THE GOOD BEER GUIDE 2022

EST 1972

MANAGING EDITOR
Emma Haines

EDITORS
Ione Brown, Claire-Michelle Taverner-Pearson, Simon Tuite

PROJECT ASSISTANCE
Katie Button, Stewart Campbell

SALES & MARKETING
Toby Langdon

D0452494

CAMRA BOOKS

© Campaign for Real Ale Ltd, 2021
www.camra.org.uk

Special thanks to the 163,000 CAMRA members who carried out research for the pub entries; the Campaign's Regional Directors and Area Organisers, who co-ordinated the pub entries; the Campaign's Brewery Liaison Coordinators and Brewery Liaison Officers, who carried out research for the brewery entries; Rick Pickup for assistance coordinating the brewery entries; Alex Presland for technical support; Iain Barker, Christine Beatty and Simon Mather at AMA Dataset; Michael Slaughter for advising on heritage pubs; James Blunt, Alex Metcalfe, Roger Protz, Elizabeth Steele and Camilla Weddell for supplying articles for the Guide; Christine Cryne for original beer styles text; Alan Murphy and Geoff Strawbridge for proofreading assistance; all CAMRA's staff and CAMRA's National Executive for their help and support.

Thanks also to the publicans, breweries, CAMRA members and others who have kindly contributed their photographs.

Photo credits: [Key: t = top; b = bottom; c = centre; l = left; r = right] p4 Dan Barrett / unsplash; p5 Michael Clement; p6 (b) Ken Paul; p8 romeovip_md / Shutterstock; p9 Mike Finn / Flickr CC BY 2.0; p10 EWY Media / Shutterstock; p12-13 Lucie Cooke Design (illustrations); p14 (l) GoodIdeas / Shutterstock; p15 (bl) Brian Mason; p612 drivethrucafe / Flickr CC BY-SA 2.0; p613 Iain Cameron / Flickr CC BY 2.0; p850 Dave_S. / Flickr CC BY 2.0.

Design: Cover design: Jack Pemberton. Page design: Jack Pemberton, Hannah Moore.

Production: Database, maps, typesetting of listings and indexes: AMA Dataset Ltd, Preston.

Printing: Printed and bound in the UK by CPI William Clowes, Beccles, Suffolk.

Published by the Campaign for Real Ale Ltd, 230 Hatfield Road, St Albans, Herts, AL1 4LW. www.camra.org.uk

ISBN 978-1-85249-376-9

Queen's Head, Newton, Cambridgeshire (p45). Photo: Helge Nareid

CONTENTS

ABOUT THE GOOD BEER GUIDE

Your Guide to the best pubs and beer in the UK.

For nearly five decades, *the Good Beer Guide* has been a comprehensive guide to the UK's breweries, their ales, and the best outlets to find them in around the country.

There may be other pub guides out there, but this book is different. Where other guides might have a small editorial board pulling together entries, *the Good Beer Guide* has a huge volunteer team, based around the country, all regularly using their local pubs, trying out the beers on offer and recommending the best of them to other beer- and pub-lovers.

We strive hard to ensure that all areas of the country are covered. Each county or region has a listing allocation based on a scientific calculation of its population, number of licensed premises and levels of tourism. As a result, the Guide's reach is unparalleled.

The Good Beer Guide is also proudly independent. Inclusion in this book is dependent on merit, not on payment. No pubs or breweries paid to be in this book.

PUBS SECTION

CAMRA has more than 160,000 members across more than 200 branches around the UK. It's within these branches that entries are democratically selected. All members are invited to rate beers served to them via the National Beer Scoring System (see p890). These scores are used by branches to identify pubs consistently serving the best real ale. Not only is the quality of the cask beer monitored, but also factors that could affect the range on offer, and the overall standard of the pub, such as change of ownership or management.

While the core purpose of the Guide is to seek out quality real ale, it also takes into account other things such as history, architecture, food, family and disabled facilities, gardens and special events (such as beer festivals). The pub listings you find in these pages paint a full picture of what you can expect before you embark on a trip to visit them.

The listings are checked many times before publication, to ensure they are accurate and up to date.

COMPREHENSIVE BREWERIES SECTION

The Good Beer Guide includes a comprehensive listing of almost 1,900 breweries currently operating in the UK – not just those producing real ale – and their core cask-conditioned beer range.

Each one is appointed a local CAMRA volunteer, as soon as they come on stream. These volunteer officers will regularly keep in touch with the brewery to stay abreast of what's being brewed, and developments that may be taking place.

SHINE ON...

I'm sorry to say, but my life is brilliant. I mean, really it is. Whenever friends ask me where we should go out in London, I can say, "I own a pub!" And honestly, buying a pub is the best thing I've ever done. Sure, I needed to do music to be able to do so, so forgive my musical output – it was for a good reason.

But that's not to say that owning and running a pub hasn't been without its challenges. As a touring musician and publican, I've pretty much chosen the worst two jobs for a global pandemic. But there have been some positives, namely — the staff. I bought the Fox & Pheasant to save a 170-year-old building. Like so many others, it was being sold to developers to turn into flats, and I felt it was a minor popstar's job to save it. But there's more to a pub than its bricks and its bar. It's the people inside who give it life and its character. So, when Boris said people shouldn't go to pubs anymore, I closed us down, and told the staff that we'd do our best to keep paying them for as long as my one hit could afford. (Generously, the government did later introduce furlough, but in the hospitality business it was limited to 80% of the minimum wage, which in real terms wasn't enough). My one saving grace is I owned the building. Many others had rent to pay, and those pubs have really struggled to stay afloat.

But as we step out of lockdown, in an industry that has a high staff turnover, we have the same team of smiling faces, all happy to be back, and when I go to the pub, it's them that I'm happy to see. We're feeling pretty positive... customers are back. And whilst, in recent years, there might have been a trend for people to drink cheap supermarket beer at home, those people have been locked away for the best part of a year, and now those people want out. They can taste real beer from the tap, and food cooked by a pro, and they can meet legally and joyfully – and you're one of them, and that's why you're in the right place. Welcome to *the Good Beer Guide*!

James Blunt

James Blunt is a best-selling singer, songwriter and record producer. He owns the Fox & Pheasant in Chelsea, London, a 17th-century pub, which he bought and renovated.

50 YEARS OF CAMRA

As we mark the publication of our 49th edition of the *Good Beer Guide*, it is impossible not to reflect on the tumultuous year our industry has had, as 2021 winds to a close.

This has also been a milestone year for CAMRA in many senses, not least the arrival of an anniversary – on 16th March 2021, we celebrated 50 years of campaigning. The organisation has come a long way from its roots, founded by four passionate young men from the North-West in 1971. CAMRA has campaigned to support pubs and ensure there is real ale in every community for 50 years, and it is safe to say the past 18 months have been some of the toughest yet.

CAMRA was founded in 1971 by four passionate young campaigners; Michael Hardman, Graham Lees, Jim Makin and Bill Mellor

CHEERS TO CAMRA AT 50

We marked the day with a #CheerstoCAMRA social media splash. Throughout 2021, we have marked our anniversary by publishing our 50th anniversary book, *50 Years of CAMRA*, by beer writer Laura Hadland, and establishing the Golden Awards recognising people, groups of people or businesses that have made a significant contribution to CAMRA's aims, as well as sharing first-hand insights into 50 campaigning milestones and launching celebratory beer boxes curated by some of the UK's leading beer experts.

Our 50th anniversary has come on the heels of a tremendously difficult year for the pub, club, beer and cider industry, after months of lockdowns and unfair restrictions.

The Steamboat, South Shields, Tyne & Wear, has been awarded a CAMRA Golden Award

In July 2021, restrictions for pubs and clubs in England finally started to lift, after months of closure due to the coronavirus pandemic, and regulations in other parts of the UK have followed suit in due course. After a period of prolonged isolation, it was wonderful to see pubs being able to open their doors, and to take up the opportunity to support our locals once more and reconnect with fellow pub-goers, friends, and family.

A CALL FOR GOVERNMENT SUPPORT

However, there is still a long road ahead to ensure as many pubs as possible survive the repercussions of the pandemic. The impact of the pandemic on pubs, clubs, and the brewers and cider makers that supply them, will continue to be felt long beyond reopening, and it is vital that this is reflected in the steps taken by the Government.

Since the start of the pandemic, we have called for further support from the Government, including a new draught beer duty rate, calls for which have gained traction over the past year. A hospitality debate in March 2021 found MPs from across the political divide agreed that a preferential rate of duty as part of a COVID support package to help pubs and brewers was a positive step.

2021 saw the launch of What's Brewing online

PULLING TOGETHER

Despite the challenges of the past year, I am proud to say that the quick actions and support of CAMRA started in March 2020 have continued. Our 'Pulling Together' campaign and Brew2You app have continued to support pubs and breweries throughout the year, helping link them to consumers as well as providing resources and information to businesses during a time when advice was changing rapidly.

The 'Cask is back - so back Cask' campaign was launched this year in conjunction with SIBA, the BII and Cask Marque

The CAMRA podcast 'Pubs. Pints. People.' has also gone from strength to strength, sharing interesting topics and industry interviews with over 1,000 listeners per episode. A major change this year involved the launch of our revamped online news service, What's Brewing Online, where members can read up on the latest beer and pub news and sign up for personalised news alerts direct to their inboxes – learn more on wb.camra.org.uk

PUBS MATTER

This year has seen new campaigns established aimed at supporting the industry – including #PubsMatter, which highlighted the vital role pubs play for their communities, and 'Cask is back – so back Cask', in conjunction with SIBA, the BII and Cask Marque, asking consumers to order a pint of fresh cask ale when they could return to the pub. As the vaccine rollout went from strength to strength, our team were hard at work preparing a relaunch of CAMRA festivals, under the 'It's Festival Season' banner and with a new COVID-secure policy to ensure the safety of beer festival goers.

We continue to be faced with uncertainty in the run up to the New Year, and questions about winter and potential return of restrictions remain unanswered. Our pubs and breweries have survived thus far, and they continue to need significant, long-term support to get back on their feet and see out the end of the pandemic. 2021 has marked a half century of CAMRA - as we acknowledge this milestone, CAMRA also reaffirms its commitment to fighting for pubs and consumers now and in the future, to ensure there are good pubs serving good beer in every community for another 50 years.

Nik Antona, National Chairman

CAMRA'S BEER STYLES

Beer is the world's third favourite drink. The most popular beer style is lager, but beer is much more than this. Most beer drinkers might have an idea what a traditional bitter is. However, do you know how this differs from a pale or golden ale? And what exactly is a barley wine?

The situation is made more complex by the growth in the number of brewers brewing international recipes, experimenting with new beer styles and digging up very old ones as well. CAMRA have cut through some of the jargon and have come up with 12 beer style categories, used to judge the prestigious Champion Beer of Britain awards each year. We have included beer style information next to each beer listed in the brewery section of the Guide this year, to help you find your favourite ones more easily. Below we take you through the beer style categories, with advice on some of the flavour profiles you can expect.

1. MILDS: UP TO AND INCLUDING 4% ABV

Mild used to mean fresh and reflected the fact that the beer was not aged. Although an old style of beer, mild is not widely available in many parts of the country but May is a good time to find it as some pubs participate in CAMRA's Make Mine Mild campaign. These beers are light drinking and not very hoppy. There are two types of mild: light/pale milds, and dark milds, so the colour can be dark brown to black to pale amber or even gold. Scottish 60 Shillings or Scottish light beer also fits into this category and can be dark brown to black in colour. Pale milds are lightly hopped and may have a light fruit character. They are malty and the beer may be sweet with a little butterscotch/toffee. Dark milds are frequently sweet with a light bitterness. The dominant flavour is of malt and roasted notes of chocolate, coffee and liquorice are often noticeable. Scottish 60 Shillings or Scottish light beers have dominant flavours of malt, with butterscotch/toffee often present.

2. SESSION BITTERS: UP TO AND INCLUDING 4.3% ABV

These are 'traditional' bitters with a thin to average body. They are often called bitters and best bitters. Usually amber to dark brown in colour these beers often have a malt character with noticeable hops; typically earthy, spicy, and peppery but may also be floral or piney. Fruit may also be present, sometimes citrus. Bitterness can range from light to strong.

3. PREMIUM BITTERS: 4.4%-6.4% ABV

Premium bitters are 'traditional' stronger bitters with an average to thick body, usually amber to dark brown in colour. They often have a medium to strong malt flavour with noticeable hops; typically earthy, spicy, and peppery but may also be floral, piney, or citrus. Fruit may be medium to strong but shouldn't dominate.

Different types of malt give different flavour profiles and aromas to beer

Worcestershire and Herefordshire are two of the main hop-growing regions of Britain

Stronger bitters may have estery notes such as pear drops, and the bitterness may range from medium to strong.

4. SESSION PALE, BLOND AND GOLDEN ALES: UP TO AND INCLUDING 4.3% ABV

These are refreshing, light drinking beers. Pale ales are dark gold to amber in colour. Malt flavours are light in character, with hop flavours more noticeable and vary from earthy or spicy to citrus and tropical. They'll be fruitier than a session bitter. Blond ales are straw to golden in colour. Malt is minimal with low to moderate fruit flavours. Hops again may vary but will not have a strong citrus character. Golden ales have pronounced fruity, citrus hop notes and may have strong bitterness.

5. PREMIUM PALE, BLOND AND GOLDEN ALES: 4.4%-6.4% ABV

These beers are refreshing but fuller-bodied than the session varieties. Pale ales are dark gold to amber, malt is light to medium in character and not dominant. Fruit can vary from minimal to strong

and is often citrus or tropical. Hops are noticeable and vary from earthy and spicy to citrus. Blonds and golden ales are straw to gold in colour. Blonds will have minimal malt and strong hop flavours, while golden ales will have pronounced fruity, citrus hop notes and may have a strong bitterness.

6. BRITISH & NEW WORLD IPAs: 5.5% AND ABOVE

IPA stands for India Pale Ale. It was the Midland town of Burton upon Trent that became famous for this style of beer, exporting it around the world including to India, hence the name. These are strong, hoppy beers with moderate to strong bitterness; usually bittersweet. The finish is long and complex. British IPAs are usually amber to pale brown and often have a biscuit malt aroma and peppery, spicy, earthy, piney or floral hop notes. New World IPAs are straw to pale brown and noticeably fruitier with citrus, tropical or white wine flavours. The malt tends to make less of an impact.

Black IPAs are typically dark brown or black with the roast character being light, complementing rather than dominating the hops and fruit in the flavour.

7. BROWN AND RED ALES, OLD ALES AND STRONG MILDS: UP TO 6.4%

These are darker beers with malty notes.

Brown ales have malt to the fore, often with roasted, smoky or nut-like flavours. Hops are sometimes evident, and they may have a moderately bitter or dry finish. Fruity flavours such as raisins or sultanas may be present. American brown ales tend to much fruitier, sometimes with pronounced bittering.

Red ales have malt to the fore, often with roast or nutty flavours. Rye may be present, creating a balanced tartness. American red ales are fruitier and hoppier.

Strong milds and unaged old ales have a light to rich malt character, sometimes with caramel and fruit notes such as raisins and sultanas.

8. SESSION STOUTS AND PORTERS: UP TO AND INCLUDING 4.9% ABV

Porters were developed in London in the eighteenth century and named after the London porters who worked on the docks in the City of London. It is thought to be the first global beer as, at one time, it was exported around the world. There is often confusion between stouts and porters. Once, stout simply meant 'strong'. CAMRA distinguishes between the two styles by describing stouts as typically black and less hopped than porters. Stouts have flavours and aromas resulting from the roasted grain malts, for example chocolate, caramel, and coffee notes. They have minimal hop and fruit notes. Porters also have roasted notes of coffee or chocolate but are balanced by a hoppy character with some fruit.

There are several types of stout brewed, each with a slightly different flavour profile. These include dry stouts, oyster stouts, oatmeal stouts and milk stouts.

9. STRONG STOUTS AND PORTERS: 5% AND ABOVE

These are stronger versions of the session varieties, usually with a smoother, fuller mouthfeel. Flavours range from sweet to dry, but with a rich, full body.

Imperial stouts and Baltic (or Imperial) porters are deep and complex with roasted

Do you know a pale ale from a golden ale, and what exactly is a barley wine?

CAMRA beer festivals are a great way to try many different styles of beer

11. SPECIALITY BEERS: DIFFERENTLY PRODUCED

Differently produced speciality beers are those brewed with non-standard ingredients or techniques, as opposed to flavoured speciality beers, which have flavour added. Non-conventional ingredients and techniques are only limited by the brewer's imagination. They can include styles such as Pilsners, Vienna lagers, Marzen, dark lagers and Kölsch, wheat beers, sours, saisons, wood-aged and smoked beers.

12. SPECIALITY BEERS: FLAVOURED

Flavoured speciality beers are beers with a flavour added. They can be similar to other styles in that any beer style can be adapted by a flavour addition to become a speciality beer. They include fruit beers or beers brewed with herbs, spices or other culinary ingredients. The latter can include beers brewed with ginger, coriander, mint, elderflower or ingredients such as honey, coffee, chocolate, vanilla or fortified wines and spirits.

The character of the base beer will influence the final taste of a fruit beer but the wide range of fruit available to brewers means that tastes can range from sour (typical of lemons or some cherries), to bitter (such as bergamot), through to sweet (such as mango or strawberry). Additional sugars may be used to sweeten the beers.'

grain, burnt fruit, fresh leather, espresso coffee, bitter chocolate, molasses, and liquorice notes. Warming alcohol is often noticeable due to the high alcohol content.

10. BARLEY WINES AND STRONG ALES: 6.5% AND ABOVE

Strong beer used to be produced to allow it to be kept, particularly to provide beer when it was too warm to brew. Many of the beers in this category are still aged before selling, leading to wine-like notes. They are rich, complex, and full-bodied with noticeable alcohol, but may vary from dry to sweet. Bitterness may be medium to strong. The term barley wine probably dates from the late 1800s, with Bass using it in the early 1900s.

THE LANGUAGE OF BEER

Nose: the aroma. Gently swirl the beer to release the aroma. You will detect malt: grainy and biscuity, often likened to crackers or Ovaltine. When darker malts are used, the nose will have powerful hints of chocolate, coffee, nuts, vanilla, liquorice, molasses and such dried fruits as raisins and sultanas. Hops add superb aromas of resins, herbs, spices, fresh-mown grass and tart citrus fruit – lemon and orange are typical, with intense grapefruit notes from some American varieties. Sulphur may also be present when waters are 'Burtonised': i.e. gypsum and magnesium salts have been added to replicate the famous spring waters of Burton upon Trent.

Palate: the appeal in the mouth (mouthfeel). The tongue can detect sweetness, bitterness and saltiness as the beer passes over it. The rich flavours of malt will come to the fore but hop bitterness will also make a substantial impact. The tongue will also pick out the natural saltiness from the brewing water and fruit from darker malts, yeast and hops. Citrus notes often have a major impact on the palate.

Finish: the aftertaste, as the beer goes over the tongue and down the throat. The finish is often radically different from the nose. The aroma may be dominated by malt whereas hop flavours and bitterness can govern the finish.

LEARN AND DISCOVER WITH CAMRA

Our Learn & Discover programme aims to support all those with an interest in beer, cider, perry, pubs and brewing to learn more about them via our books, publications, festivals and online at the CAMRA website through high-quality learner-focused content, carefully curated from trusted industry voices and the volunteer community.

In 2018 CAMRA undertook a Revitilisation Project. One of the major outcomes of that exercise was that we discovered that people want to know more about what they're drinking: what is real ale, real cider and perry? How is it brewed/ produced? What is the history behind it? How should it taste? ... and how can I brew it myself?

To that end we began a discovery programme at CAMRA beer festivals up and down the country. This was to connect festival goers to the ingredients and people behind their favourite drinks. No matter where they are on their drinker's journey there's something for everyone; whether you're a beginner, enthusiast, or connoisseur.

LEARN MORE

The Learn & Discover pages on our website follow the same journey of discovery.

'The basics' is for beginners; fundamental information anyone needs to get started enjoying beer, cider, perry and pubs. Content is free for all: you don't have to be a CAMRA member to read interesting articles by industry insiders and well known writers such as Roger Protz, Pete Brown, Emma Inch and Cath Potter.

'Learn more' is for enthusiasts, giving a more in depth look at brewing and cider making, ingredients, people and pub culture, while 'Discover' is for connoisseurs wishing to take a deep dive into it all for a more nuanced look at the drinks you love. Full access to this content is for CAMRA members only.

Visit **camra.org.uk/learn-discover** for more information.

BEER APPRECIATION

A good beer is enjoyable, but a great beer is art in a glass. The breadth of choice of beers in the UK means we have plenty to appreciate and we can increase that appreciation by sampling and tasting. To taste your ale like an expert, make sure to use your senses, particularly sight, smell and taste, and always insist on quality.

Real ale, when conditioned with care, should be bright and sparkling, with a lively head, served cool and refreshing at between 11 and 13°C.

For many years, a lot of beer drinkers believed the perfect pint should be crystal clear, but times have changed, and many beers are now being served cloudy. Hazy brews can be packed with tropical fruit and protein flavours, which filtering takes out. A good rule of thumb is if it doesn't smell right then it's probably off. As a paying consumer, don't be afraid to take your beer back to the bar if it is not in good condition. Bar staff should replace it and might not be aware of an issue unless you tell them.

Take your pint back to the bar if:

- Your beer is served either too warm or too cold (for the style)
- The pint has no head, is totally flat and out of condition
- It's not only flat but hazy and has yeast particles or protein floating in the liquid
- Your beers smells of acetone, vinegar or stale bread

Visit **camra.org.uk/learn-discover** for a handy guide to identifying off flavours and aromas in beer (illustrated below). Always remember that the style of beer matters when you're looking at its taste and 'nose'.

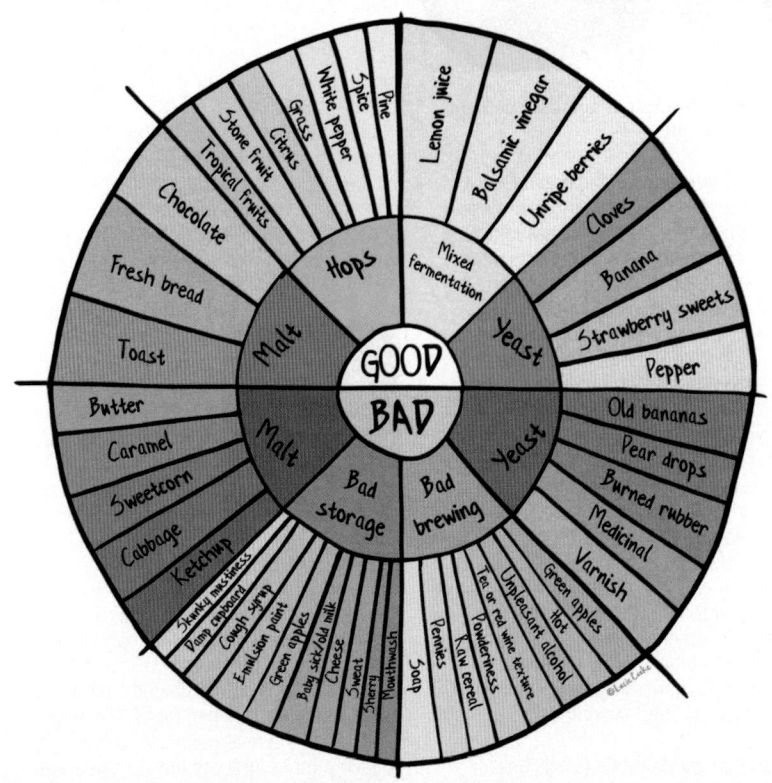

For more information on beer styles, see pages 8-11 or **camra.org.uk/learn-discover**

THE HEART OF THE COMMUNITY

Cam Weddell, CAMRA's Campaigns Assistant, tells us how CAMRA has been working with the All-Party Parliamentary Group on Pubs to promote and campaign for pubs, landlords and their communities.

CAMRA often talks about pubs as the heart of their communities. It's easy to hear these words so often they become cliché, but the pandemic leaves no doubt about exactly how true this is. Lockdowns and restrictions put many pubs on the brink of closure, but the pandemic has also reinforced the importance of community, and the vital role that pubs play in the lives and wellbeing of their regulars.

Lockdown and restrictions put many pubs on the brink of closure

I spent a decade working behind a bar and, as it turned out, February 2020 was an interesting time to leave the pub trade and begin working in CAMRA's Campaigns department. I found myself writing briefings, reading new legislation, and lobbying for increased government support, while my phone lit up with messages from the pub I had worked in just a month before. They had thousands of pounds worth of food and beer to throw away, did I need anything? Some of the regulars were shielding, could someone drop off a food package? Why were there so many eggs in stock, and who exactly had ordered them all?

The legislation, restrictions, and support schemes on which CAMRA was campaigning soon filtered through to discussions with friends and former colleagues. It was clear that the devastation of the pandemic was not only a national emergency; its impact reverberated through every level of the pub trade.

CAMRA adapted quickly to this new landscape, launching online campaigns, creating new digital tools to support consumers and the trade, and holding virtual meetings to lobby elected representatives at every level of Government.

ALL-PARTY PARLIAMENTARY GROUP ON PUBS

Towards the end of 2020, the All-Party Parliamentary Group on Pubs (Pubs APPG) elected a new Chair, and CAMRA had the opportunity to take on responsibilities as the Group's secretariat. All-Party Parliamentary Groups are informal groups of MPs and Peers who share interests and work together outside their political parties to champion a particular cause. As secretariat, CAMRA's new role would be to handle the administrative side of things.

The Campaigns Team met with the new Chair, Charlotte Nichols MP, to talk about how we could work together to fulfil the Pubs APPG's stated aim "to promote and campaign for the interests of pubs, landlords and the communities around them".

Charlotte was keen to hit the ground running. She wanted the Pubs APPG to run an inquiry into the impact of the pandemic on pubs, the people that run them, and the communities that use them. So, we got to work – building a new website, launching a Twitter account, drafting the call for

evidence, designing surveys, writing press releases and contacting everyone from individual licensees to national organisations to ask for their experiences of the pandemic.

RESILIENCE AND CREATIVITY

The response from the trade was incredible. Between licensees, pub staff, consumers, and trade organisations we received 15,000 responses detailing the unique experiences and challenges they had faced. The Pubs APPG also held a virtual evidence session, to take a more in-depth look at some key issues. This bought together MPs, trade organisations, academics and licensees to talk about pubs, the pandemic and the future of the trade.

Despite all the challenges, the resilience and creativity of the trade shone through in the evidence we collected. Pubs across the UK had played an integral part in the community response to COVID-19 – even when doing so meant taking a financial hit. They had started grocery stores, run delivery services, offered mental health support to their regulars, picked up food or prescriptions for those who were shielding, raised money for the NHS and taken countless other steps to support their communities. However, they had seen an average £285,000 drop in turnover, with one pub facing a drop of £1.6 million compared to the previous year. Pubs reported that Government support schemes had covered just over half of their fixed costs, with licensees often making up the shortfall from their savings.

The cost of Bounce Back Loans and other debt, and the restarting of fixed costs like Business Rates were huge concerns, which many pubs simply could not afford to start paying. Pub staff had struggled with furlough, with some being ineligible because of their start dates and others explaining that their tips made up a significant portion of their wages, in some cases leaving them with as little as 40% of their normal take-home pay on furlough.

The mental health impact was also clear. Both pub staff and licensees explained they were missing the social aspect of their work. This was compounded by the financial stress

Charlotte Nichols MP and CAMRA's National Chairman, Nik Antona

of the pandemic, and uncertainty about their futures. Survey respondents reported struggling with anxiety, depression and loneliness. We also asked people to look to the future and tell us what pubs would need in the months and years to come. Responses ranged from fairer Business Rates to making sure that pubs are a more welcoming and diverse environment, to calls for a new Hospitality Minister job to be created.

GREATER INVESTMENT IN PUBS AND PEOPLE

The next step was to write a report, detailing the findings of the Inquiry and making recommendations to Government on how they should support pubs. Some of these recommendations cover areas of CAMRA's campaigning – like reform of the Pubs Code to offer tied pub tenants more support. Other recommendations were outside CAMRA's normal lobbying – such as calls from licensees for better digital infrastructure to help them modernise their businesses.

At the time of writing, the Pubs APPG report hasn't yet been published, but MPs should be brandishing it in Parliament and calling for greater investment in pubs and people very soon. In the time CAMRA has been working with the Pubs APPG, membership of the Group has doubled and we're planning to reach even more MPs to ensure pubs have a strong voice in Parliament over the coming months and years.

Pubs are at the heart of our communities. The Red Lion in Preston, Herts, recently won a CAMRA Golden Award and was the first community-owned pub in Britain

For more information on The All-Party Parliamentary Group on Pubs and the inquiry, please visit **apppg.camra.org.uk**

Cam Weddell is CAMRA's Campaigns Assistant. Before joining the Campaigns Team, she spent 10 years in hospitality, doing everything from bar work in a traditional real ale pub, to a management role in a 250-seater carvery. She is passionate about all things pub!

PROUD TO SUPPORT THE GOOD BEER GUIDE

Cask Marque, the champions of beer quality, and its sister company, Stay in Pub, are pleased to jointly sponsor this year's Guide.

Cask Marque has worked closely with CAMRA to promote cask ale for over 20 years through the following:

- The Grain to Glass assessment programme resulting in the award of the highly sought-after Cask Marque accreditation
- 60 qualified assessors make over 20,000 visits to pubs each year
- Advising pubs on how to stock a good range of quality cask ales, both familiar brands and local craft beers
- Training bar staff on how to keep and serve the perfect pint
- Promoting cask ale through the CaskFinder app (QR code scanned over 1million times) and its associated Ale Trails

- Championing cask ale through an annual Cask Ale Week

Look out for the Cask Marque logo to find your perfect pint. To download the CaskFinder App go to **cask-marque.co.uk/cask-finder**, Google Play or the App Store.

Stay in a Pub was relaunched in April 2021 and is the UK's leading website dedicated to promoting and booking pub accommodation.

The team at Stay in a Pub are passionate about the great British pub and have lovingly curated a collection of boutique pubs with rooms, traditional inns, and affordable pub accommodation. The mobile-first website ensures that guests can find and book their perfect stay away in a great British pub.

- Superb search functionality by region, county, postcode, and availability on a particular date
- Filters by facilities, type of stay, activities nearby, price, dog-friendly, suitable for families and many others
- Map view to help plan your itinerary

- Our highly recommended pubs
- Special offers
- Menus
- Gift vouchers
- Things to do and places to visit nearby
- Holiday ideas

Book your perfect stay in a great British pub

To find out more and to book your Great British stay in a pub, go to **stayinapub.co.uk**

The Pubs

Dun Cow, Sunderland: City Centre, Tyne & Wear (p421). Photo: Ken Paul

NORTHERN
ISLES

SHETLAND

HIGHLANDS
&
WESTERN ISLES

ABERDEEN
& GRAMPIAN

TAYSIDE

ARGYLL &
THE ISLES

LOCH LOMOND,
STIRLING
& TROSSACHS

FIFE

GREATER
GLASGOW &
CLYDE

EDINBURGH & LOTHIANS

AYRSHIRE
& ARRAN

BORDERS

NORTHERN
IRELAND

DUMFRIES &
GALLOWAY

NORTHUMBERLAND

TYNE &
WEAR

CUMBRIA

DURHAM

ISLE OF
MAN

NORTH
YORKSHIRE

LANCASHIRE

WEST
YORKS

EAST
YORKS

MERSEYSIDE

GREATER
MANCHESTER

SOUTH
YORKS

NW WALES

NE
WALES

CHESHIRE

DERBYSHIRE

NOTTINGHAM-
SHIRE

LINCOLNSHIRE

NORFOLK

SHROPSHIRE

STAFFORD-
SHIRE

LEICESTERSHIRE

RUTLAND

CAMBRIDGE-
SHIRE

SUFFOLK

MID
WALES

WEST
MIDLANDS

NORTHAMPTON-
SHIRE

WORCESTER-
SHIRE

WARWICK-
SHIRE

BEDFORD-
SHIRE

HEREFORD-
SHIRE

HERTFORD-
SHIRE

ESSEX

WEST
WALES

GLAMORGAN

GWENT

GLOUCS &
BRISTOL

OXFORD-
SHIRE

BUCKINGHAMSHIRE

GREATER
LONDON

BERKSHIRE

SURREY

KENT

WILTSHIRE

HAMPSHIRE

WEST
SUSSEX

EAST
SUSSEX

SOMERSET

DORSET

CHANNEL
ISLANDS

DEVON

CORNWALL

ISLE OF
WIGHT

England

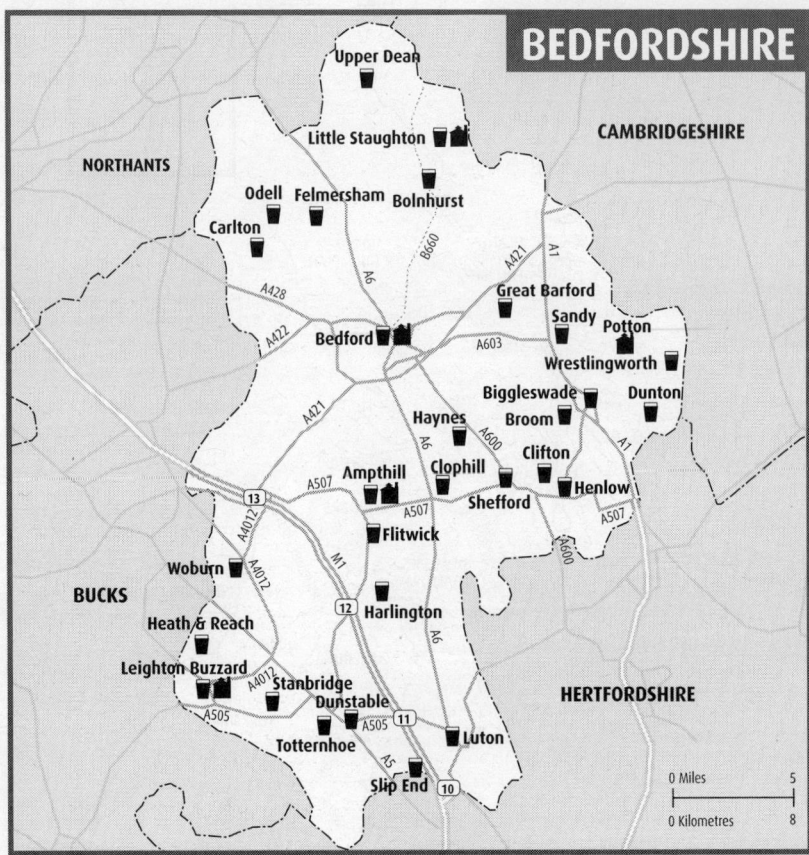

BEDFORDSHIRE

Ampthill

Albion ⅃

36 Dunstable Street, MK45 2JT

☎ (01525) 634857

B&T Golden Fox, Dragon Slayer, Shefford Bitter; Everards Tiger; 8 changing beers ⊞

An award-winning narrow-fronted Victorian pub with one large bar and 12 handpumps serving a range of local B&T beers, Everards Tiger, eight constantly changing ales mainly from microbreweries, plus one changing craft keg beer. Two regular real ciders and a guest are also on offer. There is a meeting room and a secluded patio garden towards the rear. A varied selection of local clubs and groups is supported. Twice Bedfordshire CAMRA Pub of the Year. ❂❀♣⬛❀

Engine & Tender ✅

11 Dunstable Street, MK45 2NJ

☎ (01525) 403319

Greene King IPA; St Austell Tribute; Timothy Taylor Landlord; 1 changing beer (sourced nationally; often Morland, Theakston, Wadworth) ⊞

A proper, traditional, single-bar pub with a welcoming atmosphere and a varied clientele. Regular and changing beers come from Greene King and guest brewers. Lunchtime meals are served Wednesday to Friday. Sports are very popular on the multiple TVs. There is seating out front, a covered archway and a pleasant patio area at the back. ❂◑♿♣⬛❀

Bedford

Brewhouse & Kitchen Bedford ⅃ ✅

115 High Street, MK40 1NU

☎ (01234) 342931 ⊕ brewhouseandkitchen.com/bedford

Brewhouse & Kitchen Bedford Banker's Draught, Intrepid, Invarsity; house beer (by Brewhouse) ⊞

A former bank then a Wetherspoon, relaunched by the Brewhouse & Kitchen group in 2016. The microbrewery is located within the main bar area, alongside various seating areas separated by half-height dividers that are features in themselves. Orders can be placed at the table or at the bar – the menu contains an extensive list of drinks as well as food. Seasonal and special ales are available but only in KeyKeg. ❂❀◑♿♣⬛❀🛜

Castle ⅃

17 Newnham Street, MK40 3JR

☎ (01234) 353295 ⊕ castlebedford.co.uk

Courage Directors; Eagle IPA; Young's London Original, London Special; 2 changing beers (sourced nationally) ⊞

Lively town pub with a pleasant walled patio garden, five minutes from the town centre and convenient for the Bedford Blues rugby ground. Lunches are served daily and evening meals weekdays only. Current guest beers with tasting notes are listed on the website and social media. A guesthouse behind the pub provides five en-suite bedrooms. Open mic features on a Monday evening. A former local CAMRA Pub of the Year. ❂❀◑♿♣⬛❀🛜

Devonshire Arms 🄻 ✅
32 Dudley Street, MK40 3TB (1 mile E of town centre S of A4280)
☎ (01234) 301170 ⊕ devonshirearmsbedford.co.uk
Courage Directors; Eagle IPA; 4 changing beers (sourced regionally) 🄷
Pleasant late-Victorian pub in a residential area, a Wells house for its whole 120 years. The front bar has bare floorboards and an open fire, while there is a separate rear bar. The garden has a gazebo for smokers and a no-smoking paved area. Beer and cider festivals are held twice a year. A range of wines is sold by the glass or bottle. Local CAMRA Pub of the Year 2020.
Q ᔕ ⛱ ♣ ♠ ➡ (4) ♣ 🛜

King's Arms
24 St Mary's Street, MK42 0AS
☎ (01234) 354494 ⊕ thekingsarmsbedford.co.uk
Greene King IPA; Morland Old Speckled Hen; 2 changing beers (sourced nationally) 🄷
This busy former coaching inn has been a public house since 1230. It has several interconnecting rooms and a conservatory providing a quiet area. There is free pool on Tuesday evening, a ukulele band on Wednesday, TV poker on Thursday and live performances by top local bands every Saturday evening. A selection of real bottled beer is available. No food at weekends.
ᔕ ⛱ ⇌ (St Johns) ♣ ♠ P ➡ ♣ 🛜

Pilgrim's Progress 🄻 ✅
42 Midland Road, MK40 1QB
☎ (01234) 363751
Eagle IPA; Greene King Abbot; Ruddles Best Bitter; Sharp's Doom Bar; 6 changing beers (sourced nationally) 🄷
Remodelled as a Wetherspoon hotel in 2016, the pub has five internal areas and two outdoor seating areas, one of them no-smoking. The bar is popular with all ages but doesn't usually get overcrowded, even on weekend evenings. There are views into the kitchen, and the varied food menu specifies allergens and calorie content. Wetherspoon Club offers are available. The location is convenient for public transport and offers a good view of the town centre. ᔕ ⛱ ⏻ ♿ ♠ ➡ 🛜

Three Cups 🄻
45 Newnham Street, MK40 3JR (200yds S of A4280 nr Bedford Blues rugby ground)
☎ (01234) 352153
Greene King IPA; Morland Old Speckled Hen; 4 changing beers (sourced nationally; often Kelchner) 🄷
Comfortable inn dating from the 1770s, five minutes from the town centre and now a Greene King Local Hero outlet offering Kelchner and other microbrewery beers, plus Saxby's cider. Old wood panelling helps retain some of the pub's original character. There is a largescreen TV for major matches, and an attractive garden with extra seating under cover. It has been a local CAMRA Pub of the Year, with the potential to achieve this again.
ᔕ ⛱ ⏻ ♠ P ➡ ♣

Wellington Arms 🄻
40-42 Wellington Street, MK40 2JX (N of town centre)
☎ (01234) 308033
Adnams Southwold Bitter; B&T Shefford Bitter; Draught Bass; 9 changing beers (sourced nationally; often B&T) 🄷
Traditional street-corner establishment featuring lots of breweriana. A key part of the Bedford real ale scene for 20 years, it has an interesting selection of 12 ales and two real ciders on handpump. Draught continental beers and a range of bottled Belgian beers are also available.

There is a courtyard for drinkers and smokers. The pub attracts a mixed clientele and offers a friendly welcome.
♣ ♠ ♥

White Horse 🄻 ✅
84 Newnham Avenue, MK41 9PX
☎ (01234) 409306 ⊕ thewhitehorsebedford.co.uk
Courage Directors; Eagle IPA; Marston's 61 Deep; 3 changing beers (sourced regionally) 🄷
Three seating areas, all with their own style, are served from a single bar. The smartphone quiz on Sunday and regular Tuesday quiz are popular, as is Monday evening jazz. Other musical events are advertised on Facebook. Food is freshly cooked, with a choice of roasts on Sunday (book ahead). The beer and wine selection is complemented by a wide choice of gins. Afternoon tea can be ordered for groups. ᔕ ⛱ ⏻ ♿ ♠ P ➡ (4) ♣ 🛜

Biggleswade

Golden Pheasant 🄻 ✅
71 High Street, SG18 0JH
☎ (01767) 313653 ⊕ goldenpheasantbiggleswade.co.uk
Eagle IPA; 5 changing beers (sourced nationally) 🄷
Situated in the centre of town, this pub can trace its roots back to 1876. The low beamed ceiling adds to the traditional feel, while the single-room interior is large enough to accommodate darts teams for matches alongside community groups for meetings. A good range of well-kept beers and ciders is served from the corner bar. The large outside area at the rear is a great space for live music and other charity events. Q ⛱ ⇌ ♣ ♠ ♣ 🛜

Wheatsheaf ✅
5 Lawrence Road, SG18 0LS
☎ (01767) 222220
Greene King IPA; 2 changing beers (sourced nationally; often Fuller's) 🄷
Built in 1873 and tucked away down a back street at the end of a row of terraced cottages, this comfortable and welcoming establishment is community focused and caters for local darts and dominoes teams. Horse racing and big matches feature on the large TV screens and it can get busy when popular fixtures are shown. The excellent condition of the Greene King IPA and the large family-friendly garden area make the pub worth seeking out. ᔕ ⛱ ⇌ ♣ ➡ (73,188) ♣ 🛜

Bolnhurst

Plough 🄻
Kimbolton Road, MK44 2EX (on W side of B660 S of turning to Thurleigh) TL088587
☎ (01234) 376274 ⊕ bolnhurst.com
Adnams Southwold Bitter; 2 changing beers (sourced regionally) 🄷
Award-winning pub-restaurant dating in part from the Tudor period, serving excellent food and beer. The bar area is to the left of the entrance, with the restaurant beyond and a second dining/function room to the right. Outside, the large garden has decking and a pond. The Plough has no prominent signage, just a modest hanging

sign on a post by the road entrance. Closed from Christmas until the second week of January each year. Wheelchair users should contact the pub in advance. Q❀♿◐▮P❀🐾🛜

Broom

Cock ★ ✅
23 High Street, SG18 9NA
☎ (01767) 314411 ⊕ thecockatbroom.co.uk
Greene King Abbot; 3 changing beers (sourced nationally; often St Austell, Tring, Wychwood) Ⓖ
Delightful Grade II-listed pub on CAMRA's National Inventory of Historic Pub Interiors. At the front are two rooms – a parlour with wood-burning fire and bottle collection and a games room with dartboard and Northamptonshire skittles table. Another room contains a fish tank. Outside is a beer garden and a large area for camping and caravans with access to toilets and water. Drinks are served direct from the cellar steps to customers and food is home-cooked.
Q❀♿◐▮🅟♣♠P▮(200)❀🛜

Carlton

Fox Ⓛ
High Street, MK43 7LA (off Turvey Road S of village centre)
☎ (01234) 720235 ⊕ thefoxatcarlton.pub
Eagle IPA; Fuller's London Pride; 2 changing beers (sourced regionally) Ⓗ
A charming thatched community pub with a warm welcome and an attractive garden popular with families. Guest beers are often from local microbreweries. Good-value, home-cooked lunches are served daily (no food Mon) and evening meals Tuesday to Saturday. There is a regular quiz on Thursday evening. Spring and summer bank holiday festivals are held using an outbuilding as an additional bar, plus a one-day gin festival in June. A repeat winner of local CAMRA Country Pub of the Year including 2020. Q❀♿◐▮♿♣P▮(25)❀🛜

Clifton

Admiral
1 Broad Street, SG17 5RJ
☎ (01462) 811069
5 changing beers (sourced nationally; often Brains, Harvey's, Robinsons) Ⓗ
Friendly, warm and welcoming pub with a wood-burning stove, serving five real ales, one real cider and bottled craft beers. Nautical themed pictures and model ships adorn the interior, and there are board games and darts available. Monthly pub quizzes and live music events are always popular, as is the annual beer festival. Food offerings are not to be missed, including fish & chips Fridays, weekend breakfasts, Sunday roasts, steak night Mondays and stone-baked pizzas on summer weekends. ❀♿◐▮♣♠▮(9A,9B)❀🛜

Clophill

Stone Jug
10 Back Street, MK45 4BY (off A6 at N end of village)
TL083381
☎ (01525) 860526 ⊕ stonejug.co.uk
Shepherd Neame Spitfire; Wainwright; 3 changing beers (sourced nationally) Ⓗ
Originally three 16th-century cottages, this popular village local has an L-shaped bar serving two drinking areas and a family/function room. Excellent home-made lunches are available Tuesday to Saturday. The guest

beers are often from local microbreweries, the cider is Westons. Picnic benches at the front and a rear patio garden offer outdoor drinking space in fine weather. Parking can be difficult at busy times. A good pit stop for the Greensand Ridge Walk and a former CAMRA Pub of the Year. Q❀♿◐♣♠P▮(44,81)❀

Dunstable

Gary Cooper Ⓛ ✅
Grove Park, Court Drive, LU5 4GP
☎ (01582) 471452
Greene King Abbot; Ruddles Best Bitter; Sharp's Doom Bar; 7 changing beers Ⓗ
A large, modern Wetherspoon bar serving a selection of up to seven (often local) guest ales. The usual range of JDW craft beer is also well stocked. Situated in Grove Park leisure area, the pub has a patio overlooking the Grove House gardens, with many bus routes stopping outside. It gets busy on Friday and Saturday nights. Hollywood star Gary Cooper attended the local grammar school from 1910-1913. ❀◐♿♠▮🛜

Globe Ⓛ
43 Winfield Street, LU6 1LS
☎ (01582) 512300
7 changing beers Ⓗ
Popular beer destination and community local where handpumps boast a good range of seven ever-changing microbrewery beers, a real cider and a perry. More than 20 Belgian beers are also available. Bare boards, bar stools, breweriana and a famous plank at the end of the bar create a traditional town pub atmosphere buzzing with conversation. Regular beer festivals are held. A former county and local CAMRA Pub of the Year. Q❀♿♣▮(70)❀

Victoria Ⓛ
69 West Street, LU6 1ST
☎ (01582) 662682
House beer (by Tring); 2 changing beers Ⓗ
The Victoria is a popular town-centre pub near the police station on West Street. It usually offers two varying ales from microbreweries plus a house beer from the local Tring Brewery. Darts, dominoes and crib are popular as well as televised sports in the bar. There is a separate function room next to the rear courtyard. ❀♣▮

Dunton

March Hare Ⓛ
34 High Street, SG18 8RN
☎ (01767) 600258 ⊕ themarchharedunton.co.uk
6 changing beers (sourced nationally) Ⓗ
A much-loved community hub and regular host of live music, this pub dating from the 1840s has an L-shaped, brick-faced bar and oak beam remnants. A wide-ranging selection of both local and national beers of different varieties is available. Mini beer festivals are held twice a year, plus a gin festival and a cider festival. Games and newspapers are available for drinkers to enjoy. A cosy fire and a sun-drenched beer garden add to the warm welcome at any time of year. Q❀♿❀♣♠▮(188)❀🛜

Felmersham

Sun Ⓛ
Grange Road, MK43 7EU
☎ (01234) 781355 ⊕ thesunfelmersham.com
Eagle IPA; 2 changing beers (sourced regionally) Ⓗ
Pretty thatched community pub with a family-friendly rear garden, convenient for visits to the historic parish

church and a nature reserve just across the river. Guest beers are often from local microbreweries. The creative food menu includes rotisserie-cooked chicken, hand-cut chips and seasonal ingredients from local producers. There is also a monthly food and drink theme night. The refurbished dining room can accommodate up to 40. Local CAMRA Cider Pub of the Year 2020.
ᗜᕲ❍❶♣♠️P🖳(50) ☕🐾🛜

Flitwick

Crown ✅
Station Road, MK45 1LA
☎ (01525) 713737 🌐 crownflitwick.co.uk
4 changing beers (sourced nationally) Ⓗ
This large and tidy, thriving two-bar estate pub was successfully rescued by the current tenants who are keen on their real ales, with four changing beers and a craft keg beer usually available. The front bar has TV, jukebox, pool and darts. Saturday music nights are popular. There is a large garden with patio and children's play area. Traditional pub food is served lunchtimes and evenings (lunches only on Sun). ᗜ❀❍❶♣≠♠️P🖳(2)🐾🛜

Great Barford

Anchor Inn Ⓛ ✅
High Street, MK44 3LF (by river 1 mile S of village centre) TL134517
☎ (01234) 870364 🌐 anchorinngreatbarford.co.uk
Eagle IPA; Young's London Original; 4 changing beers (sourced nationally) Ⓗ
Busy inn next to the church, overlooking a medieval bridge across the River Great Ouse. At least two guest beers are usually available from an extensive range offered by the pub company. Good home-cooked food is served in the bar and restaurant, as well as a fine selection of wines. The place is popular with river users in the summer. Occasional themed food nights are held, mainly during the winter months. Qᗜ❀❍❶P🖳(27)🛜

Harlington

Carpenters Arms
Sundon Road, LU5 6LS
☎ (01525) 872384 🌐 thecarpentersarmsharlington.com
Greene King IPA; Woodforde's Wherry; 2 changing beers (sourced nationally; often Shepherd Neame, Wainwright) Ⓗ
Situated in the heart of Harlington, this low-beamed watch-your-head traditional village inn was first licensed in 1790 and has listings of landlords from then until the present. Two regular ales and two changing guests are available. Food is reasonably priced, and themed food nights are hosted. The railway station and bus service along with a range of country walks make this a popular stop-off. Qᗜ❀❍❶♣≠♠️P🖳(42)🐾🛜

Haynes

Greyhound ✅
68 Northwood End Road, MK45 3QD (at Northwood End)
☎ (01234) 381239 🌐 thegreyhoundhaynes.co.uk
Greene King Abbot, IPA; 4 changing beers (sourced regionally; often Oakham, Wadworth) Ⓗ
A family-run village pub on the John Bunyan Trail and close to the Greensand Ridge Walk, with a large garden offering play equipment and a pétanque court. Families are welcome in the spacious lounge and dining area until 9pm. The dog-friendly public bar area hosts darts and other village teams. The fortnightly quiz is a popular

event. Four changing beers are available in summer. There is no food on Monday or Sunday evening, and Sunday lunch is a carvery. ᗜ❀❍❶♣♠️P🖳(9B)🐾🛜

Heath & Reach

Axe & Compass
Leighton Road, LU7 0AA
☎ (01525) 237394 🌐 theaxeandcompass.pub
2 changing beers (sourced nationally) Ⓗ
This village community pub has been a free house since 2014. The older front bar, with its low beams, serves as a lounge and dining area, while the rear public bar has gaming machines, a pool table and a TV screen. The large garden includes a children's play area. Regularly appearing guest beers often come from local breweries such as Hornes, Tring, Leighton Buzzard, Gun Dog and Vale. Accommodation is available in a separate lodge. ᗜ❀➰❍❶♣♠️P🖳(150)🐾🛜

Henlow

Engineers Arms Ⓛ ✅
68 High Street, SG16 6AA
☎ (01462) 812284 🌐 engineersarms.co.uk
10 changing beers (sourced nationally; often Cotleigh, Hadham, Salcombe) Ⓗ
This multi-award winning pub has enjoyed 26 consecutive years in the Guide under the same landlord. Ten beers and six ciders and perries – typically from Saxby's and Orchard Pig – are sometimes supplemented by two ales served directly from wooden barrels in the cellar. Poker, quiz and board game nights, karaoke, live bands, pub outings, a renowned beer festival, tap takeovers and TV sport ensure there is something for everyone. Local CAMRA Pub and Cider Pub of the Year 2020. Qᗜ❀❀➰♣♠️🖳(9B,188)🐾🛜

Old Transporter Ale House Ⓛ
300 Hitchin Road, SG16 6DP
☎ (01462) 817410 🌐 theoldtransporter.co.uk
4 changing beers (sourced nationally; often Potbelly, Tring) Ⓖ
Located near RAF Henlow, this single-room beer house has a friendly and welcoming atmosphere, with interesting transport-themed decoration. Real ale is served direct from barrels set up behind the bar. A good selection of ciders is available, mainly from Lilley's, plus a choice of snacks. The pub is home to a darts team and has a widescreen TV for live rugby matches. Events include live music evenings, quizzes, raffles and mini beer festivals – often featuring dark beers. ᗜ♣♠️🖳(9b,188) 🐾🛜

Leighton Buzzard

Bald Buzzard Micropub Ⓛ
6 Hockliffe Street, LU7 1HJ
☎ 07484 896131 🌐 baldbuzzard.co.uk
5 changing beers (sourced nationally) Ⓖ
This popular micropub with a bespoke chiller room opened in 2015, providing the discerning beer enthusiast with a great selection of ales and ciders. Four KeyKeg dispensers offer an interesting selection of beers not normally found locally. Four ciders are available, as well as a selection of bottled and canned beers. The bar's seating layout encourages conversation. ᗜ❀❀♣♠️❍🖳(70,150) 🐾

Black Lion
20 High Street, LU7 1EA
☎ (01525) 853725 🌐 blacklionlb.com

Draught Bass; Nethergate Suffolk County Best Bitter; Oakham Bishops Farewell; 5 changing beers (sourced nationally) ⊞
This traditional alehouse with 17th-century origins features exposed beams, wooden floors and an open fire. Eight handpumps dispense beers from the likes of Leighton Buzzard, North Cotswold, Slater's and Purity. Eight changing real ciders are also available and an impressive bottled and canned beer menu lists over 100 continental and British beers. There is a large paved garden. Bar snacks are served and bring-your-own cold lunches are welcome. Local CAMRA Pub of the Year 2015-2019. Q❀✿⊛◑♣♠☲(70,150)❀

Leighton Buzzard Brewing Company Brewery Tap ⓛ
Unit 31, Harmill Industrial Estate, Grovebury Road, LU7 4FF (second left from Grovebury Rd)
☎ 07538 903753 ⊕ leightonbuzzardbrewing.co.uk
4 changing beers (sourced locally; often Leighton Buzzard) Ⓖ
The brewery tap for the Leighton Buzzard Brewing Co, a range of four of the brewery's beers is dispensed directly from casks in the cool room, alongside bottles to drink on the premises or to take home. Real cider is also available. Open days are held one Saturday a month between March and December (check the website for dates), with local food offerings and occasional live music.
✿♿♣♠P☲(D1)❀♀

Swan Hotel ✓
50 High Street, LU7 1EA
☎ (01525) 380170
Greene King Abbot; Ruddles Best Bitter; Sharp's Doom Bar; 6 changing beers (sourced nationally) ⊞
Dating from the 17th century, this former coaching inn renovated by Wetherspoon is a High Street landmark. With good-value food and 39 guest rooms, the Swan is bustling for much of the week. One long bar provides friendly service to two rooms, a conservatory and a courtyard. Guest beers may come from local microbreweries and real cider is available in summer. Families are welcome until 11pm. Events include biannual beer festivals. Q✿❀✿✍◑♿♠☲(70,150)♀

White Horse
9 New Road, Linslade, LU7 2LS
☎ (01525) 635739 ⊕ whitehorsebandb.co.uk
Fuller's London Pride; 4 changing beers (sourced nationally) ⊞
This is a genuine back-street free house close to the Grand Union Canal and Leighton Buzzard railway station. The L-shaped bar features several sports TV screens. There is a small courtyard to the rear and a small public car park across the road. Guest beers are often from St Austell, Otter and Oakham. An interesting and varied selection of bottled and canned beers is also offered. Accommodation comprises seven rooms in a converted stable block. ✿✍♿♣♠☲❀♀

Little Staughton

Crown ⓛ
Green End, MK44 2BU (at N end of village on road to Pertenhall)
☎ (01234) 376260 ⊕ thecrownstaughton.com
Crown Pale, The Beer With No Name ⊞
A modern pub built in the 1970s after the original thatched building burnt down. The building sits back from the road behind the car park, with a large garden to the right. The main bar is L-shaped with a wood-burning stove – the fireplace is the only remaining part of the

original building. A small room to the right is used for dining and functions. The pub has its own microbrewery. ✿❀⊛◑♣P☲(28,29)❀♀

Luton

Bricklayers Arms
16-18 High Town Road, LU2 0DD
☎ (01582) 611017 ⊕ bricklayersarmsluton.co.uk
6 changing beers (sourced nationally; often Oakham) ⊞
This quirky High Town pub, run by the same landlady for over 30 years, is busy with Hatters fans on match days. It has TVs in both bars and a popular quiz night every Monday. Six handpumps serve a variety of guest beers from breweries all over the nation, including a choice of light, amber and, usually, a mild ale. Draught Belgian beers and two real ciders are also available.
❀≉♣♠❀♀

Globe ✓
26 Union Street, LU1 3AN
☎ (01582) 482259
Greene King IPA; 2 changing beers (sourced nationally) ⊞
Popular, homely, street-corner local, just off the town centre. The L-shaped single bar offers Greene King IPA complemented by two constantly changing guests from regional breweries and micros. Beer festivals feature regularly. Good-value food is served at lunchtime. Sport is shown on TV. There is an enclosed patio area to the rear of the small car park. ✿❀◑♿≉♣P❀♀

Great Northern ⓛ
63 Bute Street, LU1 2EY
☎ (01582) 729311
St Austell Tribute; Tring Side Pocket for a Toad ⊞
This may be the smallest pub in Luton. Its name was changed in the 1860s when the Great Northern Railway was built right on its doorstep. It still retains green Victorian wall tiles and a table featuring quirky brass pint glass holders at each corner. Sports are shown on TV. There is a smoking area at the rear. ≉♣❀♀

White House ⓛ ✓
1 Bridge Street, LU1 2NB
☎ (01582) 454608
10 changing beers (sourced nationally) ⊞
A large two-bar town-centre Wetherspoon with the usual keenly priced food and drinks. It offers 10 different guest ales split across the two separate bars, with local ales often from Vale, Tring or Kelchner breweries. This is a bright and clean pub in the Galaxy Centre, conveniently located for several bus routes. Q✿❀⊛◑♿≉♠☲❀♀

Odell

Bell
81 High Street, MK43 7AS
☎ (01234) 910850 ⊕ thebellinodell.co.uk
Greene King Abbot, IPA; 4 changing beers (sourced nationally) ⊞
Handsome thatched village pub with a large garden near the River Great Ouse. With the Harrold-Odell Country Park just down the lane, this is a popular stop for walkers. Sympathetic refurbishment and a series of linked but distinct seating areas help retain a traditional pub atmosphere. Good-value, quality food includes a Sunday roast, steak and chips night Monday and pie and chips night Tuesday. Brunch is served in the mornings, while tea and cakes are available all day.
Q✿❀◑P☲(25,26)❀♀

Sandy

Sir William Peel ✅
39 High Street, SG19 1AG
☎ (01767) 680607 ⊕ sirwilliampeel.wixsite.com/sirwilliampeel
Batemans XB; Oakham JHB; 2 changing beers (sourced nationally) ⊞
The inn was created in 1838 when two cottages were combined. A U-shaped bar greets you on entry. Bright patios at the front and rear contrast with the more muted interior, comfortably furnished with tables, chairs and sofas. A cabinet behind the bar contains several ciders. The pub is known for its charity fundraising and occasional live music. Separate beer and cider festivals are popular both with locals and beer tourists.
ੴ❀≠♣♠P☷(73,188) 🐾🕯

Shefford

Brewery Tap Ⓛ
14 Northbridge Street, SG17 5DH
☎ (01462) 628448
B&T Shefford Bitter; 5 changing beers (sourced nationally; often B&T) ⊞
The Tap is primarily a drinkers' pub, offering three B&T beers and three guest ales. Breweriana decorates an open-plan interior divided into two distinct areas, plus a family room at the rear. Sandwiches, toasties and other light meals are available, and it does a small selection of main meals. There is occasional live music or a quiz. The rear patio garden is heated on cool evenings.
ੴ❀◑♣♠P☷🐾🕯

Bridge Ⓛ ✅
50 High Street, SG17 5DG
☎ (01462) 351395
Eagle IPA; 1 changing beer (sourced nationally) ⊞
A corner pub next to the site of an old railway bridge, modernised to a high standard. It caters for all ages, with a large rear bar featuring three TV screens and a smaller, quieter front bar. Wednesday is quiz night. New licensees have introduced a choice of changing real ales, and food is now available. Local CAMRA Most Improved Pub 2020. ੴ❀◑♣♠P☷🐾🕯

Slip End

Rising Sun Ⓛ ✅
1-3 Front Street, LU1 4BP
☎ (01582) 731384 ⊕ therisingsunslipend.co.uk
3 changing beers (sourced nationally; often Farr Brew) ⊞
Comfortable two-bar village local, now run by the nearby Wheathampstead brewery Farr Brew following a much-needed complete refurbishment. Two rotating ales from Farr Brew are served plus a range of the brewery's bottles and a changing guest ale. One bar is primarily used as a restaurant where food is served daily. A takeaway pizza service is popular. ੴ❀◑♣P🕯

Stanbridge

Five Bells
Station Road, LU7 9JF
☎ (01525) 210224 ⊕ fivebellsstanbridge.co.uk
Fuller's London Pride; Gale's Seafarers Ale, HSB; 1 changing beer ⊞
A Fuller's-owned country pub set in extensive and attractive grounds, with wooden floors, two real fires, a cosy snug and low beams. A separate 80-seater restaurant in the 18th-century wing offers good-quality

food and can be used for weddings and other functions. Guest ales are usually from Fuller's/Gale's and may occasionally include one from a local microbrewery. The pub is named after the nearby church which once had five bells – but now has six. ੴ❀◑♣♠P☷(70)🐾🕯

Totternhoe

Old Farm Inn
16 Church Road, LU6 1RE
☎ (01582) 674053 ⊕ oldfarminn.co.uk
Fuller's London Pride; Gale's HSB; 2 changing beers ⊞
Located in the conservation area of Church End, this charming village pub boasts two inglenooks. The public bar with its low boarded ceiling is where you will find good conversation and traditional pub games. Dogs are welcome in the front bar. A quiz is held on alternate Thursdays. Tasty home-cooked food is served including popular Sunday roasts (no food Sun eve or all day Mon). Beer festivals are held in May and August. There is a child-friendly garden. ੴ❀◑♣♠P☷(61)🐾🕯

Upper Dean

Three Compasses ✅
High Street, PE28 0NE (S of village on road to Melchbourne)
☎ (01234) 708346 ⊕ thethreecompasses.co.uk
Greene King IPA; St Austell Tribute; Timothy Taylor Landlord ⊞
Attractive thatched and partly boarded inn on the southern edge of the village. The main bar is to the left of the entrance with a games area behind. There is a small lounge bar on the right which is used mainly for dining. A large garden is to the rear. Since reopening the pub several years ago, the owners have made great efforts to create a popular rural venue for food and drink.
ੴ❀◑♣P☷(28) 🐾🕯

Woburn

Woburn Ale House Ⓛ
11 Market Place, MK17 9PZ
☎ (01525) 290142 ⊕ woburnalehouse.com
4 changing beers (sourced locally; often Hornes, Leighton Buzzard, Tring) ⊞
This charming bar, previously a flower shop, has six handpumps for cask ales and two for varying ciders and perries. Local beers feature heavily, in particular from Hornes Brewery and Leighton Buzzard Brewing Company. A wide variety of up to 40 different and interesting artisan keg, canned and bottled beers is also available. There is comfortable seating towards the rear plus a small courtyard area. ❀♠♠P☷(49)🐾🕯

Wrestlingworth

Chequers Ⓛ
43 High Street, SG19 2EP
☎ (01767) 631818 ⊕ chequersfreehouse.co.uk
Adnams Southwold Bitter; Eagle IPA; 3 changing beers (sourced nationally; often Lacons) ⊞
Popular, friendly, Grade II-listed establishment with a spacious interior and several outdoor areas where you can enjoy drinking alfresco when the weather permits. Community groups, a free jukebox, unobtrusive TV sport, live music, cribbage, darts and pétanque teams, well-kept beers and good-value food help make the pub a hub of the village. Outside, there is access to footpaths and bridleways that head westward across east Bedfordshire. Ramblers, cyclists, bikers and dogs on leads are all welcome. ੴ❀◑♣P☷(188)🐾🕯

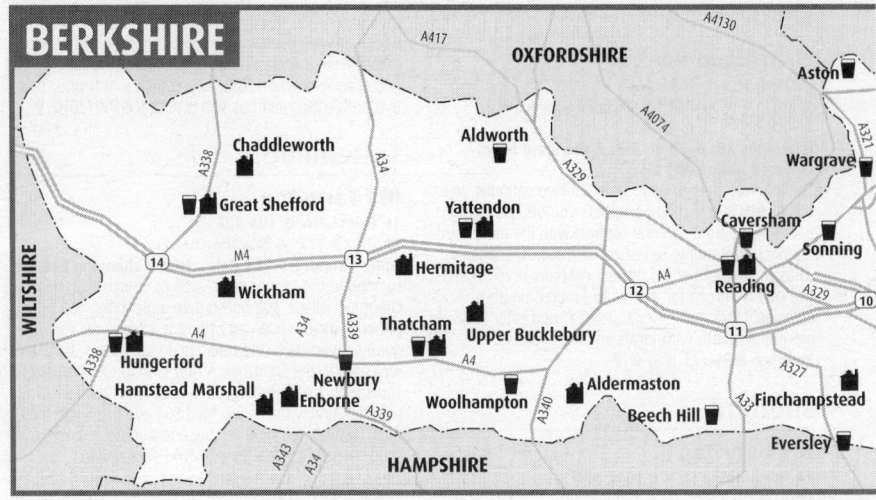

BERKSHIRE

Aldworth

Bell Inn ★ 🄻

Bell Lane, RG8 9SE (250yds off B4009)
☎ (01635) 578272
Arkell's 3B; Indigenous Baldrick; Rebellion Roasted Nuts; house beer (by West Berkshire); 2 changing beers (sourced locally; often Amwell Springs, Loose Cannon) 🄷
A long-standing Guide entry, this traditional inn has been owned by the same family for 250 years, and has been recognised by CAMRA as having a nationally important historic pub interior. Locals, walkers, cyclists and visitors rub shoulders and share tables to enjoy not only great beer but also an extensive menu of filled rolls, hot soups and proper puddings. Outside is a large, secluded garden. CAMRA National Pub of the Year in 2019.
Q🕏❀🄷♣🅟❀

Aston

Flower Pot

Ferry Lane, RG9 3DG (jct with Remenham Lane)
SU784842
☎ (01491) 574721
Brakspear Gravity; Ringwood Boondoggle 🄷
Charming rural inn set in the heart of the village, close to the River Thames with beautiful views of the countryside. The large, popular garden is a picture in summer, providing a welcoming place to enjoy food and well-kept beers. In the public bar and restaurant you will find an eclectic display of aquatic taxidermy. Licensees Tony and Pat have been here over 30 years and are Brakspear's longest-serving tenants in a single pub.
Q🕏❀🛏🄷🕭♣🅟🖵(800,850) ❀ 🛜

Beech Hill

Elm Tree

Beech Hill Road, RG7 2AZ SU695641
☎ (0118) 988 3505 🌐 theelmtreebeechhill.co.uk
Ringwood Boondoggle; Timothy Taylor Landlord; 1 changing beer (sourced nationally) 🄷
Part pub, part restaurant, the Elm Tree is popular both with locals and visitors from further afield. Diners come to this gastropub to enjoy quality food, but drinkers are equally welcome at the bars. The cosy interior features some lovely murals, a small collection of bells and a real fire. Elaborate decking outside includes palm trees and mood lighting, with spectacular countryside views. The pub may close early on Sunday if quiet. 🕏❀🄾🅟❀🛜

Binfield

Victoria Arms

Terrace Road North, RG42 5JA (100yds S of jct with Tilehurst Lane)
☎ (01344) 483856 🌐 victoriaarmsbinfield.co.uk
Dark Star Hophead; Fuller's London Pride, ESB; 1 changing beer (sourced locally; often Elusive, Rebellion, Stardust) 🄷
Welcoming village local at the heart of its community. A real fire keeps it cosy in winter while the terraced garden is popular in summer. The upper walls and beams around the bar are adorned with hundreds of beer bottles. Quality traditional pub fare is served, with a Sunday roast and children's menu. There is a heated marquee for private functions in the garden and a separate heated smoking area. Fleeces are provided outside on chilly nights. 🕏❀🄾♣🅟🖵(150,151)❀🛜

Bracknell

Cannie Man 🄻 ✅

Bywood, RG12 7RF
☎ (01344) 307620 🌐 cannieman.co.uk
Fuller's London Pride; 3 changing beers (sourced nationally; often Dartmoor, Rebellion, West Berkshire) 🄷
A welcoming, friendly estate pub with a licensee who has been running the pub for more than 10 years. Four handpumps offer a session bitter, a local ale and a selection of guest beers. A true community local, it supports charities and sponsors a local boys' football club. TVs in the large single bar area display a myriad of sporting events and music. Live weekly entertainment features on one night over the weekend.
🕏❀♣🅟🖵(171,172) 🛜

Old Manor 🄻 ✅

Grenville Place, RG12 1BP (at College roundabout jct with Church Rd)
☎ (01344) 304490
Greene King Abbot; Ruddles Best Bitter; Sharp's Doom Bar; 6 changing beers (sourced nationally; often Binghams, Oakham, Windsor & Eton) 🄷

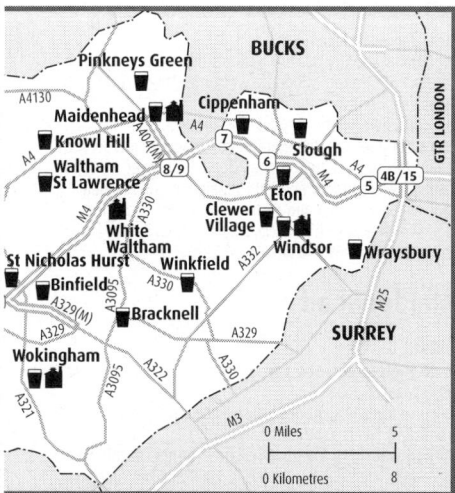

Featuring in the Guide every year since 2000, this Wetherspoon is located in one of the oldest buildings in Bracknell. Tudor origins are obvious, especially the Monk's Room where a priest hole, dating from 1682, can be seen. Two bar areas offer three regular beers and six changing guest ales plus Old Rosie and Black Dragon ciders. With a broad customer mix, the pub gets busy on Friday and Saturday evenings. There are three outside areas to enjoy. Q☆✿ⓞ☕⚤♿●P🚃(4,53)🎅🛜

Caversham

Fox & Hounds 🄻
51 Gosbrook Road, RG4 8BN
☎ 07540 816293
6 changing beers (sourced nationally; often Oakham, Siren, Wild Weather) Ⓗ
A regular winner or runner-up local CAMRA Pub of the Year, this is a popular and lively community hub. It offers eight changing beers, six craft keg lines, six or more ciders and perries, plus a good selection of bottles. A blue plaque commemorates the day in 1960 that John Lennon and Paul McCartney performed a gig here as the Nerk Twins. A quiz night every second Wednesday is always well attended. ☆✿ⓞ♣●P🚃(25,27)🎅🛜

Griffin 🄻 ✅
10/12 Church Road, RG4 7AD
☎ (0118) 947 5018
Greene King IPA, Abbot; Morland Old Speckled Hen; 1 changing beer (sourced locally; often Loddon) Ⓗ
There has been a pub on this site since the 1800s (when eels were fished in the nearby River Thames and brought to be sold inside). The current building dates from 1916 and offers good food and ale with numerous specials on the chalkboards and regular themed produce weeks. The spacious interior and heated rear patio garden provide plenty of choice for a quiet drink or a big family meal. There is usually a local ale available at the bar. ☆✿ⓞ♿●P🚃(22,23)🎅🛜

Cippenham

Barleycorn 🄻
151 Lower Cippenham Lane, SL1 5DS
☎ (01628) 603115
7 changing beers (sourced nationally) Ⓗ

Recently refurbished traditional single-bar pub that caters well for a strong local following. Seven guest beers always include one from Rebellion plus a strong ale. The rest are from both national and local breweries, along with a regularly changing real cider plus a choice of fruit ciders. A large collection of bottles and jugs features around the walls. Occasional live music and two sports TVs provide the entertainment. The nearby public car park is free. Q☆♣●P🚃(5)🎅🛜

Clewer Village

Swan 🄻
9 Mill Lane, SL4 5JG
☎ (07458) 300026 ⊕ theswanwindsor.co.uk
Windsor & Eton Guardsman; 2 changing beers (sourced locally; often Windsor & Eton) Ⓗ
Just 15 minutes' walk from Windsor town centre, this 18th-century village free house has been renovated following closure of over three years. Purchased as a community interest company, it has become the hub of the village and now provides board game nights, a knitting circle, quiz nights, occasional music and a book club. Cider offerings include Devon Red from Sandford Orchards. Q⏰✿ⓞ●🚃(71,702)🎅🛜

Eton

George Inn 🄻
77 High Street, SL4 6AF
☎ (01753) 861797 ⊕ georgeinn-eton.co.uk
Windsor & Eton Knight of the Garter, Windsor Knot, Guardsman, Conqueror; 2 changing beers (sourced locally; often Windsor & Eton) Ⓗ
Windsor & Eton Brewery's first pub has recently completed a renovation – a new bar hosts six of the brewery's ales, the range subject to change when special or seasonal ales become available. Wooden floors and lighting supplied by carriage lamps and candles help to create a warm, comfortable ambience. Breakfast is served every day. The Hop House, a separate building in the beer garden, is available for private functions. Accommodation is in eight en-suite rooms. Q⏰✿🛏ⓞ⚤●🚃(10)🎅🛜

Eversley

Tally Ho 🄻
Fleet Hill, RG27 0RR (on A327 jct with B3348)

☎ (0118) 973 2134 ⊕ tallyho-eversley.co.uk
4 changing beers (sourced regionally; often Ascot, Longdog, Red Cat) ⊞
Nestling on the Berkshire border with Hampshire, this splendid pub benefits from an extensive riverside garden. Inside it is relaxed and cosy. Many visitors come to eat in the well-regarded restaurant, but all are free to use the bar area where a good selection of local ales can be found – the house beer is believed to come from south-west England. A changing guest cider is also on handpump. A basket of reading glasses, provided for patrons to borrow, shows the attention to detail here.
Q ⏱ ❀ ⦿ ⅃ ⅄ P ⊟ (92) ❀ ☂

Great Shefford

Great Shefford ⅃
Newbury Road, RG17 7DS
☎ (01488) 648462 ⊕ thegreatshefford.com
6 changing beers (sourced nationally; often Otter, St Austell, West Berkshire) ⊞
A substantial inn with a main bar area and a separate horse-racing lounge. There are views of the River Lambourn from the rear restaurant. Outside, the adjacent terrace has comfortable seating under a canopy. A changing local beer is among six cask ales served from the long bar, and the seasonally-inspired food menu offers an eclectic mix of English and European dishes. Situated on the road from Wantage to Hungerford, the pub is a popular stop for Lambourn Valley Way walkers.
⏱ ❀ ⦿ ⅃ ⅄ P ⊟ (4,4S) ❀ ☂

Hungerford

Hungerford Club ⊘
3 The Croft, RG17 0HY (on foot via Church Lane, by road via Church St and Croft Rd)
☎ (01488) 682357 ⊕ hungerford-club.co.uk
Fuller's London Pride; 1 changing beer (sourced nationally) ⊞
A warm welcome is assured at this comfortable bowls, tennis and social club, situated in the quiet Croft, just a few yards from the High Street. Games such as billiards and snooker are also played here. Refurbishment of the bar area has given the club a fresh look. The changing guest beer, sourced nationally, is often chosen by club members. An annual beer festival is held over the August bank holiday. CAMRA members are welcome.
Q ⏱ ❀ ⅊ ♣ P ⊟ (3) ❀ ☂

John o' Gaunt ⅃ ⊘
21 Bridge Street, RG17 0EG (30yds N of canal bridge)
☎ (01488) 683535 ⊕ john-o-gaunt-hungerford.co.uk
House beer (by INNformal); 7 changing beers (sourced regionally) ⊞
A 16th-century Grade II-listed town-centre pub named after the Duke of Lancaster. There are eight handpumps offering constantly changing ales, complemented by a large selection of real ciders and bottled beers from around the world. At least two beers are always from the pub's own INNformal Brewery. Quality locally sourced food is available lunchtimes, evenings and all day Sunday. A tiki bar was added in the garden in 2019, open during the summer months.
Q ⏱ ❀ ⦿ ⅊ ♣ ⦿ P ⊟ (3X,20) ❀ ☂

Knowl Hill

Royal Oak ⅃
Round the Hill, Knowl Hill Common, RG10 9YE
☎ (01628) 822010

Brakspear Gravity; Sharp's Doom Bar; 1 changing beer (sourced locally) ⊞
Traditional country pub set back off the A4, popular with locals and offering a friendly welcome. This is a free house serving two regular beers plus a guest, often from a local brewery, and real cider on draught. Sports TV is a focus but does not dominate. Home made food is served daily. The tidy pub garden has clear views over fields to Littlewick Green and beyond to Maidenhead. An ideal stop-off for walkers and cyclists as it offers a starting point for the Berkshire Cycle Way and Knowl Hill Bridleway. ⏱ ❀ ⦿ ⅄ ♣ ⦿ P ⊟ (127,239) ❀ ☂

Maidenhead

Bear ⅃ ⊘
8-10 High Street, SL6 1QJ
☎ (01628) 763030
Greene King IPA, Abbot; Sharp's Doom Bar; 4 changing beers (sourced nationally) ⊞
A short walk from the town hall, this former coaching inn became a Wetherspoon house in 2009 and has an open-plan bar with several different seating areas, including a licensed outside space to the front. A spiral staircase leads to an upper floor with additional seating. The 10 handpumps dispense up to six guest ales, many from local breweries. Two or three ciders are often available, including Old Rosie and Black Dragon.
⏱ ❀ ⦿ ⇌ ⦿ ⊟ (3,7) ☂

Craufurd Arms ⅃
15 Gringer Hill, SL6 7LY
☎ (01628) 675410 ⊕ craufurdarms.com
Rebellion IPA; West Berkshire Good Old Boy; Windsor & Eton Knight of the Garter; 2 changing beers (sourced locally); often Stardust, Windsor & Eton) ⊞
This pint-sized local was the 50th community-owned pub in the country. The building, just outside the town centre, dates back to the 1800s. It hosts activities including live music, crib, darts and a quiz on Thursday night. Three TV screens show Sky and BT sports. A perennial award winner in the local CAMRA Pub of the Year contest, the place is well known for its friendly atmosphere and fine selection of local real and craft ales.
⏱ ❀ ⇌ (Furze Platt) ♣ P ⊟ (5,8) ❀ ☂

Maiden's Head ⅃
34 High Street, SL6 1QE
☎ (01628) 784786 ⊕ themaidenshead.co.uk
4 changing beers (sourced locally; often Rebellion, Stardust) ⊞
Large single-room high-street pub offering four constantly rotating guest ales and four keg craft beers (two American), plus Weissbier and Grimbergen Blonde, as well as a range of world bottled beers. Food is served. Outside, there is a large beer garden at the back. Terrestrial TV shows some events and live music is hosted at the weekend. Dogs are welcome outside.
⏱ ❀ ⦿ ⅃ ⇌ ♣ ⊟ (3,7) ❀ ☂

Newbury

Catherine Wheel ⅃
35 Cheap Street, RG14 5DB
☎ (01635) 569897 ⊕ thecatherinewheel.com
6 changing beers (sourced nationally; often Binghams, Long Man, Wild Weather) ⊞
Run by the current landlord since its refurbishment in 2014, this town-centre pub serves a changing selection of beers from six handpumps on the main bar plus additional cask ales on stillage in the courtyard. It also offers a large range of craft and continental beers, local

and national ciders and artisan gins. The food menu is based around Pieminister pies. A former winner of local CAMRA Pub of the Year and four times Cider Pub of the Year. ⏱❀◑≠♣🌢🖳(2,3)🌢🛜

Cow & Cask 🅛

1 Inches Yard, Market Street, RG14 5DP (SE of pedestrian crossing at corner of Market St and Bartholomew St)
☎ (07517) 658071
3 changing beers (sourced regionally; often Indigenous, Loddon, XT) 🅖

A welcoming and friendly micropub where conversation flourishes. A large blackboard lists the range of drinks and the rising number of different beers served since 2014 – usually including three locally sourced real ales on stillage, along with three or four real ciders from bag-in-box containers. Snacks include crisps, nuts and pickled eggs. There is a limited amount of outside seating. Crib is often played on Tuesday evenings. The pub is near the town's station, cinema and car parks. Q≠♣🖳(2)🌢

King Charles Tavern 🅛 🅿

54 Cheap Street, RG14 5BX
☎ (01635) 36695 🌐 kctavern.com
West Berkshire Good Old Boy; house beer (by Greene King); 6 changing beers (sourced nationally) 🅷

Over 100 years old and a former CAMRA branch Pub of the Year, this tavern is a three-minute walk from Newbury train station. It has a central bar with the cellar directly below. Eight ales are offered, all meticulously kept and available in third-pints for those who want to sample a selection. Fresh home-made food is served, with Sunday lunch a speciality. The front rooms have open fires and a mixture of sofas and chairs. Note the old map of Newbury on the ceiling. ⏱❀◑≠🖳(2,3)🌢🛜

Lion 🅿

39 West Street, RG14 1BE
☎ (01635) 528468 🌐 thelionatnewbury.co.uk
Wadworth Horizon, 6X, Swordfish; 2 changing beers (sourced nationally; often Adnams, Bath Ales, Brains) 🅷

A Wadworth Brewery pub since its 1988 rebuild. The father and son team who have run the welcoming back-street community pub since 2019 have added changing guest ales and installed a large gazebo to benefit outdoor customers. Inside, a central island bar above a traditional cellar can serve eight cask ales and a real cider. Framed historic photographs decorate the walls and the Thursday night pub quiz is popular. Sport is screened on TV and there is sometimes live music. ⏱❀◑≠♣🌢🛜

Lock, Stock & Barrel

104 Northbrook Street, RG14 1AA (alleyway 20yds NW of the canal bridge)
☎ (01635) 580550 🌐 lockstockandbarrelnewbury.co.uk
Fuller's London Pride; 4 changing beers (sourced regionally; often Dark Star, Fuller's) 🅷

Centrally located and next to the Kennet and Avon Canal, this is a popular, traditional pub with a comfortably furnished open-plan interior. There is plenty of outside seating, including a roof terrace. Beers are selected from the Fuller's range including Gale's and Dark Star. Traditional pub food is freshly cooked to order by the chef. There is regular live music and families are welcome until 9pm. Dog biscuits and blankets are provided. ⏱❀◑&≠🖳(4,4A)🌢🛜

Pinkneys Green

Boundary Arms 🅛

112 Pinkneys Road, SL6 5DN
☎ (01628) 629667
Rebellion IPA, Roasted Nuts; 1 changing beer (sourced regionally) 🅷

This large independent pub opposite the green has recently been refurbished. It has two bars, both with real fires – the public bar is at the front and at the back is a pleasant lounge bar with doors out to the garden where there is a secure children's play area. There are also two tables at the front where you can relax and watch the world go by. Q⏱❀♣P🖳(9)🌢🛜

Reading

Alehouse 🅛

2 Broad Street, RG1 2BH
☎ (0118) 950 8119
9 changing beers (sourced nationally) 🅷

Popular town centre drinking establishment that always leaves an impression on visitors with its quirky wooden fixtures and reclaimed wooden floor. As a champion of microbreweries, both local and further afield, rare and unusual ales and beer styles are frequently found on the handpumps. A selection of real ciders and perries is also available. Often busy around the bar area, those wishing for a more peaceful drink can take advantage of the secluded snugs at the back of the pub. ⏱≠⊖♣🌢🖳(4,X4)🌢

Allied Arms 🅛

57 St Mary's Butts, RG1 2LG
☎ (0118) 958 3323 🌐 allied-arms.co.uk
Loddon Hullabaloo; 9 changing beers (sourced nationally) 🅷

A small, family-run, town-centre pub dating from around 1828, with two cosy bars entered through the side passage, not the front door. An enhanced range of up to 10 ales is available each weekend. It also offers a good range of single malts, gins and rums. The large walled garden is a popular refuge from the chaos of the town, with patio heaters for colder nights. A wide and interesting selection of music is available on the jukebox. The pub hosts a regular charity quiz and is close to St Mary's Butts bus terminus. ⏱❀≠⊖♣🖳(8,9)🌢🛜

Butler 🅛

85-91 Chatham Street, RG1 7DS
☎ (0118) 959 5500 🌐 thebutlerreading.co.uk
St Austell Proper Job; Timothy Taylor Landlord; West Berkshire Mister Chubb's; 2 changing beers (sourced regionally) 🅷

Named after Butler's Wine Merchants, who operated from these premises many years ago, this is very much a local pub in the heart of town. Taken over by a consortium after a long period of Fuller's stewardship, there has been an ongoing process of upgrading both inside and out. Ales are from regional and local breweries, including some unusual choices for the area. Live music is a weekly feature and draws large crowds. ⏱❀◑≠⊖♣🖳(15,16) 🌢🛜

Castle Tap 🅛

120 Castle Street, RG1 7RJ
☎ (0118) 958 0473 🌐 thecastletap.co.uk
4 changing beers (sourced nationally) 🅷

Alongside its changing selection of real ales and ciders, the Castle Tap boasts an excellent range of bottled and canned beers. While offering a warm welcome to visiting real ale aficionados and craft beer fans, it maintains a friendly local atmosphere. Frequent live music and other events are well worth checking out. And for those feeling peckish, cheeseboards are available. The back room can be booked for functions. 🌞✿♣♠P🍴(1,2)🏃🎵📶

Greyfriar ⓛ
53 Greyfriars Road, RG1 1PA
☎ (0118) 958 0560 ⊕ thegreyfriarreading.co.uk
Hogs Back HBB; 7 changing beers (sourced locally; often Elusive, Siren, Wild Weather) 🍺
A modern-looking yet traditional pub with eight handpumps and 14 keg lines, offering an impressive choice of beers from independent breweries. Bottled and canned beers also come from countrywide and foreign suppliers. Tap takeovers by various brewers are held on occasion. A small range of paninis is available. A quiz night is held every other Monday. Convenient for the railway station and popular with the after-work crowd.
🌞◑≠⊖♠🍴(3,8)🏃📶

Nag's Head ⓛ
5 Russell Street, RG1 7XD
☎ (07765) 880137 ⊕ thenagsheadreading.co.uk
12 changing beers 🍺
With a wide range of real ales, real cider and perry always on offer, visitors are sure to find something to their taste here. There is also a craft beer wall, with vessel and dispense indicated on the adjacent blackboard. A selection of board games is available for those wanting to while away a few sociable hours. The pub gets busy on Reading FC match days. A regular in CAMRA's National Pub of the Year awards.
🌞✿◑≠(West) ⊖♣♠P🍴(1,2) 🏃📶

Park House (University of Reading) ⓛ
Park House, Whiteknights Campus, RG6 6UR
☎ (0118) 378 5098
5 changing beers (sourced nationally; often Rebellion, Siren, Titanic) 🍺
The university's old senior common room is open to the public from midday during term time and over the Christmas and Easter vacations. Five ales, mostly local, are usually sold. The bar is popular with the more mature university community and can get busy in the early evening. The large outdoor seating area is perfect for a quiet drink in the evening sun. A regular bus service drops off inside the campus. Payment is card only.
Q🌞✿◑&♣♠🍴(21,21A) 🏃📶

Retreat
8 St John's Street, RG1 4EH
☎ (0118) 376 9159 ⊕ theretreat.pub
6 changing beers (sourced nationally; often Butcombe, Harvey's, Sharp's) 🍺
A well-loved back-street boozer with a traditional layout and feel. A wide selection of real ales is squeezed into the small bar. The landlord tends to concentrate on well-known national brands; however, there is a good range of more eclectic choices available in bottles, as well as a number of ciders. The pub is locally renowned for regular live music and hosting community events. A popular quiz night is held every second Wednesday of the month.
Q🌞♠🍴(4,13) 🏃

Three Guineas
Station Approach, RG1 1LY
☎ (0118) 957 2743 ⊕ three-guineas.co.uk
Fuller's Oliver's Island, London Pride, ESB; Gale's Seafarers Ale; 4 changing beers (sourced nationally; often Butcombe, Windsor & Eton) 🍺
Large Grade II-listed outlet built in 1840 by Isambard Kingdom Brunel in the old ticket hall of Reading railway station. Thoroughly refurbished by Fuller's Brewery a few

years ago to a high standard, it features ornate tiling, old railway memorabilia and a selection of classic clocks. Outside the impressive frontage there is a large seating area but this does not have direct access to the station platforms. 🌞✿◑&≠⊖🍴(3,4)🏃📶

Weather Station ⓛ
19 Eldon Terrace, RG1 4DX
☎ (0118) 958 6048 ⊕ wildweatherales.com/the-weather-station
3 changing beers (sourced nationally; often Wild Weather) 🍺
Formerly the Eldon Arms, the premises reopened as the Weather Station in 2019, combining a dual role as a tap for Wild Weather Brewery and a back-street pub. Patrons can expect a majority of KeyKeg craft beers from the UK and overseas. However, there are always at least a couple of Wild Weather real ales and they change regularly. The modern decor features various cartoon art prints. Payment is by card only. A 10-minute walk from the centre of Reading. 🌞✿&♠🍴(3,8)🏃📶

St Nicholas Hurst

Wheelwright's Arms
Davis Way, RG10 0TR (off B3030 opp entrance to Dinton Pastures)
☎ (0118) 934 4100 ⊕ thewheelwrightsarms.co.uk
Wadworth Henry's IPA, Horizon, 6X, Swordfish; 2 changing beers (sourced nationally; often Wadworth) 🍺
Popular family-run country pub and restaurant with one main bar serving up to six real ales and two ciders, one always Westons Old Rosie. For colder months there are two log fires and, outside, the rear garden accommodates dining, sporting and music events in summer. Dogs are encouraged, and the place is a popular stop-off for walkers and cyclists. Local club and community events are held along with a quiz night on Monday and a music night on one Friday of each month.
🌞✿◑&♠P🍴(128,129) 🏃📶

Slough

Moon & Spoon ⓛ ✅
86 High Street, SL1 1EL
☎ (01753) 531650
Greene King Abbot; Ruddles Best Bitter; Sharp's Doom Bar; 4 changing beers (sourced nationally) 🍺
This Wetherspoon establishment has 12 handpumps offering three regulars beers accompanied by up to four constantly changing guest ales, always including one from a local brewery. A couple of ciders are also usually available, often Old Rosie and Black Dragon. At the entrance is an eye-catching sculpture made of 1,148 spoons. The usual Wetherspoon extensive all-day food menu is served. Soft lighting gives the pub a cosy feel, especially at quieter times. 🌞◑&≠🍴(8,2)📶

Sonning

Bull Inn
High Street, RG4 6UP (next to St Andrew's Church)
☎ (0118) 969 3901 ⊕ bullinnsonning.co.uk
Fuller's London Pride; Gale's HSB; 2 changing beers (sourced nationally; often Butcombe, Dark Star, Fuller's) 🍺
Full of character, this delightful 16th-century pub is leased to Fuller's by the adjacent church. Most of the interior is set for dining, but there is a separate Village Bar drinking area, also used as a function room. The regular beers and changing guests are mainly from the

Fuller's range. An excellent selection of quality food, from snacks to fine dining, is available seven days a week. A good stop-off for those taking a walk alongside the Thames. Q ⏚ ✿ ⌔ ⏶ ❶ P ▯ (129) ❀ 🛜

Thatcham

Wheatsheaf Inn
15 Chapel Street, RG18 4JP
☎ (01635) 876715
House beer (by Delphic); 1 changing beer (sourced locally; often Bond Brews, Flack Manor) Ⓗ
A no-nonsense, bright, traditional pub catering to the local community and passing trade alike. The bar area features a marble floor and comfortable seating arranged around wooden tables. Two TVs offer coverage of major sporting events, with a pool table, dartboard, and dominos on offer. Two handpumps serve real ale, one dedicated to Wheatsheaf Bitter from nearby Delphic Brewery, and consequently the pub is often referred to as Delphic's informal tap. There is a small, south-facing garden. ⏚ ✿ ⌔ ⅋ ♣ P ▯ (1,41) ❀ 🛜

Waltham St Lawrence

Bell ⏚
The Street, RG10 0JJ
☎ (0118) 934 1788 ⊕ thebellwalthamstlawrence.co.uk
Loddon Hoppit; 4 changing beers (sourced locally; often Binghams, Butts, Stardust) Ⓗ
A classic half-timbered 15th-century pub bequeathed to the village in 1608 by Sir Ralph Newbury. It serves as both the village local and a quality restaurant, producing exceptionally good food from fresh, seasonal ingredients and promoting real ales from small, independent breweries. Up to eight ciders and perries are served from the cellar. You will find log fires in the winter and a good-sized beer garden for sunny summer days. Local CAMRA Pub of the Year 2020. Q ⏚ ✿ ❶ ♣ ● ▯ (4A) ❀ 🛜

Wargrave

Wargrave & District Snooker Club
Woodclyffe Hostel, Church Street, RG10 8EP
⊕ wargravesnooker.co.uk
2 changing beers (sourced nationally) Ⓗ
The club opens weekday evenings only and shares the building with the local library. The regularly changing beers reflect members' recommendations, with two on in the winter months and one in the summer. The TV's default is off, though the Six Nations Rugby and World Cup are exceptions. Show this Guide or CAMRA membership card for entry (£3 fee to use the snooker tables). Winner of CAMRA branch Club of the Year for several years. ⇌ ♣ ▯ (850) ❀

Windsor

A Hoppy Place ⏚
11 St Leonard's Road, SL4 3BN
☎ (01753) 206802 ⊕ ahoppyplace.co.uk
2 changing beers (sourced locally; often Binghams) Ⓗ
Windsor's first micropub, winner of local CAMRA Pub of the Year 2021 and SIBA Best UK Craft Beer Retailer 2021. It offers two casks, 10 keg lines and five fridges full of bottled and canned beers, with a focus both on local and international brews. The fridges are arranged by beer style, plus another fridge for cider. The pub has a canning machine to can cask and keg beer for takeaway while you wait. ✿ ⇌ (Windsor & Eton Central) ♣ ● ▯ (8) ❀ 🛜

Acre ⏚ ✅
Donnelly House, Victoria Street, SL4 1EN
☎ (01753) 841083 ⊕ theacrewindsor.com
Windsor & Eton Guardsman; 2 changing beers (sourced locally) Ⓗ
Formerly the Liberal Club, now a free house with a cellar bar open to all. The name refers to the adjacent Bachelors Acre. Three ales are on offer, one permanent and two regularly changing guests, often from local breweries. Freshly made rolls, pies and pasties are available daily. Live music is hosted every Saturday night. Two screens show live sporting events and there are excellent facilities for darts. The cellar bar can be hired as a function room. ⏚ ⇌ (Windsor & Eton Central) ♣ ▯ (8,2) 🛜

Carpenters Arms ✅
4 Market Street, SL4 1PB
☎ (01753) 863739
Fuller's London Pride; St Austell Nicholson's Pale Ale; Sharp's Doom Bar; 5 changing beers (sourced nationally) Ⓗ
Situated on a narrow, cobbled street close to the castle, this excellent Nicholson's pub has been voted local CAMRA Pub of the Year several times. The elegantly decorated interior is on three levels, the lowest of which is reputed to house a passageway to the castle. Ashby's Brewery tiles are on the floor by the entrance, harking back to the pub's former owners. The three regular beers are supplemented by five interesting guests, usually including something dark. ❶ ⇌ (Windsor & Eton Central) ▯ (702,8) 🛜

Corner House ⏚
22 Sheet Street, SL4 1BG
☎ (01753) 862031 ⊕ thecornerhousepub.co.uk
Big Smoke Solaris Session Pale Ale; 9 changing beers (sourced regionally) Ⓗ
This Grade II-listed building was completely refurbished in a traditional style by new owners in 2017 and designated as an ale and cider house. Fifteen handpumps serve 10 regularly changing real ales, five ciders and 10 keg lines. A good selection of traditional pub food is available. The pub has a function room upstairs and a small, partly covered roof terrace for those wishing to savour the air. Quiz night is Monday. ✿ ❶ ⇌ (Windsor & Eton Central) ● ▯ (702,8,) ❀ 🛜

Windsor & Eton Brewery Tap Room ⏚
1 Vansittart Estate, Duke Street, SL4 1SE
☎ (01753) 854075 ⊕ webrew.co.uk
Windsor & Eton Knight of the Garter, Windsor Knot, Guardsman, Conqueror; 3 changing beers (sourced locally; often Windsor & Eton) Ⓗ
The Windsor & Eton brewery opened its on-site shop and taproom in 2016. In 2021 a bigger and better taproom was launched. Unit Four features eight handpumps dispensing six of its beers, plus two guests. In addition there are 22 keg lines for Uprising beers and guests. The decor is modern and includes a mezzanine floor. There is an interesting range of cans and bottles. A new kitchen offers tasty food. ⇌ (Windsor & Eton Central) P ▯ (8,702)

Windsor Trooper ✅
97 St Leonards Road, SL4 3BZ
☎ (01753) 670122 ⊕ thewindsortrooper.com
Adnams Southwold Bitter; Oakham Citra; 3 changing beers (sourced regionally) Ⓗ
Large recently refurbished open-plan bar on the edge of the town centre. It offers up to five cask beers plus a number of kegs. The house beer is Windsor Trooper Ale,

brewed by Caledonian. Pub food is served to accompany the beer. Major sporting events are shown and there is live music on Saturday. The pub has a large conservatory to the rear, which is also used as a function room and is available to hire. Accommodation is in nine en-suite rooms. ⊛⇦⬤◑⇌(Windsor & Eton Central)♣⬤☂

Winkfield

White Hart ⅃

Church Road, SL4 4SE (on A330 opp St Mary's Church)
☎ (01344) 882415 ⊕ thewhitehartwinkfield.co.uk
Rebellion IPA; Sharp's Doom Bar; 1 changing beer (sourced locally; often Rebellion) ℍ
Former parish courthouse, now a village community pub with a comfortable bar, stone paved floor, and sofas close to the real fire. The kitchen serves home-made food (no food Mon) in the separate dining room, which also acts as a function room (children's menu available). Wednesday quiz and fish & chip nights on Fridays are extremely popular. The extensive garden can be enjoyed in warmer weather. Dogs allowed in the bar area only.
Q☕⬤◑♣P🚃(162,162A) ☂

Wokingham

Crispin ⅃

45 Denmark Street, RG40 2AY (opp Denmark St car park)
☎ (0118) 978 0309 ⊕ crispinpub.co.uk
Hogs Back HBB; 4 changing beers (sourced regionally; often Binghams, Rebellion, Siren) ℍ
A long-established real ale and cider pub named after St Crispin, the patron saint of cobblers, hence the pub sign. Up to five real ales are available, including many from local breweries, plus ciders from Tutts Clump and Westons. No food is served but you can bring your own or order in a takeaway. The pleasant garden includes an Aunt Sally pitch and a gazebo. Seasonal beer and cider festivals are held here. ⊛⇌♣⬤🚃(4,X4)☂

Oakingham Belle

Oaks Avenue, London Road, RG40 1PB (100yds N of jct with London Rd)
☎ (0118) 324 9894 ⊕ oakinghambellepubwokingham.co.uk
House beer (by Wainright); 4 changing beers (sourced nationally; often Marston's) ℍ
Spacious newly built pub with two large areas and three smaller snug spaces. Patrons can enjoy a good selection of food and drink – 90% of the food ingredients are fresh, including home-made bread, and four handpumps serve rotating real ales from the full Marston's portfolio. An indoor dog-friendly area is available plus a beer garden and patio areas outside. Happy hour is Monday to Friday afternoons, with reduced prices on real ales.
☕◑♿P🚃(4,X4)☂

Queen's Head ⅃ ✅

23 The Terrace, RG40 1BP
☎ (0118) 978 1221 ⊕ queensheadwokingham.co.uk
Greene King Abbot; house beer (by Hardys & Hansons); 4 changing beers (sourced locally; often Binghams, Hogs Back, Loddon) ℍ
Grade II-listed 15th-century cruck-framed inn nestling in a terrace close to the station. The characterful single bar has low ceilings, timber floors and a log fire. It is home to a darts team and hosts numerous charity events. As a Greene King Local Hero pub, three local ales are available alongside three from the brewery. Beer paddles with three third-pints are offered to sample a selection. The attractive rear patio and garden are pleasant in summer. Children are welcome until 8pm. ⊛⇌♣🚃(4,X4)☂

Ship Inn

104 Peach Street, RG40 1XH (jct with London Rd on entrance to one-way system)
☎ (0118) 978 0389 ⊕ shipwokingham.co.uk
Fuller's Oliver's Island, London Pride, ESB; 1 changing beer (sourced regionally; often Fuller's) ℍ
A large establishment with three bars on the edge of the town centre. A long-established Fuller's pub, it gets busy at weekends and in the summer, particularly when rugby is shown on TV. Quality food is served lunchtimes, evenings and throughout the day Friday to Sunday. The pub has a strong community focus and runs a loneliness initiative offering free tea, coffee and a chat to senior citizens in the morning. Local CAMRA Community Pub of the Year. ☕⊛◑P🚃(4,X4)☂

Woolhampton

Rowbarge ⅃

Station Road, RG7 5SH
☎ (0118) 971 2213
House beer (by St Austell); 5 changing beers (sourced regionally; often Ascot, Delphic, Wild Weather) ℍ
Built in 1815 as a cottage and subsequently extended, the characterful village inn has added a marquee to the terrace of its large garden overlooking the Kennet and Avon Canal. The pub's attractive and accessible location is an ideal starting point for towpath walks. Six cask ales are offered, served in a choice of dining and bar areas, some with log fires. Events include beer festivals and outdoor theatre performances.
Q☕⊛◑⬤⇌(Midgham)♣⬤P🚃(1)☂

Wraysbury

Perseverance ✅

2 High Street, TW19 5DB
☎ (01784) 482375 ⊕ thepercy.co.uk
Otter Ale; 3 changing beers (sourced nationally) ℍ
Comfortable pub with several seating areas. The larger front room has sofas, a piano and a large inglenook fireplace with a real log fire. Another seating area with an open fire leads to the rear dining section, which has well-stocked bookshelves. The rear garden is delightful. Three guest ales are always varied and from some of the more interesting breweries, both LocAle and around the country. Regular beer festivals are held. Quiz night is Thursday and live music features on Sunday afternoon.
Q☕⊛◑♣⬤P🚃(10,305)☂

Yattendon

Taproom & Kitchen at West Berkshire Brewery ⅃

The Old Dairy, RG18 0XT (signed turn from Chapel Lane, S of Yattendon)
☎ (01635) 767090 ⊕ wbbrew.com
West Berkshire Mister Chubb's, Maggs' Mild, Good Old Boy, Gold Star, Maharaja IPA; 5 changing beers (sourced locally; often Amwell Springs, Loose Cannon, West Berkshire) ℍ
Situated at the side of the brewery, the Taproom & Kitchen occupies a cavernous room which is well patronised and successful. The bar showcases West Berkshire Brewery beers alongside regular guest ales. Many events are held here including brewery tours, quiz nights, films, live music, tap takeovers, live sport and the Tryanuary and OktoberWest beer festivals. There is a large seating area outside, close to a bridleway, and walkers with dogs are welcome. ☕⊛◑♿⬤P☂

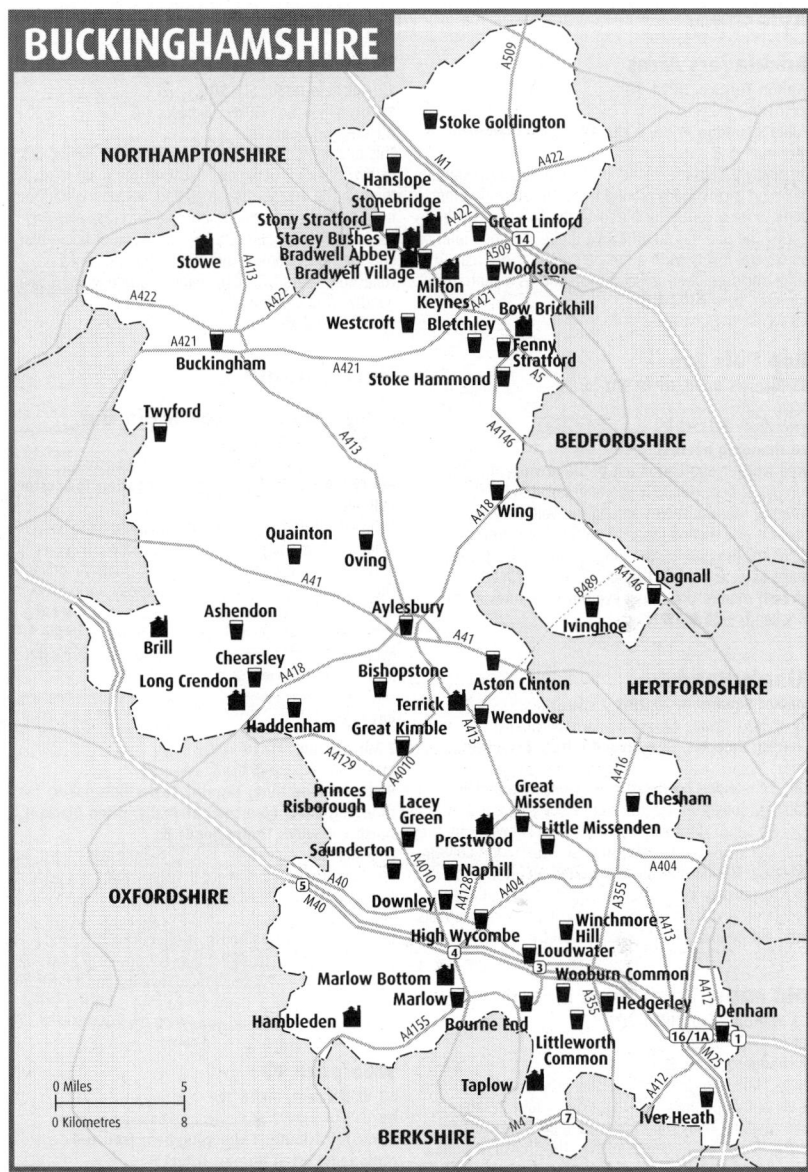

BUCKINGHAMSHIRE

NORTHAMPTONSHIRE

Stoke Goldington

Hanslope
Stonebridge
Stony Stratford
Stacey Bushes
Stowe
Bradwell Abbey
Bradwell Village
Great Linford
Woolstone
Milton
Keynes
Westcroft
Bletchley
Bow Brickhill
Buckingham
Stoke Hammond
Fenny
Stratford

Twyford

BEDFORDSHIRE

Quainton
Oving
Wing

Ashendon
Aylesbury
Dagnall

Brill
Ivinghoe

Chearsley
Long Crendon
Bishopstone
Aston Clinton
HERTFORDSHIRE

Terrick
Wendover
Haddenham
Great Kimble

Princes
Risborough
Lacey
Green
Great
Missenden
Chesham

Saunderton
Prestwood
Little Missenden

OXFORDSHIRE
Downley
Naphill

Winchmore
Hill
High Wycombe
Loudwater
Marlow Bottom
Wooburn Common
Marlow
Hedgerley
Denham
Hambleden
Bourne End
Littleworth
Common

0 Miles 5
0 Kilometres 8

Taplow
Iver Heath

BERKSHIRE

Ashendon

Hundred of Ashendon L
Lower End, HP18 0HE
☎ (01296) 651296 ⊕ thehundred.co.uk
2 changing beers (sourced locally; often Tring, Vale) ⊞

Nestling in the countryside, this family-run 17th-century inn is attractively decorated throughout, with an area dedicated to dining. The menu offers local and seasonal dishes. There are fine views from the beer garden. Dogs, muddy boots and children are all welcome. The pub is close to the National Trust property of Waddesdon Manor and has five beautifully furnished B&B rooms for those wishing to explore the local area. Q❀✿🛏🍴◐P❀🐾🛜

Aston Clinton

Oak
119 Green End Street, HP22 5EU
☎ (01296) 630466 ⊕ oakastonclinton.co.uk
Fuller's London Pride; 1 changing beer (often Fuller's) ⊞

Characterful 500-year-old inn with a large, pleasant L-shaped bar with low beams, an inglenook fireplace, wooden floor and plenty of seating. The tiled area to the left has the feel of a public bar, full of local characters and chit-chat. Freshly prepared, locally sourced food is available. The family-friendly pub boasts an extensive beer garden with attractive, leafy trees in season. ❀◐&P🚆(500,61)🐾🛜

Aylesbury

Bricklayers Arms
Walton Terrace, HP21 7QY
☎ (01296) 482930
Fuller's London Pride; 2 changing beers (sourced regionally) 🄷
Originally part of the hamlet of Walton, this 17th-century inn is on a crossroads around the corner from Walton pond, once a centre for breeding the famous Aylesbury ducks. The pub has an attractive timber-beamed interior on several levels, with a function room at the rear. The large enclosed beer garden at the back is a suntrap in summer. ❀⇌♣P🚌🐾📶

Hop Pole Inn 🄻
83 Bicester Road, HP19 9AZ (nr Gatehouse Industrial Area)
☎ (01296) 482129
10 changing beers 🄷
Well worth a short stroll out of the town centre, this temple of beer regularly sports nine cask ales including three or four guest ales among the Vale Brewery beers. There is also a good range of bottled beers, mostly from Belgium. The pub hosts a long-running quiz on Tuesday and a ukulele night on the second and fourth Wednesday of each month. Occasional live music features at the weekend. ❀◑●🚌🐾📶

King's Head 🄻
Market Square, HP20 2RW
☎ (01296) 718812 🌐 kingsheadaylesbury.co.uk
Chiltern Pale Ale, Beechwood Bitter; 2 changing beers 🄷
This is the oldest courtyard inn in England, complete with cobbles. Converted stables occupy one side and host a grocery shop. The magnificent building is owned by the National Trust; the bar and shop are run by the Chiltern Brewery. The bar has up to four Chiltern ales, with two often changing, and a guest beer – often a stout or porter in winter. A cider is also usually available. Beer festivals are held periodically. Q🍼❀◑♿⇌●🚌📶

Old Millwrights Arms 🄻
83 Walton Road, HP21 7SN
☎ (01296) 488161
7 changing beers 🄷
Now a firm fixture on the Aylesbury real ale circuit, this is a vibrant community pub that offers much to interest allcomers including open mic, comedy, Dungeons & Dragons and board games nights. The Thursday night quiz is well attended. A selection of up to seven real ales and two ciders plus occasional tap takeovers help make the pub a popular venue. 🍼❀◑♿⇌●P🚌🐾

Bishopstone

Harrow 🄻
27 Main Street, HP17 8SF
☎ (01296) 748478 🌐 theharrowbishopstone.co.uk
Chiltern Beechwood Bitter; Vale Gravitas; 1 changing beer (sourced locally; often Chiltern) 🄷
Established in 1837, this lovely village pub has been reopened by local owners following a long closure. Now sympathetically renovated and extended, it has a distinct bar area with stone flags on the floor, combined with vintage-style industrial lighting, and a central open fire adds warmth in season. There is a large area for dining, and covered seating outside as well as a spacious garden. Beers are from local breweries. 🍼❀◑♿P🐾📶

Bourne End

KEG – Craft Beer Tasting Bar
12 Oakfield Road, SL8 5QN
☎ (01628) 529369 🌐 kegcraftbeer.co.uk
2 changing beers 🄷
This micropub, newly opened in 2016 and named after its owner Kim E Georgiou, is just off the main road through the village. The small and welcoming bar goes from strength to strength, offering two cask ales and seven craft keg beers. The interior is full of bric-a-brac and the music comes from the proprietor's vinyl collection. There is limited seating outside and a car park nearby. Well worth a visit if you are in the area. ⇌●🚌(36) 🐾📶

Buckingham

King's Head Coffee & Gin Bar
7 Market Hill, MK18 1JX
☎ (01280) 812442 🌐 thekingsheadcoffeebar.com
Purity Pure UBU; 1 changing beer (often Towcester Mill) 🄷
Centrally located, this pleasant and comfortable bar has a hidden-away, good-sized courtyard garden. It serves hot drinks, spirits, cocktails, real ales and cider. Various food choices are available throughout the day, including breakfast, sandwiches, fresh pastries, burgers, salads, nachos, small plates and a tapas-style menu in the evening. Gluten-free and vegan preferences are catered for too. 🍼❀◑♿●🚌🐾📶

Mitre
2 Mitre Street, MK18 1DW
☎ (01280) 813080 🌐 themitrepub.co.uk
Blackpit Cloud Nine; Timothy Taylor Boltmaker; 2 changing beers (sourced nationally; often Blackpit, North Cotswold, Thornbridge) 🄷
Buckingham's oldest pub is a 15-minute walk from the town centre. Refurbishment in recent years has added a new oak bar, new cellar chillers and a new stone floor, but the cosy atmosphere remains, enhanced by an open fire in winter. A free house, it offers changing and interesting beers, featuring guests from local breweries. Five large-screen TVs show major events, and it hosts live music once or twice monthly. Parking is on the street. Local CAMRA Pub of the Year 2020. 🍼❀♣P🚌🐾📶

Woolpack ✔
57 Well Street, MK18 1EP
☎ (01280) 817972 🌐 thewoolpackbuckingham.com
St Austell Tribute; 1 changing beer (sourced nationally; often Hornes, Otter) 🄷
A short walk from the town centre, this busy, nicely modernised pub retains many old features. It has a separate function room with its own bar, and a large

REAL ALE BREWERIES

Blackened Sun ✦ Milton Keynes: Stacey Bushes
Blackpit ✦ Stowe
Brewhouse & Kitchen ▮ Milton Keynes: Central
Bucks Star ✦ Milton Keynes: Stonebridge
Chiltern ✦ Terrick
Concrete Cow Milton Keynes: Bradwell Abbey
Hornes ✦ Milton Keynes: Bow Brickhill
Malt ✦ Prestwood
moogBREW ✦ Taplow
Old Luxters Hambleden
Rebellion ✦ Marlow Bottom
Vale Brill
XT ✦ Long Crendon

riverside garden with a covered and heated patio. One regular beer and a guest are served. Beer festivals add more choice from time to time. Freshly cooked food features local produce where possible. Children are welcome in the large back room and the garden. Parking nearby can be difficult. Q ♿ ☕ ❀ ◑ ౹ ♣ ● ☕ (X60,X5) ✿ 🍺 🏮

Chearsley

Bell ✓

Church Lane, HP18 0DJ
☎ (01844) 208077 ⊕ thebellchearsley.co.uk
Fuller's London Pride; Gale's Seafarers Ale; 2 changing beers Ⓗ

Attractive thatched pub on the edge of the village green, often featuring in Midsomer Murders. In winter months relax by the wood-burning stove and on sunny summer days enjoy the patio and child-friendly garden. A Fuller's house, the ales are well kept and selected from across the Fuller's stable. The pub is renowned for both its ale and good wholesome food. Q ❀ ◑ P 🚌 (110)

Chesham

Trekkers Bar & Bottleshop Ⓛ

2 High Street, HP5 1EP
☎ 07943 711501 ⊕ trekkersbars.co.uk
3 changing beers (sourced locally; often Chiltern, Rebellion, Tring) Ⓐ

Local CAMRA Best Newcomer in 2020, Trekkers is a micropub in a former barbershop, dedicated to showcasing local breweries. Alongside the reasonably priced cask ales there are numerous keg beers on tap, plus traditional ciders, sparkling wines and gin. The fridge and shelves offer further national and international takeaway beer options. Tables spill out onto Chesham's Market Square. As the name suggests, Trekkers is a great place to satisfy your thirst after a walk along the nearby Chess Valley. ⊖ ● 🚌

Dagnall

Red Lion Ⓛ

21 Main Road North, HP4 1QZ
☎ (01442) 843020 ⊕ theredliondagnall.co.uk
Sharp's Doom Bar; Tring Side Pocket for a Toad; 2 changing beers (sourced nationally; often 3 Brewers of St Albans, Adnams, Tring) Ⓗ

A warm welcome awaits at this relaxing and friendly free house, with two roaring real fires in winter. The pub offers well-kept beers and freshly prepared home-made food using local produce. The rear dining room, with paintings by local artists, has a cosy atmosphere. In summer, families, cyclists and dogs enjoy the garden. The quiz night every second Monday, curry night on Tuesday and fish Friday are ever-popular. Q ❀ ☕ ◑ ♣ P ❑ ✿ 🍺

Denham

Falcon Inn ✓

Village Road, UB9 5BE
☎ (01895) 832125 ⊕ falcondenham.com
Harviestoun Bitter & Twisted; St Austell Proper Job; Timothy Taylor Landlord; 1 changing beer (sourced regionally; often Adnams, Hop Back, St Austell) Ⓗ

Small one-bar 16th-century pub in Denham Village conservation area, overlooking the village green. The entrance is via interesting old steps straight off the road. There is a lovely sunny garden to the rear. Good food is served lunchtimes and evenings, with bar snacks supplementing the full restaurant menu. Parking can be difficult, but there is easy access on foot from Denham station close by. High-quality bed and breakfast accommodation is offered. Q ❀ ☕ ❑ ◑ ➡ 🚌 🍺

Green Man Ⓛ

Village Road, UB9 5BH
☎ (01895) 832760 ⊕ greenmandenham.co.uk
Oakham JHB; Rebellion Smuggler; Sharp's Doom Bar; 2 changing beers Ⓗ

This friendly free-of-tie inn has been sympathetically refurbished. The front bar has beams, a real fire and flagged floors, opening out into a large conservatory and well-tended beer garden. With four real ales and tempting food menus, the pub is popular with diners, families and drinkers alike. Historic Denham is a picturesque rural village, a pleasant stroll from the Colne Valley Country Park Visitor Centre. ♿ ❀ ◑ ➡ ♣ ❑ ✿ 🍺

Downley

De Spencer Arms

The Common, HP13 5YQ (across common from village on flint track beyond end of Plomer Green Lane)
☎ (01494) 535317 ⊕ ledespencers.co.uk
Fuller's London Pride, ESB; 2 changing beers (sourced nationally) Ⓗ

A busy, traditional pub nestling in the woods on the edge of Downley Common. This friendly local offers a warm welcome to all including walkers and cyclists, dogs and children. The spacious garden is lovely in the summer months. The surrounding area of outstanding natural beauty offers many walks. There is car parking to the rear. ♿ ❀ ◑ ♣ P ❑ ✿ 🍺

Great Kimble

Swan Ⓛ

Lower Icknield Way, HP17 9TR
☎ (01844) 275288
Tring Side Pocket for a Toad, Moongazing; 2 changing beers (sourced locally) Ⓗ

In a village at the foot of the Chiltern Hills in excellent hiking, horse riding and cycling country, the Swan is a genuine, family-owned free house. The building dates back to the 18th century and is reputedly haunted. Sunday lunchtimes can be busy. The rear garden has been recently refurbished, and has a wood-fired pizza oven and barbecue. Late evening opening hours can be erratic, especially in the winter, as can the selection of ales. The pub adjoins the village green children's playground. ♿ ❀ ❑ ◑ ♿ ➡ (Little Kimble) ♣ P ❑ (300) ✿ 🍺

Great Missenden

George Ale House

94 High Street, HP16 0BG
☎ (01494) 865185
Harvey's Sussex Best Bitter; 3 changing beers (sourced nationally) Ⓗ

An old free house that reopened in 2018 following several years of closure. The owner's family also run two other excellent pubs nearby. There are three seating areas, some with comfy sofas and real fires, as well as a bottle shop. The pub hosts regular music nights with guitars, banjos and an accordion, all on display on the walls ready to be played. Traditional pub games including dominoes, cribbage, shut the box and board games are popular. Q ❀ ➡ ♣ ● P ✿

Haddenham

Rising Sun L ✓
9 Thame Road, HP17 8EN
☎ (01844) 291744 ⊕ risingsunhaddenham.co.uk
XT Four; 5 changing beers (sourced locally) Ⓗ
This bustling village pub boasts six real ales on handpump, with favourites from XT Brewing as well as unusual Animal Brewing Co creations, plus a changing selection of guest ales, craft beers and ciders. With a landscaped garden and treats on tap for canine companions, this family- and pooch-friendly pub seamlessly blends the best of old and new. Local CAMRA Pub of the Year 2019. Q❄☎✿✦🚲(280)♣✿🐾

Hanslope

Cock Inn
35 High Street, MK19 7LQ
☎ (01908) 510553 ⊕ cock-inn.co.uk
Greene King IPA; 1 changing beer (sourced regionally; often Great Oakley, Magpie) Ⓗ
A popular local with a large single-room L-shaped interior, featuring a pool table, dartboard and large-screen TV showing BT Sport at one end and with a real fire at the other. The bar serves one regular and one guest ale. Live music is hosted once a month, and themed events on occasion such as a Halloween fancy dress party. A kitchen is near completion so food will be available during the currency of this Guide. From the front of the pub you can admire the medieval church, which has Buckinghamshire's tallest spire.
❄☎✿&♣P🚲♣🐾

Hedgerley

White Horse L
Village Lane, SL2 3UY (in old village, near church)
☎ (01753) 643225 ⊕ thewhitehorsehedgerley.co.uk
Rebellion IPA; 7 changing beers (often Mallinsons, Mighty Oak, Oakham) Ⓖ
Local CAMRA Pub of the Year on numerous occasions, this village local offers an impressive range of real ales. New breweries often feature, as well as favourite beers from Oakham, Mallinsons and Mighty Oak. A draught Belgian beer and three real ciders are also available. This classic pub has a well-tended garden and a heated, covered patio area. Regular beer festivals are held, the largest of which is over the Whitsun weekend and a must for real ale enthusiasts. Q❄☎✿◑♣✦P♣🐾

High Wycombe

Mad Squirrel Brewery Shop Emporium
4-5 Church Street, HP11 2DE
☎ (01494) 395980 ⊕ madsquirrelbrew.co.uk
Mad Squirrel Mister Squirrel Ⓗ, **London Porter** Ⓗ/Ⓐ; **1 changing beer (sourced locally)** Ⓐ
A tasting bar and bottle shop that opened in 2016, with a bar downstairs and another upstairs with more seating. At least two cask ales are offered alongside a range of craft keg beers. There is a walk-in chiller with a selection of real ales in bottles and cans, also available to take away. You can enjoy a pizza with your favourite beer. ✿◑&✿♦P🚲🐾

Rose & Crown ✓
Desborough Road, HP11 2PR
☎ (01494) 571578
4 changing beers Ⓗ

This L-shaped pub next to the Eden Shopping Centre has steadily built up its real ale offering and now has an extensive range. It is a comfortable establishment in an area consisting mainly of small businesses. The pub holds quizzes, discos and charity events, and hosts live bands and karaoke once a month. Many sporting events are shown on two large-screen TVs. Snacks are served and Sunday roasts to order. The bus station is close by.
✿♣✦🚲♣🐾

Iver Heath

Black Horse
95 Slough Road, SL0 0DH
☎ (01753) 652631 ⊕ theblackhorseiverheath.co.uk
Hall & Woodhouse Fursty Ferret, Tanglefoot; 1 changing beer (sourced regionally) Ⓗ
Refurbished by Hall & Woodhouse, this large pub/diner has a country-house feel with oak panelling and shelving packed with interesting books. The separate drinking area has comfortable leather armchairs. A green oak timber conservatory restaurant opens onto a patio and garden. Meals and snacks, including vegetarian options, are served all day. The Uxbridge to Slough bus stops outside (last bus approximately 8pm, now with a Sunday service). Q❄☎◑&P🚲(3)♣🐾

Ivinghoe

Rose & Crown L ✓
Vicarage Lane, LU7 9EQ
☎ (01296) 668472 ⊕ roseandcrownivinghoe.co.uk
Sharp's Doom Bar; house beer (by Chiltern); 3 changing beers (sourced nationally; often Butcombe, St Austell) Ⓗ
Hidden away but clearly signposted, this 300-year-old free house has an open fire and slate floors throughout. It offers a varied choice of real ales and is popular with locals, walkers, cyclists and visitors from the campsite nearby. There is a quiet restaurant to the rear leading to a courtyard. Reasonably priced home-made British food is served. Q❄☎◑♣✦🚲(61)♣🐾

Lacey Green

Pink & Lily L
Pink Road, Parslows Hillock, HP27 0RJ
☎ (01494) 489857 ⊕ pink-lily.com
Sharp's Doom Bar; 3 changing beers (sourced locally) Ⓗ
Three-hundred-year-old family-owned pub in Parslows Hillock, a timeless hamlet in the heart of the Chilterns. Four regularly changing cask ales are available, three from local breweries. Take a look at the historic Brooke Bar room which has been preserved as it was when Rupert Brooke, the World War I poet, was a regular. The garden has a heated dining space, a play area for children, and a barbecue for summer weekends.
Q❄☎◑♣✦P♣🐾

Little Missenden

Crown Inn
HP7 0RD (off A413, between Amersham and Gt Missenden)
☎ (01494) 862571 ⊕ thecrownlittlemissenden.co.uk
St Austell Tribute; 3 changing beers (sourced nationally; often Oakham, Otter, Timothy Taylor) Ⓗ
This lovely old local has been in the same family for almost a hundred years. Former Watford footballer Trevor How and his wife took over in 1993. The village inn sits in an acre of beautiful countryside, with a patio at the

back where children are welcome. Inside you will find a traditional adults-only pub with stone and wood floors, and in winter an open fire. Good pub grub is served at lunchtimes. Three double en-suite rooms are available. Q ⏰ ✿ 🛏 ◖ ● P 🖵 (55) ● 🗢

Littleworth Common

Blackwood Arms
Common Lane, SL1 8PP SU937863
☎ (01753) 645672 ⊕ theblackwoodarms.co.uk
Brakspear Gravity, Oxford Gold; 4 changing beers Ⓗ
A delightful Victorian country pub brought back to life after a long period of closure. Close to Burnham Beeches nature reserve, it is popular with walkers and diners. An attractive garden with plenty of seating is a feature in summer, as is the roaring fire in winter. Four guest ales are offered, two from the Marston's group plus two free of tie. Dogs and horses are welcome – hay can be provided. Cider is available in summer only.
Q ⏰ ✿ ◖ ♣ ● P ● 🗢

Loudwater

Derehams Inn
5 Derehams Lane, HP10 9RH
☎ (01494) 530965 ⊕ derehamsinn.co.uk
5 changing beers Ⓗ
A friendly local up a lane off the London Road, with a car park at the rear. Outside is a garden and a covered smoking area with a pool table. An annual beer festival is held at the beginning of July. This is a traditional pub where families and dogs are welcome. Formerly known as the Bricklayers Arms, it has been run by the same couple for more than 20 years. Q ✿ ◖ P 🖵 ●

General Havelock
114 Kingsmead Road, HP11 1HZ
☎ (01494) 520391
Fuller's London Pride, ESB; Gale's Seafarers Ale; 3 changing beers Ⓗ
The General Havelock was purchased by Fuller's in 1986 and has been run by the same family since then. It was originally farm buildings before conversion to a pub. The decor is an eclectic mix of antiques and bric-a-brac. Six ales are available at all times, mostly from Fuller's. TVs are brought out for England football matches and some other events. There is an open fire in the winter and the garden is a peaceful haven in the summer.
⏰ ✿ ◖ ♣ P 🖵 (35) ● 🗢

Marlow

Royal British Legion 🅛 ✅
Station Approach, SL7 1NT (50yds from Marlow train station)
☎ (01628) 486659 ⊕ rblmarlow.co.uk
6 changing beers Ⓗ
A friendly Royal British Legion club that offers a wide range of cask ales and holds two beer festivals a year. Although a private members' club, guests are welcome – show a copy of this Guide or a CAMRA membership card for entry. Various events are held including jazz and music nights. This popular venue is a regular winner of regional CAMRA Club of the Year. ✿ ᄒ ≷ ♣ ● P 🖵 🗢

Milton Keynes: Bletchley

Captain Ridley's Shooting Party ✅
183 Queensway, MK2 2ED
☎ (01908) 621020

Greene King Abbot; Ruddles Best Bitter; Sharp's Doom Bar; 3 changing beers (sourced nationally; often Hornes, Jennings, Wells & Co) Ⓗ
Wetherspoon pub opened following complete renovation and extension in 2017. 'Captain Ridley's Shooting Party' was the cover name for MI5 agents when secretly checking whether nearby Bletchley Park would work as a wartime location. This provides the pub theme, celebrated with many pictures, artefacts and features. The pub has one large ground-floor bar with seating throughout. Twelve handpumps offer three regular beers and three guests. Bingo and quizzes are held weekly. There is ample outdoor seating in front of the pub as well as a large patio garden at the rear. ⏰ ✿ ◖ ᄒ ≷ P 🖵 (1) 🗢

Milton Keynes: Bradwell Village

Victoria Inn
Vicarage Road, MK13 9AQ
☎ (01908) 312769
4 changing beers (sourced nationally; often Hornes, St Austell, Vale) Ⓗ
Traditional 17th-century stone-built pub with a comfortable and relaxed atmosphere. As you enter, the bar with its four handpumps is directly in front of you. To the right is a room with a pool table and dartboard; to the left is a room on two levels with tables and chairs, an open fireplace, exposed beams and low ceilings. There is seating outside on the paved front terrace. ⏰ ♣ 🖵 ● 🗢

Milton Keynes: Fenny Stratford

Chequers 🅛
48 Watling Street, MK2 2BY
☎ (01908) 990718
Vale Gravitas Ⓗ**; 3 changing beers (sourced nationally)** Ⓗ /Ⓖ
Small, traditional public house with exposed beams and brickwork. Its focus is on beer, with Vale Gravitas and three changing guest ales. A small but interesting selection of bottled beers, including several from Belgium, is also stocked. Food is usually limited to Sunday roasts. There is a neat courtyard garden at the rear, furnished with wooden tables and benches, and a small car park. The pub welcomes away supporters on match days. Closed Mondays and Tuesdays.
Q ✿ ◖ ᄒ ≷ P 🖵 (18,X31) ●

Red Lion ✅
11 Lock View Lane, Simpson Road, MK1 1BY
☎ (01908) 372317 ⊕ the-red-lion-fenny-lock.co.uk
2 changing beers (sourced regionally; often Exeter, Fuller's, Timothy Taylor) Ⓗ
Popular pub by a lock on the Grand Union Canal offering two ales. Entering the pub from the road, the snug is to your left, offering comfortable seating for a quiet drink and chat. Ahead is the main bar with a variety of tables and chairs. Hot drinks are available. Through the bar, a corridor leads to a smoking area and the canalside garden. Welcomes away fans on match days.
✿ ◖ ᄒ ≷ ♣ ● P 🖵 (18) ● 🗢

Milton Keynes: Great Linford

Nag's Head ✅
30 High Street, MK14 5AX
☎ (01908) 607449 ⊕ thenagsheadmk.co.uk
Greene King IPA, Abbot; Timothy Taylor Landlord; 1 changing beer Ⓗ
Pretty thatched pub, dating from 16th century, with low ceilings and exposed beams. Its two bars have a cosy feel, especially when the log-burning stove is lit in the

saloon. Traditional and craft ales include guests from local breweries, and freshly prepared food is served. Customers enjoy monthly quiz nights, regular live music and the large, newly refurbished front and rear patio gardens. The pub is popular with ramblers, dog walkers, narrow-boaters and the local community. Local CAMRA Most Improved Pub 2020. Q♿🕮👪🍴P👌🐾🛜

Milton Keynes: Stacey Bushes

Blackened Sun Brewery Tap 🍺

Unit 3, Heathfield, MK12 6HP
☎ (01908) 990242 🌐 blackenedsunbrewing.co.uk
Blackened Sun Hédoné, Crossover, Luna Saison, Awakening; 2 changing beers (sourced locally; often Blackened Sun) ℗
The Blackened Sun microbrewery's taproom has long tables and bench seating plus some stools. Six taps serve Blackened Sun beers, sometimes a collaboration brew. All are real ales, naturally conditioned, unfined, unpasteurised and unfiltered, served from KeyKeg. Bottled house and guest beers are also available, to drink or take away, and growlers can be refilled. Under-18s are welcome before 8pm accompanied by an adult. Winner of local CAMRA branch Contribution to Local Beer Scene and Chair's Award for Excellence. ♿🕭P🖫🍴(6,14)🐾

Milton Keynes: Stony Stratford

Fox & Hounds

87 High Street, MK11 1AT
☎ (01908) 260604
Fuller's London Pride; Purity Mad Goose; St Austell Tribute; 1 changing beer (sourced nationally) 🅷
The Fox & Hounds dates from the mid-19th century, but its buildings are a century older. It has two bars, one quiet, with a small stone-walled room beyond and one with regular live bands and music, TV sport, a dartboard and a rare Northants skittle table. Outside is a garden with wooden tables and benches plus two Scandinavian-style part-open cabins – one with a log fire – where smoking is permitted. The car park is at the rear, at the end of Prospect Road. ♿🕮🕭👪P🖫🛜

Milton Keynes: Westcroft

Nut & Squirrel ✅

1 Barnsdale Drive, MK4 4DD
☎ (01908) 340031
Black Sheep Twilighter; 2 changing beers (sourced nationally; often Fuller's, Purity, St Austell) 🅷
Popular open-plan pub with nooks and crannies giving a traditional multi-room feel. The restaurant off the bar area offers the extensive Ember Inns range of food, with a dedicated menu both for vegetarians and vegans. A regularly rotating selection of quality ales is offered as well as several craft beers. The pub is located on the edge of Westcroft shopping centre and opposite Howe Park Wood. Local CAMRA Most Improved Pub in 2019. ♿🕮🕭👪P🖫🍴🛜

Milton Keynes: Woolstone

Cross Keys

34 Newport Road, MK15 0AA
☎ (01908) 528145 🌐 crosskeysmiltonkeynes.co.uk
Courage Directors; Young's London Original; 4 changing beers (sourced nationally; often Black Sheep, St Austell, Wadworth) 🅷
A traditional 16th-century building with a thatched roof. It has a bar and separate restaurant. Up to six real ales are served, as well as tea and coffee. A winner of

multiple awards, the food is home-made using fresh local produce. The large-screen TV in the bar shows terrestrial channels with subtitles. The patio and garden behind the pub are popular, now with a large marquee and outside bar during summer. Q♿🕮👪🕭P🖫(18)🍴🛜

Naphill

Wheel ✅

100 Main Road, HP14 4QA
☎ (01494) 562210 🌐 thewheelnaphill.com
Greene King Abbot; Ruddles Best Bitter; 2 changing beers 🅷
Naphill's oldest pub, dating back to the 1700s, is set in the heart of the Chilterns. Popular with locals and visitors, it has two bar areas and a dining space, as well as a large garden. It serves two regular beers and four changing guests. This friendly village local is a regular in the Guide and you can be sure of a warm welcome if you are in the area walking or visiting friends or family. Dogs and muddy boots are welcome. 🕮🕭👪P🖫🍴🛜

Oving

Black Boy 🍺 ✅

Church Lane, HP22 4HN
☎ (01296) 641258 🌐 theblackboyoving.co.uk
XT Four; 3 changing beers (sourced locally; often Chiltern, Leighton Buzzard, XT) 🅷
Delightful 17th-century inn with a roaring fire in winter. Summer visits are also a treat, with wonderful views across the local countryside from the huge beer garden. The restaurant opposite the bar is separated from it by an archway. The drinking areas offer flagstone floors and wooden beams. With good food, friendly staff and a great atmosphere, this is a cosy pub and a pleasure to visit. ♿🕮🕭👪P🖫🛜

Princes Risborough

Bird in Hand 🍺 ✅

47 Station Road, HP27 9DE
☎ (01844) 345602 🌐 birdinhandprincesrisborough.co.uk
Chiltern Beechwood Bitter; Thame Hoppiness; 2 changing beers 🅷
Situated in a residential area near Princes Risborough station, this thriving and friendly local has a compact L-shaped drinking bar supplemented by an outside drinking area and a beer garden. A good selection of real ales is available on handpump at this Thame-based Oak Taverns house. The community pub hosts entertainment including quizzes and live music. Parking can be difficult nearby. 🕮🍽👪🕭P🖫(300)🍴🛜

Quainton

George & Dragon 🍺

32 The Green, HP22 4AR
☎ (01296) 655436 🌐 georgeanddragonquainton.co.uk
6 changing beers (sourced locally) 🅷
Free house with an adjoining coffee shop, always offering four LocAles plus two guests. It has a friendly public bar with darts, a jukebox and a TV, and a saloon bar dedicated to dining, although home-cooked food is served throughout. Parts of this delightful pub date back to the 1700s, with traditional English features such as inglenook fireplaces, beams and a quarry-tiled floor. Regular beer festivals overlooking the green take place in summer. ♿🕮🕭👪🕭🍴P🖫(16)🍴🛜

Saunderton

Golden Cross

Wycombe Road, HP14 4HU

☎ (01494) 565974 ∰ thegoldencrosspub.co.uk

Adnams Ghost Ship; 2 changing beers (sourced nationally) Ⓗ

A family-friendly village inn, not far from the train station. One regular beer and two ever-changing guests are available. Meals are served daily. Outside is a large garden with a children's play area. Popular with walkers, the pub is situated in the heart of the Chiltern Hills in an area of outstanding natural beauty and surrounded by countryside. ⏳🕏🕐💒♣Pꓥ(X30)🌑🛜

Stoke Goldington

Lamb Ⓛ

16-20 High Street, MK16 8NR

☎ (01908) 551233 ∰ thelambatstokegoldington.co.uk

Tring Brock Bitter, Death or Glory; 2 changing beers (sourced regionally; often Oakham, Phipps NBC, Vale) Ⓗ

In a peaceful village midway between Milton Keynes and Northampton, the Lamb has an intimate bar, a large separate restaurant, a less formal dining room and a spacious garden with a stage for music events. The bar has a dartboard and traditional Northants skittles. Home-cooked food is served, including award-winning pies, using local seasonal produce. Walking groups are encouraged to park early and order food before their walk to enjoy on their return. Two en-suite bedrooms are available. Local CAMRA Pub of the Year 2019. Closed Mondays. Q⏳🕏🕐💒♣♠Pꓥ(37)🌑🛜

Stoke Hammond

Three Locks Ⓛ

Leighton Road, MK17 9DD

☎ (01525) 270214 ∰ threelocksstokehammond.co.uk

Fuller's London Pride; 2 changing beers (sourced regionally) Ⓗ

Popular canalside pub that supports local breweries, with several local ales on its three handpumps, plus cider, sometimes from a local producer. Following a major refurbishment in 2020, it has a brighter, fresher look and exposed beams. There is a beer festival over the May bank holiday weekend and occasional live music. The pub offers a good range of food, including vegan and gluten-free options. It is particularly busy in summer, with customers arriving by road, towpath and narrowboat. There is plenty of outdoor seating alongside the lock and canal. Boaters are welcomed, with mooring just below the locks. ⏳🕏🕐💒♠Pꓥ(70)🌑🛜

Twyford

Crown Inn

The Square, MK18 4EG

☎ (01296) 730216 ∰ thecrowntwyford.co.uk

2 changing beers Ⓗ

A freehold locals' pub central to the life of the village. The landlady has seen other pubs nearby decline and close, and has increased opening hours and food provision with the help of her family. The Crown is a deceptively large brick building opposite the village hall. A spacious bar area leads to an even larger lounge/function area on the left with a drop down screen and pool table. Serving one frequently changing beer from the barrel, it is usual to have seven different beers on during the week. ⏳🕏🕐💒♣♠Ꝕ(16)🌑🛜

Wendover

King & Queen 🅐

17 South Street, HP22 6EF

☎ (01296) 696872 ∰ thekingandqueenwendover.co.uk

Timothy Taylor Landlord; Young's London Original; 2 changing beers Ⓗ

Situated just off the High Street within easy reach of the station, the three-room village pub has a pleasant, homely ambience. Good food is served in the restaurant. There is an impressive wall map of the local countryside in one room. A wood-burning fire helps to provide a warm winter welcome for walkers returning from the nearby Chiltern Hills. Q⏳🕏🕐💒♣PꓥR🌑

Winchmore Hill

Potters Arms 🅐

Fagnall Lane, HP7 0PH (off A404 Amersham to High Wycombe road, about a mile from bypass)

☎ (01494) 726222 ∰ pottersarms.co.uk

Rebellion IPA; 3 changing beers (sourced locally; often Chiltern, Rebellion, Tring) Ⓗ

Now a free house, this village pub has been enlarged and refurbished but retains the original large fireplace. There are four beers from local breweries, and good food ranging from snacks to gastro. The front garden has a food service shack, heated umbrellas, seating for alfresco dining and a small marquee for inclement weather. Comedy nights feature monthly in the summer. Q⏳🕏🕐💒♣♠P🌑🛜

Wing

Queen's Head Ⓛ

9 High Street, LU7 0NS

☎ (01296) 688268 ∰ thequeensheadwing.co.uk

2 changing beers Ⓗ

A 16th-century village-centre free house with a comfortable public bar and restaurant with a well-deserved reputation for good food. LocAle accredited, guest beers are from nearby Tring, Vale, Hopping Mad and other micros. Log fires in winter months enhance the welcoming atmosphere, and the pub is TV-free. The large garden has a patio and a covered heated smoking area, and there is ample car parking. ⏳🕏🕐💒PꓥR(100,150)

Wooburn Common

Royal Standard Ⓛ 🅐

Wooburn Common Lane, HP10 0JS (follow signs to Odds Farm)

☎ (01628) 521121 ∰ theroyalstandard.biz

Hop Back Summer Lightning Ⓗ**; Timothy Taylor Landlord** Ⓗ/Ⓖ**; 7 changing beers** Ⓗ

This award-winning inn offers a warm welcome. Near to Burnham Beeches, it is set in the countryside and ideal for walks. Seven changing beers are served, some straight from the barrel, as well as real cider. Outside at the front is a disused red phone box with books for patrons to borrow. The pub is not served by public transport but there is a large car park. Q⏳🕏🕐💒P🌑🛜

Give my people plenty of beer, good beer and cheap beer, and you will have no revolution among them. **Queen Victoria**

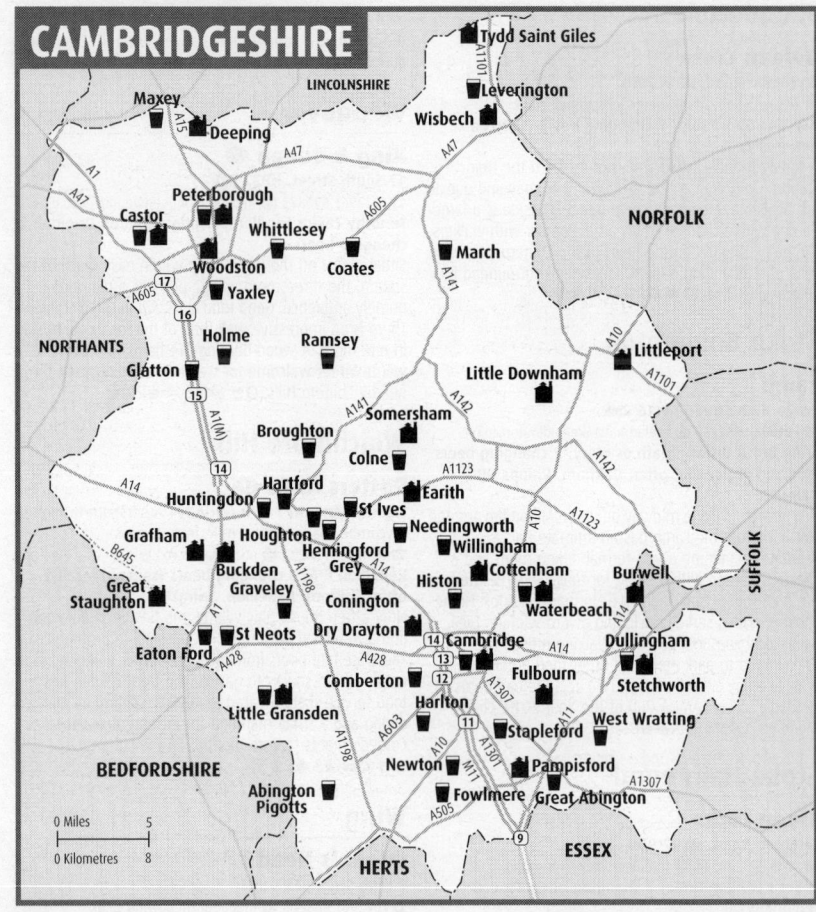

CAMBRIDGESHIRE

LINCOLNSHIRE

NORFOLK

NORTHANTS

SUFFOLK

BEDFORDSHIRE

HERTS

ESSEX

Tydd Saint Giles
Leverington
Maxey
Wisbech
Deeping
Peterborough
Castor
Whittlesey
March
Woodston
Coates
Yaxley
Holme
Ramsey
Little Downham
Littleport
Glatton
Somersham
Broughton
Colne
Earith
Hartford
Needingworth
Huntingdon
St Ives
Willingham
Grafham
Houghton
Hemingford
Grey
Cottenham
Buckden
Histon
Burwell
Great
Graveley
Conington
Waterbeach
Staughton
St Neots
Dry Drayton
Cambridge
Dullingham
Eaton Ford
Comberton
Fulbourn
Stetchworth
Little Gransden
Harlton
West Wratting
Newton
Stapleford
Abington
Pampisford
Pigotts
Fowlmere
Great Abington

0 Miles 5
0 Kilometres 8

Abington Pigotts

Pig & Abbot
High Street, SG8 0SD (off A505 through Litlington)
☎ (01763) 853515 ⊕ pigandabbot.co.uk
Adnams Southwold Bitter; Fuller's London Pride; 2 changing beers ⊞
Located in a surprisingly remote part of the south Cambridgeshire countryside, this Queen Anne-period pub offers a warm welcome. The interior has exposed oak beams, with two fires, including a large inglenook featuring a wood-burning stove. A comfortable restaurant offers home-made traditional pub food and specialises in fresh fish & chips, and steak and kidney puddings and pies. Two guest beers are stocked, often including beers from Burton Bridge, Humpty Dumpty, Mighty Oak, Timothy Taylor or Woodforde's. A former CAMRA branch Pub of the Year. Q🛏🌳❄️🍽♿♣P🐾

Broughton

Crown Inn
Bridge Road, PE28 3AY
☎ (01487) 824428 ⊕ thecrowninnrestaurant.co.uk
2 changing beers (sourced regionally) ⊞
An idyllic 19th-century inn opposite the village church. The interior is modern with a small bar area, scrubbed pine tables and a stone floor. Four handpumps serve two real ales – usually from small regional breweries – and

two ciders. Excellent seasonally changing food menus attract diners from a wide area. The pub can be busy at weekends – diners should reserve a table. Outside is a large beer garden where a beer festival is held each May.
Q🛏🌳❄️🍽P🐾🛜

Cambridge

Alexandra Arms
22 Gwydir Street, CB1 2LL (300yds from Mill Rd)
☎ (01223) 324441 ⊕ thealexcambridge.com
7 changing beers ⊞
Refurbished in 2014 in a modern kitchen style, the pub has three distinct areas on two levels, with wooden flooring and plenty of tables. The attractive enclosed garden has a garden room which can be booked for functions. A Greene King Local Hero pub, it is mainly free of tie, with guest ales frequently from Oakham and other local breweries alongside the regular beers. Food is home made and includes burgers, with bread from a local bakery. 🌳❄️🍽🚪🚌🐾🛜

Blue Moon
2 Norfolk Street, CB1 2LF (off East Road)
☎ (01223) 500238 ⊕ cambridge.pub/blue-moon
Adnams Mosaic, Ghost Ship; 2 changing beers ⊞
A 1960s pub, since 2013 it has been a sister pub to the Cambridge Blue, hence the name. As well as changing real ales, up to 20 craft keg beers are offered, with tap

takeovers featuring once a month. The front bar contains old pictures of Cambridge pubs. The larger back bar hosts events which frequently take place during the week, with live music mainly at weekends. It has a colourful outdoor area. Local CAMRA Young Members & Community (City) Pub of the Year 2020. ☎️)♣️🍴P🖥️🐾♿

Calverley's Brewery Tap 🄻
23A Hooper Street, CB1 2NZ
☎ 07769 537342 🌐 calverleys.com
Calverley's Porter Ⓖ
Close to Mill Road, the brewery was established in a former stable in 2013. It is open for on-sales on Tuesday to Friday evenings and all day Saturday. It offers one of its beers served direct from the cask plus a wide – and sometimes unusual – selection of keg beers and local real ciders. The new taproom provides more seating and frees up space in the brewery, allowing for a wider beer range. Pizzas are delivered from a nearby restaurant. Q🍴)♿🍴🖥️🐾♿

Cambridge Blue
85-87 Gwydir Street, CB1 2LG
☎ (01223) 471680 🌐 cambridge.pub/the-blue
Changing beers Ⓗ/Ⓖ
Ever-popular side-street pub close to Mill Road. A large rear extension leads to the garden, which frequently contains a marquee. Breweriana and pumpclips provide much of the decoration. Up to 14 ales from microbreweries nationwide are dispensed by handpump or by gravity from the taproom, often including XT Brewing's Animal beers. Up to seven real ciders and perries and a large selection of international bottled beers are also kept. The main beer festival is held in June. Food options include a range of pies. 🍴🎇)♿🍴🖥️🐾♿🛜

Champion of the Thames
68 King Street, CB1 1LN
☎ (01223) 351464 🌐 thechampionofthethames.com
Greene King IPA, Abbot; 3 changing beers Ⓗ
Small, two-room, city-centre establishment with a welcoming atmosphere where the chatter of customers predominates. It is one of four remaining pubs on the King Street Run pub crawl – which at one time involved a pint in each of eight pubs on the street. The oarsman of the name is commemorated in the etched windows. Wood-panelled with wooden floors, fixed benches and a part-glazed partition between the rooms, the pub is identified by CAMRA as having a regionally important historic interior. Bar snacks are available. 🎇♣️🖥️🐾🛜

Devonshire Arms 🄻
1 Devonshire Road, CB1 2BH
☎ (01223) 316610 🌐 individualpubs.co.uk/devonshire
8 changing beers (sourced nationally; often Milton) Ⓗ
Milton Brewery's first Cambridge pub. Just off Mill Road, it attracts a mix of characters for beer, food and a chat. Deceptively large inside, with tall front windows and a high ceiling with fans, outside it has small patio areas front and back. Five Milton cask ales are served, including at least one dark beer, with a further three guests from other micros. There are also bottled and keg beers, including Moravka unpasteurised lager, and two ciders. Food focuses on pizzas, burgers and hot dogs, with specials on some days of the week. 🍴🎇)≈♣️🖥️🐾🛜

Elm Tree
16A Orchard Street, CB1 1JT
☎ (01223) 322553 🌐 theelmtreecambridge.co.uk
7 changing beers (sourced nationally) Ⓗ

Back-street pub close to Parker's Piece, decorated with breweriana, quirky bric-a-brac, photos and Belgian flags. The short bar is near the entrance with seating around and beyond. Owned by Charles Wells, it has three handpumps for its own beers, plus a choice of guest ales. A real cider or perry is also served. Complementing these is a menu of around 100 bottled Belgian beers – the landlord has written a book on the subject and is happy to advise. Regular live music features. 🍴♣️🖥️🐾♿

Free Press
7 Prospect Row, CB1 1DU
☎ (01223) 368337 🌐 freepresscambridge.com
Greene King IPA, Abbot; 4 changing beers (often Morland) Ⓗ
This intimate, friendly pub serves high-quality food and great beer. Greene King-tied, the rare XX Mild was its best seller until regular production ceased. A pub since 1834, it just avoided the 1970s Kite area redevelopment. This is a loving reconstruction – only the tiny snug is original – and the pub is included on CAMRA's Outstanding Conversions & Restorations website. There is a walled garden at the rear. Named after a Temperance movement newspaper that lasted for just one edition. 🍴🎇)♣️🖥️🐾♿🛜

Geldart ✅
1 Ainsworth Street, CB1 2PF
☎ (01223) 314264 🌐 the-geldart.co.uk
Adnams Ghost Ship; Caledonian Deuchars IPA; Oakham Citra; St Austell Tribute; 4 changing beers (sourced nationally) Ⓗ
Large two-bar back-street corner pub with an enclosed patio garden behind. It is decorated throughout with film and music memorabilia, including musical instruments as handpumps and menus on 12-inch vinyl. The pub has a good reputation for its food and beers, with a restaurant area to the right of the entrance and a bar area to the left. Eight ales and a wide selection of malt whiskies and rums are available. The changing guest beers always include a dark one. Frequent live music is hosted. 🍴🎇)♿🐾🛜

Haymakers 🄻
54 High Street, CB4 1NG
☎ (01223) 311077 🌐 individualpubs.co.uk/haymakers

REAL ALE BREWERIES

Bowler's Deeping (NEW)
Burwell Burwell
Calverley's 🍴 Cambridge
Cambridge 🍴 Cambridge
Castor Castor
Crafty Beers Stetchworth
Downham Isle 🍴 Littleport
Draycott Buckden
Elgood's Wisbech
Fellows Cottenham
Grafham Grafham
IVO Somersham
Lord Conrad's Dry Drayton
Mile Tree Peterborough: Woodston
Milton Waterbeach
Moonshine Fulbourn
Oakham Peterborough
Papworth 🍴 Earith
Rocket Great Staughton
Son of Sid 🍴 Little Gransden
Three Blind Mice Little Downham
Turpin's Pampisford
Tydd Steam Tydd Saint Giles
Xtreme Peterborough: Woodston

Milton Pegasus; 7 changing beers (often Milton) Ⓗ
Milton Brewery's second of three Cambridge pubs, popular with locals and employees from the nearby science park. There are drinking areas either side of the door, plus a snug. Dark wood and warm colours abound. A good-sized beer garden is to the rear. The car park contains the largest pub cycle park in Cambridge. Eight real ales, including one dark and three guests, are on offer, plus four real ciders or perries, Moravka unpasteurised lager and a rotating Beach Brewery craft keg beer. Local CAMRA City LocAle Pub of the Year 2019 and winner of a CAMRA Lockdown Community Award in 2020. ♿🏵️🅓♣️🅿️🚃😺🛜

Maypole Ⓛ
20A Portugal Place, CB5 8AF
☎ (01223) 352999 🌐 maypolefreehouse.co.uk
Changing beers Ⓗ
The Maypole has been in the capable hands of the Castiglione family since 1982, initially as tenants, latterly as owners. Showcasing quality beers won the landlord the branch's first Real Ale Champion award. Up to 16 ever-changing beers are served, more during festivals, including LocAles, with micros predominating. The keg beers include several of interest. It has a busy front bar, a quieter back bar downstairs, a function room upstairs and a large covered patio with heaters. Food focuses on home-cooked Italian dishes although English pub classics are also available. A fomer local CAMRA Pub of the Year.
🏵️🅓♿😺🛜

Queen Edith Ⓛ
Wulfstan Way, CB1 8QN
☎ (01223) 244536 🌐 individualpubs.co.uk/queenedith
Milton Pegasus; 7 changing beers (often Milton) Ⓗ
The first new-build pub in Cambridge for around 30 years, after the demolition of a pub of the same name at the rear of the site, and the third Milton Brewery establishment in the city. The style is mock-Georgian inside and out. The bigger bar to the left of the entrance has large windows on two sides and a wood-burning stove. The second bar has wooden booths down one side. Regular and changing Milton ales are sold plus guest ales. Quiz night is Monday, open mic night first Saturday of the month. Q♿🏵️🅓♿♣️🅿️🚃😺🛜

Royal Standard Ⓛ
292 Mill Road, CB1 3NL
☎ (01223) 569065 🌐 cambridge.pub/royal-standard
4 changing beers Ⓗ
The Royal Standard reopened in 2015 after a period of non-pub use, covering around half the area of the original Victorian inn, but with well-planned use of the space available, including a small patio garden. It immediately became a fine addition to Cambridge's pub scene. Bottled beers and changing keg beers (including Duchesse de Bourgogne) are frequently from Belgium, but there are plenty of British options as well, including locally and regionally brewed cask ales. Locally produced real cider is also available, and a wide selection of gins. Greek food is served. 🏵️🅓♿♣️🚃(Citi2)😺🛜

Castor

Prince of Wales Feathers Ⓛ
38 Peterborough Road, PE5 7AL
☎ (01733) 380222 🌐 princeofwalesfeathers.co.uk
Adnams Broadside; Castor Ales Hopping Toad; Woodforde's Wherry Ⓗ**; 3 changing beers** Ⓗ/Ⓖ
This village corner pub is about 300 years old and built of stone with stained-glass windows. Originally a boot and shoe shop, it has one main bar area, divided into two by the fireplace.•There are two smaller rooms for pool and

darts – dominoes and crib are also played. Four real ales are usually served. Entertainment includes Sky Sports, plus live music every Saturday. Outside are two patios. Away football fans visiting Peterborough are warmly welcomed. ♿🏵️🅓♣️🅿️🚌🚃😺🛜

Coates

Vine Ⓛ
4 South Green, PE7 2BJ
☎ (01733) 840343
3 changing beers Ⓗ
Overlooking the village green, this free house was refurbished and extended in 2019. It has three rooms – a lively main sports bar/lounge in the middle, a conservatory at the rear and a conference suite at the front. A varying beer list always includes a LocAle. The large outdoor area has space for pétanque terrains and a children's play area. There is a pool table in the conservatory and it also has dartboards. The pub raises money for the Royal British Legion and Coates War Memorial Fund, particularly on Coates Day in late August.
♿🏵️♿♣️🅿️🚃(33)😺🛜

Colne

Green Man Ⓛ
1 East Street, PE28 3LZ
☎ (01487) 840368 🌐 greenmancolne.co.uk
Adnams Ghost Ship; Papworth Half Nelson; Three Blind Mice Lonely Snake; 1 changing beer (sourced locally) Ⓗ
A picturesque, 17th-century village local in an old Fenland fruit-growing area. The corrugated roof covers an original thatch. This busy, friendly pub provides a public bar with pool, darts and TV, plus a warm, sociable lounge with a modern dining extension serving good food. A quiz night is held fortnightly. The garden has a children's play area and hosts barbecues in summer. Camping is available nearby at Earith Lakes. Branch CAMRA Rural Pub and Pub of the Year 2020.
♿🏵️🅓🅰️♣️🅿️🚃(21,22)😺🛜

Comberton

Three Horseshoes
22 South Street, CB23 7DZ
☎ (01223) 262252
Adnams Lighthouse; Greene King IPA; 3 changing beers Ⓗ
Hanging baskets adorn this red-roofed village pub. Popular with local clubs and societies, it sponsors football and cricket teams. Historical photographs of the village and its sports players adorn the walls. The long, low-ceilinged main bar has a cosy alcove at one end and a small raised area at the other, with a games room off to the left. The brick-fronted bar takes up much of the central section. An extensive garden features children's play equipment. ♿🏵️🅓♣️🅿️🚃(18)😺🛜

Conington

White Swan
Elsworth Road, CB23 4LN
☎ (01954) 267251 🌐 thewhiteswanconington.co.uk
Adnams Southwold Bitter, Ghost Ship; 1 changing beer Ⓖ
Sturdy 18th-century brick building fronted by an impressive sward for outside drinking. The main bar has a tiled floor and a brick fireplace occupied by a fine cast-iron stove. The former cellar is now in use again, with the real ales served by gravity from behind the low,

wheelchair-friendly bar. The pub was purchased from Greene King in 2013 by the resident of Conington Hall and is run free of tie. Q✿❀⊕◗♣⭑P❀❀

Dullingham

Boot 🅛
18 Brinkley Road, CB8 9UW
☎ (01638) 507327 ⊕ thebootdullingham.co.uk
Adnams Southwold Bitter; 2 changing beers (sourced regionally) 🄷
Traditional village inn, rescued by a villager after Greene King tried to close it in 2000. It's now a welcoming community local, with several darts, crib and pétanque teams, the home pub of the village cricket team and a veterans football team. Ales (including from nearby Crafty Beers) are served direct from cask in the cellar. Food vans often visit on Thursdays and Fridays. It features live music nights and an annual beer festival. Children welcome until 8pm. Around a mile from Dulllingham railway station. ❀◗♣P❀

Eaton Ford

Barley Mow ✅
27 Crosshall Road, PE19 7AB
☎ (01480) 474435
Greene King IPA, Abbot; 2 changing beers 🄷
Simple one-bar community pub with a wide variety of activities focused on the regulars, plus live music events and seasonal celebrations. The decor is a mix of plaster, brick and wood panelling, and a long service counter dominates the centre of the bar. Images of past pub social events adorn the walls. There is a covered patio and a large beer garden with an extensive children's play area. The two changing beers are not normally from the Greene King range. ✿❀◗♣P⊟(X5)❀❀

Fowlmere

Chequers
High Street, SG8 7SR
☎ (01763) 209333 ⊕ thechequersfowlmere.co.uk
4 changing beers 🄷
Upmarket, food-oriented, 16th-century coaching inn. Drinkers will feel most comfortable in the area to the left of the bar which has a good pub feel, warmed by a roaring fire in winter. Other areas are dedicated to food – Samuel Pepys, who stayed here in 1660, would no doubt approve of the high-quality menu. Four chalet-style rooms overlooking the garden provide accommodation. The sign commemorates the 339th Fighter Group of the USAF who were based nearby. Q✿❀⊕◗P⊟(31)❀❀

Glatton

Addison Arms 🅛
Sawtry Road, PE28 5RZ
☎ (01487) 830410 ⊕ addison-arms.co.uk
Digfield Fools Nook; house beer (by Digfield) 🄷**; 2 changing beers (sourced regionally; often Digfield, Nene Valley)** 🄷/🄶
Grade II-listed pub built at the start of the 18th century and named after playwright and politician Joseph Addison (co-founder of The Spectator), who was a relative of the first landlord. The pub offers at least three real ales – the house beer, Addison Ale, is Digfield Shacklebush. Food prepared from fresh locally sourced supplies is popular. A thriving Sunday night quiz is hosted weekly. The large beer garden is busy in the summer. Q✿❀⊕◗♿P⊟(46A)❀❀

Graveley

Three Horseshoes
23 High Street, PE19 6PL
☎ (01480) 700320 ⊕ thethreehorseshoesgraveley.co.uk
Greene King IPA; Woodforde's Wherry; 2 changing beers (sourced regionally) 🄷
A late addition to the village, being built in the early 20th century after the other village pubs closed or burnt down. WW2 Graveley Airbase was used by bomber squadrons until 1946. Two real ales are available, one from Greene King, the other from a regional brewery or microbrewery. Food is served every lunchtime and evening (except Sun), with Sunday lunch a carvery. Quiz night is Tuesday. Q✿❀⊕◗♿P❀

Great Abington

Three Tuns 🅛 ✅
75 High Street, CB21 6AB
☎ (01223) 891467 ⊕ thethreetuns-greatabington.co.uk
Greene King IPA; 3 changing beers (often Crafty Beers) 🄷
Compact 16th-century two-bar free house opposite the village cricket green. One room is used by drinkers and has the main bar; there is a smaller bar in the dining room. Several shelters outside at the rear offer protection from the elements. Thai food is cooked to order by a Thai chef. The changing beer range comes from local and regional brewers, normally including one from Crafty Beers. A former local CAMRA Rural Pub of the Year. ✿❀⊕◗AP⊟❀❀

Harlton

Hare & Hounds
60 High Street, CB23 1ES
☎ (01223) 264698 ⊕ hareandhoundsharlton.co.uk
3 changing beers 🄷
Thatched 18th-century country inn with seating at the front and in the large garden, with views over the countryside, plus children's amusements and a pétanque pitch. The single bar has half-timbered walls, a beamed ceiling and a big fireplace. Closed for over a year, the pub reopened in 2017 after a Community Interest Company refurbished it and appointed managers to run it. Three changing beers come from local breweries and there are regional and national brands. Cider and perry are also often locally produced. Home-cooked food has a strong reputation, especially Sunday lunch. Quiz night is Sunday, bridge on Tuesday and cribbage on Thursday. Q✿❀⊕◗♣⭑P⊟(75)❀

Hartford

King of the Belgians 🅛
27 Main Street, PE29 1XU
☎ (01480) 52030 ⊕ kingofthebelgians.com
4 changing beers (sourced locally; often Digfield, Elgood's, Nene Valley) 🄷
This 16th-century pub at the heart of the community actively supports local charities. It hosts a beer festival in May and another in late August. A changing selection of four real ales, ciders and good-value food is served every day. The public bar is characterised by its low oak beams and a copper-topped counter, and there is a peaceful separate dining area. Entertainment includes regular quizzes, games nights and an open mic night on the first Monday of each month. Q✿❀⊕◗♣⭑P⊟❀❀

Hemingford Grey

Cock 🗍

47 High Street, PE28 9BJ (off A14, SE of Huntingdon)
☎ (01480) 463609 ⊕ thecockhemingford.co.uk
**Adnams Southwold Bitter; Brewster's Hophead; 1
changing beer** 🅷

A short walk from the River Great Ouse, this village inn
and restaurant has won local, regional and national
awards. The cosy pub is popular with regulars who enjoy
the well-kept locally sourced beers. The separate
restaurant features an extensive fish board, meat, game
and excellent home-made sausages (booking essential
at all times). During the summer, occasional beer
festivals are held in the beer garden. Q❀◐&AP❀❀❅

Histon

King William IV

8 Church Street, CB24 9EP
☎ (01223) 233930 ⊕ kingbillhiston.co.uk
**Greene King IPA; St Austell Tribute; Sharp's Doom Bar;
2 changing beers** (sourced regionally) 🅷

A traditional village local, known as the King Bill. The L-
shaped lounge comprises an old front section with
exposed timbers and brick-built open fires at each end,
plus a modern rear extension. The small lower bar has
bench seating and is devoted mostly to the playing of
pool and darts. The large patio-style garden is accessed
via the lower bar or the car park. Three regular ales are
available plus two guests. Roasts are served on
Sunday and a meat raffle held on Friday. A gourmet food
van visits on Friday evening. The King Bill Sunday league
football team are based here. ❀◐♣P₩

Red Lion 🗍

27 High Street, CB24 9JD
☎ (01223) 564437 ⊕ theredlionhiston.co.uk
9 changing beers 🅷

Two-bar free house adorned with a wonderful collection
of breweriana and historical photos. The nine
handpumps are in the right-hand bar which is quieter
and child-free. Guest beers always include a mild.
Belgian and German beers are also on draught plus a
range of world bottled beers, two ciders and a perry. Two
beer festivals are held each year – the Easter aperitif and
the main event in September – with proceeds going to
local charities. The left-hand bar welcomes families and
dogs. ᔐ❀⇆◐&♣♥P₩❅

Holme

Admiral Wells 🗍

41 Station Road, PE7 3PH (jct of B660 and Yaxley Rd)
☎ (01487) 831214 ⊕ admiralwells.co.uk
**Adnams Southwold Bitter, Ghost Ship, Broadside; 3
changing beers** (often Digfield, Oakham,
Woodforde's) 🅷

Officially the lowest-level pub in the UK. This Victorian
inn was named after one of Nelson's pallbearers, William
Wells, by its builder. Following a facelift it now has two
bar/lounge areas in a contemporary style, a conservatory
and a function room at the rear. Outside there is a beer
garden at the front, a large car park to the side, a
marquee with a bar in summer, and a children's play
area. Six ales are usually served, including two sourced
locally and one alcohol-free. Quiz night is Tuesday.
Qᔐ❀◐♣♥P❀❅

Houghton

Three Horseshoes

St Ives Road, PE28 2BE (off A1123)
☎ (01480) 462410 ⊕ threehorseshoesinnhoughton.co.uk
**Greene King IPA; Oakham JHB; Sharp's Doom Bar; 1
changing beer** 🅶

Characterful Grade II-listed 17th-century building in a
picturesque village, popular with locals as well as
walkers and cyclists. The lane opposite leads to the river
and the historic Houghton Mill. There are two bar areas
and plenty of space for diners. The real ales, including
one from a local brewery, are served by gravity dispense
from a taproom behind the bar. Home-cooked food is
available daily (not Mon and Tue in winter months).
Qᔐ❀⇆◐A♣P₩❀❅

Huntingdon

Old Bridge Hotel 🗍 ✅

1 High Street, PE29 3TQ (at S end of High St on ring
road, by river)
☎ (01480) 424300 ⊕ huntsbridge.com
3 changing beers (sourced locally; often Adnams,
Lacons, Nene Valley) 🅷

An ivy-clad hotel in what was a private bank in the 18th
century, at the southern end of the High Street with a
prominent position beside the River Great Ouse. Enjoy
imaginative and high-quality food in the Terrace
Restaurant, the covered patio and the garden area, or
simply relax with a drink in the bar or lounge. The award-
winning Old Bridge Wine Shop offers wine tasting. The
bus station is a short walk away. Qᔐ❀⇆◐&P₩❀❅

Leverington

Rising Sun Inn 🗍

Dowgate Road, PE13 5DH
☎ (01945) 583754
Elgood's Cambridge Bitter; 2 changing beers (often
Elgood's) 🅷

Comfortably furnished pub with an enclosed garden. The
building dates back to at least 1872 and was refurbished
a few years ago, but the bar retains the feel of a true
village local. It serves Cambridge Bitter and two changing
beers including Elgood's seasonals and guest beers. Well
known for good-value quality food, the restaurant hosts
regular themed nights – Wednesday is steak night. Dogs
and children are welcome. Closing time may be early if
there is no trade. A former CAMRA branch Gold Award
winner. ❀◐♣P₩(50)❀❅

Little Gransden

Chequers 🗍

71 Main Road, SG19 3DW
☎ (01767) 677348 ⊕ chequersgransden.co.uk
4 changing beers (sourced locally) 🅷

Village pub owned and run by the same family for over
60 years and in this Guide for 27 years. The unspoilt
middle bar, with its wooden benches, roaring fire and
collection of decoy birds gathering on the beam over the
bar, is a favourite spot to pick up on the local gossip. The
Chequers Son of Sid brewhouse supplies the pub and
local beer festivals. Friday is fish & chips night (booking
essential). A winner of numerous CAMRA awards, and a
Pub of the Year finalist in 2018. Q❀◐A♥P₩❀❅

March

Rose & Crown 🗍 ✅

41 St Peters Road, PE15 9NA

☎ (01354) 652077
St Austell Cornish Best Bitter; 6 changing beers (often Oakham, Tydd Steam) H
Traditional community pub, over 150 years old, with two carpeted rooms and low-beamed ceilings. There is a real fire in the main bar and a pool table in the smaller bar. Six real ales are usually on offer, mainly from microbreweries, including one from Oakham, and up to seven traditional ciders and a perry. A mini beer festival is held at Easter time. A large selection of gins and single malts is also available. Good-quality food is served lunchtimes and evenings. Quiz night is Thursday.
Q⸝❀❀◑◐❀P➽🖥🏳

Ship Inn L

1 Nene Parade, PE15 8TD
☎ (01354) 607878
Woodforde's Wherry; 4 changing beers (often Church End, Tydd Steam) H
Reopened as a free house in 2010, following a major refit, the Ship has a friendly and welcoming atmosphere. The thatched Grade II-listed riverside pub, built in 1680, has extensive moorings. Its unusual carved beams are said to have 'fallen off a barge' during the building of Ely Cathedral. A quaint wobbly floor and wall lead to the toilets and a small games room. It features a large collection of pumpclips. Attractions include monthly music from local bands and an annual beer festival in September. Winner of a CAMRA Gold Award in 2019.
Q⸝❀❀◑❀♣🖥❀🏳

Maxey

Blue Bell L

39 High Street, PE6 9EE
☎ (01778) 348182
Abbeydale Absolution; Fuller's London Pride, ESB; Oakham Bishops Farewell; 5 changing beers (sourced regionally; often Grainstore, Oakham, Woodforde's) H
Originally a limestone barn, the building was converted many years ago and reflects the rural setting in which it is found. Paraphernalia of country life adorn the stone walls and shelves of the two-roomed interior. Nine handpumps dispense a range of quality ales from large and small breweries far and wide. The pub is a popular meeting place for groups including birdwatchers and golfers. A former local CAMRA Pub of the Year and Gold Award winner. Q❀♣P➽(22,413)❀🏳

Needingworth

Pike & Eel

Overcote Lane, PE27 4TW (down a long lane off High St)
☎ (01480) 463336 ● pikeandeel.com
Adnams Broadside H/G**; 2 changing beers (sourced regionally; often Adnams, Greene King, Marston's)** H
Large riverside hotel and restaurant based around an old building dating from the 1700s with modern extensions. The oak-panelled bar and cosy snug with large inglenook fireplace are at the heart of the original building. A lounge area next to the bar is divided into a number of intimate areas with sofas. The Garden Room restaurant looks out over the river. The hotel offers 13 en-suite rooms. There is a large garden and a popular marina with moorings for up to 180 boats. Q❀🚆◑⬤❀P

Newton

Queen's Head

Fowlmere Road, CB22 7PG
☎ (01223) 870436

Adnams Southwold Bitter, Broadside; 2 changing beers G
Change comes gradually to this village local, one of a handful of pubs to have appeared in every edition of this Guide. Beers from brewers other than Adnams are now available from the stillage directly behind the bar. Regular Sunday lunches, a monthly Saturday supper club and Wednesday night food vans have been added to the soup and sandwiches on offer. Otherwise, little has changed since 1962. In fact, a list of landlords displayed in the public bar has only 18 entries since 1729.
Q◑❀♣P➽(31)❀

Peterborough

Bumble Inn

46 Westgate, PE1 1RE
● thebimbleinn.wordpress.com
5 changing beers (sourced nationally) H
A former local CAMRA Pub of the Year, this micropub opened in 2016 in what used to be a chemist's shop. Minimalist in style, it has five handpumps dispensing quality ales from far and wide, so expect the unusual. Order a taster paddle of three third-pints if you want to try a selection. Rare bottled and canned beers are stocked plus two craft keg beers, and two ciders. The pub's own Bumbling Brewery beers are also now available. Regular tap takeovers and food nights are hosted. Tea, coffee, soft drinks and home-made pies are also on offer. 🚆⬤🖥🏳

Charters L

Town Bridge, PE1 1FP (down steps at Town Bridge)
☎ (01733) 315700 ● charters-bar.co.uk
Oakham JHB, Inferno, Citra, Bishops Farewell; 4 changing beers (often Nene Valley) H/G
The converted Dutch grain barge from circa 1907 sits on the River Nene near the city centre. An oriental restaurant is on the upper deck and food is also served in the bar. Up to 12 beers are on offer plus cider. The large garden with a marquee, bar and landing stage for boats is popular in summer. Live music plays some weekends and in summer outside the pub. It gets busy on football match days. Close to the Nene Valley Railway.
🖥❀◑♣P🖥❀🏳

Draper's Arms L

29-31 Cowgate, PE1 1LZ
☎ (01733) 847570
Brewster's Hophead; Grainstore Ten Fifty; Greene King Abbot; Kelham Island Pale Rider; Ruddles Best Bitter; Sharp's Doom Bar; 5 changing beers (often Brewster's, Grainstore, Oakham) H
A converted draper's shop, built in 1899 and one of two Wetherspoons in the city. The beer range, with many from local microbreweries, is dispensed through 12 handpumps. The interior is broken up with dividers and intimate wood-panelled spaces. Food is served all day and regular beer and cider festivals are held throughout the year. Quiz night is Wednesday. A regular top 10 real ale pub within the company chain. Close to bus and railway stations. Q🖥❀◑❀🚆⬤🖥🏳

Frothblowers L

78 Storrington Way, Werrington, PE4 6QP
☎ 07756 066503 ● frothblowers.site
7 changing beers (sourced regionally; often Digfield, Hopshackle, Tydd Steam) H
This micropub is easily accessed by bus from the city centre, and is on the No.1 bus Ale Trail. It has five handpumps, and more beers available in the cellar, as well as at least 25 ciders and bottled beers. A hub of the local community, activities include tap takeovers,

acoustic music sessions, bus tours, a summer cycling club, knitting club, monthly grub club and cider festivals. Voted Peterborough and Cambridgeshire CAMRA Pub of the Year in 2019, it retained the title for 2020.
🦽😺&♣🍴P🖥🖵(1) ❀

Hand & Heart ★ 🅛
12 Highbury Street, PE1 3BE
☎ (01733) 564653 🌐 thehandandheart.com
6 changing beers (sourced regionally; often Brewster's, Rockingham, Tydd Steam) Ⓗ/Ⓖ
Rebuilt in 1938, this Art Deco-style community local has been recognised by CAMRA as having a nationally important historic pub interior. The rear room is connected to the main public bar, with its war memorial and real fire, by a drinking corridor. Traditional pub games are played. Six handpumped ales are available, with more from the cellar. The range is eclectic and forever changing. Beer festivals with live music are held in the large garden on St George's Day and in September, with occasional mini fests through the summer. A Guide regular for over 10 years and a former local CAMRA branch and county Pub of the Year. Q🦽😺&♣🍴🖵(1)❀🛜

Ostrich Inn 🅛
17 North Street, PE1 2RA
☎ 07307 195560 🌐 ostrichinnpeterborough.com
Oakham JHB; 4 changing beers (sourced regionally; often King's Cliffe, Nene Valley, St Austell) Ⓗ
This relaxing side-street pub reopened following refurbishment in 2009, with its original name restored. The single-room interior has a U-shaped bar and features many pictures for sale by local artists. Up to five regularly changing real ales are on offer, many from local breweries, alongside craft keg and 10 KeyKeg lines. A large gin selection is also stocked. Live music plays most weekends. The small enclosed patio is a suntrap. Popular on football match days. 🦽😺&≉♣🍴🐾❀

Palmerston Arms 🅛
82 Oundle Road, PE2 9PA
☎ (01733) 565865
Batemans Gold, XXXB Ⓖ**; Castle Rock Harvest Pale; Oakham Citra** Ⓗ/Ⓖ**; 10 changing beers (sourced regionally; often Lacons, Ossett, St Austell)** Ⓖ
Popular 400-year-old listed stone-built locals' pub. Owned by Batemans, three of its beers are rotated alongside nine or more other real ales, including some from Oakham. Traditional cider, perry and an extensive range of malt whiskies are also available. The majority of the beers are served straight from the cellar, which can be seen through a large glass screen. Rolls and a variety of snacks tempt customers. Live music features most weekends, and philosophy nights on occasion. Busy on football match days. 😺♣🍴🖵(1,24)❀🛜

Ploughman 🅛
1 Staniland Way, Werrington, PE4 6NA
☎ (01733) 327696
6 changing beers (sourced regionally; often Castor Ales, Hopshackle, Tiny Rebel) Ⓗ
A rejuvenated two-roomed community pub brought to the forefront of the city's real ale outlets by the enthusiastic licensee. Six handpumps serve beers from local breweries and further afield. Many activities and charity events are held regularly as well as live music at weekends. A well-supported annual beer festival is hosted in early July. A former local CAMRA Pub of the Year. 🦽😺♣🍴P🖵(1,22)

Wonky Donkey 🅛
102C High Street, Fletton, PE2 8DR
☎ 07835 594104

Phipps NBC India Pale Ale; 7 changing beers (sourced locally; often Digfield, Mile Tree, Tydd Steam) Ⓗ/Ⓖ
Micropub housed in two rooms of a former florist's, situated in a previously pub-free area. Eight beers, many straight from the cask, mostly LocAles and always including a dark ale, are available, alongside a large range of ciders, wines and gins, plus quality bottled lagers. House specials are created in conjunction with local brewery Mile Tree. Themed evenings include pop-up food nights, cheapskate Tuesday (all ales £3) and a quiz every Thursday. 🦽&♣🍴🖵(5)❀

Woolpack ◉
29 North Street, Stanground, PE2 8HR (in old part of village by River Nene)
☎ (01733) 753544
Black Sheep Best Bitter; Timothy Taylor Landlord; 1 changing beer (sourced regionally; often Mile Tree) Ⓗ
Originally constructed in 1711, a medieval wall remains in the garden and the old barn used to be the village mortuary (last used in the 1850s). The covered beer garden is used for live music and leads to the old River Nene, with boat moorings available. The L-shaped bar has TV and a dartboard, and is adorned with old photos and prints. Quiz night is Tuesday. Two guest beers are usually on tap. The pub is on the city Green Wheel route. A former local CAMRA Pub of the Year.
Q🦽😺&🕤♣❀🛜

Yard of Ale
72 Oundle Road, PE2 9PA
☎ (01733) 348000 🌐 theyardofalepub.co.uk
Lacons Encore; Rooster's Yankee; Sharp's Doom Bar; house beer (by Digfield); 5 changing beers (often Digfield, Woodforde's) Ⓗ
Built on land that was part of the nearby Palmerston Arms stable yard, this 120-year-old pub was refurbished and reopened in early 2017. Decorated in shades of grey with a warm wooden bar and surround, the large open-plan single room is divided into four distinct areas by the central supporting structure. Entertainment includes sports TV, darts and pool, plus live music most weekends. Outside is a large beer garden with a pizza oven for the summer. CAMRA branch LocAle Pub of the Year 2019. 🦽😺♣🍴🖵(1) 🛜

Ramsey

Angel
76 High Street, PE26 1BS
☎ (01487) 711968
Adnams Ghost Ship; Greene King Abbot; 2 changing beers (often Lacons, Tydd Steam) Ⓗ
This traditional brick-built two-room pub was refurbished in 2019. Entry to the main bar area, where you will find plenty of seating, two dartboards, a jukebox and a pool table, is via the rear car park and beer garden. The lounge is accessed from the main road. Friendly staff and locals help provide a great venue to enjoy a drink or two, with a LocAle always available, usually from Tydd Steam. 🦽😺♣P🖵(31) ❀🛜

St Ives

Nelson's Head 🅛
Merryland, PE27 5ED
☎ (01480) 494454 🌐 nelsonsheadstives.pub
Greene King IPA, Abbot; Morland Old Speckled Hen; 2 changing beers (sourced regionally; often Grainstore, Nene Valley, Oakham) Ⓗ
Greene King pub in a picturesque narrow street, refitted in the popular alehouse style in the late 1990s. It offers

three regular and two changing ales from local breweries, often including a dark beer. Local Cromwell cider is a permanent feature. A choice of food is served at lunchtime and pizza in the evening. On Sunday afternoon live bands perform and the pub gets extremely busy. A former local CAMRA LocAle Pub of the Year. ✿◖●🖵✿🛜

Oliver Cromwell ⬜
13 Wellington Street, PE27 5AZ
Adnams Ghost Ship; Wychwood Hobgoblin Gold; 4 changing beers (often Brewpoint) Ⓗ
Popular traditional pub near the old town quay and medieval river bridge. Originally a cottage, it became a pub in the 1840s. A well that once supplied water to a long closed brewery can be seen in the side bar. Up to six beers are served, mainly from its Brewpoint Brewery. Meals are freshly prepared using local ingredients, with Sunday roasts a speciality. The rear patio is a suntrap in the summer. Live music is hosted on Thursday evenings. ✿◖🖵✿🛜

St Neots

Ale Taster
25 Russell Street, PE19 1BA
☎ (01480) 581368
6 changing beers (sourced regionally) Ⓖ
A small, traditional, back-street pub operated in the style of a micropub. It features up to three changing ales served from a stillage behind the bar, and up to nine real ciders and perries. The owners get beer and cider from local producers as much as possible, and are happy to chat about their beers. Three large fridges display a wide selection of bottled beers from around the world. The pub encourages conversation, with quiet background music and no electronic machines. Traditional bar games are played here. Q✿✿♣●P🖵(X5)✿

Olde Sun ⬜
11 Huntingdon Street, PE19 1BL
☎ (01480) 216863
Adnams Ghost Ship; Woodforde's Wherry; 2 changing beers (often Adnams, Elgood's, Woodforde's) Ⓗ
Low-beamed and cosy traditional town-centre pub with two large inglenook fireplaces, three bar areas and a secluded patio. The jukebox is zoned, allowing quiet areas for conversation. Shove-ha'penny and bar billiards are played. Five constantly changing guest beers come from various regional breweries including Adnams, Elgood's, Marston's, Thwaites and Woodforde's. A mild and other dark beers are usually among the range. A former local CAMRA Mild/Dark Ales Pub of the Year. ✿♣🖵(X5) ✿

Pig 'n' Falcon ⬜
9 New Street, PE19 1AE (behind Barretts department store)
☎ 07951 785678 ⊕ pignfalcon.co.uk
Greene King IPA Ⓗ**, Abbot** Ⓖ**; Potbelly Best** Ⓗ**; 5 changing beers (sourced locally; often Potbelly, Three Blind Mice)** Ⓖ
This busy town-centre free house has up to six real ales and five real ciders, focusing on beers from microbreweries and unusual choices including milds, porters and stouts. A good range of bottled ciders, UK and foreign bottled beers includes Trappist ales. Beer festivals are held throughout the year. Live blues and rock nights are hosted Wednesday to Sunday. Outside is a large, imaginative, covered and heated beer garden. Three Blind Mice beers are real ale served in KeyKegs. ✿✿●🖵🖵(X5) ✿🛜

Stapleford

Three Horseshoes
2 Church Street, CB22 5DS
☎ (01223) 503402 ⊕ threehorseshoes-pub.com
Adnams Southwold Bitter; 6 changing beers Ⓗ
Friendly village inn on the southern fringe of Cambridge, attracting the local community and visitors from surrounding villages. It has three areas – the main bar, a small room to the left, and a large room to the right mainly used for dining. There is a sheltered beer garden with a barbecue at the back. A variety of food is available, with the accent on traditional Cypriot and Greek dishes. Local CAMRA Most Improved Rural Pub of the Year and winner of a CAMRA Lockdown Community Award in 2020. ✿✿◖⮑(Shelford)P🖵✿🛜

Waterbeach

Sun Inn ✅
Chapel Street, CB25 9HR
☎ (01223) 861254
Young's London Original; 3 changing beers Ⓗ
Traditional pub overlooking the village green, offering a changing list of interesting and local ales, often including a dark beer. The small, cosy lounge is dominated by a huge fireplace, while the simply appointed public bar, with its woodblock floor, is always lively. There is a small meeting room and a function room upstairs where regular gigs are hosted. An annual beer and music festival is held over the early May bank holiday weekend. ✿✿◖ᵹ⮑♣●🖵(9)✿🛜

West Wratting

Chestnut Tree
1 Mill Road, CB21 5LT
☎ (01223) 290384 ⊕ chestnuttreepub.co.uk
Greene King IPA; 3 changing beers Ⓗ
Impressive two-bar Victorian-style pub with modern extensions creating a roomy interior. The lounge to the right is mainly set out for dining. To the left is a comfortably furnished public bar with a pool table. This friendly pub hosts darts, pool and pétanque teams, and has a small lending library. It has been free of tie since the present owners bought it in 2012. Its three changing beers are mainly from micros, often local. Local CAMRA Pub of the Year 2019 and winner of a CAMRA Lockdown Community Award in 2020. Q✿✿◖♣●P🖵(19)✿

Whittlesey

Boat Inn ⬜
2 Ramsey Road, PE7 1DR
☎ (01733) 202488 ⊕ quinnboatinn.wordpress.com
Pitchfork Ales Pitchfork Ⓗ**; 4 changing beers (sourced regionally; often Grainstore)** Ⓗ/Ⓖ
This corner pub has two rooms – a public bar with sports TV and a cosy lounge. Up to 17 traditional ciders and perries supplement the real ales, some of which are served direct from the cask. A whisky club is hosted on the second Friday of the month and there are regular trips to tasting events. Outside is a pétanque terrain which is used by dancers at the Straw Bear Festival in January each year, when there is also an outside bar. ✿✿🛏ᵹ♣●P🖵(31) ✿🛜

Letter B ⬜
53-57 Church Street, PE7 1DE
☎ (01733) 206975 ⊕ theletterb.co.uk
Sharp's Doom Bar; 4 changing beers (often Digfield, Tydd Steam) Ⓗ

The Letter B is over 200 years old, with two bars, a small side room with a bar billiards table, and a decked rear patio area. A beer festival is held in January during the Straw Bear Festival weekend, which is popular with locals and visitors. Over recent years the cider range has expanded rapidly to complement the five real ales. A winner of numerous local CAMRA awards including County Pub of the Year and County Cider Pub of the Year. Accommodation is available. Q❄️🚋🍴♣🍺🚃(31,33) 🐾🛜

Willingham

Bank Micropub
9 High Street, CB24 5ES
☎ (01954) 200045 ⊕ thebankmicropub.co.uk
5 changing beers 🄶
Formerly a village bank, this single-room micropub opened in 2012. It has a short bar rescued from a closed Cambridge pub. The walls are decorated with photos of

local interest. Up to five real ales are available direct from the cask or via KeyKeg, with regional and local beers featuring strongly. A large range of craft ales includes three served from kegs. The Bank offers a warm welcome and the casual visitor is certain to be included in local conversation. Q♣🍺🚃🚃🐾

Yaxley

Farmers
200 Broadway, PE7 3NT
☎ (01733) 244885 ⊕ thefarmersyaxley.co.uk
Grainstore Ten Fifty; 3 changing beers (sourced locally; often Xtreme Ales) 🄷
Spacious 1930s pub and multi-room restaurant with large family-friendly outdoor areas. It has four handpumps, with a minimum of three ales on at any one time. House beers are from Xtreme Ales, a local brewery owned and run by the landlord's brother. A function room is available for parties and weddings. 🚋❄️🍽️🚌♿🍺P🚃(5)🛜

Three Horseshoes, Stapleford (Photo: Helge Nareid)

L⊚cAle

Many entries in the Guide refer to pubs' support for CAMRA's LocAle scheme. The ⊔ symbol is used where a pub has LocAle accreditation. The aim of the scheme is to get publicans to stock at least one cask beer that comes from a local brewery, usually no more than 30 miles away.

The aim is a simple one: to cut down on 'beer miles'. Research by CAMRA shows that food and drink transport accounts for 25 per cent of all HGV vehicle miles in Britain. Taking into account the miles that ingredients have travelled on top of distribution journeys, an imported lager produced by a multi-national brewery could have notched up more than 24,000 'beer miles' by the time it reaches a pub.

Supporters of LocAle point out that £10 spent on locally-supplied goods generates £25 for the local economy. Keeping trade local helps enterprises, creates more economic activity and jobs, and makes other services more viable. The scheme also generates consumer support for local breweries.

Support for LocAle has grown at a rapid pace since it was created in 2007. It's been embraced by pubs and CAMRA branches throughout England and has now crossed the borders into Scotland and Wales.

For more information, see camra.org.uk/locale

What is CAMRA LocAle?

- An initiative that promotes pubs which sell locally-brewed real ale
- The scheme builds on a growing consumer demand for quality local produce and an increased awareness of 'green' issues

Everyone benefits from local pubs stocking locally brewed real ale...

- Public houses, as stocking local real ales can increase pub visits
- Consumers, who enjoy greater beer choice and locally brewed beer
- Local brewers, who gain from increased sales and get better feedback from consumers
- The local economy, because more money is spent and retained in the local economy
- The environment, due to fewer 'beer miles' resulting in less road congestion and pollution
- Tourism, due to an increased sense of local identity and pride – let's celebrate what makes our locality different

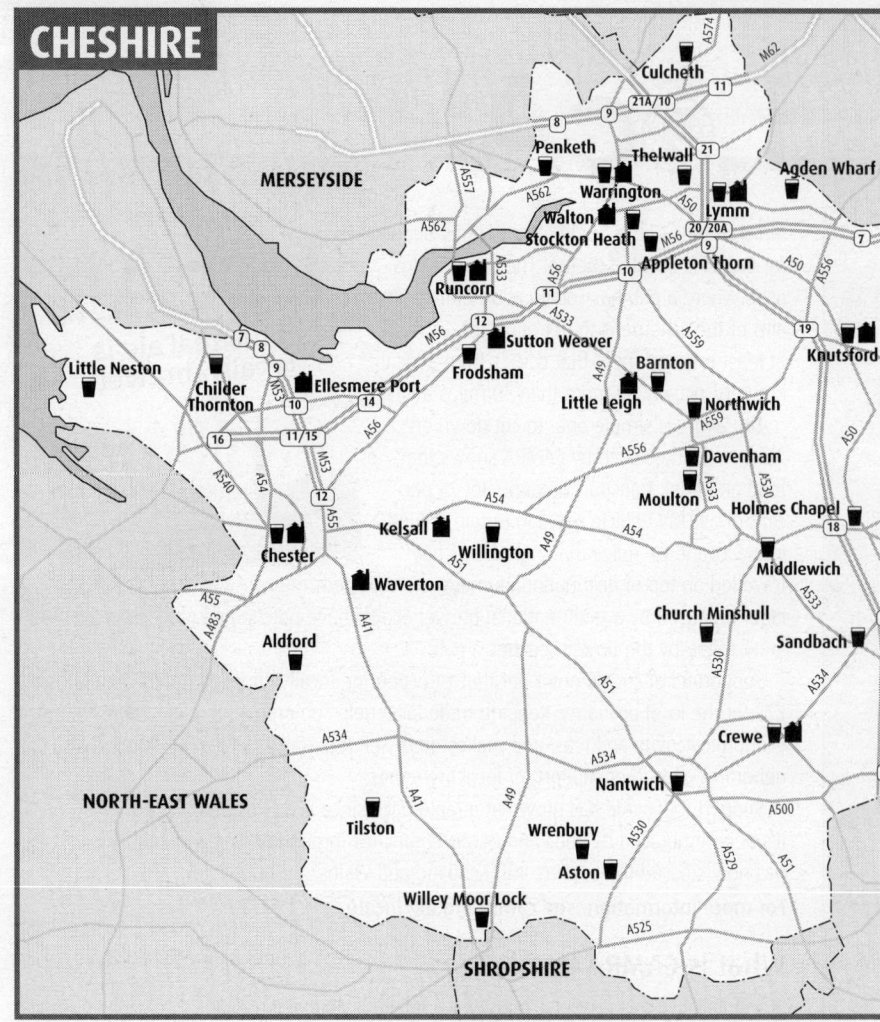

CHESHIRE

MERSEYSIDE

Culcheth

Penketh

Thelwall

Agden Wharf

Warrington

Lymm

Walton

Stockton Heath

Appleton Thorn

Runcorn

Sutton Weaver

Barnton

Little Neston

Childer Thornton

Ellesmere Port

Frodsham

Little Leigh

Northwich

Knutsford

Davenham

Moulton

Holmes Chapel

Kelsall

Willington

Chester

Waverton

Church Minshull

Sandbach

Middlewich

Aldford

Crewe

NORTH-EAST WALES

Tilston

Nantwich

Wrenbury

Aston

Willey Moor Lock

SHROPSHIRE

Agden Wharf

Barn Owl 🅛

Warrington Lane, WA13 0SW (on the Bridgewater Canal, off A56)
☎ (01925) 752020 ⊕ thebarnowlinn.co.uk
Lancaster Bomber; Moorhouse's White Witch; Wainwright; 3 changing beers (sourced locally; often Pictish, Storm, Tatton) Ⓗ
The Barn Owl sits on the banks of the Bridgewater canal with pleasant views over rolling Cheshire countryside, especially from the heated conservatory and canalside patio, the ideal place to relax in summer. The freshly-cooked food is deservedly popular and includes a Sunday carvery as well as a good value menu for the over 60's. The ales are sourced mainly from independent breweries and include at least one LocAle. Check out the large wood carvings in front of the pub. ∾⭐◑◐Ⓟ✿

Aldford

Grosvenor Arms 🅛

Chester Road, CH3 6HJ (on B5130)
☎ (01244) 620228 ⊕ grosvenorarms-aldford.co.uk

Timothy Taylor Landlord; Weetwood Eastgate; house beer (by Phoenix); 4 changing beers (sourced nationally) Ⓗ
A spacious, stylish and unashamedly upmarket pub. Full of character, it is multi-roomed with a pleasant garden room leading to a terrace and lawn with picnic tables. Inside, the decor is modern-traditional with lots of bare wood, bookcases, pictures and chalkboards. Four changing beers, which occasionally include a mild, complement the house beer brewed by Phoenix, plus beers from Weetwood and Timothy Taylor. High-quality food from an imaginative menu is popular and served all day. Q∾⭐◑◐ᕓ♣◐Ⓟ⊟(5)✿

Appleton Thorn

Appleton Thorn Village Hall

Stretton Road, WA4 4RT
☎ (01925) 261187 ⊕ appletonthornvillagehall.co.uk
7 changing beers (sourced nationally; often Bingley, Blackedge, Facer's) Ⓗ
At the hub of the community and a CAMRA National Club of the Year more than once, the Village Hall has a sizeable function room and quieter lounge area. Real

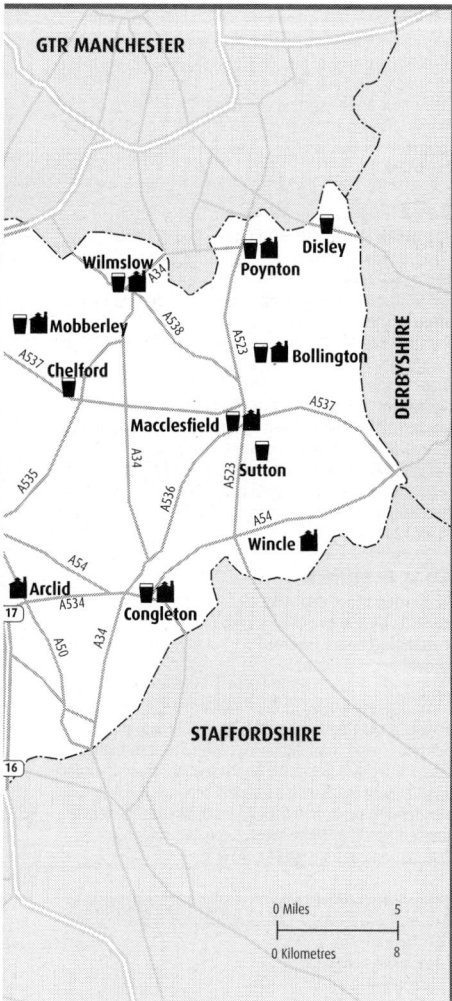

GTR MANCHESTER

Wilmslow Disley
Poynton
Mobberley
Chelford Bollington
DERBYSHIRE
Macclesfield
Sutton
Wincle
Arclid
Congleton

STAFFORDSHIRE

0 Miles 5
0 Kilometres 8

Barnton

Barnton Cricket Club L

Broomsedge, Townfield Lane, CW8 4QL (200yds from A533, down a narrow drive to left of Barnton Community Primary School)
☎ (01606) 77702 ⊕ barntoncc.co.uk
Sharp's Doom Bar; 3 changing beers (sourced nationally) Ⓗ
The Pavilion is arranged into two distinct rooms – the large Broomsedge Suite (proudly displaying an extensive range of CAMRA awards above the bar), where Sky and BT sports are shown on a projected screen, and the more intimate Townfield Lounge. The patio overlooks the cricket field. A popular beer festival is held in July. Squash, crown green bowls, darts and dominoes are all played here. Show your CAMRA membership card for admission. A former CAMRA National Club of the Year.
ॐ੬❀◑♿♣P🚍(46,4)

Bollington

Cotton Tree ✓

3-5 Ingersley Road, SK10 5RE
Adnams Southwold Bitter; Draught Bass; Sharp's Sea Fury; Wainwright; Weetwood Cheshire Cat; 1 changing beer (sourced nationally) Ⓗ
The Cotton Tree is a friendly, family-run drinkers' pub. One of a dwindling number of traditional back-street locals, it is on the corner of a terrace, built of stone, with a stone floor and warmed by a roaring fire in winter. It is next to the bus terminus and features local transport-themed memorabilia. There is a secluded beer garden tucked away at the back. Children are welcome until 7pm. It has a team in the local dominoes league and hosts frequent live music events. CAMRA branch Cider Pub of the Year 2021. ॐ❀♣●🚍😺🛜

Poachers Inn L

95 Ingersley Road, SK10 5RE
☎ (01625) 572086 ⊕ thepoachers.org
Storm Beauforts Ale; Weetwood Old Dog; 3 changing beers (sourced locally) Ⓗ
Family-run, community free house near the Gritstone Trail and Peak District National Park, popular with ramblers, cyclists and dog walkers. It supports local breweries, with regular ales from Storm and Weetwood, alongside three rotating guests including a dark beer, plus real cider and a selection of bottled craft beers. Good-value home-prepared food features locally sourced ingredients. Events include Wednesday pie night, monthly quizzes and golf days. With a coal fire in winter and a suntrap garden in summer, the pub is welcoming at any time of year. ॐ❀◑●P🚍😺🛜

Vale Inn L ✓

29-31 Adlington Road, SK10 5JT
☎ (01625) 575147 ⊕ valeinn.co.uk
Bollington Best, Long Hop, Oat Mill Stout Ⓗ
Open-plan single-room mid-terrace pub, built in the 1860s, with a real fire. The brewery tap for nearby Bollington Brewing, it features an ever-changing range of six of its beers, plus two guest ciders. Home-cooked food is highly recommended, especially the chunky chips (booking advisable for meals). Close to the Macclesfield Canal and Middlewood Way, the separate beer garden provides an ideal spot for watching cricket on the local recreation ground. Beer is available to take away in bottles and boxes. ॐ❀◑♣●P🚍😺🛜

ales are mainly from independent breweries, with third-pint paddles available, and a choice of real ciders. Show a CAMRA card for admission – a small fee may be payable. Local CAMRA Club of the Year 2021.
Qॐ❀◑੬♣●P🚍🛒😺🛜

Aston

Bhurtpore L

Wrenbury Road, CW5 8DQ (just off A530)
☎ (01270) 780917 ⊕ bhurtpore.co.uk
11 changing beers (sourced nationally) Ⓗ
Winner of local CAMRA Pub of the Year many times, including in 2019, this fine country pub boasts 29 consecutive years in the Guide. A family-owned traditional village pub, it has a relaxed, timeless atmosphere in the main bar, with a lovely open fire, where you can enjoy up to 11 real ales. Excellent home-made food – curries a speciality – is available in the separate restaurant. The bar room has a pool table and sports TV (for occasional events), and there is a large garden to the rear. It is named after Bharatpor, a fortress city in India, shown in colour photos in the side snug.
Qॐ❀◑੬▲●P🚍(72)😺🛜

Chelford

Egerton Arms 🅛
Knutsford Road, SK11 9BB
☎ (01625) 861366 ⊕ chelfordegertonarms.co.uk
5 changing beers (sourced locally; often RedWillow, Tatton) Ⓗ
Large single-roomed pub with a history dating back to the 15th century, when it served as stables. Table candles and a real fire provide a cosy atmosphere in winter, while the garden can be enjoyed in summer. Popular with diners, there is plenty to interest the casual imbiber, with five changing beers, mostly from local brewers such as Tatton or RedWillow. On weekdays, food service may finish early if it is quiet.
🕭🏵🌗&≒♣⦁P🚪(88) 🐾 🛜

Chester

Cavern of the Curious Gnome
61 Bridge Street Row East, CH1 1NW
☎ 07856 999895 ⊕ thecavernofthecuriousgnome.co.uk
4 changing beers (sourced nationally; often Salopian) Ⓗ
Belgian-themed bar located on Chester's famous Rows. Enter via Paysan wine bar, then ascend the steps up to the Cavern of the Curious Gnome, where a large, colourful papier-mache gnome gazes down on proceedings. Red-and-white spotted toadstool seats plus tables with bench seating catch the eye, with more quirkiness to be found in the decor. Four handpumps serve changing cask ales from North-West and Yorkshire breweries. Belgian offerings include lambics, gueuzes, Trappist ales plus Duvel served on draught. ⓄⓅ⦁🚪🛜

Cellar
19-21 City Road, CH1 3AE
☎ (01244) 318950 ⊕ thecellarchester.co.uk
Timothy Taylor Landlord; 5 changing beers (sourced nationally; often Hawkshead, Marble) Ⓗ
Friendly street-level bar – the name relates to the function room in the cellar below. The bar is renowned for its excellent selection of cask ales – the regular Taylor Landlord is complemented by five guest beers and three real ciders. There is also an extensive range of keg and bottled beers. Sport features on three TV screens. Bar snacks such as pork pies are available, plus complimentary food when major sporting events are screened. ≒♣⦁🚪🐾🛜

Cornerhouse
4-8 City Road, CH1 3AE
☎ (01244) 347518 ⊕ cornerhousechester.com
Salopian Oracle; Timothy Taylor Landlord; 2 changing beers (sourced nationally) Ⓗ
Situated in Chester's thriving Canal Quarter, this attractive candlelit mock-Tudor building features lots of bare brick and wood flooring. It offers two regular beers and two changing ales – usually one dark and one pale – plus an extensive bottled beer selection. Live music is hosted Thursday to Saturday and a quiz on Sunday. There is a free-to-hire function room upstairs. Outdoor seating is at the front of the pub. Food is of the platter variety (cheeses and meats) plus snacks. 🏵Ⓞ≒♣🚪🐾🛜

Cross Keys
2 Duke Street, CH1 1RP
☎ (01244) 344460
Joule's Pale Ale, Pure Blonde, Slumbering Monk; 3 changing beers (sourced nationally; often Arbor, Salopian, Joule's) Ⓗ
Attractive red-brick building with a stylish interior featuring oak floors, wood panelling and stained-glass windows depicting other Joule's hostelries. Four Joule's beers are complemented by one or two real ciders. There is usually a choice of pies on offer, and a traditional roast on Sunday. The pub hosts a quiz on Thursday and live Irish music on the second and fourth Wednesdays of the month. The terrace beer garden catches the afternoon sunshine. An upstairs room is available for hire.
🕭Ⓞ⦁🚪🐾🛜

Deva Tap
121 Brook Street, CH1 3DU (at city end of Hoole Bridge close to railway station)
☎ (01244) 314440
Rat White Rat; 5 changing beers (sourced regionally; often Ossett, Rat, Thornbridge) Ⓗ
The Deva Tap's long, narrow interior is divided into three – a small seating area by the entrance, a larger seating space in the middle and a bar at the far end. The permanent White Rat beer is complemented by four rotating ales, usually including one dark brew. Four ciders and up to 10 keg and continental beers are also available. There is outside seating in a small courtyard. Food is served Wednesday-Sunday. The pub is convenient for the railway station.
🕭🏵Ⓞ&≒♣⦁🚪🐾🛜

Goat & Munch
52 Garden Lane, CH1 4EW
☎ 07873 675298 ⊕ goatandmunch.com
4 changing beers (sourced regionally; often Chapter, RedWillow, Salopian) Ⓗ
Chester's first micropub occupies a former electrical appliance repair shop in the Garden Quarter – an area heavily populated by students. The front room features a bar front made from old pallets, with Swedish high tables and chairs plus some bench seating. There is also a brighter side room with additional seating. The four real ales tend to be from independent breweries, generally sourced from the North-West. Beers are sold at a discount on Tuesday. ⦁🚪(1,1A)🐾 🛜

Old Harkers Arms ⅃

1 Russell Street, CH3 5AL (down steps off City Rd to canal towpath)

☎ (01244) 344525 ⊕ harkersarms-chester.co.uk

Weetwood Cheshire Cat, Eastgate; house beer (by Phoenix); 6 changing beers (sourced nationally) ⒣

Upmarket pub converted from the ground floor of an old Victorian canalside warehouse. Timber flooring, traditional wooden furniture and cast-iron pillars provide an insight into its history. Blackboards show tasting notes for up to six guest ales, including a selection of bitters, stouts, milds or porters, many from local breweries. Ciders and perries are listed separately and served from the cellar. Food is available all day (booking advised for busy weekend periods). Outside seating is alongside the canal. Q❀❀⟐&≠♣●🗄❀🕸

Olde Cottage ⊘

34-36 Brook Street, CH1 3DZ

☎ (01244) 324065 ⊕ oldecottagechester.co.uk

Otter Bitter; 3 changing beers (sourced nationally; often Sharp's) ⒣

Welcoming and traditional community local on the popular eating and drinking Brook Street, between the city centre and railway station. To the left is the games room with pool, darts and a bagatelle table (rarely seen outside Chester). The main bar has another dartboard, a small TV and a real fire for the colder weather. The regular Otter Bitter is supplemented by three guests, one free of tie. Various loyalty and discount schemes are offered. ❀≠♣🗄🕸

Pied Bull ⅃

57 Northgate Street, CH1 2HQ

☎ (01244) 325829 ⊕ piedbull.co.uk

Adnams Broadside; house beer (by Pied Bull); 2 changing beers (sourced nationally; often Blackjack, Ossett) ⒣

Home to the only microbrewery inside the city walls, this oak-beamed, historic pub attracts both locals and visitors. A loyalty card is available and brewery tours can be booked. High quality pub food features local ingredients. Pop quiz every Thursday. Dogs permitted in one area. The purchase of next door cottages has enabled the construction of a smart courtyard for outside drinking and five additional guest bedrooms. House beers are usually supplemented by one or two guests. ➶❀🛏⟐&●🗄❀🕸

Telford's Warehouse ⅃

Canal Basin, Tower Wharf, CH1 4EZ (just off city walls)

☎ (01244) 390090 ⊕ telfordswarehousechester.com

Salopian Oracle; Weetwood Cheshire Cat; Young's London Original; 3 changing beers (sourced nationally) ⒣

Converted warehouse with a large glass frontage overlooking the Shropshire Union Canal basin. Some walls retain original features and are adorned with interesting industrial artefacts. Up to six changing beers are available, usually from microbreweries. The pub is a thriving live music venue, charging admission on some evenings after 9pm. Good-quality food is served, and the upstairs restaurant can be hired for private functions. Outside seating is popular in good weather. An annual beer festival is held in October. ❀⟐●P🗄(1A)❀🕸

Childer Thornton

Halfway House

New Chester Road, CH66 1QN (on A41 close to M53 jct 5)

☎ (0151) 339 2202

4 changing beers (sourced nationally; often First Chop, Ringwood, Weetwood) ⒣

Friendly, traditional former coaching inn dating from the 1770s, based at the midpoint between Chester and New Ferry (note the old prints of the pub and surrounds on the walls). The building retains much of its original character, with several drinking areas offering smart, comfortable seating. A community feel is evident, with darts and dominoes teams plus a golf society. The pub can be busy when sporting events are on TV. Quiz night is Thursday. ❀&♣🗄❀🕸

Church Minshull

Badger ⅃ ⊘

Cross Lane, CW5 6DY (in village centre beside St Bartholomew's Church)

☎ (01270) 522348 ⊕ badgerinn.co.uk

Titanic Plum Porter; house beer (by Tatton); 2 changing beers (sourced locally; often Weetwood) ⒣

A free house since 2011, this former coaching inn dating back to around 1770 is set in the heart of the Cheshire countryside. The two-roomed village pub is divided into discrete cosy areas, with a central bar in the original building. A separate dining area in the more modern extension is accessed via the lounge. A warm welcome is extended to diners and drinkers alike. Accommodation is provided in five comfortable bedrooms. ➶❀🛏⟐&♣P🗄(31,31A)❀🕸

Congleton

Beartown Tap ⅃

18 Willow Street, CW12 1RL

☎ (01260) 270775

Beartown Kodiak, Skinful; 4 changing beers (sourced locally; often Beartown, Manning) ⒣

The tap for Congleton's Beartown Brewery and Manning Brewers has been a leading real ale outlet in Congleton since 1999 and also offers brewery tours. At least five real ales are always available. The traditional, opened-out pub layout has several separate areas. There is an upstairs function room that can be booked for meetings, and a secluded outdoor beer terrace. A community pub for conversation, games, a weekly quiz and occasional music, it also hosts pizza and street-food nights. Local CAMRA Pub of the Year. ➶❀♣🗄(92)❀

Cheshire Brewhouse Tap ⅃

Unit 13, Daneside Business Park, Riverdane Road, CW12 1UN (pedestrian access via Congleton Park, vehicle access off A5365)

☎ (01260) 274788 ⊕ cheshirebrewhouse.co.uk

Cheshire Brewhouse Engine Vein, Lindow; 2 changing beers (sourced locally; often Cheshire Brewhouse) ⒣

This single-room micropub and bottle shop is within the operational brewery. It has four handpumps and two keg fonts. Cask ale from wooden casks regularly feature. No meals are served but locally sourced pork pies are available at all times. Brewery dog Jack is normally around to welcome you, and other dogs with well-behaved owners are also welcome. There is a spacious, largely covered yard which hosts live music. Accessible on foot or by bike from town through Congleton Park. Q➶❀♣P❀🕸

Wonky Pear

1A Cross Lane, CW12 3JU

☎ (01260) 278555

3 changing beers (often Beartown, Manning) ⒣

A small, modern and family-friendly bar in a converted shop near the railway station, with a large front window and two log-burners. It typically offers three cask beers, often including one from Beartown. A small room upstairs can be reserved for meetings. Tuesday is pizza night and board games are played on Wednesday. There is a monthly vinyl night and occasional live music – other events range from tap takeovers and gin nights to wreath-making. ⇌🚋(91,94)

Young Pretender 🄻

30-34 Lawton Street, CW12 1RS
☎ (01260) 273277
Wincle Sir Philip; 5 changing beers 🄷
Bonnie Prince Charlie allegedly slept here, hence the name. Set within a part Grade II-listed building, this large one-room bar is divided into several areas. Five changing real ales sourced from a wide area are available, along with one cider. Food is served during the day, catering for all appetites. Activities include a weekly quiz and movie night. The pub is also a meeting point for local community groups. ⏰🕉🌑◐♣♠♥P🚋💀🏮

Crewe

Borough Arms 🄻

33 Earle Street, CW1 2BG (on Earle St railway bridge, with entrance up steps in adjoining Thomas St)
10 changing beers (sourced nationally; often Fyne Ales, Oakham, Salopian) 🄷
This free-of-tie pub next to the railway bridge near the town centre has featured in 21 consecutive issues of the Guide. Ten handpumps pour mainly pale and golden ales from all over the UK, but there is always a dark beer on. Three distinct seating areas on split levels surround the L-shaped bar, with a much-extended seating area downstairs where the brewery used to be. Many new beer-related plaques adorn the walls. A pleasant and secluded beer garden is accessed through the downstairs room. Local CAMRA Pub of the Year.
Q⏰🕉🌑♣♠P🚋(8)💀🏮

Hops 🄻

Prince Albert Street, CW1 2DF (opp Lifestyle Centre at S end of Prince Albert St)
☎ (01270) 211100 ⊕ hopsbelgianbar.co.uk
6 changing beers (sourced nationally; often Townhouse) 🄷
A family-run bar with a friendly welcome for its wide clientele. Styled after a Belgian café-bar, it offers a fabulous choice of bottled Belgian beers to complement the range of real ales and ciders. The spacious bar room has further seating in an upstairs area. During the summer months, the European-style sun terrace situated to the front is always popular. A Guide regular in recent years, this is a must-visit establishment when visiting the town. Q⏰🕉🌑♣♠🚋💀🏮

Raven

Brookhouse Drive, CW2 6NA (jct Brookhouse Drive and Davenport Ave/Broadleigh Way)
☎ (01270) 482576
Sharp's Doom Bar; 4 changing beers (sourced regionally; often Salopian, Titanic) 🄷
A free house since 2015, the Raven has four beers, increasing to six at weekends. The pub has two seating areas and a large stage for weekend entertainment, including open mic every Wednesday; the Doom Bar is complemented by changing local and national beers, all sensibly priced. There is a pool table, darts and dominoes. Outside is a covered patio, while upstairs is a sun terrace and a separate bar. ⏰🕉🌑♣P🚋(6,12)💀🏮

Culcheth

Liberty's Gin Bar 🄻

25 Common Lane, WA3 4EW
☎ (01925) 767029
House beer (by Merlin); 2 changing beers (sourced locally) 🄷
The enthusiastic landlord takes his real ale very seriously, with three beers on offer, often from Merlin Micro Brewery and other LocAle suppliers. The house beer is brewed by Merlin. Sky Sports and BT Sports are shown on four screens in the main bar. A collection of more than 220 gins is also served. The first-floor function room has a separate bar and capacity for up to 200 people, and is available for hire. ⏰🕉🌑♣♠🚋💀🏮

Davenham

Davenham Cricket Club 🄻

Butchers Stile, Hartford Road, CW9 8JG (down a narrow signed driveway after Mount Pleasant Rd)
☎ (01606) 48922 ⊕ davenham.play-cricket.com
4 changing beers (sourced locally; often Beartown, Brimstage, Mobberley) 🄷
This welcoming family-oriented club is a community facility in an idyllic village setting. Extensive seating in front of the pavilion makes it a perfect place to enjoy beer, cricket and the summer warmth. Sporting events are shown on a large-screen TV. Four handpumps serve real ale mainly from local breweries, and two beer festivals are held each year. During the cricket season the opening hours are extended. Show your CAMRA membership card for admission. ⏰🕉🌑P🚋(37)💀🏮

Disley

Malt Disley

22 Market Street, SK12 2AA
☎ (01663) 308020 ⊕ maltdisley.co.uk
4 changing beers (sourced locally; often Mobberley, Poynton, Torrside) 🄷
A vibrant and friendly converted shop in the village centre. It is spacious for a micropub and includes a downstairs room. Five cask beers are available, some from local microbreweries, along with a cask cider. Ten KeyKeg beers, including three continental beers plus a further cider, and a range of British and continental bottled beers are also on offer. Live music plays on the last Sunday afternoon of each month. Local CAMRA Pub of the Year. ⏰🌑♥⇌🚋(199)💀🏮

Frodsham

Helter Skelter 🄻

31 Church Street, WA6 6PN
☎ (01928) 733361 ⊕ thehelterskelter.net
Oakham Bishops Farewell; Salopian Oracle; Weetwood Best Bitter; 7 changing beers (sourced nationally; often Ossett, Thornbridge) 🄷
Local CAMRA Pub of the Year numerous times, this pub offers three regular cask ales plus a further seven changing guest ales from local and national micros, including dark beers. Two rotating guest ciders and imported bottled beers are also available. The single-room bar has a welcoming, relaxed atmosphere, attracting both locals and travellers. Excellent food is served in the bar and upstairs restaurant.
◐⇌♥🚋(21,48) 💀🏮

Holmes Chapel

Bottle Bank Ⓛ

24-26 London Road, CW4 7AL
☎ (01477) 534380 🌐 beeremporiumbottlebank.co.uk
4 changing beers (often Merlin, Mobberley) Ⓗ
This bar/off-licence derives its name from its previous existence as a NatWest bank – the strong room at the rear is now used for spirit bottles. A former CAMRA branch Pub of the Year, this modern bar has four regularly changing cask ales and eight keg lines, with third-pints available. Snacks such as pork pies and Scotch eggs are served. There is an attractive beer-themed mural in the lounge area. ⏰🏵️&🚲🍴🖥️(42,316)🐾🌐

Knutsford

Rose & Crown 🏅

62 King Street, WA16 6DT
☎ (01565) 652366 🌐 knutsfordroseandcrown.co.uk
2 changing beers (sourced locally; often Dunham Massey) Ⓗ
Built in 1641, this inn has a wonderful historic charm, with a black and white exterior with leaded stained-glass windows, graced with hanging baskets. Inside, there are exposed beams and a beautiful old fireplace. The open-plan ground-floor bar and restaurant are divided into discrete areas, and there are two sharing tables near the bar. There is a good-sized rear outdoor seating area and letting rooms are available. Two hand-pumped cask beers are served, typically from Cheshire. The pub can be busy, especially at the weekends.
🏵️🛏️◐🚲P🖥️(88,89) 🐾🌐

Little Neston

Harp Ⓛ 🏅

19 Quayside, CH64 0TB (turn left at bottom of Marshlands Rd, pub is 300yds on left overlooking marshes)
☎ (0151) 336 6980
Joseph Holt Bitter; Peerless Triple Blond; Timothy Taylor Landlord; 2 changing beers (sourced nationally) Ⓗ
Former coal miners' inn converted from two cottages. It has a public bar with a real fire in winter and a basic lounge. Set in a glorious location on the Deeside to Neston part of the National Cycle Network, the pub overlooks the Dee Marshes and North Wales, with a recently enlarged garden and a drinking area abutting the edge of the marshes. A popular curry night features every Tuesday. Q⏰🏵️◐🚲P🖥️(22,487)🐾🌐

Lymm

Brewery Tap Ⓛ

18 Bridgewater Street, WA13 0AB
☎ (01925) 755451 🌐 lymmbrewing.co.uk
Dunham Massey Dunham Dark; Lymm Bitter; Bridgewater Blonde; 4 changing beers (sourced locally; often Dunham Massey, Lymm) Ⓗ
The Brewery Tap, in the red-brick former post office, is a few steps away from the Bridgewater Canal. The bar area is complemented by the front room, with subdued lighting, comfy armchairs and a wood-fired stove. Four changing beers are either from the pub's own microbrewery or nearby Dunham Massey, and include at least one dark beer, often the award-winning Porter. An open mic night features twice a month. Local pies are available at all times. ⏰🏵️&🍴🖥️🐾🌐

Saddler's Ⓛ

7 Bridgewater Street, WA13 0AB
☎ (01928) 753139
JW Lees Bitter; Wainwright; 1 changing beer (sourced locally; often Big Bog) Ⓗ
A small, traditional free house, originally owned by the local saddler, in the village centre, a few steps from the Bridgewater Canal and close to Lymm Dam and heritage walks. There is a cosy snug with a real fire to complement the larger bar area. The pub has a relaxed vibe with an emphasis on conversation and banter or just reading the paper. A popular meeting place for Formula 1 enthusiasts. Q⏰&🖥️🐾🌐

Macclesfield

Park Tavern Ⓛ 🏅

158 Park Lane, SK11 6UB
☎ (01625) 667846 🌐 park-tavern.co.uk
Bollington Best, Eastern Nights, Long Hop, Oat Mill Stout, White Nancy Ⓗ
Bollington Brewery mid-terrace pub a short walk from the town centre. Up to six beers from the Bollington range are available, plus two real ciders. An opened-out area surrounds the bar, with a snug by the front door. A popular community venue, it hosts regular events including film nights in a mini cinema function room upstairs and quizzes and science evenings downstairs. There is a small outdoor area at the rear.
⏰🏵️🌿🍴🖥️🐾🌐

RedWillow Ⓛ

32A Park Green, SK11 7NA
☎ (01625) 830718
5 changing beers (often RedWillow) Ⓗ
A local outlet for Macclesfield's RedWillow Brewery. Tastefully converted from a shop, it retains the original period frontage, complemented by an interesting modern decor. A screen above the bar shows an impressive selection of house beers, guests from other microbreweries and a real cider, along with a large selection of craft keg. A dark beer is always featured. Third-pint measures are available. The food menu features pizza and platters. There is a small pavement seating area at the front. ⏰🏵️&🌿🍴🖥️🐾🌐

Waters Green Tavern Ⓛ

96 Waters Green, SK11 6LH
☎ (01625) 422653
7 changing beers (sourced regionally; often Abbeydale, Acorn, Elland) Ⓗ
A traditional local in the town centre opposite Macclesfield railway station. The landlord's cellarmanship has kept the Waters Green in this Guide for more than 20 years. A free house, it offers a choice of up to seven cask beers from independent breweries plus a real cider or perry. Good-value home-cooked food is served Monday to Saturday lunchtimes. A real fire warms the L-shaped, open-plan main room. There is a separate pool room, and picnic tables in the back garden.
⏰🏵️◐🌿🍴🖥️🐾🌐

Wharf Ⓛ

107 Brook Street, SK11 7AW
☎ (01625) 261879 🌐 thewharfmacc.co.uk
Oakham JHB; Otter Bitter; 3 changing beers (sourced nationally) Ⓗ
A traditional end-of-terrace community pub set a short walk from the town and close to the canal wharf. This award-winning free house has five handpumps serving a good selection of beers from microbreweries. The opened-out single room has a central bar and three

distinct seating areas, plus a games area with a pool table, dartboard and bar skittles. Live music often features at the weekend. There is more seating in the well-tended back garden. ♿☀♫⬆🚪(58)🐾🛜

Middlewich

White Bear Hotel 🅛
Wheelock Street, CW10 9AG (on lower end of Wheelock St, just off A54 St Michael's Way)
☎ (01606) 837666 ⊕ thewhitebearmiddlewich.co.uk
4 changing beers (sourced locally) 🅷
This 17th-century coaching inn was comprehensively restored in 2011 by the current owner. It serves a wide variety of real ale styles, sourced locally, together with a real cider, and is also renowned for excellent food. With a large open-plan room off the bar, a separate restaurant, an alfresco patio and an upstairs function room, it appeals to a wide range of customers. Very much a regular in the Guide. ♿☀♫◑➊P🚪(37,42)🐾🛜

Mobberley

Church Inn 🅛
Church Lane, WA16 7RD (opp church, signposted from local roads)
☎ (01565) 873178 ⊕ churchinnmobberley.co.uk
House beer (by Tatton); 2 changing beers (sourced regionally) 🅷
This Grade II-listed 300-year-old dining pub, sister of the nearby Bull's Head, retains vestiges of its former multi-room layout. A house beer is named in honour of Mallory of Everest, who was born in Mobberley and is commemorated in stained glass in the church opposite (his father was a vicar there). There is a fire-lit cricket-themed main bar and dining areas, a characterful bar room, two private dining rooms upstairs, and a beer garden to the rear. Information on local walks is available. ♿☀♫◑⬆P🚪(88)🐾🛜

Moulton

Lion 🅛
74 Main Road, CW9 8PB
☎ (01606) 606049
Wainwright; Wychwood Hobgoblin Ruby; 4 changing beers (sourced locally; often Cheshire Brewhouse, RedWillow, Tatton) 🅷
Featuring in the Guide for seven consecutive years, this welcoming community-focused pub is in the centre of the village and dispenses many changing local ales and guest real ciders. It hosts a fun smartphone quiz night each Thursday. Delicious stone-baked pizzas are served in the early evening. Outside, there is a beer garden to the side and a sundeck at the front. A function room is available. Local CAMRA Pub of the Year 2021.
♿☀⬆♣⬆P🚪(31)🐾🛜

Nantwich

Black Lion 🅛
29 Welsh Row, CW5 5ED (on Welsh Row, opp Cheshire Cat)
☎ (01270) 628711 ⊕ blacklionnantwich.co.uk
Weetwood Best Bitter, Cheshire Cat, Old Dog; 3 changing beers (sourced regionally) 🅷
A traditional black-and-white-fronted inn standing among the historic buildings of Welsh Row. Its beautiful plaster and wood-beamed interior retains the expected bowed walls and creaking floorboards. An open fire welcomes you into an open-plan area which used to be

three separate rooms. The small Hop Room features hop bines on the ceiling and a pot-bellied stove for heating. Free of tie, it showcases three of Weetwood's fine ales. There is a restaurant upstairs and a covered beer garden to the side. Q☀◑♫♣⬆🚪(84)🐾🛜

Crown 🅛
High Street, CW5 5AS
☎ (01270) 625283 ⊕ crownhotelnantwich.com
Salopian Shropshire Gold; 4 changing beers (sourced regionally) 🅷
A black-and-white-timbered hotel, rebuilt in 1585 after the great Fire of Nantwich. The Grade I-listed building retains oak beams that came from Delamere Forest, and wattle and daub walls. The Long Gallery upstairs is worth a visit. Dining is available in the bar and the separate Crown Bar & Grill. Occasional live entertainment is hosted. During the Nantwich Food and Drink Festival, the Crown hosts its own beer festival.
♿🛏◑🛜♣P🚪(84, 85)🐾🛜

Vine Inn ✅
42 Hospital Street, CW5 5RP (near St Mary's Church)
☎ (01270) 619055 ⊕ vineinnnantwich.co.uk
Hydes Old Indie, Original, Lowry; 3 changing beers (sourced regionally) 🅷
The Vine is a 17th-century Grade II-listed building set on three distinct open-plan levels. There is sports TV in most rooms and a quiet board games room with a real fire at the back. The full range of Hydes beer is available including craft beers from the Beer Studio. This welcoming family- and dog-friendly pub is also popular for good food. In recent years it has become a regular in the Guide due to its consistently well-conditioned beer.
♿☀◑➊♫⬆🚪🐾🛜

Wickstead Arms 🅛 ✅
5 Mill Street, CW5 5ST (at jct of Mill St and Barker St)
☎ (01270) 610196 ⊕ wicksteadpubnantwich.co.uk
5 changing beers (sourced nationally) 🅷
Quite a small pub, the warm, friendly atmosphere is immediately evident on entering. A busy back-street local, a short stroll from Nantwich town centre, it has a sports TV bar and a dining room. Food is served throughout. Five handpumps offer a range of changing beers from the Punch Taverns list. A former local CAMRA award winner. ◑♫🚪(84,85)🐾🛜

Northwich

Baron's Lounge 🅛
13 Witton Street, CW9 5DE (in pedestrianised town centre)
☎ 07754 556497
4 changing beers (sourced locally; often Chapter, Merlin, Weetwood) 🅷
Close to the new Barons Quay development, the Baron's Lounge opened in late 2017 in what used to be a Red Cross shop and was converted into a two-storey microbar in 2018. Although small, it packs plenty in, with quiz nights, vinyl music nights, retro games and live music. There is a suntrap patio to the rear. A sister pub to the Hop Emporium in Warrington. Q☀⬆♣⬆🚪🐾🛜

Salty Dog 🅛
21-23 High Street, CW9 5BY (in pedestrianised town centre) ⊕ salty-dog.co.uk
Tatton Gold; 3 changing beers (sourced locally; often Merlin, RedWillow, Tatton) 🅷
This former shop, converted in 2017, retains its picturesque black-and-white exterior. The landlord and co-owner played drums in punk band The Business. Live music features along with comedy nights. A room at the

rear has a jukebox, table football and retro arcade games. An extensive range of bottled and canned British and European beers is available. The pub was voted one of the best small music venues in the UK by Guardian readers. ⤢⊛&♣🚾😺🛜

Penketh

Ferry Tavern
Station Road, WA5 2UJ (from car park on Station Rd, cross railway and canal) SJ5634986649
☎ (01925) 791117 ⊕ theferrytavern.com
8 changing beers (sourced nationally; often Marble, Ossett, Titanic) Ⓗ
A picturesque pub next to the River Mersey, with its car park a short walk away on the other side of the railway line. Low-beamed ceilings inside add to the unique atmosphere. Real ale events are hosted including beer festivals and tap takeovers. It is renowned for fish & chips at the weekend. The large beer garden is often busy and is a popular stopping point for users of the Transpennine Trail. Q⤢⊛◑●P🚾😺🛜

Poynton

Cask Tavern
42 Park Lane, SK12 1RE
☎ (01625) 875157 ⊕ casktavern.co.uk
Bollington Long Hop, Best, Dinner Ale; 2 changing beers (sourced regionally) Ⓗ
One of three Bollington Brewery taps in Cheshire, the Cask showcases the brewery's range of beers and a couple of guests. A mecca for real ale drinkers, national brands are conspicuous by their absence. It also features locally brewed Moravka craft lager. The one-roomed interior has comfortable seating areas, with two more drinking spaces outside. Upstairs is used for meetings by local groups. A regular clientele has developed and a warm welcome is assured to all visitors. Q⊛♣●🚾😺🛜

Runcorn

Ferry Boat ⊘
10 Church Street, WA7 1LR
☎ (01928) 583380
Greene King Abbot; Ruddles Best Bitter; Sharp's Doom Bar Ⓗ**; 2 changing beers (sourced nationally)** Ⓗ/Ⓖ
Large, busy Wetherspoon pub opposite Runcorn old town bus station. As well as the standard Wetherspoon engines there are usually at least two guest beers, plus ciders via bag-in-a-box. The pub's name derives from the river crossing that used to operate between the towns of Runcorn and Widnes (on the opposite bank of the River Mersey) before the building of the Manchester Ship Canal in the 1890s. The Brindley Theatre is 200 yards away. ⤢⊛◑&⇄●P🚾🛜

Norton Arms
125-127 Main Street, Halton, WA7 2AD
☎ (01928) 567642 ⊕ thenortonarms.co.uk
Greene King IPA; 3 changing beers (sourced nationally; often Hardys & Hansons) Ⓗ
This is the eighth year in the Guide for this Grade II-listed, two-roomed, oak-beamed inn in the centre of Halton Village. Although dominated by sports TV, the pub is still a nice find. Among the attractions are open mic nights, live music, quiz evenings and a bowling green. Due to the age of the building, wheelchair access is difficult – the entrance is up a flight of stone steps. Local CAMRA Pub of the Year 2020 and 2021. ⤢⊛◑&P🚾😺🛜

Round House
121-123 Heath Road South, Weston Village, WA7 4RP
☎ (01928) 770879
Brains Rev James; Sharp's Doom Bar Ⓗ
A large, open-plan, sports-oriented pub, hosting occasional live music. The small corner bar has two handpumps. The pub's name derives from the shape of the building – its frontage follows the natural curve of the road. Very much a community hub, it has a varied clientele. ⤢◑&♣🚾(13C)😺🛜

Society Tap Rooms (STR) Ⓛ
33 Ashridge Street, WA7 1HU (5 mins' walk from station, 10 mins' walk from Old Town)
☎ (01928) 775628 ⊕ societyltd.co.uk
Changing beers (sourced locally; often Blueball, Chapter) Ⓗ
This brewery and tap was formerly a Co-operative building and a baker's. Its beers are from Blueball, attached to the building, plus other breweries including Heavy Industry and Chapter. KeyKeg craft beer is also available. Hidden away in the Dukesfield area of the town, the entrance is under the arches of the railway line between Runcorn station and Ethelfleda Bridge which carries the line over the Mersey. ◗&⇄●🚾😺

Sandbach

Beer Emporium Ⓛ
8 Welles Street, CW11 1GT (off Hightown roundabout, down one-way street)
☎ (01270) 760113 ⊕ thebeeremporium.com
5 changing beers Ⓗ
A relaxing and friendly micropub in what was once a butcher's shop, popular with locals and visitors alike. It has a larger room at the front with seating in the window, plus a smaller room at the rear. Located in the Sandbach conservation area, it has gone from strength to strength over the past decade, offering a range of real ales and ciders, and a superb array of bottled beers. The bar staff know their stuff and are always willing to advise on beer styles. A sister pub to the Bottle Bank in Holmes Chapel. Q⤢🚾(37,38)😺🛜

Old Hall Ⓛ
High Street, CW11 2LJ (opp St Mary's Church)
☎ (01270) 758170
Timothy Taylor Boltmaker; Weetwood Cheshire Cat; house beer (by Brunning & Price); 3 changing beers (sourced regionally) Ⓗ
The Old Hall dates from the 1650s and is a Grade I-listed timber-framed building with a stone-flagged roof. It was rescued from structural decay by Brunning & Price in 2010 and reopened in 2011 as a pub and restaurant following extensive repairs and restoration. The interior is a pleasant mix of flagged and wooden floors plus Jacobean fireplaces. Beers are from a wide area but often include local brews. Excellent food menus feature locally sourced ingredients where possible.
⤢⊛◑&♣P🚾(37,38)😺🛜🔄

Stockton Heath

Costello's Bar Ⓛ
23 Walton Road, WA4 6NJ
☎ (01925) 600910 ⊕ costellosbar.co.uk
Dunham Massey Big Tree Bitter, Dunham Dark; Lymm Bridgewater Blonde; 4 changing beers (sourced locally; often Dunham Massey, Lymm) Ⓗ
A modern micro-style pub offering seven handpumps, with all beers from either the Dunham Massey or sister Lymm Brewery stables. This is an excellent venue for the

discerning drinker who prefers darker beers. Handily placed in the centre of Stockton Heath, it provides an oasis of calm at the weekend when the area is busy with a young clientele. Live music is hosted regularly on Sunday afternoons. A former local CAMRA Pub of the Year. Q⌂❀&●🖰🍽🛜

Sutton

Sutton Hall L
Bullocks Lane, SK11 0HE
☎ (01260) 253211
Brunning & Price Original; house beer (by Wincle); 4 changing beers (sourced locally) Ⓗ
More than 480 years old, this former convent and manor house has links to the notorious Lord Lucan's family. A Brunning & Price establishment, the house beer is from the brewery, alongside a selection of largely local guest beers. This is a popular dining pub but drinkers are equally welcome. Indoors there are nooks and crannies, a library and seven dining areas; outside there are extensive terraces and gardens. It is close to Macclesfield Forest in the Peak District and next to the Macclesfield Canal. Q⌂❀🛈◗&P🖰(14)🍽🛜

Thelwall

Little Manor L
Bell Lane, WA4 2SX
☎ (01925) 212070 ⊕ littlemanor-thelwall.co.uk
House beer (by Phoenix); 7 changing beers (sourced locally; often 4Ts) Ⓗ
A large upmarket food-based inn with a changing range of local and regional cask ales. It is charmingly furnished with a relaxed ambience, and has extensive garden areas for outdoor dining. A regularly changing food menu is served throughout the day. Set in picturesque surroundings, the property was originally the home for the Percival family in the 1600s, with their coat of arms adopted as the pub sign. Details of country walks in the area are available from the website or bar. Dogs are welcome in the main bar area. Q⌂❀🛈◗&♣♠P🖰🍽🛜

Tilston

Carden Arms L
Mount View, Church Road, SY14 7HB
☎ (01829) 250900 ⊕ cardenarms.co.uk
Coach House Gunpowder Mild; Salopian Shropshire Gold; Weetwood Eastgate; 2 changing beers (sourced locally; often Peerless, Spitting Feathers, Wincle) Ⓗ
Impressive rural free house at the crossroads in the village. The interior has rug-covered wood and tiled floors, real fires, traditional furniture and attractive framed pictures on the plain white walls. In addition to the three regular beers are two guests, often from local microbreweries. High-quality food is served in the bar area and the stylish dining room. Upstairs, two adjoining Georgian rooms can be booked for groups. Accommodation is available in five bedrooms. Q🛏◗&♣P🖰(41)🍽🛜

Warrington

Albion L
94 Battersby Lane, WA2 7EG (200yds N of A57/A49 jct)
☎ (01925) 231820
4 changing beers (sourced locally; often Merlin) Ⓗ
Large Victorian pub with a courtyard surrounded by the original stables. Inside, it has distinctly separate rooms, two with real fires, including a games room with a pool table. Live bands and other entertainment are hosted,

often in support of local charities. Four real ales come mainly from local independent breweries. The Albion is a former local CAMRA Community Pub of the Year. ⌂❀≷(Central)♣🖰🍽

Hop Emporium L
Unit 11, Warrington New Market, Time Square, Academy Way, WA1 2NT
☎ 07809 209254
4 changing beers (sourced regionally; often Beartown, Tiny Rebel) Ⓗ
An award-winning micropub in the new Warrington Market. There is plenty of seating inside, and also outside in an area shared by a wide variety of food outlets, based on the modern market concept. Third-pint beer paddles are available together with craft beers and a real cider. Hours are restricted to the market cookhouse's opening hours. A sister pub to Baron's Lounge in Northwich. Q⌂❀&≷(Central)●🖰🍽🛜

Tavern L
25 Church Street, WA1 2SS
☎ 07747 668817
8 changing beers (sourced nationally; often 4Ts, Mallinsons, Oakham) Ⓗ
A regular Good Beer Guide entry, the Tavern offers an excellent choice of eight beers in varying styles. Local 4Ts beers feature strongly but there is also a varied selection from bigger breweries and northern independents. Beers change all the time – this is a good place to discover something new from the regularly updated beer list at the end of the bar. Bottled craft beers, ciders and Belgian beers are also available. The pub offers a wide choice of sports TV and has an enlarged outdoor seating area. Q⌂❀≷(Central)♣🖰🍽🛜

Willey Moor Lock

Willey Moor Lock Tavern
Tarporley Road, SY13 4HF (400yds off A49, around 1½ miles N of Whitchurch)
☎ (01948) 663274 ⊕ willeymoorlock.co.uk
6 changing beers (sourced nationally) Ⓗ
This former lock-keeper's cottage is now a family-run free house. Access from the car park is via a footbridge over the Llangollen Canal. The pub is popular with boaters and also walkers on the Sandstone Trail, especially in the summer. Choose your outside seating either next to the lock or in the attractive garden. Three changing beers, many from local brewers, increase to six in summer. Good-value meals are served. Q⌂❀◗♣P🍽🛜

Willington

Boot Inn L
Boothsdale, Willington Lane, CW6 0NH (S of Kelsall, signposted from Willington Rd) SJ5304667257
☎ (01829) 751375 ⊕ thebootinnwillington.com
Weetwood Best Bitter, Cheshire Cat; 2 changing beers (sourced locally; often Weetwood) Ⓗ
Well-hidden in a picturesque location in rolling countryside, this small village pub was originally three cottages. Sandstone walls, tiled floors and low ceilings, along with open fires and a wood-burner, create a cosy atmosphere in winter, while the patios outside are popular in warmer weather. The Boot has a good reputation for food, served both in the restaurant and bar area, and also outside in summer. The two rotating beers are both from Weetwood. A number of local walks can be downloaded from the website. Q⌂❀◗♣P🍽🛜

Wilmslow

Brewhouse & Kitchen 🅛 ✅

6-12 Swan Street, SK9 1HE
☎ (01625) 441850
Brewhouse & Kitchen Bollin Ruby, Fustian Cut, Lucky Sam Ⓗ

Since opening in 2016, this brewery diner has established itself as a key destination pub in the town. The decor is beer-related, with lamps made from beer glasses and bottles. Four cask ales, all brewed on the premises, have locally themed names. Food focuses on steaks and burgers, but there are also vegetarian and vegan options. The menu gives suggested beer pairings for most dishes. The gleaming copper-coloured brewery can be viewed from the bar area.
🖖😼◐◖🦽🍴♿🍽(88,130) 📶

Wrenbury

Cotton Arms 🅛

Cholmondley Road, CW5 8HG (on right, just before Telford's lift-bridge over Llangollen Canal)
☎ (01270) 780377
Sharp's Doom Bar, Atlantic; 5 changing beers (sourced nationally) Ⓗ

A roadside venue, very popular with boaters, walkers, cyclists, campers and caravanners (two large fields behind the pub cater for the latter two) that has its own bowling green and a pavillion, both available for hire. It serves up to seven real ales on handpump plus an excellent food menu. The pub is named after Stapleton Cotton, 1st Viscount Combermere, active in the Peninsular Wars and the siege of Bharatpur.
Q🖖😼◐🍴◖▲♣🅿🚍🐾📶

White Bear, Middlewich (Photo: Marc Holmes)

CORNWALL

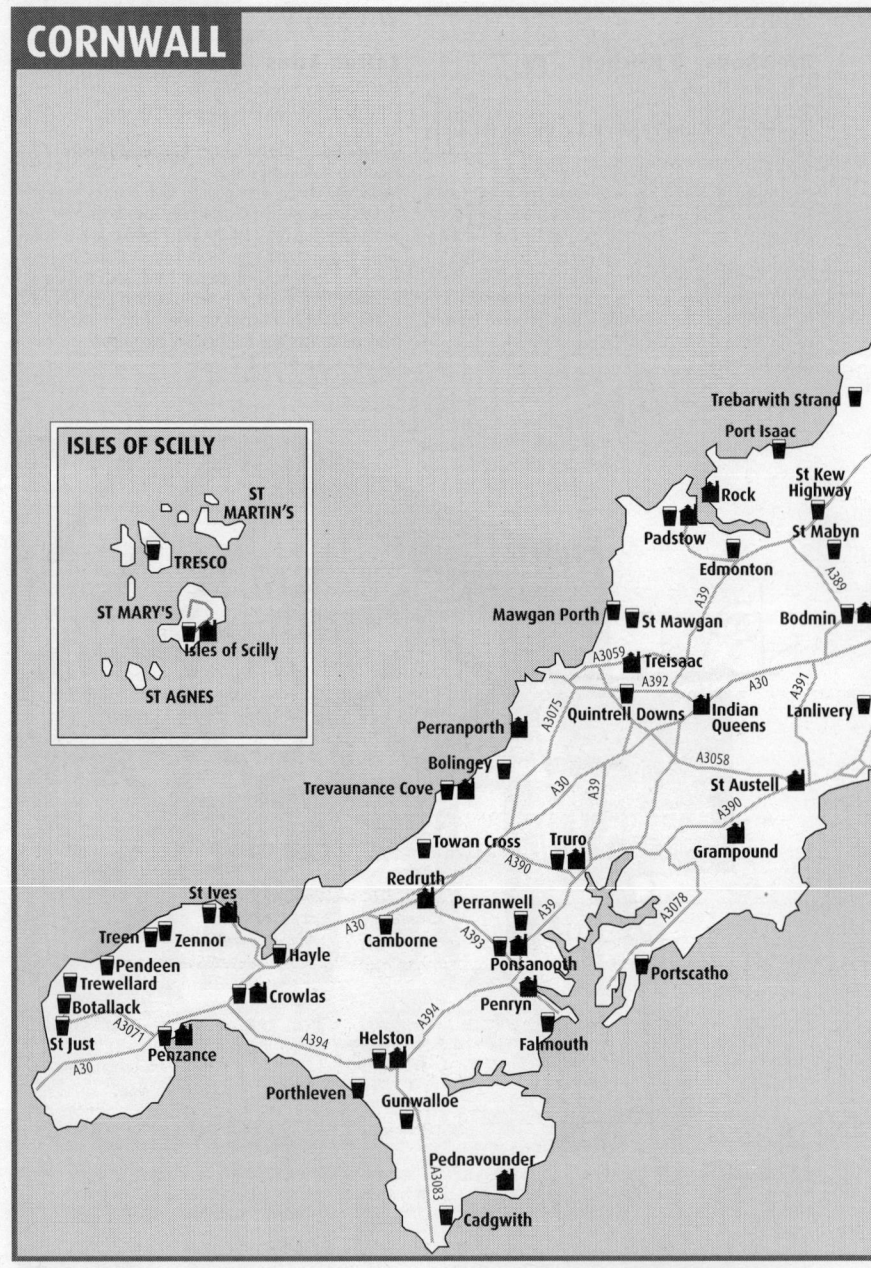

ISLES OF SCILLY

ST MARTIN'S

TRESCO

ST MARY'S

Isles of Scilly

ST AGNES

Trebarwith Strand
Port Isaac
St Kew Highway
Rock
Padstow
St Mabyn
Edmonton
A389
Bodmin
Mawgan Porth
St Mawgan
A39
A3059
Treisaac
A392
Quintrell Downs
Indian Queens
A30
A391
Lanlivery
A3075
Perranporth
Bolingey
A3058
St Austell
Trevaunance Cove
A30
A39
A390
Grampound
Towan Cross
Truro
Redruth
A3078
Perranwell
St Ives
Perranwell
A30
A39
Treen
Zennor
Camborne
A393
Hayle
Portscatho
Pendeen
Ponsanooth
Trewellard
Crowlas
Penryn
Botallack
A3071
Falmouth
St Just
Helston
A30
A394
Penzance
A514
Porthleven
Gunwalloe
Pednavounder
A3083
Cadgwith

Altarnun

Rising Sun

PL15 7SN (NW of Altarnun village) SX215825
☎ (01566) 86636 🌐 therisingsuninn.co.uk

Altarnun St Nonna's; Skinner's Lushingtons; 3 changing beers (sourced nationally) Ⓗ

A thriving community pub for more than 150 years and the tap for nearby Altarnun Brewery, this characterful building is on the outskirts of the village. The interior is cosy and warm, with beamed ceilings and an open fireplace, and antique guns and various pictures on the walls. Deceptively spacious, the pub offers ample seating in the bar, two small annexes for pool and drinkers, and a separate restaurant. Food features locally sourced ingredients. Outside, there is a large patio and grassed area for games. Q ⏰ 🏠 🍽 🕩 & ♣ ♠ 🅿 ❄ 🔌 ᯤ

Blisland

Blisland Inn

The Green, PL30 4JF (off A30 NE of Bodmin) SX100732
☎ (01208) 850739

Dowr Kammel Blisland Gold; house beer (by Sharp's) Ⓗ; **4 changing beers (sourced nationally)** Ⓗ/Ⓖ

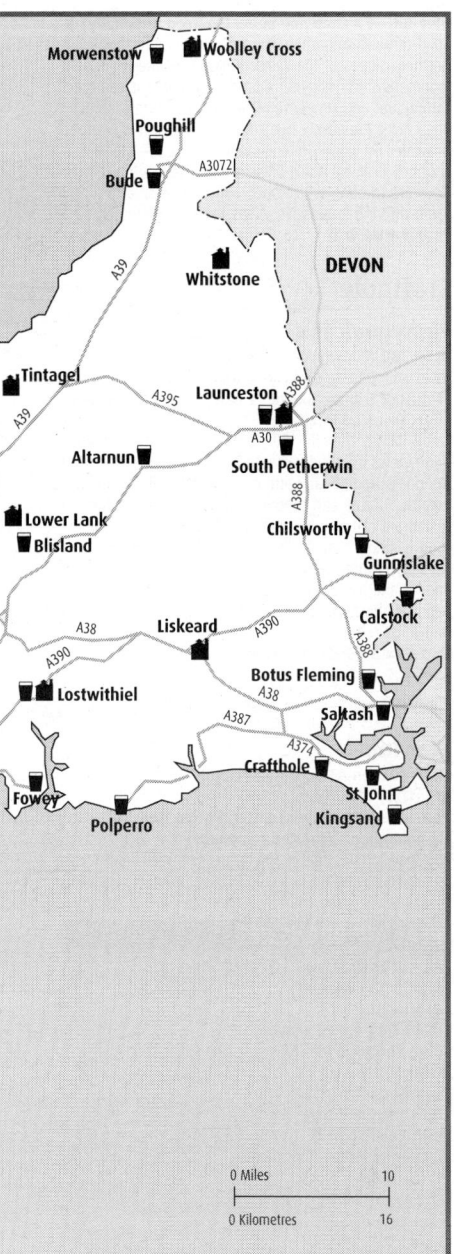

Bodmin

Hole in the Wall ✪
16 Crockwell Street, PL31 2DS (enter from town car park)
☎ (01208) 72397 ⊕ theholeinthewallbodmin.co.uk
Butcombe Original; Draught Bass; Sharp's Atlantic, Sea Fury; 2 changing beers (sourced nationally; often Skinner's, Young's) ⊞
Popular local built in the 18th century as a debtors' prison. The pub can be accessed from the public car park or through a secluded, leafy garden containing its own hop bine and stream, and presided over by a rather bleached stuffed lion. The single bar, which is subdivided by archways, contains a large and eclectic collection of antiques and military memorabilia. Upstairs is a separate function room. The pub has twice won local CAMRA Pub of the Year. Q❄♿🕏🚲♣🚌🚏(27,11A)🐾🦮🔊

Bolingey

Bolingey Inn ✪
Penwartha Road, TR6 0DH (near B3284) SW763531
☎ (01872) 571626
Sharp's Doom Bar; 3 changing beers (sourced nationally; often Dartmoor, St Austell, Wadworth) ⊞
Set in a delightful location in a small village about 20 minutes walk from Perranporth. The pub offers two bars – one mainly for drinking with a wooden floor and an open fire (especially popular with sleepy dogs), the other bar with more seating where you can dine if you wish. Four handpumps serve changing local and national ales alongside the ever-present Doom Bar. A beer festival is held twice yearly in April and October, attracting enthusiasts from near and far. Q❄🕏🍴🅰♣P🐾🦮🔊

Botallack

Queen's Arms
Botallack Road, TR19 7QG
☎ (01736) 788318 ⊕ queensarmscornwall.co.uk
Sharp's Doom Bar; 1 changing beer (sourced locally; often Tintagel) ⊞
Tucked away in a hamlet just off the St Ives to St Just coast road, the bar has exposed granite walls and is decorated with mining prints and pictures by local artists. The ceiling beams are adorned with many pumpclips, while the pub's cosy ambience is enhanced by an inglenook fireplace and log-burners. To the rear, a family/pool room leads to an attractive walled beer garden. Snacks and meals are prepared using local produce. Q❄🕏🍴🅰♣🚲P(A17)🐾🔊

Botus Fleming

Rising Sun Inn
PL12 6NJ (½ mile off A388, near Saltash) SX405613
☎ (01752) 842792
Skinner's Betty Stogs; 3 changing beers (sourced nationally; often Dartmoor, Everards, Greene King) ⊞
Tastefully refurbished after remaining largely unaltered for years, this rural gem with low ceilings and well-trodden wooden floors is tucked away in a quiet village near Saltash, just off the beaten track. The three real ales change regularly and imaginatively; there is, however, no food. The pub is dog-friendly, supports darts and euchre teams and hosts occasional live music. Regular buses pass on the A388, about a 20-minute walk away. Q🐾♣P🐾🔊

A friendly rural community pub by the village green and a former CAMRA National Pub of the Year, the Blisland retains its reputation as a real ale destination, set on the edge of Bodmin Moor. It has served well over 3,000 different real ales and normally has at least five or six beers on, with several brewed locally, plus frequently changing draught ciders including some unusual varieties. The decor is eclectic, and includes barometers, Toby jugs and coffee mugs as well as an impressive collection of pumpclips and beer mats. Food is freshly prepared using local produce. Popular with walkers and cyclists, the pub also welcomes well-behaved children and dogs. Q❄🕏🍴♣🛏🐾🔊

Bude

Barrel at Bude
36 Lansdown Road, EX23 8BN
☎ (01288) 356113 ⊕ thebarrelatbude.com
5 changing beers (sourced locally) ⊞
This small micropub opened in 2017 in a former fancy dress shop in the centre of town. All the beers and ciders are sourced from within Cornwall and Scilly by the proprietor without recourse to the wholesale trade. The philosophy is that to ensure beers are at their best, all ales in place on Thursday should be consumed by Sunday – 'drink the barrel dry' afternoon – ready for a restock the following week. Cornish organic gins and local wines are also sold. ᐳ♠P➾❀

Cadgwith

Cadgwith Cove Inn
TR12 7JX
☎ (01326) 290513 ⊕ cadgwithcoveinn.com
Sharp's Doom Bar, Sea Fury; Skinner's Betty Stogs, Lushingtons ⊞
Three-roomed inn tucked away by the harbour and the South-West Coastal Path in a compact fishing village on the Lizard peninsula. Over 300 years old, the pub remains largely unspoilt since its smuggling days. Relics from the seafaring past and photos of shipwrecks and local scenes adorn the half-panelled walls, while the bar also sports rope handles hanging from the beams for when the pub lists! Expect some lively singing in the evenings, with itinerant musicians often performing. ᐳ❀➾◑♣❀♢

Calstock

Boot Inn
Fore Street, PL18 9RN
☎ (01822) 481589
2 changing beers (sourced nationally; often Exeter) ⊞
Split-level 17th-century village inn tucked snugly amid the cottages and narrow cobbled streets of Calstock. With wood beams and wooden floors throughout, the pub's middle level hosts the bar and main drinking area, with dining spaces either side. Up to the left is a space where you can take your dog, while down to the right is a separate main dining room. Largely food-driven, the pub nevertheless welcomes customers who only want a sociable drink. Q⧖◑ᐭ➾(79)❀

Camborne

John Francis Basset ✪
21 Commercial Street, TR14 8JZ (pub entrance in Church St)
☎ (01209) 721720
Greene King Abbot, IPA; Sharp's Doom Bar; 5 changing beers ⊞
Town-centre Wetherspoon in the former Market House built by architect William Bond in 1866. Previous uses of the building have included as a cinema, a night club and a pub called the Corn Exchange. Named after a prominent former local mine owner, it is a large, airy, open-plan venue with high ceilings and tall windows. The single long bar offers an impressive selection of varying beers, often locally brewed. A real ale oasis and well worth a visit. Q⧖❀➾◑ᒻ⇌♣◑♢

Chilsworthy

White Hart
PL18 9PB (signposted from A390) SX416721
☎ (01822) 833876 ⊕ whitehartchilsworthy.com

Uley Bitter; 4 changing beers (sourced regionally) ⊞
Solid rural community free house tucked into the northern slopes of the Tamar Valley near the prominent landmark of Kit Hill. The main drinking area is carpeted throughout and simply furnished with wooden tables and chairs. Previously two separate rooms, it is warmed in winter by wood-burning stoves set in two stone chimney breasts. Horse brasses and other pub artefacts decorate the bar, which opens out at one side to a rear room offering impressive views towards Dartmoor. ᐳ❀◑♣♠P♢♢

Crafthole

Finnygook Inn
PL11 3BQ (Portwrinkle, off B3247)
☎ (01503) 230338 ⊕ finnygook.co.uk
St Austell Tribute; Skinner's Betty Stogs; 3 changing beers (sourced locally) ⊞
Large, family-friendly 15th-century coaching inn, with good views over the valley to the St Germans River. The interior is traditional, with low-beamed ceilings and a wealth of brass and copper ornaments. The separate restaurant can also be used as a function room. Quality food is made with locally sourced produce. Quiz night is Tuesday (winter only), while live music is hosted on Fridays and most Saturdays. The name refers to the resident ghost (gook) of a local smuggler, who was hung and thrown down the well.
Q⧖❀➾◑ᐭ♣P➾(70B,75) ♢♢

Crowlas

Star Inn
TR20 8DX (on A30, 2½ miles E of Penzance)
☎ (01736) 740375
Penzance Mild, Crowlas Bitter, Potion No.9; 4 changing beers (sourced nationally) ⊞
This roadside free house and former Cornwall CAMRA Pub of the Year is home to the Penzance Brewery. The long

REAL ALE BREWERIES
Ales of Scilly St Mary's: Isles of Scilly
Altarnun Launceston
Atlantic Treisaac
Black Flag ⚲ Perranporth
Blue Anchor ≣ Helston
Castle Lostwithiel
Cornish Crown ⚲ Penzance
Dowr Kammel Lower Lank
Driftwood Spars ≣ Trevaunance Cove
Dynamite Valley Ponsanooth
Forge Woolley Cross
Fowey Lostwithiel
Harbour Bodmin
Keltek Redruth
Krow Redruth
Lizard Pednavounder
Longhill Whitstone
Padstow Padstow
Penzance ≣ Crowlas
Point Break Liskeard (NEW)
Seven Stars ≣ Penryn (NEW)
Sharp's Rock
Skinner's ⚲ Truro
St Austell ⚲ St Austell
St Ives St Ives
Tintagel Tintagel
Treen's Ponsanooth
Tremethick Grampound
Woodman's Indian Queens

U-shaped bar dispenses real ales from the pub's own brewhouse and two or three from other microbreweries. There is a pool table to the right, a comfy raised seating area, a cosy lounge area with leather sofas and chairs, and an adjacent meeting room. This is essentially a beer-drinkers' local where conversation is the main entertainment, with no noisy machines to distract. ❀♣P➾❀🤶

Edmonton

Quarryman Inn

PL27 7JA (just off A39 near Royal Cornwall showground)
☎ (01208) 816444 🌐 thequarryman.co.uk
Otter Bitter; 3 changing beers (sourced regionally; often Padstow, Skinner's) ⊞
This former schoolhouse and quarrymen's accommodation is now a pub with two distinct areas. The smaller bar area has a flagstone floor and a variety of sporting memorabilia. The adjacent carpeted lounge is often busy with diners, serving locally sourced home-cooked food. The beers usually vary but with the exception of the Otter Bitter tend to be local, often from the nearby Padstow Brewery. The atmosphere is convivial and conversation flourishes – no mobile phones! Q ➚ ❀ ➊ ▲ ♣ P ➾ (11A,95) ❀ 🤶

Falmouth

Beerwolf Books

3-4 Bells Court, TR11 3AZ (up alley off main shopping street opp M&S clock)
☎ (01326) 618474 🌐 beerwolfbooks.com
6 changing beers (sourced nationally; often Blackjack, Penzance, Shiny) ⊞
Pub or bookshop? Actually, it's both. Popular with all ages, this former maritime storage loft and pleasant outside courtyard is tucked away up a side-alley off Market Street. It is accessed via a steep flight of stairs, at the top of which is the bookshop, while to the right is the bar, dispensing an adventurous selection of constantly changing beers. Cider lovers are also catered for. Basic tables and chairs are scattered throughout, so you can sit and drink beer, browse through books – or both. No food is served, but you may bring your own. ➚ ❀ ♣ ● ➾ ❀ 🤶

Oddfellows Arms

Quay Hill, TR11 3HA
☎ (01326) 218611
Sharp's Atlantic; house beer (by Sharp's) ⊞; **1 changing beer (sourced locally; often Skinner's)** ⊞/Ⓖ
Unpretentious single-bar community pub tucked up a hilly side street off the town centre and popular with locals and visitors alike. Decorated with old photographs, it has a convivial atmosphere in which to enjoy the three beers normally on offer, with sometimes a fourth racked up at the back of the bar. A small back room hosts the dartboard, pool table and real fire. The pub organises festivals throughout the year, often involving food made by the locals. Q ⇌ ♣ ➾ ❀ 🤶

Pennycomequick

16 Killigrew Street, The Moor, TR11 3PN
☎ (01326) 311912 🌐 pennycomequick.co.uk
St Austell Tribute; 2 changing beers (sourced regionally; often Bath Ales, Tintagel) ⊞
This modernised open-plan bar/restaurant with friendly and knowledgeable staff offers a relaxed and welcoming atmosphere. It has seating at the bar and front snug area for drinkers, and tables for diners. The two changing ales are generally from St Austell Brewery, but other beers from Cornwall or further afield are often available. Food

menus feature local seasonal ingredients cooked with flair (booking recommended for evening dining). Pennycomequick is derived from the former Cornish name for Falmouth. ➚ ❀ ➊ ➇ ❀ 🤶

Seaview Inn

Wodehouse Terrace, TR11 3EP
☎ (01326) 311359 🌐 seaviewinnfalmouth.co.uk
Sharp's Doom Bar; 2 changing beers (sourced locally; often Penzance, Treen's) ⊞
A traditional and comfortable town pub with a large, beamed, open-plan island bar. As the name suggests, it enjoys excellent views over Falmouth harbour and Carrick Roads, with all their maritime activity. The locals are a friendly mix of all ages, and the pub welcomes children and dogs. A games area to the rear hosts darts and pool. Accommodation is in three rooms. Q ➚ ❀ ➇ ➊ ➅ ♣ ➾ ❀ 🤶

Seven Stars ★

The Moor, TR11 3QA
☎ (01326) 312111 🌐 thesevenstarsfalmouth.com
Draught Bass; Sharp's Atlantic, Sea Fury; 2 changing beers (sourced locally; often Padstow, Skinner's, Treen's) Ⓖ
This timeless and unspoilt town-centre local has been in the same family for nearly 170 years and features on CAMRA's National Inventory of Historic Pub Interiors. It has a lively, narrow taproom where beers are served on gravity. There are two quiet rooms at the back. The old bottle-and-jug hatch remains for outdoor drinkers. Bass is ever-present, as are beers from Sharp's Brewery. A real gem that should not be missed. Q ➚ ❀ ● ➾ ❀ 🤶

Fowey

Galleon Inn

12 Fore Street, PL23 1AQ
☎ (01726) 833014 🌐 galleon-inn.co.uk
Sharp's Cornish Coaster, Doom Bar; 2 changing beers (often Bath Ales) ⊞
Riverside pub in the town centre dating back 400 years, now fully modernised, reached off Fore Street through a glass-covered corridor with a colourful marine life mural. The only free house in Fowey, it features mainly Cornish ales. A wide range of meals is available daily. The main bar and conservatory enjoy delightful harbour views and tables outside overlook the water. There is a heated, sheltered courtyard. Accommodation is en-suite, some rooms with river views. ➚ ❀ ➇ ➊ ➅ ♣ ➾ (24,25) ❀ 🤶

Gunnislake

Rising Sun Inn

Calstock Road, PL18 9BX (off A390) SX432711
☎ (01822) 832201 🌐 therisingsuninngunnislake.com
Dartmoor Legend, Jail Ale; 3 changing beers (sourced regionally) ⊞
Friendly oak-beamed community inn dating from the 17th century, lying in a conservation area in a rural setting off the beaten track. It serves a good choice of up to five varying real ales, three always changing and mainly from Cornish or other West Country breweries. Exposed stone walls and wooden beams display an extensive collection of chinaware. Outside, the beautiful terraced garden affords views of the Tamar Valley. Q ➚ ❀ ➊ ⇌ ♣ ● P ➾ (79) ❀ 🤶

Gunwalloe

Halzephron Inn

TR12 7QB (off A3083 Helston-Lizard road) SW657224

☎ (01326) 240406 ⊕ halzephron-inn.co.uk
Sharp's Doom Bar; Skinner's Porthleven; 3 changing beers (sourced nationally) Ⓗ
This quiet, welcoming 500-year-old inn was once the haunt of smugglers. The two traditional bars remain – the lounge doubling as a restaurant with an adjacent snug. Another restaurant area is in an extension to the rear. Accommodation is in two en-suite rooms. The pub name derives from the old Cornish 'als yffrin' meaning 'cliffs of hell' – timbers from many nearby shipwrecks were incorporated into the building's structure.
Q ☭ ⚙ ⛱ ◀◖ ♠ P 🖵 ♣ 🔥 🛜

Hayle

Bird in Hand
Trelissick Road, TR27 4HY
☎ (01736) 753974 ⊕ birdinhandhayle.co.uk
Treen's Essential; 2 changing beers (sourced regionally; often Dartmoor, Exeter) Ⓗ
Families are welcome in this spacious pub converted from Victorian stables, adjacent to Paradise Park wildlife sanctuary. The decor in the one-room bar is a mix of local industrial paraphernalia and horse paintings on the walls, painted casks over the bar area, and an end wall decorated with a large frieze by Terry English depicting scenes from Cornwall's industrial past. Outside is a spacious seating area. Parking is shared with the wildlife sanctuary. ☭ ⚙ ◀◖ ♣ 🖵 🖵 (T1,T2) 🔥 🛜

Helston

Blue Anchor
50 Coinagehall Street, TR13 8EL
☎ (01326) 562821 ⊕ spingoales.com
Blue Anchor Jubilee IPA, Ben's Stout; 1 changing beer (sourced locally; often Blue Anchor) Ⓗ
A former monks' rest, this 15th-century brewpub is one of the oldest in Britain, changing little over the years and retaining much of its original character. Two separate small bars are found to the right of the central passageway, one with an open fire, and two sitting rooms to the left, all with slate floors. To the rear are a skittle alley and partly covered garden area with its own bar and barbecue. An anchor is visible on the thatched roof. Q ☭ ⚙ ⛱ ♣ ♠ 🖵 🔥

Kingsand

Devonport Inn
The Cleave, PL10 1NF
☎ (01752) 822869 ⊕ devonportinn.com
Dartmoor Legend; 2 changing beers (sourced locally; often Bays, Otter) Ⓗ
Set between a narrow lane and the sea, this old pub was formerly divided into two bars but is now partly opened out to one, albeit still with distinct drinking areas. The small, wooden-floored bar has snug recesses and is ship-themed. It serves one or two constantly changing real ales, mostly from Devon. Live bands perform monthly in winter and more frequently in summer. It provides a welcome halt, both for walkers on the Cornwall coast path and the less energetic. ☭ ⚙ ◀◖ ♿ 🖵 (70) 🔥 🛜

Lanlivery

Crown Inn
PL30 5BT (in village centre)
☎ (01208) 872707 ⊕ thecrowninncornwall.co.uk
Sharp's Doom Bar; 2 changing beers (sourced locally; often Harbour, Skinner's) Ⓗ

Picturesque 12th-century pub built in a long farmhouse style, with the main bar and snug at one end. It also has a comfortable lounge with an inglenook fireplace containing a huge wood-burning stove, and a restaurant. Food is available daily, with most of the ingredients sourced locally. Snacks are served all day in summer. Accommodation is in the former piggery and is accessible by wheelchair. Q ☭ ⚙ ⛱ ◀◖ ♿ ♠ P 🖵 🔥 🛜

Launceston

Bell Inn
1 Tower Street, PL15 8BQ (next to parish church tower)
☎ (01566) 779970 ⊕ bellinnlaunceston.co.uk
House beer (by Holsworthy Ales); 5 changing beers (sourced regionally) Ⓗ
Cosy 14th-century town hostelry originally built to house stonemasons erecting the nearby church. Conversation rules in this locals' pub. The varying beer range includes mostly local beers, and two ciders, although the selection may be reduced out of season. A separate family room, available for local groups to use, features ancient frescoes uncovered when previous owners stripped away decades of modernisation. Cribbage and other pub games are played. Food is limited to a pasty or pork pie. Q ☭ ⚙ ⛱ ♣ ♠ 🖵 🔥 🛜

Lostwithiel

Globe Inn
3 North Street, PL22 0EG (on town side of river bridge near railway station)
☎ (01208) 872501
Sharp's Original, Atlantic; Skinner's Betty Stogs Ⓗ
Cosy 13th-century pub in the narrow streets of an old stannary (tin-mining) town, close to the station and medieval stone river bridge. The welcoming, rather rambling interior accommodates a single bar with several drinking and dining spaces, a restaurant and a suntrap patio at the rear. An extensive home-cooked menu features fish and game. The beer range may increase to four in summer. The pub is named after a ship that took part in a sea battle in 1813, when a member of the family that owned it at the time was killed. ☭ ⚙ ⛱ ◀◖ Å ⛲ ♣ ♠ 🔥

Royal Oak
Duke Street, PL22 0AG
☎ (01208) 872552 ⊕ royaloakcornwall.com
St Austell Tribute, Proper Job; Sharp's Doom Bar; 1 changing beer (sourced regionally; often Cotleigh) Ⓗ
This historic 13th-century inn lies just off the main road through Cornwall's old capital. A traditional stone-floored public bar contrasts with a comfortable lounge and attached restaurant; there is a patio outside. The pub has a dartboard and pool table, and hosts occasional quiz nights and live entertainment. Accommodation is in six en-suite rooms. There is reputedly a tunnel, once used by smugglers, from the pub cellar to the dungeons in the courtyard of Restormel Castle. Q ☭ ⚙ ⛱ ◀◖ Å ⛲ ♠ P 🔥 🛜

Mawgan Porth

Merrymoor ✅
TR8 4BA (beside B3276 coast road, overlooking beach)
☎ (01637) 860258 ⊕ merrymoorinn.com
St Austell Tribute; Sharp's Doom Bar; 1 changing beer (sourced locally; often Dartmoor) Ⓗ
Originally a café whose owner served in the North African Campaign, hence the name. Now an atmospheric pub run by the same family since 1961, it is very much at the heart of the local community and raises huge sums

for charity every year. Large picture windows overlook the sandy beach just 50 yards away. It is naturally busy in the season, and has a large beer garden, a spacious main bar and a separate family room.
⍭❀⇋◑▷AP⌷(A5,56) ❀ 🛜

Morwenstow

Bush Inn
Crosstown, EX23 9SR (off A39 N of Kilkhampton) SS208150
☎ (01288) 331242 ⊕ thebushinnmorwenstow.com
St Austell Tribute, Hicks; 1 changing beer (sourced locally; often Forge, Tintagel) Ⓗ
Dating back to the 13th-century and on the South West Coastal Path. Unassuming from the outside, inside it is a little gem – simply furnished, with slate floors, granite walls and exposed beams in two small bar rooms, one of which is subdivided into separate drinking areas. Conversation is the main entertainment, although there is occasional live music. A large garden offers outstanding views over the Tidna Valley and out to sea. Four en-suite rooms and a two-person holiday cottage are available. Q⍭❀⇋◑♣◐P⌷(217)❀🛜

Padstow

Golden Lion Hotel
Lanadwell Street, PL28 8AN
☎ (01841) 532797 ⊕ goldenlionpadstow.com
Sharp's Doom Bar, Atlantic; Tintagel Castle Gold Ⓗ
Padstow's oldest pub, dating back over 400 years, and still used for stabling the famous red 'oss that makes its energetic appearance every May Day during the famous 'obby-'oss celebrations. The busy low-beamed and slate-flagged public bar is partitioned to create a family dining area; the quieter lounge is spacious and comfortable. There is a patio with seating outside. The pub is situated a little way from the bustling harbour area but can get crowded during the summer season.
⍭❀⇋◑♿A⌷⌷(A5,11A) ❀🛜

Pendeen

North Inn
TR19 7DN (on B3306)
☎ (01736) 788417 ⊕ thenorthinnpendeen.co.uk
St Austell Cornish Best Bitter, Tribute, Proper Job; 1 changing beer (sourced locally; often St Austell) Ⓗ
Welcoming locals' pub serving an old mining village in an Area of Outstanding Natural Beauty, close to the coastal path and the famous Geevor and Levant tin mines. The single large room has a beamed ceiling and is carpeted throughout; in the far right corner stands a pool table. A good-value food menu features a comprehensive range of home-cooked curries, the landlord's own speciality. The inn offers accommodation in four double rooms as well as at its own campsite. Q❀⇋◑▷A♣P⌷(A17)❀🛜

Penzance

Crown
Victoria Square, TR18 2EP (on Bread St, just behind Market Jew St)
☎ (01736) 351070 ⊕ thecrownpenzance.co.uk
Cornish Crown Causeway, Porter; 2 changing beers (sourced locally; often Cornish Crown) Ⓗ
Close to the railway and bus stations, and tap for Cornish Crown Brewery, this back-street local is a gem tucked away behind the main shopping street. Offering a relaxing atmosphere, it has a tidily furnished bar with upholstered window seats and a huge mirror covering

one wall. At the rear is a cosy two-table snug with sofas and board games, while outside is a roadside patio with benches and tables. No food is served but you may bring your own, with plates provided. ⍭❀⇋♣◐P⌷❀🛜

Dock Inn
17 Quay Street, TR18 4BD
☎ (01736) 362833 ⊕ thedockinnpenzance.co.uk
Blue Anchor Ben's Stout; Penzance Potion No.9; Sharp's Doom Bar; 1 changing beer (sourced locally; often Skinner's) Ⓗ
Old and traditional one-time fishermen's pub near the dockside, close to the Isles of Scilly ferry pier. The pub extends through two old cottages, with the bar in the upper level, while a comfortable lounge next door at the lower level also serves as a dining area. The decor includes a large picture mirror, nautical and mining pictures, and bric-a-brac including a stuffed bird in a cage. A ship's figurehead oversees proceedings in the bar. Q⍭❀⇋◑⇌♣P⌷❀🛜

Perranwell

Royal Oak
TR3 7PX
☎ (01872) 863175 ⊕ theroyaloakperranwellstation.co.uk
2 changing beers (sourced locally; often Exeter, Tintagel) Ⓗ
This small 18th-century cottage-style village inn prioritises both good beer and food. Most tables are set for dining, but drinkers are equally welcome, as the many sociable regulars at the bar will testify. Booking for meals is advisable however, especially in the evening. The beers vary frequently and are mostly from local breweries. A busy community pub, it holds monthly quiz nights and fundraising events for local charities. Q⍭❀◑⇌♣◐P⌷(36,46) ❀🛜

Polperro

Blue Peter Inn
Quay Road, PL13 2QZ (far end of W side of harbour)
☎ (01503) 272743 ⊕ thebluepeterinn.com
St Austell Tribute; Sharp's Original; 4 changing beers (sourced regionally; often Cornish Crown, Dartmoor) Ⓗ
Named after the naval flag, this friendly inn is reached up a steep flight of steps near the quay, and is the only pub in the village with a sea view. In summer it offers up to six ales from Cornwall and Devon, and a varied menu of home-cooked dishes available all day. Featuring low beams, wooden floors, unusual souvenirs and work by local artists, the pub is popular with regulars, fishermen and visitors. ⍭❀◑▷A♣❀🛜

Crumplehorn Inn
The Old Mill, Crumplehorn, PL13 2RJ (on A387, top of town near coach park)
☎ (01503) 272348 ⊕ thecrumplehorninn.co.uk
St Austell Tribute, Proper Job; Tintagel Castle Gold, Harbour Special; 2 changing beers (sourced locally) Ⓗ
Once a mill and mentioned in the Domesday Book, this 14th-century inn at the entrance to the village still has a working waterwheel outside. The split-level bar has three comfortable areas with low ceilings and flagstone floors. Outside, the spacious patio by the millstream offers large umbrellas as sunshades. A varied menu includes locally sourced food. Accommodation is B&B or self-catering. In summer, catch the milk float tram down to the harbour from the nearby public car park.
⍭❀⇋◑▷A♣P⌷(72,73) ❀🛜

Ponsanooth

Stag Hunt

20 St Michael's Road, TR3 7EE (on A393)
☎ (01872) 863046
St Austell Tribute; Treen's Classic; 1 changing beer (sourced locally; often Treen's) Ⓗ
Traditional Cornish granite community pub on the main Falmouth to Redruth road, with convenient bus stops close by. The bar in the lower part of the pub is decorated with photos depicting scenes of the surrounding area. The upper back room has its own small bar and can serve as a function room; it also hosts the Thursday evening jam session and occasional beer festivals. The real ales are mostly locally brewed. Food times may vary; Indian cuisine is the house speciality. Q❀🏠❀🍴🅿🚆(U2)🐾

Port Isaac

Golden Lion

13 Fore Street, PL29 3RB
☎ (01208) 880336 ⊕ thegoldenlionportisaac.co.uk
St Austell Trelawny, Tribute, Proper Job, Hicks Ⓗ
This fine old 18th-century pub in the heart of Port Isaac has several drinking areas and a small balcony overlooking the harbour. Recognised by CAMRA as having a regionally important historic pub interior for its three slightly uneven bare-boarded rooms with old bar fittings and fireplaces. The games room downstairs was originally the Bloody Bones locals' bar, and boasts a smugglers' tunnel down to a causeway on the beach. A small flagstoned courtyard at the rear offers alfresco drinking. 🏠❀🍴❀🚆(10,95)🐾🛜

Porthleven

Ship Inn

Mount Pleasant Road, TR13 9JS
☎ (01326) 564204 ⊕ theshipinnporthleven.co.uk
Sharp's Doom Bar, Cornish Coaster; Skinner's Porthleven; Tintagel Harbour Special; 1 changing beer (sourced locally) Ⓗ
Perched on the south-west corner of the harbour, this 17th-century fishermen's inn is accessed up a steep flight of steps. It enjoys a commanding view over the harbour; here you can sit comfortably and watch the rough seas on stormy days. The rambling split-level interior has wooden and slated floors, beams decorated with an eclectic mix of coins, banknotes, beermats and brass artefacts, and sketches of local characters on the walls. A large log fire warms the pub in winter.
🏠❀🍴❀🚆(U4)🐾🛜

Portscatho

Plume of Feathers

The Square, TR2 5HW
☎ (01872) 580321 ⊕ plumeoffeathers-roseland.com
St Austell Tribute, Proper Job; 2 changing beers (often St Austell, Timothy Taylor) Ⓗ
Built in 1756, the Plume is one of the oldest buildings in the village, and the hub of the local community. Its contemporary exterior hides a traditional wood-beamed, slate-walled interior with cosy nooks, a split-room bar and separate restaurant. The selection of St Austell ales may be supplemented by a changing beer from elsewhere. The pub is focused on home-cooked and locally sourced food, and hosts events such as the August regatta. You will receive a warm welcome here.
Q🏠🛏❀🍴♿❀🚆(50)🐾🛜

Poughill

Preston Gate Inn

Poughill Road, EX23 9ET (just outside Bude, on Sandymouth Bay road) SS224077
☎ (01288) 354017 ⊕ prestongateinn.co.uk
St Austell Hicks; Sharp's Original; Skinner's Lushingtons; 1 changing beer (sourced locally; often Holsworthy Ales, Tintagel) Ⓗ
This cosy 16th-century building, originally two cottages, has been a village pub since 1983. The spacious U-shaped room hosts a dartboard at one end of the bar; the other end is roomier with more seating and a roaring log fire in winter. Conversation rules here, and the pub is home to darts and quiz teams. Meals include monthly theme nights (booking advised). The beer range may reduce in winter and the cider varies. The name Preston comes from the Cornish word for priest.
Q🏠🍴♿♣❀🚆(128,217)🐾🛜

Quintrell Downs

Two Clomes

East Road, TR8 4PD (on A392)
☎ (01637) 879737
Sharp's Doom Bar; 2 changing beers (sourced locally; often Harbour, Padstow) Ⓗ
Named after the two ovens set either side of the open fireplace – which is now fitted with a wood-burning stove – this 18th-century free house is popular for dining out. Various extensions to the original building have added a large restaurant (booking is advisable, even in winter). Background music plays and there is a TV for sporting occasions. The pub is conveniently situated on a main route into Newquay and close to campsites.
🏠❀🍴♿♿♣❀🚆(21,91)🐾

St Ives

Castle Inn

16 Fore Street, TR26 1AB
☎ (01736) 796833 ⊕ the-castle-cornwall.co.uk
Sharp's Original, Sea Fury; house beer (by Skinner's); 3 changing beers (sourced nationally; often Marston's, Skinner's) Ⓗ
This pub has had a chequered history, being by turns accommodation for men building Tregenna Castle, a brothel, and a shipping office for the former Union Castle line. Now a thriving town-centre venue, popular with locals and visitors alike, its emphasis is on a varying real ale menu, plus a cider or two, or a perry. The single bar sports an eye-catching stained-glass window at the front, and the walls are adorned with various items of nautical bric-a-brac. 🏠🍴♿♣❀🚆🐾🛜

Pilchard Press Alehouse

Wharf Road, TR26 1LF
☎ (01736) 791665
6 changing beers (sourced locally) Ⓗ/Ⓖ
Cornwall's first micropub, the Pilchard Press opened in 2016 and accommodates just 20-25 people. Situated up an alley off the harbour front, it offers the drinker a friendly atmosphere and up to six beers from casks racked up on an interesting wooden stillage. There are a few bar stools for seating, plus two tables with chairs and a smaller chessboard/draughts table. Note that the pub may close earlier if the beer runs out. Q🏠♿❀🚆🐾

St John

St John Inn

PL11 3AW

☎ (01752) 829299 ⊕ stjohninn.co.uk
Draught Bass; 2 changing beers (sourced nationally; often Exmoor, Woodforde's) Ⓗ
Reached down narrow country lanes, this 16th-century village pub was formerly two cottages. It has a pleasant, cosy ambience, with an L-shaped bar room featuring a beamed ceiling and a floor of red tiles, wooden furniture and a warming open fire for winter. A cosy snug opposite the bar, a patio with seating at the front, and an attractive beer garden add to the appeal at this picturesque and welcoming venue. Live events are hosted in a semi-permanent marquee. Q❄☽❀♪▲♠P❀

St Just

Star Inn
1 Fore Street, TR19 7LL
☎ (01736) 788767
St Austell Cornish Best Bitter, Tribute, Proper Job; 2 changing beers (sourced regionally; often Bath Ales, St Austell) Ⓗ
How pubs used to be: there is no food here, just excellent beer and friendly banter. The atmospheric main bar is enhanced by its dark, quirky décor, open fire and mining and rowing artefacts. The wood-beamed ceiling is adorned with flags of the Celtic nations, among others. A separate room opposite doubles as a meeting place for community groups, while an enclosed beer garden is at the rear of the building. Live music features on Monday and Thursday evenings. ☽❀♦▲🚃❀🛜

St Kew Highway

Red Lion Inn
PL30 3DN (just off A39)
☎ (01208) 841271 ⊕ redlionstkew.com
St Austell Tribute; 2 changing beers (sourced locally; often Padstow) Ⓗ
This picturesque family-run 17th-century pub is central to community activities. Its L-shaped single-bar interior divides distinctly in two – the front area mainly for drinking, though it includes an elevated dining space, and the rear a restaurant for more leisurely dining. Comfortable furnishings and open fires contribute to the cosy, relaxed ambience. Up to three ales are offered, mostly from Cornwall or Devon breweries. Interesting freshly cooked meals feature local produce.
Q❄☽❀◑▲P🚃(95)❀🛜

St Mabyn

St Mabyn Inn
Churchtown, PL30 3BA
☎ (01208) 841266 ⊕ stmabyninn.com
Harbour Ellensberg; Sharp's Doom Bar, Sea Fury; Tintagel Cornwall's Pride; 1 changing beer (sourced locally) Ⓗ
Near the church stands this popular, attractive, 17th-century free house, the village local where conversation thrives. It features a single bar with adjoining snug, games room and stylish well-appointed restaurant, and an attractive beer garden outside. Open fires, wood furnishings including settles, stained-glass partitions and windows add character, complemented by an interesting collection of toby jugs, horse brasses and vintage advertising. With four quality ales and a changing choice of food, including Thai nights, this pub is one to seek out.
Q❄☽❀◑▲♠P🚃(55)❀🛜

St Mawgan

Falcon Inn
TR8 4EP (in village centre)
☎ (01637) 860225 ⊕ thefalconinnstmawgan.co.uk
Dartmoor Legend; Sharp's Original; 1 changing beer (sourced locally; often Tintagel) Ⓗ
Attractive community inn in the idyllic setting of the Lanherne Valley; a quiet retreat only a few miles from the bustle of Newquay and the airport. The single-bar pub exudes a warm, welcoming atmosphere and offers three real ales, one of which always varies. It is also popular for meals. There is a games room and a large award-winning garden; dogs are welcome here and in the bar. A beer festival with a gin bar is held every July.
Q❄☽❀🛏◑♦P🚃(A5)❀🛜

Saltash

Union Inn
Tamar Street, PL12 4EL (on waterfront, beneath bridges)
☎ (01752) 844770
Dartmoor Legend, Jail Ale Ⓗ**; 2 changing beers (sourced regionally; often Bays, Cornish Crown, Summerskills)** Ⓗ/Ⓖ
The frontage of this riverside local, overlooked by the Tamar bridges, is strikingly painted as a union flag. The single bar offers a selection of real ales including a changing guest beer, usually on gravity in the cellar. The draught cider is Sam's Devon Dry. Outside, there are tables overlooking the river. Live music features on Tuesday or weekend evenings. Tamar Street, the pub's location, used to be known as Pickle Cock Alley as shellfish were sold through open windows.
❀🚄♠♦P🚃❀

South Petherwin

Frog & Bucket
PL15 7LP (just off B3254)
☎ (01566) 776988 ⊕ frogandbucket.co.uk
5 changing beers (sourced nationally) Ⓗ
Roomy pub, opened in 1989 despite local opposition, now providing a friendly focus for village social life and warmly welcoming all ages. Up to five varying guest ales are on offer. Off the main bar are a separate lounge, games room and two other rooms, one of which doubles as a restaurant or function room. Offering fine Dartmoor views, the pub is a meeting place for vintage vehicles in summer. Q❄☽❀◑♦♠P🚃(236)❀🛜

Towan Cross

Victory Inn
TR4 8BN
☎ (01209) 890359
St Austell Tribute; Skinner's Betty Stogs, Lushingtons Ⓗ
Built in 1605, this welcoming and family-run former coaching inn was originally opened to quench the thirst of local miners. Set on the clifftop, it offers impressive sea views – and breezes – to enjoy alongside Cornish ales and quality locally sourced food. The open-plan single bar separates into drinking and dining areas, extending to the conservatory and spacious beer garden. In former times, funeral corteges would stop outside, rest the coffin on the nearby horizontal Towan Cross, and take refreshment within. Q❄☽❀◑▲♠P🚃(304,315)❀🛜

Trebarwith Strand

Mill House Inn

PL34 0HD (off B3263, near Tintagel) SX058865
☎ (01840) 770200 ⏀ themillhouseinn.co.uk
Tintagel Castle Gold; house beer (by Tintagel); 1 changing beer (sourced locally; often Sharp's, Tintagel) Ⓗ
Converted 16th-century corn mill and waterwheel set beside a stream in a deep wooded valley. This friendly inn has a stone-flagged bar area accessible up a flight of steps beside the adjacent drinking terrace. The restaurant is in an extension, offering an imaginative menu that changes daily. While the Mill House is primarily a food and accommodation establishment, drinkers are nevertheless welcome in the bar, with a mix of local beers mostly from nearby Tintagel Brewery.
Q🕏🏠🛏⏵🅿🐾🛜

Treen

Gurnard's Head Hotel Ⓛ

TR26 3DE (on B3306, Lands End-St Ives coast road, nr Zennor)
☎ (01736) 796928 ⏀ gurnardshead.co.uk
St Austell Tribute; 3 changing beers (sourced locally; often Cornish Crown, Padstow, Skinner's) Ⓗ
Named after the nearby headland, this imposing and strikingly coloured inn stands near the coastal path on the rugged and beautiful granite moorland of the Penwith peninsula. It has a large bar, cosy snug and stylish restaurant. Wooden furnishings, comfy sofas and open fires add to a relaxed and unhurried ambience, with local art adorning the walls. The changing beer range features Cornish microbreweries, while daily choices in the food menu reflect the availability of local produce. Q🕏🏠🛏⏵🅿🐾🛜

Tresco: Isles of Scilly

New Inn

Townshill, New Grimsby, TR24 0QG
☎ (01720) 423006
House beer (by Skinner's); 3 changing beers (sourced locally; often Ales of Scilly, Dartmoor, St Austell) Ⓗ
Excellent old pub near New Grimsby harbour, a haven between demanding coastal walks and the boat to St Mary's. Extensions to the garden and a covered pavilion have added to the attractions of this popular real ale outlet. The varying beers are mostly from Cornish breweries, usually Skinner's and St Austell, and local brewer Ales of Scilly is frequently represented. The Driftwood Bar is adorned with wreck wood and marine relics. Beer festivals are held over the spring and late summer bank holidays. Accommodation is available in 16 en-suite rooms. 🕏🏠🛏⏵🐾🛜

Trevaunance Cove

Driftwood Spars ✅

Quay Road, TR5 0RT
☎ (01872) 552428 ⏀ driftwoodspars.co.uk
Driftwood Spars; 5 changing beers (sourced locally; often Atlantic, Driftwood Spars, Harbour) Ⓗ
Friendly community-oriented brewpub, well worth a visit. A former 17th-century sail loft and mine warehouse, it features three wood-beamed bars on different levels, with lead-light windows and granite fireplaces. The decor is mainly nautical and shipwreck-themed. Upstairs, the restaurant affords panoramic views across the bay, while over the road the beer garden adjoins the Driftwood Brewery, whose beers are always

on the bar alongside favourite regional guests. The pub holds three beer festivals a year, and occasional tutored tastings. Q🕏🏠🛏🍴⏵&🐾🅿🚃(87,315)🐾🛜

Trewellard

Trewellard Arms

Trewellard Road, TR19 7TA (on B3318/B3306 jct)
☎ (01736) 788634
5 changing beers (sourced regionally; often Cotleigh, Tintagel) Ⓗ
Formerly a mining count house, then a hotel, this is now a thriving family-run free house, where a warm welcome is assured. Its cosy interior accommodates a spacious open-beamed single bar and a pleasant restaurant with secluded dining space. Open fires enhance the homely atmosphere. A varying beer menu offers up to five ales and two ciders, and good-value home-cooked food is available. Outside is a paved patio area. A beer festival is held each May.
Q🕏🏠🛏⛺⏵🐾🅿🚃(A17)🐾🛜

Truro

Old Ale House

7 Quay Street, TR1 2HD (near bus station)
☎ (01872) 271122 ⏀ old-ale-house.co.uk
Skinner's Betty Stogs, Hops 'n Honey, Lushingtons, Porthleven; 4 changing beers (sourced nationally; often Skinner's) Ⓗ
This friendly and lively city-centre pub is Skinner's Brewery tap. The main bar is atmospheric, with a beamed ceiling, subtle lighting, wooden floors and scattered artefacts. Seating is plentiful, while upstairs is a quieter drinking area and function room. Up to 13 real ales and five real ciders are on offer, in addition to an impressive range of up to 40 craft keg and foreign beers. Customers may bring their own food. Q🕏&🐾🅿🚃🐾🛜

Rising Sun

Mitchell Hill, TR1 1ED
☎ (01872) 240003 ⏀ therisingsuntruro.co.uk
Fuller's London Pride; Skinner's Betty Stogs Ⓗ**; 2 changing beers (sourced locally; often Skinner's)** Ⓖ
Near the city centre up a steep hill, this award-winning hostelry is worth seeking out. Its narrow frontage belies a spacious interior accommodating a small public bar with adjacent dining area, a lounge bar, and a raised restaurant section. Outside is a sheltered patio where periodic beer festivals are held. The pub is comfortably furnished throughout, its decor including old Truro scenes. The changing beer menu offers up to four ales, two dispensed straight from casks. The popular food menu features locally sourced ingredients – booking is advised. Q🕏🏠🛏⏵🅿🐾🛜

Zennor

Tinners Arms

TR26 3BY (off B3306 St Ives-St Just coast road)
☎ (01736) 796927 ⏀ tinnersarms.com
Skinner's Lushingtons, Porthleven; house beer (by Sharp's) Ⓗ
An ancient granite village pub lying on the north coast of the Penwith peninsula. An atmospheric interior accommodates a single bar and adjacent restaurant, the ambience enhanced by exposed granite walls and wood beams, open fires, wall panels and rustic furnishings. The food menu features local produce (phone the pub first if planning to eat here). Folk music features on Thursday evening, Sunday is quiz night.
🕏🏠🛏⏵🐾🅿🚃(16A)🐾🛜

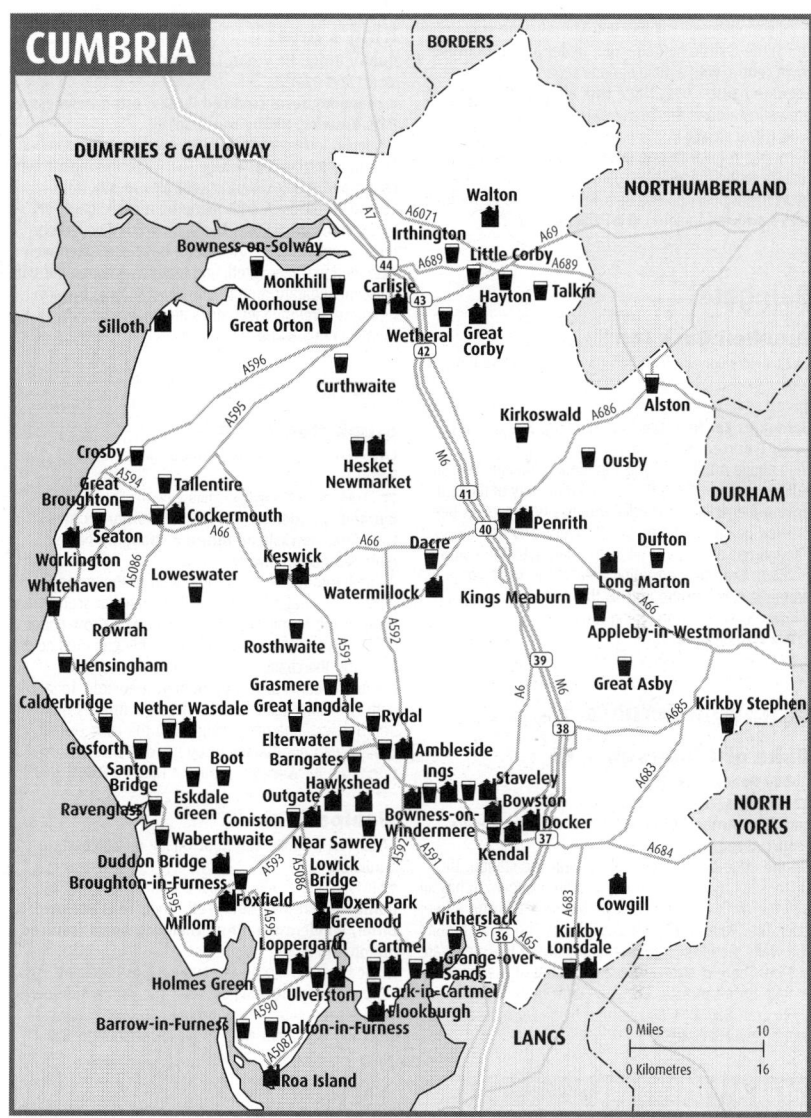

CUMBRIA

ENGLAND

BORDERS

DUMFRIES & GALLOWAY

NORTHUMBERLAND

Walton

Bowness-on-Solway
Irthington
Little Corby
Monkhill
Carlisle
Hayton
Talkin
Moorhouse
Great Orton
Wetheral
Great Corby
Silloth
Curthwaite
Kirkoswald
Alston
Crosby
Hesket Newmarket
Ousby
Great Broughton
Tallentire
Penrith
DURHAM
Seaton
Cockermouth
Dacre
Dufton
Workington
Keswick
Long Marton
Whitehaven
Loweswater
Watermillock
Kings Meaburn
Rowrah
Rosthwaite
Appleby-in-Westmorland
Hensingham
Grasmere
Great Asby
Calderbridge
Nether Wasdale
Great Langdale
Rydal
Kirkby Stephen
Gosforth
Elterwater
Ambleside
Santon Bridge
Barngates
Ings
Staveley
Eskdale
Boot
Hawkshead
Bowston
Ravenglass
Green
Outgate
Bowness-on-Windermere
Docker
NORTH YORKS
Waberthwaite
Coniston
Near Sawrey
Kendal
Duddon Bridge
Lowick Bridge
Broughton-in-Furness
Foxfield
Oxen Park
Cowgill
Millom
Greenodd
Witherslack
Kirkby Lonsdale
Loppergarth
Cartmel
Grange-over-Sands
Holmes Green
Ulverston
Cark-in-Cartmel
Barrow-in-Furness
Flookburgh
LANCS
Dalton-in-Furness
Roa Island

0 Miles 10
0 Kilometres 16

Alston

Cumberland Inn 🅛
Townfoot, CA9 3HX
☎ (01434) 381875 ⊕ cumberlandalston.co.uk
Firebrick Blaydon Brick; 3 changing beers 🅷
A 19th-century inn overlooking the South Tyne river.
Close to the Coast-to-Coast cycle route and Pennine Way,
it is an ideal base to explore the highest market town in
England. Guest beers are dispensed from four
handpumps. The Cumberland has won many local
CAMRA awards, including for cider, and always has a
wide selection of beers, ciders and perries to choose
from. Q🕯️❄️🍴◑👤🍽️🐾🤶🛜

Ambleside

Golden Rule ✅
Smithy Brow, LA22 9AS
☎ (015394) 32257

**Robinsons Wizard, Dizzy Blonde, Cumbria Way,
Cascade IPA; 3 changing beers (sourced regionally;
often Robinsons)** 🅷
A Guide feature since 1977, time has stood still for three
generations of loyal Lakes lovers who enjoy a refreshing
pint and a natter by the cosy fire after a day on the fells.
The simple old pub serves Robinsons' regular range of
beers as well as seasonal small-batch brews, especially
in winter. The separate snug room is handy for families
and card games. A small sheltered courtyard at the back
has additional seating for sunny days and busy sessions.
Q🕯️🚲👤♣️🍴🚪🐾🛜

Appleby-in-Westmorland

Midland Hotel 🅛
25 Clifford Street, CA16 6TS
☎ (017683) 51524 ⊕ themidlandhotelappleby.co.uk
**3 changing beers (sourced nationally; often Cross
Bay, Eden River, Malvern Hills)** 🅷

A fully modernised railway hotel next to the station on the Settle-Carlisle heritage line, under a mile from the town centre, with a main bar and separate smaller room. The free house serves three cask ales mostly from local breweries around the Eden Valley and the North-East, with Oliver's cider in the summer. The unusual toilet decor is a regular talking point; however, the best feature is the hidden back garden with lots of tables. It hosts the annual Appleby Beer Festival every September. Q ‍‍‍‍‍‍‍‍‍‍‍‍‍‍(Appleby) ♣♠P♿🚐(563) 🐾🐶📶

Barngates

Drunken Duck Inn L
LA22 0NG (signed off B5286 Hawkshead to Ambleside road)
☎ (015394) 36347 ⊕ drunkenduckinn.co.uk
Barngates Cat Nap, Cracker, Tag Lag; 3 changing beers (sourced locally; often Barngates) Ⓗ
High above Ambleside, this traditional Lakeland dwelling reflects the simplicity, beauty and longevity of its natural environment. From the fells, it draws water for its beers brewed on-site by Barngates Brewery. The bar has six handpumps and serves all of the Barngates beers on rotation. The outside seating area at the front offers dramatic views of the fells to the north-east. Dogs are allowed except in the dining room.
Q ‍‍‍‍‍‍‍‍‍‍‍‍‍‍ÅP🐶📶

Barrow-in-Furness

Duke of Edinburgh L ✅
Abbey Road, LA14 5QR
☎ (01229) 821039 ⊕ dukeofedinburghhotel.co.uk
Lancaster Amber, Blonde, Red; 5 changing beers (sourced regionally) Ⓗ
On the edge of the town centre near the station, the Duke is not as noisy as similar bars in the town. It has an airy feel with modern, comfortable furniture and a fine open fire. Paintings by local artists are displayed around the walls. Good-quality, reasonably priced bar meals are served. There is also a separate restaurant. Beers are mainly from Lancaster Brewery, with guest ales plus three craft keg ales, and bottled beers from around the world. ‍‍‍‍‍‍‍‍‍‍‍P📶

King's Arms L
Quarry Brow, Hawcoat, LA14 4HY
☎ (01229) 828137
4 changing beers (sourced locally; often Bowness Bay, Keswick, Kirkby Lonsdale) Ⓗ
A popular local conveniently situated near the number 1 bus route in Hawcoat village (between the main town centre and the hospital). It sells ales mostly from Cumbrian micros. A beer menu on a chalkboard lists forthcoming attractions. The pub, which has been on these premises since the 1860s, has been extensively extended and renovated, and features an open bar with adjacent separate rooms. Friendly staff give a warm welcome. Well-behaved dogs are allowed in one of the rooms. Q ‍‍‍‍♣🚐🐶📶

Boot

Brook House Inn L
CA19 1TG (200yds walk from Dalegarth station – La'al Ratty)
☎ (019467) 23288 ⊕ brookhouseinn.co.uk
Barngates Goodhew's Dry Stout; Cumbrian Ales Langdale; Hawkshead Bitter; 6 changing beers (sourced nationally) Ⓗ
A family-run tourist inn, at the heart of the western Lake District, in beautiful Eskdale with its majestic scenery and close to the terminus of the La'al Ratty narrow gauge railway. The inn is renowned for freshly prepared quality food and the changing variety of cask ales, and frequently earns local CAMRA branch awards. Together with two other Eskdale pubs close by, it hosts the June beer festival, one of the biggest in the Lake District, usually with entertainment by morris dancers.
Q ‍‍‍‍‍‍‍‍‍‍Å‍(Dalegarth for Boot) ♠P🐶📶

Woolpack Inn L
CA19 1TH (¾ mile E of Boot village on approach to Hardknott Pass)
☎ (019467) 23230 ⊕ woolpack.co.uk
Barngates Brathay Gold; Fell Ghyll; Tirril Borrowdale Bitter; Windermere IPA; 6 changing beers (sourced nationally) Ⓗ
Iconic Lakeland inn on the approach to Hardknott Pass, surrounded by stunning scenery. This family-run tourist venue is renowned for good food and well-kept cask ales, and is popular with families. The lounge and

REAL ALE BREWERIES
Appleby Kendal
Barngates Ambleside
Beckstones Millom
Bowness Bay ✦ Kendal
Brack'N'Brew Watermillock
Carlisle Carlisle
Coniston Coniston
Cumbrian Hawkshead
Dent Cowgill
Derwent Silloth
Eden River Penrith
Ennerdale Rowrah
Fell Flookburgh
Foxfield 🍺 Foxfield (brewing suspended)
Gan Yam Kendal
Grasmere Grasmere
Great Corby Great Corby
Greenodd 🍺 Greenodd (brewing suspended)
Handsome Bowston
Hawkshead ✦ Flookburgh / Staveley
Healey's 🍺 Loppergarth
Hesket Newmarket Hesket Newmarket

Jennings Cockermouth
Keswick ✦ Keswick
Kirkby Lonsdale ✦ Kirkby Lonsdale
Lakeland Ulverston
Lakes ✦ Kendal (NEW)
Langdale Docker
Logan Beck Duddon Bridge
Old Friends 🍺 Ulverston
Old Vicarage Walton
Roa Island 🍺 Roa Island
Shaws of Grange Grange-over-Sands
South Lakes Ulverston
Strands 🍺 Nether Wasdale
Tarn Hows Outgate
Tirril Long Marton
Tractor Shed Workington
Twisted Magnolia 🍺 Keswick
Ulverston ✦ Ulverston
Unsworth's Yard ✦ Cartmel
Westmorland Kendal
Wild Boar 🍺 Bowness-on-Windermere
Windermere 🍺 Ings

walkers bars offer an attractive mix of traditional and modern styles, with wood-burning stoves in both areas. Together with other nearby pubs in the Eskdale Valley, the Woolpack Inn participates in the annual Eskdale Beer Festival held in June. It also holds a cider festival in April. Q ﹩⚘🍴◑Ａ⇌(Dalegarth for Boot) ♣●P🖵❀🛜

Bowness-on-Solway

King's Arms
CA7 5AF
☎ (016973) 51426 ⊕ kingsarmsbowness.co.uk
2 changing beers (sourced nationally; often Jennings, Marston's) Ⓗ
In the centre of the village, the King's Arms is a regular stopping-off point for visitors to the area walking the Hadrian's Wall route. It is a community pub, with a library, band practice every other Sunday, and a quiz on Thursday nights. It also has pool, darts and dominoes teams. Set on the Solway coast in an area of outstanding natural beauty, it is popular with birdwatchers and cyclists as well as walkers. Snacks are available thoughout the day in summer. Q ﹩⚘🍴◑♣P❀🛜

Broughton-in-Furness

Manor Arms ⒧
The Square, LA20 6HY
☎ (01229) 716286 ⊕ manorarmsthesquare.co.uk
Great Corby Blonde; Hawkshead Windermere Pale; 6 changing beers (sourced regionally) Ⓗ
An outstanding free house owned by the Varty family for more than 30 years. Set in an attractive Georgian square, it has been the recipient of many CAMRA awards. Real ale dominates, always including a dark beer, along with traditional cider and perry. A mini beer festival is held every day. Two fires keep the pub warm and the bar staff are always friendly. Q ﹩🍴♣🖵❀🛜

Calderbridge

Stanley Arms Hotel
CA20 1DN
☎ (01946) 841235 ⊕ stanleyarmshotel.com
Wychwood Hobgoblin Gold; 4 changing beers (sourced nationally) Ⓗ
This small family-run village hotel, bordering the Lake District National Park, has a delightful beer garden beside the River Calder, with full fishing rights. Situated on the A595, it gives easy access to western beaches, lakes, fells and valleys. Hearty meals, using locally sourced produce, are available in the two-room bar and restaurant. It offers a well-equipped function/conference room. Attractions close by include the riverside walk along the Calder past the ruined 12th-century Calder Abbey. Q ﹩⚘🍴◑♣P❀🛜

Cark-in-Cartmel

Engine Inn ⒧ ✅
LA11 7NZ
☎ (015395) 58341 ⊕ theengineinncartmel.co.uk
Black Sheep Best Bitter; Laine Piston Ale; Lancaster Blonde; Timothy Taylor Landlord Ⓗ
This 17th-century inn, refurbished in 2010, makes an excellent end to the walk from Grange described in CAMRA's Lake District Pub Walks book. Beers are selected to provide a range of styles. There is an open bar area with a cosy fire, separate rooms away from the bar, and a riverside beer garden. Five en-suite rooms are available. Opening hours and food service times are reduced in winter. ﹩⚘🍴◑Ａ♿⇌♣●🖵(530)❀🛜

Carlisle

Fat Gadgie ⒧
5 Devonshire Street, CA3 8LG
☎ (01228) 812880 ⊕ thefatgadgie.co.uk
6 changing beers Ⓗ
Opened in 2017 after the closure of a specialist ale bar in the same premises, the space has been refurbished by the owner to provide a pleasant, quiet drinking environment without the distraction of TV or gaming machines. This city-centre bar serves a range of beers from far and wide, changing the selection frequently and targeting the discerning drinker. The Fat Gadgie adds to a series of unusual bar names in this area of the city. ♿⇌♣🖵❀🛜

King's Head Inn ⒧
Fisher Street, CA3 8RF
⊕ kingsheadcarlisle.co.uk
4 changing beers Ⓗ
An excellent city-centre pub, and winner of many CAMRA awards. It offers a range of guest ales from four handpumps. Pictures of old Carlisle adorn the internal walls, and outside is an explanation of why the city isn't in the Domesday Book. Good-value meals are served at lunchtime. The spacious, covered outdoor courtyard has a large-screen TV and regularly features live music. Children and dogs are not allowed. ⚘◑⇌♣🖵❀🛜

Spinners Arms ⒧
Cummersdale, CA2 6BD
☎ (01228) 532928
Carlisle Spun Gold, Flaxen, Magic Number; 1 changing beer (sourced locally; often Carlisle) Ⓗ
Cosy family-friendly hostelry, an original Redfern pub with unique and original features. Less than half a mile from Carlisle's south-western boundary, it is close to the Cumbrian Way and National Cycle Route 7, which run alongside the picturesque river Caldew. There is regular live music, with Irish music sessions every first and third Wednesday. Children are welcome until 9pm and well-behaved dogs are permitted. The pub is the brewery tap for Carlisle Brewing Co, showcasing its beer on five pumps. ﹩⚘♿♣P🖵(75)❀🛜

Thin White Duke
1 Devonshire Street, CA3 8LG
☎ (01228) 402334 ⊕ thinwhiteduke.info
Cumbrian Ales Loweswater Gold; 1 changing beer Ⓗ
Popular city-centre cocktail bar and restaurant in the heart of Carlisle's nightlife zone, mainly serving a young clientele in the evenings, but busy with all ages at lunchtimes. It has an interesting basement drinking area downstairs that still retains many of the old features from its monastic days, including a tunnel that once ran under the city to the cathedral. The name is a nod to David Bowie, with a musical influence creating a cool, vibrant atmosphere. ◑⇌🖵🛜

Woodrow Wilson ⒧ ✅
48 Botchergate, CA1 1QS
☎ (01228) 819942
Great Corby Session Ale, Blonde; Greene King Abbot; Marston's Old Empire; Ruddles Best Bitter; Sharp's Doom Bar; 6 changing beers (sourced nationally) Ⓗ
One of two almost adjacent Wetherspoons, this pub is in a refurbished Co-op building named after the former US president, whose mother was born in Carlisle. Up to 14 handpumps offer the largest range of real ales to be found in the city. Food is served all day till 11pm. At the rear there is a spacious outdoor seating area, heated patio and smokers' section. Children are welcome in some parts until 8pm. ﹩⚘◑♿⇌♣●P🖵❀🛜

Cartmel

Unsworth Yard Brewery L

4 Unsworth's Yard, LA11 6PG
☎ 07810 461313 ⊕ unsworthsyardbrewery.co.uk
Unsworth's Yard Crusader Gold; 2 changing beers (sourced nationally) ⊞

A tasting room at the front of a five-barrel brewery with up to three of the brewery's beers available at all times it is open. The room, which is available for functions by appointment, opens out on to a courtyard with extensive outdoor seating. High quality bread and cheese shops, as well as a shop specialising in fine wines, surround the courtyard giving this an almost continental ambience. ✿⑤⇢🚪(532,530)

Cockermouth

Castle Bar L ✓

14 Market Place, CA13 9NQ
☎ (01900) 829904 ⊕ castlebarcockermouth.co.uk
Cumbrian Ales Loweswater Gold; Jennings Night Vision, Cumberland Ale; Titanic Plum Porter; 2 changing beers (sourced nationally) ⊞

Set in the town's marketplace, 150 yards from the Jennings Brewery, parts of the building date from the 16th century. It was refurbished in the 2000s (commended in CAMRA Pub Design Awards 2009). The publican is keen on requests for beers from around the UK, and the chalkboard outside lists current and upcoming real ales and ciders. Three TVs show sports across the mazy ground floor. There is a restaurant on the first floor and a relaxing second-floor room with sofas. ⑤✿①◗🚪❀🍺

Cock & Bull

7 South Street, CA13 9RT (centre of town opp Sainsbury's)
☎ (01900) 827999 ⊕ thenewcockandbull.co.uk
Coniston Bluebird Bitter; Great Corby Blonde, Fox Brown Ale; 2 changing beers (sourced nationally) ⊞

A community pub in the centre of town. It does not serve food apart from bar snacks, but there is a constantly changing range of real ales on two of the handpumps, mainly from smaller Cumbrian breweries. The venue is on three levels, with bar stools in the main area, plus two seating areas and a TV showing sports in the front corner. The top level has a pool table and dartboard. Below this, off the main bar, is a quieter small room. ⑤✿❀🍺

Swan Inn L

52-56 Kirkgate, CA13 9PH
☎ (01900) 822425
Jennings Cumberland Ale; Wainwright; house beer (by Jennings); 3 changing beers (sourced nationally) ⊞

A true community pub well supported by locals, this 17th-century hostelry has flagged floors, exposed beams, a real fire and quiet nooks and crannies. It hosts a monthly whisky club and folk music sessions. There are six handpumps, with three of the beers served coming from the Jennings Brewery nearby. The large-screen TV at the back is used for showing sports. The pub is a short walk from the centre of the town. ⑤♣🚪❀🍺

Coniston

Black Bull Inn & Hotel L

LA21 8DU
☎ (015394) 41335 ⊕ blackbullconiston.co.uk
Coniston Oliver's Light Ale, Bluebird Bitter, Bluebird Premium XB, Old Man Ale, Special Oatmeal Stout,

No.9 Barley Wine; 3 changing beers (sourced locally; often Coniston) ⊞

A 16th-century coaching inn, this is Coniston Brewing Company's on-site taphouse, also serving good food in traditional, comfortable surroundings. A full menu is available from noon. Six regular ales are supplemented by other beers from the brewery on a rotation basis – try a tasting paddle. The spacious bar and lounge are frequented by tourists in this popular, spectacular location near Coniston Old Man. The outside seating area is perfect in summer. Dogs are not allowed in the restaurant. ⑤✿🚪①⑤♣P🚪(X12,505)❀🍺

Sun L

LA21 8HQ
☎ (015394) 41248 ⊕ thesunconiston.com
6 changing beers (sourced locally) ⊞

Take the Walna Scar road up from Coniston village, or down from the Old Man of Coniston, to visit this 16th-century pub and hotel. The deliberately unmodernised dual-level bar has atmosphere and character, with a slate-topped bar, slate flooring, exposed beams and stone walls, heated by a large open range. Up to eight cask ales are on tap, mostly from local brewers. The conservatory and terrace enjoy delightful views over the garden. Winter opening hours vary. Q⑤✿🚪①⑤♣P🚪(505,X12)❀🍺

Yewdale Inn L

2 Yewdale Road, LA21 8DU
☎ (015394) 23132 ⊕ yewdaleinn.com
Barngates Tag Lag; Cumbrian Ales Loweswater Gold; Theakston Old Peculier; 1 changing beer (sourced nationally) ⊞

Welcoming village inn in the centre of Coniston, attracting locals and visitors alike. In winter a cosy fire and jovial atmosphere prevail; in summer you can enjoy a drink on the terrace with stunning views of the Old Man of Coniston and surrounding fells, and Church Beck, a babbling brook running through the village. Opening hours and the availability of food are reduced in winter – see the website for information. Breakfast is served. ⑤✿🚪①⑤♣P(505,X12)❀🍺

Crosby

Stag Inn ✓

Lowside, CA15 6SH
☎ (01900) 812549 ⊕ staginncrosby.com
Sharp's Doom Bar; Tetley Bitter; 3 changing beers (sourced nationally) ⊞

A friendly pub well supported by locals and visitors alike. It is in a great location, with views over the Solway Firth to Scotland. The large bar room has two serving points, plus quiet corners and a restaurant area with an extensive menu to suit all tastes. There is also a function room and a sheltered beer garden. ⑤✿①⑤♣P🚪(300)❀🍺

Curthwaite

Royal Oak L

CA7 8BG
☎ (01228) 936978
3 changing beers ⊞

A welcoming traditional country inn less than a mile south of Thursby, which is fairly well served by public transport. The pub has a good reputation for excellent food with an emphasis on local produce. Three changing real ales are on tap and these are usually from local breweries including Carlisle, Cumberland, Eden, Hesket Newmarket and Jennings. ⑤✿①⑤♣P

Dacre

Horse & Farrier 🅛

Eden, CA11 0HL (1 mile S of A66)
☎ (017684) 86022 ⊕ horseandfarrierdacre.com
3 changing beers (sourced locally; often Allendale, Eden River, Hesket Newmarket) Ⓗ
Off the beaten track, but worth seeking out en route to Keswick or Pooley Bridge, this old Cumbrian inn was saved from closure by an enthusiastic young team. The main focus is food, but it also serves a small range of local cask and unusual keg beers. The pub holds beer festivals twice a year and regular events – see social media. Dacre is a lovely quiet village on the new round-Ullswater walk. The pagan stone bears are a unique attraction. Q➲❀🖨🕮Å♣♠P🐾🧡

Dalton-in-Furness

Brown Cow Inn 🅛

10 Goose Green, LA15 8AQ
☎ (01229) 462553
Black Sheep Best Bitter; 5 changing beers (sourced locally) Ⓗ
A warm and friendly atmosphere awaits visitors to this 400-year-old coaching house, which has retained many original features including beams, brasses, local prints and an open fire. A winner of many awards for its six real ales, the pub also serves excellent food from a full and varied menu. Meals can be enjoyed in the large dining room or, on warmer days, on the charming patio with heating and lighting. ➲❀🖨🕮P🚻(6,X6)🧡

Dufton

Stag Inn

CA16 6DB
☎ (017683) 51608 ⊕ thestagdufton.co.uk
4 changing beers (sourced regionally; often Allendale, Bowness Bay, Cross Bay) Ⓗ
A pink sandstone pub overlooking a picture-book green in a chocolate-box village on the popular Pennine Way. The small and old bar room and cosy snug lead to a new extension at the back, where large windows open onto a long garden with fantastic views of the fells. Four cask ales are from Westmorland and the North-East, and there is also a modern keg line. The nearby butcher supplies the kitchen. Dufton has holiday cottages, a campsite and a seasonal youth hostel. A beer festival takes place in August. Q➲❀🖨🕮Å♠P🐾🧡

Elterwater

Britannia Inn 🅛 ✅

LA22 9HP
☎ (015394) 37210 ⊕ britinn.co.uk
Coniston Bluebird Bitter; Langdale Elterwater Gold; house beer (by Langdale); 3 changing beers (sourced locally; often Barngates, Eden River, Langdale) Ⓗ
A tiny pub in a tiny village, the Brit magically squeezes in a surprising number of thirsty walkers hot from the fells in search of beer and sustenance. The four small rooms and hallway expand to fit the need, with tables and covered seating spilling out over the green. Langdale and Coniston beers are house staples alongside other well-kept local brews. Book in early for the busy autumn beer festival. Residents have use of Langdale Spa. ➲❀🖨🕮👤Å♠P🚻(516)🧡

Eskdale Green

Bower House Inn

CA19 1TD (short walk from Irton Rd station – La'al Ratty)
☎ (019467) 23244 ⊕ bowerhouseinn.com
Cumbrian Ales Loweswater Gold; Hawkshead Windermere Pale; Timothy Taylor Landlord; 1 changing beer (sourced nationally) Ⓗ
An 18th-century Eskdale Valley coaching inn on the edge of the village and close to the Outward Bound School. It is renowned for cask ales and good food and is a recent local CAMRA branch award winner. The dining room has oak-panelled seating and beamed ceilings, and there is a real fire in the bar. Outside is an attractive beer garden, and a play area for children. The pub has a community focus, with local cricket and darts teams, and Sunday quizzes for charities in the area.
Q➲❀🖨🕮Å🚲(Irton Rd) ♠♣P🐾🧡

Gosforth

Gosforth Hall Inn

Wasdale Road, CA20 1AZ (from A595 follow road signed to Wasdale; adjacent to St Mary's church)
☎ (019467) 25322 ⊕ gosforthhall.co.uk
4 changing beers (sourced nationally) Ⓗ
Situated on the edge of the village, this popular 16th-century locals' and visitors' pub is renowned for a range of well-kept ales and good food. The former 17th-century farmhouse is Grade II* listed and boasts a priest's hole, a spiral staircase to the upper floors and the widest single-span sandstone hearth in England. An annual beer festival is held in August. A previous winner of local CAMRA Pub of the Year. Q➲❀🖨🕮👤♠P🐾🧡

Grange-over-Sands

Keg & Kitchen 🅛

Main Street, LA11 6AB
☎ (015395) 83003 ⊕ kegandkitchen.co.uk
Unsworth's Yard Sir Edgar Harrington's Last Wolf; Wainwright; Wychwood Hobgoblin Gold; 1 changing beer (sourced locally; often Unsworth's Yard) Ⓗ
Large venue in the centre of Grange opposite the post office. The main bar and entrance are on the middle floor, while the upstairs has been converted to a games area containing a pool table. The lower area, called the Gin Pig, can be accessed from the pub or from a separate entrance. It is open Friday and Saturday evenings and sells bottled beers from Shaws of Grange.
➲❀🕮👤Å🚲♣🚻🐾🧡

Grasmere

Tweedies Bar & Lodge 🅛

Red Bank Road, LA22 9SW
☎ (015394) 35300 ⊕ tweediesgrasmere.com
Cumbrian Ales Loweswater Gold; 12 changing beers (sourced nationally; often Coniston, Salopian, Wylam) Ⓗ
A legend in its own opening time, the bar is an institution for regular visitors from near and far and offers a wide-ranging selection of excellent ales – both familiar and new. Even with the third-pint beer bats it is a challenge to sample every ale and cider – but it's great fun to try! There are lots of outdoor tables and seating in the large garden. The famous Grasmere Guzzler beer and music festival is hosted in September. Visit and enjoy!
➲❀🖨🕮👤Å🚲P🚻(555,599) 🐾🧡

Great Asby

Three Greyhounds 🅛

CA16 6EX

☎ (017683) 51428 ⊕ asbyparish.org.uk/
the-three-greyhounds

2 changing beers (sourced locally; often Allendale, Derwent, Great Corby) Ⓗ

An unspoilt little pub with a beamed ceiling, flagstone floor and iron range fireplace, overlooking the village green and Asby Beck. It serves two changing local ales from a very long list chosen by regular customers. Simple meals are available including Sunday lunch – book ahead. Occasional events including live music and quizzes are hosted. On the Pennine Route 68 Cycleway, this pub is well worth a visit. During lockdown it catered for isolated residents in this remote village with takeaway meals and beers. Check opening hours, especially in winter. Q⊛🅗⑷🚷🅰♣❀🤶🎱

Great Broughton

Punch Bowl Inn

19 Main Street, CA13 0YJ

☎ (01900) 267070

3 changing beers (sourced nationally) Ⓗ

This small community pub, originally a 17th-century coaching inn, is run by a committee of volunteers. Although it has limited opening hours, this is more than compensated for by the quality and variation of the real ales, which usually come from Cumbria. A guest beer weekend is held in February. Q⊛♣P❀🎱

Great Langdale

Old Dungeon Ghyll Hotel 🅛

LA22 9JY

☎ (015394) 37272 ⊕ odg.co.uk

Theakston Old Peculier; 5 changing beers (sourced locally; often Barngates, Fell, Hawkshead) Ⓗ

The Hikers Bar is famous as a timeless watering hole for generations of weary walkers. The fare is basic, as are the facilities (a converted cow shed with stalls), but the beer always hits the spot! Ales from local breweries are popular on the bar, with occasional outsiders for variety, however Loweswater Gold is a firm favourite. There are plenty of tables in the garden and car park. A useful bus service runs from Ambleside.
Q⊛🅗⑷🅰♣P🚍(516) ❀🎱

Great Orton

Wellington Inn

CA5 6LZ

☎ (01228) 710775

3 changing beers (sourced locally; often Derwent, Keswick) Ⓗ

Set in a quiet village, this is an attractive country inn. It does good-value meals using ingredients sourced locally, including meat from the area's renowned butcher. Three handpumps mainly serve ales from nearby breweries like Derwent and Keswick. Live music is being reintroduced here, with open mic nights on an occasional basis. There is space for 10 touring caravans on the adjacent camp site. Q⊛🅗⑷♣P

Hayton

Stone Inn

CA8 9HR

☎ (01228) 670896 ⊕ stoneinnhayton.co.uk

Thwaites Original; 2 changing beers (often Hadrian Border) Ⓗ

A traditional family-run outlet, this community pub is home to the local leek club. A fine pair of 1904 Christ Church boat club oars adorns one wall; ask to see the CAMRA mirror. The upstairs dining room can be hired for small gatherings. There is a guest ale, often from a brewery nearby, as well as the regular Thwaites Original bitter. 🕭⑷♣P❀🎱

Hensingham

Globe Inn

95 Main Street, CA28 8QX (take A595 from Whitehaven and follow signs for Cleator Moor)

☎ (01946) 590772

2 changing beers (sourced nationally) Ⓗ

Nestled among a terrace of houses, the friendly character of this pub takes hold as soon as you walk in. There are two separate rooms downstairs and a dining area upstairs. Food is freshly cooked to order. With two handpumps on offer, the beer range changes frequently. Sports TV is available, as well as a dartboard, jukebox and quiz machine. Very much a locals' pub, and welcoming to dogs. 🕭⊛⑷🚍🎱

Hesket Newmarket

Old Crown 🅛 ✅

CA7 8JG

☎ (016974) 78288 ⊕ theoldcrownpub.co.uk

Hesket Newmarket Haystacks, Black Sail, Helvellyn Gold, High Pike, Doris' 90th Birthday Ale, Brim Fell IPA; 4 changing beers (sourced locally; often Hesket Newmarket) Ⓗ

Sitting in the heart of this lovely fellside village, the Old Crown is a showcase for the Hesket Newmarket Brewery immediately behind it. It is well known as the first co-operatively owned pub in the country, and is popular with locals and visitors alike, with Prince Charles and Sir Chris Bonington among its supporters. Opening hours are subject to change so please check the website before travelling. Q🕭⊛🅗⑷♣❀🎱

Holmes Green

Black Dog Inn 🅛

Broughton Road, LA15 8JP SD233761

☎ (01229) 462975

Cumbrian Ales Esthwaite Bitter, Langdale, Loweswater Gold; 5 changing beers (sourced nationally; often Abbeydale, Cumbrian Ales, Oakham) Ⓗ

You can be sure of a warm welcome from the landlord and locals alike at the Black Dog. This former coaching inn, with two real fires, quarry-tiled floor and rustic beams, was recently refurbished but retains plenty of character. Five real ales are on offer. There is live music monthly, and the Dog Fest music festival is usually on the August bank holiday Sunday. Outside there is a decked seating area. 🕭⊛🅗⑷♣❀🎱

Ings

Watermill Inn 🅛

LA8 9PY

☎ (01539) 821309 ⊕ watermillinn.co.uk

Windermere Collie Wobbles, A Bit'er Ruff, Windermere Blonde; 8 changing beers (sourced locally; often Windermere) Ⓗ

Windermere Brewery is housed in the centre of this old watermill with its mill race alongside. The bar showcases

its many beers and all have dog-based names. The food menu and eight bedrooms also cater for four-legged friends. The family owners have extended the car park and added new seating areas both front and back. There is a nearby campsite and the Lakes bus stops outside – handy if you are sampling Shi Tzu Faced at 7% ABV.
Q✿🕮🚐◑🕭♿▲♣P🅿🐾☀🛜

Irthington

Sally
CA6 4NJ
☎ (016977) 42954 ⊕ thesallyirthington.co.uk
Wainwright; 1 changing beer (sourced nationally; often Thwaites) 🅷
Fully refurbished and extended former coaching inn in a village popular as a rest stop for Hadrian's Wall walkers. This is a gastro-pub and boutique hotel that serves real ale from the Thwaites range. Note the superb slate fireplace in the dining area which has a roaring fire in colder weather. Food is served daily and booking is recommended. The unusual name is a diminutive of the original, the Salutation Inn. 🕮◑♿♣P

Kendal

Barrel House 🅛
Unit 10, Castle Mills, Aynam Road, LA9 7DE
☎ 07498 203351 ⊕ bownessbaybrewing.co.uk
Bowness Bay Swan Blonde, Fellwalker, Raven Red, Swan Gold, Swan Black; 7 changing beers (sourced locally; often Appleby, Bowness Bay) 🅷
Hidden behind the old carpet factory below the castle is a repurposed industrial estate in the old mill complex. One converted unit houses the tap for Bowness Bay Brewing. The folding glass wall opens to reveal a long oak bar showcasing 12 cask and keg beers brewed on-site. The yard accommodates various events in temporary tents, with cosy booths for intimate encounters. Always a hive of activity, beer was delivered to outlying pubs throughout the pandemic and bottled for Booths supermarkets. Lockdown heroes! 🕭◑♿🚐♣P🅿🐾☀🛜

Factory Tap 🅛
5 Aynam Road, LA9 7DE
☎ (015394) 82541 ⊕ thefactorytap.co.uk
Fyne Ales Jarl; Handsome Lakes Blonde 🅷; 9 changing beers (sourced nationally; often Blackjack, Bradfield, Brass Castle) 🅷/🅐
The Tap has an enthusiastic following for its broad selection of moreish beers from far afield and closer to home. There is always something new to tempt the tastebuds and the brewery takeovers are a runaway success – Brass Castle is a special treat. The assorted tables and chairs are seemingly saleroom specials, and add to the idiosyncratic design appeal, both inside on two floors and in the three outside areas. Frequent pop-up food events and mini festivals take place as advertised. 🕮🕭◑♿🚐P🅿🐾🛜

Fell Bar 🅛
3 Lowther Street, LA9 4DH
☎ 07725 987600 ⊕ fellbrewery.co.uk
Fell Ghyll 🅷, Crag, Tinderbox IPA 🅐; 11 changing beers (sourced regionally; often Chapter, Flagship, Fyne Ales) 🅷/🅐
At the side of the town hall, the four-storey town house is the first of two tap bars for artisan Fell Brewery and offers house and guest beers in modern styles. The well-informed staff help navigate the exciting craft voyage around the wide-ranging choice of cask and keg ales, including unctuous stouts and fruity sours alongside

more traditional styles. Small-plate snacks enhance the taste experience of the beer adventure. Live music and brewery takeovers take place as advertised. The bar is vibrant and lively; everyone is welcome. 🕭◑🚐♣🕭♿🐾☀🛜

Indie Craft Beer 🅛
32 Finkle Street, LA9 4AB
☎ (01539) 721450 ⊕ indiecraftbeer.co.uk
4 changing beers (sourced nationally; often Cloudwater, Marble, Northern Monk) 🅐
An exciting, adventurous craft haven in the town centre on a pedestrianised shopping street with outdoor tables and benches. It has a peaceful chillout room upstairs with a spacious toilet facility. Around 200 bottles and cans line the shop shelves and fridges, including quality Belgian and other European beers. A small range of speciality glasses is sold. The four keg lines offer classic keg favourites and carefully selected special treats. A vinyl music selection is available for customer requests – or bring your own. Note the Madchester connections.
🕭♣🕮🚐(555,X6) 🛜

New Union 🅛
159 Stricklandgate, LA9 4RF
☎ (01539) 726019 ⊕ thenewunion.co.uk
Bowness Bay Swan Blonde; Fyne Ales Jarl 🅷; 3 changing beers (sourced regionally; often Bowness Bay, Kirkby Lonsdale, Thornbridge) 🅷/🅐
An old town hostelry on the Windermere road with one large modernised bar, plus a car park with tables, a stage and covered terrace. Justly famous for its many ciders and perries, the Union has an equal passion for real ales – whether cask or keg – with plenty of choice, embracing traditional and modern styles. A wide range of European bottled beers, a good whisky selection and special gins are also offered. It holds occasional tap takeovers, tasting events and an annual festival (see social media). A short food menu is offered at certain times. Local CAMRA Pub and Cider Pub of the Year 2019 and 2020.
🕮🕭◑🚐♣🕭♿P🅿(555) 🐾🛜

Keswick

Wainwright 🅛
Lake Road, CA12 5BZ
☎ (017687) 44927 ⊕ thewainwright.pub
Fell Tinderbox IPA; Wainwright; 5 changing beers (sourced nationally) 🅷
The Wainwright has a distinctive black and white frontage and oak flooring within, with two drinking areas served by an L-shaped bar. The interior is mountain-themed and has a cosy ambience. The beer and the food come mostly from Cumbria. The pub also brews its own cider. It has frequently been a winner of local CAMRA branch awards, and has a good reputation for food in terms of quality, quantity and price.
Q✿🕮🚐◑♣🕭🐾☀🛜

Kings Meaburn

White Horse Inn 🅛
CA10 3BU
☎ (01931) 714256
3 changing beers (sourced locally; often Bowness Bay, Eden River, Fell) 🅷
A lockdown hero pub that fed and watered its community throughout, so although it is remote, seek this place out and enjoy the real welcome, real pies and real ale! The bar serves beers from three or four local breweries, always including Bowness Bay. There is a special Pie & Pint deal on Friday and Saturday, and

frequent charity events. The pub has a pleasant sunny patio at the side. It hosts a popular summer beer and music festival, attracting visitors from a wide area for the fun and games. Q☺☎◑◐♿♣P♥☀⊛

Kirkby Lonsdale

King's Arms Hotel Ⓛ
7 Market Street, LA6 2AU
☎ (015242) 71220 ⊕ kingsarmshotelkirkbylonsdale.co.uk
Moorhouse's Blond Witch; Titanic Plum Porter Ⓗ; 3 changing beers (sourced regionally) Ⓗ/Ⓐ
Two music and real ale enthusiasts have run this vibrant inn since 2017. It has a large following for its imaginative food menu, spurred on by the success of lockdown takeaways. The restored long bar features interesting modern beers alongside traditional out-of-town and local ales. An inglenook fireplace warms the bar; the upstairs room, with a pool table, doubles as a private dining room. Occasional live music takes place. The building has a bijou back garden beside three self-catering cottages. An old pub for the young at heart.
☺☎☀◑◐♿♣P🚃☀⊛

Orange Tree Ⓛ ⊘
9 Fairbank, LA6 2BD (turn left past churchyard, hotel is on your right)
☎ (015242) 71716 ⊕ theorangetreehotel.co.uk
Kirkby Lonsdale Stanley's Pale Ale, Singletrack, Monumental Blonde; 3 changing beers (sourced locally; often Handsome, Kirkby Lonsdale) Ⓗ
The cosy old pub by the church acts as a second tap for Kirkby Lonsdale Brewery – but with food and rooms. The central bar offers six cask beers, including Jubilee Stout as a special. There are daily meal deals and a popular happy hour on Friday for local beer lovers, so the pub and separate dining room behind the bar rapidly fill up. Accommodation is in six en-suite rooms, with occasional offers. There's always a warm welcome.
☺🛏◑♣🚃(567)♥☀⊛

Royal Barn Ⓛ ⊘
New Road, LA6 2AB
☎ (015242) 71918 ⊕ klbrewery.com/the-royal-barn
Kirkby Lonsdale Tiffin Gold, Stanley's Pale Ale, Ruskins Bitter, Singletrack, Monumental Blonde, Jubilee Stout; 4 changing beers (sourced locally; often Kirkby Lonsdale) Ⓗ
The Barn has transformed into a stable as a result of lockdown alterations and now houses separate stalls, with a new mezzanine floor overlooking the bar plus a kitchen with pizza oven. Fortunately the beers remain a constant and the 12 handpulls and eight keg lines are still dispensing your favourite Kirkby Lonsd'ale' beers along with real cider and coffee freshly ground on-site. Get down there and catch some of the action!
☺◑♣P🚃♥☀⊛

Kirkby Stephen

Taggy Man Ⓛ
4 Market Street, CA17 4QS
☎ (017683) 72531 ⊕ taggyman.co.uk
4 changing beers (sourced regionally; often Black Sheep, Cross Bay, Keswick) Ⓗ
A traditional old Cumbrian free house below the town centre that is treasured for its warm and happy atmosphere. The jolly team is dedicated to serving a good selection of well-kept local beers along with the requisite nationals. The U-shaped bar serves two distinct areas that are filled with friendly local drinkers for regular live music, open-mic nights and the popular quiz

(advertised on social media). Hot food is offered during the week. Dogs and muddy boots are welcome.
☺☀◑◐♿ÅP🚃(563,564)🐾♥⊛

Kirkoswald

Fetherston Arms
The Square, CA10 1DQ
☎ (01768) 898284 ⊕ fetherston-arms.co.uk
Theakston Best Bitter; 3 changing beers (often Allendale, Hesket Newmarket) Ⓗ
The Fethers is in the centre of this historic village. Extensive alterations and the friendly enthusiasm of the owners have helped convert it into a truly outstanding pub, with a deservedly excellent reputation for its food. Three changing real ales are sold from breweries such as Allendale and Hesket Newmarket. The village is not on a bus route, but it is a 20-minute stroll from Lazonby station on the Carlisle-Settle line. Check hours in winter.
Q☺☀◑◐♥☀⊛

Little Corby

Otter Inn
Little Corby Road, CA4 8QQ
☎ (01228) 560906
1 changing beer (often Great Corby) Ⓗ
Formerly known as The Haywain, this is the only pub in the area not under state management control from WWI to the early 1970s. Close to the River Eden, this altered village venue now has a larger bar area but has lost none of its character, and has a cosy lounge with a log-burner. Occasionally open on Thursday evenings for a monthly quiz and darts evenings, other community activities also take place, such as a local leek show. Local road signs are confusing and it is difficult to separate Little Corby from Corby Hill. ☺♿♣P♥

Loppergarth

Wellington Inn Ⓛ
Main Street, LA12 0JL (1 mile from A590 between Lindal and Pennington)
☎ (01229) 582388
Healey's Blonde; 4 changing beers (sourced locally; often Healey's) Ⓗ
This superb village local has its own microbrewery, Healey's, a custom-made stainless steel plant which is viewable from the snug. Four handpumps dispense Healey's beers, including an award-winning blonde and a golden bitter. A traditional darker best bitter, and a superb mild are occasionally available. Wood-burning stoves make this a cosy pub, with games, books and good conversation. There is a quiz on alternate Saturdays. Well-behaved dogs on leads are welcome.
☺☀♿♣♥☀⊛

Loweswater

Kirkstile Inn
CA13 0RU (off B5289, 7 miles S from Cockermouth) NY140210
☎ (01900) 85219 ⊕ kirkstile.com
Cumbrian Ales Esthwaite Bitter, Langdale, Loweswater Gold; 3 changing beers (sourced regionally; often Cumbrian Ales) Ⓗ
CAMRA award-winning 16th-century coaching inn, scenically located below Melbreak, Crummock Water and Loweswater. It has low-beamed ceilings, solid wood tables, chairs and settles in three bar areas, and an open fire for chilly days. Substantial bar meals are served from noon, and there is a well-established restaurant. The

building was the original home of Loweswater Brewery, and is now the brewery tap for Cumbrian Ales. An annual beer festival is held in April. There is an outdoor seated drinking area in stunning surroundings. Dogs are welcome during the day. Q ➸ ⏱ ✖ ◑ ⏱ ♣ ⊕ P ☏ ● ☏

Lowick Bridge

Red Lion Inn 🅛

LA12 8EF (just off A5084 on Ulverston-Torver road)
☎ (01229) 885366 ⊕ redlion-lowick.co.uk
Bank Top Flat Cap; Great Corby Session Ale; 1 changing beer (sourced locally) ⅄
This former Hartleys ale house, worth finding just off the road from Greenodd to Coniston, was purchased by the present owners from Robinsons in 2014. It is now a charming, comfortable country inn, popular both with locals and visitors to the Lakes. Friendly and welcoming, it is an ideal base to explore the hidden corners of the southern Lakes and the Furness and Cartmel Peninsulas.
Q ➸ ⏱ ✖ ◑ ⏱ P ⊟ (X12) ● ☏

Monkhill

Drovers Rest

CA5 6DB
☎ (01228) 576141
4 changing beers ⅄
A traditional country pub close to the popular Hadrian's Wall Path, with a strong community focus. Although opened up, the interior still has the feel of three distinct rooms. The bar area is cosy and welcoming, with a roaring fire in winter. Some interesting historical State Management Scheme documents adorn the walls. The Drovers is an oasis for lots of different real ales, sometimes obscure for the area. Winner of multiple CAMRA awards including at regional level.
➸ ⏱ ◑ ⏱ ♣ P ⊟ (93) ●

Moorhouse

Royal Oak

CA5 6EZ
☎ (01228) 576475
Cumbrian Ales Loweswater Gold; Theakston XB; 1 changing beer ⅄
A small country pub on the outskirts of Carlisle. It is over 250 years old, so be prepared to duck as you go through some of the doors. Log-burning stoves help provide a rustic atmosphere. A traditional home-cooked menu is served along with real ale from local breweries.
⏱ ◑ ⏱ ● ● ☏

Near Sawrey

Tower Bank Arms 🅛

LA22 0LF (on B5285 2 miles S of Hawkshead)
☎ (015394) 36334 ⊕ towerbankarms.co.uk
Barngates Tag Lag; Cumbrian Ales Loweswater Gold; Hawkshead Bitter; 3 changing beers (sourced locally) ⅄
A 17th-century Lakeland inn, with slate floors, oak beams and a cast-iron range creating a lovely atmosphere, next to the National Trust's Hill Top (Beatrix Potter's home). Five handpumps serve local beer, with cider and perry dispensed by gravity. Booking is essential for evening meals. Families and dogs are welcomed, and accommodation is available in four en-suite rooms. There is a seasonal bus service connecting to the Windermere ferry and Hawkshead. Note that it is closed Mondays in winter. Q ➸ ⏱ ✖ ◑ ⏱ ♣ P ⊟ ● ☏

Nether Wasdale

Strands Inn 🅛

CA20 1ET
☎ (019467) 26237 ⊕ thestrandsinn.com
Strands Brown Bitter, Errrmmm...; 6 changing beers (sourced nationally) ⅄
In a pretty Lakeland village with superb views across to the Wasdale Screes and up towards Wasdale Head, Strands is a justifiably popular inn both for tourists and locals. A range of excellent beers is available, all dispensed by handpump; some are regular favourites but there is always something new to sample, and all come from the adjacent Strands Brewery. It has a comfortable and welcoming atmosphere, usually with open fires in winter, and serves excellent bar food.
Q ➸ ⏱ ✖ ◑ ⏱ ♣ P ● ☏

Ousby

Fox Inn 🅛

CA10 1QA
☎ (01768) 881374
2 changing beers (often Cross Bay, Eden River) ⅄
Nicely refurbished pub with unusual seating in the bar. In the lee of the Pennines with extensive views over the Eden Valley, this is a good village outlet catering for locals as well as tourists. The large games area offers two pool tables and darts. A touring caravan site with camping is opposite. Two changing guest ales are on sale, usually from breweries nearby such as Eden and Cross Bay. There is a quiz on Thursday evenings.
➸ ⏱ ◑ ⏱ ♣ P ● ☏

Oxen Park

Manor House Hotel 🅛

LA12 8HG
☎ (01229) 861345 ⊕ manorhouseoxenpark.co.uk
2 changing beers (sourced regionally) ⅄
In a small village on the outskirts of the Lake District, this former Hartleys pub reopened in 2017 as a free house after an extensive refurbishment to a modern high standard. The beer range varies but includes ales from local breweries. The excellent menu features a number of vegan dishes (booking is recommended at weekends). Free overnight parking is available for campervans, with access to toilets and electric hook up.
➸ ⏱ ✖ ◑ ⏱ ♣ A P ● ☏

Penrith

Agricultural Hotel 🅛 ✓

Castlegate, CA11 7JE
☎ (01768) 862622 ⊕ the-agricultural-hotel.co.uk
6 changing beers ⅄
The hotel is built from local sandstone and the bar and dining room are open plan, with steps from one to the other. There is also a small reception area. The Victorian shuttered sash screen bar has six handpumps. Food is served in the large dining area, as well as in the bar at quiet times. The premises became freehold in 2018 and extended the range of local beers. Convenient for the local railway station and nearby bus stops.
➸ ⏱ ✖ ◑ ⏱ ➥ ♣ P ⊟

Fell Bar 🅛

52 King Street, CA11 7AY
☎ (01768) 866860
6 changing beers ⅄
A small and intimate venue in the centre of Penrith, on three floors, which became a pub in 2012. It serves as

the tap for Fell Brewery but offers a range of other cask ales and craft beers as listed on the blackboard near the bar. Regular quiz, comedy and music nights are held, details of which are on its Facebook page. ☺⇌🚬♿☻🛜

Royal 🅛
Wilson Row, CA11 7PZ
☎ (01768) 862670 🌐 royalpubpenrith.co.uk
3 changing beers 🅷
Traditional pub on the edge of the town centre with tiled walls and lots of mellow wood. It has three separate areas served by one bar. Two handpumps offer beers from all over the UK including LocAles. It is home to darts, dominoes and pool teams, and there is full sports TV coverage. Live music sessions with a broad appeal are held on Sunday afternoons outside the football season. Food is served weekday evenings except Friday and weekend afternoons. ☺🍴◑👍⇌♣🚬☻🛜

Ravenglass

Inn at Ravenglass
Main Street, CA18 1SQ (N end of village, overlooking Irish Sea)
☎ (01229) 717230 🌐 theinnatravenglass.co.uk
Bowness Bay Swan Blonde; 3 changing beers (sourced nationally) 🅷
This 17th-century inn is in a national park hamlet that was once a Roman port, at the junction of the rivers Esk, Irt and Mite. It offers a good choice of real ales, to be enjoyed after a day on the fells, messing about in boats, or just relaxing round the wood-burning stove in winter, and is a great place for sunset views over the estuary. Close to Ravenglass stations for mainline and La'al Ratty. Q☺👺🍴◑👍⇌♣🚬P🚌(6) ☻🛜

Rosthwaite

Scafell Hotel ✅
Borrowdale, CA12 5XB (on B5289)
☎ (017687) 77208 🌐 scafell.co.uk
Tirril Borrowdale Bitter, 1823; 6 changing beers (sourced nationally) 🅷
In the heart of the Lake District and the home of the annual Borrowdale Fell Race, the Riverside Bar here welcomes walkers, cyclists and all those who enjoy the outdoor life. The River Derwent rushes past the windows of the bar, where food is served. A selection of malt whiskies is stocked and open fires create a homely feel. Q☺👺🍴◑👍⇌♣A🚌P🚌(78) ☻🛜

Rydal

Badger Bar (Glen Rothay Hotel) 🅛
LA22 9LR
☎ (015394) 34500 🌐 theglenrothay.co.uk
Barngates Goodhew's Dry Stout; house beer (by Old School); 4 changing beers (sourced locally; often Bowness Bay, Fell, Great Corby) 🅷
The badgers are real – just like the ale – but fortunately they do not live in the bar! The quirky original inn is near Wordsworth's Rydal home and would be his local. It has a Victorian hotel attached and a large garden overlooking Rydal Water, with a sheltered side terrace near the bus stop. All the beers are from breweries in the area including Badger Ale. The live Badgercam is on the website so if you cannot join them – watch them! Q☺👺🍴◑👍A♣P🚌(555,599) ☻🛜

Santon Bridge

Bridge Inn
CA19 1UX (on road from Gosforth to Eskdale)
☎ (019467) 26221 🌐 santonbridgeinn.com
6 changing beers (sourced nationally) 🅷
Once a modest mail coach halt, this is now a country inn on the banks of the River Irt and at a junction of roads into Wasdale and Eskdale. The place is cosy, with low beams, creaking floors and a log fire, and is licensed for civil marriage ceremonies. Seven beers from local, regional and national breweries are on the bar. It holds the World's Biggest Liar competition in November. Food comes from nearby. Q☺👺🍴◑👍⇌♣A♣P☻🛜

Seaton

Royal Oak
49 Main Road, CA14 1HU
☎ 07393 864592
Butcombe Original; Robinsons Dizzy Blonde; 2 changing beers (sourced nationally) 🅷
A lively community pub popular with locals. The front bar has a TV and seated drinking area, and there is a rear room with a pool table and dartboard. A quiz is held on a Wednesday night. The bar has three handpumps offering two regular beers and one changing guest, with most ales sourced nationally. 🅿P🚌(47)☻🛜

Staveley

Beer Hall 🅛 ✅
Hawkshead Brewery, Mill Yard, LA8 9LR
☎ (01539) 825260 🌐 hawksheadbrewery.co.uk
Hawkshead Bitter, Red 🅷, Lakeland Lager Ⓐ; 16 changing beers (sourced locally; often Hawkshead) 🅷
The tap for Hawkshead Brewery, set in a picturesque Lakeland village between Kendal and Windermere. The Beer Hall is the brewery's flagship outlet and now reflects the ongoing changes implemented centrally by the new owners, Halewood, who have moved bulk production from Staveley to Flookburgh. The beers have unfortunately lost their award-winning historic names and keg beers have become more prominent at this sprawling venue. Q☺👺◑👍⇌♣🚌P🚌(555)☻🛜

Eagle & Child Hotel 🅛
Kendal Road, LA8 9LP
☎ (01539) 821320 🌐 eaglechildinn.co.uk
5 changing beers (sourced locally; often Bowness Bay, Cumbrian Ales, Fell) 🅷
A traditional village pub with rooms, in a lovely location, with a garden beside the river Kent, plus a tranquil orchard behind the large function room. There is a good choice of mainly local beers to complement the Lakeland food. A popular quiz is hosted on Thursdays. Staveley is home to a wide range of small craft businesses and can be visited by train or by bus – with a stop outside the hotel. Q👺🍴◑👍⇌♣P🚌(555)☻🛜

Talkin

Blacksmiths Arms 🅛
CA8 1LE
☎ (016977) 3452 🌐 blacksmithstalkin.co.uk
Black Sheep Special Ale; 2 changing beers 🅷
Since taking over in 1997, the present owners have made this probably the most popular pub in the vicinity. The winning formula includes four real ales, a superbly stocked bar, friendly efficient staff, no TV and meticulous attention to detail. Set in an area of outstanding natural beauty, with a golf course and country park within two

miles and plenty of other outdoor activities locally, the pub attracts visitors from far outside north Cumbria. Q🛇⛄🏠🍴◑&♣P🛜

Tallentire

Bush Inn

CA13 0PT

☎ (01900) 823707

3 changing beers (sourced nationally) Ⓗ

A genuine old-fashioned, Grade II-listed pub with exposed beams, stone floors and a wood-burning stove. A changing selection of ales is offered, usually including at least one from a Cumbrian brewery. Folk music is hosted on the last Wednesday of the month. Food is served in the bar and in the separate dining room Thursday to Saturday, March to December. Home to the local cricket and darts teams. Q🏠🍴♣♠🐾🛜

Ulverston

Beerwolf Ⓛ

7 Market Street, LA12 7AY

🌐 wearebeerwolf.com

2 changing beers (sourced nationally) Ⓗ

A micropub and bottle shop owned by a CAMRA member. It has two handpumps plus eight KeyKeg beers, with an extensive range of interesting local, national and international bottled and canned beers and ciders, plus growler fills in cans to take away. Tap takeovers and other events are occasionally held – check Facebook. The pub has been recently refurbished to give more seating downstairs, with additional seating upstairs making for a pleasant and relaxing atmosphere. ⇌🖥🐾

Devonshire Arms Ⓛ

Braddyll Terrace, Victoria Road, LA12 0DH (next to railway bridge in town centre)

☎ (01229) 582537

Abbeydale Moonshine; 4 changing beers (sourced regionally; often Abbeydale, Cross Bay, Moorhouse's) Ⓗ

Conveniently situated between the bus and train stations, the Dev is a real locals' pub with a welcoming atmosphere. Four TVs provide comprehensive sports coverage, and there are two dartboards and a pool table. Five constantly changing cask ales and a cider are all dispensed on handpump. The outside seating area is popular in summer. A meat raffle is held on Sunday evening. It has received numerous awards from CAMRA over the years. 🛇🏠&♠⇌♣P🖥🐾🛜

Mill Ⓛ ✅

Mill Street, LA12 7EB

☎ (01229) 581384 🌐 mill-at-ulverston.co.uk

Lancaster Amber, Blonde, Black, Red; 6 changing beers (sourced nationally) Ⓗ

The Mill has an interesting characterful layout, centred around a restored original, but now static, waterwheel. The Cask Bar is on the ground floor. On Friday and Saturday both the Loft Bar on the second floor, serving evening cocktails, and the first-floor Terrace Bar, with a separate outdoor patio area and large-screen TV, are open. It is deservedly popular for quality food; booking is essential for the restaurant. There are picnic tables outside to the front. 🛇🏠◑&⇌🖥(6,X6)🐾🛜

Old Friends Ⓛ

49 Soutergate, LA12 7ES

☎ (01229) 208195 🌐 oldfriendsulverston.co.uk

6 changing beers (sourced nationally; often Old Friends) Ⓗ

A 17th-century Grade II-listed locals' pub 200 yards uphill from the town centre. It has a cosy snug with an open fire in front of the bar. Another room with a TV is separated by a passageway, with a hatch to the bar. Beers are mostly from the area, with three produced in the pub's own brewery. A popular quiz night is held every Tuesday. There is a wonderful beer garden with heating in the winter. 🛇🏠♣🖥🐾🛜

Rose & Crown

22 King Street, LA12 7DZ

☎ (01229) 583094 🌐 the-rose-ulverston.co.uk

Robinsons Dizzy Blonde, Cumbria Way, Cascade IPA, Trooper; 1 changing beer (sourced nationally; often Robinsons) Ⓗ

A warm welcome awaits at this 400-year-old inn, which retains many original features including low beams and real fires. There are five distinct areas (check out Sid's Room, named after a regular who ran the bakery next door). Four handpumps serve Robinsons beers in excellent condition, and high-quality home-cooked food is available at lunchtimes and evenings. Well-behaved dogs are welcomed in the front bar. Enjoy the patio in warmer weather, or sit in the covered area when cooler. Q🛇🏠⛄◑⇌🖥🐾

Swan Inn Ⓛ

Swan Street, LA12 7JX

☎ (01229) 582519

9 changing beers (sourced nationally) Ⓗ

On the edge of the town centre, overlooking the A590, there's an open-plan feel here, yet there are three distinct drinking areas. Premier League football and major sports events are screened, live music features occasionally, and a jukebox allows for all genres of music. A Sunday night quiz rounds off the entertainment. The beer garden is popular, especially in summer. Children are allowed until 8pm. 🏠&♣🖥🖨(6,X6)🐾🛜

Waberthwaite

Brown Cow Inn

LA19 5YJ

☎ (01229) 717243 🌐 thebrowncow-inn.simplesite.com

7 changing beers (sourced locally) Ⓗ

A lively centre for the village, this 100-year-old family-run inn has been refurbished, with a cosy fire in the main bar. The ales change regularly and cider is on tap in summer. It serves pub food made using local produce. There is an annual beer festival, regular quiz nights, and live music occasionally at weekends. A conference room is available. Situated on the A595, with easy access to the western fells, beaches and Eskmeals nature reserve. Q🛇⛄🏠◑&♠♣🖥🖨🐾🛜

Wetheral

Wheatsheaf Inn Ⓛ ✅

CA4 8HD

☎ (01228) 560686

Great Corby Session Ale; 2 changing beers Ⓗ

Early 19th-century village pub just a few minutes' walk from the village green and railway station. It is deservedly popular with locals and visitors. Along with Corby Ale from the Great Corby Brewery nearby, there are two changing ales that come from local breweries. Good-value bar meals are served Wednesday to Sunday; booking is advisable at weekends. The regular Tuesday quiz nights are well supported. 🛇🏠◑⇌♣P🖨(75)🐾🛜

Whitehaven

Candlestick ✔

21-22 Tangier Street, CA28 7UX

☎ (01946) 66288

3 changing beers (sourced nationally) Ⓗ

A town-centre pub close to Whitehaven harbour, with a local crowd of regulars. It used to be known as the Welsh Arms and is in a part of town with four pubs. The interior comprises a bar area and a comfortable seating area. The bar has live music and caters for sports enthusiasts, and can be busy on Friday and Saturday nights. ≋🖥🌢🛜

Vagabond

9 Marlborough Street, CA28 7LL (on continuation of Lowther St, leading to harbour)

☎ (01946) 66653 ⊕ thevagabondpub.co.uk

4 changing beers (sourced nationally) Ⓗ

Just off the historic harbourside of this Georgian town, the present and former name, American Connection, commemorate the pirate raid of John Paul Jones in 1778. It is a traditional two-storey wooden-floored building with a welcoming atmosphere. Beers change frequently, with choices and styles from Cumbrian, Scottish and national breweries. Food includes stone-baked pizzas. 🌢◖≋🖥🌢🛜

Witherslack

Derby Arms Hotel Ⓛ

LA11 6RH

☎ (015395) 52207 ⊕ thederbyarms.co.uk

Bowness Bay Swan Blonde; Cumbrian Ales Loweswater Gold; 4 changing beers (sourced regionally; often Fell, Keswick, Kirkby Lonsdale) Ⓗ

The new road bypasses the village, so the old coaching inn that was once a busy dinner-dance venue for charabanc parties is now a hidden haven for walkers and cyclists on the coastal route. The excellent selection of well-kept beers changes regularly but always includes popular favourites from Bowness Bay. The spacious main bar has a real fire, plus a large dining room, and two small rooms leading from it. There is a separate pool room above the bike store. The X6 bus stops nearby. 🛏🏠🍴◖🌢♣🅿🐾🌢🛜

King's Arms, Barrow-in-Furness (Photo: Jack Summers-Glass)

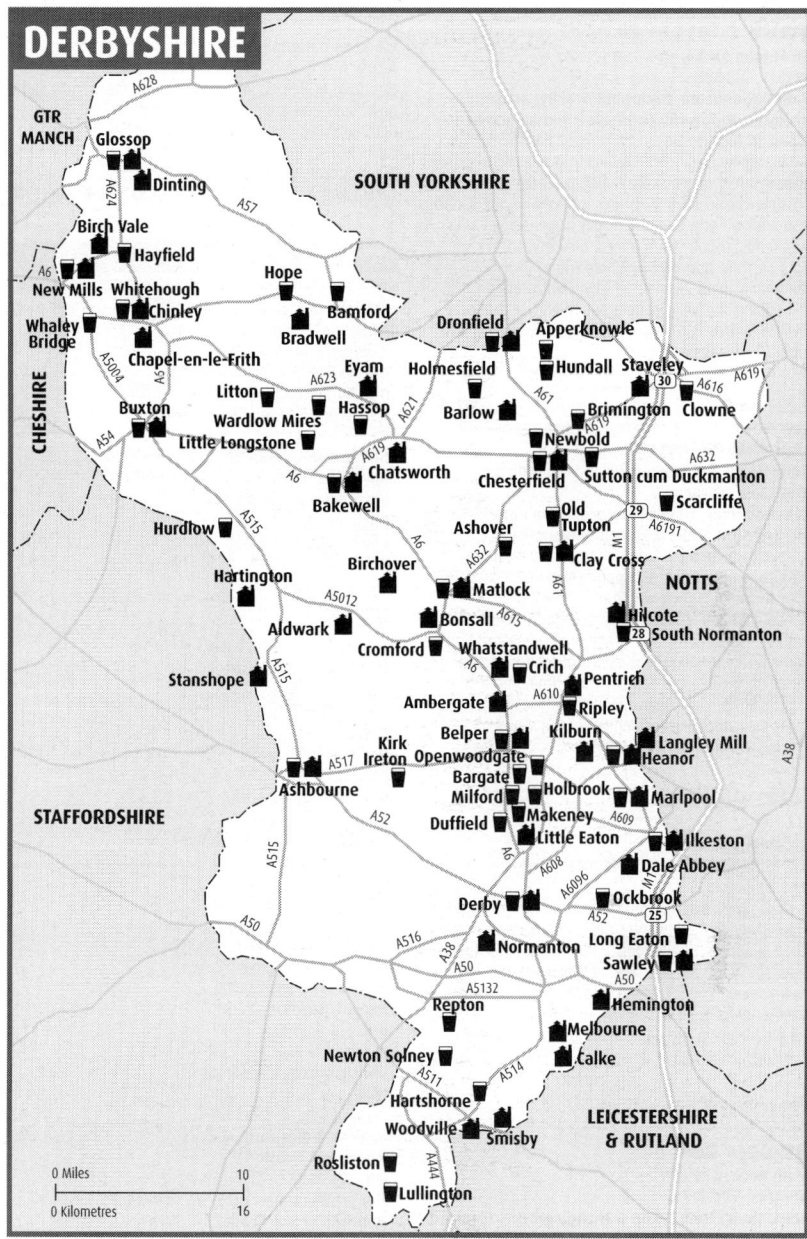

Apperknowle

Traveller's Rest 🅛

High Street, S18 4BD SK384782

☎ (01246) 460169

Neepsend Blonde; Timothy Taylor Landlord 🅗; 4
changing beers (sourced nationally) 🅗/🅖
The Travs, sometimes referred to as the Corner Pin, is a
traditional country pub, serving an excellent and
changing range of real ales, ciders and perries. The
outdoor drinking area provides sweeping views over the
Drone Valley. Good-quality food is on offer including the
ever-popular cheese and pork pie platters.
Q☺🕭🕪◑♣♠P🖵(14) 🐱🗢

Ashbourne

House of Beer

28B Church Street, DE6 1AE

☎ (01335) 343669

10 changing beers 🅗
Combined bottle shop and craft ale taproom in a former
antique shop. It has 10 KeyKeg taps, three permanent
and seven varying ales, plus four cider taps. The front
area contains 400 world beers and ciders, including a
good selection from British breweries nearby and
nationwide. Many examples of RAIB and mini pins are
also on sale. Locally sourced pies are served, and there is
free coffee for any designated driver. 🖐🐱🐾🗢

Smith's Tavern ✔

36 St John Street, DE6 1GH
☎ (01335) 300809
Banks's Sunbeam; Brakspear Gravity; Marston's
Pedigree; Ringwood Fortyniner; 1 changing beer
(sourced locally) Ⓗ

Small, highly traditional town centre pub, with as many
as seven real ales on. The landlord selects the widest
possible choice from Marston's portfolio of beers, and is
also allowed one free choice guest ale, served at
weekends, usually from a local brewery. Locally sourced
pork pies are normally available. There is also a good
range of around 25 malt whiskies, with tutored tastings
throughout the year. A frequent winner of the local
CAMRA branch Pub of the Year, five times in the last
eight years. Q❧♣❀🚭

Ashover

Old Poets' Corner Ⓛ

Butts Road, S45 0EW (downhill from church)
☎ (01246) 590888
Everards Tiger; Titanic Steerage, Plum Porter, Captain
Smith's Strong Ale; 2 changing beers Ⓗ

An award-winning village pub with a welcoming
atmosphere, warmed by open fires on cold days. Taken
over by Titanic Brewery in June 2019, it offers 10
handpulled ales, mainly from the Titanic range, along
with changing guest ales, traditional ciders and bottled
world beers. An excellent choice of food is served,
including a carvery at Sunday lunchtime, and a curry
night on Thursday. Open mic night is Tuesday and quiz
night Wednesday. Dogs and walkers are welcome.
Q❀✉◐&♣●P🚌(63,64)❀🚭

Bakewell

Joiners Arms Ⓛ

1-2 Rutland Buildings, DE45 1BZ
☎ 07834 950693
6 changing beers (often Peak Ales, Thornbridge) Ⓗ

Small, friendly town-centre micropub, opened in May
2019 in a former newsagents, run by a cask ale and craft
cider specialist. Six cask ales and six craft keg ales, as
well as vegan beers, are always on, sourced locally, as
are the selection of wines, gins and whiskies. Open mic is
on Wednesdays and light, live music on Sunday
evenings, from March onwards. Q❧❀●🚌❀🚭

Bamford

Anglers Rest Ⓛ

Main Road, S33 0DY
☎ (01433) 659317 🌐 anglers.rest
Black Sheep Best Bitter; 5 changing beers (sourced
locally; often Abbeydale, Bradfield, Little Critters) Ⓗ

At the heart of Bamford and not far from Ladybower
Reservoir, this is a community hub in every sense, where
the locals have been running the pub (and associated
post office and café) since 2013. The main bar is the focal
point and is extremely popular with families, walkers
and – particularly – cyclists, who have access to dedicated
cycle parking and a DIY repair shop. There is also a
quieter snug. Good-value, rustic bar food is served
Wednesday to Sunday. Q❧❀◐&▲♣P🚌(257)❀🚭

Bargate

White Hart

Sandbed Lane, DE56 0JA
☎ (01773) 827397

Fuller's London Pride; Oakham Citra; 5 changing beers
(sourced nationally) Ⓗ

A cosy two-roomed pub in the heart of this village above
the town of Belper. With a reputation for friendly staff,
good beer and a welcoming atmosphere, it is popular
with locals and has an excellent selection of changing
cask ales. A large beer garden is to the rear and walkers
are welcome any time. Bar snacks are usually available.
Local CAMRA Pub of the Year 2020. Q❧❀♣P🚌(71)❀

REAL ALE BREWERIES

3P's Woodville (NEW)
Aldwark Artisan Aldwark
Alter Ego Heanor
Ashover Clay Cross
Aurora Ilkeston
Bad Bunny Ambergate
Bang The Elephant Langley Mill
Bartleby's Belper
Bentley Brook ⚒ Matlock
Big Stone Chinley
Birch Cottage Sawley
Birchover ⬛ Birchover
Black Hole Little Eaton
Bottle Brook Kilburn
Brampton Chesterfield
Brunswick ⬛ Derby
Buxton Buxton
Chapel-en-le-Frith Chapel-en-le-Frith
Chickenfoot ⬛ Bonsall
Collyfobble ⬛ ⚒ Barlow
Dancing Duck Derby
Derby Derby
Dovedale Stanshope
Draycott Dale Abbey
Drone Valley Dronfield
Eyam Eyam
Falstaff ⬛ Derby: Normanton
Furnace ⬛ Derby
Globe ⬛ Glossop
Grasshopper Langley Mill
Hartshorns Derby
Haywood Bad Ram Ashbourne
Hemlock Hemington
Hollow Tree Whatstandwell
Howard Town ⚒ Glossop
Intrepid Bradwell
Leadmill Heanor
Leatherbritches ⬛ Smisby
Littleover Derby
Marlpool ⬛ Marlpool
Matlock Wolds Farm Matlock
Moody Fox Hilcote
Moot ⬛ Matlock
Morgan Brewmasters ⬛ ⚒ Melbourne (NEW)
Mouselow Farm Dinting
Muirhouse Ilkeston
Old Sawley ⬛ Sawley
Peak Chatsworth
Pentrich Pentrich
RBA Derby
Rock Mill New Mills
Shiny ⚒ Little Eaton
Silver Staveley
Thorley & Sons Ilkeston
Thornbridge Bakewell
Thornsett Birch Vale (NEW)
Tollgate ⚒ Calke
Torrside ⚒ New Mills
Townes ⬛ Staveley
Urban Chicken Ilkeston
Whim Hartington

Belper

Angels Micro Pub
Market Place, DE56 1FZ (top right-hand side of Market Place)
☎ 07527 163316
Oakham Citra; Thornbridge Jaipur IPA; Titanic Plum Porter; 5 changing beers (sourced nationally) Ⓖ
A quirky and friendly bar offering real ales, an excellent choice of real ciders, wines and gins. More like a mini beer festival than a pub, a full selection of ales (up to eight plus eight ciders at times) from Thursday gradually decreases as Sunday approaches and the beer is drunk. Locally sourced pork pies and cheeses are served. Live artists perform most Sunday afternoons. ▷⊛⅏≉♣●P☐❀ᗑ

Railway ✪
25 King Street, DE56 1PW
☎ (01773) 689987 ⊕ railwaybelper.co.uk
Lincoln Green Marion, Hood, Bowman, Tuck; 4 changing beers (sourced nationally; often Lincoln Green) Ⓗ
Refurbished to a good standard and now operated by Lincoln Green Brewery, the Railway offers eight cask and six keg ales. It has become a welcome addition to the main shopping street in Belper, providing a link between Bridge Street and Market Place pubs. A loyalty card scheme is available and meals are served. A quiz is held on Wednesday night. ▷⊛⊄⅊⅄≉●☐❀ᗑ

Brimington

Brimming with Beer Ⓛ
Patrick Hinds House, Chesterfield Road, S43 1AD (adjacent to Ark Tavern pub)
☎ (01246) 278888
3 changing beers (often Thornbridge) Ⓗ
Beer shop opened in 2016, with an on-licence. A vast range of bottled beers from around the world is stocked, together with British bottled beers. Between three and five cask ales are served on the bar, plus three permanent and two changing keg beers, together with a choice of ciders. A selection of advertising signs and presentation packs is usually available, together with snuff and cigars. No dogs allowed Friday and Saturday evenings. ☐❀

Buxton

53 @ Buxton Tap House Ⓛ
11-16 The Old Court House, George Street, SK17 6AT
☎ (01298) 214085 ⊕ buxtonbrewery.co.uk/tap-house
4 changing beers (sourced locally; often Buxton) Ⓗ
The 53 @ Buxton Tap House is in Buxton's café quarter at the rear of the crescent. The tap for Buxton Brewery, it has four handpumps serving a regularly changing range of the brewery's cask beers; in addition, up to 16 fonts dispense KeyKeg beers in a variety of styles and strengths (listed on the beer blackboard). A varied food menu is available Monday-Saturday. The cellar is shared by the nearby Cellar Bar (also run by the same owners). ⊛⊄⅊≉☐❀ᗑ

Ale Stop Ⓛ
Chapel Street, SK17 6HX
☎ 07801 364619
3 changing beers (sourced nationally) Ⓗ
Recently refurbished, this is the first micropub in the High Peak, its two rooms converted from a former wine shop off Buxton market square. Beer is the thing here, with three changing ones from microbreweries up and down the country, as well as three real ciders. The objective is

to bring to Buxton beers that are rarely, if ever, seen in the town. The enthusiastic staff ensure a warm and friendly welcome. An eclectic choice of background music on vinyl is played. ▷⅊●☐❀ᗑ

Buxton Brewery Cellar Bar
George Street, SK17 6AT
☎ (01298) 214085 ⊕ buxtonbrewery.co.uk/tap-house
2 changing beers (sourced locally; often Buxton) Ⓗ
Owned and run in conjunction with Buxton Brewery, the Cellar Bar is next door but one to the Tap House bar but is focused on drinks, with no food available. The single room is divided into two seating areas; the decor is simple with an original brick vaulted ceiling. Two cask and 12 keg beers, mainly from Buxton Brewery, are served from taps behind the bar alongside a selection of the brewery's canned and bottled beers. An outdoor covered seating area is provided at the front. ⊛≉☐❀ᗑ

Cheshire Cheese Ⓛ
37-39 High Street, SK17 6HA
☎ (01298) 212453
Everards Tiger; Titanic Steerage, Iceberg, White Star, Plum Porter, Captain Smith's Strong Ale; 4 changing beers Ⓗ
A double-fronted building of considerable age, which was refurbished before reopening under the management of Titanic in 2013. The pub is essentially open plan but is split into several distinct areas. Low ceilings with original beams add to the cosy atmosphere and there are two open fires. The bar boasts an array of 10 handpumps serving a range of Titanic beers and guests. Home-made food is available. Entertainment is provided on Saturday evenings and there is a quiz on Sundays. Q▷⊛⊄⅊⅄♣●P☐❀ᗑ

RedWillow Buxton Ⓛ
1 Cavendish Circus, SK17 6AT
⊕ redwillowbrewery.com
RedWillow Wreckless; 4 changing beers (sourced locally) Ⓗ
Opened in 2017 and located in a former bank in the centre of Buxton, this is the RedWillow Brewery's second bar. Original features have been retained such as etched windows and the mahogany and glass office, alongside a new bar and a smaller mezzanine area. The five cask ales comprise four RedWillow beers and a guest. Small plates and stone-baked pizzas are served and private beer tastings are held. There is also live music monthly. ▷⅊⅄≉♣☐❀ᗑ

Chesterfield

Beer Parlour Ⓛ
1 King Street North, Whittington Moor, S41 9BA
☎ 07870 693411 ⊕ the-beer-parlour.co.uk
8 changing beers Ⓗ
The Parlour is a rustic one-roomed bar that is warm and friendly, with comfy seating that gives a real homely micropub feel. A choice of up to eight real ales, often local, is usually on tap. Many different ciders are also offered as well as Belgian and continental beers on draught, and you can opt to take a beer home too. Close to Chesterfield FC Technique Stadium. A winner of CAMRA awards. Q⅄●☐❀

Chesterfield Alehouse Ⓛ
37 West Bars, S40 1AG
⊕ chesterfieldalehouse.co.uk
6 changing beers Ⓗ
Chesterfield's first micropub is a few minutes' walk from the marketplace. Previously a furniture shop, the split-

level room has a small seating space leading up a few steps to the serving area, where you'll find six regularly changing beers, always including a stout or a porter. Up to 12 keg lines – many of them KeyKeg – are also on offer, and a growing range of bottled world beers, ciders and wines. Free-to-air sports are often shown in the upstairs room. Q&♣♠♥☆🖶♨🅿️

Neptune Beer Emporium 🅛
46 St Helen's Street, S41 7QD
☎ (01246) 220146 ⊕ neptunebeeremporium.co.uk
8 changing beers (sourced locally) 🅗
Now a free house and a self-styled beer emporium, this is a compact back-street pub divided into two drinking areas either side of a central bar. The list of real ales is always changing and includes many from breweries in the area. An extensive range of continental and craft beers on draught and in bottles is also offered, all listed on a descriptive chalkboard. Voted local CAMRA Pub of the Year and Town Pub of the Year 2020, Neptune is also renowned as a live music venue. ☷◖≈♣♠♥☆♨🅿️

Pig & Pump 🅛
16 St Mary's Gate, S41 7TJ
☎ (01246) 229570 ⊕ pigandpump.co.uk
Brains Rev James; Castle Rock Harvest Pale; Oakham Citra; Titanic Plum Porter; 8 changing beers (often Abbeydale, Peak Ales, Thornbridge) 🅗
Formerly the White Swan, this friendly hostelry is opposite Chesterfield's parish church with its famous crooked spire. It is open plan, split into two areas, one slightly raised and leading to a long bar, and is popular for food – the home-made Sunday roast is recommended. The pub has live music on Saturdays and a quirky quiz on Tuesdays. An upstairs function room is available for hire. There is parking in the public car park adjoining. ☷♨◖&♠♥🅿️🖶♨🅿️

Rose & Crown 🅛 ✔
104 Old Road, Brampton, S40 2QT
☎ (01246) 563750 ⊕ roseandcrownbrampton.co.uk
Brampton Golden Bud, Best; Everards Tiger; 6 changing beers (often Brampton) 🅗
Everards' Project William renovation enabled the Brampton Brewery to open its first tied house. A compact snug provides room for group meetings, while the main room has plenty of quiet corners. Memorabilia from the original Brampton Brewery festoon the walls. There are outdoor drinking areas to the front and rear, with covered decking. Quiz night is Tuesday, it does Sunday lunches, and an annual beer festival is held for St George's Day. Four Brampton beers are always available, including a dark ale. Winner of numerous local CAMRA awards. ☷♨◖♣♥🅿️🖶(170)♨🅿️

Spa Lane Vaults 🅛 ✔
34 St Mary's Gate, S41 7TH
☎ (01246) 246300
Greene King Abbot; Ruddles Best Bitter; 5 changing beers 🅗
For many years this was known as the Phoenix Hotel, until the building was converted by Wetherspoon. It is the smaller of the two Wetherspoon pubs in town, close to the Crooked Spire. The interior is spacious and modern, divided into separate areas. It can get busy at weekends and on club nights. Music, sport TV and games machines feature. The patio at the back is split for smoking and non-smoking, and is popular in summer. Public parking is close by. ☷♨◖&≈♥🅿️🖶♨

Clay Cross

Rykneld Turnpyke 🅛
4 John Street, S45 9NQ
☎ (01246) 250366
12 changing beers 🅗
Formerly Egstow Working Men's Club, the Rykneld Turnpyke (named after Rykneld Street, the old road between Chesterfield and Derby) is the brewery tap for the on-site Instant Karma brewing company. It features a large bar with 12 cask ales, craft keg and a variety of bottles. The large open room is divided into different areas, with comfortable seating and two log-burners. It has a cosy, welcoming, eclectic feel, and is dog-friendly. A previous winner of Chesterfield CAMRA Pub of the Year. ♣♥🅿️(54)♨

Three Horseshoes 🅛
49 Market Street, S45 9JE
☎ (01246) 861789
Neepsend Blonde; Thornbridge Jaipur IPA; 2 changing beers 🅗
Previously called Corner Pin and Three Bar, this pub returned to its original name when it reopened in 2013. Refurbished in an attractive, modern style, it serves breakfast, tea and coffee as well as real ales in a café-bar environment. Open mic night is Tuesday, quiz night is Thursday, there is a singer or a band on Friday, steak night is also Friday, and there is karaoke on Sunday. Catering is available for weddings and parties. ♨◖🅿️🖶♨

Clowne

Centre 🅛 ✔
Recreation Close, S43 4PL
☎ (01246) 819546
4 changing beers (often Timothy Taylor) 🅗
A council-run community centre widely used by locals for functions, which can be booked for weddings, parties and special events. There is a popular quiz night with free food on Tuesday, and live music on the last Friday of the month. Regular beers come from the Timothy Taylor range, and there are changing guests. A real ale beer festival is also hosted. The place is well cared for, with a relaxed and friendly atmosphere. Ample car parking is available. ☷♨&🅿️🖶

Crich

Old Black Swan 🅛
12 Bowns Hill, DE4 5DG
☎ (01773) 856406
6 changing beers (sourced nationally) 🅗
Situated close to the centre of the village, this former 17th-century coaching inn now boasts a fine selection of real ales along with an excellent food menu. Upcoming beers are shown on a chalkboard together with their ABV and a brief description. The two large rooms have plenty of character, with beamed ceilings and real fires. Outside there is a quirky yard area with tables and benches for summer evenings. Near to the historic Tramway Museum. Q☷♨◖&♣♠♥☆🖶♨🅿️

Cromford

Boat Inn 🅛
Scarthin, DE4 3QF (small road behind shops from Greyhound car park)
☎ (01629) 258083
4 changing beers (sourced locally) 🅗
Built in 1772, the beamed ceilings, exposed stone walls and open fire give the main bar a cosy atmosphere. A

small snug area, dining room and cellar sports bar with Sky and BT Sports cater for a range of different needs. Home-cooked meals are served every day from lunchtime onwards. Live music features every Friday and Saturday night. The beer garden overlooks the large mill pond. Cromford is within the Derwent Mills Valley, which is part of the World Heritage Site along the River Derwent. ♿🕮⬧▲🚃(6.1)❀🛜

Derby

Alexandra Hotel 🄻

203 Siddals Road, DE1 2QE
☎ (01332) 293993 ⊕ alexandrahotelderby.co.uk
Castle Rock Harvest Pale; 7 changing beers (sourced nationally) Ⓗ
A Castle Rock pub serving its own beers and up to five guest ales, including a mild and a stout or porter. There are also more than 50 UK and continental bottled beers of varying styles. Themed food nights are held approximately monthly. The lounge is adorned with breweriana and the bar has railway memorabilia. A Class 37 locomotive cab resides in the car park. The birthplace of Derby CAMRA in 1974. Q♿🕮⬧🚭♿≉♣●P🚃❀🛜

Babington Arms 🄻 ✅

11-13 Babington Lane, DE1 1TA
☎ (01332) 383647
Draught Bass; Greene King Abbot; Marston's Pedigree; Ruddles Best Bitter; Small World Thunderbridge Stout, Twin Falls; 11 changing beers (sourced nationally) Ⓗ
This Wetherspoon is a converted furniture showroom close to the city centre. It boasts a huge range of real ales, many from local microbreweries, and typically has six ciders on handpump or gravity dispense. The back end of the large bar includes some half-partitioned banquette seating and caters for family dining. Outside at the front of the pub there is a small fenced-off area for drinkers. ♿🕮⬧🚭♿🚃🛜

Brunswick Inn 🄻

1 Railway Terrace, DE1 2RU
☎ (01332) 290677 ⊕ brunswickderby.co.uk
Brunswick White Feather, Triple Hop, The Usual; Everards Beacon Hill, Tiger; Timothy Taylor Landlord; 10 changing beers (sourced nationally) Ⓗ
Originally part of the railway village, this multi-roomed establishment was restored and opened as Derby's first multiple choice real ale house in 1987. A purpose-built brewery was added in 1991 and the pub has since become one of the best-known free houses in the country. Owned by Everards, the range of up to 16 real ales includes at least six from Brunswick, the in-house brewery. Busy on Derby County match days. Q♿🕮⬧🚭♿≉♣●P🚃❀🛜

Creaky Floorboard 🄻

179 Kedleston Road, DE22 1FT
☎ 07974 749517
House beer (by Derby); 4 changing beers (sourced locally) Ⓗ
A micropub, opened in 2018, on the end of a line of terraced houses and formerly a guesthouse. The interior is made up of two rooms off a central entrance way, and retains the feel of a private home. The small bar is located in the left-hand room and normally serves locally produced ales. Q🕮🚃♿

Exeter Arms 🄻 ✅

13 Exeter Place, DE1 2EU
☎ (01332) 605323 ⊕ exeterarms.co.uk

Dancing Duck Ay Up; Marston's Pedigree; 2 changing beers Ⓗ
A joint venture between Dancing Duck Brewery and a local food and drink entrepreneur has resulted in a fine range of beers and an excellent dining experience, all put together in a venue with old-world charm. The small bar has an open fire and leads to several other rooms, including a wooden-settled snug with an old-fashioned range. The adjoining atmospheric cottage dating from around 1815 has now been incorporated into the pub. A popular and quirky quiz is held on Monday evening. ♿🕮⬧●P🚃❀🛜

Falstaff 🄻

74 Silverhill Road, Normanton, DE23 6UJ
☎ (01332) 342902 ⊕ falstaffbrewery.co.uk
Falstaff Fist Full of Hops, Phoenix, Smiling Assassin; 1 changing beer Ⓗ
A 20-minute walk from the city centre into the Normanton district rewards you with this atmospheric and reputedly haunted free house. Originally a coaching inn before the neighbourhood was built up, it is now the Falstaff Brewery tap and has long been the best real ale house in the area. The rear lounge is a shrine to Offilers' Brewery, with a display of memorabilia. Other collectibles can be viewed throughout the games room and second bar room. Q♿🕮♣🚃(4,7)❀

Five Lamps 🄻 ✅

25 Duffield Road, DE1 3BH
☎ (01332) 348730 ⊕ fivelampsderby.co.uk
Draught Bass; Everards Tiger; Peak Ales Chatsworth Gold; St Austell Proper Job; Thornbridge Jaipur IPA; house beer (by Derby); 8 changing beers (sourced regionally) Ⓗ
Since it reopened in 2010, the pub has gone from strength to strength thanks to the dedication of the licensees and staff. Fourteen handpumps showcase many local ales from breweries such as Derby, Peak and Whim. The Lamps is essentially open plan, but has many little nooks and crannies, giving it a homely feel. It has been tastefully refurbished with wood panelling and leather seating in a traditional style. 🕮⬧♿●P🚃❀🛜

Flowerpot 🄻

23-25 King Street, DE1 3DZ
☎ (01332) 204955 ⊕ flowerpotderby.com
Marston's Pedigree; Oakham Bishops Farewell; Sharp's Doom Bar Ⓗ**; Whim Hartington IPA; 3 changing beers (sourced nationally)** Ⓗ/🄶
Dating from around 1800 but much expanded from its original premises, this vibrant pub reaches back from the roadside frontage and divides into several interlinking rooms. One room provides the stage for regular live bands; another has a glass cellar wall revealing rows of stillaged firkins, which can be seen from the bar and from the road outside. Up to 14 real ales and two ciders are offered. Good en-suite accommodation is available. 🕮♿🛏♿♣●🚃❀🛜

Furnace Inn 🄻

Duke Street, DE1 3BX
☎ (01332) 385981
Furnace Fun Sponge; Shiny 4 Wood; 6 changing beers (sourced nationally) Ⓗ
A former Hardys & Hansons pub, reopened in 2012 and transformed into a real ale mecca It is now the tap for Furnace Brewery. Up to eight real ales and three ciders/ perries are served, complemented by a variety of UK craft beers. There are two distinct open-plan rooms with a central bar. Poker and cheese nights feature weekly, and there are regular beer festivals throughout the year. ♿🕮⬧♿♣P❀🛜

Hole in the Wall L

Station Road, Mickleover, DE3 9GH
☎ (01332) 501301 🌐 holeinthewall-dbc.co.uk
6 changing beers [H]
Opened in March 2020, this is a former NatWest bank corner building at the start of Station Road in the centre of Mickleover. The pub has a large single room with the bar at the back to one side. Operated by the Derby Brewing Co, there are six handpulled beers on offer, one of which is a guest. 🚌

Little Chester Ale House L

4A Chester Green Road, Chester Green, DE1 3SF
Hartshorns Ignite; 3 changing beers (sourced nationally) [H]
On the edge of a tree-lined conservation area, Derby's first micropub is in the historic Little Chester part of the city, the site of Roman Derventio, where two ancient wells can still been seen nearby. This former shop has one small main room with a narrower passageway containing the bar. It has four changing beers, including three from local Hartshorns Brewery, the pub's owner. Q♿♣🍎🚌🐾📶

Malt Shovel ★ ✔

Potter Street, Spondon, DE21 7LH
☎ (01332) 674203
Banks's Sunbeam; Brakspear Gravity; Marston's 61 Deep, Pedigree [H]**; Wychwood Hobgoblin Gold** [H]/[G]
There has been a pub on this site since 1340, although it has been rebuilt twice since then. The unusual layout features a copper-topped bar in the main corridor with two snugs opposite, a lounge and a larger games room with a full-size snooker table. A large lawned garden is at the rear. At least four guest beers from the Marston's range are on sale, some dispensed by gravity. Good-value food is served at lunchtimes, but there is no evening food except fish & chips on Wednesdays. Q❀◑♣🍎P🚌🐾📶

No.189

189 Blenheim Drive, Allestree, DE22 2GN
Littleover Gold, King George's Bitter; 3 changing beers (sourced nationally) [H]
Opened in 2018 in the large Allestree estate, this former launderette, and then beauticians', has proved popular. The single-roomed micropub offers a choice of five real ales, including two from Littleover Brewery. Three craft ale taps are also on the bar. Furnishings include a mix of high and low seating, while outside there are benches. The centre of Derby is a 15-minute bus ride. Q❀P🚌🐾📶

Old Bell Hotel L ✔

51 Sadler Gate, DE1 3NQ
☎ (01332) 723090 🌐 bellhotelderby.co.uk
Draught Bass; house beer (by Imperial); 1 changing beer (sourced regionally) [H]
This 18th-century coaching inn, with a large frontage, is a welcome oasis in Sadler Gate, a premier shopping street in the Cathedral Quarter. The exterior Tudor-style half timbering was only added in 1929. The Tavern Bar features a range of real ale and craft kegs, including a house beer. Drinkers after a historic atmosphere should seek out the Tudor Bar to the rear (open Friday and Saturday), which only ceased being a men-only bar in 1975. ❀◑🐾

Olde Dolphin Inne ★ L

5A Queen Street, DE1 3DL (close to cathedral)
☎ (01332) 267711 🌐 yeoldedolphin.co.uk
Draught Bass; Greene King Abbot; Marston's Pedigree; Sharp's Doom Bar; 4 changing beers (sourced nationally) [H]
Claimed to be Derby's oldest pub, it certainly looks the part, with a number of small rooms including a traditional snug which has a real fire in winter and conversation all year round. There is regular live music on the large outdoor patio. Food is served in the bar areas, plus the steak restaurant upstairs, open Thursday to Saturday evenings. A music quiz is held on Tuesday evening and a general knowledge quiz on Sunday evening. Q❀◑♣🍎P🚌📶

Silk Mill Ale & Cider House L ✔

19 Full Street, DE1 3AF
☎ (01332) 365439 🌐 silkmillderby.co.uk
Dancing Duck Ay Up; Sharp's Doom Bar; 6 changing beers [H]
Handsome stone-faced building named after the historic silk mill nearby, which marks the start of the Derwent Valley World Heritage Trail. To the right of the entrance is the Offilers' Lounge with a cosy real fire, ideal for drinkers. There is a dedicated dining area to the rear of pub – booking is recommended at peak times. The central bar has nine handpumps shared between real ales and ciders. Quirky decorative ornaments and fittings are used throughout. ❀◑🍎P📶

Smithfield L

Meadow Road, DE1 2BH
☎ (01332) 986601
Draught Bass; 7 changing beers (sourced nationally) [H]
The Smithfield rests near the town centre on the banks of the River Derwent opposite Bass's Rec and a short walk from the main bus station. The large main bar boasts an eclectic range of new and interesting beers supported by Draught Bass. A separate quiet room with a real fire overlooks the patio next to the river. The pub has regular live music and many beer-related activities. ❀◑♣🍎P🚌🐾📶

Standing Order ✔

28-32 Iron Gate, DE1 3GL
☎ (01332) 207591
Draught Bass; Greene King Abbot; Kelham Island Pale Rider; Marston's Pedigree; Ruddles Best Bitter; Sharp's Doom Bar; 12 changing beers [H]
Named after its former role as a bank, this establishment became the first, grandest and certainly the tallest of the three Wetherspoons in Derby. It features full-size reproductions of paintings of Derby worthies from the time of the Industrial Revolution. There are a few quieter corners but generally this has the feeling of a busy city-centre pub. There is a good changing selection of guest ales. Alcoholic drinks are served from 9am. Q◑♿🍎📶

Dronfield

Coach & Horses L

Sheffield Road, S18 2GD
☎ (01246) 413269 🌐 mycoachandhorses.co.uk
Thornbridge Lord Marples, Jaipur IPA; 4 changing beers (sourced nationally; often Drone Valley, Mallinsons, Thornbridge) [H]
The pub is next to the ground of Sheffield FC (the world's oldest football club), on the northern edge of Dronfield. It is operated by Thornbridge and showcases a good range of the brewery's beers, with guest ales across a wide range of styles. The large outdoor drinking area is particularly popular. Meals are provided daily from lunchtime onwards. The pub hosts a regular quiz night on Thursday and open mic acoustic session on Monday evening. ❀◑🍎P🚌(43)🐾📶

Duffield

Town Street Tap 🄻
17 Town Street, DE56 4EH (on main road through Duffield)
☎ 07925 461706
6 changing beers (sourced nationally) 🄶
This micropub for Tollgate Brewery has been converted into a modern, uncluttered drinking space with table service. Of the six changing real ales, two are from the Tollgate range and at least one is dark. In addition, four ciders are available and take-outs are offered in containers or from the bottle shop. Walkers with boots are welcome. There is free tea and coffee for drivers, pork pies and Scotch eggs for the hungry. Q₮♣♠P🖥🛇🐕

Glossop

Bar 2 🄻
9 High Street East, SK13 8DA
☎ 07597 704447
Bradfield Farmers Blonde; Nook Best; 3 changing beers (sourced locally; often Bradfield, Donkeystone, Stockport) 🄷
Micropub in a converted shop opened in 2018 (originally called Tweed 2). In addition to the cask beers on offer there are also craft keg lagers, together with a good selection of wines and gins. It is a pleasant place, and the discrete background music allows drinkers to play traditional pub games, or simply to chat. There is also a retro video games table. Children are welcome until 8pm. Close to Glossop train station and local bus routes. ಹ₮♣🖥🚍🐕☂

Smithy Fold 🗸
Unit 11, Howard Town Shopping Park, Victoria Street, SK13 8HS
☎ (01457) 890070
8 changing beers 🄷
This popular Wetherspoon is in the town centre on the ground floor of an old cotton mill. There remain some original features, and there is interesting artwork showing the history of the mill and some notable figures from the town. Breakfast is served each day until noon. Beers are usually three national brands, with the remainder from regional and local breweries. ಹ🛇🌆&₮♠🖥☂

Star Inn 🗸
2 Howard Street, SK13 7DD (next to railway station)
☎ (01457) 761816
4 changing beers (sourced regionally; often Abbeydale, Howard Town, Pictish) 🄷
A very popular town centre pub, run by a dedicated CAMRA member. Conversation predominates in the large, comfortable, wood-panelled main room. A smaller room to the rear displays a large map of part of the Peak District National Park on one wall. Guest beers are mainly from local microbreweries. Close to the railway station, the pub is an ideal starting/finishing point for walking or cycling within the Dark Peak area. QÅ₮P🖥🐕☂

Hartshorne

Admiral Rodney Inn 🗸
65 Main Street, DE11 7ES (on A514)
☎ (01283) 227771
Draught Bass; 5 changing beers (sourced nationally) 🄷
Traditional village local dating back to the early 19th century, but rebuilt and extended in the late 20th century to provide an open-plan L-shaped drinking space

while retaining the original oak beams in the former snug. There is also a secluded raised area tucked away behind the bar. Cheese tasting takes place on the first Monday of the month, open mic night on the third Tuesday, and a quiz night on Sunday. Real cider (choice varies) is available at weekends. The grounds include a cricket pitch, home of Hartshorne Cricket Club. ಹ🌆&♠P🖥(2)🐕☂

Hassop

Eyre Arms ★ 🄻
Hassop Road, DE45 1NS
☎ (01629) 640390 ⊕ oldeyrearms.co.uk
Peak Ales Swift Nick; 3 changing beers (sourced locally; often Abbeydale, Bradfield, Kelham Island) 🄷
A 300-year-old country inn with two comfortably furnished rooms and a small snug squeezed in between, watched over by an imposing grandfather clock. The impressive Eyre family coat of arms is displayed above the fireplace. Excellent, good-value, home-cooked food is served lunchtimes and evenings, otherwise bar snacks are available. The service in this characterful, unspoilt pub is friendly. Qಹ🌆◑♣P🖽🖥(218)🐕

Hayfield

Pack Horse 🗸
3-5 Market Street, SK22 2EP
☎ (01663) 749126 ⊕ thepackhorsehayfield.uk
4 changing beers (sourced regionally) 🄷
A large comfortable open-plan pub in the centre of the village, it welcomes all and is dog friendly. A function room is also available. There are real fires and three distinct areas, with one of them mainly for dining. It offers four changing cask beers from near and far. A small outdoor drinking area is used in the summer months. Although usually closed on Mondays the pub opens on bank holidays. ಹ🌆◑P🖥🐕☂

Heanor

Crooked Cask 🄻
8 Ray Street, DE75 7GE
☎ (01773) 688140
6 changing beers 🄷/🄶
Opened in 2018 and now an established local, this is a friendly place to enjoy a drink. The front bar is wood-panelled and on a split level, and there is a smaller room to the rear. Beers are offered on up to six handpulls and on gravity from a variety of sources. The landlord is enthusiastic in stocking different ales. Also on the bar are seven ciders and one premium lager. Q🌆◑&♣P🖥🐕☂

Redemption Ale House 🄻
Ray Street, DE75 7GE
☎ 07887 568576
7 changing beers 🄷
A large open-plan micropub that opened in 2016 in a former butcher's shop. The original abattoir is still outside and is used as an area for the regular beer festivals. Six varying beers are available and up to 20 real ciders. A large collection of pumpclips adorns the walls, along with old framed photographs showing the building's previous life. There is an upstairs area with a variety of board games. Q🌆&♠🖥🐕☂

Holbrook

Dead Poets Inn 🄻
38 Chapel Street, DE56 0TQ

☎ (01332) 780301

Draught Bass; Oakham Citra; 6 changing beers (sourced regionally; often Brunswick, Everards) Ⓗ
Built around 1800 and originally called the Cross Keys, this inn was renamed after an imaginative alteration, and has enjoyed iconic status since then. The Poets is now owned by Everards and leased by the Brunswick Inn in Derby, and is a favourite destination for drinkers near and far. It was the first winner of the local CAMRA branch's Pub of the Year award. Q✿☎◑♠P⊟(71)❀✿

Holmesfield

Rutland Arms Ⓛ

96 Main Road, S18 7WT
☎ (0114) 289 0374

Black Sheep Best Bitter; Bradfield Farmers Blonde; Theakston Best Bitter; 2 changing beers (often Bradfield, Everards, Theakston) Ⓗ
A winner of many local CAMRA branch awards, this extremely popular traditional village country pub with open fires and low wooden beams has a relaxing, warm and snug atmosphere. The beer range has increased steadily over the years to six hand-pulled cask ales. Outside, the extensive seating area with grassed children's play space is idyllic in late spring and summer. A collection of books and magazines of local interest is available for customers to enjoy.
Q✿☎❀◑♣♠P⊟(15) ❀✿

Hope

Cheshire Cheese Inn Ⓛ

Edale Road, S33 6ZF
☎ (01433) 620381 ● thecheshirecheeseinn.co.uk

Abbeydale Moonshine; Bradfield Farmers Blonde; 4 changing beers (sourced locally; often Abbeydale, Bradfield, Peak Ales) Ⓗ
A cosy country inn dating from 1578, with an open-plan bar area and a smaller room at a lower level that was probably originally used to house animals, but is now mainly used as a dining area. Home-cooked meals using local produce are served lunchtimes and evenings. The pub is in good walking country but the parking is limited as the road outside is narrow.
Q✿☎❀✿◑P⊟❀✿

Hundall

Miners Arms Ⓛ

Hundall Lane, S18 4BP
☎ (01246) 414505

Drone Valley Dronny Bottom Bitter; Pictish Alchemists Ale; 3 changing beers (sourced nationally; often Church End, Vocation, Welbeck Abbey) Ⓗ
A traditional village hostelry which has won many local and regional CAMRA branch awards and offers a wide range of beers and real ciders. Regular ales come from Pictish and the nearby community Drone Valley Brewery, and there are also three changing guests. It operates a Monday Club with real ales discounted for all customers, and serves a limited range of pub snacks. Large-screen TVs show sport. There is an excellent beer garden to the rear. ✿☎♣♠P⊟⊟(14)❀✿

Hurdlow

Royal Oak Ⓛ

SK17 9QJ (just off A515 Buxton-Ashbourne road, Monyash crossroads)
☎ (01298) 83288 ● peakpub.co.uk

Sharp's Doom Bar; 2 changing beers (often Abbeydale, Bradfield) Ⓗ
Remote pub with the advantage of being only a few minutes' walk away from the Tissington and High Peak Trail, and ideal for exploring the Peak District National Park. It has open fires and hidden corners, and the emphasis is on food, which also includes breakfast. Accommodation is provided in the Bunk Barn and 20-pitch campsite (no motor homes). Breakfast is available, and main meals from lunchtime. Q✿☎❀✿◑ẂP❀✿

Ilkeston

Burnt Pig Ⓛ

53 Market Street, DE7 5RB
☎ 07538 723722

5 changing beers Ⓗ/Ⓖ
This micropub is well-established and has become a regular in the Guide. Regulars and newcomers are welcomed with equal gusto. The interior features a collection of historic pub memorabilia and is spread over three sections, from the busy bar area to two rooms to the rear. The bar offers a wide range of top-quality ales, normally chosen personally by the landlord. There is also a variety of bottled continental beers, and a range of pork pies and cheeses to eat in or take away. Q♣♠⊟✿

Dew Drop Inn Ⓛ

24 Station Road, DE7 5TE
☎ (0115) 932 9684

Oakham Bishops Farewell; house beer (by Oakham); changing beers (often Acorn, Blue Monkey, Castle Rock) Ⓗ
A longstanding entrant in the Guide, this is an historic unchanged three-roomed pub, with roaring fires in winter. There is a bar and lounge either side of the serving area and a separate snug. It serves up to eight real ales, all to an excellent standard. Also on offer are two ciders and a bar menu during the day. Only a short walk away from the reopened Ilkeston railway station. Q✿☎❀◑≼♣♠⊟(27) ✿

Kirk Ireton

Barley Mow Inn

Main Street, DE6 3JP (off B5023) SK266501
☎ (01335) 370306

Whim Hartington IPA; 4 changing beers Ⓖ
A firm favourite for generations, this is one of Britain's most venerated pubs, set in a charming village. The gabled Jacobean building houses several interconnecting rooms, and has low beams, mullioned windows and well-worn woodwork, with a welcoming open fire in the main room. It has no bar as such, but a small serving hatch through which the cask ales are fetched from the cellar. Good home-cooked food is served. As of early 2020, brewing has begun on-site. Local CAMRA Pub of the Year 2020. Q❀✿◑P✿

Little Longstone

Packhorse Inn

Main Street, DE45 1NN
☎ (01629) 640471 ● packhorselongstone.co.uk

Black Sheep Best Bitter; Thornbridge Wild Swan, Lord Marples, Jaipur IPA; 2 changing beers (often Thornbridge) Ⓗ
This small pub began life as two miners' cottages and has been welcoming drinkers since 1787. It is just a short walk from stunning views of Monsal Head, and dogs and walkers are welcome. Fresh produce from the area is a passion, an ethos also extended to the beers, which

always include a choice from the nearby Thornbridge Brewery. There is a pleasant beer garden, and food is available all day at weekends. ⌂❀⬤▶▲♣☒(173)✿☞

Litton

Red Lion ⎣ ✅
Church Lane, SK17 8QU
☎ (01298) 871458 ⊕ theredlionlitton.co.uk
Abbeydale Absolution; Peak Ales Bakewell Best Bitter; 2 changing beers (sourced locally; often Acorn, Bradfield, Moorhouse's) ⊞
Nestling on the green and the only pub in the village, the Red Lion is a welcome refuge for locals and visitors alike. There is a large fireplace warming several rooms off a central passageway. Not to be missed, the annual Wakes Week is at the end of June, when the village hosts events including a well dressing on the green and the pub holds a beer festival. Fresh food is served all day, every day. ⌂❀⬤⬤♣P☒(65,173) ✿☞

Long Eaton

Hole in the Wall ⎣
Regent Street, NG10 1JX
1 changing beer ⊞
An unchanged, traditional two-roomed pub. The landlord, of over 30 years' service, offers five quality real ales. These are normally from the Oakham and Nottingham Ales range. The smaller public bar has a pool table and is complemented by a quieter lounge, with its own serving hatch. An attractive beer garden is hidden away at the rear. A varied clientele includes local trade and real ale enthusiasts. Q❀♿♣⬤☒✿☞

Lullington

Colvile Arms
Main Street, DE12 8EG (centre of village)
☎ 07510 870980 ⊕ thecolvilearms.com
Draught Bass; Marston's Pedigree; 2 changing beers (sourced regionally) ⊞
Leased from the Lullington Estate, seat of the Colvile family until the early 1900s, this popular 18th-century free house is at the heart of an attractive hamlet at the southern tip of the county. The public bar incorporates an adjoining hallway and features high-backed settles with wood panelling. The bar and a comfortable lounge are on opposite sides of a central serving area. A snug/function room (where dogs are allowed) overlooks the beer garden and lawn. Pop-up food vans visit Wednesday and Friday evenings. Q⌂❀▶♣⬤P✿☞

Makeney

Holly Bush ★ ✅
Holly Bush Lane, DE56 0RX
☎ (01332) 841729 ⊕ hollybushinnmakeney.co.uk
Greene King Abbot; Marston's Pedigree; Thornbridge Jaipur IPA; Timothy Taylor Landlord; 4 changing beers (sourced nationally) ⊞
An excellent late 17th-century Grade II-listed hostelry with great character. Once a farmhouse and brewery on the Strutt Estate, it stood on the main Derby turnpike before the new road (now the A6) opened in 1818. Dick Turpin reputedly drank here, and the pub, recognised by CAMRA as having a nationally important historic interior, has various stone-flagged hideaways, with welcoming fires in winter. A home-cooked lunchtime food menu is available as well as bar snacks. Regular beer festivals are staged. Walkers, families and dogs are welcome. Q⌂❀⬤♿♣P☒✿☞

Marlpool

Marlpool Ale House ⎣
5 Breach Road, DE75 7NJ
☎ 07963 511855 ⊕ marlpoolbrewing.co.uk
Marlpool Blind Boris, Otters Pocket, Scratty Ratty, Frank ⊞**; 5 changing beers (sourced regionally)** ⊞/Ⓖ
A true micropub with entry almost straight into the bar, which is an old Methodist chapel pulpit. Ales come from the two-barrel brewery in the yard at the rear. Guest beers are normally from small breweries from far and wide. Family-run, this a friendly place to meet up with friends and strangers. Beers are drawn from handpump or direct from the barrel in the cellar. Real ciders are also on offer. Q❀⬤☒✿

Matlock

Farmacy ⎣
76 Smedley Street, DE4 3JJ (jct of Bank Rd/Smedley St)
☎ (01629) 583350 ⊕ aaabrewery.co.uk
5 changing beers (sourced locally; often Aldwark Artisan) ⊞
Up the steep hill from the town centre and behind County Hall, this cosy, split-level micropub – a former chemist's – is the tap for Aldwark Artisan Ales. It has five handpulls, one dispensing real cider, and usually features several Aldwark beers, as well as a choice of gins and wines. Pork pies and other snacks are available. Themed nights include music and quizzes. ⌂⇌⬤☒✿☞

Newsroom ⎣
75-77 Smedley Street East, DE4 3FQ
☎ (01629) 583625
4 changing beers (sourced regionally)
This smart conversion from a newsagent to a micropub is an L-shaped room with some exposed brickwork and renovated sash windows. There are four real ales from interesting local and sometimes national microbreweries. Six craft ales normally include a stout and a lager; at least one will be KeyKeg. Upwards of 60 different bottled and canned beers for drinking in or taking away are stocked, as well as a good range of gins and wines. CAMRA branch Pub of the Year winner. ♿⇌☒✿

Thorn Tree Inn
48 Jackson Road, DE4 3JQ
☎ (01629) 580295
Draught Bass; Nottingham Extra Pale Ale; Timothy Taylor Landlord; 4 changing beers (sourced nationally) ⊞
Set high above Matlock, this traditional two-roomed pub boasts far-reaching views down the Derwent Valley from its heated patio area. Dogs and families are welcome but due to the compact nature of the pub it can feel quite cosy. There are always three permanent real ales on, with a further selection of four guest ales. Q❀⬤⇌♣⎚☒✿☞

Twenty Ten ⎣
16 Dale Road, DE4 3LT
☎ (01629) 259793 ⊕ twentytenmatlock.co.uk
4 changing beers (sourced locally)
A stone's throw from the train and bus stations, the bar nestles among the antique shops of Dale Road. It serves four real ales, with the focus on LocAle - Thornbridge is regularly on the handpulls. These are complemented by 16 draught craft beers, at least eight KeyKeg. Food is served at lunchtime followed by a light bites menu until the evening. Live music is performed most Friday and Saturday nights. ⌂❀⬤⇌⬤☒✿☞

Milford

King William
The Bridge, DE56 0RR
☎ (01332) 840842
Draught Bass; Greene King Abbot Ⓖ; Timothy Taylor
Landlord; 3 changing beers (sourced nationally) Ⓗ
On the A6 between Derby and Belper, this stone-built
Georgian inn is dramatically sited at the foot of
sandstone cliffs. An open fire at one end of the elongated
bar often adds to the ambience of the cosy interior.
Original period furniture and quarry-tiled flooring date
from the time the place was built. Regular beer festivals
and live music are an added attraction at this popular
pub. ⏚🏠♿♣🖳🐾🛜

New Mills

Beer Shed
47B Market Street, SK22 4AA
☎ (01663) 742005
3 changing beers (sourced locally; often Rock Mill,
Torride) Ⓗ
The first micropub in this town is handily situated in the
centre close to New Mills Central railway station and bus
station. The layout is unusual – it has a very small
frontage but a long and narrow interior with a squeeze
past the bar, and a small downstairs room. The three
changing beers include some from local micros, in
addition to six KeyKeg fonts and German Flensburger
lager on draught. The cheerful, intimate atmosphere
makes for a pleasant drinking experience. Q⇌🚶🖳🐾

Rock Mill Brewery
Unit 1B, Rock Mill Lane, SK22 3BN (behind carpentry
workshop off top of Union Rd)
☎ (01633) 743999
4 changing beers (sourced locally; often Rock Mill) Ⓗ
Opened in 2018, the bar is located within the secluded
RB Pine Joinery courtyard. The enterprise started up in an
adjacent building as a small craft brewery producing
traditional-style English ales and a few speciality beers.
The small bar now sits in the old garage premises next
door, with seating above the original pits where
mechanics previously examined the cars. Three to four
Rock Mill cask beers are sold plus a keg beer, Flensburger
lager, cider and wine. Walkers and dogs are welcome.
Q🌣⇌🚶🖳🐾

Newbold

Nag's Head Inn Ⓛ
37 Newbold Village, S41 8RJ
☎ (01246) 297446
Sharp's Doom Bar; 5 changing beers (often Ashover,
Pheasantry, Shiny) Ⓗ
Built in 1760, this inn is Grade II listed, retaining its
central bar layout, surrounded by four separate rooms,
one of them with an open fire. Another historic building
lies directly behind; also Grade II listed, access to the
medieval Eyre Chapel is through the car park. Adjoining
this is the Newbold Observatory, which has public open
evenings. There is a Tuesday discount on cask ales, and
traditional cider is available in the summer months.
⏚🌣♣🚶🖳🐾

Newton Solney

Brickmakers Arms
9-11 Main Street, DE15 0SJ (on B5008, opp jct with
Trent Lane)
☎ 07525 220103 ⊕ brickmakersarms.pub

Burton Bridge Sovereign Gold, Bridge Bitter, Stairway
to Heaven, Top Dog Stout; 1 changing beer (sourced
regionally) Ⓗ
This cosy local at the end of an 18th-century terrace of
cottages was converted into a pub in the early 19th
century for workers at a nearby brickworks. It features a
narrow central bar leading at one end to a room served
through a hatch, and at the other to an impressive oak-
panelled room. The street entrance hallway houses a
small bring-and-take library, beyond which is a function/
meeting room. Monday is quiz night, Tuesday is bingo
and Thursday poker. Q⏚🌣♣🚶🖳(V3)🐾🛜

Ockbrook

Cross Keys ✅
Green Lane, DE72 3SE
☎ (01332) 662308 ⊕ crosskeys-ockbrook.co.uk
Marston's Pedigree; Sharp's Doom Bar; 2 changing
beers Ⓗ
A traditional village pub with a quirky character stocking
a selection of five real ales and one real cider. The bar
has a low-beamed ceiling, a darts playing area, several
screens for sports TV and a wood-burner for the winter
months. Events include karaoke, quizzes and theme
nights. Stone-baked pizza features on the home-made
food menu. Outside there is a small terrace with seating
at the front and an enclosed garden and play space to
the side. ⏚🌣🍴♣🚶🖳(9,9A)🐾🛜

Royal Oak Ⓛ
55 Green Lane, DE72 3SE
☎ (01332) 662378 ⊕ royaloakockbrook.com
Draught Bass; 4 changing beers Ⓗ
An attractive 18th-century pub with a number of small
rooms. Since 1953 it has been run by the Wilson family,
who have brought about many improvements while
retaining the original character and features. Excellent
home-cooked food is served every day. A large function
room allows the venue to host many community and
public events including live music and open mic nights.
Outside there are two pleasant gardens, one with an
enclosed play area for children.
Q⏚🌣🍴♿♣🚶🖳(9,9A) 🐾🛜

Old Tupton

Tupton Tap Ⓛ
Derby Road, S42 6LA (on main A61 Chesterfield to
Derby road)
☎ (01246) 862180
Oakham Citra; house beer (by Ashover); 5 changing
beers Ⓗ
After a period of closure, this place, originally called the
Royal Oak, was reopened following extensive
refurbishment by the Old Poets Corner. The pub has a
central bar with a large drinking lobby serving both
entrances, and there are cosy drinking areas and corners
situated around the bar. It now sports eight handpulls,
traditional cider and craft beers, with regular beers from
Ashover Brewery. Friday is pizza night.
⏚🌣🍴♣🚶🖳(51) 🐾

Openwoodgate

Black Bull's Head
2 Kilburn Lane, DE56 0SF
☎ 07432 687239
4 changing beers (sourced regionally; often Blue
Monkey, Castle Rock, Dancing Duck) Ⓗ
A two-roomed former Greene King pub, now a free
house serving many real ales and ciders. It offers a warm

welcome in pleasant surroundings, with real fires in the winter. The walls are adorned with historic photographs and newspaper clippings of local and national interest, and one wall is dedicated to the RAF.
Q🕏🏵🍴♣♿P🚆🐾🛜

Repton

Boot 🅛 ✅

12 Boot Hill, DE65 6FT
☎ (01283) 346047 ⊕ thebootatrepton.co.uk
Boot Clod Hopper, Bitter, ESB; 4 changing beers (sourced regionally) 🅗
Close to the Repton Cross at the centre of the village, this inn has been brought back to life by the local Bespoke pub company with a refurbishment and the addition of an on-site microbrewery. Up to six of the real ales on the bar are brewed here. There are two main rooms, one devoted to dining. Accommodation is available.
🕏🏵🍴🛏🍺♿P🚆(V3)🐾🛜

Ripley

Beehive Inn

151 Peasehill, DE5 3JN
☎ (01773) 749593
Blue Monkey Infinity; Dancing Duck Dark Drake 🅗**, Abduction; Draught Bass; 3 changing beers (sourced nationally)** 🅖
Half a mile from the town centre, this three-roomed free house is a hub for local rugby and pub league teams. It has welcoming fires in winter, Sky TV in the public bar and a large, pleasant beer garden. The Honeypot Bar in a building at the top of the garden has six real ales plus ciders. Q🕏🏵♣♿P🚆(9.1,9.3)🐾🛜

Talbot

1 Butterley Hill, DE5 3LT
8 changing beers (sourced nationally) 🅗
In a traditional Victorian flat-iron-shaped building, the Talbot is blissfully free of music, instead preferring the sounds of conversation, laughter and traditional games. It offers an excellent selection of real ales pulled from casks stored on an original stone stillage. Look for the locally turned pump handles in various designs. Bar snacks are usually available. This welcoming and popular place, with a real fire in winter, was local CAMRA branch Pub of the Year in 2019. Q🕏♿♣♿P🚆🐾

Tom Said

1 Well Street, DE5 3AE
5 changing beers 🅖
Ripley's latest micropub, just off Oxford Street in the former Ripley Dry Cleaners shop. It is small and cosy with a good atmosphere and room for outside seating in fine weather. Five cask and four keg ales are on offer, with a large range of craft cans and bottles, plus ciders and assorted spirits. Q♿♿🚆🐾

Rosliston

Bull's Head

Burton Road, DE12 8JU (NW edge of village)
☎ (01283) 762642
Draught Bass; Marston's Pedigree; 2 changing beers (sourced regionally) 🅗
Late 19th-century brick-built free house with a comfortable public bar and smart, cosy lounge, both featuring open fires and beamed ceilings. There is also a large function room in a converted stable block. A collection of china bulls is displayed behind the bar, and intricate encased models of a Burton union brewing

system can be found in both the public bar and the function room. Filled cobs with chips are available at Sunday lunchtime. The National Forest Rosliston Forestry Centre is about half a mile away.
🕏🏵🅓♣♿P🚆(22)🐾🛜

Sawley

Sawley Junction 🅛

176 Tamworth Road, NG10 3JU
☎ 07966 757407
5 changing beers (sourced regionally) 🅖
This one-roomed family-run pub has been renovated to a high standard. Already a popular local, it has the feel of a snug station bar and is wood-panelled, with railway memorabilia adorning the walls. Four to five gravity-fed cask ales are available, rotating on a regular basis, as well as a variety of real ciders and craft ales. Bar snacks, freshly made sandwiches, savouries and hot drinks are served throughout the day.
Q🕏🍴🚆(Long Eaton)♿P🚆🐾

Scarcliffe

Horse & Groom

Mansfield Road, S44 6ST
☎ (01246) 823152
Black Sheep Best Bitter; Greene King Abbot; Morland Old Golden Hen; Sharp's Doom Bar; 3 changing beers 🅗
Up to seven beers are stocked at this charming rural two-room pub, along with a choice of cider. This inn, over 500 years old, has been owned and run by the same family for more than 20 years. The locally made pork pies should be tried. Dogs and young families are welcome in the large conservatory. Buses stop right outside, there is a large car park to the front, and accommodation is available on-site in a couple of cottages.
Q🕏🏵🛏♿P🚆(53)🐾

South Normanton

Devonshire Arms

137 Market Street, DE55 2AA
☎ (01773) 810748 ⊕ TheDevonshireArms.pub
Sarah Hughes Dark Ruby Mild; Theakston XB; 4 changing beers (often Little Critters, Moody Fox, Thornbridge) 🅗
Multi-roomed and a genuine free house, the bar offers up to six real ales and two real ciders or perries. Customers' suggestions are used to determine some of the guest ales. Home-cooked food is served lunchtimes every day, including a popular Sunday carvery (booking is recommended). Sports TV is an attraction. A regular winner of local CAMRA Pub of the Year.
🕏🅓♣♿P🚆(9.1)🐾🛜

Market Tavern 🅛 ✅

41 High Street, DE55 2BP
5 changing beers (often Blue Monkey, Marble, Thornbridge) 🅗
A two-roomed micropub, once a charity shop and now lovingly renovated. Located on the marketplace, this establishment offers up to five changing beers, usually from local breweries, and three traditional ciders. Dogs and children are welcome at all times. A small selection of filled rolls is available at weekends, and food can be brought in. Cask Marque accredited.
Q🕏♣♿P🚆🚆(9.1)🐾🛜

Sutton cum Duckmanton

Arkwright Arms 🅛

Chesterfield Road, S44 5JG (on A632 between Chesterfield and Bolsover)
☎ (01246) 232053 ⊕ arkwrightarms.co.uk
Greene King Abbot; Whim Arbor Light; changing beers ℍ

There is always a warm welcome at this Brewers' Tudor-fronted free house. A changing range of 10 guest ales, many from local micros, is complemented by 12 ciders and four perries. Beer festivals are held at Easter and bank holidays, with mini events throughout the year. Quality food is served until mid-evening Monday to Saturday, and until mid-afternoon on Sunday. The spacious beer garden has play equipment for children. A winner of numerous CAMRA awards, including East Midlands Cider Pub of the Year and local CAMRA Pub of the Year. ➄❀❂◗⅄♣➔●P🚇🐾

Wardlow Mires

Three Stags' Heads ★ 🅛

Mires Lane, SK17 8RW (jct A623/B6465)
☎ (01298) 872268
Abbeydale Deception, Absolution; house beer (by Abbeydale); 1 changing beer (sourced regionally) ℍ

A quaint 300-year-old inn with two small rooms, stone-flagged floors and low ceilings. Unspoilt, it is one of the few outlets in the area identified by CAMRA as having a nationally important historic pub interior. An ancient range warms the bar and it has house dogs, one of which gave its name to the house beer (Black Lurcher). Traditional cider is only available in summer.
Q❀♣AP🚇(173) 🐾⏉

Whaley Bridge

Whaley Nook

20 Old Road, SK23 7HR (turn up Old Road opp Co-op; bar is on left)
Abbeydale Deception; 3 changing beers (sourced locally; often Eyam) ℍ

Following the closure of the Whaley Brewery, the tap reopened as the Whaley Nook. It has a cosy front bar and a small separate room to the rear. Four handpumps offer three changing beers from breweries in the area, typically including Eyam Real Ale Company, and a regular beer. A loyalty card system operates during the week. An interesting selection of gins from far and wide is also stocked. Works of art by local artists are displayed on the walls and are for sale. ➔●🚇(199,61)🐾⏉

Whitehough

Old Hall Inn 🅛

SK23 6EJ (nr Chinley, 750yds off B6062)
☎ (01663) 750529 ⊕ old-hall-inn.co.uk
8 changing beers (sourced locally; often Abbeydale, Big Stone Beer, RedWillow) ℍ

The 16th-century Whitehough Hall forms part of this quintessential country inn, which has previously won CAMRA regional Pub of the Year, the Great British Pub award for best cask pub in the region for several years, and is a regular Guide entry. Eight ales, including seven regularly changing guests from quality micros nearby, complement those available at the adjacent Paper Mill Inn (under the same ownership). A popular menu features dishes using local produce. Well-attended beer festivals run in September.
➄❀❂◗⅄♣➔P🚇(189,190) 🐾⏉

Brickmakers Arms, Newton Solney (Photo: Mike Gibson)

CASK MARQUE – WHO ARE WE?

Cask Marque was founded in 1998 by Paul Nunny, a former Director of Adnams, to improve the quality of cask ale in pubs and raise industry standards.

"We are a not-for-profit organisation set up to ensure that the cask ale you drink in pubs is in perfect condition. Today the Directors are made up of representatives from large and small breweries, pub companies and trade bodies, all engaged in continuing to drive beer quality."

In just over twenty years Cask Marque has:

- Accredited over 10,000 pubs for the quality of their beer
- Visited over 20,000 pubs each year
- Improved standards of cellarmanship through training, qualifications, and star ratings
- Ensured that your beer in the glass is cellar-cool by installing ale python cooling systems
- Communicated what Cask Marque stands for with 77% of consumers recognising the plaque (YouGov 2018)
- Launched the Cask Finder app to find Cask Marque pubs with over 60,000 users per month
- Championed cask ales through the annual Cask Report

Look out for our Marque in the Guide and you are guaranteed to find a great pint of cask ale ✅

Pubs who apply for a Cask Marque accreditation receive two unannounced visits per year from one of 60 assessors who are qualified brewers or senior technical services personnel. On a visit they sample up to six cask ales in the glass and check for temperature, aroma, appearance, and taste. In addition, new pubs must pass an 11-point check list to establish their beer cellar rating.

Use the free Cask Finder app and you are guaranteed to receive a great pint of cask ale

To find out more about Cask Marque visit **www.cask-marque.co.uk** and join us in championing beer quality in the glass

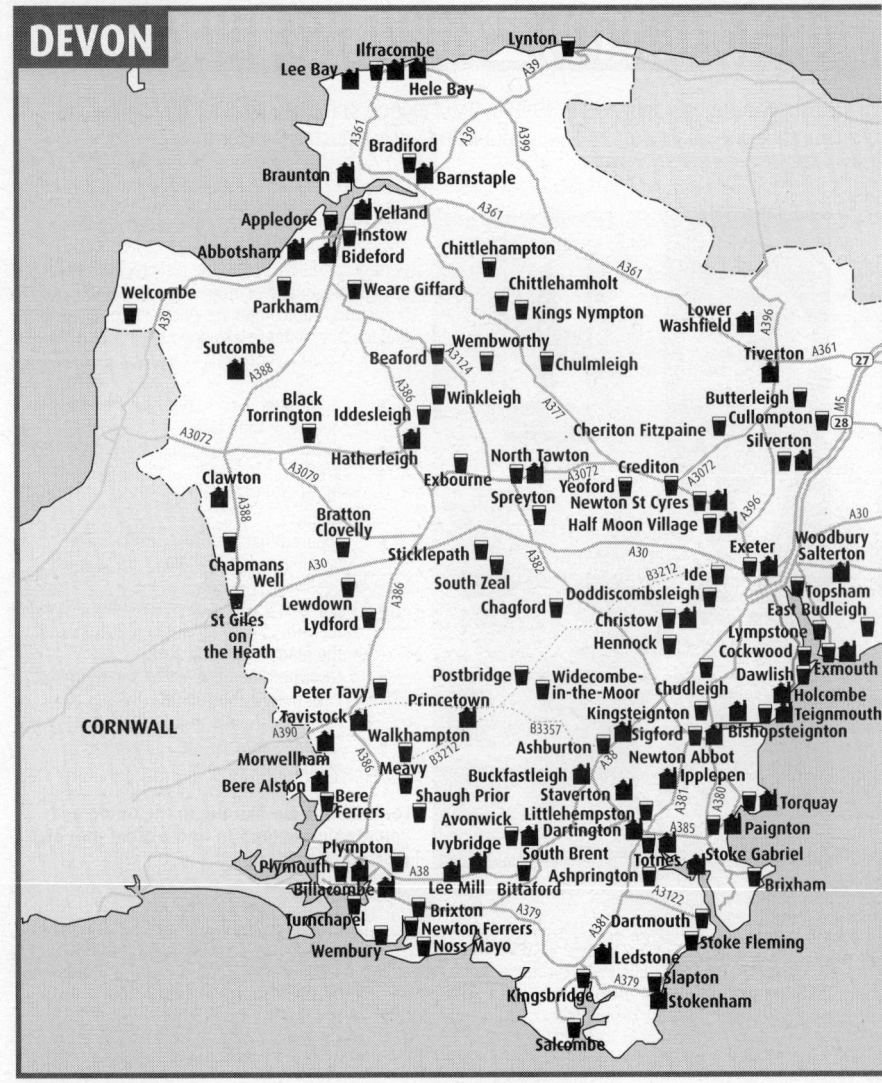

DEVON

CORNWALL

Appledore

Champ 🗌

Meeting Street, EX39 1RJ (just off Appledore Quay)
☎ (01237) 421662
Clearwater Expedition Ale; 3 changing beers (sourced locally) 🖽
Cosy and quirky evening pub – the brewery tap for nearby Clearwater Brewery, with up to four of its ales generally available on tap. The Champ is renowned for live music which features regularly on Fridays and Saturdays, together with popular open-mic evenings on Tuesdays, Wednesdays and Thursdays (advertised on social media), including blues and folk nights. Customers are welcome to bring in food to eat on the premises, while a nearby public car park accommodates camper vans overnight for a modest fee. 🌮♿♣🛏🚌🖵🐾🛜

Ashburton

Old Exeter Inn 🗌

26 West Street, TQ13 7DU (on main road through centre of Ashburton, opp church)
☎ (01364) 652013 ⊕ oldexeterinn.com
3 changing beers 🖸
The oldest pub in the town, originally built in 1130 to house workers constructing the nearby church, with additions in the 17th century. This friendly inn has seating areas either side of the entrance, leading to a wood-panelled L-shaped bar, with a granite shelf behind for serving the gravity-fed ales. There are also two rear seating areas and a flagstone-floored corridor that takes you to the lovely secluded walled garden at the back. Local cider and perry are sold.
Q🌮♿🛏🍴🛏🖵(88,X38) 🐾🛜

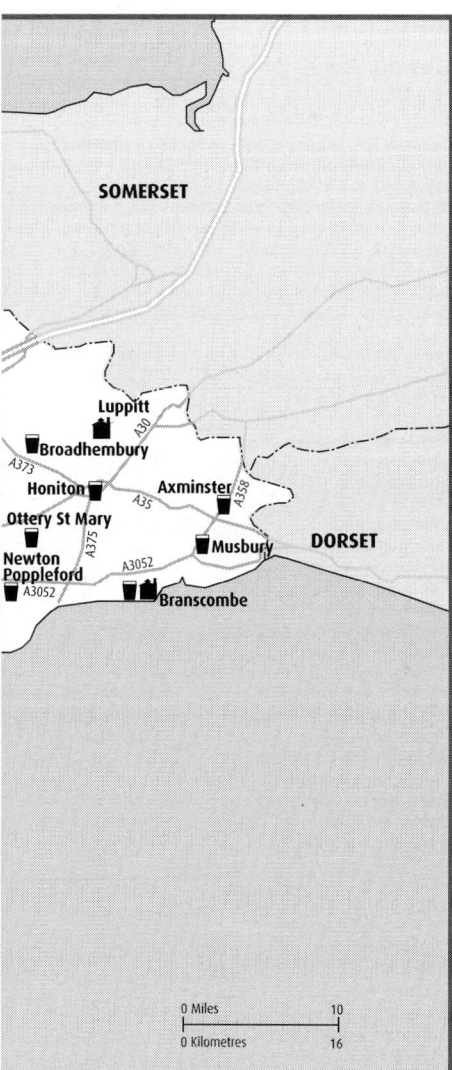

Avonwick

Avon Inn 🄻

TQ10 9NB

☎ (01364) 73475 ∰ avon-inn.org.uk

Dartmoor Legend, Jail Ale; Draught Bass; 1 changing beer (sourced regionally) Ⓗ

At the crossroads in the centre of the village, the inn is at the heart of the community, with various events regularly taking place including quiz nights, barbecues and live music. The lounge is now the restaurant. Alongside the ale, up to 10 ciders are stocked from Ashridge, Countryman, Sandford Orchards and Westons. The village is served by Country Bus number 91 between Plymouth and Totnes. Closing times may vary depending on custom. ⌂✿🍴♿🅰♣🌢🅿🚌(91)❀

Axminster

Axminster Inn 🄻 ✅

Silver Street, EX13 5AH

☎ (01297) 34947 ∰ axminsterinn.pub

Palmers Copper Ale, IPA, Dorset Gold, Tally Ho!; 1 changing beer (sourced locally) Ⓗ

A friendly traditional pub, lying just off the town centre, with a real log fire for the winter months and a lovely enclosed beer garden to enjoy in the warmer weather. A Palmers house, it offers a good range of the brewery's real ales. Live music is featured. Free Wi-Fi is available and there is a skittle alley and dartboard. Children are welcome up until 7pm. ⌂✿🚆♣🌢🅿❀🛜

Beaford

Globe Inn 🄻

Exeter Road, EX19 8LR (on main road, A3124, in centre of village)

☎ (01805) 603920

3 changing beers (sourced regionally) Ⓗ

Traditional and cosy country inn, with a particular passion for real ale and craft beers to suit all tastes. Three changing and mainly local ales are usually available, alongside a comprehensive drinks menu that includes more than 40, often legendary, bottled and bottle-conditioned beers from around the globe. Proud of its environmental credentials, the pub also offers a seasonal and attractively priced food menu, which uses the best of ingredients from producers in the area. Local CAMRA branch Pub of the Year 2020. Q⌂✿🚐🍴♣🌢🚌❀🛜

Ashprington

Durant Arms

TQ9 7UP (exit Totnes on A381; left turn signposted after 1,500yds)

☎ (01803) 732240 ∰ durantarms.co.uk

Noss Beer Works Church Ledge; Otter Amber Ⓗ**; 2 changing beers (sourced regionally)** Ⓗ/Ⓖ

A lovely family-run pub in the heart of a traditional Devon village. The building is 18th century, with wood-burning fires, traditional furnishings and slate floors. There is a seating area outside to the front and a picturesque garden to the rear. The pub is both family- and dog-friendly, with rooms available for B&B. A variety of themed events are hosted throughout the year. It has a good reputation for quality beer and fresh, home-cooked food (served Tue to Fri). Popular with walkers and cyclists it was originally part of the Sharpham estate until 1940, and is close to Sharpham Vineyard on the River Dart, on the South Devon national cycle route no. 28 and the Dart Valley scenic walking trail from Totnes. Q⌂✿🚐🍴🌢🅿🚌(B2C)❀🛜

Bere Ferrers

Olde Plough Inn 🄻

Fore Street, PL20 7JG (close to church and river)

☎ (01822) 840358 ∰ theoldeploughinn.co.uk

Hunters Half Bore; 3 changing beers (sourced locally; often Roam, Salcombe, Summerskills) Ⓗ

This 16th-century village inn has outstanding views over the River Tavy from the beer garden, and is only a 15-minute walk from the station on the picturesque Tamar Valley line. Inside, there are flagstone floors, exposed stonework walls, beamed ceilings, real fires and a welcoming atmosphere. Acoustic music, jam sessions, quizzes and themed food nights take place. Up to three guest beers are sourced from local and national breweries, alongside bottled beers from Bere Brewery. Food is served to suit all ages and appetites. Q⌂✿🍴🚆♣🌢🚌(87)❀🛜

Bittaford

Horse & Groom L
Exeter Road, PL21 0EL
☎ (01752) 892358
Dartmoor Jail Ale; house beer (by Hunters); 3 changing beers (sourced locally; often Exeter, South Hams, Summerskills) Ⓗ
A family-owned pub run by a real ale enthusiast, with good home-cooked food and seven pumps, two dedicated to real cider. The other pumps predominantly offer ales from regional breweries in south Devon and Cornwall. Third-pint tapas are available. There is a long bar and a separate dining space, with pictures of the former Moorhaven Hospital on the wall. A beer festival and a cider and sausage festival are hosted during the year, supporting charities in the area. Local CAMRA branch Pub of the Year 2020. ⬤⬤⬤⬤⬤⬤⬤⬤⬤P🚲(X38)⬤

Black Torrington

Black River Inn L
EX21 5PT
☎ (01409) 231888 ⊕ blackriverinn.co.uk
Hanlons Brewers Blend; 3 changing beers (sourced locally) Ⓗ
Village pub with a growing reputation for real ale and good food. Three regularly changing beers are kept, together with two local ciders. The tastefully decorated public bar with adjacent dining area leads through to a separate restaurant (which can also be used as a function room). Outside, the attractive garden has views over the Torridge Valley and surrounding countryside. Near to both the Tarka Trail and Ruby Way, the pub is popular with walkers and cyclists. Bar snacks only on Tuesday and Wednesday. Q⬤⬤⬤⬤⬤P⬤⬤🛜

Bradiford

Windsor Arms L
55 Bradiford, EX31 4AD (on main road through village, approximately ½ mile N of Pilton)
☎ (01271) 343583
GT Ales Thirst of Many; 1 changing beer (sourced nationally; often Greene King, Timothy Taylor, Wadworth) Ⓗ
A community-oriented and friendly village inn within easy walking distance of Barnstaple. Two changing real ales are kept, with one of these invariably from nearby GT Ales. Good, freshly-cooked and locally sourced food is served Friday to Sunday in the separate lounge bar. A function room, with skittle alley, pool table and dartboard, lies to the rear. ⬤⬤⬤⬤⬤🚲⬤🛜

Branscombe

Fountain Head Inn L
EX12 3BG (in main street, 1 mile S of A3052)
☎ (01297) 680359 ⊕ fountainheadinn.com
Branscombe Branoc, Golden Fiddle; 1 changing beer (sourced locally) Ⓗ
Set in a beautiful coastal valley, this old, walker-friendly pub is at the west end of one of England's longest villages. Ancient features such as the inglenook fireplace, wood panelling and flagstone floors greet customers, while the bar offers Branscombe Vale ales and ciders. Good-value home cooked food is served, with breakfast also on offer Monday to Saturday in summer. A beer festival is held on the closest weekend to the longest day. Q⬤⬤⬤⬤⬤⬤P🚲(899)⬤

Bratton Clovelly

Clovelly Inn L ✓
EX20 4JZ (between A30 and A3079) SX464919
☎ (01837) 871447 ⊕ clovellyinn.co.uk
Dartmoor IPA, Jail Ale; Sharp's Doom Bar; 1 changing beer (sourced nationally) Ⓗ
Dating back to the 18th century and with the bar featuring an oak fireplace lintel inscribed 1789, this truly authentic rural Devon pub lies at the heart of the local community. The cosy main bar, with a large wood-burning stove, is complemented by two separate dining areas (it's advisable to book in the evenings) and a games room. Three real ales are kept, with Sam's

REAL ALE BREWERIES

Art Brew ✔ Sutcombe
Barnaby's Staverton
Barum 🍺 Barnstaple
Bays Paignton
Beer Engine 🍺 Newton St Cyres
Bere ✔ Bere Alston
Black Tor Christow
Branscombe Branscombe
Bridgetown Totnes
Buckland Bideford
Checkstone 🍺 Exmouth
Clearwater Bideford
Combe ✔ Ilfracombe
Cottage Beer Project Tiverton (NEW)
Country Life Abbotsham
Crossed Anchors 🍺 Exmouth
Dartmoor Princetown
Devil's Pleasure Sigford (NEW)
Devon Earth Buckfastleigh
Exe Valley Silverton
Exeter ✔ Exeter
Fat Belly Ilfracombe
Fat Pig 🍺 Exeter
Grampus 🍺 Lee Bay
GT Braunton
Hanlons Half Moon Village
Hatherland Lower Washfield (NEW)
Holsworthy Clawton
Hunters Ipplepen
Isca Holcombe
Ivybridge ✔ Ivybridge
Madrigal ✔ Hele Bay
Morwell Morwellham
New Devon Exeter
New Lion ✔ Dartington
Noss Beer Works Lee Mill
Otter ✔ Luppitt
Platform 5 Torquay
Powderkeg Woodbury Salterton
Red Rock ✔ Bishopsteignton
Riviera Stoke Gabriel
Roam ✔ Plymouth
Salcombe ✔ Ledstone
South Hams Stokenham
Stannary ✔ Tavistock
Steel Brew ✔ Plymouth
Summerskills Plymouth: Billacombe
Tally Ho! 🍺 Hatherleigh
Taw Valley North Tawton
Teignmouth Teignmouth
Teignworthy Newton Abbot
Topsham ✔ Exeter
Totnes 🍺 Totnes
TQ South Brent
Turk's Head 🍺 Exeter (NEW)
Yelland Manor Yelland

Medium cider also stocked in summer. Good home-cooked food is served seven days a week.
ﾇ❄◗ﾆゐⒶ♣ⅢPﾖ(633) ❀

Brixham

Queen's Arms Ⓛ ✅
31 Station Hill, TQ5 8BN (from Brixham Library go up Church Hill East, then up Station Hill)
☎ (01803) 852074 ● thequeensarmsbrixham.co.uk
House beer (by Teignworthy); 5 changing beers (sourced nationally; often Branscombe) Ⓗ
This single-bar end-of-terrace inn has a well deserved reputation for the quality of its six beers and multiple real ales. The pub has a friendly atmosphere with a strong community ethos and, for cold winter nights, wood-burning stoves. Good-value Sunday lunches and Monday evening meals feature, plus live music at weekends. A charity beer festival is hosted in early December with over 50 real ales and ciders.
ﾇ❄◗♣ⅢPﾖ(17)

Brixton

Foxhound Inn Ⓛ
Kingsbridge Road, PL8 2AH
☎ (01752) 880271 ● foxhoundinn.co.uk
Courage Directors; house beer (by Summerskills); 3 changing beers (sourced nationally; often Caledonian, Courage, Summerskills) Ⓗ
An 18th-century former coaching house in a rural village just east of Plymouth, with two separate bars and a small restaurant. Traditional English meals are served daily, featuring locally sourced ingredients. Look out for Red Coat, an ale crafted by the landlord, among four guest ales. A monthly charity quiz night is held. Brixton has a frequent daytime bus service. Qﾇ❄◗ゐⒶ♣ⅢPﾖ❀

Broadhembury

Drewe Arms Ⓛ
EX14 3NF
☎ (01404) 841267 ● drewearmsinn.co.uk
Bays Devon Dumpling; Dartmoor Jail Ale; Otter Ale, Amber; 1 changing beer (sourced locally) Ⓗ
Grade II-listed 16th-century thatched pub with a secluded garden, set in a picturesque estate village of cob and limewashed cottages within the Blackdown Hills. There are low-beamed ceilings and uneven floor levels throughout the many rooms. This is a friendly and welcoming family-run venue with the emphasis on local real ales and produce. Good-value food is served Tuesday to Saturday (plus Monday in the summer) and lunchtime on Sunday, with a takeaway menu also available.
Qﾇ❄◗♣ⅢP❀

Butterleigh

Butterleigh Inn Ⓛ
The Green, EX15 1PN (opp church) SS9746108212
☎ (01884) 855433 ● butterleighinn.co.uk
4 changing beers (sourced regionally) Ⓗ
In this small, quaint village, hidden along narrow country lanes, the Butterleigh Inn has now been in the Guide for 35 years. The regular customers create a great atmosphere, with diverse conversation. There are two rooms around the bar, with a modern dining room at the back. The outside covered patio has grapevines in summer. Good-value home-cooked food is served, with a carvery Sunday lunchtime. There is a choice of up to four real ales and three ciders. Qﾇ❄◗♣ⅢP❀🎓

Chagford

Globe Inn Ⓛ ✅
9 High Street, TQ13 8AJ
☎ (01647) 433485 ● theglobeinnchagford.co.uk
Dartmoor IPA; Otter Bitter Ⓗ; **1 changing beer (sourced locally)** Ⓗ/Ⓖ
Overlooking the parish church, the Globe was once a coaching inn and coopery. The pub has become a focal point of this historic Dartmoor stannary town, providing good food, music, a cinema club and many other events. There is a splendid public bar, a separate lounge bar and a dining room, with large open log fires. A small courtyard garden is at the rear and parking is nearby. The ciders are Sam's and Westons Old Rosie.
ﾇ❄◗◗Ⅲﾖ(173,178) ❀🎓

Ring o' Bells Ⓛ
44 The Square, TQ13 8AH
☎ (01647) 432466 ● ringobellschagford.co.uk
Dartmoor IPA, Jail Ale; Otter Bitter Ⓗ
A 16th-century inn in the centre of the town, although archives reveal there had been an inn on this site well before this. Both the bar, comfortably furnished with bench and booth seating, and the separate dining room to the rear, have open fireplaces. A passageway leads to a pretty walled garden with plenty of seating and a covered smoker's area. There is parking nearby.
ﾇ❄◗◗♣ⅢPﾖ(173,178) ❀🎓

Chapmans Well

Arscott Arms Ⓛ
PL15 9SG
☎ (01409) 211113 ● arscottarms.co.uk
2 changing beers (sourced locally) Ⓗ
Approximately halfway between Holsworthy and Launceston, this welcoming roadside pub was tastefully renovated and refurbished to a high standard prior to reopening in 2018. Since then it has developed a growing reputation for its well-kept ales and good food. The front bar leads through to an attractive dining area, while outside there is a pleasant beer garden with decking and a good-sized car park. Locally brewed Holsworthy Ales feature regularly. Qﾇ❄◗Ⓐ♣P❀🎓

Cheriton Fitzpaine

Ring of Bells Ⓛ
EX17 4JG
☎ (01363) 860111 ● theringofbells.com
2 changing beers (sourced regionally) Ⓗ
A thatched Grade II-listed pub in the heart of this picturesque village, by the parish church. Two changing beers are normally available at the single bar. Fine food is served lunchtimes and evenings, but those seeking a snack, a quiet pint by the fire or a few drinks with friends in the garden are equally welcome. Binka the landlady has made this a destination for everyone, including children and dogs. ﾇ❄◗♣ⅢP❀

Chittlehamholt

Exeter Inn Ⓛ
EX37 9NS
☎ (01769) 540281 ● exeterinn.co.uk
Exmoor Fox; Otter Ale; 2 changing beers (sourced locally) Ⓗ
Traditional 16th-century thatched inn on the old road from Barnstaple to Exeter. There are four separate dining areas serving locally sourced, home-cooked food from a seasonal menu. The pub retains many original

architectural features including two real fires, one of which has a bread oven, while various photographs of historical interest adorn the walls. Outside there is a pleasant south-facing patio. Opening hours vary, check the website. Q✿❀❍❑♪♣♠P❀❄❃

Chittlehampton

Bell Inn 🅛

The Square, EX37 9QL (opp St Hieritha's parish church) SS636254

☎ (01769) 540368 ⊕ thebellatchittlehampton.co.uk

Exmoor Ale; 6 changing beers (sourced regionally) 🄷

In the same family since 1975 and popular with locals and visitors alike, this busy village inn celebrated 26 continuous years of Guide inclusion in 2021. An impressive selection of real ales is kept, with up to nine regularly available. The bar area is notable for its sporting memorabilia, with good-value home-cooked food served both here and in the adjoining restaurant. Local CAMRA branch Pub of the Year 2019.

✿❀❄❍❑♪❆▲♣♠P❑(658,859)❀❃

Christow

Teign House Inn 🅛

Teign Valley Road, EX6 7PL

☎ (01647) 252286 ⊕ teignhouseinn.co.uk

Otter Bitter; 3 changing beers (sourced regionally; often Black Tor, Hunters, Powderkeg) 🄷

On the edge of Dartmoor in the scenic Teign Valley you'll find this welcoming, atmospheric country pub, with exposed beams and a warming log fire in winter. It is supported strongly by the locals, with a large garden attracting families; the adjoining field has space for caravans, campervans and campers. There's live music every third Tuesday evening and every fourth Sunday afternoon. Great food is served, all home cooked, with a special Thai menu, also available to take away.

Q✿❀❍❑♪❆▲♣♠P❑(360)❀❃

Chudleigh

Bishop Lacy Inn 🅛

52-53 Fore Street, TQ13 0HY

☎ (01626) 854585

3 changing beers (sourced regionally; often Black Tor, Greene King, South Hams) 🄷/🄶

A warm welcome is guaranteed from an ebullient landlady to this Grade II-listed premises opposite the church and named after the Bishop of Exeter (1420-1455). The left-hand bar is dominated by a magnificent fireplace which was originally used to cure ham and where most of the locals congregate. Witch dolls are suspended around the bar and you are challenged to ask the landlady why! Child- and dog-friendly throughout, with Sambuca the pub dog greeting well-behaved fellow canines. Q✿❀❍❑♪❆▲♣♠P❑(39,182)❀❃

Chulmleigh

Old Court House

South Molton Street, EX18 7BW

☎ (01769) 580045 ⊕ oldcourthouseinn.co.uk

Dartmoor IPA; Butcombe Original; 1 changing beer (sourced regionally) 🄷

Charles I stayed here in 1634 when he held court (hence the name) and this is commemorated with an original coat of arms in one of the bedrooms, while a replica hangs above the fireplace in the main bar. Today this friendly, cosy local features two regular real ales, usually joined by a guest beer in summer. Good home-cooked food can be taken in the bar area, in the separate dining room, or in the pretty cobbled courtyard garden.

✿❀❄❍❑♪♣❆♣P❑(377)❀❃

Cockwood

Anchor Inn 🅛 ✅

EX6 8RA (just off A379, outside Starcross, next to Cockwood harbour) SX9756480692

☎ (01626) 890203 ⊕ anchorinncockwood.com

Dartmoor Jail Ale; 2 changing beers (sourced locally) 🄷

On a picturesque harbour, this 450-year-old inn and former seaman's mission has many old settles, timber panelling, low beams and snugs, with an impressive display of old nautical memorabilia. It offers an extensive award-winning seafood menu, with mussels a speciality. Up to five ales are usually available. Reportedly haunted by a friendly ghost and his dog, this is a really atmospheric Devon gem. Close to the main GWR line, it is a steam train spotters' paradise. Parking is limited and the bus stop is over the bridge.

Q✿❀❍❑♪❆▲♣♠P❑(2)❀

Ship Inn 🅛 ✅

Church Road, EX6 8NU (just off A379, outside Starcross)

☎ (01626) 890373 ⊕ shipinncockwood.co.uk

Dartmoor Jail Ale; St Austell Tribute, Proper Job; 2 changing beers (sourced nationally) 🄷

A busy family-run pub, close to the picturesque harbour at Cockwood, with a large beer garden with views of the estuary, and a log fire in winter. Popular with drinkers and diners alike, it offers a choice of three regular ales and, usually, two rotating guests, and has an excellent menu. Meals are prepared with produce from the area where possible, including a varied choice of locally caught fish. The bus stops 100 yards across the bridge.

Q✿❀❍❑▲♣♠P❑(2)❀❃

Crediton

Duke of York

74 High Street, EX17 3JX

☎ (01363) 775289

Dartmoor IPA; 2 changing beers (sourced regionally) 🄷

A one-bar, Grade II-listed pub, re-established in 2002 as a family-run free house. It has one regular beer and one or two changing beers on offer, depending on demand – often Sharp's Atlantic or brews from Exe Valley and Bays. Sky and BT sports are televised on up to three screens. Men's and women's darts teams play here. There is a south-facing garden. The number 5 bus passes the door. ❀❍♣P❑❀❃

Cullompton

Pony & Trap 🅛 ✅

10 Exeter Hill, EX15 1DJ (on B3181 S of town)

☎ (01884) 34182

Dartmoor Jail Ale; Draught Bass; Exmoor Ale; Otter Bright; 4 changing beers (sourced regionally) 🄷

A traditional inn with good atmosphere and a mixed clientele. Many local darts and skittles teams are based here. It has a smart interior featuring a log-burner, making it cosy in winter; flowers and ornaments give it a homely feel. Up to eight real ales are on the bar including a house beer, plus three real ciders. There is a garden and seating area. Live music features once a month and pub games are played. Q❀❍♣♠❑(1)❀

Dartmouth

Cherub Inn ✓

13 Higher Street, TQ6 9RB
☎ (01803) 832571 ⊕ the-cherub.co.uk
Exeter Ferryman; St Austell Proper Job; South Hams Devon Pride; house beer (by St Austell); 1 changing beer (sourced locally) ⊞
This nautical town is famous for its Tudor buildings, and the Cherub is one of the best and oldest, a Grade II*-listed 14th-century merchant's house. The bar has many original features, with beams made from old ship's timbers, and boasts three handpumps serving local and national cask ales. An intricate winding staircase leads to the cosy restaurant and facilities on the two upper floors.
Q✿🍷◐♿≷(Kingswear) ●P🚲❀

Seven Stars

8 Smith Street, TQ6 9QR
☎ (01803) 839635 ⊕ sevenstars-dartmouth.co.uk
Dartmoor Jail Ale; 3 changing beers (sourced locally; often Exeter, Otter) ⊞
Grade II listed and near to the church, the inn reopened after an extensive refurbishment in 2017. The present building was originally two cottages which were merged in the 18th century and, with 16th- and 17th-century features, enables it to claim to be the oldest alehouse in Dartmouth. The ground floor bar is both atmospheric and contemporary, with two fireplaces, and it welcomes children and dogs. Upstairs there is a restaurant and function room, and also six ensuite rooms.
🛏◐♿≷(Kingswear) ♣●P🚲❀🛜

Dawlish

White Hart

6 Albert Street, EX7 9JY
☎ (01626) 866476
3 changing beers ⊞
Popular with drinkers, the pub serves two or three changing ales, mostly from Teignworthy Brewery. This is a single-room outlet central to the ale trail, and a friendly welcome greets old and new visitors. Local licensees have produced a Dawlish Ale Trail leaflet for 10 pubs within walking distance of each other, and all based around the beautiful Dawlish Water and central area. It has a welcoming winter fire. No food is served.
✿≷🚲(2) ❀

Doddiscombsleigh

NoBody Inn ✓

EX6 7PS (best approached from A38 at top of Haldon Hill)
☎ (01647) 252394 ⊕ nobodyinn.co.uk
House beer (by St Austell); 2 changing beers (sourced locally) ⊞
A venerable village inn, mainly 17th century with some later additions, full of old beams and antique furniture. There is a pub garden for the summer and a log fire in the winter. It has an extensive whisky list (more than 240) and wine list (more than 150). There are five comfortable bedrooms, and high-quality food is served every lunchtime and evening. Dogs are welcome in the bar. Only four miles from Exeter Haldon racecourse.
Q✿🛏◐P🚲(360) ❀🛜

East Budleigh

Sir Walter Raleigh Inn ⬡

22 High Street, EX9 7ED (off B3178 opp Hayes Lane)
☎ (01395) 442510
4 changing beers (sourced regionally) ⊞
Set in the middle of a delightful village, the birthplace of Sir Walter Raleigh, this free house is a truly welcoming 16th-century country inn. Good-quality local pub food is served lunchtimes and evenings in addition to four varying real ales, and up to six real ciders. Originally two cottages, the buildings were converted into a Jacobean-style hostelry, retaining the original wooden beams throughout. Q✿🛏◐♿●🚲(157)❀

Exbourne

Red Lion ⬡ ✓

High Street, EX20 3RY (200yds N of jct with A3072) SS602018
☎ (01837) 851551 ⊕ theredlionexbourne.co.uk
Dartmoor IPA, Legend; 1 changing beer (sourced regionally) Ⓖ
This friendly village venue has a well-deserved reputation for the quality and consistency of its ales and has been local CAMRA branch Pub of the Year several times in recent years. Casks are set on stillage at the end of the L-shaped bar, which is notable for the absence of handpumps, as the landlord refuses to serve draught lager. There is always good conversation to be enjoyed here. Live music also features regularly.
Q✿🛏●P🚲❀🛜

Exeter

Blue Ball Inn

Sandygate Lane, Sandygate, EX2 7JL
☎ (01392) 873401 ⊕ blueballpub.co.uk
St Austell Tribute, Proper Job; 2 changing beers ⊞
A 300-year-old thatched inn, which has recently extended the restaurant. A superb place, it has a large garden, children's play area and parking. There are usually four real ales and two real ciders on tap. Fine food, using locally sourced ingredients where possible, is served lunchtimes and evenings. This is the closest pub to Sandy Park, home of Exeter Chiefs, and four B&B rooms are available. Q✿🛏◐♿▲●P🚲❀🛜

Bowling Green ⬡ ✓

29-30 Blackboy Road, EX4 6ST
☎ (01392) 490300 ⊕ bowlinggreenexeter.co.uk
4 changing beers (sourced locally) ⊞
Originally an 18th-century establishment called The Ropemakers, this is a cosy place away from the main city centre close to Exeter City football club at St James Park. It has an extensive selection of reasonably priced pub food including pizzas and gluten-free and vegetarian options. Four real ales are available; three are rotating and come from local breweries. Live music takes place every Saturday night and Sunday afternoon, followed by a quiz in the evening.
Q✿🛏◐♿≷(St James Park) ♣●🚲❀🛜

Fat Pig ⬡

2 John Street, EX1 1BL (behind Fore St)
☎ (01392) 437217
3 changing beers (sourced locally) ⊞
Formerly the Coachmakers Arms, this Victorian corner inn was brought back to life in 2008 as a traditional pub, featuring a range of locally sourced food, including brewery-fed pork and sausages, from a herd of rare-breed pigs. There are malt whisky evenings, a Monday quiz, and homebrew competitions. It has two sister bars nearby, one of which has the Fat Pig brewery and tap bar, and distillery, producing a cider, a wide range of ales, and numerous whiskies. ◐♿≷(Central)♣●🚲❀🛜

George's Meeting House ✪

38 South Street, EX1 1ED (nr bottom of South St)
☎ (01392) 454250
Greene King IPA, Abbot; Sharp's Doom Bar; 6 changing beers ⊞

This Wetherspoon opened in 2005 having been sympathetically converted from a Unitarian chapel dating from 1760. Many of the original features remain unaltered; these include two upstairs galleries, a pulpit and stained-glass windows. A range of national, regional and local ales and five real ciders is served. Food is available throughout the day until 10pm. A newer extension, which is at the rear of the main building, leads to more seating outdoors.
Q❄️🍴🐕♿🚲≷(Central) ♟🚃🐾🛜

Great Western Hotel 🅛

St David's Station, EX4 4NU
☎ (01392) 274039 ⊕ greatwesternhotel.co.uk
9 changing beers ⊞

This hotel dates from 1840, and is close to St David's railway station. A range of up to nine ales is offered from around the country. It has a good community atmosphere, with wheelchair users most welcome and easy access to the bar and toilet. Ideal for stopovers, a variety of 35 en-suite rooms is available. The Karma restaurant serves traditional bar snacks and also has an exclusive Indian cuisine. A two-times winner of CAMRA branch Pub of the Year.
Q❄️🛏♿≷(St David's) 🚃🐾🛜

Imperial 🅛 ✪

New North Road, EX4 4AH
☎ (01392) 434050
Greene King IPA, Abbot; changing beers ⊞

This large pub features a range of beers from regional and national breweries. It was built in 1810 as a private house, converted to a hotel, and opened as a Wetherspoon in 1996. It has an orangery, and a large beer garden, which offers plenty of seating to enjoy in warmer weather. Located close to the university and near St David's railway station, there is a bus stop directly outside the premises. Regular beer festivals are held, featuring local, national and international breweries. Food is served all day. Q❄️🍴♿≷(St David's)♟P🚃🛜

Ship Inn ✪

1-3 Martins Lane, EX1 1EY
☎ (01392) 272040
Exeter Avocet; Greene King IPA, Abbot; Otter Ale; 2 changing beers (sourced regionally) ⊞

A historic city-centre venue situated along a narrow passageway between the high street and Cathedral Green. It is one of the oldest pubs in Exeter and Sir Francis Drake used to visit. Four regular ales are served along with two guests, mostly local, and up to three ciders. It offers good-value food all day, including a children's menu. Live entertainment features on Wednesdays, Fridays and Saturdays.
❄️🍴♿≷(Central) ♟🚃🐾🛜

Thatched House Inn ✪

Exwick Road, EX4 2BQ
☎ (01392) 272920 ⊕ thatchedhouse.net
Greene King Abbot; 6 changing beers (sourced locally; often Dartmoor, Hanlons, Salcombe) ⊞

This thatched building dates from the 1600s and is a community establishment next to the Exwick playing fields, opposite the Exeter College Sports Hub. It is close to the river, convenient for dog walkers, cyclists and sightseers. Seven real ales and one real cider are usually on sale, together with great-value home-cooked food featuring local ingredients and producers. On-street

parking is available nearby, and the pub is on the Stagecoach F1 and F2 bus route.
Q❄️🍴♿≷(St David's) ♟🚃🐾🛜

Topsham Brewery Taproom

Haven Road, EX2 8GR
☎ 07735 591557
3 changing beers (sourced locally) ⊞

Taproom in an attractive historic stone building on the Haven Banks side of Exeter Quay, adjacent to the brewery (which is visible from the bar). The bar is family and dog-friendly during the day but becomes lively in the evening with frequent DJs or live music. Cask beers are from the Topsham range, served on gravity – guest keg craft beers and ciders are also on sale.
🐾≷(St Thomas) 🐕

Exmouth

Bicton Inn 🅛 ✪

5 Bicton Street, EX8 2RU
☎ (01395) 272589 ⊕ bictoninn.co.uk
Dartmoor Jail Ale; Hanlons Citra IPA, Port Stout; 5 changing beers (sourced locally) ⊞

A friendly and popular back-street local, offering good beer and chat. It has twice been CAMRA branch Community Pub of the Year and is a former branch Pub of the Year. Traditional games are played such as darts, pool and euchre, and regular live music events are featured. Up to eight real ales and two ciders are normally on offer, including several LocAles. The snug is available for small gatherings and meetings. Two beer festivals are held throughout the year. ❄️≷♣♟🚃🐾🛜

First & Last Inn 🅛

10 Church Street, EX8 1PE (off B3178 Rolle St)
☎ (01395) 263275
Dartmoor Jail Ale; Otter Ale; Teignworthy Neap Tide ⊞; **2 changing beers (sourced locally; often Checkstone)** Ⓖ

Victorian outlet near the town centre with a public car park opposite. A genuine free house, it has three distinct areas and a courtyard patio with heated awnings. The Checkstone Brewery started here in 2016 and supplies the pub with changing ales from an increasing range. Games include pool and darts, and there is a skittle alley. Televised sport is prominent and there is regular live music early on Sunday evenings. Up to nine ciders are on sale including Westons Old Rosie and Thatchers Traditional. 🐕♿≷♣♟🚃(57)🐾

Grapevine

2 Victoria Road, EX8 1DL
☎ (01395) 222208 ⊕ thegrapevineexmouth.com
Crossed Anchors Bitter Exe, Devon Steam Gold; 4 changing beers ⊞

The Grapevine brewhouse is a stylish Victorian free house in the centre of Exmouth which underwent a minor refurbishment in January 2020. It is home to Crossed Anchors Brewing and Ruby Diner burger specialists. There are 12 craft taps and three bag-in-box ciders that are rotated on a regular basis. Discounts are offered on weekday afternoons. Live music takes place on most Friday and Saturday nights, and there is an open mic session on Wednesday. ❄️🍴♿≷♣♟🚃(57)🐾🛜

GWRSA Railway Club

3-5 Royal Avenue, EX8 1EN
☎ (01395) 274010
Dartmoor Jail Ale; Otter Amber; 4 changing beers ⊞

This club, with superb views of the Exe estuary, has five handpumps offering changing beers, usually one from Otter and Dartmoor breweries, the others sourced regionally, occasionally nationally. Traditional games are played and weekly live music is featured. Bar snacks are available. There is a quiz night every Thursday. CAMRA members can gain entry on production of a membership card. ♿🕮❄♣P🚃🐾🛜

Holly Tree

161 Withycombe Village Road, EX8 3AN (leave A376 at Gipsy Lane lights, then turn left)
☎ (01395) 273740
Dartmoor Jail Ale; St Austell Tribute, Proper Job; 2 changing beers Ⓗ
A popular pub selling good beer. Although owned by St Austell, the other regular ales are guest beers from a variety of breweries, sourced nationally. It is well supported by the local community, with two ladies' and two gents' darts teams, six pool teams, two euchre teams and a Sunday night quiz. Dogs are welcome at all times, and families until 7pm. Although wheelchair access is straightforward, access to the toilets can be difficult. ♿🕮♣P🚃(97)🐾

Half Moon Village

Hanlons Beer Factory & Kitchen

Hill Farm, EX5 5AE (off food caravan lay-by on A377)
☎ (01392) 851160
3 changing beers (sourced locally) Ⓗ
The bar and restaurant are on the first floor overlooking the working brewery, which has produced numerous award-winning beers since 2013. The three handpumps deliver a range of Hanlons ales including seasonals and varieties. Prescott beers also feature frequently since Hanlons purchased Prescott Ales of Cheltenham in 2019. The kitchen serves a burger-based menu suited to all ages, and champions local produce. Booking is essential, as seating is limited to 50 persons. ♿🕮🍴♿P🚃(5)🐾🛜

Hennock

Palk Arms Ⓛ

Church Road, TQ13 9QB (take B3344 from A38 to Chudleigh Knighton, and follow Hennock signs)
☎ (01626) 836584 ⊕ theonlypalkarms.co.uk
3 changing beers (often Dartmoor, Otter, Teignworthy) Ⓗ
A 16th-century free house with stunning views over the Teign valley, well worth seeking out. Popular with cyclists, dog walkers and hikers, it has car parking and camping sites very close to hand. The pub, reputed to be haunted, boasts two log-burning stoves, which adds to the warm, welcoming atmosphere. It is close to the unique local library, and is an ideal starting point to explore Hennock's mining heritage and the outstanding surrounding countryside. Q♿🕮🍴♿▲♣●P🚃🐾🛜

Honiton

Holt Ⓛ

178 High Street, EX14 1LA
☎ (01404) 47707 ⊕ theholt-honiton.com
Otter Bitter, Amber, Bright, Ale Ⓗ
The Holt has a cosy bar at street level, with a fine dining restaurant upstairs, both smartly decorated. The kitchen is in full view of the clientele. A lunch menu of tapas and home-cooked food is served in the bar. Independently owned by two sons of the Otter Brewery family, the Holt has won Gastro-Pub of the Year and Taste of the West, and currently holds two AA Rosettes. The head chef also runs popular breadmaking and cookery courses.
Q♿🕮🍴❄♣🚃🐾🛜

Iddesleigh

Duke of York

EX19 8BG (off B3217 next to church) SS570083
☎ (01837) 810253 ⊕ dukeofyorkdevon.co.uk
Adnams Broadside; Bays Topsail; 1 changing beer (sourced nationally) Ⓖ
Dating from the 15th century, this traditional thatched village inn has old beams, inglenook fires and an unfailingly friendly atmosphere. Real ales are dispensed on gravity, while cider comes from nearby Sam's. The pub is renowned for its generous portions of locally sourced, home-cooked food. It is close to the Tarka Trail, River Torridge and Stafford Moor Fishery, and there are seven en-suite rooms for visitors. A popular beer festival is held every August bank holiday weekend.
Q♿🕮🍴🛏️♿▲♣●P🚃🐾🛜

Ide

Poachers Inn Ⓛ

55 High Street, EX2 9RW (3 miles from M5 jct 31, via A30)
☎ (01392) 273847 ⊕ poachersinn.co.uk
Branscombe Branoc; Exeter Tomahawk; 4 changing beers (sourced locally; often Exeter, Palmers, Sharp's) Ⓗ
Typical busy village pub, with a friendly atmosphere, serving a varied menu of home-made locally sourced produce, including excellent-value fish & chips to eat in or take away on Wednesday evenings. Dogs are welcome in the comfortably furnished bar, with old sofas, chairs and a big log fire in winter. There is also a large beer garden overlooking the glorious Devon countryside. Usually five or six ales are on tap, with various guest beers from the West Country.
Q♿🕮🍴🛏️▲P🚃(360)🐾🛜

Ilfracombe

Hip & Pistol Ⓛ

8 St James Place, EX34 9BH
☎ (01271) 549651
Exmoor Stag; GT Ales Thirst of Many, North Coast IPA; 2 changing beers (sourced nationally) Ⓗ
This extensively modernised Georgian house has a nautical theme, with the flooring a special feature. It shows the bay around Ilfracombe in pictorial form, with local landmarks and shipwrecks plotted, together with an impressive pub logo in an image of a compass. Outside, there is a pleasant beer garden at the front. There is always a good selection of real ales, ciders and food offerings. North Devon CAMRA branch Cider Pub of the Year 2020. ♿🕮🍴♿▲●🚃(21)🐾🛜

Second Stage Ⓛ

Wilder Road, EX34 9AJ
☎ 07967 530936
Exmoor Stag; 1 changing beer (sourced locally) Ⓗ
Opposite the theatre, this old Victorian building is on the seafront and within easy reach of Ilfracombe's seaside attractions. There is a strong commitment to real ale, with the regular Exmoor Stag invariably accompanied by one from the GT Ales range. The bar area has a film-oriented theme, while the raised level pool room, with its high-quality tables, makes the pub something of a mecca for local enthusiasts. Opens from noon in summer.
♿🍴♣🚃🐾

Wellington Arms Ⓛ

66-67 High Street, EX34 9QE
☎ (01271) 864720

Fuller's London Pride; Greene King Abbot; Sharp's Doom Bar; 2 changing beers (sourced nationally) Ⓗ
Grade II-listed, this friendly town local was originally two pubs. There are separate public and lounge bars and a games room – the cosy lounge retains its original beams and large open fire. TVs and sound systems enable different channels to be shown, making the place particularly popular with sports enthusiasts. Up to five competitively priced ales are usually on tap. Regular live music sessions, quiz nights and beer festivals are held. No under-18s allowed. ✿▲♣P꠸✿🕏

Instow

Quay Inn Ⓛ ✅
EX39 4HY
☎ (01271) 860624
Sharp's Doom Bar; 2 changing beers (sourced locally) Ⓗ
Delightful contemporary riverfront bar with three ales on handpump, one of which is always a local north Devon ale, and two ciders. It has a 20-seater function room and separate restaurant upstairs. Sunday roast is popular all year round. Families and dogs are welcome. The Quay claims to be the first in the village to be Cask Marque accredited. ⭢🕽&P✿🕏

Kings Nympton

Grove Inn Ⓛ
EX37 9ST (in centre of village) SS683194
☎ (01769) 580406 ⊕ thegroveinn.co.uk
Exmoor Ale Ⓖ; 3 changing beers (sourced regionally) Ⓗ
Thatched, Grade II-listed 17th-century inn, with low beams, flagstone floors, an open fire in winter, and a pretty enclosed terrace to enjoy in summer. A recent local CAMRA branch Pub of the Year and Cider Pub of the Year, it usually has four real ales on, together with a good range of ciders. It also has a reputation for its excellent home-cooked food, which can be enjoyed in the dining area, adjacent to the bar.
Q⭢✿🕽🍴🕽♣●P✿🕏

Kingsbridge

Hermitage Inn
8 Mill Street, TQ7 1ED
☎ (01548) 853234
2 changing beers (sourced regionally; often Cotleigh, Teignworthy) Ⓗ
Popular with the inhabitants of Kingsbridge, this extremely friendly pub with log fires and a traditional interior also has an enclosed pleasant beer garden to the rear. It boasts an eclectic range of local beers, normally two at any given time, with bar snacks and basket meals on Friday nights and lunchtimes during the summer. Live music is staged regularly, which proves popular. Facebook is a key source of information if you are planning a visit. Q⭢✿&♣●P꠸✿🕏

Kingsteignton

Ten Tors Inn
Exeter Road, TQ12 3NP
☎ (01626) 365434 ⊕ tentorsinn.co.uk
St Austell Tribute, Proper Job; 1 changing beer (sourced locally; often Dartmoor) Ⓗ
An imposing building set back from the main road, having previously been the site of a petrol station and a transport café on the old A380. Entrance is through the large car park and up some steps to a porch (there is

separate wheelchair access). It has one long bar with distinct spacious areas throughout, and has a strong food emphasis including a restaurant and a carvery (with discounts for the over-55s). There is a drinking area outside and a children's play area.
Q⭢✿🕽🍴&♣P꠸(2,X64)✿🕏

Lewdown

Blue Lion Inn Ⓛ
EX20 4DL
☎ (01566) 783238
Dartmoor Jail Ale; Otter Amber; Sharp's Doom Bar; 1 changing beer (sourced regionally) Ⓗ
Family-owned and family-run roadside inn, set on the now-bypassed old A30 between Okehampton and Launceston. Originally a 17th-century farmhouse on the Lewtrenchard Estate, the property was extended in the early 1900s. It is home to numerous local groups, and several pub teams are also supported. Although predominantly wet sales-oriented, good-value food is served Tuesday-Saturday evenings. Accommodation is available in two well-appointed rooms. No visiting dogs allowed. ⭢✿🍴🕽&♣●P꠸🕏

Littlehempston

Tally Ho Ⓛ
TQ9 6LY SX813627
☎ (01803) 862316 ⊕ tallyhoinn.co.uk
Dartmoor Legend; 1 changing beer (sourced locally; often Teignworthy) Ⓗ
Idyllic 14th-century stone-built pub. Community-owned since 2014, the single-roomed bar with timber beams has a cosy feel, complemented by two wood-burners, and is furnished with pews and wooden settles. Guest beers are from breweries nearby and a real cider is sold. The pub hosts numerous events including an annual beer festival, occasional local live music and a regular Sunday night quiz. The enclosed beer garden is to the rear.
Q⭢✿🕽&●P꠸꠸(X64,177)✿🕏

Lydford

Castle Inn
School Road, EX20 4BH
☎ (01822) 820242 ⊕ castleinnlydford.co.uk
St Austell Tribute, Proper Job; 3 changing beers (sourced nationally) Ⓗ
With its low ceilings, slate flooring and exposed beams, this cosy 16th-century inn has bundles of atmosphere. Be sure to check out the rustic main bar area, as well as the snug, restaurant, lounge and delightful garden. The four regular beers are supplemented by a varying guest ale in summer. Local attractions include the scenic Lydford Gorge, St Petroc's Church and the Castle. The pub is on the National Cycle Network 27 Devon Coast-to-Coast, Dartmoor Way and West Devon Way cycle/walking routes. ✿🍴🕽▲P꠸(46)✿🕏

Lympstone

Redwing Bar & Dining
Church Road, EX8 5JT
☎ (01395) 222156 ⊕ redwingbar-dining.co.uk
Branscombe Branoc; St Austell Proper Job; Sharp's Doom Bar Ⓗ
This welcoming, tastefully decorated venue was once known as the Redwing Inn. While the accent is now more on food, there is plenty of space for drinkers near the bar at small tables or on comfortable seating near the entrance. The restaurant area extends into a

conservatory, there is a small function room upstairs, and the garden is a suntrap. Excellent fresh food is served, with a set-price menu for weekday lunchtimes. Dogs are welcome in the bar area. Q🅥🐕🍴◑🛴⇌P❀🌶📶

Lynton

Cottage Inn 🅛
Lynbridge, EX35 6NR (on B3234 between Barbrook and Lynton)
☎ (01598) 753496
Fat Belly Guzzler, Ocean Gold, Carver Doone; 2 changing beers (sourced nationally) Ⓗ
Characterful 17th-century riverside inn with accommodation and an authentic Thai restaurant. Fat Belly ales began here and, although now brewed nearby at Mullacott, they remain a key part of the business. At least three of these are always in stock, often accompanied by other specials from the brewery. A further selection of craft beers is served through a USA-style craft beer dispenser. Please check first if visiting in midwinter, as opening hours and meal times can then vary. 🛴🐕🍴◑🌳♠P🚍❀📶

Meavy

Royal Oak Inn 🅛
PL20 6PJ
☎ (01822) 852944 ⊕ royaloakinn.org.uk
Dartmoor Jail Ale; Otter Amber; St Austell Tribute; 1 changing beer (sourced regionally; often Dartmoor, Otter) Ⓗ
People come from miles around to enjoy the food and drink at this tucked-away, civilised but unpretentious 16th-century inn. In the summer, sit outside on one of the benches by the legendary tree and watch children play on the village green. In winter, relax in the public bar and enjoy the conversation, dogs and roaring fire. There is an interesting range of cider, with a festival in August and occasional live music. Local CAMRA branch Country Pub of the Year runner-up in 2020.
Q🅥🐕🍴◑♠♣P🚍(56) ❀📶

Musbury

Hind 🅛
The Street, EX13 8AU
☎ (01297) 553553 ⊕ thehindmusbury.co.uk
3 changing beers Ⓗ
Free house on the crossroads of the A358, three miles south of Axminster. It has a public bar and a lounge/restaurant where good-value home-cooked food is served lunchtimes and evenings (no food Mon or Sun eve). There are two outside areas: a front courtyard with stunning views over the Axe Valley, and an enclosed rear beer garden with a lawn. Dogs are welcome.
Q🅥🐕🍴◑♣P🚍(885) ❀📶

Newton Abbot

Maltings Taphouse & Bottle Shop
Tuckers Maltings, Teign Road, TQ12 4AA (500yds from Newton Abbot railway station)
☎ (01626) 334734 ⊕ themaltingstaphouse.co.uk
House beer (by Teignworthy); 2 changing beers (sourced nationally; often New Lion) Ⓗ
A micropub based in the historic but recently closed Tuckers Maltings, also home to the Teignworthy Brewery. The interior reflects its previous use, with low ceilings. The walls are covered with historic images of the maltings, the adjacent railway, the local racecourse and the town. A vast range of bottled and canned beers is

available, with several craft keg lines. No jukebox, TV or fruit machines here; beer and conversation prevail.
Q🅥🐕🍴⇌♣P🚍(12) ❀📶

Teign Cellars 🅛
67 East Street, TQ12 2JR
☎ (01626) 332991 ⊕ teigncellars.com
4 changing beers (sourced nationally) Ⓗ/Ⓖ
This venue has been reincarnated from its previous existence as the Greene Man and, further back, as an annexe of the 1836 workhouse opposite. There are three or four beers on handpumps, with others dispensed from KeyKegs, plus a selection of boxed ciders. It has one bar with a combination of hard stools, soft furnishings and a periodic beer table, and a shop to the rear selling 170 bottled beers and cans. The food is excellent and popular, which can make the place crowded at times.
Q🅥🐕🍴⇌♣P🚍❀📶

Newton Ferrers

Dolphin Inn
Riverside Road East, PL8 1AE
☎ (01752) 872007 ⊕ dolphininn.weebly.com
Draught Bass; Salcombe Shingle Bay; St Austell Tribute; 1 changing beer (sourced locally; often Hanlons, Salcombe, Summerskills) Ⓗ
The pub is situated close to the tidal estuary, with views across to Noss Mayo. It reopened under new management in early 2019 after a short period of closure. Good home-cooked food is served daily, lunchtimes and evenings. Up to four real ales are usually on offer, mainly sourced from within the West Country. There is a small car park. Friendly dogs are welcome.
Q🅥🐕🍴◑♣P🚍(94) ❀📶

Newton Poppleford

Cannon Inn
High Street, EX10 0DW
☎ (01395) 568266 ⊕ pubindevon.com
2 changing beers (sourced nationally) Ⓖ
Cheery, welcoming, two-bar pub, the only one in the village and a community hub, with tables for dining in the lounge bar and restaurant area. Real ales are served by gravity from stillage behind the bar. This is a friendly place with busy passing trade. Good-value home-cooked food, served lunchtimes and evenings, covers most traditional favourites and, locals say, is of a tasty standard. Well-behaved dogs are allowed. There are two large gardens and a skittle alley.
Q🅥🐕🍴◑♠♣P🚍(52,157) ❀📶

Newton St Cyres

Beer Engine 🅛
EX5 5AX (beside railway station ½ mile N of A377)
☎ (01392) 851282 ⊕ thebeerengine.co.uk
Beer Engine Rail Ale, Piston Bitter; 3 changing beers Ⓗ
Victorian hostelry, built in 1850 on the Exeter to Barnstaple Tarka Line. The pub brews its own ales and five are usually available. Home-cooked food made with locally sourced produce is served lunchtimes and evenings. Part of the downstairs area has been converted into a second bar to accommodate sports fans and to serve those in the large, covered area between the pub and the railway line. The downstairs bar also allows views of the brewery. Q🅥🐕◑⇌P❀

103

North Tawton

Railway Inn ⃝Ⓛ

Whiddon Down Road, EX20 2BE (1 mile S of town, just off A3124) SS666000

☎ (01837) 82789 ∰ therailwaynorthtawton.co.uk

Teignworthy Reel Ale; 1 changing beer (sourced regionally) Ⓗ

Good value and a warm welcome always await you at this friendly Devon local. Adjacent to the former North Tawton railway station that closed in 1971, there are numerous old railway photos on the walls. Reel Ale from Teignworthy is normally joined by a guest ale from one of the other West Country breweries, together with a real cider in summer. The dining room is popular in the evening (no food Thu), with light meals served at lunchtime. Assistance dogs only. Q☆✿❶♣♠P⎕🛜

Noss Mayo

Ship Inn Ⓛ

PL8 1EW

☎ (01752) 872387 ∰ nossmayo.com

Dartmoor Jail Ale; Noss Beer Works Church Ledge, Ebb Rock; St Austell Tribute; 1 changing beer (sourced regionally; often Bath Ales, Noss Beer Works) Ⓗ

Popular with ramblers and seafarers alike, this fine split-level pub is on an inlet of the Yealm estuary. Four ales and excellent food are served daily. A former local CAMRA Pub of the Year, it is an ideal start or finish point for a walk to sample the breathtaking river and sea views along the route of Lord Revelstoke's Drive. If sailing, ring ahead to check the tide times and mooring availability. There is no bus service in the evening or on Sunday. Q☆✿❶♿♠P⎕(3)🐾

Ottery St Mary

London Inn

4 Gold Street, EX11 1DG

☎ (01404) 812045

6 changing beers (sourced nationally) Ⓗ

A 17th-century coaching inn close to the historic 14th-century parish church and a friendly locals' pub. There are two separate bars offering six changing real ales from breweries near and far, with a good range of styles and strengths, all at the same price. Good-value home-cooked food, including roast on Sunday, is served, and four B&B rooms are available. There is a pool room and a function room, and live music is regularly promoted. Q☆✿🛏❶♿♣⎕(4,4A)🐾🛜

Paignton

Henry's Bar Ⓛ ⃝

53 Torbay Road, TQ4 6AJ

☎ (01803) 551190 ∰ henrysbarpaignton.co.uk

Sharp's Doom Bar; house beer (by Sharp's); 2 changing beers (sourced nationally; often Dartmoor) Ⓗ

An excellent example of a traditional-style town-centre pub serving real ales and ciders from near and far. It has close ties with people and events in the area, and is a real hub of the community. The impressive long bar has four handpumps with three regular beers plus one guest, and a fifth handpump dedicated to cider, plus various bottles and polyboxes. Home-cooked food is served daily, with a renowned roast on Sundays. Families are welcome until the evening. ☆✿❶≠♠P⎕🐾🛜

Paignton Conservative & Unionist Club

34 Palace Ave, TQ3 3HB

☎ (01803) 551065

Dartmoor Jail Ale; 3 changing beers (often Exmoor, Salcombe, Skinner's) Ⓗ

Set in an old building that has been a private members' club since 1885, CAMRA members are now welcome here. The Tardis-like entrance brings you into the covered ale bar and leads through to the spacious Palace lounge which hosts cabaret nights, quiz and bingo sessions. Upstairs is a snooker room with two tables, and a sports room that is used for the bridge club and euchre games as well as serving as a lunchtime restaurant. Q☆❶♿≠♣P⎕🛜

Torbay Inn ⃝

34 Fisher Street, TQ4 5ER (300yds from big tree bus stop – the local landmark)

☎ (01803) 392729

St Austell Tribute; Sharp's Sea Fury; Twickenham Naked Ladies; Wye Valley HPA; 1 changing beer (often St Austell) Ⓗ

A traditional pub with separate lounge and public bars dating back to the early 1600s when the sea was on its doorstep and it was opposite a fish market – hence the name of the street. Time is called via a ship's bell recovered by a local diver from an old wreck, and it's documented that the Roundhead General Fairfax stayed here prior to a civil war battle in Exeter. A warming welcome awaits all visitors. Q☆✿♿≠♣P⎕(12,120)🐾🛜

Parkham

Bell Inn Ⓛ ⃝

Rectory Lane, EX39 5PL (½ mile S of A39 at Horns Cross, on opp corner to village primary school) SS387212

☎ (01237) 451201 ∰ thebellinnparkham.co.uk

3 changing beers (sourced regionally) Ⓗ

Sympathetically restored after a serious fire in 2017, this 13th-century thatched inn, with its cob walls, oak beams and wood-burner fires, has retained all of its old-world charm. Three, and sometimes four, changing real ales are on the bar, with usually at least one coming from a local brewery. Good home-cooked food is served, both in the bar and the adjacent raised restaurant area, including the popular Friday night fish & chips and Sunday roast lunch. Q☆✿❶♣♠P⎕(372)🐾🛜

Peter Tavy

Peter Tavy Inn

Lane Head, PL19 9NN

☎ (01822) 810348 ∰ petertavyinn.com

Dartmoor Jail Ale; 4 changing beers (sourced regionally; often Black Tor, Roam, Salcombe) Ⓗ

In a quiet village on the edge of Dartmoor, the inn has a small central bar serving Dartmoor Jail Ale, supplemented by a varying range of up to four local guest beers. Traditionally fitted out throughout, it also has two larger rooms. A patio and hidden garden are added attractions. The pub is renowned for its food, but drinkers are made welcome. It is on the No.27 cycle route, near a caravan and camping site. Q☆✿❶🏕♣P⎕(46,95)🐾🛜

Plymouth

Artillery Arms 🄻

6 Pound Street, Stonehouse, PL1 3RH (behind Stonehouse Barracks and Millbay Docks)
☎ (01752) 262515
Draught Bass; 1 changing beer (sourced locally; often Black Tor, Dartmoor, Summerskills) 🄷
Cracking back-street local tucked away in the old quarter of Stonehouse, close to the magnificent Grade I-listed Royal William Yard and maintaining the area's military connections. One South-West guest beer and Thatchers Heritage cider are normally stocked. An out-of-season beach party takes place on the last weekend of February, and charity monkey games also feature. Also popular with local hockey teams, this place is a real find. ✿●🏠(34,34A) 🐾 🛜

Brass Monkey 🄻 ✅

12-14 Royal Parade, PL1 1DS
☎ (01752) 260442
House beer (by Hunters); changing beers (sourced nationally; often Batemans, McMullen, Roam) 🄷
Modern bustling city centre pub with a wide clientele. It is conveniently situated, with easy access to shopping, buses, Plymouth Hoe and The Barbican. The decor includes photographs of pre-war Plymouth. Good-value family meals are served. Up to eight real ales and two real ciders feature from Devon and Cornwall as well as some national favourites. Several ale festivals are held each year. ➜🕽&●🏠🛜

Bread & Roses 🄻

62 Ebrington Street, PL4 9AF
☎ (01752) 659861 ⊕ breadandrosesplymouth.co.uk
Exeter Avocet; 2 changing beers (sourced regionally; often Altarnun, Red Rock) 🄷
A friendly, sympathetically restored late-Victorian inn popular with university staff, but also with a mixed clientele. Up to three real ales are sold, which are organic/Fairtrade wherever possible, just like the snacks. The ales are selected from local and regional breweries, including small batch and speciality beers unusual for Plymouth. The pub promotes artistic and musical creativity, and is a vibrant music hub for talent from the area. ●🏠(23,24)🐾🛜

Britannia Inn 🄻 ✅

2 Wolesely Road, Milehouse, PL2 3BH
☎ (01752) 607596
Dartmoor Jail Ale; Greene King Abbot; Ruddles Best Bitter; Sharp's Doom Bar; changing beers (sourced nationally; often Bays, Exmoor, Summerskills) 🄷
A Georgian hostelry from the 1830s, situated opposite the Plymouth City bus depot, Central Park and the Life Centre, and a short walk from Home Park, Plymouth Argyle FC. The premises itself was built by the grandfather of Captain Scott (of Antarctic fame). Ten handpumps dispense at least one real cider, with Westons and other local ciders appearing regularly. Since becoming a Wetherspoon in 1999, it has established a well-earned reputation for its beer. Q➜✿🕽&●🏠🛜

Dolphin Hotel 🄻 ✅

14 The Barbican, Barbican, PL1 2LS
☎ (01752) 660876
Dartmoor Jail Ale; Draught Bass; Roam Tavy IPA; St Austell Tribute; Sharp's Doom Bar; Skinner's Betty Stogs; 2 changing beers (sourced regionally; often Roam, St Austell, Sharp's) 🄶
A Plymouth institution, this unpretentious hostelry is steeped in history. Up to eight ales are all dispensed by gravity from the cask. Full of character, this charming pub has tiled floors, well-used wooden benches and a traditional open fire, all creating the perfect ambience. The walls are adorned with paintings by local artist, the late Beryl Cook, who depicted many of the characters she encountered in the Dolphin. Plymouth CAMRA City Pub of the Year 2020. ●🏠(25)🐾

Fawn Private Members Club 🄻

39 Prospect Street, Greenbank, PL4 8NY
☎ (01752) 226385
Bays Topsail; 4 changing beers (sourced regionally; often St Austell, Sharp's, Teignworthy) 🄷
This mid 19th-century establishment was originally the Fawn Inn/Hotel, prior to converting to a club. CAMRA members are welcome with a valid membership card; regular visitors will be required to join. Four guest ales from the area are generally served, as well as a rotating range of local cider from Countryman. The club is popular for rugby and other televised sports, and supports multiple darts and euchre teams. Local CAMRA branch Club of the Year 2020. ➜♣●🏠🐾

Ferry House Inn 🄻 ✅

888 Wolseley Road, Saltash Passage, PL5 1LA
☎ (01752) 361063 ⊕ ferryhouseinn.com
Dartmoor Jail Ale; Sharp's Doom Bar; Dartmoor IPA 🄷
A warm welcome awaits you and your dog from the landlord and locals at this picturesque riverside pub on the River Tamar. Three regular West Country ales are served, as well as good home-cooked food. A decking area on the edge of the river gives spectacular views of both the road bridge and Brunel's iconic 1859 railway bridge. Photos, some dating back to the turn of the 20th century, adorn the walls. Quiz night is Sunday. ➜✿🕽&●🏠(13)🐾🛜

Fisherman's Arms 🄻

31 Lambhay Street, Barbican, PL1 2NN
☎ (01752) 268243 ⊕ fishermansarms.co.uk
Dartmoor Jail Ale; house beer (by Summerskills); 1 changing beer (often Otter) 🄷
The family owners have returned this former St Austell inn into a traditional free house. The interior is welcoming, with several distinctly decorated areas. The dartboard is back and there is a variety of games and puzzles on offer. Ale and cider festivals are held twice a year. Traditional pub grub at affordable prices is supplemented by specials, with the famous roast available on Sundays. Close to the Royal Citadel and the Barbican. ➜🕽♣●🏠(25)🐾🛜

Fortescue Hotel 🄻 ✅

37 Mutley Plain, PL4 6JQ
☎ (01752) 660673
Bays Devon Dumpling; Dartmoor Legend; Roam Tavy IPA; St Austell Proper Job; Skinner's Betty Stogs; Summerskills Devon Dew; 4 changing beers (sourced nationally; often Cornish Crown, Exeter, South Hams) 🄷
A multi award-winning and lively venue frequented by a broad section of the community, where conversation flourishes. Nine real ales are usually on tap, and up to eight real ciders. A perfect Sunday can be spent here – a good-value home-cooked roast washed down with a pint of Spingo Special, followed by a brain-teasing quiz in the Cellar Bar in the evening. The patio beer garden draws crowds in the summer and is heated in winter. ➜✿🕽➜♣●🏠🐾🛜

Mannamead 🄻 ✅

61 Mutley Plain, PL4 6JH
☎ (01752) 825610

Dartmoor Jail Ale; Greene King Abbot; Ruddles Best Bitter; Sharp's Doom Bar; changing beers (sourced nationally; often Dartmoor, Roam, Summerskills) [H]
A Wetherspoon establishment converted from a former NatWest bank. A wide range of ales from near and far can be found, with at least two local brews usually on the pumps. There is also a good choice of real cider and perry. Beer and cider festivals take place several times a year. Brewery showcase events are also held, featuring a large number of regional beers, as well as a Devon ale festival. 🐴❀◐◑♿⇌🍎🚌📶

Minerva Inn [L]
31 Looe Street, Barbican, PL4 0EA
☎ (01752) 223047 🌐 minervainn.co.uk
St Austell Trelawny, Tribute; 2 changing beers (sourced locally; often Dartmoor, Roam, Summerskills) [H]
Plymouth's oldest hostelry, dating from around 1540, and within easy walking distance of the city centre and the historic Barbican. It has a long and narrow bar, leading through to a cosy seating area at the rear. Two guest beers are supplemented by spring and autumn beer festivals, where beer could, and does, come from all over the country. Live music takes place Thursday to Sunday evenings and Sunday lunchtimes. The pub benefits from a varied clientele. 🐴❀♣🍎🚌🐾📶

Prince Maurice [L] ✔
3 Church Hill, Eggbuckland, PL6 5RJ
☎ (01752) 771515
Dartmoor Jail Ale; St Austell Tribute, Proper Job, Hicks; Sharp's Doom Bar; 2 changing beers (sourced locally; often Hunters, Roam, Summerskills) [H]
There is very much a village feel to this four-times local CAMRA Pub of the Year, which sits between the church and village green. The six regular ales are supplemented by a changing guest ale. The pub is named after the Royalist general, the King's nephew, who had his headquarters nearby during the siege of Plymouth in the Civil War. Two log fires keep you warm in winter, adding to the ambience. No food at weekends.
🐴❀◐♣🍎P🚌(28A)🐾

Providence [L]
20 Providence Street, Greenbank, PL4 8JQ
☎ (01752) 946251
3 changing beers (sourced nationally; often Brains, Dartmoor, St Austell) [H]
A welcoming hostelry, tucked away within the back-street labyrinth of Greenbank. One of the smallest pubs in Plymouth, what it lacks in size it makes up for in atmosphere and character. The interior is smart but comfortable and the real fire in winter is wonderful. Three competitively priced beers from a range of breweries are generally available, as are two or three real ciders. There are no fruit machines here, and the only sound is the buzz of conversation. Q⇌♣🍎🚌🐾📶

Pub on the Hoe [L]
159 Citadel Road, The Hoe, PL1 2HU
☎ (01752) 202405
House beer (by Hunters); 5 changing beers (sourced locally; often Bays, Roam) [H]
A busy street-corner pub serving a mixed clientele and near Plymouth Hoe, where Sir Francis Drake famously played bowls. Up to four varying real ales supplement the house beer, Drunken Hoe, and two local real ciders. Good home-cooked food is served all day. The wood-panelled raised and lower deck seating areas add to the nautical theme. It is just a short walk from the historic Barbican and is well worth a visit.
🐴❀🛏◐◑♣🍎🚌(25)🐾📶

Plympton

Union Inn [L]
17 Underwood Road, Underwood, PL7 1SY
☎ (01752) 336756 🌐 unioninnplympton.com
4 changing beers (sourced regionally; often Exeter, Summerskills, Tintagel) [H]
The landlord of this family-run community pub is a beer hunter, getting in changing brews to charm his regulars' palates and to create a year-round beer festival. The four beers on offer are regional, but could be from almost anywhere. The cider selection is also from far and wide, but Old Rosie is a regular. A warm welcome is assured at this traditional, cosy, early 19th-century hostelry. A former local CAMRA branch Cider Pub of the Year runner-up. Q🐴❀♣🍎P🚌🐾📶

Postbridge

Warren House Inn [L]
PL20 6TA (on B3212 between Postbridge and Bennett's Cross)
☎ (01822) 880208 🌐 warrenhouseinn.co.uk
Otter Ale; 3 changing beers (sourced regionally; often Black Tor, Exeter, Summerskills) [H]
Isolated and exposed at 1,425 feet above sea level, this is one of England's highest pubs. Up to three varying guest beers, mainly from the West Country, are stocked, with Countryman cider also featuring regularly. The characterful main bar boasts two log fires – one never goes out! Excellent-value home-made food includes the famous rabbit pie, local lamb and delicious puddings with clotted cream. There is a large family room, and tables outside give breathtaking views over the moors. Open all day in summer. Q🐴❀◐◑⛺🍎P🐾

St Giles on the Heath

Pint & Post [L]
PL15 9SA
☎ (01566) 779933
2 changing beers (sourced locally) [H]
This thatched village local was once two cottages and then a pub and post office, hence the name. A friendly family-run inn close to the Cornish border, it offers good home-cooked food including takeaways and hosts a regular Wednesday quiz night. Legend from Dartmoor is one of the two well-kept ales, joined by a locally sourced guest beer. Q🐴❀◐◑⛺♣P🐾📶

Salcombe

Ferry Inn ✔
Fore Street, TQ8 8JE
☎ (01548) 844000 🌐 theferryinnsalcombe.com
Palmers Copper Ale, IPA, Dorset Gold [H]
Grade II-listed building dating from 1739, a Palmers Brewery house. The waterside location provides superb views over the estuary, and the patio close to the water can be busy during fine weather. It offers a choice of real ales and wholesome pub food at reasonable prices. There are roasts on Sunday afternoons, and wine and cheese on Sunday evenings. 🐴❀◐♣P🚌(606)🐾📶↺

Fortescue Inn ✔
Union Street, TQ8 8BZ
☎ (01548) 842868 🌐 thefortsalcombe.co.uk
Otter Bitter; 2 changing beers (often Salcombe, Sharp's) [H]
Grade II-listed 18th-century pub built on reclaimed land; up until 1951 it was called the Union Inn. It is nestled away from prevailing winds on the high street, which is

busy with pedestrians. Sometimes the sea advances up Union Street on a high tide. There are three log fires, the menu is varied, and you can eat either in the bar area or in the restaurant. A wide choice of beer is offered from Salcombe Brewery. ⮝🗴🖾🕪🅰♣🅿🖳(606,164)🌑🛜

Shaugh Prior

White Thorn Inn 🗍

PL7 5HA (on Cornwood to Bickleigh road, S of Yelverton)
☎ (01752) 839245
Dartmoor Jail Ale; Fuller's London Pride; St Austell Tribute; 1 changing beer (sourced regionally; often Bays, Dartmoor, St Austell) 🅷
Very much a community village pub, it was completely refurbished by local musician Michael Mathieson, better known as Mad Dog McRea. The open-plan bar has a central fireplace, and hosts regular entertainment including folk music on Wednesday, live music on Saturday evening, and a quiz on the last Thursday evening of the month. The three regular beers are supplemented by one other West Country beer. A mile from the Plym Valley Walking and Cycle Path.
⮝🗴🕪♣🅿🖳(59) 🌑🛜

Silverton

Lamb Inn 🗍

Fore Street, EX5 4HZ
☎ (01392) 860272 ⊕ thelambinnsilverton.co.uk
Salcombe Seahorse; 2 changing beers (sourced locally) 🅶
Family-run pub in the centre of Silverton, with stone floors, stripped timber, old pine furniture, and a large open real fire. Three competitively priced ales are served by gravity from a temperature-controlled stillage behind the bar. There is a well-used function room and skittle alley, regular quiz nights and occasional live music. Good-value home-cooked food is served lunchtimes and evenings, plus a popular Sunday roast.
Q⮝🗴🕪🅖♣🖳(55B) 🌑🛜

Slapton

Queen's Arms 🗍

TQ7 2PN
☎ (01548) 580800 ⊕ queensarmsslapton.co.uk
Dartmoor Jail Ale; Otter Bitter; South Hams Wild Blonde; 1 changing beer (sourced regionally; often Salcombe, South Hams) 🅷
Splendid 14th-century pub deep in the South Hams countryside only half a mile from the beach, boasting a flower-filled garden in the summer with a patio at the rear and an open fire inside in the winter. The walls depict local life and history including WWII evacuation photographs. An extensive menu is available with daily specials; the chef is known for his home-made pies in winter. Sunday roasts are popular (booking advisable), and children and dogs are welcome.
Q⮝🗴🕪🅰♣🖿🅿🌑🛜

South Zeal

King's Arms 🗍

EX20 2JP (centre of village) SX649936
☎ (01837) 840300 ⊕ thekingsarmssouthzeal.com
Dartmoor IPA, Legend; 1 changing beer (sourced regionally) 🅷
Thatched 14th-century village inn, which is not only at the hub of the community but also attracts many visitors exploring the area. Well-behaved dogs are made particularly welcome here. The regular Dartmoor beers

are accompanied by a changing guest ale and locally made cider. Good food is served lunchtimes and evenings every day. Regular live music sessions are held throughout the year and the pub plays a central role during the Dartmoor Folk Festival in August.
Q⮝🗴🕪🅖♿♣🖿🅿🖳🌑🛜

Spreyton

Tom Cobley Tavern 🗍

EX17 5AL (off A3124 in village) SX6986096761
☎ (01647) 231314 ⊕ tomcobleytavern.co.uk
10 changing beers (sourced regionally) 🅷/🅶
Named after the well-known folklore figure, this family-run traditional 16th-century village pub provides a warm welcome to visitors and locals alike. With several West Country ales, some served straight from the cask, and 12 ciders and perries usually on offer, it's no wonder the walls are decorated with certificates of CAMRA awards won over the years. In colder months an open fire can be enjoyed in the bar area, with its unique thatched bar. The beer garden offers views over Dartmoor and the surrounding countryside. Excellent meals and snacks are available lunchtimes and evenings. Quizzes, darts and other events are supported and there are six en-suite guest rooms. Q⮝🗴🖾🕪♣🖿🅿🌑🛜

Sticklepath

Taw River Inn 🗍

EX20 2NW (on main road, old A30, going through village) SX642941
☎ (01837) 840377 ⊕ tawriver.co.uk
Dartmoor Jail Ale; St Austell Tribute; Sharp's Doom Bar; 1 changing beer (sourced regionally) 🅷
Popular thatched inn set in an attractive village on the edge of Dartmoor, close to picturesque walks and numerous places of historical interest. The real ales, together with a real cider made in the village, are all competitively priced, while good-value food is served in both the bar area and adjacent dining room. There is a TV in the large single bar, where numerous sports and pub games are played by friendly locals.
⮝🗴🕪♿♣🖿🅿🖳🌑🛜

Stoke Fleming

Green Dragon 🗸

Church Road, TQ6 0PX (opp village church)
☎ (01803) 770238 ⊕ thegreendragon-pub.business.site
St Austell Tribute; Salcombe Seahorse; house beer (by Otter); 1 changing beer (sourced regionally) 🅷
On the South West Coast Path and half a mile from Blackpool Sands, there has been a building on the site since the 12th century. The cosy bar, adjacent restaurant and kitchen were refurbished in 2018, and there is an open log fire. Local legend suggests there is a tunnel underneath the floor to the nearby beach and, some say, a ghost. The garden benefited from landscaping in April 2021 and the addition of an outside bar.
⮝🗴🕪🅰🅿🖳(3) 🌑🛜

Teignmouth

Blue Anchor Inn 🗍

Teign Street, TQ14 8EG
☎ (01626) 772741
6 changing beers (sourced regionally; often Exeter, Summerskills, Teignworthy) 🅷
Situated in a conservation area and close to the docks, this is a free house not to be missed. There is one single bar with eight handpumps, some of which are devoted

to cider, and the landlord is keen to provide dark beer. Drinking areas outside burst with floral colour in summer, and at Christmas there is an impressive display of decorations – but mind the reindeer! Note the rare VR letterbox. ✪♿≉♣🚐🚌(2,22)✿

Topsham

Bridge Inn ★ L
Bridge Hill, EX3 0QQ
☎ (01392) 873862 ⊕ cheffers.co.uk
Branscombe Branoc; changing beers (sourced regionally) G
An historic, cosy, 16th-century inn, beautifully positioned overlooking the River Clyst, run by six generations of the same family since 1897, and visited by the Queen in 1998. It is a delight for real ale fans, with a continually varying range of beers dispensed by gravity direct from the cellar. There are two rooms in the unspoilt interior, and it also has the malthouse, which is used at busy times and for functions. Traditional lunches such as ploughman's and sandwiches served.
Q✪◑≉♣🚐P🚌(57,T)✿

Exeter Inn L
68 High Street, EX3 0DY
☎ (01392) 873131
Teignworthy Beachcomber; 3 changing beers (sourced regionally) H
A pub since at least 1860, although some of this partially thatched building dates from the 17th century, when it was a coaching inn and blacksmith's. The Exeter Inn is a friendly local serving four ales and two ciders plus, occasionally, snacks such as rolls. Three TVs show various sports, while the front area is devoted to pool and darts. There is a small sheltered garden and smoking area at the side. ⇆✪♿≉♣🚐🚌✿🛜

Globe Hotel
Fore Street, EX3 0HR
☎ (01392) 873471 ⊕ globehotel.com
St Austell Trelawny, Tribute, Proper Job; 1 changing beer H
A characterful 16th-century coaching inn, acquired by St Austell Brewery in 2011, in this popular town on the Exe estuary, selling real ales are from the brewery's range. The hotel offers 19 en-suite rooms, and the restaurant serves good-quality food. The Malt House out back is used as a function room. Opens at 8am for breakfast.
⇆🛏◑♿≉P🚌(T,57)✿🛜

Torquay

Buccaneer Inn
41 Babbacombe Downs Road, TQ1 3LN
☎ (01803) 312661 ⊕ thebuccaneerinn.co.uk
St Austell Tribute, Proper Job, Hicks H
Located atop the highest clifftop promenade in England, this warm and welcoming pub has spectacular views across Lyme Bay from both the lounge bar and patio. An extensive and varied menu is served daily, with local seafood specials in the summer and a popular Sunday lunch. ⇆✪🛏◑♿♣P🚌✿🛜

Totnes

Albert Inn L
32 Bridgetown, TQ9 5AD (from town centre cross river, 100yds on left)
☎ (01803) 863214 ⊕ albertinntotnes.com

Bridgetown Albert Ale, Bitter, Cheeky Blonde, Shark Island Stout, West Coast IPA; 2 changing beers (sourced locally) H
A shining example of a traditional pub, the only hostelry across the river in the Bridgetown area of Totnes. Celebrating the scientist, Albert Einstein, this community venue holds culinary nights, quizzes, regular cider and beer festivals plus live music and pub teams. Based in a former chapel of ease, it is the brewery tap for the Bridgetown Brewery and is noted for its hideaway beer garden which affords views of the River Dart.
Q⇆✪◑♿♣▲♣P🚌✿🛜

Bay Horse Inn L
8 Cistern Street, TQ9 5SP (at top of main shopping street)
☎ (01803) 862088 ⊕ bayhorsetotnes.com
New Lion Totnes Stout, Pandit IPA; 2 changing beers (sourced locally; often Noss Beer Works, Salcombe, Teignworthy) H
Grade II-listed 15th-century coaching inn at the top of this historic town, holding several beer festivals through the year and normally serving a minimum of three ales and two ciders. A Guide regular, it is the brewery tap for New Lion Brewery, based close by in neighbouring Dartington. At the rear there's an attractive large beer garden with bench seating and a covered smoking area. Although bus stops are at the bottom of town, the walk up is worth it. This community-minded and friendly place hosts live music and quiz nights.
Q⇆✪⍟🛏◑♿≉♣P🚌(92,164)✿🛜

Totnes Brewing Company
59A High Street, TQ9 5PB (at top of High St by Market Square) ⊕ thetotnesbrewingco.co.uk
8 changing beers (sourced nationally; often Totnes) H /P
Modern craft brewpub serving a large and diverse range of beers. The constantly changing range usually includes at least one ale brewed in-house on handpump, together with guests on up to seven other handpumps. There is also a good range of KeyKeg ales. Takeaway food may be brought in. There is a Saxon castle at the rear of the premises. Q⇆✪♿▲≉✿🛜

Waterman's Arms
Victoria Street, TQ9 5EF
☎ (01803) 863038
Dartmoor Jail Ale H**; 2 changing beers (sourced locally; often Hunters)** H/G
A cosy and friendly single bar, this gem of a pub is in the back streets of town near the main bus stop. It serves one beer on gravity from a stillage behind the bar, another two are on handpump. Comfortably furnished with perimeter banquette seating, wooden tables and chairs, together with stools at the bar, it has a dartboard, gaming and quiz machines, and a jukebox. Outside, to the right, is a small paved patio area with three picnic tables. Q⇆✪♿▲≉♣P🚌✿🛜

Turnchapel

Boringdon Arms L ✓
13 Boringdon Terrace, PL9 9TQ
☎ (01752) 402053 ⊕ boringdon-arms.net
Dartmoor Jail Ale; Fuller's London Pride; Sharp's Atlantic, Sea Fury H
The Bori is a traditional and dog-friendly former CAMRA Regional Pub of the Year, with six letting rooms. It sits in a waterside village on the South West Coast Path, and benefits from a regular bus service from Plymouth or a water taxi from the Barbican. Four regular ales are available, with more at the four beer festivals held

during the year. Good-value, home-cooked food is served daily. There are two secluded gardens to the rear. Q❄🛏🍴❤◀♣🚪(2,2A)🐾📶

Walkhampton

Walkhampton Inn L

PL20 6JY

☎ (01822) 258697 ⊕ walkhamptoninn.co.uk

3 changing beers (sourced regionally; often Bays, Dartmoor, Sharp's) 🅷

Set in the centre of the village, this welcoming 17th-century local displays traditional features throughout the bar, dining areas and snug. Up to four different real ales are sold and six real ciders. There are quiz nights, live music and open mic nights throughout the year, and annual real ale and cider festivals. The pleasant courtyard beer garden hosts summer events. This is a good old-fashioned country pub. Q❄◀🅰♣❤🚪(55,56)🐾📶

Weare Giffard

Cyder Presse L

EX39 4QR

☎ (01237) 425517 ⊕ cyderpresse.co.uk

Timothy Taylor Landlord; 3 changing beers (sourced regionally) 🅷

Family-run premises in a picturesque village on the banks of the River Torridge, with cosy bar and restaurant areas, a beer garden and two en-suite twin rooms. Local CAMRA Cider Pub of the Year in 2019, it usually features more than nine real ciders, alongside up to four real ales. Home-cooked food made with regional produce is served Wednesday to Saturday and Sunday lunchtime. On Tuesday there is a regular live folk music night. Q❄🏵🛏◀🅰♣❤🚪(7A)🐾📶

Welcombe

Old Smithy Inn L

EX39 6HG (turn off A39 Bideford to Kilkhampton road at Welcombe Cross; follow signs to Welcombe and then to pub)

☎ (01288) 331305 ⊕ theoldsmithyinn.co.uk

3 changing beers (sourced regionally) 🅷

A 13th-century thatched inn, nestled at the top of the Welcombe Valley and just a mile from the sea near the Cornish border. Quality ales, from Forge and other nearby breweries, good ciders and a range of excellent, locally sourced food can all be enjoyed here in a most welcoming atmosphere. Outside there is a pleasant garden and a separate function room. An outstanding beer and music festival is held in July. ❄🏵🛏◀🅰♣❤🐾📶

Wembury

Odd Wheel L

Knighton Road, PL9 0JD

☎ (01752) 862504 ⊕ theoddwheel.co.uk

Dartmoor Jail Ale; Draught Bass; St Austell Tribute; 3 changing beers (sourced regionally) 🅷

At the northern end of a picturesque village, this friendly country pub was tastefully refurbished several years ago. The three regular beers are supplemented by up to three guest beers, mainly from Devon and Cornwall. Regular beer festivals are held. Food is served daily, with ingredients from local suppliers. Outside, there is a terraced garden and play area for children. Many walking routes are close by, including the South West Coast Path. ❄🏵◀♣❤🚪(48)🐾📶

Wembworthy

Lymington Arms

Lama Cross, EX18 7SA (on minor road, midway between Eggesford and Winkleigh)

☎ (01837) 83572 ⊕ lymingtonarms.co.uk

Teignworthy Reel Ale; 2 changing beers (sourced regionally) 🅷

Friendly, welcoming pub set in mid-Devon countryside, with a large car park, attractive outdoor seating, a sunny bar/dining area and a characterful restaurant. Although seemingly remote, Eggesford Station, where all Tarka Line trains stop, lies only two miles away and is fairly easily walked or cycled. The regular Teignworthy Reel Ale is usually accompanied by at least two other West Country beers, while good locally sourced and home-cooked food is served. Q❄🏵◀♿🅿🐾

Widecombe-in-the-Moor

Rugglestone Inn L

TQ13 7TF (¼ mile from centre of village)

☎ (01364) 621327 ⊕ rugglestoneinn.co.uk

Dartmoor Legend; house beer (by Teignworthy); 2 changing beers (sourced regionally) 🅶

An unspoilt Grade II-listed Dartmoor building which was converted to a pub in 1832. Beer can be served through a hatch in the passageway or from a cosy bar with a wood-burner. There are two further rooms, one with an open fire. A wide selection of home-cooked food is available. Across the stream is a large grassed seating area with the car park just down the road. Real local farm cider from Ashridge is sold, plus additional real cider and perry. Q❄🏵🛏◀🅰♣❤🚪(271,672)🐾

Winkleigh

King's Arms L

The Square, Fore Street, EX19 8HQ (in village square)

☎ (01837) 682681 ⊕ kingarmswinkleigh.co.uk

Hanlons Yellow Hammer; Teignworthy Reel Ale; 3 changing beers (sourced locally) 🅷

Thatched Grade II-listed 16th-century village pub. The single bar has low-beamed ceilings, a flagstone floor and a welcoming wood-burning fire for colder months. Good food from a varied menu can be enjoyed in a series of intimate dining rooms featuring naval memorabilia, books and an intriguing glass-capped well. To the rear is a cosy private function room. Up to five real ales, mainly from Devon, are usually sold, together with two ciders from nearby Sam's. Q❄🏵◀🅰♣❤🚪(315)🐾📶

Yeoford

Duck ✅

EX17 5JD (right out of train station or, by car from Crediton, take left fork opp green)

☎ (01392) 85273 ⊕ theduckatyeoford.co.uk

3 changing beers (sourced locally) 🅷

Set in beautiful countryside, this multi-roomed 1860 free house is easily accessible from the train station on the Tarka Line connecting Exeter and Barnstaple. It offers locally brewed Devon ales, including its own-label Muddy Duck ale. Good food showcases local suppliers and there is a Pub-up-Shop selling a huge variety of essentials and a variety of pre-cooked meals to take away. The large beer garden benefits from a children's play area. ❄🏵◀♿≷❤🐾📶

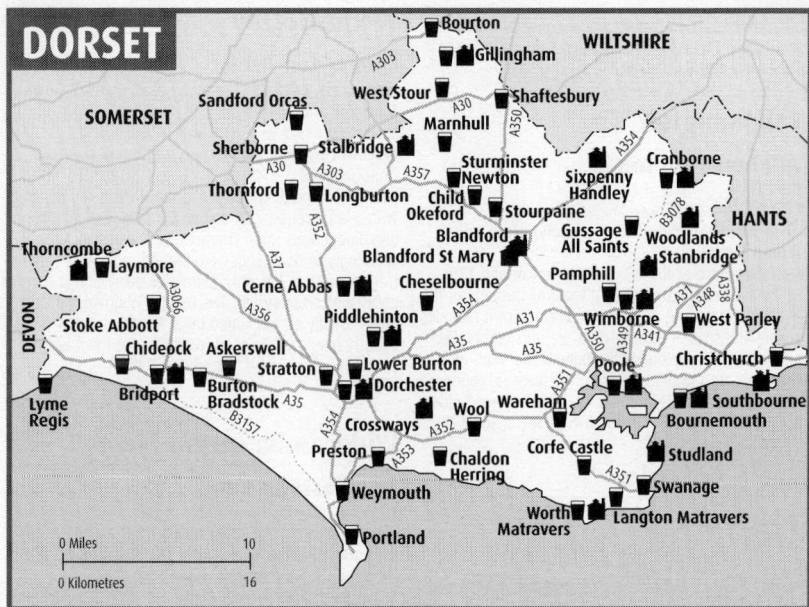

Askerswell

Spyway Inn

DT2 9EP

☎ (01308) 485250 ⊕ thespywayinn.com

3 changing beers (sourced locally; often Copper Street, Otter) Ⓖ

Family-friendly 16th-century smugglers' inn perched on a hill outside Askerswell. It offers a selection of local ciders as well as a continuously changing range of beers on gravity, mainly from local breweries. The lounge bar has beams and a wood-burner; a further bar has tables for dining. The menu includes dishes made with locally produced ingredients. There are three sheltered pods in the large garden, which provides spectacular views and is popular with locals, walkers and dog owners.
Q ⑤ ✿ ♨ ⊕ ● P ❄ ☂

Bournemouth

Acorn

1492 Wimborne Road, Kinson, BH11 9AD

☎ (01202) 575062

6 changing beers (sourced regionally; often Sixpenny) Ⓗ

This imposing 17th-century pub, originally built as a coaching inn, is rich in history and has a connection with local smuggler Isaac Gulliver. It is now in the safe hands of a family who previously ran an award-winning pub close by. A well-chosen selection of ales is on offer at the large L-shaped bar, which serves two distinct areas. The landlord plays music on Sunday afternoon, and live music sometimes also features. No children after 6pm.
♣ ● P ⊒ ❄

All Hail Ale

10 Queens Road, Westbourne, BH2 6BE

☎ 07786 045996

4 changing beers (sourced nationally) Ⓗ

A vibrant micropub and bottle shop, this former restaurant has been skilfully converted, with wooden flooring and polished-wood bar and tables. Five handpumps serve a range of ales from independent breweries nationwide, and a real cider. Ten keg pumps offer a varied and well-chosen selection of beers. Popular tap takeovers are held to showcase some of the major new craft ales, and a large blackboard lists the beers available. ● ⊒ ❄ ☂ ☐

Firkin Shed

279 Holdenhurst Road, Springbourne, BH8 8BZ

☎ (01202) 302340

2 changing beers (sourced nationally; often Cerne Abbas, Farmageddon, Vibrant Forest) Ⓗ

A former CAMRA National Cider Pub of the Year, the Shed is a quirky, friendly, family-run micropub. Tables and benches hug the walls of the main bar area and snug, which are decorated with flags, musical instruments, puppets and skulls. A shed is used as the bar, hosting a constantly changing selection of cask and keg beers alongside an impressive cider range. The garden is a great place to relax and enjoy the summer sunshine.
✿ ➜ ● ⊒ (2,6A) ❄

Micro Moose

326 Wimborne Road, Winton, BH9 2HH

⊕ micromoose.co.uk

6 changing beers (sourced nationally) Ⓗ /Ⓖ

This friendly and cosy bar was established when the Canadian owner decided to convert her coffee shop into a micropub offering 'Great British Ales with Canadian Hospitality'. It serves a selection of local and regional ales on both handpump and gravity. The bottled beer range is Canadian-themed, as is the decor, complete with fluffy moose head. In common with other micropubs, sharing tables is encouraged. Local cider is also available, along with a good selection of bar snacks.
Q ● ⊒ ❄

Silverback Alehouse

518 Wimborne Road, Winton, BH9 2EX

⊕ silverbackalehouse.co.uk

5 changing beers (sourced regionally) Ⓖ

Set on Winton's bustling high street, this micropub offers a welcome respite from the weekly shop. Carefully chosen real ales are served on gravity, often including beers from the Nottinghamshire area. Six ciders from small independent cider makers are also on offer. Benches and tables line the perimeter, with table service by friendly staff. Light snacks are available and you are welcome to bring in your takeaway. The bar has a relaxed and friendly atmosphere, making it popular with locals and visitors alike. Q♣●♬🖵❀🐾♿

Bourton

White Lion
High Street, SP8 5AT
☎ (01747) 840866 ⊕ whitelionbourton.co.uk
Otter Amber; 1 changing beer Ⓗ
The White Lion is a traditional inn dating from 1712. The stone-flagged bar has an open fireplace and many quiet corners for a meal or a drink. A separate restaurant leads off the bar for more formal dining. There is a large beer garden to the rear. Parking is either opposite the pub or in the car park. Close to Stourhead house and gardens and convenient for local attractions including Stonehenge. Q❀🚪◗●P🖵(X4)❀🐾

Bridport

Pursuit of Hoppiness
15 West Street, DT6 3QJ
☎ (01308) 427111 ⊕ hoppiness.co.uk
6 changing beers (sourced nationally; often Eight Arch, Tapstone) Ⓗ
Popular town-centre micropub with a single room that accommodates up to 25 people. There are six handpumps serving beers of all styles, changing regularly every few days and sourced from small West Country brewers as well as further afield. Six ciders are normally available including regulars Dorset Nectar and West Milton. Outdoor seating is at the front. Q🚶♣●P🖵❀🐾

Ropemakers Ⓛ ✅
36 West Street, DT6 3QP
☎ (01308) 421255 ⊕ theropemakers.com
Palmers Copper Ale, IPA, Dorset Gold, 200, Tally Ho!; 1 changing beer (often) Ⓗ
Deceptively large pub in the centre of town serving the full Palmers range of beers. The interior is divided into numerous themed areas decorated with memorabilia and items depicting local history. There is a large, partially covered courtyard at the rear and wheelchair access via the back door. Music features on Friday and Saturday evenings. The pub closes around 4pm on Sunday in winter (later on bank holiday weekends or if there is live music). 🚶❀◗🅰♣●P🖵❀🐾

Woodman Inn
61 South Street, DT6 3NZ
☎ (01308) 456455 ⊕ thewoodman.pub
4 changing beers (sourced regionally; often Cerne Abbas, Copper Street, Exmoor) Ⓗ
A friendly pub with a focus on quality beers and ciders. Handy for the twice-weekly markets, it has a cosy one-bar interior with a stone floor and log-burner. There are sunny pavement tables at the front, a pleasant garden to the rear and a skittle alley. Real ales change frequently, and up to 12 boxed ciders are available. Regular music events include a folk night, story-telling and DJs. The pub stays open later on Sunday in the summer. 🚶❀🅰●P🖵❀🐾

Burton Bradstock

Anchor Inn
High Street, DT6 4QF
☎ (01308) 897228 ⊕ anchorinn.pub
4 changing beers (sourced regionally; often Dorset, St Austell, Sharp's) Ⓗ
One of the few free houses in this part of Dorset, the Anchor is in the centre of a pretty village with an excellent beach nearby. Inside, the Stables Bar has a traditional pub feel (and bar food) and there is also a larger restaurant area with an extensive menu of high quality, locally sourced food. Local shellfish and seafood is the speciality. Up to four beers are selected from Dartmoor, Dorset, Exmoor, Sharp's and St Austell breweries. The pub also has its own gin menu, offering a premium range. En-suite accommodation in three rooms is available. Q🚶❀🚪◗🅰♣P🖵(X53)❀

Three Horseshoes Ⓛ ✅
Mill Street, DT6 4QZ
☎ (01308) 897259 ⊕ threehorseshoesburtonbradstock.co.uk
Palmers Copper Ale, IPA, Dorset Gold, 200, Tally Ho!; 1 changing beer Ⓗ
Three-hundred-year-old thatched pub and restaurant with suntrap seating at the front and in the beer garden. It serves good home-cooked food and is popular with families using the beach. The full Palmers range is available plus a Palmers seasonal beer or Dorset Orchards First Press cider. Closed Mondays (and Tuesday in Winter). Food is served throughout the day on Saturdays in winter and Tuesday to Saturday in summer. Dogs are welcome in the bar and garden.
🚶❀◗🅰♣●P🖵(X53)❀🐾

Cerne Abbas

Giant Inn Ⓛ ✅
24 Long Street, DT2 7JF
☎ (01300) 341441 ⊕ thegiantcerneabbas.co.uk
Butcombe Adam Henson's Rare Breed; 3 changing beers (sourced locally; often Cerne Abbas, Ringwood, Wriggle Valley) Ⓗ
A warm welcome is assured at this pub in the centre of the village. The exterior frontage is Victorian; the interior features an original 15th-century fireplace. Home-cooked food is served alongside a good selection of up to four real ales from Dorset and the West Country, including

REAL ALE BREWERIES

Barefaced ✦ Blandford
Brew Shack Sixpenny Handley
Brewers Folly Stanbridge
Brewhouse & Kitchen 🍺 Bournemouth
Brewhouse & Kitchen 🍺 Dorchester
Brewhouse & Kitchen 🍺 Poole
Brewhouse & Kitchen 🍺 Southbourne
Cerne Abbas ✦ Cerne Abbas
Copper Street ✦ Dorchester
Dorset ✦ Crossways
Eight Arch ✦ Wimborne
Gyle 59 Thorncombe
Hall and Woodhouse (Badger) ✦ Blandford St Mary
Hattie Brown's Worth Matravers
Isle of Purbeck 🍺 Studland
Palmers Bridport
Piddle Piddlehinton
Remedy Oak ✦ Woodlands (NEW)
Sandbanks ✦ Poole
Sixpenny ✦ Cranborne
Small Paul's Gillingham
Southbourne Bournemouth
Stripey Cat 🍺 Bridport
Way Outback ✦ Southbourne
Wriggle Valley ✦ Stalbridge

one from the Cerne Abbas brewery. Skittles and darts are played. Definitely worth popping into on the way to visit the Cerne Giant. Q♿🅿🕑♣🚌(X11)🌸🛜

Chaldon Herring

Sailor's Return 🅛
DT2 8DN
☎ (01305) 854441 🌐 sailorsreturnpub.com
Cerne Abbas Ale; Otter Ale; Palmers Copper Ale; 1 changing beer (sourced regionally; often Cerne Abbas, Flack Manor, Palmers) 🅗
Historic thatched inn on the edge of a tranquil village, a few miles from the Jurassic Coast. The pub dates from the 1860s but the buildings are much earlier. There are several dining and drinking areas, with flagstone floors throughout. An original inn sign hangs in the main bar. Wednesday is pie night. On Friday night food is only served in the restaurant area (booking advisable). Q♿🕑🅿🅿🛜

Cheselbourne

Rivers Arms
Cheselbourne, DT2 7NW
☎ (01305) 236586 🌐 theriversarms.co.uk
Hardys & Hansons Olde Trip; Morland Old Golden Hen 🅗
Unspoilt inn on the outskirts of the village, believed to have been built to cater for drovers en route to Dorchester. It was threatened with change to residential use but, thanks to a successful local campaign, was saved and has been totally refurbished with a rustic theme. There is an upstairs room, conservatory area, large veranda and a stove in the bar. The pub serves real home-cooked food. Seven en-suite log cabins with valley views provide accommodation. Q♿🕑🅿🅿🛜

Chideock

George Inn 🅛 ✅
Main Street, DT6 6JD
☎ (01297) 489419 🌐 georgeinnchideock.co.uk
Palmers Copper Ale, IPA, Dorset Gold, 200, Tally Ho! 🅗
Traditional Dorset thatched pub, popular with locals and visitors alike. Real ales and ciders are served in a friendly atmosphere, with log fires in winter. For summer there is a sun terrace, where you will find a wood-fired oven cooking pizzas on Thursday nights. An award-winning menu of local and seasonal food is offered seven days per week, lunch and evening. 🕑♿🅿♣🅿🚌(31,X53)🌸

Child Okeford

Saxon Inn
Gold Hill, DT11 8HD
☎ (01258) 860310 🌐 saxoninn.co.uk
Butcombe Original; Otter Bitter; 2 changing beers (sourced regionally) 🅗
This 300-year-old village inn is hidden behind a row of cottages. Its bar and restaurant areas are cosy, boasting a log fire, and are popular with locals and visitors. The large garden is perfect for alfresco dining and hosts a beer and cider festival. Quality home-cooked food is served. The two guest ales are chosen on the recommendation of customers, and there are two real ciders. The pub also offers B&B and is an ideal base for exploring the Dorset countryside. 🕑♿🅿♣🅿🚌(X10)🛜

Christchurch

Saxon Bar
5 The Saxon Centre, Fountain Way, BH23 1QN
☎ (01202) 488931
4 changing beers (sourced nationally; often Downton, Sixpenny, Vibrant Forest) 🅖
A friendly single-room micropub, close to the town centre, featuring perimeter seating and high tables made from reclaimed wood from Bournemouth Pier. The pub offers a variety of well-chosen ales plus up to 10 real ciders, all served direct to your table. Four KeyKeg beers are also available, along with local and international spirits and speciality bar snacks. Winter hours vary. Local CAMRA Cider Pub of the Year 2020. Q♿🍴♣🅿🌸

Corfe Castle

Bankes Arms Hotel 🅛 ✅
23 East Street, BH20 5ED
☎ (01929) 288188 🌐 bankesarmshotel.co.uk
Palmers IPA, 200; 2 changing beers (sourced regionally) 🅗
This historic 16th-century Grade II listed hotel, owned by the National Trust, retains many of its original features including a front drinkers' bar. The restaurant to the rear serves excellent home-cooked food. A large picturesque garden overlooks Swanage Steam Railway and Corfe Castle station and enjoys fantastic views of the Purbeck Hills. Regular beers are from Palmers, and ales recreated by the Dead Brewers Society, brewed by Barnet, are available. Occasional beer festivals are held in summer. 🕑♿🍴🕑🚂🅿🚌(40)🌸🛜

Corfe Castle Club
70 East Street, BH20 5EQ (off A351)
☎ (01929) 480591
Ringwood Razorback; Timothy Taylor Landlord; 1 changing beer (sourced nationally) 🅗
Friendly club in a Purbeck stone-built former school in the village centre. The main bar features upholstered bench seating and a TV for major sporting events, plus darts and Purbeck longboard shove-ha'penny. An upstairs room has a pool table and can be hired for meetings. Filled rolls are available all day. The spectacular garden boasts a boules court and views over the Purbeck hills. Visitors are welcome with a CAMRA membership card or copy of the Guide. Convenient for the castle or steam railway. ♿🚂(Swanage)♣🅿🚌(40)🌸🛜

Fox Inn 🅛
8 West Street, BH20 5HD
☎ (01929) 480449 🌐 thefoxinncorfecastle.com
Box Steam Soul Train; Butcombe Adam Henson's Rare Breed; Hattie Brown's Moonlite; 1 changing beer 🅗
Delightful 16th-century inn nestled in the heart of historic Corfe Castle and retaining many original features. Its front door opens into a small traditional snug with steps down to the main bar area, where good pub food is served. Towards the rear is a fabulous garden, complete with barbecue shack, offering fine views over the castle and surrounding Purbeck Hills. Q🕑♿🅿🅰🚂(Swanage)🅿🚌(40)🌸

Cranborne

Sixpenny Tap 🅛
Holwell Farm, Holwell, BH21 5QP (1 mile from village centre on B3078)
☎ (01725) 762006 🌐 sixpennybrewery.co.uk
Sixpenny 6d Best Bitter, 6d Gold, 6d IPA; 2 changing beers (often Sixpenny) 🅗

Housed in a converted Victorian stables and packed full of quirky miscellaneous items, the Sixpenny Tap has established itself at the heart of the local community. With the brewery located next door, its popular range of ales is served with pride and enthusiasm. The pub hosts many successful and colourful community and charity events in the extensive courtyard, with a warm welcome for all who visit. This is a real countryside gem set within picturesque farmland, and it even has its own Tardis.
Q ✿ ❀ ᕼ ♣ ♠ P ♠ 🖤 ☎

Dorchester

Convivial Rabbit
1 Trinity House, Trinity Street, DT1 1TT
🌐 convivialrabbit.co.uk
6 changing beers (sourced nationally) 🄶
Popular micropub with a changing choice of around six real ales of varying styles and strengths from micro and independent British breweries. Local ciders, gins and wines are also available in addition to cans of craft beer and lager. Rustically decorated and run by friendly and knowledgeable licensees, the pub is tucked away down an alley off Trinity Street, but well worth seeking out when visiting Dorchester town centre. Regular folk, jazz and vinyl nights are hosted. Q ✿ ❀ ♣ ♠ ᕼ ♠

Tom Browns 🄻 ✪
47 High East Street, DT1 1HU
☎ (01305) 264020 🌐 tombrownspub.co.uk
Copper Street Saxon Gold; Dorset Tom Brown's; 2 changing beers (sourced nationally; often Cerne Abbas, Copper Street, Plain) 🄷
Formerly home to the Goldfinch Brewery, this town-centre alehouse has an open fire, skittle alley and a function room, and hosts regular live music and other events. In addition to the four real ales, there are up to five real ciders and a selection of more than 20 gins. The large, beautiful riverside garden is ideal for lazy pints in the sun. Food is not served but you are welcome to bring in a takeaway from one of the nearby establishments. Dogs are welcome, except when live music plays.
✿ ❀ ♣ ♠ ᕼ ♠ ☎

Gillingham

Buffalo
2 Lydford Lane, SP8 4NJ (100yds S of B3081)
☎ (01747) 823759 🌐 ristorantedamassimo.co.uk
Hall & Woodhouse Fursty Ferret, Tanglefoot; 1 changing beer (often Hall & Woodhouse) 🄷
A traditional old stone pub, formerly the Drum & Monkey, tucked away on a side road opposite the old Matthews Brewery, which closed in the 1960s. The building has been extended and refurbished to capitalise on the large car park, beautiful garden and patio areas. It now caters for up to 60 diners while retaining a well-used public bar. The restaurant trades as Ristorante Da Massimo. ✿ ❀ ◑ ♿ Å ♣ P ᕼ (X2)

Dolphin
Peacemarsh, SP8 4HB
☎ (01747) 824007
2 changing beers (sourced regionally; often Cotleigh, Exmoor, St Austell) 🄷
Following refurbishment, this pub has two dining rooms plus seating for drinkers in the bar. Meals are cooked to order and are always popular (booking is recommended). The beer garden has had a makeover and there is a covered smoking area outside.
Q ✿ ❀ ◑ P ᕼ (X2,25) 🖤 ☎

Phoenix
High Street, SP8 4AY
☎ (01747) 823277
St Austell Proper Job; Sharp's Doom Bar; 1 changing beer (often Hattie Brown) 🄷
Originally a 15th-century coaching inn with its own brewery and stables, this pub was rebuilt and renamed the Phoenix following a fire in the 17th century. It has an open-plan layout with a dining area to one side and a log fire. Picnic tables now occupy the former car park outside; parking is available on-street and in two public car parks nearby. 🚲 ᕼ (X2) 🖤 ☎

Gussage All Saints

Drovers Inn
Bowerswain Hollow, BH21 5ET
☎ (01258) 840550 🌐 thedroversinn.info
Ringwood Fortyniner; Sixpenny 6d Best Bitter; 2 changing beers (sourced regionally) 🄷
Located in a picturesque village in the heart of rural Dorset and Cranborne Chase, this thriving, award-winning community-owned pub is very much at the centre of local life. With its cosy atmosphere and warm welcome, the Drovers entices you in to sample its changing range of real ales and good-quality food. Although great conversation is the order of the day, the pub hosts many events throughout the year such as festivals and music nights. ✿ ❀ ᕼ ◑ Å ♠ P 🖤 ☎

Langton Matravers

King's Arms
27 High Street, BH19 3HA
☎ (01929) 422979
Ringwood Razorback; 3 changing beers (sourced nationally) 🄷
Dating back to 1743, this Purbeck stone-built pub, with original flagstone floors, has many quirky little rooms off a central bar area, and a suntrap rear garden. The seaside town of Swanage with its steam railway is close by, as are many fine walks where you can explore the Purbecks and the South West Coast Path. A welcoming family pub serving good food and well-chosen ales, this is a magnet both for locals and visitors. Q ✿ ❀ ◑ Å ♣ ♠ ᕼ (40) 🖤 ☎

Laymore

Squirrel Inn
TA20 4NT ST387048
☎ (01460) 30298 🌐 squirrelinn.co.uk
1 changing beer (sourced nationally; often Fuller's, Otter) 🄷
Modernised country pub with a large single-bar area plus a separate function room featuring a double skittle alley and pool table. At least one real ale, three draught ciders and a huge selection of bottled gins are available. Good home-made food is cooked to order, with gluten-free and vegetarian options if arranged in advance. There is a beer garden with a gazebo and camping can be booked in the field opposite. Families are welcome. Opens late depending on demand. ❀ ᕼ ◑ ♿ Å ♣ ♠ P 🖤 ☎

Longburton

Rose & Crown
DT9 5PD
☎ (01963) 210202
5 changing beers (sourced nationally; often Fine Tuned, Otter, St Austell) 🄷

This thatched 17th-century former coaching inn is a fascinating blend of old beams, stone flags and open fireplaces, set off by contemporary decor. A free house, it offers five constantly rotating national, regional and local beers. Traditional pub food is served in the bar and restaurant (booking essential on Sunday). There is a large beer garden plus a separate self-contained cottage available to hire. Real cider is served in summer. Open all day on bank holidays. Local CAMRA pub of the year 2021, providing a real community focus during the pandemic. Q✿❀⇦❃◑♣⛾P🚲🚍(X11) ☸ 🛜

Lower Burton

Sun Inn

DT2 7RZ

☎ (01305) 250445 🌐 sun-inn-dorchester.co.uk

2 changing beers (sourced nationally; often Dark Star) Ⓗ

Attractive old-feel 17th-century family-owned free house, less than a mile from Dorchester. Popular for food with a carvery available lunchtime and evening (all day Sat and Sun). Ideal for the sunny summer months with a front courtyard and rear patio area and garden, which also has a play area for children. In winter the roaring log fires welcome and warm you. There are two large, well-lit car parks. Dogs are welcome in the garden. ✿❀◑♿Å♣⛾P🚍(X11) ☸ 🛜

Lyme Regis

Pilot Boat Inn ✅

1 Bridge Street, DT7 3QA

☎ (01297) 443157 🌐 thepilotboat.co.uk

Palmers Copper Ale, IPA, Dorset Gold, 200 Ⓗ

A 'tardis' of a pub, tastefully renovated to provide a large main bar opening out to a courtyard and overlooked by a roof terrace. There is a 110 seat restaurant at the rear and an open-plan kitchen providing pizzas and other modern pub-style food, which is open all day. Additional Palmers beers may be available as well as First Press cider. The accommodation comprises three sea-view rooms, which are named after Palmers beers. ✿❀⇦◑♿Å♣🚍☸🛜

Rock Point Inn

Broad Street, DT7 3QD

☎ (01297) 443153 🌐 rockpointinn.co.uk

St Austell Tribute, Proper Job; 2 changing beers (sourced regionally; often Bath Ales, St Austell) Ⓗ

Large 18th century inn, which was extensively renovated and expanded in 2020. There are fabulous sea views to be had from inside the pub and the outdoor balcony area. The outside space has gas heaters for those cold evenings but can be closed in rough weather. Proper Job and Tribute are regulars with two changing beers from the St Austell and Bath Ales ranges. There are nine bedrooms, some having a sea view. ✿❀⇦❃◑Å🚍☸🛜

Royal Standard Ⓛ ✅

25 Marine Parade, DT7 3JF

☎ (01297) 442637 🌐 theroyalstandardlymeregis.co.uk

Palmers Copper Ale, IPA, Dorset Gold, 200 Ⓗ

Popular 400-year-old pub with a restaurant and beer garden fronting on to the beach. Interior stained glass, originally from the Three Cups Hotel, depicts the Duke of Monmouth landing on the nearby beach in the 1685 rebellion. Palmers Tally Ho! is available in the winter. Home-cooked meals feature local produce and freshly caught fish, with several vegetarian and Greek dishes on the menu. Ideal for families, the pub can be busy in the summer. ✿❀◑♿Å♣⛾(71)☸

Marnhull

Blackmore Vale Inn

Burton Street, DT10 1JJ

☎ (01258) 820701

St Austell Tribute; Wriggle Valley Ryme Rambler; 1 changing beer (sourced regionally; often Bath Ales, Otter, Sharp's) Ⓗ

Despite a recent refurbishment this 15th-century building retains some traditional character, featuring a spacious bar area with a wood-burning stove and low beams. A separate dining area leads off the bar. An extension is being built, and there are plans for a bottle store and microbrewery. Music night is Friday, quiz night is Sunday. Q✿◑Å♣⛾P🚍(X4) ☸

Pamphill

Vine Inn ★

Vine Hill, BH21 4EE (off B3082)

☎ (01202) 882259

2 changing beers (sourced regionally; often Hop Back, Plain) Ⓗ/Ⓖ

Identified by CAMRA as having a nationally important historic pub interior, this multi-award winning country pub, owned by the National Trust, has been managed by the same family for 120 years – the current landlady residing for over 30 of these. The pub has two cosy bars, an upstairs room, and a large suntrap patio and garden providing the perfect place to relax and enjoy a drink. Light snacks including ploughman's and toasties are served at lunchtime. Popular with walkers and cyclists, this is a true rural gem. Q✿◑♣⛾P🚲☸

Piddlehinton

Thimble Inn Ⓛ ✅

14 High Street, DT2 7TD

☎ (01300) 348270 🌐 thimbleinn.co.uk

Palmers Copper Ale, IPA, Dorset Gold Ⓗ

Large, partly thatched village pub on the River Piddle. The spacious low-beamed bar has a brick fireplace and plenty of nooks and crannies for cosy twosomes and larger groups. The pub offers a well-kept range of Palmers ales, often including Tally Ho! and its seasonal ales. Food is served Monday to Saturday and Sunday lunchtimes. The river runs through the large garden, and there is plenty of parking – motorhomes and camper vans allowed overnight. ✿❀◑♿Å♣P☸🛜

Poole

Barking Cat Alehouse

182-184 Ashley Road, Upper Parkstone, BH14 9BY

☎ (01202) 258465

🌐 the-barking-cat-alehouse.ueniweb.com

8 changing beers (sourced nationally) Ⓗ

A bustling alehouse serving an interesting choice of beers from local and national microbreweries alongside six ciders, all on handpull. There are also 10 craft keg lines, providing an excellent range for all beer tastes. Customers are welcome to bring in a takeaway – there is a Chinese next door. The large function room has a pool table and dartboards. Entertainment includes a quiz night on alternate Thursdays and live music on Saturday nights. ✿≋♣⛾🚍☸🛜

Bermuda Triangle

10 Parr Street, Lower Parkstone, BH14 0JY

☎ (01202) 748047 🌐 bermudatrianglepub.com

5 changing beers (sourced nationally; often Dark Star, Oakham, Palmers) Ⓗ

Established in 1870, this great local drinkers' pub is at the heart of Ashley Cross. The cosy interior has five distinct bar areas – find your way through the bookcase to discover the hidden sixth room. It is nautically themed and decorated to reflect the Bermuda Triangle story. Five ales on handpump are complemented by two real ciders and speciality keg beers. With a welcoming atmosphere, the pub hosts occasional live music. The outside drinking area with fairy lights is a must in summertime.
🏶🌫🍴🍺🗒🏵📶

Branksome Railway Hotel
429 Poole Road, Branksome, BH12 1DQ
☎ (01202) 769555
2 changing beers (sourced nationally; often Dark Star, Otter) Ⓗ
Victorian railway hotel, dating from 1894, opposite Branksome station on the Waterloo to Weymouth line, and on the main bus routes between Poole and Bournemouth. The large, open-plan interior is divided into three areas with a log fire between two of them. Up to two guest beers are served, often from the Dark Star range, to complement the two permanent ales. Live major sporting events are shown on TV, and live music and open mic sessions are occasionally held at weekends. 🦽🌫P🛏🗒🏵📶

Brewhouse
68 High Street, BH15 1DA
☎ (01202) 685288
Frome Funky Monkey, Beer; 3 changing beers (sourced nationally) Ⓗ
This multi-award winning venue is a long-established feature of the town, and a reliable source of interesting ales from Frome Brewery as well as from national microbreweries. Real cider is also available. Entering from the High Street you find tables in the window; past the busy bar area is a space for pool and darts. Dogs are welcome in this no-frills traditional community pub, which has outside seating areas to the front and rear.
🏶🌫🌳🍺🗒🏵📶

Poole Arms Ⓛ ✅
19 The Quay, BH15 1HJ
☎ (01202) 673450 ⊕ poolearms.co.uk
Dorset Jurassic; Flack Manor Flack's Double Drop; Ringwood Fortyniner; St Austell Proper Job; 1 changing beer (sourced regionally) Ⓗ
Originating from 1635 and steeped in history, this distinctive green-tiled quayside pub is popular with locals and tourists alike. Its cosy and small, single-room interior is dominated by pews and the bar, plus wood-panelled walls displaying photographs of historic Poole. Bench seating at the front provides a great place to watch activities taking place on the quay. A fifth bar is available during the busier summer months. The extensive menu of locally sourced seafood is among the best in the area. 🏵🍴🌫🗒

Portland

George Inn ✅
133 Reforne, DT5 2AP
☎ (01305) 820011
Greene King Abbot; 3 changing beers (sourced nationally; often Fuller's, St Austell, Timothy Taylor) Ⓗ
A friendly, family-oriented local dating from the mid-18th century. It has four separate bar and dining areas plus a large enclosed beer garden. There are usually three constantly rotated guest ales on offer. Food is available daily Thursday to Sunday – Sunday roasts are popular, as is the Thursday evening curry and quiz. Live

music plays on some Saturday evenings and Sunday afternoons. A beer festival is held in April.
🦽🏶🍴🍺🗒(1) 🏵📶

Preston

Bridge Inn
Bridge Inn Lane, DT3 6BD
☎ (01305) 833380
Butcombe Original; Sharp's Doom Bar, Sea Fury Ⓗ
Traditional village inn built in the 18th century alongside the River Jordan, surrounded by stone cottages. The entrance leads to the lounge with its single bar; to the left is a snug with dartboard, to the right is a pool table. The separate restaurant serves traditional pub fare. Outside, the extensive beer garden has a children's play area. There is a paved path from the car park providing level access to the pub. Q🦽🏶🍴👶🍴♿P🗒🏵📶

Sandford Orcas

Mitre Inn
DT9 4RU
☎ (01963) 220271 ⊕ mitreinn.co.uk
3 changing beers (sourced nationally; often Church End, Quantock, Yeovil) Ⓗ
Run by the same couple since 1992, the Mitre is a homely, family-friendly pub with a cosy bar and separate restaurant area. There are flagstoned floors throughout, and two open fires, but mind your head on the door lintels. The regularly changing guest beers are usually from local breweries Apex and Yeovil. Booking is recommended for Sunday lunch. The elevated garden at the rear is accessed via steps.
Q🦽🏶🍴🍴♿P🗒(39) 🏵📶

Shaftesbury

Ship Inn ✅
24 Bleke Street, SP7 8JZ
☎ (01747) 853219
Butcombe Original; Sixpenny 6d IPA; 2 changing beers Ⓗ
Stone-built town pub at the top of the steep Tout Hill. The single bar serves four different areas – the main bar, lounge bar, a snug with an open fire, and a games room with pool, darts, fruit machine and jukebox. Outside are a sunny patio and covered smoking area. No hot food is available but you can order from local takeaways or bring your own. 🏶🍺🗒🏵📶

Sherborne

Digby Tap ✅
Cooks Lane, DT9 3NS
☎ (01935) 813148 ⊕ digbytap.co.uk
4 changing beers (sourced regionally; often Cerne Abbas, Otter, Teignworthy) Ⓗ
A lively, long-established free house close to the abbey, railway station and all town-centre amenities. The owners of over 20 years have retained the character and atmosphere of the old building, with its four separate drinking areas, pine panelling, flagstone floors, old beams, settles, and three fireplaces. Three or four changing beers, mostly from West Country independent brewers, are sold at extremely reasonable prices.
Q🏶🍴👶🌫🌳🗒🏵

Stoke Abbott

New Inn Ⓛ ✅
DT8 3JW

☎ (01308) 868333 ⊕ newinnstokeabbott.co.uk
Palmers Copper Ale, Dorset Gold Ⓗ
Comfortable 17th-century inn situated in the middle of a picturesque village. The bar's unusual thatched roof reflects the thatch covering the building outside. Good quality freshly-cooked food is offered with ingredients sourced locally where possible. The pub hosts themed events throughout the month, such as quiz night, pie and a pint night, and steak night. Advance table booking for meals is advisable at busy times. An impressive fireplace warms the pub in winter. Q ➜ ☻ ◖ ♣ P ♀ ✿

Stourpaine

White Horse Inn ✓
Shaston Road, DT11 8TA
☎ (01258) 453535 ⊕ whitehorse-stourpaine.co.uk
Sharp's Doom Bar; house beer (by Flack Manor); 3 changing beers (sourced regionally; often Cerne Abbas, Gritchie, Sixpenny) Ⓗ
Wonderful village free house incorporating the local shop and post office. Originally two adjoining cottages, the pub has multiple cosy spaces with beams and open fireplaces. Five handpumps serve national and regional ales, and cider lovers can enjoy Cranborne Chase direct from the box. Close to the North Dorset Trailway, the pub offers walkers and cyclists a well-earned break; dogs are welcomed with their own firkin of water. Pleasant gardens help make this an appealing destination throughout the year. Q ➜ ☻ ◖ ♣ ♠ P ☒ (X3) ✿ ⬤

Stratton

Saxon Arms
20 The Square, DT2 9WG
☎ (01305) 260020 ⊕ thesaxon-stratton.co.uk
Butcombe Original; St Austell Tribute; Timothy Taylor Landlord; 1 changing beer (sourced nationally; often Cerne Abbas) Ⓗ
Set in the village square, with the church and village hall nearby, this is a thatched inn built of stone and flint in 2001, offering a warm, friendly welcome and a real fire. The pub serves three or four ales plus cider and has a decent wine list. There is a good menu of locally sourced food – check the website for offers. Dogs are welcome but not in the main restaurant area. Open all day from 11.30am in August. Q ➜ ☻ ◖ ⓱ ♣ ♠ P ✿ ⬤

Sturminster Newton

White Hart Alehouse ✓
Market Place, DT10 1AN
☎ (01258) 472558
Fuller's London Pride; 5 changing beers (sourced locally; often Gritchie, Wild Beer, Yeovil) Ⓗ
A thatched Grade II-listed pub in the town centre. Now a free house, it has an open-plan beamed bar with ample seating and a piano. Half a dozen real ales are served alongside a selection of bottled craft beers. Local breweries are well supported and a range of boxed cider adds to the choice. ➜ ☻ ☍ ◖ ♣ ♠ P ☒ (X4)

Swanage

Black Swan Ⓛ ✓
159-161 High Street, BH19 2NE
☎ (01929) 423846 ⊕ blackswanswanage.co.uk
Dorset Knob; 2 changing beers (sourced regionally; often Sharp's, Skinner's, Timothy Taylor) Ⓗ
Deservedly popular Grade II-listed pub on the historic High Street in the heart of Swanage. It has two bars with stone floors and log fires, and serves three well-kept ales

– the locally produced Dorset Knob is named after a local biscuit. The pub is renowned for its quality food and booking is recommended. The suntrap garden is the perfect place to enjoy the last of the evening sunshine. Swanage station is the terminus of the steam railway. Q ➜ ☻ ◖ ⩫ ☒ (40,50) ✿

Red Lion
63 High Street, BH19 2LY
☎ (01929) 423533 ⊕ redlionswanage.co.uk
Hop Back GFB; Otter Bitter; Sharp's Doom Bar; Timothy Taylor Landlord; 2 changing beers (sourced nationally) Ⓖ
Traditional 17th-century inn serving up to six ales on gravity from the ground-floor cellar behind the bar. A large selection of real ciders and perries is a big draw, with the range displayed on blackboards in both bars. The lounge has a restaurant area where quality food is served, with curry and steak nights always popular. The large, partly covered garden is busy throughout the year. Q ➜ ☻ ☍ ◖ ⩫ ♣ ♠ P ☒ (40,50) ✿ ⬤

Thornford

King's Arms Ⓛ
Pound Road, DT9 6QD
☎ (01935) 872294 ⊕ kingsarmsthornford.com
Butcombe Original; Palmers IPA; 2 changing beers (sourced regionally; often Palmers, Plain, Yeovil) Ⓗ
The pub is at the heart of the village, next to an unusual red-brick Victorian clock tower, erected to commemorate Queen Victoria's Diamond Jubilee. There is a traditional bar plus a separate restaurant. Outside are pleasant seating areas and children's play facilities adjacent to a large skittle alley. The car park is small but on-road parking is available. Guest ale news is posted weekly on Facebook. Closed Mondays except bank holidays. Local CAMRA Pub of the Year 2020. ➜ ☻ ◖ ♣ ♠ P ✿ ⬤

Wareham

Horse & Groom Ⓛ ✓
St Johns Hill, BH20 4LZ
☎ (01929) 552222
4 changing beers (sourced regionally; often Copper Street, Hattie Brown's, Palmers) Ⓗ
Free house offering four real ales, with a proud emphasis on those brewed in Dorset, plus real cider. Comfortable, welcoming and spacious, it has a reputation for good pub food. Cosy in winter, with two real fires, it also delivers in the summer months, with a pleasant garden tucked away at the rear. The pub hosts quiz nights and occasional curry evenings, offering something for everyone. Local CAMRA Pub of the Year 2020. ➜ ☻ ◖ ♠ ☒ (40,X54) ✿ ⬤

King's Arms ✓
41 North Street, BH20 4AD
☎ (01929) 552503 ⊕ kingsarmswareham.co.uk
5 changing beers (sourced nationally; often Exmoor, Otter, St Austell) Ⓗ
An award-winning traditional thatched inn that dates back to the 1500s and which survived the Great Fire of 1762. The flagstone-floored public bar is adorned with interesting artefacts including old armament shell casings. There is a dedicated dining area with an excellent range of home-cooked food on offer, a drinking corridor and a large garden to the rear with a covered area for smokers. The five varied guest beers are usually from the West Country. Live music often features at weekends. Q ➜ ☻ ◖ ⩫ ♠ P ☒ (40,X54) ✿ ⬤

West Parley

Owls Nest
196 Christchurch Road, BH22 8SS
☎ (01202) 572793 ⊕ theowlsnest-westparley.com
4 changing beers (sourced regionally; often Flack Manor, Otter, Sixpenny) Ⓗ
Charming and welcoming, this Tudor-style building with beamed ceilings and a wood-burner has a comfortable vibe. Four handpumps dispense local and regional ales. The pub is popular for its home-made food; booking is recommended. A beer and home-made pie festival has become an early-in-the-year favourite. There is occasional live music, with an Irish session on the first Thursday of the month. Closed Sunday evening January to March. 🌳🕮🍴🅿️🚌(13,X6)🐾🤶

West Stour

Ship Inn
A30, SP8 5RP
☎ (01747) 838640 ⊕ shipinn-dorset.com
3 changing beers Ⓗ
Once a coaching inn, this popular roadside pub has views across the Blackmore Vale. The public bar features a flagstone floor; the separate light and airy restaurant area has stripped-oak floorboards. There is a patio and large garden at the rear. This friendly hostelry is renowned for superb home-cooked food (no meals Sun eve) and comfortable accommodation. It usually has six local ciders to choose from and always three ales. Dogs are welcome in the bar. A beer festival is held each July. Q🌞🛏🕮🍴🍴🅿️🤶

Weymouth

Belvedere Inn ✅
High West Street, DT4 8JH
☎ (01305) 459099
4 changing beers (sourced nationally; often Isle of Purbeck, New Bristol, Otter) Ⓗ
A Victorian bar on the fringes of the town centre with bare-wood flooring throughout. It is a real gem, serving a varied selection of interesting real ales from microbreweries alongside up to nine ciders. Music features most days (see Facebook for details), and this is one of very few pubs that still has a piano in the bar. A quiz is hosted on Tuesdays. The must-see terrace garden is referred to as the Narden. Families and dogs are welcome. 🌳🌞🍴🍴🚌(1)🤶

Doghouse Micro Pub
2 Great George Street, DT4 8NN
☎ (01305) 567134 ⊕ weymouthmicropub.co.uk
3 changing beers (sourced nationally) Ⓖ
Micropub in a side street near to the Esplanade consisting of one long room stretching several yards to the bar at the back. The bar area has a quirky floor decoration. Three real ales on gravity are mainly from the South West; there are also ciders, gins and country wines. Various bottled Belgian and German beers are sold from the fridge. Only traditional pub snacks are served including pork pies and pickled eggs. Dogs are welcome. Q🌳🚂🍴🚌(1,2)🤶

Globe Inn
24 East Street, DT4 8BN
☎ (01305) 786061
Dartmoor Jail Ale; St Austell Cornish Best Bitter, Proper Job; Sharp's Doom Bar; 2 changing beers (sourced regionally; often Cerne Abbas, Palmers) Ⓗ
Free house with a friendly welcome, tucked away on a street corner just 30 yards from the iconic harbourside.

The Globe is only a short distance from the town centre, the beach and the esplanade, and offers a distinct change from the packed waterside. There is a jukebox and a separate games room with pool table, darts and pub games. A fun quiz is held on Sunday afternoon. Guest ales are not always available in the low season. The cider is Thatchers Cheddar Valley. 🌳🍴🍴🚌🤶🤶

William Henry ✅
1 Frederick Place, DT4 8HQ
☎ (01305) 763730
Greene King IPA; Sharp's Doom Bar; Thornbridge Jaipur IPA; 5 changing beers (sourced nationally; often Adnams, Dorset, Titanic) Ⓗ
A popular Wetherspoon, centrally located close to main transport links. It serves an excellent range of three regular ales and at least five guests, plus ciders. The bars are on two levels but wheelchair access is good, including toilets. The pub is family-friendly and appeals to all ages. It was built in the gardens of the summer residence of Prince William Henry, Duke of Gloucester and brother of George III. 🌳🕮🍴♿🚂🍴🤶

Wimborne

Taphouse
11 West Borough, BH21 1LT
☎ (01202) 911200
9 changing beers (sourced nationally; often Brew Shack, Eight Arch, Sixpenny) Ⓗ
Close to the historic town centre, this narrow wood-panelled pub is known for its long hardwood bar. It serves nine real ales from local, regional and national breweries, including familiar favourites. It has an appealing atmosphere, and conversation rules both in the cosy window-seating area and on the suntrap patio outside. Live acoustic music features on Sunday. 🌞🍴🚌🤶🤶

Wool

Black Bear Inn
High Street, BH20 6BP
☎ (01929) 405541 ⊕ blackbear.website
House beer (by Flack Manor); 3 changing beers (sourced nationally) Ⓗ
Award-winning inn close to the many attractions of the Purbecks. It offers so much more than its four well-kept cask ales. Hearty home-cooked food is served in the front bar and in the restaurant area to the rear. Curry nights, quizzes, walks and a breakfast club all contribute to the pub being a real community asset. The outside seating area is perfect for relaxing in the summer sun. Q🌳🌞🕮🚂🅿️🚌(X54)🤶🤶

Worth Matravers

Square & Compass ★ Ⓛ
Weston Road, BH19 3LF (off B3069)
☎ (01929) 439229 ⊕ squareandcompasspub.co.uk
Hattie Brown's HBA, Moonlite; 3 changing beers (sourced regionally) Ⓖ
A real gem, identified by CAMRA as having a nationally important historic pub interior. It has been in the same family since 1907, and has appeared in every edition of the Guide. Two rooms either side of a serving hatch convey an impression that little has changed over the years. Pasties are available. The sea-facing garden offers views across the Purbecks, and fossils are displayed in the adjacent museum. Beer and cider festivals are held in October and November. Q🌳🌞🍴🤶🤶

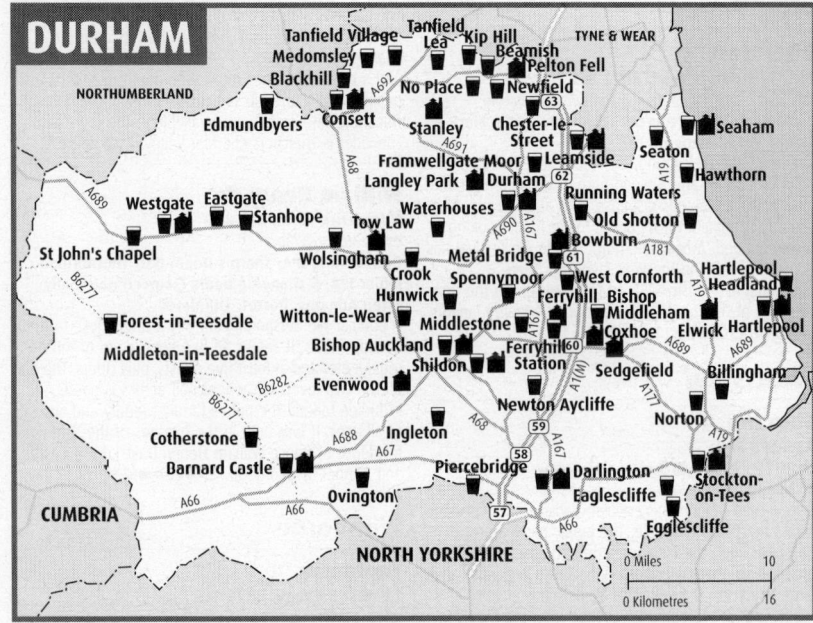

DURHAM

Tanfield Village Tanfield Lea Kip Hill
Medomsley Blackhill
NORTHUMBERLAND
Edmundbyers Consett
Stanley Chester-le-Street
No Place Newfield
Beamish Pelton Fell
TYNE & WEAR
Seaham
Seaton
Hawthorn
Framwellgate Moor Leamside
Langley Park Durham
Waterhouses
Westgate Eastgate Stanhope
St John's Chapel Tow Law
Wolsingham Metal Bridge
Running Waters
Old Shotton Bowburn
Hartlepool Headland
Crook Spennymoor West Cornforth
Hunwick Ferryhill Bishop
Forest-in-Teesdale Witton-le-Wear Middlestone Middleham Hartlepool
Middleton-in-Teesdale Bishop Auckland Coxhoe Elwick
Shildon Ferryhill Station Sedgefield Billingham
Evenwood Newton Aycliffe Norton
Cotherstone Ingleton
Barnard Castle Piercebridge Stockton-on-Tees
Ovington Darlington Eaglescliffe
CUMBRIA Eaglescliffe
Egglescliffe
NORTH YORKSHIRE

Co Durham incorporates part of the former county of Cleveland

Barnard Castle

Old Well Inn L ✅
21 The Bank, DL12 8PH
☎ (01833) 690130 ● theoldwellinn.co.uk
Camerons Strongarm; Timothy Taylor Landlord; 3 changing beers (sourced locally) Ⓗ
The boundary of this 17th-century town-centre inn incorporates part of the medieval castle wall. The pub has a cosy front bar and a comfortable lounge, a separate restaurant and an airy conservatory, plus an enclosed beer garden. At least five well-kept beers are available including three guests from local microbreweries, often Mithril. Excellent food is served daily, and there is accommodation in 10 rooms. A five-day beer festival is held at Easter. The Castle Players meet here.
Q ☮ ❀ ☎ ◐ ♨ ♿ 🚌 (75,76) ❀ 🎵

Beamish

Shepherd & Shepherdess ✅
DH9 0RS (follow signs for Beamish Museum)
☎ (0191) 370 0349 ● shepherdbeamish.co.uk
Timothy Taylor Landlord; 2 changing beers (sourced nationally) Ⓗ
Traditional country pub handily located next to the open-air Beamish Museum. Walkers and cyclists from the nearby Coast-to-Coast trail are welcome; there is a large outdoor seating area with space for parking bikes. The pub is family-friendly, with an outdoor play area. Quality home-cooked, locally sourced food is served.
☮ ❀ ◐ ♿ P 🎵

Billingham

Billingham Catholic Club L
37 Wolviston Road, TS23 2RU (on E side of old A19, just S of Roseberry Rd roundabout, next to bus stop)
☎ (01642) 901143 ● billinghamcatholicclub.webs.com
3 changing beers Ⓗ
Now in its 12th year of continuous Guide recognition, this Victorian mansion and former school is a friendly club, where actively supporting the local community comes high on the agenda. Dedicated volunteers ensure that the club's reputation for offering 150 different beers annually continues. Three beers and two ciders are normally served, with eight ales available throughout the popular bank holiday beer and music festivals. Local CAMRA Community Pub of the Year and Club of the Year 2020. ❀ ♿ ♣ ♥ P 🚌 🚌 (35,36) ❀

Crafty Cock L
113 Station Road, TS23 2RL (at N end of Station Rd, among a row of shops)
☎ (01642) 881478
3 changing beers Ⓗ
This small, cosy bar is one of several micropub-style outlets in Old Billingham. Friendly and knowledgeable bar staff dispense three beers, including offerings from local breweries, as well as real cider. Third-pint tasting bats are available. This popular micro has become renowned locally for its varied live bands. Mexican food is offered Tuesday to Thursday evenings and Sunday lunches are served, with a take-away and local delivery service also available. ◐ ♿ ♥ P 🚌 (36,X9)

Bishop Auckland

Bay Horse
38-40 Fore Bondgate, DL14 7PE (50yds N of bus station)
☎ (01388) 609765 ● dorbiere.co.uk/bay-horse
Timothy Taylor Landlord; 1 changing beer (sourced nationally; often Maxim) Ⓗ
There has been an inn on this site since 1530, and this lively, open-plan bar is a quiet relief from shopping during the week. With live music on Friday and karaoke on Saturday, it becomes joyfully boisterous at the weekend, and is popular for televised sport. It retains its roots as a long-established, proper pub, with pub games teams and an eclectic choice of ales. ❀ ♣ ♥ 🚌 ❀ 🎵

Pollards 🄻
104 Etherley Lane, DL14 6TU (400yds W of railway station)
☎ (01388) 603539
Wainwright; house beer (by Camerons); 3 changing beers (sourced nationally; often Allendale, Consett, Marston's) Ⓗ
A comfortable and busy establishment that combines traditional pub and pleasant diner, a 10-minute stroll from the town centre. Two of the four original areas, including the bar, boast open fires or log-burners, and there is a spacious restaurant to the rear where the famous Sunday carvery can be enjoyed. Five well-kept ales, good conversation and a popular Sunday-evening quiz are among the attractions. **Q🐎❀◐♿⇌♣P🐾**

Welcome
Low Waldron Street, DL14 7DS
☎ (01388) 662492
1 changing beer (sourced nationally) Ⓗ
Very much a cosy, local pub, only a minute's walk from the bus station and main street. There is a single L-shaped room with a dartboard to the rear. It is a welcoming place for a chat, with a great community feel. Live music is hosted on Friday. Closed Tuesday.
Q🐎❀♿⇌♣P🚌🐾📶

Bishop Middleham

Cross Keys 🄻
9 High Street, DL17 9AR (1 mile from A177)
☎ (01740) 651231 🌐 crosskeysbm.com
2 changing beers (sourced nationally; often Consett, S43) Ⓗ
A busy family-run village inn with a good reputation for food. It has a bar with a real fire, a lounge and a large restaurant at the back. There is a large beer garden to the rear and a pool table in the bar, which also has a widescreen TV for live sport. The pub is opposite the remains of Forsters Brewery which closed in 1913 and it may well have been the tap house. The village has a series of walks exploring beautiful countryside and the remains of Bishop Middleham Castle. **Q🐎❀◐♣🚌🐾**

Blackhill

Scotch Arms 🄻 ✔
48 Derwent Street, DH8 8LZ
☎ (01207) 593709
Sharp's Atlantic; 3 changing beers (sourced nationally; often Big Lamp, Caledonian) Ⓗ
A traditional community hostelry off the main street in Blackhill with a large L-shaped bar. The interior was freshened up to celebrate the licensee's 10-year anniversary in 2018. Up to four cask ales are on offer, always including local beers. The welcoming pub is home to pool and darts teams plus a local football club, and is popular for sports TV. Charity nights and other live events often feature. Toasted sandwiches are available.
🐎♿♣⚽🐾📶

Chester-le-Street

Butchers Arms ✔
Middle Chare, DH3 3QD (off Front St on left from Market Place)
☎ (0191) 388 3605 🌐 butchersarms.org.uk
Marston's Pedigree; Jennings Cumberland Ale; 3 changing beers (sourced nationally; often Ringwood, Wainwright, Wychwood) Ⓗ
A cosy pub acknowledged for the quality and quantity of its beers, selling at least five cask ales from the Marston's range. It is also noted for its food, with home-cooking a speciality; Sunday lunches are popular and good value. Teas and coffees are also served. Dogs are welcome and it is convenient for the railway station and all buses through the town. Quiz night is Tuesday.
Q🐎❀🛏◐♿⇌♣🚌(21)🐾

Masonic Centre 🄻
Station Road, DH3 3DU
☎ (0191) 388 4905
4 changing beers (sourced nationally; often Cheviot, Marston's, Oakham) Ⓗ
Guests are more than welcome at the Masonic Centre just off Front Street in the heart of the town. Press the buzzer on the front door and walk in. As well as four changing real ales, you will also find one of the biggest selections of single malt whisky in the area. Sunday lunches and Friday fish suppers are popular. Local CAMRA Club of the Year 2020. **🐎◐♿⇌P🚌(21)🐾📶**

Sticky Wicket 🄻
Emirates Durham International Cricket Ground, Riverside, DH3 3QR
☎ (0191) 387 5502 🌐 thestickywicket.co.uk
Timothy Taylor Landlord; 2 changing beers (sourced nationally; often Durham, Camerons, Maxim) Ⓗ
Sports bar within the grounds of the Emirates Riverside cricket venue, home to Durham County Cricket Club. The bar is open Tuesday to Sunday, with food served daily until early evening. Quiz night is Tuesday; live music features on Thursday, Friday and Saturday nights. An admission fee to the ground may apply during a cricket match. **🐎◐♿⚽P🚌(71)🐾**

Consett

Company Row 🄻 ✔
Victoria Road, DH8 5BQ
☎ (01207) 585600
Greene King Abbot; Ruddles Best Bitter; Sharp's Doom Bar; 3 changing beers (sourced nationally) Ⓗ
Modern pub named after the rows of houses built by the Derwent Iron Company for its workers; most of the buildings were demolished in the 1920s. This spacious

REAL ALE BREWERIES

Barnard Castle ✎ Barnard Castle
Black Storm Pelton Fell
Camerons Hartlepool
Caps Off Bishop Auckland
Castle Eden Seaham
Consett ▤ Consett
Crafty Monkey Elwick
Crafty Pint ▤ Darlington
Devilstone Langley Park (NEW)
Durham Bowburn
George Samuel ✎ Shildon
Hill Island Durham
Hopper House Brew Farm ✎ Sedgefield
Hops & Dots Bishop Auckland
Mad Scientist ▤ Darlington
McColl's ✎ Evenwood
North Pier Tow Law (NEW)
S43 Coxhoe
Saints Row ✎ Darlington
South Causey Stanley (brewing suspended)
Three Brothers Stockton-on-Tees
Village Brewer: Brew 22 ▤ Darlington
Weard'ALE ▤ Westgate
Working Hand ▤ Leamside (brewing suspended)
Yard of Ale ▤ Ferryhill

and well-decorated Wetherspoon establishment is a real asset to Consett town centre. An excellent beer selection, including local ales, and good food, make this social pub popular with a clientele of all ages. ⌂❀◐⌕♣☀⌂⌂❄

Grey Horse L

115 Sherburn Terrace, DH8 6NE (A692, then right along Sherburn Terrace)

☎ (01207) 502585 ⊕ consettaleworks.co.uk/the-grey-horse

Consett Pale Ale, Steel Town Bitter, White Hot, Red Dust; 5 changing beers (sourced nationally) ⊞
Traditional pub dating back to 1848. The interior comprises a lounge and L-shaped bar, with a wood-beamed ceiling. Consett Ale Works Brewery is located at the rear. Beer festivals are held twice a year, live entertainment is hosted on Thursday and a quiz on Wednesday. The Coast-to-Coast cycle route is close by. There is some bench seating outside at the front of the pub. Local CAMRA Town Pub of the Year 2019 and 2020.
❀⌂⌂❄❄

Cotherstone

Red Lion L

Main Street, DL12 9QE

☎ (01833) 650236 ⊕ theredlionhotel.blogspot.com

House beer (by Yorkshire Dales) ⊞
An 18th-century Grade II-listed coaching inn, built in stone and set in an idyllic village. This homely local, simply furnished and featuring two open fires, has changed little since the 1960s. It has no TV, jukebox or one-armed bandit, just good beer and conversation. Two house ales from Yorkshire Dales are served alongside up to six real ciders. The pub is used by various local clubs, and welcomes children, dogs and clean boots. The small garden is a suntrap. Local CAMRA Community Pub of the Year 2020. ⌂❀♣⌂⌂(95)❄❄

Crook

Copper Mine L

26 High Jobs Hill, DL15 0UL

☎ (01388) 763333 ⊕ copperminecrook.com

3 changing beers (sourced locally; often Allendale, Yard of Ale) ⊞
A comfortable family-run local on the edge of Weardale, up the hill from Crook towards Durham. The interior is open plan but with distinct drinking and dining areas. The beers are nearly always from local breweries. Home-cooked quality food is available to suit all tastes.
⌂❀◐P⌂(X46)❄❄

Horse Shoe L ✓

4 Church Street, DL15 9BG

☎ (01388) 744980

Greene King Abbot; Maxim Double Maxim; Ruddles Best Bitter; 6 changing beers (sourced nationally) ⊞
A busy and attractive pub with four interlinked drinking areas in the main building, plus a pleasant sheltered patio to the side. There is the usual Wetherspoon acknowledgement of previous use, in this case a butcher's, in the metal bar top. Local history is reflected in the decor, with a surprise at the top of the stairs in the shape of old mining equipment. ⌂❀◐⌂⌂(X1,X46)❄

Darlington

Bondgate Tavern

94 Bondgate, DL3 7JY

☎ (01325) 962114

4 changing beers (sourced nationally) ⊞

One of the newest town-centre bars, handily located on Bondgate where a number of venues serving good beer can be found. Up to four competitively priced real ales are served, with a focus on local breweries. The busy calendar features live music, sport on TV and quizzes during the week. The pub hosts darts and has a pool table and function room. ⌕♣❄

Britannia L ✓

1 Archer Street, DL3 6LR (next to ring road W of town centre)

☎ (01325) 463787

Camerons Strongarm; Draught Bass; John Smith's Bitter; 3 changing beers (sourced nationally) ⊞
Warm, friendly, local CAMRA award-winning inn – a bastion of cask beer since 1859. The comfortable, traditional pub retains much of the appearance and layout of the private house it once was – a modestly enlarged bar and small parlour sit either side of a central corridor. Grade II listed for its historic association, it was the birthplace of teetotal 19th-century publisher JM Dent. Three changing guest ales complement the three regular ales. ♣⌂P❄❄

Darlington Snooker Club L

1 Corporation Road, DL3 6AE (corner of Northgate)

☎ (01325) 241388

4 changing beers (sourced nationally) ⊞
First-floor, family-run and family-oriented private snooker club that was founded over 100 years ago. A cosy, comfortable TV lounge is available for those not playing on one of the 10 top-quality snooker tables. Twice yearly, the club hosts a professional celebrity. Four guest beers from micros countrywide are stocked and two beer festivals are held annually. Frequently voted CAMRA Regional Club of the Year and a former National finalist, it welcomes CAMRA members on production of a membership card or copy of this Guide. ⌂◐⇌⌂

Half Moon L

130 Northgate, DL1 1QS

☎ (01325) 469965

7 changing beers (sourced nationally) ⊞
Old-school pub just across the ring road from the town centre with friendly staff and customers creating a relaxed atmosphere. It offers seven changing cask ales including brews from micros unusual for the area and occasional beers from the on-site Crafty Pint nano brewery. There is a library area to borrow and exchange books. ⌂♣❄❄

House of Hop L

4B Houndgate, DL1 5RL

4 changing beers (sourced nationally) ⊞
Smart, contemporary bar in the town centre's Imperial Quarter, with links to the local Three Brothers brewery. The pub serves four changing real ales from across the North-East and beyond. It also offers one of the town's widest ranges of craft keg beers, plus ciders and cocktails. Live music is played regularly. Q❄❄❄

Number Twenty 2 L ✓

22 Coniscliffe Road, DL3 7RG

☎ (01325) 354590

Village White Boar, Bull, Old Raby; 7 changing beers (sourced nationally) ⊞
Town-centre alehouse with a passion for cask beer, a winner of many CAMRA awards. Ales are dispensed from up to 16 handpumps, including a stout or porter, plus two real ciders and 10 draught European beers. Huge curved windows, stained-glass panels and a high ceiling give the interior an airy, spacious feel. To the rear is an in-house nano distillery and microbrewery producing gin,

vodka and ale. Sandwiches and snacks are available at lunchtime. Home of Village Brewer beers, commissioned from Hambleton by the licensee. Q❧♿☂

Old Yard Tapas Bar ⓛ
98 Bondgate, DL3 7JY
☎ (01325) 467385 ⊕ tapasbar.co.uk
John Smith's Bitter; house beer (by Tyne Bank); 4 changing beers (sourced nationally) Ⓗ
Interesting mixture of a bar and Mediterranean taverna, offering real ales alongside a blend of international wines and spirits in a friendly setting. Five guest beers are stocked, some from local micros, with two more sometimes available in a separate room. Although this is a restaurant it welcomes customers for a pint and tapas. Food is served lunchtime and evening Sunday to Friday and all day Saturday. The pavement café is popular in good weather. A TV shows sport only. Q❧❀◑♿♣♨☂

ORB Micropub ⓛ
28 Coniscliffe Road, DL3 7RG
☎ 07903 237246
6 changing beers (sourced nationally) Ⓗ
Traditional micropub with friendly, knowledgeable staff in a former beauty salon, the first of its kind in Darlington. There is no TV or loud music so this is a place to relax and engage in conversation. It serves six local real ales, with the town's Saints Row a regular supplier, plus craft beers, two real ciders and a large range of single malt whiskies. ORB stands for Orchard Road Brewery. A recent local CAMRA Pub of the Year. Q♣♨

Quakerhouse ⓛ
2 Mechanics Yard, DL3 7QF (off High Row)
⊕ quakerhouse.co.uk
9 changing beers (sourced nationally) Ⓗ
Seventeen times local CAMRA Town Pub of the Year, and a former North-East Pub of the Year, this gem is located in one of the town's historic Yards. The lively bar offers nine handpulled guest beers from local and regional breweries plus two changing real ciders. This friendly and welcoming establishment is a popular music venue, catering for all tastes from acoustic to rock. It hosts live music every Wednesday and some other nights, with free entry. Home to the Mad Scientist microbrewery.
❀♿♣♦P🖵♨☂

Tanners Hall ✅
63-64 Skinnergate, DL3 7LL
☎ (01325) 369939
Greene King Abbot; Ruddles Best Bitter; 7 changing beers (sourced nationally) Ⓗ
A popular Wetherspoon named after the local 18th-century leather trade that dominated the town. Its 12 handpumps provide a good selection of real ales including up to nine guests, often from local micros. A spacious interior makes this an ideal venue for the pub's beer festivals and Meet the Brewer nights, and the chain's national events. Reasonably priced food is served until late. Q❧❀◑♿♨☂

Durham

Bridge Hotel
40 North Road, DH1 4SE (200yds from Durham rail station)
☎ (0191) 386 8090 ⊕ bridgehoteldurham.com
Wainwright; 2 changing beers (sourced nationally) Ⓗ
Friendly pub that attracts a good mix of regulars and visitors to the region. It was built in the 1850s as lodgings for railway workers constructing the viaduct under which it sits, becoming a public house a few years later. The pub has a comfortable bar and lower dining

area. It serves good-quality home-cooked food every day at reasonable prices, and hosts quizzes on Tuesday and Sunday night with a free hot buffet.
❧🏠◑⇌🖵(21) ♨☂

Colpitts Hotel
Colpitts Terrace, DH1 4EG
☎ (0191) 386 9913
Samuel Smith Old Brewery Bitter Ⓗ
A late-Victorian pub that has been smartened but remains little changed from when it was first built, and continues to thrive on its traditional charm. As with all Samuel Smith's pubs, the noise comes from the chatter of conversation rather than from music or TV. The unusual A-shaped building comprises a cosy snug, a pool room and the main bar area partially divided by a fireplace. If you want to take a step back in time, this is the pub for you. Q❧⇌🖵♨

Dun Cow ⓛ ✅
37 Old Elvet, DH1 3HN
☎ (0191) 386 9219
Black Sheep Best Bitter; Castle Eden Ale; Moorhouse's White Witch; 1 changing beer (sourced nationally) Ⓗ
A Grade II-listed pub, parts of which date back to the 15th century. In 995AD, Lindisfarne monks searching for a resting place for the body of St Cuthbert came across a milkmaid looking for her lost cow. She directed them to Dun Holm (Durham), and the pub is named after the historic animal. There is a friendly front snug with a larger lounge to the rear. It occasionally has a guest beer. Q❧◑🖵(6,X12) ♨☂

Half Moon Inn ⓛ ✅
86 New Elvet, DH1 3AQ
☎ (0191) 374 1918 ⊕ thehalfmooninndurham.co.uk
Draught Bass; Durham White Gold; Sharp's Doom Bar; Timothy Taylor Landlord Ⓗ
Popular city-centre pub, reputedly named after the crescent-shaped bar that runs through it. The decor throughout is traditional, featuring photos of the pub at the beginning of the 20th century, including many from the Miners' Gala. A friendly venue with a relaxed atmosphere, it offers a good selection of ales. The large beer garden overlooks the river. ❀♿🖵(6)♨☂

Head of Steam ⓛ
Reform Place, DH1 4RZ (through archway from North Rd)
☎ (0191) 383 2173
5 changing beers (sourced nationally; often Camerons, Leeds) Ⓗ
Vibrant pub with a continental feel, attracting beer lovers of all ages. As well as five real ales, it offers an extensive choice of draught and bottled beers from around the world. Tasting events are often held featuring a wide choice of ales and ciders. Excellent, good-value food is available during the day, and families are welcome during the day. ❧❀◑♿⇌♦🖵☂

Old Elm Tree ⓛ
12 Crossgate, DH1 4PS
☎ (0191) 386 4621
6 changing beers (sourced nationally; often Durham, Great Corby, Marston's) Ⓗ
One of Durham's oldest inns, dating back to at least 1600, with a friendly atmosphere attracting a good mix of locals, students and visitors to the city. The interior comprises an L-shaped bar and a top room linked by stairs. The pub hosts a Wednesday quiz (arrive early), and a folk group on Monday and Tuesday. A former local CAMRA Town Pub of the Year. ❧❀◑⇌♦P🖵♨☂

Station House ⓛ

North Road, DH1 4SE
🌐 stationhousedurham.co.uk
4 changing beers (sourced nationally; often Fyne Ales, North Riding Brewery, Yorkshire Dales) Ⓗ/Ⓖ
A wedge-shaped pub in the shadow of the railway viaduct, opened in 2015 by CAMRA members. It is very friendly, with a back-to-basics approach and an emphasis on conversation. A changing range of real ale and cider is served directly through a hatch from the cold room. Handpumps have recently been installed, with gravity dispense remaining an option. A dark beer is always available, and an extra ale is often added at weekends. Reigning CAMRA branch City Cider Pub of the Year. Closed Monday. Q♿🚶♿⚖🕮🛏🐕🐾🛜

Victoria Inn ★ ⓛ

86 Hallgarth Street, DH1 3AS
☎ (0191) 386 5269 🌐 victoriainn-durhamcity.co.uk
Big Lamp Bitter; 4 changing beers (sourced regionally; often Durham, Fyne Ales, S43) Ⓗ
A welcoming, family-run, Grade II-listed pub that has remained almost unchanged since it was built in 1899. Its quaint decor, coal fires, cosy snug and genuine Victorian cash drawer help create an olde-world feel. No meals are served but toasties are available. Voted local CAMRA City Pub of the Year yet again in 2020, the Victoria is popular with locals, students and visitors to the city. Q♿🚶🍴🐕🛏🛜(6,PR2)🐾🛜

Waiting Room ⓛ

Northbound Platform, Durham Railway Station, DH1 4RB
☎ (0191) 386 7773
Hadrian Border Tyneside Blonde; 2 changing beers (sourced locally; often Durham, Hadrian Border, Yard of Ale) Ⓗ
This attractive venue on Durham railway station's northbound platform is an interesting relaunch of the original 1872 Ladies' Waiting Room, out of use for many years other than as a storage facility. In keeping with the building's Grade II-listed status, the design is traditional, with chesterfield-style seating, original floorboards and fireplaces, wood panelling and a dark-wood bar. Three handpumps showcase local beers. Q♿♿⚖🛏🛜(40)🐾🛜

Water House ⓛ ✅

65 North Road, DH1 4SQ
☎ (0191) 370 6540
Greene King Abbot; Ruddles Best Bitter; Sharp's Doom Bar; 5 changing beers (sourced nationally) Ⓗ
Situated in former Water Board offices, this popular Wetherspoon gets busy at weekends. It offers a good selection of beers from micro and regional brewers, and hosts a beer festival twice a year plus an annual cider festival. The modern decor is complemented by coal-effect open fires. The pub serves good-value food, and hosts a poker night on Monday and a quiz evening on Wednesday. Alcoholic drinks are available from 9am. 🚶🍴♿⚖🕮🛏🛜

Eaglescliffe

Cleveland Bay

718 Yarm Road, TS16 0JE (jct of A67 and A135, N of Tees bridge)
☎ (01642) 780275 🌐 clevelandbay.co.uk
2 changing beers (sourced nationally) Ⓗ
A large three-roomed locals' pub with an enthusiastic licensee and a reputation for fine premium bitters. Third-pint glasses and tasting notes are available for the four handpumps. The pub's Blues at the Bay live music

evening on Friday features bands of national and international repute. A free buffet lunch is served on Sunday. A former CAMRA branch Community Pub of the Year. Q♿♿♣P🛏🛜(7,17)🐾🛜

Eastgate

Cross Keys ⓛ

A689, DL13 2HW (on main road)
☎ (01388) 517234 🌐 crosskeyseastgate.co.uk
2 changing beers (sourced locally; often Allendale) Ⓗ
A proper family-run Weardale pub, popular with holidaymakers and locals. The ancient 17th-century building has a pleasant interior with a lively, welcoming bar and a restaurant providing relaxed dining. Allendale Brewery beers feature regularly. There is a beer garden to the rear. Comfortable B&B accommodation is available for those wishing to explore the beautiful surrounding countryside. Q♿🚶🍴🛏♿A♣P🛏(101)🐾

Edmundbyers

Baa ⓛ

Low House Haven, DH8 9NL
☎ (01207) 255651 🌐 thebaabar.com/thebaa
2 changing beers (sourced locally; often Cullercoats) Ⓗ
Former Youth Hostel Association building and now an independent hostel close to Derwent Reservoir, dating back to 1600 when it began life as an inn. The cycle sheds have been converted into a welcoming stone-floored micropub-style bar, offering two well-kept ales, invariably from local breweries and often produced just for the pub. Opening hours may vary, especially out of season, so check before travelling. Q🚶🍴A🛏🐾

Egglescliffe

Pot & Glass ✅

Church Road, TS16 9DQ (300yds E of A167, opp parish church)
☎ (01642) 651009
Caledonian Deuchars IPA; Greene King IPA, Abbot; Jennings Cumberland Ale; Wychwood Hobgoblin Gold; 2 changing beers Ⓗ
This old-fashioned and ever-popular local CAMRA multi award-winner, with the same licensee for over 20 years, is a classic, many-roomed 17th-century village local situated in a quiet cul-de-sac. A former licensee and cabinet maker Charlie Abbey, whose resting place overlooks the pub, fashioned the ornate bar fronts from old country furniture. Tasting notes are available for the seven handpumps. Themed food evenings complement the good-value home-cooked food. Outside is a large, sometimes sunny, south-facing garden.
Q🚶🍴🕮♿♣P🛏(7,17)

Ferryhill Station

Surtees Arms ⓛ

Chilton Lane, DL17 0DH
☎ (01740) 655933 🌐 yardofalebrewery.com
Yard of Ale One Foot in the Yard; 4 changing beers (sourced locally; often Yard of Ale) Ⓗ
Traditional pub serving local and national ales and ciders as well as beers from the on-site Yard of Ale Brewery (est 2008). Annual beer festivals are held in the summer and at Halloween. Live music and charity nights are regular events. Lunches are served on Sunday only. A large function room is available. Local CAMRA Country Pub of the Year 2020 and a former regional Pub of the Year. Q♿🚶🍴🕮🛏🐕🛜🐾🛜

Forest-in-Teesdale

Langdon Beck Hotel

DL12 0XP (on B6277, 8 miles NW of Middleton in Teesdale)
☎ (01833) 622267 ● langdonbeckhotel.com
1 changing beer (sourced nationally) Ⓗ
Known as the Sportsman's Rest in the early 1800s, this pub is in the North Pennines, three miles from the spectacular High Force and Cauldron Snout waterfalls and close to the Pennine Way. The welcoming inn has long been a destination for walkers, anglers and those seeking hospitality in scenic and peaceful surroundings, whether staying overnight or just long enough to enjoy the excellent food and drink. A beer festival takes place over the late May bank holiday weekend.
Q❀☺❀╌◑❍ᕔ♣P☙

Framwellgate Moor

Fram Ferment Ⓛ

29B Front Street, DH1 5EE
● framferment.co.uk
2 changing beers (sourced nationally; often Anarchy, Cullercoats, Fyne Ales) Ⓟ
A bottle shop and tap room since 2019, this was formerly an NHS clinic. One wall is lined with large fridges full of bottles and cans of both beer and cider. A large oak bar, believed to have previously been a Methodist pulpit, sits in front of a tiled tap wall, through which both the cask and keg beers are served. Seating options include a monk's bench, cinema seats and pub stools, plus a couple of tables outside the front window.
☺❀ᕔ╤◑☙☙ᕃ

Hartlepool

Anchor Tap Room & Bottle Shop Ⓛ

Stockton Street, TS24 7QY (on A689, in front of Camerons Brewery)
☎ (01429) 868686
2 changing beers (sourced locally) Ⓗ
When Camerons Brewery discovered that it owned an adjacent derelict pub, the building was converted into the brewery's tap and visitor centre. Now in its 18th successful year, it has been rebranded as a bar and bottle shop. Strongarm and the brewery's monthly specials are always available, together with an array of limited edition and continental bottled beers. Meetings, conferences and social events, as well as superb buffets, can all be arranged. ❀ᕔ╤P╌(1,36)☙

Hops & Cheese Ⓛ

9-11 Tower Street, TS24 7HH (100yds S of bus interchange and station)
☎ 07704 660417 ● hopsandcheese.co.uk
3 changing beers Ⓗ
Run by enthusiastic hosts fulfilling a vision of bringing home a flavour of the tapas-style bars experienced on their continental holidays, this welcoming venue represents something modern, original and different. Several interesting beers and a real cider are served in a relaxed atmosphere, along with artisan cheeses and charcuterie. Jazz evenings are hosted. Newspapers, a book club, off-sales and low-key background music enhance the experience. ☺◑ᕔ╤╌(1,36)

Rat Race Ale House

Station Approach, Hartlepool Railway Station, TS24 7ED (on Platform 1)
☎ 07903 479378 ● ratracealehouse.co.uk
4 changing beers (sourced nationally) Ⓗ

The second micropub in the country, now celebrating 12 years of continuous Guide recognition, adheres to the original micropub norms: no fizzy lager or beer, no spirits or alcopops, no TV or jukebox, no one-armed bandit, and even no bar. Since opening in 2009, the pub has offered more than 1,900 beers, sourced from over 500 breweries and served direct to the table by the landlord himself. Two real ciders are also available, as well as crisps, nuts and scratchings. A winner of multiple local CAMRA branch awards. Qᕔ╤♣❍╌(1,36)

Hartlepool Headland

Fisherman's Arms Ⓛ ✪

Southgate, TS24 0JJ (on headland close to Fish Quay in Old Hartlepool)
☎ 07847 208599 ● thefishhartlepool.co.uk
3 changing beers Ⓗ
The Fish, a local CAMRA multi award-winner, is a friendly one-room local. Now free of tie, it serves up to four beers, plus a cider in summer. The pub's theme is keeping music alive – it hosts well-supported open mic nights together with live music on Saturday. A popular quiz is held on Sunday. There is no jukebox, TV or one-armed-bandit. Two beer festivals, also with live music, are held annually. Winter opening hours may vary.
Q❍╌(7)☙ᕃ

Globe Ⓛ

26 Northgate, TS24 0LJ (on headland towards Fish Quay in Old Hartlepool)
☎ (01429) 860097
Camerons Strongarm Ⓗ
Opposite the port that was once bustling with shipbuilding, fishing boats, coal staithes and pit props, this typical two-roomed local is under the stewardship of a friendly and experienced licensee with over 25 years of service to the trade. The price of Strongarm (ask for a Hartlepool Head) still represents remarkable value, reflecting the pub's freehold status, as savings negotiated with Camerons are passed on to customers. A recent local CAMRA Community Pub of the Year.
Qᕔ♣╌(7)

Hawthorn

Stapylton Arms Ⓛ

Village Green, SR7 8SD
☎ (0191) 527 0778 ● thestaps.co.uk
3 changing beers (sourced regionally; often Consett, Maxim, S43) Ⓗ
Delightfully welcoming, locally owned village inn serving excellent food. It has two comfortable, well-appointed rooms – one a bar and the other a lounge/restaurant. Three cask ales in top condition showcase the best of North-East breweries. The Monday evening quiz is well-attended and contested. This hidden-away pub is in an ideal location for walkers exploring the nearby Hawthorn Dene. Q☺❀◑P☙ᕃ

Hunwick

Joiners Arms

13 South View, DL15 0JW
☎ (01388) 417878 ● thejoinersarms.webnode.com
3 changing beers (sourced nationally; often Timothy Taylor) Ⓗ
Family-run village local with a welcoming bar, restaurant, tiny snug and covered yard/pool room. The bar, whose three handpumps serving a changing selection, is the place for proper conversation. Quality locally sourced food is served Wednesday to Saturday

evenings, and Sunday lunchtime in the restaurant. On Monday evening the pub hosts a cheese night.
❀◐♣🅿🍴 (108,109) 🛜

Ingleton

Black Horse 🅛
Front Street, DL2 3HS
☎ (01325) 730374
4 changing beers (sourced nationally) 🄷
Free house and restaurant in a picturesque village. This is a popular community hostelry with a relaxed atmosphere, and a friendly bar that runs into the dining area. Four guest ales come from local micros within a 30-mile radius of the Black Horse. Excellent Italian food is served in the restaurant Wednesday to Sunday. The pub hosts local darts teams and a Sunday night quiz. It is set back from the road and has a large car park.
Q👫❀◐&♣🅿🍴 (84) 🐾🛜

Kip Hill

South Causey Inn 🅛
Beamish Burn Road, DH9 0LS
☎ (01207) 235555 🌐 southcausey.co.uk
Bombardier; 3 changing beers (sourced nationally; often South Causey) 🄷
A large and attractive inn with hotel and restaurant facilities. Extensive seating includes soft leather sofas in front of open fires and dining tables. Beers are always available from the on-site South Causey Brewery. The pub opens early for cooked breakfasts, with non-residents welcome. Several rooms can be booked for private functions. Q👫❀🛏◐&♣🅿🛜

Leamside

Three Horseshoes 🅛
Pit House Lane, DH4 6QQ (about ½ mile N of A690, just outside West Rainton)
☎ (0191) 584 2394 🌐 threehorseshoesleamside.co.uk
Timothy Taylor Landlord; 5 changing beers (sourced nationally) 🄷
A country pub with an excellent restaurant, the Back Room (booking advisable). The traditional bar has open fires in winter and a large TV for sport. Five real ales and a real cider are served. It is home to a local cycle club and hosts a quiz on Sunday evening. Local CAMRA Country Pub of the Year 2019, and runner-up in 2020.
Q👫❀◐&♣🅿🐾🛜

Medomsley

Royal Oak 🅛
7 Manor Road, DH8 6QN
☎ (01207) 560336
Hadrian Border Tyneside Blonde; 2 changing beers (sourced nationally; often Consett, Hadrian Border) 🄷
Traditional country-style pub with a warm, welcoming feel. It has a large bar with a selection of seating including soft sofas and leather chairs, and plenty of dining space. It serves a rotation of quality beers as well as good food. There is a large, attractive rear garden and ample parking to the front. Quiz night is Sunday.
Q👫❀◐&🅿🐾🛜

Metal Bridge

Old Mill 🅛
Thinford Road, DH6 5NX (off A1M jct 61; follow signs on A177)
☎ (01740) 652928 🌐 oldmilldurham.co.uk

4 changing beers (sourced nationally; often Durham, Bowland, Rudgate) 🄷
Originally a paper mill in 1813, the pub offers good-quality food and well-kept ales – four handpumps serve a diverse range, with local breweries supplying at least one of the beers. The food menu is extensive, with daily specials listed on a board above the bar. Larger groups are welcome in the conservatory. Accommodation is of a high standard, with all rooms en-suite. Q🛏❀🛏◐🅿🛜

Middlestone

Ship Inn 🅛
Low Road, DL14 8AB (between Coundon and Kirk Merrington)
☎ (01388) 810904 🌐 theshipinnmiddlestonevillage.co.uk
Timothy Taylor Landlord; 5 changing beers (sourced nationally) 🄷
Regular drinkers come from far and wide to the Ship. It has a bar divided into three distinct areas with an open fire, and a large function room upstairs which is the location for occasional beer festivals. The rooftop patio has spectacular views. Various pieces of Vaux memorabilia are on display – one of the many subjects of conversation. Sunday lunches are popular. A former local CAMRA Country Pub of the Year.
Q🛏❀◐&♣🅿🍴 (56,99) 🐾

Middleton-in-Teesdale

Teesdale Hotel ✅
Market Place, DL12 0QG
☎ (01833) 640264 🌐 teesdalehotel.co.uk
Black Sheep Best Bitter; 2 changing beers (sourced nationally) 🄷
A former coaching inn updated to provide excellent accommodation. This is a popular village local as well as a resting place for Pennine walkers; Middleton-in-Teesdale is often referred to as 'the capital of Upper Teesdale', with High Force and Cauldron Snout nearby. Up to two guest beers, often from local micros are served. Meals can be enjoyed in the main bar or the comfortable restaurant. A farmers' market is held on the last Sunday of the month. Q🛏◐ 🅿🍴 (95,96)🐾

Newfield

Newfield Inn 🅛
Front Street, DH2 2SP
☎ (0191) 370 0565
Maxim Double Maxim; 1 changing beer (sourced nationally) 🄷
A friendly two-roomed pub in the centre of the village, known locally simply as the Inn. It serves one beer from owner Maxim Brewery from nearby Houghton-le-Spring, plus one guest. It hosts a Tuesday night quiz, monthly live music and football on TV, and also offers accommodation. Families are welcome and there is a pleasant beer garden. 🛏🛏&🅿🍴 (78)🐾

Newton Aycliffe

Turbinia 🅛
Parsons Centre, Sid Chaplin Drive, DL5 7PA (off Burnhill Way, next to Methodist church)
☎ (01325) 313034 🌐 turbiniapub.co.uk
4 changing beers (sourced nationally; often Mithril, Three Brothers, Revolutions) 🄷
Named after the famous Tyneside steamship, this friendly free house comprises a large lounge and function room, with traditional pub decor featuring a pictorial history of the Turbinia – the world's fastest ship

on its construction in 1894. The place serves a variety of beers sourced locally and nationally, as well as craft gins. It hosts a beer and cider festival twice yearly. Darts, dominoes and pool are played in the main bar during the week and live music at the weekend. ⚅⚆♿♣⬤P🍴(7) 🐾 📶

No Place

Beamish Mary Inn L
DH9 0QH (follow signs to No Place off A693 from Chester-le-Street to Stanley)
☎ (0191) 392 0543 ⊕ beamish-mary-inn.co.uk
5 changing beers (sourced nationally; often Consett, Big Lamp) Ⓗ
Full of character, this pub is well respected for its warm welcome, generously portioned pub grub and ample selection of well-kept real ale. The location is handy for visitors to the renowned open-air Beamish Museum nearby. Consett Ale Works and Big Lamp beers are usually included among the range of LocAles on offer. Accommodation is available in twin, double and family rooms. Q⚅⚆♿🚭⬤♿⬤P🍴(8,8A,78A)🐾 📶

Norton

Hydes Bar L
Rowan Yard, Billingham Road, TS20 2RZ (in a former builder's yard, at S end of High St)
☎ (01642) 550662
4 changing beers Ⓗ
Contemporary, friendly bar in the former workshop of John Hyde, a family-run joiner and builder's merchant for more than 50 years. The workshop highlights its former use with old items and photographs on display. Large patio doors open onto a south-facing courtyard. Four guest beers and four real ciders are served. Music nights feature throughout the week. ⚆♿⬤🍴(36,37)🐾

Old Shotton

Royal George L
The Village, SR8 2ND
☎ (0191) 586 6500 ⊕ royalgeorgeoldshotton.co.uk
Timothy Taylor Landlord; 2 changing beers (sourced nationally; often Harviestoun, Rooster's) Ⓗ
A well-established pub and restaurant on the old village green, featuring a bar plus larger lounge and dining area. Handpulled cider is often on tap alongside the cask ale. Traditional pub grub and bar snacks are available. Dogs are welcome, with treats at the bar. Q⚅⚆⬤⬤P🐾 📶

Ovington

Four Alls L
The Green, DL11 7BP (2 miles S of Winston & A67)
☎ (01833) 627302 ⊕ thefouralls-ovington.co.uk
2 changing beers (sourced locally) Ⓗ
Friendly stone-built 18th-century inn opposite the village green in what is known as the 'maypole village'. A Victorian sign denotes the four alls: 'I govern all (queen), I fight for all (soldier), I pray for all (parson), I pay for all (farmer).' The single-room interior has an 'upstairs' snug serving excellent, good-value food made with local ingredients. Two real ales are available – a dark and a light from local Mithril Ales. There is seating outside at the front and the rear beer garden is perfect on sunny days. Q⚅⚆⬤♿♣P🐾 📶

Piercebridge

Fox Hole L
Carlbury, DL2 3SJ (on B6275)
☎ (01325) 374286 ⊕ the-foxhole.co.uk
Camerons Strongarm; Timothy Taylor Landlord; 1 changing beer (sourced nationally) Ⓗ
In a village built on the site of a Roman fort, the Fox Hole sits almost centrally between the towns of Darlington, Barnard Castle, Bishop Auckland and Richmond. From the welcoming Wellie bar through to the relaxed yet elegant dining room and alfresco dining terrace, the emphasis is on high-quality, locally sourced food and drink, combined with traditional pub values. The friendly service and three beers – two regulars plus a guest from local micros including Mithril – help make this place a must-visit. ⚆◐♿P🍴(75,76) 🐾 📶

Running Waters

Three Horse Shoes
Sherburn House, DH1 2SR
☎ (0191) 372 0286 ⊕ threehorseshoesdurham.co.uk
3 changing beers (sourced nationally) Ⓗ
Country inn nicely situated a few miles from Durham city, offering good food and drink plus comfortable accommodation. Three cask ales are served, usually at least one sourced locally, with alcohol available from noon. The rear beer garden provides excellent views over open countryside. Q⚅⚆🚭◐♿P🍴📶

St John's Chapel

Blue Bell Inn L
Hood Street, DL13 1QJ
☎ (01388) 537256 ⊕ thebluebellinn.pub
2 changing beers (sourced regionally; often Allendale, Consett, Firebrick) Ⓗ
Originally a pair of terraced cottages, the Blue Bell is a friendly and cosy pub with a bar across the front of the building leading to a small pool room, and a garden to the rear. Situated on the A689, it serves the local community and those who holiday in Upper Weardale. Popular for pub games, it also has books to borrow. Q⚅⚆▲♣🍴(101) 🐾 📶

Seaham

Coalhouse L
39 Church Street, SR7 7EJ
☎ (0191) 581 6235 ⊕ seahamcoalhouse.uk
4 changing beers (sourced locally; often Cullercoats, Yard of Ale) Ⓗ
A former bookmakers', now a much valued part of Seaham's licensed trade. The pub building incorporates 100-year-old timbers salvaged from the town's demolished Co-op. The decor celebrates the area's coal mining heritage, notably one wall's impressive mural depicting Seaham pits. Four changing cask beers are offered along with up to four real ciders and five keg taps. ⚆≈♣🍴(265,60)🐾

Seaton

Dun Cow L
The Village, SR7 0NA
☎ (0191) 513 1133
4 changing beers (sourced nationally; often Jennings, Maxim, Wainwright) Ⓗ
Friendly and unspoilt inn on the village green, featuring a public bar and lounge areas. This is a pub for good conversation or a game of darts; the TV is used only for

special events. The changing guest beer selection usually comprises two light and two dark ales. No meals are served but toasties are always available. Regular busker and acoustic music nights are hosted. A former local CAMRA Country Pub of the Year. 🐴🌼♿♣P🚌(238)🐾📶

Shildon

Canteen Bar & Kitchen [L]

Norland House, Byerley Road, DL4 1HE

🌐 canteen-bar-kitchen.co.uk

George Samuel Locomotion No.1, Harvey, Travelling Light [H]

An ambitious conversion of the former canteen of the famous Shildon Wagon Works. The bar and brewery share a single space, and an entrance with other businesses in the building. There is a spacious drinking area with picnic-style tables, where you can sit within feet of the brewing vessels. The pub's railway heritage is reflected in its decor. Q◐♿🚆P🚌(X21)

Spennymoor

Frog & Ferret [L]

Coulson Street, DL16 7RS

☎ (01388) 815840

6 changing beers (sourced nationally; often Camerons, Consett, Hadrian Border) [H]

Friendly family-run free house offering up to six constantly changing real ales. These come from far and wide, with local and northern microbreweries well represented. The comfortable lounge has a bar with brick, stone and wood cladding and a solid-fuel burner. Sports TV is featured and children are welcome until mid-evening. Live music is hosted on Saturday night. 🐴♣🍎🚌(6,X21)🐾📶

Little Tap [L]

King Street, DL16 6QQ

☎ (01388) 304001

5 changing beers (sourced regionally; often Daleside, Durham) [H]

Clever remodelling of a former sandwich shop as a smart little bar, conveniently located next door to a Chinese takeaway. A plush carpet makes it unusually comfortable for a micropub. Beer is housed in cleverly converted fridges directly beneath the bar. Outside is a small yard in which to take advantage of any sunshine. Q🌼♿🚌🐾

Stanhope

Grey Bull

17 West Terrace, DL13 2PB

☎ (01388) 529428

3 changing beers (sourced nationally) [H]

A community-focused hostelry with a warm welcome, at the foot of Crawleyside Bank at the west end of town. It has a busy bar area at the front and a lounge to the rear, served by a central bar. Tables to the front are popular in fine weather. Convenient for the Coast-to-Coast cycle route. Q🌼🛏♣🚌(101)🐾📶

The Campaign for Real Ale has been fighting for 50 years to save Britain's proud heritage of cask-conditioned ales, independent breweries, and pubs that offer a good choice of beer. You can help that fight by joining the campaign: see **www.camra.org.uk**

Stockton-on-Tees

Golden Smog

1 Hambletonian Yard, TS18 1DS (in a ginnel between High St and West Row)

☎ (01642) 385022

4 changing beers [H]

The town's original micropub is named after the environmental conditions that formerly prevailed on Teesside. Four real beers and two real ciders are on handpump alongside an impressive range of Belgian beers – some familiar, most not so familiar, all served in matching glasses in the continental fashion. Third-pints are also available, on bespoke Smog tasting tables. An extensive selection of free bar snacks is offered on Sunday. Winner of many awards including local CAMRA Pub of the Year 2019. Q🍎🚌🐾

Hope & Union [L]

9-10 Silver Court, TS18 1SL (E of High St, through a ginnel off Silver St)

☎ (01642) 385022

4 changing beers [H]

A bright, modern pub tucked away in a quiet square in the town's cultural quarter. Hope was Robert Stephenson's second locomotive and Union was a horse-drawn coach, both operated in the 1820s by the world's first passenger railway, the Stockton & Darlington. The pub serves four interesting beers, real cider and a large selection of craft ales, gins and whiskies. The cellar is on open display, as is the kitchen, which offers locally sourced, freshly cooked and good-value dishes all day, every day. ◐🚆🍎🚌

Lucifers [L]

Calvin House, Green Dragon Yard, TS18 1AE (E of High St, through a ginnel off Finkle St)

🌐 lucifers-stockton.business.site

3 changing beers [H]

Friendly staff provide a warm welcome at this micropub within a Grade II-listed former warehouse. It is named after local chemist John Walker's 19th-century invention of the friction match, known as the lucifer. The place is billed as the smallest bar in town and can get busy, its benches, booths and stools making for a cosy atmosphere. Three rotating guest beers, normally including a dark ale, are served alongside two ciders. Third-pint glasses are available. Local CAMRA Pub of the Year 2020. 🚆🍎🚌🐾📶

Thomas Sheraton [L] ✔

4 Bridge Road, TS18 3BW (at S end of High St)

☎ (01642) 606134

7 changing beers [H]

This pub in a Grade II-listed Victorian building, a fine conversion of Stockton's law courts, is named after the great Georgian cabinet maker who was born in the town in 1751. It features a large, airy interior comprising several separate drinking and dining areas, plus a pleasant balcony and outdoor terrace upstairs. The guest beers, usually from the area, are served alongside an extensive and varied range of real ciders. A recent local CAMRA Cider Pub of the Year. Q🐴🌼◐♿🚆♣🍎🚌📶

Wasps Nest [L]

Wasps Nest Yard, 1 Calvert's Square, TS18 1TB (E of High St, through a ginnel off Silver St)

☎ 07789 277364

3 changing beers [H]

Tucked away in a quiet square in the town's cultural quarter, between the Grade II-listed Georgian Theatre and the River Tees, the Wasps is firmly established as a feature of Stockton social life. It is a modern and lively pub serving a selection of local beers, real cider and perry. Third-pint bats are available. The pub's claim to fame is that it has the town's only outdoor courtyard patio drinking area. Q❀☘⇌●☕❀

Tanfield Lea

Tanfield Lea Working Men's Club
West Street, DH9 9NA
☎ (01207) 238783
2 changing beers (sourced nationally) Ⓗ
The village has no pub, reflecting its strong Methodist history, but guests are most welcome in this CIU-affiliated club, which has become something of a flagship for real ale in the area after a diet of keg beer for many years. TV sport is shown in the bar and there is a quiet, comfortable lounge. Traditional club activities such as bingo take place and there is usually a live act on Sunday. Local CAMRA Club of the Year 2016-2019. ☎&♣P☕(V7,V8) ☂

Tanfield Village

Peacock ✅
Front Street, DH9 9PX
☎ (01207) 232720
Black Sheep Best Bitter; 1 changing beer (sourced nationally) Ⓗ
A warm welcome is guaranteed in this friendly, traditional, two-bar pub in a pretty village. The Peacock is popular with locals and visitors alike, including bell ringers from the church opposite. Black Sheep is always available alongside a changing guest beer. Lovely home-cooked meals are served Wednesday to Saturday evenings and Sunday lunchtime – the portions are generous and great value for money. There is a small beer garden and ample parking. Q☎❀◑♣P☕(V8)

Waterhouses

Black Horse Ⓛ
Hamilton Row, DH7 9AU
☎ (0191) 373 4576
2 changing beers (sourced nationally; often Castle Rock, S43) Ⓗ
A friendly local with a warm, cosy atmosphere, helped by an open fire at one end and a glass-fronted fire at the other. It dispenses two well-kept real ales, always including one from a local brewery. Good-value Sunday lunches are served. There is a pool table. An excellent pub for walkers, handily situated adjacent to the Deerness Valley Way. Q☎◑♣●P☕(52,725)❀☂

West Cornforth

Square & Compass Ⓛ
7 The Green, DL17 9JQ (off Coxhoe-West Cornforth road)

3 changing beers (sourced nationally) Ⓗ
A proper drinking pub and friendly local on the village green in the old part of Doggy (the village's local nickname). It has sold real ale for more than 40 years and usually offers at least one local beer among its three guests. It is home to darts and dominoes clubs and hosts a well-attended Thursday night quiz. There are good views towards the Wear Valley and Durham city. Q☎❀♣P☕(56)❀

Westgate

Hare & Hounds Ⓛ
24 Front Street, DL13 1RX
☎ (01388) 517212
⊕ hareandhoundswestgate.blogspot.co.uk
Weard'ALE Chilled Nights, Pilsner, Gold, Dark Nights Ⓗ
On the banks of the Wear, on the A689. The spacious stone-flagged bar is partially fitted out with items salvaged from the former village chapel, and is a great place to catch up on local news. The restaurant's patio overlooks the river; here the beer is being brewed beneath your feet. Food, including the famous Sunday carvery, is locally sourced. Q☎❀◑&Å♣P☕(101)

Witton-le-Wear

Dun Cow
19 High Street, DL14 0AY
☎ (01388) 488294
3 changing beers (sourced nationally; often Timothy Taylor) Ⓗ
A welcoming local set back from the road through the village, with a single L-shaped room warmed by open fires at both ends. Dating from 1799, the bar is guarded by a sleeping fox who always seems to have just closed his eyes. There are benches to the left of the bar, and seating outside offering pleasant views over the Wear valley. The decor includes some interesting football memorabilia. Q❀♣P

Wolsingham

Black Lion Ⓛ
21 Meadhope Street, DL13 3EN (50yds N of Market Place)
☎ (01388) 527772
5 changing beers (sourced nationally) Ⓗ
Nationally recognised for its commitment to real cider, hidden away a minute from Market Place, this welcoming, comfortable gem is a great spot for relaxing. An open fire features in the single open-plan room, with a pool table to the rear and TV sport to the front. Local charities benefit from the efforts of the pub. Six or more ciders can be on offer. Local CAMRA Country Cider Pub of the Year 2020. Q❀&♣●☕(101)❀☂

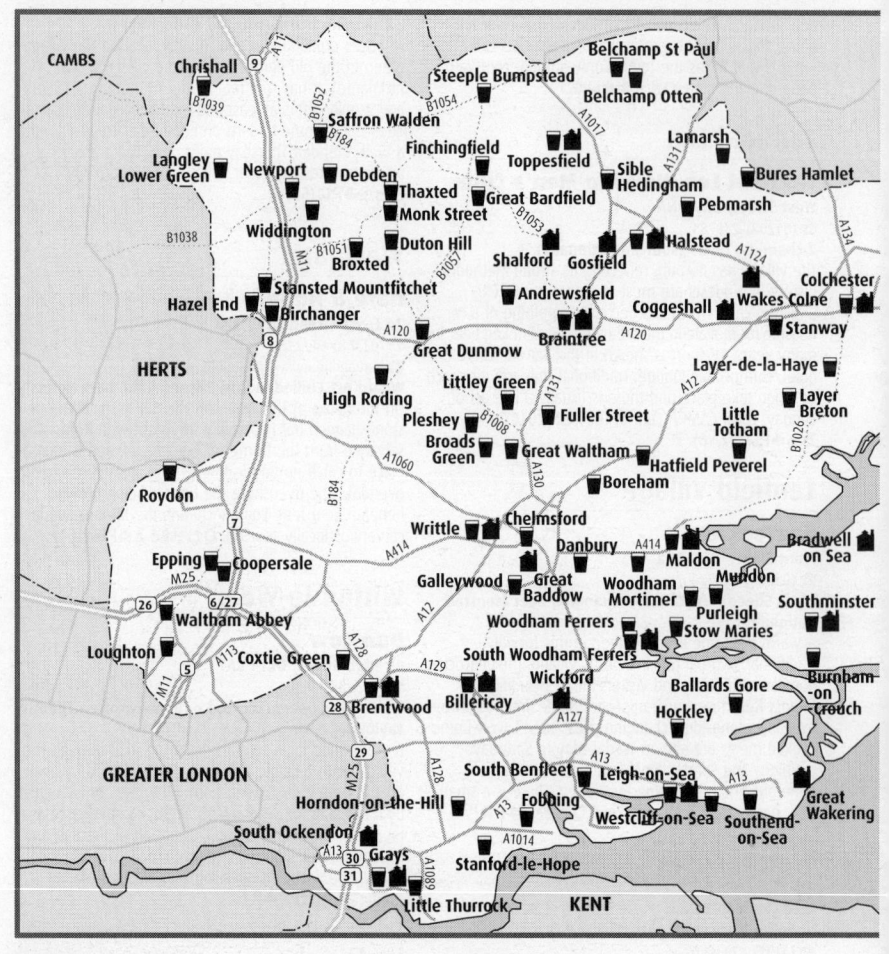

Map locations shown:

CAMBS · Chrishall · A11 · B1039 · Steeple Bumpstead · Belchamp St Paul · Belchamp Otten · B1052 · B1054 · Saffron Walden · Finchingfield · Lamarsh · A1017 · Toppesfield · Sible Hedingham · Bures Hamlet · Langley Lower Green · Newport · Debden · B184 · Great Bardfield · Pebmarsh · B1038 · Widdington · Thaxted · Monk Street · B1051 · Duton Hill · B1053 · Shalford · Gosfield · Halstead · A1124 · Colchester · Broxted · B1057 · Andrewsfield · Coggeshall · Wakes Colne · A134 · Hazel End · Stansted Mountfitchet · Birchanger · Braintree · A120 · Stanway · HERTS · A120 · Great Dunmow · A131 · Layer-de-la-Haye · Littley Green · A12 · Layer Breton · High Roding · Pleshey · Fuller Street · Little Totham · B1026 · Broads Green · B1008 · Great Waltham · Roydon · B184 · A1060 · A130 · Hatfield Peverel · Boreham · Epping · 7 · Writtle · Chelmsford · Bradwell on Sea · Coopersale · M25 · A414 · Danbury · A414 · Maldon · Waltham Abbey · 26 · 6/27 · Galleywood · Great Baddow · Woodham Mortimer · Mundon · Southminster · Loughton · A12 · Woodham Ferrers · Purleigh · Stow Maries · 5 · A113 · Coxtie Green · A128 · A129 · South Woodham Ferrers · Wickford · Ballards Gore · Burnham-on-Crouch · 28 · Brentwood · Billericay · A127 · Hockley · GREATER LONDON · M25 · A128 · A13 · South Benfleet · Leigh-on-Sea · A13 · Great Wakering · Horndon-on-the-Hill · A13 · Fobbing · Westcliff-on-Sea · Southend-on-Sea · South Ockendon · A1014 · A13 · 30 · Grays · Stanford-le-Hope · A1089 · 31 · Little Thurrock · KENT

Andrewsfield

Millibar ⃝L

Stebbing Airfield, New Pasture Lane, CM6 3TH
(accessed by a track beside runway, nr Stebbing Green)
TL689248
☎ 07923 981900 ⊕ andrewsfield.com/andrewsfield-millibar
Bishop Nick Ridley's Rite Ⓗ
The manager of the bar at this flying school is keen on local supply and has installed Ridley's Rite from Bishop Nick Brewery as his sole ale. There is also a range of Bishop Nick bottled beers. The training airfield is a small grass strip dominated by single-engine Cessna aircraft, a Mustang III and B17 Meteor IIIs, and trial flying lessons are available. The public are welcome in the bar and it stays open until 11pm if there are customers.
Q ♿ 🕸 ⊛ ◖ ● P ❀ 🛜

Ballards Gore

Shepherd & Dog

Gore Road, SS4 2DA (between Rochford and Paglesham)
☎ (01702) 258658 ⊕ theshepherdanddogstambridge.co.uk
2 changing beers (sourced locally; often George's) Ⓗ
A traditional country pub with an L-shaped interior, beams throughout and a real fire. The bar at the front offers up to six changing real ales, at least two from breweries nearby, plus a range of real ciders. Towards

the back is the restaurant, serving home-cooked food made with produce from the area. There is seating outside at the front and in the beer garden to the rear, plus an outside bar. Regular music events are popular.
♿ 🕸 ⊛ ◖ ● P 🚃 (60) ❀

Belchamp Otten

Red Lion ⃝L

Fowes Lane, CO10 7BQ (on very small single track lane, signed by duck pond) TL799415
☎ (01787) 278301
Adnams Southwold Bitter; 2 changing beers (sourced nationally) Ⓗ
Lovely inn, hidden away in the smallest of the Belchamps. The owner and his friendly labrador provide a warm welcome, with an open fire in winter. The pub does not currently serve food, but has delivery arrangements with nearby takeaway restaurants. It has darts and a pool table, and occasional events are run. There are excellent views, good walks and cycle rides from here. Closed Tuesday. ♿ 🕸 ♣ ● P ❀ 🛜

Belchamp St Paul

Half Moon ✅

Cole Green, CO10 7DP TL792423
☎ (01787) 277402 ⊕ halfmoonbelchamp.co.uk

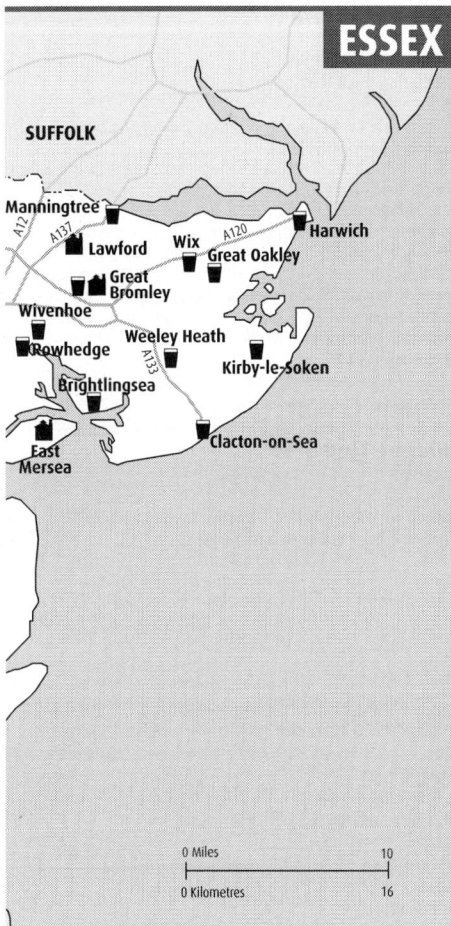

ESSEX

SUFFOLK

Manningtree

Lawford Wix Great Oakley Harwich

Great Bromley

Wivenhoe

Rowhedge Weeley Heath

Brightlingsea Kirby-le-Soken

East Mersea Clacton-on-Sea

0 Miles 10
0 Kilometres 16

Coach & Horses Ⓛ

36 Chapel Street, CM12 9LU

☎ (01277) 622873 ⊕ thecoachandhorses.org *

Adnams Broadside; Mighty Oak Captain Bob; Oakham Citra; Wibblers Dengie IPA; 2 changing beers (sourced nationally) Ⓗ

Close to the High Street, this inviting pub has appeared in this Guide for over 20 years. Six ales are on tap, with one always from Oakham. Good-quality, home-made food is available lunchtimes and evenings, with a popular Sunday roast, plus themed menus including curry nights. The bar service is efficient and friendly. The walls are adorned with prints and decorative plates, and a collection of tankards hangs from the ceiling. There is a cosy and attractive courtyard garden.

❀◑♿⬌♦Pᵉ(100) 🛜

Railway

1 High Street, CM12 9BE

☎ (01277) 652173 ⊕ therailwaybillericay.co.uk

Dark Star Hophead; Wibblers Dengie IPA; 3 changing beers (sourced nationally) Ⓗ

Friendly pub with a welcoming atmosphere, which earns the tag line: Number 1 in the High Street. It has served over 800 different real ales and won several local CAMRA awards. Guest beers are updated on social media. Regular events include a quiz, live music and charity days. This community-oriented venue has two darts teams and sponsors a local rugby team. Traditional bar games include shove-ha'penny with real ha'pennies. A beer garden is outside, and an open fire indoors during winter. ᔑ❀♿⬌♣Pᵉ🐾🛜

Birchanger

Birchanger Sports & Social Club

229 Birchanger Lane, CM23 5QJ

☎ (01279) 813441 ⊕ birchangerclub.com

Greene King IPA; 2 changing beers (sourced nationally) Ⓗ

Greene King IPA; 2 changing beers (sourced nationally) Ⓗ

Beautiful thatched pub dating from about 1685, opposite the village green, with original wooden beams and low ceilings in places. Three real ales and guest beers change regularly. This friendly venue is popular with regulars and has an excellent choice of freshly made and locally sourced bar and restaurant meals (no food Sun eve or Mon). It provided one of the locations for the first Lovejoy TV series. Qᔑ❀◑♿♣Pᵉ🛜

Billericay

Billericay Brewing Co Shop & Micropub

52 Chapel Street, CM12 9LS

☎ (01277) 500121 ⊕ billericaybrewing.co.uk

Billericay Zeppelin, Blonde, Dickie; 4 changing beers (sourced locally; often Billericay) Ⓖ

Brewery tap micropub next door to the brewery. It serves up to four ales on gravity, mostly from the brewery, plus two other beers on KeyKeg. It is also a beer shop, with bottles from Billericay plus other breweries, as well as foreign beers. Beer festivals are held each year in March, June, September and December. Seating is on high stools next to solid wooden tables. There is an extra pop-up bar in the brewery at busy times.

ᔑ❀⬌♦🖶(100,222) 🐾🛜

REAL ALE BREWERIES

Billericay Billericay
Bishop Nick Braintree
Brentwood Brentwood
Chelmsford ✦ Great Baddow
Colchester Wakes Colne
Colne Valley Colchester (NEW)
Courtyard ✦ Gosfield
Crouch Vale ✦ South Woodham Ferrers
Fallen Angel Writtle
George's Great Wakering
JackRabbit Lawford
Leigh on Sea ✦ Leigh-on-Sea
Mersea Island East Mersea
Mighty Oak Maldon
Moody Goose 🍺 Braintree
Mr Majolica Grays (brewing suspended)
Neolithic Bradwell on Sea
Other Monkey Colchester
Posh Boys ✦ Wickford
Pumphouse Community Toppesfield
Red Fox Coggeshall
Shalford Shalford
St Botolphs Colchester
Sticklegs Great Bromley (brewing suspended)
Vendetta South Ockendon
Watson's Colchester
White Hart 🍺 Halstead
Wibblers ✦ Southminster

A friendly local social club where CAMRA members are welcome as guests. Many matches and events take place here, so it can get busy. Beers change frequently as the turnover is high. The club has football, cricket, bowls, darts, crib and snooker teams, and hosts regular quizzes, plus bingo and bottle draws. It has won CAMRA branch Club of the Year awards on several occasions.
🏠🏵️🌓◗👩‍🦽♣️👜🏘️(7,7A) 🛜

Boreham

Queen's Head
Church Road, CM3 3EG
☎ (01245) 467298
4 changing beers (sourced nationally) Ⓗ
In the same family for over 20 years, this friendly pub, dating from the 16th century, is tucked away behind houses just past the church. It has two contrasting bars, one with bench seating, where darts, dominoes and crib are played; the other is for dining. In the warmer months the garden is a lovely area in which to sit at one of the picnic benches and enjoy the tranquil setting, within sight of the village church. Home-cooked food is served Wednesday to Sunday. Beer festivals take place over the bank holiday weekends of Easter and August.
🏠🏵️🌓◗♣️👜🏘️(40,71A) 🛜

Braintree

King William IV Ⓛ
114 London Road, CM77 7PU
☎ (01376) 567755 ⊕ kingwilliamiv.co.uk
4 changing beers (sourced nationally) Ⓖ
Friendly free house serving a changing range of real ales, usually featuring Essex microbreweries and at least one from the Moody Goose Brewery, located in the grounds. An interesting selection of ciders is also on offer. There is a main bar and a small back bar with a dartboard. Outside, a large patio area and extensive gardens host beer festivals and other events. This is a traditional drinking pub and does not offer food other than snacks.
Q🏵️♣️👜🏘️🐕🛜

Brentwood

Rising Sun ✅
144 Ongar Road, CM15 9DJ (on A128, at Western Rd jct)
☎ (01277) 227400
Fuller's London Pride; Greene King IPA; Sharp's Atlantic; Timothy Taylor Landlord; 1 changing beer (sourced nationally) Ⓗ
Superb community local with five real ales, extensively refurbished and extended in spring 2020. A charity quiz is held on Monday evenings, there are frequent darts matches in the public bar, and occasional charity nights. Five handpumps in the saloon bar dispense four regular ales plus a guest. Signed film and sports prints adorn the walls. Outside there is a covered, heated smokers' area, a new garden and a patio. 🏠🏵️♣️👜🏘️(21,71)🐕🛜

Victoria Arms
50 Ongar Road, CM15 9AX (on A128)
☎ (01277) 223371
Adnams Ghost Ship; Harvey's IPA, Sussex Best Bitter; 3 changing beers (sourced nationally) Ⓗ
Pleasant and comfortable Gray & Sons pub with a friendly atmosphere. Unusually for the area, there are normally two Harvey's beers on tap, as well as Ghost Ship and three changing ales. There are several TV screens which mostly show sports matches, and an outside smoking area. Cribbage and other card games are played. Local CAMRA Pub of the Year 2021. 🏵️♣️👜🏘️(498,21)

Brightlingsea

Railway Tavern Ⓛ
58 Station Road, CO7 0DT
⊕ alesattherails.co.uk
Crouch Vale Essex Boys Best Bitter; 2 changing beers (sourced nationally) Ⓗ
Originally built as a hotel in 1865 to service the railway, the building has been a public house for many years. The refurbishment that began over a year ago was completed during periods of lockdown. New owners in 2018 have not only maintained the ales in excellent condition, and put on the annual real cider festival each May (circumstances allowing), but have added a new lounge bar area in 2019 and refurbished the existing bar areas and toilets. Local CAMRA Pub of the Year 2020.
Q🏠🏵️🏵️👜🏘️(62) 🐕

Broads Green

Walnut Tree Ⓛ ✅
CM3 1DT
☎ (01245) 360222
Bishop Nick Ridley's Rite; Timothy Taylor Landlord; 1 changing beer (sourced nationally) Ⓖ
Handsome Victorian pub overlooking the green. The front door opens into what was the bottle and jug, but is now a small snug. To the left is the wood-panelled public bar, little-changed since it was built in 1888. To the right is the slightly more modern saloon bar. Outside there is seating at the front, a children's play area and a large garden. There is no food, the landlord preferring to concentrate on his beers and to maintain a traditional atmosphere. Q🏠🏵️🏵️👣♣️👜🏘️🐕🛜

Broxted

Prince of Wales Ⓛ ✅
Brick End, CM6 2BJ
☎ (01279) 850256 ⊕ princeofwalesbroxted.co.uk
Greene King IPA; 5 changing beers (sourced nationally) Ⓗ
This former Charrington pub has been turned into a welcoming community venue after the current landlords took over in 2011. It has a comfortable split-level bar, an adjoining room with two wood-burners, and a conservatory seating up to 50. Generous portions of food, mostly locally sourced, will satisfy the most demanding appetite. A small garden is to the rear. Up to five guest beers are sold, with LocAle from Bishop Nick. Closed Monday. 🏠🏵️🌓◗👜🏘️(6)🐕🛜

Bures Hamlet

Eight Bells Ⓛ
6 Colchester Road, CO8 5AE
☎ (01787) 227354
Greene King Abbot, IPA; 4 changing beers (sourced nationally) Ⓗ
A real gem, this is a traditional village local with a longstanding landlord in his 41st year here. It has three drinking and dining areas, served by a large bar, and a separate function area. Monthly open mic nights are hosted. Traditional pub food is available daily, with a roast on Sunday. Walkers and cyclists are always welcome. Only five minutes' stroll from Bures station. Q🏠🏵️🌓◗👣🚆(Bures) 👜🏘️🐕🛜

Burnham-on-Crouch

Queen's Head
26 Providence, CM0 8JU

☎ (01621) 784825
Dark Star Hophead; Wibblers Dengie IPA; 2 changing beers (sourced nationally) ⊞
A true locals' pub just off the High Street, owned by Gray & Sons. It is frequently busy, with a good and varied range of beers and ciders. The basic no-frills interior is warmed in winter by a log-burning stove. The pool table is a popular feature. A small sheltered courtyard to the rear provides a delightful outside space, with a heated smoking area. Beer festivals are hosted. Burnham-on-Crouch railway station is 15 minutes' walk away.
⌖♣●🖪🖳(31X) ❀🛜

Chelmsford

Ale House 🅛
24-26 Viaduct Road, CM1 1TS
☎ (01245) 260535 ⊕ the-ale-house-chelmsford.co.uk
12 changing beers (sourced nationally) ⊞
A unique bar in Chelmsford, located under the arches at the railway station, with one of the widest ranges of continuously changing beers in Essex, always including dark and stronger beers, plus eight craft keg beers and 12 real ciders. There are also imported ales on tap and a wide range of bottled beers from around the world. No food is served but customers are welcome to bring their own or order a takeaway. A quiz is held on the last Sunday of the month and there are regular beer festivals. Only 10 minutes' walk from Essex County Cricket ground and a five minute walk to the High Street.
ॐ⌖&≒♣●🖪❀🛜

Endeavour 🅛
351 Springfield Road, CM2 6AW
☎ (01245) 257717
Adnams Ghost Ship; Mighty Oak Captain Bob, Maldon Gold; Wibblers Dengie IPA; 1 changing beer (sourced nationally) ⊞
Busy and friendly pub, comprising three rooms. Four regular ales are on tap as well as one changing guest beer. Cooked meals are served lunchtimes and evenings, and sandwiches are available all day (Mon-Sat). Booking is recommended for the roast dinner on Sunday. All food is good value, locally sourced and home cooked. This is a true community venue, with sport on TV, darts and crib teams, and regular charity events. Outside is an attractive courtyard garden. ⌖◑♣🖪❀🛜

Hop Beer Shop 🅛
173 Moulsham Street, CM2 0LD
☎ (01245) 353570
4 changing beers (sourced nationally) 🅖
Essex's first micropub. Four beers are served by gravity, with local breweries always represented, alongside interesting ales from around the country – usually including a stout or porter and a golden beer. There are also craft keg beers, 100 or so bottled beers from regional and international breweries, and bottled cider, which may be drunk here or purchased to take home. Local CAMRA Cider Pub of the Year 2018-2020. Closed Monday. Q●🖪❀🛜

Oddfellows Arms Smokehouse 🅛
195 Springfield Road, CM2 6JP
☎ (01245) 490514 ⊕ theoddfellowsarms.com
Bishop Nick 1555; Dark Star Hophead; St Austell Tribute; Wibblers Dengie IPA; 1 changing beer (sourced nationally) ⊞
The pub has a modern wood interior but maintains the feel of a local. There is a large U-shaped bar area and a back room with a pool table, leading out to the attractive decked garden/smoking area. An extensive menu of home-made food is served weekday lunchtimes and

evenings, and all day at weekends, including wood-smoked brisket, ribs and pulled pork. Poker nights are hosted twice a week, live music monthly and a beer festival every year. ⌖◑♣🖪🖳🛜

Orange Tree 🅛
6 Lower Anchor Street, CM2 0AS
☎ (01245) 262664 ⊕ the-ot.com
Mighty Oak Oscar Wilde; 7 changing beers (sourced nationally) ⊞
One of the best real ale destinations in Chelmsford and local CAMRA Pub of the Year 2020. It is a place for conversation and meeting friends, with separate public and saloon bars. A great range of real ales is on tap, always including something dark, plus craft keg beers. Food is served at lunchtime, including a roast on Sunday, and a steak and curry night on Thursday evening. Quiz night is Tuesday. Q⌖⌖◑&♣●🖪❀🛜

Queen's Head 🅛
30 Lower Anchor Street, CM2 0AS
☎ (01245) 265181
Crouch Vale Essex Boys Best Bitter, Brewers Gold; 5 changing beers (sourced nationally) ⊞
Crouch Vale Brewery's first pub in the city, selling three of its beers permanently, with four guests which may include a Crouch Vale seasonal and always include a dark beer. The Victorian L-shaped bar has bare-board flooring and comfortable bench seating. Two fires make it cosy in winter. This popular local can be busy when there is a match at the nearby county cricket ground. The Essex Beard Club meets here once a year in February.
Q⌖♣🖪❀🛜

Railway Tavern 🅛
63 Duke Street, CM1 1LW
☎ (01245) 280679
Greene King Abbot; Red Fox IPA; 5 changing beers (sourced nationally) ⊞
A Tardis-like corner pub, right outside Chelmsford station. Not surprisingly, a railway theme dominates. It is long and narrow, with banks of handpumps at opposite ends of the central bar counter. There is a small enclosed garden where you can listen to the station announcements and marvel at the ever-changing mural. It may stay open later on Sundays in the summer. This traditional hostelry also sells craft beers and over 50 different gins. ⌖◑≒♣●🖪❀🛜

Chrishall

Red Cow
11 High Street, SG8 8RN (N of B1039) TL446393
☎ (01763) 838792 ⊕ theredcow.com
Adnams Southwold Bitter; Woodforde's Wherry; 2 changing beers (sourced nationally) ⊞
Thatched 14th-century inn in a small village near the Cambridgeshire/Hertfordshire borders. Guest beers are usually from East Anglia. It is frequented by many local groups including the cricket club, the village book group, stallholders from the farmers' market and the WI. Special occasions can be celebrated with meals from the extensive award-winning menu, either in the tiled bar or in the restaurant, separated by original open timbering. There is also a small sweet shop. Situated on the ancient Icknield Way, the pub is a popular stop-off for ramblers.
Q⌖⌖🚤◑P❀🛜

Clacton-on-Sea

Old Lifeboat House
39 Marine Parade East, CO15 6AD

☎ (01255) 476799
Greene King Abbot; St Austell Proper Job; 3 changing beers (sourced nationally; often Colchester, Greene King, St Austell) H
A regular in the Guide since 2011, this family-run establishment sells five ales, with local brews from Colchester, Mauldons and Mighty Oak featuring regularly, as well as numerous ciders and perries. Food is served on Wednesday evening. Snacks are on offer Tuesday evening and Sunday lunchtime, with a monthly roast instead during the winter months. Darts teams play on Monday or Thursday. ☆❀◗♿⇌♣●P🚂🚌📶

Colchester

Ale House L
82 Butt Road, CO3 3DA
☎ (01206) 573464 🌐 thealehousecolchester.co.uk
10 changing beers (sourced nationally) H/G
A free house with a friendly landlady and staff, and relaxing decor. A wide range of ales is sold, dispensed via handpump and also on gravity (including at least one dark beer), as well as real cider. Quiz night is every third Wednesday, with a folk music session on the fourth Tuesday of the month. Darts, bar billiards and TV sport are available. There is a large walled garden at the rear. Currently the CAMRA Town Pub of the Year for Colchester. ❀⇌(Town) ♣●🚌(64) 📶

Bricklayers L ✔
27 Bergholt Road, CO4 5AA
☎ (01206) 852008
Adnams Broadside; Sharp's Atlantic, Doom Bar; 4 changing beers (sourced nationally) H
Close to Colchester mainline station, the Brick is a lively two-bar hostelry. It has a public bar with darts and pool, a saloon bar with two large TVs showing various sports, plus a snug and a conservatory. There is a car park at the rear, an outside area and a garden. Food is served, with a curry night on Thursday. There are quizzes twice a month and live music on the last weekend of the month.
Q☆❀◐◗⇌♣●P🚌🐾📶

British Grenadier L
67 Military Road, CO1 2AP
☎ 07832 215118
4 changing beers (sourced nationally) H
This welcoming hostelry, run by a knowledgeable publican, has featured in the Guide for over 10 years. It is a traditional Victorian two-bar pub with a pool table in the small rear bar and a dartboard in the main bar, heated by an open fire in the winter months. This venue is LocAle accredited, and serves a changing range of local, regional and nationally sourced beers and ciders via handpumps. ☆❀♿⇌(Town)♣●🚂🚌(6,61)🐾📶

Fat Cat
65 Butt Road, CO3 3BZ (nr police station)
☎ (01206) 577990 🌐 fatcatcolchester.co.uk
Crouch Vale Brewers Gold; Fat Cat Honey Ale; Hop Back Summer Lightning; Woodforde's Wherry; 8 changing beers (sourced nationally) G
A welcome return to the Guide for this popular single-bar, split-level establishment just outside the town centre. You are always assured of good banter and a pleasing choice of quality ales, all on gravity dispense from a central taproom; there is also a large selection of ciders and Belgian beers. Food is served in the evenings and at lunchtimes from Wednesday to Sunday. It boasts the town's smallest pub garden and has regular crib competitions and a Sunday quiz.
☆❀◐◗♿⇌(Town) ♣●🚌(64,63) 🐾📶

New Inn L
36 Chapel Street South, CO2 7AX
☎ (01206) 575277 🌐 theoldnewinnpub.co.uk
Bishop Nick Ridley's Rite; 7 changing beers (sourced nationally) H
With a quiet, comfortable and cosy saloon bar, an open fire and a stripped-back public bar featuring music, TV sports and friendly conversation, this is definitely a venue of two halves. There are up to eight real ales and four real ciders, and regular brewery tap takeovers take place throughout the year. Traditional pub food is served Tuesday to Saturday lunchtimes and evenings, with a roast lunch on Sunday. Numerous board games are available in the saloon bar.
Q☆❀◐◗♿⇌(Town) ♣●P🚌(64) 🐾📶

Odd One Out L
28 Mersea Road, CO2 7ET
☎ (01206) 615102
Colchester Metropolis, Number One; 7 changing beers (sourced nationally) H
The multi award-winning Odd One Out features two bars. It offers at least two beers from Colchester Brewery and a range of changing guest ales over seven handpumps, as well as a varied range of ciders. There is a small secluded rear garden allowing for a quiet pint, and a small function room that is well used by a range of community groups. Check Facebook for regular evening quizzes, impromptu music sessions and barbecues.
Q☆❀⇌(Town) ●🚌(8,67) 🐾📶

Purple Dog L ✔
42 Eld Lane, CO1 1LS
☎ (01206) 564995 🌐 thepurpledogpub.co.uk
Adnams Ghost Ship; Fuller's London Pride; Sharp's Doom Bar; 3 changing beers (sourced nationally) H
This wood-beamed corner pub in the town centre is one of the oldest bars in Colchester, dating back to 1647, and has an outdoor drinking area. Six handpumps provide mainly regional beers alongside the usual town-centre offerings. An extensive menu, complemented by changing special dishes, is served daily. Regular music events, including DJs and occasional live bands, are hosted and there is a monthly quiz night.
☆❀◐◗⇌(Town) 🚌📶

Victoria Inn L
10 North Station Road, CO1 1RB
☎ (01206) 514510 🌐 victoriainncolchester.co.uk
5 changing beers (sourced nationally) H
A multi award-winning hostelry with friendly, knowledgeable staff, on the edge of the town centre. It serves two unique house ales and three guests from microbreweries, both in the area and further afield, as well as up to nine real ciders, three craft keg taps and an impressive range of cans and bottles. Keg lager, cider and stout are all locally brewed (no mainstream brands). Live music plays on Sunday afternoon. The pub is dog-friendly and child-tolerant, and has a cosy courtyard and a covered area outside. ❀⇌♣●🚌🐾📶

Coopersale

Theydon Oak L
9 Coopersale Street, CM16 7QJ
☎ (01992) 572618
Adnams Ghost Ship; Fuller's London Pride; St Austell Tribute; Woodforde's Wherry; 2 changing beers (sourced locally) H
A quaint and ancient inn, parts of which date back 400 years, with log-burners and comfortable seating, lots of exposed beams, horse brasses and antiques. Rumours

abound locally that a ghost has been seen several times in the cellar, and occasionally passing by the inglenook fireplace. The pub has a good reputation for its wide assortment of home-cooked food. A beer festival is held in May and there are various events throughout the year. The pub is set in beautiful countryside not far from Epping – there is a footpath from Epping underground station. Q🕏🌭🅭◐●🅿🚫(381)🕸

Coxtie Green

White Horse 🅛
173 Coxtie Green Road, CM14 5PX (1 mile W of A128, at jct with Mores Lane) TQ564959
☎ (01277) 372410 ⊕ whitehorsebrentwood.co.uk
Brentwood Marvellous Maple Mild; Fuller's London Pride; Greene King Abbot; house beer (by Brentwood); 6 changing beers (sourced nationally) 🅗
Pleasant country free house with an extended and comfortable saloon bar. Badged as the Brentwood Brewery tap, it has 10 handpumps usually dispensing four regular beers and six guests, of which three are usually from Brentwood and the rest from anywhere. There is a large play area in the garden to keep children happy. The local bus service is limited but reliable. 🕏🌭🅭🅵♣●🅿🚫(71,72)🕸🕸

Danbury

Cricketers Arms
Penny Royal Road, CM3 4ED
☎ (01245) 222022 ⊕ cricketersarmsdanbury.com
Shepherd Neame Whitstable Bay Pale Ale, Spitfire, Bishops Finger; 2 changing beers (sourced nationally; often Shepherd Neame) 🅗
The building is 400 years old and has been an inn for about 200 years. This Shepherd Neame outlet has been refurbished and has a public bar, main bar, lounge and dining room, plus plenty of outdoor seating. It hosts monthly quiz nights, a magic circle on a Tuesday, and an annual beer festival in August. Popular with ramblers and cyclists, it also provides towels and snacks for dogs. An arts and crafts centre is attached, and it is close to National Trust properties – Danbury Common, Danbury Park and lakes. Q🕏🌭🅭◐🅵♣🅿🚫🕸🕸

Debden

Plough 🅛
High Street, CB11 3LE
☎ (01799) 541899 ⊕ theploughatdebden.co.uk
Greene King IPA; 3 changing beers (sourced nationally) 🅗
The sole remaining village pub, with a restaurant and garden, now revitalised by a young energetic couple. It offers a warm and friendly welcome and runs beer festivals, other events and local celebrations. An interesting and varied range of beers from the area is served alongside an extensive food menu. The Plough is an important social centre for this village and the surrounding area, and a good base for walkers and cyclists. A monthly quiz night is normally held on the third Wednesday. Closed Monday. Q🕏🌭◐●🅿🚫(6,313)

Duton Hill

Three Horseshoes 🅛
CM6 2DX (1 mile W of B184) TL606268
☎ (01371) 870681
Mighty Oak Maldon Gold; 2 changing beers (sourced nationally) 🅗

Outstanding village inn with a garden, wildlife pond and terrace overlooking the Chelmer Valley and farmland. The landlord often hosts a weekend of open-air theatre in July. A millennium beacon in the garden, breweriana and a remarkable collection of Butlin's memorabilia are features. A beer festival is held on the late spring bank holiday in the Duton Hill Den. Look for the pub sign depicting a famous painting, Our Blacksmith, by former Duton Hill resident Sir George Clausen. Local and parish newspapers are available. Local CAMRA Pub of the Year 2021. 🕏🌭🅭♣🅿🚫(313)🕸

Epping

Forest Gate Inn 🅛
111 Bell Common, CM16 4DZ (turn off main road opp Bell Hotel)
☎ (01992) 572312 ⊕ forestgateinnepping.co.uk
Adnams Southwold Bitter, Broadside; Bishop Nick Ridley's Rite 🅗**; 1 changing beer** 🅗/🅖
On the edge of Epping Forest, this is a 17th-century building with low ceilings and flag floors, run by the same family for 50 years. It is popular with locals, walkers and their dogs. Hot meals and soups are served in the bar, as well as in Haywards Restaurant next door. There is a large grassed seating area. The town centre and London underground station are around a mile away. Q🕏🌭🅵◐●🅿🚫🕸

Finchingfield

Finchingfield Lion 🅛
6 Church Hill, CM7 4NN (on B1053, opp guildhall)
☎ (01371) 810400 ⊕ thefinchingfieldlion.co.uk
Adnams Southwold Bitter; Greene King IPA; 2 changing beers 🅗
Fifteenth-century coaching inn in a famously picturesque village, just up the hill from the pond. A friendly venue with a warm atmosphere, it has a heavily beamed bar area with an open fire, and a separate restaurant and function room. There is a garden for better weather. Good-value home-cooked food is served. Cyclists, walkers, locals and families are all made welcome. Q🕏🌭◐♣●🅿🚫🕸🕸

Fobbing

White Lion ✅
1 Lion Hill, SS17 9JR (nr B1420)
☎ (01375) 673281 ⊕ thewhitelionfobbing.com
Greene King IPA; St Austell Tribute; Sharp's Atlantic; Wadworth 6X 🅗
Attractive hilltop pub in a 15th century building that was originally used as a chandlery, making sails for ships that used the nearby wharf. It was licensed to sell alcohol in 1605. This traditional village local has home-cooked food and a large beer garden, which includes a small bar. The famous author Daniel Defoe and the Peasants Revolt leader Jack Straw reputedly frequented the pub. 🌭🅵◐🅿🚫(11,374)

Fuller Street

Square & Compasses
CM3 2BB TL748161
☎ (01245) 361470 ⊕ thesquareandcompasses.co.uk
2 changing beers (sourced nationally) 🅖
A 17th-century free house known locally as the Stokehole. Set in attractive countryside and handy for the Essex Way long distance footpath, this is a small, well-looked-after country pub. There are exposed beams throughout and two wood-burning stoves in inglenook

fireplaces. Old woodworking tools adorn the taproom bar. Up to three real ales and Berties cider from Braintree are served. Fresh locally sourced home-cooked food is available daily including game from the surrounding estates (no food Sun eves). ✪❍♿♠P🐾

Galleywood

Horse & Groom
The Common, CM2 8PL
☎ (01245) 261653
Greene King IPA; Sharp's Doom Bar; 3 changing beers (sourced nationally) Ⓗ
Traditional pub tucked away on Galleywood Common, overlooking the old racecourse. It has two bars, one quiet and the other with music, a pool table and dartboard. Home-cooked meals are served. Many photos of Old Chelmsford are on the walls, in particular of the old racecourse, as well as a 1908 map of Essex. The location is ideal for walkers, and various car and biker clubs meet here, often holding barbecues. There is occasional live music and a winter beer festival.
Q✪❍♿♣P🚍(42,100) 🐾 🛜

Grays

Theobald Arms
141 Argent Street, RM17 6HR (5-7 mins' walk from Grays rail and bus stations, down Kings Walk)
☎ (01375) 372253 ⊕ theosarms.co.uk
Courage Best; 3 changing beers (sourced nationally; often Brentwood) Ⓗ
Genuine, traditional inn with a public bar that has an unusual hexagonal pool table. Darts and cards are also played. The changing selection of four guest beers features local independent breweries, alongside a range of British bottled beers. Lunchtime meals are served Monday to Friday. Regular summer beer festivals are held in the old stables and on the rear enclosed patio.
✪❍♿⇌♠P🚍

White Hart Ⓛ ✅
Kings Walk, RM17 6HR (5-7 mins' walk from Grays rail and bus stations)
☎ (01375) 373319 ⊕ whitehartgrays.co.uk
Dartmoor Best, IPA; 3 changing beers (sourced nationally) Ⓗ
Traditional local just outside the town centre, rejuvenated since it was taken over in 2006. The regular beers are supplemented by three guests (one usually dark) and a selection of over 30 bottled Belgian beers. Good-value meals are served weekday lunchtimes. There is a meeting/function room and a large, secluded beer garden. Live music features on Saturday. An extensive collection of old-fashioned soft toys is displayed on the historic bar-back. The pub supports pool and darts teams, and sport is screened. Local CAMRA Pub of the Year 2019 and 2020. 🚃✪🏠❍♿⇌♠P🚍🐾🛜

Great Bardfield

Bell Inn Ⓛ
Dunmow Road, CM7 4SA
☎ (01371) 239165
Bishop Nick Ridley's Rite, Heresy; 1 changing beer (sourced locally) Ⓗ
A friendly local with a warm welcome, featuring beers mainly from Bishop Nick. It has a beamed bar and restaurant area, an open fire and a separate public bar with TV and darts, and now has a pool table. Outside there is a patio area. Good-value, locally-sourced food is served. The pub is available for private functions and is

linked to the Great Bardfield artists. There is a quiz on Sunday afternoon. It is also a refreshment stop on the Dunwich Dynamo cycle trip. 🚃✪❍♠🚍🐾🛜

Great Bromley

Cross Inn
Ardleigh Road, CO7 7TL
☎ (01206) 621772 ⊕ greatbromleycross.pub
2 changing beers (sourced nationally) Ⓗ
This remote country inn is an absolute gem and well worth a visit. It was formerly the home of Frank Goddard, a British heavyweight boxing champion. Saved by the community in 2016 after much campaigning, fundraising and a share offer, it now also hosts the post office, coffee shop and library on Wednesday mornings. Since reopening, the interior (including cellar and kitchen) has been refurbished and the toilets extended and twinned, with wheelchair access by radar key 24 hours per day. ✪♿♠P🚍(77A,105) 🐾

Great Dunmow

Boar's Head
37 High Street, CM6 1AB
☎ (01371) 873630
Adnams Southwold Bitter; Fuller's London Pride; 1 changing beer (sourced nationally) Ⓗ
A 400-year-old traditional town-centre pub also accessible from the main public car park. The timber-framed lath and plaster building has beamed low ceilings and three large-screen TVs for sport. Live music is performed on Saturday evenings throughout most of the year. A large decking area at the rear includes covered seating for smokers. No food is served – this is a pub to enjoy for social drinking. ✪P🚍(42A,133)🛜

Great Oakley

Maybush Inn Ⓛ
Farm Road, CO12 5AL
☎ (01255) 880123 ⊕ maybushinn.co.uk
Courage Directors; house beer (by Eagle); 1 changing beer (sourced nationally) Ⓗ
This extremely welcoming and friendly village local is owned by the community and entirely staffed and managed by volunteers. A regular entry in this Guide in recent years, the pub keeps its ales in excellent condition. It is exceptionally community-focused, with various activities such as quizzes, bingo, crib and music every week. A quiet beer garden has been added. A beer festival to mark the anniversary of the initial opening is held each February. Q🚃✪♠🐾🚍(102,104)🐾🛜

Great Waltham

Rose & Crown Ⓛ
Minnows End, Chelmsford Road, CM3 1AG
☎ (01245) 360359 ⊕ roseandcrowngreatwaltham.co.uk
Bishop Nick 1555; Greene King IPA; 1 changing beer (sourced nationally) Ⓗ
A rural pub with a traditional bar, a separate snug seating 10 people and a small function room. It also has a restaurant serving up to 22 people with home cooking from mainly local produce, with a discount on food for NHS workers. Outside, there is a patio area and decking with themed table tops. An open mic night features on the second Wednesday and a jazz night on the last Wednesday of each month. Q🚃❍P🚍(10,42)🐾🛜

Halstead

Dog Inn L

37 Hedingham Road, CO9 2DB
☎ (01787) 477774
5 changing beers (sourced nationally) H
Welcoming traditional venue with two bars, close to the town centre. The public bar has a TV with sports, and the comfortable saloon has a real fire. Five changing beers are on tap, often from local microbreweries. A large beer garden is at the rear, perfect for sunny days. The pub hosts regular live music including a folk session on the first Sunday afternoon, and acoustic sessions on the third Sunday afternoon and on one Saturday evening each month. B&B is available with en-suite rooms.
Q ☏ ☺ 🛏 ♣ P 🚃 (88) ● 🌐 ᯤ

White Hart Inn L

15 High Street, CO9 2AA
☎ (01787) 475657 ⊕ whitehartinnhalstead.co.uk
White Hart Halstead Bitter, Golden Hart; 2 changing beers (sourced nationally) H
One of the oldest coaching inns in Essex, in a medieval hall believed to have been built in the 13th century. It has its own brewery and gin distillery in the old stables; the distillery produces London dry and hop gins. Ales include those from its own brewery as well as local and national beers. Comfortable en-suite bedrooms and traditional home-cooked food are on offer.
☺ 🛏 ◖ P 🚃 (88) ● 🌐 ᯤ

Harwich

Alma Inn L ✅

25 Kings Head Street, CO12 3EE
☎ (01255) 318681 ⊕ almaharwich.co.uk
Adnams Southwold Bitter, Broadside; 4 changing beers (sourced regionally) H
Close to Harwich Quay in the old town, this fascinating medieval building has been a pub since 1859 and is the embodiment of an ancient inn, providing excellent food, drink and accommodation, but with a distinctly modern twist. It has plenty of nooks and crannies to hide away in, or you can sit amongst it all in the main bar, with plenty of history and artefacts to look at. Core ales from Adnams are complemented by changing guests, including local brews from Harwich Town Brewery.
☏ ☺ 🛏 ◖ ≠ (Town) ● 🚃 ● ᯤ

New Bell Inn L

Outpart Eastward, CO12 3EN
☎ (01255) 503545 ⊕ thenewbell.co.uk
Greene King IPA; Mighty Oak Oscar Wilde; 2 changing beers (sourced regionally) H
A historic inn that has always been a community favourite, with many local groups meeting within its 18th-century walls. A changing guest real ale and cider line-up is underpinned by that great rarity these days – a regular mild from Mighty Oak, much loved by the locals. Hearty lunchtime food makes this a great refuelling stop for those wanting to explore Old Harwich, and there is a secret walled garden for sunny weekends and summer evenings. Q ☏ ☺ ◖ ≠ (Town) ♣ ● P 🚃 ● ᯤ

Hatfield Peverel

Cross Keys

The Green, CM3 2JQ
☎ (01245) 633339
Sharp's Doom Bar; 2 changing beers (sourced nationally) H
A traditional open-plan drinking pub where you will receive a friendly welcome whether you are 20 or 90. It offers home-cooked food, and there is free pool every Thursday, a quiz every Sunday lunchtime, and occasional karaoke. The pub is about a 20-minute walk from Hatfield Peverel station and parking is also available. Open on bank holiday Mondays. Q ☏ ☺ & ♣ P 🚃 (73) ● ᯤ

Hazel End

Three Horseshoes

CM23 1HB
☎ (01279) 813429 ⊕ threehorseshoeshazelend.co.uk
Adnams Southwold Bitter; Sharp's Doom Bar; 1 changing beer (sourced nationally) H
A clean and friendly pub opposite the cricket green at Hazel End. It has been completely renovated – a large extension has created more space to both eat and drink here comfortably. Food includes an impressive fish menu. This is a good example of a once run-down premises transformed into a thriving, successful establishment. It has low ceilings, black wooden beams and two wood-burning stoves. ☺ ◖ ▶ P ●

High Roding

Black Lion L

3 The Street, CM6 1NT (on B184 Dunmow to Ongar road)
☎ (01371) 872847 ⊕ theblacklionhighroding.co.uk
4 changing beers (sourced locally; often Colchester, Hadham, New River) H
A former coaching inn on the London to Norwich road, this striking half-timbered 14th-century building has low ceilings, oak beams and a huge fire in the winter. The restaurant serves good locally sourced food, with a popular roast on Sunday. There is a TV in the end bar, usually showing rugby on Saturday. Tasting evenings feature throughout the year. Outside is a pleasant courtyard garden. Q ☏ ☺ ◖ & P 🚃 (17,18) ●

Hockley

White Hart

274 Main Road, Hawkwell, SS5 4NS
☎ (01702) 203438 ⊕ whiteharthockley.co.uk
House beer (by Caledonian); 2 changing beers (sourced nationally) H
A friendly village pub facing Hawkwell village green, this old coaching inn has a modern, comfortable interior, and stages a popular quiz night on the first Monday of the month. The housing that surrounds this hostelry has made it the centre of village life for over 200 years. It still retains original sash windows, a central open fire and horse brasses. One house beer and two changing guest ales are served. There is a large rear garden with seating and a patio area, plus picnic tables at the front.
☺ ◖ & ≠ ♣ P 🚃 (7,8) ᯤ

Horndon-on-the-Hill

Bell Inn

High Road, SS17 8LD (nr centre of village, almost opp Woolmarket and Orsett Rd)
☎ (01375) 642463 ⊕ bell-inn.co.uk
Crouch Vale Brewers Gold; Greene King IPA, Abbot; 2 changing beers (sourced nationally) H
Popular 15th-century coaching inn, where beamed bars feature wood panelling and carvings, run by the same family since 1938. Note the hot cross bun collection; a bun has been added every Good Friday for more than 100 years. Three regular beers are on the bar, plus two guests, including ales from Essex breweries. The award-winning restaurant is open daily, lunchtimes and

evenings (booking advisable). Gourmet nights are held – see website for details. Accommodation is available in 27 bedrooms. Q✤⬤❀☎◑⬤&P🛏(11)❀🅫

Kirby-le-Soken

Ship

35 Walton Road, CO13 0DT

☎ (01255) 679149 ⊕ theshipkirbylesoken.co.uk

Adnams Southwold Bitter, Ghost Ship, Broadside; 3 changing beers (sourced nationally) Ⓗ

A free house with a restaurant area offering a wide selection of menus. The Ship has a large beer garden to the rear and an outside seating area to the front. The garden contains a marquee that is used for various events throughout the year, including an annual beer festival. For cider lovers, trays of three third-pints are on offer to help you choose a favourite. Well-behaved dogs are welcome. Q✤❀☎◑⬤♣⬤P🛏(98,98A)❀🅫

Lamarsh

Lamarsh Lion

Bures Road, CO8 5EP (1¼ miles NW of Bures) TL892355

☎ (01787) 227007 ⊕ lamarshlion.co.uk

4 changing beers (sourced nationally) Ⓗ

A popular 14th-century community venue that boasts Constable and Gainsborough as former customers – their paintings feature outstanding views of the Stour Valley. Formerly an Independent newspaper Top 20 new UK pub, its beautifully renovated interior showcases many social events including live music. The varied daily menu includes specials and all-day breakfasts. Cyclists and ramblers are welcome, as are dogs. There is parking to the side and rear, and outside seating in the garden and at the front. Camping is available from spring and a minibus shuttle runs for parties within an eight-mile radius. Q✤⬤❀☎◑⬤&♣⬤P🛏(754)❀🅫

Langley Lower Green

Bull

Park Lane, CB11 4SB TL437345

☎ (01279) 777307 ⊕ thebullpub.co.uk

Adnams Mosaic; Greene King IPA; 2 changing beers (sourced regionally) Ⓗ

Classic Victorian village local with original cast-iron lattice windows, in a tiny isolated hamlet close to both Hertfordshire and Cambridgeshire. The pub has a band of local regulars. There is an aquarium in the lounge bar. Occasional quiz nights are held, and open mic nights feature on the last Tuesday of the month. An annual beer festival takes place in September. ✤❀◑♣P❀🅫

Layer Breton

Hare & Hounds

Crayes Green, CO2 0PN

☎ (01206) 330459 ⊕ thehareandhound.co.uk

3 changing beers (sourced nationally) Ⓗ

Attractive country pub with a single bar and a separate room for dining and functions. It has cosy log-burners, and a garden with a pergola for alfresco eating and drinking. Three beer festivals are held a year including one on St George's Day. The community shop sells newspapers, and operates a post office on Tuesday morning and Thursday afternoon. It has been a regional finalist in the Countryside Alliance awards, and has a good-quality food menu. Quiz night is on the first Wednesday of the month.
✤⬤❀☎◑⬤&🅰⬤P🛏(92) ❀🅫

Layer-de-la-Haye

Donkey & Buskins Ⓛ

Layer Road, CO2 0HU

☎ (01206) 734774 ⊕ donkeyandbuskins.co.uk

Adnams Southwold Bitter; Greene King IPA; 2 changing beers (sourced nationally) Ⓗ

Built circa 1840, this hostelry, run by the same family since 1985, is now an aspiring fresh food gastro-pub supporting neighbourhood produce suppliers. Up to five ales are available from local and national brewers. It has a bar and three restaurant rooms, a large beer garden off the main road, surrounded by woodland, and a large car park. Q✤⬤❀☎◑⬤&♣P🛏(50)❀🅫

Leigh-on-Sea

Leigh on Sea Brewery Tap Ⓛ

35 Progress Road, SS9 5PR (N of A127 and standing behind an industrial unit, it is reached by a signposted gravel and concrete path around that building)

☎ (01702) 817255 ⊕ leighonseabrewery.co.uk

8 changing beers (sourced locally; often Leigh on Sea) Ⓗ

The brewery taproom is on the Progress Road industrial estate and offers a rotation of core beers on either handpump or KeyKeg dispense, plus one or two guest beers. The decor features exposed brickwork, tall tables and stools, industrial lighting and a bar top of cockleshells. International rugby and other major sporting events are shown on terrestrial TV. Regular music events take place. It is open Thursday to Saturday – hours can vary, so check the website or social media.
❀⬤🛏(25,20) ❀🅫

Mayflower Ⓛ

5-6 High Street, Old Leigh, SS9 2EN (at far end of Old Leigh from railway station, behind chip shop)

☎ (01702) 478535 ⊕ mayfloweroldleigh.com

Crouch Vale Brewers Gold; George's Cockleboats; St Austell Proper Job; 3 changing beers (sourced regionally) Ⓗ

Popular pub selling six beers and one cider, including some from local breweries. It has been the local CAMRA Pub of the Year three times in the past. Food is mainly fish & chips from the attached restaurant. One wall lists the names of all who sailed on the Mayflower, and there is a pleasant seating area at the back with views of the estuary. ❀❀◑&⬤P🛏(26)❀🅫

Little Thurrock

Traitors' Gate Ⓛ

40-42 Broadway, RM17 6EW (on A126)

☎ (01375) 372628 ⊕ traitorsgatepub.wordpress.com

Greene King Abbot; 4 changing beers (sourced regionally) Ⓗ

Taken over by the current operator in 2013, this hostelry has established a reputation for live bands on Fridays and Saturdays and open mic sessions on Thursdays. The quieter, traditional end is to the right of the front bar. It has five handpumps, with four dispensing a rotating selection of guest beers. The small chalkboards above the bar list current and forthcoming beers. Real ales are discounted at various times through the week. The pub is not easy to find due to the lack of external signage.
❀❀&♣🛏(66,66A) ❀🅫

Little Totham

Swan

School Road, CM9 8LB

☎ (01621) 331713 ⊕ theswanlittletotham.com
Crouch Vale Brewers Gold; Mighty Oak Oscar Wilde, Captain Bob; St Austell Tribute; 3 changing beers (sourced nationally) Ⓖ
Grade II-listed, three-roomed, cottage-style inn, which includes a cosy public bar and restaurant. It was twice the National CAMRA Pub of the Year and offers a superb range of beers, mostly local, served direct from the cask in the cooled cellar, and a dozen or so ciders including Westons Rosie's Pig and Abrahalls Cracklin' Rosie perry. The walled front garden provides a safe play area and there is a large space to the rear for outdoor activities and events. A two-week beer festival is hosted in June.
Q🕏❀⏰👭♣👆P🛗❀🎱

Littley Green

Compasses Ⓛ
CM3 1BU
☎ (01245) 362308 ⊕ compasseslittleygreen.co.uk
Bishop Nick Ridley's Rite; Crouch Vale Essex Boys Best Bitter; 3 changing beers (sourced nationally) Ⓖ
Formerly Ridley's Brewery tap, this is a picturesque Victorian country pub in a quiet hamlet. A wood-panelled bar has benches around the walls and a tiled floor. Beers are drawn directly from casks, and it has an interesting range of three ciders and a perry. Renowned filled huffers (giant baps) are available lunchtimes and evenings, plus other traditional dishes. There are seats and tables outside and in the large gardens. Regular beer festivals are held. Accommodation comprises five high-quality rooms. Q🕏❀🛏⏰♣👆P🛗❀🎱

Loughton

Victoria Tavern ⓥ
165 Smarts Lane, IG10 4BP
☎ (020) 8508 1779 ⊕ thevictoriatavern.co.uk
Adnams Southwold Bitter; Greene King IPA; Sharp's Doom Bar; Timothy Taylor Landlord; 2 changing beers Ⓗ
This is an old-fashioned traditional tavern that prides itself on real ale and inclusive conversation. It lies between Loughton and Epping Forest and is a 10-15 minute walk from Loughton tube station. Outside, the pleasant gated garden is popular with locals and walkers; well-behaved dogs are welcome. The pub serves generous portions of fresh seasonal food and has no TV – just good ale, good food and good company.
Q🕏❀⏰P🚃🎱

Maldon

Blue Boar Hotel
Silver Street, CM9 4QE
☎ (01621) 855888 ⊕ blueboarmaldon.co.uk
Adnams Southwold Bitter; Timothy Taylor Landlord Ⓖ
A historic and architecturally interesting hotel in an ideal town-centre location. There are several distinct bars and an outside courtyard and garden areas in which to enjoy a range of ales dispensed on gravity. Musical entertainment features on Fridays, Saturday evenings and Sunday lunchtime (see website). The impressive long room may be hired out for private functions. Parts of the pub date back to the 14th century, when it was a hostel for the friars of nearby Beeleigh Abbey.
Q🕏❀🛏P🚃❀

Queen Victoria
Spital Road, CM9 6ED
☎ (01621) 852923 ⊕ queenvictoriamaldon.co.uk

Adnams Southwold Bitter; Greene King Abbot; Mighty Oak Captain Bob; 3 changing beers (sourced nationally; often Dartmoor, Elgood's, Skinner's) Ⓗ
A warm and friendly welcome awaits everyone at this convivial Gray's establishment, with four well-kept ales from local and regional breweries, and up to three guest ales and three real ciders. Extensive menus offer locally sourced, home-cooked meals, with vegetarian and vegan options (booking is recommended). Families are welcome throughout, as are dogs, in the beer garden and public bar. Seasonal events are joyfully celebrated, together with beer festivals, darts, dominoes and bar skittles. Local CAMRA Pub of the Year 2020.
🕏❀⏰👭♣👆P🚃❀🎱

Manningtree

Red Lion
42 South Street, CO11 1BG
☎ (01206) 391880 ⊕ redlionmanningtree.co.uk
Adnams Southwold Bitter; 2 changing beers (sourced regionally; often Colchester, Mighty Oak, Woodforde's) Ⓗ
The Red Lion's history dates back to 1603. Many changes have taken place over the intervening centuries, but recent ones have improved customer space, modernised the toilets and added a small function room, all while maintaining the quality of the ales and the high level of service from the friendly staff. Larger events such as live music and the Oktoberfest take place in a large function room upstairs. The pub doesn't provide food beyond bar snacks, but you can bring in takeaways. 🕏❀♣👆🚃❀🎱

Monk Street

Farmhouse Inn Ⓛ
CM6 2NR (off B184, 2 miles S of Thaxted) TL614288
☎ (01371) 830864 ⊕ farmhouseinn.org
Greene King IPA; 2 changing beers (sourced locally) Ⓗ
Built in the 16th century, this former Dunmow Brewery establishment has been enlarged to incorporate a restaurant and accommodation; the bar is in the original part of the building. The quiet hamlet here overlooks the Chelmer Valley, two miles from historic Thaxted. A disused well in the garden supplied Monk Street with water during World War II. There is a rear patio, front garden and a top field. Draught cider from Westons is usually available. 🕏❀🛏⏰👆P🚃(313)❀🎱

Mundon

White Horse
Main Road, CM9 6PB TL869026
☎ (01621) 740276
3 changing beers (often Colchester, Mighty Oak) Ⓗ
The White Horse is a Grade II-listed building, with many characteristics of an old-style pub including exposed beams and a large open fire. There is a large bar with three handpumps serving local ales. Food is available, including popular Sunday roasts. Darts and pool are played and there are quiz nights. Occasional music events take place monthly. The pub is a popular stop off for walkers in the area and visitors to St Mary's Church. ❀⏰♣P🚃❀

Newport

Coach & Horses
Cambridge Road, CB11 3TR (on B1383)
☎ (01799) 540292

Adnams Southwold Bitter; Fuller's London Pride; 1 changing beer (sourced nationally) ⊞
A former coaching inn with a warm welcome, on the main road through Newport, at the north end of the village. It has an excellent kitchen serving great locally sourced traditional food, and is available for functions. There is a large garden with interesting children's activities. Q⚭❀◑●P⊟🐾ᯤ

Pebmarsh

King's Head
The Street, CO9 2NH
☎ (01787) 267942 🌐 kingsheadpebmarsh.com
Adnams Ghost Ship; 3 changing beers (sourced nationally) ⊞
The King's Head, dating back to 1450, was saved by the community and reopened in 2017 after an extensive refurbishment, while maintaining a traditional character. A plaque on the wall displays the names of the many shareholders. There is a single bar serving three areas: one for drinking, one for dining, and another with comfortable seating. The main bar has a real fire. Outside, there are benches in the large garden area. There is a good menu of freshly prepared home-cooked food. Closed Mondays except bank holidays.
⚭❀◑P⊟🐾ᯤ

Pleshey

Leather Bottle 𝕃
The Street, CM3 1HG
☎ (01245) 237291
3 changing beers (sourced nationally) ⊞
Grade II-listed village pub with two rooms. The older part of the building (single-storied and believed to date back to the 15th century) is to the right, with tables, chairs and a cushioned bench along one wall. To the left is a room that is part of a later two-storey house, where you'll find the bar, an open fire and more chairs and tables. Beers are shown on the bar, but served from a room behind it. There is a substantial food menu.
⚭❀◑♿P⊟(10)

Purleigh

Bell
The Street, CM3 6QJ
☎ (01621) 828348 🌐 purleighbell.co.uk
Adnams Southwold Bitter; Crouch Vale Brewers Gold; Mighty Oak Captain Bob; 1 changing beer (sourced regionally) ⊞
This historic building, dating from the 14th century and with links to George Washington, has recently had a two-storey extension. It is situated next to the village church, on a hill with views over the countryside. The large bar is warmed by an open fire. There is an emphasis on high-quality food, but beer drinkers are welcome. The pub caters for many local clubs including walking groups, and has regular quiz nights. Q⚭❀◑♿♣P🗑🐾ᯤ

Rowhedge

Olde Albion
High Street, CO5 7ES
☎ (01206) 728972
3 changing beers (sourced nationally) ⊞
A free house on the waterfront, playing a substantial role in local village life. The pub serves an interesting range of changing ales from various breweries. There is usually a cheeseboard on Sunday. A fire adds warmth in cold weather, and on fine days there are tables and chairs on the greensward overlooking the River Colne. Beer festivals are held on St George's Day and during the Rowhedge Regatta. ❀♣●⊟(66)🐾ᯤ

Roydon

New Inn ✔
90 High Street, CM19 5EE
☎ (01279) 792225 🌐 thenewinnroydon.co.uk
Adnams Broadside; Greene King IPA; Sharp's Doom Bar; 1 changing beer (sourced nationally) ⊞
The New Inn was built in the 18th century in this charming village and retains many period features. Situated a short walk from Roydon station and the River Stort Navigation, it welcomes many walkers and boaters as well as a local clientele. It was nominated for 2020 Parliamentary Pub of the Year by the local MP. The large garden has a children's play area. A beer festival is held each September, barbecues on fine Friday evenings, and a Wednesday senior citizens' lunch. ❀◑⇄P🐾ᯤ

Saffron Walden

King's Arms 𝕃
10 Market Hill, CB10 1HQ
☎ (01799) 522768 🌐 thekingsarmssaffronwalden.co.uk
Adnams Southwold Bitter; Otter Bitter; Timothy Taylor Landlord; 2 changing beers (sourced nationally) ⊞
Venerable wooden-beamed, multi-roomed pub, just off the market square (market days are Tuesday and Saturday). It has welcoming log fires in cold weather and a pleasant patio for alfresco dining and drinking. A mild or dark beer is often sold in winter. There is live music at weekends, acoustic music on Thursdays, and a monthly quiz. Food is served at lunchtimes. Q⚭❀◐⊟🐾ᯤ

Old English Gentleman ✔
11 Gold Street, CB10 1EJ (E of B184/B1052 jct)
☎ (01799) 523595 🌐 oldenglishgentleman.com
Woodforde's Wherry; 2 changing beers (sourced regionally) ⊞
An 18th-century town-centre pub with log fires and a welcoming atmosphere. It serves a selection of guest ales and an extensive menu of bar food and sandwiches that changes regularly. Traditional roasts and chef's specials are available on Sunday in the bar or dining area. A variety of works of art is displayed. There is a heated patio at the rear and a wood-burning stove too. Saffron Walden is busy on Tuesday and Saturday market days.
⚭❀◐⊟🐾ᯤ

Railway Arms 𝕃
Station Road, CB11 3HQ (300yds SE of war memorial)
☎ (01799) 619660 🌐 railwayarms.co.uk
5 changing beers (sourced locally) ⊞
A Victorian street-corner local, it sits opposite the former Saffron Walden railway station, which closed in 1964 as a result of the Beeching cuts. Now community owned by some 500 local shareholders, there has been significant renovation both inside and out, largely undertaken by volunteers. Fully open inside, plus a large quantity of outside seating and tables in the garden and courtyard; it serves a range of beer styles exclusively from local breweries, usually including a stout or mild. ❀◑●P⊟

Sible Hedingham

White Lion 𝕃
6 Church Street, CO9 3NS
☎ (01787) 462534
3 changing beers (sourced nationally) ⊞

The last remaining pub in Sible Hedingham is proving popular with locals and visitors, featuring regular events and live music. Friendly and hospitable, it offers homemade lunches (not Mon) with a good range of bar snacks. Sunday lunch (please book) is served in the function room, which has a small stage and is available for private hire. The bar has numerous wines and spirits, including 30 gins. It boasts an attractive beer garden and games room with darts, pool and sport TV. Homemade afternoon teas by appointment. ♿❀◖♣P🐕🕸🛜

South Benfleet

South Benfleet Social Club L
8 Vicarage Hill, SS7 1PB (at jct with B1006 High Road)
☎ (01268) 206159
6 changing beers H/G
A popular social club that is a huge asset to the community. Two beer festivals are held in May and December, and a good range of beers and ciders is always enjoyed. It is the local CAMRA branch Club of the Year and has been for many years. Games include pool and poker, with quiz nights, sport on TV and live music at weekends all adding to the ambience. CAMRA members and Guide holders are always welcome.
♿❀◖&≥(Benfleet) ♣●P🖵🕸🛜

South Woodham Ferrers

Tap Room 19
19 Haltwhistle Road, CM3 5ZA
☎ (01245) 322744 🌐 crouchvale.co.uk/tap-room-19
Crouch Vale Blackwater Mild, Essex Boys Best Bitter, Brewers Gold, Yakima Gold; 2 changing beers (sourced locally; often Crouch Vale) G
Tucked away on the town's Western Industrial Estate in front of the Crouch Vale brewery, the pub is about 10-minutes' walk through side streets from the railway station. Simply furnished, with understated decor, it is a welcome real ale oasis in a town with few others. Beers are served from a taproom, visible through windows at the rear of the bar. There is a small outdoor seating area to the front. Up to four ciders are on offer.
Q🕸≥♣●P🖵🚌(36) 🕸🛜

Southend-on-Sea

Mawson's L
781 Southchurch Road, SS1 2PP (on A13)
☎ (01702) 601781
George's Wallasea Wench, Cockleboats; 4 changing beers (sourced nationally) H
This converted shop was Southend's first micropub and has up to six cask ales, with a least two from the local George's Brewery. Six real ciders, three craft keg pumps, two draught German pilsners and two draught ciders, one of which is Rocquette of Guernsey, are exclusively sold in Essex by Mawson's. Set in the Southchurch village area, the bar has a large gallery of Laurel and Hardy pictures. Quiet music adds to happy conversation, with occasional live music and quiz nights.
♿&≥(East) ●🖵🚌(1,14) 🕸🛜

Southminster

Station Arms
39 Station Road, CM0 7EW
☎ (01621) 772225 🌐 thestationarms.co.uk
Adnams Southwold Bitter; 4 changing beers (sourced regionally; often Bishop Nick, George's, Mighty Oak) H

A traditional weatherboarded Essex pub that has featured in this Guide for 30 consecutive years. It is a welcoming and thriving community local. The comfortable bare-boarded bar, with its open log fire, is decorated with railway and brewery memorabilia. An attractive courtyard is popular in fine weather and a barn with a wood-burning stove provides shelter if required. Live blues and folk music is hosted monthly. Annually, a harvest festival charity auction and a conker championship are held. Q🕸❀≥♣🖵

Wibblers Brewery Taproom & Kitchen
Goldsands Road, CM0 7JW
☎ (01621) 772044 🌐 wibblers.co.uk/taproomkitchen
Wibblers Dengie IPA H; 6 changing beers (sourced locally; often Wibblers) H/G
The taproom is attached to an award-winning, restored medieval tithe barn housing Wibblers' Brewery. The kitchen offers a wide-ranging menu of excellent home-cooked food, using mostly local produce. The bar is attractively furnished and – weather permitting – you can sit outside in the countryside. The brewery and taproom host open days and various other events throughout the year, including televised rugby and themed food evenings. Southminster railway station is only a five-minute walk away. Closed Monday and Tuesday.
Q♿❀◖&≥●P🖵(31X) 🕸🛜

Stanford-le-Hope

Rising Sun L
Church Hill, SS17 0EU (opp church and nr A1014)
☎ (01375) 671097
Greene King IPA; 4 changing beers (sourced nationally) H
Much-improved traditional two-bar pub in the shadow of the church. The five guest beers are mainly from independent breweries, including LocAle beers, and up to three ciders or perries are stocked. Regular monthly live music takes place, and beer festivals are held three times a year in spring, summer and winter, with the summer festival in the large rear garden. The back bar is available for private functions. 🕸≥♣P🖵🕸🛜

Stansted Mountfitchet

Rose & Crown L
31 Bentfield Green, CM24 8HX (½ mile W of B1383)
TL505256
☎ (01279) 812107 🌐 roseandcrownstansted.co.uk
3 changing beers (sourced regionally) H
Family-run Victorian pub near a duck pond, on the edge of a small hamlet. This free house has been modernised to provide one large bar but retains the welcoming atmosphere of an active village venue. It has been extended to include a fairly large new snug. Food is home cooked and uses locally sourced produce. A large variety of gins is stocked. There is an old seven-inch singles jukebox on which you can play your own records.
♿❀◖♣P🖵(7,7A) 🕸🛜

Stanway

Live & Let Live L
12 Millers Lane, CO3 0PS (in a small lane 100yds from London Rd, W of Colchester)
☎ (01206) 574071 🌐 theliveandletlive.co.uk
4 changing beers (sourced nationally) H
A traditional, welcoming establishment that continues to delight, with a homely saloon bar and public bar, offering sports TV, darts, pool and a comprehensive jukebox. The

publicans regularly support local breweries and take great pride in the condition and quality of their real ales. The beers are competitively priced, as is the traditional home-cooked food, served most lunchtimes and Friday and Saturday evenings. The place is renowned for its beer, sausage and pie festivals. Runner-up and highly commended local CAMRA Pub of the Year in 2020.
Q🔥❀◐♿♣🍎P🚌(65,70) 🐾📶

Steeple Bumpstead

Fox & Hounds [L]

3 Chapel Street, CB9 7DQ
☎ (01440) 731810 🌐 foxinsteeple.co.uk
Greene King IPA; 3 changing beers (sourced nationally) [H]
A 17th-century coaching inn in a picturesque village on the Essex/Suffolk border, featuring an open fire in the main bar, two restaurants, a courtyard rear garden and further seating at the front. Freshly prepared local food from a seasonal and varied menu is served six days a week (booking recommended). On Wednesday evening a complimentary cheeseboard is offered, with reduced-price real ale and wine all evening. Live bands perform and quiz nights take place throughout the year.
Q🔥❀◐♣🚌(18) 🐾📶

Stow Maries

Prince of Wales

Woodham Road, CM3 6SA
☎ (01621) 828971 🌐 prince-stowmaries.net
6 changing beers (sourced nationally) [H]
This classic weatherboarded pub boasts several characterful drinking areas, and has open fires and an old bread oven used for baking pizza in the winter months. The extensive garden and courtyards provide plenty of options for outside drinking. Good food is on the menu, made with local produce where possible. Many special events are held including Burns Night, a firework display on the last Saturday in October, and live music. The historic Stow Maries World War I airfield is nearby.
Q🔥❀🛏◐♿🍎P📺🚌(593) 🐾📶

Thaxted

Maypole

31 Mill End, CM6 2LT (by B184)
☎ (01371) 831599 🌐 maypolethaxted.com
Greene King IPA; 4 changing beers (sourced nationally) [H]
A renamed ex-Ridley's local all in one room with a games and TV area, sofas, chairs and a drinking area with tables. Up to four guest ales are available. The pub holds musical events and runs beer festivals, and is a hospitable place for beer drinkers. There is a pleasant patio and garden and a car park at the rear.
🔥❀◐♣P🚌(6,312) 🐾📶

Toppesfield

Green Man [L]

3 Church Lane, CO9 4DR
☎ (01787) 237418
4 changing beers (sourced nationally; often PumpHouse Community) [H]
A community-owned local that hosts beer festivals and events throughout the year. It has two pool teams, and darts is played in the public bar. There is a brewery next door, PumpHouse Community Brewery. In fact, this village is the only place in the UK to have a pub, brewery and shop all owned by the community. It is advisable to book ahead for meals. Sunday lunch is served, fish & chips (including to take away) on Friday, and bacon rolls on Saturday. 🔥❀◐♿♣🍎P🐾📶

Waltham Abbey

Woodbine Inn [L] ✔

Honey Lane, EN9 3QT
☎ (01992) 713050 🌐 thewoodbine.co.uk
Adnams Ghost Ship [H]; Bishop Nick Divine [H]/[G]; Mighty Oak Oscar Wilde [G], Captain Bob [H]; 4 changing beers (sourced locally) [H]/[G]
National finalist for Cider Pub of the Year 2019 and local CAMRA branch Pub of the Year 2020, the pub is situated in Epping Forest and close to junction 26 of the M25. It concentrates on real ales and over 40 small producer ciders, and brews London Glider cider on-site. Food is home made, with local sausages, ham and steak as specialities. Dogs are welcome in the main bar. Bar billiards is played. The Ale Sampling Society and Comedy Club meet here monthly. 🔥◐♣🍎P🚌(66,66A)🐾

Weeley Heath

White Hart

Clacton Road, CO16 9ED (on B1441, 1 mile from Weeley station) TM153208
☎ (01255) 830384
2 changing beers (sourced nationally; often Greene King, Mauldons, Woodforde's) [H]
In 2021 Mark and Sally clocked up 25 years as landlords of this free house, which hosts pool and darts teams and has a real ale club. A great venue for sports enthusiasts, it shows Sky TV and BT Sport. Community-focused, it hosts occasional music and quiz evenings. The garden has a covered patio for smokers. Local CAMRA Cider Pub of the Year in 2020. ❀⛺♣🍎P🚌📶

Westcliff-on-Sea

Cricketers

228 London Road, SS0 7JG (on A13)
☎ (01702) 345053 🌐 thecricketersbarandfood.co.uk
Adnams Ghost Ship; Dark Star Hophead; Greene King Abbot; Mighty Oak Oscar Wilde, Maldon Gold; 1 changing beer (sourced regionally) [H]
A Gray & Sons establishment with well-kept beer, not far from Southend town centre. A music venue adjoins the pub so it can get busy on music nights. There are also jazz nights featuring Digby Fairweather and guests every second Wednesday of the month, and a quiz on Monday. The five regular beers, one of which is dark, are joined by an extra ale on days when Southend United are playing at home. 🔥❀◐♿🚆🚌🐾📶

Mile & a Third

67 Hamlet Court Road, SS0 7EU
☎ (01702) 902120 🌐 mileandathird.com
2 changing beers (sourced nationally) [G]
Run by two beer managers from the Rochford beer festival, this is an L-shaped former shop, the front being the bottle shop, while the bar is on the side. There are also four trees inside the premises. Two real ales are served on gravity, and eight keg lines, plus three real ciders from bag-in-box. The bottle shop's three fridges have bottles and cans featuring national and international brewers. All ales and ciders are £3 a pint on Wednesday and Thursday. Music is mainly played on vinyl. Local CAMRA Pub of the Year 2020. Closed Monday and Tuesday. 🔥♿🚆♣🍎📺🚌🐾📶

West Road Tap
2 West Road, SS0 9DA
☎ (01702) 330647 ⊕ westroadtap.com
3 changing beers (sourced nationally) Ⓖ
Near the Palace Theatre in Westcliff, this is a two-level micropub and bottle shop, serving up to three cask ales, sourced nationally, on gravity in the upstairs bar. Beer is also served from six KeyKeg taps upstairs, with a further six KeyKeg taps downstairs, and there is an extensive fridge selection of craft beer in bottles and cans, available to drink on the premises or to take home. Two real ciders in boxes are also sold. Children are welcome until early evening. Local CAMRA Pub of the Year 2019. Closed Monday. Q♣❀➤●♬(1,27)♣

Widdington

Fleur de Lys Ⓛ ✪
High Street, CB11 3SG TL538316
☎ (01799) 543280 ⊕ thefleurdelys.co.uk
Adnams Southwold Bitter, Broadside; Woodforde's Wherry; 2 changing beers (sourced nationally) Ⓗ
Rumours of a ghost abound at this welcoming 400-year-old village hostelry, which boasts a large open fireplace and beams. This was the first pub to be saved from closure by the local branch of CAMRA after the branch's formation. Quality meals are offered with fresh ingredients from the area; the kitchen is closed on Tuesdays but there is an outdoor food truck in the evening. A bridge club is held on Monday night. The source of the River Cam, and Prior's Hall Barn, an English heritage site, are both nearby. Local CAMRA Pub of the Year 2020. ♣❀❀➤●♬(301)♣

Wivenhoe

Black Buoy
Black Buoy Hill, CO7 9BS
☎ (01206) 822425 ⊕ blackbuoy.co.uk
Colchester Number One; 5 changing beers (sourced nationally) Ⓗ
Local CAMRA Pub of the Year 2020, the Black Buoy is a popular and welcoming community-owned venue. There is a small public bar for drinkers at the front and other areas for drinking and dining, with a range of traditional home-cooked food available every day. It hosts beer festivals in May and August in the pleasant outdoor area and garden. Regular quiz and open mic nights take place throughout the year. Q♣❀❀➤●➤♬♣♥

Horse & Groom ✪
55 The Cross, CO7 9QL
☎ (01206) 824928 ⊕ handgwivenhoe.co.uk
Adnams Southwold Bitter, Ghost Ship, Broadside; 3 changing beers (sourced nationally) Ⓗ
A real locals' two-bar pub with a large garden to the rear. Children and dogs are always welcome, and the garden has a small play area. It sells Adnams beers as well as a range of guests. Quality home-cooked lunches are served Monday to Saturday, with an ever-popular roast lunch on a Thursday (no food Sun). Regular curry nights take place each month. Q♣❀❀➤♬♣♥

Wix

Waggon
Clacton Road, CO11 2RU
☎ (01255) 870279
Bombardier; 2 changing beers (sourced nationally) Ⓗ
The earliest known reference to this establishment standing on the crossroads in Wix was in 1810 – the current landlord has been here since 1987. A free house, it serves a choice of reasonably priced beers. There is a pool and darts room, and regular live music and event nights are hosted. A patio area at the rear has access to picnic tables next to the car park. The pool room is occasionally used as a function room.
♣❀❀➤♬(102,104)♣♥

Woodham Ferrers

Bell Inn
Main Road, CM3 8RF
☎ (01245) 320443
Crouch Vale Brewers Gold; Fuller's London Pride; Mighty Oak Captain Bob, Gorgeous George; 2 changing beers (sourced regionally) Ⓗ
A traditional locals' pub with darts, pool and cards, in the same family for 35 years. Ales are drawn from handpumps in a bar apart from the main bar. There is a separate function room and a large garden with a millpond, an ideal area for summer outdoor drinking. Phone ahead to book meals. Q❀❀➤♬(36)♣

Woodham Mortimer

Hurdlemakers Arms
Post Office Road, CM9 6ST
☎ (01245) 225169 ⊕ hurdlemakersarms.co.uk
5 changing beers (sourced locally; often George's, Mighty Oak, Wibblers) Ⓗ
A Gray's house, this 400-year-old former farmhouse seamlessly blends restaurant with pub, and good food and beer are both on offer here. One area is dedicated to diners, while drinkers are catered for in a smaller bar. There is a huge beer garden ideal for families, with a play area and shady trees. Barbecues are held on summer weekends, functions are catered for in a marquee or Mortimer's Barn, and a popular beer festival is held in the last week of June.
Q♣❀❀➤●♬♣♥

Writtle

Wheatsheaf Ⓛ
70 The Green, CM1 3DU
☎ (01245) 420672 ⊕ thewheatsheafwrittle.co.uk
2 changing beers (sourced nationally) Ⓖ
Traditional village inn built in 1813, with a small public bar, an equally compact lounge, and a covered patio by the road. It is a long-time favourite of the local CAMRA branch. The atmosphere is generally quiet, with the TV switched on only for occasional sporting events. Traditional food is served Tuesday to Saturday lunchtimes. Note the old Gray's sign in the public bar. Q♬♣➤♬

By George!
It was my Uncle George who discovered that alcohol was a food well in advance of modern medical thought.
P G Wodehouse, The Inimitable Jeeves

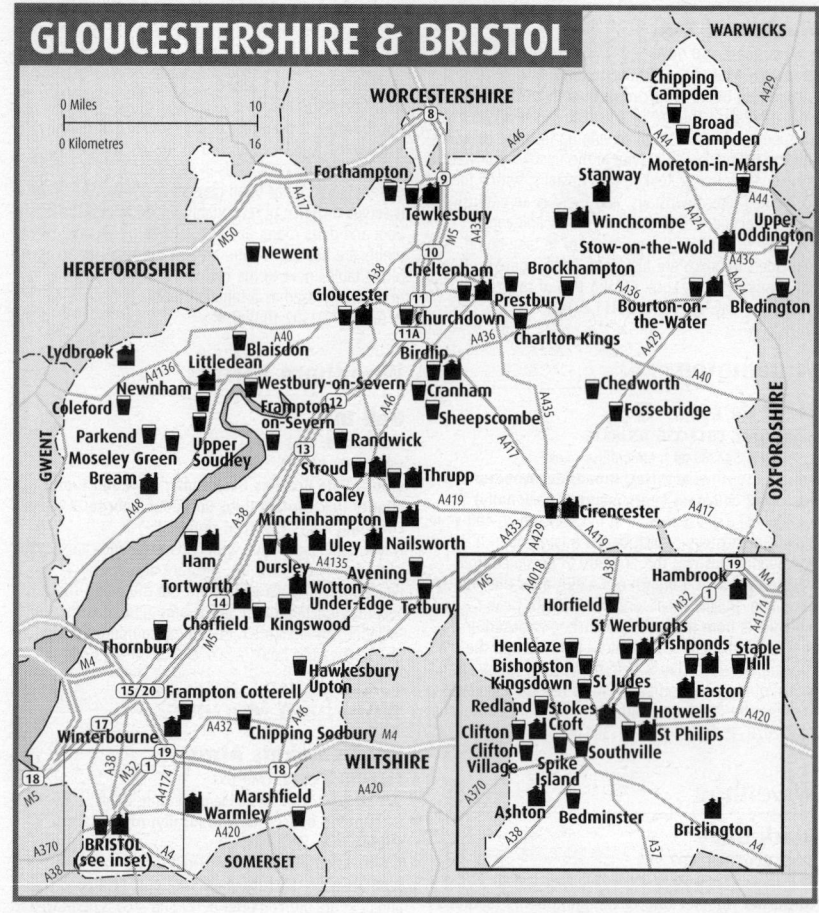

GLOUCESTERSHIRE & BRISTOL

Avening

Bell L

29 High Street, GL8 8NF (at bottom of High St on B4014)
☎ (01453) 836422 ⊕ thebellavening.co.uk
Box Steam Soul Train; Timothy Taylor Landlord; Wickwar BOB; 1 changing beer (often Butcombe) ⊞
This pleasant old village inn is friendly and confidently run, with exposed stone walls, two bay window seats and a roaring wood-burner. The jovial, amicable regulars are always chatty, enjoying the offerings from the attractive open bar, which features up to four different ales at busy times. The refurbished, comfortable dining area serves a competitively priced menu in collaboration with a local Indian restaurant. This pub can be quietly addictive and quite difficult to leave. Q ⌖ ⊛ ⏴ ♣ 🚲 🚌 ?

Birdlip

Golden Heart

Nettleton Bottom, GL4 8LA (on A417)
☎ (01242) 870261 ⊕ thegoldenheart.co.uk
3 changing beers (sourced nationally) ⊞
A welcome oasis of tranquillity beside the single-carriageway section of the Gloucester to Swindon road, this 400-year old Cotswold free house retains most of its original features. The small bar, almost hidden beyond a huge open fireplace, overlooks a stone-paved patio and garden with views over the valley. The menu uses the finest award-winning meats and local produce. Dogs are welcome, with treats available for them at the bar. Q ⌖ ⊛ ⏴ ⏴ P ☀ ?

Blaisdon

Red Hart L

GL17 0AH (signed from A4136 E of Longhope or N of A48)
☎ (01452) 831717 ⊕ redhartinn.co.uk
Otter Bitter; 3 changing beers (sourced nationally; often Bespoke, Kingstone, Wye Valley) ⊞
Local CAMRA branch Pub of the Year 2020, the Red Hart is a lovely old tavern deservedly popular for its excellent food and well-kept ales. A warm welcome is assured. There are designated dining spaces, but no separate restaurant, so everyone can enjoy the convivial atmosphere. The well-tended garden is an ideal place for families to enjoy in the summer. The bar area has flagstones, worn through generations of use, and the walls are adorned with memorabilia. Paintings from local artists displayed are for sale. ⌖ ⊛ ⏴ ♣ A ♣ ♦ P ☀

Bledington

King's Head L ✓

The Green, OX7 6XQ (off B4450 on village green)
☎ (01608) 658365 ⊕ kingsheadinn.net

Hook Norton Hooky; 3 changing beers (sourced regionally) Ⓗ
Delightful 16th-century stone-built inn overlooking the village green, and about four miles from Stow-on-the-Wold. In 1614 Prince Rupert of the Rhine supposedly lodged here, prior to the Battle of Stow. The pub has original old beams and an open inglenook log fire with high-backed settles. This free house, with 12 comfortable letting rooms, is renowned for its wide range of ale and food. There are good walks to nearby villages, with Kingham station close by. The two guest beers are selected from brewers in Gloucestershire and Oxfordshire. Q ☺ ➎ ❀ ➍ ➊ ♣ P ♣ ☆ 🛈

Bourton-on-the-Water

Mousetrap Inn Ⓛ
Lansdowne, GL54 2AR (300yds W of village centre)
☎ (01451) 820579 🌐 themousetrapinn.co.uk
3 changing beers (sourced locally) Ⓗ
Traditional Cotswold stone free house recently refurbished, in the Lansdowne part of Bourton close to the centre, with three changing beers from the area on offer. A friendly welcome is assured for locals, tourists, children and dogs, with food including breakfast available. The patio out front with tables and hanging baskets provides a suntrap in the summer. Local CAMRA Pub of the Year runner-up in 2020.
Q ☺ ❀ ➍ ➊ ♣ P 🖴 (801,855) ♣ 🛈

Bristol

Bank Tavern ●
8 John Street, BS1 2HR (take lane next to arcade on All Saints St)
☎ (0117) 930 4691 🌐 banktavern.com
4 changing beers Ⓗ
Popular and compact one-bar pub, hidden away near the old city wall. The four beers of varying styles are often from microbreweries from the South-West or sometimes further afield, alongside one changing real cider. Quirky humour and many varied events define the place – it is a great alternative to the more predictable establishments all around. Quiz night is Tuesday and live music features every other Thursday. Quality food is served lunchtimes, with booking essential for the award-winning Sunday lunch. ☺ ❀ ➊ ♣ ➎ 🖴 ♣ 🛈

Bridge Inn
16 Passage Street, BS2 0JF
☎ (0117) 929 0942
Quantock QPA; 3 changing beers Ⓗ
Conveniently placed near Temple Meads station and Cabot Circus shopping centre, this small, friendly venue is a good place to start a visit to Bristol. An adventurous choice of ales is offered, and exceptionally good-value weekday lunches are served from a small menu. Musical memorabilia adorn the walls and board games are available to play. Thirty malt whiskies and selected vodkas, gins and rums are also stocked, together with Belgian bottled beers. Outside tables increase capacity during good weather. ❀ ➎ ➔ ♣ 🖴 ♣ 🛈

Christmas Steps
2 Christmas Steps, BS1 5BS
☎ (0117) 925 3077 🌐 thechristmassteps.com
5 changing beers (often Arbor, Bristol Beer Factory, Twisted Oak) Ⓗ
Just off the city centre, this fascinating place has welcomed drinkers since the 17th century and is one of Bristol's heritage treasures. The compact, cosy drinking areas reveal many original features, with dining on the

top level. Food and drink are sourced locally where possible. Five real ales in a variety of styles are served from the lower bar, including Crack ales brewed for the pub by Twisted Oak Brewery, as well as two real ciders. ☺ ❀ ➊ ➔ ♣ 🖴 ♣ 🛈

Cornubia
142 Temple Street, BS1 6EN
☎ 07961 796406 🌐 thecornubia.co.uk
8 changing beers Ⓗ
Originally built in 1775, this cosy, traditional inn has recently been refurbished to give it a lighter feel, with pictures and horse brasses on the walls. It is a long-term Guide entry, with a good range of daily changing real ales, usually including a dark ale. The attractive beer garden has an extended seating area to both the front and side of the building, some of which is lit and covered. Bar snacks, including filled rolls and pork pies, are usually available. ❀ ➔ ♣ ➎ 🖴 ♣ 🛈

REAL ALE BREWERIES

Arbor Bristol
Artisan Minchinhampton
Ashton Cheltenham
Basement Beer Bristol: Stokes Croft
Bath ✦ Bristol: Warmley
Battledown Cheltenham
Bespoke ✦ Littledean
Brewhouse & Kitchen 🍴 Bristol: Clifton
Brewhouse & Kitchen 🍴 Cheltenham
Brewhouse & Kitchen 🍴 Gloucester
Bristol Beer Factory Bristol: Ashton
Clavell & Hind ✦ Birdlip
Corinium ✦ Cirencester
Cotswold Bourton-on-the-Water
Cotswold Lion Cheltenham
Dawkins ✦ Bristol: Easton
DEYA ✦ Cheltenham
Donnington Stow-on-the-Wold
Fierce & Noble ✦ Bristol: St Werburgh's
Fishponds 🍴 Bristol: Fishponds
Forest, The Bream
Fresh Standard Stroud (NEW)
Gloucester ✦ Gloucester
Goff's Winchcombe
Good Chemistry Bristol: St Philips
Great Western Bristol: Hambrook
Hal's Dursley (brewing suspended)
Incredible Bristol: Brislington
Inferno Tewkesbury
Keep Brewing 🍴 Nailsworth
King Street 🍴 Bristol
Left Handed Giant ✦ Bristol: St Philips
Little Giant Bristol: Fishponds
Lucifer Wotton-Under-Edge (NEW)
Lydbrook Valley 🍴 Lydbrook
Masquerade Bristol: St Werburgh's
Moor ✦ Bristol
New Bristol ✦ Bristol
Severn Tortworth
Stanway Stanway (brewing suspended)
Stroud ✦ Thrupp
TAP Cirencester
Tapestry ✦ Bristol: St Philips
Three Engineers ✦ Winterbourne
Tiley's 🍴 Ham
Uley Uley
Volunteer Tavern 🍴 Bristol (NEW)
Wiper and True ✦ Bristol: St Werburghs
Wookey Bristol (NEW)
Zerodegrees 🍴 Bristol

Famous Royal Navy Volunteer

17-18 King Street, BS1 4EF
☎ (0117) 316 9237 ⊕ navyvolunteer.co.uk
5 changing beers Ⓗ

One of several popular pubs on historic King Street. Customers can keep warm in front of the snug fireplace, or on fine days enjoy the suntrap roof terrace. Although there are no pumpclips, beer boards on both sides of the bar display what's on offer, with prices for third, half and full pints. Sports are often shown on TVs, although the building is big enough to avoid the match if desired. Wheelchair access is at the rear entrance.
🏃🕸�🕽🚃💺🖥🎛🛜

Gryphon

41 Colston Street, BS1 5AP
☎ 07894 239567
6 changing beers Ⓗ

A shrine to dark beer and great rock and heavy metal music. Posters, guitars and many pumpclips adorn the walls. Triangular in shape due to its corner plot, and just a few yards uphill from the Bristol Beacon concert hall (formerly Colston Hall), the Gryphon has six handpumps dispensing rapidly changing brews, many dark and often strong. Live bands sometimes play upstairs, and 'MetAle' beer festivals are held in March and September. Children and dogs are admitted at the licensee's discretion.
🖥🎛🛜

LHG Brewpub

Compressor Building, Hawkins Lane, BS1 6EU
⊕ lhgbrewpub.com
2 changing beers (often Burning Sky, Left Handed Giant) Ⓗ

Popular three-floor brewpub which opened in June 2019 in part of the old Courage brewery, and which saw brewing come back on the site in August that year after a number of decades of inactivity. The wide range of beer is served in a variety of styles, including by cask handpump, tank-conditioned, or via KeyKeg and keg. The second floor has its own bar for those who want to use the three dartboards and two pool tables. Card payment only. 🕸🕽🚃🖥🎛🛜

Lime Kiln

17 St Georges Road, BS1 5UU (behind City Hall – formerly Council House)
☎ 07903 068256
6 changing beers Ⓗ

Located near College Green, this cosy free house has a small outdoor drinking area at the front. The six handpumps dispense a range of beers in a variety of styles. Many of the breweries featured are seldom seen in Bristol, but local beers are also often stocked, along with one traditional cider. You are welcome to bring your own food. Several beer festivals are hosted throughout the year, some in conjunction with other pubs nearby.
🏃🕽P🖥🎛🛜

Old Fish Market

59-63 Baldwin Street, BS1 1QZ (200yds from city centre)
☎ (0117) 921 1515
Fuller's Oliver's Island, London Pride, ESB; Moor Beer Nor'Hop; 1 changing beer (sourced nationally; often Dark Star, Fuller's, Moor Beer) Ⓗ

There's something for everyone at this Fuller's outlet, which was refurbished in 2014 with decor, seating and lighting in the style of a relaxed lounge. There is a stadium-like atmosphere when major sporting events are shown on the big screen. Live jazz music features every Sunday evening. Between 20 and 30 gins are a great attraction for any fan of the spirit. Food includes a range of chowders, stone-baked pizzas and Sunday roasts. Dog-friendly, with treats and water bowls provided. 🏃🕽&🛩🖥🎛🛜

Seven Stars

1 Thomas Lane, BS1 6JG (just off Victoria St)
☎ (0117) 927 2845 ⊕ 7stars.co.uk
8 changing beers Ⓗ

Popular free house tucked away in a lane 10 minutes' walk from the city centre and Temple Meads station. For many years one of Bristol's premier ale houses, it serves eight beers of all styles and strengths, plus ciders and perries. Quality live acoustic music features on Sunday afternoon. No food is served but you may bring your own. There is an outdoor seating area and an informative plaque detailing how the pub featured in the 18th-century anti-slavery campaign. 🕸≋♣🛩🖥🎛🛜

Shakespeare Tavern ✓

68 Prince Street, BS1 4QD
☎ (0117) 929 7695
Greene King IPA, Abbot; St Austell Tribute; 4 changing beers (sourced locally; often Bristol Beer Factory, Gloucester, Plain) Ⓗ

By Bristol's historic docks, close to the city centre and Queen's Square, this converted Georgian town house claims to have the longest continuous ale licence in Bristol. Seven handpumps offer three regular ales plus four changing guests of varying styles from breweries near and far. Seasonal beer-related events are held, hosted by local breweries. A large selection of classic meals is on offer. There are benches on the front terrace for watching the world pass by. Q🏃🕽♣🛩🖥🎛🛜

Volunteer Tavern Ⓛ

9 New Street, BS2 9DX (close to main Cabot Circus car park across carriageway from shops)
☎ (0117) 955 8498 ⊕ volunteertavern.co.uk
4 changing beers Ⓗ

Vibrant 17th-century hostelry tucked away in a quiet side street and convenient for Old Market bus interchange. Up to six real ales are served including two from a new brewery in a carbon-neutral shipping container adjacent to the pub. The large, fully enclosed, paved and heated garden hosts beer festivals, live music and DJs. Food comes from rotating pop-up kitchens, run by local chefs – check the website for times. Sunday roasts are hugely popular. 🏃🕸🛩🖥🎛🛜

Bristol: Bedminster

Bristol Beer Factory Tap Room

291 North Street, BS3 1JP
☎ (0117) 902 6317
Bristol Beer Factory Fortitude; 3 changing beers (often Bristol Beer Factory) Ⓗ

A short walk from Ashton Gate Stadium, and busy on match days, this comfortable brewery taproom showcases four rotating real ales from Bristol Beer Factory, along with six keg lines. Visitors are welcome to bring in food from local North Street bakeries and shops; the taproom provides on- and off-sales. Regular beer events are held, both for the Bristol Beer Club and the general public. A large TV screen is used to show Six Nations rugby. There is a small outdoor seating area on the pavement. 🕸🛩🖥(24)🎛🛜

Tobacco Factory Café Bar

Raleigh Road, BS3 1TF
☎ (0117) 902 0060 ⊕ tobaccofactory.com/cafe-bar
Bristol Beer Factory Fortitude; 5 changing beers (often Arbor, Good Chemistry, Siren) Ⓗ

Built in 1912, the Tobacco Factory was part of the vast Imperial Tobacco estate across south Bristol. Saved from demolition in 1993, the café bar opened in 2001 and has been transformed into a vibrant venue offering good-quality, locally produced food and drink, with a number of nearby breweries' beers served from six cask handpumps and numerous keg fonts. The outside yard is used for special events, such as local brewery tap takeovers and the popular Factoberfest beer festival in mid-September. ॐ❀◑よ♖(24)❖

Bristol: Bishopston

Annexe
Seymour Road, BS7 9EQ (directly behind Sportsman pub)
☎ (0117) 949 3931
Wickwar BOB, Falling Star; Wye Valley HPA; 2 changing beers Ⓗ
Spacious community pub close to Gloucestershire county cricket ground and not far from the Memorial Stadium, which means it can be busy on match days. At one side is a conservatory where families are welcome until 8.30pm. Several TVs show live sport, including one on the partially covered patio outside. Good-value food is served including pizzas until late every evening. The two changing guest beers can include some interesting options. No dogs are allowed, even on the patio. ॐ❀◑♖❖

Bristol: Clifton

Brewhouse & Kitchen Ⓛ ✅
31-35 Cotham Hill, BS6 6JY
☎ (0117) 973 3793
Brewhouse & Kitchen (Bristol) Hornigold, Crockers, Ameryck, Yankee Cabot; 1 changing beer (often Brewhouse & Kitchen (Bristol)) Ⓗ
Popular brewpub and dining spot reopened in 2015, on the site of the 18th-century Whitelladies Tavern. The brewery is at one end of the large bar and catches the eye (and nose, on brewing days) upon entry. The in-house brewed beers are all suitable for vegans, except Treason milk stout. Brewery experience days can be booked throughout the year. A function room is available upstairs and a patio area is just across the road. ॐ❀◑⇌♦♖❖❖

Eldon House
6 Lower Clifton Hill, BS8 1BT (off top of Jacobs Wells Rd)
☎ (0117) 922 1271 ⊕ theeldonhouse.com
Bath Ales Gem; 3 changing beers (often Arbor, Bath Ales, St Austell) Ⓗ
Cosy end-of-terrace pub close to the busy Clifton Triangle. Get off a bus near the top of Park Street and head a short way down Jacobs Wells Road. The beers include guests from well-chosen independent brewers, often local, and occasionally from further afield. Many events are hosted, including a Monday quiz, live music every Sunday and occasional Saturdays, and a tango night every third Wednesday. Part of the pub can be hired for private functions at no cost. ॐ♖❖❖

Bristol: Clifton Village

Portcullis
3 Wellington Terrace, BS8 4LE
☎ (0117) 973 0270 ⊕ theportcullisclifton.com
Dawkins Bristol Blonde; Bristol Best; 4 changing beers (sourced nationally) Ⓗ
A pub since 1821, rescued by Dawkins in 2008, featuring a downstairs bar and an upstairs lounge that is also used

for functions. The building is part of a Georgian terrace close to the Clifton side of the Suspension Bridge, and has a cosy decor with many photos of film stars. Two to three Dawkins beers and guests from other microbreweries nationwide are served, plus a traditional cider. A large range of Belgian beers is also stocked. The rear garden is accessed from upstairs. ॐ❀◑♦♖(8,505)❖❖

Bristol: Fishponds

Snuffy Jack's
800 Fishponds Road, BS16 3TE
8 changing beers Ⓖ
The name of Bristol's third micropub, opened in 2017, relates to a former head miller at the nearby Snuff Mills. Between four and eight real ales are served on gravity from a chilled cabinet, plus two or more changing real ciders. Local beers feature plus some from further afield, with all styles offered. Food is limited to bar snacks. A quiz is held on the first Wednesday of the month. Conveniently close to multiple bus routes with direct links to many areas. Qॐ♦♖❖

Bristol: Henleaze

Westbury Park Ⓛ
Northumbria Drive, BS9 4HP
☎ (0117) 962 4235 ⊕ westburyparkpub.co.uk
Butcombe Original; St Austell Tribute; Timothy Taylor Landlord; 2 changing beers (often Arbor, Thornbridge) Ⓗ
Featured as the Kebab & Calculator in the BBC series The Young Ones, this circular pub reopened in 2016 after a major refurbishment. It is smartly decorated and furnished, with stools at the bar, and dining tables and comfortable seating throughout the open-plan interior. Outside, nine wooden cabins have been added, each with lighting and heating, accommodating six people. Emphasis is on well-kept, interesting beers, often from breweries in the area, and quality fresh, locally sourced food, with regularly changing seasonal menus. ॐ❀◑よP♖❖❖

Bristol: Horfield

Drapers Arms Ⓛ
447 Gloucester Road, BS7 8TZ
⊕ thedrapersarms.co.uk
7 changing beers Ⓖ
Bristol's first micropub, opened in 2015, prides itself on a changing selection of up to eight real ales on gravity, mostly from Bristol and the surrounding counties. Wine, local gins and bar snacks are also served, but no keg beer, bottled beer, lager or cider. This popular and friendly place follows the micropub tradition of focusing on good beer and conversation, with no music or TV. Two beer festivals are held each year. Qॐ♖❖

Bristol: Hotwells

Bag of Nails
141 St Georges Road, BS1 5UW (5 mins' walk from cathedral towards Hotwells)
☎ 07927 041014 ⊕ catpub.co.uk
7 changing beers Ⓗ
Close to the floating harbour, this small, partially gas-lit, terraced free house dates from the 1860s and serves up to nine changing cask ales, mainly from microbreweries, as well as a real cider. An eccentric list of rules includes no children, dogs or idiot pub crawls. The interior features terracotta colours, portholes in the floor, many

cats roaming free, and eclectic music from a proper record player. There are board games for the customers and toys for the cats. ♿🖵

Grain Barge

Mardyke Wharf, Hotwell Road, BS8 4RU (moored opp Baltic Wharf marina)

☎ (0117) 929 9347 ⊕ grainbarge.co.uk

Bristol Beer Factory Notorious, Fortitude, Independence; 2 changing beers (sourced locally; often Arbor, Good Chemistry, New Bristol) Ⓗ

This moored barge, built in 1936 and converted into a floating bar by Bristol Beer Factory in 2007, boasts great views of the SS Great Britain, the floating harbour and passing boats. There is seating with wooden tables at either end of the central bar, an extended shelf by the window overlooking the water, and an outdoor drinking area on the top deck. It hosts regular themed food nights, a quiz on Mondays, and live music some evenings. ᏏⓀ◑🖵🐾🛜

Merchants Arms

5 Merchants Road, BS8 4PZ

☎ (0117) 907 3047

4 changing beers Ⓗ

A traditional inn, free of tie, close to the Cumberland Basin, selling mainly South-West cask-conditioned ales. It has been completely refurbished after a car entered the bar! Both rooms are furnished with dark-wood seating and there is a real log fire in the front room. Sport is sometimes shown on the TV and a wide range of board games is available. Regular poetry nights take place. Renowned for home-made Scotch eggs, hand-finished pork pies and real Cornish pasties. QᏏ♣P🖵🐾🛜

Bristol: Kingsdown

Hare on the Hill

41 Thomas Street North, BS2 8LX

☎ (0117) 987 8462

4 changing beers (sourced locally; often Arbor, Bristol Beer Factory, Moor Beer) Ⓗ

Small street-corner venue with an impressive traditional green-tiled frontage. It is simply furnished and has a warm and welcoming feel throughout the stripped-back wood interior. Four handpumps offer a range of locally brewed beers as well as some from further afield. Six craft keg fonts also feature several Bristol-based brewers. The pub hosts an array of events including a weekly quiz, live music, low-key DJs on Saturday nights, and jazz piano evenings twice a month on a Wednesday. Ⓚ◑⇄●🖵🐾🛜

Hillgrove Porter Stores

53 Hillgrove Street North, BS2 8LT

☎ (0117) 924 9818

Dawkins Bristol Blonde, Bristol Best; 12 changing beers (sourced regionally) Ⓗ

This traditional community venue has a horseshoe-shaped interior, with a lounge area behind the bar and a pleasant patio. Alongside the two regular Dawkins beers there are up to 12 guests, including dark ales and rare styles, many from South-West breweries, plus a real cider. Japanese meals and bar snacks are served, as well as a popular Sunday afternoon roast. The style is eclectic and relaxed, with a lively atmosphere, a wide range of customers, and occasional DJ sets. Ⓚ◑⇄●🖵🐾🛜

Bristol: Redland

Chums

22 Chandos Road, BS6 6PF

☎ (0117) 973 1498 ⊕ chumsmicropub.co.uk

Wye Valley Bitter; 5 changing beers (often Cheddar Ales, Dawkins, Great Western) Ⓗ

A micropub in a converted shop, opened in 2016. Conversation rules, and electronic communication devices should be used with discretion. Real ales are dispensed from six handpumps – two from regular breweries – and a dark ale is always on the bar. Six traditional ciders are also available as well as a selection of wines and spirits. Simple bar snacks are served including filled rolls. Two beer festivals are held annually, one of which coincides with the community street party. Q🐕⇄♣●🖵🐾

Good Measure Ⓛ

2B Chandos Road, BS6 6PE

☎ (0117) 903 9930

Good Chemistry Time Lapse; 3 changing beers (often Burning Sky, Good Chemistry) Ⓗ

Good Chemistry Brewery's first outlet, opened in 2018, is a boutique bar in the increasingly popular Chandos Road neighbourhood of Redland. A wide range of drinks from the local area, the rest of the UK and the world, is served. Supplementing the four cask ales, which always include one dark ale and one from Good Chemistry, are eight taps serving seven craft beers, often in KeyKegs. Bottled Belgian beers and organic wines are also sold. There's a quiz every Monday evening. ᏏⓀ◑⇄🖵🐾🛜

Bristol: St Judes

Swan with Two Necks

12 Little Ann Street, BS2 9EB (off Wade St)

☎ (0117) 955 1837

Good Chemistry Time Lapse; Moor Beer Stout; 3 changing beers (sourced locally; often Arbor, Good Chemistry, Moor Beer) Ⓗ

Under new ownership since 2019, this small, single-bar venue, tucked away in a side street near Old Market, is rapidly becoming a beer destination as it was back in the 1990s. Two real ales and three guest beers are served, mainly, but not always, from local breweries, plus a real cider. In addition 14 keg lines dispense a variety of beers, lagers and cider. Food is limited to simple snacks, and music is from the vinyl collection behind the bar. ♿🖵🐾🛜

Bristol: St Philips

Barley Mow

39 Barton Road, BS2 0LF (400yds from rear exit of Temple Meads station over footbridge)

☎ (0117) 930 4709

Bristol Beer Factory Notorious, Fortitude; 6 changing beers (often Bristol Beer Factory, Siren, Tapestry) Ⓗ

Bristol Beer Factory's flagship outlet has eight handpumps offering up to three beers from the brewery plus constantly changing guests of varying styles from all over the UK, as well as a real cider. It also has an extensive bottled beer selection from around the world. Occasional beer-related events are held and it stages a quiz on Tuesdays. A small range of quality dishes changes frequently, with vegan-friendly options. There is a walled rear beer garden and benches at the front. ᏏⓀ◑⇄●🖵(506)🐾🛜

Bristol: St Werburghs

Duke of York Ⓛ

2 Jubilee Road, BS2 9RS (S side of Mina Rd park)

☎ (0117) 941 3677

4 changing beers (sourced locally; often Arbor, Electric Bear, Moor Beer) Ⓗ

Tucked away in a side street, this popular outlet has an eclectic clientele and decor to match. The wooden floors, coloured fairy lights, and intriguing range of memorabilia and artefacts create a welcoming grotto-like atmosphere. Notable features include a rare refurbished skittle alley, carved wooden mirrors and a Grand Old Duke of York exterior mural painted by a local artist. Upstairs is a room with sofas to lounge on. Four changing beers are served, mostly from breweries in Bristol and the surrounding area. ➄❀♣♠➡️(5)🛜

Bristol: Southville

Coronation

18 Dean Lane, BS3 1DD

☎ (0117) 940 9044

Bath Ales Gem; Butcombe Original; 2 changing beers (often Bristol Beer Factory, Twisted) Ⓗ

Popular traditional local in a residential area a short walk from Gaol Ferry Bridge. Five reasonably priced real ales are served as well as a good range of cans and bottles. Straightforward food, with extensive vegan options, is available most evenings, as well as a Sunday roast. Furnishings are simple and cosy and the licensee is the creator of the eclectic artwork that decorates the walls. There is a small raised seating section at the rear and on-street seating outside. ➄❀◑≒➡️(24)🍽🛜

Bristol: Spike Island

Orchard Inn

12 Hanover Place, BS1 6XT (off Cumberland Rd nr SS Great Britain)

☎ 07405 360994 ⊕ orchardinn.co.uk

Otter Bitter; St Austell Tribute; 3 changing beers (sourced regionally; often Box Steam, Gloucester, Otter) Ⓖ

Nestled on a corner in Spike Island, this friendly, traditional pub is close to the marina and just a short stroll or ferry ride from the city centre. Up to six ales are available, either straight from the barrel behind the bar or fetched from the cellar, where they share space with up to 20 ciders and perries. Sport is occasionally shown on TV in a raised area that doubles up as stage space for live jazz or blues music. ➄❀♠➡️(506,M2)🍽

Broad Campden

Bakers Arms Ⓛ

GL55 6UR (signed off B4081, at NW end of village)

☎ (01386) 840515 ⊕ bakersarmscampden.com

Prescott Hill Climb; Wickwar BOB; Wye Valley HPA, Butty Bach; 1 changing beer (sourced locally) Ⓗ

Fine old village local and genuine free house, first licensed as a public house in 1724. A photograph of the building in 1905 shows it as the village bakery and grain store. It boasts Cotswold stone walls, exposed beams and a fine inglenook. Excellent food is available in the bar and dining room extension, and there is a large garden and children's play area. Local guest beers alongside regular ales are served from the handsome oak bar. Q➄❀◑♣♠P🍽🛜

Brockhampton

Craven Arms Ⓛ

Kingsbury Street, GL54 5XQ (off A436 in centre of village in a cul-de-sac)

☎ (01242) 820410 ⊕ thecravenarms.co.uk

3 changing beers (sourced regionally; often XT) Ⓗ

A 17th-century free house set in an attractive hillside village with outstanding views and walks. It has a cosy bar area with an open fire and a dining room separated by church-style stone windows. Three carefully selected beers are well kept by the owner-chef. This pub is a regular Guide entry and a gem well-managed by a friendly family who organise functions for locals each month and a summer beer festival. Local CAMRA Pub of the Year winner 2019. Q➄❀�ᗑ◑▲♣P🍽🛜

Charfield

Pear Tree Micro Pub Ⓛ

6 Wotton Road, GL12 8TP (on B4058 1½ miles from jct 14 on M5)

☎ (01454) 260663

Great Western Maiden Voyage; 3 changing beers (sourced regionally; often Abbey, Cheddar Ales, St Austell) Ⓖ

A small, attractive, one-roomed pub, popular with regulars and visitors alike, with restored tiled flooring and a small wooden bar. Humorous murals cover most of the walls. It offers up to four beers, dispensed through wooden casks mounted in an old fireplace, usually from local and regional breweries. There is a large fenced outdoor seating area at the front. Q♣♠P➡️🍽

Plough Inn

68 Wotton Road, GL12 8SR

☎ (01453) 845297

4 changing beers Ⓗ

This attractive single-room micropub with two open fireplaces was extensively remodelled in 2019. It has a large outdoor seating space, heated in winter, with service via the original off-sales hatch. Four real ales are available plus lagers and ciders. There is a piano in the bar, and live music is a regular feature. One of its more unusual features is the large gnu head above the fireplace that gives its name to the occasional house beer. Q➄❀P➡️(60,85)

Charlton Kings

Royal

54 Horsefair Street, GL53 8JH (in centre of village opp church)

☎ (01242) 228937 ⊕ royalpub.co.uk

4 changing beers (often Bath Ales, Dartmoor, Otter) Ⓗ

Spacious, popular village restaurant/pub built in 1830 on the eastern fringe of town, which underwent a major refurbishment a few years ago in a contemporary style. The central bar, with comfy sofas, is adjacent to a lounge area. Regular live music, quizzes and Meet the Brewer evenings are hosted. Guest ales are typically from Hogs Back and Bath breweries. Beer festivals with live music are staged most bank holidays. Outside is a patio and large garden. No food Sunday evenings. Q➄❀◑♣P➡️(B,P/Q)🍽🛜

Chedworth

Seven Tuns

Queen Street, GL54 4AE (NE of village and nr church)

☎ (01285) 720630 ⊕ seventuns.co.uk

Hook Norton Hooky; Otter Amber; TAP Old Dairy Gold; house beer (by TAP); 1 changing beer (sourced locally) Ⓗ

Attractive 17th-century stone-built village pub, reopened as a free house after extensive refurbishment. There is a main bar, a snug and a converted barn restaurant, with exposed stone walls and a fireplace. Five handpumps

serve local and regional beers; the house beer is brewed by Tap Brewery. The local area has excellent walks.
Q❄️☆◑⚫&♿P🍴🅿❄️🎵

Cheltenham

Cheltenham Motor Club 🅛

Upper Park Street, GL52 6SA (first right off Hales Rd from London Rd lights, 100yds on right; pedestrian access from A40 via Crown Passage opp Sandford Mill Rd jct)
☎ (01242) 522590 🌐 cheltmc.com
6 changing beers (often Moor Beer, Tiley's) 🅷
Friendly club, winner of CAMRA National Club of the Year in 2013, 2017 and 2020, as well as multiple other awards. Five regularly changing ales are on the bar from across the country, plus a regular ale from the area, often from Tiley's Brewery. At least one KeyKeg, generally from Deya, is also served, alongside three real ciders and a range of bottled Belgian beers. An annual beer festival is hosted plus Meet the Brewer/takeover evenings. Local darts and pool teams play here. Non-members are welcome without charge for occasional visits.
Q❄️♣♿P🚃(B,51) ❄️🎵

Jolly Brewmaster 🅛

39 Painswick Road, GL50 2EZ
☎ (01242) 772261
7 changing beers (often Arbor, Bespoke, Moor Beer) 🅷
A frequent local CAMRA Pub of the Year with 13 handpumps featuring a changing range of nationally sourced ales and up to six ciders. This busy and friendly community hub features original etched windows, a horseshoe bar and open fire. It is a traditional drinking establishment with no food menu, but hot bar snacks such as pasties and pies are generally available later in the week. The attractive courtyard garden is popular in the summer, with regular Friday barbecues.
Q❄️☆⚫🚃(10,94U) ❄️🎵

Kemble Brewery 🅛 ✅

27 Fairview Street, GL52 2JF (off Northern ring road, jct of Fairview Rd/St Johns Avenue, turn left into Fairview St beside Machine Mart, pub is 100yds on right)
☎ (01242) 701053
Wye Valley HPA, Butty Bach; 4 changing beers 🅷
Small, popular, back-street local, current Cheltenham CAMRA Pub of the Year, hard to find, but well worth the effort. Originally a butcher's shop in 1845, it became a public house in 1847 and was soon brewing ciders, hence the name, although no brewing has taken place in recent times. It was fully refurbished in 2016. Six ales from near and far are generally available. There is a small attractive walled garden to the rear featuring a new servery for summer barbecues and pizzas.
Q❄️☆◑♣❄️🎵

Moon under Water 🅛 ✅

16-28 Bath Road, GL53 7HA
☎ (01242) 583945
Greene King Abbot; Ruddles Best Bitter; Sharp's Doom Bar; 5 changing beers 🅷
Open-plan Lloyds No.1 just off the pedestrianised high street (Strand). A decked area at the back overlooks the River Chelt and Sandford Park. Some five changing guest ales – local to countrywide – supplement the regular beers, plus a selection of real ciders. The dance floor is only used in the evening Friday and Saturday; there is a generally quiet atmosphere at other times. An interactive quiz night is hosted on Monday.
❄️☆◑&♿🚃❄️🎵

Railway Inn

New Street, GL50 3QL (400yds W of Wilson Museum)
☎ (01242) 522925
Stroud Tom Long; 2 changing beers 🅷
This smart local, just west of the town centre off the lower end of the High Street beside Waitrose, has recently become free of tie. There are two main rooms: a large lounge with comfy sofas at one end, and a small cosy bar facing the road. It has a garden with a terrace for smokers. Thai food and smoky barbecue cuisine are the main food focus, available every day. Q❄️☆☆◑P🍴❄️

Sandford Park Alehouse 🅛

20 High Street, GL50 1DZ (E end of High St, past Strand on right)
☎ (01242) 690242 🌐 sandfordparkalehouse.co.uk
Wye Valley Butty Bach; 8 changing beers (often Oakham) 🅷
CAMRA National Pub of the Year 2015 and a local winner in recent years, this contemporary alehouse has a U-shaped main bar area complete with bar billiards, a cosy front snug with a wood-burning stove, and a large south-facing patio and garden. A function room/lounge is on the first floor. Ten handpumps feature constantly changing ales from microbreweries sourced nationally and locally, plus at least one cider and 16 speciality lagers and craft beers. Internal screens plus the website keep you informed. Q❄️☆☆◑♣♿🚃❄️🎵

Chipping Campden

Eight Bells 🅛

Church Street, GL55 6JG
☎ (01386) 840371 🌐 eightbellsinn.co.uk
Hook Norton Hooky; North Cotswold Best; Purity Pure UBU; Wye Valley HPA 🅷
The Eight Bells was originally built in the 14th century to house the stonemasons who were constructing St James' church, and was later used to store the peal of eight bells. It was rebuilt using most of the original stone and timbers during the 17th century. What exists today is an outstanding example of a traditional Cotswold inn with a cobbled courtyard. Four handpumps dispense local and regional ales and two real ciders. CAMRA branch Pub of the Year winner 2020. Q❄️☆☆◑◑♣♿🚃(21)❄️

Chipping Sodbury

Horseshoe

2 High Street, BS37 6AH
☎ (01454) 325658 🌐 horseshoechippingsodbury.co.uk
7 changing beers (sourced regionally) 🅷
One of the oldest buildings in the town, this was formerly a stationery shop, then briefly a wine bar, and was converted into a pub at the start of 2014. It serves seven beers, often unusual but mostly from the West Country, including dark or strong choices, as well as real ciders. There are three linked rooms with assorted furniture, a gin bar upstairs, a pleasant rear garden and a cellar. A selection of freshly made rolls is available at lunchtimes. ❄️☆♣♿🚃❄️🎵

Churchdown

Old Elm 🅛 ✅

Church Road, GL3 2ER
☎ (01452) 530961 🌐 theoldelminn.co.uk
Sharp's Atlantic; 4 changing beers (sourced locally; often Hillside, Stroud) 🅷
Set in the heart of this village, the Old Elm has become popular since its refurbishment in 2015. It has gained a deserved reputation for the food – the menu features

good vegetarian options – and serves five quality beers, including LocAles. The pub hosts lively quiz and music nights, and food and drink tasting evenings; main sporting events are shown in the sports bar. Families are welcome and the garden has a children's play area. There are five letting rooms. ♿🏠🛋🍴♿♣🅿🚲🐾📶

Cirencester

Drillman's Arms

34 Gloucester Road, GL7 2JY (on old A417, 200yds from A435 jct)

☎ (01285) 653892

Sharp's Doom Bar; 3 changing beers (sourced nationally) 🅷

A lively Georgian inn perched beside a busy thoroughfare, offering a convivial lounge with wood-burner, a pub games dominated public bar and a popular skittle alley. Graced by the same landlady for over 25 years, this cracking free house features low-beamed ceilings, horse brasses, fresh flowers and brewery pictures, and serves well-priced pub food (lunchtimes only). An annual beer festival swamps the small front car park on August bank holiday weekends. Past winner of local CAMRA Pub of the Year awards. ❀🍴♣🅿🐾📶

Marlborough Arms 🅛

1 Sheep Street, GL7 1QW

☎ (01285) 651474

Box Steam Piston Broke; North Cotswold Windrush Ale; 6 changing beers (sourced nationally; often Corinium) 🅷

A real ale haven offering eight beers from regionals and microbreweries, plus a plethora of interesting boxed ciders and perries, and bottles. This lively, wooden-floored venue lies opposite the old GWR station, and is local CAMRA Pub and Cider Pub of the Year once again. Brewery memorabilia adorn the walls, with pews and a deep-set fireplace adding character. The ceiling is disappearing beneath the encroaching pumpclip collection. The rear patio is used for barbecues during beer and cider festivals. ❀♣🐾📶

Twelve Bells 🅛 ✅

12 Lewis Lane, GL7 1EA (straight ahead at traffic lights off A435 roundabout)

☎ (01285) 652230 🌐 twelvebellscirencester.com

Wye Valley Bitter; 3 changing beers (often Slater's, Three Castles) 🅷

This Grade II-listed pub is named after the 12-strong peal in the parish church. It comprises three areas: the front room with the bar is a popular spot for a beer and a chat, the middle and back rooms are primarily (but not exclusively) for dining. There is a TV but it is only used for major events. Outside is a sunny and colourful garden. Car parking is limited but there is a large car park 200 yards away (free after 3pm) and on-street parking after 6.30pm. Q♿❀🛋🍴👤♿🅿🚲🐾📶

Coaley

Old Fox 🅛

The Street, GL11 5EG

☎ (01453) 890905 🌐 oldfoxatcoaley.co.uk

Otter Bitter; Uley Pig's Ear Strong Beer; 4 changing beers 🅷

This attractive 300-year-old stone-built village local is in the centre of the village on the Cotswold Way. The single room interior was refurbished in 2018 and features a large oak bar, with seating on benches and at tables. A wood-burning stove provides a focal point. Now a free house, it has six real ale handpumps and three for cider.

A traditional pub food menu is available. There are outdoor seating areas to the front and side. Q♿❀🛋🍴👤♿♣👤🅿🚲🐾📶

Coleford

Dog House Micro Pub

13-15 St John Street, GL16 8AP

☎ 07442 787015

4 changing beers (sourced locally) 🅷/🅶

A friendly welcome is guaranteed, both for two- and four-legged customers. The small front bar extends back into another room. Four changing ales are served, almost invariably including a strong ale or stout. A good selection of cider in boxes is available, alongside a fine gin and rum collection. Social events include charity quiz nights, vinyl nights, Knit and Natter and a fishing club. Acoustic live music and talent showcase evenings take place most weekends. Closed Monday, Tuesday and weekday afternoons, and there is no admittance after 10.30pm. Local CAMRA branch Cider Pub of the Year 2019. Q♿👤🅿🚲🐾

Cranham

Black Horse Inn 🅛

GL4 8HP (off A46 or B4070)

☎ (01452) 812217

4 changing beers (sourced regionally; often Wye Valley) 🅷

A 17th-century, stone-built free house almost hidden up a side lane in the village. It is idyllically quiet, with a proper fire, but with no jukebox, TV or fruit machines. The lack of a reliable mobile phone signal in the village means that patrons here indulge in the traditional pursuit of conversation with friends, strangers and the walkers who have explored the myriad woodland paths nearby. Q♿🛋♣👤🅿🐾

Dursley

New Inn 🅛

82-84 Woodmancote, GL11 4AJ (on A4135 Tetbury road)

☎ (01453) 519288

5 changing beers (sourced regionally; often Hal's) 🅷

A dog-friendly establishment where the owners' pooches often provide a greeting. The pub is welcoming and comfortable, offering a large L-shaped public bar with a tiled floor and a smaller lounge. The eclectic selection of changing guest beers – usually, but not exclusively, from smaller breweries – is often chosen by regulars. There is a garden at the rear which is popular on sunny days. ♿❀♣👤🅿🚲(61)🐾

Old Spot Inn 🅛

2 Hill Road, GL11 4JQ (by bus station and free car park)

☎ (01453) 542870 🌐 oldspotinn.co.uk

Uley Old Ric; 7 changing beers (sourced nationally) 🅷

Excellent free house dating from 1776, serving great ales, ciders and perries. It is named after the Gloucestershire Old Spot pig, and a porcine theme blends with the extensive brewery memorabilia, low ceilings, wood-burning stove and welcoming staff to create a convivial atmosphere. There is an attractive garden and a heated outdoor covered area. Freshly prepared food is served lunchtimes. On the Cotswold Way, it is popular with walkers, and hosts regular events in the evenings. Q♿❀🛋👤♿👤🐾📶

Forthampton

Lower Lode Inn Ⓛ

GL19 4RE (follow sign to Forthampton from A438
Tewkesbury to Ledbury road) SO8788231809
☎ (01684) 293224 ⊕ lowerlodeinn.co.uk
4 changing beers Ⓗ
Blessed with views across the River Severn to
Tewkesbury Abbey, this attractive 15th-century brick-
built venue, with its three acres of lawns, is a popular
stopover for boats and is a Camping and Caravan Club
site. Food, advertised as simple and wholesome, is
excellent quality and value for money. A beer festival is
held in September. Day fishing is available, plus en-suite
accommodation. Opening times are reduced in winter so
check ahead. Q ☺ ❀ ✍ ◐ ▲ ♣ ⬤ P ❀

Fossebridge

Inn at Fossebridge ⊘

GL54 3JS (on A429)
☎ (01285) 720721 ⊕ innatfossebridge.co.uk
**Butcombe Original; North Cotswold Windrush Ale;
Wadworth 6X; 2 changing beers (sourced locally)** Ⓗ
This inn is in a pretty hamlet, where the Fosse Way drops
into the Cotswolds valley of the River Coln, an area of
outstanding natural beauty. An attractive one-bar tavern
with old timbers and a fine flagstone floor with open
fires, the premises also benefit from an outstanding four-
acre garden with a lake and river. A selection of regional
ales and guests from local breweries is served in cosy
surroundings. Q ☺ ❀ ✍ ◐ ⬤ P ❀ ☞

Frampton Cotterell

Globe Inn

366 Church Road, BS36 2AB
☎ (01454) 778286 ⊕ theglobeframptoncotterell.co.uk
**Butcombe Original; Fuller's London Pride; St Austell
Proper Job, Tribute; 1 changing beer (often Bristol
Beer Factory, Otter)** Ⓗ
Independent free house opposite the parish church and
situated on the Frome Valley Walkway, which links the
Cotswold Way with Bristol. It is open-plan with an L-
shaped bar, and low ceilings and carpet give the pub a
comfortable feel. At the far end of the bar is a large
function room. The pub specialises in home-made,
freshly cooked food. The large enclosed lawned garden
with children's play area is very popular in the summer.
☺ ❀ ◐ ⬤ P 🖃 ☞

Rising Sun

43 Ryecroft Road, BS36 2HN
☎ (01454) 772330 ⊕ gwbrewery.co.uk/rising-sun
**Great Western HPA, Maiden Voyage, Moose River; 3
changing beers (often Butcombe, Draught Bass,
Wadworth)** Ⓗ
Village local and brewery tap for the Great Western
Brewing Company in nearby Hambrook. There is a room
as you enter with a log-burning stove, then three
archways past slate pillars to the bar, additional seating
up the stairs to the left, and a restaurant in the warm
conservatory. Lunchtime snacks and more substantial
evening meals are served from an extensive menu, with
all food made in-house. The skittle alley can also be used
for private functions. Q ❀ ◐ ♣ P 🖃 (Y4,Y6) ❀ ☞

Frampton-on-Severn

Three Horseshoes Ⓛ

The Green, GL2 7DY (off B4071)
☎ (01452) 742100

**Timothy Taylor Landlord; Uley Bitter; 1 changing
beer** Ⓗ
There is always a warm welcome in this two-bar rural
community pub, originally built by a farrier in the 19th
century at the south end of England's longest village
green. The food is home-cooked, especially the unique
3-Shu pie, which is freshly baked to order. Both bars
have coal fires, and dogs are welcome in the flagstoned
public bar. Evening jamming sessions are popular
(largely biased towards folk music) and there are regular
community events. A double boules court hosts annual
championships. Q ☺ ❀ ◐ ⬤ ▲ ♣ ⬤ ❀ ☞

Gloucester

Brewhouse & Kitchen (Gloucester Quays)

Unit R1, St Anne Walk, Gloucester Quay, GL1 5SH
☎ (01452) 222965
**Brewhouse & Kitchen Shed Head, Stevedore, (Down
A) Pegg, SSB** Ⓗ
Based in the bustling Gloucester Quays development,
this smart bar and restaurant is part of the growing
Brewhouse & Kitchen chain, crafting its own range of
ales on-site. Customers can sit in comfort and enjoy a
quality beer, while watching the brewing process. Four
cask ales are available, with seasonal specials on keg. On
a fine day you can relax by the side of the Gloucester-
Sharpness Canal in the outdoor seating area.
☺ ◐ ⬤ 🖃 ❀ ☞

Fountain Inn Ⓛ ⊘

53 Westgate Street, GL1 2NW (down an alley between
nos 51 & 55)
☎ (01452) 522562 ⊕ thefountaininngloucester.com
**Bristol Beer Factory Independence; Dartmoor Jail Ale;
St Austell Tribute; 3 changing beers** Ⓗ
A stone's throw away from Gloucester Cathedral, this
interesting 17th-century inn is on the site of an ale house
known to have existed in 1216. A passage leads from
Westgate Street into an attractive courtyard where there
is a plaque to commemorate King William III riding his
horse up the stairs. The Cathedral Bar has a panelled
ceiling and carved stone fireplace. The Orange Room
serves as a restaurant or as a room for private functions.
❀ ◐ ⬤ ❀ ☞

Pelican Inn Ⓛ ⊘

4 St Marys Street, GL1 2QR
☎ (01452) 582966
**4 changing beers (sourced regionally; often Wye
Valley)** Ⓗ
The Pelican was licensed as an alehouse in the 17th
century. People believe that some of its beams are from
Drake's ship the Golden Hind, which began life as the
Pelican. After a chequered history, Wye Valley Brewery
refurbished it in 2012, since when its popularity has
grown steadily. There is a main bar area, a side room and
an attractive outdoor drinking space. The growing range
of cider and perry increases during the summer to
complement the 10 ales on offer, including a guest beer.
Q ❀ ⬤ ≈ ♣ ⬤ 🖃 ❀ ☞

Tank ⊘

12-14 Llanthony Road, GL1 2EH
☎ (01452) 690541 ⊕ tankgloucester.com
4 changing beers (sourced nationally) Ⓗ
This brewery tap is a welcoming, urban warehouse-style
bar with a contemporary feel, located in the heart of the
Gloucester Docks redevelopment. The decor utilises the
building's strengths, and is well worth a look. Though
primarily selling Gloucester beers, there is a wide range

of guest beers, craft and bottled beers, and ciders. Food comes in the shape of local meats and cheeses served on platters, along with a selection of hand-made pizzas. ◐♿●🚌(10) 🐾📶

Ham

Salutation Inn [L]

Ham Green, GL13 9QH (from Berkeley take road signposted to Jenner Museum)
☎ (01453) 810284 🌐 the-sally-at-ham.com
Tiley's Ordinary Bitter; 5 changing beers (sourced nationally; often Arbor, Bristol Beer Factory, Moor Beer) [H]
An attractive multi award-winning rural free house, popular with locals and visitors alike, offering up to seven real ales and nine real ciders and perries, plus an extensive bottled beer and cider menu. The on-site microbrewery, Tiley's Ales, produces a range of traditional ales. There are three bars – two cosy ones share a central wood-burner – and a skittles alley/function room. Food is served at lunchtimes and on occasional evenings only; there are also folk nights and singalongs. Situated in the Severn Valley it is within walking distance of the Jenner Museum and Berkeley Castle and Deer Park. Q🐴❀◐♿♣●P🐾📶

Hawkesbury Upton

Beaufort Arms [L]

High Street, GL9 1AU (off A46, 6 miles N of M4 jct 18)
☎ (01454) 238217 🌐 beaufortarms.com
Bristol Beer Factory Independence; Butcombe Original; 3 changing beers (sourced regionally) [H]
A wonderful Grade II-listed Cotswold stone free house, built in 1602, close to the historic Somerset Monument. It features separate public and lounge bars, a dining room and a skittle alley/function room, which house a veritable plethora of ancient brewery and local memorabilia. Up to five ales and a traditional cider are served on handpump. Outside is an attractive garden with a barbecue used for local community activities. A great bunch of regulars assures a warm welcome. Q🐴❀◐♿♣●P🚌🐾📶

Kingswood

Lyons Den

121 Regent Street, BS15 8LJ
6 changing beers (often Bristol Beer Factory, New Bristol, Tiny Rebel) [G]
Micropub opened in May 2019 in a former charity shop at the eastern end of the main shopping street. The bar area as you enter is simply furnished and there is a small snug space at the rear. The beers and ciders for sale are displayed on a retro-style computer screen on the wall. Board games are available to play and there is low-volume background music. Look out for regular tap takeovers from local breweries and some from further afield. Q🐴❀●🚌🐾

Marshfield

Catherine Wheel

39 High Street, SN14 8LR (if using postcode in sat nav check it is not showing Colerne)
☎ (01225) 892220 🌐 thecatherinewheel.co.uk
Butcombe Original; Stroud Organic Pale Ale; 1 changing beer (sourced locally; often Bath Ales) [H]
The Catherine Wheel is an impressive example of provincial baroque architecture, much of it dating back to the 17th century, although some interior features look older. Simple, sympathetic decor complements the exposed stone walls and large open fireplaces. It feels like a traditional Cotswold pub inside, offering good ale, good food and a warm interior. It has a large cosy bar area, with rooms off. Q🐴❀🛏◐♣P🚌🐾📶

Minchinhampton

Crown Inn

High Street, GL6 9BN (opp Market House)
☎ (01453) 488160 🌐 thecrown-minchinhampton.com
Butcombe Adam Henson's Rare Breed; 5 changing beers (sourced nationally; often Arbor, Cheddar, Thornbridge) [H]
A late 17th-century Cotswold stone coaching inn triumphantly resurrected in 2019 after being closed for seven years. It is run by an enthusiastic landlord with an adventurous approach to beer sourcing – including exclusive brews and one-off casks. Light streams in through two bay windows on to a spectacular carved bar front salvaged from France, topped with a copper counter and eight handpumps – three of them devoted to a changing selection of ciders. Towards the rear it becomes dark and alluring, with tables set for dining, subdued lighting and candles. A large courtyard garden features an outdoor bar with four DEYA craft keg beers on tap. Local CAMRA Pub of the Year 2021.
🐴❀◐♿⛺●🚌(69) 🐾📶

Moreton-in-Marsh

Bell Inn [L] ✔

High Street, GL56 0AF (on A429)
☎ (01608) 651688 🌐 thebellinnmoreton.co.uk
Prescott Hill Climb; Purity Pure UBU; Timothy Taylor Landlord; 2 changing beers (sourced locally; often Hook Norton, North Cotswold) [H]
An old High Street coaching inn dating from the 18th century, now pleasantly refurbished. The interior is mainly open plan, sympathetically divided into more intimate snug sections with a real fire. Local and national ales are stocked along with good food. A large courtyard is found through the old arched entrance, with an enclosed garden at the rear. The Bell is famed for its links with JRR Tolkien, Lord of the Rings author – a map of Middle Earth adorns the walls.
Q🐴❀🛏◐♿⛺🚆P🚌(801) 🐾📶

Moseley Green

Rising Sun [L] ✔

GL15 4HN
☎ (01594) 562008 🌐 risingsunmoseleygreen.co.uk
Wickwar BOB; 3 changing beers (sourced nationally) [H]
Set in splendid isolation deep in the woodlands of the Forest of Dean, this pub is popular with walkers, cyclists and locals. It originally served miners working at the nearby collieries and, enjoying the panoramic views, it is difficult to imagine that this was once a scene of industrial activity. There are extensive grounds with patios for alfresco dining, ideal for families. Brass bands play in the garden on Sunday evenings in summer.
🐴❀🛏◐♣●P🎯🐾

Newent

Black Dog

47 Church Street, GL18 1AA
☎ (01531) 248260 🌐 blackdognewent.co.uk
Sharp's Doom Bar; 3 changing beers (often Bespoke, Inferno, Prescott) [H]

A recently refurbished 18th-century half-timbered pub in the heart of Newent. It is family friendly, welcoming both children and dogs. There is an open lounge and separate dining room serving daytime and evening meals. Entertainment includes evenings of live music, traditional games and a large sports TV. Outside, there is a sheltered smoking area and parking.
ᵹ❀🛏◑♣P🚌🐾📶

King's Arms

Ross Road, GL18 1BD (on B4221)
☎ (01531) 820035 🌐 kings-arms-newent.business.site
4 changing beers (often Bespoke, Shepherd Neame, Titanic) H
Following major improvements, the pub has a comfortable refitted bar area with open fires, a large function room and skittle alley, and a big lower bar and dining room. There is also a spacious outdoor decked courtyard. With a good reputation for home-cooked food, the pub offers a wide menu including speciality pizzas, midweek offers and popular Sunday lunches. Qᵹ◑♣P

Newnham

Black Pig Ale House

High Street, GL14 1BY (up alleyway to side of Ship Inn)
☎ (01594) 516283
4 changing beers (sourced nationally; often St Austell, Wickwar) G
This wonderful new venture is situated inside a 16th-century Grade II-listed horse stable, within the grounds of the Ship Inn. Effectively a micropub, an impressive wooden bar lies opposite a huge fireplace, and there is an upstairs mezzanine area for darts, space invaders and conversation. Drinks are stillaged against the thick stone walls – the regularly changing ales are served direct from the barrel. Outside, the charming garden and courtyard are an enjoyable spot on warmer evenings. Dogs are welcome. ❀♣🚌(23)🐾

Parkend

Fountain Inn

Fountain Way, GL15 4JD (off B4234)
☎ (01594) 562189 🌐 thefountaininn.info
Wye Valley HPA, Butty Bach; 2 changing beers (often Hillside) H
This inn makes an ideal refreshment stop after a leisurely journey on the Dean Forest Railway to its present terminus at Parkend nearby. (In the height of the tourist season Parkend can be a bustling place.) A branch line once passed directly in front of the pub. The Fountain offers accommodation and an adjoining bunkhouse caters for larger groups. A footpath leads directly to the Whitemead Forest Park. Good food and well-kept beer provide sustenance for visitors and regulars. Interesting artefacts depicting local and railway history adorn the walls. Qᵹ❀🛏◑♿▲♣P🐾📶

Prestbury

Plough ✔

Mill Street, GL52 3BG (opp church, can be accessed by walking through churchyard from High St)
☎ (01242) 361506 🌐 theploughprestbury.co.uk
3 changing beers (often Bath Ales, St Austell) G
Half-timbered thatched inn with an attractive garden. It has a wood-panelled lounge and a stone-flagged public bar. Low ceilings and serving hatches help to make this the definitive traditional pub. It serves good-value food in an expanded restaurant area, and beers are drawn straight from the barrel. The garden has been refurbished and now includes a new equipped play area, more seating, and a boules pitch. Summer opening hours are longer than in winter, so check ahead. Qᵹ❀◑♣●

Randwick

Vine Tree Inn L

The Stocks, GL6 6JA
☎ (01453) 763748 🌐 thevinetreerandwick.co.uk
3 changing beers (sourced regionally; often Purity, Tiley's, Tiny Rebel) H
A secluded gem nestling in the flank of a steep hill with spectacular views. It comprises three interconnected spaces, the walls a mixture of grey-painted matchboard wainscots, rustic stone and artex, while the furniture is scrubbed tables and wheel-backed chairs. The landlord has thrown his heart and soul into the pub and the community – it is a centre for village football, cricket, table tennis and darts teams, and a mecca for walkers. Qᵹ❀◑▲♣●P🚌🐾📶

Sheepscombe

Butchers Arms L ✔

GL6 7RH (signed off A46 N of Painswick and B4070 N of Slad) SO8911610434
☎ (01452) 812113 🌐 butchers-arms.co.uk
Bristol Beer Factory Notorious; 2 changing beers (sourced nationally; often Blue Monkey, Fresh Standard, Vocation) H
A handsome 17th-century Cotswold-stone pub overlooking a wooded valley. Its inn sign, a painted three-dimensional carving of a butcher quaffing ale while tethered to a pig, is world famous. The guest pumps offer an adventurous range of ales from across the country. In 2014 the lean-to outdoor toilets metamorphosed into a new bar, seamlessly executed in reclaimed stone and Welsh oak. This complements a quality inter-war refurbishment that added the generous bay windows and porch. A wood-burning stove offers warmth in winter while the forecourt tables and sloping side garden are suntraps in summer.
Qᵹ❀◑♿▲♣●P▯🐾📶

Staple Hill

Wooden Walls Micropub

30 Broad Street, BS16 5NU
☎ 07858 266596 🌐 thewoodenwallsmicropub.com
5 changing beers H
Micropub opened in 2018 in a former carpet shop on the main shopping street. The single room is pleasantly furnished with wooden booths and walls. Drinks for sale are displayed on a large blackboard that surrounds the serving hatch. Between five and 10 real ales are on offer alongside several real ciders, in addition to gin and wine, but no lager. There are a few steps up to the toilets and paved rear garden. Q❀♣●🚌🐾

Stroud

Ale House L

9 John Street, GL5 2HA (opp Cornhill Farmers' Market)
☎ (01453) 755447 🌐 thealehousestroud.com
Burning Sky Plateau; Tiley's Zappa Talus Pale; 6 changing beers (sourced nationally; often Electric Bear, Grey Trees, Red Cat) H
Built in 1837 for the Poor Law Guardians, this Grade-II listed building is a mecca for ale lovers. The bar occupies the double-height top-lit former boardroom, where an all year round beer festival showcases beers from Fyne Ales, Vocation and many others – plus a cider and perry.

Opposite is a blazing log fire and adjoining are two smaller rooms. Live music is hosted at weekends, with jazz once a month on Thursday. Quiz night is Sunday. Food consists of home-made curries, chilli and more. A restored bar billiards table is a welcome recent addition. Q✿❶ঙ✦♣♠♥❄✿

Bowbridge Arms 🄻

London Road, Bowbridge, GL5 2AY (on A419 at junction with Butterrow Hill)
☎ (01453) 298914 ⊕ thebowbridgearms.co.uk
St Austell Proper Job; 1 changing beer (often Bath Ales, Box Steam, Stroud) Ⓗ
Friendly, traditional, Cotswold-stone pub at the eastern edge of Stroud. Close to Bowbridge Lock on the Thames and Severn Canal, it is a 15-minute walk from the town centre and railway station. The comfortable modernised interior is dominated by a stonking Clearview stove. At the back, a small lounge, also with a stove, leads to an even smaller room with a large flat-screen TV, available to hire for meetings or private dining. The large south-facing suntrap patio has a children's play area and views across the valley to Rodborough Common. Good-value home-cooked food includes typical pub grub (lasagne, burgers and pizzas). Q✿✿♣❶ঙ✦AP♥❄✿

Crown & Sceptre 🄻

98 Horns Road, GL5 1EG
☎ (01453) 762588 ⊕ crownandsceptrestroud.com
Stroud Budding; Uley Bitter; Pig's Ear Strong Beer; 1 changing beer (sourced regionally; often Blue Anchor) Ⓗ
Lively back-street local that is at the heart of its community. The walls display an eclectic mix of framed prints, posters and clocks. Local groups meet round a large oak table in a side room – including Knit and Natter on Tuesdays. The pub also has its own motorcycle society. It is famed for its Up the Workers good-value set meal on Wednesdays, and Sunday roasts. Sport is screened in the back bar. A terrace to the rear offers panoramic views across the valley to Rodborough Common. ✿✿❶A♣♠♥(8)❄✿

Prince Albert 🄻 ✪

Rodborough Hill, GL5 3SS (corner of Walkley Hill)
☎ (01453) 755600 ⊕ theprincealbertstroud.co.uk
Bristol Beer Factory Independence; Timothy Taylor Landlord; 3 changing beers (sourced nationally; often Clavell & Hind, Pitchfork, Tiley's) Ⓗ
This lively, cosmopolitan, Cotswold-stone inn below Rodborough Common has been run by the same family for 25 years. It manages to be simultaneously bohemian, homely and welcoming, with a big reputation for live music. The L-shaped single bar is filled with local art, music and film posters, and an idiosyncratic mix of furniture, fittings and memorabilia. Home-made pizzas and burgers are served from a brand-new kitchen adjoining a large covered courtyard. Stairs lead up to a walled garden with an elegant cruck-framed shelter. Live music on Sunday and Monday evenings is ticketed. ✿✿❶A♣♠♥(40) ❄✿

Tetbury

Royal Oak 🄻 ✪

1 Cirencester Road, GL8 8EY (on B4067)
☎ (01666) 500021 ⊕ theroyaloaktetbury.co.uk

> A fine beer may be judged with only a sip, but it's better to be thoroughly sure.
> **Czech proverb**

Butcombe Haka; Moor Beer So'Hop; Stroud Tom Long; 2 changing beers (sourced regionally) Ⓗ
This wonderful award-winning pub utilises clever design to marry a traditional feel to a modern layout. The swathe of wooden surfaces creates a welcoming feel, with a small fireplace adding warmth. Six handpumps include Severn Cider and a vegan ale from Moor – chosen to match the vegan menu option. The one-pot dish is popular, especially on quiz nights. Upstairs dining rooms and six letting rooms are popular, as are the lively music and beer festivals. ✿✿🛏❶ঙ✦♣♠P♥❄✿

Tewkesbury

Berkeley Arms ✪

8 Church Street, GL20 5PA (between Tewkesbury Cross and abbey on old A38)
☎ (01684) 290555 ⊕ berkeleyarms.pub
Wadworth Henry's IPA, 6X, Swordfish; 2 changing beers Ⓗ
A 15th-century half-timbered Grade II inn, just off Tewkesbury Cross. The entrance to the public bar is from the street, while the lounge is accessed from one of Tewkesbury's many alleyways. At the rear of this two-bar venue, a barn, believed to be the oldest non-ecclesiastical building in this historic town, is used as a meeting room year round. Live music is performed on Friday and Saturday evenings. Buses to Cheltenham and Gloucester stop close by. ✿✿ঙ♣A♠♥♥(41)❄✿

Cross House Tavern 🄻

108 Church Street, GL20 5AB
☎ 07931 692227
5 changing beers (often Goff's, Inferno, Ledbury) Ⓗ
Tewkesbury's first micropub was originally two houses in the early 16th century. It was extended in the 17th century, and extensively renovated throughout in about 1865. The Cross House Tavern's heritage has been restored with a great deal of dedication. It has again become a Victorian-style establishment serving real local ales (including vegan beer), ciders, perries, wines and snacks (all sourced within 20 miles). The beer is dispensed from tapped casks, much as it was when the building was known as the Tolsey Inn & Coach House in the early 20th century. QA♣♠♥❄

Nottingham Arms 🄻 ✪

129 High Street, GL20 5JU (on A38 in town centre)
☎ (01684) 491514
Sharp's Doom Bar; St Austell Tribute; Wye Valley Butty Bach, HPA Ⓗ
Fourteenth-century town-centre hostelry with two welcoming rooms, a public bar at the front and the restaurant behind, with timber predominating. Framed photographs of old Tewkesbury adorn the walls. The pub is gaining a reputation for excellent, well-priced food, served lunchtimes and evenings. Knowledgeable staff will happily tell you about the resident ghosts. Live music is hosted on most Sunday evenings and Thursday is quiz night. ✿❶A♣♠♥❄✿

Royal Hop Pole 🄻 ✪

94 Church Street, GL20 5RS (centre of town)
☎ (01684) 278670
Great Western Old Higby; Greene King IPA; Hook Norton Old Hooky; Ruddles County; 4 changing beers (sourced locally) Ⓗ
This well-known landmark is an amalgamation of historic buildings from the 15th and 18th centuries. It has been known as the Royal Hop Pole since it was visited in 1891 by Princess Mary of Teck (Queen Mary, Royal Consort of George V). The Hop Pole is mentioned in Dickens' Pickwick Papers. Purchased by JD Wetherspoon, it

reopened in 2008. There is wood panelling on almost every wall of this spacious, multi-roomed drinking establishment, with a large patio and garden area at the rear. Q ⮜ ❀ ⇦ ◖ ⬥ ♿ P 🚃 ❀ 🛜

Thornbury

Anchor Inn 🅛 ✅
Gloucester Road, BS35 1JY
☎ (01454) 281375 ⊕ theanchorthornbury.co.uk
Draught Bass; 7 changing beers (often Exmoor, Fuller's, St Austell) Ⓗ
Licensed since 1695, this friendly, traditional inn serves one regular beer and between five and seven changing guests, plus a real cider. Good home-cooked food is available daily. There are two large rooms, one of which has been split to provide a function/meeting area and is also used by local artists. The pub has its own darts, cribbage, dominoes and cricket teams, and angling syndicate. The garden includes a boules piste and children's play area. ⮜ ❀ ◖ ♣ ♿ P 🚃 ❀ 🛜

Thrupp

Stroud Brewery Tap 🅛
Kingfisher Business Park, London Road, GL5 2BY (take A419 from Stroud, turn right down Hope Mill Lane just before the red, white and blue-painted bus shelter, take the immediate right and the brewery is on your left over the bridge at the end)
☎ (01453) 887122 ⊕ stroudbrewery.co.uk
Stroud Tom Long, Organic Pale Ale, Budding; 1 changing beer (often Stroud) Ⓗ
Stroud Brewery occupies a new purpose-designed building beside the Thames and Severn Canal. The taproom opens directly onto a terrace beside the towpath. To one side is an open kitchen with an Italian wood-fired pizza oven. Seating consists mostly of wooden benches beside long tables – resembling at times a diminutive Bavarian beer hall. These benches are augmented by squishy leather sofas and large oak casks for vertical drinking. At the far end – and with small windows allowing glimpses of the brewery – is a small stage with an upright piano. ⮜ ❀ ◖ & ♣ P 🚃 ❀ 🛜

Upper Oddington

Horse & Groom 🅛 ✅
GL56 0XH (top of village signed off A436 E of Stow)
☎ (01451) 830584 ⊕ horseandgroom.uk.com
Prescott Hill Climb; Wye Valley Butty Bach; 1 changing beer (sourced locally) Ⓗ
You are assured of a warm welcome at this privately owned 16th-century inn run by friendly licensees. It has an extended bar area for locals with its own sitting room

linked by a real open log fire in an inglenook setting. On the bar are Wye Valley beers plus a weekly changing guest, usually from a Gloucestershire brewer. The pub has an attractive garden and patio, a large car park, and eight letting bedrooms. Situated in good walking country close to Stow. Q ⮜ ❀ ⇦ ◖ P 🚃 ❀ 🛜

Upper Soudley

White Horse Inn
Church Road, GL14 2UA (on B4227)
☎ (01594) 825968
2 changing beers (sourced nationally) Ⓗ
This pub was originally built as a railway hotel, next to the now defunct Soudley Halt, and has fine views across the valley from the garden. The lovely old inn has a small main bar with a welcoming fireplace and two regularly changing guest ales. The old dining room down the passageway is used for functions, and leads through to a much-loved skittle alley. An appealing stop-off for geologists and walkers, with the Blue Rock Trail and Soudley ponds nearby. ⮜ ❀ & ♣ ♿ P 🚃 (717) ❀

Westbury-on-Severn

Lyon Inn
The Village, GL14 1PA (on A48)
☎ (01452) 760221 ⊕ thelyoninn.com
3 changing beers Ⓗ
Conveniently situated on the main Gloucester to Chepstow road, and dominated by the recently refurbished and imposing spire of the parish church, the Lyon has welcomed travellers for generations. Earliest references go back as far as the 16th century, but the ancient-looking timbers are an early 20th-century addition. The new owners have sensitively revived the fortunes of the former Red Lion, sensitively opening up previously underused areas to create dining spaces while retaining the traditional ambience. Q ⮜ ❀ ⇦ ◖ ♣ P 🚃

Winchcombe

Lion Inn ✅
37 North Street, GL54 5PS
☎ (01242) 603300 ⊕ thelionwinchcombe.co.uk
Marston's EPA; North Cotswold Cotswold Best; Prescott Grand Prix; Wye Valley Butty Bach Ⓗ
Comfortable 15th-century coaching inn in the centre of the town, renovated in 2011. It retains a traditional appearance, with exposed oak timbers and stone fireplaces. A popular venue with regulars and visitors, the bar offers changing local real ales on four handpumps. The pub also has an attractive restaurant and accommodation, and a secluded lawn and patio at the rear. ⮜ ❀ ⇦ ◖ ♣ P 🚃 ❀ 🛜

Beer not brandy

Before brandy, which has now become common and sold in every little alehouse, came to England in such quantities as it now doth, we drank good strong beer and ale, and all laborious people (which are the greater part of the kingdom), their bodies requiring after hard labour some strong drink to refresh them, did therefore every morning and evening used to drink a pot of ale or a flagon of strong beer, which greatly helped the promotion of our grains and did them no great prejudice; it hindereth not their work, neither did it take away their senses nor cost them much money, whereas the prohibition of brandy would prevent the destruction of his majesty's subjects, many of whom have been killed by drinking thereof, it not agreeing with their constitution.
Petition to the House of Commons, 1673

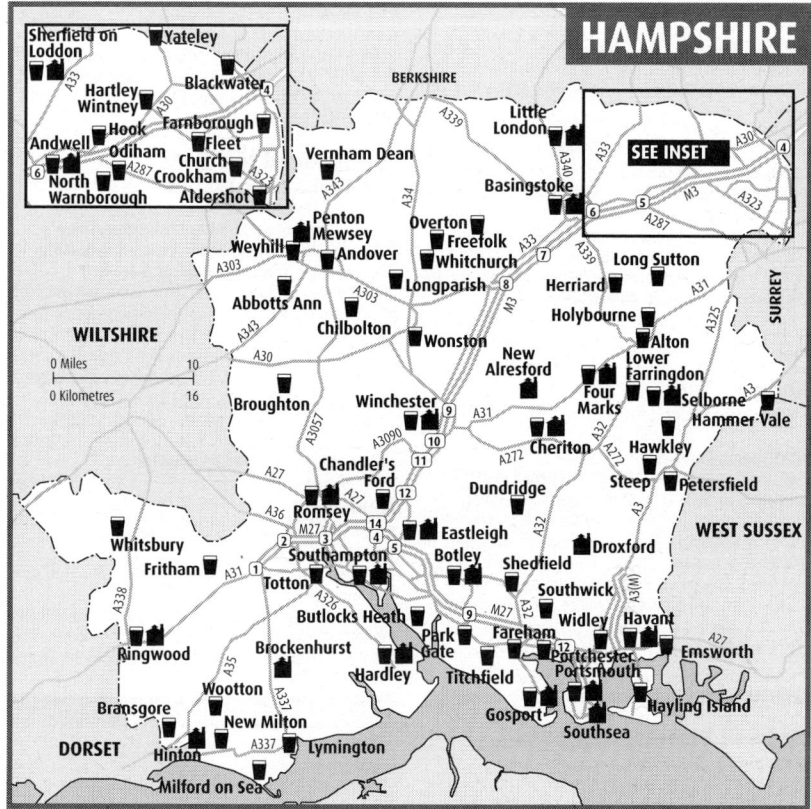

HAMPSHIRE

Please note: Ringwood Brewery renamed Best Bitter to Razorback but it is still available in some outlets as Best Bitter

Abbotts Ann

Eagle Inn 🄻
Duck Street, SP11 7BG
☎ (01264) 710339 🌐 theeagleinn.wordpress.com
Bowman Wallops Wood; 3 changing beers (sourced locally) 🄷
In a picturesque village just two miles south-west of Andover, this pub is at the heart of the community, and friendly conversation rules the house. The regular Wallops Wood is supplemented by three changing beers, often from regional breweries. A beer and cider festival is held in the summer. The public bar has pool and there is a skittle alley at the rear. Locally sourced food features.
🏵🍴♣🅿🚆(87)🐾🛜

Aldershot

Garden Gate 🄻 ✅
2 Church Lane East, GU11 3BT
☎ (01252) 219717
Courage Best Bitter; Surrey Hills Ranmore; house beer (by Marston's); 1 changing beer (sourced regionally; often Banks's, Surrey Hills) 🄷
Close to Aldershot's bus and railway station, this friendly pub with background music repays a visit. Three or four handpumps are on the bar, with the licensee preferring to source predominantly from local breweries. The Thursday night quiz is well attended and a music quiz is held on the first Sunday of the month. Popular with dogs and their owners. 🏵🚆🅿🚆🐾🛜

Alton

Eight Bells 🄻
33 Church Street, GU34 2DA
☎ (01420) 82417
Flower Pots Perridge Pale, Pots Bitter; 1 changing beer (sourced regionally; often Flack Manor, Crafty Brewing) 🄷
This genuine free house, a pub since at least the 1840s, is a regular outlet for Flower Pots ales, and the guest beer turnover can be rapid. The main bar is a haven for good beer and conversation, while the rear drinking area has a TV for major sporting events. An open fire is welcoming in the winter and, outside, the paved patio, with floral shrub borders in summer, has a covered smoking refuge and an old well. Q🏵🚆🚆(13)🐾🛜

Railway Arms 🄻
26 Anstey Road, GU34 2RB
☎ (01420) 542316
Triple fff Alton's Pride, Moondance; 5 changing beers (sourced nationally; often Fuller's, Red Cat) 🄷
Friendly pub close to the Watercress Line and mainline station. A striking sculpture of a steam locomotive emerges from the front over outside seating. Owned by Triple fff Brewery, its beers are supplemented by guest ales, often from local micros, and the real cider is Seacider. The rear bar can be hired. The patio area at the back, designed with a traditional railway theme, incorporates a covered smoking area. Local CAMRA Cider Pub of the Year 2020. 🏵🚆♣🅿🚆(64,65)🐾🛜

Ten Tun Tap House Ⓛ

1 Westbrook Walk, GU34 1HZ
☎ 07971 076657
4 changing beers (sourced nationally; often Red Cat, Siren) Ⓕ
Opened in March 2020 two days before the first Covid lockdown as a real ale and craft beer micropub, this bar kept going through the subsequent restrictions with a local delivery service. Four handpumps plus eight taps dispense real ale, craft keg and cider from around the country, although Hampshire and Sussex brews are usually available. The style is bare-wood minimalist but a vibrant buzz is generated by the varied clientele and the jazzy background music. ⏁≠●🚌🐱🐾📶

Andover

Andover Tap

2 Winchester Street, SP10 2EA
☎ 07866 555243 ⊕ theandovertap.co.uk
10 changing beers Ⓕ
This small, independent micropub, opened in 2019, specialises in the supply of local beers in a simply furnished former patisserie near the High Street. There are up to 12 available – four on handpump, four casks on gravity dispense and four keg beers – and three or four real ciders. The pub is owned and run by the former brewer from Test Brewing. Families are welcome until 8pm and simple snacks are served at all times.
Q⏁🐜●🚌🐾

Andwell

Andwell Brewery Taproom Ⓛ

Andwell Lane, RG27 9PA
☎ (01256) 761044 ⊕ andwells.com
Andwell Resolute Bitter, Gold Muddler, King John, Ruddy Darter Ⓖ
The Brewhouse Café and Bar is found by the riverside in this attractive hamlet, and serves rotating seasonal draught ales, craft beers, wines and spirits along with cakes, coffees and sandwiches. Flights of three beers are sold. Outside there is a fine terrace overlooking a stream. Guest street food vendors usually visit on Friday evenings and takeaways are available. QP🚌🐾📶

Basingstoke

Angel ✅

Unit R6, Lower Ground, Festival Place, RG21 7BB
☎ (01256) 854800
Greene King IPA, Abbot; Sharp's Doom Bar; 4 changing beers (often Andwell, Ascot, Longdog) Ⓕ
This modern, spacious one-bar pub is at the edge of the restaurant quarter in the town's Festival Place shopping centre, handy for the nearby bus station and five minutes' walk from the rail station. Popular with younger people, it can get busy and often noisy in the evenings, especially at weekends. Lunchtimes attract a wider age range and tend to be quieter. The walls are adorned with TVs, all in silent mode. ⏁🐜◑&≠●🚌📶

Basingstoke Sports & Social Club ✅

Fairfields Road, RG21 3DR
☎ (01256) 473646 ⊕ basingstokesportsandsocialclub.com
Dark Star Hophead; Fuller's London Pride; Gale's HSB; 2 changing beers (sourced nationally; often Andwell, Little London, Longdog) Ⓕ
This sports-based members' club has a pub licence so the bar is open to all. The premises are home to cricket, squash, football and rugby. Widescreen TVs show major sports events. An annual programme of social activities is

held and facilities can be hired including a small function room. Opening hours and meal times change according to the season and sporting fixtures, so phone for details. The home of Hampshire OctoberFest Beer Festival and local CAMRA Club of the Year 2019 and 2020.
⏁◑♣🅿🚌(1,3)🐾📶

Maidenhead Inn Ⓛ ✅

17 Winchester Street, RG21 7ED
☎ (01256) 316030
Greene King Abbot; Ruddles Best Bitter; Sharp's Doom Bar; 3 changing beers (sourced nationally; often Loddon, Longdog, Windsor & Eton) Ⓕ
On the site of an old inn of the same name, this relatively small Wetherspoon is in the Top of Town pedestrian area. The long, narrow, split-level layout has a single bar and an additional downstairs area. There is a small garden/ smoking area at the rear. The guest ales vary but are usually local. The bar gets exceptionally busy on weekend evenings with nearby nightclub visitors. Children are welcome until 8.30pm and a public pay car park is at the rear. ⏁🐾◑&≠●🚌📶

New Inn

Sarum Hill, RG21 8SS
☎ (01256) 323292
Rebellion IPA; 2 changing beers (often Marston's, Thwaites) Ⓕ
Corner pub at a crossroads in a residential area between the town centre and the college. The single spacious bar has three main areas, including one to the right, slightly

REAL ALE BREWERIES

Alfred's Winchester
Andwell ✦ Andwell
Botley Botley
Bowman Droxford
Brewhouse & Kitchen 🍴 Portsmouth
Brewhouse & Kitchen 🍴 Southampton
Brewhouse & Kitchen 🍴 Southsea
CrackleRock Botley
Dancing Man ✦ Southampton
Drop The Anchor Hinton
Emsworth ✦ Havant
Fallen Acorn ✦ Gosport
Flack Manor Romsey
Flower Pots Cheriton
Gilbert White's Selborne (NEW)
Irving Portsmouth
Itchen Valley New Alresford
Laverstoke Park Basingstoke
Little London Little London
London Road Brew House 🍴 ✦ Southampton
Longdog Basingstoke
Makemake 🍴 Southsea
Newtown Gosport
Penton Park Penton Mewsey (brewing suspended)
Pig Beer Brockenhurst
Queen Inn 🍴 Winchester
Red Cat Winchester
Red Shoot 🍴 Ringwood
Ringwood Ringwood
Sherfield Village Sherfield on Loddon
Southsea Portsmouth
Staggeringly Good ✦ Southsea
Steam Town 🍴 Eastleigh
Stratton Lane ✦ Winchester
Tap It ✦ Southampton
Triple fff Four Marks
Unity ✦ Southampton
Urban Island ✦ Portsmouth
Vibrant Forest ✦ Hardley

raised, with a pool table. The other to the left has a large wall photo of the inn and Sarum Hill taken in times of yore. The evenings see much conversation at the bar. ⏣◑≒♣🖵

Queen's Arms 🅛
Bunnian Place, RG21 7JE
☎ (01256) 465488 ⊕ thequeensarmspub.co.uk
Fuller's London Pride; Sharp's Doom Bar; 4 changing beers (sourced nationally) 🄷
Just outside the main shopping area, this cosy pub is handy for all transport links. It attracts a wide-ranging clientele of all ages from all walks of life, and is a regular port of call for rail commuters. The choice of up to four guest beers is imaginative and the turnaround can be swift. Good-value home-cooked food is served lunchtimes and evenings. During warmer weather the shady courtyard garden at the rear is a popular attraction. Q⏣◑≒P🖵🛜

Wheatsheaf
Winton Square, RG21 8EU
☎ (01256) 479601
Butcombe Original; Otter Ale; Sharp's Atlantic, Doom Bar 🄷
This is a lively wet-led local with the atmosphere you would expect from a popular town-centre pub. It is basically a traditional boozer with no frills but a warm welcome. A broad choice of well-kept cask beers is served at good prices for the area. Large screens show sports fixtures at weekends and some evenings. ≒🖵

Blackwater

Mr Bumble 🅛
19 London Road, GU17 9AP
☎ (01276) 32691
Fuller's London Pride; 3 changing beers (sourced regionally; often Dark Star, Triple fff, Windsor & Eton) 🄷
Very much a community local, Mr Bumble is near the station and bus stops. It has a large L-shaped bar with comfortable seating, tables and chairs. The regular London Pride is accompanied by a wide range of real ales and four still ciders. A few steps around the corner from the main bar takes you to the Sports Bar with darts and three pool tables. There are widescreen TVs for major sporting events, and live music is staged on Thursday and Saturday. ⏩≒♣🌭P🖵(3)⏣🛜

Botley

CrackleRock Tap Room 🅛
30A High Street, SO30 2EA (down alley between Clarke Mews and Botley MTB) SU5130213037
☎ 07733 232806 ⊕ cracklerock.co.uk
CrackleRock Verified, Fire Cracker, Gold Rush, Dark Destroyer, Crafty Shag, Crackatoa IPA; 3 changing beers (sourced locally; often Bowman, Steam Town, Urban Island) 🄷
Cosy, friendly L-shaped brewery pub, hidden down an alleyway off the main road. The bar has nine handpumps and seven keg taps dispensing mainly its own beers from the brewery across the road (where the original taproom was located) plus a few local guest beers. An impressive range of flights is available offering four or six third-pints of beer, plus vodka, gin or wine. A cider festival is held in the summer plus other occasional events. 👣♣🌭🖵(3,X9)⏣

Bransgore

Three Tuns
Ringwood Road, BH23 8JH
☎ (01425) 672232 ⊕ threetunsinn.com
Otter Amber; Ringwood Fortyniner; house beer (by Ringwood); 6 changing beers (sourced nationally; often Crafty Brewing, Flack Manor) 🄷
A 17th-century pub with two bars and up to 10 different real ales. The new covered outside seating area has its own order station for meals and snacks. Live music is now a regular feature during the summer. A local cider may also be available in summertime. Pétanque (boules) is a popular sport, with the New Forest league team based here. The annual beer festival is on the last weekend in September. Q⏠⏣◑🍴♿🅰♣🌭P🖵(125)⏣🛜

Broughton

Tally Ho!
High Street, SO20 8AA
☎ (01794) 301280 ⊕ thetallyhobroughton.co.uk
House beer (by Ringwood); 2 changing beers (sourced nationally) 🄷
Located at the heart of this rural village community, the pub is 50 yards from the Clarendon Way between Winchester and Salisbury. The landlord is the chef and serves high-quality food complemented by a selection of real ales and other drinks. Real cider is usually available during the summer. The garden features an outdoor dining area in addition to more traditional pub garden furniture. Dogs are welcome. A beer and cider festival is held over the August bank holiday weekend. ⏠⏣◑🅰♣🌭P🖵(16)⏣🛜

Butlocks Heath

Roll Call 🅛 ✅
Woolston Road, SO31 5FJ
☎ (023) 8045 2358 ⊕ therollcall.co.uk
Butcombe Original; Flower Pots Pots Bitter; Ringwood Fortyniner; 1 changing beer (sourced locally; often Bowman, Flower Pots) 🄷
Welcoming two-bar establishment with pub signs and historic pictures on the walls. A log-burner is situated between the bars, and tankards hang from the ceiling of the public bar. Three out of four handpumps dispense beers from local breweries, including one guest ale. Food, served Thursday to Sunday, consists of home-made traditional pub favourites plus a varied range of authentic curries. Outside is a patio and garden with a small children's assault course. ⏠⏣◑♿🅰P🖵(6,X15)⏣🛜

Chandler's Ford

Steel Tank Alehouse 🅛
1 The Central Precinct, Winchester Road, SO53 2GA
☎ 07379 553025 ⊕ thesteeltank.com
Alfred's Saxon Bronze; 8 changing beers (sourced nationally; often Eight Arch, Flower Pots, Steam Town) 🄷
Local CAMRA's 2020 Pub of the Year, this is a friendly family-run enterprise offering up to eight changing beers, national and local, with Alfred's Brewery's Saxon Bronze as house beer. Up to 12 keg beers, mainly KeyKeg, and up to six ciders from bag-in-box, will put a smile on your face. A surprisingly spacious interior plus some outside covered seating make this the ideal place to enjoy beer and company at its best. Q♿≒🌭🖵(1,X6)⏣🛜

Cheriton

Flower Pots Inn L

Brandy Mount, SO24 0QQ (¾ mile N of A272 Cheriton/
Beauworth crossroads) SU5812928293
☎ (01962) 771318 ⊕ theflowerpots.co.uk
**Flower Pots Perridge Pale, Pots Bitter, Buster's Best,
Cheriton Porter, Goodens Gold, IPA; 1 changing beer
(sourced locally; often Flower Pots)** Ⓖ
Early 19th-century inn that has recently been hugely
extended. All its gravity-dispensed beers are provided by
the adjoining brewery. The central bar serves three out
of the five rooms at the front, one of which has a glass-
covered well. To the rear, a glass-sided walkway leads to
a Hampshire-style barn and a second bar that also serves
the extensive garden, which has plenty of seating.
Affordable, home-cooked, locally sourced food is sold.
Q☺≠◑&♣◑P☐(67)♥🎜🛜

Chilbolton

Abbots Mitre

Village Street, SO20 6BA
☎ (01264) 860348 ⊕ abbotsmitre.co.uk
4 changing beers Ⓗ
A traditional local in the village centre with a good
garden and a covered outside terrace. The area has many
walks and there are nearby nature reserves. Beers are
changing, coming mainly from breweries nearby such as
Itchen Valley, Alfred's, Andwell and Hogs Back, and
sometimes there is a more unusual ale. It offers an
extensive food menu with specials. ☺☺◑P☐

Church Crookham

Wyvern

75 Aldershot Road, GU52 8JY
☎ (01252) 624772 ⊕ thewyvernpub.co.uk
**Morland Old Speckled Hen; Wadworth 6X; 3 changing
beers (often Andwell)** Ⓗ
Pronounced 'Wivvern', to rhyme with 'given', this is a
community venue, which can become lively at times,
especially during sporting events, but it is always family
friendly. Darts are played and there is a regular Thursday
quiz night. Six screens show premier league football and
other sporting events. There is a sunny garden with
heated beach huts. The pub has live music, often tribute
acts, and it supports local charities with fundraising
events. ☺☺◑&♣P☐(10)♥

Dundridge

Hampshire Bowman L

Dundridge Lane, SO32 1GD (turn E off B3035 ½ mile N
of Bishops Waltham, then it's another 1½ miles)
SU5778218424
☎ (01489) 892940 ⊕ hampshirebowman.com
**Bowman Swift One, Quiver Bitter; West Berkshire
Good Old Boy; 2 changing beers (sourced nationally;
often Andwell, Flack Manor)** Ⓖ
An 18th-century coaching inn, well off the beaten track
and ideally placed for walkers and cyclists. Dogs are
welcomed. A traditional brick-floored bar is
supplemented by a larger rear bar, with tables for dining
and access to the garden. Up to five beers are served
direct from the cask, together with 10 ciders, plus a wide
variety of home-cooked locally sourced food (no food
Sun eve). The large garden with patio and children's play
area is popular during summer weekends.
Q☺☺◑&♣P♥🛜

Eastleigh

Steam Town Brew Co L

1 Bishopstoke Road, SO50 6AD
☎ (023) 8235 9139 ⊕ steamtownbrewco.co.uk
**7 changing beers (sourced locally; often Steam
Town)** Ⓗ
Eastleigh's first new-style combined pub, brewery and
restaurant, which has built up a loyal customer base. The
brewery is visible from the repurposed first-class railway
seating area in the restaurant. The main bar serves new
and seasonal brews along with the much-loved
favourites. Gourmet burgers are the house speciality.
Additional restaurant seating is in the upstairs room,
which is also available to hire. There is additional seating
outside on the pavement area. ☺☺◑◑≠◑☐♥🛜

Emsworth

Coal Exchange ✓

21 South Street, PO10 7EG
☎ (01243) 375866 ⊕ thecoalexchange.co.uk
**Dark Star Hophead; Fuller's London Pride; Gale's
Seafarers Ale, HSB; 2 changing beers (sourced
nationally; often Butcombe, Fuller's)** Ⓗ
A former Gale's outlet with a single L-shaped bar and
open fireplaces. To the rear is a small walled garden
which offers alfresco dining and is a real suntrap in
summer. In addition to lunchtime meals, themed dining
is on offer most weekday evenings. The pub is handy for
walks from the harbour along the shore to Langstone
(but check the state of the tide). The name derives from
coal delivered by sea to be traded locally.
☺☺◑≠☐(700)♥

Fareham

West Street Alehouse L

164A West Street, PO16 0EH
☎ 07927 004735 ⊕ southernalehouseltd.selz.com
3 changing beers (sourced regionally) Ⓗ
Fareham's first micropub is ideally situated close to rail
and bus stations. Opened in 2019, the bar serves three
ales on handpump, five craft beers from the tap wall and
up to four ciders, all of which are listed on a TV screen.
With plenty of seating and no loud music, it is easy to
converse while drinking. There is a bottle shop with local
and foreign cans and bottles available to take away. A
gem, to be recommended. Q☺≠◑☐♥

Farnborough

Goat in the Garden L

21 Church Avenue, GU14 7AT
☎ 07920 153452
**3 changing beers (sourced nationally; often Church
End, Fallen Acorn, Loddon)** Ⓗ
An attractive bar, hidden away in the grounds of a small
hotel – Melford House – but accessed via its own
entrance. The single bar stocks up to three changing
guest beers, primarily from local breweries. Outside
there is a split-level patio with appropriate seating for
the summer. The bar is only for invited guests – CAMRA
members have an open invitation but please send a
message first as the bar may be closed from time to
time. ☺☺≠♣P☐(1)🛜

Prince of Wales L ✓

184 Rectory Road, GU14 8AL
☎ (01252) 545578 ⊕ theprincepub.uk

Dark Star Hophead; Fuller's London Pride; Hop Back Summer Lightning; West Berkshire Maggs' Mild; 6 changing beers (sourced nationally) ⊞
This cosy free house has featured in the Guide for over 30 years, offering four regular beers, six guests, five kegs and a real cider. A popular beer festival is held every October. Good lunches are served throughout the week, with evening meals Monday and Friday only. Quiz night is on the first Sunday and live music on the third Sunday of each month. Various charity events are held during the year. ⅀❀❀◑≠♠P❀令

Tilly Shilling ✔

Units 2 to 5, Victoria Road, GU14 7PG
☎ (01252) 893560
Greene King Abbot; Ruddles Best Bitter; Sharp's Doom Bar; 4 changing beers (sourced nationally; often Ascot, Hogs Back) ⊞
Modern town-centre Wetherspoon named after Beatrice 'Tilly' Shilling, a celebrated local engineer at the nearby former Royal Aircraft Establishment. Its aviation theme includes a row of airline seats and various Spitfire memorabilia. The large rectangular open-plan lounge features a glass frontage that slides open in good weather, extending the pub onto the pavement. Ten handpumps serve three regular and four changing guest beers. Real cider is dispensed from boxes in fridges at the end of the bar. Alcoholic drinks are on sale from 9am. ⅀◑&≠♠令

Fleet

Prince Arthur 🅛 ✔

238 Fleet Road, GU51 4BX
☎ (01252) 622660
Greene King Abbot; Ruddles Best Bitter; Sharp's Doom Bar; 4 changing beers (sourced nationally; often Langham, Twickenham, Windsor & Eton) ⊞
A traditionally designed pub in a former grocery shop building over 100 years old, with alcoves, wood surrounds and a rustic feel. It is named by Wetherspoon after Prince Arthur, son of Queen Victoria, who lived in Fleet in the 1890s while he was British Army Commander at Aldershot. Seven different casks ales are on tap, including local ales supplied direct from 12 breweries across Hampshire, Berkshire and Surrey. Two different route 7 buses serve this pub. Q⅀❀◑&♠局(7,10)令

Four Marks

Offf the Rails 🅛

Unit 3, Magpie Works, Station Approach, GU34 5HN
☎ (01420) 561422
Triple fff Alton's Pride, Moondance; 3 changing beers (sourced locally; often Triple fff) Ⓖ
Offf the Rails was extended at the end of 2019 to create two distinct drinking areas centred on a bar serving two regular and up to three seasonal or more obscure ales from the adjoining Triple fff Brewery. Bottled Mr Whitehead ciders are also sold. The pub adjoins the Triple fff off-licence featuring bottled ales from microbreweries from far and wide. The brewery holds an open day in August. Situated by Medstead & Four Marks station on the preserved Watercress line. ⅀&≠♠P局(64)❀令

Freefolk

Watership Down Inn 🅛

Freefolk Priors, RG28 7NJ
☎ (01256) 892254 ⊕ watershipdowninn.com
5 changing beers (sourced locally) ⊞

Built in 1840 in the Upper Test Valley and still affectionately known in the area as the Jerry, the inn has been named in honour of local author Richard Adams' book Watership Down, set in downland just to the north of the pub. Outside there is an extensive garden, patio and family area. Occasional live music evenings are arranged and each May a beer festival is held. The place is popular with walkers and cyclists in the Test Valley and close to the Bombay Sapphire gin distillery. Food is locally sourced. Q⅀❀❀◑P局(76)❀令

Fritham

Royal Oak 🅛 ✔

SO43 7HJ (W end of village on no through road)
SU2321614135
☎ (023) 8081 2606 ⊕ royaloakfritham.co.uk
Flack Manor Flack's Double Drop; Hop Back Crop Circle, Summer Lightning; house beer (by Bowman); 4 changing beers (sourced locally; often Hattie Brown's, Stonehenge, Three Daggers) Ⓖ
This tiny award-winning establishment in the heart of the New Forest is a must-visit. Thatched, with a small, beamed interior, it has two rooms with log fires, and an interconnected back room with a hatched bar service. Real ales are on stillage and are locally sourced, as is the legendary ploughman's lunch. The pub caters for walkers, cyclists, equestrians and dog owners. It has a large garden which is popular in the summer, with a huge marquee for colder and wetter times. Parking in the narrow, dead-end lane can be tricky. Q⅀❀❀◑&❀

Gosport

Four-Ale Taproom 🅛

45 Stoke Road, PO12 1LS
☎ (023) 9258 4455 ⊕ fouraletaproom.co.uk
4 changing beers (sourced regionally; often Fallen Acorn, Urban Island) Ⓖ
Gosport's first micropub opened in 2018 in previously unlicensed premises. There is no bar and the four cask beers, from small and independent breweries, are on a gravity stillage along one wall. Four ciders are on the go plus keg real ale and an interesting range of bottled and canned beers. On the walls there is a map of the breweries supplying beer and pumpclips of beers and ciders recently served. A free cheeseboard is put out on Sunday lunchtime. Q♣♠P局❀❀令

Junction Tavern 🅛

1 Leesland Road, Camden Town, PO12 3ND
☎ (023) 9258 5140
3 changing beers (sourced regionally; often Cotleigh, XT) ⊞
This venue is on the now-disused railway line between Gosport and Fareham, which closed in 1953 and is now a cycle track and footpath. The three real ales usually include a dark beer, and there are four ciders and a perry. The canopy over the bar is decorated with pumpclips of the beers sold. A beer festival takes place over the Easter weekend. ⅀❀♣♠局(E1)❀令

Queen's Hotel 🅛

143 Queens Road, Forton, PO12 1LG
☎ 07974 031671 ⊕ cliveluff.wixsite.com/queenshotel
Fallen Acorn Expedition IPA; Ringwood Fortyniner; Young's London Original; 2 changing beers (sourced nationally; often Newtown, Titanic) ⊞
No trip to Gosport is complete without a visit to this street-corner local, a regular entry in the Guide for over 36 years. The guest beer range always includes a dark beer, and up to two ciders are stocked. The main feature

of the bar is a large fireplace with a carved wood surround. Snacks are served Friday lunchtimes and a regular beer festival takes place in October. Local CAMRA Pub of the Year 2020. ✿♣●🖵

Hammer Vale

Prince of Wales

Hammer Lane, GU27 1QH

☎ (01428) 652600 ⊕ princeofwaleshaslemere.co.uk

Dark Star Hophead; Fuller's London Pride; Gale's HSB; 2 changing beers (sourced nationally; often Fuller's) Ⓗ

An interesting hostelry dating from 1924, with many original features such as stained-glass windows, including one for Amey's of Petersfield, who built the pub. It is definitely worth visiting in order to sample the Pride, HSB and Fuller's and Dark Star guests. Outside is a large seating area and car park, well sited for walkers and campers. Excellent meals and bar snacks are served (no food Mon). Stories abound as to how a large roadhouse was sited away from the main road.
Q✿🕭🛈👤🍴♣P✿☀🐾

Hardley

Vibrant Forest Brewery Taproom Ⓛ

Unit 3, The Purlieu Centre, Hardley Industrial Estate, SO45 3AE

☎ (023) 8200 2200 ⊕ vibrantforest.co.uk

7 changing beers (sourced locally; often Vibrant Forest) Ⓖ

The Taproom is warm and well-equipped with tables and benches (heated in winter). Beers come from the Vibrant Forest range in all formats, with occasional guests. Ciders, perries, wines and soft drinks are also available. Snacks are served and a street-food truck is on-site most weekends, with food ranging from Thai to curry, burger or pizza. There is a large, outside covered seating area and a smaller smoking area. Well-behaved children and dogs are welcomed. Q✿🕭🛈●P🖵(8,9)✿☀

Hartley Wintney

Waggon & Horses

High Street, RG27 8NY

☎ (01252) 842119 ⊕ thewagg.co.uk

Butcombe Original; Gale's HSB; 4 changing beers (sourced nationally; often Castle Rock, Flower Pots, Sharp's) Ⓗ

This award-winning village pub is recognised by CAMRA as having a regionally important historic pub interior. The changing guest beers here often include Courage Best and others from microbreweries. The lively public bar contrasts with a quieter lounge. Tables outside on the pavement enable guests to enjoy the atmosphere of the village, renowned for its unique shops. At the rear is a large, pleasant courtyard garden and a heated, covered smokers' area. Food is served lunchtimes only Monday to Saturday. Q✿🕭●🖵(7)✿☀

Havant

Wheelwright's Arms Ⓛ ✔

27 Emsworth Road, PO9 2SN

☎ (023) 9247 6502 ⊕ wheelwrightshavant.co.uk

Fallen Acorn Pompey Royal; 3 changing beers (sourced locally; often Crafty Brewing, Irving, Langham) Ⓗ

This imposing Edwardian hostelry serves up to four cask beers, mainly from local microbreweries, with handpulled ciders also offered. A range of bottled beers

from the UK and abroad is also stocked, plus a selection of quality wines and spirits. The south-facing front terrace and secluded courtyard garden are popular in warm weather. The pub hosts a number of area organisations and offers private hire space. Major sporting fixtures are shown on TV.
Q✿🕭🛈👤🚃♣●P🖵(27,700) ✿☀

Hawkley

Hawkley Inn ✔

Pococks Lane, GU33 6NE

☎ 07540 160187 ⊕ hawkleyinn.co.uk

Flower Pots Perridge Pale, Goodens Gold; house beer (by Greyhound); 4 changing beers (sourced regionally; often Flower Pots, Red Cat, Triple fff) Ⓗ

A genuine free house set in the South Downs National Park. Popular with locals and passers-by alike, it has a good selection of guest beers, showcasing 164 ales from 42 breweries in the last year. The annual beer festival takes place in May/June (see the website for details). The inn serves great food and has five rooms available for B&B, ideal for a walking holiday in the Hampshire countryside. ✿☀🛏🕭🛈👤☀☀

Hayling Island

Maypole

9 Havant Road, PO11 0PS

☎ (023) 9246 3670 ⊕ maypoleonhayling.co.uk

Fuller's London Pride; Gale's Seafarers Ale, HSB; 1 changing beer (sourced nationally; often Fuller's, Gale's) Ⓗ

A pleasant roadside house with friendly and welcoming staff. It has a single quiet bar and a separate restaurant. There are plenty of tables and seating space in the bar area. The large beer garden at the back looks over fields. The Maypole has a good local reputation for its food as well as for keeping its draught beers in fine condition, and typifies what a good traditional pub should be.
✿🕭🛈👤P🖵(30,31) ✿☀

Herriard

Fur & Feathers Ⓛ

Back Lane, RG25 2PN

☎ (01256) 510510 ⊕ thefurandfeathers.co.uk

Hogs Back TEA; 2 changing beers (sourced locally; often Fallen Acorn, Itchen Valley, Red Cat) Ⓗ

Family-owned and family-run free house built in 1855 to service farm workers, now open plan with a central bar area. Beers are mainly from Hampshire breweries such as Flack Manor and Longdog. Two dining areas provide a pleasant atmosphere to enjoy the mouthwatering locally sourced menu that changes on a daily basis. Reservations are recommended, but a quiet pint can be enjoyed at any time. A well-appointed secluded garden features partly paved and grassed areas. Seasonal hours may vary so phone ahead. Q✿🕭🛈👤P🖵(13X)✿

Holybourne

Queen's Head

20 London Road, GU34 4EG

☎ (01420) 768213

Greene King Abbot; St Austell Tribute; 1 changing beer (sourced regionally; often Goddards) Ⓗ

Traditional friendly pub with two beers from the Greene King list and a rapidly changing guest usually from the southern counties. The separate restaurant area serves home-made food with generous portions. There is a games room with darts and pool. The extensive garden is popular in the summer months, when licensing hours may be extended (check website). Live music events are held throughout the year. Q🍽️🕒🏠◑♣P🚃(65)🐾🛜

Hook

Crooked Billet
London Road, RG27 9EH
☎ (01256) 762118
Courage Best Bitter; Sharp's Doom Bar; 2 changing beers (often Timothy Taylor) 🅷
A free house just outside Hook which has been under the same ownership for 33 years. Enjoy the pleasant riverside garden in fine weather and the air-conditioned bars, restaurant and snug at any time. In winter, warm up by a traditional log fire. Good food and real ales are always on offer here. Q🍽️🕒🏠◑♿🐾🛜

Little London

Plough Inn
Silchester Road, RG26 5EP
☎ (01256) 850628
Little London Hoppy Hilda; Otter Amber; Ringwood Razorback 🅷; 2 changing beers (sourced regionally; often Butts, Church End, Dark Star) 🅖
Excellent traditional village hostelry and former CAMRA Regional Pub of the Year. Enjoy beer fed on gravity from casks behind the bar and sit in front of a log fire or in the peaceful garden. A good range of baguettes is available (no food Sun eve). Popular with locals and also visitors to Pamber Forest and nearby Roman Silchester. Q🍽️🕒♣♠P🚃(14)🐾

Long Sutton

Four Horseshoes
The Street, RG29 1TA (signed from B3349) SU748470
☎ (01256) 862488
2 changing beers (sourced nationally; often Andwell, Palmers, Slater's) 🅷
A truly rural pub, simply decorated and situated to the east of Long Sutton in a popular walking area. Formerly a Gale's tied house, it is now a free house normally offering two low-strength guest beers. There are twice-monthly quiz and jazz nights in the spacious but cosy bar which has two real fires. Simple English dishes are served, with a popular roast on Sunday. Midweek lunchtime opening is only by prior arrangement. Q🍽️🕒🏠◑P🐾🛜

Longparish

Cricketers Inn
SP11 6PZ
☎ (01264) 720424 🌐 thecricketersinnlongparish.com
Flower Pots Perridge Pale, Buster's Best; 3 changing beers 🅷
A rural village inn full of character with a large beer garden and an outdoor wood-fired pizza oven. The garden has some covered marquee seating with picnic tables as well as a permanent summer house and fire pits. Specialising in game and seafood dishes, the pub also has its own smokehouse. The area is popular with walkers and cyclists and families and well-behaved dogs are welcome here. Q🍽️🕒🏠◑♿🐾🛜

Lower Farringdon

Golden Pheasant 🄻 ✅
Gosport Road, GU34 3DJ
☎ (01420) 588255 🌐 golden-pheasant.com

Crafty Brewing One; Sharp's Doom Bar, Atlantic; 3 changing beers (sourced regionally; often Andwell, Dark Star, Otter) 🅷
The owners have run pubs in the area for many years and 10 years ago brought their expertise to this delightful privately owned free house. The beers are well kept, with seven handpumps serving three permanent and four guest beers. The food is freshly cooked, with vegetarian options; the fish & chips warrants special mention thanks to the secret recipe batter used. It opens early in the morning for tea and coffee. Accessible down the A32 four miles from Alton, this place is not to be missed. Q🍽️🕒🏠◑♣P🐾🛜

Lymington

Monkey Brewhouse 🄻
167 Southampton Road, SO41 9HA
☎ (01590) 676754 🌐 monkeybrewhouse.co.uk
Sixpenny Best Bitter; 4 changing beers (sourced locally; often Hop Back, Red Cat, Sixpenny) 🅷
Prominent, historical and popular roadside pub north of the town noted for its food and with its own on-site brewery supplying the beer. The much rearranged and redecorated bar and dining room have increased space. An 18th-century turnpike tollhouse survives in the garden. A former landlord kept monkeys, and monkey-themed artefacts adorn the rooms. There is a notable fireplace with brick surround in the dining room, and wooden floors and wood-panelled walls in the bar. Regular live music takes place at weekends. Q🍽️🕒🏠◑◑♿P🚃(6)🐾🛜

Milford on Sea

Wash House
27 High Street, SO41 0QF
☎ (01590) 644665 🌐 thewashhousebar.co.uk
4 changing beers (sourced locally; often Andwell, Hop Back, Piddle) 🅷
A former launderette, now a welcoming and friendly single-room village micropub, decorated with mismatched furniture and artefacts from its former life. Four different real ales and four real ciders are served, plus a selection of other alcoholic drinks and fresh coffee. Customers can order gourmet burgers from a nearby takeaway. Dogs are welcomed, and can be walked along the beach which is about half a mile away. Q🍽️🕒♿🐾🚃(X1)🐾

New Milton

Hourglass
8 Station Road, BH25 6JU
☎ (01425) 616074 🌐 hourglassmicropub.co.uk
4 changing beers (sourced nationally) 🅖
New Milton's first micropub is a family-run free house focusing on a constantly changing selection of cask and keg beers, plus ciders alongside wines and spirits. It has a quiet, friendly atmosphere, hosting a music jam the first Sunday of every month, a pub quiz every other Thursday, and offering an extensive collection of board games and puzzles, all helping to give the Hourglass its strong community feel. Tap takeovers and Meet the Brewer events also feature regularly. Q≈♣🍽️🚃🐾🛜

North Warnborough

Mill House 🄻
Hook Road, RG29 1ET
☎ (01256) 702953 🌐 millhouse-hook.co.uk

Hogs Back TEA; house beer (by St Austell); 4 changing beers (sourced regionally; often Andwell, Longdog, Triple fff) Ⓗ

Listed as one of eight mills of Odiham in the Domesday Book, current sections are 17th-century additions, and the building was last used as a corn mill in 1895. It has a pleasant central bar space, separate dining areas and a landscaped lower-level view of the waterwheel and restaurant. The area surrounding the millpond, fed from the Whitewater, provides pleasant outdoor seating.
Q ⑤ ⊛ ◑ ⅊ ☖ (13) ☙ 🛜

Odiham

Red Lion
102 High Street, RG29 1LP
☎ (01256) 701145 ⊕ redlionodiham.co.uk
Hogs Back TEA; Tilford Red Mist; 3 changing beers (sourced locally) Ⓗ
The Red Lion was opened in 2017 after an extensive refurbishment of a former restaurant. There was, however, a Red Lion ale house on this site in the 17th century. A small traditional pub with rustic beams, it has a modern design and atmosphere. Part of the Red Mist Leisure Group, changing beers are from its Tilford Brewery as well as a guest ale from the Odiham area. The menu is fresh local Hampshire fare. There are seven B&B rooms and a front pavement seating area.
⑤ ⇤ ◑ ☖ (13) 🛜

Overton

Old House at Home
Station Road, RG25 3DU
☎ (01256) 770335 ⊕ theoldhouseathome.com
Black Sheep Best Bitter; Dark Star Hophead; St Austell Tribute; 2 changing beers (often Brains, Exmoor, Penton Park) Ⓗ
A hostelry with an old-fashioned feel and an excellent Thai restaurant and takeaway, also serving traditional pub food and great-value dinners on a Sunday. It has five ale pumps dispensing three regular and two changing beers. There is a large garden with a play area and decking. A fun quiz is hosted on a Sunday and there are teams in local crib, pool and quiz leagues.
Q ⑤ ⊛ ⇤ ◑ ♣ ⅊ ☖ (76) ☙ 🛜

Park Gate

Gate Ⓛ
27 Middle Road, SO31 7GH
3 changing beers (sourced locally; often Eight Arch, Steam Town, Urban Island) Ⓗ
A relatively new addition to the local drinking scene, this micropub has been converted from an estate agent's office. The decor is modern with a mix of tables and booths. It retains the previous owner's map of the local area on one wall. Beers are sourced from small independent breweries throughout the country, with a local offering usually available. The pub hosts meetings of home brewers, who can bring along their beers and discuss them with local brewing companies.
⑤ ⅊ ⇤ ♣ ⅊ ☖ (X4) 🛜

Village Inn ✪
67 Botley Road, SO31 1AZ
☎ (01489) 573223
Ember Pale Ale; 4 changing beers (sourced nationally) Ⓗ
A large, sprawling, single-storey Ember Inn, modern in style, with plenty of tables and an emphasis on meals. Beer drinkers aren't ignored though, with at least four

rotating ales always on handpump. In keeping with current trends, there are some alcohol-free beers and wines too. The comfortable pub has a large car park and is close to Swanwick station.
⑤ ⊛ ◑ ⅊ ⇤ ⅊ ☖ (28,28A) ☙ 🛜

Petersfield

Townhouse Ⓛ
28 High Street, GU32 3JL
☎ (01730) 265630 ⊕ townhousepetersfield.co.uk
3 changing beers (sourced regionally; often Downlands, Langham, Red Cat) Ⓗ
In the heart of Petersfield, this is a bistro-style establishment offering food (breakfast, lunch and dinner), with a variety of keg beers and a good selection of ales, both local and from further afield. It has a family environment where children and dogs are welcome. A separate function room, upstairs, is available for hire. To the rear is a small patio garden.
⑤ ⊛ ◑ ⇤ ♣ ⅊ ☖ (67) ☙ 🛜

Portchester

Cormorant ✪
181 Castle Street, PO16 9QX
☎ (023) 9237 9374 ⊕ thecormorant.co.uk
Gale's Seafarers Ale, HSB; Sharp's Doom Bar; 2 changing beers (sourced nationally; often Fuller's, Skinner's) Ⓗ
A traditional pub a stone's throw from Portchester Castle – said to be the best preserved Roman fortress in Europe. Around the walls are numerous seafaring-inspired pictures and photos, and several stuffed seabirds are displayed. Outside is a part-covered patio area with picnic tables and chairs. Dogs are welcome in the bar but not in the raised restaurant area which, although not large, is well laid out. ⑤ ⊛ ◑ ⅊ ☖ (3)

Portsmouth

Admiral Drake Ⓛ
8 Kingston Crescent, Rudmore, PO2 8DH
☎ (023) 9265 1599
Greene King Abbot; 3 changing beers (sourced nationally; often Irving, Urban Island, Yeovil) Ⓗ
Dating from 1936, this pub now stands isolated – dwarfed by the Rudmore flyover. The U-shaped bar room is bare boarded and furnished with a mix of traditional tables and chairs as well as high tables and bar stools. There is a performance area for live bands to the right as you enter. In winter a real log fire is a welcome sight opposite the bar counter. Outside events are held during the summer in the large car park. ⑤ ⊛ ◑ ⅊ ♣ ⅊ ☖ ☙ 🛜

Apsley House
13 Auckland Road West, Southsea, PO5 3NY
☎ (023) 9282 1294
Hop Back Summer Lightning; Sharp's Doom Bar; Timothy Taylor Landlord Ⓗ
A small traditional back-street pub tucked away between Southsea Common and the bars of Palmerston Road. It gets busy when events are held locally, and the benches on the front patio are at a premium. It is home to both darts and pool teams and hosts occasional live music. There is a raised section with seating that is usually a lot quieter than the main bar. ⊛ ♣ ☖ 🛜

Barley Mow ✪
39 Castle Road, Southsea, PO5 3DE
☎ (023) 9282 3492 ⊕ barleymowsouthsea.com

Fuller's London Pride; Gale's HSB; 6 changing beers
(sourced nationally) Ⓗ
This large community pub dates from 1924 and is a lucky
survivor of WWII when a delayed action bomb landed in
the cellar. It retains its two bars and the outside toilets
for the public bar, which is at a lower level and smaller
than the wood-panelled lounge. There is an award-
winning patio garden to the rear, a real suntrap on
warmer days. Various games, including bar billiards and
shove-ha'penny, are played, and the Barley Mow hosts
many events. ✿&♣●₪(3)✿🤝

Brewhouse & Kitchen Ⓛ ✪

26 Guildhall Walk, Landport, PO1 2DD
☎ (023) 9289 1340
Brewhouse & Kitchen Portsmouth Mucky Duck,
Sexton, Mary Rose, Black Swan; 1 changing beer
(sourced locally; often Brewhouse & Kitchen
Portsmouth) Ⓗ
Known locally as the Mucky Duck, this pub is distinctive
from the outside, with its Brewers' Tudor timber-clad
Grade II-listed façade. It brews its own beer in a 2.5-
barrel plant. Next door is the newly refurbished New
Theatre Royal and 30 seconds away is the Portsmouth
Guildhall venue. On brew day, there's a chance to
become a brewer for the day. Food is served all day.
🤝✿Ⓓ⇌♣●₪(7,25) 🤝🤝

Bridge Tavern

54 East Street, Old Portsmouth, PO1 2JJ
☎ (023) 9275 2992 ⊕ bridge-tavern-portsmouth.co.uk
Fuller's London Pride; Gale's Seafarers Ale, HSB; 2
changing beers (sourced nationally; often Fuller's) Ⓗ
A former fishermen's pub, this is the only survivor in the
Camber Docks area. One side of the exterior is decorated
with a large mural of Thomas Rowlandson's cartoon
Portsmouth Point. Inside, the bar is divided into several
drinking areas and there is an upstairs dining room. The
dock used to be spanned by an adjacent double swing
bridge and is now the home of Portsmouth's fishing
fleet. Not surprisingly, the decor has a strong nautical
theme. ✿Ⓓ₪(16)🤝

Eastney Tavern Ⓛ

100 Cromwell Road, Eastney, PO4 9PN
☎ (023) 9282 6246 ⊕ eastneytavern.co.uk
Sharp's Doom Bar, Atlantic; 3 changing beers
(sourced locally; often Fallen Acorn, Goddards) Ⓗ
A large wooden bar greets you as you walk in. Floor
space is cleverly split into three: to the right, seating and
space to watch Sky and BT Sport, to the left a cosy
restaurant, and then an open seating area. This Victorian
pub occupies a prominent corner plot and is a two-
minute walk to the seafront. LocAle is supported with
Fallen Acorn and Goddards Brewery, and two handpulls
are for Sharp's Brewery. 🤝✿Ⓓ&₪(16)🤝🤝

Fawcett Inn Ⓛ

176 Fawcett Road, Southsea, PO4 0DP
☎ (023) 9229 8656
Ringwood Razorback; Titanic Plum Porter; 1 changing
beer (sourced locally; often Banks's, Irving,
Marston's) Ⓗ
Designed by AH Bone and built in 1886 for the
Brickwoods Brewery, the Fawcett Inn occupies a
prominent position on a busy street corner. With its half-
timbered Brewers' Tudor style and witch's hat tower, it
has an imposing presence. It now sports one large,
curved bar room, having been knocked through in the
days of Whitbread. A popular venue for Pompey football
fans on match days, the pub is boarded throughout and
furnishings are mostly traditional.
🤝✿&♣●₪(18) 🤝🤝

Hole in the Wall Ⓛ

36 Great Southsea Street, Southsea, PO5 3BY
☎ (023) 9229 8085 ⊕ theholeinthewallpub.co.uk
Flower Pots Goodens Gold Ⓖ; 5 changing beers
(sourced nationally) Ⓗ
The Hole is a wood-panelled gem that may be one of the
smaller pubs in Portsmouth but, as a genuine free house,
offers a good range of beers from a wide selection of
local and national breweries. Check the website for the
current beer range. Real ciders are usually stocked as
well. Open on Saturdays from noon for Pompey home
games; no admittance after 11pm. Dogs must be on
leads. ●₪₪(3)🤝🤝

Lawrence Arms Ⓛ

63 Lawrence Road, Southsea, PO5 1NU
☎ (023) 9282 1280 ⊕ lawrence-arms-portsmouth.co.uk
Harvey's Sussex Best Bitter; 5 changing beers
(sourced nationally; often Irving, Langham, Urban
Island) Ⓗ
A large street-corner venue a short walk from both
Fratton station and Albert Road. Six real ales are usually
served, sourced from around the country, always
including a local beer and a dark one. A selection of cans
and bottles is also on offer to drink in or take away. Cider
and perry lovers are well catered for, with six available in
winter and up to 12 at other times. Local CAMRA Cider
Pub of the Year. 🤝✿♣●₪(18)🤝

Merchant House

9-11 Highland Road, Eastney, PO4 9DA
4 changing beers (sourced nationally) Ⓗ
A modern-style pub featuring a range of cask, KeyKeg,
canned and bottled beers from different parts of the
country. A large screen on the wall displays the current
offerings. The main bar is divided into two, one part
being on a slightly higher level. The floor and walls are
bare wood and brick. To the rear is a staircase leading
down to a third drinking area. ✿Ⓓ●₪(1,2)

Northcote Ⓛ

35 Francis Avenue, Southsea, PO4 0HL
☎ (023) 9278 9888
Irving Invincible; Long Man American Pale Ale;
Timothy Taylor Landlord; house beer (by Wadworth);
1 changing beer (sourced nationally; often Irving,
Langham) Ⓗ
Close to Albert Road, this is a large two-bar community
pub with a partly covered patio. The public bar is plainly
decorated and has a dartboard and pool table, while the
lounge has comfortable seating that divides the bar into
several open booths. The walls are adorned with
memorabilia of comedy acts from the early days of stage
and screen and portrayals of Conan Doyle's Sherlock
Holmes. The bar-back dividing the bars includes a clear
glass panel. ✿♣●₪(2)

Old Customs House

Gunwharf Quays, Gunwharf, PO1 3TY
☎ (023) 9283 2333 ⊕ theoldcustomshouse.com
Fuller's London Pride, ESB; Gale's Seafarers Ale, HSB;
2 changing beers (sourced nationally; often Dark
Star) Ⓗ
Proclaiming itself the only traditional pub in the
Gunwharf Quays retail complex and marina, this Grade II-
listed building retains the layout of the former naval
offices of HMS Vernon. A stone's throw from Spinnaker
Tower, it has a heated rear patio area and seating at the
front which is ideal for people-watching during the
summer. It is open all day for food, including breakfast,
and a number of dishes include Fuller's ales in their
recipes. 🤝✿Ⓓ⇌&●🤝🤝

Pembroke

20 Pembroke Road, Old Portsmouth, PO1 2NR
☎ (023) 9282 3961
Draught Bass; Fuller's London Pride; Greene King Abbot Ⓗ

A traditional drinkers' pub a short walk from the Hot Walls at the mouth of Portsmouth harbour and where Lord Nelson joined HMS Victory to sail to Trafalgar. Opposite is the Royal Garrison Church, the oldest garrison church in the country and a survivor of a fire bomb raid in WWII. The pub was originally called the Little Blue Line and as such it featured in books by Captain Marryat. Not surprisingly, the decor here also has a nautical theme. ♣🖵😼🛜

Phoenix

13 Duncan Road, Southsea, PO5 2QU
☎ (023) 9278 1055
Ringwood Fortyniner; 2 changing beers (sourced nationally; often Irving, Red Cat, Urban Island) Ⓗ

A hidden gem, the Phoenix is a classic community pub just off Albert Road. The lounge bar has many photos of people who have appeared at the nearby King's Theatre as well as some of the theatre's interior, a working piano and a number of quirky artefacts including an old wooden telephone and a post box. The larger public bar has posters of Portsmouth Football Club teams from earlier years and a tabletop Space Invaders game. A small walled patio garden provides outdoor drinking space. 🌞♣🖵(2)😻

Porters Ⓛ

31-35 Albert Road, Southsea, PO5 2SE
☎ (023) 9229 3474
Otter Ale; Sharp's Doom Bar; 3 changing beers (sourced nationally; often Irving) Ⓗ

A large pub with a single bar divided into several drinking areas. It is simply decorated with a tiled and flagstoned floor and wooden tables and chairs, church pews and with a few comfortable sofas to relax in. To the rear of the bar area is a small raised seating section. Good value food is available daily, specialising in Mexican dishes and including vegetarian options. The beer range usually includes an offering from a local brewery. ◑&😼🖵(2)🛜

Rose in June Ⓛ ✅

102 Milton Road, Milton, PO3 6AR
☎ (023) 9282 4191 ⊕ theroseinjune.co.uk
Gale's HSB; Hop Back Summer Lightning; Irving Frigate; Purity Pure Gold; Pure UBU; West Berkshire Good Old Boy; 2 changing beers Ⓗ

Four of the listed beers are always on the bar, plus weekend specials. Situated about 10 minutes' walk from Fratton Park, this two-bar (three for football) pub is popular with football fans. Events include quizzes and pool and darts matches. The extensive garden has a play area and is used for barbecues and a summer beer festival. A February winter beer festival is also held. Seven real ciders are stocked and roast dinners are served on the third Sunday of the month. Q🕏🌞😼🅿🖵😻🛜

Winchester Arms

99 Winchester Road, Buckland, PO2 7PS
☎ (023) 9266 2443
Wychwood Hobgoblin Gold; 3 changing beers (sourced regionally) Ⓗ

The Winch is a proper back-street local, offering one regular beer and two or three varying guests. Every third Sunday evening of the month is open mic night with music and comedy, and live music is featured on the other weekends. A beer festival is held over the spring

bank holiday weekend. The garden has a covered smoking shelter. Closing time may be later on Friday and Saturday if busy. 🌞😼🖵😼🛜

Ringwood

Railway Ⓛ

35 Hightown Road, BH24 1NQ
☎ (01425) 473701 ⊕ therailway.co
House beer (by Ringwood); 4 changing beers (sourced nationally) Ⓗ

Four changing beers, both local and national plus Ringwood Best as a regular, with bag-in-box cider and a great kitchen, make the Railway the place to visit for lunch or just a beer in a pleasant, comfortable atmosphere. The landlord and landlady have taken big steps to improve their ample outdoor space, planting a combination of native trees and hedges and installing a new festival tent. A true unspoilt, Victorian two-bar traditional community pub, it features a public bar on the right with a small snug area and a lounge bar. Q🕏🌞◑👤♣😼🅿🖵😻🛜

Romsey

Old House at Home

62 Love Lane, SO51 8DE (adjoining Waitrose car park)
☎ (01794) 513175 ⊕ theoldhouseathomeromsey.co.uk
Fuller's London Pride; Gale's Seafarers Ale, HSB; 2 changing beers (often Fuller's) Ⓗ

This well-established and popular Fuller's outlet has appeared in every Guide since 2005. It is a few minutes' walk from the town centre, midway between the railway and bus stations and adjacent to a large public car park. The pub has an L-shaped bar on two levels and a walled garden with a patio at the rear. Good-quality meals are served in the bar and in a separate restaurant area. 🌞◑▶≒🅿🖵😻🛜

Selborne

Selborne Arms Ⓛ

High Street, GU34 3JR
☎ (01420) 511247 ⊕ selbornearms.co.uk
Bowman Swift One; Ringwood Fortyniner; 3 changing beers (sourced regionally; often Gilbert White's, Itchen Valley, Triple fff) Ⓗ

A traditional two-bar village pub but greatly extended, with real fires and a friendly atmosphere throughout. Up to three guest beers, many from microbreweries in the area, are on sale. Bats offering three third-pints of cask beers for the price of a pint are a welcome feature. Extensive menus showcase local and home-made produce, with vegetarian and gluten-free options. The safe play area in the garden is popular with children. Q🕏🌞◑▶🅿🖵(38)😻🛜

Shedfield

Wheatsheaf Inn Ⓛ

Botley Road, SO32 2JG
☎ (01329) 833024
Flower Pots Pots Bitter, Goodens Gold; 4 changing beers (sourced locally; often Flower Pots, Steam Town, Stonehenge) Ⓖ

Popular and friendly roadside village pub serving ales direct from their casks, in addition to Westons ciders. The interior is split into two distinct rooms, both with bars, separated by a double-sided wood-burning stove. Home-cooked food is served at lunchtimes and on Tuesday and Wednesday evenings. The rear garden's flowers are delightful in summer. Live jazz, folk or blues feature on most Saturday evenings, and there is a meat draw on Sundays. An annual beer festival is held each late May bank holiday weekend. Q🕮🅰🍴👪♣♠P🚃(69)🐾🐱🛜

Sherfield on Loddon

Four Horseshoes 🄻 ✅
Reading Road, RG27 0EX
☎ (01256) 882296 ● the4horseshoes.co.uk
Sharp's Doom Bar; 1 changing beer (often Sherfield Village) Ⓗ
This family-run village inn is Grade II listed and dates back to the 16th century, with traditional low beams, some bench seating and wood-burners. The single bar with three handpumps serves four areas, one with a sports TV. At the front is a pleasant patio and at the rear a summer beer garden with play equipment. Families and dogs are welcome. Sherfield Village beers are on one handpump, with another LocAle as guest.
Q🕭🐶🍴👪♣P🚃(14) 🐱

Southampton

Beards & Boards
33 Bedford Place, SO15 2DG
● beardsandboards.co.uk
3 changing beers (sourced nationally; often Steam Town, Vibrant Forest) Ⓗ
A friendly micropub featuring a varied selection of real ales on three handpumps. There are also 10 keg taps and four draught ciders. The bar has a stripped-back industrial decor with displays of skateboarding activities. Music turntables provide the option to bring and play your own vinyl. The pub is popular with all ages and holds dedicated music evenings, and has a range of board games and a Sega games console. You may bring your own food or order in a takeaway. 🐶🕮👪🚃🐱🛜

Bitter Virtue 🄻
70 Cambridge Road, SO14 6US
☎ (023) 8055 4881 ● bittervirtue.co.uk
2 changing beers (sourced regionally; often Siren, Steam Town, Vibrant Forest) Ⓖ
Hidden in the back streets, but close to main roads, this world-class street-corner beer shop attracts customers from far and wide. Now in its 24th consecutive year in the Guide, it is Southampton's longest-standing entry. Over 1,000 beers and ciders in bottles and cans are stocked from Britain, Belgium, the US, and many other countries worldwide. Two cask beers and a draught cider are also available. The side wall of the building has a community historical mural. Q🍴🚃🐱

Bookshop Alehouse
21 Portswood Road, SO17 2ES
4 changing beers (sourced locally; often Eight Arch, Elusive, Vibrant Forest) Ⓗ
TBA for short, this community-led bookshop and micropub serves four cask ales and four craft keg beers, locally and nationally sourced, along with real cider – all clearly listed on a blackboard. The cellar is a quiet social meeting room, used occasionally for poetry and story-telling events. No food is served but you are welcome to bring in a takeaway. Dogs are loved.
Q👤♿🍴🚃(2,7)🐱🛜

Butcher's Hook
7 Manor Farm Road, SO18 1NN
☎ (023) 8178 2280 ● butchershookpub.com
4 changing beers (sourced nationally) Ⓖ
Southampton's first micropub, opened in 2014 and named after the butcher's shop that it used to be. It

serves four changing real ales straight from the cask and around six craft keg beers. A hub of the local community, the pub's small interior makes for a lively, sociable and conversational drinking atmosphere. It gets busy at weekends but it is well worth the detour to find this gem, hidden behind the Bitterne Triangle clock tower. Private events are hosted on occasion – check social media. Q♿🍴♣🚃(7)🐱🛜

Crammed Inn
48 High Street, SO14 2NS
☎ (023) 8057 6252
3 changing beers (sourced regionally) Ⓗ
This friendly, quirky place, in the historic part of the city, is an attractive establishment. The name is no exaggeration – blink and you will have walked by, which would be a shame as the long, thin, cosy bar has some great beers on offer. Three mainly local ales, often including a dark brew, are served. Look out for the Happy Hour and Wednesday night quiz. Close to the waterfront and the Isle of Wight and Hythe ferry terminals.
🕮♿🚃🐱🛜

Dancing Man 🄻
Wool House, Town Quay, SO14 2AR
☎ (023) 8083 6666 ● dancingmanbrewery.co.uk
6 changing beers (sourced nationally; often Dancing Man) Ⓗ
The Dancing Man brewery is housed in the iconic 14th-century Grade I-listed Wool House. Most beers are from the brewery, which promotes unfined beers and is a frequent award winner at local and regional CAMRA beer festivals. The food served is high quality with vegan options. Proximity to the registry office makes the restaurant sought after by wedding groups and the first floor can be reserved for private functions.
🕮🅰♿🍴🚃🐱🛜

Duke of Wellington
36 Bugle Street, SO14 2AH
☎ (023) 8033 9222 ● thedukeatsouthampton.co.uk
Wadworth Henry's IPA, Horizon, 6X, Swordfish; 4 changing beers (sourced regionally) Ⓗ
An historic pub in the heart of Southampton's old town with roots back to the medieval period. It was carefully rebuilt and restored to continue reflecting its Tudor past after extensive war damage. With beamed ceilings and half-timbered walls, this friendly and cosy venue opens from the main bar area into a back room for dining, and has a function room on the first floor. Serving a range of Wadworth beers, it is popular with tourists and regulars alike. Q🕭🅰♣🚃🐱🛜

Fox & Hounds 🄻
106 Pound Street, SO18 6BP (off West End road to the N of A3024 Bitterne bypass) SU4532613386
☎ 07766 614300
Flower Pots Goodens Gold; Steam Town Stoke Ⓖ
Excellent two-bar community local which sells Flower Pots Goodens Gold and Steam Town Stoke from the cask. It boasts a billiards table, an excellent jukebox (free on Sunday) and runs various themed nights including poker, crib, dominoes, a quiz and a meat draw. Families and dogs are welcome. The large, enclosed garden has plenty of seating. This is possibly the only pub in Southampton that has a humane moth trap to help identify passing specimens. 🐶🕮♣🚃🐱🛜

Freemantle Arms 🄻
31 Albany Road, SO15 3EF
☎ (023) 8077 2536 ● thefreemantlearms.co.uk

House beer (by Ringwood); 4 changing beers (sourced regionally; often Courage, Fallen Acorn, Goddards) ⊞

Popular real ale pub in a cul-de-sac only a few minutes' walk from Shirley Road, which has a regular bus service to and from Southampton Central station. Handpumps can be found at both ends of the bar. The rear conservatory leads through to a well-established garden with a covered area for smokers. Children are welcome inside and in the beer garden up until 8.30pm. ❀✿(Millbrook) ♣🖥😺🔶

Guide Dog 🅛
38 Earl's Road, SO14 6SF
☎ (023) 8063 8947
Dark Star American Pale Ale; Flower Pots Pots Bitter, Goodens Gold; Steam Town Stoke; 7 changing beers (sourced nationally; often Arbor, Red Cat, Steam Town) ⊞

A beer mecca hosting 11 handpumps, hidden away in a residential back street. Public transport is easily accessible on nearby main roads. To the rear is the Dog House function room, which extends the pub's seating area as well as hosting occasional folk music and private events. Outside is a small, covered seating space. Within walking distance of St Mary's football stadium – home and away fans welcome. Wednesday is Thai curry night (booking advised). Q🖥(7,U6)😺🔶

Handle Bar 🅛
69 The Avenue, SO17 1XS
☎ 07754 769620 ⊕ handlebarale.com
6 changing beers (sourced regionally; often Fallen Acorn, Red Cat, Steam Town) ⊞

A friendly multi-level pub, with old pictures and memorabilia on the walls giving it a rustic feel. The bar has six handpumps serving a varied range of beers, predominantly from local breweries. Food includes a range of Mediterranean tapas and other dishes. Additional seating is provided by a partially covered decked area at the front. Northbound buses stop right outside. Bar staff often have the appropriate moustache! ❀🕐♣🖥😺🔶

Hop Inn 🅛
199 Woodmill Lane, SO18 2PH
☎ (023) 8055 7723
Bowman Swift One; Sharp's Doom Bar; Steam Town Stoke, Firebox; 1 changing beer (sourced nationally) ⊞

Traditional 1930s pub, shaped to fit its triangular site in a residential area close to Riverside Park. It retains a two-bar layout with separate entrances for each one, with some interesting internal architechture where it seems no two walls meet at right angles. The lounge is homely, with a central fireplace that splits the area into two. The public bar is more spartan, with a jukebox and the usual games. There is a small garden behind the public bar plus a patio adjacent to the lounge bar. The menu is interesting and reasonably priced. ✿❀🕐&♣P🖥(16,7)😺🔶

Key & Anchor
90 Millbrook Road East, Freemantle, SO15 1JQ (jct of Cracknore Rd)
☎ (023) 8022 5674
Dartmoor Jail Ale; St Austell Proper Job; Wadworth 6X ⊞

A friendly street-corner local dating back to 1862. Three handpumps on the bar serve cask ale. The open hearth fire and comfortable sofas, combined with the excellent real ale, make for enjoyable visits. Bar stools and tables and chairs suit the more traditional pub-goer; there is a

terrace at the front and comfortable garden to the rear. Bingo and quizzes alternate Wednesdays. Weekly Saturday afternoon meat draw. ❀✿♣🖥😺🔶

Olaf's Tun
8 Portsmouth Road, SO19 9AA
☎ (023) 8044 7887 ⊕ olafstun.co.uk
6 changing beers (sourced nationally) ⊞

Originally opened in 2016, the pub was taken over by new owners in November 2020. Six handpumps serve a changing selection of local and national cask ales alongside eight rotating keg lines, bag-in-a-box ciders and a copious range of cans and bottles. A tasteful refurbishment includes comfortable seating, a raised decked area, outdoor seating, and the addition of a cellar and new bar. A small kitchen is also on hand for those who are a little peckish. Q❀&✿♦🖥😺🔶

Park Inn
37 Carlisle Road, SO16 4FN
☎ (023) 8078 7835 ⊕ theparkinn.co.uk
Wadworth Henry's IPA, 6X, Swordfish; 3 changing beers (sourced nationally) ⊞

A beautiful street-corner pub from the Victorian era. With a U-shaped bar in the middle of the room, it manages to maintain both the public and lounge atmospheres of the original two rooms. During 2020 the dartboard was removed and that area converted to additional seating. Two or three guest beers complement the three regular Wadworth ales. Snacks are provided on Sunday lunchtimes. ❀♣♦🖥😺🔶

Platform Tavern 🅛 ✅
Town Quay, SO14 2NY
☎ (023) 8033 7232 ⊕ platformtavern.com
Dark Star Hophead; Gale's Seafarers Ale; 4 changing beers (sourced locally) ⊞

Situated close to the Isle of Wight ferry terminal, the Platform Tavern is popular with visitors to the Island. It is built into the remnants of the city's ancient walls (a small portion is visible behind glass in the bar). African art, including musical instruments and batik panels, as well as tented celiing fabric create an exotic atmosphere. As well as being a popular watering hole for its real ale, the pub also serves restaurant-quality food and stone-baked pizzas at pub prices. Frequent live music sessions can make weekends busy. 🕐♣♦🖥😺🔶

South Western Arms
38-40 Adelaide Road, SO17 2HW
☎ (023) 8122 0817
9 changing beers (sourced nationally; often Bowman, Exmoor) ⊞

Adjoining St Denys railway station, this spacious Victorian establishment with two floors and a large paved beer garden is a regular in this Guide. The decor includes exposed brick walls and period bric-a-brac, and there is a jukebox. The single bar serves up to nine different national and local real ales. Live music features regularly downstairs on Saturday evenings, while upstairs has table football, pool and darts. A friendly and popular place. ❀✿♣P🖥(7)😺

Witch's Brew 🅛
220 Shirley Road, SO15 3FL
☎ 07803 347775 ⊕ thewitchsbrewsouthampton.com
5 changing beers (sourced nationally; often Bedlam, Flower Pots, Steam Town) 🅖

A quirky witch-themed micropub with bespoke furnishings on Southampton's busy Shirley Road. Multiple connected rooms lead to the tiny bar and decked garden to the rear. A varied selection of quality ales and ciders are dispensed by gravity into oversized glasses, supplemented by bottles and cans from the fridge. The friendly pub dog warmly welcomes customers – visiting dogs on leads please. A regular finalist in the local CAMRA Pub of the Year competitions. Q✿♣●▯🚌🐾

Southwick

Golden Lion 🄻

High Street, PO17 6EB

☎ (023) 9221 0437 🌐 goldenlionsouthwick.co.uk

Suthwyk Old Dick, Skew Sunshine Ale; 4 changing beers (sourced regionally; often Langham, Palmers, Urban Island) 🄷

Famous historic free house in a privately owned village. It has many military artefacts, and Montgomery and Eisenhower were visitors, partly planning D-Day in the snug. A number of vintage vehicle societies visit during the warmer months. The Old Dick beer is named after the last brewer at the historic brewhouse behind the pub. The award-winning food can be enjoyed in the main bar or in the quieter dining area. Jazz night is every Tuesday. Members of the Britstop Motorhome Club are welcome. Q🛋✿◐◑♿⛺♣●P🐾📶

Steep

Harrow ★ 🄻

Harrow Lane, GU32 2DA

☎ (01730) 262685 🌐 theharrowinnsteep.co.uk

2 changing beers (sourced locally; often Flack Manor, Hop Back, Langham) 🄶

Genuinely unspoilt, the Harrow is a timeless rural gem featuring two cosy rooms with serving hatches. It can be hard to find and has limited parking, but it is more than worth the hunt. Beer is always 4% ABV or less, coming from a range of local breweries, while ciders are from Cheddar Valley and Meon Valley. There are several benches at the front, and a lovely well-kept garden. The toilets are across the road. The Harrow has been identified by CAMRA as having a nationally important historic pub interior. Q✿◐◑●P🐾

Titchfield

Wheatsheaf 🄻

1 East Street, PO14 4AD

☎ (01329) 842965

Fallen Acorn Hole Hearted; Flower Pots Pots Bitter; 4 changing beers (sourced regionally; often Fallen Acorn) 🄷

A 17th-century free house, owned by the licensee since 2017, which has established a reputation for top-quality real ale. The premises comprise a main bar with a real fire, a cosy snug and a bistro restaurant. Separate bar and restaurant menus are available. Regular beer and cider festivals are held at the end of January and July each year. No food is served Sunday evening. Q🛋✿◐◑♿●P🚌(X4)🐾

Totton

6 Barrels

31 Salisbury Road, SO40 3HX

☎ (023) 8178 3030 🌐 6barrels.co.uk

Steam Town Stoke, Barton; 4 changing beers (sourced locally; often Vibrant Forest) 🄷

Formerly a Thai takeaway, now a micropub, furnished with wood-panelled walls and benched tables. Four handpumps supply locally brewed ales, and a good selection of craft keg beers, ciders and perries is also offered. Customers can buy pizza from next door to eat in the bar, should they choose. A selection of board games is also available for visitors if they run out of conversation. Outside are more tables and benches in a covered seating area. ♿⇌●🚌🐾📶

Vernham Dean

George Inn

Back Lane, SP11 0JY

☎ (01264) 737279 🌐 thegeorgeatvernhamdean.co.uk

Bowman Swift One; Flack Manor Flack's Double Drop; Stonehenge Pigswill; 2 changing beers 🄷

Beautiful old-fashioned village pub dating back to the 17th century, with eyebrow windows, while inside are oak beams and fireplaces. Sited in the upper reaches of the Bourne valley, numerous footpaths and cycling routes, including to Fosbury hill fort, surround the village. Outside there is a beer garden and seating to the front. Fresh cooked food is available most of the day and themed nights are regularly held. A beer festival is staged in August, with camping available. Q🛋✿◐◑P🐾📶

Weyhill

Weyhill Fair

Weyhill Road, SP11 0PP

☎ (01264) 773722 🌐 weyhillfairandover.co.uk

Fuller's London Pride; Gale's Seafarers Ale, HSB; 2 changing beers (often Butcombe, Castle Rock, Wychwood) 🄷

Country-style pub three miles west of Andover, standing on the site of the historic Weyhill fairground. The three regular Fuller's beers are usually supplemented by both a seasonal and a guest beer from the Fuller's portfolio. Good food uses locally sourced ingredients where possible and is available to eat in or take away. Fish Friday is ever popular. Closed on Monday in winter. 🛋✿◐◑⛺P🚌🐾📶

Whitchurch

King's Arms

10 Church Street, RG28 7AB

☎ (01256) 896333 🌐 kingsarmswhitchurch.co.uk

6 changing beers 🄷

A traditional two-bar community-style pub in the town centre. Beers often include local and regional offerings, with three usually on tap. One bar has a large screen and pool table with a cosy snug off, while the other bar is comfortable for socialising or for a good meal. Built in 1575, the building became an inn in 1675. A sympathetic refurbishment in 2013 has retained the original period character and features. Numerous events and themed evenings are hosted. 🛋✿◐◑⇌♣P🚌(76,86)🐾📶

Prince Regent 🄻

104 London Road, RG28 7LT

☎ (01256) 895525

Hop Back Summer Lightning; Young's London Gold 🄷

The pub up the hill, as it is known, is a basic single-bar free house on the edge of this pleasant country town, overlooking the Test Valley. Local conversation takes pride of place among a mixed clientele. There is an excellent jukebox, a pool table and sports TV, with an emphasis on football matches. Occasional live music and quizzes feature. The location is ideal for walks into the countryside. ♣P🚌(76)🐾

Whitsbury

Cartwheel Inn

Whitsbury Road, SP6 3PZ

☎ (01725) 518362 ⊕ cartwheelinnwhitsbury.com
3 changing beers (sourced locally; often Andwell, Brew Shack, Eight Arch) Ⓗ
A wonderful example of an 18th-century country pub, created originally from farm cottages and once housing a wheelwright's and the village bakery (a defunct oven remains). Here Hampshire hills roll towards Dorset and Wiltshire; the famous racehorse Desert Orchid was trained nearby. It is well situated for visiting the New Forest and Salisbury. A proud free house, it serves good local beers and highly rated food in convivial surroundings both inside and outside.
Q🌣🕭❀◑🕯♣♿P🐾☀🎝

Widley

George Inn
Portsdown Hill Road, PO6 1BE
☎ (023) 9222 1079 ⊕ the-george-inn.co.uk
Flower Pots Goodens Gold; Fuller's London Pride; Greene King Abbot; Sharp's Doom Bar; Timothy Taylor Boltmaker; 2 changing beers (sourced nationally; often Goddards, Irving, Langham) Ⓗ
Offering views across Portsmouth to the Isle of Wight, this Grade II-listed pub is a comfortable place to relax after the climb up Portsdown Hill. It is also of interest to transport enthusiasts, being a former coaching inn on the London to Portsmouth route and a tram stop on the Portsdown & Horndean Light Railway. The bar is decorated with brewing memorabilia, mainly on the theme of the former Brickwoods brewery. Chess, shove-ha'penny and board games are available to entertain you. 🕭◑P🖳(7,8)🐾☀🎝

Winchester

Albion Ⓛ
2 Stockbridge Road, SO23 7BZ
☎ (01962) 867991
Flower Pots Perridge Pale, Pots Bitter, Goodens Gold; 1 changing beer (sourced locally)
A stone's throw from Winchester railway station, this cosy L-shaped street-corner pub is a traditional straightforward drinking venue, serving three to four quality Flower Pots beers on draught – three regular and one seasonal/guest. Celebrated for its friendly atmosphere, the Albion is popular as a stop-off to and from the station, for meeting friends, or to just enjoy watching the world going by its windows. Q≉🖳🐾☀🎝

Black Boy Ⓛ
1 Wharf Hill, SO23 9NQ (just off Chesil St B3404)
☎ (01962) 861754 ⊕ theblackboypub.com
Alfred's Saxon Bronze; Flower Pots Pots Bitter; 3 changing beers (sourced locally; often Bowman, Hop Back, Itchen Valley) Ⓗ
A rambling centuries-old building, stuffed full of unusual, interesting, even disturbing bric-a-brac, and comprising many interconnected rooms serviced from a central bar. Popular with residents and tourists alike, whether for a local real ale or delicious food, you would need several visits to take it all in. Outside, in the secluded garden, there is a splendid medieval-style covered seating area. The Black Rat restaurant opposite and the Black Hole B&B next door are under the same ownership.
Q🕭🛏◑♣♿🖳(4)☀🎝

Fulflood Arms Ⓛ
28 Cheriton Road, SO22 5EF
☎ (01962) 842996 ⊕ thefulfloodarms.co.uk
Greene King IPA; Morland Old Speckled Hen; Red Cat Prowler Pale; Steam Town Stoke; 6 changing beers

(sourced locally; often Alfred's, Flower Pots, Red Cat) Ⓗ
Classic 19th-century back-street pub with the original dark-green tiled façade, frosted-glass windows and signage of its former Winchester Brewery ownership. Inside is a smart and comfy, capacious single bar with a wood-burning stove and a library with newspapers. Note the city map on the ceiling. Patios, both front and rear, are an attraction. Sports events shown on TV attract an enthusiastic local following. No food is served but takeaways may be ordered. 🕭≉♣●🖳(4,3)🐾☀🎝

Hyde Tavern Ⓛ
57 Hyde Street, SO23 7DY
☎ (01962) 862592 ⊕ hydetavern.co.uk
Flower Pots Pots Bitter; Harvey's Sussex Best Bitter Ⓗ**; 4 changing beers (sourced locally; often Flower Pots, Red Cat, West Berkshire)** Ⓖ
A Grade II-listed building, with low beams and prominent double-gable frontage, which has barely changed over generations. The small front room, with its tiny bar, is a delightful place to quaff locally sourced ales. A larger room to the rear leads, via a stairway, to the secluded garden. A cellar area, equipped with a bar, is used by groups as a regular function room. No food is served, but customers may bring food in (small fee for plates and cutlery). Q🕭≉♣●🖳🐾☀🎝

Old Vine Ⓛ ✔
8 Great Minster Street, SO23 9HA
☎ (01962) 854616 ⊕ oldvinewinchester.com
Alfred's Saxon Bronze; Timothy Taylor Landlord; 2 changing beers (sourced locally; often Andwell, Bowman, Steam Town) Ⓗ
A vine-clad, 18th-century, Grade II-listed inn, with views across the city museum and cathedral green. The cosy oak-beamed bar, with four handpumps, serves beers mainly from local breweries. To the left, through a curtain, is a restaurant serving quality home-cooked food using produce from the area where possible. At the rear there is a further room and beyond that a small smoke-free terraced courtyard. Accommodation is available in six stylish en-suite rooms. Q🕭🛏◑♣🖳(1,69)🐾☀🎝

Wykeham Arms
75 Kingsgate Street, SO23 9PE
☎ (01962) 853834 ⊕ wykehamarmswinchester.co.uk
Dark Star Hophead; Flower Pots Goodens Gold; Fuller's London Pride; Gale's Seafarers Ale, HSB; 1 changing beer (sourced regionally) Ⓗ
An historic and iconic pub near Winchester College, where school memorabilia fills the walls and ceilings and old school desks are used as tables. Entry through the curved glass doors leads to the main bar area, with a welcoming real fire, interconnecting seating and dining rooms leading off. A friendly conversational atmosphere fills the rooms (supported by the active discouragement of mobile phones). The kitchen offers a two AA rosette-rated menu seven days a week. Q🕭🛏◑🖳(1,69)🐾☀🎝

Wonston

Wonston Arms Ⓛ
Stoke Charity Road, SO21 3LS
☎ 07909 993388 ⊕ thewonston.co.uk
4 changing beers (sourced locally; often Bowman, Oakham, Red Cat) Ⓗ
This is a gem of a pub in the heart of the village, around a 15-minute walk from Sutton Scotney and the nearest bus stop. It is a true community local catering for everyone. Although it doesn't serve food, there are pop-up street-food vendors most nights. Folk music is on the second and fourth Wednesdays of the month, and jazz

sessions, a pop-up café, quizzes and a photography club also feature. Local CAMRA Pub of the Year 2017-2020, and CAMRA National Pub of the Year 2018.
Q✿♣👜P🐾🛜

tethered in the extensive car park – the local riding stables is nearby. The location is handy for forest walks.
♿✿🕊♿P🚪(C32,C33) 🐾🛜

Wootton

Rising Sun Ⓛ ✔

Bashley Common Road, BH25 5SF
☎ (01425) 610360 ⊕ therisingsunbashley.co.uk
Flack Manor Flack's Double Drop; Otter Ale; 2 changing beers (sourced regionally; often Andwell, Fine Tuned, Hop Back) Ⓗ

Welcoming and prominent 1900s roadside pub with something for everyone. Staff are knowledgeable and enthusiastic about the real ale sold. In summer, a draught cider is sometimes served. A wide food menu and daily specials cater for all food tastes throughout the day. A large family room and adventure playground will keep children amused. Horses are welcome and may be

Yateley

Dog & Partridge

105 Reading Road, GU46 7LR
☎ (01252) 870648 ⊕ dogandpartridgeyateley.co.uk
Sharp's Doom Bar; 3 changing beers (sourced nationally) Ⓗ

Customers are assured of a friendly welcome in this village pub at the heart of the local community next to the green. It has built up an excellent reputation for quality cask beer and home-made food. Sharp's Doom Bar is the main ale, while there are three changing guests. Sunday lunch is popular and booking is essential. Quiz night is Monday and live music plays on Saturday. TV sport is shown at the far end. ♿✿🕊♿P🚪(3)🐾🛜

Merchant House, Portsmouth (Photo: Geoff Marsh)

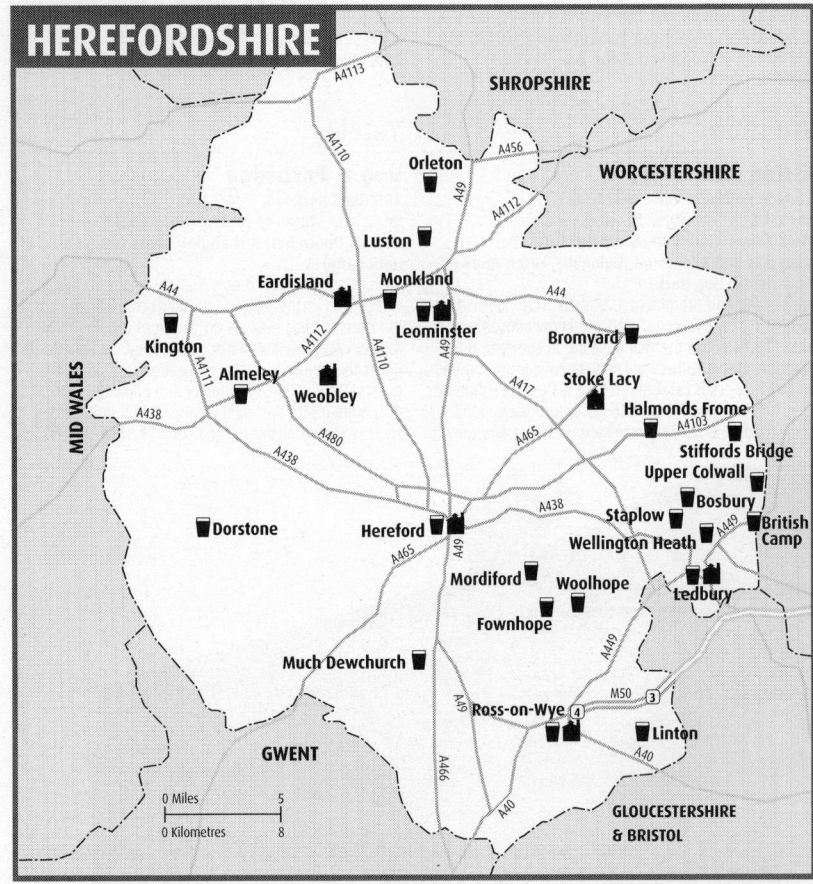

HEREFORDSHIRE

Almeley

Bells Inn L

HR3 6LF

☎ (01544) 327216 ⊕ thebellsinnalmeley.com

Goff's Lancer; 2 changing beers (sourced locally; often Hobsons, Swan, Wood) Ⓗ

A genuine welcome is guaranteed at this enthusiastically run, traditional country inn set in the heart of its rural community, which incorporates an award-winning farm shop and delicatessen. The bar has a low ceiling and an alcove housing the dartboard. Home-prepared lunches are served Tuesday-Saturday, and evening meals Friday (booking required). The guest beers are typically from local breweries. Runner-up Herefordshire CAMRA Pub of the Year 2020. ☙☻⟐♣●Ｐ☲☺ ᗡ ●

Bosbury

Bell Inn L ✔

HR8 1PX (on B4220, in village)

☎ (01531) 640285 ⊕ bosburyandcoddington.co.uk/the-bell-inn-bosbury

Otter Bitter; Wye Valley Butty Bach; 1 changing beer Ⓗ

A two-bar black and white half-timbered inn in a terrace opposite the imposing village church, the bells of which lend the place its name. The dining area (no food served Sun eve or all day Mon) contrasts with the basic yet comfortable public bar, replete with grand fireplace,

alcoves, books and newspapers. Friendly and welcoming, this pub lies at the heart of its community. A large garden features at the rear. Plenty of on-street parking is available. Ｑ☙☻⟐♣●☲(417)☺ ᗡ

British Camp

Malvern Hills Hotel L

Jubilee Drive, WR13 6DW (at jct of A449 and B4232)

☎ (01684) 540690 ⊕ malvernhillshotel.co.uk

Wye Valley Bitter, HPA, Butty Bach; 1 changing beer Ⓗ

Located high on the Malvern Hills, in the shadow of the Herefordshire Beacon, this enthusiastically run and comfortable venue has been popular with walkers and locals for generations. Drinkers can enjoy five local ales in the welcoming wood-panelled main bar. Two stylish restaurants provide affordable quality dining including a

REAL ALE BREWERIES

Hereford 🍺 Hereford
Ledbury Ledbury
Little Dewchurch 🍺 Hereford
Motley Hog 🍺 Ross on Wye (NEW)
Simpsons 🍺 Eardisland
Swan Leominster
Weobley 🍺 Weobley
Wobbly ✦ Hereford
Wye Valley Stoke Lacy

good range of bar meals. Refurbished accommodation and a conference room top it off nicely. Dry dogs and children are welcome – the latter until 4pm.
🏨🛏️🕽◑🍴&P🐾❀

Bromyard

Rose & Lion L ✓
5 New Road, HR7 4AJ
☎ (01885) 482381
Wye Valley Bitter, HPA, Butty Bach Ⓗ
A longstanding member of the expanding Wye Valley pub estate, the Rosie is very much a town pub of the old school, with a loyal following from locals. Two small, largely unaltered rooms are complemented by a further bar area to the rear, plus a more contemporary annexe and a pleasant garden. Furnished throughout in a modern but appropriate style, there is always a buzz about the place. No food is served. The car park is small, but there is free on-street parking nearby.
Q🕽🏨&♣P🕽🖵(420) ❀

Dorstone

Pandy Inn L
HR3 6AN (signed off B4348)
☎ (01981) 550273 ⊕ thepandyinn.co.uk
Sharp's Atlantic; Wye Valley Butty Bach; house beer (by Grey Trees); 1 changing beer Ⓗ
Opposite the small village green, the Pandy has a history dating back to the 12th century. Although opened out inside, discrete areas give an intimate feel, alongside timber framing, exposed stone walls and a huge fireplace. The pub caters equally for drinkers and diners, with an interesting range of dishes, including vegetarian ones. It will open on weekday lunchtimes for groups by prior arrangement. Gwatkins cider is on handpump. A monthly quiz and curry night is hosted (booking advisable). Winter hours apply early October to early April. Q🕽🏨◑♣●P🖵🐾❀

Fownhope

New Inn L
HR1 4PE (on B4224, in village)
☎ (01432) 860350 ⊕ thenewinnfownhope.co.uk
Hobsons Best; house beer (by Wye Valley); 1 changing beer (often Hobsons, Swan, Wye Valley) Ⓗ
A genuine locals' pub at the heart of a thriving village community. The single room with exposed beams and light decor is divided into more discrete spaces by a central, bare-brick fireplace. Outside is a large, lawned garden. Typical pub food is served lunchtimes plus Friday and Saturday evenings, with a roast on Sunday. A quiz is held on the last Thursday of the month. Fownhope football team use the inn as a base.
🕽🏨◑&▲♣P🖵(454) ❀🍴

Halmonds Frome

Major's Arms L
WR6 5AX (¾ mile N of A4103 at Bishops Frome)
SO675481
☎ (01531) 640261
Otter Bitter; Purity Pure Gold; Wye Valley HPA Ⓗ
An isolated hillside pub, once a cider mill, that achieved national fame in 1991 when it temporarily became the Miners Arms as the coal mines were being closed wholesale. Entry is via a simple, no-frills, high-ceilinged room with stone walls and a large wood-burner. An archway leads through to another drinking area and a patio, from which there are superb views, particularly

sunsets, over west Herefordshire and into Wales. Complimentary bar snacks are often provided, and occasionally live music. 🕽🏨▲♣P🐾❀🍴

Hereford

Barrels L ✓
69 St Owen Street, HR1 2JQ
☎ (01432) 274968
Wye Valley Bitter, The Hopfather, HPA, Butty Bach, Wholesome Stout; 1 changing beer (sourced locally; often Wye Valley) Ⓗ
Local CAMRA Pub of the Year seven times, The Barrels is a must-visit Hereford institution with a warm welcome for all. With no food, no gimmicks, but oodles of character across five rooms, this is a community inn of the highest order. It has a fantastic covered courtyard to the rear which hosts a charity beer and music festival each August bank holiday weekend. Events include jazz on the first Monday of the month and comedy on some Wednesday evenings. There are TVs throughout turned on for major events. 🕽🏨🍴♣●🖵🐾❀

Beer in Hand
136 Eign Street, HR4 0AP
☎ 07543 327548
5 changing beers Ⓖ
Herefordshire's first micropub, this minimalist, single-bar establishment was converted from a launderette in 2013. In recent years it has won CAMRA Herefordshire Pub of the Year and Cider Pub of the Year. With an impressive chilled racking system, it typically sells up to five ales on cask, six keg beers (including one from Odyssey Brew Co) and eight mainly local ciders and perries. Snacks are always available and artisan pizzas are made on-site Thursday and Friday evenings. Quiz night is the first Wednesday and folk night the third Thursday of the month. Q🕽🏨◑&♣●🖵🐾

Britannia L ✓
7 Cotterell Street, HR4 0HH
☎ (01432) 341780
Wye Valley Bitter, HPA, Butty Bach Ⓗ
Reopened by Wye Valley Brewery following an impressive refurbishment which included a new extension with an oak-vaulted ceiling and a landscaped rear garden/patio, this is a back-street venue with real pedigree. The large central bar-servery is bookended by two distinct seating areas with modern decor. Snacks such as sandwiches are always available, and pork pies and barbecues in summer. A quiz is held monthly on a Thursday. A popular pub for an area of the city otherwise devoid of quality choices. 🕽🏨&♣🖵🐾❀

Kington

Olde Tavern ★ L
22 Victoria Road, HR5 3BX
☎ (01544) 231417
Hobsons Mild; 4 changing beers (often Ludlow, Salopian, Swan) Ⓗ
A living and breathing Victorian time warp – once called the Railway Tavern (the railway closed in the 1950s) and before that the Tavern in the Fields – the pub is a microcosm of the town's development. On entering the lobby, with original serving hatch intact, to the left is a small bar with original timberwork, bench and alcove seating, and multifarious curios. To the right is the old smoke room with its fine flagstone floor and bench seating. The place has a strong local following.
Q🕽🏨▲♣🖵🐾

Ledbury

Feathers Hotel

25 High Street, HR8 1DS
☎ (01531) 635266 ⊕ feathersledbury.co.uk
Ledbury Bitter; house beer (by Wadworth); 2 changing beers (often Malvern Hills, St Austell) ⊞
An elegant black and white Elizabethan coaching inn, one of the flagship hotels for the county, the Feathers has recently benefited from a major refurbishment. Features inside this fine Grade II*-listed building include a function room that was once the town theatre, and hand-painted murals in the upstairs corridors. The smart, plush, quiet bar is complemented by a restaurant and separate coffee shop and eatery. The toilets are fully accessible. Q ✿ ⎅ ⚘ ⟐ ◐ ◑ ⚘ P ⋒ ⚘ 🛜

Prince of Wales ⫪ ⦿

Church Lane, HR8 1DL
☎ (01531) 632250 ⊕ powledbury.com
Eagle IPA; Hobsons Town Crier; Ledbury Dark; Otter Amber; Wainwright; 2 changing beers ⊞
Tucked away down a picturesque cobbled alley leading up to the church, this 16th-century timber-framed pub boasts two bars, plus an alcove where a folk jam session is held each Wednesday evening. A frequent award winner, it is a genuine community pub – always bustling with locals and visitors. Rosie's Pig and Snailsbank draught ciders are available as well as one rotating craft beer and an extensive range of foreign beers in bottles and cans. The bar meals are good value (booking advisable for Sunday roasts). ✿ ⊛ ◐ ◑ ⚘ ◐ ⋒ ⚘ 🛜

Leominster

Chequers ⫪ ⦿

63 Etnam Street, HR6 8AE
☎ (01568) 612473
Wye Valley Bitter; HPA, The Hopfather, Butty Bach, Wholesome Stout; 1 changing beer (often Wye Valley) ⊞
Probably the oldest pub in the town, Chequers has a fine timber-framed façade and interesting protruding gables. A wonderful front bar was at one time two bars, but still has much charm, with a fine tiled floor, original fireplace, timbers and cosy window alcoves. To the rear is a more conventional lounge bar, a games room and a patio with a feature oak-timbered shelter. Snack food is available. Children over 13 are admitted. A quiz is held monthly on Wednesdays, and jazz on the first Fridays in summer. Q ⊛ ⫴ ⚘ ◐ P ⋒ ⚘ 🛜

Linton

Alma Inn ⫪

HR9 7RY (off B4221, W of M50 jct 3) SO659255
☎ (01989) 720355 ⊕ almainnlinton.co.uk
Butcombe Original; Ludlow Gold; Malvern Hills Black Pear; Oakham JHB; 1 changing beer (often Bristol Beer Factory, Hop Shed, Swan) ⊞
Hidden behind a plain façade is an understated but award-winning pub of outstanding calibre. The convivial front bar with wood-burner and original timber furniture contrasts with the rear pool room and a separate wood-panelled dining room. Hearty, freshly prepared pub classics are offered, with seasonal specials, light bites and bar snacks. Events include the nationally renowned Linton Music Festival in July, hosted in the extensive gardens along with a beer festival. A quiz is held every last Sunday of the month. CAMRA Herefordshire Pub of the Year 2020. Q ✿ ✤ ⊛ ◐ ◑ ⚘ ⚘

Luston

Balance ⫪

HR6 0EB (on B4361, in village)
☎ (01568) 616801 ⊕ thebalanceinnluston.business.site
Hobsons Best; Wye Valley HPA, Butty Bach; 1 changing beer (often Swan) ⊞
Located on the site of an old wool weighing station – hence the name – in a small village, the Balance has an unspoilt interior with exposed beams and open fires. The main bar is complemented by a snug with chesterfield sofa, a games room with pool table and dartboard, and a large conservatory. Locally sourced meals are served daily, including in-house stone-baked pizzas, and takeaways are available. ✿ ⊛ ◐ ✤ ⚘ ⋒ (490) ⚘ 🛜

Monkland

Monkland Arms ⫪

HR6 9DE (on A44, W end of village)
☎ (01568) 720510 ⊕ themonklandarms.co.uk
Hobsons Best; Wye Valley Butty Bach; 2 changing beers (sourced locally; often Ludlow, Swan, Wood) ⊞
A single bar serves the drinking area, with dining areas to the side and rear. The beer garden has seating under cover, with views across open country. Home-cooked, locally sourced food is served, including traditional Sunday lunches. Up to seven local draught ciders are available and a range of four real ales. Quiz night is the last Wednesday of the month and live music is hosted on some Saturdays and Sundays. ✿ ⊛ ◐ ✤ ⚘ P ⋒ (502) ⚘ 🛜

Mordiford

Moon Inn

HR1 4LW (on B4224, in village)
☎ (01432) 873067 ⊕ mooninnmordiford.co.uk
Otter Bitter; St Austell Proper Job; Timothy Taylor Landlord; Wychwood Hobgoblin Ruby ⊞
This comfortable half-timbered two-bar village inn started life as a farmhouse over 400 years ago. Popular with locals and with families tripping out from Hereford, it benefits from its proximity to the Mordiford Loop – a well-known local walk – as well as the rivers Lugg and Wye. Traditional, locally sourced pub food is served There is a children's play area in the garden, plus a camping and caravan site to the rear. ✿ ⊛ ◐ ◑ ▲ ✤ ⚘ P ⋒ (453) ⚘ 🛜

Much Dewchurch

Black Swan

HR2 8DJ (on B4348, in village)
☎ (01981) 540295
Timothy Taylor Landlord; 2 changing beers (often Butcombe, Slater's, Swan) ⊞
One of the oldest pubs in Herefordshire, this delightful 15th-century beamed village inn comes complete with its own priest hole. It has a small lounge leading to the dining room with open fire, a separate public bar with flagstone floors, and a pool and darts room. Home-prepared, mainly locally sourced food is available every session. The guest beers are typically from regional breweries. Draught Gwatkins perry is stocked as well as ciders from Cockyard, Colcombe House and other local makers. Thursday is folk night. Herefordshire CAMRA Cider Pub of the Year 2019. ✿ ⊛ ◐ ✤ ⚘ P ⋒ ⚘ 🛜

Orleton

Boot Inn ⫪

SY8 4HN (off B4361, in village)
☎ (01568) 780228 ⊕ bootinnorleton.co.uk

Hobsons Best, Twisted Spire; Ludlow Blonde; 1 changing beer ℍ

The Boot reopened under community ownership in 2019, following a period of closure. A major refurbishment of this Grade II-listed, 16th-century, half-timbered masterpiece has been carried out to good effect – it has been sympathetically opened out while maintaining a separate dining room, snug and original inglenook fireplace. Good seasonal food is served and booking is advised (and essential at weekends). ᗡ❀ÅP🖵(490)

Ross-on-Wye

Tap House 🅛

1 Millpond Street, HR9 7BZ

☎ 07510 156708

6 changing beers (sourced nationally; often Hop Shed, Motley Hog, New Bristol) ℍ

Opened in 2018, this micropub occupies what was, until 1965, the tap for Alton Court Brewery. Serving six real ales from smaller breweries far and wide plus a local cider, it has transformed the choice of real ale in Ross. Consisting of a simply furnished room and a snug, the Tap does not serve meals, but cobs are available Friday to Sunday. A new brewery, Motley Hog, installed upstairs, is now in operation. Herefordshire CAMRA Pub of the Year 2019. Q🖤🖵❀

Staplow

Oak Inn 🅛

HR8 1NP (on B4214)

☎ (01531) 640954 ⊕ oakinnstaplow.co.uk

Bathams Best Bitter; Ledbury Gold; Wye Valley Bitter; 1 changing beer ℍ

A stylishly renovated and well-run roadside country inn offering exceptional food, good beer and quality accommodation. The contemporary public area neatly divides into three – a reception bar area with modern sofas and low tables, a snug, and a main dining area featuring an open kitchen. At the rear is a further room with scrubbed tables. Such is the reputation of the Oak that booking is essential for food and accommodation. Qᗡ❀🛏◑ḋP🖵(417)❀🎋

Stiffords Bridge

Red Lion Inn 🅛

WR13 5NN (on A4103)

☎ (01886) 880318 ⊕ redlioncradley.com

Pitchfork Golden Ale; Wye Valley Butty Bach; 4 changing beers (often Malvern Hills, Purity, Salopian) ℍ

This multi-roomed roadside pub is as popular with out-of-town diners as it is with locals and drinkers. A survivor of multiple floods, it is characterised by modern flagstone floors, wood panelling, bare brick walls, cosy window alcoves and a large fireplace with a wood-burner. There are pleasant and extensive gardens to the rear where events are hosted. Traditional locally sourced

food dominates the menu. The guest beers are from breweries far and near, many unusual for the area, supplemented by a craft keg beer and two real ciders. ᗡ❀◑ḋ♣🖤P❀🎋 ⬤

Upper Colwall

Chase Inn 🅛

Chase Road, WR13 6DJ (off B4218, turning at upper hairpin bend signed British Camp) SO766431

☎ (01684) 540276 ⊕ thechaseinnmalvern.co.uk

Enville Ale; Malvern Hills Black Pear; 2 changing beers (often Bathams) ℍ

Small and cosy two-bar free house hidden away in a quiet wooded backwater on the western slopes of the Malvern Hills. With a genteel atmosphere, it is popular with walkers and locals alike. It comprises a small lounge for dining (booking advisable at weekends) and a long, narrow public bar, both adorned with many artefacts and curios. A delightful manicured rear beer garden commands panoramic views across Herefordshire to the Welsh Hills. A quiz is held on the first Monday of the month. Q❀ᗡ◑♣🖤P🖵🖵(675)❀🎋

Wellington Heath

Farmers Arms 🅛

Horse Road, HR8 1LS (in village, E of B4214)

☎ (01531) 634776 ⊕ farmersarmswellingtonheath.co.uk

Wye Valley HPA, Butty Bach; 2 changing beers (often Ledbury, Purple Moose, Salopian) ℍ

Follow the signs carefully to find this pub in its dispersed rural community. The bar and main dining area are in the original mid-19th century building, and on either side are more modern extensions housing a games room with pool table and a restaurant. The food ranges from burgers and pub classics to steaks and speciality dishes. Eight local draught ciders are available. A popular Beer & Beast festival is held in July. Open on bank holiday Mondays. ᗡ❀◑ḋ♣🖤P🖵(675)❀🎋

Woolhope

Crown Inn 🅛

HR1 4QP (in village) SO611357

☎ (01432) 860468 ⊕ crowninnwoolhope.co.uk

Ledbury Bitter; Wye Valley HPA; 1 changing beer ℍ

Situated next to the church, the Crown has a large bar, complemented by a restaurant and a public bar area in the conservatory by the front door. Sandwiches and meals are all locally sourced and home-prepared. Curries feature on Monday evenings and a gourmet night is held on the third Thursday of the month. A wide range of local cider and perry is stocked, in bottle and on draught, the latter including the pub's own produce under the brand name Kings. ᗡ❀◑ḋÅ♣🖤P🖵(453)❀🎋

Drunken primates

Brehm asserts that the natives of north-eastern Africa catch the wild baboons by exposing vessels with strong beer, by which they are made drunk. On the following morning they (the baboons) were very cross and dismal; they held their aching heads with both hands, and wore a most pitiable expression: when beer was offered them, they turned away in disgust.

Charles Darwin, The Origin of Species, 1859

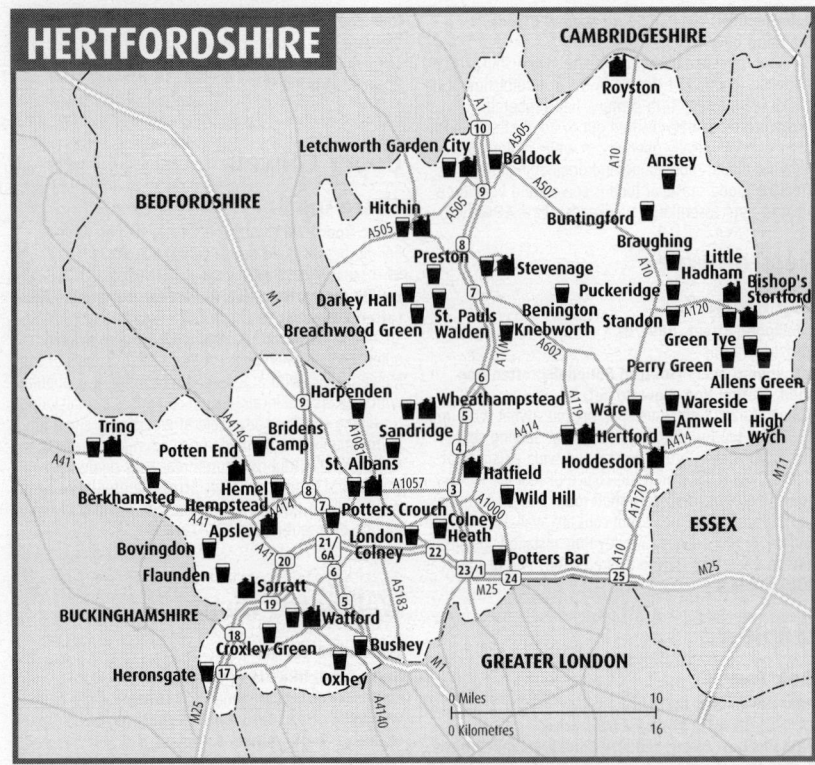

HERTFORDSHIRE

Allens Green

Queen's Head 🄻
CM21 0LS TL455170
☎ (01279) 723393
Fuller's London Pride; Mighty Oak Maldon Gold; 2 changing beers (sourced locally) 🄶
This village inn serves a changing range of beers. Hot snacks are available except in especially busy periods. It boasts a large garden and is popular with walkers and cyclists as well as regulars. A frequent winner of local CAMRA Pub of the Year over the past decade and Hertfordshire Cider Pub of the Year 2020. Q❀&♿P🐾🎵

Amwell

Elephant & Castle 🄻 ✅
Amwell Lane, AL4 8EA TL167131
☎ (01582) 832175 ⊕ theelephantandcastle.co.uk
Farr Brew Chief Jester, Our Greatest Golden, The Best Bitter; Greene King Abbot; 1 changing beer (sourced nationally) 🄷
Hidden away in a peaceful setting, this rural community pub is now leased by Farr Brew, the local brewer, and is popular with cyclists and walkers. Its front bar features terracotta tiles and a large fireplace; the rear bar has a 100-foot well. There are two gardens, one child-friendly. Lunches are served daily, and evening meals Tuesday to Saturday. The pub holds regular charity events and shows TV sports and films. English wines and locally distilled gins are available. Q🍽❀🐕♿P🚌🐾🎵

Anstey

Blind Fiddler
SG9 0BW
☎ (01763) 848000
Buntingford Twitchell; Fuller's London Pride; 1 changing beer (sourced nationally) 🄷
Named after the local legend of Fiddler George, the Blind Fiddler has been opened out into one large bar area with a separate restaurant. Regular beers come from Buntingford and Fuller's and entertainment includes monthly quiz nights and live music. Pétanque, played in the garden, is popular, and there is a rare bar billiards table. 🐕❀🍽♣P🐾🎵

Baldock

Cock
43 High Street, SG7 6BG
☎ (01462) 896594
Greene King IPA, Abbot; Morland Old Speckled Hen; 2 changing beers (sourced nationally) 🄷
The Cock dates from the 17th century, and features a cosy beamed interior and a welcoming open log fire. It is a traditional pub in a historic Roman market town. The split-level layout enhances this popular, friendly local's character. An enclosed outside drinking area can be enjoyed in good weather. Regular live music events take place. 🐕❀&♿🚌🚆(635,98)🐾🎵

Orange Tree 🄻 ✅
Norton Road, SG7 5AW
☎ (01462) 892341 ⊕ theorangetreebaldock.com
Greene King IPA, Abbot; Tring Mansion Mild; 9 changing beers (sourced nationally) 🄷
A multi-roomed pub that dates back over 300 years and is home to more than 10 local clubs and societies. It serves nine guest ales from small breweries, always including two from the local Buntingford Brewery, plus five local real ciders. There is a huge malt whisky

collection on display, alongside a large selection of vintage bottled beers. Good home-cooked food is available, including meat from local, award-winning Chapman's Butchers. Quiz night is Tuesday. Rugby internationals are shown in all rooms.
ॐ֎ᐤ₺♧⇌♣♠P☐֍ຈ

Benington

Lordship Arms
42 Whempstead Road, SG2 7BX
☎ (01438) 869665 ∰ lordshiparms.com
Black Sheep Best Bitter; Crouch Vale Brewers Gold; Timothy Taylor Landlord; 6 changing beers (sourced nationally) Ⓗ
Under the same ownership for 28 years, this pub is a repeat winner of local and county CAMRA awards, and is local CAMRA Pub of the Year 2021. Its single bar is decorated with telephone memorabilia. The garden features floral displays to be enjoyed in the summer. Wednesday evening curries are popular, and lunchtime snacks are served. There is a classic car gathering on the third Tuesday of the month from April to September. Sunday hours can vary in winter – call to check.
Q֎ᐤ♠P☐ຈ

Berkhamsted

Bull
10 High Street, HP4 2BS
☎ (01442) 767440 ∰ thebullberkhamsted.co.uk
Tring Side Pocket for a Toad; 1 changing beer (sourced locally; often Tring) Ⓗ
This stunning high-street establishment is the oldest surviving pub in Berkhamsted, dating back to at least 1535. It has a large red-brick fireplace, wood panelling and an extensive canalside beer garden. Beers are well-kept and mostly local. The pub holds regular quizzes, frequently shows sport on TV and serves breakfast, lunch and dinner. ॐ֎ᐤ⇌♣P☐(500,501)♠ຈ

Rising Sun Ⓛ
1 Canal Side, George Street, HP4 2EG (at lock 55 on Grand Union Canal, a five-minute walk along canal from station)
☎ (01442) 864913
Tring Drop Bar Pale Ale; house beer (by Tring); 3 changing beers (sourced nationally; often Chiltern, Froth Blowers, Milestone) Ⓗ
The Riser is a thriving canalside pub with plenty of outdoor space – a firm favourite with local hikers, dog walkers and cyclists. The recipient of many well-deserved CAMRA awards, it serves five well-kept real ales and up to 20 real ciders. The pub hosts many popular events including quiz nights, folk music afternoons, a cheese club and quarterly beer and cider festivals. A range of bar snacks is offered such as pork pies and nachos, as well as the renowned ploughman's.
ॐ֎ᐤ⇌♣♠☐(500,501) ♠ຈ

Bishop's Stortford

Bishop's Stortford Sports Trust Ⓛ
Cricketfield Lane, CM23 2TD
☎ (01279) 654463
6 changing beers (sourced locally; often Hadham, Mauldons, New River) Ⓗ
Everyone is welcome at this pub within a club – no membership required. Conversation flourishes in the comfortable seating area as the TV sports screens usually have the sound off. Outside drinking in summer comes with an attractive view. The venue is easily reached from

town via Chantry Road; turn left at the end to see the grounds on the right. Local CAMRA Club of Year 2020 and a recent national finalist. ॐ֎֍P

Star Ⓛ ✅
7 Bridge Street, CM23 2JU
☎ (01279) 654211
5 changing beers (sourced regionally) Ⓗ
A 17th-century town-centre pub catering for all ages. It is busy on Friday and Saturday evenings with a young crowd, but normally attracts a mixed clientele. Tuesday is quiz night. A quiet pint can be enjoyed on other evenings and at lunchtimes. Beers from regional and local breweries are offered on a changing basis. Reasonably priced traditional pub food is freshly prepared throughout the day. ֎ᐤ⇌♦☐ຈ

Bovingdon

Bell Ⓛ ✅
79 High Street, HP3 0HP
☎ (01442) 832800 ∰ bellbovingdon.co.uk
Tring Side Pocket for a Toad; 3 changing beers (sourced nationally; often Timothy Taylor, Tring, Young's) Ⓗ
Welcoming 18th-century beamed village inn. It has a split-level main bar, plus a smaller adjoining snug and a restaurant to the rear. The pub has gained an excellent reputation for its food. Log fires ensure a cosy atmosphere in winter, while the garden terrace is an ideal place to relax in summer. Events include a monthly charity quiz and occasional live music.
ॐ֎ᐤ♣P☐(1,352) ♠ຈ

Braughing

Brown Bear
14 The Street, SG11 2QF
☎ (01920) 822157 ∰ brownbearbraughing.co.uk
3 changing beers (sourced nationally) Ⓗ
A pub since at least 1740, the Brown Bear has a public bar and a restaurant, both with impressive fireplaces – have a go at identifying the implements. A widely varying choice of three real ales is usually available. There is something for everyone here, including a Thursday quiz, darts and pétanque teams, a large garden with a pizza oven, occasional outside bars and monthly live music. ॐ֎ᐤ♣P☐(331)♠ຈ

REAL ALE BREWERIES

3 Brewers of St Albans ✐ Hatfield
Belgian Brewer, The ✐ Bishop's Stortford
Bowtie Watford
Buntingford Royston
Farr Brew ✐ Wheathampstead
Garden City 🍺 Letchworth Garden City
Hadham Little Hadham
Hitchin Hitchin
Lock 81 Watford
Mad Squirrel ✐ Potten End
McMullen Hertford
New River Hoddesdon
Oxhey Village Watford
Paradigm Sarratt
Pope's Yard Apsley
Six Hills ✐ Stevenage
Tring Tring
White Hart Tap 🍺 St Albans (brewing suspended)

Breachwood Green

Red Lion ✓
16 Chapel Road, SG4 8NU
☎ (01438) 833123 ⊕ redlionbreachwoodgreen.co.uk
Greene King Abbot; St Austell Tribute; Woodforde's Wherry; 1 changing beer (sourced nationally) Ⓗ
Being the only pub in the village the Red Lion attracts many locals as well as visitors from further afield. It has a TV showing main sporting events as well as a quiet dining area. The garden provides views of the countryside and a good vantage point to view the aircraft approaching Luton Airport. The pub has darts, dominoes teams and associated football and cricket sides. Good home made food is served, and the guest beers are unusual for the area. Accommodation is also available. ⏲✿❀◗♣♿P🚪🐾❄🛜

Bridens Camp

Crown & Sceptre Ⓛ
Red Lion Hill, HP2 6EY (from A4146 at Water End take Red Lion Lane opp Red Lion up hill for 1km) TL044111
☎ (01442) 234660 ⊕ crownandsceptrepub.co.uk
Greene King Abbot, IPA; 4 changing beers (sourced regionally; often Tring, Vale) Ⓗ
The Crown & Sceptre is thought to date back to the mid-1800s, with a classic pub interior that includes a dark wood-panelled bar and roaring fire. Located in the quiet village of Bridens Camp, it provides a refreshing stop on a country walk. The home-cooked traditional pub food is always excellent and reasonably priced. It boasts four changing handpumps serving a variety of local and regional ales. There is always a warm welcome from the locals. Q⏲✿◗♿P🚪(29)🐾❄🛜

Buntingford

Crown
17 High Street, SG9 9AB
☎ (01763) 271422
Draught Bass; St Austell Trelawny; 1 changing beer (sourced nationally) Ⓗ
This town-centre pub has a large front bar with dartboard, plus a cosy back bar and function room. Outside are a covered patio and a secluded garden with pétanque piste. Traditional fish & chips is served on Friday evenings and an acoustic music night takes place on the third Monday of the month. On CAMRA's Regional Inventory of Historic Pub Interiors.
Q⏲✿◗♣🚪(386,331)🐾

Bushey

Swan
25 Park Road, WD23 3EE
☎ (020) 8950 2256 ⊕ swanpubbushey.co.uk
Black Sheep Best Bitter; Greene King Abbot; Timothy Taylor Landlord; Young's Bitter Ⓗ
Traditional Victorian pub just off the main high street with a single bar and two coal fires. A real gem, it has old photos and sporting mementos adorning the walls. The original jug-and-bottle window has been retained. Hot snacks are available at all times including toasties and pies. The pub hosts a book club, and offers entertainment including darts, board games and shut the box. The Ladies is accessed via the garden. ✿♣🚪(142,258)🐾❄🛜

Colney Heath

Crooked Billet Ⓛ
88 High Street, AL4 0NP
☎ (01727) 822128 ⊕ thecrookedbilletpub.com
Sharp's Doom Bar; Tring Side Pocket for a Toad; Young's London Special Ⓗ
Popular and friendly cottage-style village pub dating back over 200 years. A genuine free house, it stocks three beers from national and regional breweries and micros. A wide selection of good-value, home-made food is served lunchtimes plus Friday and Saturday evenings. Summer barbecues and Saturday events are held occasionally. This is a favourite stop-off for walkers on the many local footpaths. Families are welcome in the bar until 9pm and in the large garden, where there is play equipment. ⏲✿❀♣P🚪(304)🐾

Croxley Green

Sportsman Ⓛ
2 Scots Hill, WD3 3AD (at A412 jct with the green)
☎ (01923) 443360
Oakham JHB; Sharp's Doom Bar; 5 changing beers (sourced nationally; often New River, Paradigm, Vale) Ⓗ
A family-run community pub with friendly, welcoming service, providing a traditional pub atmosphere in a modern context. It serves two regular real ales plus five varying guest beers from near and far. Craft keg versions of the prize-winning Paradigm Black Friday and Oakham Green Dragon are regularly available. The pool table and dartboard continue to be well used. Comfortable outdoor seating is provided. Quiz night is Wednesday; live music features every other Sunday afternoon. Croxley tube station is a 12-minute walk. ⏲✿♣♿P🚪🚌

Darley Hall

Fox
Darley Road, LU2 8PP
☎ (01582) 731366 ⊕ thefoxdarleyhall.co.uk
4 changing beers (sourced locally) Ⓗ
Late 19th century pub in a small hamlet close to Luton Airport. This double fronted pub is first recorded as having a landlord in the 1891 census. The single bar pub with an adjoining dining area is welcoming to all whether drinking or dining. There is a walled garden open for children / dogs and a large mezzanine decking area linked to the excellent restaurant, which overlooks the Hertfordshire countryside. ⏲✿◗P🚪🐾

Flaunden

Green Dragon ★
Flaunden Hill, HP3 0PP TL015008
☎ (01442) 832020 ⊕ greendragonflaunden.co.uk
6 changing beers (sourced nationally; often Hop Back, Timothy Taylor, Young's) Ⓗ
A 17th-century pub that reopened in 2020 under new ownership after a sympathetic refurbishment, with an additional function room and extended garden. In addition to the historic taproom, which has been carefully preserved (and has been identified by CAMRA as a nationally important historic pub interior), there are two areas with wooden beams, exposed bricks and open fires. The food range includes pizza cooked in a wood-fired oven, a trattoria menu and Sunday roast. ⏲✿◗♣🐾❄🛜

Green Tye

Prince of Wales Ⓛ
Green Tye, Much Hadham, SG10 6JP TL444184
☎ (01279) 842139 ⊕ thepow.co.uk

Abbeydale Moonshine; Hadham Gold; Wadworth Henry's IPA; 1 changing beer (sourced locally) Ⓗ
A traditional and friendly village local, whether you are a walker, cyclist, dog owner or just plain thirsty. Food includes sandwiches and great-value pub grub. There is a small garden for fine weather. Well-established beer festivals in May and September feature a barbecue and entertainment. Q🕏🕸🕭P🐾🕏

Harpenden

Carpenters Arms
14 Cravells Road, AL5 1BD (bottom of Cravells Rd by car park)
☎ (01582) 460311
Adnams Southwold Bitter; Courage Best Bitter; Greene King Abbot; 2 changing beers (sourced nationally) Ⓗ
Landlord Tony has been running Harpenden's smallest pub since 2006, offering five real ales including two changing guest beers. It is popular with all sections of the community – and their dogs. The cosy interior is comfortably furnished, with an open fire warming the bar in cold weather. The spacious, secluded patio is a suntrap in summer. BT and terrestrial sport are shown on TV, with rugby union internationals especially popular. Meals are available Tuesday to Saturday lunchtimes. Q🕸◑P🖳(321,657)🐾🕏

Cross Keys Ⓛ ✔
39 High Street, AL5 2SD (opp war memorial)
☎ (01582) 763989
Rebellion IPA; Timothy Taylor Landlord; Tring Side Pocket for a Toad Ⓗ
A regular entry in the Guide, located on the lower High Street, this two-bar pub has retained its traditional charm with a rare fine pewter bar top and flagstone floors. The original oak-beamed ceiling has tankards from past and present customers. In spring and summer, enjoy your pint in the secluded, attractive rear garden, and in autumn or winter savour your beer in front of the saloon bar's fire. Traditional home-cooked lunches are served Monday to Saturday. Q🕏🕸◑🗲♣🖳🐾🕏

Gibraltar Castle
70 Lower Luton Road, Batford, AL5 5AH (on B653)
☎ (01582) 460005 ⊕ gibraltar-castle.co.uk
Fuller's London Pride; 3 Brewers of St Albans Ruby English Ale; 1 changing beer (sourced nationally) Ⓗ
An old building dating back to 1799 with several interesting internal nooks and crannies, original oak beams, bread ovens and an open fire. Outside, the pleasant drinking area has recently been updated with the inclusion of sheltering. The leaseholders also run the Garibaldi pub in St Albans. This is one of the few Fuller's establishments stocking a regular beer from outside the company range. The pub participates in the local darts league. Good home-cooked food is served daily.
Q🕏🕸◑♣🕭P🖳🐾🕏

Hemel Hempstead

Full House Ⓛ ✔
128 Marlowes, HP1 1EZ
☎ (01442) 265512
Greene King Abbot; Ruddles County; Sharp's Doom Bar; 6 changing beers (sourced nationally; often Tring) Ⓗ
A former cinema and bingo hall (hence the name), which is spacious with extensive seating, the pub has a decor reminiscent of its past. Consistent beer quality and a wide range of changing ales, often local, ensure it is

always interesting to visit this pub. Food is served all day. There are regular beer festivals in spring and autumn. The ladies' toilets are notably ornate. Q🕏🕸◑🕭🖳♿🕏

Monks Inn Ⓛ
31-32 The Square, HP1 1EP
☎ 07554 661877
10 changing beers (sourced nationally) Ⓗ/Ⓖ
The town's first micropub cemented its position in this Guide by becoming the local CAMRA Pub of the Year. The landlord stocks an impressive array of well-kept, ever-changing beers in a comprehensive range of styles. Six ciders are available too. The small interior, converted from an old betting shop, is complemented by gazebos outside. Customers are welcome to bring in food from local eateries and fast-food outlets. Comedy nights, quizzes and music nights are held regularly.
Q🕏🕸●🖳🐾🕏

Heronsgate

Land of Liberty, Peace & Plenty Ⓛ
Long Lane, WD3 5BS (off jct 17 of M25) TQ023949
☎ (01923) 282226 ⊕ landoflibertypub.com
8 changing beers (sourced nationally; often Downton, Tring, XT) Ⓗ
Welcoming, award-winning pub just off the motorway, popular with walkers, cyclists, locals and real ale enthusiasts. It has historic connections to the Chartists, who had a short-lived rural community nearby. Up to eight microbrewery beers are offered in a range of styles and strengths. Real cider, perry and a wide choice of whiskies are also available, as are gins and bottled beers. Beer festivals, tastings and a monthly charity quiz are held throughout the year. Bar snacks are served all day. There is a large outside pavilion and garden for families. 🕸♣🕭P🖳(R2)🐾🕏

Hertford

Black Horse Ⓛ ✔
29-31 West Street, SG13 8EZ
☎ (01992) 583630 ⊕ theblackhorse.biz
6 changing beers (sourced nationally) Ⓗ
A community-focused, timbered free house, dating from 1642 and situated in one of Hertford's most attractive streets, near the start of the Cole Green Way. Six real ales from around Britain are on offer, including one from Hertfordshire. An interesting menu features curries, game and daily specials, and the pub has its own bakery producing pastries. The well-kept garden has a separate and safe children's area. Handy for Hertford Town FC supporters, the pub also has its own Black Horse Rugby Club which plays home games at nearby Hertford RFC.
🕏🕸◑🗲♣🖳🐾🕏

Great Eastern Tavern
29 Railway Place, SG13 7BS
☎ (01992) 582048
McMullen AK Original Mild, Cask Ale; 1 changing beer (sourced nationally) Ⓗ
Popular, buoyant and traditional back-street McMullen local with two contrasting bars bedecked with pictures and artefacts. There is live TV sport and interesting rock and blues piped music. A folk club is hosted on the first Thursday of the month and a quiz on the first Sunday. Sandwiches are available at lunchtimes. A chilli challenge is held every February. Outside are two small gardens – the larger, to the rear, is paved and adorned with a stunning array of plants.
🕏🕸🗲♣🖳(395,310)🐾🕏

Hertford Club

Lombard House, Bull Plain, SG14 1DT
☎ (01992) 421422 ⊕ hertford.club
3 changing beers (sourced nationally) ℍ
Dating from the 15th century with later additions, Lombard House, on the River Lea, was built as an English hall house and is one of the oldest buildings in Hertford. It has been the home of this private members' club since 1897. CAMRA members are welcome and may be signed in on production of a membership card. You will find two or three changing beers and real cider, which in summer can be enjoyed in the delightful walled garden and riverside terrace. Home-cooked food is served at lunchtimes and on Friday evening. ⏰❄◐≢♣♠🚌🚃🛜

Old Barge

2 The Folly, SG14 1QD
☎ (01992) 581871 ⊕ theoldbarge.com
Marston's 61 Deep; 3 changing beers (sourced nationally) ℍ
A free house on Folly Island, pleasantly situated canalside on the River Lea, offering a good selection of ales – often including a dark brew – and a range of ciders and perries. Locally sourced home-cooked food is served all day with roasts on Sundays. There is a popular Sunday night quiz and a music quiz on the last Thursday of the month. The Spring Fling music festival takes place on the second May bank holiday Monday. Look out for the annual duck race. ⏰❄◐≢♣♠🚃🛜

Old Cross Tavern ⓛ

8 St Andrew Street, SG14 1JA
☎ (01992) 583133 ⊕ oldcrosstavern.com
Timothy Taylor Landlord; 5 changing beers (sourced nationally) ℍ
Superb town free house offering a friendly welcome. Up to six real ales, usually including a dark beer of some distinction, come from brewers large and small, and there is a fine choice of Belgian bottle-conditioned beers. Two beer festivals are held each year – one over a spring bank holiday weekend, the other in October. No TV or music here, just good old-fashioned conversation. Home-made pork pies and Scotch eggs are available. Local CAMRA Pub of the Year 2020. Q≢♣🚃(395)❄

White Horse

33 Castle Street, SG14 1HH
☎ (01992) 500557 ⊕ white-horse-hertford.co.uk
Dark Star Hophead; Fuller's London Pride, ESB; Gale's Seafarers Ale; 2 changing beers (sourced nationally) ℍ
A charming old timber-framed building with two downstairs bars and additional rooms upstairs, one featuring bar billiards, others where children are welcome. Guest beers are from Fuller's and different breweries around Britain. Home-cooked Thai food and pub favourites are available all day. The White Horse welcomes dogs and has no gaming machines to interrupt its atmosphere of engaging chat.
Q⏰❄◐≢♣♠🚃❄🛜

High Wych

Rising Sun

High Wych Road, CM21 0HZ
☎ (01279) 724099
4 changing beers (often Oakham, Woodforde's) 🄶
Friendly village local, popular with locals and walkers. It has never used handpumps; the range of four or five beers is served on gravity, often featuring East Anglian breweries. Although refurbished, the building retains its original character with a stone floor, attractive fireplace

and wood panelling. The pub holds an annual vegetable competition. Parking is in the village hall car park opposite. Q❄♣P🚃(347)❄

Hitchin

BB's Bar

Bridge Street, SG5 2DE
☎ (01462) 656084
Fuller's London Pride; Oakham Citra; 2 changing beers (sourced nationally) ℍ
A sport and music Bar named after Blues legend BB King, which maintains a friendly pub atmosphere. The cask taps bar counter is at the rear of the front room and separate from the main bar counter. A second room at the back is only open when busy, but is also available for private functions. Beer range usually includes two Oakham beers plus two others. ⏰❄❄

Half Moon ⓛ

57 Queen Street, SG4 9TZ
☎ (01462) 453010 ⊕ thehalfmoonhitchin.com
Adnams Southwold Bitter; Young's Bitter; 10 changing beers (sourced nationally) ℍ
This welcoming one-bar pub dates from the 18th century. The two house ales and eight guest ales ensure a variety of beer styles is always on offer from a range of breweries near and far, alongside a choice of traditional ciders. Bar snacks are always available. Twice-yearly beer festivals, regular quizzes and music nights are popular in this friendly community pub. ⏰❄◐≢♣♠P🚃❄🛜

Victoria ✅

1 Ickleford Road, SG5 1TJ (off A505)
☎ (01462) 432682 ⊕ thevictoriahitchin.com
Greene King IPA, Abbot; 4 changing beers (sourced nationally) ℍ
This popular and busy pub dates from 1865. It hosts a range of events from quiz nights and live music to comedy and cabaret, as well as an annual beer and cider festival and the Vic Fest music festival. Two regular Greene King beers are complemented by two guests. Good-value, home-cooked food is served every day, with roasts on Sunday. Pie nights feature regularly. The historic barn is available for community use and live events. ⏰❄◐♿≢♣🚃🛜

Knebworth

Station

1 Station Approach, SG3 6AT
☎ (01438) 812224 ⊕ stationpubknebworth.com
Shepherd Neame Spitfire; Timothy Taylor Landlord; 3 changing beers (sourced nationally) ℍ
An attractively refurbished pub next to the railway station. Now owned by the local parish council, it recently reopened after a campaign lasting almost three years to save it from residential development. Four cask ales are served, covering a range of styles, and delicious food is available every day. ⏰❄◐♿≢P❄🛜

Letchworth Garden City

Garden City Brewery & Bar ⓛ

22 The Wynd, SG6 3EN
☎ 07932 739558 ⊕ gardencitybrewery.co.uk
8 changing beers (sourced nationally) 🄶
An award-winning, family-run brew-bar in a converted café on a charming pedestrianised street. All ales are on gravity: usually four of the brewery's own, only available here, and four guests. A large selection of local and UK-wide ciders is also on offer, alongside locally produced

bar snacks. The paved beer garden has a weatherproof awning. There is a regular events programme and the TV shows tennis and rugby. The bar is five minutes' walk from the station, with parking adjacent and a playground opposite. Local CAMRA Cider & Perry Pub of the Year 2020. Q🍴🐾🚶♿⇌♠P🚃😺🔄🛜

London Colney

Bull 🅛
Barnet Road, AL2 1QU
☎ (01727) 823160 🌐 thebullpublondoncolney.co.uk
St Austell Tribute; Timothy Taylor Landlord; 2 changing beers (sourced nationally) 🅷
A lovely 17th-century timbered building near the River Colne, offering a range of real ales. It has a cosy lounge featuring an original fireplace, and a large public bar with a dartboard and TV. Evening events include live music sessions. Good-value home-made meals are served Monday to Saturday lunchtimes and evenings, with breakfast on Saturday and a roast on Sunday. Outside is a children's play area. 😺🌚🍴♠P🚃😺🔄🛜

Oxhey

Railway Arms ✓
1 Aldenham Road, WD19 4AB
☎ 07976 647569
Greene King IPA, Abbot; 2 changing beers (sourced nationally; often Purity, St Austell, Timothy Taylor) 🅷
Friendly and welcoming two-bar pub opposite Bushey station. Railway memorabilia adorn the pub, befitting its name. Historically it was used as a masons' meeting house, as indicated by the coat of arms on the side of the pub. Now it is a multi-screen TV sports venue with a wide variety shown, including Gaelic football. The public bar features a pool table and signed Watford FC shirts. 😺🌚⇌(Bushey) ⊖(Bushey) ♠P🚃😺🛜

Villiers Arms
108 Villiers Road, WD19 4AJ
☎ (01923) 448848
3 changing beers (sourced nationally; often Rebellion, Timothy Taylor, Tring) 🅷
Traditional family-run village pub, popular with the locals. Its layout dates from the 1970s, with a single semicircular bar. Numerous drink-related items are among the memorabilia in the lounge bar. Up to three real ales are served, together with a selection of other drinks. The pub has a cosy feeling in winter and a bright, airy feel in summer, making it a year-round favourite. Q😺🌚⇌(Bushey) ⊖(Bushey) ♠🚃😺🛜

Perry Green

Hoops 🅛
SG10 6EF
☎ (01279) 843568
Hadham Gold, Oddy, First 🅷
A traditional country pub on the edge of the Henry Moore estate, the Hoops is a rural gem. Food is served and drinkers are always welcome in the bar area. The superb large gardens are ideal for fine-weather drinking. Opening hours are extended in summer. Closing time can depend on how busy the pub is, so phone to check if you're planning a late visit. Q😺🌚🍴P

Potters Bar

Admiral Byng ✓
186-192 Darkes Lane, EN6 1AF (corner of Byng Drive)
☎ (01707) 645484

Greene King Abbot; Ruddles Best Bitter; Sharp's Doom Bar; 8 changing beers (sourced nationally) 🅷
A friendly community Wetherspoon with a display of two model sailing ships and other memorabilia celebrating the exploits and death of Admiral Byng, who was executed for 'failing to do his utmost' to save Minorca from falling to the French in 1756. (The family estate is nearby.) In summer the frontage of the pub is opened onto the street, with additional seating provided. There is a good choice of real cider. 😺🌚🍴♿⇌♣♠🚃(84,610) 🛜

Potters Crouch

Holly Bush
Bedmond Lane, Potters Crouch, AL2 3NN (off B5183 at jct of Potters Crouch Lane and Ragged Hall Lane)
TL16052
☎ (01727) 851792 🌐 thehollybushpub.co.uk
Fuller's London Pride, ESB; Gale's Seafarers Ale 🅷
This charming wisteria-covered 17th-century pub sits in rural surroundings. It is attractively furnished throughout, containing large oak tables and period chairs. The atmosphere in the three pleasant bar areas is convivial and conversational, with no jukeboxes, slot machines or TVs to disturb guests. The food menu is not extensive but is of high quality. Children are welcome. The garden is ideal in summer. Q😺🌚🍴♿P🚃

Preston

Red Lion 🅛
The Green, School Lane, SG4 7UD
☎ (01462) 459585 🌐 theredlionpreston.co.uk
Fuller's London Pride; Young's Bitter; 3 changing beers (sourced nationally) 🅷
This attractive free house on the village green was the first community-owned pub in Britain. It offers a variety of beers, many from small breweries. Fresh home-made food is served, often featuring locally sourced ingredients (no food Sun eve and Mon). The pub hosts the village cricket teams. Winner of numerous local CAMRA Pub of the Year awards in recent years, and national finalist for the 2019 Pub of the Year. Q😺🌚🍴♣♠🚃😺🛜

Puckeridge

White Hart 🅛
Braughing Road, SG11 1RR
☎ (01920) 821309 🌐 thewhitehartpuckeridge.co.uk
McMullen AK Original Mild, Country Bitter; 1 changing beer (sourced nationally) 🅷
A 14th century pub, named after the emblem of Richard II. It has many interior rooms with a huge fireplace in the dining room, ask about the story of the beam over the fireplace. The large garden features a children's play area. A thatched gazebo is built around a tree in the car park. Breakfast is available Saturdays from 8.30-11am. 😺🌚🍴P🚃(386,331) 😺🛜

St Albans

Garibaldi ✓
61 Albert Street, AL1 1RT
☎ (01727) 894745 🌐 garibaldistalbans.co.uk
Fuller's London Pride, ESB; Gale's HSB; 1 changing beer (sourced nationally) 🅷
A fine example of a back-street local, in the heart of Sopwell near the cathedral. The pub serves an extensive range of Fuller's ales; the landlord is a past winner of the Fuller's Master Cellarman award. Home-cooked food is available weekend lunchtimes and afternoons (booking

advised for Sunday roasts), with excellent service provided by friendly bar staff. A genuine community pub, it hosts live music on Saturday nights plus occasional quiz nights, food nights and charity events throughout the year. ⚡😃🕪🚲⇖♣☺🚫🐾🐾🛜

Great Northern ✅
172 London Road, AL1 1PQ
☎ (01727) 730867 ⊕ greatnorthernpub.co.uk
4 changing beers (sourced nationally) Ⓗ
A lively free house, this independent Grade II-listed pub has been modernised and features a pumpclip wall. It serves four regularly changing cask beers and a wide selection of UK and international craft keg beers, bottles and cans. The menu of locally sourced modern European food is available Wednesday to Sunday lunchtimes and Tuesday to Saturday evenings. The pub hosts a quiz every Tuesday and beer festivals in summer, plus tap takeovers throughout the year. ⚡😃🕪🚲⇖♣☺🚫🐾🛜

Lower Red Lion Ⓛ
34-36 Fishpool Street, AL3 4RX
☎ (01727) 855669
Tring Side Pocket for a Toad; 4 changing beers (sourced nationally) Ⓗ
Classic Grade II-listed pub in a conservation area in one of St Albans' most picturesque streets. The Lower Red was an early champion of CAMRA's values in the real ale revival movement and continues to stock quality real ales, ciders and perries. Home-cooked food is served lunchtimes and weekday evenings. A recently added function room serves as an additional dining area on Sunday. B&B is available. Q😃🚲🕪♣🚫🐾🛜

Mad Squirrel Tap & Bottle Shop
17 High Street, AL3 4EW
☎ (01727) 236867
Mad Squirrel Mister Squirrel; 2 changing beers (sourced locally) Ⓗ
In the shadow of St Albans Abbey, this modern beer experience, split over two levels, could hardly offer a starker contrast – yet somehow works so well. Three handpumps and an array of craft keg taps showcase Mad Squirrel's full range of beers, plus unusual guest ales – and if you can't choose, a special 20-sided dice is available to decide for you. There are also bottles and cans to drink in or take away, and pizzas are served all day. ⚡😃🕪🚲⇖🚫🐾🛜

Mermaid
98 Hatfield Road, AL1 3RL
☎ (01727) 845700
Oakham Citra; 5 changing beers (sourced nationally) Ⓗ
Welcoming community venue catering for regulars and the after-work crowd, a short walk from the city centre and St Albans City railway station. It serves a good choice of ales, usually including a stout or porter, plus ciders and bottled foreign beers, and has won several local CAMRA awards for both beer and cider. Beer festivals are held on the May Day and August bank holiday weekends, with a cider festival over the spring bank holiday. Wednesday is live music night. 😃🕪⇖♣🚫🐾🛜

Robin Hood ✅
126 Victoria Street, AL1 3TG
☎ (01727) 856459 ⊕ robin-hood-st-albans.co.uk
Harvey's Sussex Best Bitter; 2 changing beers (sourced nationally) Ⓗ
Friendly single-bar pub that is handy for St Albans City station and football ground. Real cider or perry is always available to complement the rotating beer range. A secluded garden to the rear offers summer enjoyment.

The traditional jukebox and table skittles provide entertainment all year round, and folk music is performed on Wednesday evenings. Toasted sandwiches are available lunchtimes on weekdays. ⚡😃⇖♣☺🐾🛜

Six Bells Ⓛ ✅
16-18 St Michael's Street, AL3 4SH
☎ (01727) 856945 ⊕ the-six-bells.com
Oakham JHB; Timothy Taylor Landlord; Tring Ridgeway; 3 changing beers (sourced nationally) Ⓗ
Characterful 16th-century pub in the attractive St Michael's village, a short walk from the city centre and Abbey, and close to Verulamium Park and Museum. It offers three regular beers and three changing guests – one always from a Hertfordshire brewer – plus real cider in summer. Good-quality home-cooked food is served lunchtimes and evenings (no food Sun eve). Outside is a pleasant patio area. ⚡😃🕪♣🚫🐾🛜

White Hart Tap Ⓛ
4 Keyfield Terrace, AL1 1QJ
☎ (01727) 860974 ⊕ whiteharttap.co.uk
Timothy Taylor Boltmaker, Landlord; Tring Side Pocket for a Toad; 4 changing beers (sourced nationally) Ⓗ
One-bar back-street local featuring three beers free of tie, mostly from microbreweries. The pub also brews occasional ales on the premises in various styles. Good-value, home-cooked food is served lunchtimes and Monday to Saturday evenings, with roasts on Sunday and monthly themed food nights. Quiz night is Wednesday; other attractions include summer barbecues and, now and again, beer festivals. There is a heated, covered smoking area outside and a public car park opposite. ⚡😃🕪🚲⇖♣☺🚫🐾🛜

St Pauls Walden

Strathmore Arms Ⓛ
London Road, SG4 8BT TL193222
☎ (01438) 871654 ⊕ thestrathmorearms.co.uk
Tring Side Pocket for a Toad; 3 changing beers (sourced nationally) Ⓗ
This traditional, no-nonsense rural pub on the Bowes-Lyon estate has been serving drinkers since 1882. Specialising in a wide range of draught real ales, craft beer and real cider, it has offered more than 4,000 beers since 2002. There are no fruit machines or jukeboxes here, just good conversation and great beer. Bar food is offered at lunchtimes Tuesday to Friday, with a barbecue on summer Sundays when weather permits. Q⚡😃🕪🅰♣🚫🐾🛜

Sandridge

Green Man ✅
31 High Street, AL4 9DD
☎ (01727) 854845
Greene King Abbot; Sharp's Atlantic; Tring Side Pocket for a Toad Ⓖ
This village community pub, refurbished in 2019, extends a warm welcome to beer and cider drinkers alike. All ales are served direct from the cask, alongside up to six real ciders. Traditional home-cooked food is available daily. Sandridge is close to the 850-acre Heartwood Forest, making the pub an ideal place for refreshment after a stroll in the woods. Dogs are welcome in the conservatory; the garden has a small aviary. Q⚡😃🕪♣🚫🐾🛜

Standon

Star ✅
62 High Street, SG11 1LB
☎ (01920) 823725 ⊕ starstandon.com
Greene King IPA, Abbot; 2 changing beers Ⓗ
Traditional 17th-century pub with exposed wooden beams. It has a separate sports-themed public bar and a quiet and comfortable saloon/restaurant. Food is classic pub grub with roasts on Sunday. Two guest beers are offered, at least one not via Greene King – usually from a small independent local brewer.
ᗺ❀ⓘ♣P➡(331,386) 🐾 📶

Stevenage

Broken Seal Ⓛ
29b High Street, SG1 3AU (entrance to the pub is on Basils Road)
☎ 07973 673040 ⊕ sixhillsbrewing.co.uk
4 changing beers (sourced nationally; often Six Hills) Ⓟ
Stevenage's first brewpub was opened in 2019 as the taproom for Six Hills Brewing. In addition to serving their regular beers, special limited edition beers are brewed at the pub. Usually serves four cask beers, plus ten craft or international beers on keg. Large range of bottled and canned beers to drink in or take away. Q&➡

Tring

King's Arms Ⓛ
King Street, HP23 6BE (corner of Queen St and King St) SP921111
☎ (01442) 823318 ⊕ kingsarmstring.co.uk
Tring Moongazing; 4 changing beers (sourced nationally; often Leighton Buzzard, Oakham, Vale) Ⓗ
A light, open and airy pub in the centre of Tring, popular with all ages. The atmosphere is bustling, with a friendly welcome assured. It offers an ever-changing range of five beers and one real cider. Pub snacks and home-cooked food are served daily. There are two open fires inside and a stable yard with heated canopies outside; in summer this transforms into a beer garden and venue for live music and beer festivals. Children and dogs are welcome. Q ᗺ❀ⓘ♣♠P🐾📶

Ware

Crooked Billet ✅
140 Musley Hill, SG12 7NL (via New Rd from High St)
☎ (01920) 462516
4 changing beers (sourced nationally) Ⓗ
Friendly gem of a traditional community pub, well worth the 15-minute walk up New Road and Musley Hill from the town centre. The two small bars feature TV sport, pool and darts. It serves a varying range of four or five ales, including a mild, porter or stout. Filled rolls are available on Saturday evenings. Outside there are tables to the front and rear. ᗺ❀&♣♠P➡(395)🐾📶

Wareside

Chequers Ⓛ
Ware Road, SG12 7QY
☎ (01920) 467010 ⊕ chequerswareside.com
Timothy Taylor Landlord; house beer (by Hadham); 1 changing beer (sourced regionally) Ⓗ
A rural free house dating from the 15th century, the Chequers was originally a coaching inn and has three distinct bars plus a restaurant. The rotating complement of three beers includes local brewers and some from

further afield. The house IPA is exclusively brewed for the pub by the local Hadham Brewery. All food is home-made and reasonably priced, with plenty of vegetarian options. Walkers and cyclists are welcome, making this a good base for a ramble. No games machines, no music, and a ban on swearing! Q ᗺ ⓘ & ♣ ♠P➡(M3,M4)🐾📶

Watford

Wellington Arms Ⓛ
2 Woodford Road, WD17 1PA
☎ (01923) 220739
Fuller's London Pride; 2 changing beers (sourced locally; often Tring) Ⓗ
Modernised street-corner free house close to Watford Junction station and a short walk from the town centre. Run by the same family for over 30 years, the pub serves good-quality cask ales. Traditional British food is available weekdays, and occasionally at weekends before Watford FC home games. Sporting events are shown on TV screens around the pub. There are 12 letting rooms available. ᗺ❀&ⓘ⊏≠(Jct)⊖(Jct)♣P➡🐾📶

West Herts Sports Club Ⓛ
8 Park Avenue, WD18 7HP (S of A412 near town hall)
☎ (01923) 229239 ⊕ westhertssportsclub.co.uk
Tring Side Pocket for a Toad; Young's Bitter; 3 changing beers (sourced nationally; often Farr Brew, Paradigm, Vale) Ⓗ
The clubhouse is being redeveloped with the intention of moving the bar to a new first-floor extension. Until that is complete, drinks will be served from either the old function room (home of the Watford Beer Festival) or a revamped ground-floor bar. Show a CAMRA membership card or a copy of this Guide to gain entry up to four times a year. Can get very busy on Watford FC match days. ᗺ❀⊖♣♠P⏸📶

Wheathampstead

Reading Rooms Ⓛ
36 The High Street, AL4 8AA
☎ (01582) 833000
3 changing beers (sourced locally; often Farr Brew) Ⓗ
The first brewery-owned micropub and bottle shop in south Hertfordshire, opened in 2018. It is run by Farr Brew who are based two miles away at Samuels Farm, where there has been a taproom open on Saturday for several years. This former florist's consists of three distinct rooms including the whole upper floor. Two beers from Farr Brew feature, along with one guest and a real cider. Spirits from the local Black Bridge Distillery are also stocked. Q&♣♠➡🐾📶

Wild Hill

Woodman Ⓛ
45 Wildhill Road, AL9 6EA (between A1000 and B158) TL264068
☎ (01707) 642618 ⊕ thewoodman.uk
Greene King IPA, Abbot; 4 changing beers (sourced nationally) Ⓗ
A friendly and unpretentious rural pub that is very community oriented. It thrives on and is a staunch supporter of real ale, serving up to six beers including four guests. Lined oversized glasses are available on request. The large garden is ideal in summer. Good pub grub is served lunchtimes (no food Sun). Look for God's Waiting Room. A frequent winner of local and Hertfordshire CAMRA Pub of the Year. ᗺ❀ⓘ♣♠P🐾📶

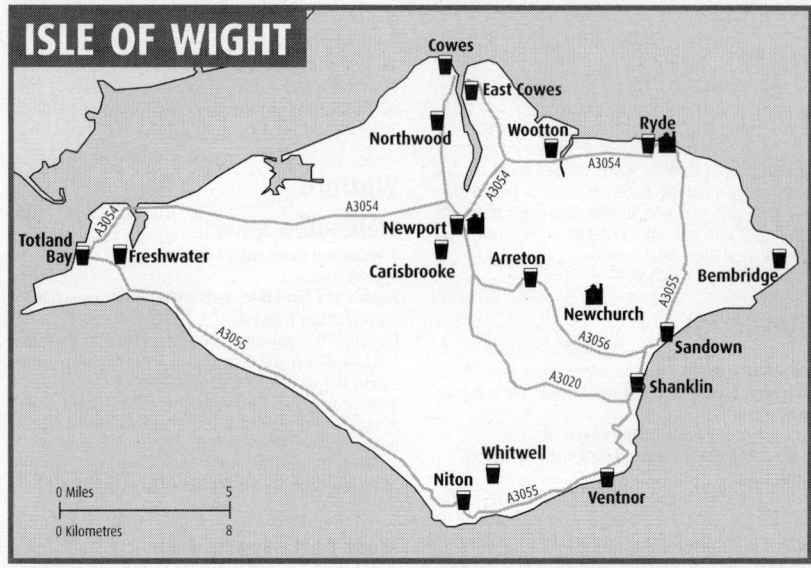

ISLE OF WIGHT

Arreton

Dairyman's Daughter 🅛

Main Road, PO30 3AA (main road from Newport)
SZ53258680

☎ (01983) 539361 ⊕ dairymansdaughter.co.uk

Ringwood Fortyniner; 5 changing beers (sourced nationally; often Lancaster Bomber, Ringwood) 🅗
Arreton Barns Craft Village includes the Dairyman's, Shipwreck Centre and Maritime Museum and IW Studio Glass, all worth visiting, plus the 11th-century church of St George and the grave of the original Dairyman's Daughter. The pub provides up to six beers including local ales, as well as a large selection of Island bottled beers in the old brewery. Lunchtime and evening meals can be enjoyed indoors or in the garden.
🅑🏵🅘🅓♿P🖵(8)🐾🛜

Bembridge

Old Village Inn ✪

61 High Street, PO35 5SF

☎ (01983) 872616 ⊕ yeoldevillageinn.co.uk

4 changing beers (sourced nationally; often Brains, Joseph Holt, Marston's) 🅗
The Old Village is reputed to have been serving pints since 1787, and now offers a fine choice of real ales and wines in a refined and relaxed atmosphere. The menu specialises in local meat and fish dishes. Live music plays on Friday and Saturday, and a popular quiz is held on Monday. There is a patio area to the rear and a pétanque terrain. Q🅑🏵🅘🅓♣P🖵(8)🐾🛜

Carisbrooke

Waverley Inn 🅛

2 Clatterford Road, PO30 1PA

☎ (01983) 522338 ⊕ waverleyinn.co.uk

Goddards Wight Squirrel, Fuggle-Dee-Dum; Island Yachtsmans Ale 🅗**; 1 changing beer (sourced regionally; often Goddards, Island, Otter)** 🅖
This is a large comfortable pub at the crossroads in Carisbrooke village. It has a beautiful lounge with painted Victorian ceiling, a superb public bar offering a range of local real ales, and a comfortable children's

room. Food is served all day, starting with breakfast from 8am, from a good, well-priced menu. The bar opens at 11am. Coffee and home-made cake are available at any time of day. Six en-suite rooms provide overnight accommodation. 🅑🏵🛏🅘🅓♿♣P🖵🐾🛜

Cowes

Anchor Inn 🅛

1 High Street, PO31 7SA (opp Sainsbury's)

☎ (01983) 292823 ⊕ theanchorcowes.co.uk

3 changing beers (often Adnams, Goddards, Yates') 🅗
Originally the Three Trumpeters back in 1704, this inn is close to the marina, tempting visiting yachtsmen for their first pint ashore. A good selection of beer is on offer, with one Island ale and three or more guests always available. The varied menu is served in prodigious quantities. Live entertainment features regularly. Outside is a pleasant beer garden. Accommodation is in seven comfortable rooms.
🅑🏵🛏🅘🅓🖵(1)🐾🛜

Cowes Ale House

5A Shooters Hill, PO31 7BE (up hill from Sainsbury's)

☎ (01983) 294027

4 changing beers (sourced nationally) 🅖
Like its sister pub, Newport Ale House, this venue, conveniently situated in the main street, is small, friendly and sometimes crowded. Four real ales are usually on stillage in a range that rotates regularly - expect to find the occasional mild or porter. Bar snacks are available. Events feature throughout the week including a well-supported Irish night on Monday, the ever-popular quiz on Wednesday and music Friday and Sunday. Q🅑♿🖵(1)🐾🛜

Painters Arms ✪

51 Cross Street, PO31 7TA

☎ (01983) 300977 ⊕ thepaintersarms.co.uk

Sharp's Doom Bar; Timothy Taylor Landlord 🅗
Join in with the friendly banter at the bar, dominated by sport TV, or find a secluded corner in the bar or garden, which now has TV and a wagon with burritos and burgers, including vegetarian options. More tables can be found outside in Francki Place. Redecoration has

maintained the traditional character of this superb building, dating from around 1903. An earlier Painters Arms stood at the head of Temperance Terrace, a renowned Cowes alley, now sadly a car park. ♿❀P🚃(1) ❀ 🐾 🛜

East Cowes

Ship & Castle 🅛

21 Castle Street, PO32 6RB
☎ (01983) 716230
Fuller's London Pride; 2 changing beers (sourced regionally; often Adnams, Goddards, Island) 🅗
Handy for the ferry terminal and near the floating bridge to Cowes, this town-centre drinking establishment is now a free house, offering three well-kept real ales throughout the year. It is not overly large, but you are assured of a warm welcome. Prices are reasonable, especially during happy hour. Frequent and lively music sessions are held. Q♿◗🔥🚶🏧🚃❀🛜

Freshwater

Red Lion 🅛

Church Place, PO40 9BP SZ34508738
☎ (01983) 754925 ⊕ redlion-freshwater.co.uk
St Austell Proper Job; 3 changing beers (sourced nationally; often Butcombe, Timothy Taylor, West Berkshire) 🅗
Former three-bar coaching inn dating back to the 11th century, now converted to one large bar but still retaining much of its character. It is situated in the most picture-postcard area of Freshwater in the church square and by the Causeway, and enjoys splendid views of the River Yar towards Yarmouth. The pub is noted for its fine food (diners are advised to book ahead). Closing time may be earlier in winter. A guide is available for a walk to the Wheatsheaf in Yarmouth. Nearby attractions include Freshwater Golf Club and Tennyson's Monument. Q❀◗P🚃(7,12) ❀ 🛜

Newport

Bargeman's Rest 🅛

Little London Quay, PO30 5BS
☎ (01983) 525828 ⊕ bargemansrest.com
Goddards Fuggle-Dee-Dum; Ringwood Razorback, Fortyniner; 4 changing beers (often Andwell, Marston's, Wychwood) 🅗
This massive, locally owned pub has previously been an animal feed store and a sail and rigging loft for the barge fleet that once used the river. The huge bar room provides intimate drinking areas, and the nautical memorabilia, decor and ambience are what you would expect from a traditional, well-seasoned pub. The outdoor drinking area is only a few feet from the bustling River Medina. Beer and food are consistently good and the range is varied. Live entertainment features most nights. ♿❀◗🔥P🚃❀🛜

Man in the Moon 🅛 ✅

16-17 St James Street, PO30 5HB
☎ (01983) 530126
Greene King Abbot; Sharp's Doom Bar; 7 changing beers (often Goddards, Island) 🅗
Opened in 2014, this impressive Wetherspoon conversion of the former Congregational Church maintains the character of the original while adding sympathetic extensions. The drinking and dining areas include an upstairs gallery and an outdoor area where dogs and children are welcome. Although a food-led pub, the beers are well kept, with a good selection of

local brews among the large rotating selection of ales. You may find the excellent Island Brewery RDA here and often a cider on handpump. ♿❀◗🚃🔥🐾🛜

Newport Ale House 🅛

24A Holyrood Street, PO30 5AZ
☎ (01983) 559376
3 changing beers (sourced nationally) 🅖
Situated in a Grade II-listed building that has previously traded as a hairdresser's, undertaker's and also a posting house and stables. It is the Island's smallest pub, recalling the days when there were many such establishments in Newport. This is a hugely popular venue with all generations, where conversation comes easy – it can get crowded and noisy. Live music is often hosted, including on a Sunday afternoon. The beer choice is always interesting and varied. No meals, but snacks are high quality. Local CAMRA Pub of the Year 2020. Q♿🚃❀🛜

Niton

Joe's Bar 🅛 ✅

High Street, PO38 2AZ
☎ (01983) 730280
Greene King Abbot; 2 changing beers (often Dark Star, Goddards) 🅗
Joe's opened when the village inn closed for a short time and has since become the hub of village life, also serving as a post office, newsagent, confectioner and tea room. Pizzas from the wood-fired oven are ever-popular, with soup and jacket potatoes also offered. Ruby Mild, Plum Porter and local specialities are regular visitors. A unique establishment with an excellent garden and patio. Q♿❀◗🚃(6)

Northwood

Travellers Joy 🅛 ✅

85 Pallance Road, PO31 8LS (ask bus driver for Four Cross) SZ48009360
☎ (01983) 298024 ⊕ travellersjoycowes.co.uk
Brains Rev James; Island Wight Gold; 3 changing beers (sourced nationally; often Theakston) 🅗
This long-standing country inn was the Island's first beer exhibition house and offers up to five ales including local favourite Island Brewery Wight Gold. Real cider is usually available. A good range of home-cooked food is served. With a garden and play area that is recently refurbished, and camping nearby, the pub is a good base for visitors as well as a thriving local community centre. Popular events are Derek's Sunday quiz and bingo night on Monday. Q♿❀◗🚶🏧P🚃(1)❀🛜

Ryde

S Fowler & Co 🅛 ✅

41-43 Union Street, PO33 2LF (top of Union St)
☎ (01983) 812112
10 changing beers (sourced nationally) 🅗
Although not the most charismatic pub in the Wetherspoon chain, this converted drapery store offers a constantly changing range of well-kept beers and is popular. Its name was at the suggestion of the local CAMRA branch – not only is Fowler the name of the former store, but also that of the first local CAMRA

REAL ALE BREWERIES

Goddards Ryde
Island Newport
Yates' Newchurch

chairman and revered early campaigner. The family-friendly food area is upstairs. Situated in the centre of town, there is a bus stop conveniently outside.
Q ✤ ◑ & ≠ ⬛ 🛜

Solent Inn
7 Monkton Street, PO33 1JW
☎ (01983) 613761
Timothy Taylor Landlord; Wychwood Hobgoblin Gold; 1 changing beer (sourced nationally; often St Austell) Ⓗ
Excellent street-corner local with a warm, welcoming atmosphere. Parts of this handsome pub are ancient, going back to medieval times. It originally fronted the sea before reclamation of land, hence the name. Meal times can change depending on the season. There is live music at the weekend. Beware – the public bar slopes alarmingly! Q ✤ ⚘ ◑ ≠ ♣ ⬛ 🐾

Sandown

Castle Inn Ⓛ
12-14 Fitzroy Street, PO36 8HY (off High St)
☎ (01983) 403169 ⊕ sandowncastle.co.uk
Gale's HSB; Goddards Fuggle-Dee-Dum; Wychwood Hobgoblin Gold; 3 changing beers (sourced regionally; often Adnams, Andwell, Island) Ⓗ
The Castle is an excellent town free house and locals' pub, home to crib and darts teams. Six real ales are on offer including the best from local breweries. There is a children's room at the back and a patio for warm weather. The TV is not allowed to intrude and only turned on for special events. Happy hour (5-7pm nightly) is popular, as is the Sunday quiz. Beer festivals are held twice a year, usually featuring local ales and cider.
Q ✤ ⚘ ≠ ♣ ⬛ (3,8) 🐾 🛜

Shanklin

King Harry's Bar Ⓛ
6 Church Road, PO37 6NU
☎ (01983) 863119 ⊕ kingharrysbar.co.uk
Fuller's ESB; 3 changing beers (often Goddards, Shepherd Neame, Young's) Ⓗ
Charming 19th-century thatched property with two established Tudor-themed bars, restaurants, decked gardens and the Chine walk, plus car parking front and rear. Up to three guest beers are offered, chosen for their originality. The long-established Henry VIII kitchen specialises in steaks (food is served in the evening May-September only). Opening hours vary – the pub often stays open until midnight in summer.
Q ✤ ⚘ ➔ ◑ ▲ ♣ P ⬛ (3,2) 🐾

Totland Bay

Highdown Inn Ⓛ
Highdown Lane, PO39 0HY (W of Alum Bay)
SZ32348596
☎ (01983) 752450 ⊕ highdowninn.com
3 changing beers (sourced regionally; often Island, Ringwood, Wychwood) Ⓗ
Situated close to Farringford House, once home to Alfred Lord Tennyson, this hospitable pub is an ideal base for walkers and cyclists alike. A range of home-cooked food includes a seasonal variety of fresh local game, fish and vegetables, and a children's menu. B&B accommodation is in three comfortable rooms, and there is a campsite

close by. A large covered area outside is good for all seasons. Unfortunately, no buses serve the pub in winter.
Q ✤ ➔ ◑ ▲ P ⬛ (7,12) 🛜

Waterfront Ⓛ
The Beach, PO39 0BQ
☎ (01983) 756969 ⊕ thewaterfront-iow.co.uk
Sharp's Doom Bar; 3 changing beers (sourced regionally; often Andwell, Dorset, Island) Ⓗ
Pleasant and popular pub-restaurant beside the sea, enjoying excellent Solent views to Portland and beyond. Beers are reasonably priced and the constantly changing range has increased in recent years, with up to 12 ales in the cellar including stouts and milds. During the summer months a tented area provides more space outside, and the pub is accessible from the cliff path. Food includes a Sunday roast. Closes at 6pm on Sunday in the winter.
Q ✤ ⚘ ◑ P ⬛ 🐾 🛜

Ventnor

Volunteer Ⓛ
30 Victoria Street, PO38 1ES
☎ (01983) 852537
5 changing beers (sourced regionally) Ⓗ
Built in 1866, the Volunteer is one of the smallest pubs on the island and a former local CAMRA Pub of the Year. It has recently been tastefully refurbished. Up to five beers are available including a local brew. No chips, no children, no fruit machines, no video games – just a pure adult drinking house and one of the few places where you can still play rings and enjoy a traditional games night. A wonderful old pub. Q ♣ ⬛ (3,6) 🐾

Whitwell

White Horse Inn Ⓛ
High Street, PO38 2PY SZ52007800
☎ (01983) 730375 ⊕ whitehorseiow.co.uk
4 changing beers (sourced nationally; often Bombardier, Rudgate, Young's) Ⓗ
Built in 1454, this ancient stone building is considered to be the oldest established inn on the Isle of Wight. An extension to the side adds a family area and additional dining space. The remainder of the building is traditional, with intimate areas to the rear. Four handpumps serve a changing range of beers and the excellent menu is extensive; it also does breakfast. A large garden is fine for children on warmer days. Q ✤ ⚘ ◑ & P ⬛ (6) 🐾 🛜

Wootton

Cedars
2 Station Road, PO33 4QU
☎ (01983) 882593 ⊕ cedarsisleofwight.co.uk
Fuller's London Pride; Gale's Seafarers Ale, HSB Ⓗ
In a prominent position, this late-Victorian two-bar village local is a large pub though, curiously, it has one of the smallest front doors on the Island. There is a children's room and a large garden with a children's play area. Smokers are spoilt as the outdoor smoking area is adapted from a beautiful Victorian outbuilding. An extensive food menu is offered, and the friendly bar staff ensure a welcoming atmosphere. The steam railway is nearby. Q ✤ ⚘ ◑ ≠ ♣ P ⬛ (4,9) 🐾 🛜

Is there anywhere in this damned place where we can get a decent bottle of Bass?
Alfred, Lord Tennyson, during a public performance of one of his poems, 1862

Public transport information

Leave the car behind and travel to the pub by bus, train, tram or even ferry...

Using public transport is an excellent way to get to the pub, but many people use it irregularly, and systems can be slightly different from place to place. So, below are some useful websites and phone numbers where you can find all the information you might need.

Combined travel information

The national **Traveline** system gives information on all rail and local bus services throughout England, Scotland and Wales. Calls are put through to a local call centre and if necessary your call will be switched through to a more relevant one. There are also services for mobiles, including a next-bus text service and smart-phone app. The website offers other services including timetables and a journey planner with mapping.

- 0871 200 22 33
  www.traveline.info

LONDON

In London use Traveline or **Transport for London (TfL)** travel services. TfL provides information and route planning for all of London's Underground and Overground, Docklands Light Railway, National Rail, buses, River Buses, Tramlink. Detailed ticketing information helps you find the most cost-effective ways to travel.

- 0343 222 1234
  www.tfl.gov.uk

Train travel

National Rail Enquiries covers the whole of Great Britain's rail network and provides service information, ticketing, online journey planning and other information.

- 03457 48 49 50
  www.nationalrail.co.uk

Coach travel

The two main UK coach companies are **National Express** and **Scottish Citylink**. Between them, they serve everywhere from Cornwall to the Highlands. Their websites offer timetables, journey planning, ticketing, route mapping, and other useful information. CAMRA members can benefit from 20% off travel with National Express*. See **camra.org.uk/benefits** for details.

- National Express: 08717 81 81 81
  www.nationalexpress.com

- Scottish Citylink: 0141 352 4444
  www.citylink.co.uk

Megabus

(A Stagecoach Company) operate various long-distance services between major cities and towns in England and Scotland, also Cardiff in Wales.

- 0900 160 0900 (Premium phone line).

Scottish ferries

Caledonian MacBrayne (CalMac) operate throughout Scotland's islands, stretching from Arran in the south to Lewis in the north.

- 0800 066 5000
  www.calmac.co.uk

Northern Ireland & islands

For travel outside mainland Britain but within the area of this Guide, information is available from the following companies:

NORTHERN IRELAND

- Translink: 028 9066 6630
  www.translink.co.uk

ISLE OF MAN

- Isle of Man Transport: 01624 662 525
  www.iombusandrail.info

ISLE OF WIGHT

- Southern Vectus Bus services covering all the Island: 0330 0539 182

JERSEY

- Liberty Bus: 01534 828 555
  www.libertybus.je

GUERNSEY

- Island Coachways: 01481 720 210
  www.buses.gg

Public transport symbols in the Guide

Pub entries in the Guide include helpful symbols to show if there are stations and/or bus routes close to a pub. There are symbols for railway stations (⇌); tram or light rail stations (🚊); London Underground, Overground or DLR stations (⊖); and bus routes (🚌). See the 'Key to symbols' on the inside front cover for more details.

Membership benefits are subject to change.

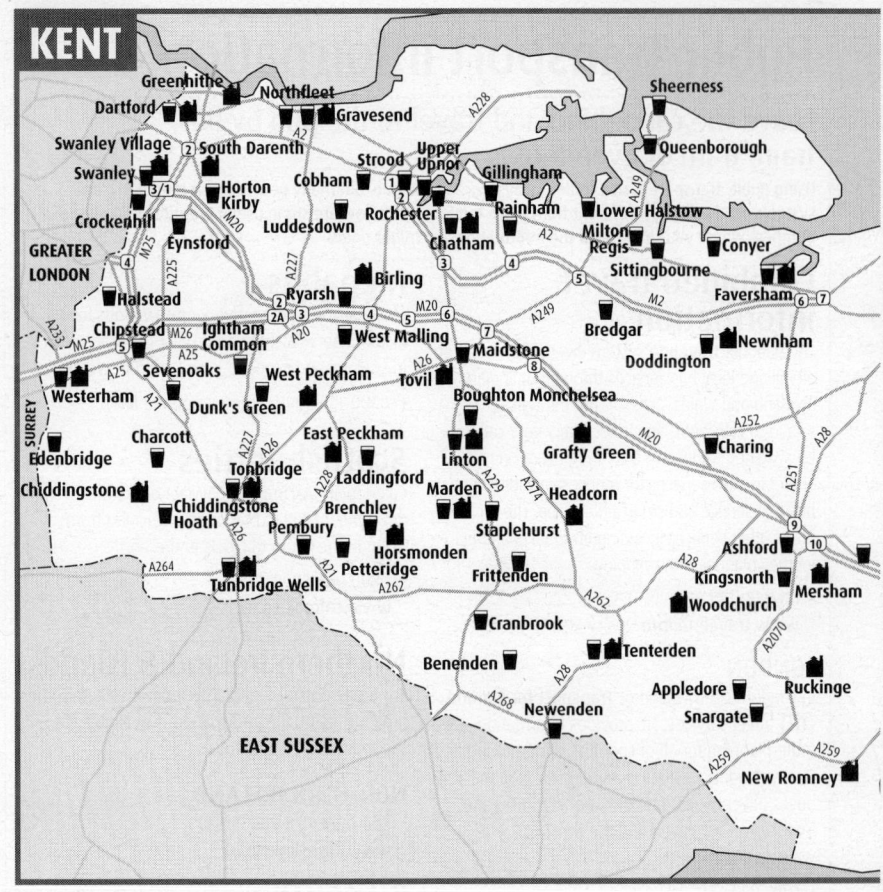

KENT

Appledore

Black Lion ⓛ
15 The Street, TN26 2BU (in centre of village)
☎ (01233) 758206 ⊕ blacklion-pub.com
**Greene King IPA; 4 changing beers (sourced
locally)** Ⓗ
A traditional pub and restaurant set in a historic village
which can trace its history back to Viking times, when it
was a busy port. It is handy for ramblers on the Saxon
Shore Way and the Royal Military Canal. The bar is
decorated with an interesting collection of ancient
pumpclips and blowlamps. An extensive menu is
available every day that includes locally reared lamb and
freshly caught fish as a speciality. Q⏰☕🕗🌙&🚲�(11B)🛜

Ash

Chequer Inn ⓛ
4 Chequer Lane, CT3 2ET
☎ (01304) 273680 ⊕ chequerinnash.co.uk
**Harvey's Sussex Best Bitter; 2 changing beers
(sourced locally; often Canterbury Ales)** Ⓗ
A 14th-century timber-framed community-owned pub.
Sympathetically refurbished, the wooden floors,
panelling and furniture give warmth to the main bar and
restaurant. Up to three real ales, including one from a
nearby brewery, are available alongside local wines and
gins. Home-made food, featuring ingredients from the

area, ranges from vegan dishes to Sunday roasts, with
seafood a speciality. Events, many community-oriented,
include Meet-up Monday and Wednesday Family Night.
There is a large garden with a bat and trap pitch. A free
public car park is close by. ⏰☕🕗🌙♣🚲�(43)🐾🛜

Ashford

County Hotel ⊘
10 High Street, TN24 8TD (at lower end of High St)
☎ (01233) 646891
**Greene King Abbot; Ruddles Best Bitter; Sharp's
Doom Bar; 4 changing beers (sourced nationally)** Ⓗ
This building dates from around 1710 and was originally
a doctor's home and medical practice. It became a hotel
in the 19th century and was acquired by Wetherspoon in
1988. It has a spacious bar with three separate seating
areas, and a courtyard outside. Food is available every
day all day. Children are allowed in the dining area until
9pm. Two real ciders are dispensed from polypins in the
fridge. Summer and autumn national and international
beer festivals are staged. Q⏰☕🕗🌙&🚆♦🚲�🛜

Beltinge

Copper Pottle ⓛ
84 Reculver Road, CT6 6ND
☎ 07710 001261

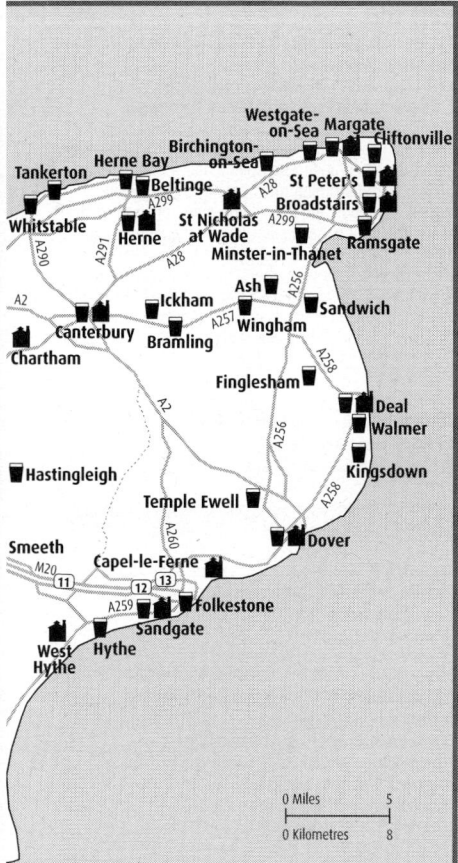

Westgate-on-Sea
Margate
Cliftonville
Birchington-on-Sea
Tankerton
Herne Bay
Beltinge
St Peter's
Broadstairs
Whitstable
St Nicholas at Wade
Herne
Ramsgate
Minster-in-Thanet
Ash
Ickham
Sandwich
Canterbury
Wingham
Chartham
Bramling
Finglesham
Deal
Walmer
Hastingleigh
Kingsdown
Temple Ewell
Smeeth
Dover
Capel-le-Ferne
Folkestone
Sandgate
West Hythe
Hythe

0 Miles 5
0 Kilometres 8

Birchington-on-Sea

Old Bay Alehouse
137 Minnis Road, CT7 9NS
3 changing beers G

A fine micropub an easy five-minute stroll from the beach at Minnis Bay, near Birchington. The bar counter on the right serves real ales and ciders on gravity dispense from a temperature-controlled cool room behind. Seating is at wall-mounted benches with high tables, plus some low tables and chairs. There are a few comfy armchairs in the front window. The real ale selection always includes at least one local beer. Bar snacks are available and there are occasional pop-up food events. Q♿≋♣☀🚌(34)🌼

Boughton Monchelsea

Cock Inn L
Heath Road, ME17 4JD TQ776512
☎ (01622) 743166 🌐 cockinnmaidstone.co.uk
Shepherd Neame Master Brew, Spitfire Gold; 2 changing beers (sourced regionally; often Shepherd Neame) H

A 16th-century coaching inn built to provide lodgings for Canterbury pilgrims, full of character, with oak beams and an inglenook fireplace, and with a large patio. A broad and varied menu complemented by real ales is served in both the bar and restaurant; Sunday roasts are a popular speciality (no food Sun eve). You can play various board games here. It is near the Greensand Way, and dogs and walkers are welcome.
Q♿🕮🅿🚌(59)🌼🛜

Bramling

Haywain L
Canterbury Road, CT3 1NB
☎ (01227) 720676 🌐 thehaywainbramling.co.uk
Fuller's London Pride; 3 changing beers (sourced regionally; often Goacher's, Ramsgate, Whitstable) H

Classic friendly country pub featuring hop bines, a cosy snug and a charity library where books are sold for 50p each. Traditional games include darts and bat and trap. There is a Monday quiz night and a Wednesday crib night. Guest beers are usually from Kent breweries, and an annual beer festival is hosted over the late spring bank holiday weekend in a marquee in the attractive garden. Excellent home-cooked food is served, using local produce. 🕮🅿♣🚌🌼🛜

Ramsgate Gadds' No.5 Best Bitter Ale; 3 changing beers (sourced regionally) G

Originally a pet food shop, this friendly micropub has an attractive blue-tiled frontage. Drinks are dispensed via a small bar counter. Conversation is encouraged with a layout of high and low narrow tables, and the walls are decorated with amusing posters and postcards. Every six weeks there is a charity fundraising event, which might be a quiz evening, food evening or a barbecue. The south-facing garden is a good place to enjoy a beer, cider or wine. Open on bank holiday Mondays. Q♿🕮♣☀🚌🌼

Benenden

Bull L
The Street, TN17 4DE
☎ (01580) 240054 🌐 thebullatbenenden.co.uk
Dark Star Hophead; Harvey's Sussex Best Bitter; Larkins Traditional Ale; 1 changing beer (sourced locally; often Long Man) H

A genuine free house, dating back to 1608, overlooking the picturesque village green. The public bar features a large inglenook fireplace and the interior has wooden floors and exposed oak beams throughout. A separate restaurant/function room offers good food featuring locally grown produce, although meals are also served in the public bar. Booking is advisable for Friday fish & chips and the Sunday lunchtime carvery. A monthly acoustic music session is held on a Sunday afternoon (details on website). Q♿🕮🅘♣🅿🚌(297)🌼🛜

Bredgar

Sun Inn
The Street, ME9 8EY
☎ (01622) 884221 🌐 thesuninn.co.uk
Sharp's Sea Fury; Shepherd Neame Master Brew; 1 changing beer (often Adnams, Musket) H

A village inn since the early 1700s, it has a sizeable front bar area with a long bar separating it from the large Old Barn restaurant to the rear. The front bar has a real fire. The clientele is a mixture of locals plus passing trade. Tastefully in keeping with its surroundings, the pub is food-led but does offer a fair choice of cask beers. There is a quiz on the first Wednesday of the month and monthly music nights are planned. ♿🕮🅘🅿🌼

Brenchley

Halfway House L ✔

Horsmonden Road, TN12 7AX (½ mile SE of village)
☎ (01892) 722526 ⊕ halfwayhousebrenchley.co.uk
Goacher's Fine Light Ale; Kent Pale; Long Man Best Bitter; Tonbridge Brenchley Bitter, Rustic; 3 changing beers (sourced locally; often Canterbury Ales, Cellar Head, Rother Valley) Ⓖ
In an attractive rural setting, this award-winning free house and Guide entry of 15 years' standing offers up to 10 beers direct from cooled casks, along with Chiddingstone and Turners ciders. Substantial home-made dishes using local produce are served, including traditional Sunday roasts. Choose between the cosy, rustic interior complete with hanging hops, farming instruments and an open fire, or the spacious garden incorporating an outside bar and a separate family area. Beer festivals are held on Whitsun and August bank holidays. Q ➠ ⊛ ◑ ♣ ⬤ P ⬚ (297) ❀ ☎

Broadstairs

White Swan

17 Reading Street, CT10 3AZ
☎ (01843) 863051 ⊕ whiteswanbroadstairs.co.uk
4 changing beers Ⓗ
This superb hostelry is situated on the far outskirts of Broadstairs. The present pub dates from 1913, although the building dates back to 1704. The ales, which change on a continual basis, come from all around the country. To the rear is a garden where children are welcome. It has a separate saloon and public bar – and in keeping with times past when pubs charged different prices between the public bar and 'better' rooms, there is 4p difference between the bars. The pub is believed to be the only one in the UK that keeps this tradition.
⊛ ◑ ♣ ⬚ ❀

Canterbury

Eight Bells ✔

34 London Road, CT2 8LN
☎ (01227) 454794
Young's London Original, London Special Ⓗ
A small, traditional local dating from 1708 and rebuilt in 1902, retaining original embossed windows and outside toilets, and decorated with memorabilia. There is live music monthly on a Friday, and a quiz, usually on the first Wednesday of the month. Five darts teams play every week and their trophies are on display. The only food is a Sunday lunchtime roast (booking advisable). There is an attractive small walled garden and a comfortable heated smoking area. ➠ ⊛ ◑ ≠ (West) ♣ ⬚ ❀ ☎

Foundry Brew Pub L

77 Stour Street, CT1 2NR (just off High St)
☎ (01227) 455899 ⊕ thefoundrycanterbury.co.uk
Canterbury Brewers & Distillers Foundryman's Gold, Foundry Torpedo, Streetlight Porter; 3 changing beers (often Canterbury Brewers & Distillers) Ⓗ
The home of Canterbury Brewers & Distillers. Double doors from the bar open into the attractive brewery and restaurant area, which is available for functions and brewery tours. Six ales are usually on tap, all brewed on the premises. Cider, vodka, rum and gin are also made here. Food is served every day. Winner of Kent Tourism Pub of the Year 2019. ➠ ⊛ ◑ ♿ ≠ (East) ⬤ ⬚ ☎

New Inn

19 Havelock Street, CT1 1NP (off ring road nr St Augustine's Abbey)
☎ (01227) 464584 ⊕ newinncanterbury.co.uk
7 changing beers (often Oakham, Ramsgate, Thornbridge) Ⓗ
A Victorian back-street terraced pub a few minutes' walk from the cathedral, St Augustine's Abbey and the bus station. The welcoming main bar has a cosy wood-burner, and a changing range of seven cask beers. The floor is hand-stencilled by the landlady, and there are other creative features. At the back is a long, bright conservatory with newspapers and a range of board games. Beer festivals are held on the Whitsun and August bank holiday weekends indoors and in the attractive garden. Q ➠ ⊛ ♣ ⬤ ⬚ ❀ ☎

Thomas Tallis Alehouse L

48 Northgate, CT1 1BE
⊕ thethomastallisalehouse.co.uk

REAL ALE BREWERIES

Alpha State Horsmonden
Amazing ⬚ Sandgate
Angels & Demons Capel-le-Ferne
Boutilliers Faversham
Breakwater Dover
Brew Buddies ✦ Swanley Village
Brumaison Marden
By The Mile Broadstairs (brewing suspended)
Canterbury Ales Chartham
Canterbury Brewers ⬚ ✦ Canterbury
Constellation ✦ Tonbridge (NEW)
Dartford Wobbler South Darenth
Farriers Arms ⬚ Mersham
Fonthill ⬚ Tunbridge Wells
Four Candles ⬚ St Peter's
Goacher's Tovil
Goody Herne
Headcorn Hop Headcorn
Hildenborough Tonbridge (NEW)
Hinks Ruckinge
Hop Fuzz West Hythe
Hopdaemon Newnham
Iron Pier ✦ Gravesend
Isla Vale Margate
Kent Birling
Koomor Dartford (NEW)
Larkins Chiddingstone
Mad Cat Faversham
Musket ✦ Linton
NauticAles Broadstairs
Nelson ✦ Chatham
No Frills Joe ✦ Greenhithe
Northdown ✦ Margate
Old Dairy ✦ Tenterden
Pig & Porter Tunbridge Wells
Ramsgate Broadstairs
Romney Marsh New Romney
Running Man Chatham
Shepherd Neame Faversham
Stag (Kent) Woodchurch
Swan ⬚ West Peckham
Time & Tide Deal
Tír Dhá Ghlas ⬚ Dover
Tonbridge East Peckham
Wantsum ✦ St Nicholas at Wade
Westerham ✦ Westerham
Whitstable Grafty Green
XYLO ⬚ Margate

3 changing beers (sourced locally; often Kent, Old Dairy, Ramsgate) G

Canterbury's first micropub ale house, located in a lovely 15th-century half-timbered building, part of the historic Hospital of St John. Three different Kent cask beers and many national and international beers are stocked – in KeyKeg, bottles and cans – as well as five to six Kentish ciders. One of the two front rooms has a log-burning stove, while the rear snug has armchairs and a sofa. Generally a seat/table service applies. Outside seating is available on the street. Q ॐ ❀ ⇌ (West) ♣ ● 🚲 ❀ 🛜

Unicorn 🅛 ✅

61 St Dunstan's Street, CT2 8BS

☎ (01227) 463187 ⊕ unicorninn.com

4 changing beers (often Hopdaemon, Long Man, Shepherd Neame) H

Comfortable pub, near the historic Westgate, that dates from 1604 and has an attractive suntrap garden. Bar billiards is played and a quiz, set by regular customers, is held every Sunday evening. One guest beer is often from one of several Kent microbreweries, and beer updates are posted on Facebook and Twitter. There is a good range of bottled beers. Food is good value, with a meal deal on selected dishes. Sporting events (not Sky) are televised unobtrusively. Q ॐ ❀ ◑ ⇌ (West) ♣ ● 🚲 ❀ 🛜

Charcott

Greyhound 🅛

off Camp Hill, TN11 8LG (½ mile N of B2027 at Chiddingstone Causeway)

☎ (01892) 870275 ⊕ thegreyhoundcharcott.co.uk

Larkins Traditional Ale; 3 changing beers (sourced locally; often Gun, Old Dairy, Titsey) H

Reopened with new owners in 2017, this small hamlet pub has become a firm favourite with locals and those from surrounding villages, making it the very heart of the community. The beers and ciders are from within a 30-mile radius and much attention is given to supporting nearby producers when creating the menus. Although seemingly remote, the Greyhound is easily accessible from Penshurst railway station via a surfaced footpath across fields. Check the website for news of live music evenings and special events.
Q ॐ ❀ ◑ ⇌ ♣ ● 🚲 (210) ❀ 🛜

Charing

Bowl Inn

Egg Hill Road, TN27 0HG (signposted from A20 and A251)

☎ (01233) 712256 ⊕ bowlinncharing.com

4 changing beers (sourced locally; often Old Dairy, Ramsgate, Tonbridge) H

A 16th-century free house on the top of the North Downs in an Area of Outstanding Natural Beauty. An inglenook fire warms the bar and there is a spacious garden with a heated patio. With a large well-reputed restaurant, the pub is a popular stop-off point for walkers and cyclists and offers five rooms for overnight stays. Camping is also available. Opening hours are longer in summertime.
Q ॐ ❀ 🛏 ◑ 🅟 ♿ 🅟 ❀

Chatham

Thomas Waghorn 🅛 ✅

14 Railway Street, ME4 4JL

☎ (01634) 405422

Greene King IPA, Abbot; Sharp's Doom Bar; 3 changing beers (sourced nationally; often Wantsum) H

Ideally sited in the heart of Chatham, with both the railway and bus stations within easy walking distance. A former post office, this Wetherspoon is named after a 19th-century Chatham-born naval officer. It is on two levels, both having outside drinking areas, and has various seating arrangements including some booths. A quiz is held every Wednesday. A number of interesting and unusual guest ales figure alongside the usual fare offered by Wetherspoons. ॐ ❀ ◑ ♿ ⇌ ● 🚲 🛜

Chiddingstone Hoath

Rock 🅛

Hoath Corner, Rywell Road, TN8 7BS (1½ miles S of Chiddingstone)

☎ (01892) 870296 ⊕ therockpub.co.uk

Larkins Traditional Ale; 2 changing beers (sourced locally; often Dark Star, Long Man) H

Featuring brick flooring, an inviting inglenook fireplace, extensive wooden beams and the ancient game of ring the bull, the Rock oozes character. Despite its rural location, it attracts visitors in cars, on foot and even on horseback. Cosy and informal, the desire is to remain a proper pub with proper grub, catering for a community dedicated to rural pursuits. The staple Larkins Traditional is brewed just a couple of miles down the road. Here's to another half millennium of history! Q ॐ ❀ ◑ ♣ 🅟 🚲 ❀ 🛜

Chipstead

Bricklayers Arms ✅

39-41 Chevening Road, TN13 2RZ (opp entrance to sailing club)

☎ (01732) 743424 ⊕ the-bricklayers-arms.co.uk

Harvey's Sussex Best Bitter, IPA G; 1 changing beer (sourced locally; often Harvey's) H

Located opposite Chipstead sailing lake, this vibrant Harvey's brewery-owned community pub features Winston Churchill, who once lived nearby, on its sign, laying bricks. Sussex Best is served direct from casks behind the bar, while the brewery's monthly seasonal brews are dispensed by handpump. An excellent choice of home-cooked meals, supplemented by many themed food nights, can be enjoyed either in the side cottage restaurant, in the flagstone-floored bar complete with log fire, or in the adjacent dining space. Walkers and their dogs are welcome. Q ॐ ❀ ◑ ♿ ♣ 🅟 🚲 (401) ❀ 🛜

Cliftonville

Banks Ale & Wine House

244 Northdown Road, CT9 2PX

☎ (01843) 221251

3 changing beers H

Ale and wine house in a former bank in the Cliftonville district of Margate. It is tastefully decorated with low tables and chairs, with a collection of old keg beer fonts displayed on shelves and the window ledges. The front bar counter has four handpumps which are purely decorative. Real ales are served either via two handpumps or by gravity dispense through wall taps connected to casks in the cellar room behind the wall.
Q ॐ ● 🚲

Laughing Barrel

35A Summerfield Road, CT9 3EZ

☎ 07970 867189

5 changing beers (often Breakwater, Goody Ales, Ramsgate) G

This micropub opened in 2018 serving ales, cider and wines in part of the former 60s estate pub, the Northdown – the rest of the premises now houses a pharmacy. The real ales and a large range of ciders and perries are dispensed by gravity from a room behind the L-shaped bar counter, the real ale being stored in jacket-cooled casks. The focus for the ales and ciders is on local Kentish producers. ➹❀❦⌂ (8A,38)❀

Cobham

Darnley Arms

40 The Street, DA12 3BZ

☎ (01474) 814218 ⊕ thedarnleyarms.com

Dark Star Hophead; Greene King IPA; 2 changing beers (sourced locally; often Iron Pier, Pig & Porter) H

Situated in the centre of a charming little village, this is a friendly venue. It has a large horseshoe-shaped bar with a separate small side room for meetings. The décor features local memorabilia including the coat of arms of the Darnley family, who lived at Cobham Hall not far away. It stocks two regular real ales and two changing beers, mainly from nearby breweries in Kent. The wide menu features traditional English food, with fish specialities. Q➹❀❦⌬⍾❦⌂⍾P⌂(416)❀ ≋

Conyer

Ship

Conyer Quay, ME9 9HR

☎ (01795) 520881 ⊕ shipinnconyer.co.uk

3 changing beers (sourced regionally; often Adnams, Old Dairy) H

An 18th-century creekside pub with a nautical-themed interior. Bare floorboards and scrubbed pine tables add rustic charm, and a real fire adds character. Popular with the boating fraternity, walkers and cyclists, it is located on the Saxon Shore Way, and is a 20-minute walk from Teynham train station. Food, with an emphasis on local produce, is served from noon daily. It has a small courtyard garden overlooking the creek. ➹❀⍾❦P⌂❀ ≋

Cranbrook

Larkins' Alehouse L

7 High Street, TN17 3EB

☎ 07786 707476 ⊕ larkins-alehouse.co.uk

4 changing beers (sourced locally; often Cellar Head, Goacher's, Larkins) G

Opened in 2017, this community-focused micropub has put the heart back into the town. It comprises a single room simply furnished with a small bar, plus a courtyard beer garden. Welcoming staff will guide you to the chalkboard displaying current beers and Kentish ciders (Biddenden, Turners) as well as wines, spirits and soft drinks. Home-made pork pies, rolls and chutneys are for sale, although you're welcome to bring your own food and order a takeaway. Sunday lunchtime food is provided by the pub and customers. Q➹❀❦⍾P⌂(5,297)❀ ≋

Crockenhill

Chequers ✔

Cray Road, BR8 8LP

☎ (01322) 662132 ⊕ chequerscrockenhill.co.uk

Courage Best Bitter; 3 changing beers (sourced regionally; often Fuller's, Woodforde's, Wychwood) H

Friendly village local offering one permanent beer and three changing guest ales from a wide selection of breweries. Lunches and evening meals are served, with discounts for over-55s at the beginning of the week. There is a quiz on Monday evenings and various other events on regular occasions, including live music and theme nights. Several pictures of old Crockenhill indicate that the pub has been a hub of village life for many years. ➹❀⍾❦P⌂(477)❀ ≋

Dartford

Dartford Working Men's Club L

Essex Road, DA1 2AU

☎ (01322) 223646 ⊕ dartfordwm.club

Courage Best Bitter H; 14 changing beers (sourced regionally; often Dark Star, Leatherbritches, Oakham) H/G

CAMRA National Club of the Year in 2006 and finalist in 2017, this modern CIU club serves 15 ales on handpump plus ciders on gravity. The club hosts the BBC award-winning Dartford Folk Club every Tuesday night, and has free live music every Thursday and Saturday night as well as on the last Sunday afternoon of the month. Tribute acts perform every other Friday night and a quiz takes place on the first Wednesday of the month. CAMRA members are welcome as guests. ❀⍾≋❦P⌂ ≋

Foresters ✔

15-16 Great Queen Street, DA1 1TJ

☎ (01322) 223087

Adnams Ghost Ship; Harvey's Sussex Best Bitter; 1 changing beer (sourced nationally) H

Pleasant Victorian side-street local, just off East Hill, five minutes' walk from the town centre. It is quiet at lunchtimes but busy in the evenings, with live sports on TV and darts, pool and crib teams. The U-shaped bar has a log-burning fire at one end. The graveyard opposite contains the unmarked pauper's grave of famed steam pioneer Richard Trevithick, its approximate location being indicated by a plaque on the north wall. ➹❀≋❦P⌂❀ ≋

Malt Shovel

3 Darenth Road, DA1 1LP

☎ (01322) 224381 ⊕ maltshovelda1.co.uk

St Austell Tribute; Young's London Original, London Special; 2 changing beers (sourced nationally) H

Traditional country-style inn, dating from 1673, five minutes' walk from the town centre. It has two separate bars, a small taproom with a low ceiling featuring an 1880s Dartford Brewery mirror, and a larger saloon bar leading to a conservatory, where meals are served lunchtimes Tuesday to Thursday, all day Friday and Saturday, plus Sunday lunchtime roasts. The large beer garden is accessed from the conservatory. A popular open quiz is hosted on Monday evening and cribbage on Tuesday. Q❀⍾≋❦⍾P⌂

Deal

Farrier L ✔

90 Manor Road, CT14 9DB

☎ (01304) 360080

Fuller's London Pride; St Austell Proper Job; 2 changing beers (often Old Dairy, Ramsgate) H

This Grade II-listed traditional black and white-beamed pub is reputedly the oldest in Deal. It has a friendly atmosphere with a real community feel to it, and is a relaxing place to chat and enjoy the four ales on offer. Inside are three open fires and plenty of seating. At the back there is a large covered and heated patio. Events include darts matches, monthly quiz nights and a Sunday meat raffle. You can bring your own food. 🛏️👪♿🚲🚌🐕🍴🛜

Just Reproach L
14 King Street, CT14 6HX
4 changing beers (sourced nationally) G
A town-centre micropub with a welcoming ambience. Its high benches and table service make for a friendly, convivial atmosphere. Up to five real ales are served, with at least one from a Kent brewery, and at least one Kentish cider. A wide selection of craft beers is available, alongside wines, gins and soft drinks. Snacks include pork pies, Scotch eggs and local cheese. The pub has no keg beer, fruit machines or music, and do not let your mobile phone ring! Local CAMRA Pub of the Year 2021. Q🛏️🚲🐕🍴🛜

Ship Inn L
141 Middle Street, CT14 6JZ
☎ (01304) 372222
Dark Star Hophead; Ramsgate Gadds' No.7 Bitter Ale; Gadds' No.5 Best Bitter Ale; Timothy Taylor Landlord; 1 changing beer (often Ramsgate) H
Only 10 minutes' walk from the town centre, this unspoilt, traditional inn is in Deal's historic conservation area. Dark wooden floors and subdued lighting create a warm and comfortable atmosphere, complemented by the nautical theme. A wide mix of drinkers enjoy the good range of beers dispensed from five handpumps, including beers from Ramsgate and Dark Star. The small cosy rear bar overlooks a large patio garden, accessed by a staircase, with a covered smoking area. 🛏️👪🚲🐕🍴

Doddington

Chequers
The Street, ME9 0BG (6 miles W of Faversham)
☎ (01795) 886366 ⊕ chequersinndoddington.co.uk
Shepherd Neame Master Brew; 1 changing beer (sourced regionally; often Shepherd Neame) H
A Grade II listed coaching inn with oak timbers, mullioned windows and an inglenook fireplace. It is reported to have two resident ghosts —a Cavalier from the English Civil War and a ghoul with a passion for the piano. This centre of village life provides a full post office service every Tuesday 1-3pm. It also hosts regular live music and other events. Up to three ales are available during the summer. 🛏️👪🚲🅿🚌(345)🐕🛜

Dover

Breakwater Brewery Taproom L
St Martin's Yard, Lorne Road, CT16 2AA
☎ 07866 198075
Breakwater Dover Pale Ale; 6 changing beers (sourced locally; often Breakwater) G
Opened in 2016, the brewery tap is on the site of the Harding's Wellington Brewery, which closed in 1890. The bar is modern, well lit and furnished with chunky, wooden furniture, and the bar counter resembles a stone breakwater. Cask ales from the brewery are served on gravity along with the pub's own house ciders. Stone-baked pizzas are available from the in-house pizzeria (Thu-Sat). Regular live music events are held and tours of the brewery are possible by prior arrangement. 🛏️👪♿🚲🐕🍴

Eight Bells L ✓
19 Cannon Street, CT16 1BZ
☎ (01304) 205030
Greene King Abbot; Ruddles Best Bitter; Sharp's Doom Bar; 9 changing beers (often Wantsum, Whitstable) H
This popular and bustling Wetherspoon is situated on the precinct, its name linked to the church opposite. Inside, it has a large open-plan room with a long bar and a raised restaurant section. At the front an enclosed seating area looks out onto the precinct. Twelve handpumps dispense a range of regular and guest beers, including at least two from a Kent microbrewery. There are real ale offers on Mondays and two beer festivals each year. Q🛏️👪🍴♿🚲🐕🍴🛜

Elephant & Hind L
18-19 Market Square, CT16 1NX
☎ (01304) 215654 ⊕ elephantandhind.co.uk
1 changing beer (sourced locally; often Breakwater, Canterbury Ales, Ramsgate) G
The pub is situated in the heart of Dover, overlooking the Market Square. The main bar has been furnished in contemporary pastel shades around three sides of a central servery. At the front, there's plenty of pavement seating. One regular ale is served from a Kent brewery, typically Ramsgate or Breakwater. Real cider is available in the summer. A varied menu is available, with sourdough pizza and burgers a speciality. Events include live music, poker and quiz nights. Free one hour parking is available nearby. 🛏️👪🍴♿🚲🐕🍴🛜

Hoptimist Taproom & Bar L
3 Bench Street, CT16 1JH
☎ 07515 367802 ⊕ thehoptimisttaproomandbar.co.uk
6 changing beers (sourced locally; often Kent, Northdown Brewery, Time & Tide)
This modern taproom, near Dover's Market Square, provides a comfortable environment in which to enjoy a pint of cask ale or real cider. Ales are from Kent breweries with occasional guests from further afield. There's also modern craft beer, premium keg beers and an ever-changing gin menu. The aim is to have a range of beer styles on at all times. Food is simple, consisting of ploughman's and a cheeseboard. There's a selection of board games and regular music events are held. Free car parking can be found nearby. 🛏️👪🍴🚲🐕🅿🚌(62,68)🐕

Louis Armstrong L
58 Maison Dieu Road, CT16 1RA
☎ (01304) 204759
4 changing beers (sourced locally) H
Down-to-earth pub and music venue that has featured live music for over 50 years. The large L-shaped bar and stage is surrounded by music posters, a large mirror and long bench seating. Up to four real ales are sold, principally from Kent microbreweries, with an occasional real cider from a Kent cider maker. On Wednesday evenings good-value food is served. It has a pleasant beer garden, is easily accessible by bus, and has car parking nearby. 🛏️👪🚲🐕🍴🛜

White Horse
St James Street, CT16 1QF
☎ (01304) 213066 ⊕ thewhitehorsedover.co.uk
Harvey's Sussex Best Bitter; Timothy Taylor Landlord; 1 changing beer (sourced nationally; often St Austell) H
The inn's history can be traced back to 1574, making this probably the oldest pub in Dover. The furniture is simple but comfortable. In 2002 the venue was adopted by Channel swimmers, and the walls are covered with their signatures. Up to three real ales are served from national

breweries, and real cider is available in summer. It is only a short walk from the bus station and there is public car parking nearby. ♿🌞🍴◗🍺🚃🐾🌸

Dunk's Green

Kentish Rifleman 🅛

Roughway Lane, TN11 9RU (jct with Dunks Green Rd, 4 miles N of Tonbridge, off A227)
☎ (01732) 810727 ⊕ thekentishrifleman.co.uk
Harvey's Sussex Best Bitter; 2 changing beers (sourced locally; often Old Dairy, Tonbridge) Ⓗ

A charming old-English pub complete with low oak-beamed ceilings and open fireplaces. The Rifleman serves up quality beer and food (no food Sun and Mon eves), in an informal atmosphere that is welcoming to villagers and visitors alike. Local suppliers feature throughout a menu that emphasises seasonal produce, while the beer offer will please those eager to sample well-maintained Kent and Sussex ales. Full of bonhomie since the 16th century, this place is well worth seeking out. Q♿🌞🍴◗P🚃(222)🐾🌸

Edenbridge

Secret Cask

91 High Street, TN8 5AU (at S end of High St nr bridge)
☎ 07595 262247
5 changing beers (sourced locally; often Gun, Iron Pier, Kent) Ⓖ

Housed in a former florist's shop, this micropub was opened in 2018 and consists of two simply furnished cosy rooms with a small bar. A changing selection of five real ales, mainly from Kent and Sussex, is served direct from the cask and displayed on the wall alongside the ciders from Biddenden. Four craft beers on keg are also available, as well as wines and local gins. The walls are decorated with beer pumpclips, which are a testament to the variety served. Q�🍺🚃🐾🌸

Eynsford

Five Bells

High Street, DA4 0AB
☎ (01322) 863135
Harvey's Sussex Best Bitter; 1 changing beer (sourced nationally; often Adnams, Fuller's, St Austell) Ⓗ

Traditional community hostelry in the heart of an attractive village. The public bar retains a homely atmosphere, with wooden tables and a wood-burning fire in winter. It also has a comfortable separate saloon bar with a dartboard. There is a pleasant garden to the rear and a small car park. Dogs are welcome in the public bar. Food is not served here but try its larger sister pub, the Malt Shovel, nearby. Q🌞♣P🚃(421)🐾🌸

Faversham

Bear Inn

3 Market Place, ME13 7AG
☎ (01795) 532668 ⊕ bearinnfaversham.co.uk
Shepherd Neame Master Brew; 1 changing beer (sourced locally; often Shepherd Neame) Ⓗ

A 16th-century inn in the historic market square, with a couple of tables at the front for summer drinking. It has a regionally important historic pub interior with wood panelling, and three separate bar areas off a corridor running the length of the building. A general knowledge quiz is held on the last Monday of the month. The Bear is

a good place to try Shepherd Neame beers, and it often serves a seasonal or guest beer. Popular both with locals and visitors to Faversham. Q◗�♣🚃🛜

Elephant 🅛

31 The Mall, ME13 8JN
☎ (01795) 590157
5 changing beers (sourced regionally; often Hopdaemon, Mighty Oak, Rother Valley) Ⓗ

A two-roomed, traditional free house with a function room at the back, and much nautical memorabilia on the walls. The landlord takes pride in serving good real ale, occasionally including a beer matured in the cellar, and has won numerous CAMRA awards over many years. The pub is host to local clubs and has regular live music. A well-tended walled garden at the back and a log fire within make it a great place to visit at any time of year. ♿🌞🚋♣🍺🚃🐾🌸

Furlongs Ale House

6A Preston Street, ME13 8NS
☎ 07747 776200
5 changing beers (sourced locally; often Canterbury Ales, Kent, Ramsgate) Ⓗ

Faversham's first micropub opened in 2014 and has expanded to include an outside seating area at the rear. There are wooden benches and solid tables within. Beers are drawn by handpump from the cellar to the small bar, many from Kent microbreweries, although others from across the UK feature. The emphasis is on the hop. Kent gin, wines and ciders are also served. Q♿🌞🚋🍺🚃🐾🌸

Shipwrights Arms 🅛

Hollowshore, ME13 7TU (over 1 mile N of Faversham at confluence of Faversham and Oare creeks) TR017636
☎ (01795) 590088 ⊕ theshipwrightsathollowshore.co.uk
Kent Prohibition; house beer (by Goacher's); 3 changing beers (sourced locally; often Goacher's, Harvey's) Ⓖ

A 300-year-old family-run free house with welcoming old-style hosts, both young and old. It is well worth the 45-minute walk across countryside from Faversham, or the slightly longer sea wall path. The wooden-clad building's cosy interior reflects a nautical heritage, with associated ornaments and pictures on display, and a choice of comfortable seating around the fireplaces. The large garden at the rear is open spring to autumn, and there is outside seating at the front for all seasons. Opening hours are extended in summer, but in severe winter weather telephone to check opening times. Q♿🌞◗♣P🌸

Finglesham

Crown Inn 🅛

The Street, CT14 0NA
☎ (01304) 612555 ⊕ thecrowninnfinglesham.co.uk
Dark Star Hophead; 2 changing beers (often Old Dairy, Ringwood, Romney Marsh) Ⓗ

Traditional village pub with a warm welcome and a friendly atmosphere. Three to four real ales are sold, one usually from a local microbrewery. Quality home-made food is served lunchtimes and evenings, including a roast on Sunday. You can eat in the bar or the restaurant, which opens onto the pleasant garden, with a children's play area. Occasional live music events take place and bat and trap is played in summer. B&B accommodation is available in the modern lodges behind it. Hours may be extended in summer. ♿🌞🚋◗♣P🚃(81)🐾🛜

Folkestone

Bouverie Tap [L]

45 Bouverie Road West, CT20 2SZ

☎ (01303) 255977 🌐 thebouverietap.co.uk

3 changing beers (sourced locally) [H]

This alehouse was extended into the adjacent shop and courtyard in 2020, and is decorated with interesting old posters. It offers three changing local ales and cider. Food is prepared from locally sourced ingredients, with wholesome roasts served on Sundays. Breakfasts are available on Saturday and Sunday. Well-behaved children welcome up to 7pm. 🎠❀◑♿🚆🍏🚌🐾📶

Chambers [L]

Radnor Chambers, Cheriton Place, CT20 2BB (off Hythe end of Sandgate Rd)

☎ (01303) 223333 🌐 thechamberspub.co.uk

Adnams Lighthouse; 3 changing beers (sourced regionally) [H]

A spacious cellar bar with six handpumps beneath a licensed coffee shop; beers include some from local breweries and at least two real ciders. A beer festival is held over the Easter weekend. Food, including Mexican, European and daily specials, is served except on Mondays and Friday evenings. There is a disco on Fridays and a quiz on the first Sunday of the month (see Facebook for details), and live music on Thursdays, usually with free admission. 🎠◑🚆🍏🚌📶

East Cliff Tavern

13-15 East Cliff, CT19 6BU

☎ (01303) 251132

2 changing beers (sourced regionally) [H]

A friendly, terraced back-street venue since 1862, run by the same family for over 50 years, which can be approached via the footpath across the disused railway line, a short walk from the harbour. It usually stocks two beers, often from local breweries, with Biddenden or Kingswood cider on gravity behind the bar. Old photographs of Folkestone decorate the walls and community events include weekly raffles. Opening hours may vary. Q❀♣🍏🚌(91)🐾

Firkin Alehouse

20 Cheriton Place, CT20 2AZ

☎ 07894 068432 🌐 firkinalehouse.co.uk

4 changing beers (sourced regionally) [G]

This welcoming micropub offers up to four cask beers, usually one from a Kent microbrewery, and up to six ciders served by gravity from a temperature-controlled room. The display fridge offers a selection of bottled and canned foreign and British beers, and there is a limited wine selection. Bar snacks include pickled eggs, pickled onions, and other basic fare. No music or pub games, just good company and conversation, make this a place to enjoy a good drink and relax. Q🚆🍏🚌🐾

Kipps' Alehouse

11-15 Old High Street, CT20 1RL

☎ (01303) 246766 🌐 kippsalehouse.co.uk

3 changing beers (sourced regionally; often Mad Cat) [G]

This alehouse follows the general principle of a micropub, serving real ale directly from the cask, usually including one Kentish ale, one award winner, and then another unusual beer from around the country from a small independent microbrewery. Several ciders are on sale from boxes, and there is a variety of bottled craft beers and draught international lagers. A range of international vegetarian food is available. Music features on some Sunday afternoons. 🎠❀◑♿♣🍏🚌🐾📶

Mariner [L] ✔

16 The Stade, CT19 6AB

☎ (01303) 254546

Adnams Ghost Ship; Harvey's Sussex Best Bitter; Sharp's Doom Bar; 2 changing beers (sourced regionally; often St Austell, Shepherd Neame, Timothy Taylor) [H]

Formerly the Jubilee in Mackeson's days, this welcoming pub has an outstanding location overlooking the old fishing harbour and the revived harbour arm, while just 50 yards away are the Sunny Sands, one of Kent's best bathing beaches. Approached through mid-19th century railway arches, the Stade was rebuilt in the 1930s. All major sporting events are shown and there's even a handy postbox for those holiday postcards. ♣🚌(91,102) 📶

Frittenden

Bell & Jorrocks ✔

Biddenden Road, TN17 2EJ TQ815412

☎ (01580) 852415 🌐 thebellandjorrocks.co.uk

Black Sheep Best Bitter; Harvey's Sussex Best Bitter; 2 changing beers (sourced nationally; often Dark Star, Fuller's, Tonbridge) [H]

An archetypal village venue and the social centre of the local community. Previously called the Bell, it gained its current name when the pub opposite, the John Jorrocks, closed in 1969. Excellent food is served. Originally a coaching inn dating from the early 18th century, its stables are used for a mid-April beer festival with about 25 different beers. It is a good base for walks in the picturesque Low Weald countryside surrounding the village and for nearby Sissinghurst Castle.
🎠❀◑⛺♣🍏🐾📶

Knoxbridge [L]

Cranbrook Road, TN17 2BT TQ788406

☎ (01580) 895374

🌐 theknoxbridge-frittenden.foodndrink.uk

3 changing beers (sourced regionally; often Brumaison, Harvey's, Musket) [H]

A relaxed family-friendly pub serving great food cooked by a French chef, complemented by up to three changing ales from local and distant breweries. If you'd like to sample them all, they can be bought as three third-pint glasses in a wooden tray. A beer festival is held on the weekend of St George's Day, with a large number of military vehicles in attendance. A selection of gins is also stocked and a gin festival is held in September. An hourly bus stops outside the door. 🎠❀◑P🚌(5)📶

Gillingham

Frog & Toad ✔

38 Burnt Oak Terrace, ME7 1DR

☎ (01634) 852231

4 changing beers (sourced nationally; often Cotleigh, Parkway, Wadworth) [H]

A three-times winner of local CAMRA Pub of the Year, this traditional back-street one-bar pub is just 10 minutes' walk from the town centre. In keeping with the frog theme, there is a treat to be found on the over-bar glass rack for the musically minded. The large patio garden at the rear has covered wooden tables and seating. A permanent outdoor stillage is in place to serve real ale and ciders during regular beer festivals. A collection of vintage photos of the area adorns the walls.
🎠❀🚆♣🍏🚌(176,177) 🐾📶

Past & Present Ale House L

15 Canterbury Street, ME7 5TP
☎ 07725 072293
4 changing beers (sourced nationally; often Dartmoor, Nelson, Titanic) G

Medway's first micropub and local CAMRA's Pub and Cider Pub of the Year once again for 2020. It moved to larger premises in April 2020 but retains the same ethos of selling between three and five cask ales and up to 12 ciders. True to micropub form it has high seating at the front, with more low seating to the rear, and a bar serving rums, whiskies, gins and KeyKeg beers. Regular cider and ale festivals are staged throughout the year. A good assortment of bar snacks is available. There is a smoking area outside. Dogs are welcome on a lead.
Q ☺ ⇌ ♣ ● 🖪 🖵 (116,176) ❀

Will Adams

73 Saxton Street, ME7 5EG (on corner with Lock St)
☎ (01634) 575902
3 changing beers (sourced nationally; often Adnams, Oakham, St Austell) H

A real ale oasis, this traditional back-street hostelry close to the town centre has had 27 consecutive entries in this Guide. Offering up to three ales and five ciders, it has been run by the owners for 28 years. Some sporting events are shown on the TV. On Gillingham FC match days it opens earlier, and offers varied food for fans, with the chilli a speciality – but beware, it is not for the fainthearted! The pub is a member of the Oakademy of Excellence, which grants access to limited and special brews from Oakham Brewery. Will Adams was a mariner born in Gillingham who opened up Japan to the West and became a Samurai. ❀◖⇌♣●🖵❀⏾

Gravesend

Compass Alehouse L

7 Manor Road, DA12 1AA
☎ 07951 550949 ⊕ thecompassalehouse.co.uk
4 changing beers (sourced nationally) G

Genuine micropub opened in 2014. It has a small front room with high bench seats and a smaller snug off a little courtyard to the rear. Four ever-changing real ales and five ciders are available, often from Kent producers. A convivial atmosphere and conversation are paramount – talking on mobile phones is discouraged and incurs a fine for charity. A water bowl is provided for dogs. Regular events include a games night on Tuesdays, bi-monthly Belgian beer tasting and two beer festivals.
Q ☺ ❀ ♿ ⇌ ● 🖪 🖵 ❀

Jolly Drayman

1 Love Lane, Wellington Street, DA12 1JA (off Milton Rd, E of town centre)
☎ (01474) 352355 ⊕ jollydrayman.co.uk
Dark Star Hophead; St Austell Proper Job; Skinner's Betty Stogs; 2 changing beers (sourced nationally; often Iron Pier) H

This cosy pub on the eastern edge of the town, also known as the Coke Oven, is part of the former Walker's Brewery. It features quirky low ceilings and a relaxed atmosphere. Daddlums (Kentish skittles) is played most Sunday evenings, and men's and women's darts teams are hosted. Lunchtime meals are served. Live music takes place on the first Saturday of the month, monthly open mic sessions and quizzes on alternate Tuesdays.
☺ ❀ 🍴 ◖ ♿ ⇌ ♣ P 🖵 ❀ ⏾

Three Daws L

7 Town Pier, DA11 0BJ
☎ (01474) 566869 ⊕ threedaws.co.uk

6 changing beers (sourced locally; often Canterbury Ales, Dartford Wobbler, Iron Pier) H

Historic riverside inn with stories of ghosts, press gangs, smugglers, secret tunnels and more, offering views of the Thames and passing river traffic. The bar is upstairs, with a large function room below. The interior is divided into small rooms with very few right angles, displaying photos and pictures of local and marine interest. Meals are served until 9pm every day using ingredients from the area. Live music is hosted on Fridays, a quiz on Sundays, and beer festivals in August and October.
☺ ❀ ◖ ⇌ ♣ 🖵 ⏾

Three Pillars L

25 Wrotham Road, DA11 0PA (on A227 opp Civic Centre)
☎ 07794 348529
5 changing beers (sourced nationally; often Kent, Mighty Oak, Wantsum) G

A small cellar bar underneath the Masonic Hall, reached by steep steps to the right. Two carpeted front rooms lead to the brick-floored bar area. The ceilings are low throughout and there are photos of Gravesend pubs past and present. There is a quiz on the third Thursday of each month and live music on some Sundays, featuring solo acts or small groups. Patrons must not use the Masonic Hall car park. ☺ ⇌ ● 🖵 ❀

Halstead

Rose & Crown

Otford Lane, TN14 7EA
☎ (01959) 533120
Larkins Traditional Ale; Mighty Oak Captain Bob; St Austell Proper Job; Timothy Taylor Landlord; 2 changing beers (sourced nationally; often Rudgate, Tonbridge) H

Accessible from junction 4 of the M25 and bordering Greater London, this is still unmistakably a village pub. Two equal-sized rooms are differentiated solely by the dartboard in the public bar and a roaring fire in the lounge. The owner's passion for cask beer is reflected in the choice of six ales, with half from local breweries and the remainder from national ones. Good-value lunches include an over-50s menu. The place has a timeless quality that modern establishments cannot match.
☺ ❀ ◖ ♣ P 🖵 (3,R5) ❀ ⏾

Hastingleigh

Bowl Inn L

The Street, TN25 5HU TR095449
☎ (01233) 750354 ⊕ thebowlonline.co.uk
3 changing beers (sourced locally) H

This lovingly restored listed village pub near the Wye National Nature Reserve displays vintage advertising material and retains many period features. The main bar welcomes families but the snug room is child-free and used for village meetings. A beer festival is held on the August bank holiday Monday. Excellent sandwiches and baguettes are available weekends. CAMRA branch Pub of the Year in 2019. Q ☺ ❀ ◖ ♣ ● ⏾

Herne

Butcher's Arms L

29A Herne Street, CT6 7HL (opp church)
☎ 07908 370685 ⊕ micropub.co.uk

Fuller's ESB; Oakham Citra; Old Dairy Copper Top; 2 changing beers (sourced locally; often Adnams, Old Dairy) G

Britain's first micropub, opened in 2005, is a real ale gem and the inspiration for others since. Once a butcher's shop, it still has the original chopping tables with hooks and other implements. There is seating for 12 customers and standing room for 20 – the compact drinking area ensuring lively banter. The range of ales changes frequently and customers can also buy beer to drink at home. The pub has won many CAMRA awards and the landlord was voted one of CAMRA's top 40 campaigners. There is a public car park in School Lane, nearby. Q▲●🛇🖩🕏

Herne Bay

Bouncing Barrel L

20 Bank Street, CT6 5EA

☎ 07777 630685

4 changing beers (sourced regionally; often Goody Ales, Old Dairy, Ramsgate) G

A welcoming micropub with bench seating for 20 customers around old workshop tables. The beer range changes regularly and comes mainly from microbreweries, with generally at least one from a Kent brewery. Local snacks are available. The venue is named after the bombs used in the Dam Buster raids, which were tested off the coast nearby, and there is a mural of a bomber flying past the Reculver Towers. Regular small beer festivals are held throughout the year. Q🏴🚲♿♣●🖩🕏

Parkerville

219 High Street, CT6 5AD

☎ 07939 106172

4 changing beers (sourced locally) G

Lively micropub in a former music store. The spacious front seating area has a corner bar, and a small stage with a piano in the front window. The back bar has a TV screen for big events only. Beers are often from local microbreweries and there is a good selection of ciders, whiskies, rums, artisan gins and wines. Occasional live music is staged, and the pub celebrates its birthday every 24 July with music and food. Q🏴🚲♿●🖩🕏

Horton Kirby

Bull L

Lombard Street, DA4 9DF

☎ (01322) 860341

Dark Star Hophead; 4 changing beers (sourced locally; often Kent, Oakham, Whitstable) H

Friendly, comfortable one-bar village local with a large garden affording views across the Darent Valley, within walking distance of Farningham Road railway station. It has five handpumps, with one regular and four rotating guest ales. There is an open mic night on the first Friday of each month and a quiz on the last Monday. The pub hosts regular beer festivals, normally over the Whitsun and August bank holidays, supported by Ron's garden bar. 🏴🛂◐♣●🖩(414)🕏🛜

Hythe

Potting Shed L

160A High Street, CT21 5JR (at Folkestone end of High St)

☎ 07780 877226

4 changing beers (sourced regionally) G

Hythe's only micro-alehouse serves an interesting range of ales from around the country, most on gravity although one ale may sometimes be pulled through a handpump. One local Kentish beer is usually available. A range of three chilled ciders is also normally dispensed from boxes. Bar snacks are limited. This is a good place to enjoy a drink and interesting conversation after visiting the High Street. 🏴●🖩🕏🛜

Three Mariners L

37 Windmill Street, CT21 6BH

☎ (01303) 260406

Young's Bitter; 4 changing beers (sourced regionally) H

This traditional back-street pub with a partly heated outdoor area is well worth a visit and is an ideal place for a relaxing drink when visiting Hythe. Friendly staff and local customers are happy to have a chat over a pint of local or regional beer. No food is served – it is the excellent quality and selection of real ales and cider that makes this a popular destination. 🏴🛆♣●🖩🕏

Ickham

Duke William

The Street, CT3 1QP

☎ (01227) 721308 ⊕ thedukewilliamickham.com

3 changing beers (sourced locally; often Angels and Demons, Hop Fuzz, Whitstable) G

An attractive, busy establishment in a quintessentially English village, welcoming towards locals, diners and drinkers, with a roaring log fire in winter and a conservatory dining area at the rear. There is also a large patio. Guest ales are mostly from local microbreweries. The venue is a welcome addition to Michelin-starred chef Mark Sargeant's portfolio: his aim is to 'mirror simplistic but perfect pub meals'. There is also a bar menu served Monday to Saturday. 🛂🏴🚐◐🖩(11)🕏🛜

Ightham Common

Old House ★ L

Redwell Lane, Redwell, TN15 9EE (½ mile SW of Ightham village, between A25 and A227) TQ590558

☎ (01732) 886077 ⊕ oldhouse.pub

6 changing beers (sourced locally; often Harvey's, Larkins, Long Man) G

A Kentish red-brick, tile-hung cottage in a narrow, isolated country lane, with a nationally important historic pub interior. The main bar features a Victorian wood-panelled counter, parquet flooring and an imposing inglenook fireplace. Up to six changing beers are dispensed by gravity, often from wooden casks, including at least one bitter, a golden ale and a dark beer. Kentish ciders always available. Local CAMRA branch Pub of the Year 2019 and 2020. May close earlier in the evening if not busy. Q🏴▲♣●P🕏🛜

Kingsdown

King's Head L

Upper Street, CT14 8BJ

☎ (01304) 373915 ⊕ kingsheadkingsdown.co.uk

3 changing beers (often Goacher's, Ramsgate) H

A traditional 18th-century village pub with three beamed rooms surrounding the central bar. It has a dining/family room, a rear courtyard, a skittle alley and a heated smoking area. Local historical photos adorn the walls, and in winter a log fire warms the public bar. Three to four real ales feature, including beers from Goacher's and

Ramsgate. Cider is on sale in the summer. Home-made food is served lunchtimes and evenings on Saturday and Sunday. Events include quiz nights and a guitar club. 🐎✿◐◑⛺♣🍎🚌(82)🐾📶

Kingsnorth

Queen's Head [L]

Ashford Road, TN23 3ED

☎ (01233) 620769 🌐 queenshead-kingsnorth.co.uk

Harvey's Sussex Best Bitter; 2 changing beers (sourced regionally) [H]

This family-run 18th-century Grade II-listed pub to the south of Ashford provides a warm and inviting environment, and serves great food and a range of quality ales, two of which change at least weekly. Live music, quiz nights, and additional events are listed on its website and social media. Well-behaved children and dogs are welcome. Closed on Mondays during the winter months. ✿◐◑♿⛺♣P🚌(11,2A)🐾📶

Laddingford

Chequers ✔

The Street, ME18 6BP TQ689481

☎ (01622) 871266 🌐 chequerladdingford.co.uk

Adnams Southwold Bitter; 3 changing beers (sourced nationally) [H]

An attractive oak-beamed inn dating from the 15th century and the heart of village life. A variety of events is held throughout the year, including a beer festival at the end of April. A log fire burns in winter, and the pub frontage is a sea of flowers in summer. Good food is served, including a wide selection of sausage dishes on Thursdays. The large garden has children's play equipment. Accommodation is available (book ahead). Buses stop outside. Q🐎✿🛏◐◑♣P🚌(23,25)🐾📶

Linton

Armoury [L]

Loddington Farm, Loddington Lane, ME17 4AG

☎ (01622) 749931

6 changing beers (sourced locally; often Musket) [G]

The Musket Brewery tap overlooks the new brewhouse that is visible through the windows. There are up to eight casks on the stillage, and beer may also be ordered for collection. Comfortable seating is provided in a good-sized area. Pizzas are usually available, and monthly bookable themed dining events like Burns Night or St George's Night are held. A large grassed area opposite offers tables and cushioned casks on sunny days, with shade under the trees. Q🐎✿◐◑♿🍎P📺🚌(59)🐾📶

Lower Halstow

Three Tuns [L]

The Street, ME9 7DY

☎ (01795) 842840 🌐 thethreetunsrestaurant.co.uk

Goacher's Real Mild Ale; 3 changing beers (sourced locally; often Hop Fuzz, Romney Marsh, Wantsum) [H]

A true family village pub with a friendly, bustling, cheerful atmosphere and lively chatter. A log fire, sofa seating, brick walls and beams add character. The owners actively support real ale, offering mainly Kentish beers; third-pint flights are available for the indecisive, and several local ciders are on the bar, including Dudda's Tun. The pub has a good reputation for high-quality locally sourced food and has won many awards. A beer festival is held during the summer bank holiday and there are monthly quizzes. The owners celebrated their 10th year in 2020. 🐎✿🛏◐◑♿♣🍎P🚌🐾📶

Luddesdown

Cock Inn [L] ✔

Henley Street, DA13 0XB (1 mile SE of Sole Street station) TQ664672

☎ (01474) 814208 🌐 cockluddesdowne.com

Adnams Southwold Bitter, Lighthouse, Broadside; Goacher's Real Mild Ale; Harvey's Sussex Best Bitter; St Austell Trelawny [H]

A proudly traditional rural free house dating from 1713, under the same ownership since 1984. It has two distinct bars, a large conservatory, a comfortable heated smoking area and a separate function room where many local clubs and societies meet. There are eight real ales on handpump, and doorstep sandwiches are available at all times. Traditional pub games are played including pétanque and bar billiards, and there is a free quiz on Tuesday evenings devised and hosted by the landlord. Children are not allowed in the bars or garden. Q✿♣P🐾

Maidstone

Cellars Alehouse [L]

The Old Brewery, Buckland Road, ME16 0DZ (if front gates are closed use rear via alley alongside railway)

☎ (01622) 761045 🌐 thecellarsalehouse.co.uk

6 changing beers (sourced nationally; often Bristol Beer Factory, Cellar Head, Gun) [G]

In a former barley wine cellar of the old Style & Winch brewery, with access down a flight of steps. This alehouse has a surprisingly spacious interior with wooden pews, seats and tables. The barrel-vaulted ceiling is adorned with pumpclips and hops. Real ales are served by gravity from the capacious cool room, and at least 10 real ciders, a few craft keg beers and gins are also stocked. Evening events may include quizzes, folk music, comedy and Meet the Brewer sessions. Q🚆♣🍎🚌🐾

Flower Pot [L]

96 Sandling Road, ME14 2RJ

☎ (01622) 757705 🌐 flowerpotpub.com

Goacher's Gold Star Strong Ale; 8 changing beers (sourced nationally; often Fyne Ales, Thornbridge) [H]

A street-corner alehouse where the upper bar has nine handpumps delivering ales mainly from microbreweries. Up to four ciders and perries are served directly from the container and there is a small selection of KeyKeg beers. Beers and ciders are displayed on video screens. There are music nights on some Saturdays, jam nights on Tuesdays, monthly vinyl nights on Fridays, and an annual beer festival. Maidstone United football ground is nearby. A previous winner of Kent CAMRA Pub of the Year. ✿◐◑🚆♣🍎📺🚌(101,155)🐾📶

Olde Thirsty Pig [L] ✔

4A Knightrider Street, ME15 6LP

☎ (01622) 299283 🌐 thethirstypig.co.uk

4 changing beers (sourced locally; often Musket, Tonbridge) [H]

Reputedly the third-oldest building in the town, it dates from around 1430 and has massive timber beams, and sloping floors with curious nooks and crannies on two storeys. It was originally a farmhouse within the estate of the archbishop's palace. There is a heated and covered courtyard area. The bar has four handpumps dispensing ales mainly from Kent microbreweries. Draught cider is stocked, and many bottled beers including several foreign ones. Two small meeting rooms are available. 🏠🍺🅿♿🐾🛜

Rifle Volunteers 🅛

28 Wyatt Street, ME14 1EU
☎ (01622) 750540 ● theriflevolunteers.co.uk
Goacher's Real Mild Ale, Fine Light Ale, Crown Imperial Stout, Gold Star Strong Ale; 1 changing beer (sourced locally; often Goacher's) ⊞
One of only two Goacher's tied houses, a short walk away from Maidstone town centre, this little-altered Victorian pub has been recognised by CAMRA as having a regionally important historic interior. With no jukebox or gaming machines, it is a place for conversation and a quiet drink. A popular fun quiz open to all is held on alternate Tuesdays and a local winter quiz league on other weeks. Snacks can be made to order. Q🏠⇌🐸♿🐾🛜

Stag 🅛

11 Middle Row, ME14 1TG
☎ (01622) 296420
Rockin' Robin Reliant Robin; 2 changing beers (sourced locally; often Kent, Old Dairy) ⊞
Run by Rockin' Robin Brewery since August 2019 when it was renamed the Stag, this is a historic pub in the town centre, decorated in mid-grey with beams stripped back to their original colour. Enter from either the High Street or Bank Street to the room at the rear. It has pavement tables and chairs outside for when there isn't room inside. Up to three handpumps are on the bar, and bar snacks are available. It is three steps down to the toilets from the front room. A fire in each room may be lit in winter. 🏠⇌🅿🐾🛜

Marden

Marden Village Club 🅛

Albion Road, TN12 9DT
☎ (01622) 831427 ● mardenvillageclub.co.uk
Shepherd Neame Master Brew; 5 changing beers (sourced regionally; often Goacher's, Kent, Ramsgate) ⊞
At this Grade II-listed club and community hub six real ales are now offered, five changing regularly and generally from local Kent microbreweries. Many members are followers of football and rugby on the TV and are also involved in the club's snooker and darts teams; others simply enjoy the friendly ambience. Bingo and music evenings are held. It has regularly been voted CAMRA branch Club of the Year. Card-carrying CAMRA members are welcome but regular visitors will be required to join. ♿⇌♣🅿(23)🐾🛜

Margate

Fez

40 High Street, CT9 1DS
4 changing beers ⒼΙ
This eclectically furnished micropub which opened in 2015 has a mixture of high and low tables along with some raised bench seating. Brewery and fairground memorabilia adorn the walls while musical instruments are fixed on the ceiling. The small bar counter at the rear has a temperature-controlled cellar room from which cask ales and ciders are served on gravity dispense. A limited wine range along with a selection of soft drinks are also sold. 🐦⇌♦🅿(56,33)🐾🛜

Two Halves

2 Marine Drive, CT9 1DH
☎ 07538 771904
3 changing beers Ⓖ
This small, friendly and welcoming micropub has an incredible location on Margate's seafront. The landlord knows his ale, sourcing beers from all regions of the country and changing them regularly. No matter what the weather, this place has a great aspect; enjoy sunsets out of the window or just watch the world go by. The beer and cider are kept in immaculate condition in a large stillage room. Look for the old-fashioned postcards in the loo. Q⇌♦🅿(56)🐾

Milton Regis

Three Hats

93 High Street, ME10 2AR
☎ (01795) 427645
4 changing beers (sourced nationally) ⊞
The Three Hats is in the medieval High Street, the focal point for many social activities. An open-plan interior with low beams to the front rises just enough at the rear to accommodate a dartboard, beyond which is a large patio area and garden. Occasional live music and karaoke take place, with a meat raffle on Sunday. 🐦🏠♦🅿(347)🐾🛜

Minster-in-Thanet

Hair of the Dog

73 High Street, CT12 4AB
☎ 07885 362326 ● hairofthedogpub.co.uk
3 changing beers Ⓖ
This micropub, previously a dog groomer's, offers a warm welcome on the village high street. Usually serving three real ales and at least three ciders, all are dispensed from casks in a cool room directly off the bar. The furniture is rustic with a mix of high and low seating and tables, where customers can play a mix of old games such as shove-ha'penny or try and crack some of the puzzles left out. Dogs always welcome. Q🐦⇌(Minster)♣♦🅿🐾

Newenden

White Hart 🅛

Rye Road, TN18 5PN (on A28 in centre of village)
TQ834273
☎ (01797) 252166 ● thewhitehartnewenden.co.uk
Harvey's Sussex Best Bitter; Rother Valley Level Best; 2 changing beers ⊞
A characterful 16th-century free house serving the local community with its ever-changing selection of fine cask ales. It is an ideal base from which to explore the area – perhaps a nostalgic steam train journey through beautiful countryside with the Kent and East Sussex Railway, a visit to one of the many National Trust properties on its doorstep, or a drive down to the coast. Pub quizzes are held on the first Monday of the month (except on bank holidays). 🐦🏠🛏🍴♿🅿▲⇌(Northiam)♣♦🅿(2)🐾🛜

Northfleet

Earl Grey

177 Vale Road, DA11 8BP
☎ (01474) 365240 ● earlgreynorthfleet.co.uk
Shepherd Neame Master Brew, Spitfire; 1 changing beer (sourced regionally; often Shepherd Neame) ⊞

A distinctive late 18th-century cottage-style building with a Kentish red-brick and flint exterior. Internally there is an L-shaped bar with a raised seating area at the rear. The pub hosts regular darts and pool teams. Outside is a large garden with children's play equipment. Seasonal ales come from the Shepherd Neame range. Children are not permitted in the evening.

🐕⚘♣🅿🚆(481,483) ⚘

Iron Pier Taproom 🅛

Units 6 & 7, May Industrial Estate, May Avenue, DA11 8RU

☎ (01474) 569460 🌐 ironpier.beer

Iron Pier Perry St Pale, Bitter Ⓗ

Iron Pier is only the second brewery to operate in Gravesend since Russell's was swallowed by Truman's in the 1930s, and it opened its new taproom in 2018. Inside, there is plenty of seating and an excellent view of the brewery itself. Up to four Iron Pier beers are served. A selection of gins, wines, bottled beers and soft drinks is also available. 🅿🚆⚘

Pembury

King William IV

87 Hastings Road, TN2 4JS

☎ (01892) 458241 🌐 kingwilliampembury.com

Greene King IPA; St Austell Proper Job; 4 changing beers (sourced regionally; often Fuller's, Long Man, Titsey) Ⓗ

A refurbished free house under family ownership, the King Will has been given a new lease of life as a thriving community pub. Spacious, with ample seating, it has large front and rear gardens, room for darts and bar billiards games, and regular live music evenings – something for everyone. The menu includes home-made Cornish pasties which complement the regular appearance of a Cornish beer, reflecting the landlord's origins. Local breweries are well supported, and a real cider from Biddenden or Seacider is usually on offer. 🐕⚘🅾♣⚪🅿🚆(6,297) ⚘🛜

Petteridge

Hopbine

Petteridge Lane, TN12 7NE (1 mile E of Matfield)

☎ (01892) 722561 🌐 thehopbine.pub

Long Man Best Bitter; Tonbridge Traditional Ale; house beer (by Cellar Head); 1 changing beer (sourced locally; often Gun) Ⓗ

A picturesque tiled and weatherboarded gem of a pub with affable staff and local clientele, perched on the junction of Petteridge and Tibbs Court Lanes. Customers may be welcomed by a log fire and the aroma of freshly home-made pizza (not served Monday and Sunday eves) baked in a wood-fired oven. A choice of Kent and Sussex beers are accompanied by a local cider such as Chiddingstone or Turners. A regular stopping place for ramblers taking advantage of the landscaped garden and patio. Q🐕⚘🅾♣⚪🅿🚆(297)⚘🛜

Queenborough

Admiral's Arm 🅛

West Street, ME11 5AD (in Trafalgar Court, 30yds left from High St and Park Rd crossroads)

☎ (01795) 668598 🌐 admiralsarm.co.uk

4 changing beers (sourced nationally; often Ilkley, Oakham, Ramsgate) Ⓗ/Ⓖ

Located in the historic heart of town, this micropub has a nautical theme including local shipping maps, and is frequented by regulars and visitors alike. The welcoming owners happily serve a good range of beers direct from the cask or via handpump, plus eight KeyKeg beers, ciders and many gins. Excellent pizzas are available at weekends, cooked in the pizza oven. Regular quiz nights and cheese Sundays are held. Local CAMRA branch Pub and Cider Pub of the Year 2019 and 2020, and Kent Pub of the Year 2019. Q🐕⚘🅾◑≈♣⚪🚆(334)⚘🛜

Rainham

Mackland Arms

213 Station Road, ME8 7PS (5 mins walk N of railway station)

☎ (01634) 232178 🌐 macklandarms.co.uk

Shepherd Neame Master Brew, Spitfire; 1 changing beer (sourced nationally) Ⓗ

A popular traditional local, this Shepherd Neame tied house has three linked areas and a large rear garden. The island bar displays three ales on handpumps, and an Orchard View 4.5% ABV cider is on tap. Darts teams play twice a week, there is a pool table at the rear, and two screens for watching sport. Red plush seating and pleasant décor feature. No food is served. A bus stop opposite will connect with the main routes of the A2. 🐕⚘🅾♣⚪🚆(327) ⚘

Prince of Ales 🅛

121 High Street, ME8 8AN (nr centre of Rainham, next to post office)

☎ 07982 756412 🌐 princeofales.co.uk

4 changing beers (sourced nationally; often Kent, Oakham, Tonbridge) Ⓖ

On the main A2, opposite the Citroen dealer and two minutes from bus stops, this attractive micropub is run by a dedicated team. Four changing, mostly Kent-based, ales are served direct from casks in the chiller room, as are three ciders of the bag-in-box type. It also sells wine, prosecco and soft drinks. Wooden tables and benches predominate, and there is a small outside area similarly fitted out. An annual beer festival is held. Food is not available, and children and animals are not permitted. Q⚘≈♣⚪🍴🚆(132)

Ramsgate

Artillery Arms

36 Westcliff Road, CT11 9JS

☎ (01843) 853202

Oakham Citra; Ramsgate Gadds' No.5 Best Bitter Ale; 2 changing beers (often Ramsgate, Wantsum) Ⓗ

A celebrated alehouse a short walk from the town attracting a diverse clientèle. The lower bar area with stairs leads to an upper area with more seating. The landlord maintains a long tradition of stocking a carefully considered range of real ales. Handpumps serve a selection of beers from Kent and around the country. Interesting old painted windows depict battle scenes and the theme is continued with displays of other militaria. ♣⚪🚆⚘

Montefiore Arms

1 Trinity Place, CT11 7HJ

☎ (01843) 593265

Ramsgate Gadds' No.7 Bitter Ale; 4 changing beers Ⓗ

This award-winning traditional back-street venue enjoys a good reputation with real ale drinkers in the Thanet area. The name and sign are unique, honouring the great Jewish financier and philanthropist, Sir Moses

Montefiore, who lived locally for many years and was a benefactor to the town's poor. The pub showcases the beers of the Ramsgate Brewery along with changing guest ales and Biddenden cider. ♣🍴🖵🛜

Royal Victoria Pavilion ✅
Harbour Parade, CT11 8LS
☎ (01843) 854420
Greene King Abbot; Ruddles Best Bitter; Sharp's Doom Bar; 6 changing beers ⒣
This splendid establishment opened as a Wetherspoon pub in 2017 in a dilapidated Grade II pavilion. The building was designed by architect Stanley Davenport Adshead in the early 1900s as a concert hall/assembly rooms based on the style of a Robert Adam orangery. It features two floors and two bars, and is said to be the largest Wetherspoon in the country. The pub has a ground-floor rear beer garden, along with a first-floor roof terrace. Children permitted until 9pm. 🛏🏨🍴🖵🍴🖵🛜

Rochester

Coopers Arms
10 St Margarets Street, ME1 1TL
☎ (01634) 404298 ⊕ thecoopersarms.co.uk
Courage Best Bitter; Young's London Special; house beer (by Tonbridge); 4 changing beers (sourced regionally; often Canterbury Ales, Tonbridge, Westerham) ⒣
This charming building dating from the reign of Richard I (1189-1199) was originally the home of monks, and did not become an inn until 1543. The original character remains in this historic two-bar pub. Local and regional ales are offered. On a Sunday evening musicians from the surrounding area entertain in a wide variety of styles. Quiz nights are held on a regular basis. 🏨🍴🖵P🖵🐾🛜

Golden Lion Hotel Ⓛ ✅
147-149 High Street, ME1 1EL
☎ (01634) 880521
Greene King Abbot; Ruddles Best Bitter; Sharp's Doom Bar; 4 changing beers (sourced nationally) ⒣
A short walk from the railway station, this large split-level Wetherspoon's outlet also has nine hotel rooms. It is in the Dickensian High Street where the original Golden Lion pub stood from the early 19th century until 1920. The old fireplace is still in use. There are various types of seating, including booths, throughout, and it has a large garden to the rear with many shrubs in planters. Extremely busy at weekends. 🛏🏨🍴🍴🐾🍴🖵🛜

Man of Kent Ale House Ⓛ
6-8 John Street, ME1 1YN (200yds off A2 from bottom of Star Hill)
☎ 07772 214315
Goacher's Gold Star Strong Ale; 10 changing beers (sourced locally; often Bexley, Ramsgate, Tonbridge) ⒣
This wonderful establishment keeps evolving. Already renowned for its selection of Kentish ales, ciders, wines and bottled beers, German keg beer, and a wide range of gins, it has now added vegan and gluten-free beers and ciders to the collection. Live music acts perform on Wednesday and Thursday evenings, when the pub gets busy. It has an enclosed garden at the rear, which is a real suntrap. 🏨🍴♣🍴🖵🖵(155)🐾

Who'd Ha' Thought It
9 Baker Street, ME1 3DN (off Rochester-Maidstone road)
☎ (01634) 830144 ⊕ whodha.com

3 changing beers (sourced nationally; often Harvey's, Skinner's, Titanic) ⒣
A friendly back-street local with a spacious wood-panelled bar and a log fire for winter months. To the rear is a snug area with books and games, ideal for small groups. Three TVs, one large-screen, show major sporting events. The dog-friendly garden is a real suntrap and has a covered smoking area. A selection of three ales is served and they are rotated regularly. The pub hosts monthly quiz nights and charity events, and celebrates major calendar landmarks. 🛏🏨♣P🖵(155)🐾🛜

Ryarsh

Duke of Wellington Ⓛ
Birling Road, ME19 5LS
☎ (01732) 842318 ⊕ dukeofwellingtonryarsh.com
Harvey's Sussex Best Bitter; Kent Pale; 2 changing beers (sourced nationally; often Musket, St Austell, Twickenham) ⒣
A 16th-century pub with two bars, both with inglenook fireplaces. The main bar to the left includes a snug, and the restaurant to the right has part of an original wattle and daub wall displayed behind glass. A covered and heated patio opens onto the garden, with additional tables outside at the front. The varied menu includes takeaways and Sunday roasts. A popular jazz music evening is held on the first Thursday of the month, quiz night on alternate Sunday evenings. Ramblers are welcome. Q🛏🏨🍴P🖵(58)🐾🛜

St Peter's

Four Candles Alehouse
1 Sowell Street, CT10 2AT
☎ 07947 062063 ⊕ thefourcandles.co.uk
3 changing beers Ⓖ
This former shop is now firmly established on the local micropub scene, and is renowned for its friendly atmosphere. Seating is provided at high bench tables, with the beer served from a cooled cabinet in an adjacent room. The pub has its own microbrewery in the cellar, supplying excellent one-off beers to complement the offerings from other brewers. Benches outside are ideal for enjoying the sunshine. Q🍴(Broadstairs)🍴🖵(56)🐾

Sandgate

Earl of Clarendon
Brewers Hill, CT20 3DH (25yds up footpath off A259 from seafront between Seabrook and Sandgate next to public phone box)
☎ (01303) 248684 ⊕ the-earl-of-clarendon.business.site
3 changing beers ⒣
This ex-Mackeson, Whitbread and Shepherd Neame free house was originally built as a hotel and provided refreshment to troops as it is on a path between Shorncliffe Camp and the sea. It has continuously changing beers from all over Britain, usually including at least one local beer. Live music takes place occasionally during the summer, tasty home-made food is served every day, bar billiards and third-pint glasses are available, and it shows football, cricket and snooker on satellite TV. Outdoor tables overlook the sea. 🍴♣🖵🐾

Inn Doors
96 Sandgate High Street, CT20 3BY
☎ 07958 474473 ⊕ inndoorsmicropub.co.uk

House beer (by Four Candles); 2 changing beers (sourced regionally) G

A micropub at the west end of Sandgate styled on a 1930s living room, with a small bar and two-level seating. Beers are served from a cold room visible through a window. The landlord brews his own beers at the Four Candles brewery in Broadstairs. Tasty snacks are served as well as a large variety of gins. The pub hosts Bring Your Own Vinyl nights played on a vintage record player, and monthly charity quiz evenings. Q⏚♣♦🚲🚌

Sandwich

Crispin Inn ⏚ ✔

4 High Street, CT13 9EA

☎ (01304) 621967 ⊕ sandwichpubs.co.uk

Adnams Broadside; Harvey's Sussex Best Bitter; house beer (by Mad Cat); 3 changing beers (often Adnams) ⊞

A Grade II-listed public house by the medieval barbican and toll bridge. Low ceilings, wooden beams and brick walls create a congenial ambience. Relax by the window and watch the world go by, or sit in the back courtyard overlooking the river. Three or four real ales are on the bar, including an ale from Mad Cat; real cider is from Westons or Thatchers. A good range of home-made food and snacks usually features Caribbean specialities, for example goat curry. Regular live music events are held. ⏚❀🕽♦🅰🍴≈♣♦🚌😺🛜

Sevenoaks

Anchor ⏚

32 London Road, TN13 1AS

☎ (01732) 454898

House beer (by Wantsum); 2 changing beers (sourced locally; often Kent, Ramsgate) ⊞

One of the last real traditional hostelries in the area, with landlord Barry at the helm for more than 40 years. A pub full of friendly banter makes for a unique experience, while enjoying one of three exceptionally well-kept real ales, usually from Kent breweries. This is an established venue for live music, featuring twice-monthly blues and open mic nights. Darts, poker and pool are also played. Good home-made food, including roasts, is served every day, with snacks in the evening. 🕽♣🚌😺

Sheerness

Flying Sheep Micropub

193 High Street, ME12 1UJ

☎ 07958 134282

4 changing beers (sourced regionally) ⊞

Opened in 2018, this micropub has an aviation and local sheep theme reflecting Sheppey's past involvement in aircraft manufacture and sheep farming. The seating is mainly high tables and high stools, but there are several comfortable airline seats. The bar counter offers an interesting and changing range of beers from near and far, and ciders on gravity dispense. A themed night is held on Wednesday. The bar may occasionally close for private functions. Runner-up local CAMRA branch Pub of the Year 2020. May occasionally close for private functions – check ahead. ⏚♿≈♣♦🚇🚌(360)😺🛜

Sittingbourne

Donna's Ale House ⏚

20 West Street, ME10 1AB

5 changing beers (sourced locally; often Goody Ales, Mad Cat, Wantsum) ⊞

Micropub premises opened in 2017. It has a contemporary decor inside, with seating at high benches, tables and stools. Four handpumps dispense ales with an emphasis on Kentish makers, but occasionally from out of county; a blackboard gives a description of the beers on offer. Over 100 gins are also stocked. A selection of snacks is available, typically ranging from cheeseboards to pie and mash and chilli with nachos. A welcome town-centre addition to the real ale scene and proving popular with all who visit. ⏚🕽≈♦🚌

Paper Mill ⏚

2 Charlotte Street, ME10 2JN (N of station, almost in Milton Regis at corner of Church St and Charlotte St)

☎ 07927 073584 ⊕ thepapermillmicropub.co.uk

3 changing beers (sourced regionally; often Dark Revolution, Goacher's, Salopian) G

Popular micropub close to the town centre and railway station, a one-room establishment with bench seating around four large tables. Local beers feature alongside national beers such as Blue Monkey and Cloudwater. A range of real cider is available, and blackboards with the beer list include KeyKeg offerings. Occasional events such as Meet the Brewer and quizzes take place. Opening hours are flexible with advance notice. Q⏚♿≈♣♦🚇🚌(334,347) 😺

Yellow Stocks

22A High Street, ME10 4PD

☎ 07572 180627

2 changing beers (sourced locally; often Canterbury Ales, Iron Pier, Ramsgate) G

A micropub opened in 2018 in a former clothes shop and named after a type of hand-made building brick, once manufactured in large quantities in the surrounding countryside. The real ales, ciders and perries come from a temperature-controlled cellar room behind the small bar counter. Real ales and ciders are mainly with a Kentish provenance, but some unusual regional beers are offered. Outside, there is a garden at the rear. Occasional comfort food is on the bar. ⏚❀≈♣♦🚌😺🛜

Smeeth

Dog House Pub ⏚

Evegate Business Park, Station Road, TN25 6SX (S of A20 at Smeeth crossroads and rear of business park)

☎ 07340 985064 ⊕ thedoghousepub.co.uk

3 changing beers (sourced locally) G

This small pub/cafe offers a changing selection of local ales and ciders, and home-made food. There is a small patio providing space for smokers and alfresco drinking and dining in fine weather. Live music is performed most Friday and Saturday evenings and there are periodic live jam nights. Families and dogs are welcome in this old vets' dogs convalescing barn. Ample parking available. ⏚❀🕽♿♦P😺🛜

Snargate

Red Lion ★ ⏚

TN29 9UQ (on B2080, 1 mile NW of Brenzett) TQ990285

☎ (01797) 344648

3 changing beers G

A regular Guide entry since 1981, this superb, multi-room 16th-century smugglers' inn has been in the same family for over 100 years, and has a nationally important pub interior. It passed to the next generation in 2016, but is still universally known as Doris's. It is decorated with posters from the 1940s and the Women's Land Army. A beer festival is held in June near to the summer solstice and a mini festival in October. Q❀♣●P🚌(11B)🐾

Staplehurst

Lord Raglan 🄻

Chart Hill Road, TN12 0DE (½ mile N of A229 from no.5 bus stop at Cross at Hand) TQ786472

☎ (01622) 843747 🌐 lord-raglan.co.uk

Goacher's Fine Light Ale; Harvey's Sussex Best Bitter; 1 changing beer (sourced locally) 🄷

Owned by the same family for many years, this is an unspoilt free house retaining the atmosphere of a country pub from bygone days. The bar is hung with hops and warmed by two log fires and a stove. It serves excellent food from a popular menu, and perry and local Double Vision cider are stocked. The large orchard garden catches the evening sun. Well-behaved children and dogs are welcome. Q❀◐●P🐾

Strood

10:50 From Victoria 🄻

Rear of 37 North Street, ME2 4SJ (in a railway arch opp Asda car park)

☎ 07941 449137

Grainstore Ten Fifty; Kent Session Pale 🄶**; 5 changing beers (sourced locally)** 🄷/🄶

A beer oasis in an ale desert. This micropub, local CAMRA 2019 Pub of the Year, is hugely popular both with regulars and real ale fans. Wood-panelled throughout, the walls are adorned with railway and other memorabilia. Alongside six ciders, five ales are stocked including regulars Grainstore Ten Fifty and Kent Session Pale, the remainder being a mix of Kent and regional micros. A log-burner keeps customers cosy in the colder months and there is an outside patio and garden area for warmer times. Q❀♿⇌♣●P🚌(191)🐾

Swanley

Cotton Mill 🄻 ✔

10 Station Road, BR8 8ET

☎ (01322) 669619 🌐 thecottonmillpub.com

4 changing beers (often Iron Pier, Park, Whitstable) 🄷

A micropub, opened in 2018, serving four changing real ales on handpump, several real ciders in boxes, and four craft beers. It has an interesting tiled floor with bottle tops inlaid in mosaic patterns. The pleasantly renovated building, with comfortable seating, is shared with a taxi office in a former public WC, and has a pleasant outside drinking area. It holds a quiz night every Thursday evening. There are plans for expansion and beer festivals in summer. ♘❀⇌♣●P🚌🐾ᯤ

Tankerton

Tankerton Arms 🄻

135 Tankerton Road, CT5 2AW

☎ 07897 741811 🌐 thetankertonarms.co.uk

3 changing beers (sourced locally; often Mad Cat, Old Dairy) 🄶

This friendly micropub, with a firm policy of supporting Kent microbreweries, is situated among Tankerton's small shops. There are occasional beer swaps with regional breweries. The pleasant, airy room is lined with high wooden tables and stools, encouraging good conversation among customers, and adorned with bunting and pictures of Thames sailing barges and the sea forts. Italian antipasti evenings are held every few weeks. There is a patio in front for outdoor drinking. Q♘❀♿♣●🚌🐾ᯤ

Temple Ewell

Fox

14 High Street, CT16 3DU

☎ (01304) 823598

Exmoor Fox; 2 changing beers (often Breakwater) 🄷

A traditional village pub with a warm welcome for locals and visitors. Enjoy real ales in a good range of styles and strengths in the main bar or in one of the smaller rooms. A variety of events, quiz nights, curry nights and occasional music evenings keeps the place busy. In June a charity beer festival is organised by the Rotary Club. There is an attractive streamside garden with a skittle alley. Close to Kearnsey Abbey gardens and public transport. ♘❀◐⇌♣P🚌(15,68)🐾ᯤ

Tenterden

Old Dairy Tap Room

Tenterden Station Yard, Station Road, TN30 6HE

☎ 07961 769672 🌐 cattleshedbrew.co/taproom

4 changing beers (sourced locally; often Old Dairy) 🄷

The Tap Room is located at the front of the brewery and offers the range of Old Dairy and Cow Shed beers along with a selection of bottled beers. There is also a choice of ciders from the area from the Nightingale Cider Company. Kentish gin, whisky, vodka, and local wines and soft drinks, including a variety of teas and coffees, are also available. ❀⇌(Town)●P🚌

This Ancient Boro'

3 East Cross, TN30 6AD

☎ (01580) 388815 🌐 thisancientboro.com

9 changing beers (sourced nationally) 🄶

A Whitbread outlet which closed in 1968 and reopened as an alehouse and tapas bar in 2018, becoming the CAMRA branch Pub of the Year in 2020. It is a hybrid of the original and a micropub, with no live music or gaming machines. A variety of beers is available dispensed by gravity from cooled casks on stillage behind the bar, together with various ciders served from a fridge. An interesting snack/tapas menu is served. Q♘◐⇌(Town)♣●🚌🐾ᯤ

Tonbridge

Beer Seller

64 High Street, TN9 1EH

☎ (01732) 666336 🌐 thebeerseller.co.uk

Cellar Head Session Pale Ale; Constellation Draco; Goacher's Gold Star Strong Ale; 3 changing beers (sourced locally; often 360 Degrees, Iron Pier, Kent) 🄶

Reminiscent of its sister pub, the Halfway House at Brenchley, this former shop has been uniquely styled as a Kentish barn, with farmyard implements and rustic paraphernalia to give a relaxed feel of the countryside in the centre of town. Up to 10 cask beers are served by gravity from a cold room behind the bar, along with eight real ciders. Snack food is available until half an hour before closing. A function room and a separate off-licence are to be found upstairs. Q♿⇌●🚌🐾ᯤ

Fuggles Beer Café ✓

165 High Street, TN9 1BX (N end of High St nr parish church)
☎ (01732) 666071

Tonbridge Coppernob; 3 changing beers (sourced nationally; often Cellar Head, Downlands, Iron Pier) ⊞

A welcome recent addition to the town, Fuggles was converted from a former shop to a café/bar with a light, airy and relaxed feel. In addition to the cask ales there are 18 draught lines, a huge range of bottled beers from around the world, and two cask ciders, giving customers an amazing choice. Regular Meet the Brewer and tap takeovers are advertised, while takeouts are also available in one litre growlers. Meals come in the form of cheeseboards, charcuterie and toasties.
🛇🕽🕭�●🟥🐾🐱🛜

Humphrey Bean ✓

94 High Street, TN9 1AP
☎ (01732) 773850

Greene King Abbot; Ruddles Best Bitter; Sharp's Doom Bar; 4 changing beers (sourced nationally; often Dorking, Oakham, Tonbridge) ⊞

A regular Guide entry, the Bean continues to provide a comprehensive selection of six guest ales and to stage occasional Meet the Brewer evenings. Westons Old Rosie, together with an additional cider such as Marcle Hill or Black Dragon, is kept in the chiller. An attractive and spacious garden overlooks the River Medway and Tonbridge Castle. Inside, there is plenty of seating, and a flame-effect gas fire keeps customers warm in winter. Community events, such as a Wednesday quiz, are hosted. Q🛇🕽�●🕭�●🟥🛜

Nelson Arms

19 Cromer Street, TN9 1UP
☎ (01732) 358284 ⊕ thenelsonarms.com

6 changing beers (sourced nationally; often Fyne, Hop Back, Kent) ⊞

Saved from extinction by multi award-winning owners, this pub was revitalised in 2018 to become a destination of choice close to the station. The Nelson commemorates the naval hero with a nautical theme of pictures, artefacts and bar names, and is smartly furnished with tiling, hop decoration and plenty of seating and tables. Ten handpumps dispense a well-chosen range of beer styles, along with Turners and Chiddingstone cider. Food service is until late, TV sports fans are well catered for, and live music is performed on Friday evenings.
🌑🕽🌯🌘🟥🐱🛜

Tunbridge Wells

Fuggles Beer Café Ⓛ ✓

28 Grosvenor Road, TN1 2AP (opp Tesco bus stop)
☎ (01892) 457739

Burning Sky Plateau; Tonbridge Coppernob; 3 changing beers (sourced nationally; often 360 Degree, Bristol Beer Factory, Downlands) ⊞

Respected town-centre drinking establishment catering for a wide range of tastes. It offers cask ales, ciders, wines, spirits and a huge range of bottled beers reflecting quality throughout, often served in a bustling atmosphere. The distinct European feel runs through to the cured meat and cheeseboards, open sandwiches and salads. Informed, friendly staff contribute to the impression of a well-run and welcoming destination. Frequent events, including brewery tap takeovers, are organised, and are advertised on the website and within the beer café. 🛇🕽🌯🌘🟥🐱🛜

George ✓

29 Mount Ephraim, TN4 8AA
☎ (01892) 539492 ⊕ thegeorgepubtunbridgewells.co.uk

Fonthill Good Morning Captain; Long Man Best Bitter; 4 changing beers (sourced locally; often 360 Degrees, Gun, Tonbridge) ⊞

After several incarnations in other guises, this Georgian coaching inn has rediscovered itself as a smart and friendly pub. A free house, it is home to the Fonthill nanobrewery whose beers often appear on the bar, alongside a selection of ales from Kent and Sussex, and a local cider such as Turners or Seacider. It has front terrace seating, and a rear staircase leads down to the haven of a secluded courtyard garden. Light bites are served every day beyond lunchtimes. 🛇🕮🕿🌯🌘🟥🐱🛜

Grove Tavern Ⓛ

19 Berkeley Road, TN1 1YR
☎ (01892) 526549 ⊕ grovetavern.co.uk

Harvey's Sussex Best Bitter; Timothy Taylor Landlord; 2 changing beers (sourced nationally; often Black Sheep, Otter, Salcombe) ⊞

Ascending cobbled Warwick Road from the High Street leads you to the old village area and an integral part of it, the Grove – a long-term Guide fixture. Any newcomer here will find themselves readily included in friendly conversation while selecting between firm favourites Harvey's Best and Landlord, or two interesting guest beers. The social nature of the pub is emphasised with a display of images of fondly remembered former patrons, friends and their dogs on the far wall. Q🛇🌯🌘🟥🐱🛜

Mount Edgcumbe

The Common, TN4 8BX (signposted lane off Mt Ephraim)
☎ (01892) 618854 ⊕ themountedgcumbe.com

Harvey's Sussex Best Bitter; 3 changing beers (sourced locally; often Cellar Head, Northdown, Old Dairy) ⊞

Tunbridge Wells's country pub in the middle of town; a Georgian gem situated a short walk from the railway station and High Street yet surrounded by woodland. Set in isolation, the Grade II listed building enjoys a countryside feel and has a large terrace overlooking the common and sandstone rock formations, as well as its own sixth-century sandstone cave. There is an extensive food menu featuring locally sourced produce, with light meals served through the afternoon on Friday and Saturday. 🛇🕮🌯🕽🌯🌘🟥🐱🛜

Royal Oak Ⓛ

92 Prospect Road, TN2 4SY
☎ (01892) 542546

Cellar Head Varies; Five Points Varies; Harvey's Sussex Best Bitter; 2 changing beers (sourced nationally; often Iron Pier, Kent, Salopian) ⊞

Deservedly popular community venue a short walk from the town centre. The large open-plan panelled room has a central bar serving an eclectic range of real ales and ciders. Third-pint taster racks are available. Pub classics and snacks are served every day (except Mon), including the popular Sunday roasts. The atmosphere varies from a gentle buzz at quieter times to a lively vibe during televised sports events or when live music plays on Saturday evenings. 🛇🕮🕽🌯🌘🟥 (6,285)🐱🛜

Sussex Arms

Sussex Mews, TN2 5TE
☎ (01892) 549579 ⊕ thesussextw.co.uk

Long Man Long Blonde; Timothy Taylor Landlord; 4 changing beers (sourced regionally; often Adnams, Downlands, Musket) ⊞

Tucked away behind the Corn Exchange just off the Pantiles, the Sussex offers a retreat away from the crowds, with a sunny patio on one side and a covered, traffic-free terrace on the other. The interior is cosily lit, homely and comfortable, with wooden furnishings, sofas and a log fire. Ascension cider is served alongside ales that come mostly from South-East breweries. A programme of regular live music and comedy entertainment in the pub's Forum basement is displayed on the walls. 🌳♿🍴♣🍺🚃🐾🛇

Upper Upnor

King's Arms
2 High Street, ME2 4XG
☎ (01634) 717490 ⊕ kingsarmsupnor.co.uk
5 changing beers (sourced nationally) Ⓗ
Situated close to the free village car park, you will find a good choice of five guest real ales here, including a mild, and a selection of ciders, perries and European bottled beers. The large garden often hosts beer festivals. The pub has a reputation for quality food, and offers restaurant and bar menus. Upnor Castle sits at the far end of the high street. Q🌳🛇🏵🍴♣🍺P🚃(197)🐾🛇

Tudor Rose
29 High Street, ME2 4XG
☎ (01634) 714175 ⊕ tudorroseupnor.co.uk
Shepherd Neame Master Brew, Whitstable Bay Pale Ale; 2 changing beers (sourced nationally) Ⓗ
An inn with character, and numerous rooms linked to its L-shaped bar, in this quaint village overlooking the River Medway and next to Upnor Castle. The narrow cobbled street dates from the 17th century. There is a large walled garden at the rear. The pub has a good reputation for quality food. Customers may use the free car park at the far end of the High Street.
Q🌳🛇🏵🍴♣🍺P🚃(197)🐾🛇

Walmer

Berry Ⓛ
23 Canada Road, CT14 7EQ
☎ (01304) 362411 ⊕ theberrywalmer.co.uk
Harvey's Sussex Best Bitter; Oakham Citra; 12 changing beers (often Ramsgate, Time & Tide) Ⓗ
A multi award-winning alehouse with a warm welcome and friendly service, located off the seafront. The bar has a light and airy feel and at the back there is a pleasant patio. There is plenty of choice of quality ales and ciders, with up to 11 cask beers, seven KeyKeg ales (many from Time & Tide), and more than 12 ciders. Three beer festivals are hosted annually. Events include monthly quizzes, live music and pop-up food nights.
🌳🏵♣🍺🚃🐾🛇

Freed Man Ⓛ
329 Dover Road, CT14 7NX
☎ (01304) 364457 ⊕ thefreed-man.co.uk

> There is not a brewer who doesn't doctor his beer with something or other. Really something is in it. Four glasses made a Brooklyn man shoot down Dr Duggan in cold blood. Beer made a New York husband put a hole through his wife with a 22-calibre defender. Murder is in it. Who drinks lager beer is too apt to swallow the murder with it.
>
> **Elisha Chenery MD, 1889**

4 changing beers Ⓗ
This venue offers everything for the discerning drinker in a micropub atmosphere. The decor is cosy and warm, with nautical memorabilia covering the reclaimed wood walls. Up to four real ales, predominantly from local breweries, are served from the Victorian beer engine. Alongside these are real ciders, wines, selected spirits and authentic draught and bottled European lagers. Food can be brought in and the staff provide plates and cutlery. Regular events include a Thursday ladies' night and a monthly quiz night. Q🌳🍴♣🍺🚃🐾🛇

West Malling

Bull Inn Ⓛ
1 High Street, ME19 6QH
☎ (01732) 842753
Goacher's Gold Star Strong Ale; Timothy Taylor Landlord; Young's London Original; 4 changing beers (sourced nationally; often Goacher's, Musket, Ramsgate) Ⓗ
At the north end of the town, near the railway bridge, is this friendly free house, with wood panelling and a real fire. There is a terrace outside at the rear. The focus is on beers and ciders from the area, with one cider on handpump. A quiz is held on Monday evening and live music on some Saturdays. Good food using locally sourced ingredients is offered (no food Mon). A lower-priced beer labelled Bull's Malling Special is normally from Musket. Q🌳🛇🏵🍴♣🍺🚃(72,151)🐾🛇

Malling Jug
52 High Street, ME19 6LU (in narrow alley opp Swan St between funeral director's and charity shop)
☎ (01732) 667832
Kent Session Pale; 7 changing beers (sourced nationally; often Goacher's, Kent, Tiny Rebel) Ⓖ
A small, modern stylish pub down an alleyway off the High Street. Current and forthcoming beers are shown on a board near the bar and on clipboards dotted around. Various bottled and canned beers, mainly from the UK and Belgium, are listed at sensible prices. A periodic table of beer styles helps you to choose. Newspapers are supplied but there is no music or electronic machines. Snacks are available to accompany the drinks. There is table service at busy times. 🏵♿🚃♣🍺🚃(72,151)🐾

Westerham

Real Ale Way
23 High Street, TN16 1RA
⊕ therealaleway.com
4 changing beers (sourced locally; often Larkins, Tonbridge, Westerham) Ⓖ
Westerham welcomed the 'little sister' of the Real Ale Way in Hayes, Kent, in 2019, which showcases Kentish beers and ciders. A changing selection of up to six cask ales and a similar number of ciders are chalked on a large board adjacent to the bar, and are served from a cool room behind. Stairs lead up to a cosy cottage-style retreat which may also serve as a function space by prior arrangement. Bus services connect to the towns of Sevenoaks, Edenbridge, Biggin Hill and Bromley. Q♣🍺🐾🛇

Westerham Brewery Tap Room
Beggars Lane, TN16 1QP
☎ (01732) 864427 ⊕ westerhambrewery.co.uk
Westerham British Bulldog, Spirit of Kent; 2 changing beers (sourced locally; often Westerham) Ⓗ

Brewing was proudly restored to Westerham town after an absence of half a century with this modern development comprising brewery, taproom and shop. The stylish bar offers four core or seasonal cask ales along with a range of keg beers, and is surrounded by tempting merchandise, bottles and mini-casks to take home. Further seating extends among the brewing vessels. Street-food operators provide pizzas, burgers and moules Friday through Sunday. Brewery tours are bookable every Friday and Saturday, and many other events are listed on the website.
ᗷ੭Ⓘ&ⓦＰ☕(1,246) ✿ 奈

Westgate-on-Sea

Bake & Alehouse
21 St Mildred's Road, CT8 8RE
☎ 07913 368787 ⊕ bakeandalehouse.com
5 changing beers Ⓖ
Welcoming micropub down the alleyway between the Carlton Cinema and a bookmaker's, an oasis for real ale drinkers in the area. A selection of around five changing beers mainly from Kentish breweries is served straight from the barrel, kept in a temperature-controlled room, along with a range of Kentish ciders. With seating for around 20 people, the small interior has been managed well, creating a welcoming atmosphere. Locally produced cheese and pork pies are available. Local CAMRA Pub of the Year 2019 and 2020. Q➳♣♦Ｒ✿

Whitstable

Ship Centurion Ⓛ ✅
111 High Street, CT5 1AY
☎ (01227) 264740
Adnams Southwold Bitter; 4 changing beers (sourced regionally; often Canterbury Ales, Goacher's, Ramsgate) Ⓗ
A friendly and traditional town-centre pub. Colourful hanging baskets add to its charm in summer, and pictures of Whitstable are displayed in the bar. A Kentish

beer is always served. Home-cooked bar food often includes authentic German dishes, and there is a schnitzel on Saturday (no food Sun). Live music plays on Thursday evenings (except in January). A good place to watch sport on Sky. ᗷⓘ➳♣♦Ｒ✿奈

Twelve Taps
102 High Street, CT5 1AZ
☎ (01227) 770777 ⊕ thetwelvetaps.co.uk
House beer (by Time); 11 changing beers (sourced regionally; often Buxton, Pig & Porter, Wild Beer) Ⓗ
A craft beer bar decorated in warm colours, with wooden floors and a pleasant suntrap courtyard. Try a sample paddle of three beers to find your favourites. There are many artisan gins (free tonic on Tuesdays), plus organic wines, bottled ciders and interesting soft drinks. The bar is open on bank holiday Mondays. There is a quiz on the last Wednesday of each month. Check Twitter for the winner of the Dog of the Day award. ᗷ੭&➳Ｒ✿奈

Wingham

Anchor Inn Ⓛ ✅
High Street, CT3 1BJ
☎ (01227) 720392 ⊕ theanchoratwingham.com
Harvey's Sussex Best Bitter; 4 changing beers (often Hopdaemon, Old Dairy, Timothy Taylor) Ⓗ
This traditional family-run pub has a welcoming environment, with its rambling interior, dark beams and wooden floors. Multiple awards are evidence of the work and effort that has gone into running it. There are two real ales, usually including one from Kent, and one real cider. Music events, quiz nights, clubs, social and charity activities make for a busy calendar. The function room/ Arts Centre doubles as a community resource and the large garden has bat and trap and pétanque pitches.
ᗷ੭Ⓘ♣♦Ｒ☕(11,43) ✿奈

Duke of Wellington, Ryarsh (Photo: John K Thorne/Flickr CC BY 2.0)

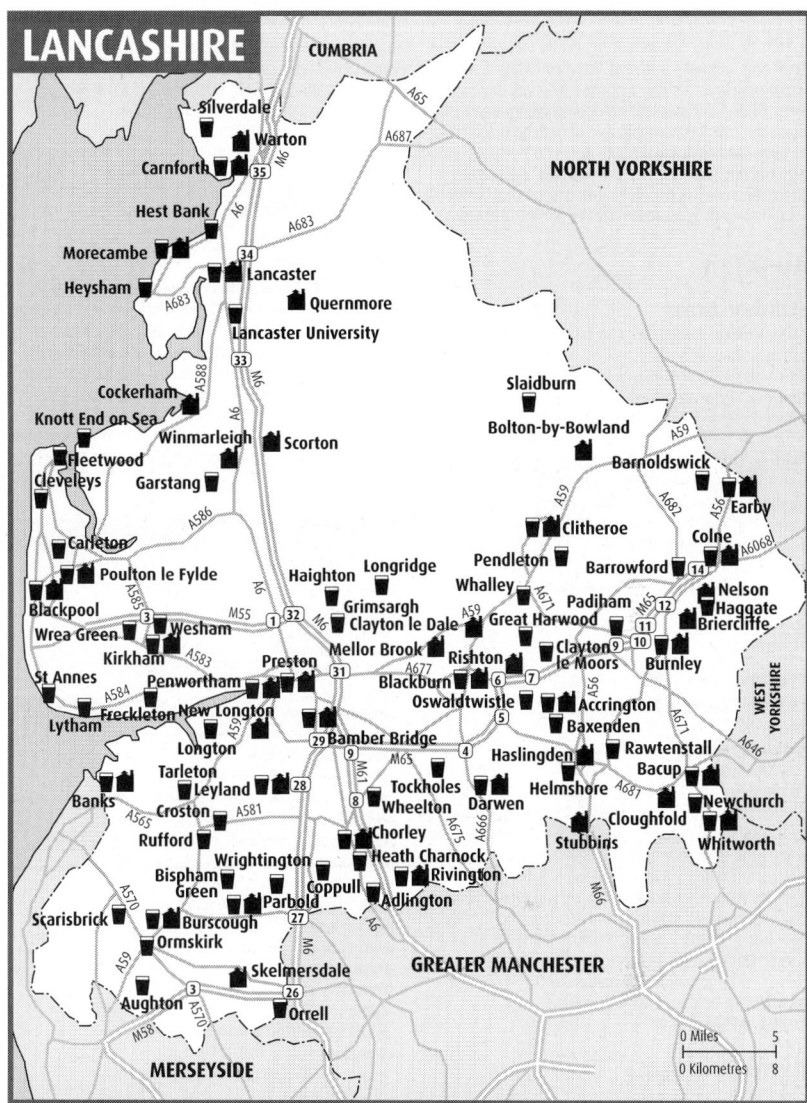

LANCASHIRE

CUMBRIA

NORTH YORKSHIRE

Silverdale
Warton
Carnforth (35)
Hest Bank
Morecambe (34)
Heysham
Lancaster
Quernmore
Lancaster University (33)
Cockerham
Knott End on Sea
Winmarleigh
Scorton
Fleetwood
Cleveleys
Garstang
Slaidburn
Bolton-by-Bowland
Barnoldswick
Carleton
Haighton
Longridge
Pendleton
Clitheroe
Barrowford
Colne
Earby
Poulton le Fylde
Whalley
Padiham
Nelson
Haggate
Blackpool (3)
Grimsargh
Clayton le Dale
Great Harwood (11) (12) Briercliffe
Wrea Green
Wesham
Mellor Brook
Rishton
Clayton (10)
le Moors
Burnley
Kirkham
Preston (31)
Blackburn (6) (7)
St Annes
Penwortham
Oswaldtwistle
Accrington
Freckleton New Longton
Baxenden
Lytham
Longton (29) Bamber Bridge
Haslingden
Rawtenstall
Tarleton
Leyland (9)
Bacup
Banks
Croston (28)
Tockholes
Helmshore
Newchurch
Rufford
Wheelton
Darwen
Cloughfold
Whitworth
Wrightington
Chorley
Stubbins
Bispham
Heath Charnock
Green
Coppull
Rivington
Scarisbrick
Parbold (27)
Adlington
Burscough
Ormskirk
Skelmersdale
GREATER MANCHESTER
Aughton (3) (26)
Orrell
MERSEYSIDE

0 Miles 5
0 Kilometres 8

WEST YORKSHIRE

Accrington

Canine Club 🄻

45-47 Abbey Street, BB5 1EN
☎ (01254) 233999
Tetley Bitter; 3 changing beers (sourced nationally; often Old School, Reedley Hallows, Worsthorne) 🄷
An award-winning social club on a busy street in an area of the town centre known for its many independent retailers. The central bar serves a comfortable lounge to the front, and a games room to the rear where snooker, pool and darts are played. There is a large upstairs function room. This traditional club is always busy but is welcoming to all. Alongside the Tetley bitter there is a changing range, usually featuring local breweries, plus a visitor from further afield. ➧♣🚲(464,X41)🛜

Grants 🄻

1 Manchester Road, BB5 2BQ
☎ (01254) 393938 🌐 grantsbar.co.uk

Big Clock Pals 1916, Bitter & Twisted, Dirty Blonde, Ruby 100; 4 changing beers 🄷
A large, imposing building close to the college on the edge of the town centre. The pub is home to the impressive Big Clock Brewery, which can be viewed from the main drinking area. Up to eight Big Clock ales are on handpump along with a good range of boxed real ciders. Beers and ciders can be served in third-pint glasses on a wooden platter for those who want to sample a range. A menu of pizzas and pasta dishes includes many vegetarian options, and a wood-fired pizza oven provides a proper Italian twist. Q❄️🞉❄️➧♿P🚲

Adlington

Spinners Arms 🄻

23 Church Street, PR7 4EX
☎ (01257) 483331
Moorhouse's Pride of Pendle; Rudgate Ruby Mild; 5 changing beers (often Abbeydale, Oakham) 🄷

The pub is known as the Bottom Spinners to differentiate it from the other Spinners Arms in the village. Built in 1838 and originally a row of three cottages, it is welcoming and friendly; a single bar serves three seating areas. There is a pleasant outdoor drinking area to the front. The pub has no pool table or gaming machine, just an open log fire. The bar menu offers home-cooked food, with Sunday specials. Two regular cask ales and five alternating guests are served, often from local breweries. Small functions are catered for. ⏳❄🚲⇌🅿️🚌(8A)🐾🛜

Aughton

Stanley Arms

24 St Michael Road, L39 6SA (off A59 at Aughton Springs) SD391055

☎ (01695) 423241 ⊕ thestanleyarmsaughton.co.uk

Timothy Taylor Landlord; 3 changing beers Ⓗ

Situated beside a historic Norman church, the Stanley has distinctive 18th-century architecture and was originally a coaching stop for postal deliveries. Decorated throughout with Tudor-style woodwork, there are several side rooms containing brewing memorabilia around the centrally placed bar, which dispenses from five handpumps. Immaculately kept both inside and out, the pub is exceptionally popular for its excellent home-cooked and locally sourced food. ⏳❄🚲🅿️🚌🛜

Bacup

Crown Inn Ⓛ ✅

19 Greave Road, OL13 9HQ

☎ (01706) 873982

Pictish Brewers Gold; 3 changing beers Ⓗ

Cosy traditional country pub, just off the road out to Todmorden, with a spacious L-shaped bar and stone-flagged floors throughout, built in 1865 and once owned by Baxter's of Glentop Brewery. A welcoming coal fire warms the atmosphere in the cooler months. There are always three beers available, usually local, and traditional home-cooked food is served most evenings. Quiz nights are Wednesday and Sunday, and the second floor has a function room accommodating up to 35 guests. Other events including live music are also staged. There is a large patio beer garden to the front. Beer festivals are held in July and October. ⏳❄🅿️🚌(465)🐾

Bamber Bridge

Beer Box Ⓛ

Unit 3, 143 Station Road, PR5 6LA

☎ (01772) 339619

5 changing beers (sourced locally) Ⓗ

Bamber Bridge's second micropub opened in 2018 on the main road running through the northern end of the town, and is in premises previously operated by North West Domestic Services. There is one relatively large room with plenty of seating and some standing room, as well as an outside seating area to the front. Up to five real ales are available, mainly from local breweries and including one dark beer. A previous winner of local CAMRA Pub of the Season. Q♿⇌♿🚌(125)🐾🛜

Brig 'n' Barrel Ⓛ

188 Station Road, PR5 6TP

☎ 07728 794755 ⊕ brig-n-barrel.business.site

6 changing beers (sourced locally) Ⓗ

The Brig 'n' Barrel was Bamber Bridge's first micropub, opening in June 2018 in a former electrical shop premises. It specialises in quality cask and craft beers and gins. There are six handpumps serving a changing

selection of, mostly, locally brewed beers from smaller breweries; two real ciders are also stocked. There is just one room in this cosy rustic bar, with a small amount of outside seating as well. Q⏳❄⇌♿🚌(125)🐾🛜

Banks

Ralph's Wife's

Hoole Lane, PR9 8BD

☎ (01704) 214678

Fell Crag; 2 changing beers (sourced locally) Ⓗ

A coffee shop and bar with two changing real ales, now the only real ale outlet in Banks since the closure of the New Fleetwood in July 2020. It has the usual friendly, welcoming attributes of micropubs, and benefits from some seating outside. Tea and coffee are also served, including a range of speciality teas. It has held tapas nights and cheese and wine events. A welcome addition to the real ale scene in Southport and west Lancashire. QP🚌(2,X2)🐾🛜

REAL ALE BREWERIES

4 Mice 🛢 Bolton-by-Bowland
Accidental 🛢 Lancaster
Avid Quernmore
BB18 🛢 Earby (NEW)
Beer Brothers ✦ Bamber Bridge
Ben's ✦ Chorley (NEW)
Big Clock 🛢 Accrington
Bishop's Crook Penwortham (brewing suspended)
Bowland Clitheroe
Brewsmith Stubbins
Chain House New Longton
Chapel Street 🛢 Poulton-le-Fylde
Clay Brow Skelmersdale
Crankshaft ✦ Leyland
Cross Bay ✦ Morecambe
Farm Yard ✦ Cockerham
Folly Clayton le Dale (NEW)
Fuzzy Duck Poulton-le-Fylde
Hop Vine 🛢 Burscough
Hopstar Darwen
Lancaster Lancaster
Lytham ✦ Kirkham
Mighty Medicine ✦ Whitworth
Moorhouse's Burnley
Northern Whisper ✦ Cloughfold
Old Boot Bacup (NEW)
Old School ✦ Warton
Oscars Nelson
Parker Banks
Patten 🛢 Winmarleigh
Peregrine Rishton (NEW)
Priest Town Preston
Problem Child 🛢 Parbold
Q Brew Carnforth
Reedley Hallows Burnley
Rivington ✦ Rivington
Rock Solid Blackpool
Rossendale 🛢 Haslingden
Snaggletooth Darwen
Snowhill Scorton
Tap & Vent 🛢 Kirkham (NEW)
Three B's 🛢 Blackburn
Three Peaks Nelson
Thwaites Mellor Brook
Unbound Colne (NEW)
West Coast Rock 🛢 Blackpool
Withnell's ✦ Chorley
Worsthorne Briercliffe

Barnoldswick

Barlick Tap Ale House 🅛
8 Newtown, BB18 5UQ
☎ 07739 088846
5 changing beers (sourced nationally) 🅗
This friendly one-room micropub was the first to be set up in Barnoldswick and is just off the town square, two minutes from the main bus stop. A choice of five constantly changing cask beers is offered, one of which will be a dark beer and one a LocAle. There is a large selection of continental bottled beers, and it always has two ciders. It hosts occasional events and tastings. No music is played. Q✿●🖵(M1)✿

Rolls-Royce Leisure
Skipton Road, BB18 6HJ
☎ (01282) 818093 ● rollsleisurebarnoldswick.co.uk
3 changing beers (sourced regionally) 🅗
The expansive Rolls-Royce leisure club incorporates a number of fitness and sporting facilities and the award-winning Trent lounge bar, which was voted local CAMRA's branch Club of the Year 2020. There is a smart function room which hosts regular live entertainment and private functions and is licensed for weddings. The Trent restaurant serves quality food. You do not have to work at Rolls-Royce to enjoy the facilities. ♣🖵

Barrowford

Bankers Draft
143 Gisburn Road, BB9 6HQ
☎ 07739 870880
5 changing beers (sourced nationally) 🅗
This imposing detached former bank is now a small and friendly micropub, specialising in real ale and conversation, with no loud music or TVs. The five handpumps dispense continually rotating cask ales from small brewers nationwide, offering a great variety of beer styles from hoppy blondes and traditional bitters to dark beers. There is also a good selection of wines and bottled craft lagers and wheat beers, with at least one real cider normally on draught. Q⌂●P🖵(2)✿

Baxenden

Dog & Partridge ✔
41 Back Lane, BB5 2RE
☎ (01254) 239992
Theakston Best Bitter; 4 changing beers (sourced nationally) 🅗
A popular village pub that sits on Back Lane, the original road from Accrington to Manchester, a short walk uphill from Manchester Road. Behind the pub is Baxenden Cricket Club and a sign on the pub wall indicates right for cricket and left for golf. The Dog has been partially opened up but retains separate areas for drinking. There is usually entertainment on Saturday nights, as well as a weekly quiz. Note the etched glass Lion Ales on the entrance door. Buses from Accrington to Manchester and the Rossendale Valley pass close by. ✿♣P🖵

Bispham Green

Eagle & Child
Maltkiln Lane, L40 3SG
☎ (01257) 462297 ● eagleandchildbispham.co.uk
Southport Golden Sands; Thwaites Original; Wainwright; 5 changing beers 🅗
An 18th-century hostelry with eight handpumps that showcases local ales; Southport Golden Sands is always available, and a variety of guest ales includes Prospect,

Wigan Brewhouse and Moorhouse's. This busy country hostelry has been Lancashire Dining Pub of the Year and is noted for its food. The huge beer garden, with its wildlife area and great views, hosts a beer festival on the first May bank holiday. Quiz night is every Monday. ♿✿◑●P🖵(337)✿🐾

Blackburn

Black Bull 🅛
Brokenstone Road, BB3 0LL (corner of Brokenstone Rd and Heys Lane) SD666247
☎ (01254) 581381 ● threebsbrewery.co.uk
Three B's Stoker's Slake, Bobbin's Bitter, Black Bull, Weavers Brew, Knocker Up, Oatmeal Stout; 2 changing beers (sourced locally; often Three B's) 🅗
In the heart of rural Lancashire, this is an independent award-winning family-run pub with brewery attached. There are eight handpumps serving a fine selection of Three B's ales including the exclusive Black Bull Bitter. The three beer wedges are popular. It was built on a farmhouse in the 18th century, purchased by Robert Bell from Thwaites and transformed now into a place for those who appreciate fine beer and friendly conversation. There is no jukebox, fruit machines or food served, it just provides a friendly, relaxing atmosphere. Q⌂✿♿♣P✿

Drummers Arms 🅛
65 King William Street, BB1 7DT
☎ (01254) 941075
Three B's Stoker's Slake; 4 changing beers (sourced locally; often Big Clock, Cross Bay, Hopstar) 🅗
Single-room bar opposite the town hall on the edge of the main shopping area, run by a mother and daughter team. The walls are adorned with breweriana and old pub signs. The majority of beers are sourced from Lancashire breweries, though a visitor from across the Pennines sometimes makes an appearance. Live music followed by an open mic session features on the first Sunday of every month. There is a pleasant terrace out front for alfresco drinking with upcycled drum tables and attractive bespoke garden planters. Blackburn with Darwen CAMRA Pub of the Year 2020. ✿≉●🖵✿

Blackpool

1887 The Brew Room 🅛
139-141 Church Street, FY1 3NU
☎ (01253) 319165 ● thebrewroom1887.co.uk
West Coast Rock Golden Mile, Blackpool Blonde, Oyster Stout, Tangerine Dream, Wonky Donkey; 5 changing beers (sourced nationally; often Cross Bay, Tiny Rebel) 🅗
Blackpool's only brewpub, home to the West Coast Rock Brewing Company, is approximately 150 yards from the Winter Gardens complex. It is a large Victorian establishment which, although open plan, has many quiet corners. Through a door to the rear a viewing platform overlooks the brewery. It offers a selection of 10 real ales (five from the on-site brewery), ciders, and craft beers as well as authentic German lagers. A simple menu of sizeable snacks is served all day. Live music features most Friday and Saturday nights and a popular quiz is held on Mondays. ♿≉✿●🖵✿🐾

Albert's Ale Micropub 🅛
117 Albert Road, FY1 4PW
☎ (01253) 292827 ● blackpoolmicrobar.co.uk
4 changing beers (sourced locally) 🅗/🅖
Forget preconceptions of Blackpool B&Bs at this quirky, hotel cellar bar close to the Winter Gardens complex in

the heart of Blackpool's hotel quarter, just 10 minutes' walk from the promenade and tower. At least four changing ales are on tap, mostly supporting local brewers and normally including a dark beer. A wide range of predominantly Belgian bottled beers is also stocked. The hotel has 11 comfortable bedrooms. Level access is available on request. May also open on bank holiday Mondays. ✿☆≠♂❶🅟🖵❀🛜

Blackpool Cricket Club

Barlow Crescent, West Park Drive, FY3 9EQ (follow signs to Stanley Park)
☎ (01253) 393347 ⊕ blackpoolcricket.co.uk
Wainwright; 4 changing beers (sourced regionally; often Cumbrian Ales, Moorhouse's, Reedley Hallows) Ⓗ
On the western edge of Stanley Park, this club hosts many sports teams. Several TVs show various sporting fixtures. Upstairs functions rooms are available for social events. It has its own squash courts and holds quiz and entertainment nights, as well as an annual beer festival. It has frequently been voted local CAMRA Club of the Year. There is free entry to all cricket games except Lancashire's. ☎☆◑👶🅿🖵(18)❀🛜

Cask

9 Layton Road, FY3 8EA
☎ (01253) 396321
4 changing beers (sourced nationally) Ⓗ
Situated about a mile inland from the centre of Blackpool on main bus routes, Cask provides a range of rapidly changing cask beers from near and far in a pleasant single-room micropub. There is a pavement area to the front and a small drinking yard to the rear. The cemetery opposite contains the grave of the last survivor of the charge of the Light Brigade. Q☎☆🖵❀

No.10 Ale House & Thai Kitchen

258 Whitegate Drive, FY3 9JW
☎ (01253) 694913
5 changing beers (sourced nationally) Ⓗ
Sister pub to No.10 in St Annes on Sea, this place opened in 2018. Enter first into a bright, front room and bar area, and then pass into a comfortable rear room. There is also an upstairs room where diners can partake of a popular Thai menu. The bar has five ales sourced from all over. The walls indicate the owners' support for Blackpool FC and display many fine prints of bygone Blackpool. The bus stop is virtually outside. ☎☆◑🖵🛜

Burnley

Bridge Bier Huis Ⓛ

2 Bank Parade, BB11 1UH
☎ (01282) 411304
Moorhouse's Premier Bitter; 4 changing beers (sourced regionally) Ⓗ
An award-winning true free house with a large open-plan bar that has a log-burner and a small snug to one side. It mainly offers microbrewery beers alongside a changing real cider. More than 60 foreign bottled beers are also sold, plus seven foreign beers on tap including rare German brews. Wednesday is quiz night and live music is hosted on occasional weekends. This welcoming pub opens 5pm Monday or Tuesday if Burnley FC are at home. ☎☆◑≠❤🅿🖵❀

New Brew-m Ⓛ

11 St James Row, BB11 1DR
☎ 07902 961426
Reedley Hallows Pendleside; 5 changing beers (sourced nationally) Ⓗ

This smart micropub in the centre of town is run as the Reedley Hallows Brewery tap. There is always at least one of its own beers on the bar alongside five others sourced nationwide using the head brewer's contacts from years in the trade. A good range of foreign bottled beers and bottled ciders is available. The fully glazed frontage makes the bar feel light and airy. There is a small room upstairs for extra seating. Will open if Burnley FC are at home on a Tuesday night. Q≠🖵❀

Burscough

Old Packet House Ⓛ ✔

29 Liverpool Road North, L40 5TN
☎ (01704) 807330 ⊕ the-old-packet-house.edan.io
Coach House Blonde; 3 changing beers (often Bank Top, Prospect) Ⓗ
A typical canalside pub in the centre of town, featuring a series of old prints of Burscough on the walls. It concentrates on selling real ale but also hosts food afternoons and evenings (no food Mon or Tue). You can watch the boats go past from the garden or from the side of the canal. The pub is over the road from Burscough Wharf, and is ideal for a ramble along the canal. ☎☆◑👶≠(Bridge)🖵(2A,3)❀🛜

Thirsty Duck Ⓛ

Unit 9 & 10 Burscough Wharf, L40 5RZ
☎ (01704) 894600
Hawkshead Bitter; 4 changing beers Ⓗ
A new bar and bottle shop opened up in the Burscough wharf complex making a welcome addition to the thriving real ale scene here. It is tastefully decorated modern bar with five cask lines, 10 keg lines and real cider, as well as a full range of wine and spirits. The bottle shop, the Beer Haul, is just over the courtyard from the bar and is open at the same times; to obtain access ring the bell or speak to the staff in the Thirsty Duck. Q☆👶≠(Bridge)♣❤🅿🖵(2A,3)❀🛜

Carleton

Castle Gardens ✔

Poulton Road, FY6 7NH
☎ (01253) 890015
Moorhouse's White Witch; Purity Pure UBU; Wainwright; house beer (by Black Sheep); 5 changing beers (sourced nationally) Ⓗ
There has been an inn on this site since about 1750. It is a popular outlet which successfully mixes being a food-led destination and local community pub. A range of nine ales is normally on the bar, including five changing guests. A weekly quiz is held on Tuesdays and live music is performed regularly at weekends. There is an outdoor drinking area to the side. ☎☆◑👶🅿🖵(14)❀🛜

Carnforth

Royal Station

Market Street, LA5 9BT
☎ (01524) 733636 ⊕ royalstation.co.uk
6 changing beers Ⓗ
A traditional Victorian station hotel which is slowly getting a facelift. A grand entrance and a foyer lead to a tapas bar, while round the back is the larger and more basic (2016 revamp) Junction Bar, where you will find games, real ale and live music (Fri and Sat). In 1900 the Royal part of the name was added in recognition of the fact that the Duke of York, later to become George V, availed himself of the hotel's hospitality during a shooting trip. A microbrewery is planned. ☆◑≠♣🖵❀🛜

Snug

Unit 6, Carnforth Gateway Building, LA5 9TR (at N end of former mainline up platform)
☎ 07927 396861 ⊕ thesnugmicropub.blogspot.co.uk
5 changing beers ⊞
The area's first micropub. The only drinks are ale, cider, wine, a few soft drinks and at least 10 good-quality gins; the only food is a few light snacks; the only sounds are conversation and the roar of the passing trains. Decor is similarly stripped back: painted walls, bare floorboards and chunky tall tables. The eye is naturally drawn to a beautiful glazed wooden cabinet, where all the drinks are stored. Parking is on the station car park (for which there is a charge). Q🌑🕭≷♣🌑🗑🖵🌑

Chorley

Ale Station 🅛

60 Chapel Street, PR7 1BS
☎ (01257) 368003
9 changing beers (sourced locally; often Hawkshead, Rock the Boat) ⊞
Family-run micropub conveniently situated near both the bus and train stations. A modern-looking venue with a wine-bar feel, this inviting place offers a full range of drinks. Up to nine changing real ales are served, mainly from north-western microbreweries, although expect to find others from far and wide. There are also two changing real ciders. A state-of-the-art digital display board provides full price information and real ale details, in addition to updated train times for the railway traveller. Pictures of old Chorley adorn the walls.
Q🕭≷🌑🖵🌑🛜

Bob Inn

24 Market Place, PR7 1DA
☎ 07767 238410
3 changing beers (sourced nationally) ⊞
The smallest pub in the area, this is a tiny bar in a market stall with an adjacent unit used as a lounge space. It has outside seating and drinkers often spill over into the market. Conversation and banter are an important part of the experience. The pub has something for every taste, with three changing cask beers from smaller breweries nationally and at least two local ciders. No food is served, but you are welcome to bring your own. This is a local CAMRA multi award-winning pub. Q🌑🛋🕭≷🌑🖵🌑

Malt 'n' Hops 🅛

50-52 Friday Street, PR6 0AA
☎ (01257) 260074
Bank Top Dark Mild; 8 changing beers (sourced nationally; often Fernandes, Moorhouse's, Rat) ⊞
Converted from an old shop in 1989, this pub is close to the town's railway and bus stations. The single L-shaped bar is on two levels with a bright yet traditional feel, and has a pleasant beer garden. This is a genuine free house with up to nine guest ales, usually from Lancashire and Yorkshire micros, including Rat, Wily Fox, Ossett, Elland, Lancaster, Fernandes, Goose Eye and Blackedge. A regular mild, good-value filled rolls and pork pies are usually on sale. 🛋🌑≷🌑🖵🌑🛜

Masons Arms 🅛

98 Harpers Lane, PR6 0HU
☎ 07464 841589
6 changing beers (sourced locally; often Blackedge, Pictish) ⊞
Tastefully modernised multi-room pub a mile from the town centre. This light and airy yet cosy pub has a growing reputation for good beer. The taproom serves six changing ales, usually including a dark brew. Most are

sourced from north-western micros but beers from further afield are also sold. The taproom and two lounges with wood-burning stoves give distinctly different drinking areas, and there is a partly covered beer garden to the rear. Pizzas are served daily. 🛋🌑🖵(24,125)🌑🛜

Prince of Wales 🗸

9-11 Cowling Brow, PR6 0QE
☎ (01257) 260815
Banks's Sunbeam; Jennings Cumberland Ale; Marston's 61 Deep; Wainwright; 4 changing beers (sourced nationally) ⊞
Friendly multi-roomed local with a central bar that serves a taproom, large lounge and pool room, with a further room off the entrance hall. There are real fires in both lounges, and a beer garden to the rear. The pub normally stocks eight beers from the Marston's stable, with the guest ales changing regularly. No meals are served but sandwiches and pies may be available. Live music is hosted at the weekends but the place is quiet at other times. Close to the Leeds-Liverpool Canal with access nearby, this is a great walkers' pub; dogs are welcome and treats provided. 🛋🌑♣🌑🖵🌑🛜

Shepherds' Hall Ale House 🅛

67 Chapel Street, PR7 1BS
5 changing beers (sourced nationally) ⊞
This welcoming bar next door to the bus station was the first micropub in Chorley when it opened in 2014, and was extended into adjoining premises all in 2021. It serves up to five ales from microbreweries all over the country, with a wide range of beer styles, always including a dark brew. Two craft keg lines often feature Rivington beers, and third-pint beer paddles are available. Two real ciders and a variety of other drinks ensure there is something to suit all tastes. Q≷♣🌑🗑🖵🌑🛜

Clayton le Moors

Old England Forever 🅛 🗸

13 Church Street, BB5 5HT
☎ (01254) 383332
Bank Top Dark Mild, Flat Cap; 4 changing beers (sourced regionally; often Bank Top, Prospect) ⊞
Acquired by the Bank Top Brewery in 2018, this Edwardian terraced pub was completely refurbished prior to reopening in a style reminiscent of its establishments in and around Bolton. It sits just off Barnes Square and is easily reached from the towpath of the Leeds-Liverpool canal. A long bar faces the only room in the pub. An unusual feature is the section of glass flooring in front of the bar from where the cellar can be viewed. The pub is wheelchair friendly and has fully accessible toilets. Q🌑🕭♣🌑🖵(6,7)

Cleveleys

Jolly Tars 🗸

154-158 Victoria Road West, FY5 3NE
☎ (01253) 856042
Greene King Abbot; Ruddles Best Bitter; Sharp's Doom Bar; 7 changing beers (sourced nationally; often Bank Top, Moorhouse's, Phoenix) ⊞
Named after a nine-strong, highly popular family troupe of entertainers who pleased the locals and visiting crowds during the 1940s, this busy place has a great reputation for food and drinks and friendly staff. It is also a welcoming environment in which to enjoy a quiet drink in several secluded booths. The popular front drinking area can get busy. Several bespoke pieces of John Ditchfield Glasform glass decorate the pub. 🛋🌑🕼🕭🌑🖵🌑🛜

Shipwreck Brewhouse 🅛

53 Victoria Road West, FY5 1AJ
☎ (01253) 540597
4 changing beers (sourced locally) 🅗
An oasis of calm on the popular, main shopping street of town. A range of four mostly local beers is sold along with a selection of bottled and canned beers and ciders. A large covered seating area is at the front and a secret beer garden at the rear, along with a function room. Open from 9.30am daily for the sale of teas and coffees, snacks and home-made cakes. 🏠🌙🕃🔔🚃🐾

Clitheroe

Bowland Beer Hall 🅛 ✔

Greenacre Street, BB7 1EB
☎ (01200) 401035 ⊕ holmesmill.co.uk/beer-hall
Bowland Pheasant Plucker, Gold, AONB, Boxer Blonde, Hen Harrier, Buster IPA; changing beers (sourced nationally) 🅗
The popular beer hall is now a major part of Clitheroe's thriving beer scene. Up to 24 guest beers are on offer alongside the large number from the on-site Bowland Brewery, visible from the main bar area. There are many beery events such as Meet the Brewer evenings. A completely new selection of beers is offered every Thursday, with weekly drink-up sessions. The complex hosts a hotel, cinema, coffee shop and delicatessen and is a short walk from Clitheroe castle and the town centre. Many buses stop close by. 🏃🏠🌙🕃🚃🐾🍴P🚃🐾

New Inn 🅛

20 Parson Lane, BB7 2JN
☎ (01200) 423312
Moorhouse's Premier Bitter; Coach House Gunpowder Mild, Farrier's Best Bitter; Moorhouse's Pride of Pendle, Blond Witch; Coach House Blueberry Classic Bitter; 5 changing beers (sourced regionally; often Prospect, Saltaire, Worsthorne) 🅗
The bar at the New Inn is a welcome sight, with at least 10 beers on offer. The bar itself is central, with a number of smaller rooms clustered around it. In addition to the regular beers from Coach House and Moorhouse's you may also find the likes of Saltaire, Ilkley, Prospect or Wharfedale breweries represented. The pub dates from the early 1800s and faces Clitheroe Castle. It is just a short walk from the bus and railway stations.
Q🏠🅐🚃🐾

Colne

Admiral Lord Rodney 🅛

Mill Green, BB8 0TA
☎ (01282) 219759
9 changing beers (sourced regionally; often Goose Eye, Ilkley, Reedley Hallows) 🅗
A much-loved community pub in Colne's South Valley area, the old industrial heart of the town. The stone-flagged floor includes mosaics and there are beautiful tiles up the inner staircase. Set out in three rooms, the pub has become the meeting place for a number of clubs. There is regular live entertainment during the evenings, plus local history and art displays. There has been a recent refurbishment with open fires and flagged floors, plus a much-improved outdoor seating area and a separate smokers' space. Q🏃🏠🌙🕃🍴🐾🎏

Boyce's Barrel

7 New Market Street, BB8 9BJ
☎ 07736 900111
5 changing beers (sourced nationally) 🅗

The first micropub in Colne, a member of the Micropub Association, offering five high-quality real ales, no music, no lager, just a great atmosphere and plenty of banter. Tastefully styled with tall polished wooden sleeper tables, it is reminiscent of a rail staging post. Ales are rotated often, with new beers put on the bar almost as soon as a barrel runs dry. All ales come from non-local breweries, and always include one mild and one porter or stout. A place that is sure to suit any real ale fan's tastes. Q🕃🚃🍴🚃🐾

Coppull

Wheatsheaf 🅛

1 Westerton Court, Spendmore Lane, PR7 4NY
☎ 0871 951 1000
3 changing beers 🅗
The Wheatsheaf has been at the centre of the local community since the 1700s, although the current building is not original. It underwent an extensive refurbishment a few years ago and has a smart, modern interior. Recent improvements include a new outdoor drinking area. Three handpumps serve a changing selection of real ales with a focus on beers from local microbreweries – Prospect, Bank Top and Blackedge often feature. Q🏃🏠🌙🕃🍴P🚃🐾🎏

Croston

Wheatsheaf

Town Road, PR26 9RA
☎ (01772) 600370 ⊕ wheatsheaf-croston.com
Goose Eye Chinook Blonde; Hawkshead Windermere Pale; Hop Back Summer Lightning; 2 changing beers (sourced nationally) 🅗
On the main road and overlooking the village green, this recently refurbished pub has a contemporary feel. It has a distinct area for dining as well as a comfortable drinking space with sofas and chairs. There is a large patio to the front, venue for an annual beer festival in October. Three regular and two changing ales are on tap. Food is available lunchtimes and evenings during the week and all day at weekends, when breakfast is also served. Children are welcome. 🏃🏠🌙🕃🚃P🚃🐾🎏

Darwen

Bird in th'hand 🅛

225 Duckworth Street, BB3 1AU
☎ 07926 115292
4 changing beers (sourced regionally; often Blackedge, Hopstar, Three B's) 🅗
A bar-cum-bottle shop named after the pub that stood here over 100 years ago. One room contains benches and a log-burner; another has relaxing sofas. The pub has four handpumps and offers one boxed cider, alongside 10 craft lines, three for ciders. Shelves on one wall stock a wide range of international and UK bottled beers, some of them bottle conditioned, which can be consumed on or off the premises. Toilets are upstairs. May close early if quiet at the start of the week. 🚃🍴🚃(1)🐾

Number 39 Hopstar Brewery Tap 🅛

39-41 Bridge Street, BB3 2AA
☎ 07531 425352 ⊕ hopstarbrewery.co.uk
Hopstar Dizzy Danny Ale, Dark Knight, Off t'Mill, Smokey Joe's Black Beer, JC, Lancashire Gold; 2 changing beers (sourced nationally; often Slater's) 🅗
A classic single-roomed continental-styled bar with an eclectic range of background music serving a variety of Hopstar beers. It is a strong supporter of real cider, and two or more ciders or perries are available. Bottled

continental and world beers and draught Timmermans are also on offer. Thursday nights usually feature quality live music concerts, Friday is tapas day and Sunday afternoon has the legendary apple, cheese and perry session. Frequent buses between Blackburn and Bolton pass close by. ☕️✿❄♣🌓🖳(1)🌸🎱📶

Earby

Red Lion 🅛
72 Red Lion Street, BB18 6RD
☎ (01282) 843395
Naylor's Gold, Pinnacle Blonde; 4 changing beers (sourced locally; often Settle) 🅗
A warm and friendly welcome awaits you both from the host and regulars. This is a traditional country local, owned by local people. Both rooms have been attractively renovated – the lounge is heated with a wood-burner. An extensive menu is served in the lounge lunchtime and evenings. The pub is close to a Youth Hostel and is a drinkers' delight. Q☕️🌓🖳🌸

Fleetwood

Royal Oak Hotel 🅛
171 Lord Street, FY7 6SR
☎ (01253) 873486
Banks's Sunbeam; house beer (by Reedley Hallows); 5 changing beers (sourced locally; often Blackedge, Moorhouse's, Worsthorne) 🅗
Known locally as Dead 'Uns, this pub was rescued from closure in 2013, and still retains many original features. Up to five beers are served, most sourced from within a 50-mile radius. There is a small outside drinking area to the rear. Live music takes place regularly at weekends. Away fans of clubs playing Fleetwood Town FC are welcome. Dogs are allowed in the vaults only. ✿🖳♣🐾🌸📶

Steamer
Queens Terrace, FY7 6BT
☎ (01253) 681001
Lancaster Red; Reedley Hallows Pendleside; 3 changing beers (sourced nationally; often Bowness Bay, Cross Bay, Kirkby Lonsdale) 🅗
One of Fleetwood's oldest pubs, this former coaching inn is close to the town's museum and Fleetwood Market. It is convenient for buses, trams and the Knott End ferry. Up to five beers are on the bar. There is live music on Friday and Saturday nights, a singer on Tuesday afternoon and charity karaoke on a Friday afternoon. Pool, darts, dominoes and snooker can be played. If you are lucky, you might be served by TV legend Syd Little. Food is available Tuesday to Sunday. ☕️✿🌓👟🚋(Victoria Street) ♣🖳🌸📶

Thomas Drummond ✅
London Street, FY7 6JE
☎ (01253) 775020
Greene King Abbot; Ruddles Best Bitter; 8 changing beers (often Bank Top, Moorhouse's) 🅗
Converted from a former Sunday school, this spacious yet cosy pub guarantees a warm and friendly welcome to all. A great range of ales from light to dark and medium to strong come mainly from the North's brewers. Regulars are encouraged to help in the selection of beers. Cider-in-a-box is also available. There is a pleasant small garden to the rear. ☕️✿🌓👟🍺🖳🌸📶

Freckleton

Vestry Taproom
68-74 Lytham Road, PR4 1XA
☎ (01772) 634924
3 changing beers (sourced regionally) 🅗
Situated a short walk from the centre of Freckleton, this micropub opened its door at the end of 2019. Awaiting the thirsty drinker is a range of three ales, mostly from local brewers, along with a selection of craft beers. There is a pleasant outdoor area to the front. Although a TV shows sporting events and live music is played on many weekends, this is mostly unobtrusive, and the pub is an ideal spot for conversation. ✿🌓🖳🌸📶

Garstang

Th'Owd Tithe Barn ✅
Church Street, PR3 1PA
☎ (01995) 604486 ⊕ tithebarngarstang.com
Wainwright; 3 changing beers 🅗
A pub-restaurant since 1973, this building dates back to 1701. The canal company later dug a large basin next to the barn, creating an ideal space for patio drinking in the summer. Most of the interior is a large dining area heated by a wood-burning stove. Two smaller rooms are comfortably pubby and well-used by locals. The building is open to the rafters and the space aloft houses a display of obsolete agricultural implements. Quiz night is Tuesday. ✿🌓♣🖳🌸

Great Harwood

1B Tap 🅛
1B Glebe Street, BB6 7AA
4 changing beers (sourced nationally; often Snaggletooth) 🅗
Welcoming two-roomed bar opened in former office premises by three real ale enthusiasts. It is close to Towngate square and preservation area, on a side street opposite the post office. The main room, featuring plenty of beer- and brewery-related items, sells a changing and skilfully selected range of cask beers which usually includes a stout or porter. Local breweries predominate. A side room housing a separate bar serving gin and world beers offers additional seating. Note the collection of beer festival glasses on display in the bar. Local CAMRA Pub of the Year 2020. 🍺🖳📶

Grimsargh

Plough 🅛 ✅
187 Preston Road, PR2 5JR
☎ (01772) 700666 ⊕ ploughgrimsargh.co.uk
Timothy Taylor Landlord; house beer (by Theakston); 3 changing beers (often Blackedge, Lancaster, Titanic) 🅗
Large traditional village pub on the main Preston-Longridge road in the centre of the village, with a friendly and welcoming atmosphere. It has a bar and a separate dining area that serves home-cooked food. Five handpumps dispense two regular beers – Timothy Taylor Landlord and Grimsargh Wetlands (Theakston's Lightfoot) – plus three guests ales, one of which is a LocAle from the SIBA list. This family-friendly place is popular with the locals and has a large garden at the rear. Dogs are welcome in the bar area. ☕️✿🌓👟🅐♣🖳(1)🌸📶

Haggate

Hare & Hounds ✅
1 Halifax Road, BB10 3QH

☎ (01282) 424612
4 changing beers (sourced locally) Ⓗ
A traditional multi-roomed country pub in the Briercliffe area of Burnley, with superb open views over Pennine moorland to the rear. There are separate rooms at the front and a large dining area at the back. The pleasant beer garden offers comfortable alfresco drinking. Rightly proud of its cider offering, it was local CAMRA Cider Pub of the Year 2020. Q♿❁◐♣♠P♫🐾🐾🛜

Haighton

Haighton Manor Ⓛ
Haighton Green Lane, PR2 5SQ
☎ (01772) 706350
House beer (by Phoenix); 6 changing beers (often Hawkshead, Moorhouse's, Worsthorne) Ⓗ
Refurbished and extended in 2016, this former country house hotel is now a bustling pub and dining venue. Stone walls, flagged and wooden floors, low-beamed ceilings and open fires maintain the country house feel. Seven handpumps offer a varied range of real ales, including a dark mild or stout, and a real cider. Quality locally sourced food is served as well as a selection of beer tapas. A conservatory and patio provide views across the fields. Walkers and dogs are welcome. ❁❁◐♿Å♠P🐾🛜

Heath Charnock

Yew Tree Ⓛ
Dill Hall Brow, PR6 9HA
☎ (01257) 480344 ⊕ yewtreeinnanglezarke.co.uk
4 changing beers (sourced locally; often Blackedge, Northern Monkey) Ⓗ
Attractive, isolated pub with fine views over open countryside. The stone-built building has flagged floors on two levels and is essentially open plan, but walls and partitions create cosy areas. Beers from the nearby Blackedge brewery are served alongside a guest ale or two from another independent local brewery. The pub has a reputation for quality food, and offers a full range of meals featuring locally sourced produce. Dogs are welcome in the bar but not the restaurant. Closing times can vary. Q❁❁◐♿Å♠P🐾🛜

Helmshore

Robin Hood Inn Ⓛ ✓
280 Holcombe Road, BB4 4NP
☎ (01706) 404200
Hydes Original; 4 changing beers Ⓗ
Traditional stone-built village pub which, although opened up, still retains the impression of having three separate rooms with two open fires. The original Glen Top brewery windows are a feature. Beers from the seasonal ranges of Hydes and Beer Studio dominate the guest ales. Quiz nights are held on Thursdays. A small beer garden overlooking Helmshore Textile Museum and the lodge can be reached by steps to the side. Q❁❁◐♿♠(11) 🐾

Hest Bank

Crossing
6 Coastal Road, LA2 6HN
☎ 07584 660075
5 changing beers Ⓗ
A former café that opened as a micropub in 2018. The stone Victorian-style building has a timber extension and a plate-glass window from café days. The layout is U-shaped, with the bar counter near the entrance and a wood-burning stove in the middle. A back room features games, bound copies of Railway magazine and photos of Hest Bank station, which closed in 1969. The pub's name refers to the fact that it is close to both one of the last level crossings on the West Coast Main Line and the ancient route over the sands. Q♣♠(5,55A)🐾🛜

Heysham

Bookmakers ✓
364 Heysham Road, LA3 2BJ
☎ 07785 257648
5 changing beers Ⓗ
This micropub in a former betting shop, set among other shops in a suburban neighbourhood, has been a popular addition to the micropub scene in this area. The single wedge-shaped room is done out in industrial chic with a few comfy chairs and bar stools, and an arrangement of standing and seated areas. It attracts large numbers of locals. ♿♣♠🐾

Kirkham

Tap & Vent Brewhouse Ⓛ
26 Poulton Street, PR4 2AB
☎ (01772) 382401 ⊕ tapandventbrewhouse.co.uk
8 changing beers (sourced regionally; often Lytham) Ⓗ
A traditional-looking shop from the outside, a modern pub on the inside, and located right in the centre of Kirkham, just up from the Market Square and bus stops. It offers good range of guest ales, continental lagers and bottled beers. A quieter snug is hidden behind the bar and a pavement area is to the front. A large range of international bottled beers features in two large fridges. Q❁❁♿♣♠🛜

Knott End on Sea

Knott End Working Men's Club
Salisbury Avenue, FY6 0BP
☎ (01253) 812226 ⊕ knottendwmc.co.uk
3 changing beers (often Bank Top) Ⓗ
Friendly private club which allows CAMRA members free entry on production of a membership card or a copy of the Guide, otherwise entry costs £1. There are three main rooms with one central bar. Three cask beers are served, mostly from fairly local breweries. There is a comfortable lounge to the right on entry, and a large games room featuring snooker and pool tables to the rear. A function room is available for private parties, live music and other club events. ❁❁◐♿♣♠P♠(2C,89)🛜

Lancaster

Bobbin ✓
36 Cable Street, LA1 1HH
☎ (01524) 32606
5 changing beers (often Anarchy, Dark Star, Tiny Rebel) Ⓗ
A large pub that is mainly Victorian and part 18th century, entirely open plan but still divided up by raised areas and pillars. It is frequented by a goth/metal crowd but they are by no means the only customers. The pub features 70s-style flock wallpaper, a laminate floor and an extremely eclectic jukebox. Live music is hosted on Friday and Saturday; Wednesday is pool night. Handy for the bus station. ❁❁🥪♣♠♫🐾🛜

Cornerhouse
34 New Street, LA1 1HU
☎ (01524) 845939 ⊕ cornerhouselancaster.co.uk

8 changing beers (sourced locally; often Cumbrian Ales, Farm Yard) Ⓗ

A conversion of one end of an old department store, comprehensively refitted in 2018 in a modern interpretation of gin-palace style. Most of the space is restaurant, but there is a large bar offering the choice of communal drinking at a long marble-topped table or more discreet areas around the walls. There is also plenty of standing room. A couple of Farm Yard ales are usually in the range of beers on offer. Cocktails are a speciality, with an amazing selection of spirits and mixers. Live music is staged most week nights. Outside tables are sheltered from the worst of the weather. ⚘♿≉♣🖵🐱🛜

Jailor's Barrel ✪
64 Market Street, LA1 1HP
☎ (01524) 840316 ⊕ jailorsbarrel.co.uk
Hydes Original, Lowry; 4 changing beers (often Hydes) Ⓗ

This pub was converted from retail premises in 2007, retaining the façade with its huge curved windows. Inside, wooden screens and various furnishings break up the area. An upstairs room is also open to the public, and can be reserved. Alongside the changing handpumped ales is a selection of bottled beers, some quite rare, strong and expensive. There is 50p off cask ales for everyone on Monday. Food is served daily.
Q⊕≉♣🖵(BS) 🐱🛜

John o' Gaunt ✪
53 Market Street, LA1 1JG
☎ (01524) 65356
6 changing beers (often Titanic, Wainwright, Wychwood) Ⓗ

A handsome Victorian frontage hides a narrow pub, dating from 1871, in which the walls are crammed with a variety of objects collected by the former licensee – beer mats, jazz posters and photos of musicians (reflecting one of his enthusiasms). At lunchtime the majority of the customers are from nearby banks and offices, in the evening it's mainly regulars. There is music most evenings, a Sunday lunch, and a quiz on Thursdays.
⚘≉♣🖵🐱🛜

Merchant's ✪
29 Castle Hill, LA1 1YN
☎ (01524) 66466 ⊕ merchants1688.co.uk
House beer (by Old School); 7 changing beers (sourced regionally; often Allendale, Kirkby Lonsdale, Tirril) Ⓗ

Converted wine merchants' cellars, built in 1688, create a peaceful haven from the hubbub of the city centre, enhanced by an extensive outdoor drinking area. The main drinking spaces are in three separate tunnels, with a fourth forming the entrance and bar. One tunnel is now a restaurant, another is used for functions as required. Look out for the stoneware bottles used in the construction of the cellar walls. The house beer, Castle Blonde, is brewed by Old School. Numerous board games are available. Live music is performed late every Saturday evening; quiz night is Sunday. ⚘⊕≉🖵🐱🛜

Three Mariners
Bridge Lane, LA1 1EE (nr Parksafe car park entrance)
☎ (01524) 388957 ⊕ thethreemarinerslancaster.co.uk
Oakham Citra; Robinsons Wizard, Dizzy Blonde; 7 changing beers Ⓗ

Commonly claimed to be the oldest pub in Lancaster, and it certainly looks it. It had a comprehensive revamp in 2004, and the cellar is excavated at first-floor level. It is now a popular watering hole with a thriving local clientele. Home-cooked, reasonably priced food is

served. Music is a feature, with Irish folk on Tuesday, folk on the first Friday of the month, and bluegrass on the third Friday of the month. Parking is limited.
Q⚘🕯⊕♿♣≉♣🖵🐱🛜

Lancaster University

Graduate College Bar
Bailrigg, LA2 0PF (on Graduate Square in Alexandra Park; college is signposted)
☎ (01524) 592824 ⊕ lancaster.ac.uk/eat
4 changing beers (sourced nationally) Ⓗ

The Graduate College Bar is much pubbier and attracts a higher age range than the usual student watering hole. The choice of beer is good, with eight handpumps. There is a beer fest in June. Curry night is on Friday, and open mic night alternates with live bands on Thursdays. The university bars all have alternative names: this one, for some reason, is Herdwick. Snacks are pork pies and pickled eggs. The beer list is on Untappd. Reduced hours in vacations. ⚘♿♣🖵(2,4)🐱🛜

Leyland

Market Ale House Ⓛ
33 Hough Lane, PR25 2SB
☎ (01772) 623363
6 changing beers (sourced locally) Ⓗ

Opened in 2013, this was the area's first micropub. It is located at the entrance to the former Leyland Motors North Works, which now serves as the town's market hall. With an extension into the adjoining premises, added in 2021, and an upstairs lounge, there is plenty of seating. Six varying real ales come from local and national breweries. Changing ciders, wines and a few spirits are also served. There is no TV but live acoustic music plays on Sunday afternoon. Tables on the wide pavement create an outside drinking area in summer.
≉♣🖵🐱🛜

Longridge

Hoppy Days Ⓛ
36A Derby Road, PR3 3JT
☎ 07772 901515
5 changing beers Ⓗ

A warm and friendly welcome awaits you at this pleasant single-roomed real ale house with a relaxed atmosphere. There are five handpumps showcasing a variety of beers, many from small local microbreweries. There is normally a range of strengths and styles including a dark beer. The quality ales are kept in a temperature-controlled chiller room. Bottled beers, wines and real cider are also served. Q♠♣🖵(1)🐱🛜

Tap & Vent ✪
4 Towneley Parade, PR3 3HU
☎ (01772) 875781
4 changing beers Ⓗ

The Tap & Vent was the first micropub in Longridge when it opened in 2016. Situated in a row of shops, it has a welcoming and friendly atmosphere. Four handpumps serve a selection of changing cask ales, typically from microbreweries, with a fifth devoted to real cider. Craft, bottled and keg beers are also sold, as well as fine wines, Prosecco and a large range of gins. ♿♣🖵(1)🐱🛜

Longton

Dolphin
Marsh Lane, PR4 5JY
☎ (01772) 612032

4 changing beers (sourced locally) ⊞
Isolated country pub (also known locally as the Flying Fish) at the end of a lane on Longton Marsh, close to the Ribble Way. The cask ales can be found in the wood-floored public bar to the right of the main entrance. There is a restaurant in the rear conservatory and a varied menu covers everything from sandwiches to man vs food challenges. Up to four real ales and a cider are on tap, offering a changing selection with an emphasis on microbreweries in the area. Evening closing time is flexible dependent on trade. 🚶😋◑🍴♿🅰🏕🅿😊

Lytham

Craft House Beer Café
5 Clifton Street, FY8 5EP
☎ (01253) 730512
4 changing beers (sourced regionally; often Cumbrian Ales, Rat) ⊞
Twice winner of CAMRA branch Pub of the Year and now in its fifth year, this cosy micropub guarantees a warm and friendly welcome. It has fast developed into a popular destination for real ale drinkers. Four varying beers are served, always including a dark brew, coming from far and wide and supplemented by a wide selection of world and British bottled ales. The bar offers pavement seating, weather permitting. A small food menu is offered daily. Q😋◑🚲🍴🚌😊🛜

Taps ✅
12 Henry Street, FY8 5LE
☎ (01253) 736226
Greene King IPA; Moorhouse's Pendle Witches Brew; Morland Old Speckled Hen; Robinsons Dizzy Blonde; 6 changing beers (sourced nationally) ⊞
A multi award-winning pub that makes this Guide for the 27th consecutive year. The Taps continues to provide a wide range of well-kept ales from near and far, always including a mild and normally a stout or porter. It also usually stocks at least two ciders. Food is home cooked, mostly using locally sourced ingredients. A popular quiz takes place on Monday evening; regular charity events include an annual 30-mile bike ride. 🚶😋◑🚲♿🚄♣🍴🚌😊🛜

Morecambe

Eric Bartholomew ✅
10-18 Euston Road, LA4 5DD
☎ (01524) 405860
Greene King Abbot; Ruddles Best Bitter; Sharp's Doom Bar; 3 changing beers (often Cross Bay) ⊞
Opened in 2004, this Wetherspoon near the sea front is dedicated to Eric Morecambe (born Eric Bartholomew). It functions on two levels, with an upstairs lounge and dinner area. The long bar services an open-plan pub with pictures of 19th-century Morecambe and artwork with a Morecambe and Wise theme. There is some outside seating at the front for smokers but no drinking is allowed there. Close to shops and a public car park. Q😋◑♿🚄🍴🚌🛜

Little Bare
23 Princes Crescent, LA4 6BY
☎ 07817 892370
5 changing beers ⊞
Micropub that opened in 2017 in a former off-licence, retaining the shop window. With grey paint, bare floorboards and candles after dark, it follows the micropub formula: no food, no music, no machines. A second room, down a corridor, provides extra seating. There is a small beer garden to the rear, accessed through the back room. 😋🚄(Bare Lane)♣🚌😊

Morecambe Hotel
25 Lord Street, LA4 5HX
☎ (01524) 415239 ∰ themorecambehotel.co.uk
Cross Bay Halo; 4 changing beers ⊞
The place to come if you want a choice of Cross Bay beers. Reopened in 2015 after renovation in contemporary style, it is light and airy with flagged floors and a variety of seating and tables. The bar is faced with unplaned wood. There are four rooms around a bar and to the rear a surprisingly spacious garden. Screens show videos of 20th-century Morecambe. For most of the day, food dominates. This hotel was a coaching inn built long before there was a town called Morecambe. 😋🛏◑♿🚄🚌😊🛜

Royal 🅛
257 Marine Road Central, LA4 4BJ
☎ (01524) 416668 ∰ theroyalmorecambe.co.uk
House beer (by Cross Bay); 5 changing beers ⊞
A survival from Victorian Morecambe, built around 1850, although not unaltered since. The 2012 renovation respected the remaining features and blended with them. A single-bar room stretching from the handsome bay window, overlooking the bay and the Eric Morecambe statue, to the back windows, is complemented by an upstairs room variously used for dining or functions. Steak nights feature on Thursdays and live music Thursday (acoustic), Friday, Saturday, and Sunday. The house beer from Cross Bay is on offer at a reduced price. 😋🛏◑♿🚄🚌(4,6)🛜

Newchurch

Boar's Head 🅛
69 Church Street, BB4 9EH
☎ (01706) 557422
4 changing beers (sourced nationally) ⊞
A large three-storey building on the corner of Church Street and Newchurch Road and close to St Nicholas church. The stone above the door indicates that the building was constructed in 1674, and was once owned by Kenyons brewery. The central bar, with its four handpumps, serves three drinking areas. It is said that somewhere in the cellar is a sealed up door to an underground passage leading to the church. 🚶😋♣🚌(10)

Ormskirk

Cricketers 🅛
24 Chapel Street, L39 4QF
☎ (01695) 571123 ∰ thecricketers-ormskirk.co.uk
4 changing beers (sourced regionally; often Old School, Reedley Hallows) ⊞
Close to Ormskirk town centre, the pub prides itself on quality food and cask ales, featuring six beers from local and regional breweries. The extensive food menu is served all day in its restaurant or bar area. Cricket memorabilia around the walls reflect the pub's close relationship with Ormskirk cricket club. 🚶😋◑♿🚄🅿🚌(375,385) 🛜

Tap Room No.12 🅛
12 Burscough Street, L39 2ER
☎ (01695) 581928
4 changing beers (sourced regionally) ⊞
This former shop has had a customised conversion into a Belgian-style single-room bar with wooden panels. It features four changing cask ales from the region and aims to offer a porter or stout, an amber bitter and two pale beers of different strengths. There is also an extensive range of foreign bottled beers and authentic

foreign lagers on draught. There is a quiz every Wednesday and live music Friday and Saturday, with background music during the rest of the week. ≈♣🖥🐱📶

Orrell

Delph Tavern
Tontine, WN5 8UJ
☎ (01695) 622239
5 changing beers Ⓗ
Free house frequented by regulars and visitors selling five different ales, with an emphasis on local breweries. Food is served every day and offers a balance of traditional pub classics alongside innovative street food. Live sports are shown on a number of unobtrusive screens, while a vault offers pool and darts. The outside space has a small play area as well as tables to enjoy food and drinks. Weekly quiz nights are popular. Ꮬ❀《♿♣P🐱📶

Oswaldtwistle

Vault Ⓛ
343 Union Road, BB5 3HS
☎ (01254) 872279
Moorhouse's White Witch; 4 changing beers (sourced regionally) Ⓗ
This single-roomed bar with separate seating areas is on the busy main road through Oswaldtwistle. It is easy to reach by public transport as buses from Accrington and Blackburn pass the door every few minutes. There is high bench seating around the walls and a standing area at the bar. The six handpumps dispense four changing beers and two ciders. Q🖕🖥🐱

Padiham

Hare & Hounds Ⓛ ✅
58 West Street, BB12 8JD
☎ (01282) 545308
5 changing beers (sourced regionally; often Big Clock, Reedley Hallows, Worsthorne) Ⓗ
A true free house with a changing choice of five beers. There are two rooms off the bar and a large separate room to the side, all with real fires. The pub is at the entrance to both Padiham cricket club and Padiham FC football ground. There is a large beer garden to the rear. BT and Sky sports are shown and there is occasional live music at weekends. Ꮬ❀《♿♣🖥(M2,152)🐱📶

Molly Rigby's Ⓛ ✅
17-19 Mill Street, BB12 8EX
☎ (01282) 778997 ⊕ mollyrigbys.co.uk
House beer (by Worsthorne); 3 changing beers (sourced locally; often Reedley Hallows, Worsthorne) Ⓗ
A comfortable, friendly members' club which opened in Padiham town centre in 2004 and has a strict over 25s policy. It serves up to four real ales mainly from local breweries, with the Worsthorne house beer available at a reduced price. Home to many local community groups, it was Burnley CAMRA Club Of The Year in 2020. Ꮬ❀《♿♣🖥

Parbold

Wayfarer Ⓛ
1-3 Alder Lane, WN8 7NL
☎ (01257) 464600 ⊕ wayfarerparbold.co.uk
Problem Child Good Spankin'; 5 changing beers Ⓗ
A country inn with a focus on dining. It has six handpulls (one of them for cider) and a range of craft keg beers. There are low-beam ceilings, with cosy nooks and crannies, and it has a countryside beer garden with pleasant views. The place is popular with walkers, being close to the Leeds-Liverpool canal and Parbold Hill – suitable walks are shown on the website. Landlord and brewer Jonny Birkett is happy to show you around his on-site microbrewery, Problem Child Brewing. Q⏏Ꮬ❀《♿≈🖕P🖥🐱📶

Windmill Hotel
3 Mill Lane, WN8 7NW
☎ (01257) 462935 ⊕ thewindmillparbold.co.uk
Wainwright; 4 changing beers (sourced nationally) Ⓗ
A former grainstore to the adjacent windmill, with parts of the building dating back to 1794. Two open fires provide a warm welcome to drinkers, diners, bargees and walkers. It is often busy with diners during the early evening. Up to five real ales feature on the bar, including some from the Windmill brewery. A separate snug to the right of the doorway features delightful carved animals in the wooden panels. Unfortunately this pub has no wheelchair access due to its steep stone steps. Q⏏Ꮬ❀≈P🖥🐱

Pendleton

Swan with Two Necks Ⓛ
Main Street, BB7 1PT
☎ (01200) 423112 ⊕ swanwithtwonecks.co.uk
5 changing beers (sourced regionally; often Goose Eye, Phoenix, Tiny Rebel) Ⓗ
A plethora of awards acknowledge that this has been one of the best pubs in north-west England for a decade. It has been run by the same owners for over 30 years. The five handpulls offer a range that may feature beers from Blackedge, Fernandes, Rat and Goose Eye. Real cider is also sold. Rumour has it that the beer is so good because the landlord talks to it. Food is of high quality yet reasonably priced. Attractions include real fires in winter, and a large beer garden with spectacular views for summer. Q❀《♣🖕P🐱

Penwortham

Tap & Vine
69 Liverpool Road, PR1 9XD
☎ (01772) 751116 ⊕ tapandvine.co.uk
4 changing beers (sourced locally) Ⓗ
Penwortham's first micropub, an upmarket wine bar-type establishment housed in a former arts and crafts shop. It has limited seating and can get quite busy at times, although to the rear there is a small secluded room with a wood-burning stove, as well as outside seating in the summer months. Four changing beers are always available, often including some from lesser known microbreweries. The food consists of snacks and serving platters. Q Ꮬ♣🖕🖥🐱📶

Poulton le Fylde

Old Town Hall
5 Church Street, FY6 7AP
☎ (01253) 892257
6 changing beers (sourced locally; often Bank Top, Moorhouse's, Reedley Hallows) Ⓗ
Located in the heart of Poulton facing the old churchyard; as the name suggests, this building was once the town hall. The now open-plan layout retains some of its heritage features, attracting many local real ale enthusiasts. Live bands play at weekends and an upstairs

function room is available. Live sports are shown on many TVs, with horse racing always popular. ⛄🚫♿🍴♣🚆🚍🐱🛇

Poulton Elk ✓

22 Hardhorn Road, FY6 7SR

☎ (01253) 895265

Greene King Abbot; Ruddles Best Bitter; Sharp's Doom Bar; 7 changing beers (sourced nationally; often Bowland, Cross Bay, Saltaire) Ⓗ

A thriving, well-run Wetherspoon's, formerly a night club and before that the area telephone exchange. It was the 900th pub to be opened by its owners. Popular for its food, it can get busy at weekends. There are two outdoor drinking areas, a front terrace and a pleasant suntrap area to the rear. A skeleton of a 13,000-year-old elk was discovered nearby; a sharpened flint found with it is the earliest evidence of man in the area. ⛄🚫♿🍴♣🚆🚍🐱🛇

Preston

Black Horse ★ ✓

166 Friargate, PR1 2EJ

☎ (01772) 204855

Robinsons Dizzy Blonde, Unicorn, Trooper, Old Tom; 4 changing beers (sourced nationally) Ⓗ

A Victorian Grade II-listed pub close to the historic open market. With its tiled bar and walls and mosaic floor, the building has been identified by CAMRA as having a nationally important historic pub interior. Two front rooms are adorned with Robinsons memorabilia and photos of old Preston. The famous hall of mirrors seating area is to the rear. Real cider and a selection of pork pies are always on offer. Four Robinsons beers are available, together with four changing guest ales from far and wide. Awarded the 2019/20 George Lee Memorial Trophy, the local CAMRA branch's premier award. ⛄🚆♣🐱🚍🐱🛇

Continental

South Meadow Lane, PR1 8JP

☎ (01772) 499425 🌐 newcontinental.net

House beer (by Marble); 6 changing beers (sourced nationally) Ⓗ

Vibrant pub alongside the River Ribble, Miller Park and the railway line. It has a main bar area plus a lounge with a real fire in winter, and a conservatory overlooking the large beer garden. Live music and theatre are hosted regularly in a separate events space, which is also used for beer festivals. Eight handpumps serve a cider plus up to seven microbrewery beers, including the house beer from Marble and a dark brew. Freshly cooked meals are available Wednesday to Sunday. Q⛄🚫♿🍴♣🚆🚍P🐱🛇

Guild Ale House

56 Lancaster Road, PR1 1DD

☎ 07932 517444

7 changing beers (sourced regionally; often Bank Top, Elland, Pomona Island) Ⓗ

Preston's first micropub, opened in 2016 just a few doors away from the city's Guild Hall complex. The main room has high- and low-level seating, with tall ceilings giving a light and airy feel. A small lounge is tucked away to the rear and there is a comfortable lounge upstairs. Seven changing beers are served, mainly local or from Yorkshire, and at least one dark ale. The pub also offers a range of continental beers in keg and bottle. There is no jukebox, music, TV, or food, but live acoustic sessions take place on Sunday afternoons. Q⛄🚫♿🍴♣🚆🚍🐱🛇

Moorbrook

370 North Road, PR1 1RU

☎ (01772) 823302 🌐 themoorbrook.co.uk

8 changing beers (sourced nationally) Ⓗ

This pub is where the local CAMRA branch was formed in 1973. It has a traditional-style wood-panelled bar with two rooms off the main bar area, and a suntrap beer garden to the side and rear. Eight guest beers come from all over the country, providing a wide choice of regional ale types while retaining a strong emphasis on microbreweries from the area. The food menu features authentic wood-fired pizzas and home-made shortcrust pies. The venue gets busy on Preston North End match days. Local CAMRA Pub of the Year 2019. ⛄🚫🍴♿🐱🛇

Old Vic Ⓛ ✓

79 Fishergate, PR1 2UH

☎ (01772) 828519

Bombardier; 6 changing beers Ⓗ

Opposite the railway station and on bus routes into the city, this pub helpfully provides travellers with a TV screen showing live updates of train departures. The place can get busy, particularly at weekends. The rear of the building has recently been extended, with pool players and darts enthusiasts now having a separate area. Seven handpumps offer a good range of beers with Yorkshire breweries, Ossett and Rat being particularly popular. The car park is only available on a Sunday and in the evenings. ⛄🚫🍴🚆♣🚍P🐱🛇

Orchard

Earl Street, PR1 2JA

☎ 07756 583621

3 changing beers (sourced nationally; often Farm Yard, Nightjar, Wily Fox) Ⓗ

The Orchard was opened in 2018 as a sister pub to the Guild Ale House. Located within the Grade II-listed covered market, the decor and framework is of wood recycled from the old market trestle boards, plus lots of modern glass. Two cask ales and 10 craft ales are always sold, alongside real cider. No food is served but there is plenty on the neighbouring market, which can be ordered and taken in. Q🚫🚆♣🐱🚍

Plau

115 Friargate, PR1 2EE

☎ (01772) 561404 🌐 plau.co.uk

House beer (by Kirkstall); 3 changing beers (sourced nationally) Ⓗ

Recently restored and reopened on the site of a former pub, The Plough, which originally closed in 1913. The building dates back to the 18th century and the main bar is spread over three levels, with further bars in the vault, which includes a restored and exposed 40-foot-deep stone well. Four cask ales are on tap, with three always changing, typically coming from a wide range of local microbreweries, alongside the house beer, 1668, from Kirstall Brewery. Up to eight craft keg beers are also stocked, along with an extensive range of gins. ⛄🍴♿🚆♣🚍🐱🛇

Plug & Taps

32 Lune Street, PR1 2NN

4 changing beers Ⓗ

Craft-beer-cum-real-ale-bar consisting of 10 keg lines and four handpumps, as well as a large can and bottle fridge with occasional real cider boxes. Changing beers can come from anywhere in the country and internationally, with three house beers from Outstanding Brewery and a permanent Rivington Brewery line. There are also occasional tap takeovers from various breweries. The pub has a large function room upstairs with a jukebox, air conditioning in the main bar, and an outside seating area for use in warm weather. ⛄🚆♣🚍🐱🛇

Princess Alice L ✅

29-31 Cambridge Walk, PR1 7SL

☎ (01772) 823737

4 changing beers (sourced regionally; often Lancaster, Worsthorne) H

Warm and friendly Victorian street corner local in a redeveloped residential area. Ornate tilework reflects the former Matthew Brown brewery ownership. The interior has been modernised and opened out, with a large number of TV screens showing multiple (often sports) channels. The regular beer is Lancaster Blonde and changing ales are normally from small Lancashire breweries, often Lancaster and Worsthorne. The pub is only 15 minutes' walk from Deepdale stadium and is popular on match days. ❀&♣P☐(23)🛜

Vinyl Tap

28 Adelphi Street, PR1 7BE

☎ (01772) 561871

6 changing beers (sourced nationally) H

A single-room bar adjacent to the university; open since 2018. There are six real ale pumps serving a wide range of microbrewery beers, often from unusual breweries for the area. The pub features vinyl-themed events and a jukebox Sunday to Thursday; customers can choose from an ever-growing collection or bring their own to be played, while enjoying a drink and a bite to eat throughout the day. Fridays and Saturdays vary between live music and guest vinyl DJ slots, with music spanning most genres. Local CAMRA Most Improved Pub of the Year 2019. ♦🕿☐🛜

Winckley Street Ale House ✅

8B Winckley Street, PR1 2AA

☎ (01772) 563797 ⊕ winckleyale.co.uk

4 changing beers (sourced regionally) H

This premises initially opened as the Otter's Pocket in 2018 – a single-room bar and restaurant occupying the whole ground floor of the former shop. In March 2020 the pub was closed for renovation and it has since reopened as the Winckley Street Ale House, offering a wider menu and great range of beers. Up to four regularly changing cask ales are now available as well as up to 10 keg lines, with a strong focus on local and regional breweries. ☺🕀&☐❀

Rawtenstall

Casked Ale House & Ginporium L

14-16 Bury Road, BB4 6AA

☎ 07764 695261

House beer (by Reedley Hallows); 5 changing beers (sourced regionally; often Brewsmith, Irwell Works, Nightjar) H

A large open-plan single-room bar with varied seating and imaginative lighting. On the edge of Rawtenstall town centre, it is a short walk from the bus station and East Lancs heritage railway station, and just along from Fitzpatrick's famous Temperance Bar. Up to six mainly local cask ales are available on handpump plus several modern keg beers. Many beers are sourced from breweries around the Rossendale Valley. Rossendale CAMRA Pub of the Year 2019. 🕿♦☐(464,X43)❀

Hop Micro Pub L

70 Bank Street, BB4 8EG

☎ 07753 775150 ⊕ hopmicropubs.com

Deeply Vale Hop; 5 changing beers H

Situated at the top end of Rawtenstall's cobbled Bank Street, close to the market, Hop is a pleasant and congenial venue with the atmosphere of the traditional local pub. It has a bar room, first floor lounge and a

heated drinking area outside. With six handpulled cask ales, including the permanent Hop from Deeply Vale, as well as keg craft beers and ciders available, there is always a fantastic choice. A short walk from the bus station and from the northern terminus of the East Lancashire heritage railway. ❀🕿♦P☐❀

Rivington

Rivington

Horrobin Lane, BL6 7SE

☎ (01204) 691509 ⊕ rivingtonbowlingclub.co.uk

Abbeydale Deception; 1 changing beer (often Abbeydale) H

The Rivington is a tearoom and bar attached to Rivington Bowling Club, and has a full pub licence with non-members welcome at all times. There is a single room with a bar serving two cask ales. The garden is in an elevated position overlooking the reservoir. Sandwiches, soup and cakes are available in the tearoom. Occasional live music is staged. Opening hours are complicated depending on the time of year, so it is advisable to ring before setting out. Q☺🕿♣P❀

Rivington Brewery Co Tap L

Home Farm, Horrobin Lane, PR6 9HE

☎ 07859 248779 ⊕ rivingtonbrewing.co.uk

Rivington range H

Rivington Brewery Tap opened in 2019, housed in a converted stable block at the farm where the brewery is situated. It showcases the brewery's extensive range of ales, two on handpump and a further 15 keg taps with cider and lager also available. It is in a beautiful setting with outdoor seating providing breathtaking views across the reservoir towards Winter Hill. The bar is lofty with bare stone walls and a large stone-topped bar counter. During summer opening, food is also served daily by Dough 'n' Co (pizzas and burgers) and by other local food suppliers. ☺❀🕀◐AP❀

Rufford

Hesketh Arms

81 Liverpool Road, L40 1SB (on A59 at jct with B5246)

☎ (01704) 821002

Moorhouse's White Witch, Pride of Pendle; 7 changing beers (sourced regionally; often Cross Bay, Phoenix, Reedley Hallows) H

A spacious former Greenall's inn, the Hesketh is now a free house serving up to six ales, mostly from local microbreweries. Set in a charming village, it is near to the National Trust property of Rufford Old Hall, the delightful St Mary's Marina, and the popular Mere Sands nature reserve. A large split-level venue with several dining areas, the pub serves good-quality food throughout the day. Monthly live entertainment and a Tuesday quiz attract a mixed clientele. Q☺❀◐&🕿P☐(2A,347)

St Annes

Fifteens at St Annes ✅

42 St Annes Road West, FY8 1RF

☎ (01253) 725852 ⊕ fifteensstannes.com

House beer (by Coach House); 5 changing beers (sourced regionally; often Acorn, Bradfield, Titanic) H

This splendid conversion of a former Lloyds Bank is a multi award-winning Guide regular and attracts a varied and loyal clientele. Many original features have been retained, including glorious stained-glass windows and probably the world's most comfortable (and tranquil) bank vault. The landlord's obsessive pride in the six cask ales from near and far is obvious. Two ciders are normally sold. The pub has regular entertainment, with live bands at weekends and a Sunday night quiz. ≠♣�🖶😣

Keg 'n' Cask

17 St Andrews Road South, FY8 1SX

☎ 07913 791476

5 changing beers (sourced locally) Ⓗ

A two-roomed micropub just inland of the main square in St Annes, close to the railway station and located in what was the town's first post office. A range of five beers is stocked, mostly from brewers within a 30-mile radius. Conversation is king in the front room; the rear room is generally quieter. 🖒😣&≠🖶😣

No.10 Ale House Ⓛ ✅

10 Park Road, FY8 1QX

☎ (01253) 423240

5 changing beers (sourced nationally) Ⓗ

Quirky and original in style, this single-room micropub was the first of its ilk to open on the Fylde, just off St Annes Square and a five-minute walk from the beach. There are usually five well-chosen beers to choose from. Quality bar snacks and pizzas are available, as well as coffee. Live music is hosted occasionally, and there is a monthly quiz, but conversation is king here. The background music is usually muted and the TV shows only major sporting events. 😣&≠🖶😣

Scarisbrick

Heatons Bridge Inn ✅

2 Heatons Bridge Road, L40 8JG (on B5242 by Leeds-Liverpool Canal)

☎ (01704) 840549

2 changing beers (sourced regionally; often Moorhouse's, Tetley) Ⓗ

Great canalside venue dating from 1837, when it served as offices for the Leeds and Liverpool freight services. It is now a traditional inn with separate areas and provides home-cooked food. Pillbox beer is often served to commemorate WWII, and there is a lookout post outside. Twice-yearly military displays and annual classic bus services take place, with themed beers for the occasion. Popular with families, walkers and cyclists, the pub is in an excellent rural setting and has a garden with eating area. 🖒😣🕪♣▲🖶(375)😣🛜

Silverdale

Woodlands

Woodlands Drive, LA5 0RU

☎ (01524) 701655

4 changing beers Ⓗ

Large country house on an elevated site built circa 1878 and converted to a pub with only minimal alterations. Most of the trade is provided by locals. The bar has a large fireplace as big as the counter and offers great views across Morecambe Bay. Beer pumps are in another room, with a list of the four available ales on the wall facing the bar. Home-made sandwiches are served at weekends. The smoking area is covered and sheltered. A beer festival of 30 ales is held in October and a quiz on the last Sunday of the month. To telephone you need to ring twice. Q🖒😣♣●P🖶😣

Slaidburn

Hark to Bounty Ⓛ

Townend, BB7 3EP

☎ (01200) 446246 ● harktobounty.co.uk

Theakston Best Bitter, Old Peculier; 2 changing beers (sourced regionally) Ⓗ

This traditional family-run inn has nine en-suite bedrooms, and is an ideal base for exploring the Forest of Bowland AONB. Either side of the central bar, with four ales on handpump, are comfortable lounges with real fires. Home-cooked meals, including daily changing specials, are served lunchtimes and evenings; check the service times before travelling in winter. A 16th-century court room, serving as a function room, can be viewed by request. The large beer garden is popular in summer. Q🖒😣🕪●🕪&▲P🖶(10)😣🛜

Tarleton

Vestry Tap Room

109 Church Road, PR4 6UP

☎ (01772) 301976

Bowland AONB; 2 changing beers (often Beer Brothers, Parker, Salopian) Ⓗ

A micropub that opened in 2019 in an old tapas restaurant in the centre of the village. It has a wide range of high and low seating, plus a small upstairs lounge/function room. Three handpumps and eight craft keg lines offer a wide choice of ales. Tea and coffee are also served, in addition to wines and spirits. A temporary marquee at the back, containing numerous tables and lounge chairs, creates a substantial extension to the pub. Q😣♣●P🖶(2,2A)😣🛜

Tockholes

Royal Arms Ⓛ

Tockholes Road, Rydal Fold, BB3 0PA (3 miles W of Darwen)

☎ (01254) 705373

3 changing beers (sourced nationally; often Hopstar, Moorhouse's, Three B's) Ⓗ

Traditional free house formed from two cottages knocked together. It is small, but has a great atmosphere within its four back-to-back rooms where the original stone walls, real fires and flagged or wooden floors have been retained. Most beers are from local microbreweries. In the West Pennine Moors, close to Darwen Tower and adjacent to Roddlesworth Visitor Centre, it looks over moors, woods and reservoirs. Friendly staff welcome walkers, cyclists, ramblers and dogs alike, and offer a good menu. Summer and winter opening and food times are liable to change, so check before travelling. Q🖒😣🕪♣P😣🛜

Wesham

Stanley Arms

8 Garstang Road South, PR4 3BL

☎ (01772) 469495

Butcombe Original; 2 changing beers (sourced nationally) Ⓗ

Originally formed from three terraced houses, this welcoming community pub is on a side street just three minutes' walk from Kirkham railway station and bus stops. The comfortable open-plan interior contains many photos of old Preston and Blackpool landmarks. The landlord is the longest-serving in the area and provides good food (often cooked by himself), including breakfasts at weekends. The Stanley Arms is approximately three-quarters of a mile walk from AFC Fylde's football ground. 🖒😣🕪&≠♣🖶😣🛜

Whalley

Dog Inn 𝕃
55 King Street, BB7 9SP
☎ (01254) 823009
6 changing beers (sourced regionally) ⊞
Deservedly popular and usually crowded, especially at weekends, the Dog has been run by the same family since the early 1990s. Six handpumps serve a range of beers, changed continually, from breweries such as Acorn, Hetton, Moorhouse's, Peerless and Wishbone. Food is served only at lunchtimes and is always excellent. This traditional, historic inn is very close to the ruins of Whalley Abbey and is handy for exploring the picturesque Ribble Valley. ⑤⊛⑪≼⊟⬤❖

Wheelton

Red Lion
Blackburn Road, PR6 8EU (in centre of village opp clock tower)
☎ (01254) 659890 ⊕ theredlionatwheelton.co.uk/#top
Hawkshead Iti, Lakeland Gold; Oakham JHB; Timothy Taylor Landlord; 4 changing beers (sourced nationally; often Rudgate, Salopian, Saltaire) ⊞
Built around 1826, this former Matthew Brown house retains many original features including a large stone lion at roof level above the door. It features a comfortable lounge with an open fire and a second room up a few steps. Food is served seven days a week. There are eight handpumps showcasing four regular beers and four changing real ales from larger independents, usually including a stout and a strong ale (over 6.0% ABV). Close to the West Pennine Moors; many local walks pass by. Dogs are welcome. Q⑤⊛⑪❫P⊟(24)❖

Whitworth

Whitworth Vale & Healey Band Club 𝕃 ✅
498 Market Street, OL12 8DP
☎ (01706) 852484
Banks's Amber Ale; 3 changing beers (sourced nationally) ⊞

Popular social club, notable for being the home of the local brass band of the same name. It is part of a terrace on the main road through the town, with the regular 464 bus service passing by the door. It is quite spacious despite the low ceiling, and there is an outside seating area. A recent winner of local CAMRA Branch and Regional Club of the Year awards. ⊛⊟❫(464)⬤❖

Wrea Green

Wrea Green Institute
Station Road, PR4 2PH
☎ (01772) 682118 ⊕ wreagreentute.co.uk
Coniston Bluebird Bitter; Wainwright; 3 changing beers (sourced nationally) ⊞
The 'Tute has been a community club near the centre of this picturesque village for over a century. Nicely renovated, it provides a main bar with pool tables and a comfortable lounge with old village pictures. There is also a function room downstairs. A beer festival is held in September and there are regular music, folk and poker nights. Snacks are available. Visitors should present a copy of this Guide or a membership card to be signed in. ⊛⬥♣P⊟(61,76) ⬤❖

Wrightington

White Lion ✅
117 Mossy Lea Road, WN6 9RE
☎ (01257) 425977 ⊕ thewhitelionwrightington.co.uk
Banks's Amber Ale; Jennings Cumberland Ale; 6 changing beers ⊞
A popular country pub with a good range of food and beers for diners and drinkers, with eight handpumps. It hosts a Monday Club with drinks offers, a quiz on Tuesdays, a poker league on Thursdays, a monthly cocktail night and live music every Saturday. It is community-oriented, running the village scarecrow festival and themed evenings throughout the year. Families are welcome – there is a large beach hut-themed garden area, and board games for inside. Q⑤⊛⑪⬥P⊟(113)

Of Ale
Ale is made of malte and water, and they the which do put any other thynge to ale than is rehersed, except yest, barme or godisgood (other forms of yeast) do sofysticat (adulterate) theyr ale. Ale for an englysshe man is a natural drynke. Ale must have these propertyes, it must be freshe and cleare, it must not be ropy (cloudy) or smoky, nor it must have no welt nor tayle (sediment or dregs). Ale should not be dronke under V days olde. Newe ale is unholsome for all men. And soure ale and deade ale the which doth stande a tylt is good for no man. Barley malte maketh better ale then oten malte or any other corne doth, it doth engender grosse humoures, but yette it maketh a man stronge.

Of Bere
Bere is made of malte, of hoppes, and water, it is a natural drinke for a dutche man. And nowe of late dayes it is moche used in Englande to the detryment of many englysshe men, specyally it kylleth them the which be troubled with the colycke and the stone & strangulion (quinsy), for the drynke is a colde drynke: yet it doth make a man fat and doth inflate the bely, as it doth appere by the dutche mens faces & belyes. If the beer be well served and be fyned & not newe, it doth qualify ye heat of the lyver.

Andrew Boorde (c. 1490-1549),
A 'Compendyous Regyment' or 'a Dyetary of Helth', 1542

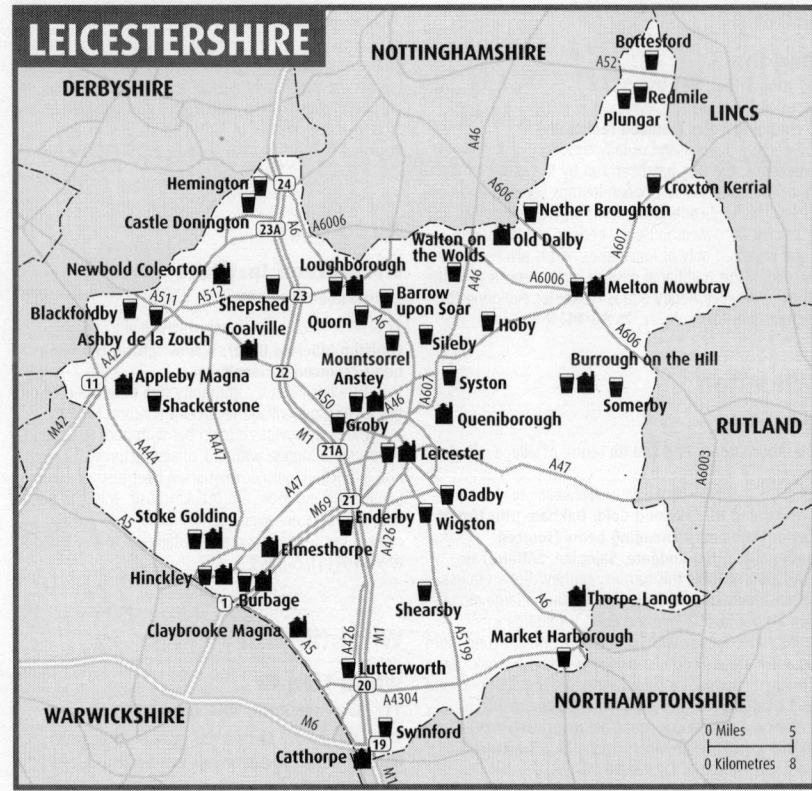

LEICESTERSHIRE

Anstey

Anstey Ale Brewery (Mash & Press)
46A Albion Street, LE7 7DE
☎ 07960 776843 ⊕ ansteyale.co.uk
House beer (by Anstey); 3 changing beers (often Anstey) Ⓗ
The Mash and Press is a collaboration between Anstey Ale Brewery and Charnwood Cider, and serves as tap house for both. The upstairs bar offers up to four changing cask ales on handpull, plus several keg lines and up to eight real ciders. Local wines, a wide range of gins and other spirits are also available. Outside is a refurbished beer garden with plenty of seating.
🌤🕭🏮🖵(74,54A) 🏵🛜

Ashby de la Zouch

Tap at No. 76
76 Market Street, LE65 1AP
Tollgate Ashby Pale; 4 changing beers Ⓗ
This Tollgate Brewery micropub on the high street is a relatively recent addition to the Ashby scene. It offers five real ales – four on handpump and one on gravity. Third-pint tasting trays are available for those wishing to try the full range of beers. Pork pies are served. 🖵

Barrow upon Soar

Soar Bridge Inn
29 Bridge Street, LE12 8PN
☎ (01509) 412686 ⊕ soarbridgeinn.co.uk
Everards Tiger, Old Original; 1 changing beer (often Everards) Ⓗ

Situated next to the bridge that gave it its name, this pub is popular with walkers, boaters and drinkers. The large single-room interior divides into distinct areas, with a separate restaurant, function room and skittle alley. Outside there is a floodlit pétanque court, beer terrace and garden. Children and well-behaved dogs are welcome. Home-made food is available Tuesday to Sunday, with a different theme each evening.
Q🌤🕭🐕🖐🛆🏮🚆♣♠🖵🚇(K2,CB27) 🏵🛜

Blackfordby

Black Lion
3 Main Street, DE11 8AB
☎ (01283) 337551 ⊕ theblacklionblackfordby.com
Draught Bass; 5 changing beers (sourced locally; often Blue Monkey, Derby) Ⓗ
Popular local free house in a quiet village in north-west Leicestershire. Grade II listed, with old beams and open fires, it has a lovely courtyard and a covered smoking area. Guest beers are often sourced from small local breweries, and up to four ciders are on draught. Ham and cheese cobs are available. Quiz night is the first Sunday of each month, jam night the last Wednesday.
Q🌤🕭🛆♣🏮🖵🏵🛜

Bottesford

Bull ⒧
Market Street, NG13 0BW
☎ (01949) 842288
Castle Rock Harvest Pale; Fuller's London Pride; Theakston Best Bitter Ⓗ

Set on the main road through this busy village, well served by train and bus, the Bull has a large bar area with a real fire, pool table and plenty of seating. There is also a separate lounge for quieter drinking, plus a function room and outdoor seating area. Three cask ales are served, including one LocAle. Memorabilia in the lounge and a plaque outside commemorate Stan Laurel and Oliver Hardy's visits in the 1950s, when Laurel's sister was the landlady. ⊛&≠♣P🖳🛜

Burbage

Burbage & District Constitutional Club L
Church Street, LE10 2DE
☎ (01455) 615142 ⊕ burbageconclub1911.com
Greene King Abbot; Marston's Saddle Tank; 3 changing beers (often Church End, Grainstore) 🅗
Formerly the home of Prime Minister George Canning, the club was founded here in 1911. This Grade II-listed building, in the heart of the village, features a comfortable lounge with open fire, wheelchair access and a garden. Attractions include a function room equipped with skittle alley, plus snooker and pool tables, darts, dominoes, crib, chess and table tennis. A regular CAMRA branch Club of the Year and former East Midlands Club of the Year. 🛇⊛&♣🖳🛜

Lime Kilns Brew Pub L ⊘
Watling Street, LE10 3ED
☎ (01455) 631158 ⊕ limekilnsinn.co.uk
St Austell Tribute; Timothy Taylor Landlord; 2 changing beers (sourced locally; often Buswells) 🅗
An 18th-century coaching inn alongside the Ashby Canal and A5, featuring free gardenside moorings and a large canalside beer garden. The first-floor lounge has canal views and an open fire. The ground-floor stable bar has a wood-burner and opens to the beer garden, where there is a marquee for functions. Traditional food is served all week, with special deals Monday to Thursday evenings. Buswells microbrewery is on-site. Q🛇⊛◑&♣♦P🛜

Burrough on the Hill

Stag & Hounds L
4 Main Street, LE14 2JQ
☎ (01664) 454250
Parish PSB; 1 changing beer (sourced nationally) 🅗
A 16th-century inn, the Stag & Hounds operated more recently as Grant's Free House before reclaiming its original name following refurbishment in 2019. It has a bar on two levels, a cosy lounge and a restaurant to the rear. A central servery dispenses PSB from the Parish Brewery, located in an adjacent outbuilding, plus a guest ale. The restaurant serves locally sourced food and champions the area's best suppliers. 🛇⊛◑♣P🖳🛜

Castle Donington

Flag
32 Borough Street, DE74 2LA
☎ 07841 374441
House beer (by Dancing Duck) 🅖; 6 changing beers 🅗
A thriving micropub in the heart of a busy street. It serves real ale straight from the cask, visible from a temperature-controlled cool-room cellar. A range of six ciders and quality wines is also kept. Skylink bus services make the pub accessible from Derby, Nottingham, Loughborough and Leicester. Q♦🖳🛜

Croxton Kerrial

Geese & Fountain L
1 School Lane, NG32 1QR
☎ (01476) 870350 ⊕ thegeeseandfountain.co.uk
5 changing beers 🅗
Traditional village inn with a quie, relaxed atmosphere, featuring wood fires, a flagstone floor and rustic seating. Children, cyclists, walkers and dogs are all welcome. Local ales always feature on the five handpumps, with guest beers from nearby microbreweries, plus lagers and three real ciders. Food is served every day, and B&B rooms are available. Regular live music nights and occasional mini beer and cider festivals are held throughout the year. Q🛇⊛🛏◑&♣♦P🖳🛜

Enderby

Mill Hill Cask & Coffee
12-14 Mill Hill, LE19 4AL
⊕ millhillcaskandcoffee.com
4 changing beers 🅗
Micropub with modern decor, a relaxed atmosphere and a growing clientele of locals and passing trade. The owners have established a reputation for well-conditioned ales from top UK breweries, with up to four cask ales and up to 10 KeyKegs to choose from. Food includes home-made sandwiches, cakes, locally sourced pies and Scotch eggs. An outside seating area with heaters and a retractable roof is a popular addition. Q🛇⊛◑&≠♦P🖳(50,X55) 🐾🛜

Groby

Stamford Arms L
2 Leicester Road, LE6 0DJ
☎ (0116) 287 5616 ⊕ stamfordarms.co.uk
Everards Beacon Hill, Tiger; 4 changing beers (sourced nationally; often Everards) 🅗
A superb village pub that serves food, modernised in 2020 and continuing to develop into an outstanding venue. It offers seven cask ales plus craft beer, cider and an extensive gin selection. The food is traditional, with a pizza oven and daily specials. The neighbouring 17th-century thatched Blacksmith's Cottage is let for holidays and nightly bookings. The pub is ideally located for Bradgate Park and the National Space Centre. 🛇⊛🛏◑&♣♦P🖳🐾🛜

REAL ALE BREWERIES

Anstey ✦ Anstey
Belvoir Old Dalby
Buswells 🍺 Burbage
Charnwood ✦ Loughborough
Dow Bridge Catthorpe
Elmesthorpe Elmesthorpe
Emperor's Newbold Coleorton (NEW)
Everards Leicester
Framework Leicester
Golden Duck Appleby Magna
Great Central Leicester
Langton Thorpe Langton
Market Bosworth Stoke Golding
Moonface ✦ Loughborough
Mount St Bernard Coalville
New Buildings Hinckley
Parish Burrough on the Hill
Pig Pub 🍺 ✦ Claybrooke Magna
Q Brewery Queniborough
Round Corner ✦ Melton Mowbray
West End 🍺 ✦ Leicester

Hemington

Jolly Sailor
21 Main Street, DE74 2RB
☎ (01332) 812665
Black Iris Snake Eyes; Marston's Pedigree; Oakham Bishops Farewell; 3 changing beers Ⓗ
This 17th-century building is thought to have once been a weaver's cottage. A pub since the 19th century, it retains many original features including old timbers, open fires and a beamed ceiling – convenient for hanging a collection of blowlamps and beer mugs. Well-filled rolls are available. ❀❀Ⓞ▶❀❀ 🤖

Hinckley

Elbow Room Ale & Cider House
26 Station Road, LE10 1AW (below Cineworld at The Crescent)
☎ 07900 191388
House beer (by Furnace); 6 changing beers Ⓖ
Family-run micropub decorated in an industrial style, offering a warm welcome and a great atmosphere. The ales and ciders are served by gravity directly from the cellar behind sliding glass doors. More than 40 gins are available, along with high-quality wines, whiskies, vodkas, world craft beers and lagers plus a range of soft drinks. Pork pies and Scotch eggs complement the drinks. There is no TV, jukebox or gaming machine as conversation is king. Children are welcome until early evening. Ｑ❀❀Ⓞ❀❀❀🚍(3,7)❀🤖

New Plough Inn ✅
Leicester Road, LE10 1LS
☎ (01455) 615037 ⊕ thenewploughinn.co.uk
Marston's Pedigree, Saddle Tank; 3 changing beers (often Jennings, Ringwood, Wychwood) Ⓗ
Award-winning Victorian pub offering old settles, more than 50 gins and a comfortable ambience. Rugby and cricket memorabilia reflect sponsorship of local teams. Darts, dominoes, skittles, crib and shooting teams involve the local community, and the Stables function room is available for parties and meetings. Popular quizzes have raised large sums for charity. The owners are CAMRA members who also run the historic Greyhound nearby. ❀❀❀❀🚍(159,1)❀🤖

Pestle & Mortar Ⓛ
81 Castle Street, LE10 1DA
☎ 07715 106876 ⊕ thepestlehinckley.co.uk
Draught Bass; 8 changing beers (sourced locally) Ⓗ
Comfortable and pleasantly quirky micropub with a friendly atmosphere, catering for a wide range of drinking tastes. As many as eight handpumps dispense up to eight changing real ales from casks behind the bar. As many as 22 changing real ciders are also served, including Westons Old Rosie Rhubarb. Cobs are available. Local CAMRA Pub of the Year and Cider Pub of the Year 2020.
Ｑ❀❀❀🚍(8,X55) ❀🤖

Queen's Head
Upper Bond Street, LE10 1RJ
☎ 07748 100212
4 changing beers Ⓗ
A warm welcome awaits at this multi award-winning Victorian free house serving four varying real ales. It has been sympathetically refurbished and features open fires, a Victorian range and a recently added snug, helping to generate a cosy atmosphere. A local CAMRA Pub of the Year on several occasions, it has been a regular in the Guide since 2013. Sorry, no children and no pets. ❀❀🚍

Hoby

Blue Bell Ⓛ
36 Main Street, LE14 3DT
☎ (01664) 434247 ⊕ bluebell-hoby.co.uk
2 changing beers (sourced nationally) Ⓗ
A picturesque thatched village pub with a beer garden providing fine views across the Wreake Valley. Exposed wooden beams and tiled floors with rug coverings give it a cosy and pleasant feel. There is always a good range of Everards beers available, and usually a guest ale or two. The pub is frequently busy – it is an ideal stop-off point for those seeking refreshment while walking the Leicestershire Round footpath. ❀❀Ⓞ❀❀Ｐ🚍❀🤖

Leicester

Ale Stone
660 Aylestone Road, LE2 8PR
☎ (0116) 319 2320
House beer (by Leatherbritches); 4 changing beers Ⓗ
Micropub in a converted shop unit, featuring a nicely furnished interior with wooden benches and dados all round. Up to five real ales, plus four ciders and perries, are stillaged in a temperature-controlled glass-fronted cellar. Ham and cheese cobs and coffee are available. This and sister pub the Blue Boar are unique in the city in using oversize glasses to guarantee a full pint. The two pubs arrange regular tap takeovers and beer bus trips.
Ｑ❀❀🚍❀🤖

Ale Wagon
27 Rutland Street, LE1 1RE
☎ (0116) 262 3330 ⊕ alewagon.co.uk
Hoskins Hob Bitter, IPA Ⓗ**; house beer (by Hoskins)** Ⓟ**; 4 changing beers (sourced regionally; often Hoskins)** Ⓗ
City-centre pub whose 1930s interior features an original oak staircase, two rooms with tiled and parquet floors and a central bar. The walls display photos of the former Queen's Hotel, which was across the road from the pub, and the old Hoskins Brewery. A function room is available to hire. The pub is handy for the nearby Curve Theatre. ❀❀❀🚍

Black Horse
65 Narrow Lane, Aylestone, LE2 8NA
☎ (0116) 283 7225
Everards Beacon Hill, Tiger; 4 changing beers (sourced nationally; often Brunswick, Everards, Titanic) Ⓗ
Welcoming, traditional Victorian pub with a distinctive bar servery, set in a village conservation area on the city's edge. Up to eight real ales are offered alongside home-cooked food. Quiz night is Sunday and comedy features regularly. There is a large beer garden, and a skittle alley and function room available to hire. Beer festivals and community events are regularly hosted. Coaches are welcome by prior arrangement.
Ｑ❀❀Ⓞ❀❀❀🤖

Black Horse Ⓛ
1 Foxon Street, LE3 5LT
☎ (0116) 254 0446
Everards Beacon Hill, Sunchaser, Tiger; 2 changing beers (sourced nationally) Ⓗ
The only remaining traditional community pub in a street of youth-oriented bars. It has two rooms separated by a central bar, with wood-panelled walls and practical furniture providing a comfortable setting. Guest beers are selected through Everards; the cider is Westons Old Rosie. The pub hosts live music four nights a week and a quiz on the first Sunday of the month. A roof terrace is popular for open-air drinking. ❀❀❀🚍❀🤖

Blue Boar 🏠

16 Millstone Lane, LE1 5JN
☎ (0116) 319 6230 🌐 blueboarleicester.co.uk
Beowulf Finn's Hall Porter; house beer (by Shiny); 11 changing beers ⓗ
Light, airy, single-room micropub, named after the Blue Boar Inn where Richard III stayed before the Battle of Bosworth Field. The cellar is visible through a glass partition behind the bar. The house beer is brewed by Bang the Elephant, and guest ales come from microbreweries around the country. This and sister pub the Ale Stone are the only pubs in the city using lined glasses to ensure customers get a full pint.
Q🍴🕙◐⇄♣🍴🚪☕🧡🛜

Globe

43 Silver Street, LE1 5EU
☎ (0116) 253 9492 🌐 theglobeleicester.com
Everards Beacon Hill, Sunchaser, Tiger; 3 changing beers (often Everards) ⓗ
Dating back to 1720, this pub retains original features including a snug near the entrance. It has an island servery surrounded by small rooms, and offers a range of beers and ciders alongside good food. Upstairs is a function room with its own servery. There is a pleasing collection of local photos and bric-a-brac throughout. Restored gas lights are used on special occasions.
🍴◐&🍴🚪🧡🛜

King's Head

36 King Street, LE1 6RL
☎ (0116) 254 8240
Black Country Bradley's Finest Golden, Pig on the Wall, Fireside; 7 changing beers ⓗ
A traditional one-room city-centre local owned by Black Country Ales. Its 12 handpulls dispense seven regularly changing guest beers and two varying ciders. Two changing keg ales and a range of bottles are also stocked. Meals are not served but filled cobs are often available. The pub shows sport on TV and hosts seasonal beer festivals. Its open fire and roof terrace help make it popular throughout the year with real ale and cider enthusiasts and visitors to the local football and rugby grounds. There is rear access to the pub from New Walk.
🌞⇄🍴🚪🧡🛜

Marquis Wellington

139 London Road, LE2 1EF
☎ (0116) 254 0542 🌐 themarquiswellington.com
Everards Beacon Hill, Sunchaser, Tiger; 3 changing beers ⓗ
Historic pub whose richly decorated façade stands out on the London Road thoroughfare. Popular with local workers, shoppers and students, it serves a good range of real ales plus ciders and quality food, including a vegan menu. The pub hosts live music nights and a weekly quiz night on a Monday, raising money for charity. Beach huts in the garden provide shelter from the sun and can be heated for cooler nights.
🍴🌞◐&⇄🍴🚪🧡🛜

Old Horse ✅

198 London Road, LE2 1NE
☎ (0116) 254 8384 🌐 oldhorseleicester.co.uk
Everards Beacon Hill, Tiger; 4 changing beers (sourced nationally; often Everards) ⓗ
Traditional 19th-century coaching inn, handy for dog walkers, students and sports fans. It has four guest beers which change monthly. The addition of a cider bar serving eight handpulled ciders earned the pub local CAMRA Cider Pub of the Year awards. Tasty, good-value food is served, including a Sunday carvery. Behind the building is the largest pub garden in Leicester, complete

with children's play equipment. Regular quiz nights, karaoke and special events take place.
🍴🌞◐&♣🍴P🚪🧡🛜

Queens Road Tap

109 Queens Road, LE2 1TT
🌐 tollgatebrewery.co.uk/the-queens-road-tap
6 changing beers (often Tollgate) ⓗ
Micropub that was opened in what was once a shop in 2017 by the Tollgate Brewery, based at the Calke Estate in south-east Derbyshire. The modern single-room interior has rustic furniture. The bar serves a constantly varying range of six real ales, including three or four from Tollgate, plus several guests and two ciders. There is no music or TV. Pizza can be ordered and delivered to your table from an outlet down the road. Dogs, walkers and cyclists welcome. The bus to Leicester stops right outside but evening services are limited. Q🍴🚪(44A,83A)🧡

Real Ale Classroom 🏠

22 Allandale Road, LE2 2DA
☎ (0116) 319 6998 🌐 therealaleclassroom.com
5 changing beers (sourced regionally; often Grainstore, Oakham) Ⓖ
A classroom-themed micropub run by career-change teachers in a converted shop. The furniture includes reclaimed desks with original graffiti; the beers are written up on a blackboard. Cask ales and ciders are served from a home-made chiller cabinet behind the high bar. A log-burner warms the rear room. In both rooms seating around large tables encourages conversation between regulars and visitors. Crisps, nuts, scratchings and take-away cans are available.
Q🌞♣🍴🚪🧡🛜

Rutland & Derby 🏠

21 Millstone Lane, LE1 5JN
☎ (0116) 262 3299 🌐 therutlandanddderby.co.uk
Everards Sunchaser, Tiger; 2 changing beers ⓗ
Local ales and good food prepared from uncomplicated, ethically sourced ingredients are features of this pub, whose open-plan interior helps give a contemporary ambience. The long servery bar is directly facing the front entrance. Off to the left is a lounge-style bar, leading to a restaurant area on a raised level. Out back is a block-paved courtyard with a metallic spiral staircase leading up to a rooftop terrace. 🍴🌞◐&⇄🍴🚪🧡🛜

Salmon

19 Butt Close Lane, LE1 4QA (from clock tower walk down Churchgate; Butt Close Lane is second left)
☎ (0116) 253 2301 🌐 bca.charlesdesign.co.uk/pubs/the-salmon
Black Country Bradley's Finest Golden, Pig on the Wall, Fireside; 7 changing beers (sourced nationally) ⓗ
A small corner local with a U-shaped single room and a bright, traditional interior. A Black Country Ales pub since 2016, the Salmon has a friendly, welcoming atmosphere and a strong sports following. Its 12 handpumps dispense the brewery's ales alongside guest beers and two real ciders. Cobs, pork pies and Scotch eggs are offered throughout the day. Bus stations are nearby.
Q🍴🌞&♣🍴🚪🧡🛜

Sir Robert Peel

50 Jarrom Street, LE2 7DD
☎ (0116) 255 9419 🌐 sirrobertpeel.net
Everards Beacon Hill, Sunchaser, Tiger; 3 changing beers ⓗ
Run by a friendly, knowledgeable couple, this is one of the few original pubs left in the city. It serves well-kept Everards beers alongside a range of guests and a real

cider. The traditional pub food is popular. A large beer garden provides a relaxing space for dining and drinking. The pub gets busy on football and rugby match days. ✿◑♿🍴🚪🐾☙

Two-Tailed Lion

22 Millstone Lane, LE1 5JN
☎ (0116) 224 4769 ⊕ thetwotailedlion.com
3 changing beers Ⓗ
Modern, newly refurbished beer-oriented pub. Three handpumps and six keg taps provide a regular rotation of beers. There is also a well-stocked bottle shop. Unobtrusive music is played. As well as the small downstairs bar with a range of comfortable seating there are two upstairs rooms that can be hired. A mobile wood-fired pizza van serves food at weekends. ☙♥🚪🐾☙🛜

West End Brewery

68-70 Braunstone Gate, LE3 5LG
☎ 07875 745302 ⊕ thewestendbrewery.co.uk
West End Project Pale, Stout, West Coast IPA; 3 changing beers (sourced nationally; often West End) Ⓗ
Leicester's original brewpub, opened in 2016. The owner/brewer aims to produce innovative beers, and plans to extend the range over time – capacity increased to a five-barrel plant in 2019. He likes to experiment with his recipes and takes on board customers' feedback. The brewery is behind the pub and is open to visitors. Four house beers are available plus at least two guests or farmhouse ciders from quality local microbreweries or from further afield. Live music is hosted once a month. ☙♣🚪🐾☙🛜

Wygston's House

12 Applegate, LE1 5LD
☎ (0116) 296 4301 ⊕ wygstonshouse.co.uk
Charnwood Vixen; 3 changing beers (sourced locally) Ⓗ
The best-preserved medieval house in Leicester, Wygston's opened as a bar and restaurant in 2017. Its central entrance leads into a stone-flagged passage, with small, elegant rooms on either side. The corridor opens out at the back into the medieval part of the house, a bar area with a wood-beamed ceiling. Upstairs is a light, airy room also with an old beamed ceiling and views over historic Leicester. There is an extensive and attractive patio outside. ☙✿◑♿♥🚪🐾☙🛜

Loughborough

Moon & Bell 🏅

6 Wards End, LE11 3HA
☎ (01509) 241504
Greene King IPA, Abbot; Kelham Island Pale Rider; Ruddles Best Bitter; Sharp's Doom Bar; 4 changing beers Ⓗ
A large Wetherspoon venue in the Grade II-listed Atherstone House. The pub serves a fine selection of house and guest ales, plus an extensive food menu. Beer and cider festivals are held frequently, including twice-yearly real ale festivals. A marquee in the spacious rear garden serves many beers on handpull in addition to those available inside. Q☙✿◑P🚪🐾🛜

Moonface Brewery & Tap

13 Moira Street, LE11 1AU
☎ (01509) 700171
5 changing beers Ⓖ
A small, neat bar that opened in 2018 in a former warehouse building and art studio. Three to five real ales are served direct from casks stillaged behind the counter,

with a constantly changing range. There are no keg beers. The in-house Moonface microbrewery, visible in a room directly behind the bar, is now in full production. Local CAMRA Pub of the Year 2020 and 2021. ♥

Needle & Pin

The Rushes, LE11 5BE
☎ 07973 754236
4 changing beers Ⓗ
A micropub in what was the old H&R Electronics shop. Beer is served downstairs in a continental-style bar with high stools. The upstairs room has board games and music. More than 80 continental and craft beers are stocked. ☙♥🐾

Organ Grinder

4 WoodGate, LE11 2TY
☎ (01509) 264008
Blue Monkey BG Sips, Infinity, Guerrilla, Ape Ale; 4 changing beers (sourced locally; often Blue Monkey) Ⓗ
Previously known as the Pack Horse, and bought by Blue Monkey in 2012, the building has received a top-to-bottom renovation, uncovering lots of interesting original features. The stable bar at the back reflects the pub's past life as a coaching inn. Eight cask ales are always available alongside a choice of four real ciders, sometimes a perry, and Belgian bottled beers. Bar snacks include an interesting range of pork pies. ☙✿♥🍴🚪🐾☙🛜

Swan in the Rushes

21 The Rushes, LE11 5BE
☎ (01509) 217014
Castle Rock Sheriff's Tipple, Harvest Pale, Elsie Mo; 6 changing beers (often Castle Rock, Charnwood) Ⓗ
Traditional three-room Castle Rock pub comprising a quiet, traditionally styled lounge, a contemporary dining room and a lively bar with a jukebox. A constantly changing range of up to seven guest beers is on offer. Real cider, perry, a wide variety of continental bottled and draught beers and a good choice of malt whiskies and country wines are also available. Upstairs is the Hop Loft function room and a first-floor outside terrace. Q☙✿◑♿♥▲🍴P🚪🐾☙🛜

White Hart

27 Churchgate, LE11 1UD
☎ (01509) 236976 ⊕ benpimlico.com/whitehart/home
Charnwood Salvation, Vixen; Draught Bass; Timothy Taylor Landlord; 2 changing beers (sourced locally; often Leatherbritches, Sarah Hughes) Ⓗ
Free house that combines quality ales with attractions including a secluded patio and beer garden to the rear. It serves changing guest beers from local breweries such as Leatherbritches and Charnwood. Bar snacks and tapas are available until early evening. Live music plays on occasional Friday and Saturday evenings. ✿◑♣♥🚪🐾☙

Lutterworth

Fox

34 Rugby Road, LE17 4BN (½ mile on main road from M1, 400yds from Whittle roundabout)
☎ (01455) 550935 ⊕ fox-lutterworth.co.uk
Draught Bass; Sharp's Doom Bar; 2 changing beers (sourced nationally; often Timothy Taylor, Wadworth) Ⓗ
Welcoming 18th-century establishment at the southern end of Lutterworth, described as the town's village pub. An L-shaped, open-plan interior with a wooden-floored bar and carpeted dining area is warmed by two open fires. Meals are served lunchtimes and evenings, including excellent Sunday roasts. Thai food is available

in the evenings in the adjacent Sawasdee restaurant. Outside is a large garden and drinking area. Quiz night is Tuesday. ⚶◖◑⬥P🖶(58,X44)❀ 📶

Greyhound L

9 Market Street, LE17 4EJ (on main road)
☎ (01455) 553307 ⊕ greyhoundinn.co.uk
4 changing beers Ⓗ

A Grade II-listed coach house on the main thoroughfare, dating from 1758 and offering a warm welcome. The lounge contains original features and period-style furnishings, with nautical pictures and old clocks. The bar includes a wood-block floor. A variety of food including light meals is available all day, with an evening menu served in the plush restaurant. The pub is a popular venue for private parties and weddings. It has a paved courtyard outside for summer drinks. Q⚶❀⬅◖◑🖶❀ 📶

Real Ale Classroom

4 Station Road, LE17 4AP
☎ (0116) 319 6998 ⊕ therealaleclassroom.com
4 changing beers (sourced nationally) Ⓖ

A spacious micropub with a schoolroom theme, owned by former teachers. It offers a constantly changing line-up of four cask and four craft keg ales plus a wide range of bottled and canned beers and five ciders. The bar has a log-burner for winter and a fantastic beer garden to enjoy in summer. Friendly staff are knowledgeable about the drinks on offer, including excellent gins and spirits from local distillers. Snacks are from local suppliers. Q⚶❀♣⬥🖶(X84,58) ❀ 📶

Unicorn ✓

29 Church Street, LE17 4AE (near church)
☎ (01455) 552486
Adnams Southwold Bitter; Draught Bass; Greene King IPA; 2 changing beers (sourced nationally; often Sharp's) Ⓗ

Traditional street-corner local with a black and white frontage, built in 1919 on the site of an 18th-century coach house in the town centre. The large public bar, with its open fire, shows TV sport and hosts teams playing darts, dominoes and skittles. The small, comfortable lounge, divided by a central fireplace, displays photographs of old Lutterworth. Alongside the adjacent dining room it forms a family-friendly area that is used to serve the pub's good, inexpensive, lunchtime food, which includes vegetarian and children's options. ⚶◑♣P🖶(8,X44) ❀ 📶

Market Harborough

Beerhouse

76 St Mary's Road, LE16 7DX (behind St Mary's Fish Bar)
☎ (01858) 465317
8 changing beers (sourced nationally) Ⓟ

Market Harborough's first micropub, set in a converted furniture shop directly behind the chip shop on St Mary's Road. The focus is very much on beer – no food, gaming machines or loud music. There are 20 taps for draught products – eight for cask ales, the rest for KeyKegs and ciders. Monday is quiz night, and the pub hosts occasional comedy nights, vinyl nights and live music. Other attractions include a book club and cider festival. ⚶❀♣⬅⬥P🖬❀ 📶

Melton Mowbray

Anne of Cleves L

12, Burton Street, LE13 1AE
☎ (01664) 481336 ⊕ theanneofcleves.com
3 changing beers (sourced nationally) Ⓗ

One of Melton Mowbray and Everards' most historic pubs and an icon for the town. Part of the property dates back to 1327 when it was home to monks. The house was gifted to Anne of Cleves by Henry VIII as part of her divorce settlement. It is now a popular hostelry following a sympathetic restoration in 1996. It has stone-flagg floors, exposed timber beams and tapestries throughout. The beer garden recently won a silver award from 'East Midlands in Bloom'. ⚶❀◖◑⬅♣P🖶❀ 📶

Boat ✓

57, Burton Street, LE13 1AF
☎ (01664) 500969
Draught Bass; Bombardier; 1 changing beer Ⓗ

A traditional single-roomed pub that takes its name from a canal basin that was once adjacent. Many of the walls are wood panelled and decorated with old pictures of the town and a map of the old Melton-Oakham canal. The pub is always busy and popular with those who enjoy good conversation with their pint. An open fire gives plenty of warmth and adds to the atmosphere in winter. ⬅♣🖶❀ 📶

Paint the Town Red

7 King Street, LE13 1XA
☎ (01664) 561958
2 changing beers (sourced nationally) Ⓗ

Previously a BeerHeadZ company micropub, but now under local independent ownership. It offers a wide choice of beer styles, many from innovative and new breweries. Real cider and a good range of craft ales (most of which are KeyKeg) are also available. It occupies a manor house that dates from the 14th century and is one of Melton Mowbray's oldest buildings, with a timber frame going back to 1301; in the 1500s it was the manor of John Mowbray. More recently it was a dressmaker's; the signage remains on the front of the pub. Q⚶❀⬅⬥🖬🖶(5,19) ❀

Mountsorrel

Sorrel Fox

75 Leicester Road, LE12 7AJ
☎ (0116) 230 3777
Charnwood Salvation, Vixen; 2 changing beers (sourced locally; often Charnwood) Ⓗ

The Sorrel Fox is Charnwood Brewery's first micropub in the village. It is cosy with a lovely log-burner, and welcomes dogs. Charnwood's popular cask ales and craft beers are served alongside an imported Austrian lager, complemented by quality wines, a selection of gins and a couple of rums. The pub is close to the A6, with a bus stop for routes to Leicester, Loughborough and Shepshed. 🖶❀

Swan

10 Loughborough Road, LE12 7AT
☎ (0116) 230 2340
Black Sheep Best Bitter; Castle Rock Harvest Pale; 2 changing beers (often Dancing Duck, Greene King) Ⓗ

Seventeenth-century, Grade II-listed coaching inn on the banks of the River Soar, entered via a narrow arch into a courtyard. The split-level interior has open fires, stone floors and low ceilings, and includes a small dining area with a polished wood floor. Good-quality, interesting food is cooked to order, the menu changing weekly and featuring regular themes. Outside is a long, secluded riverside garden. A beer festival is held annually. Q⚶❀◖◑P🖶❀

Nether Broughton

Anchor
Main Road, LE14 3HB
☎ (01664) 822461
Ringwood Razorback; 1 changing beer Ⓗ
A cosy village roadside pub on the A606, featuring a main bar with a real fire and dartboard, plus a separate dining area offering a quieter space. Traditional fare is served regularly, with occasional themed nights. The pub hosts regular charity events, and welcomes families and dogs. Outside there is a large car park and pleasant seating. The house beer is Ringwood Razorback, served under its old name of Best Bitter. ❀❁❂❃❄♣P🚽🐾

Oadby

Cow & Plough
Gartree Road, LE2 2FB
☎ (0116) 272 0852
Fuller's London Pride; Steamin' Billy Bitter, Skydiver; 4 changing beers (sourced regionally; often Abbeydale, Belvoir, Charnwood) Ⓗ
Situated in what was a farm building with a conservatory, the pub is decked out with breweriana. It is home to Steamin' Billy beers, named after the owner's now departed Jack Russell who features on the logo and pumpclips. A mild is always available and a real cider in the summer months. An annual beer festival is held. The renowned restaurant is in the old dairy buildings. Q❀❁❂❃❅♣🐾P🚽🐾📶

Plungar

Anchor ⒧
Granby Lane, NG13 0JJ
☎ (01949) 860589
3 changing beers Ⓗ
This brick-built pub in the heart of the village dates from 1774 and previously served as the local courtroom. It has a large bar, lounge area and separate restaurant, plus an annexe housing the pool table, and an attractive beer garden. Up to three beers, at least one local, are available in a range of styles. The pub is popular with locals and visitors, cycling groups, horse riders and anglers using the nearby fishing lakes. Q❀❁❂❃❅♣P🚽(24)🐾📶

Quorn

Manor House
Woodhouse Road, LE12 8AL
☎ (01509) 413416 ⊕ themanorhouseatquorn.co.uk
Charnwood Salvation; Draught Bass Ⓗ
Built in 1899 by the Great Central Railway, the Manor House was designed to serve passengers arriving at Quorn and Woodhouse station, which it still does today – the heritage railway's steam and diesel trains pass by 150 yards from the door. It is a free house serving two guest beers during the week and three at weekends. The interior features an open-plan bar and award-winning restaurant, plus a function and meeting room that can be hired. Q❀❁❂❅🅰🚉♣P🚽🐾

Redmile

Windmill ✅
4 Main Street, NG13 0GA
☎ (01949) 842281 ⊕ thewindmillinnredmile.co.uk
2 changing beers (sourced locally; often Castle Rock, Shipstone's) Ⓗ
The Windmill is a privately owned freehold restaurant and bar, owner operated, one mile down the hill from Belvoir Castle. It has two rooms, a stone-floored bar complete with log fire, and a lounge, plus a generous terrace. It enjoys a cult status among fans of the TV show Auf Wiedersehen, Pet, in which it appeared as the Barley Mow. Photos taken during filming are on display. Q❀❁❂❃🅰P🚽🐾📶

Shackerstone

Rising Sun
Church Road, CV13 6NN
☎ (01827) 880215 ⊕ risingsunpub.com
Draught Bass; Marston's Pedigree; Timothy Taylor Landlord; 1 changing beer Ⓗ
A traditional family-owned free house in the heart of Shackerstone, near the Ashby Canal and preserved Battlefield Railway. It has a wood-panelled bar serving traditional ales, a restaurant, pool room with Sky Sports, family-friendly conservatory and an attractive garden. The pub, popular with locals and visitors alike, is renowned for the quality and variety of its ales and serves good food – the ideal hub for visiting this rural part of Leicestershire. ❀❁❂❃🅰🚉(Battlefield)♣🐾P🚽(7)🐾📶

Shearsby

Chandlers Arms ⒧
Fenny Lane, LE17 6PL
☎ (0116) 247 8384 ⊕ thechandlersinshearsby.co.uk
Dow Bridge Acris; 4 changing beers (sourced regionally) Ⓗ
Quintessential local inn with a big reputation – the pub is a community hub for the village and welcoming to visitors. Its name derives from the building's original use as a tallow candlemaker's premises. The beer garden overlooks the village green from a high vantage point and an undercover terraced area has recently been added. Microbrewery beers are always on the bar, often locally sourced, including a stout or porter. Good food is available, but the owners see it primarily as a drinkers' pub. ❀❁❂❃♣🐾🐾📶

Shepshed

Black Swan ✅
21 Loughborough Road, LE12 9DL
☎ (01509) 506222
Draught Bass; Greene King Abbot; Timothy Taylor Landlord; 2 changing beers Ⓗ
Multi-roomed pub in a prominent position close to the town centre, offering two guest beers alongside the regulars. An extremely good range of whiskies is also kept. The main room has two drinking areas, both with comfortable seating. A further small room can be used by families and is available to hire for functions. Wednesday is quiz night. Local events include music by a ukulele orchestra. Shepshed Dynamo football ground is nearby. ❀🅸P🚽

Horse
196 Ashby Road West, LE12 9EF
☎ (01509) 507006 ⊕ thehorseshepshed.co.uk
Draught Bass; Greene King Abbot; Leatherbritches Hairy Helmet; 1 changing beer (often Charnwood) Ⓗ
The Horse, one of the oldest free houses in the town, is traditionally built, with a restaurant and bar. A good range of beers is available and the pub takes pride in serving freshly prepared food made on the premises, where possible using produce sourced within a five-mile

radius of Shepshed. The interior has a feature fireplace with wood-burning stove; outside is an alfresco dining area with wood-fired pizza oven. ৬❀⛆P🖳

Sileby

Horse & Trumpet
4 Barrow Road, LE12 7LP
☎ (01509) 812549
Charnwood Salvation; Steamin' Billy Bitter Ⓗ
This multi-room inn with open fires has undergone a huge transformation since becoming part of the Steamin' Billy chain. A real cider and perry are on offer. No hot food is served but cobs are available, and there is a monthly curry club. The pub has a function room. Well-behaved dogs are welcome in the bar and outside seating area. Q❀⇌♣●P🖳(KB2)

Somerby

Stilton Cheese Ⓛ
High Street, LE14 2QB
☎ (01664) 454394 ⊕ stiltoncheeseinn.co.uk
Grainstore Ten Fifty; Marston's Pedigree; 3 changing beers (sourced nationally) Ⓗ
Welcoming family-run pub, built in local ironstone in the late 16th century. Inside is a cosy bar and an adjoining room displaying an eclectic collection of copper pots and pans, horse brasses, pictures of hunting scenes and a stuffed pike and badger. At least four real ales are always available, often from local breweries. Local CAMRA Pub of the Year 2019 and 2020. Q৬❀⛆♣●P🖳🤙

Stoke Golding

George & Dragon Ⓛ
Station Road, CV13 6EZ
☎ (01455) 213268 ⊕ churchendbrewery.co.uk/pubs
Church End Goat's Milk, Gravediggers Ale, What the Fox's Hat, Stout Coffin, Fallen Angel; 3 changing beers (sourced locally; often Church End) Ⓗ
Renowned village local serving eight real ales from the Church End range, plus a real cider. Excellent home-cooked lunches feature local produce. There is a steak night on the second Tuesday of each month, and Sunday lunch on the last Sunday. Bar snacks are made on the premises and always available. The pub is close to the historic Bosworth battlefield. It supports a number of clubs and societies, and is popular with walkers, cyclists and boaters from the nearby Ashby Canal. Q৬❀⛆▲♣●P🖳(66) 🐾🤙

Swinford

Chequers ✓
High Street, LE17 6BL (near church)
☎ (01788) 860318 ⊕ chequersswinford.co.uk
Adnams Southwold Bitter; 2 changing beers (sourced nationally; often St Austell, Timothy Taylor) Ⓗ
A warm welcome is assured at this family-run community local, whose landlord has been in place for more than 34 years. The menu caters for all and includes vegetarian and children's options. The large garden and play area are popular with families in good weather. A marquee provides the venue for the annual beer festival and is available for private hire. Pub games include table skittles. Within a mile is the 18th-century Stanford Hall, with a caravan park and museum. ৬❀⛆▲♣🐾🤙

Syston

Beer Pharmacie Ⓛ
3 High Street, LE7 1GP
☎ (0116) 269 6933
Shipstone's Mild, Original; 3 changing beers (sourced nationally; often Framework, Oakham, Pentrich) Ⓗ
Syston's first micropub opened in 2018 with a 1950s pharmacy theme, displaying medical artefacts, equipment, advertisements and a friendly skeleton sitting on a dentist's chair. Upstairs, the theme is 1950s movies in a vinyl lounge with seating for about 70 people. Another room is available for private hire. The pub offers a varying selection of real ales plus up to six craft kegs. No meals are served but cheese cobs and other snacks are available. Q৬&♣●ⱷ🖳🐾🤙

Syston & District Social Club
36 High Street, LE7 1GP
☎ (0116) 260 9086 ⊕ systonsocial.weebly.com
Banks's Amber Ale; Wychwood Hobgoblin Ruby; 3 changing beers (often Castle Rock, Church End) Ⓗ
Historically, this old building was a pub, the Bull's Head. It became a Labour club for a while, and is now an independent non-political members' club. It is home to many local societies and sports clubs including darts, skittles, chess and crib. The range of six beers includes four regularly rotating guests. Beer festivals are held in February and June. For entry, show a CAMRA membership card or a copy of this Guide. ৬❀&♣🖳(5,5A) 🐾🤙

Walton on the Wolds

Anchor
2 Loughborough Road, LE12 8HT
☎ (01509) 880018
Draught Bass; Timothy Taylor Landlord; 1 changing beer (often Charnwood) Ⓗ
The Anchor is in the centre of a small village within easy reach of Leicester and Nottingham via the A46. It is a popular venue for walkers who stop for a well-earned home-cooked lunch in front of the log fire. There is a menu to suit all tastes plus an extensive specials board. Outside is an elevated seating area to the front and a garden and large car park to the rear. Q৬❀⇌⛆P🖳🐾

Wigston

Tap & Barrel
58 Leicester Road, LE18 1DR
☎ (0116) 319 0123 ⊕ tapandbarrelwigston.co.uk
5 changing beers Ⓖ
A rustic timber bar gives this micropub an unpretentious ambience, enhanced by bare wooden floorboards, and exposed ceiling joists braced with traditional herringbone strutting. It offers five cask handpumps (all five not always in use) and up to four gravity fed casks from the chiller, eight keg lines and up to 16 traditional ciders served from a chiller behind the bar. Recent modifications have seen the bar moved to the rear of the venue, giving an open spacious feel and more seating, including a cosy chillout area upstairs. The alterations have allowed room for a small kitchen, which serves stone-baked pizzas, burgers, pies, chips and their take on a Sunday lunch. ৬⛆&♣●P🖳🐾🤙

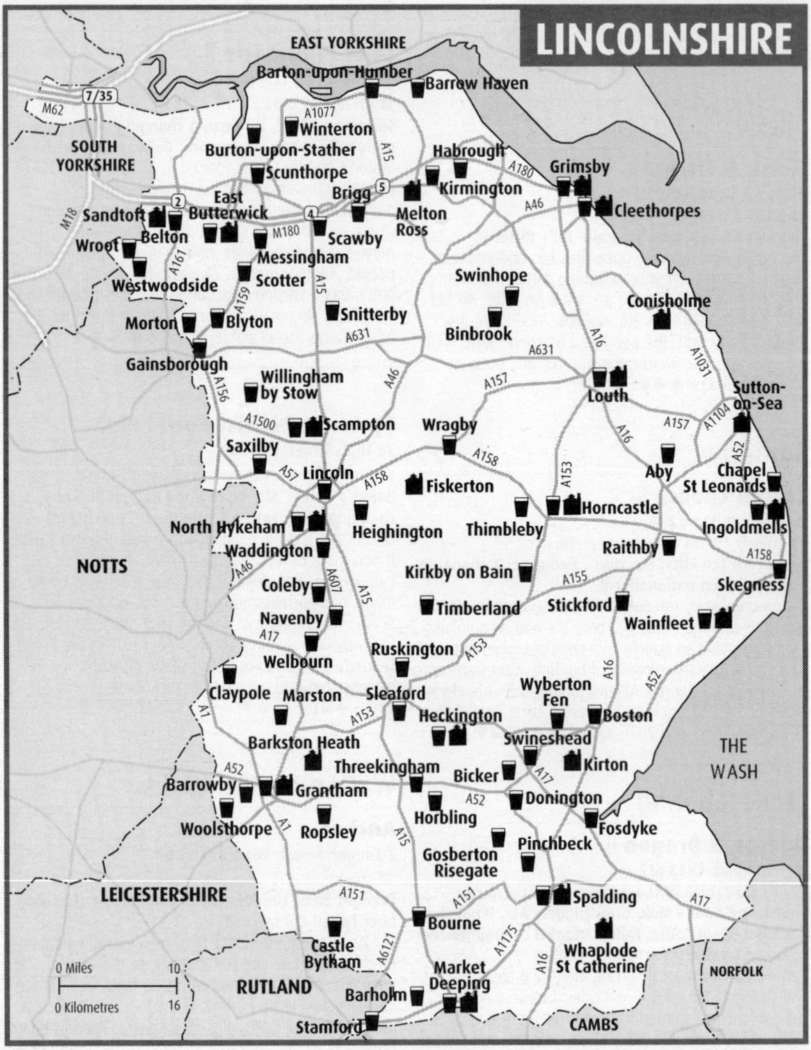
LINCOLNSHIRE
EAST YORKSHIRE
Barton-upon-Humber
Barrow Haven
7/35
M62
A1077
Winterton
SOUTH
YORKSHIRE
Burton-upon-Stather
A15
Habrough
A180
Grimsby
Scunthorpe
Kirmington
5
Brigg
East
Butterwick
2
A46
Cleethorpes
M18
Sandtoft
4
Melton
Ross
Belton
M180
Scawby
Wroot
Messingham
A161
Westwoodside
Scotter
Swinhope
A159
Conisholme
Morton
Blyton
Snitterby
A631
Binbrook
A16
Gainsborough
A631
A1031
Willingham
by Stow
A46
A157
Louth
Sutton-
on-Sea
A156
A1500
Scampton
Wragby
A1104
A157
Saxilby
A16
A52
A158
Aby
Chapel
St Leonards
A57
Lincoln
A158
A153
Fiskerton
Horncastle
Thimbleby
North Hykeham
Heighington
Ingoldmells
Raithby
Waddington
NOTTS
A46
A158
Kirkby on Bain
A155
Skegness
Coleby
A607
A15
Stickford
Timberland
Navenby
Wainfleet
A17
Welbourn
Ruskington
A153
A16
Claypole
Marston
Sleaford
Wyberton
Fen
A52
A1
A153
Heckington
Boston
Barkston Heath
Swineshead
THE
WASH
Threekingham
Kirton
A52
Barrowby
Grantham
Bicker
A17
A52
Donington
Horbling
Woolsthorpe
A1
Ropsley
Fosdyke
A15
Pinchbeck
Gosberton
Risegate
LEICESTERSHIRE
A151
Spalding
A151
A17
Bourne
A1175
Castle
Bytham
A6121
A16
Whaplode
St Catherine
0 Miles
10
NORFOLK
RUTLAND
Market
Deeping
0 Kilometres
16
Barholm
Stamford
CAMBS

Aby

Railway Tavern

Main Road, LN13 0DR (off A16 via South Thoresby)

☎ (01507) 480676 🌐 railwaytavern-aby.co.uk

2 changing beers (sourced nationally) [H]

A rural inn that was closed when the licensees took it on over 15 years ago; since then it has grown to the successful pub it is now, serving the community and raising money for charity. It has won numerous awards including local CAMRA Country Pub of the Year four times. It offers a wide range of real ales and a menu based on produce from the area. Two holiday cottages are available for short breaks or week-long bookings. Q☕❀⇌◑♿⛺♣P🐾

Barholm

Five Horseshoes [L]

PE9 4RA

☎ (01778) 560238

Adnams Southwold Bitter; Draught Bass; Oakham JHB; 3 changing beers (often Grainstore, Hopshackle) [H]

An 18th-century stone-built country pub, well known for supporting many charities. It comprises two bars, two cosy side rooms and a pool room. A wood fire burns throughout the winter. A real cider is served along with three permanent and three changing ales. Pizzas are available on Friday and Saturday evenings, while barbecues and live music events in the large garden are a feature of the summer months. Q☕❀◑♿🍏P🐾📶

Barrow Haven

Haven Inn [L]

Ferry Road, DN19 7EX (approx 1½ miles E of Barrow-upon-Humber)

☎ (01469) 530247

Sharp's Doom Bar; Timothy Taylor Landlord; 1 changing beer (sourced nationally) [H]

Built in 1730 as a coaching inn in the quiet north Lincolnshire countryside for travellers using the former ferry, the Haven has been renowned for hospitality, good food and drink, and comfortable lodgings ever since. Full of character, a warm welcome awaits, with a bar, lounge and large comfortable conservatory. It is ideally located for walkers from the Humber Bank to call in for a well-kept pint. 🐴❀🛏🍴♿🚆P🐾

Barrowby

White Swan ✔

Main Street, NG32 1BH

☎ (01476) 562375

Castle Rock Harvest Pale; Sharp's Doom Bar; 2 changing beers [H]

Popular village pub run by the same landlord for 28 years, who is an enthusiastic CAMRA member. There is a comfortable lounge, a separate bar area and a further section where the local darts, cribbage and pool teams play. Offering two regular and two changing guest ales, it also provides locally sourced traditional home-made food Wednesday to Saturday. Outside, there is a heated smoking space and a secluded garden. Quiz night is on the first Sunday of the month. Q🐴❀🍴♿♣P🚌🐾📶

Barton-upon-Humber

Sloop Inn [L]

81 Waterside Road, DN18 5BA (follow Humber Bridge viewing signs)

☎ (01652) 637287

Batemans Gold; Timothy Taylor Boltmaker; Theakston Best Bitter; 1 changing beer (sourced nationally) [H]

This welcoming 19th-century multi-roomed pub, popular with locals and walkers, has recently been taken over by experienced local hosts. It has been refurbished throughout but original features such as the Delft fireplace tiles and stained glass windows remain. The Far Ings Nature Reserve, Waters Edge Visitor Centre, Ropewalk, Ropery Hall and the Humber Bridge are all nearby attractions. 🐴❀🍴♿⛺🚆♣P📺🚌(250,350)🐾

White Swan [L]

66 Fleetgate, DN18 5QD (follow signs for railway station)

☎ (01652) 661222

House beer (by Westgate); 4 changing beers (sourced nationally; often Great Newsome, Horncastle Ales) [H]

Multi award-winning, renovated 17th-century coaching inn, directly opposite the bus/train interchange. It offers a warm welcome to all, hosting community groups, traditional pub games, a monthly vinyl night, music and quiz evenings. Four ever-changing cask ales and regular house beer Golden Ale are complemented by a rotating craft keg beer and changing ciders and perry in summer. The pub is an outlet for new local brewery Little Big Dog. The deceptively spacious covered rear courtyard is ideal for outdoor drinking. Q🐴❀🛏🍴♿🚆♣🍐P🚌📶

Belton

Crown Inn [L]

Church Lane, DN9 1PA (turn off A161 at All Saints Church and follow road behind)

☎ (01427) 872834

Bradfield Farmers Blonde; Brakspear Gravity; Jennings Cocker Hoop; Oakham Citra; 2 changing beers (sourced regionally; often Abbeydale, Ringwood) [H]

Difficult to find but well worth the effort, this pub has long been a haven for the discerning drinker. Six cask ales are always on tap, one of which is usually from the Cuckoo Brewery, part-owned by the licensees. It is active in the community, and quizzes, beer festivals and live entertainment are all features of this multi-roomed venue. A winner of several local CAMRA awards including a District Pub of the Year. Does not use Autovacs. 🐴❀⛺♣🍐P📺🚌(399) 🐾📶

Bicker

Red Lion

Donington Road, PE20 3EF

☎ (01775) 821200 🌐 redlionbicker.co.uk

Adnams Southwold Bitter; Courage Directors; Greene King IPA; 1 changing beer [H]

A typical country inn in a pleasant setting, with low beams and a tiled floor. It was extensively and tastefully redecorated in 2015 and reopened after two years' closure. The welcoming multi-roomed pub has a small bar, and is popular for dining, with a varied, extensive menu. The pub is known to date from at least 1665. 🐴❀🍴♿♣P🚌(59) 📶

Binbrook

Plough

Market Place, LN8 6DE

☎ (01472) 398808 🌐 theploughbinbrook.co.uk

4 changing beers (sourced regionally; often Horncastle Ales) [H]

A Victorian pub in the heart of the this Lincolnshire Wolds village which has been well maintained over the decades. Its aviation links to the nearby defunct airbase are proudly displayed on the walls with pictures of Lightning jet planes which used to fly past. Good home-cooked food is served regularly and is getting a much-sought-after reputation. Live music can be heard most weekends. No dogs allowed during food service. 🐴❀🍴♣P🚌(3) 🐾

Blyton

Black Horse

93 High Street, DN21 3JX

☎ (01427) 628277 🌐 blackhorseblyton.co.uk

Batemans XB; 2 changing beers [H]

One of two pubs in the village, sited at the northern end. The interior is divided into five distinct areas: two for

REAL ALE BREWERIES

8 Sail ◆ Heckington
Austendyke Spalding (brewing suspended)
Bacchus 🛢 Sutton-on-Sea
Batemans ◆ Wainfleet
Blue Bell 🛢 Whaplode St Catherine
Brewsters Grantham
Consortium 🛢 ◆ Louth
Dark Tribe 🛢 East Butterwick
Docks Grimsby
Don Valley Sandtoft
Ferry Ales Fiskerton
Firehouse Louth
Fuddy Duck Kirton
Greg's 🛢 Scampton
Hopshackle Market Deeping
Horncastle 🛢 Horncastle
Leila Cottage 🛢 Ingoldmells
Lincolnshire Craft Melton Ross
Newby Wyke Grantham
Poachers ◆ North Hykeham
Welland Spalding
Wickham House Conisholme
Willy's 🛢 Cleethorpes
Zest Barkston Heath

dining, two for drinking, and one for the pool table and darts. There is also an outside drinking space. One beer is often from Batemans, alongside two changing choices, sometimes from local brewers. Self-contained accommodation is available and there is generous parking. ⌖🛏🍴🕪👌♣🅿🚌🛜

Boston

Coach & Horses
86 Main Ridge, PE21 6SY
☎ (01205) 612649
Batemans XB, XXXB; 1 changing beer (sourced locally; often Batemans) Ⓗ
The open-plan lounge here has a polished wooden bar frontage and wood-panelled ceiling. Wooden cabinets showcase a large collection of miniature bottles. Other items such as a deer's antlers, a large clock and photographs of musicians adorn the walls. The pub hosts pool, darts, poker, and quiz teams. Close to the Boston United football ground, it is popular with football supporters. There is regular entertainment at weekends.
❀♣🐾🛜

Eagle
144 West Street, PE21 8RE
☎ (01205) 361116
Castle Rock Black Gold, Harvest Pale, Preservation, Screech Owl; 7 changing beers Ⓗ
Part of the Castle Rock chain, the Eagle is known as the real ale pub of Boston. This friendly two-roomed hostelry has an L-shaped bar with a large TV screen for big sports events. The small cosy lounge has an open fire. It stocks a wide range of guest ales, and at least one cider. A function room upstairs is home to Boston folk club. Friday is quiz night – allegedly the hardest in town.
Q❀👌🗦♣🍴🚌🐾🛜

Goodbarns Yard ✅
8 Wormgate, PE21 6NP
☎ (01205) 355717 ⊕ goodbarnsyard.com
Morland Old Speckled Hen; Timothy Taylor Landlord; 1 changing beer (sourced nationally) Ⓗ
The 700-year-old pub is in a cobbled medieval street, which runs northwards away from the Boston Stump, parallel to the River Witham. It is popular for meals, with a busy restaurant. Old signs and pictures of Boston adorn the walls. A large garden with tables and covered patio areas overlooks the river. In winter, an open fire welcomes you. ⌖❀🕪🗦🛜

Bourne

Anchor
44 Eastgate, PE10 9JY
☎ (01778) 422347
House beer (by Dancing Duck); 4 changing beers (sourced regionally; often Nene Valley, St Austell, Thornbridge) Ⓗ
A traditional two-roomed local with a patio by the banks of a tributary of the River Glen, strong on sports, with pool and darts played, Sky Sports on TV and several sporting trophies on display. It raises funds for the local Air Ambulance service. The house beer, Bourne Particular, is supplied by Dancing Duck, as is Roundheart, brewed for sister pub the Hand & Heart in Nottingham. There is a small car park. ⌖❀👌♣🍴🅿🛜

Brigg

Yarborough Hunt Ⓛ
49 Bridge Street, DN20 8NS (across bridge from marketplace)
☎ (01652) 658333
Lincolnshire Craft Best Bitter, Bomber County, Lincoln Gold; 4 changing beers (sourced nationally; often Skinner's, Timothy Taylor, Wychwood) Ⓗ
A traditional pub in the town centre with a main bar and a number of interconnecting rooms, some with real fires. Many vintage photographs and old brewery signs and notices are displayed. There are three real ales from Lincolnshire Craft Beers plus four rotating guest beers and a real cider. Fourteen keg taps also offer a collection of continental and craft beers. An enclosed beer garden is at the rear. No food is served, but customers can bring their own sandwiches. Q⌖❀👌🗦♣🍴🚌(4,X4)🐾🛜

Burton-upon-Stather

Ferry House Inn Ⓛ ✅
Stather Road, DN15 9DJ (follow campsite signs through village; down hill at church)
☎ (01724) 721783
2 changing beers (sourced locally; often Lincolnshire Craft, Wold Top) Ⓗ
Friendly village inn on the banks of the River Trent, in the same family for over 60 years. It has its own microbrewery (check for availability of beers) and real cider is sold. The pub is a popular meeting place for local heritage groups – the heritage group beer festival is held on the last weekend in August – and hosts live music events. Good-value home-cooked food is served Friday night, all day Saturday, and Sunday lunchtime. There is a large outdoor play area. Opening hours are reduced in January so check ahead.
Q⌖❀🕪👌🛏♣🍴🅿🚌(60)🐾🛜

Castle Bytham

Castle Inn Ⓛ
High Sreet, NG33 4RZ
☎ (01780) 411223
Hop Back Summer Lightning; Oakham Citra; 2 changing beers Ⓗ
One of the original public houses in an historic village, the decor here consists of old oak beams, period furnishings and walls hung with antique prints. This 17th-century gem has Summer Lightning permanently on offer, alongside regularly changing guest ales sourced regionally and nationally. An excellent food menu is available, with home-made food cooked on a wood-fired stove in the bar served lunchtime and evening.
Q⌖❀🕪♣🐾🛜

Fox & Hounds
6 High Street, NG33 4RZ
☎ (01780) 410336
Marston's Pedigree; 3 changing beers (often Oakham, Timothy Taylor) Ⓗ
This welcoming village local has been in the same family for over 20 years. The regular beer on the bar is Marston's Pedigree, alongside up to three guests, typically Oakham JHB and Timothy Taylor Landlord. Excellent home-cooked food is supplemented by regular curry nights, with curries from Bombay Cottage in Stamford. ❀🕪♣🅿

Chapel St Leonards

Admiral Benbow
The Promenade, PE24 5BQ
☎ (01754) 871847 ⏻ admiralbenbowbeachbar.co.uk
Black Sheep Best Bitter; 2 changing beers Ⓗ
A beach bar on the promenade, with an outside seating area on the Hispaniola boat deck. Opening times and facilities are dependent on the weather and are limited in winter (see the website for current times). Bar snacks and hot food are sold, with picnic trays and plastic glasses to take your favourite food and ale onto the beach. Dogs are welcome on leads, with blankets and dog treats available. If the flag is flying the bar is open. ⏰❀⏻⏚❀❖

Claypole

Five Bells ⎣
95 Main Street, NG23 5BJ
☎ (01636) 626261 ⏻ thefivebellsclaypole.co.uk
4 changing beers (sourced nationally; often Tetley) Ⓗ
This is a popular and well-supported village pub. Four beers and two ciders are always on the bar, with the guest ales coming predominantly from local micros. It holds an annual beer festival in June. There is a large public bar and a small lounge and restaurant serving delicious home-cooked food. Outside is a spacious beer garden and children's play area. There are four en-suite rooms available. Q⏰❀⏚⏻❖♣⏻P⏚❖❖

Cleethorpes

Crow's Nest
Balmoral Road, DN35 9ND
☎ (01472) 698867
Samuel Smith Old Brewery Bitter Ⓗ
A short drive away from Cleethorpes seafront, this is a lovely example of a traditional estate pub. Built in the 1950s, it offers a warm and friendly welcome to the local community and any new visitors. This Sam Smith's establishment also provides accommodation if booked in advance. Recently refurbished to a good standard, with a garden, it is worth a visit. Q⏰❀♣⏻P⏚(7,4)

No.1 Pub
Railway Station, DN35 8AX
☎ (01472) 696221
Batemans XXXB; Draught Bass; 6 changing beers (sourced regionally) Ⓗ
Large railway bar on Cleethorpes station. This popular venue has a main bar with a smaller real ale themed back room overlooking the station platform. The walls are adorned with local railway memorabilia. There is outside seating at the front for the warmer weather. The pub is known for its home-cooked meals. Most weekends live music is a feature, and it also hosts a yearly music festival. ⏻❈❀♣⏻P⏚❖❖

No.2 Refreshment Room
Station Approach, DN35 8AX
☎ 07905 375587
Hancocks HB; Rudgate Ruby Mild; Sharp's Atlantic, Sea Fury; 2 changing beers (sourced nationally) Ⓗ
A local CAMRA award-winning pub, set on the railway station forecourt itself and therefore handy for train travellers. An excellent choice of quality real ales is always served, in a convivial atmosphere. There is also a range of ciders. Known as Under the Clock, this small one-roomed bar is a regular in this Guide. ❀❈❀⏻⏚❖

Willy's
17 High Cliff, DN35 8RQ
☎ (01472) 602145
Draught Bass; Willy's Original; 2 changing beers (sourced nationally) Ⓗ
A seafront bar with views over the Humber Estuary to the Yorkshire coast. It mainly operates from the downstairs bar; an upstairs bar is used for functions. There is some outdoor seating. Willy's Original Bitter is brewed in the on-site microbrewery. Good-quality locally sourced home-made food is served. A mix of ages sees a gentler, quieter crowd of an afternoon, with DJs at weekends. ⏰❀⏻❈❀⏻⏚❖

Coleby

Tempest Arms
Hill Rise, LN5 0AG
☎ (01522) 810258 ⏻ thetempestcoleby.co.uk
Brains Rev James; Castle Rock Harvest Pale; St Austell Cornish Best Bitter; Timothy Taylor Landlord; 2 changing beers (sourced nationally) Ⓗ
Despite its recently enlarged dining area, and sturdy dining tables throughout, this warm and friendly local is still very much a drinkers' pub. Two stove-heated seating areas surround the well-stocked central bar. Immaculately kept, and now locally owned, the pub attracts Viking Way trekkers, regional bus users and villagers alike. Meals and snacks are served all day (except Mon). Diners enjoy views over the terraced beer gardens and the panoramic Witham-Trent valley. Q⏰❀⏻P⏚(1) ❖❖

Donington

Black Bull
7 Market Place, PE11 4ST
☎ (01775) 822228 ⏻ theblackbulldonington.co.uk
Batemans XB; Sharp's Doom Bar; 3 changing beers (often Batemans) Ⓗ
Busy local just off the A52. Five handpumps feature three regular beers, and occasionally two varying guest beers from small brewers as well as large regionals. The comfortable bar has low, beamed ceilings, wooden settles and a cosy fire in winter. Due to the return in 2020 of the remains of Captain Matthew Flinders, navigator and cartographer, born 1774, to his birthplace in Donington, the pub has an exclusive beer named in his honour, brewed by Batemans. ⏰❀⏻♣⏻P⏚❖❖

East Butterwick

Dog & Gun ⎣
High Street, DN17 3AJ (off A18 at Keadby Bridge, E bank)
☎ (01724) 782324 ⏻ doggunpub.com
3 changing beers (sourced locally; often Dark Tribe) Ⓗ
Village pub on the main road alongside the River Trent, with seating outside at the front and side of the building and across the road on the river bank. Inside are three rooms, two with open fires lit in winter. Rustic decor includes wooden tables, chairs and padded bench seats, and flagstone and wooden floors. The pub's own Dark Tribe microbrewery is at the back. Food times are popular and reservations are advised. ⏰❀⏻⏚♣⏻P⏚(12)❖

Fosdyke

Ship Inn
Moulton Washway, PE12 6LH

☎ (01205) 260764 ⊕ shipinnfosdyke.com
Adnams Southwold Bitter, Broadside; Batemans XB ⊞
Just outside Fosdyke when travelling from Boston on the A17 next to the bridge, this former Batemans pub, as its name suggests, is dedicated to things maritime – maps, photographs, charts, model ships and artefacts of many descriptions are plentiful. The week's tidetable is also detailed on a blackboard. The inn is near the busy Fosdyke Marina – boaters and landlubbers are all well catered for, with excellent home-cooked food, good beer and a warm welcome. Q ➢ ◖I ▶ P ✿ 🛜

Gainsborough

Blues Club
Northolme, North Street, DN21 2QW
☎ (01427) 613688
1 changing beer (often Horncastle Ales)
The club has a bar area with several TVs showing sport, a quieter lounge and a large function room which hosts regular live entertainment (admission charges may apply). Two or three changing real ales are usually sold, and details of forthcoming beers can be emailed to customers on request. CAMRA guests are always welcome on production of a membership card.
➢ ≠ (Central) ♣ ☰ 🛜

Elm Cottage ▯
138 Church Street, DN21 2JU
☎ 07591 501070
Timothy Taylor Landlord ⊞
This pub is close to Gainsborough Trinity's football ground and the Blues Club, and gets busy on home match days. There are six changing beers, some from the Marston's portfolio, but microbrewery beers are frequently available. The pub is popular with local amateur sports teams, and weekly live music is featured. The Elm Cottage is a previous winner of several CAMRA branch awards. Q ➢ ✿ & ≠ (Central) ◖ P ☰ ✿ 🛜

Sweyn Forkbeard ✓
22-24 Silver Street, DN21 2DP
☎ (01427) 675000
Greene King Abbot; Ruddles Best Bitter ⊞
This town-centre Wetherspoon, the local CAMRA branch's Pub of the Year 2019, is one of the must-visit pubs in town. Three rotating guest beers often include some oddities for this part of the country. Customers can ask for their favourite beer and it frequently appears. The pub is named after the Danish King of England in 1013, whose son Canute is rumoured to have tried to stop the aegir (the tidal bore on the River Trent). Great value, tasty food is available until 10pm. ➢ ◖I & ≠ (Central) ◖ ☰ 🛜

Gosberton Risegate

Duke of York ▯
106 Risegate Road, PE11 4EY
☎ (01775) 840193
Batemans XB; St Austell Tribute; 1 changing beer (sourced locally) ⊞
A friendly pub and a longstanding entry in this Guide, with a deserved reputation for value-for-money beers and food. Alongside the regular ales, guests come from a range of independent brewers. A wide choice of food is served, with portions to suit the largest appetite. Local community life is supported through charities, sports teams, and other social events. Q ➢ ✿ ◖I ♣ P ✿

Grantham

Chequers ▯
25 Market Place, NG31 6LR
☎ (01476) 570149
3 changing beers (sourced nationally; often Brewsters) ⊞
A cosmopolitan and contemporary bar with a real fire that features ales from local breweries Brewsters and Zest. Other regular beers come from Bakers Dozen, supplemented further with changing guest beers. Located on a paved side street between the High Street and the market square, known locally as Butchers Row, it has a relaxing atmosphere during the day and comes alive on evenings and weekends. Q ✿ ≠ ◖ ☰ ✿ 🛜

Grantham Railway Club ▯
Huntingtower Road, NG31 7AU
☎ (01476) 564860
2 changing beers ⊞
A community-run establishment voted CAMRA branch Club of the Year for 2020 and 2021, which supports Grantham's three local brewers. This former British Rail Staff Association club hosts numerous cribbage, darts and dominoes teams as well as supporting various social and community organisations. There is live music every Saturday night, with a spacious back room available to hire. CAMRA members are welcome. ➢ ✿ & ≠ ♣ P ✿ 🛜

Nobody Inn ▯
9 North Street, NG31 6NU (opp Asda car park)
☎ (01476) 562206 ⊕ nobody-inn.business.site
6 changing beers (often Castle Rock, Newby Wyke, Timothy Taylor) ⊞
The Nobody is famous for its hidden toilet door behind the bookcase. It sells beer from the award-winning Newby Wyke brewery in Grantham. The bar can get lively at weekends and when a big sporting event is taking place, but it is also a nice place for a quiet drink, with great staff. Popular live music is staged most Saturday nights. Watch out for the giant spider!
♣ ◖ ☰ ✿ 🛜

Grimsby

Docks Beers
The Church, King Edward Street, DN31 3JD
☎ (01472) 289795 ⊕ docksbeers.com
2 changing beers ⊞
Docks Beers brewery taproom is set in an old church, selling three cask ales and a craft beer selection. It also offers Axholme beers, often in collaboration with other breweries. The brewery has recently increased capacity and you can sit and watch it at work producing ale. A space upstairs hosts different events, and there are food stalls outside most weekends. ➢ ≠ ☰ ✿

Rutland Arms
26 Rutland Street, DN31 3AF
☎ (01472) 357362
Old Mill Traditional Bitter; 3 changing beers ⊞
Close to both bus and train stations, this hostelry is easy to find, and tends to be a favourite with local football supporters. Inside, it has one single long room with a pool table and dartboard at the end. The pub has been taken over and is being refurbished. It has four handpumps and sells a selection of Old Mill beers. A TV shows live sporting events. Q ➢ ✿ ≠ ♣ P ☰ 🛜

Spiders Web
180 Carr Lane, DN32 8LN
☎ (01472) 692065

John Smith's Bitter; 3 changing beers (sourced nationally; often Leeds, Wainwright) Ⓗ
This friendly family-run community pub has a lively bar, a quiet lounge and a function room which holds frequent live music events from artists of many genres. In the bar, games such as poker, darts and pool are played. There is also a weekly quiz night. Outside is a large suntrap garden with a smoking area. Q❄️🕮♣️P🖵(4)🐾🛜

Yarborough Hotel ✿
29 Bethlehem Street, DN31 1JN
☎ (01472) 268283
Greene King Abbot; Kelham Island Easy Rider; Ruddles Best Bitter; 12 changing beers (sourced regionally) Ⓗ
Large, thriving, open-plan pub serving 15 real ales from national brands through to more local ales from the Lincolnshire area. Like many in the Wetherspoon chain, it can be busy on Tuesday steak night and again on Thursday curry night. After a troubled past where it was under threat of demolition, the building has been restored and is once again a grand hotel, next door to Grimsby Town railway station. Q❄️🕮🛏️🕮♿🛤🖵

Habrough

Station Inn
Station Road, DN40 3AP
☎ (01469) 572896
3 changing beers (sourced regionally; often Bradfield, Theakston, Timothy Taylor) Ⓗ
Originally a hotel built in 1848 for the Great Grimsby & Sheffield Junction Railway, this inn has a single large room with access to the bar and a smaller area for pool and bar games. It has a good community spirit – live bands play once a month on Saturday, and with karaoke, theme nights and traditional pub games, this is a lively environment. Three handpumps feature changing beers from regional brewers. ❄️🕮🛤♣️🕮P🐾

Heckington

8 Sail Brewery Bar
Heckington Mill, Hale Road, NG34 9JW
☎ (01529) 469308 ⊕ 8sailbrewery.co.uk
8 Sail Windmill Bitter, Blonde, Rolling Stone, King John's Jewels, Oat Malt Stout; 3 changing beers (sourced locally; often 8 Sail) Ⓗ
Situated in part of the Heckington Windmill complex, this is a single-room brewery bar featuring a restored Victorian counter with church pew and Britannia bar seating. It usually serves three changing 8 Sail Brewery beers and occasional guest beers. A selection of German bottled beer and local cider is also available. Beer festivals are held in mid-July over the Heckington Show weekend. On Saturdays and Sundays in winter it tends to close at 3pm. Q❄️🕮♿🛤🕮P🖵🐾🛜

Heighington

Butcher & Beast
High Street, LN4 1JS
☎ (01522) 790386 ⊕ butcherandbeast.co.uk
Batemans XB, XXXB; Timothy Taylor Landlord; 3 changing beers (sourced nationally) Ⓗ
Welcoming old stone Batemans pub adorned with splendid floral displays. Inside, it has distinctive drinking areas, a real fire, and old photographs on the walls. Along with a fine selection of gins there is at least one real cider. The restaurant at the rear offers quality food and has a steak night on Monday, a fish night on Tuesday, and serves a roast on Sunday. Quizzes and

charity nights are popular. The garden boasts a beautiful patio. Local buses run until early evening.
Q❄️🕮♿🕮♣️🕮P🖵(2,10)🐾🛜

Horbling

Plough Inn
4 Spring Lane, NG34 0PF
☎ (01529) 240263 ⊕ ploughinnhorbling.co.uk
Grainstore Ten Fifty; 2 changing beers Ⓗ
A community pub owned by the parish of Horbling, built in 1832 and set just off the main road. Alongside the lounge/bar, it has a snug that is surely one of the smallest and most intimate of its kind. Guest beers come from a wide range of breweries, often micros, and change frequently. Quality meals are served throughout the pub and in a separate restaurant. The Spring Wells, a feature worth seeing, are just a few yards down the lane.
❄️🕮♿♣️🕮P🐾🛜

Horncastle

King's Head
16 Bull Ring, LN9 5HU
☎ (01507) 523360
Batemans Gold, XB, XXXB; 1 changing beer (sourced regionally) Ⓗ
A comfortable, cosy and friendly venue. Unusually for this area, the building has a thatched roof, hence its local name, The Thatch. Three beers from Batemans are generally on tap, plus a guest. Reputedly this place inspired an OO-gauge Hornby model, an example of which is displayed behind the bar. Summertime sees the pub resplendent with hanging baskets and it has been the winner of Batemans' Floral Display competition. Try spotting the resident cat, Rufus. ❄️🕮🕮♣️🖵🐾🛜

Old Nick's Tavern
8 North Street, LN9 5DX
☎ (01507) 526862
4 changing beers (sourced locally; often Horncastle Ales) Ⓗ
Built in 1752 as a coaching inn, this original building is now a town-centre pub with its own microbrewery, the home of Horncastle Ales – the head brewster is the landlord's daughter. It has been refurbished and incorporates the old hanging sign and old photos of the pub. Regular live bands are featured. There are five handpumps, four of which usually offer Horncastle ales. No food is served. ❄️🕮♣️🕮🖵🐾🛜

Ingoldmells

Countryman Ⓛ
Chapel Road, PE25 1ND
☎ (01754) 872268
Leila Cottage Leila's Lazy Days, Ace Ale2, Leila's One Off Ⓗ
The privately owned Countryman appears to be a modern building but it incorporates the early 19th-century Leila Cottage, which gives its name to the brewery behind it. A notorious smuggler, James Waite, used to reside here when Ingoldmells was a wild and lonely place, but he certainly would not recognise the current holiday coast, with Skegness, Butlin's and Fantasy Island nearby. Information boards give brewery, pub and beer information for visitors. It is on northern bus routes from Skegness. ❄️🕮🕮♿🅰️♣️P🖵

Kirkby on Bain

Ebrington Arms
Main Street, LN10 6YT
☎ (01526) 354560 ⊕ ebringtonarms.com
Batemans XB; Sharp's Doom Bar; Timothy Taylor
Landlord; 1 changing beer (often Adnams) ⊞
Attractive country pub close to the River Bain and dating
from 1610. World War II airmen used to slot coins into
the ceiling beams to pay for beer when they returned
from missions over Germany. Sadly, many of these coins
are still in situ and make a unique memorial to the dead.
The popular restaurant offers good food made with local
produce (booking advised). A guest beer is served in
winter, often two in summer.
Q ☎ ⊛ ◖ ◖ ᄫ ♣ P ☷ (65) ❀ ☞

Kirmington

Marrowbone & Cleaver
High Street, DN39 6YZ
☎ (01652) 688335 ⊕ marrowboneandcleaver.com
Sharp's Doom Bar; house beer (by Batemans); 1
changing beer ⊞
After a period of closure, this village pub was refurbished
and reopened by motorbike racer Guy Martin. It is
adorned inside with racing memorabilia as well as items
from 166 Squadron. It is family-run, with Guy's sister
Sally managing it. Although it is mainly food-oriented it
has three handpumps. Drinkers are given a warm
welcome as well as diners. The house beer was
developed through a collaboration between Guy Martin
and Batemans Brewery. Q ☎ ⊛ ◖ ◖ ᄫ ♣ P ❀

Lincoln

Adam & Eve Tavern
25 Lindum Road, LN2 1NT
☎ (01522) 537108 ⊕ adamandevelincoln.co.uk
Castle Rock Harvest Pale; Morland Old Speckled Hen;
2 changing beers (sourced nationally) ⊞
A short walk from the cathedral or a hill climb from
downtown Lincoln, this multi-room tavern is ideal for
small to mid-sized gatherings. Helping to keep music live
with weekly music nights, it is also home to popular
Sunday quiz nights and a monthly music quiz. The pub is
great for watching sporting events, and if games are your
thing, darts and pool feature, along with gaming
machines and a selection of board games.
☎ ⊛ ◖ ♣ P ☷ ❀ ☞

BeerHeadZ
4 Eastgate, LN2 1QA
☎ (01522) 255430
4 changing beers (sourced nationally) ⊞
Situated in the uphill city area, this bright, colourful
hostelry has an industrial feel. It is part of a small chain of
new generation indie pubs. It serves up to six cask ales,
craft keg beers, two ciders and a range of bottled and
canned beers, and uses oversized glasses. Customers are
welcome to bring in their own food. Regular events
taking place include quizzes, live music and tap
takeovers. ◖ ☷ ❀ ☞

Cardinal's Hat
268 High Street, LN2 1HW
☎ (01522) 527084
Adnams Mosaic; Lincolnshire Craft Lincoln Gold; Rat
White Rat; house beer (by Lincolnshire Craft); 4
changing beers (sourced nationally) ⊞
A Grade II*-listed tavern at the foot of Lincoln's Steep Hill,
this three-storey, half-timbered building was an inn
during the 16th-18th centuries. The sensitive conversion

to a pub in 2015 revealed a number of historical features.
It has a large ground-floor bar area plus smaller
atmospheric snugs and rooms. Eight ales, four ciders and
other drinks can be enjoyed alongside a menu of
charcuterie and cheese. ☎ ⊛ ◖ ◖ ᄫ ♣ ❀ ☞

Golden Eagle
21 High Street, LN5 8BD
☎ (01522) 521058
Castle Rock Harvest Pale; Sharp's Doom Bar; 7
changing beers (sourced nationally) ⊞
A thriving, traditional two-roomed venue on the lower
High Street, close to the LNER Stadium, and therefore
busy on match days. It stocks up to nine real ales and
over 50 craft ales from the fridge in the bar area. Outside
is a large garden with cosy sheltered seating. Two annual
beer festivals are the highlight of the social calendar.
Harvey the pub dog is always happy to greet customers.
A small function room is available to hire.
Q ☎ ⊛ ♣ ♣ P ☷ ❀ ☞

Joiners Arms
4 Victoria Street, LN1 1HU
☎ (01522) 244470
5 changing beers (sourced nationally) ⊞
A short walk from the High Street, this traditional back-
street boozer features five changing ales, and has an
increasing selection of gins. It is a popular venue for live
entertainment and beer festivals. Traditional pub games
include Lincoln's only bar billiards table. A quiz takes
place every Tuesday and open mic every Friday. Enjoy a
drink by the open fires. Football fans (home and away)
will find a warm welcome. A characterful beer garden is
to the rear. ⊛ ♣ ❀ ☞

Ritz ⓛ ⊘
143-147 High Street, LN5 7PJ
☎ (01522) 512103
Greene King Abbot; Ruddles Best Bitter; Sharp's
Doom Bar; 6 changing beers (sourced nationally) ⊞
Part of the Wetherspoon chain, the Ritz was originally a
cinema and entertainments centre. The venue is a split-
level building with a family area on the ground floor and
the bar, with seating above, and a lift for access if
required. Its past use is reflected in both the interior and
exterior decor. Food is served all day, with speciality
nights. A Meet the Brewer event is held on the last
Thursday of each month. Close to the city's transport hub.
Q ☎ ⊛ ◖ ◖ ᄫ ♣ ◖ ☷ ❀ ☞

Strugglers Inn ⓛ
83 Westgate, LN1 3BG
☎ (01522) 535023
Ossett Yorkshire Blonde; Sharp's Sea Fury; Timothy
Taylor Landlord; 7 changing beers (sourced
nationally) ⊞
A small hostelry big on character, this traditional two-
roomed pub next to Lincoln Castle is in a great location
for locals and tourists alike. Myriad pumpclips of previous
beers adorn the walls and ceilings in both the main bar
and the snug. The hidden beer garden is great for
summer drinking, while two real fires make for a warm
winter welcome. Regular live music plays on Sundays.
Q ⊛ ♣ ☷ ❀ ☞

Tiny Tavern
107 High Street, LN5 7PY
☎ 07761 123697
5 changing beers (sourced nationally) ⊞
This micropub opened in March 2020 in what was
originally two 17th-century cottages in the Grade II-listed
St Andrew's Row. The cosy lounge has a window seat
and fireplace. Towards the rear is a bar area with a

dartboard. An additional room is available for community activities. There is a large garden, part of which will be set aside as a community allotment. The five handpumps feature beers from microbreweries near and far.
❀≠♣🍎🚌

Victoria

6 Union Road, LN1 3BJ
☎ (01522) 541000 🌐 thevictoriapub.co.uk
Batemans XB; Castle Rock Harvest Pale; Timothy Taylor Landlord; 3 changing beers (sourced nationally) 🄷
Thirty-eight continuous years in this Guide are a tribute to the long-time manager and testament to the consistent provision of good ale in the city. The Victoria is in the most historic part of Lincoln and has a sunny outdoor area for drinkers to enjoy a pint. A refurbishment is on the horizon but we are assured that the character and simplicity of this traditional two-room pub will be preserved. Q❀◖🍎🚌🐾📶

Louth

Boar's Head

12 Newmarket, LN11 9HH
☎ (01507) 654127 🌐 theboarsheadlouth.co.uk
Caledonian Deuchars IPA; Theakston Best Bitter; Timothy Taylor Landlord; 1 changing beer 🄷
A traditional three-roomed pub just outside the centre of this market town. It is well known locally for its real ales. Games include darts, dominoes and pool. On Thursday – cattle market day – it may open early.
Q🐴❀◐♿♣🍎🚌🐾📶

Brown Cow ✔

133 Newmarket, LN11 9EG (top of Newmarket on jct with Church St)
☎ (01507) 605146
Black Sheep Best Bitter; Castle Rock Harvest Pale; Fuller's London Pride; 1 changing beer 🄷
The owners Nigel and Victoria are celebrating 10 years behind the bar of this friendly free house. With a great atmosphere and excellent beer, it is a must when visiting Louth. A free quiz is held every first Sunday of the month. The kitchen serves traditional, home-cooked food, made with locally sourced products. This pub is a popular community meeting place. 🐴❀◐♿⛺🚌🐾📶

Cobbles Bar

New Street, LN11 9PU (off Cornmarket)
Black Sheep Best Bitter; 1 changing beer 🄷
Traditional pub-style bar based in the centre of town, with friendly staff at all times. This small but accommodating venue has multiple personalities, from a bustling coffee shop serving light lunches to a busy pre-club local, with a DJ and live music at weekends. Regular quizzes are held. It has a good beer trade, with two contrasting cask ales, as well as a huge selection of exotic spirits. Wheelchair access is right through the front doors. ◐♿🚌

Consortium Micropub 🄻

13C Cornmarket, LN11 9PY
☎ (01507) 600754
Consortium ZigZag, Wet Pocket, Best Bitter, Pleasant Blonde, Willy Wickams Posthumous Ale 🄷
The Micropub was opened in 2017 to give people a chance to taste various ales, ciders and lagers from around the UK. It is situated in a small courtyard 50 yards from the Market Place next to the Masons Arms Hotel. The pub has its own microbrewery and distillery on the industrial estate and produces a massive range of diverse real ales and gins. It usually has six ales on the bar plus a well-stocked gin shelf, as well as a local market stall selling bottled ales ciders and lagers.
Q🐴♿⛺🍎P🚉🚌(51)🐾📶

Olde Whyte Swanne ✔

45 Eastgate, LN11 9NP
☎ (01507) 824141 🌐 whyteswannelouth.co.uk
Rudgate Ruby Mild; 3 changing beers 🄷
The oldest pub in a pretty market town, established in the early 1600s. Upon entering this Grade II-listed building you are met by traditional low-beamed ceilings and a real fire. Beyond this is another modern room which is used for dining and meetings. The bar offers a good variety of beers and cider on handpump.
Q🐴❀◐♿🚉🚌🐾📶

Woolpack 🄻

Riverhead Road, LN11 0DA
☎ (01507) 606568 🌐 woolpacklouth.com
Batemans XB, Gold, XXXB; 1 changing beer 🄷
The Woolpack is close to the theatre and is popular with drinkers and diners alike, with good home-cooked food available. It usually offers four or five real ales on handpump. Located next to the canal, the Grade II-listed building is dog-friendly, and has wheelchair access and baby-changing facilities. There is a large beer garden and ample parking. 🐴❀◐♿P🚌🐾📶

Market Deeping

Vine Inn 🄻

19 Church Street, PE6 8AN
☎ (01778) 348741
Sharp's Doom Bar; house beer (by Worthington's); 3 changing beers (often Abbeydale, Courage, Skinner's) 🄷
Formerly a Charles Wells outlet and now a free house, this small, friendly pub features oak beams and stone floors, with many 20th-century prints on the walls. There is a large patio at the rear. Five handpumps dispense Sharp's Doom Bar and Vine Ale (Hancocks HB) plus a changing range of guests. Boxed real cider is stocked. Free nibbles are provided Sunday lunchtime and early evenings during the week. The television is only used for major sporting events. ❀🍎P🚌(101)🐾📶

Marston

Thorold

Main Street, NG32 2HH
☎ (01400) 251849
Batemans XB, Gold; Timothy Taylor Landlord 🄷
This establishment is owned by the village community, with its own shop serving amazing home-cooked food. Through many hours of hard work the insides have been refurbished beautifully, with a flagstone floor, an all-wooden bar and two log-burners. Three beers are usually on tap. 🐴❀◐P🚌🐾📶

Messingham

Pooley's

46 High Street, DN17 3NT
☎ 07860 799178
5 changing beers (sourced regionally; often Batemans, Ossett, Rat) 🄷
Comfortable, traditionally styled village inn, which is only open in the evenings. A bar at one end serves three distinct drinking areas with bare brick walls, rustic furniture, wooden and flagstone floors and real fires. The walls display attractive vintage posters and signs. Five changing real ales are stocked, often from Adnams,

Batemans, Fernandes, Oakham, Ossett and Rat, plus a large selection of malt whiskies, gins and wines. Winner of several local CAMRA awards. Q&⌂🖩(100,103)❁🖢

Morton

Ship Inn ✅
34 Front Street, DN21 3AE
☎ (01427) 613298
Bradfield Farmers Blond; Wainwright; Wychwood Hobgoblin Gold ⓗ
To the north of Gainsborough, this is a quaint, typical village pub. There are weekly darts, dominoes and pool matches and regular quiz evenings. It has two rotating cask ales and food is served six days a week, with Sunday lunches proving to be popular. ⌂♣🖩

Navenby

Lion & Royal
57 High Street, LN5 0DZ
☎ (01522) 810368
Greene King IPA, Abbot; 3 changing beers (sourced nationally) ⓗ
An imposing stone building in the centre of the village. Cosy real fires are lit when needed and there is a large beer garden for the warmer weather. Royal was added to the pub's name following a visit by the Prince of Wales in 1870, and Guy Gibson of RAF 617 Squadron fame spent his wedding night here. It is on the Lincoln to Grantham bus route and is popular with walkers on the nearby Viking Way. ⌂❁◑&♣P🖩(1)🖢

North Hykeham

Centurion ✅
Newark Road, LN6 8LB
☎ (01522) 509814
Bombardier Gold; Sharp's Doom Bar; house beer (by Black Sheep); 2 changing beers (sourced nationally) ⓗ
The pub's name reflects the Roman history of the area, as it is near the route of the ancient Fosse Way linking Lincoln to Exeter. Built in 1969, the Centurion is a hive of activity and a great meeting point for the local community and beyond. A warm welcome awaits diners and drinkers alike. Food and ale offers feature throughout the week, and there are twice-weekly quizzes. Regular bus services from the city mean you can leave the car at home and properly enjoy the range of ales. ⌂❁◑&P🖩🖢

Pinchbeck

Ship
Northgate, PE11 3SE
☎ (01775) 711746
Greene King Abbot; Morland Old Speckled Hen; 2 changing beers (often Hopshackle, Welland) ⓗ
Thatched pub on the banks of the River Glen by the railway bridge at the western end of Knight Street. It has been given a sympathetic update and is smart, neat and tidy, but retains a warm and cosy appeal. Food is farm to fork, locally sourced, fresh quality produce. Events throughout the year range from beer, wine and spirit tasting evenings to an annual garden party, car shows and live music. ⌂❁◑P🖩🖢

Raithby

Red Lion
Raithby Road, PE23 4DS

☎ (01790) 753727 ⊕ redlioninn.pub
Batemans XB; 2 changing beers (often Ferry Ales, Batemans) ⓗ
Cosy Grade II-listed village pub built around 1650, with beamed low ceilings in its many small rooms that surround the bar, and pictures of outdoor pursuits and old photographs adorning the walls. Situated in an attractive quiet village in the Wolds, it is an excellent base for walking and cycling. It changed hands in 2018 and is now popular for dining, offering fresh locally sourced food. Q⌂🖙❁◑&♣P🖩🖢

Ropsley

Green Man
24 High Street, NG33 4BE
☎ (01476) 585897 ⊕ the-green-man-ropsley.com
Wainwright; 3 changing beers (sourced nationally; often Caledonian, Grainstore, Theakston) ⓗ
Crowned local CAMRA Pub of the Year 2020 and 2021, and Country Pub of the Year 2019, this 17th-century village inn has a growing reputation for innovative food, including exotic meats, locally sourced game and seafood, and is also renowned for an extensive bottled range. A relaxed tearoom area is frequented by walkers and cyclists, and there is a pleasant, tranquil beer garden. Themed food and drink matching evenings are held regularly. ⌂❁◑♣P🖩🖢

Ruskington

Shoulder of Mutton
11 Church Street, NG34 9DU
☎ (01526) 832220
Bombardier; John Smith's Bitter; 2 changing beers (sourced regionally; often Sharp's) ⓗ
A popular and thriving pub in the heart of the village attracting customers of all ages. It is one of the oldest buildings in the village and was once a butcher's shop, hence the name. A few old meat hooks can still be seen in the wooden ceiling in the bar. Changes have been made in recent years but have not spoilt the essential character. Standing guard outside is Knight and Day, a sculpture from Lincoln's 2017 Knight's Trail. ❁⇌♣P🖩(31)🖢

Saxilby

Anglers ✅
65 High Street, LN1 2HA
☎ (01522) 702200 ⊕ anglerspublichouse.com
Theakston Best Bitter; 3 changing beers (sourced nationally) ⓗ
A family-run village local, with a strong community and pub sport focus. Regular charity fundraising events are held, along with darts, dominoes, pool and cribbage matches. The quieter lounge has old village photos, and the outside drinking area has a boules court. Pop-up food stalls visit on some Friday and Saturday evenings. Close to the railway station, bus stops and visitor moorings on the Fossdyke, the country's oldest canal. Q❁⇌♣P🖩🖢

Scampton

Dambusters Inn 🄻
23 High Street, LN1 2SD
☎ (01522) 731333 ⊕ dambustersinn.co.uk
Greg's Scampton Ale, Dambusters Ale; 5 changing beers (sourced nationally) ⓗ
Some pubs are special places of pilgrimage, and 10 visitors' books are testament to the international

reputation of this multi award-winning village local honouring the eponymous WWII squadron. It has memorabilia displays worthy of a national museum and an annual commemorative beer festival drawing drinkers from near and far to toast the 617 heroes. This is a proper pub, a flourishing micro-brewery and a popular food destination – a true reminder of good old England! Q🌑🕐🍴P🚃(103) 🌑🕐🛜

Scawby

Sutton Arms

10 West Street, DN20 9AN (on main road through village)

☎ (01652) 652430 🌐 suttonarmsscawby.co.uk

Black Sheep Best Bitter; Sharp's Doom Bar; 2 changing beers (sourced nationally; often Great Newsome, Hawkshead, Milestone) Ⓗ

A village inn with a strong emphasis on food; the extensive menu includes daily specials. The two-sided central bar serves a large dining area and separate restaurant, plus a narrow snug bar used mainly for drinking. The interior is classic country pub style, including ceiling beams and dark-wood fittings. Two regular real ales are always on the bar plus two rotating guests from all over the country. Quiz night is on Sunday evening. 🌑🕐🍴P♿🌑🛜

Scotter

Sun & Anchor

54 High Street, DN21 3RX

☎ (01724) 763444

Butcombe Original; Rat White Rat Ⓗ

A warm and inviting traditional village inn with a bar and lounge serving a wide selection of refreshing drinks and traditional pub food including the popular Sunday roast. All the latest sporting matches and events are shown. There is a darts and pool area, dominoes is played regularly, and there is a spacious private beer garden with a children's play area, plus a car park. The pub's history has been traced back to 1216. 🌑🕐♿♣P🚃(101) 🌑🛜

Scunthorpe

Blue Bell ✓

1-7 Oswald Road, DN15 7PU (at town-centre crossroads)

☎ (01724) 863921

Ruddles Best Bitter; Sharp's Doom Bar; 6 changing beers (sourced regionally; often Bradfield, Kelham Island, Ossett) Ⓗ

Popular town-centre Wetherspoon, now refurbished and enlarged, taking over three neighbouring properties to double its size. It also boasts a large ground-floor beer garden and smoking area, plus a large open terrace on the first floor accessed by stairs and a lift. The usual Wetherspoon food menu is served daily up to 11pm, and there are occasional themed events and beer, cider and gin festivals. 🌑🕐🍴♿🍴P🚃🛜

Malt Shovel

219 Ashby High Street, DN16 2JP (in Ashby Broadway shopping area)

☎ (01724) 843318

Rat White Rat; 5 changing beers (sourced regionally; often Abbeydale, Rat, Rooster's) Ⓗ

Recently refurbished, popular High Street pub, with a beer garden at the front. It has a comfortably furnished, carpeted lounge, with more seating in a conservatory leading out to the beer garden. Often busy at meal

times, booking for food is recommended. Quiz night is usually Thursday, live music night usually Friday. Five rotating guest beers, craft keg, real ciders and perries are served from the cellar. There is a members' only social and snooker club and a new sports bar upstairs. 🌑🕐🍴♿🍴🚃

Skegness

Seathorne Arms

Seathorne Crescent, PE25 1RP

☎ (01754) 767797

2 changing beers (often Greene King, Morland) Ⓗ

Set back from Roman Bank and 15 minutes' walk from Butlin's, the pub has a large outside seating area and a spacious single-room interior with partitioned spaces for eating, pub games, drinking and TV watching. The landlord operates a constantly rotating two-beer selection, and there is an extensive food menu featuring locally sourced meat. The pub's trade is seasonal, depending on nearby caravan sites; it is closed January and hours may vary February-March. 🌑🕐🍴♿♣🚃🛜

Vine Hotel

Vine Road, PE25 3DB (off Drummond Rd)

☎ (01754) 763018

Batemans XB, XXXB; 1 changing beer (often Batemans) Ⓗ

A delightful building, one of the oldest in Skegness, dating from the 18th century and set in two acres of pleasant grounds. Inside are comfortable wood-panelled bars in which to enjoy a quiet pint or two after experiencing some of the noisier attractions and bustle of Skegness. It is within striking distance of the Gibraltar Point National Nature Reserve, walking trails, beach and golf links, and is reputed to have connections with the poet Tennyson. 🌑🕐🍴🍴♿P🚃🌑🛜

Sleaford

Carre Arms Hotel

Mareham Lane, NG34 7JP

☎ (01529) 303156 🌐 carrearmshotel.co.uk

3 changing beers (often Draught Bass, Marston's, Springhead) Ⓗ

A privately run hotel previously owned by Bass, next to the Bass Sleaford Maltings complex which is now awaiting a regeneration scheme. It has a comfortable bar area with two rooms, offering three real ales which regularly change, featuring both larger regional and local breweries. There is often a cider on handpump. An extensive menu is offered, served in the bar or restaurant. Outside is a pleasant covered courtyard, ideal on inclement days. 🌑🕐🍴♿🍴P🚃

White Horse

Boston Road, NG34 7HD

☎ (01529) 968003

Bombardier; 2 changing beers (often Batemans, Horncastle Ales) Ⓗ

On the junction of Carre Street and Boston Road, the White Horse serves the housing area along the Boston Road. It is one of the few remaining traditional locals' pubs in Sleaford, with wet sales only. The interior has been opened out into a single L-shaped room, but retains a cosy feel. Sports predominate, with both darts and pool teams. 🌑🍴♣P🌑🛜

Snitterby

Royal Oak

High Street, DN21 4TP (1½ miles from A15)

☎ (01673) 818273 ⊕ royaloaksnitterby.co.uk
JW Lees Bitter; Rooster's Buckeye Ⓗ**; 4 changing beers (sourced nationally; often Big Drop, Greene King, Ossett)** Ⓗ**/**Ⓖ
Traditional family-run, community pub in a village setting, selling four or five real ales year round, with up to eight on bank holiday weekends. The comfortable, spacious interior is light and airy, with real fires and wooden floors. Outside there's an extensive beer garden with a mix of patio areas, decking and attractively planted raised beds overlooking a bubbling stream, providing a relaxing backdrop to an alfresco pint.
Q✿❀🅟🗴♣♠P✿

Spalding

Priors Oven Ⓛ

1 Sheep Market, PE11 1BH
6 changing beers (sourced locally) Ⓖ
The first micropub to be opened in Lincolnshire. The building was part of the Priory of Spalding and is believed to be almost 800 years old. Because of its shape it has always been known as The Oven or The Prior's Oven, and has been used as Spalding's monastic prison. Its more recent use was as a bakery and it became a pub in 2013. The ground-floor bar has a vaulted ceiling, while a stone spiral staircase leads up to a gin bar. Beers can be served in third-pint measures. Q➸♠🗴🖿

Red Lion Hotel

Market Place, PE11 1SU
☎ (01775) 722869 ⊕ redlionhotel-spalding.co.uk
Bombardier; Draught Bass; Greene King Abbot Ⓗ
A carefully refurbished 18th-century family-run hotel with a cosy, comfortable and welcoming bar overlooking the marketplace. A rare outlet for Bass in the locality, it offers a consistently well-kept range of cask ales, which the staff take great pride in serving in top condition. For fine sunny days there are outside tables and chairs beneath attractive floral displays. ✿🛏🗴➸P🖿✿🛜

Stamford

Bull & Swan Ⓛ

High Street, St Martins, PE9 2LG
☎ (01780) 766412 ⊕ thebullandswan.co.uk
5 changing beers (often Bakers Dozen, Nene Valley, Oakham) Ⓗ
A 17th-century coaching inn which retains many original features, with three small interconnecting low-beamed rooms, decorated with brass and copper. It has a large patio garden. Described by Stamford Living as the most improved pub in Stamford, it was renovated by Burghley Estates and reopened in 2011. It has a separate dining room and themed guest rooms. Run by the Hillbrooke hotel chain. ✿🛏🅟➸🖿(201)✿🛜

Jolly Brewer Ⓛ

1 Foundry Road, PE9 2PP
☎ (01780) 755141 ⊕ thejollybrewer.com
Brewsters Marquis; Oakham JHB; 4 changing beers (sourced locally; often Baker's Dozen) Ⓗ
A locals' hostelry dating back to 1830 and twice local CAMRA Pub of the Year, the Brewer boasts a roomy split-level drinking area with open fires in the winter and a separate dining room. Six handpumps dispense LocAles, national ales and its own Baker's Dozen beers. The real cider is usually Old Rosie. The car park and large patio host a beer festival in the autumn, while pub games, including the World Pushpenny Championships, are a feature. Q✿🅟➸♣♠P🖿(9,202)✿🛜

King's Head

19 Maiden Lane, PE9 2AZ
☎ (01780) 753510 ⊕ kingsheadstamford.co.uk
5 changing beers Ⓗ
A compact 19th-century pub just off the High Street. This is a one-roomed, but split-level, house, featuring a wood-burning stove and wooden-beamed ceiling as well as a pleasant patio area to the rear. It operates a one-barrel policy, with five constantly changing ales from the length and breadth of the country. Over 400 were promoted in the first two years of the scheme. Popular with diners at lunchtime. Q✿🅟➸🖿

Tobie Norris

12 Saint Pauls Street, PE9 2BE
☎ (01780) 753800
Fuller's London Pride; Oakham JHB Ⓗ**; 6 changing beers (sourced regionally; often Adnams)** Ⓗ**/**Ⓖ
The building, parts of which date back to 1280, was bought by Tobie Norris in 1617 and used as a bell foundry. Formerly a RAFA club, it received a major refurbishment in 2007. It now has many small rooms with real fires, stone floors and low beams. Three handpumps serve beers from local and countrywide breweries, with more available directly from the cask. A former local CAMRA Pub of the Year.
Q✿🅟➸➸♣🖿(202,203)✿

Stickford

Red Lion Inn Ⓛ

Church Road, PE22 8EP
☎ (01205) 480395
Black Hole Lincoln Imperial Ale; 2 changing beers (often Settle, Sharp's) Ⓗ
The pub name Red Lion, one of the most common in England, is frequently found hereabouts because it was a heraldic emblem of the 14th-century John of Gaunt, Earl of Lancaster and Lord of the Manor at nearby Bolingbroke Castle. This pub has one larger open-plan room, with a small separate dining and function room. The owners are keen on live music and host regular events (see Facebook for details). ✿🅟➸♠♣P🖿(113)✿🛜

Swineshead

Green Dragon

Market Place, PE20 3LJ
☎ (01205) 821381
Batemans XB; Theakston Traditional Mild; 3 changing beers (sourced regionally) Ⓗ
Originally called the Green Dragon, the pub's fortunes gradually declined until new owners brought it back to life with a new name. A change of ownership has now seen it revert to its original name, and it is a vibrant and thriving village local, successfully blending old and new to create a genuine community venue with an emphasis on beer and traditional pub games. Pizza and bar snacks to eat in or take away are available Thursday to Saturday. ✿🅟♣♠P🖿(K59)✿🛜

Swinhope

Clickem Inn

Binbrook Road, LN8 6BS (2 miles N of Binbrook on B1203)
☎ (01472) 398253
Batemans XXXB; Timothy Taylor Landlord; house beer (by Pheasantry); 3 changing beers (sourced regionally; often Horncastle Ales, Rudgate, Springhead) Ⓗ

Set in the picturesque Lincolnshire Wolds, this is a popular stopping place for walkers and cyclists. The name originates from the counting of sheep passing through a nearby clicking gate. The pub is renowned for its home-cooked food served in the bar and conservatory, and offers a choice of drinks, including six real ales and a traditional cider. The house beer is Terry's Tipple. There is pool, darts and a jukebox. Monday is quiz night. A covered area is provided for smokers. Q✿◑➧♣♠P✿⚲

Thimbleby

Durham Ox

Main Road, LN9 5RB

☎ (01507) 527152 ⊕ durhamoxpubthimbleby.co.uk

Adnams Ghost Ship; Batemans XB; 1 changing beer (sourced regionally) Ⓗ

Fine country inn over 200 years old and reopened in 2013. This welcoming place with its beamed ceilings, cowshed bar and RAF corner also has a large field at the rear for caravans and camper vans. There is an extensive menu serving local produce. The name comes from a huge 18th-century ox which toured the country and which at its largest weighed 270 stone. ⚲✿◑Å♠P➧✿

Threekingham

Three Kings Inn

Saltersway, NG34 0AU

☎ (01529) 240249

Draught Bass; Morland Old Speckled Hen; Timothy Taylor Landlord; 1 changing beer (sourced regionally) Ⓗ

A classic country inn with charm and character. Its bright and comfortable lounge bar, with attractive rural prints, and panelled dining room serving regionally sourced food, are deservedly popular with locals and visitors. Guest beers are usually from independent brewers. There's a pleasant beer terrace and garden for summer months and a large function room. The pub's name refers to the slaying, by the Saxons, of three Danish chieftains in battle in 870 at nearby Stow; look for the effigies above the entrance. Q⚲✿◑P✿

Timberland

Penny Farthing

4 Station Road, LN4 3SA

☎ (01526) 378881 ⊕ thepennyfarthinginn.co.uk

2 changing beers (sourced nationally) Ⓗ

A country pub in the heart of the village serving at least two changing beers, often from breweries nearby. It has a large open-plan layout with various spaces for dining and a comfortable seating area. Families and dogs are welcome. Food is locally sourced, specials are on offer Tuesday to Friday, and there is a popular Sunday lunch. A regular quiz is held on Tuesday plus occasional comedy and music evenings. Five en-suite bedrooms are available. Q⚲✿↩◑&♣P✿⚲

Waddington

Three Horseshoes

High Street, LN5 9RF

☎ (01522) 720448

John Smith's Bitter; 5 changing beers (sourced nationally) Ⓗ

In the heart of the village, next to the church and with easy access to the bus route, this is a real community local providing social gatherings on most nights. Darts, quizzes, poker and live entertainment feature regularly.

Two bars with real fires provide a cosy environment in which to play traditional pub games and enjoy real ale from five handpumps. Large screens show sports events. ⚲✿♣➧(1,13) ✿⚲

Wainfleet

Batemans Brewery Visitor Centre Ⓛ

Salem Bridge Brewery, Mill Lane, PE24 4JE

☎ (01754) 880317 ⊕ bateman.co.uk

Batemans XB, Gold, Salem Porter, XXXB; 1 changing beer (sourced locally; often Batemans) Ⓗ

Visiting Batemans brewery provides the chance to experience the blend of its proud 140-plus years of craft brewing tradition with its forward-looking outlook. Mr George's Bar, within the attractive windmill, is the ideal venue for sampling a range of its beers. Further entertainment is to be found with brewery tours, featuring the Theatre of Beers, and in the pleasant beer garden with its games. Opening days and times vary throughout the year – see the Batemans website for details. Usually closed in January. ⚲✿◑&Å⇄♣P➧(7) ✿⚲

Welbourn

Joiners Arms

21 High Street, LN5 0NH

☎ (01400) 279356

Joseph Holt Bitter; Sharp's Doom Bar; 1 changing beer (sourced nationally) Ⓗ

This brick-built free house is the sole pub in the village. Inside is a single long bar area with a small alcove at one end, and there is a cosy and welcoming atmosphere. Good homely food is available Friday to Sunday with special feature nights. There are occasional quiz and music nights, plus other social events. Two en-suite letting rooms are available. ⚲✿↩◑♣P➧(1)✿⚲

Westwoodside

Carpenters Arms

Newbigg, DN9 2AT (follow B1396 to centre of village)

☎ (01427) 752416

Black Sheep Best Bitter; Bradfield Farmers Blonde; Brains Rev James; 2 changing beers (sourced nationally; often Marston's, Welbeck Abbey, Wychwood) Ⓗ

A regular in the Guide for many years, this friendly village inn takes an active part in community events, and has raised significant sums for local charities. A recent change of ownership has not altered the pub's long-held reputation for beer quality. Four cask ales are available, two of which change frequently. A past winner of several CAMRA awards and previous holder of the local Haxey Hood trophy. Autovacs are not used here. ⚲✿◑♣P➧(399) ✿⚲

Willingham by Stow

Half Moon Ⓛ

23 High Street, DN21 5JZ

☎ (01427) 788340

Batemans XB Ⓗ

Traditional-style village pub in a building dating back to 1850, with a public bar, lounge bar, an open fire and a beer garden. There are four beers on tap, one regular and three changing. Food is served from Thursday to Sunday and the fish & chips are popular with locals and visitors. There are entertainment nights on a relatively frequent basis and themed charity nights. Q⚲✿◑&♣➧✿

Winterton

George Hogg Ⓛ ✅

25 Market Street, DN15 9PT

☎ (01724) 732270 ● thegeorgehogg.co.uk

Draught Bass; 4 changing beers (sourced regionally; often Batemans, Lincolnshire Craft) Ⓗ

A Grade II listed building situated in the marketplace, this is a friendly local CAMRA award-winning pub with a large lounge and public bar, both with real fires. Guest beers change on a regular basis, often sourced from local breweries. The George is a popular meeting place for local football teams and supporters' clubs, and hosts occasional live music. Tea and coffee are served but no hot food. There is an outdoor seating area, and the Fastcat bus stops outside. Q ☺ ❀ ♣ P ➯ (350) ❀ 🛜

Woolsthorpe

Dirty Duck

Woolsthorpe Wharf, NG32 1NY

☎ (01476) 870111 ● thedirtyduckpub.co.uk

Batemans XB, Gold; Sharp's Doom Bar; 1 changing beer Ⓗ

A hidden gem in the Lincolnshire countryside. On the bank of the Grantham Canal, this pub attracts walkers and cyclists. The quality restaurant makes it a popular place for diners. There is also a separate function room and bar that can be hired for private events. With an outdoor seating area overlooking the canal, live music and barbecues in the summer months, it is truly worth a visit. ☺ ❀ ◑ ▶ A P ❀ 🛜

Wragby

Ivy

Market Place, LN8 5QU

☎ (01673) 858768

Batemans XB; Draught Bass; Timothy Taylor Boltmaker; 2 changing beers (sourced nationally) Ⓗ

A 17th-century village-centre pub with three separate areas, including a restaurant, offering a varied selection of real ales. The wood-burning stove gives a homely feeling in winter. Tasty home-cooked food is served, including vegan and gluten-free options. There is a popular quiz on Sunday evenings and sport is screened in the main bar. En-suite letting rooms are available and there is free parking opposite. Q ☺ ⇔ ◑ ➯ (50,56) ❀ 🛜

Wroot

Cross Keys

High Street, DN9 2BT (in centre of village)

☎ (01302) 770231

Theakston Best Bitter; 3 changing beers (sourced regionally; often Acorn, Pheasantry, Welbeck Abbey) Ⓗ

A highly successful community pub serving a remote village of fewer than 500 inhabitants. It takes part in a whole range of local events and always has a friendly, welcoming atmosphere. This multi-roomed venue offers four cask ales – the three guests usually come from nearby breweries. Evening meals are served on Thursdays and also at weekends. Autovacs are not used here. Q ☺ ❀ ◑ A ♣ P ❀ 🛜

Wyberton Fen

Hammer & Pincers ✅

Swineshead Road, PE21 7JE

☎ (01205) 361323 ● hammerandpincers-boston.co.uk

Adnams Ghost Ship; Fuller's London Pride; Sharp's Doom Bar; Woodforde's Wherry Ⓗ

A lively family-run community establishment on the outskirts of Boston, close to the Downtown shopping centre and supermarket. It has two rooms and a conservatory, with a 1970s feel to the main public bar. Popular for reasonably priced food, the menu includes breakfast, snacks, traditional pub meals and daily specials. An outside seating space to the front is decorated with flower baskets in the summer. ☺ ❀ ◑ & ♣ P ➯ ❀ 🛜

Joiners Arms, Lincoln (Photo: Tom Bastin/Flickr CC BY 2.0)

London index

*Shown on Inner London map

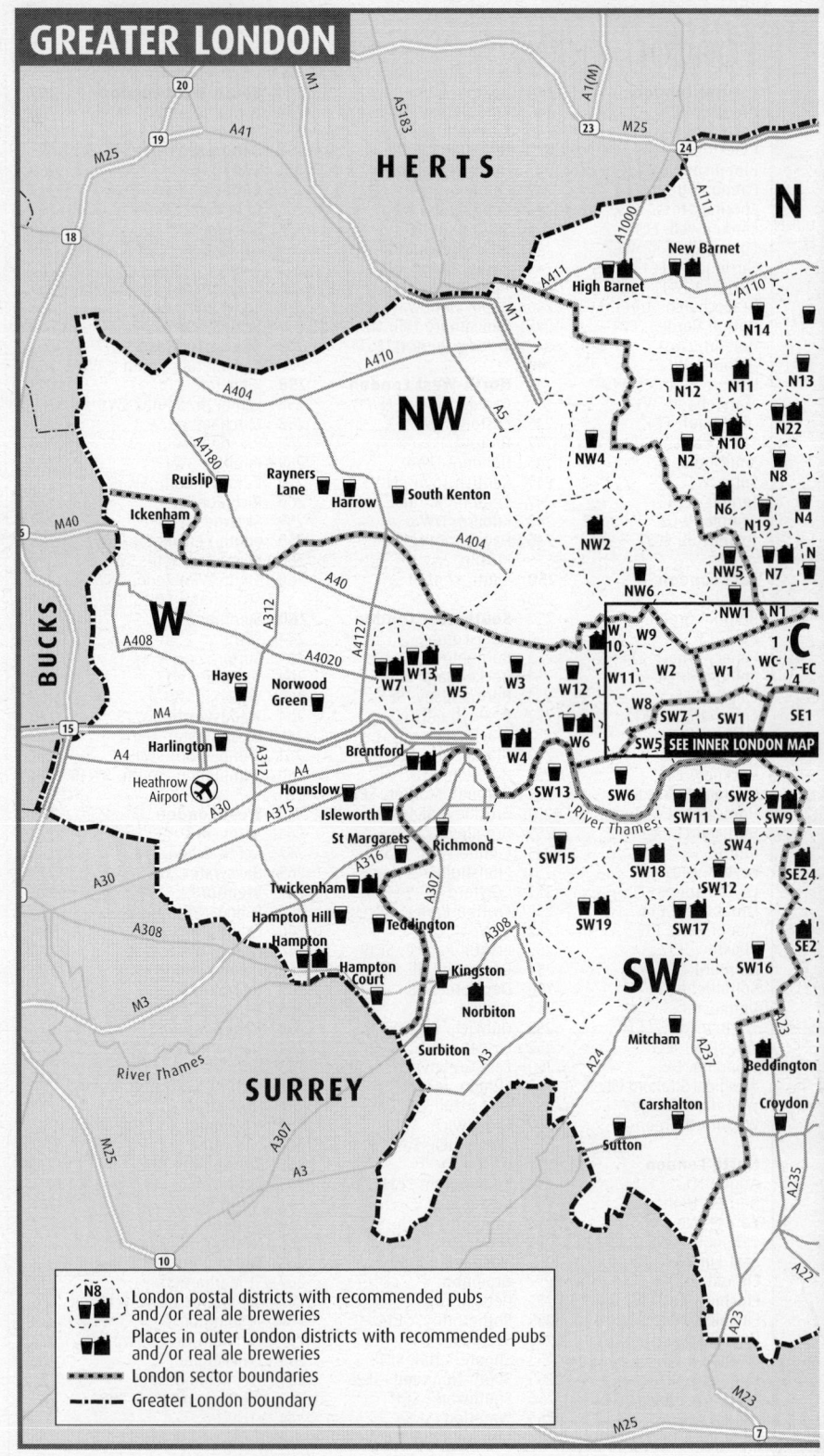

GREATER LONDON

ENGLAND

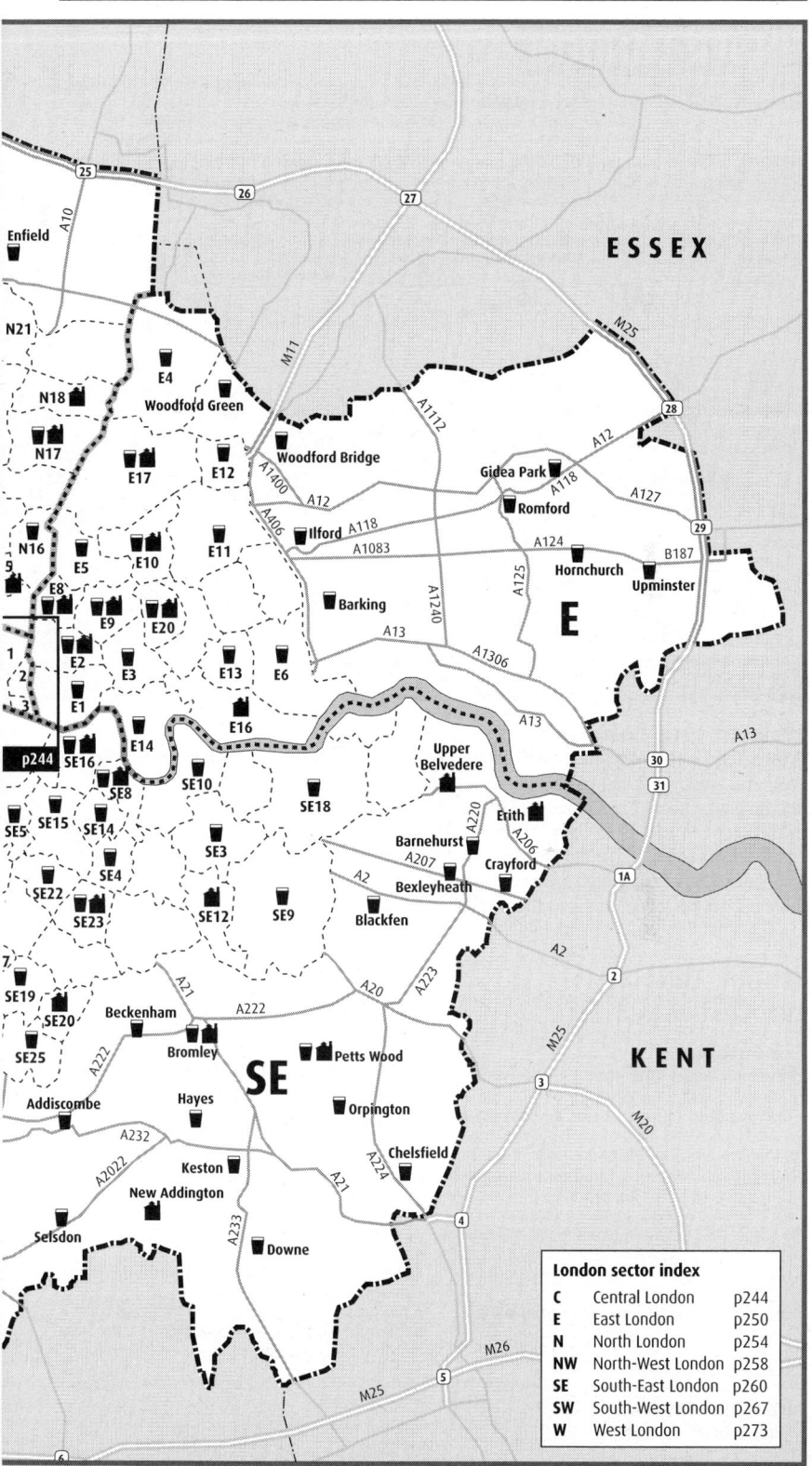

ESSEX

E

KENT

Enfield
N21
E4
N18
Woodford Green
N17
E17
E12
Woodford Bridge
Gidea Park
Romford
Ilford
Barking
N16
E5
E10
E11
E8
E9
E20
E2
E3
E13
E6
E1
E16
E14
SE16
SE8
Upper Belvedere
SE10
SE18
Erith
Barnehurst
Crayford
Bexleyheath
Blackfen
SE5
SE15
SE14
SE3
SE22
SE4
SE23
SE12
SE9
SE19
SE20
Beckenham
SE25
Bromley
Petts Wood
SE
Addiscombe
Hayes
Orpington
Keston
Chelsfield
New Addington
Selsdon
Downe

M11
M25
A10
A1112
A12
A118
A127
A1400
A406
A12
A118
A1083
A124
A125
B187
Hornchurch
Upminster
A1240
A13
A1306
A13
A13
A220
A206
A207
A2
A2
A2
M25
M20
A21
A222
A20
A223
A222
A232
A2022
A21
A224
A233
M26
M25

p244

ESSEX

London sector index

C	Central London	p244
E	East London	p250
N	North London	p254
NW	North-West London	p258
SE	South-East London	p260
SW	South-West London	p267
W	West London	p273

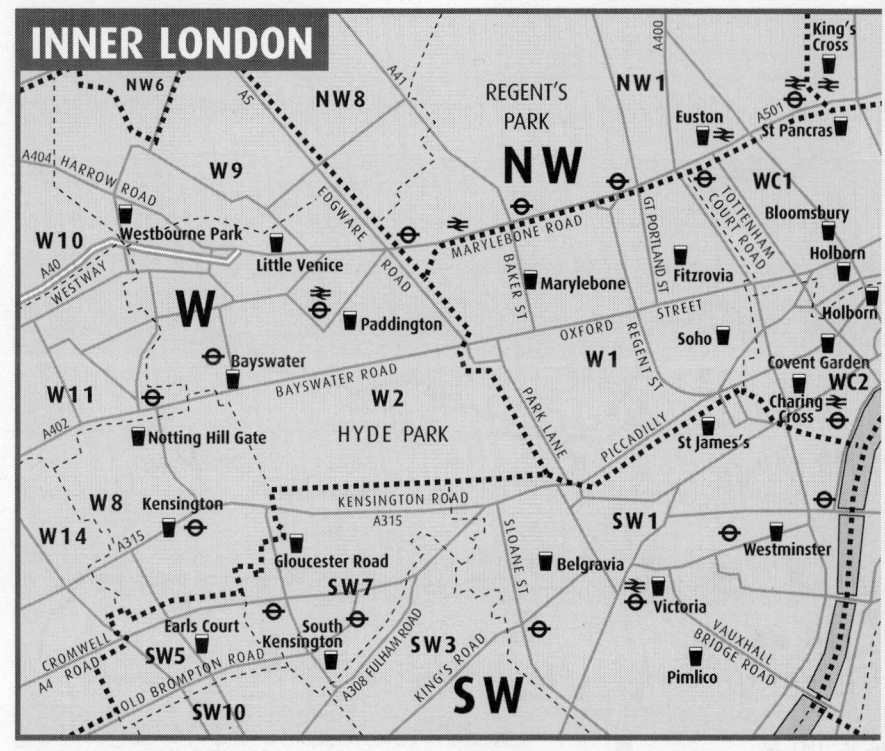

INNER LONDON

How to find London pubs

Greater London is divided into seven sectors: Central, East, North, North-West, South-East, South-West and West, reflecting postal boundaries. The Central sector includes the City (EC1 to EC4) and Holborn, Covent Garden and the Strand (WC1/2) plus W1, where pubs are listed in postal district order. In each of the other six sectors the pubs with London postcodes are listed first in postal district order (E1, E2 etc), followed by those in outer London districts, which are listed in alphabetical order (Barking, Chadwell Heath, etc) – see Greater London map. Postal district numbers can be found on every street name plate in the London postcode area.

CENTRAL LONDON
EC1: Clerkenwell

Exmouth Arms 🅛

23 Exmouth Market, EC1R 4QL
☎ (020) 3551 4772
4 changing beers (often Dark Star, Revolutions) Ⓗ
Operated by Barworks, this hostelry has four constantly changing real ales alongside a wide range of bottled beers and a dozen keg beers. Bar snacks and main meals are available. The last rebuilding was in 1915 (see date stone); the exterior shows former Courage ownership. The interior has been totally reconstructed in minimalist fashion but it feels like a proper pub. A small bar upstairs is now a cocktail bar and is used for overflow on busy nights.
🏚🌰🕽✇(Farringdon) ⊖(Angel/Farringdon) ♣🖨🐾🛜

EC1: Farringdon

Jerusalem Tavern

55 Britton Street, EC1M 5UQ
☎ (020) 7490 4281
6 changing beers (often St Peter's) Ⓐ

The premises date from 1719/20, with the frontage added in 1810. Originally a merchant's house, then a workshop for the clock-making trades, it was converted to a pub in 1996. The interior is a recreation of an 18th-century tavern, complete with real fire. The only outlet in London belonging to St Peter's Brewery in Suffolk, its dispense system is unusual, with beer from the cellar pumped by air pressure to emerge from fake cask ends behind the bar. Q🏚🕽✇⊖♣🖨🛜

Sutton Arms ✔

16 Great Sutton Street, EC1V 0DH
☎ (020) 7253 2462 ⊕ suttonarms.co.uk
Fuller's London Pride; 2 changing beers (often Ilkley, Oakham) Ⓗ
A free house since 1991, this former Whitbread outlet is named after 17th-century plutocrat Thomas Sutton, who founded nearby Charterhouse. If you are looking for a traditional after-work venue with a friendly atmosphere and a knowledgeable manager, this is it. A corner pub with side bar, plus a dining/function room upstairs, it sells the three cask beers, KeyKeg choices from local breweries such as Five Points, and a variety of foreign bottled beers. 🏚🌰🕽✇⊖(Barbican)♣🖨🐾🛜

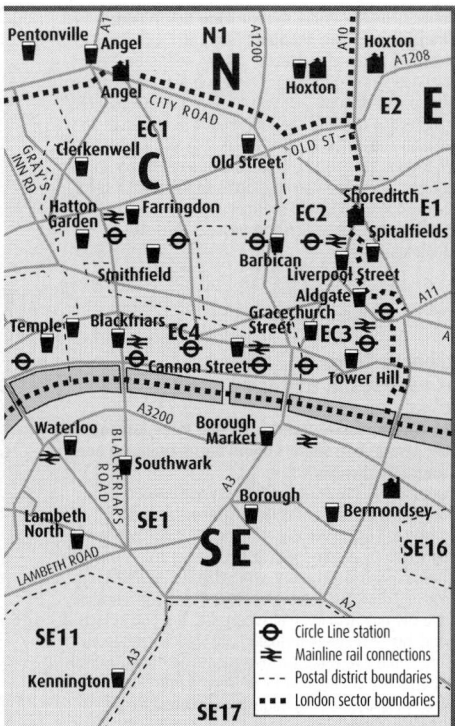

Map legend:
- ✛ Circle Line station
- ⇌ Mainline rail connections
- - - - Postal district boundaries
- ■■■ London sector boundaries

EC1: Hatton Garden

Craft Beer Co 🅛

82 Leather Lane, EC1N 7TR

☎ (020) 7404 7049

House beer (by Kent); changing beers (sourced nationally) Ⓗ

This popular pub on a historic site on Leather Lane offers up to 14 cask ales, 20 keg lines, many international bottled beers and two ciders. Downstairs it has stools and tables around the walls and plenty of standing room. There is more seating upstairs and a small standing area outside. Food is pies and Scotch eggs, though you can order in a takeaway. Grade II-listed, interesting features include a distinctive glass ceiling and chandelier and a large Bass mirror.

ॐ❀⇌(Farringdon) ⊖(Chancery Lane/Farringdon) ♠🖵❀🛜

Olde Mitre ★ 🅛 ✓

1 Ely Court, Ely Place, EC1N 6SJ

☎ (020) 7405 4751

Fuller's Oliver's Island, London Pride; Gale's Seafarers Ale; 4 changing beers (often East London, Sambrook's, Windsor & Eton) Ⓗ

Hidden in an alley between Hatton Garden and Ely Place, there has been a tavern on this site since 1546. Mainly dating from the 18th century, the current building has two bars and an upstairs function room, reached by a narrow staircase. All are wood panelled, giving a traditional feel, and the pub has been identified by CAMRA as having a nationally important historic interior. Bar snacks include a range of toasties.

Q❀⇌(City Thameslink) ⊖(Chancery Lane/Farringdon) ♠🖵🛜

EC1: Old Street

Artillery Arms 🅛

102 Bunhill Row, EC1Y 8ND

☎ (020) 7253 4683 ⊕ artillery-arms.co.uk

Fuller's Oliver's Island, London Pride, ESB; 2 changing beers (often Dark Star, Gale's) Ⓗ

Small, single-room pub with a central bar, bare wooden floor and plain walls, giving it a relaxed and comfortable feel. The five handpumps usually serve four beers, with one ready to change. The guest beer is from the Fuller's list, with one choice a month from the London Brewers' Alliance. It has dining areas at the rear, with military prints on the wall, and extra seating upstairs. Sunday roasts are served from noon until they run out.

◧⇌⊖♠🐾❀

Old Fountain 🅛

3 Baldwin Street, EC1V 9NU

☎ (020) 7253 2970 ⊕ oldfountain.co.uk

5 changing beers (sourced regionally) Ⓗ

A privately owned free house with a single bar on two levels, a fish tank gracing the upper area. It is popular with workers from nearby Silicon Roundabout. You can relax upstairs on the roof garden with its two large parasols and heating. The extensive beer range comes mainly from breweries nearby, featuring new brews and including many local bottled beers.

ॐ❀◧⇌⊖♠🖵❀🛜

EC1: Smithfield

Hand & Shears ★ ✓

1 Middle Street, EC1A 7JA

☎ (020) 7600 0257 ⊕ thehandandshears.com

St Austell Tribute; Timothy Taylor Landlord; 3 changing beers (often Black Sheep, Sharp's) Ⓗ

Close to the site of St Bartholomew's Fair, this Grade II-listed pub has long associations with the cloth trades. In various forms it has served Smithfield since 1123 and was given a Justice's Licence in 1552. The current building dates from 1843 and has a nationally important historic interior with a wealth of Victorian and inter-war features. A central island bar serves a number of separate areas. The wooden floors and panelling contribute to the atmospheric character.

◧⇌(Farringdon) ⊖(Barbican) ♠🖵❀🛜

EC2: Barbican

Wood Street

53 Fore Street, EC2Y 5EJ

☎ (020) 7256 6990 ⊕ woodstreetbar.co.uk

Dark Star Hophead; Harvey's Sussex Best Bitter, Old Ale; Purity Mad Goose; 1 changing beer (sourced nationally) Ⓗ

An independent hidden gem, open on weekdays, tucked away at the south edge of the Barbican complex at the north end of Wood Street. The modern interior is light and airy. A downstairs bar has two pool tables, two dartboards and a separate poker room. The wood-panelled main bar has plentiful and varied seating. Observe the Barbican water feature ponds from the rear windows. Burgers and bites are served lunchtimes and evenings. Dark beers appear on rotation.

ॐ◧⇌⊖(Moorgate) ♠🖵❀🛜

EC2: Liverpool Street

Hamilton Hall ✓

Unit 32, Street-level Concourse, Liverpool Street Station, EC2M 7PY

☎ (020) 7247 3579
Greene King IPA, Abbot; Sharp's Doom Bar; 7 changing beers (sourced nationally) Ⓗ
Once a ballroom, this is now a Wetherspoon pub that has retained a lavish interior. Real ale is dispensed from 10 handpumps on the entrance level bar and from five on the upstairs bar. There is an outside seating area and children are welcome during the day. Breakfasts are served on weekdays. The pub can at times be busy. TV screens show train departure and arrival times.
Q ⏰ 🐕 ❀ ◑ ♿ ⇄ ☷ 🚆 ☏

EC3: Aldgate

Hoop & Grapes Ⓛ ✔
47 Aldgate High Street, EC3N 1AL
☎ (020) 7481 4583
Fuller's London Pride; St Austell Nicholson's Pale Ale; Sharp's Doom Bar; 5 changing beers (sourced nationally) Ⓗ
On the eastern edge of the City, this Grade II*-listed pub survived the Great Fire of London by 50 yards and is a rare example of a timbered building in London. Although only called the Hoop & Grapes since 1920, the inn on this site goes back to the 13th century and had a licence in 1580. It was renovated in 1983, preserving the sense of antiquity. Now an M&B Nicholson's outlet, it boasts an extensive food menu.
🐕 ◑ ≈ (Fenchurch St) ↔ (Aldgate/Aldgate E) ● 🚆 ❀ ☏

EC3: Gracechurch Street

Crosse Keys Ⓛ ✔
7-12 Gracechurch Street, EC3V 0DR
☎ (020) 7623 4824

Fuller's London Pride; Greene King IPA, Abbot; Sharp's Doom Bar; changing beers Ⓗ
Housed in a grandiose building that used to be the headquarters of a banking corporation, this pub is named after a coaching inn that was once nearby. Twenty four handpumps dispense the four regular beers, up to 18 rotating guest ales and two ciders. The ales are listed on TV screens above the bar and are ordered by pump number. There are function rooms to the rear. A spiral staircase leads down to the toilets.
Q 🐕 ◑ ♿ ≈ (Cannon St/Fenchurch St) ↔ (Bank/Monument) 🚆 ☏

EC3: Tower Hill

Liberty Bounds Ⓛ ✔
15 Trinity Square, EC3N 4AA
☎ (020) 7481 0513
Adnams Broadside; Fuller's London Pride; Greene King IPA, Abbot; Sharp's Doom Bar; 5 changing beers (sourced nationally) Ⓗ
Opposite the Tower of London, and surrounded by handsome buildings, this large Wetherspoon is a converted bank. Recently refurbished, it has two levels connected by a grand staircase. Displays reflect the unusually rich local history, with a bias to the Tudors. The food and drink are good value for the area and, unusually for a city pub, it is open at weekends. The pub attracts a good mix of clientele including city workers and tourists. It hosts the two usual Wetherspoon major beer festivals during the year. Breakfasts are served from 8am. Wheelchair access is through the rear entrance in Muscovy Street.
Q ⏰ 🐕 ◑ ♿ ≈ (Fenchurch St) ↔ (Tower Gateway/Tower Hill) ● 🚆 ☏

REAL ALE BREWERIES

Affinity ✦ SW9: Brixton
Anspach & Hobday ✦ Beddington
Barnet ⬟ ✦ High Barnet
Battersea ⬟ SW11: Battersea Power Station
Beerblefish ✦ E17: Walthamstow
Bexley Erith
Block ⬟ N1: Hoxton
Boxcar ✦ E2: Bethnal Green
Brew By Numbers ✦ SE16: Bermondsey
Brewhouse & Kitchen ⬟ E2: Hoxton
Brewhouse & Kitchen ⬟ EC1: Angel
Brewhouse & Kitchen ⬟ N5: Highbury
Brick SE8: Deptford
Brixton ✦ SW9: Brixton
Brockley ✦ SE12: Hither Green
Broken Drum Upper Belvedere
Bullfinch ✦ SE24: Herne Hill
By The Horns ✦ SW17: Summerstown
Canopy ✦ SE24: Herne Hill
Clarkshaws ✦ SW9: Loughborough Junction
Cronx New Addington
Ealing ✦ Brentford
East London E10: Leyton
Enfield N18: Upper Edmonton
Fearless Nomad ⬟ Brentford
Five Points ✦ E8: London Fields
Fuller's W4: Chiswick
Gipsy Hill ✦ SE27: West Norwood
Goodness ✦ N22: Wood Green
Goose Island ⬟ E1: Shoreditch
Gorgeous ⬟ ✦ N6: Highgate
Greywood N22: Wood Green (brewing suspended)
Hammerton ✦ N7: Barnsbury
Howling Hops ⬟ ✦ E9: Hackney Wick

Husk ✦ E16: West Silvertown
London Brewing ⬟ ✦ N12: North Finchley
Macintosh W6: Stamford Brook (NEW)
Marko Paulo ⬟ W13: Northfields
Marlix Petts Wood (NEW)
Mellors N8: Harringay (NEW)
Moncada ✦ NW2: Dollis Hill
Muswell Hillbilly ✦ N10: Muswell Hill
Mutineers Bromley
Oddly N11: Friern Barnet
One Mile End ✦ N17: Tottenham
Park ✦ Norbiton
Portobello W10: North Kensington
Pressure Drop ✦ N17: Tottenham Hale
Redemption ✦ N17: Tottenham
Sambrook's ✦ SW18: Wandsworth
Signal ✦ Beddington
Signature ✦ E17: Walthamstow
SlyBeast ⬟ SW18: Wandsworth
Southey ✦ SE20: Penge
Southwark ✦ SE1: Bermondsey
Spartan ✦ SE16: South Bermondsey
Tap East ⬟ E20: Stratford
Three Hills SE16: Bermondsey
Three Sods ✦ E8: London Fields
Tiny Vessel Hampton
Truman's ✦ E9: Hackney Wick
Twickenham ✦ Twickenham
Up the Creek ⬟ SE10: Greenwich
Urban Alchemy New Barnet
Volden SE23: Forest Hill
Weird Beard W7: Hanwell
Wild Card ✦ E17: Walthamstow
Wimbledon ✦ SW19: Colliers Wood

EC4: Blackfriars

Black Friar ★ ⃝ ✔

174 Queen Victoria Street, EC4V 4EG

☎ (020) 7236 5474

Fuller's London Pride; St Austell Nicholson's Pale Ale; Sharp's Doom Bar; 7 changing beers ⊞

The Black Friar has been identified by CAMRA as having a nationally important historic pub interior and is a stunning example of the rare Art Nouveau style. It was famously saved from demolition by Sir John Betjeman in the 1960s. Just opposite Blackfriars station, it is lively, frequented both by office workers and tourists. Look out for the friars in marble and brass who line the walls under the coving. ♿❀❁◑➤⊖🚃♣🐱🛜

EC4: Cannon Street

Bell ✔

29 Bush Lane, EC4R 0AN

☎ (020) 7283 0029

Courage Best Bitter; Harvey's Sussex Best Bitter; Sharp's Doom Bar; Timothy Taylor Landlord; 1 changing beer (sourced locally) ⊞

Copper pots and pans hang from the ceiling of this no-nonsense, ex-Courage, one-bar drinking house near Cannon Street station. A list of previous licensees going back centuries hangs on the back wall next to the photo of Sid James. Televised sports are quietly shown, with tasteful background music gently playing. Food is mainly pie and mash, with the small upstairs dining area doubling as a function room. ◑➤⊖🚃🛜

Pelt Trader

Arch 3, Dowgate Hill, EC4N 6AP

☎ (020) 7160 0253 ● pelttrader.com

6 changing beers (sourced nationally) Ⓐ

Nestled under an archway beneath Cannon Street station, this independent venue offers six cask taps behind the bar along with 14 keg taps showcasing a variety of modern craft beer and cider. Owned by the Bloomsbury Leisure Group, the archway opened as a bar in 2013. Decorative mirrors portray pelt traders; Skinners' Hall is directly opposite the front door. Pizzas can be ordered from the bar. Available for private hire at weekends. ♿❀❁◑➤⊖🚃♣🛜

Sir John Hawkshaw ⃝ ✔

Cannon Street Station, EC4N 6AP

☎ (020) 3206 1004

Fuller's London Pride; Greene King IPA; Sharp's Doom Bar; 2 changing beers ⊞

A Wetherspoon bar next to Platform 1. You navigate to the well-lit interior via an external seating area. A departure and arrival screen hangs by the bar. You can see the cellar section through the windows of the right-hand room. Seating comprises a mix of high stools and comfortable leather bench seats. As it is within the station, no smoking is allowed. (The free toilets are by Platform 7.) Q♿◑❁🅶➤⊖🚃🛜

EC4: Temple

Old Bank Of England

194 Fleet Street, EC4A 2LT

☎ (020) 7430 2255 ● oldbankofengland.com

Fuller's London Pride; McMullen AK Original Mild, Country Bitter, IPA ⊞

A Grade II-listed building that was Bank of England premises until 1975, sensitively refurbished as a Fuller's Ale & Pie house in 1994. It has an island bar, a gallery and various murals depicting the rich history of the area. Note the ornate high ceiling and chandeliers. New owner

McMullen has been in charge since early 2019. There are two dining/function rooms. At the back is a beer garden. Occasionally the whole pub may be hired out, so check before visiting. ❀❁◑➤(City Thameslink)⊖🚃♣🛜

WC1: Bloomsbury

Museum Tavern ✔

49 Great Russell Street, WC1B 3BA

☎ (020) 7242 8987

Greene King IPA, London Glory; Theakston Old Peculier; 2 changing beers (often Hammerton) ⊞

A magnificent Grade II-listed Victorian pub opposite the British Museum. In 1855 William Finch Hill designed the ground floor front and classic mahogany bar-back still evident today. In 1889 five separate bars were created, with partitions and decorations of stained glass, two rare examples of which survive. Five bars were reduced to three in 1935, becoming one in the 1960s. The five sets of entrance doors are all that now remain of the historic arrangement. ♿❀❁◑🅶⊖(Tottenham Court Rd)♣🚃🛜

Swan ⃝ ✔

7 Cosmo Place, WC1N 3AP

☎ (020) 7837 6223

Greene King IPA, Abbot; Hammerton N1; 4 changing beers (often Five Points, Greene King) ⊞

Popular family-oriented venue among the tourist hotels on Southampton Row, close to Great Ormond Street Children's Hospital. It has a single long bar room plus tables out the front on a pedestrian passage. This lively venue has eight handpumps offering three regular real ales and four guests, mainly from London breweries, together with a real cider. An extensive menu of pub grub and snacks are served all day. A large-screen TV shows live sports events. Q♿❀❁◑🅶⊖(Russell Sq)♣🚃🐱🛜

WC1: Holborn

Craft Beer Co

168 High Holborn, WC1V 7AA

☎ (020) 7240 0431

Kent Pale; 14 changing beers (sourced nationally) ⊞

Though in the ancient parish of St Giles, whose church featured in several of Hogarth's etchings, including Gin Lane, the location of this pub on the north-eastern edge of Covent Garden will probably have a more modern resonance. On two levels, the sixth Craft Beer Co outlet would be more at home in Beer Street, with its 15 pumps dispensing a changing range of ales from across the UK. There are frequent tap takeovers and Meet the Brewer events. ◑⊖(Covent Garden/Holborn)🚃

WC1: St Pancras

Queen's Head ⃝

66 Acton Street, WC1X 9NB

☎ (020) 7713 5772 ● queensheadlondon.com

Redemption Trinity; 2 changing beers (sourced regionally) ⊞

Narrow, late-Georgian premises off Gray's Inn Road, with a single bar, a smoking patio at the rear and benches in front. The piano is used for jazz and blues on Thursdays and late Sunday afternoons. Microbrewery guest beers usually include a dark one. One handpump serves cider, with three more real ciders and a range of other draught and bottled beers in stock. Sharing snack platters are on offer at this comfortable pub frequented by locals and the occasional tourist. ❀❁◑➤⊖(King's Cross St Pancras)♣🚃🛜

Skinners Arms

114 Judd Street, WC1H 9NT

☎ (020) 7837 6521 🌐 skinnersarmslondon.com

Greene King IPA, Abbot; 4 changing beers (often Siren) ⊞

Named after the City livery company and standing on a street named after a past master of the company, this traditional, quiet, corner pub has in effect been converted to one bar, despite the signs on the doors and in the stained glass. A raised seating area is on the left as you enter and the previously separate room at the back is now a large alcove with more seating.

❀◖≠⊖(King's Cross St Pancras) ⊟

WC2: Charing Cross

Harp ⃒ ✅

47 Chandos Place, WC2N 4HS

☎ (020) 7836 0291

Dark Star Hophead, American Pale Ale; Fuller's London Pride; Harvey's Sussex Best Bitter; 5 changing beers (sourced nationally) ⊞

Small friendly Fuller's premises that became a haven for beer choice as a free house run by the late, legendary, Binnie Walsh. Ciders and perries complement the fine beer range. The narrow bar is adorned with mirrors and portraits, and a cosy upstairs room provides a refuge from the throng. Since 2019 beers from the wood have occasionally been available, usually on a Wednesday. Current local CAMRA Pub of the Year. Q◖≠⊖♠⊟♀

Lemon Tree ✅

4 Bedfordbury, WC2N 4BP

☎ (020) 7831 1391 🌐 lemontreecoventgarden.com

Harvey's Sussex Best Bitter; St Austell Tribute; 3 changing beers (often Adnams, Portobello, Truman's) ⊞

This one-bar pub next to the stage door of the Coliseum is a favourite among locals, musicians and theatregoers. The Thai restaurant upstairs doubles as a function room. Look out for the entrance, slightly set back. There is an emphasis on London brews among the guest beers by popular demand. The premises are operated by All Our Bars, a small chain based in Edenbridge. ◖≠⊖⊟♀

Ship & Shovell

1-3 Craven Passage, WC2N 5PH

☎ (020) 7839 1311 🌐 shipandshovell.co.uk

Hall & Woodhouse Badger Best Bitter, Fursty Ferret, Tanglefoot; 1 changing beer (often Hall & Woodhouse) ⊞

An attractive, welcoming pub almost underneath Charing Cross station. Perhaps uniquely (for London, at least), it is divided into separate halves, facing each other across Craven Passage alleyway between Villiers Street and Craven Street. Acquired by Hall & Woodhouse in 1997, it commemorates Admiral Sir Cloudesley Shovell, drowned with 2,000 men when his fleet was grounded off the Scilly Isles in 1707 – the catastrophe believed to have inspired the Admiralty to offer the Longitude Prize for an accurate nautical timepiece. Q❧❀◖≠⊖⊟♣♀

WC2: Covent Garden

Lamb & Flag

33 Rose Street, WC2E 9EB

☎ (020) 7497 9504

Dark Star Hophead; Fuller's Oliver's Island, London Pride, ESB; Gale's Seafarers Ale; 2 changing beers (sourced nationally) ⊞

Owned by Fuller's since 2013, this Grade II-listed building remains a pleasant traditional local without muzak or games machines, tucked away up Rose Street from Garrick Street. It has two dark wood-panelled rooms, the rear one with an attractive fireplace and a connecting passage from the main bar on the ground floor. Note that the upstairs bar and restaurant has table service only. Charles Dickens and Karl Marx were both regulars. ❧❀◖≠(Charing Cross) ⊖(Covent Garden/Leicester Sq) ⊟♣♀

White Swan ✅

14 New Row, WC2N 4LF

☎ (020) 3077 1129

Fuller's London Pride; St Austell Nicholson's Pale Ale; Sharp's Doom Bar; 5 changing beers (sourced nationally) ⊞

Grade II listed, once owned by the London banking firm of Hoare & Co, this M&B Nicholson's establishment is popular with Covent Garden tourists and is a rare WC2 outlet for real cider. It may appear crowded at first glance, but it is longer than it looks and there are more seats at the back. The first-floor dining room can be booked for functions. Note the contrasting fireplaces. The premises had a spruce-up in February 2020. ❧◖≠(Charing Cross) ⊖(Leicester Sq) ♣⊟♀

WC2: Holborn

Shakespeare's Head

Africa House, 64-68 Kingsway, WC2B 6BG

☎ (020) 7404 8846

Fuller's London Pride; Greene King IPA, Abbot; Sharp's Doom Bar; house beer (by Windsor); 5 changing beers (sourced nationally) ⊞

Large Wetherspoon bank conversion from 1998, named after a famous pub in the locality until the demolition of Wych Street over 100 years ago. It is usually busy with shoppers, tourists, local office workers and, during term time, students from the nearby London School of Economics. Here is a convenient place for a couple of pints after your cultural sojourn at the nearby Sir John Soane's Museum. Q❧❀◖&⊖⊟♀

WC2: Temple

Devereux

20 Devereux Court, WC2R 3JJ

☎ (020) 7583 4530 🌐 thedevereux.co.uk

Fuller's London Pride; Gale's Seafarers Ale; 2 changing beers (sourced regionally) ⊞

An attractive Grade II-listed pub built in 1844; part of the site was once the Grecian Coffee House. The comfortable lounge with wood panelling has a bar with five handpumps. Prints on the walls show local places of interest and historic figures, the judges and wigs reflecting proximity to the law courts. Upstairs is a restaurant available for hire. Q❧&≠(City Thameslink) ⊖♣⊟♀

Edgar Wallace

40 Essex Street, WC2R 3JF

☎ (020) 7353 3120

Crouch Vale Brewers Gold; 7 changing beers (often Dark Star, East London, Timothy Taylor) ⊞

Just off Fleet Street near the Royal Courts of Justice, this is a real gem of a one-room pub, with additional seating upstairs. The comfortable downstairs room, its walls and ceiling covered with beer mats and old advertising signs, has a fine wooden bar offering a wide range of rotating ales. This quiet place allows no music, laptops, mobiles and so on. Good-value food is served all day. Q❧◖⊖⊟♣

George 🄻 ✅
213 Strand, WC2R 1AP
☎ (020) 7353 9638 ⊕ georgeinthestrand.com
Greene King IPA, Abbot; house beer (by Greene King); 4 changing beers ⓗ
Opposite the Royal Courts of Justice, the George has a splendid exterior dating from an 1898 rebuild. It is believed to be named after a previous landlord; former reference to royalty has been removed from the current signs. Inside, the bar is long, with some partitioned seating areas opposite, leading to a room at the back and the upstairs Pig & Goose restaurant. For details of theatre ticket food offers and pre-theatre special deals, see the website. ◖▸≷(City Thameslink)⊖🖫

W1: Fitzrovia

Queen Charlotte
43 Goodge Street, W1T 1TA
☎ (020) 7323 9361
3 changing beers (often Siren) ⓗ
A big welcome awaits you in this small, single-bar corner pub with bare wooden floors and simple furnishings. Changing offerings from Siren and other smaller breweries are available in one-third and two-third pint measures in addition to the usual halves and pints. Plenty of other interesting draught and bottled beers are also stocked. Meals, including speciality burgers, are served all day, as well as brunch on Saturday.
🖫❀◖⊖(Goodge St) 🖫 ☎

Stag's Head 🄻
102 New Cavendish Street, W1W 6XW
☎ (020) 7580 8313
Fuller's London Pride; 1 changing beer (often Tring) ⓗ
A smart, oak-panelled building with a historic interior of regional importance, offering a friendly welcome to regulars and visitors alike. Rebuilt in the late 1930s by brewers William Younger, it has a marvellous Art Deco exterior, sporting a curved corner profile. Vertical drinking is assisted by unusual peninsular shelf projections to the bar and elsewhere. Sun lovers and smokers can relax on shaded benches outside. Traditional pub food is available lunchtimes only except Sunday, when service continues through the afternoon.
🖫❀◖⊖(Great Portland St) 🖫

W1: Marylebone

Barley Mow ★
8 Dorset Street, W1U 6QW
☎ (020) 7487 4773
Fuller's London Pride; Sharp's Doom Bar; 4 changing beers (sourced nationally) ⓗ
Dating from 1791, the pub is Grade II listed and identified by CAMRA as having a nationally important historic interior, with a main bar and a small snug at the rear. It retains both its original matchboard panelling, now displaying prints of 18th-century Marylebone and, most notably, two small drinking compartments fronting the main bar counter. Both bars are furnished with upholstered pews, benches and stools. Food from a short menu of home-made items is served weekday lunchtimes only. 🖫❀◖◖⊖(Baker St)♣🖫 ☎

Golden Eagle
59 Marylebone Lane, W1U 2NY
☎ (020) 7935 3228
Fuller's London Pride; St Austell Tribute; 2 changing beers (often North Cotswold, Twickenham) ⓗ

First licensed in 1842 and rebuilt in 1890, this single-bar pub is traditional in every way: small and cosy, with smart decor, a fine etched bar-back mirror and leaded windows. The historic interior is of regional importance. The landlady and her family celebrated 30 years here in 2021. Piano singalongs on Tuesday, Thursday and Friday evenings maintain the timeless atmosphere. Real ales are quality, not quantity. Q♿⊖(Bond St)🖫

Jackalope
43 Weymouth Mews, W1G 7EQ
☎ (020) 3455 2871 ⊕ jackalopelondon.com
4 changing beers (often Adnams, Five Points, Redemption) ⓗ
One of Marylebone's two remaining mews pubs, formerly the Dover Castle, built in 1777 and Grade II listed, with a regionally important historic interior. The mirrors underneath the dividing beam allowed coachmen to observe when their passengers wanted to depart. Now owned by Bloomsbury Leisure, operators of the Euston Tap, it has, downstairs, London's first Liu Xiaomian noodle kitchen, specialising in ramen dishes.
🖫◖⊖(Great Portland St/Regent's Park) 🖫❀☎

Thornbury Castle 🄻
29a Enford Street, W1H 1DN
☎ (020) 7723 8540 ⊕ thornbury-castle.business.site
6 changing beers (sourced regionally; often Park, Tring, Vale) ⓗ
A small, family-run pub in a side street near Marylebone station, with wood panelling throughout and a raised seating area at the back. There is a strong Rugby Union connection (Wasps) and the pub may open at weekends for big games on TV. Discerning drinkers will find it a worthwhile alternative to the more mainstream pubs in the area. Thai food is served. Q❀◖▸⊖♣🖫❀☎

W1: Soho

Dog & Duck ★ ✅
18 Bateman Street, W1D 3AJ
☎ (020) 7494 0697
St Austell Nicholson's Pale Ale; Sharp's Doom Bar; 5 changing beers (often St Austell, Sharp's) ⓗ
In the heart of Soho, this Grade II-listed Nicholson's outlet, built in 1897, has a nationally important historic pub interior. An elaborate mosaic depicts dogs and ducks, and wonderful advertising mirrors adorn the walls. The upstairs Orwell Bar can be hired for functions. The place is small and so popular, especially with media people, that it is not just smokers who have to drink outside. The bar extends towards the Frith Street door.
◖⊖(Tottenham Court Rd) 🖫 ☎

Lyric 🄻
37 Great Windmill Street, W1D 7LT
☎ (020) 7434 0604 ⊕ lyricsoho.co.uk
Harvey's Sussex Best Bitter; 8 changing beers (often Big Smoke, Siren, Southwark) ⓗ
A small, independently owned bar just off Shaftesbury Avenue, bay fronted with a tiled, panelled interior, popular with local trade. Once two adjacent taverns, the Windmill and the Ham, it merged in the mid-18th century to form the Windmill & Ham, renamed in 1890 and rebuilt 16 years later. Alongside other draught beers, including London specialities, the cask ales come from a wide range of mainly smaller breweries all over the country. 🖫◖⊖(Piccadilly Circus)●🖫❀☎

Old Coffee House
49 Beak Street, W1F 9SF
☎ (020) 7437 2197
3 changing beers (sourced locally) ⓗ

A large but cosy venue, close to the buzz of Carnaby Street. First licensed as the Silver Street Coffee House, it was rebuilt in 1894 and is now Grade II listed. The long bar and dark panelling are adorned with Watney's Red Barrel signage, brewery mirrors and sundry prints, posters, pictures and brassware. At lunchtimes you will find good-sized portions of pub grub, all reasonably priced. ≿🌢◑❶⊖(Piccadilly Circus)🚃❀

Queen's Head 🅛
15 Denman Street, W1D 7HN
☎ (020) 7437 1540 ⊕ queensheadpiccadilly.com
Fuller's London Pride; Sambrook's Wandle Ale; 3 changing beers (often Dark Star, Gun, Sambrook's) Ⓗ
A rare West End free house with plenty of vertical drinking space below and a restaurant upstairs. The traditional feel is enhanced by an attractive bar-back and wall mirroring downstairs, and an unusual leather-fronted bar in the restaurant. With its real ales, good-value pies and other pub food, including snacks and cheeseboards at the bar, this venue is popular both before and after theatre visits.
≿◑❶⊖(Piccadilly Circus) 🚃❀🛜

EAST LONDON
E1: Spitalfields

Commercial Tavern
142 Commercial Street, E1 6NU
☎ (020) 3137 9563 ⊕ commercial-tavern.com
4 changing beers (often Burning Sky, Thornbridge, Tiny Rebel) Ⓗ
Built in 1865, this Grade II-listed pub has an unusual curved frontage and interesting features. The warm, vibrant atmosphere welcomes you as you walk through the tabled area to the bar at the rear. Alongside the four cask beers are 10 keg fonts. The larger of the two upstairs rooms has its own bar; the smaller is more intimate. The selection of freshly cooked sourdough pizzas includes cheese-free options.
≿◑❶&≉(Liverpool St) ⊖(Liverpool St/Shoreditch High St) 🚃❀🛜

King's Stores 🅛 ✅
14 Widegate Street, E1 7HP
☎ (020) 7247 4089 ⊕ kingsstores.co.uk
Greene King IPA; 4 changing beers (sourced nationally) Ⓗ
A Greene King Metropolitan outlet, this is a corner pub in the narrow streets near Old Spitalfields Market. The decor is minimal, with bare floorboards and brick walls. The front is the main drinking area while the rear is more for eating, and there is also a restaurant upstairs. Five real ales always include at least one London brew. TVs show sporting events. ≿◑❶&≉⊖(Liverpool St)🚃❀🛜

Pride of Spitalfields 🅛
3 Heneage Street, E1 5LJ
☎ (020) 7247 8933
Crouch Vale Brewers Gold; Fuller's London Pride, ESB; Sharp's Doom Bar; 1 changing beer (often Truman's) Ⓗ
Just off Brick Lane, this single-bar free house has been run by the same landlady for the past 30 years and with most of the same staff. A real ale enthusiast, she has all the ales delivered direct from the brewery. Food at lunchtime is simple fare. Originally tied to the Star Brewery in Romford, the pub had changed its name from the Romford Arms by the early 1980s. Many local pictures adorn the walls.
≿◑❶⊖(Aldgate East/Shoreditch High St) 🚃❀

Williams Ale & Cider House 🅛 ✅
22-24 Artillery Lane, E1 7LS
☎ (020) 7247 5163 ⊕ williamsspitalfields.com
Greene King IPA, Yardbird; 5 changing beers (often Southwark, Truman's, Twickenham) Ⓗ
In a narrow street near Old Spitalfields Market, here is a large, comfortably furnished venue with bare floorboards and brick walls. The beer range always features London breweries, and seven ciders are also on handpump. TVs are switched on for major sporting events only. This is one of the few pubs in the area with dartboards. Food from a varied menu is served all day. Children are not admitted. ◑≉⊖(Liverpool St)♣●🚃❀🛜

E1: Wapping

Prospect of Whitby 🅛 ✅
57 Wapping Wall, E1W 3SH
☎ (020) 7481 1095
Greene King IPA, Abbot; 4 changing beers (often East London, Redemption, Sambrook's) Ⓗ
A traditional establishment, popular with tourists and locals alike for its historical relevance and tales. On the ground floor, the ancient pewter bar is supported by old beer barrels and has six handpumps. There are several seating areas including an atmospheric riverside terrace with the shade of a tree, and additional seating can be found upstairs on the balcony. Food is served all day from an extensive menu. Occasional sporting events are shown. Three function rooms are available for hire.
≿🌢◑❶⊖🚃(100,D3) ❀

E2: Bethnal Green

Camel 🅛 ✅
277 Globe Road, E2 0JD
☎ 07305 470811
Adnams Mosaic; Sambrook's Wandle Ale; 3 changing beers (often Five Points, St Austell, Three Sods) Ⓗ
A small refurbished Victorian pub with a single bar and a traditional feel. One of the guest beers is usually from Five Points Brewery in Hackney. There is food throughout the day, with a range of pies and mash, toasties and puddings. The distinctive exterior tiling gives a clue to the original brewery; the last one with a tie was Ind Coope. Convenient for the Museum of Childhood and York Hall. ≿🌢◑⊖🚃❀🛜

King's Arms
11A Buckfast Street, E2 6EY
☎ (020) 7729 2627 ⊕ thekingsarmspub.com
3 changing beers (often Five Points, Howling Hops, Siren) Ⓗ
A single-bar back-street local run by Barworks since refurbishment seven years ago. Three cask ales are offered along with over a dozen keg beers and a large range of bottles. Two ciders are available. There are no pumpclips; the beer menu is on the tables and the wall, and can also be found on the website. The only food offerings are Scotch eggs and tortas with cheese or meat. There is seating outside.
≿🌢&⊖(Bethnal Green/Shoreditch High St) ●🚃❀🛜

E3: Bow

Eleanor Arms
460 Old Ford Road, E3 5JP
☎ (020) 8980 6992 ⊕ eleanorarms.co.uk
Shepherd Neame Master Brew, Whitstable Bay Pale Ale; 2 changing beers (sourced nationally; often Shepherd Neame) Ⓗ

This multi award-winning pub, slightly off the beaten track but convenient for Victoria Park, is well worth visiting. Quiz night is the first Thursday of the month. On Sunday evening it becomes the Old Ford Jazz Club and usually hosts a jam session. It retains 1930s wood panelling and has a beer garden to the rear. The management team is in its second decade and enjoys occasional help from its customers. ⏰✿&♣🚆(8)🛜

E4: Chingford

King's Head L ✓
2B Kings Head Hill, E4 7EA
☎ (020) 8529 6283
Fuller's London Pride; Morland Old Speckled Hen; St Austell Tribute; Sharp's Doom Bar; 6 changing beers (sourced regionally) Ⓗ
This roomy Stonegate pub is in an old building with a contemporary interior. The six changing beers are often from London, Essex and Hertfordshire brewers. Popular with diners, it has seating outside and, unusually for London, there is a car park. Six Nations rugby is shown. Quiz nights are on Sunday and Wednesday; music on Friday nights alternates each week between live bands and a DJ. ⏰✿◑&P🚆✿🛜

E4: Highams Park

Stag & Lantern
11-12 The Broadway, E4 9LQ
☎ (020) 7998 8930 ⊕ thestagandlantern.co.uk
3 changing beers (sourced nationally) Ⓗ
The first micropub in north-east London, converted in early 2020 from two shops that had been knocked into one. At least three cask ales and ciders rotate, complemented with a range of bottles and cans. Seating is around a few tables both inside and outside the venue. No food is served but snacks are available. ⊖🚆

E5: Clapton

Anchor & Hope L ✓
15 High Hill Ferry, E5 9HG (800yds N of Lea Bridge Rd, along river path)
☎ (020) 8806 1730 ⊕ anchor-and-hope-clapton.co.uk
Fuller's London Pride, ESB; 1 changing beer (often Fuller's) Ⓗ
One of Fuller's smallest pubs, on the bank of the River Lea and dating from about 1850. Refurbished a couple of years ago, it has one bar with wood panelling and a dartboard at the rear, a wood fire and the bar at the front. Drinkers include wildlife enthusiasts and birdwatchers, boaters and locals. Food is served at weekends and there are barbecues in summer. You can moor outside if you arrive by boat. ⏰✿♣🚆(393)✿🛜

E6: East Ham

Miller's Well ✓
419-421 Barking Road, E6 2JX
☎ (020) 8471 8404
Greene King Abbot; Ruddles Best Bitter; Sharp's Doom Bar; 3 changing beers (sourced nationally) Ⓗ
A popular Wetherspoon outlet, across the road from East Ham town hall, converted from three shops in 1993. The walls are decorated with the usual mix of local historic photographs and pictures. In the back bar there is a memorial to John Travers (Jack) Cornwall VC and Edgar Kingborne Myles VC, and the British Legion poppy appeal. The pub now has a darts team. Q⏰✿◑&⊖♣🚆🛜

E8: Hackney

Cock Tavern L
315 Mare Street, E8 1EJ
⊕ thecocktavern.co.uk
8 changing beers (sourced locally; often Howling Hops) Ⓗ
A bustling, friendly, town-centre establishment, built in the 1930s, now a single-room bar with exposed floorboards. The cellar currently houses Short Stack brewery which makes small-batch brews. Eight handpumps dispense varying guest beers, another eight an excellent selection of real ciders. The Cock has become the Howling Hops brewery cask taproom. Bar snacks include a selection of pickled eggs. You can bring outside food in – try the vegan vish & chip shop nearby. ⏰✿◑🚆(Downs) ⊖(Central/Downs) ●🚆✿🛜

Pembury Tavern L
90 Amhurst Road, E8 1JH
☎ (020) 8986 8597 ⊕ pemburytavern.co.uk
Five Points Pale, Railway Porter; house beer (by Five Points); 2 changing beers (often Harvey's, Milton) Ⓗ
A large corner pub now run by the Five Points Brewery, located under nearby railway arches. On occasion instead of the regular beers there may be tap takeovers by other breweries. There is always a friendly vibe. Pizzas are available Monday to Saturday, and roasts (including vegan options) on Sunday. Monday quizzes and occasional comedy nights are held; check the website for forthcoming events. Local CAMRA Community Pub of the Year 2020/21. ⏰◑&🚆(Downs) ⊖(Central/Downs) ♣●🚆✿🛜

E9: Homerton

Chesham Arms
15 Mehetabel Road, E9 6DU
☎ (020) 8986 6717 ⊕ cheshamarms.com
4 changing beers (sourced nationally) Ⓗ
This lovely traditional back-street local was saved from closure following a high profile campaign a few years ago. There are two real fires inside and an attractive garden down at the back. Very much part of the community, it has a book swap shop and occasional singalongs on the piano. Four changing ales and one cider are served in winter, three and two respectively in summer. Pizzas are available from the Yard Sale Pizza eatery nearby. ⏰✿◑🚆⊖(Hackney Central)♣●🚆✿🛜

E10: Leyton

Coach & Horses
391 High Road, E10 5NA
☎ (020) 8281 3398 ⊕ thecoachleyton.com
Mighty Oak Captain Bob; 5 changing beers (often East London, Purity, Sharp's) Ⓗ
A recently refurbished pub with a horseshoe bar. Some beers from London breweries are among those on the handpumps and 20 keg fonts. There is ample seating in the two rooms and rear beer garden. Monday is quiz night; Dungeon and Dragon games and Escape Room adventures are also played here (book ahead). The menu includes speciality burgers, steak & Guinness and vegetarian pies, and Sunday roasts. The place gets busy on Leyton Orient match days. ⏰✿◑⊖●🚆✿🛜

Leyton Orient Supporters Club L
Breyer Group Stadium, Oliver Road, E10 5NF
☎ (020) 8988 8288 ⊕ orientsupporters.org
Mighty Oak Oscar Wilde Ⓖ; 10 changing beers Ⓗ
Multi award-winning club, once a CAMRA national finalist and now local CAMRA Club of the Year for 2020/21. Open

only on home match days (but not during the matches) and for England soccer fixtures, it hosts four brewery tap takeovers every year. The bar can get busy but the volunteer staff are efficient. On match days CAMRA members may need to show their membership card, but other events are open to all. Q🚼❀⊖🍎🚌

E11: Leytonstone

North Star [L]

24 Browning Road, E11 3AR

☎ 07747 010013 🌐 thenorthstarpub.co.uk

East London Foundation Bitter; Oakham JHB; 4 changing beers (sourced nationally) [H]

A recent local CAMRA Pub of the Year and named after a steamship, this community-oriented side-street venue has a long-serving landlord. Separate rooms either side are served from a central bar. Pizzas and Thai dishes are available from late afternoon (not Mon). There is a garden to the rear and pavement tables at the front. England sports matches are shown on terrestrial channels, and a jukebox supplies music.

🚼❀◑⊖(Leytonstone) ♣🚌🐾

Northcote Arms [L]

110 Grove Green Road, E11 4EL

☎ (020) 8518 7516

4 changing beers (often East London, Redemption, Signature) [H]

A local community venue between Leyton and Leytonstone. The regionally important historic interior is divided into different areas including a small snug, and is comfortably furnished. Entertainment includes quizzes, vinyl record nights, live music and drag cabaret on Sunday evenings. There are two gardens to the rear, with a whisky bar, and pavement tables at the front. Highly regarded pizzas are served. The TV shows only major sporting events. Local CAMRA Pub of the Year 2020/21.

🚼❀◑⊖(Leyton) ♣🚌🐾📶

Red Lion [L]

640 High Road, E11 3AA

☎ (020) 8988 2929 🌐 theredlionleytonstone.com

Sharp's Atlantic; Volden Session Ale, Pale Ale; 7 changing beers (sourced nationally; often Volden) [H]

Popular with young families, this pub has a decor with retro touches from Antic such as stylus record players and vinyl records on the shelves. There is a large semi-covered garden to the rear and also a restaurant. As well as the real ale and cider, a good selection of bottles is available. The ballroom upstairs hosts live music every Sunday, usually jazz/funk, with a DJ on Friday and Saturday nights and a quiz night on Monday.

🚼❀🛏◑♿⊖♣🍎🚌🐾📶

E11: Wanstead

George [L] ✔

159 High Street, E11 2RL

☎ (020) 8989 2921

Fuller's London Pride; Greene King IPA, Abbot; Sharp's Doom Bar; 8 changing beers (sourced nationally) [H]

Interior decorations reflect the name of the original tavern on this site, from about 1716, which was the George & Dragon. A large dragon hangs from the ceiling above the main bar and there is a carved wooden dragon chair for the solo drinker. The walls are adorned with pictures of famous Georges. Cask beers are served at the downstairs bar only. The smoking area and car park are at the rear. Q🚼❀◑♿⊖🚌📶

E12: Manor Park

Golden Fleece ✔

166 Capel Road, E12 5DB

☎ (020) 8478 0024

Greene King IPA, Abbot; Timothy Taylor Landlord; 3 changing beers (often Castle Rock, Greene King) [H]

With its large family-friendly garden, this pub is busy in the summer. Recently refurbished, it has a comfortable atmosphere. Food is served all day, all week. There is regular entertainment, including a quiz night on Wednesday and a jam session for local musicians most Friday evenings. TV screens show sporting events.

🚼❀◑♿⊖♣P🚌🐾📶

E13: Plaistow

Black Lion ✔

59-61 High Street, E13 0AD

☎ (020) 8472 2351 🌐 blacklionplaistow.co.uk

Mighty Oak Captain Bob; 3 changing beers (sourced nationally) [H]

A freehold pub, rare for East London, run by the same landlord for 35 years. Rebuilt in the 18th century, it has two bars, an original cobbled courtyard, a function room in a converted outbuilding, and a garden. The narrow main bar is where four ales are on offer. There is a smaller back bar accessible by a separate door or through the main bar. Sports TVs can be viewed from all points.

🚼❀◑⊖♣P🚌📶

E14: Canary Wharf

Ledger Building [L] ✔

4 Hertsmere Road, E14 4AL

☎ (020) 7536 7770

Fuller's London Pride; Greene King IPA, Abbot; Sharp's Doom Bar; 5 changing beers (often Truman's, Twickenham) [H]

In a building dating from 1800, this pub stands on the north-west corner of the former Import Dock and takes its name from the original use, which was to hold the ledgers of the West India Docks. The rotating guest ales on the large single bar often come from London breweries. Pictures of the area adorn the walls. Three further rooms provide plenty of space, and a smoking area is out front. Q🚼❀◑♿⊖(West India Quay)🚌📶

E14: Crossharbour

Pepper Saint Ontiod

21 Pepper Street, E14 9RP

☎ (020) 7987 5205 🌐 peppersaintontiod.com

3 changing beers (often East London, Five Points, Truman's) [H]

A stylish 1990s pub, run by Antic since 2009, with outside seating and lovely views across the Inner Millwall Dock. Ontiod is the estate agents' contraction of On the Isle of Dogs. Expect a friendly welcome; children are allowed until the evening every day. The downstairs bar usually has at least one guest ale. The upstairs area offers pool, table football and sports TV. 🚼❀◑♿⊖♣🚌🐾📶

E14: Limehouse

Craft Beer Co

576 Commercial Road, E14 7JD

☎ (020) 7790 2726

House beer (by Kent); 5 changing beers (sourced nationally) [H]

Very close to Limehouse station, this Craft Beer Co pub since 2016 gives a nod to its origins, with displays of

memorabilia from Charrington, Bass and Worthington. Children are welcome during the day and dogs too. Cask beers include either a stout or a porter, and a wide range of keg beers is available. On Sunday late afternoon live music plays in the downstairs bar area. There is extra room upstairs and also a secret garden.
꒰🕑🏵🅲➊➤≈⊖🚃🐾🛜

E17: Walthamstow

Bell 🄻 ✅
617 Forest Road, E17 4NE
☎ (020) 8523 2277 ⊕ belle17.com
Sharp's Doom Bar; Timothy Taylor Landlord; 8 changing beers (sourced nationally) ⊞
An imposing pub at a busy junction. The spacious interior has two distinct areas, while a sizeable garden at the rear has sheltered seating. There is a quiz on Tuesday evening, live music every second Saturday and a DJ on Fridays and other Saturdays. Live jazz features on the second Sunday of the month. A TV screen is used only for major sporting events. Accompanied children are welcome until the evening. ꒰🏵🅲➊➤♣🚃🚏🐾🛜

Olde Rose & Crown 🄻 ✅
53-55 Hoe Street, E17 4SA
☎ (020) 8509 3880 ⊕ yeolderoseandcrowntheatrepub.co.uk
6 changing beers (sourced nationally; often East London) ⊞
A spacious Victorian community pub with a welcoming atmosphere. There is a theatre upstairs and a function room downstairs. Various events are held including a folk club on Sunday evening, open mic on the first Wednesday, and a 78rpm record night on the second Wednesday of each month. Live music often features in the bar on other nights. Though on an Ei (Stonegate) lease, it is now free of tie. Alcoholic drinks are served from noon. ꒰🏵🅲➊⊖(Central)♣🚏🐾🛜

E20: Westfield Stratford City

Tap East 🄻
7 International Square, Montfichet Road, E20 1EE
☎ (020) 8555 4467 ⊕ tapeast.co.uk
6 changing beers (sourced nationally; often Tap East) ⊞
A brewpub oasis with comfortable seating in the Great Eastern Market, down at the end by the international station. You can see the brewery through a glass door and windows. Behind the bar a screen shows the current three house beers, three guests and real cider. A good range of international bottled beers is also stocked, with occasional tasting sessions (book in advance). Snacks and pies are served all day. The bar can be busy on West Ham match days. ꒰🏵&⊖(Stratford/Stratford Intl) ♣🚏🛜

Barking

Barking Dog ✅
61 Station Parade, IG11 8TU
☎ (020) 8507 9109
Adnams Broadside; Greene King Abbot; Ruddles Best Bitter; Sharp's Doom Bar; 6 changing beers (sourced nationally) ⊞
A busy town-centre Wetherspoon's, close to Barking station and many bus routes, and popular with locals and passing commuters alike. There can be up to five regular and seven changing beers. Food is served all day, alcoholic drinks from 9am. Muted TV screens show rolling news and occasional sport. ꒰🅲➊&⊖🚏🛜

Gidea Park

Gidea Park Micropub
236 Main Road, RM2 5HA (on A118)
☎ (01708) 397290
6 changing beers (sourced nationally) 🄶
Havering Borough and East London's second micropub opened in 2017 after winning a planning appeal for the change of use. Four to eight real ales from microbreweries are served (in all legal measures) from casks in the ground-floor cellar, as well as real ciders, wines and gins. There are high and low tables and chairs, unusual spider lighting and an ever-growing display of pumpclips from beers sold here. Mobile phones should be silent. Local CAMRA Pub of the Year 2020.
Q꒰🏵🅲➊&⊖♣➤🚃🚏(174,498) 🐾🛜

Ship ✅
93 Main Road, RM2 5EL (on A118)
☎ (01708) 741571 ⊕ theshipgideapark.co.uk
Greene King IPA; Sharp's Doom Bar; Timothy Taylor Landlord; 1 changing beer (sourced nationally) ⊞
More than 250 years old, this Grade II-listed split-level pub has extensive dark-wood panelling, timber beams and huge fireplaces. The building is largely unchanged and has low ceilings in places – so duck or grouse! It is a family-run business. A quiz night is held on Thursday and live music is hosted on Saturday.
Q꒰🏵🅲➊⊖🚏(174,498) 🐾🛜

Hornchurch

Hop Inn
122 North Street, RM11 1SU
⊕ hopinnhornchurch.co.uk
Timothy Taylor Landlord; 3 changing beers (sourced nationally) 🄶
Havering Borough and East London's third micropub was converted from a skin clinic and opened in 2019. Up to five cask beers are served direct from the cooled cabinets behind the bar, together with two KeyKeg beers, real ciders and perry. Also available are craft beer cans and bottles, wines, soft drinks, plenty of gins, malt whiskies and other spirits. Comfortable seating is at high and low tables. Sorry, no children under 18 admitted. Mobile phones should be silent. Current local CAMRA Pub of the Year. Q⊖(Emerson Park)♣🚏🚃🐾

J.J. Moon's
48-52 High Street, RM12 4UN (on A124)
☎ (01708) 478410
Greene King Abbot; Ruddles Best Bitter; Sharp's Doom Bar; 8 changing beers (sourced nationally) ⊞
A busy Wetherspoon pub, opened in 1993 and popular with all age groups, featuring a good variety of ales with an emphasis on breweries from London and the South-East. Watercolour paintings of nearby scenes provide the main decoration, with the usual local interest panels to the rear. Families are welcome until 6pm, and alcoholic drinks are served from 9am. Silent TVs show subtitles.
Q꒰➊&⊖(Emerson Park) 🚏🛜

Ilford

Jono's ✅
37 Cranbrook Road, IG1 4PA (on A123)
☎ (020) 8514 6676
Castle Rock Harvest Pale; St Austell Tribute ⊞
Just one minute's walk from the station, Jono's is a converted shop with an unusual style. The front of the bar is in dark wood and the rear is half-timbered, with a patch of thatch over the seating. Large-screen TVs show sports fixtures; it can be noisy at times. Friendly and

efficient bar staff serve well-kept ales; Castle Rock beer is rare in East London. The pub hosts a Thursday quiz and live music on Friday and Saturday evenings. ⊖🖳🛜

Romford

Moon & Stars ✓
99-103 South Street, RM1 1NX
☎ (01708) 730117
Greene King Abbot; Ruddles Best Bitter; Sharp's Doom Bar; 6 changing beers (sourced nationally) Ⓗ
Reopened with a new roof terrace and lift after a £1.1 million refurbishment, this Wetherspoon has a raised rear area where children are welcome. Food is served all day. Wall panels display local history, and an assortment of books fills the shelves. Close to Romford station and buses, the pub is busy on Thursday and Friday evenings. Toilets (except accessible) are upstairs.
Q🌝🏵🍴🏵🕭🛒🖳🛜

Upminster

Upminster TapRoom 🅛
1B Sunnyside Gardens, RM14 3DT (off St Mary's Lane)
☎ 07841 676225
Dark Star Hophead; 6 changing beers (sourced locally) Ⓖ
Upminster and East London's first micropub, the TapRoom opened in a converted office in 2015 as a snack bar selling real ale before obtaining change of use on appeal. Garlands of hops adorn the walls. The ales are served straight from casks in the cool cellar visible from the bar. Walk or use public transport to get here, and silence mobile phones or pay a fee for charity.
Q🌝🏵🍴🕭🛒⊖🍴🖳🌝

Woodford Bridge

Crown & Crooked Billet ✓
13 Cross Road, IG8 8BN (off B173)
☎ (020) 8502 9192
Fuller's London Pride; Sharp's Doom Bar; 3 changing beers (sourced nationally) Ⓗ
Spacious multi-room pub overlooking the village green, church spire and duckpond, complete with large weeping willow tree. Recently refurbished, the pub is clean and stylish, with wooden beams and a conservatory, as well as plenty of outdoor seating, making for a pleasant venue in which to enjoy drinks and meals from an inviting menu. 🌝🏵🍴🕭P🖳(275,W14)🌝🛜

Woodford Green

Cricketers 🅛
299-301 High Road Woodford Green, IG8 9HQ (on A1199)
☎ (020) 8504 2734
McMullen AK Original Mild, Cask Ale, Country Bitter; 1 changing beer Ⓗ
Warm and friendly, this two-bar local has a dartboard in the public bar and plaques in the saloon for all 18 first class cricket counties, together with photographs of former MP Sir Winston Churchill, whose statue stands on the green almost opposite. Good value food is served weekday lunchtimes (with pensioners' specials Mon-Thu). Picnic tables are on the front patio and seats within a covered smoking area at the rear, where a Boules pitch is sometimes in use. Q🏵🍴♣P🖳(179,W13)🌝🛜

NORTH LONDON
N1: Angel

Angel 🅛 ✓
3-5 Islington High Street, N1 9LQ
☎ (020) 7837 2218
Greene King IPA; Sharp's Doom Bar; 6 changing beers (often Truman's, Twickenham, Windsor & Eton) Ⓗ
A large, modern, open-plan Wetherspoon conversion with some booths towards the back giving slightly more privacy. The adjacent tower was a part of the Angel, one of the first talkie cinemas, which was sadly mostly demolished. With the long-gone Philharmonic Hall (subsequently Grand Theatre), this was always a centre of popular entertainment. Its classic columns and caryatids can apparently be seen in the Museum of London. 🌝🏵🍴🕭⊖🍴🖳🛜

N1: Hoxton

Wenlock Arms 🅛
26 Wenlock Road, N1 7TA
☎ (020) 7608 3406 🌐 wenlockarms.com
Mighty Oak Oscar Wilde; 7 changing beers (sourced nationally) Ⓗ
Free house saved from closure by a vigorous local campaign. It features beers from small and medium-sized breweries across the UK, usually including a mild and subject to regular change. With up to seven ciders and perries, and a small snacks menu of toasties, Scotch eggs, sausage rolls and pickled eggs, this is a truly welcoming street-corner venue with an international reputation. Occasionally it serves beer from the in-house Block Brewery in the cellar.
🌝🍴🕭⊖(Old St) ♣🍴🌝🛜

N1: King's Cross

Parcel Yard
King's Cross Railway Station, Euston Road, N1C 4AH
☎ (020) 7713 7258
Dark Star Hophead; Fuller's Oliver's Island, London Pride, ESB; Gale's Seafarers Ale, HSB; 4 changing beers (often Adnams, Dark Star, Fuller's) Ⓗ
A large pub, upstairs at the rear of the concourse, converted from the former station parcel office. It is used by local workers and commuters, and to host meetings. As well as bars on two levels, there are semi-private rooms converted from offices (available to book) and an indoor balcony. The decor is minimal and features rescued furniture; no music is played. Food, starting with breakfast, is served throughout the day. Wheelchair access is by lift. Smoking is not permitted.
🌝🍴🕭⊖(King's Cross St Pancras) ♣🖳🛜

N1: Pentonville

King Charles I
55-57 Northdown Street, N1 9BL
☎ (020) 7837 7758
4 changing beers (sourced nationally) Ⓗ
The regionally important historic 1930s interior of this Georgian building is small and cosy, containing knick-knacks and homely artefacts, warmed by real fires in the winter. Food can be ordered at the bar or from the Blue River café opposite during the day. Live blues, folk and indie music can be impromptu or planned. Since 2015 the pub has been community owned, with a 20-year lease shared by local residents and regulars.
🏵🕭⊖(King's Cross St Pancras) 🖳🌝🛜

N2: East Finchley

Bald Faced Stag ✓
69 High Road, N2 8AB
☎ (020) 8442 1201 ⊕ thebaldfacedstagn2.co.uk
Greene King IPA, Yardbird; 1 changing beer (often Redemption) ⊞
A short walk from the underground station, this pub's four handpumps in prime position are a welcome sight as you enter. The guest ale is often from a south-eastern brewery. There is a separate dining room on the left, and comfy seating at the front and to the right of the bar. A decked garden for outside drinking surrounds a historic sycamore tree. Note that wheelchair access is through the rear car park. Children are admitted until mid evening. ⏱✿❶♿⊖Ⓟ🚌🐾🛜

N4: Stroud Green

Brave Sir Robin
29 Crouch Hill, N4 4AP
☎ (020) 7018 3830 ⊕ bravesirrobin.co.uk
4 changing beers (often Hammerton, Moor Beer) ⊞
Occupying a street-corner site, with what might best be described as modern decor, this pub has been through various guises but now seems to have hit on a winning formula. Regularly changing cask beers and ciders (see the website for what's on) are complemented by the food – seasonal and modern European-style dishes. For those who like to try the non-cask side there is a range of over 10 such beers, many from London. Local CAMRA Cider Pub of the Year 2020. ❶⊖(Crouch Hill)🍴🐾🛜

N5: Canonbury

Snooty Fox Ⓛ
75 Grosvenor Avenue, N5 2NN
☎ (020) 7354 9532 ⊕ snootyfoxlondon.co.uk
Otter Ale; 3 changing beers (sourced nationally) ⊞
A vibrant community establishment with 1960s icons depicted throughout, serving up to five real ales and a real cider. The airy bar features a 45rpm jukebox. A function room accommodates local groups and private dining, and outside there is a pleasant patio with seating. The pub is well known for its ale and cider festivals, which attract people from far and wide. The kitchen serves quality modern British food and an excellent Sunday roast. Local CAMRA Pub of the Year 2019. ✿❶⊖🍴🚌

N5: Highbury

Brewhouse & Kitchen Ⓛ ✓
2A Corsica Street, N5 1JJ
☎ (020) 7226 1026
Brewhouse & Kitchen Goalscorer, Astronomer, Romford Pele ⊞
The former tramshed at Highbury Corner, refurbished and reopened with an in-house brewery. The company continues to expand, opening new outlets across the UK, but this location offers a lovely outdoor space at the front, a large interior to accommodate private parties, brewing classes in its academy, and plenty of room to enjoy some pub classics with a delicious twist. On Arsenal home match days it is only open to season ticket holders. ⏱✿❶♿≷⊖(Highbury & Islington)🚌🐾🛜

N7: Holloway

Coronet Ⓛ ✓
338-346 Holloway Road, N7 6NJ
☎ (020) 7609 5014

Fuller's London Pride; Greene King IPA, Abbot; Ruddles Best Bitter; Sharp's Doom Bar; 6 changing beers (sourced nationally) ⊞
Impressive Wetherspoon conversion of a cinema, the Savoy, designed by William Glen, which showed its last film in 1983. The pub displays large prints of movie stars and former local entertainers, with an old projector the centrepiece of a raised dais towards the rear. Sometimes there are single-brewery festivals. Expect plastic glasses and higher prices when Arsenal are playing at home. Tables (some under cover) are on the pavement. Q⏱✿❶♿⊖(Holloway Rd)🚌🛜

Lamb Ⓛ
54 Holloway Road, N7 8JL
☎ (020) 7619 9187 ⊕ thelambn7.co.uk
3 changing beers (often Five Points, Signature) ⊞
Highbury Brewery's tap, taken over by Taylor Walker in 1912, later becoming the Flounder & Firkin before the demise of that chain. Three cask beers rotate, typically a best bitter and a pale ale, alongside an amber, rye beer or porter from Redemption, Howling Hops, Five Points, Signature and many more local breweries. The beautiful interior has handsome wood panelling and skylights; the façade parades its painstakingly stripped back original green tiles. Live music is a speciality. ✿♿≷⊖(Highbury & Islington)🚌🐾🛜

N8: Hornsey

Toll Gate Ⓛ ✓
26-30 Turnpike Lane, N8 0PS
☎ (020) 8889 9085
Adnams Broadside; Greene King Abbot; Redemption Hopspur; Ruddles Best Bitter; 4 changing beers ⊞
Large, early (1988) Wetherspoon with a central bar and an outside seating area in front. Up to five guest beers come from small breweries, the local beers varying regularly. Very much a community pub, it can be busy and loud on weekend evenings. It takes its name from the toll gate erected in 1765 where High Road meets Green Lanes, which was dismantled soon after the system of turnpikes (private roads) was abolished in 1872. ✿❶≷⊖(Turnpike Lane)🚌🛜

N10: Muswell Hill

Mossy Well ✓
258 Muswell Hill Broadway, N10 3SH
☎ (020) 8444 2914
Fuller's London Pride; Greene King IPA, Abbot; Sharp's Doom Bar; 8 changing beers (often Redemption, Truman's) ⊞
A former Express Dairies tearoom and milk depot but a pub since 1984, reopened by Wetherspoon in 2015. Its name derives from the etymology of Muswell. Many internal features reflect its milky history. It is spacious inside, with a mezzanine floor and outdoor drinking areas at both front and back. Despite the size it can be packed. Q⏱✿❶♿🚌🛜

N12: North Finchley

Bohemia Ⓛ
762-764 High Road, N12 9QH
☎ (020) 8446 0294 ⊕ thebohemia.co.uk
London Brewing Beer Street, London Lush; 2 changing beers (often London Brewing) ⊞
A lively brewpub, home to the London Brewing Company. Three or four real ales are on sale, mainly from the on-site brewery, as well as a wide range of craft keg and bottled beers. Five more handpumps dispense cider.

Table tennis, table football and a selection of board games can be played. There are also monthly jazz and comedy nights, together with a weekly Tuesday quiz night. Outside seating is at the front and rear. Good food is served all day.

ⓈⓍⓇ♿⊖(Woodside Park)♣●🚌🐾🔽

Elephant Inn
283 Ballards Lane, N12 8NR
☎ (020) 8343 6110
Fuller's London Pride, ESB; 2 changing beers (often Adnams, Dark Star, Fuller's) Ⓗ
Formerly the Moss Hall Tavern, this corner pub, with a regionally important historic interior, has a U-shaped bar with televised sports to the right, a relaxed TV-free area to the left, and raised tables and stools in the middle. Newspapers are usually provided. In front, there is a large patio with wooden seating below a wooden pagoda. Dark Star or Fuller's seasonal ales are often complemented by a true guest ale. Food from the Thai restaurant upstairs can be served in any of the drinking areas. ⓈⓍⓇ♿⊖(West Finchley)♣🐾🔽

N13: Palmers Green

Alfred Herring ✅
316-322 Green Lanes, N13 5TT
☎ (020) 3232 1083
Greene King Abbot; Ruddles Best Bitter; Sharp's Doom Bar; 7 changing beers (often East London, Redemption, Sambrook's) Ⓗ
A busy Wetherspoon shop conversion dating from 2006 in the heart of the Green Lanes retail area, comprising a large open drinking and dining space with side booths. Seven of the 10 handpumps offer a varying range, with the manager regularly obtaining beers from the wide choice of London breweries. Alfred Herring was a local First World War soldier awarded the Victoria Cross for his heroic action in France in 1918. Photos and information on the history of the area adorn the walls.
QⓈⓇ♿⊖🚲🚌🔽

N14: Southgate

New Crown ✅
80-84 Chase Side, N14 5PH
☎ (020) 8882 8758
Greene King Abbot; Ruddles Best Bitter; Sharp's Doom Bar; 6 changing beers (often Redemption, Sambrook's, Wimbledon) Ⓗ
There was an Old Crown on Chase Side until its demolition in the 1960s, hence the name. This large well-established Wetherspoon's is convenient for the tube, and four bus routes stop outside. Converted from a Sainsbury's store more than 20 years ago, it has a single open-plan seating area. Up to six guest ales come from small and large breweries across the country, but with an emphasis on London brews whenever possible.
QⓈⓇ♿⊖♣●🚌🔽

N16: Stoke Newington

Rochester Castle ✅
143-145 Stoke Newington High Street, N16 0NY
☎ (020) 7249 6016
Greene King IPA, Abbot; Sharp's Doom Bar; 4 changing beers (sourced nationally) Ⓗ
A Grade II-listed building, with an impressive frontage featuring some fine tiling and a large skylight at the back, is a welcome outlet for cask beer and is now Wetherspoon's longest-trading venue. The pub here dates from 1702 as the Green Dragon, subsequently

demolished and rebuilt by Richard Payne from Rochester (hence the name) although it was briefly the Tanners Hall in the 1980s. The cider is stored in polypins in a fridge behind the bar. ⓈⓍ⊖●🚌🔽

N17: Tottenham

Antwerp Arms Ⓛ
168-170 Church Road, N17 8AS
☎ (020) 8216 9289 ⊕ antwerparms.co.uk
Redemption Pale Ale, Hopspur; 2 changing beers (often Redemption) Ⓗ
Tucked away in the historic and atmospheric Bruce Castle Park area, this Georgian building with beer garden is Tottenham's longest-established working pub, serving people in the neighbourhood since 1822. Facing demolition in 2013, it was saved by the local community and CAMRA campaigners and is now owned as a community collective, and is in effect a permanent outlet for Redemption Brewery beers. Food is served at limited times, so do check the Antwerp's website. Local CAMRA Pub of the Year 2020.
ⓈⓍⓇ⊖(White Hart Lane)♣P🚌🐾🔽

N19: Upper Holloway

Landseer Arms Ⓛ
37 Landseer Road, N19 4JU
☎ (020) 7281 2569 ⊕ landseerarms.com
Hammerton N1; 4 changing beers (sourced locally) Ⓗ
A Victorian pub, quite different from most of the places on nearby Holloway Road, and one that has been through many incarnations, eventually renamed after the artist whose works included the Trafalgar Square lions and the painting Monarch of the Glen. The spacious interior includes a conservatory-style area (sometimes used for dining) on the other side of the bar. There is plenty of pavement seating, with retractable awnings and heaters. Food is available all day.
ⓈⓍⓇ♿⊖♣🚌🐾🔽

Shaftesbury Tavern Ⓛ
534 Hornsey Road, N19 3QN
☎ (020) 7272 7950 ⊕ theshaftesburytavern.co.uk
Hammerton N1; 3 changing beers (often Fuller's, Sambrook's) Ⓗ
A nice old venue, now operated by Remarkable Pubs and comprehensively restored following a 2014 refurbishment, with the former pool room turned into the restaurant area under a fine skylight. The historic interior is identified by CAMRA as of regional importance. Outside at the front there is seating on the terrace. Food comes from a predominantly Thai menu, with some classics such as fish & chips or sausage and mash. Quiz night is Tuesday. ⓈⓍⓇ♿⊖(Crouch Hill)●🚌🐾🔽

St John's Tavern
91 Junction Road, N19 5QU
☎ (020) 7272 1587 ⊕ stjohnstavern.com
Fuller's London Pride; 4 changing beers (often Hammerton, Howling Hops) Ⓗ
Another piece of the real ale renaissance taking place in this part of London. Although the emphasis here is undeniably on food (hams hanging in the food preparation area are visible from the bar), this gastro-pub has up to five real ales on at any one time and has room for those who just want to relax with a drink. The whole impression is one of space, helped by a large bar area and high ceilings. Ⓧ⊖(Archway)♣●🚌🔽

N21: Winchmore Hill

Dog & Duck ✔
74 Hoppers Road, N21 3LH
☎ (020) 8886 1987 🌐 dogandduckn21.co.uk
Greene King IPA; Timothy Taylor Landlord; Young's London Original; 1 changing beer (sourced nationally) Ⓗ
Friendly one-bar pub, popular with locals and welcoming to visitors. Sporting events are shown on a large-screen TV, local football teams meet and it hosts a golf society. The fortnightly quiz night is on Monday when you can enjoy a takeaway pizza. Music nights are every other Sunday. There is a pretty walled patio garden at the rear. Dogs are welcome at quiet times. The pub has now appeared in this Guide 30 times since 1987.
❀♣🚌(W9) 🐾 ᯤ

Little Green Dragon
928 Green Lanes, N21 2AD
☎ (020) 8351 3530 🌐 littlegreendragonenfield.com
5 changing beers (often Hammerton, Thornbridge, Vibrant Forest) Ⓖ
This micropub was local CAMRA Pub of the Year in 2020 and is a former Greater London Pub of the Year. Meet the Brewer events are often held as well as regular music nights. The cosy interior, with a variety of seating including a church pew, bus seats and padded kegs, contributes to the friendly community atmosphere. Pavement benches and a small courtyard at the back provide for alfresco drinking. No excuses for missing your bus – electronic live times are displayed.
Q❀≉♣●▯🚌(125,329) 🐾 ᯤ

Orange Tree
18 Highfield Road, N21 3HA
☎ (020) 8360 4853
Greene King IPA; 2 changing beers (often New River, Redemption, St Austell) Ⓗ
A traditional back-street venue with a large garden and play area for children. The garden also hosts summer barbecues. The landlord is proud to have been in this Guide continuously since 1995 and the pub has the feel of a well-used community local. Major sports events are shown, and there is a pool table and dartboard. Quiz night is every Wednesday. The New River Walk is close by. ❀◐≉♣P🚌(329)ᯤ

N22: Wood Green

Prince
1 Finsbury Road, N22 8PA
☎ (020) 8888 6698 🌐 theprincen22.co.uk
4 changing beers (often Hammerton) Ⓗ
A handsome two-roomed venue occupying a prominent corner site, brought back to life in 2016 with up to four regularly changing cask ales, nine keg beers and a range of ciders. The beers come from small breweries across the UK and are listed on the website as they change. Snacks are served weekday lunchtimes, Japanese dishes in the evenings and all day at weekends.
❀◐◑≉(Alexandra Palace) ⊖●

Westbury
57 Westbury Avenue, N22 6SA
☎ (020) 8889 2059 🌐 westburyn22.co.uk
Timothy Taylor Landlord; 5 changing beers (often Goodness, Hammerton, Redemption) Ⓗ
Large, impressive corner house taken over in 2014 by London Village Inns and extensively renovated as a pub and kitchen with lots of space, big windows throughout and heated outside seating. A wide choice of beers is offered including a number from London breweries. Quiz night is Tuesday and there is live music on a Saturday. Payment is by card only.
❀◐◑♿⊖(Turnpike Lane) ●🚌ᯤ

Enfield

Moon under Water 𝕃 ✔
115/117 Chase Side, EN2 6NN
☎ (020) 8366 9855
Greene King Abbot; Ruddles Best Bitter; Sharp's Doom Bar; 5 changing beers (often New River, Redemption, Twickenham) Ⓗ
An early Wetherspoon in what used to be the British School, which opened in 1838 and closed in 1901. It has since been a public hall, a dairy and then a restaurant. The building has a church-like appearance and has light flooding in on three sides. Popular with all age groups, it has a dedicated area for families. The beers often include local and London brews. Sparklers may be used; if you are concerned, ask for them to be removed.
❀◐◑♿≉(Chase) P🚌(191,W9) ᯤ

Wonder 𝕃
1 Batley Road, EN2 0JG
☎ (020) 8363 0202
McMullen AK Original Mild, Country Bitter; 1 changing beer (sourced locally; often McMullen) Ⓗ
An old-fashioned two-bar back-street local with a regionally important historic interior. The seasonal offer might be one of its own Rivertown beers. The large public bar has a real fire and a dartboard, and is where live honky tonk piano and spoons are played on Saturday evening and Sunday afternoon. Some tables feature table-top games boards such as backgammon and snakes and ladders. There is also a quiet lounge area. Outside are traditional pub tables on the pavement. Dogs are welcome.
Q❀♿≉(Gordon Hill) ♣P🚌(191,W8) 🐾 ᯤ

High Barnet

Lord Nelson ✔
14 West End Lane, EN5 2SA
☎ (020) 8449 7249
Young's London Original, London Special; 1 changing beer (often Ringwood, Young's) Ⓗ
A friendly one-bar pub hidden away off Wood Street. There is often a guest beer alongside the Young's regulars. Among its interesting features are a fabulous collection of novelty salt and pepper pots, various nautical objects including a display of model ships above the bar, and an example of a snob screen by the side door. It hosts regular events such as Tuesday night bingo and a Thursday night quiz. Lunch is served Wednesday and Friday. ❀◐♣🚌🐾ᯤ

Olde Mitre Inne
58 High Street, EN5 5SJ
☎ (020) 8449 5701
Greene King Abbot; Timothy Taylor Landlord; Tring Side Pocket for a Toad; 4 changing beers (often Five Points, Redemption, Tiny Rebel) Ⓗ
The oldest coaching inn in Barnet, this Grade II-listed building oozes character and charm. A traditional pub, it has beams, exposed brickwork, wood panelling, open fires and efficient and well-trained staff. Families are welcome. Outside is a large courtyard that can be heated and covered in winter months. Live music is hosted every Sunday evening, a quiz every Thursday and monthly bingo nights. ❀◐◑⊖♣●🚌🐾ᯤ

Olde Monken Holt ✔

193 High Street, EN5 5SU
☎ (020) 3674 3145 ⊕ ye-olde-monken-holt.business.site
Greene King IPA, Abbot; St Austell Tribute; Timothy Taylor Landlord ⊞
This historic pub, close to the site of the 1471 Battle of Barnet, can be found at the northern end of the High Street. Dating from 1863, the premises are welcoming and popular, with attentive staff serving four regular beers. Recognised as a music venue, it hosts a Wednesday open mic night, a Friday DJ, Saturday live music, and then a Sunday Irish music night. Popular sports events are shown on many TVs towards the rear.
Ὅ✿♿♣🖼(84,399) ✿ ♠ ?

New Barnet

Railway Bell ✔

13 East Barnet Road, EN4 8RR
☎ (020) 8449 1369
Courage Directors; Greene King IPA, Abbot; Sharp's Doom Bar; 6 changing beers (often Adnams, East London, Enfield) ⊞
There has been a pub on this site since the late 19th century. Photographs and information about railways and the local area adorn the walls. With a large conservatory giving it a bright and spacious feel, it also has a generous patio and garden with a no-smoking section where you can watch the trains go by. One of the earliest Wetherspoons, it has featured in over 20 editions of this Guide since 1977. Q Ὅ✿🕽♿⇌🖼 ♠ ?

NORTH-WEST LONDON
NW1: Camden Town

Camden Road Arms

102-104 Camden Road, NW1 9EA
☎ (020) 7485 4530
3 changing beers (often Sambrook's, Siren) ⊞
Previously the Eagle, Rosie O'Grady's, Mac Bar and Grand Union, this huge pub was massively improved by the Draft House group in 2017 and in turn by BrewDog in 2018. It has a horseshoe-shaped bar, eclectic lighting and music memorabilia; a large mural reflects Camden's musical history. A board lists the various beers available, and food includes Sunday roasts. A function area to the side can be reserved. There is a quiz on Tuesday and a DJ on Friday. Ὅ✿🕽♿⊖(Camden Rd/Town)●🖼♠?

Colonel Fawcett 🅛

1 Randolph Street, NW1 0SS
☎ (020) 7267 9829 ⊕ thecolonelfawcett.co.uk
3 changing beers (sourced nationally; often Hammerton) ⊞
Dating from 1843 and originally known as the Camden Arms, this was the site of one of the last fatal duels in England in 1873, and the place is now named after its victim. He died upstairs and his ghost is reputed to still drink here. Hidden down the back streets of Camden, this pub has gone from strength to strength under its new independent operators, with regular events including quiz nights and Friday/Saturday DJ nights.
✿🕽⊖(Camden Rd) 🖼 ?

Golden Lion 🅛

88 Royal College Street, NW1 0TH
☎ (020) 7097 4760 ⊕ goldenlioncamden.com
Dark Star Hophead; Fuller's London Pride; Sambrook's Junction Ale ⊞
A lovely and popular community pub, saved from closure in 2013; the licensee and the local community,

supported by Camden Council, waged a long campaign to prevent its conversion into flats. This came to its final and excellent conclusion with the sitting tenant buying the building, which he now leases out. Tasteful decor complements the pub's regionally important historic interior features - mainly the mirrored bar-back. A real back-street community boozer.
Ὅ✿🕽♿⊖(Camden Rd) ♣●🖼♠?

Tapping the Admiral 🅛

77 Castle Road, NW1 8SU
☎ (020) 7267 6118 ⊕ tappingtheadmiral.co.uk
House beer (by Brakspear); 7 changing beers (sourced regionally) ⊞
A lively and enjoyable community venue where friendly, knowledgeable staff offer a warm welcome. Guest ales come mainly from local breweries. Great British food includes speciality home-made pies. Outside at the back is a well-designed, heated and covered beer garden. There is a popular Wednesday quiz and live traditional music on Thursday evening. Look out for monthly tap takeovers, pop-up events, and also the pub's cat, Nelson.
Q Ὅ✿🕽♿⊖(Kentish Town West) ●🖼♠?

NW1: Euston

Doric Arch 🅛

Euston Station Colonnade, 1 Eversholt Street, NW1 2DN
☎ (020) 7383 3359
Dark Star Hophead, American Pale Ale; Fuller's Oliver's Island, London Pride, ESB; 3 changing beers (often Adnams, Dark Star, Fuller's) ⊞
Up a flight of stairs, the large picture windows afford a bird's eye view of the busy urban world below. Right next to Euston station, the bar is used extensively by commuters, aided by the train times screen. Excellent staff are helpful and informative about the ales, including guest beers, increasingly from Dark Star. Brewery and railway memorabilia adorn the walls. Alcoholic drinks are served from 10am, food all day. Toilets are at basement level. Ὅ🕽⇌⊖(Euston/Euston Sq)●🖼?

Euston Tap

West & East Lodges, 190 Euston Road, NW1 2EF
☎ (020) 3137 8837 ⊕ eustontap.com
10 changing beers (sourced nationally) ℗
Fronting the main station building, these impressive Grade II-listed Portland stone lodges, separated by a bus lane, are relics from the original 1830s station. Up to 10 changing beers, mostly from smaller breweries, are pumped up to taps behind the bar. Small ground-floor spaces are augmented by seating (and toilets) up the wrought iron spiral staircases and large heated drinking areas outside. The East Lodge opens later in the afternoon. Both sides offer traditional cider.
✿⇌⊖(Euston/Euston Sq) ●🖼♠?

Exmouth Arms ✔

1 Starcross Street, NW1 2HR
☎ (020) 7387 5440
Titanic Plum Porter; 4 changing beers (often Sambrook's, Signature, Southwark) ⊞
Adjacent to the HS2 works, this lively venue has a boutique hostel on the upper floors and an open-plan kitchen offering burgers and tapas from Burger Craft. The interior has large picture windows and comfortable seating - booths by the windows, high tables and benches - around a large L-shaped bar fronted by mosaic tiles. Local cask beers appear regularly; bottled and canned beers are displayed on the wall of beer. Breakfasts are served. Outside there is plentiful bench seating. ✿🖾🕽⇌⊖(Euston/Euston Sq)●🖼♠?

Royal George 🅛
8-14 Eversholt Street, NW1 1DG
☎ (020) 7387 2431
Greene King IPA, Abbot; 4 changing beers (often Portobello, Southwark) Ⓗ
Directly opposite Euston station, this large pub was built in 1939 and is named after HMS Royal George, a flagship vessel for the Royal Navy in the 1800s. It is Grade II listed and arranged as interconnecting areas facing the three street frontages, with a central bar. One side has an unusual fireplace with marquetry work on the surounds. Local London beer are augmented by regional guests or Greene King seasonal beers. Its many TV screens often show different sporting events.
🌫️❀◑≉⊖(Euston/Euston Sq)🚃❀☎

NW4: Hendon

Midland Hotel
29 Station Road, NW4 4PN
☎ (020) 3602 1320
Oakham Citra; 1 changing beer (often 3 Brewers of St Albans, New River) Ⓗ
A surviving and characterful Victorian local, a stone's throw from the railway station. The main bar area is at the front, and a larger room with snooker table at the rear occasionally hosts live music. One cask beer is usually available, two at busier times. Also known as the Mids, this is a community pub; it offers a warm welcome to all. A large outside space houses a small collection of classic cars, including a Trabant.
🌫️❀◑≉♠🅿️🚃(83,183) ☎

NW5: Kentish Town

Grafton 🅛 ✅
20 Prince of Wales Road, NW5 3LG
☎ (020) 7482 4466 ⊕ thegraftonnw5.co.uk
3 changing beers (sourced nationally) Ⓗ
Popular award-winning pub with beautiful Victorian features, combining a traditional feel with many contemporary touches and specialising in local cask beers. The spacious ground-floor horseshoe bar is partly tiled, with ample seating. There is also an upstairs bar/function room (no real ale) and an elegant covered roof garden. Knowledgeable and friendly bar staff are happy to advise you. Quiz night is Tuesday and there is comedy on Wednesday, as well as the piano and board games.
🌫️❀◑≈⊖(Kentish Town/Kentish Town West)
🍴🚃☎☎

Lion & Unicorn 🅛
42 Gaisford Street, NW5 2ED
☎ (020) 7267 2304 ⊕ thelionandunicornnw5.co.uk
Young's London Original, London Special; 1 changing beer (often Redemption) Ⓗ
This popular community venue is a great favourite, with its genuine homely feel, open fire and comfortable seating. Run by friendly management and staff as a Geronimo-branded gastro-pub, it offers a good-quality cask ale range featuring several breweries from the area. Front and back gardens have both won local and regional awards. A quiz is held on Sunday. Comedy nights are hosted on occasion. Upstairs is the Proforca theatre – details of productions can be found on the Proforca website. 🌫️❀◑≈⊖🍴☎☎

Pineapple 🅛
51 Leverton Street, NW5 2NX
☎ (020) 7284 4631 ⊕ thepineapplepubnw5.com
House beer (by Marston's); 4 changing beers (sourced nationally) Ⓗ

An authentic and friendly community venue, saved from closure by the locals, Grade II listed and with a regionally important historic interior, notable for its mirrors and splendid bar-back. The front bar, with comfortable seating around tables, leads through to an informal conservatory overlooking the patio garden. The menu is Thai kitchen cuisine. Some of the beers come from across London and, the pub being free of tie, the range changes regularly. Q🌫️❀◑≈⊖🍴🚃☎☎

Southampton Arms
139 Highgate Road, NW5 1LE
⊕ thesouthamptonarms.co.uk
8 changing beers (sourced nationally) Ⓗ
The pub does what it says on the sign outside: Ale, Cider, Meat. This multiple CAMRA award-winning venue has 14 handpumps and behind the bar, serving almost equal amounts of cider and different beers from microbreweries across the UK. Snacks include pork pies, roast pork in baps, cheese and meat baps, plus veggie options. Music is played on vinyl only and the piano is in regular use. Down at the back is a secluded patio.
❀◑≈⊖(Gospel Oak/Kentish Town) 🍴🚃

NW6: Kilburn

Sir Colin Campbell 🅛
264-266 Kilburn High Road, NW6 2BY
☎ (020) 7693 5443 ⊕ thesircolincampbell.co.uk
Timothy Taylor Landlord; 2 changing beers (sourced nationally) Ⓗ
This establishment was acquired and restored to its original beauty in early 2017 by three local people. Cask beer returned, plus a good selection of bottled and canned beers, and there is live traditional Irish music every Friday, Saturday and Sunday night. Two separate rooms around a central bar give a real feel of how traditional pubs used to be. Rotating pop-up kitchen opening times vary with the supplier; check the website.
🌫️❀◑♿⊖(Brondesbury/Kilburn)🚃☎☎

Harrow

Castle ★
30 West Street, HA1 3EF
☎ (020) 8422 3155
Dark Star Hophead; Fuller's London Pride, ESB; 1 changing beer (often Dark Star, Gale's, Wimbledon) Ⓗ
A lively and friendly Fuller's house in the heart of historic Harrow-on-the-Hill. Built in 1901 and Grade II listed, it has a nationally important historic interior. Food is served until 9.30pm (8pm Sun); reservations are recommended for Sunday lunchtimes. Three real coal fires help to keep the pub warm and cosy in the colder months, and a secluded beer garden is popular during the summer. Local CAMRA Pub of the Year 2019.
🌫️❀◑♠🚃(258,H17) ☎☎

Rayners Lane

Village Inn ✅
402-408 Rayners Lane, HA5 5DY
☎ (020) 8868 8551
Greene King IPA, Abbot; Sharp's Doom Bar; Twickenham Naked Ladies; 4 changing beers Ⓗ
A split-level, double-fronted shop conversion. The rear of the pub, accessed down a few steps, sports the traditional Wetherspoon booths, with a row of tables down the centre. A terraced area behind has a variety of large potted plants among the picnic tables, and the

front pavement has a few tables and chairs for that alfresco moment. A good cross-section of customers mingle quite happily together. Alcoholic drinks are served from 9am. Q✿⌘❀❄◐●◆➡☐⌚

Ruislip

Hop & Vine
18 High Street, HA4 7AN
5 changing beers (sourced nationally) G
Converted from a former café, seating is at low tables, chairs and benches. The small bar counter in the right-hand corner dispenses real ales, keg beers and ciders from a temperature-controlled cellar room behind it. Bottled and canned beers, wines and spirits are also sold. Snacks are enhanced by cheeseboard and charcuterie board options. There may be six or seven cask beers at weekends, often with table service. Q✿⌚◐●◆➡✿

Woodman ★ ✅
Breakspear Road, HA4 7SE
☎ (01895) 635763 ⊕ thewoodmanruislip.com
Courage Best Bitter; Timothy Taylor Golden Best, Landlord; 1 changing beer (sourced nationally) H
A cheerful and welcoming two-bar local with a nationally important historic interior, opposite Hillingdon Borough Football Club and close to Ruislip Lido and woods. The cosy lounge bar is traditional in atmosphere with no intrusive electronic machines, although the TV may be on for sports matches. Note the collection of bottled beers on display. There is also a good selection of single malt whiskies. The public bar is friendly and comfortable, with a dartboard and other pub games.
Q✿⌘❄⌚◆P☐(331) ✿⌚

South Kenton

Windermere ★
Windermere Avenue, HA9 8QT
☎ (020) 3632 0020
⊕ windermerepub-com.stackstaging.com
Gale's Seafarers Ale; Young's London Special H
Built in 1939 and next to South Kenton station, the Windermere has been identified by CAMRA as having a nationally important historic interior. It is a genuine community pub with three bars, although the public bar is now only used for functions. The saloon and lounge retain many original features, including the large inner porches, bar counters, back fittings, wall panelling and fireplaces. A quiz is held on alternate Thursdays and there is sometimes live entertainment.
✿✿⌚◐❀P☐(223) ⌚

SOUTH-EAST LONDON
SE1: Bermondsey

Simon the Tanner L
231 Long Lane, SE1 4PR
☎ (020) 7357 8740 ⊕ simonthetanner.co.uk
3 changing beers (often Anspach & Hobday, Firehouse, Henry Smith) H
In a quiet road off busy Bermondsey Street, the Simon is a mid-terrace, modestly sized Grade II-listed pub. A former Shepherd Neame outlet, it is now a free house. The three regularly changing real ales are from small breweries, and there is often real cider. Food ranges from Scotch eggs, vegetarian bar snacks, burgers, and cheese and meat sharing platters to a three-course dinner, with roasts on Sunday. A quiz is held on a Tuesday. Children are welcome until early evening. ✿◐❀●◆☐⌚⌚

SE1: Borough

King's Arms
65 Newcomen Street, SE1 1YT
☎ (020) 7407 1132 ⊕ kingsarmsborough.co.uk
Harvey's Sussex Best Bitter; Purity Mad Goose; Timothy Taylor Landlord; Truman's Swift; 1 changing beer (often Five Points, Theakston) H
A Grade II-listed single-room pub just off the busy Borough High Street, with a traditional and comfortable interior. The striking plaque above the entrance originally adorned the old London Bridge. Five cask beers are usually on tap and traditional, mainly British, meals are served lunchtimes and evenings (lunch only Sun). A first-floor function room is available for hire.
✿◐≷(London Bridge) ❀☐

Libertine ✅
125 Great Suffolk Street, SE1 1PQ
☎ (020) 7378 7877 ⊕ thelibertine.co.uk
Sharp's Doom Bar; 2 changing beers (often Signature, Twickenham) H
Originally a Whitbread house, this lively and spacious pub is popular with a mix of workers, locals and students. The food menu specialises in pizzas and there is a discount for students on Monday and Wednesday. Live music or a DJ play Thursday to Sunday evenings and a quiz is held on Tuesdays. Major sporting events are also shown and there is a dartboard. ◐❀◆●◆☐✿⌚

Lord Clyde
27 Clennam Street, SE1 1ER
☎ (020) 7407 5643
Fuller's London Pride; Sharp's Doom Bar; house beer (by Anspach & Hobday) H
A gem of a street-corner pub that has changed little since being rebuilt in 1913, including beautiful Truman's Brewery exterior tilework. It has been identified by CAMRA as having a regionally important historic pub interior with its traditional decor, comfortable seating and curtains over the doors. In addition to the main bar is a side room with its own serving hatch. After being run by three generations of the same family, the pub is now under new management. ◐≷(London Bridge)❀☐✿

Royal Oak ✅
44 Tabard Street, SE1 4JU
☎ (020) 7357 7173 ⊕ royaloaklondon.co.uk
Harvey's Dark Mild, Sussex Best Bitter; 2 changing beers (often Harvey's) H
A brick built Victorian pub just down the road from Borough Market, this charming back-to-basics drinkers' pub is separated into two sections by the bar counter and an off-sales hatch. This is Sussex-based Harvey's Brewery's first London tied house and is renowned for friendly and attentive service. The range of beers includes seasonal brews, a mild, which is unusual for London, plus several Harvey's bottled beers. The pub is something of a local institution, with regulars coming from miles around to spend time here.
Q✿◐≷(London Bridge) ❀◆●☐✿⌚

Ship
68 Borough Road, SE1 1DX
☎ (020) 7403 7059 ⊕ shipborough.co.uk
Fuller's ESB, London Pride; 3 changing beers (often Adnams, Fuller's, Gales) H
Situated midway between Borough and the Elephant & Castle, this is a great example of a pub that combines good beer, good food, sport and music. As part of the local Victorian landscape, the pub is long and thin with the bar running along most of its length and larger seating areas at the front and rear. As with all Fuller's

pubs, the menu is hearty and a pie is always the perfect accompaniment to a pint.
❀◐➧≹(Elephant & Castle) ⊖🚌ᯤ

SE1: Borough Market

Barrowboy & Banker
6-8 Borough High Street, SE1 9QQ
☎ (020) 7403 5415
Dark Star Hophead; Fuller's Oliver's Island, London Pride, ESB; 2 changing beers (often Fuller's, Wimbledon) Ⓗ
The interior of this busy Fuller's Ale & Pie establishment retains much of the opulence from its time as the first branch of the National Westminster Bank. The double-height ceiling and enormous windows provide a sense of spaciousness. A sweeping staircase leads up to one of two dining areas, with an extensive menu, including chef's specials, available daily. Major non-football sporting events are shown. The pub is handily located for Southwark Cathedral, Borough Market and the many Bankside tourist attractions.
(London Bridge)

Market Porter
9 Stoney Street, SE1 9AA
☎ (020) 7407 2495 🌐 themarketporter.co.uk
Harvey's Sussex Best; 7 changing beers (sourced nationally) Ⓗ
This classic, rustic market pub next to the famous Borough Market still retains its traditional 6am-8.30am weekday opening hours. It's a Guide regular, with a wide range of changing real ales and at least one cider on handpump. Adorning the walls is a vast array of pumpclips reflecting the huge range of beers offered over the years. Popular with locals and visitors alike, it can get busy, with drinkers spilling out onto the street. An upstairs restaurant serves lunches.
(London Bridge) ⊖(London Bridge)

Old King's Head
King's Head Yard, 45-49 Borough High Street, SE1 1NA
☎ (020) 7407 1550 🌐 theoldkingshead.uk.com
Adnams Ghost Ship; St Austell Proper Job; 1 changing beer (often Southwark) Ⓗ
A traditional hostelry down a narrow, cobbled lane off Borough High Street. Stained-glass windows hint at a bygone era and the pictures adorning the walls tell the story of a pub, and an area, that has a rich history. The layout inside is simple, with an L-shaped bar in one corner usually offering at least three real ales on handpump. The clientele is a mix of tourists, office workers and visitors to the nearby Borough Market.
(London Bridge)

Rake
14 Winchester Walk, SE1 9AG
☎ (020) 7407 0557
4 changing beers (sourced nationally) Ⓗ
On the edge of Borough Market, this small pub prides itself on offering a high-quality, varied beer selection, and over the years has become a real global destination for beer aficionados and brewers. Four handpumps are complemented by a comprehensive range of bottled beers, mainly from North America and Europe, plus a small range of wines and spirits. Beer festivals, brewery tap takeovers and other themed beer selections all feature. Q(London Bridge)

SE1: Lambeth North

Hercules
2 Kennington Road, SE1 7BL
☎ (020) 7920 9092 🌐 thehercules.co.uk
Dark Star Hophead; Fuller's London Pride; 2 changing beers (sourced nationally) Ⓗ
After being a variety of restaurants in recent years, the Hercules is now back as a pub under the ownership of Fuller's. The decor is contemporary, including exposed brickwork and large, modern chandeliers. There are both ground floor and first floor bars, the former serving cask beer and the latter featuring a large shuffleboard table. A separate meeting room is also available. Food is served all day including breakfast. (Waterloo)

SE1: Southwark

Ring
72 Blackfriars Road, SE1 8HA
☎ (020) 7620 0811 🌐 theringbarlondon.co.uk
Sharp's Doom Bar; 3 changing beers (often East London, Sharp's) Ⓗ
A pleasant bar named after the boxing arena that stood opposite the pub during the early part of the 20th century, with boxers calling in for a drink before and after bouts. It has a gym and a ring upstairs, and pictures of the rich local boxing history adorn the walls of the bar. There is additional outdoor seating on the pavement. Major sporting events on terrestrial TV are shown.
(Waterloo/Waterloo East)

SE1: Waterloo

King's Arms 🄻
25 Roupell Street, SE1 8TB
☎ (020) 7207 0784 🌐 thekingsarmslondon.co.uk
Adnams Southwold Bitter; house beer (by Sharp's); 7 changing beers (sourced nationally) Ⓗ
Tucked away in a back street, this popular outlet is worth seeking out, and it gets busy in the early evenings. It has been identified by CAMRA as having a regionally important historic pub interior. Two small rooms are separated by a central bar and drinking is also allowed on the pavement outside at the front. Nine real ales usually include two or more from London breweries and at least one dark beer. Thai food is served in public bar and rear conservatory.
(Waterloo/Waterloo East)

Waterloo Tap
Arch 147, Sutton Walk, SE1 7ES
☎ (020) 3455 7436 🌐 waterlootap.com
5 changing beers (often East London, Siren) Ⓐ
This fairly compact, modern sister pub to the Euston Tap is in a railway arch close to Waterloo station and a short stroll from the South Bank, making it handy for visitors to the BFI IMAX and Royal Festival Hall complex. The cask ales are all dispensed from taps mounted on the copper bar-back. Details of the current beers are listed on a blackboard above the bar.

SE3: Blackheath

Hare & Billet ✔
1A Eliot Cottages, Hare & Billet Road, SE3 0QJ
☎ (020) 8852 2352 🌐 hareandbillet.com
Greene King IPA; house beer (by Greene King); 4 changing beers (often Old Dairy, Sambrook's, Twickenham) Ⓗ
An inn of this name has existed on the site since at least 1732, though the current building dates from the 19th

century. The decor is faux Victorian in a contemporary style, with stripped natural-finish wood cladding and bare floorboards. Up to six real ales may be on offer. Plastic glasses are used in summer for outdoor drinking overlooking the heath's open expanse. The pub part-sponsors the cleaning and maintenance of the pond opposite. ♉◑♿⇌♣🚌(380)🐾📶

SE4: Brockley

Brockley Barge ✔

184 Brockley Road, SE4 2RR

☎ (020) 8694 7690

Greene King IPA, Abbot; Sharp's Doom Bar; 4 changing beers (often Portobello, Sambrook's, Twickenham) [H]

A former Courage public house, now part of the Wetherspoon chain, a stone's throw from the railway station. It is a popular, thriving hub whose clientele reflects the vibrant local area. The premises are laid out in a semi-horseshoe shape with a variety of seating spaces. A small courtyard to the south side is well used in the summer. The name recalls the former Croydon Canal, which was replaced (in 1836) by the railway line, laid largely along the same course. Q♉❀◑♿⇌⊖🚌📶

SE4: Crofton Park

London Beer Dispensary

389 Brockley Road, SE4 2PH

☎ (020) 8694 6962

3 changing beers (often Siren, Southey) [H]

This former wine bar is one of the handful of Beer Dispensary pubs run by Penge-based Southey Brewery. A bar counter was added in 2019 and sports a set of handpumps, one of which serves a real cider. Alongside a Southey beer are two changing guest beers, usually from microbreweries. The bar is popular with families; children are welcome until the evening. Pizza is served from Wednesday to Sunday, including vegetarian and vegan options, with meal deals often available.
♉❀◑⇌🍎🚌🐾📶

SE5: Camberwell

Hermits Cave

28 Camberwell Church Street, SE5 8QU

☎ (020) 7703 3188

Dark Star Hophead; 5 changing beers (often Five Points) [H]

An imposing corner pub run by the same family for 25 years and popular with a cross-section of local residents and art college students. The premises have remained essentially unchanged, with etched windows and wooden floors adding to the traditional feel. A corner TV provides the only distraction to convivial conversation. Guest beers come from independent breweries. Three real ciders on handpump increase to five during summer months. An impressive range of whiskies includes examples from Wales and Japan.
♿⇌⊖(Denmark Hill) 🍎P🚌🐾

SE5: Denmark Hill

Fox on the Hill ✔

149 Denmark Hill, SE5 8EH

☎ (020) 7738 4756

Ruddles Best Bitter; Sharp's Doom Bar; 4 changing beers (often By the Horns, Sambrook's) [H]

An attractive brick-built Wetherspoon pub opposite Ruskin Park. A series of rooms, with quiet alcoves and screened booths, surrounds a central bar area. Framed prints celebrate the numerous historic figures and notable thinkers who lived nearby, often lending their names to the streets. A lawned space to the front affords views across to central London and there are large gardens at the rear. The pub is popular when Dulwich Hamlet FC are playing at home. ♉❀◑♿⇌⊖P🚌📶

SE8: Deptford

Brookmill

65 Cranbrook Road, SE8 4EJ

☎ (020) 8333 0899 🌐 thebrookmill.co.uk

House beer (by Bexley); 1 changing beer (often Brixton, Brockley) [H]

This spacious Victorian corner pub retains much of its original exterior, but a modernised interior gives a more contemporary feel with bare-board flooring and part-exposed brickwork. There is an outdoor area and also an upstairs function room. Good-quality food is served daily. The Brookmill house beer by Bexley Brewery is complemented by a changing real ale usually sourced from a local south London brewer.
Q♉❀◑⇌(St Johns) ⊖(Elverson Rd) ♣🚌(47,225) 🐾📶

Dog & Bell L ✔

116 Prince Street, SE8 3JD

☎ (020) 8692 5664

Fuller's London Pride; 4 changing beers (often Clarkshaws, Dent, Old Dairy) [H]

A Guide stalwart for over 30 years, this is a traditional and welcoming pub down a side street a short stroll from the centre of Deptford. Complementing the real ales is a selection of Belgian bottled beers, malt whiskies and simple, tasty meals. A lively bar and a real fire in winter greet a good mixed clientele including locals, cyclists and those strolling along the nearby Thames Path. Regular beer festivals are often themed around the UK patron saints' days. Current local CAMRA Pub of the Year.
Q♉❀◑♿⇌♣🚌🐾📶

SE9: Eltham

Long Pond L

110 Westmount Road, SE9 1UT

☎ (020) 8331 6767 🌐 thelongpond.co.uk

House beer (by Tonbridge); 5 changing beers (often Hop Fuzz, Pig & Porter, Tonbridge) [G]

A micropub in a former plumbers' merchants and named after the pond in nearby Eltham Park North. Mainly Kentish ales are served from a rear, chilled stillage room. Wine, several gins, a malt whisky and Dudda's Tun real cider or perry are also sold, with limited bar snacks. Seating is mainly at high benches and tables, though the rear snug features low tables and chairs. Winner of several local CAMRA awards. Children or dogs are not admitted. Q♿⇌🍎🚌(B16)

Park Tavern

45 Passey Place, SE9 5DA

☎ (020) 8850 3216 🌐 parktaverneltham.co.uk

8 changing beers (sourced nationally) [H]

Traditional Victorian pub with an original Truman's Brewery tiled frontage and signage. The compact interior has an L-shaped bar with stylish lamps and chandeliers. Etched windows feature elegant drapes, and decorative plates and pictures line the walls. Light background music is played. There is a well-kept, heated rear garden and further seating to the front and side. Alongside the range of real ales is an impressive selection of craft beers and lagers, whiskies and wine. ❀◑⇌🚌🐾

Rusty Bucket

11 Court Yard, SE9 5PR

☎ 07776 145990 ● therustybucket.pub

3 changing beers (often Kent, Oakham, Siren) Ⓖ

This venue reopened in 2018 after the redevelopment of the former Crown pub, retaining the original frontage. Inside, the walls are half-panelled and brightly painted. It is run along micropub lines by a couple of friends who are enthusiastic and knowledgeable about beers. The cask ales and some real ciders are dispensed from a walk-in chilled cellar cupboard. A host of other draught, bottled and canned beers is on offer. Live music sessions are held on Sunday. ⏰👪≠♣●🖵♿🐾🛜

SE10: East Greenwich

River Ale House

131 Woolwich Road, SE10 0RJ

☎ 07963 127595

7 changing beers (often East London, Kent, Siren) Ⓗ/Ⓖ

A converted shop unit opened in 2017 in the micropub style, comprising two rooms with a rustic feel and a small ramp between them. Real ales and ciders are dispensed from a temperature-controlled cellar room behind the bar counter. Wines and spirits are available too. This friendly, family-run house, where conversations with strangers are inevitable, has quickly become a part of the neighbourhood community and developed a wider following too. Local CAMRA branch Pub of the Year 2019. Q♿≠(Westcombe Park) ♣●🖵🐾🛜

SE10: Greenwich

Morden Arms

1 Brand Street, SE10 8SP

☎ (020) 8858 2189

4 changing beers (often Brockley, Truman's) Ⓗ

Unpretentious, without an external pub sign or even name, this ex-Courage corner house is now an independent establishment with a strong orientation to live music. One of a dying breed of back-street boozers in these parts, it has a clientele of locals and music lovers. Cribbage night is on Monday. The beer range is mainly from London breweries, with other guest beers from further afield appearing occasionally. ⏰🌳≠⊖♣🖵🐾🛜

Plume of Feathers ✪

19 Park Vista, SE10 9LZ

☎ (020) 8858 1661 ● plumeoffeathers-greenwich.co.uk

Harvey's Sussex Best Bitter; 2 changing beers (often Pig & Porter, West Berkshire) Ⓗ

With parts dating from 1691, this cosy and quiet pub sits opposite the northern wall of Greenwich Park, close to the National Maritime Museum. Maritime memorabilia and interesting historical paintings are on display inside the bar. Bar meals are served and there is a separate restaurant at the rear. Afternoon tea can be booked for a minimum of eight people. Outside is a pleasant garden area. It has its own football team, the Plume Rockets, and a golf society. ⏰🌳●≠(Maze Hill) ⊖(Cutty Sark) 🖵🐾🛜

SE11: Kennington

Mansion House

48 Kennington Park Road, SE11 4RS

☎ (020) 7582 5599 ● oakalondon.com

Oakham JHB, Inferno, Citra, Bishops Farewell; 1 changing beer (often Oakham) Ⓗ

Oakham Ales' flagship pub in London was previously a cocktail lounge and piano bar. A modern interior with an oriental flavour is styled Oaka at the Mansion House, a setting for enjoying pan-Asian meals served by attentive staff. During the summer, the front glass doors open out onto the outside seating area. A seasonal Oakham beer often complements the permanent range. ⏰🍴♿≠(Elephant & Castle) ⊖🖵🐾🛜

SE14: New Cross

Royal Albert

460 New Cross Road, SE14 6TJ

☎ (020) 8692 3737 ● royalalbertpub.co.uk

4 changing beers (often Five Points, Moor Beer, Portobello) Ⓗ

A Portobello, ex-Antic, pub, this Grade II-listed Victorian inn retains the original etched-glass windows and bar-back. It has a spacious interior furnished with wood panelling, ornate lamps and a mix of seating including chesterfield sofas. The open kitchen at the rear serves a selection of distinctive and enticing dishes. The cask beer range usually includes one from Portobello, and there is often a bag-in-box cider on handpump, though not always a real cider. A quiz is hosted on Monday and live jazz on Sunday. ⏰🌳🍴≠⊖♣🖵🐾🛜

SE15: Nunhead

Beer Shop London

40 Nunhead Green, SE15 3QF

☎ (020) 7732 5555 ● thebeershoplondon.co.uk

3 changing beers (often Anspach & Hobday, Moor Beer, Squawk) Ⓖ

A former corner shop, haberdashery and, latterly, a recording studio. The knowledgeable staff serve a varied selection of three real ales direct from the cask, along with an extensive range of bottled beers, plus wines, spirits and soft drinks. Boxed cider, from various producers, is also on offer, as are snacks. Events such as Meet the Brewer evenings are hosted on occasion. ⏰🌳♿●🖵(78,P12) 🐾🛜

SE16: Rotherhithe

Mayflower

117 Rotherhithe Street, SE16 4NF

☎ (020) 7237 4088 ● mayflowerpub.co.uk

House beer (by Greene King); 5 changing beers (often Bexley, St Austell) Ⓗ

A nautical-themed venue celebrating the Mayflower's historic journey taking the Pilgrim Fathers to New England. Those with a family connection may sign the Mayflower Descendants Book. The interior is in the style of a 17th-century tavern and at the rear is a wooden jetty over the River Thames. This is a popular place for tourists and the only pub licensed to sell UK and US postage stamps. The house beer is the appropriately named Scurvy Ale. Q🌳🍴⊖●🖵(381,C10)

SE18: Shooters Hill

Bull

151 Shooters Hill, SE18 3HP

Harvey's Sussex Best; 3 changing beers (often Exmoor, Greene King, Long Man) Ⓗ

On the brow of a hill, this reputedly haunted Grade II-listed premises was rebuilt in 1881. It retains separate public and saloon bars with individual street entrance doors, and a central circular bar counter serving both rooms. The saloon bar is well appointed, whereas the public bar has a more basic appearance. There is a pool table, and occasional live music events are held. ⏰🌳♣🖵🐾🛜

SE19: Crystal Palace

Westow House
79 Westow Hill, SE19 1TX
☎ (020) 8670 0654 ⊕ westowhouse.co.uk
Portobello Westway Pale Ale; 2 changing beers (often Arbor, Marble, Portobello) Ⓗ
Large Victorian corner hostelry, now operated by Portobello Brewing, bordering the edge of the Crystal Palace triangle, with a varied clientele. Former Antic vintage shabby-chic furnishings provide a warm ambience, and there is a spacious, partly covered outdoor seating area at the front. The three cask ales are complemented by two changing ciders, though not always real ciders. The pub hosts regular live music and a weekly quiz. ⌂❀⌨◖≈⊖♣⌖❀�;

SE22: East Dulwich

East Dulwich Tavern
1 Lordship Lane, SE22 8EW
☎ (020) 8693 1316 ⊕ eastdulwichtavern.com
Dark Star Hophead; Volden Session Ale; 5 changing beers (often Brick, Truman's, Twickenham) Ⓗ
An imposing building in a prominent corner position and the home of the Antic pub company. The interior is classic boozer, but in tune with the times and alive with customers. Previously a hotel, the upper storeys are now offices, although the first-floor masonic hall with its own bar opens occasionally for music and events, including a monthly film club. There is usually real cider available during summer months, and good-quality food is on offer. ⌂❀◖⌖≈♣⌖❀?

SE23: Forest Hill

Blythe Hill Tavern ★
319 Stanstead Road, SE23 1JB
☎ (020) 8690 5176 ⊕ blythehilltavern.org.uk
Dark Star Hophead; Harvey's Sussex Best Bitter; Sharp's Doom Bar; 2 changing beers (often Brockley, St Austell) Ⓗ
A multiple award-winning house, this friendly Victorian local has an unusual three-bar layout, identified by CAMRA as a nationally important historic pub interior. Usually five cask beers and up to 13 real ciders are available. In two of the bars TV screens show sporting events, especially horse racing. Live traditional Irish music is performed on Thursday evening and there are regular poetry nights. The pretty rear garden includes a children's play area.
Q⌂❀≈(Catford/Catford Bridge) ●⌖❀?

SE25: South Norwood

Portland Arms
152 Portland Road, SE25 4PT
☎ (020) 8655 0098 ⊕ portlandarmspub.co.uk
House beer (by Sambrook's); 3 changing beers (sourced locally; often Bexley, Truman's)
Tagged as a Pub & Kitchen, and with a modern feel, this traditional local reopened in 2016. The single bar is light and airy with a mixture of seating. Real ales selected from London breweries complement a range of other draught beers. A loyalty membership scheme is available. Food includes burgers, pub classics and Sunday roasts. There is an outside drinking area to the rear.
⌂❀◖⌖≈(Woodside) ⊖(Norwood Jct) ⌖❀?

Addiscombe

Claret & Ale
5 Bingham Corner, Lower Addiscombe Road, CR0 7AA
☎ (020) 8656 7452
Palmers IPA; 5 changing beers (sourced nationally) Ⓗ
Small and friendly privately owned free house around the corner from Addiscombe tram stop, making its 34th appearance in this Guide. The Claret is a community pub where conversation is king. The changing beers come from all over the UK, and mainly from microbreweries. A board opposite the bar indicates beers that are on and coming up. Up to four draught ciders are also stocked, served from the cellar. Events are held regularly to raise money for charity. ⌖⌂●⌖❀?

Barnehurst

Bird & Barrel Ⓛ
100 Barnehurst Road, DA7 6HG
House beer (by Bexley); 2 changing beers (sourced nationally; often Bexley) Ⓗ
A micropub opened in 2018 in a former tropical fish emporium. Owned by Cliff and Jane of Bexley Brewery, it is in effect the brewery tap, with one guest beer. House beer Hills & Holes commemorates the old name of the lane serving nearby Barnehurst station. Seating is at a handful of standard-height tables, and there is a decent-sized beer garden. Three keg beers and wines and spirits are also available. Last orders are 30 minutes before closing time. Q⌂❀≈●⌖❀?

Beckenham

Bricklayers Arms
237 High Street, BR3 1BN
☎ (020) 8402 0007 ⊕ bricklayersarms.co
St Austell Tribute, Proper Job; Young's London Special; 1 changing beer (sourced nationally) Ⓗ
Traditional high-street pub providing a friendly welcome to a clientele of all ages, conveniently located opposite the cinema. There is an open log fire in winter and a covered outdoor seating area with heaters and even a TV screen. The changing guest ales often reflect customers' recommendations, and occasional beer festivals are held. Live music is popular; both local and visiting bands play here. Live sports fixtures are also shown. Sunday hours apply on most bank holidays.
⌂❀≈(Junction/Clock House) ⌖(Junction) ♣●⌖❀?

Bexleyheath

Robin Hood & Little John Ⓛ
78 Lion Road, DA6 8PF
☎ (020) 8303 1128 ⊕ robinhoodbexleyheath.co.uk
Adnams Southwold Bitter; Bexley Bexley's Own Beer; Fuller's London Pride; Harvey's Sussex Best Bitter; Shepherd Neame Whitstable Bay Pale Ale; 3 changing beers (often Bexley, Shepherd Neame, Westerham) Ⓗ
A back-street local dating from the 1830s when it was surrounded by fields. The real ales come mostly from independent breweries, including Bexley. The pub has a good reputation for its home-cooked lunchtime meals (no food Sun) with Italian specials, which can be eaten at tables made from old Singer sewing machines. A frequent local CAMRA Pub of the Year and regional winner three times. The year 2020 marked 40 years of Ray and Katerina running this pub. Over-21s only.
Q❀◖⌖(B13) ❀

Volunteer

46 Church Road, DA7 4DQ

☎ (020) 8306 0287 ⊕ thevolunteerpub.co.uk

Morland Old Speckled Hen; 2 changing beers (sourced nationally; often Morland) Ⓗ

Truly a back-street local, now a rare breed, just 200 yards down a side road away from the busy Bexleyheath Broadway, where friendly staff make you feel welcome. With a real ale voucher system, you can buy six pints and get the seventh free. Now on a six-year lease from Wellington Pub Company to a community group, it was saved from total closure in 2018 by campaigners who were awarded a national CAMRA Pub Saving runner-up accolade that year. ➲✿Ⓓ≼♣P🖳

Wrong 'Un Ⓛ ✅

234-236 Broadway, DA6 8AS

☎ (020) 8298 0439

Greene King Abbot; Ruddles Best Bitter; Sharp's Doom Bar; 5 changing beers (sourced nationally; often Brewsters, Flack Manor, Shepherd Neame) Ⓗ

Bexleyheath's first Wetherspoon, opened in 1994. There are records of cricket being played locally since 1746, and the unusual pub name is an alternative expression for a googly. There are comfortable booths to sit in as well as an open-plan area. Opens 8am for cooked breakfast with self-service tea and coffee, and for alcoholic drinks from 9am. Pizza is served from a pizza oven. New admittances are not allowed after 11pm on Fridays and Saturdays. Q➲✿Ⓓ&≼♣🖳🖳🛜

Yacht Ⓛ ✅

167 Long Lane, DA7 5AE

☎ (020) 8303 4889

Greene King IPA, London Glory; Morland Old Speckled Hen Ⓗ

A spacious open-plan roadhouse pub serving good food, with a car park at the front and to the left. Two or three large-screen TVs show live sport or news throughout the day. It stands near a parade of local shops; alight at the Heversham Road bus stop. The original Yacht Inn, in Erith High Street facing the river, was demolished for a road widening scheme in 1937, when the licence was transferred to this new premises. Q➲✿Ⓓ&♣P🖳

Blackfen

Broken Drum Ⓛ

308 Westwood Lane, DA15 9PT

☎ 07803 131678 ⊕ thebrokendrum.co.uk

3 changing beers (sourced nationally) Ⓖ

A micropub named after an inn in a Terry Pratchett novel – you can't beat it! Seating comprises bay window settles and a variety of tables and chairs, plus pavement facilities for fair-weather drinking. Cheesy Thursday is the first Thursday of each month. With occasional quizzes and excursions, this is a real community pub. Q➲♣●P🖬🖳(51,132)✿🛜

Bromley

Partridge

194 High Street, BR1 1HE

☎ (020) 8464 7656

Dark Star Hophead; Fuller's London Pride, ESB; Gale's HSB; 2 changing beers (often Butcombe, Fuller's) Ⓗ

Grade II-listed former NatWest bank, now a spacious Fuller's Ale & Pie House, retaining many original features including the high ceilings and chandeliers. There are two snug rooms off the long main bar, plus a small back patio. An upmarket food menu – including vegetarian choices – is offered. Located by the Market Square, the pub is popular with shoppers and theatregoers for the nearby Churchill Theatre, as well as for its live music on Saturday evenings. Q➲✿Ⓓ&≼(North/South)🖳✿🛜

Red Lion ✅

10 North Road, BR1 3LG

☎ (020) 8460 2691 ⊕ redlionbromley.co.uk

Greene King IPA, Abbot; Harvey's Sussex Best Bitter; 2 changing beers (often Black Sheep, Jennings, Oakham) Ⓗ

A traditional, well-kept hostelry in the quiet back streets just north of Bromley town centre, the Red Lion is well worth seeking out. Now in its 25th consecutive appearance in the Guide, this is the only pub in the borough to have featured in every edition since the local branch was formed in 2011. It retains many original features, including tiling. An extensive library of books dominates one wall, while a real fire adds warmth in winter. Q✿Ⓓ≼(North)♣🖳

Star & Garter

227 High Street, BR1 1NZ

☎ (020) 3730 9458 ⊕ starandgarterbromley.com

7 changing beers (often Bristol Beer Factory, Fyne Ales, Siren) Ⓗ

A late 19th-century Grade II-listed pub, reopened in 2016 after more than two years' closure and offering real ale for the first time. The building has been completely refurbished and now boasts eight handpumps, one of which frequently dispenses real cider. Real ales are usually from outside the mainstream, with local and regional microbreweries strongly represented. Customers are welcome to order in food from nearby takeaways. Local CAMRA Pub of the Year for 2018-2020. Q➲&≼(North/South) ●🖳✿🛜

Chelsfield

Five Bells ✅

Church Road, BR6 7RE TQ482682

☎ (01689) 821044 ⊕ thefivebells-chelsfieldvillage.co.uk

Courage Best Bitter; 3 changing beers (often Otter, Timothy Taylor, Young's) Ⓗ

At the centre of an unspoilt 17th-century village, this pub is at the heart of the local community and retains a rural feel despite being just inside the M25 (use the nearby junction 4). It retains a traditional public bar, with separate entrances providing access to the saloon and dining sections. Guest beers sometimes come from small breweries in the area and at least one beer festival is held every year. The large garden has a children's play area. Q➲✿Ⓓ♣P🖳(R7)✿🛜

Crayford

Penny Farthing Ⓛ

3 Waterside, DA1 4JJ

☎ 07772 866645 ⊕ pennyfarthingcrayford.co.uk

4 changing beers (often Old Dairy, Wantsum, Whitstable) Ⓖ

Bexley's second micropub, opened in 2014. Ale and cider are served from a cold room with a viewing window. A charity fine is levied should your mobile phone ring. Kentish brewers predominate, with an increasing cider range supplementing Dudda's Tun and Westons. Pavement seating during summer overlooks a small riverside park. Usually open bank holidays, this is a good place to watch local public events. Q✿≼♣●🖬🖳✿

Croydon

Dog & Bull
24 Surrey Street, CR0 1RG
☎ (020) 3971 5747 ⊕ dogandbullcroydon.co.uk
Young's London Original, London Special; 2 changing beers (sourced nationally) Ⓗ
This historic Grade II-listed pub, with an island bar and stained-glass windows, is a favourite with local traders as well as visitors to the Surrey Street market. The large garden is unexpected, and has been brought up to date with booths equipped with TV, large awnings and a bar and barbecue in the summer. A small upstairs function room is available for hire.
⏱❀⏺≹(East/West) ☷(George St/Reeves Corner) ⊖(West) ☷❀☎

George Ⓛ ✅
17-21 George Street, CR0 1LA
☎ (020) 8649 9077
Greene King IPA, Abbot; Sharp's Doom Bar; Thornbridge Jaipur IPA; 11 changing beers (often Surrey Hills, Tillingbourne) Ⓗ
A converted shop, this town-centre pub's name commemorates a former Croydon coaching inn, the George & Dragon. It has two bars – the rear one is raised (with a ramp for access) and lined with booths, and has six handpumps often showcasing beers from breweries such as Dark Star, Oakham, Saltaire and Thornbridge. The front bar offers a wider mix of beers, including real ales from local breweries and the Wetherspoon national range.
⏱⏺≹(East/West) ☷(George St/Reeves Corner) ⊖(West) ☷❀☎

Green Dragon Ⓛ ✅
58 High Street, CR0 1NA
☎ (020) 8667 0684
8 changing beers Ⓗ
A converted bank with a modern twist, the pub boasts a vast range of ales and other draught beers from local and national breweries, as well as ciders. Located between the historic Surrey Street market and the south Croydon restaurant quarter, it attracts a wide clientele. The upstairs function room hosts weekly events such as quizzes, poker and open mic nights.
⏱⏺≹(East/West) ☷(George St/Reeves Corner) ⊖(West) ♣●☷☎

Oval Tavern ✅
131 Oval Road, CR0 6BR
☎ (020) 8686 6023 ⊕ theovaltavern.co.uk
4 changing beers (sourced nationally; often Robinsons, St Austell) Ⓗ
Back-street family-friendly pub with a good reputation for live music, including jam sessions, acoustic acts and the occasional DJ. The decor is unusual – half-timbering creates an interesting interior with a rural atmosphere. Tasty home-made food is served; the kedgeree and huge sausage rolls are especially recommended. A quiz is held on Wednesdays. There is a large garden and barbecue area to the rear. The pub continues to improve and promote its range of cask ale, often featuring local beers.
⏱❀⏺≹☷(East) ♣●☷☎

Royal Standard
1 Sheldon Street, CR0 1SS
☎ (020) 8680 3106 ⊕ royalstandardcroydon.co.uk
Fuller's ESB, London Pride; Gales HSB; 1 changing beer (often Dark Star) Ⓗ
A street-corner local dwarfed by the adjacent Croydon flyover and multi-storey car park. This quiet retreat just south of the town centre offers a single bar with four

different drinking areas, each with its own character. A small secluded garden area is located across the road. Football and rugby are often shown on the TV with the sound turned down. ⏱❀☷(George St/Church St)♣☷

Skylark ✅
34-36 South End, CR0 1DP
☎ (020) 8649 9909
Greene King Abbot; Ruddles Best Bitter; Sharp's Doom Bar; 6 changing beers Ⓗ
A spacious Wetherspoon pub in the restaurant quarter south of the town centre. The main bar is wood-panelled, with a raised library area to the rear. The decor includes pictures of nearby former Croydon airport, London's first civil airport. A grand staircase at the rear leads to an upstairs bar, not always in use and offering a reduced range of beers. Changing ales are mainly from microbreweries, often local ones.
⏱❀⏺≹(South) ☷☎

Spreadeagle
39-41 Katharine Street, CR0 1NX
☎ (020) 8781 1134 ⊕ spreadeaglecroydon.co.uk
Fuller's Oliver's Island, London Pride, ESB; Gale's HSB; 2 changing beers Ⓗ
Large street-corner venue built in 1893 as a bank. The spacious interior boasts wood panelling, high ceilings, glass mirrors and an imposing staircase leading up to two function rooms, one occasionally used as a 50-seater theatre/cinema. As well as real ale from six handpumps, a good range of other draught and bottled beers is on offer. The pub has Fuller's Master Cellarman accreditation. Quiz night is Sunday.
❀⏺≹(East/West) ☷(George St/Reeves Corner) ⊖(West) ☷☎

Downe

Queen's Head Ⓛ ✅
25 High Street, BR6 7US TQ432616
☎ (01689) 852145 ⊕ queensheaddowne.com
Fuller's London Pride; 3 changing beers (often Adnams, Westerham) Ⓗ
Attractive and traditional venue with open fireplaces, dating from 1565 and named following a visit by Queen Elizabeth I. Though in the centre of this historic country village, it is less than 20 minutes by bus from Bromley or Orpington. It may have enjoyed the patronage of Charles Darwin, who lived locally at Down House. There are several dining areas benefiting from a daily menu including home-made pies. The pub is popular with walkers all year round. ⏱❀⏺♣●☷(146,R8)❀☎

Hayes

Real Ale Way Ⓛ
55 Station Approach, BR2 7EB
☎ 07446 897885 ⊕ therealaleway.com
House beer (by Tonbridge); 9 changing beers (often Larkins, Mad Cat, Whitstable) Ⓖ
Opened in 2018, this family-owned micropub offers a welcome new choice for local drinkers and rail commuters alike. It overlooks the entrance to Hayes station, and numerous bus routes stop outside. Up to nine Kentish real ales are served from a cold room. The Kent theme extends to the wines and spirits, as well as to the bar snacks. The premises, once a bank and more recently an accountancy office, are quite large by micropub standards. Q≹●☷❀

Keston

Greyhound ✓

Commonside, BR2 6BP TQ413646
☎ (01689) 856338 ⊕ greyhound.pub
**Sharp's Doom Bar; Timothy Taylor Landlord; 4
changing beers (sourced nationally)** Ⓗ
A popular local with an enthusiastic and welcoming
landlord. It overlooks the common and is on walking
routes including the London Outer Orbital Path, but is also
easily accessed by bus from Bromley. The pub is at the
heart of village life, with a crowded calendar of events,
detailed in the newsletter. A beer festival is held during
the Easter weekend, when up to 15 less well-known
beers can be enjoyed. Q❀⛅️❀◑➔ P🚪(146,246)🐾🐱🛜

Orpington

Orpington Liberal Club Ⓛ

7 Station Road, BR6 0RZ
☎ (01689) 820882 ⊕ orpingtonliberalclub.co.uk
5 changing beers
Friendly club serving a changing selection of beers (over
200 different real ales every year) mainly from smaller
breweries. Real cider and bottled lower-alcohol and
gluten-free beers are also available. Two real ale
festivals are held each year. The club is a hub of the
community, hosting many events in its spacious hall and
supporting local charities. It reached the last four in the
CAMRA 2020 National Club of the Year competition. A
CAMRA/NULC card is required for entry.
Q❀⛅️❀≉♣♠ P🅿️🚪🐱🛜

Petts Wood

One Inn the Wood Ⓛ

209 Petts Wood Road, BR5 1LA
☎ 07799 535982 ⊕ oneinnthewood.co.uk
**House beer (by Tonbridge); 4 changing beers
(sourced regionally; often Kent, Ramsgate,
Tonbridge)** Ⓖ
The first micropub in the area, opened in a former wine
bar near the station in 2014 and winner of several
CAMRA awards. Seating is on benches, with a large
woodland backdrop dominating the left-hand wall. Beer
is served from a glass-fronted cool room. Wine, gin and
soft drinks are also sold, together with a range of mainly
locally produced snacks. Families and dogs are welcome.
Q❀⛅️≉♠🚪🐱

Selsdon

Golden Ark

186 Addington Road, CR2 8LB
☎ (020) 8651 0700 ⊕ thegoldenark.co.uk
4 changing beers (sourced locally) Ⓗ
A newish micropub in the main street, offering a full
range of alcoholic drinks. Bottled and canned beers and
cider are also available for off-sales. Boards detailing
current beers are hung on the ceiling beam above the
corner bar. The bar and some of the wooden tabletops
have been artistically finished, and artworks adorn the
walls. The venue has strong links with the local
community. Q❀⛅️♿♣♠🚪🐱🛜

SOUTH-WEST LONDON
SW1: Belgravia

Antelope

22-24 Eaton Terrace, SW1W 8EZ
☎ (020) 7824 8512

**Fuller's Oliver's Island, London Pride, ESB; Gale's
Seafarers Ale; 1 changing beer (sourced nationally)** Ⓗ
Dating back to 1827, this Fuller's venue used to be a
Nicholson's pub until 2005. Original preserved features
include etched-glass windows, a side room used as a
snug, and the central bar. This is an upmarket house and
the clientele consists mainly of local professionals. The
Antelope plays cricket matches against the Churchill
Arms (Notting Hill). The upstairs bar and side room can
be hired for functions. Q❀◑➔(Sloane Sq)🚪🛜

Star Tavern

6 Belgrave Mews West, SW1X 8HT
☎ (020) 7235 3019
**Fuller's London Pride, ESB; 3 changing beers (often
Butcombe, Dark Star, Wimbledon)** Ⓗ
Down a mews, near embassies and rich in the history of
the powerful and famous, this is rumoured to be the
place where the Great Train Robbery was planned. A
popular Fuller's pub where local residents, business
people and embassy staff rub shoulders with casual
visitors, it has featured in all 49 editions of this Guide. A
Fuller's special brew or, now, a beer from the wood, may
occasionally be served. Upstairs is a function room.
⛅️◑➔(Hyde Park Corner/Knightsbridge) ♣🚪🐱🛜

SW1: Pimlico

Cask Pub & Kitchen

6 Charlwood Street, SW1V 2EE
☎ (020) 7630 7225 ⊕ caskpubandkitchen.com
10 changing beers Ⓗ
Formerly the Pimlico Tram, the Cask was converted 10
years ago to a beer destination by new owners, who
have since rescued several more pubs. Ten handpumps
serve a changing choice of beers from selected
microbreweries. A vast range of bottled beers from the
UK and around the world complements some unusual
keg offerings. Burgers feature on the weekday menu,
with roasts on Sundays until late afternoon. Local CAMRA
Pub of the Year 2019 and a runner-up several times.
❀◑≉(Victoria) ➔🚪🐱🛜

SW1: St James's

Red Lion ★

2 Duke of York Street, SW1Y 6JP
☎ (020) 7321 0782
**Fuller's Oliver's Island, London Pride, ESB; Gale's
Seafarers Ale; 2 changing beers (often Fuller's)** Ⓗ
Close to the upmarket shops in Jermyn Street, this is a
deservedly celebrated little gem, worth visiting just for
its nationally important historic pub interior and, in
particular, its spectacular Victorian etched and cut mirrors
and glass. The Grade II-listed building dates from 1821
and was given a new frontage in 1871. With little space
inside, visitors often spill out onto the pavement. Beware
of the precipitous steps down to the toilets. Food is
served until late afternoon.
Q❀⛅️◑➔(Green Park/Piccadilly Circus) 🚪🐱🛜

SW1: Victoria

Willow Walk Ⓛ ✓

25 Wilton Road, SW1V 1LW
☎ (020) 7828 2953
**Fuller's London Pride; Greene King IPA, Abbot;
Sharp's Doom Bar; 6 changing beers** Ⓗ
Ground-floor Wetherspoon conversion from a
Woolworth's in 1999, extending from opposite the
eastern side entrance to Victoria station back to Vauxhall
Bridge Road, with entrances on both streets. Some wood

panelling, a fairly low ceiling and subdued lighting create a warm atmosphere. Friendly and attentive staff look after a mixed clientele including families. There are usually some London-brewed guest beers. Alcoholic drinks are served from 9am. Q ᗱ ◑ ﴾ ᵭ ≠ ⊖ ⮕ 🛜

SW1: Westminster

Buckingham Arms
62 Petty France, SW1H 9EU
☎ (020) 7222 3386 ⊕ buckinghamarms.com
Young's London Original, London Gold, London Special; 3 changing beers (often Young's) 🅗
Said to have once been a hat shop, the building became an inn called the Bell in the 1720s. Renamed the Black Horse soon after, rebuilt in 1898, renamed again in 1901 and substantially renovated in recent years, this is another pub that has appeared in all 49 editions of the Guide. A mix of modern and traditional seats and tables draws civil servants, visitors and the occasional MP. Open during the day on Sunday from the end of March through the summer. ᗱ ◑ ⊖(St James's Park)⮕

Speaker ✔
46 Great Peter Street, SW1P 2HA
☎ (020) 7222 4589
Timothy Taylor Landlord; 4 changing beers (often London Brewing, Mad Squirrel) 🅗
A friendly pine-panelled one-bar venue decorated with parliamentary caricatures. Dating from 1729 or earlier, the Castle, renamed the Elephant & Castle around 1800 and the Speaker from 1999, was part of the Devil's Acre, a notorious slum next to the world's first public gasworks. Local estate residents and office workers are welcome, not to mention an occasional MP or two, all to enjoy the attractive range of beers and the hot bagels. No music, TV or children. Closed at weekends.
⊖(St James's Park) ⮕ 🛜

SW4: Clapham

Abbeville ✔
67-69 Abbeville Road, SW4 9JW
☎ (020) 8675 2201
Harvey's Sussex Best Bitter; Timothy Taylor Landlord 🅗
A cosy, mostly half-panelled gastro-pub, halfway down a bus-free, residential road running parallel behind Clapham Common South Side. Separate drinking areas are at different levels in front of and around two small side bars, and there are tables outside. Cream walls display old prints. Deservedly popular with a mixed, youngish clientele, it welcomes families and pets. Food is served all day on Saturday, small functions are bookable, and sports may be shown on a big screen by request. ᗱ 🐾 ◑ ⊖(South)⮕

King & Co Ⓛ
100 Clapham Park Road, SW4 7BZ
☎ (020) 7498 1971 ⊕ thekingandco.uk
4 changing beers (sourced nationally; often Portobello) 🅗
An innovative pub offering an enterprising and changing range of beers from microbreweries throughout the UK, plus real ciders from smaller producers. The single bar is basically furnished, with current beer offerings displayed on a large board. The kitchen is periodically taken over by street-food specialists, and the Sunday roast lunches are popular. There are tables outside at the front.
ᗱ 🐾 ◑ ⊖(Common) ♣ ♠ ⮕ 🐾 🛜

SW5: Earls Court

King's Head
17 Hogarth Place, SW5 0QT
☎ (020) 7373 5239
Fuller's Oliver's Island, London Pride; 2 changing beers (often Fuller's) 🅗
A comfortable, friendly corner pub with a modernised interior, hidden away off the busy Earls Court Road; it is a 1937 rebuild of the oldest (circa 17th century) licensed premises in the area. Seating is a mixture of high stools around tall tables, dining tables and settees with low tables. Three Fuller's cask ales are supplemented by a guest, usually from another local brewery. Alcoholic drinks are served from 11am. On Monday evening there is a quiz. ᗱ ◑ ᵭ ≠(West Brompton)⊖⮕ 🐾 🛜

SW6: Fulham

Lillie Langtry ✔
19 Lillie Road, SW6 1UE
☎ (020) 3637 6690 ⊕ thelillielangtry.co.uk
3 changing beers (often Hogs Back, Timothy Taylor) 🅗
Fulham's oldest surviving 19th-century pub, built in 1835 as the Lillie Arms, named after its freeholder owner, Sir John Scott Lillie. Enlarged in 1875 with a new ground-floor addition and revamped frontage, it was given its present name in 1979 in tribute to the famous actress and courtesan. It served no real ale until 2016, when Hippo took over and carried out an extensive refurbishment. 🐾 ◑ ᵭ ≠ ⊖(West Brompton)⮕ 🐾 🛜

SW6: Parsons Green

White Horse Ⓛ
1-3 Parsons Green, SW6 4UL
☎ (020) 7736 2115 ⊕ whitehorsesw6.com
Harvey's Sussex Best Bitter; Oakham JHB; 6 changing beers (often Hogs Back, Saltaire) 🅗
Destination Mitchells & Butler pub that normally boasts five guest beers on handpump and an international selection of bottled beers. Regular beer and food matching events take place as well as beer festivals; the Old Ale festival in late November has run for 36 years, with a stillage in the Coach House, normally reserved for dining. The pub can get busy when Chelsea FC is playing at home, but upstairs there is room to escape the crowds. Q ᗱ 🐾 ◑ ᵭ ⊖ ⮕ (22,424)🐾 🛜

SW7: Gloucester Road

Queen's Arms
30 Queen's Gate Mews, SW7 5QL
☎ (020) 7823 9293 ⊕ thequeensarmskensington.co.uk
St Austell Proper Job; Sharp's Doom Bar; Timothy Taylor Landlord; 5 changing beers (sourced nationally)
Lovely corner mews pub, discreetly tucked away off Queen's Gate, well worth seeking out for its real ales and its large range of interesting draught and bottled beers, malt whiskies and other spirits. Note the unusual curved doors. The L-shaped room has wooden floors and panelling. The clientele reflects the location: glamorous locals, students from Imperial College and musicians from, and visitors to, the nearby Royal Albert Hall – all of whom, if wise, reserve tables. ◑ ᵭ ⊖ ⮕ 🐾 🛜

SW7: South Kensington

Anglesea Arms ✔
15 Selwood Terrace, SW7 3QG

☎ (020) 7373 7960 ⊕ angleseaarms.com
Greene King IPA, Abbot; 4 changing beers (sourced nationally; often Sambrook's, Timothy Taylor, Vale) Ⓗ
A real ale stalwart from CAMRA's early years. Built in 1827, it was a Meux tied house for more than a century. Now a Grade II-listed Greene King Metropolitan pub, it has the air of a country inn, with outside seating and an interior featuring a diverse collection of mirrors, prints, photographs and paintings. As well as the range of real ales, it offers a variety of food at reasonable prices for the area. Q🏠⛶🛈🚆�"⛵🐕📶

SW8: Battersea Park

Mason's Arms

169 Battersea Park Road, SW8 4BT
☎ (020) 7622 2007 ⊕ masons-arms-battersea.co.uk
Fuller's London Pride; 2 changing beers (often Dark Star, Fuller's) Ⓗ
Extensively refurbished in 2019, this stripped-back Fuller's gastro-pub in a Grade II-listed building almost opposite Battersea Park station attracts a mainly young, upmarket clientele. The bar has 23 draught lines – 20 keg and 3 cask – with space for 15 rotational beers. There is a dining area towards the rear and a patio to the side for alfresco dining. Alcoholic drinks are served from 10am. 🏠🐕♿⇌(Park/Queenstown Rd) ⊖(Power Station) 🚆🐕📶

SW8: South Lambeth

Fentiman Arms

64 Fentiman Road, SW8 1LA
☎ (020) 7793 9796 ⊕ thefentimanarms.co.uk
St Austell Proper Job; Young's London Original, London Special Ⓗ
Within easy reach of the Oval cricket ground, this elegant, 19th-century end-of-terrace building is now impressively refurbished as a comfortable, popular dining pub, where drinkers are also welcome. Locally brewed guest beers may also be served. There is a front terrace and, at the back, an enclosed, split-level garden patio with a Burger Shack and views over the adjacent post-war estate. The decor includes Penguin paperback covers in the rear anteroom. An upstairs function room is available for hire. 🏠🐕🛈⊖(Oval)🚆🐕📶

Surprise

16 Southville, SW8 2PP
☎ (020) 7622 4623
Young's London Original, London Special Ⓗ
Tucked away next to Larkhall Park, this small, down-to-earth, L-shaped local was refurbished in 2018 and now includes a conservatory extension. It is the only building remaining from streets that were replaced by the park after WWII bomb damage. The back room walls display caricatures of regular customers, while the middle section has black and white photographs of Battersea Power Station. A third real ale is occasionally available. A pizza menu was introduced in summer 2021. 🏠🐕🛈⊖(Nine Elms) ♣🚆🐕

SW9: Brixton

Craft Beer Co

11-13 Brixton Station Road, SW9 8PA
☎ (020) 7274 8383
House beer (by Kent); 3 changing beers (often Siren) Ⓗ
Close to Brixton market, this modern pub has a retro feel with hints of an American diner. Downstairs there is an

industrial vibe, with red high stools, while upstairs there are bright blue bench seats, a tumbling blocks parquet floor, neon signs and enamel brewery advertisements from Belgium and France. London microbreweries are represented among the draught and bottled beers, as are Belgian Trappists and Lambic. The bar gets busy when concerts are on at the nearby O2 Academy. 🏠🐕⇌⊖🛈🚆🐕📶

SW11: Battersea Power Station

Battersea Brewery Tap Room

12-14 Arches Lane, SW11 8AB
☎ (020) 8161 2366 ⊕ batterseabrew.co.uk
2 changing beers (often Battersea) Ⓗ
Opened in 2018 as the tap to the adjacent Battersea Brewery, both housed in railway arches alongside the Power Station development. Although the brewery mainly produces keg beers, two cask-conditioned ales will always be available on handpump, sometimes including a guest beer. Bar snacks include chicken wings and a selection of toasted sandwiches. Terrestrial TV sport is on screen for major events. Close to the new underground station on the Northern line. 🐕♿⇌(Park) ⊖♣🚆🐕📶

SW11: Clapham Junction

Beehive ⊘

197 St Johns Hill, SW11 1TH
☎ (020) 7450 1756 ⊕ beehivewandsworth.co.uk
Dark Star Hophead; Fuller's London Pride Ⓗ
Tasteful and elegant refurbishment and enthusiastic management have revitalised this classic Fuller's local. A traditional terraced pub it has an intimate, friendly atmosphere. A roll-up TV screen shows major sporting events. The rear area is available for functions and there is now a sheltered garden. Blankets are thoughtfully supplied for guests wishing to sit outside. Look out for the wonderful 1898 housing survey map of SW London; since then the Luftwaffe and town planners have altered things somewhat! 🏠🐕⇌⊖🚆🐕📶

Eagle Ale House Ⓛ

104 Chatham Road, SW11 6HG
☎ (020) 7228 2328
Surrey Hills Shere Drop; changing beers (often Downton, Hackney, Pilgrim) Ⓗ
A short uphill walk from Northcote Road, this traditional pub has a warm, friendly welcome for everyone and their dog. Guest beers are from microbreweries, including local choices. Major sporting events are shown on four TV screens including one in the heated marquee in the garden, which can be hired for private events. Live music sessions are also popular. Local CAMRA Pub of the Year more than once and usually among the top three. 🏠🐕🚆(319,G1) 🐕📶

SW12: Balham

Bedford ⊘

77 Bedford Hill, SW12 9HD
☎ (020) 3976 8007 ⊕ thebedford.com
Sambrook's Wandle Ale; Timothy Taylor Landlord; 2 changing beers Ⓗ
A thriving landmark Grade II-listed building with several Art Deco features dating from its construction in 1931. In addition to the busy front bar and restaurant area in the former saloon, there is an impressive circular galleried theatre space at the rear, regularly used for comedy and live music. Other events run from bridge and dance classes to yoga and zumba. Accompanied children are

welcome until the evening. Outside seating is provided in a small, partly covered yard.
♿🏠🍴🕙🍺♿�ᵉ♠🚗➡🚗♿📶

Nightingale 🄻
97 Nightingale Lane, SW12 8NX
☎ (020) 8673 1637 ⊕ thenightingalebalham.co.uk
Young's London Original, London Special; 1 changing beer (often St Austell) 🅷
Recent renovation has not altered the basic layout of this country pub in town, dating from the mid-19th century and featuring some fine etched-glass windows. It has outdoor seating in front of the public bar area and in a spacious, part-covered beer garden behind the rear saloon. A summer walk, raising funds for charity, has been held annually for over 40 years. There is a warm welcome here for everyone, both regulars and occasional visitors.
♿🏵🕙🍴🚶≈(Wandsworth Common) ⊖(Clapham South) ♣🚗(G1)♿📶

SW13: Barnes

Red Lion
2 Castelnau, SW13 9RU
☎ (020) 8748 2984
Fuller's London Pride, ESB; 3 changing beers (often Dark Star) 🅷
Large Victorian landmark establishment at the entrance to the Wetland Centre, comprising a front bar area and a spacious rear dining room with a mosaic domed ceiling light, leaded stained-glass windows and an impressive fireplace. Outside is a covered patio and a large artificial grass garden with a children's play area. A garden bar is open on busy summer days. There is seating around the front and side, including two four-seater heated cabins.
Q♿🏵🕙🚶♿P🚗♿📶

SW15: Putney Heath

Telegraph 🄻
Putney Heath, SW15 3TU
☎ (020) 8194 2808 ⊕ telegraphputney.co.uk
Brunning & Price Traditional Bitter; 7 changing beers (sourced nationally) 🅷
Accessible via a woodland footpath from Tibbets Ride on the 93 bus route from Wimbledon, this spacious country-style pub has been impressively renovated by new owners, Brunning & Price. A dining destination, it welcomes ale drinkers, offering variety and including local brews. With an extensive garden, it is especially busy on fine days and popular wiht local dog walkers and cyclists. The name records the Admiralty Telegraph shutter semaphore station in use nearby during the Napoleonic wars. ♿🏵🕙🍴♿P🚗♿📶

SW16: Streatham

Railway 🄻 ✅
2 Greyhound Lane, SW16 5SD
☎ (020) 8769 9448 ⊕ therailwaysw16.co.uk
Sambrook's Wandle Ale; 4 changing beers (sourced locally; often By the Horns, Portobello, Southwark) 🅷
Showcasing beers exclusively from London microbreweries, both cask and bottled, this is a busy two-bar community venue close to Streatham Common station. The back bar, which is available for hire, opens in the afternoon as a popular tearoom. There is seating outside and in the back yard. It hosts a quiz on Tuesday, music nights and a popular comedy night on the last Sunday of the month. Local CAMRA Pub of the Year 2019 and 2021. ♿🏵🕙🍴♿≈(Common)🚗(60,118)♿📶

SW17: Summerstown

By The Horns Brewery Tap 🄻
25 Summerstown, SW17 0BQ
☎ (020) 3417 7338 ⊕ bythehorns.co.uk
3 changing beers (sourced locally) 🅷
A friendly brewery taproom open Tuesday to Sunday, near AFC Wimbledon's new stadium (home fans only on match-days). Two cask beers are usually on, with other draught and canned choices and occasional guests from small breweries. There is plenty of room in the two bar areas and a covered space outside. Major sporting events are shown on two large projection TVs, and board games are available also. Pizzas available Friday and Saturday, at other times food can be ordered in. ♿🏵P🚗♿

SW17: Tooting

Antelope
76 Mitcham Road, SW17 9NG
☎ (020) 8672 3888 ⊕ theantelopepub.com
Sambrook's Wandle Ale; Thornbridge Jaipur IPA; Volden Session Ale; 3 changing beers (often Volden) 🅷
A lively pub in Tooting's bustling town centre, the Antelope has a historic interior of regional importance, decorated in the shabby-chic style typical of its operators, Antic. The main bar area, retaining some Barclays signage, leads into a dining space at the rear that adjoins the large Rankin Room used to show big-screen sports, and a back yard with seating. Regular events include a quiz on Monday and live music. Children are welcome until mid-evening. ♿🏵🕙🍴🚶≈⊖(Broadway)♠🚗♿📶

SW18: Wandsworth

Grapes
39 Fairfield Street, SW18 1DX
☎ (020) 8874 1840
Young's London Original 🅷
Sensitively refurbished, this street-corner Wandsworth institution a few minutes' walk from the former brewery site retains its reputation for serving Young's beer in excellent condition. The interior is traditional, with dark wood, cut and etched glass, bench seating and an interesting carved bar-back. Outside, an airy conservatory leads out to patio seating and a suntrap garden, offering refuge from the infamous one-way system.
♿🏵🕙🍴≈(Town) 🚗♿📶

Old Sergeant 🄻
104 Garratt Lane, SW18 4DJ
☎ (020) 8874 4099 ⊕ theoldsergeant.co.uk
SlyBeast Beam Engine Bitter; Ram Street Special 🅷
This small public house, now decorated in Young's contemporary style, is a longstanding local favourite and deservedly popular with drinkers and diners alike. The John Young Room upstairs has a remarkable collection of brewery memorabilia on display and is available for hire. Outside seating is provided on the pavement at the front and in the enclosed beer garden.
♿🏵🕙🍴🚶🚗(44,270)♿📶

Ram Inn
68 Wandsworth High Street, SW18 4LB
☎ (020) 8871 9752 ⊕ theraminnsw18.co.uk
SlyBeast 4 Foot 2 London Porter, Beam Engine Bitter, Ram Street Special; 2 changing beers (often SlyBeast) 🅷
After 13 years' closure since Young's moved out of Wandsworth, its Grade II-listed Brewery Tap reopened with a new name in October 2019 under the care of Lee and Keris de Villiers, tenants of the Old Sergeant and the

Pig & Whistle. The SlyBeast Brewery is next to the main bar, where the walls commemorate Young's Brewery history. Upstairs is a little different, with shuffleboards and a Citroen H2 van serving tacos. Altogether an impressive restoration. ♿🍽️🚆(Town)♣🍴🐾🛜

SW19: South Wimbledon

Sultan
78 Norman Road, SW19 1BT
☎ (020) 8544 9323
Hop Back GFB, Summer Lightning; 4 changing beers (often Downton, Hop Back) Ⓗ
Hop Back's only London tied house, an attractive two-bar 1950s brick building, identified by CAMRA as having a regionally important historic interior. Mostly carpeted, it has dark-wood walls, large tables with chairs, some fixed seating, and settees in the conservatory. Two guest ciders are on handpump in the small saloon bar. Bottled Crop Circle and Typhoon are gluten-free real ales. ♿🐾♿🚆(Haydons Rd) ⊖(Colliers Wood/S Wimbledon) ♣P🍴🐾🛜

SW19: Wimbledon

Crooked Billet
14-15 Crooked Billet, SW19 4RQ
☎ (020) 8946 4942 🌐 thecrookedbilletwimbledon.com
St Austell Proper Job; Young's London Original, London Special; 1 changing beer (often Wimbledon) Ⓗ
A homely late 18th-century building, extended in 1969 into an adjacent cottage, and again more recently to increase dining space. The wood-panelled walls are adorned with old prints, photographs and local painters' works. It has flagstone and wooden floors, a variety of seating and a real fire in winter. Good food is served throughout, including in the intimate restaurant room at the back. Quiz night is Monday. Plastic glasses are used outside in the summer. ♿🐾🍽️🚆(200)🐾🛜

Hand in Hand Ⓛ
7 Crooked Billet, SW19 4RQ
☎ (020) 8946 5720 🌐 thehandinhandwimbledon.co.uk
Courage Directors; St Austell Proper Job; Young's London Original, London Special; 2 changing beers (often Twickenham) Ⓗ
Recently refurbished dog-friendly ale house on the edge of Wimbledon Common with separate drinking areas and a variety of seating. Up to three guest beers are usually sold, increasingly from local breweries. Children are welcome in the family room. This is a great place to eat, inside or on the front patio, with beer included in several recipes. There is poker on Monday, a quiz on Tuesday and occasional beer tastings and cellar tours. Q♿🐾🍽️♿♣🚆(200) 🐾🛜

Wibbas Down Inn Ⓛ ✅
6-12 Gladstone Road, SW19 1QT
☎ (020) 8540 6788
Greene King IPA, Abbot; Oakham JHB; Sharp's Doom Bar; 14 changing beers Ⓗ
An enormous two-bar Wetherspoon pub stretching from Gladstone Road to Russell Road, unusual in its 1995 conversion from a Tesco supermarket. It is a favourite haunt for drinkers owing to its low prices and the proximity of the back bar to the Wimbledon Theatre across the road. Fourteen guest beers change frequently and many are sourced from local breweries. Up to 50 beers are available at the frequent festivals. Food and coffee are served all day. Q♿🐾🍽️♿🚆⊖🍴🐾🛜

Carshalton

Hope Ⓛ
48 West Street, SM5 2PR
☎ (020) 8240 1255 🌐 hopecarshalton.co.uk
Downton New Forest Ale; Windsor & Eton Knight of the Garter; 5 changing beers Ⓗ
Traditional multi award-winning free house owned by several of its regulars. Seven handpumps dispense a range of the country's finest beers, served in measures from a third-pint upwards. A good range of craft keg and bottled ale is also sold, and knowledgeable staff are always ready to advise you about your choices. A marquee with its permanent bar is used for events and private hire. Good-value pub grub is served until mid-afternoon, and pot meals during the evening. Over-14s only. Current local CAMRA Pub of the Year. Q🐾🍽️♿🚆♣♿P🍴🐾🛜

Railway Tavern ✅
47 North Street, SM5 2HG
☎ 07710 476437
Fuller's London Pride; Gale's Seafarers Ale, HSB Ⓗ
Street-corner community local in Carshalton village, with hanging baskets and window boxes beneath the fine etched windows. Inside is a small U-shaped drinking area around a central bar. As well as various items of railwayana, the walls display certificates and awards to mark achievements and qualifications of the pub and its staff. The landlord is a Fuller's Master Cellarman. ♿🐾♿🚆♣🚆🐾🛜

Sun
4 North Street, SM5 2HU
☎ (020) 8773 4549 🌐 thesuncarshalton.com
6 changing beers (sourced nationally) Ⓗ
This handsome and imposing Victorian pub was given a tasteful makeover several years ago and has not looked back since. Several distinct areas accommodate diners with excellent food, and discerning drinkers with a wide beer choice on six handpumps. In summer the large courtyard garden, with its continental-style veranda, is popular. A huge upstairs function room can be hired. Q♿🐾🍽️🚆♣🚆🐾🛜

Kingston

Albion Ⓛ
45 Fairfield Road, KT1 2PY
☎ (020) 8541 1691 🌐 thealbionkingston.com
Big Smoke Solaris Session Pale Ale; 9 changing beers (often Big Smoke) Ⓗ
One of a small chain that includes the Big Smoke Brewery. Ales come from small breweries nationwide alongside up to five changing ciders. Varnished wooden floors and comfortable wood-panelled seating areas extend back to a rear patio garden with heaters, a new gin distillery and a glazed garden room (available for hire). Music is from an extensive collection of vinyl LPs. Home-cooked food is served all day. Local CAMRA Pub of the Year 2019. ♿🐾🍽️♿♣🍴🐾🛜

Canbury Arms Ⓛ
49 Canbury Park Road, KT2 6LQ
☎ (020) 8255 9129 🌐 canburyarmskingston.co.uk
Harvey's Sussex Best Bitter; Surrey Hills Shere Drop; Young's Bitter Ⓗ
A delightful Art Deco-style pub with a separate restaurant and first floor function room. Party bookings are welcome, with special menus by arrangement. The extensive home-cooked menu and snacks are available all day in the bar and restaurant, with children welcome until the evening. Wine makers',

gourmet and brewer's evenings are hosted. There is a patio area to the side and a paved garden at the rear. See the website for details of local parking arrangements. ⏃✿◑⏃♿⇌🚌❀🛜

Willoughby Arms 🅛

47 Willoughby Road, KT2 6LN
☎ (020) 8546 4236 ⊕ thewilloughbyarms.com
7 changing beers (sourced locally; often Twickenham) 🅗
Friendly Victorian back-street premises, with a games and TV sports bar and a quieter lounge area. Upstairs is a soundproofed function room. Free of tie, beers are sourced from smaller breweries. Pizzas and pies are cooked to order. The spacious garden includes beach huts and a covered, heated and lit smoking area with a large TV screen. Quiz night is Sunday. Beer festivals are held around St George's Day and Halloween. Local CAMRA Pub of the Year 2020. Q⏃✿❀♣●🚌(371,K5)❀🛜

Wych Elm 🅛 ✅

93 Elm Road, KT2 6HT
☎ (020) 8546 3271 ⊕ thewychelmkingston.co.uk
Dark Star Hophead; Fuller's London Pride, ESB; Gale's Seafarers Ale; 2 changing beers (often Dark Star) 🅗
This traditional hostelry with a secluded garden nestles in the heart of north Kingston. Run by independent operators, it is a proper local offering great freshly prepared food and friendly service. The guest ale is supplied by Fuller's but is often from another brewery – a Master Cellarman takes care of the beers. There are logburners in winter. Some major sporting events are shown on a projection screen and parties and celebrations can be hosted. Charity quizzes, piano and wine evenings are also held. Q⏃✿◑🚌(K5)❀🛜

Mitcham

Windmill

40 Commonside West, CR4 4HA
☎ (020) 8685 0333
Young's London Original; 1 changing beer (often Sharp's) 🅗
A warm, friendly, independent free house facing the common, with stained-glass windmills in attractive bow-windows. This is a local community pub, with terrestrial TV for sports highlights, a dartboard and occasional live music. There is sometimes a second guest beer. To the side is a spacious heated and covered patio with plenty of seating for smokers. ⏃✿❀♣🚌

Richmond

Mitre

20 St Mary's Grove, TW9 1UY
☎ (020) 8940 1336 ⊕ themitretw9.co.uk
Timothy Taylor Landlord; 6 changing beers (often Oakham, Siren, Thornbridge) 🅗
A simply furnished tavern tucked away off Sheen Road, with a decked area at the front and patio garden at the back. Leaded stained-glass windows feature different colourful church mitres. Cask beers are on constant rotation from independent brewers outside the M25, with three handpumps dispensing cider or perry. A bar billiards table is available. Food can be delivered from Basilico Pizza. Rudi lives here, officially the cutest pub dog in Britain. ⏃✿❀⇌⊖♣●P🚌❀

Roebuck ✅

130 Richmond Hill, TW10 6RN
☎ (020) 8948 2329

Greene King IPA, Abbot; 5 changing beers (often Purity, Surrey Hills, Thames Side) 🅗
Close to Richmond Park, this 200-year-old pub, rebuilt in 1741, commands the famous view over the Thames painted by Turner – the only view protected by Act of Parliament. Inside are a number of comfortable secluded areas and upstairs is a function room and bar for hire. Guest beers are on constant rotation and Westons Old Rosie is now a regular cider. Patrons can also use the outside terrace across the road. ⏃◑⏃♿🚌(371)❀🛜

Surbiton

Antelope 🅛

87 Maple Road, KT6 4AW
☎ (020) 8399 5565 ⊕ theantelope.co.uk
Big Smoke Solaris Session Pale Ale; 9 changing beers (sourced nationally; often Big Smoke) 🅗
The original home of the Big Smoke Brewery, with two or three of its beers usually on the bar. The spacious split-level interior has a real fire in winter and a covered, heated and lit courtyard behind, beyond which the old brewhouse now acts as dining or function room. Five changing ciders are usually sold. Home-cooked food includes roasts on Sunday. Popular with locals and commuters, it can be particularly busy evenings and weekends. A former local CAMRA Pub of the Year. ⏃✿◑⇌♣🚌❀🛜

Coronation Hall 🅛 ✅

St Marks Hill, KT6 4LQ (b3370)
☎ (020) 8390 6164
Greene King Abbot; Ruddles County; Sharp's Doom Bar; 9 changing beers (sourced nationally) 🅗
Across the road from Surbiton station, this Wetherspoon is in a 1911 building that has had a variety of former uses including music hall, cinema, bingo hall and nudist club. The decor is a mix of film artefacts and images of movie stars, the coronation of George V, and the planets. Guest beers change regularly, many from nearby microbreweries. Occasionally the pub hosts local beer festivals. Children are welcome until 9pm. Q⏃✿◑♿🚌🛜

Lamb 🅛

73 Brighton Road, KT6 5NF
☎ (020) 8390 9229 ⊕ lambsurbiton.co.uk
Hop Back Summer Lightning; Surrey Hills Shere Drop; 2 changing beers (sourced nationally) 🅗
This small, family-run free house hosts many community events, especially those bringing people together through creativity. Live music is often hosted. Built in 1850 and formerly four separate rooms, it retains the original horseshoe-shaped bar. It had a small brewery in Victorian times. The changing beers are usually from a microbrewery, sometimes local. An outdoor pop-up kitchen hosts guest chefs for lunch and dinner every day. ⏃✿◑⇌🚌🛜

Sutton

Moon on the Hill ✅

5-9 Hill Road, SM1 1DZ
☎ (020) 8643 1202
Greene King Abbot; Ringwood Fortyniner; Ruddles Best Bitter; Sharp's Doom Bar; 6 changing beers (sourced regionally) 🅗
Formerly the furniture depository of a department store, this is a popular and well-established Wetherspoon pub, conveniently situated for Sutton's main shopping area. It comprises a single bar with ample seating on three levels and a garden for those preferring to drink and eat

alfresco. The guest beers are local whenever possible and mini beer festivals are held throughout the year. Draught ciders on offer come from different parts of the country. ⏱🏵🕊◗&♿🖥🅿🛜

Shinner & Sudtone 🄻
67 High Street, SM1 1DT
☎ (020) 8643 8395 🌐 shinnerandsudtone.co.uk
3 changing beers (sourced nationally) 🄷
In the shopping area of Sutton, this Portobello – ex Antic – pub's interior is decorated in a shabby-chic style. Its name combines that of a former department store nearby and an old name for Sutton. The long bar has tables and chairs either side of a central walkway, leading to a small raised section at the rear. Up to three ales are usually sold, and a board indicates beers waiting in the cellar. Acoustic and open mic nights are held regularly. ⏱◗&♣♠🖥🅿🛜

WEST LONDON
W2: Bayswater
Champion ✔
1 Wellington Terrace, W2 4LW
☎ (020) 7792 4527 🌐 thechampionpub.co.uk
Adnams Ghost Ship; 4 changing beers (often By the Horns, Dark Star, Oakham) 🄷
The nearest pub to Kensington Palace, opposite the security-protected road on the northern side of Kensington Gardens. Built in 1838 and Grade II listed, it was refurbished in 2004 and spruced up more recently by owners Mitchells & Butlers. In warm weather the front windows are often opened into the bar. A plush basement area leads on to a sunken beer garden, with patio heaters for cold weather. ⏱🏵◗&⊖(Notting Hill Gate/Queensway) ●🖥🐾🛜

W2: Little Venice
Bridge House ✔
13 Westbourne Terrace Road, W2 6NG
☎ (020) 7266 4326 🌐 thebridgehouselittlevenice.co.uk
Sharp's Doom Bar; Timothy Taylor Landlord; 2 changing beers (often St Austell, Thornbridge) 🄷
Dating from 1848, this pub beside the canal is now a lounge-style bar, ideal for a quiet afternoon drink. It has a good solid bar counter, wooden floor and panelling, with old mirrors (Bass, and H D Rawlings' High Class Mineral Waters) above the fireplace. A chandelier, pastel-painted walls, high and standard tables and chairs, and low easy chairs complete the setting. An extensive food menu is offered for lunch and dinner.
Q⏱🏵◗🚆(Paddington) ⊖(Warwick Ave) 🖥🐾🛜

W2: Paddington
Mad Bishop & Bear
Upper Level, The Lawn, Paddington Station Concourse, W2 1HB
☎ (020) 7402 2441 🌐 madbishopandbear.co.uk
Dark Star Hophead; Fuller's London Pride, ESB; 5 changing beers (often Tiny Rebel, Wild Beer, Wimbledon) 🄷
Above the shopping complex just behind the station concourse, the modern pub interior features one long bar, railway memorabilia and train information screens. The raised areas can be hired for events and there are café-style seats outside. It may not be crowded even in the rush hour, but the bar could close early if football crowds are passing through. ⏱🏵◗&🚆⊖🅿🐾🛜

Victoria ★
10A Strathearn Place, W2 2NH
☎ (020) 7724 1191
Fuller's Oliver's Island 🄷/🅿**, London Pride, ESB; 3 changing beers (often Dark Star, Thornbridge, Tiny Rebel)** 🄷
There is plenty to admire in this Grade II-listed mid-Victorian inn, popular with tourists and locals alike. The nationally important historic interior includes ornately gilded mirrors above a crescent-shaped bar, painted tiles in wall niches and numerous portraits of Queen Victoria. The walls display cartoons, paperweights and a Silver Jubilee plate. Upstairs, via a spiral staircase, the Library and Theatre Bar provide extra space. Tuesday is quiz night. Paddington Station is a few minutes away.
Q⏱🏵◗🚆⊖(Lancaster Gate/Paddington) 🖥🐾🛜

W3: Acton
Red Lion & Pineapple ✔
281 High Street, W3 9BP
☎ (020) 8896 2248
Greene King IPA, Abbot; Sharp's Doom Bar; 6 changing beers 🄷
A Wetherspoon at the top of Acton Hill formerly owned by Fuller's, it was originally two pubs which then combined in 1906 – hence the unique name. The larger room is home to the circular bar, surrounded by red and black tiles. The windows are large, with etched and stained tops, and the walls are decorated with historical photographs of Acton. The smaller room is mainly used by diners and families. Alcoholic drinks are served from 9am. ⏱🏵◗&⊖(Town)🖥🛜

West London Trades Union Club
33-35 High Street, W3 6ND
☎ (020) 8992 4557 🌐 wltuc.com
2 changing beers (often Nelson) 🄷
Small, friendly club, run as a co-operative, that combines excellent beer with a busy cultural and social life. Two real ales are served from a variety of independent breweries, and particularly from the wide Nelson range. The Acton Community Theatre is upstairs, and regular film shows are also held. The local CAMRA branch is an associate member; show a CAMRA membership card or this Guide for entry. Closed on most Saturdays (check the website for exceptions). Q⏱🏵⊖(Central)🖥🐾🛜

W4: Acton Green
Duke of Sussex 🄻 ✔
75 South Parade, W4 5LF
☎ (020) 8742 8801 🌐 thedukeofsussex.co.uk
Greene King IPA; 3 changing beers (often Sambrook's, Twickenham) 🄷
On a pub site dating from the 1840s, this 1898 building with mock-Tudor frontage has a regionally important historic interior. It retains a central island counter, exposed floorboards, alcove seating and etched-glass screens. Between three and five rotating guest ales are served, mostly from London and the home counties. Both a local and a gastro-pub, the rear room is dedicated to diners and leads to a large garden with hidden corners. A quiz is held on Sunday evening.
Q⏱🏵◗&⊖(Chiswick Park) 🖥🐾🛜

Swan
1 Evershed Walk, 119 Acton Lane, W4 5HH
☎ (020) 8994 8262 🌐 theswanchiswick.co.uk
Timothy Taylor Landlord; 2 changing beers 🄷
This street-corner hostelry, dating from 1871, retains a local drinking character despite the addition of a well-

regarded dining area in part of the original garden – still one of the best pub gardens in West London. The ever-present Timothy Taylor Landlord is joined by two guest beers, often from the West Country. The exterior regularly appeared in a 1980s sitcom, and familiar faces from current TV can often now be seen here. ♿☀️◑➊⊖(Chiswick Park) ♣🚃🐾

W4: Turnham Green

George IV

185 Chiswick High Road, W4 2DR
☎ (020) 8994 4624 ⊕ georgeiv.co.uk
Dark Star Hophead; Fuller's London Pride, ESB; 1 changing beer (often Dark Star, Fuller's) Ⓗ
There has been an inn here in the heart of Chiswick since 1777, and the present inter-war pub is reputed to have its own ghost, George. Inside, the different areas include the board game-themed mezzanine, and the Boston Room across the rear courtyard hosts events including a comedy club, and is available for private hire. Fuller's small-batch brews are among the beers on offer. Up to two staff here have Fuller's Master Cellarman qualifications. ♿☀️◑♿🍴⊖🍽️🚃🐾🛜

Tabard Ⓛ ✅

2 Bath Road, W4 1LW
☎ (020) 8994 3492
Greene King IPA, Abbot; 2 changing beers (sourced nationally) Ⓗ
Built in 1880 as part of the Bedford Park estate, the first London garden suburb, this Grade II°-listed inn has a regionally important historic pub interior. Features include the replica swing sign (the original was painted by TM Rooke), interior tiling by William de Morgan and Walter Crane, and Arts & Crafts mirrors and pictures. The dining area usually has live music on Saturday evening and a quiz on Wednesday. An intimate fringe theatre is upstairs. ♿☀️◑♿♣🚃🐾🛜

W5: Ealing

Questors Grapevine Bar Ⓛ

12 Mattock Lane, W5 5BQ
☎ (020) 8567 0011 ⊕ questors.org.uk/grapevine
Fuller's London Pride; 2 changing beers Ⓗ
A friendly theatre club bar near the centre of Ealing and Walpole Park, run by enthusiastic volunteers. CAMRA members and Questors Theatre ticket holders are welcome. Guest beers include some from breweries in the area. Beer festivals are held twice-yearly and there are malt whisky tastings. Some books and the odd board game are available. Local CAMRA Club of the Year 2019 and winner of the CAMRA national award in 2012. Q♿☀️♿🚃⊖(Broadway) ♣P🚃🐾🛜

W5: North Ealing

Greystoke Ⓛ ✅

7 Queens Parade, Hanger Lane, W5 3HU
☎ (020) 8997 6388
Greene King IPA, Abbot; 5 changing beers (often Wimbledon) Ⓗ
A spacious family dining pub opposite North Ealing station, built in typical 1930s style, with affordable hot food and a changing selection of Greene King beers. The single open-plan bar is comfortably furnished. All major sporting events from around the world, including NFL, are shown. A weekly quiz is hosted on Thursday as well as regular live music events. ♿☀️◑♿⊖♣P🚌(112,483) 🐾🛜

W6: Hammersmith

Andover Arms ✅

57 Aldensley Road, W6 0DL
☎ (020) 8748 2155 ⊕ theandoverarms.com
Fuller's London Pride; Gale's Seafarers Ale; 1 changing beer (often Fuller's) Ⓗ
Hidden away in the back streets of Hammersmith, this popular and welcoming local is an enduring real ale champion with a rural feel about it. The attractive panelled bar counter, with its elaborate bar-back, separates two areas furnished with an assortment of dining tables and chairs. The kitchen offers a wide range of dishes lunchtimes and evenings. Quiz night is Sunday. ♿☀️◑⊖(Ravenscourt Park) ♣🚃🐾🛜

Dove

19 Upper Mall, W6 9TA
☎ (020) 8748 9474
Fuller's Oliver's Island, London Pride, ESB; 1 changing beer (often Fuller's, Gale's) Ⓗ
A Grade II-listed pub dating from the 1740s, with a regionally important historic interior, overlooking the Thames and hence often crowded in summer. The likes of Dylan Thomas, Ernest Hemingway and Alec Guinness have enjoyed a pint or two here. Down off the main bar, a tiny public bar holds the Guinness world record for the smallest bar area. The food service can be slow at busy times but is usually worth the wait. ♿☀️◑⊖(Ravenscourt Park) 🍴🚃🐾🛜

Plough & Harrow Ⓛ ✅

120-124 King Street, W6 0QU
☎ (020) 8735 6020
Fuller's London Pride; Greene King IPA, Abbot; Sharp's Doom Bar; 6 changing beers Ⓗ
On the site of an inn established in 1419, and more recently a Rolls-Royce showroom, this light and airy Wetherspoon pub dates from 2002. It has a mixture of stone and carpeted floors and a long metal-topped bar. Many of the guest beers come from microbreweries. There are several tables outside. Alcoholic drinks are served from 9am. Q♿◑♿⊖(Hammersmith/Ravenscourt Park) 🚃🛜

Prince of Wales Townhouse

73 Dalling Road, W6 0JD
☎ (020) 8563 1713 ⊕ princeofwales-townhouse.co.uk
Big Smoke Solaris Session Pale Ale, Underworld; Park Killcat Pale; house beer (by Laine); 2 changing beers (often Big Smoke, Oakham) Ⓗ
Big Smoke Brewery returned what had become the Rook's Nest to essentially its original name on taking it over in 2020. Some 20 keg beers and three ciders complement the cask beers. Breakfast is served from 8am, alcoholic drinks from 11am. The pub has an open kitchen, open brickwork, white tiling, and wood panelling painted green. The chain has a loyalty card scheme; after buying nine pints you get the 10th free. ☀️♿◑♿⊖(Ravenscourt Park) 🍴🚃🐾🛜

William Morris Ⓛ

2-4 King Street, W6 0QA
☎ (020) 8741 7175
Greene King Abbott; Ruddles Best Bitter; Sharp's Doom Bar; 7 changing beers (sourced nationally) Ⓗ
Close to Hammersmith's two underground stations and Lyric Theatre and not far from the Apollo music venue, this large, popular Wetherspoon is named after the Arts & Crafts designer who had a home nearby. A modern pub, with entrances on both King Street and the pedestrianised Lyric Square, on which there is terrace seating, the interior stretches in an L-shape, with the bar

in the middle. Frequently changing interesting ales, often from smaller breweries, are usually on offer. Alcoholic drinks are served from 9am. ♿🐾🗲🌢➊🚪🚼🛜

W7: Hanwell

Dodo Micropub 🄻
52 Boston Road, W7 3TR
☎ (020) 8567 5959 ⊕ thedodomicropub.com
5 changing beers (sourced locally) Ꮆ
A classic micropub shop conversion that landed in Hanwell in 2017. Up to five cask beers are served from a temperature-controlled cellar room at the rear, along with cider and wine. Beers almost always include some from local breweries. There is a small bar counter by the front door but table service is the order of the day here. Current local CAMRA Pub of the Year. Q♿🌢➊🍴🚪🚼🛜

Fox
Green Lane, W7 2PJ
☎ (020) 8567 4021 ⊕ thefoxpub.co.uk
Fuller's London Pride; 3 changing beers (sourced nationally) Ⓗ
Wonderful back-street free house in the welcoming multicultural town of Hanwell, as popular with walkers, cyclists and other nearby canal users as with locals. A good range of beers, with changing guest ales from independent breweries, is complemented by excellent, inexpensive food, including a popular Sunday lunch (booking recommended). Two annual beer festivals are hosted and occasional jazz sessions. Local CAMRA Pub of the Year on many occasions. ♿🐾🗲➊🐶🌢🚪🚆(195,E8) 🚼🛜

Green W7 🄻
13 Lower Boston Road, W7 3TX
☎ (020) 8840 6789 ⊕ thegreenw7.com
Fuller's London Pride; 2 changing beers (often Portobello, Twickenham, Windsor & Eton) Ⓗ
Previously the White Hart, the Dolphin and the Inn on the Green, this pub dates from at least 1860 and retains some wood panelling, tiling and lots of exposed brickwork. A pizza oven was installed in 2017 and burgers are also served. There may be up to four changing beers on tap, with the Monday club offering draft beer at £3 per pint. ♿🐾🗲🗲🌢🚪🐶🌢🚪🚪🛜

Viaduct ✅
221 Uxbridge Road, W7 3TD
☎ (020) 8567 5866 ⊕ viaduct-hanwell.co.uk
Dark Star Hophead; Fuller's 1845 Ⓗ
A friendly Fuller's house, much larger on the inside than it looks from the outside. The separate function room used for Friday comedy nights is otherwise available for hire. The pub was renamed circa 1838 after the Wharncliffe Viaduct behind it – the first viaduct to carry a commercial electric telegraph. Ealing Hospital is close by. Q♿🐾🗲➊🌢🐶🚪🚼🛜

W8: Kensington

Elephant & Castle ✅
40 Holland Street, W8 4LT
☎ (020) 7937 6382
Fuller's London Pride; St Austell Nicholson's Pale Ale; Sharp's Doom Bar; 3 changing beers (sourced nationally) Ⓗ
First licensed in 1865 as a beer house in what were two adjacent houses, and tucked away north-east of Kensington Town Hall, this busy wood-panelled Nicholson's pub has a regionally important historic interior. With its cosy rural feel it is a welcome refuge

from the hurly-burly of Kensington High Street. Guest beers come from a wide range of breweries. Food, especially pies and sausages, is available throughout the day. Note the fine Charrington's bar-back. ♿🐾🗲➊➊(High St Kensington) 🚪🚼🛜

Scarsdale Tavern
23A Edwardes Square, W8 6HE
☎ (020) 7937 1811
Fuller's London Pride; Gale's Seafarers Ale; 2 changing beers (often Fuller's) Ⓗ
On a secluded square off Kensington High Street, this upmarket 1867 pub was reportedly a haunt of the late Diana, Princess of Wales. Behind the half-frosted windows lies an L-shaped dark-wood bar with an ornate etched and mirrored bar-back. Walls are decorated with elegantly framed paintings, the most striking of which is a reproduction of David's Napoleon Crossing the Alps. The front patio has tables and heating. The pub is said to be the local in the 1970s TV crime series The Professionals.
🐾➊🚆(Kensington Olympia) ➊(High St Kensington) 🚪🛜

W8: Notting Hill Gate

Churchill Arms
119 Kensington Church Street, W8 7LN
☎ (020) 7727 4242
Fuller's Oliver's Island, London Pride, ESB; 2 changing beers (often Fuller's) Ⓗ
A multi award-winning, deservedly popular establishment with a regionally important historic interior including snob screens, now rare. Churchillian and Irish memorabilia are among the bric-a-brac suspended from the panelled ceiling. The Thai restaurant in the conservatory was one of the first in a London pub. Outside, at busy times, drinkers stand on the pavement below the numerous hanging flower baskets. At Christmas, the tree decorations are quite something to behold. Q♿➊➊🚪🚼🛜

Windsor Castle ★ ✅
114 Campden Hill Road, W8 7AR
☎ (020) 7243 8797 ⊕ thewindsorcastlekensington.co.uk
Marston's Pedigree; Timothy Taylor Landlord; 4 changing beers Ⓗ
A back-street, Grade II-listed pub dating from 1830. Sited on a corner, it contrasts an old-world rural feel with a modern upmarket service and menu style. The bar room is divided into three drinking compartments separated by partitions that date from a 1933 refurbishment; recognised by CAMRA as having a nationally important historic interior. Four of the real ales on offer rotate through some interesting brews. The beer garden to the rear boasts its own bar. Q♿🐾➊➊🚪🚼🛜

W9: Westbourne Park

Union Tavern 🄻
45 Woodfield Road, W9 2BA
☎ (020) 7286 1886
Dark Star Hophead; Fuller's London Pride Ⓗ
Following a takeover by Fuller's, this is now a part-tied beer house offering craft keg beers and cask ales produced within 30 miles and, with just one brewery exception, in London. The mainly young crowd enjoys reduced beer prices on Monday, various music nights and a Meet the Brewer event on the first Tuesday of the month. Good-value food is another attraction, with traditional Sunday lunches. The canalside terrace comes into its own on a warm sunny day. ♿🐾➊➊🚪🚼🛜

W12: Shepherds Bush

Central Bar ✅

Unit 1, West 12 Shopping Centre, Shepherds Bush Green, W12 8PH
☎ (020) 8746 4290
Greene King IPA, Abbot; changing beers Ⓗ
A Wetherspoon pub opened in 2002 on the upper floor of a new shopping centre. Access from the ground floor is via escalator or lift. A wide entrance leads into a long bar area with large windows overlooking the Green. The venue is named after the Central London Railway (or tuppenny tube), now the Central Line, which reached Shepherds Bush with a station opposite the pub opened by the Prince of Wales (later Edward VII) in 1900.
Q🕏🕾◗≉⊖(Shepherd's Bush/Market) ●🚃🛜

Defector's Weld Ⓛ

170 Uxbridge Road, W12 8AA
☎ (020) 8749 0008 ⊕ defectors-weld.co.uk
Young's London Original, London Special; 3 changing beers (often Redemption, Truman's, Twickenham) Ⓗ
Since Young's took over this pub, it has continued to rotate local guest beers. The large horseshoe-shaped main bar has a welcoming mix of sofas, tables and chairs. An upstairs bar is available for hire. DJs play music Thursday to Sunday evenings (no admission after midnight Fri & Sat). Home fans only are allowed here on Queen's Park Rangers match days, but card-carrying CAMRA members not wearing team colours are welcome.
Q🕏◗&≉⊖(Shepherd's Bush/Market) 🍴🚃🐾🛜

W13: West Ealing

Drayton Court Hotel

2 The Avenue, W13 8PH
☎ (020) 8997 1019
Dark Star Hophead; Fuller's London Pride Ⓗ
Known locally as Dracula's Castle owing to its neo-Gothic and towered brick construction, this large establishment was fairly recently reconverted to a hotel. Ho Chi Minh is believed to have worked as a chef here. The downstairs function room has been completely refurbished and has its own bar. Regular music nights are held, particularly jazz. Quiz evenings, chess tournaments and an annual beer festival are also featured. It has one of the largest pub gardens in West London.
🕏🕭🍴◗&⊖♣●P🐾🛜

Forester ★ ✅

2 Leighton Road, W13 9EP
☎ (020) 8567 1654
Dark Star Hophead; Fuller's London Pride; 4 changing beers Ⓗ
Built in 1909 from designs by Nowell Parr for the Royal Brewery of Brentford and bought by Fuller's in 2012, this pub has a nationally important historic interior. Thai and English food are available daily, except on Sunday when the traditional carvery is served until 6pm. Wednesday is quiz night and on Thursday there are poker tournaments. Two guest beers are supplemented by two additional beers from Fuller's (often Gale's HSB) and two beer festivals are held annually.
🕏🕭🍴◗&⊖(Northfields/West Ealing) ♣●🚃(E2,E3) 🐾🛜

Owl & The Pussycat Ⓛ

106 Northfield Avenue, W13 9RT
⊕ markopaulo.co.uk
6 changing beers (sourced locally; often Ealing, Marko Paulo) Ⓗ

Unique to West London, this combination of microbrewery and pub has retained the atmosphere of the former bookshop. Drinkers can view the brewing process while avid readers can browse through the beer-related books and magazines. All the beers are currently brewed on the premises. The ciders are often from Oliver's if not home-produced. Conversation is all-important in this small, friendly environment. Local CAMRA Pub of the Year 2019 and Cider Pub of the Year 2019 and 2020. Q⊖(Northfields)♣●🚃(E2,E3)🛜

Brentford

Black Dog Beer House

17 Albany Road, TW8 0NF
☎ (020) 8568 5688 ⊕ blackdogbeerhouse.co.uk
7 changing beers (often East London, Manchester, Tiny Rebel) Ⓗ
This landmark building, a former Royal Brewery (Brentford) pub dating back to at least 1861, has become a neighbourhood favourite after reopening in 2018. The light, open L-shaped room has plenty of seating, no TVs, music from classic vinyl LPs and an eclectic food menu. The real ales, five real ciders, 14 more beers and ciders on keg taps are listed on two chalkboards. Dogs are welcome, though the eponymous hound lives elsewhere. Local CAMRA Pub of the Year 2020.
🕏◗≉♣●🚃🐾🛜

Express Tavern

56 Kew Bridge Road, TW8 0EW
☎ (020) 8560 8484 ⊕ expresstavern.co.uk
Big Smoke Solaris Session Pale Ale; Draught Bass; Harvey's Sussex Best Bitter; 7 changing beers (sourced nationally) Ⓗ
A local landmark since the 1800s, still featuring its illuminated external Bass signage, with Draught Bass remaining a fixture on the bar. It has a regionally important historic pub interior. The Chiswick Bar has 10 ale handpumps and an upright piano, with music also on vinyl LPs. The Saloon and Lounge Bar handpumps serve five ciders and perries. To the rear is a glazed conservatory and a beer garden with a covered and heated terrace. 🕏◗&≉(Kew Bridge)♣●🚃🐾🛜

Hampton

Jolly Coopers

16 High Street, TW12 2SJ
☎ (020) 8979 3384
Courage Best Bitter; Hop Back Summer Lightning; 3 changing beers (sourced locally; often Ascot, Park) Ⓗ
A popular, traditional community pub, proud of its heritage; a wooden wall panel lists landlords from 1727 to the present owners, who took over in 1986. The small horseshoe bar features guest beers, mainly from breweries in the area. Walls are adorned with water jugs and local memorabilia, including some coopers' tools. Extensive tapas and traditional food, including Sunday lunches (booking essential), are served in Squiffy's restaurant and, weather permitting, on the sun patio outside. 🕏🕭◗&≉🚃🐾🛜

Railway Bell ✅

Station Road, TW12 2AP
☎ (020) 8979 1897 ⊕ therailwaybellhampton.co.uk
Skinner's Betty Stogs; 3 changing beers (often Fuller's, Sharp's, Twickenham) Ⓗ
A friendly, cottage-style, two-room pub, approached across a large, inviting front terrace area down a driveway beside the railway bridge (Tudor Road) just to the east of Hampton station. Known locally as the Dip, it

has two separate, simply furnished bars, one of them decorated with old photographs of the locality. Home-cooked food is served all week except Mondays; afternoon coffee and Sunday lunches are provided. ✿◑≈♣🖵(111,216) ✿

Hampton Court

Mute Swan
3 Palace Gate, Hampton Court Road, KT8 9BN
☎ (020) 8941 5959
House beer (by St Austell); 3 changing beers (often Park, Surrey Hills, Twickenham) Ⓗ
A friendly Brunning & Price pub and dining room opposite the gates of Hampton court Palace. A good selection of food is served both upstairs and in the main bar. Bar bites are listed on a chalkboard. The cask beers change frequently, with a cider on handpump often also on the go. Seating and tables are provided outside. There are no TV screens to spoil the atmosphere, which draws locals and tourists alike. No prams are allowed inside. ◑≈♣♠🖵✿🛜

Hampton Hill

Roebuck
72 Hampton Road, TW12 1JN
☎ (020) 8255 8133 ⊕ roebuck-hamptonhill.co.uk
St Austell Tribute; Sambrook's Junction Ale; Young's London Original; 2 changing beers (often Park, Triple fff, Windsor & Eton) Ⓗ
Comfortable and traditional Victorian street-corner pub with screens dividing the single bar into various seating areas. An amazing array of bric-a-brac and other displays (framed banknotes, military memorabilia, model seaplanes, a wickerwork Harley-Davidson) keeps growing but does not detract from the comfort of the place. Good, old-fashioned pub food is served. The small garden has a gazebo for smokers and there is a garden room (available for hire) for cooler evenings. The real fire never goes out in winter. ✿♠◑≈(Fulwell)🖵🛜

Harlington

White Hart
158 High Street, UB3 5DP
☎ (020) 8759 9608
Fuller's London Pride, ESB; 1 changing beer (often Dark Star, Fuller's, Gale's) Ⓗ
Large, Grade II-listed Fuller's pub standing proud at the north end of the village. The bar provides access to an open-plan area with comfortable seating, leading to an area favoured by diners. The interior was refurbished in 2009 to improve facilities and create the open feel it has now. Local history is the theme of the wall displays, enjoyed by regulars and visitors from the nearby Heathrow airport. Quiz night is Thursday. Fuller's or Gale's seasonal ales are sometimes on the bar. ঠ✿◑&P🖵✿🛜

Hayes

Botwell Inn ✓
25-29 Coldharbour Lane, UB3 3EB
☎ (020) 8848 3112
Greene King Abbot; Ruddles Best Bitter; Sharp's Doom Bar; 3 changing beers (often Adnams, Hogs Back, Windsor & Eton) Ⓗ
A large Wetherspoon opened in 2000 following a shop conversion from furnishers S Moore and Son, with several sections for dining and drinking. There is a fenced paved area to the front and a patio at the rear with large

parasols and heaters. At least one Westons cider is stocked. Several beer festivals are held annually. Qঠ✿◑&≈⊖(Hayes & Harlington) ●🖵🛜

Hounslow

Moon under Water ✓
84-88 Staines Road, TW3 3LF
☎ (020) 8572 7506
Greene King Abbot; Ruddles Best Bitter; Sharp's Doom Bar; 5 changing beers (sourced nationally) Ⓗ
Licensed from 9am, this is a 1991 Wetherspoon shop conversion still in original style, displaying many local history panels and photographs. It is a regular venue for the town's beer lovers, also attracting others from surrounding areas. Up to five guest ales are offered, both national and local, with more at festival times, when 10 handpumps are put to work. Families are welcome during the day. Qঠ✿◑&⊖(Central)🖵🛜

Ickenham

Tichenham Inn ✓
11 Swakeleys Road, UB10 8DF
☎ (01895) 678916
Greene King Abbot; Ruddles Best Bitter; Sharp's Doom Bar; 4 changing beers Ⓗ
Small and friendly Wetherspoon pub with a strong local following. Food and beers are good value, with the usual chain promotions. The pub has its own festivals with more guest ales, in conjunction with other nearby Wetherspoons. Alcoholic drinks are available from 9am. Qঠ✿◑&⊖🖵🛜

Isleworth

London Apprentice ✓
62 Church Street, TW7 6BG
☎ (020) 8560 1915
Greene King IPA, Abbot; 3 changing beers (often Exeter, Sambrook's, Timothy Taylor) Ⓗ
Famous Grade II-listed former Isleworth Brewery pub on the river in old Isleworth. Rebuilt in the early 1700s, the interior is classic traditional, although opened out, with an upstairs function room with superb views. The large patio has many tables, with more on the riverbank. A real cider is served in summer. Food is popular. There is usually music on Friday evening, a poker night on Thursday and a quiz on Sunday. ঠ✿◑&●P🖵

Norwood Green

Plough
Tentelow Lane, UB2 4LG
☎ (020) 8574 7473 ⊕ ploughinnnorwoodgreen.co.uk
Fuller's London Pride, ESB; Gale's Seafarers Ale; 1 changing beer (often Fuller's, Harvey's, St Austell) Ⓗ
Dating back to circa 1650, this Grade II-listed building with low exposed beams and two real fires is Fuller's oldest tied house. The landlord takes pride in friendly service, a well-kept range of real ales and ciders, and good food served every day of the week. Musicians entertain from time to time inside the pub as well as in the garden during the summer. There is patio seating at the front. ঠ✿◑&♣♠🖵(120)✿🛜

St Margarets

Crown
174 Richmond Road, TW1 2NH
☎ (020) 8892 5896 ⊕ crowntwickenham.co.uk

Harvey's Sussex Best Bitter; Surrey Hills Shere Drop;
Young's London Original Ⓗ
A large pub dating from about 1730 and Grade II listed,
with a substantial refurbishment enhancing the Georgian
heritage of the original building. Several windows and
doors are original. The Victorian hall at the back has been
opened up for dining and the courtyard garden
attractively remodelled. Inside are various seating areas
and three fireplaces – the one in the bar with a real fire.
Food is served throughout the day. ⃰⃰⃰⃰⃰⃰⃰⃰⃰⃰

Teddington

Masons Arms

41 Walpole Road, TW11 8PJ
☎ (020) 8977 6521 ⊕ the-masons-arms.co.uk
Sambrook's Junction Ale; Vale Best IPA; 2 changing
beers (sourced nationally; often Andwell, Kissingate,
Sambrook's) Ⓗ
A small, friendly back-street community free house built
in 1860. It is a beer drinkers' haven, with bottles, pictures
and pub memorabilia on display. Carpeting and
comfortable seating create a cosy atmosphere. There is a
log-burning stove, a dartboard and a small secluded rear
patio. Music evenings include a bring-your-own-vinyl
night on the third Tuesday of the month. Guest beers
come from a wide range of UK independent brewers.
Local CAMRA Pub of the Year 2019. ⃰⃰⃰⃰⃰⃰⃰⃰

Twickenham

Prince Albert

30 Hampton Road, TW2 5QB
☎ (020) 8894 3963
Fuller's Oliver's Island, London Pride, ESB; 1 changing
beer (often Big Smoke) Ⓗ
Opened by the Star Brewery in 1840, this convivial pub
was unofficially known later as Wiffen's, run by three
generations of the family whose name is still displayed
behind the bar. It has an attractive garden, a Thai
restaurant and live music on a Saturday evening. Two
annual beer festivals feature small brewers. The smoking
patio has a sports screen.
⃰⃰⃰⃰⃰⃰(Strawberry Hill) ⃰⃰⃰

Rifleman

7 Fourth Cross Road, TW2 5EL
☎ (020) 8255 0205
Butcombe Original; Young's Bitter; 3 changing beers
(often Twickenham) Ⓗ
A gem of a traditional late-Victorian pub, originally a
19th-century beer house whose name commemorates
riflemen billeted nearby in Napoleonic times. It benefits
from a small beer garden, front patio and close proximity
to several bus routes. Definitely a community hub, it has
board games, TV sport and events on Thursdays.
Twickenham Stadium and Harlequins rugby clubs are a
15-minute walk. A Twickenham Fine Ales house since
July 2019. ⃰⃰(Strawberry Hill)⃰⃰⃰⃰⃰

White Swan

Riverside, TW1 3DN
☎ (020) 8744 2951 ⊕ whiteswantwickenham.co.uk
Otter Bitter; Twickenham Naked Ladies Ⓗ
A Grade II-listed building and an award-winning
traditional pub, built around 1690. Entry is via steps up to
the first floor, with real fires and walls covered with
rugby and other memorabilia. A small veranda/balcony
and a triclinium (a three-sided room with window seats)
afford views of the river and Eel Pie Island. Directly
opposite is a larger beer garden (tides permitting), right
on the water's edge. A summer beer festival and an
annual raft race are held. Q⃰⃰⃰⃰⃰⃰⃰⃰⃰

William Webb Ellis

24 London Road, TW1 3RR
☎ (020) 8744 4300
Greene King IPA, Abbot; Sharp's Doom Bar;
Twickenham Naked Ladies; 8 changing beers (often
Oakham, Twickenham, Windsor & Eton) Ⓗ
What was Twickenham's post office is now a spacious
Wetherspoon venue in the centre of the home of English
rugby, named after the schoolboy said to have invented
the game. Twelve handpumps are in constant use and
food is served all day. Silent screens show live news and
sport. There is a patio outside to the rear. Licensing
restrictions stipulate there is no new admittance an hour
before last orders. ⃰⃰⃰⃰⃰⃰⃰⃰

Definitions

bivvy – beer
bumclink – inferior beer
bunker – beer
cooper – half stout, half porter
gatters – beer
shant of gatter – glass of beer
half and half – mixture of ale and porter, much favoured by medical students
humming – strong (as applied to drink)
ponge or pongelow – beer, half and half
purl – mixture of hot ale and sugar, with wormwood infused
rot-gut – bad
small beer shandy – gaffs ale and gingerbeer
shant – pot or quart (shant of bivvy – quart of beer)
swipes – soup or small beer
wobble-shop – shop where beer sold without a licence

J C Hotten, The Slang Dictionary, 1887

GREATER MANCHESTER

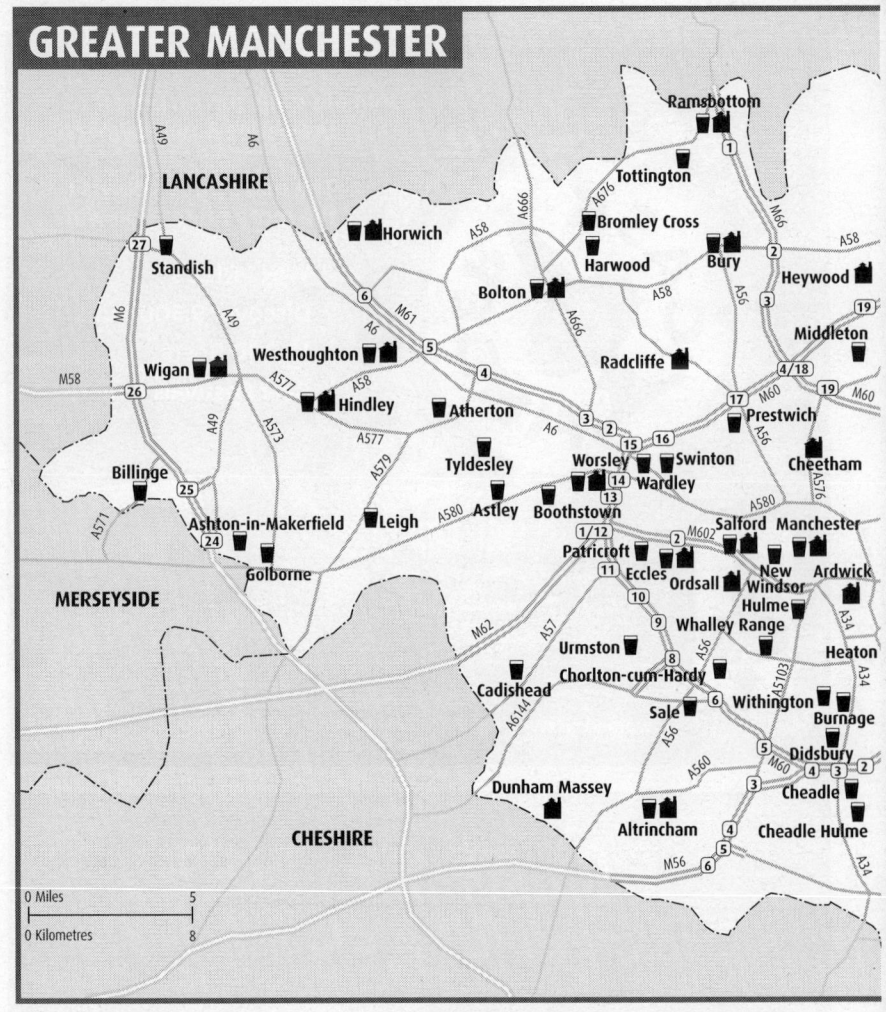

Altrincham

Costello's Bar Ⓛ

18 Goose Green, WA14 1DW (alleyway from Stamford New Rd/opp Regent Rd, adjacent to new hospital)
☎ (0161) 929 0903 ⊕ costellosbar.co.uk
Dunham Massey Big Tree Bitter, Dunham Dark; 5 changing beers (sourced locally; often Dunham Massey) Ⓗ
Small bar in Altrincham's attractive and popular Goose Green, behind the new hospital. The taphouse for Dunham Massey Brewery, it has a modern feel with smart, clean decor, and is a favourite both with locals and visitors. On the bar there are seven handpumps that feature a continually changing selection of beers from the brewery's 25 recipes. Numerous award certificates adorn the walls, reflecting the bar's fine reputation. 🛏️🏵️🍴♿🕏🚌🅿️🐾☀️🛜

Jack in the Box

Altrincham Market Hall, Market Street, WA14 1SA
☎ 07917 792060
House beer (by Blackjack); 4 changing beers (sourced nationally) Ⓗ

A Blackjack Brewery bar in the popular Altrincham Market House, part of the town's historic market. The small bar houses six handpumps, two dispensing beers from Blackjack and the others mostly ales from elsewhere including local breweries such as Track, Squawk and Stubborn Mule. Eight keg taps are on the back wall. The casks and kegs are housed in a chilled cellar behind the bar. Food is available throughout the Market House. 🛏️🏵️🍴♿🕏🚌🅿️🐾☀️🛜

Old Packet House

1 Navigation Road, WA14 1LW
☎ (0161) 929 1331
Tatton Blonde; Timothy Taylor Landlord Ⓗ
Dating back to the 18th century, this was once the second inn on the journey from Manchester along the Bridgewater Canal, which runs just behind the pub. Leaded and stained glass feature in the back bar and partitions around the pub. The main bar area is divided by an impressive central chimney, warmed by a real fire in winter. Home-cooked food is popular with local office workers at lunchtime. Attractions include a quiz night on Monday, karaoke on Friday and frequent football on TV. 🛏️🏵️🍴🕏♣️🅿️🐾☀️🛜

This sister pub to Cask Liverpool Road is on the ground floor of a newly built complex, adjacent to the Rochdale Canal and within the marina area at New Islington. It serves a changing range of six handpulled ales from local and regional breweries, plus a cider on handpump and 20 keg beers, some from Spain and other European countries. A courtyard overlooking the marina is open to 9pm every day. ♿🚃(New Islington)♣🐕🌸

Ashton-in-Makerfield

Twisted Vine Ale House 🅛

15 Wigan Road, WN4 9AR

☎ (01942) 716472

7 changing beers (sourced regionally) 🅗

A microbar from Hophurst Brewery opened in 2018, offering seven cask handpumps, six keg taps, three real ciders and a selection of gins, spirits and wines. It has a quiz night and beer club, and hosts live music on Sundays and the first Thursday of the month. It is open to over-18s only and welcomes dogs. Local CAMRA Pub of the Year 2019. 🐕🚋🌸

Ashton-under-Lyne

Ash Tree ✔

9-11 Wellington Road, OL6 6DA

☎ (0161) 339 9670

Greene King Abbot; Moorhouse's Blond Witch; Ruddles Best Bitter 🅗**; Sharp's Doom Bar** 🅗**/**🅖**; 4 changing beers (sourced regionally)** 🅗

Directly facing the Victorian Market Hall, this pub was extended into the former snooker hall next door in 2019. Its upper-floor veranda overlooks a beer garden that stretches the depth of the building, creating a space that is particularly attractive in fine weather. The pub's 11 handpumps serve Wetherspoon's regular beers plus others sourced locally and nationwide. It is easily accessible by bus, train and tram from all over Greater Manchester. Families are welcome in the lower dining level. 🌞🏛️🍽️♿🚃🐕🚲🅿️🚋📶

Astley

Cart & Horses Hotel

221 Manchester Road, M29 7SD

☎ (01942) 886530

Joseph Holt Bitter 🅗

Friendly traditional roadside community pub with darts and dominoes teams. The lounge has two separate seating areas with a third used for dining. The vault is through the door on the right as you enter. There is a large beer garden and patio at the back and some benches at the front. Good-value food is served every day and there are regular live music nights.
Q🌞🏛️🍽️♣🅿️🚌(34)🌸

Atherton

Pendle Witch

2-4 Warburton Place, M46 0EQ

☎ (01942) 884537

Moorhouse's Black Cat, Premier Bitter, Pride of Pendle, Blond Witch, Pendle Witches Brew; 2 changing beers 🅗

The Pendle is hidden down a narrow alley near the church and Market Place. Here you will find the full range of Moorhouse's beers plus guests and a selection of Belgian bottled beers. There is a conservatory at the front and a games area and bar to the rear. The well-kept patio is popular in summer. 🌞🏛️♿🌳♣🅿️🚌(V2)

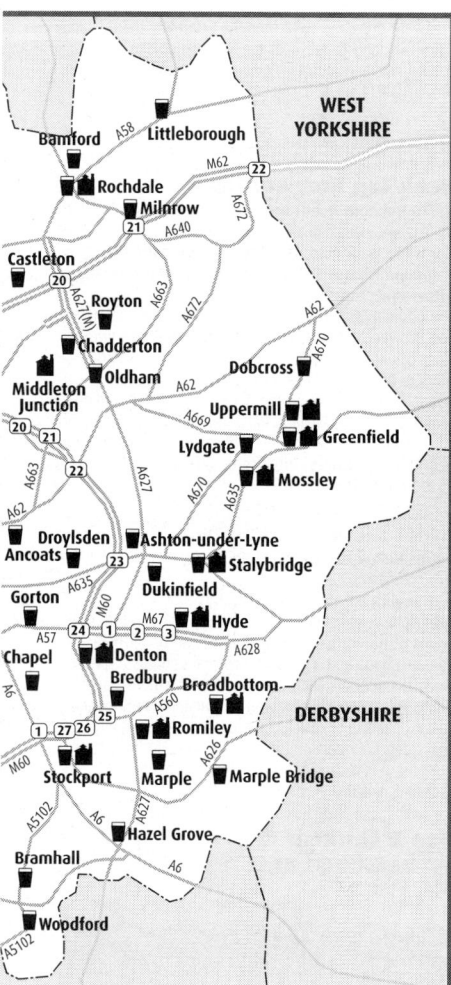

Pi 🅛

18 Shaws Road, WA14 1QU

☎ (0161) 929 9098

Tatton Blonde; 2 changing beers (sourced nationally; often RedWillow, Saltaire, Stubborn Mule) 🅗

Next door to the bustling Market Hall eatery, the smaller Pi is quieter but still popular. Its three handpumps serve one regular beer from Tatton and two guests. There are also guest keg beers from breweries such as Cloudwater and Lervig, plus a wide selection of bottles and cans in the large fridges. More seating is available upstairs. Outside at the front are pavement tables with blankets for cooler weather. Pieminister pies and mash are served daily. 🌞🏛️🍽️♿🚃🐕🍴🚋🌸📶

Ancoats

Cask

2 New Union Street, Cotton Field Wharf, M4 6FQ (over bridge from Redhill St)

☎ (0161) 392 0809

6 changing beers (sourced regionally; often Squawk) 🅗

Taphouse

119 Market Street, M46 0DF

☎ (01942) 367519

4 changing beers (sourced regionally) ⊞

The Taphouse is a micropub on the main street in the centre of Atherton. Inside this comfortable, friendly one-room bar there are four tables with extra seating at the sides. There is also a small yard area at the back. Beers are generally from small regional microbreweries and are competitively priced. ⛷❀&●🖵(V2)🛜

Bamford

Elephant & Castle ✓

608 Bury Road, OL11 4AU

☎ (01706) 640793

Wainwright; 3 changing beers (often Acorn, Ascot) ⊞

An attractive stone-built gastro-pub on the main road between Rochdale and Bury, recently extended at the rear. The building was destined to become housing and was bought by a family to retain it as a community resource. The focus is on good-quality dining at reasonable prices, and also well-kept real ales on four handpumps and a well-stocked gin bar. Independent of tie, this traditional friendly local serves Wainwright alongside three guest ales from smaller breweries. ❀◑&P🖵

Billinge

Masons Arms

99 Carr Mill Road, WN5 7TY

☎ (01744) 603572

5 changing beers (sourced regionally) ⊞

Friendly, traditional, community-based pub on the edge of open countryside, run by members of the same family for over 200 years. The warm and welcoming bar, where the single TV allows the opportunity to chat without glaring music or noise, is adorned with rugby memorabilia. There is also a quiet side lounge area. All areas are dog- and child-friendly. Externally there is an extensive landscaped beer garden overlooking the countryside and an interesting smoking shelter. ❀&●P🖵(137)🐾🛜

Bolton

Bank Top Brewery Tap �Ⓛ

68-70 Belmont Road, Astley Bridge, BL1 7AN

☎ (01204) 302837 ⊕ banktopbrewery.com

Bank Top Dark Mild, Flat Cap, Pavilion Pale Ale, Palomino Rising; 5 changing beers (sourced locally; often Bank Top) ⊞

The original taphouse for the multi award-winning Bank Top Brewery, based less than a mile away. This two-room street-corner community local also has a large outdoor area with smoking shelter. There are nine handpumps showcasing the brewery's ales – including regulars Flat Cap, Pavilion Pale and Dark Mild plus the current seasonal – and a guest beer. Up to six cellar-cool bag-in-box real ciders are also on offer. ⛷❀&♣●🖵🐾🛜

Great Ale at the Vaults Ⓛ

Vaults Below Market Place, BL1 2AL

☎ (01204) 773458

4 changing beers (sourced locally) ⊞

Atmospheric bar situated in the centre of the refurbished vaults of the former Market Hall, whose upper floors contain shops and a cinema. Four handpumps dispense three guest beers from near and far, plus house beer Vaults Bitter specially brewed by Outstanding Brewery. Tasting paddles of cask ale are available, plus usually one real cider. Cold bar food is offered, while in the Vaults area there is a choice of other food outlets. Q⛷◑&⇌●P🖵🛜

Hen & Chickens ✓

143 Deansgate, BL1 1EX

☎ 07850 026681

5 changing beers (sourced locally; often Lancaster, Northern Monkey, Three B's) ⊞

The Hen & Chickens has long been one of the most pleasant and popular of town-centre pubs. Its smart exterior and colourful floral displays brighten up this end of Deansgate. Inside, there is a central horseshoe bar serving both sides of the pub. Although now open plan, to the left is a smaller vault with a comfortable raised seating area, and to the right is the lounge where food is served. ❀⊙❯⇌♣🖵🛜

Northern Monkey 🅛

Nelson Square, BL1 1AQ
☎ 07737 125629 ⊕ northernmonkeybrew.co.uk
Northern Monkey Film Club, Winter Hill; 2 changing beers (sourced locally) ⊞

This pub was set up and renovated from what was previously a restaurant, though originally it was the dining room of the Pack Horse Hotel which dominated this side of Nelson Square. The four real ales include Northern Monkey beers, now brewed off-site to provide more space inside, and sometimes a couple of guests. At least one dark ale is normally available. Eight fonts serve modern keg beers from Northern Monkey and elsewhere. 🛏⊙⇌🖵❀🛜

One for the Road

Stalls F14-F15 Ashburner Street Lifestyle Hall, BL1 1TJ
☎ 07725 338773
3 changing beers (sourced locally) ⊞

This microbar is in the Lifestyle Hall of Bolton's award-winning indoor market. It serves a choice of three beers from a wide range of smaller breweries. Sharing the same large seating area at the front of the bar is a choice of take-away food stalls, with dishes from Malaysia to Cameroon alongside more standard sandwiches and pasties. Opening days and hours are restricted to those of the main market. A former local CAMRA Pub of the Year. Q🛏♿⇌●P🖵🛜

Swan & Barristers Bar

7 Bradshawgate, BL1 1EL (entrance to both bars is in the passageway between them)
☎ (01204) 365174
Bank Top Flat Cap; Moorhouse's Blond Witch; 5 changing beers (sourced locally; often Abbeydale, Blackedge, Wainwright) ⊞

A prominent Grade II-listed building comprising two separate bars with a shared courtyard and toilet area between them. The Swan is a comfortable, spacious bar which converts to a nightclub on weekend evenings. Barristers has a wood-panelled interior with a traditional pub atmosphere. Cask beers from local breweries such as Bank Top, Moorhouse's and Blackedge are supplemented by ales from breweries further afield such as Fyne, Coniston and St Austell. ❀⊙♿⇌●🖵❀🛜

Boothstown

Royal British Legion

Victoria Street, M28 1HQ (close to jct with Vicars Hall Lane)
☎ (0161) 790 2928
Joseph Holt Bitter; Wainwright ⊞

A large, friendly club, welcoming to non-members. A lounge to the right of the entrance leads to a games and TV room, and there is a function room at the rear. The spacious garden is ideal for summer drinking. Live entertainment features and a beer festival is held in November. The steward and stewardess have been awarded the Queen's medal for voluntary service. A regular winner in the Club Mirror awards and local CAMRA Club of the Year. Q🛏❀♿♣P🖵🛜

Royal Oak

18-20 Leigh Road, M28 1LZ (close to jct of Leigh Rd, Simpson Rd and Chaddock Lane)
☎ (0161) 703 8582
Joseph Holt Bitter; 1 changing beer (sourced nationally; often Marston's) ⊞

A thriving and friendly community pub with three rooms. A small, cosy room to the left of the entrance leads to a larger room where live music events, discos and darts are sometimes hosted. A vault to the right has a fire for the colder weather and a dartboard. No meals are served but there are nine different pork pies to choose from! Q🛏❀♣🖵(34,553)🐾❀🛜

Bramhall

Mounting Stone

8 Woodford Road, SK7 1JJ (at jct with Bramhall Lane South)
☎ (0161) 439 7563 ⊕ themountingstone.co.uk
Bollington Best, Long Hop; 4 changing beers (sourced locally) ⊞

The sister venue to Cheadle Hulme's Chiverton Tap, this is a cosy, friendly micropub right in the village centre. The former blacksmith's operates over two floors - ground and basement - with a small beer garden to the rear. The name derives from a local large stone that allowed riders to mount their horses. Alongside the Bollington ales are four from microbrewers, one usually a dark beer. It opened an on-site, one-barrel brewery named Made of Stone in 2018. Q🛏❀♿♣⇌●🖵❀🛜

Bredbury

Arden Arms 🅛

Ashton Road, SK6 2RY
☎ (0161) 879 4844
House beer (by Stockport); 2 changing beers (often Stockport) ⊞

A comfortable inn in a rural setting, popular with walkers and horse riders. This place, previously a Robinsons pub, was reopened in 2018. Three ales include Arden Best Bitter (Stockport Brewing's Crown Best Bitter rebadged) plus two guest ales, also typically from Stockport Brewing. The comfortable interior is open plan with lots of dark wood. Food is served daily except Tuesday. There are children's play areas indoors and outside. Barbecues are held regularly in summer. The site is reputedly haunted. Q🛏❀⊙♿♣P🖵

Broadbottom

Harewood Arms 🅛 ✔

2 Market Street, SK14 6AX
☎ (01457) 762500 ⊕ theharewoodarms.co.uk
Green Mill Chief, Old Git; 4 changing beers (sourced locally; often Green Mill) ⊞

A large pub for all the community in this quiet village on the edge of the Peak District. Home to the Green Mill Brewery, it serves five regular Green Mill ales plus seasonals, guests and a rotating real cider. Partially open plan, with various seating areas and two real fires, it also has a beer garden to the rear. Approximately five minutes' walk from Broadbottom railway station and on local bus routes. 🛏❀⊙♿▲⇌♣●🖵❀🛜

Bromley Cross

Nook & Cranny

211/213 Darwen Road, BL7 9BS
☎ 07403 030394

3 changing beers (sourced locally; often Northern Monkey, Northern Whisper) Ⓗ

Classy and friendly micropub that opened in 2018 in what was once a shop, extended into the adjacent premises a year later to provide additional seating. Large bench tables help spark a convivial atmosphere that attracts locals and visitors alike. Three handpumps dispense real ales, most from local breweries. There is also a good range of real ciders and modern keg beers. ✿≠♦P♣❀❀

Burnage

Reasons to be Cheerful

228 Fog Lane, M20 6EL (at jct with Elmsmere Rd)
☎ (0161) 425 9678 🌐 reasonsbeercafe.co.uk
3 changing beers (sourced locally) Ⓗ

Modern beer café in former beer shop premises on a shopping parade near Burnage railway station. The small, inconspicuous frontage hides a long but welcoming interior, including an alcove providing seating and a view of the street. The L-shaped bar is fitted with three handpumps, often serving a porter/stout, a bitter and a pale ale. Eight craft beer taps are mounted on the back bar, and there is also a display rack for off-sales. A secluded rear room can accommodate up to 20 people. Outside at the front is a small drinking area.
Q✿≠Ҁ(Didsbury Village) ♦❀❀☗

Bury

Art Picture House Ⓛ ✅

36 Haymarket Street, BL9 0AY (opp metro/bus station interchange)
☎ (0161) 705 4040
Brightside Odin Blonde; Greene King Abbot; Moorhouse's Blond Witch; Ruddles Best Bitter; changing beers Ⓗ

A town-centre Wetherspoon pub in a beautifully restored former 1920s cinema, opposite the Bury Interchange, handy for buses and Metrolink trams. It is on two levels and has a large seating area with several private booths facing the back bar. Eight handpumps dispense regular and changing beers from near and far, served by a team of experienced bar staff who can help with your selection. Food is available every day.
Ҁ🕭❀(Bolton St ELR) ❀♦❀☗

Broad Street Social

9 Broad Street, BL9 0DA
☎ (0161) 204 7387 🌐 broadstreetsocial.co.uk
Brewsmith Bitter, New Zealand Pale, Oatmeal Stout, IPA; 2 changing beers (often Brewsmith) Ⓗ

The new Brewsmith Brewery tap, opened in August 2020. Tastefully renovated and equipped, the interior is open plan and stripped back to the bare brickwork, allowing those with an archaeological interest to see the phases in the building's history. Six handpumps on the bar dispense a variety of Brewsmith's beers including the ever-popular Oatmeal Stout. Craft taps are also serve various guest keg beers. ❶≠(Bolton St ELR)❀❀

Elton Liberal Club

New George Street, BL8 1NW
☎ (0161) 764 1776 🌐 eltonliberalclub.co.uk
2 changing beers Ⓗ

This is a private members club (non-political) where guests have to be signed in at one per visit. The facilities include two function rooms, which members can hire, three snooker tables, sport TV and three bars. Two ever-changing real ales are served through two handpumps. The club has a bowling green surrounded by an outside

seating area. Live music features every Saturday and Sunday with a live group on the last Sunday in the month. Ҁ✿❀❀♣P❀☗

Rose & Crown Ⓛ

36 Manchester Old Road, BL9 0TR
☎ (0161) 764 6234
Moorhouse's White Witch; Oakham Citra; Phoenix Arizona; 5 changing beers (often Bradfield) Ⓗ

A traditional small but perfectly formed venue on the edge of Bury town centre, an easy walk or just two stops from Manchester Road on the 135/524 bus. The friendly pub welcomes families and dogs. It operates a loyalty beer card, with local ales among the range on its eight handpulls. An acoustic night is held on the first Thursday of every month, and live music on Saturday nights. Recently renovated, there are plans to build a beer garden. Ҁ✿≠(Bolton St ELR)❀♣❀☗

Thirsty Fish Ⓛ

Unit 1A, Princess Parade, Millgate Shopping Centre, BL9 0QL
Beartown Creme Bearlee; Brewsmith Bitter; house beer (by Beartown); 8 changing beers (often Moorhouse's, Phoenix) Ⓗ

A true microbar that opened in 2018 in what used to be a shop unit on the outside of the Mill Gate Shopping Centre. It is close to the famous Bury Market and adjacent to Bury Interchange transport hub. The bar sells eight constantly changing real ales. It also has a good selection of continental lagers. Dogs are welcome but children are not permitted. ♿≠(Bolton St ELR)❀❀☗

Trackside Bar Ⓛ ✅

Bolton Street Station, BL9 0EY (platform 2 on ELR)
☎ (0161) 764 6461
House beer (by Northern Whisper); changing beers Ⓗ

The Trackside combines some excellent ales and ciders with the nostalgia of the East Lancashire Railway. It has 12 handpumps offering a varying range of guest ales plus ELR Pale, the house beer from Northern Whisper, alongside a choice of craft keg and foreign bottled beers. A former local CAMRA branch Cider Pub of the Year, the real ciders and perries it sells are on gravity from the cellar. The station platform just outside has seating under a roof canopy for those wanting the real railway experience. ✿❀Ҁ♿A≠(Bolton St ELR)❀♦P❀☗

Cadishead

Grocers

152A Liverpool Road, M44 5DD (close to Moss Lane next to Plough)
☎ 07950 522468
3 changing beers (sourced regionally; often Blackedge, Brewsmith, Dunham Massey) Ⓗ/Ⓖ

This micropub is the 2020 CAMRA branch Pub and Cider Pub of the Year. It has one room and no bar; beers are brought to your table by the proprietor from a separate air-chilled room. One beer is on handpull and two on gravity, alongside three ciders or perries. The lack of TV, jukebox or other electronic entertainment means conversation is king. It has a yard to the rear for outside drinking. May close early if quiet.
Q✿❀❀♦❀(67,100) ❀

Castleton

Blue Pits Inn

842 Manchester Road, OL11 2SP
☎ (01706) 632151

JW Lees Bitter, Manchester Pale Ale Ⓗ; 1 changing beer (sourced locally; often JW Lees) Ⓗ/Ⓟ
Friendly local in the centre of Castleton, easily accessible by bus or train. It offers three JW Lees beers including seasonal and Boilerhouse ales. The bar has three distinct drinking areas, with pub games in the taproom and a pleasant, quieter side room. Quiz and karaoke nights regularly feature. Spot the rare tiled JW Lees mosaic on the gable wall of this former railway building.
⯊❀♿➳♣P🚊(17)🐾🐾🛜

Old Post Office Ale House 🅛

858 Manchester Road, OL11 2SP
☎ (01706) 645464
House beer (by Pictish); 4 changing beers (sourced locally; often Beartown, Outstanding) Ⓗ
Now celebrating its fifth year, this popular and award-winning microbar is always welcoming, with a roaring open fire in colder weather. Easily accessible by public transport, the bus stop to Rochdale is outside the door and the railway station is across the road. Five handpulled real ales are permanently on, of consistently good quality, together with a selection of real cider, wines and gins. The bar welcomes dogs and there is a well laid-out beer garden at the rear.
Q❀➳🚊(17)🐾🛜

Chadderton

Rose of Lancaster ✅

7 Haigh Lane, OL1 2TQ
☎ (0161) 624 3031 🌐 roseoflancaster.co.uk
JW Lees Bitter, Manchester Pale Ale; 3 changing beers (sourced locally; often JW Lees) Ⓗ
A lounge bar, conservatory restaurant and separate vault where sporting events are screened providing plenty of choice for the pub's varied clientele. Drinkers and diners mix easily in the busy lounge, and keen management ensures swift and cheerful service. Outside, a covered patio with views of the Rochdale Canal is popular in fine weather. Nearby bus and train links make for easy travel to this well-run pub. JW Lees' seasonal and Boilerhouse beers are always available. ❀◑♿➳(Mills Hill)♣P🚊🛜

Cheadle

James Watts ✅

13 High Street, SK8 1AX (on A560, jct Manchester Rd)
☎ (0161) 428 3361 🌐 thejameswatts.co.uk
House beer (by Hydes); 6 changing beers (sourced regionally; often Hydes) Ⓗ
An old pub given new life by a tasteful refit in 2017. What was once the Old Star is now an upmarket, well-appointed bar. It is traditional at the front, with various seating areas throughout, including a space at the back with tables for both dining and drinking. Outside is a gravelled patio area. Although a Hydes house, this is one of the few in its estate to offer guest ales from other local and regional brewers. Q❀◑♣🛖🚊

Cheadle Hulme

Archive Bar & Bottle

2 Mellor Road, SK8 5AU (at jct with Station Rd)
4 changing beers (sourced regionally) Ⓗ
Opened in 2019, this homely, modern micropub occupies what were once restaurant premises opposite the station. The place operates over two floors with the upstairs accessed by a spiral staircase, divided into a lounge area and snug (toilets are here too). Four changing ales are served, one usually a dark beer. The bar also offers 12 eclectic keg lines and two keg ciders. A

well-stocked fridge holds over 300 beers. Note the archive display of beer bottles on shelves throughout every room. ⯊❀◑➳🛖🐾🛜

Chiverton Tap

8 Mellor Road, SK8 5AU (off Station Rd)
☎ (0161) 485 4149 🌐 thechivertontap.co.uk
Bollington Best, Long Hop; 4 changing beers (sourced locally) Ⓗ
Friendly micropub in what was once Arthur Chiverton's draper's shop. Note the mosaic in the doorway and framed displays of photographs and drapery tools on the walls and bar. Alongside its cask and keg beers, the venue serves a wide variety of gins and a changing bag-in-box real cider. In 2019 it added a first-floor function room and an outside area at the rear with tables.
Q⯊❀♿➳🛖🐾🛜

Chorlton-cum-Hardy

Beer House 🅛

57 Manchester Road, M21 9PW
☎ (0161) 881 9206
Marble Pint, Manchester Bitter; 4 changing beers (sourced locally; often Ilkley, Pomona Island, Squawk) Ⓗ
Ever-popular micropub whose knowledgeable staff provide a warm welcome. The focus is on quality beer, with regulars Manchester Bitter and Pint plus a changing selection of guests. Top-quality craft beers are served from the keg, along with excellent canned and bottled brews. Traditional games supplement games console favourites from the 1980s. No food is served but bar snacks are available. ⯊❀🚊🛖🚊(86)🐾🛜

Chorlton Tap 🅛

533 Wilbraham Road, M21 0UE
☎ (0161) 861 7576 🌐 chorltontap.wixsite.com/chorltontap
Wander Beyond Peak; 5 changing beers (sourced regionally; often Howard Town, Pictish, Wander Beyond) Ⓗ
This taproom for the Wander Beyond brewery was previously a beer specialist for 25 years as the Bar. What was once two distinct properties is now a small bar area and spacious adjacent room. Two handpumps and several keg lines dispense the brewery's beers, alongside four guests on handpump. Monday is quiz night. Food is available Friday to Sunday. There is outside seating front and back. ⯊❀◑🚊🛖🚊🐾🛜

Font 🅛

115-117 Manchester Road, M21 9PG
☎ (0161) 871 2022 🌐 thefontbar.wordpress.com
6 changing beers (sourced nationally; often Mallinsons, RedWillow, Track) Ⓗ
This notable beer and cider haven has been voted local CAMRA Cider Pub of the Year seven times in the last eight years. It features up to six varying real ales on the bar, one usually from RedWillow. There are also 16 keg lines of which roughly half are regularly changing guests. A small font wall dispenses up to six ciders. The open kitchen serves breakfast as well as a full menu daily. A quiz is held on Tuesday. ⯊❀◑🚊🛖🚊(86)🐾🛜

Sedge Lynn 🅛 ✅

21A Manchester Road, M21 9PN
☎ (0161) 860 0141
Moorhouse's Blond Witch; Phoenix Wobbly Bob; Ruddles Best Bitter; house beer (by Brightside); 6 changing beers (sourced nationally; often Acorn, Hawkshead, Kelham Island) Ⓗ
Built by Norman Evans as a billiard hall for the temperance movement, this Grade II-listed building with

a barrelled roof and Art Deco styling is well worth a look. Now a Wetherspoon establishment, it provides a typical selection of ales – the manager's aim is to ensure there is always a range of light to darker beers available on the 10 handpumps, with six changing guests.
Q❀◐♿⚲♣🚌📶

Denton

Carters Arms

Stockport Road, M34 6AQ
☎ (0161) 320 3752
Black Sheep Best Bitter; Wainwright; 2 changing beers (sourced locally) H
Friendly local with two large open-plan rooms. The lounge-style room to the left is regularly hired out for functions for up to 70 people; the traditional bar/games room on the right features wood panelling and dark leather seating. The pool team plays on Wednesday, live music happens on Friday, karaoke and disco night is Saturday. Children are welcome until 8pm. There is wheelchair access to the rear. You can get to the pub by bus from Manchester and Stockport. Q♿♣P🚌🐾

Crown Point Tavern L

16 Market Street, M34 2XW (in pedestrianised Denton Civic Square)
☎ (0161) 337 9615 🌐 thecrownpointtavern.co.uk
5 changing beers (sourced locally) H
A micropub on the pedestrianised Denton Civic Square, popular for watching sports TV. Six real ales are served, typically from Greater Manchester, with tasting notes on a chalkboard. They are complemented by an extensive selection of bottled local craft beers, two real ciders and a range of gins. Entertainment includes a DJ on Sunday.
Q❀♿♣🚌🐾📶

Howard's Neighbourhood Bar

49 Manchester Road, M34 2AF
☎ 07951 972015
House beer (by Beartown); 2 changing beers (sourced locally; often Beartown) H
Opened in December 2019 opposite Denton post office, this spacious open-plan bar serves three handpulled real ales, usually including one from Beartown Brewery who helped install the cellar. It also has six craft keg taps, one dedicated to cider (usually Mortimers from Westons). Cheese and meat boards are available daily. A quiz is hosted every other Wednesday. Children are welcome until 7pm. Easily reached by buses that serve Crown Point. ◐♿🚌🐾📶

Lowes Arms

301 Hyde Road, M34 3FF
☎ (0161) 336 3064 🌐 lowesarms.co.uk
Lowes Arms Apex EGA, Into the Light, Force 8 SB, Into the Shadows; 4 changing beers (sourced locally) H
Built in 1824 to serve the new Manchester Road, this thriving local has a reputation for quality beers and good-value food. The real ales served are all brewed on-site in the cellar, where traditional stillage is used. The comfortable lounge to the left is the main food area. To the right is the vault with a pool table; the room can be used for functions. It holds occasional beer festivals over bank holiday weekends, and there is a large beer garden. Q❀◐♿♣P🚌(201)🐾📶

Didsbury

Fletcher Moss ✔

1 William Street, M20 6RQ (off Wilmslow Rd, A5145 via Albert Hill St)
☎ (0161) 438 0073
Hydes Lowry, Original; 5 changing beers (sourced nationally; often Hydes) H
Named after the alderman who donated the nearby botanical gardens, this thriving community local provides a haven for lively conversation. Three traditional front snugs display a collection of pretty porcelain teapots. The rear opens into a conservatory leading to covered terraces and a beer garden. A quiz is held on Tuesday and acoustic music plays on alternate Mondays. The TVs are silent except for major sporting events.
Q❀♿⇄⚲(Village) 🚌📶

Gateway ✔

882 Wilmslow Road, M20 5PG (jct Kingsway and Manchester Rd)
☎ (0161) 438 1700
Greene King Abbot; Ruddles Best Bitter; house beer (by Brightside); 5 changing beers (sourced nationally) H
This comfortable and popular late-1930s roadhouse, conveniently located opposite the Parrs Wood leisure complex and public transport interchange, stands out due to its welcoming atmosphere, enthusiastic staff and excellent beer. The large Wetherspoon pub's central island bar is surrounded by distinct seating areas, ensuring that you can always have a quiet drink somewhere. An upstairs function room hosts local social activities and groups.
Q❀◐♿⇄(E Didsbury) ⚲(E Didsbury) ♣P🚌📶

Dobcross

Dobcross Band Social Club L

Platt Lane, OL3 5AD
☎ (01457) 873741 🌐 dobcross.club
Bradfield Farmers Blonde; JW Lees Manchester Pale Ale; 2 changing beers (sourced locally; often Joseph Holt, Ossett) H
This not-for-profit members' club welcomes visitors at all times, offering great views of the Saddleworth Moors and a good choice of great beers. The present building dates from 1967, although the club has been in existence for over 100 years. The function room is available for hire, with a snooker table and BT Sports. Crown Green bowling takes place in the summer and the Whit Friday brass band contest is held here. Current local CAMRA Club of the Year. ♿♣P🚌(356)🐾📶

Navigation Inn L

21-23 Wool Road, OL3 5NS
☎ (01457) 872418 🌐 thenavigationdobcross.com
Greene King Abbot; Millstone Tiger Rut; Timothy Taylor Landlord; 1 changing beer (often Millstone) H
A popular, traditional inn next to the Huddersfield Narrow Canal, with four beers on handpump. The family-run pub dates from 1806 and was originally built for the benefit of the navvies on the canal. It offers locally sourced, home-made and freshly prepared food every day lunchtime and early evening, and welcomes families and dogs. The annual August Saddleworth Rushcart Festival event stops off here.
Q❀◐♿P🚌(350,356) 🐾📶

Droylsden

Silly Country Bar & Bottle Shop L

121 Market Street, M43 7AR
4 changing beers (sourced locally) H
Modern open-plan bar and bottle shop on the corner of Droylsden Shopping Centre. Opened in 2018 by a small group of local real ale enthusiasts, it has provided a

much-needed boost to the real ale scene in the area. Five handpumps dispense four mostly local ales and a cider, complemented by an extensive range of bottled beers and ciders. Droylsden tram stop is across the road from the bar. Q✿❄☗☘♣●♬(216,168)❀☂

Dukinfield

Angel
197 King Street, SK16 4TH
☎ (0161) 830 0223 ● theangeldukinfield.co.uk
4 changing beers (sourced nationally) Ⓗ
Popular and well-furnished community pub near the centre of Dukinfield, featuring a traditional snug to the left and lounge to the right. The bar offers four constantly changing beers from national and local breweries. A quiz is hosted on Sunday and the pub has local league teams in pool, darts, dominoes and crib. Children are welcome until 8pm. The sizeable upstairs function room has its own bar and is available to hire. ☗✿☗♣P♬(330)❀☂

Victoria Hotel
92 Victoria Road, SK16 4UP
☎ (0161) 330 2916
1 changing beer (sourced regionally; often Robinsons) Ⓗ
Lively suburban community pub owned by Robinsons, offering one rotating real ale from the Robinsons range. Although open plan, the three rooms are still quite distinct, with a pool table in one. The pub hosts free pool on Wednesday, karaoke/DJ on Friday and live acts alternating Saturday and Sunday. Regular family events, particularly on bank holidays, often including children's entertainment such as a bouncy castle.
☗✿☗♬≒♣P♬(330) ❀☂

Eccles

Lamb Hotel ★
33 Regent Street, M30 0BP (opp Metrolink station)
☎ 07827 850252
Joseph Holt Bitter, Mild; 1 changing beer (sourced nationally) Ⓗ
Classic Grade II-listed red-brick and terracotta Joseph Holt Edwardian pub dating from 1906. A central bar serves a vault on one side and on the other a lobby that leads to lounges and a billiard room with a full-sized original Burroughes & Watts table. The interior features Jacobean-style door surrounds, a terrazzo floor and a dado of green tiles leading to a screened, curved mahogany bar displaying polished brass and exquisite etched glass. The pub has featured in several TV dramas. Q≒☗♣P♬❀☂

Golborne

Queen Anne
14 Bridge Street, WA3 3PZ
☎ (01942) 726922 ● queenanne-golborne.co.uk
2 changing beers (sourced regionally) Ⓗ
Tucked away on Bridge Street just off the East Lancs Road, the Queen Anne is handy for Haydock Park racecourse and caters for pre-race parties. Home-cooked food is served in the bar and separate dining area, with early-bird specials on weekdays plus Sunday roasts. The beer garden is a suntrap in summer. Q☗✿☗P♬(10)☂

Gorton

Vale Cottage
Kirk Street, M18 8UE (off Hyde Rd A57)
☎ (0161) 223 4568 ● thevalecottage.co.uk

Timothy Taylor Landlord; 2 changing beers (sourced nationally) Ⓗ
Well hidden in the Gore Brook conservation area, the Vale Cottage has the feel of a country pub. Parts date from the 17th century, hence the low-beamed ceilings, multiple drinking areas and reputed ghost. A relaxed, friendly atmosphere, where conversation predominates, is disturbed on Tuesday by a lively and popular general knowledge quiz. Indulge in an excellent home-cooked meal in the garden, or even join in the music quiz and steak night on the last Thursday of the month.
Q✿❄◗☗≒P♬☂

Greenfield

Wellington Inn 🅛
29 Chew Valley Road, OL3 7AF
Coach House Gunpowder Mild; Mansfield Cask Ale; Millstone Tiger Rut; Phoenix Arizona; Salopian Lemon Dream; Wainwright; 2 changing beers (sourced locally; often Donkeystone, Phoenix) Ⓗ
A stone-built free house on the main road through the village. The building comprises a small bar area offering seven handpulled beers, a main room popular with diners, and a recently refurbished side room with a dartboard, cribbage and dominoes. Some sports are shown on TVs in both rooms. Good-value home-cooked food is usually available on Wednesday, Friday and Sunday. There is limited pavement seating at the front. ☗Å≒♣♬(180,350) ❀☂

Harwood

House without a Name 🅛
75 Lea Gate, BL2 3ET
☎ (01204) 457802 ● housewithoutaname.co.uk
Joseph Holt Bitter; Sharp's Doom Bar; 4 changing beers (sourced locally; often Moorhouse's, Northern Monkey, Titanic) Ⓗ
Locally known as the No Name, this cosy terraced venue was two 1830s cottages before being refurbished and sensitively modernised, retaining the flag floors and wooden beams. Its main lounge has a bar servery and features a chalkboard beer listing, real fire and TV showing sport. There is also a small bar to the left. Simple bar food is served during opening hours.
☗♬(480,507) ❀☂

Hazel Grove

Grove Alehouse
145 London Road, SK7 4HH (opp Hope St)
☎ 07594 123174
5 changing beers (sourced regionally) Ⓗ
Micropub with an airy feel, set in a former butcher's premises. Its bar is made from reclaimed wood and sits in an L-shaped drinking area with a good mix of bench seating, bar stools, tables and chairs. The five handpumped beers include a dark ale and are mostly from local producers. Three real ciders are served from the fridge. Bring-your-own cheese tastings are held on the first Sunday of the month. Q☗✿❄≒♣●♬❀☂

Heaton Chapel

Heaton Hops
7 School Lane, SK4 5DE (jct with Manchester Rd)
☎ (0161) 442 3541 ● heatonhops.co.uk
2 changing beers (sourced regionally) Ⓗ
Since opening in 2015, this cosy, intimate and popular micropub has won several local awards. As well as the main bar area, there is a small room downstairs and a

modest amount of seating outside on the pavement. Two cask ales are on handpump plus eight beers on keg taps, with takeaways available in special flagons. A large range of bottle-conditioned beers is also on sale. Heaton Chapel railway station is a short walk away. ⏴☸❄🚆

Hindley

Hare & Hounds 🄻
31 Ladies Lane, WN2 2QA
☎ (01942) 200370
5 changing beers 🄷
This small but traditional pub is located between Hindley railway station and the town centre. It has a large, cosy lounge and a distinct bar/vault area. The lounge displays pictures from bygone Hindley and has a large-screen TV for sports. The pub has darts teams playing in the local league. Quiz night is on Thursday evening. Beers are from Wigan Brewhouse along with other local breweries and further afield. ⏴☸❄♣♥🎕

Horwich

Bank Top Brewery Ale House 🄻 ✔
36 Church Street, BL6 6AD
☎ (01204) 693793 🌐 banktopbrewery.com
Bank Top Bad to the Bone, Dark Mild, Flat Cap, Pavilion Pale Ale, Palomino Rising, Port o' Call; 3 changing beers (sourced locally; often Bank Top) 🄷
Award-winning Bank Top Brewery pub, in a conservation area opposite Horwich parish church and alongside 18th and 19th-century cottages associated with the area's history of textiles and bleaching. The pub serves eight beers from Bank Top, including Dark Mild, a former Champion Mild of Britain, plus one changing guest. Alongside are up to six real ciders and perries, most kept cellar cool. Walkers and their dogs are welcome.
Q⏴☸♣♥🚆(125) 🎕

Brewery Bar 🄻
Moreton Mill, Hampson Street, BL6 7JH (just behind Old Original Bay Horse)
☎ (01204) 692976 🌐 thebrewerybar.co.uk
Blackedge Hop, Black, Pike; 4 changing beers (sourced locally; often Blackedge) 🄷
This bar above the award-winning Blackedge Brewery has seven handpumps serving its beers, plus a range of real ciders. Converted from a former industrial premises and retaining some original features, it has varnished bench tables and stools spread throughout a large drinking area. Locally made pork and Blackedge Ale pies are usually available. The brewery is visible through large glass windows as you enter. Note: there is no lift.
⏴☸♣♥🚆🎕

Crown 🄻
1 Chorley New Road, BL6 7QJ
☎ 07827 850221
Joseph Holt Mild, IPA, Bitter, Two Hoots; 4 changing beers (sourced locally; often Bank Top, Blackedge, Bootleg) 🄷
A spacious, comfortable and popular landmark pub whose multi-room layout provides a home to many community activities. The separate pool and games room with its own bar hosts darts, dominoes and pool teams. Elsewhere are quiet drinking areas and a large sports TV. There is live entertainment on Saturday and Sunday evening and home-cooked food is served every day. The Crown's location attracts outdoor enthusiasts stopping for a pint after enjoying the beautiful countryside of the neighbouring West Pennine Moors.
⏴☸🍴♣🚆(125,575) 🎕🎕

Hulme

Salutation
12 Higher Chatham Street, M15 6ED
☎ (0161) 247 6465 🌐 thesalutationpub.com
Bollington Best, Long Hop; 3 changing beers (sourced nationally) 🄷
A gem of a pub hidden away from the busy Oxford Road, tucked away inside the expanded Manchester Metropolitan University and adjacent to the Students' Union. Now owned by the University, the pub was built on the site of lodgings used by Charlotte Bronte and her father, where she began to write Jane Eyre. The late Chris Sievey gave his last performance here, as his alter ego Frank Sidebottom. Quality traditional pub food is served. ⏴🍴♿🚆(Oxford Rd) ♣♥🚆🎕

Hyde

Cheshire Ring Hotel 🄻
72-74 Manchester Road, SK14 2BJ
☎ 07917 055629
6 changing beers 🄷
One of the oldest pubs in Hyde. Seven handpumps offer a range of ales from Beartown Brewery plus micros near and far, in addition to ciders, perries and continental beers. A selection of bottled beers is also stocked. Home-made curries are available on Thursday evening and Sunday is quiz night. Opening hours vary with the season. ⏴☸❄♥🚆(201)🎕

Sportsman Inn 🄻
57 Mottram Road, SK14 2NN (exit of Morrisons car park)
☎ (0161) 368 5000
Rossendale Floral Dance, Glen Top Bitter, Ale, Halo Pale, Pitch Porter, Sunshine 🄷
This former regional CAMRA award winner is popular with locals and retains its character while offering a full range of Rossendale Brewery ales. Upstairs, a restaurant serves Cuban tapas and vegetarian options. Wednesday is curry night and on Sunday there is a traditional roast from noon until it's gone. The pub is home to pool and chess teams. Its rear patio includes a covered and heated smoking area. ⏴☸🍴❄♣🚆🎕🎕

Leigh

Bobbin
38A Leigh Road, WN7 1QR
☎ (01942) 581242 🌐 thebobbinleigh.co.uk
4 changing beers (sourced locally) 🄷
One-room micropub on the edge of the town centre, offering a warm welcome and comfortable seating. Beers are from regional microbreweries, with current and future selections shown on the website. A dark beer and a real cider are always available, and prices are competitive. Open from 1pm on Sundays when Leigh RLFC are at home. Q♿♥🚆🎕🎕

Weavers Arms ✔
9-13 Lord Street, WN7 1DP
☎ (01942) 267510
3 changing beers (sourced nationally) 🄷
The Weavers Arms is situated in the centre of town just off the main shopping street. During the day it has a relaxed atmosphere, with shoppers and families dining. In the evening it is a popular meeting place, with football and rugby shown on TV and entertainment at weekends. There are special offers on cask beers on Tuesday and Wednesday. ⏴☸🍴♿♣🚆🎕

Littleborough

Hare on the Hill

132 Hare Hill Road, OL15 9HL

☎ 07955 542787 ● hare-on-the-hill.co.uk

Vocation Bread & Butter; 4 changing beers (often Pictish, Saltaire, Tiny Rebel) Ⓗ

A small, busy pub just up from the centre of the village. Four changing cask ales are available plus four craft kegs, two craft lagers and the occasional real cider. Excellent fresh food from an inventive menu is cooked on the premises daily (book ahead at weekends). There is a large beer garden to the rear with plenty of cover, and dogs are welcome. The bus stop is across the road.
❀◗≠●🅿🚍(518) ❀🛜

White House Ⓛ

Blackstone Edge, Halifax Road, OL15 0LG

☎ (01706) 378456 ● thewhitehousepub.co.uk

Theakston Best Bitter; 3 changing beers (often Abbeydale, Newby Wyke) Ⓗ

This old coaching house, originally called the Coach & Horses, dates from 1671 and is 1,300 feet above sea level. A family-run establishment for 30 years, it offers a warm and friendly welcome. Theakston Best is a regular, complemented by three changing beers. Good food is served daily from an extensive menu. There is a bus stop on the Rochdale to Halifax route outside the front door. The famous Pennine Way passes this hostelry.
Q❀❀◗&🅿🚍(X58) 🛜

Lydgate

White Hart Inn Ⓛ ✅

51 Stockport Road, OL4 4JJ

☎ (01457) 872566 ● thewhitehart.co.uk

JW Lees Bitter; Timothy Taylor Golden Best, Boltmaker; 3 changing beers Ⓗ

A country pub-restaurant with impressive views over the surrounding countryside and Greater Manchester. A free house, it serves three regular beers from JW Lees and Timothy Taylor plus guest ales usually from local breweries. The building dates from 1788 and was once a police station. The multi-room layout has log-burning stoves in the bar area and brasserie. Quality food is served daily from an award-winning kitchen. The pub hosts a variety of events including themed dinners and wine tastings. Q❀❀🛏◗&🅿🚍(180,184)❀🛜

Manchester

Angel

6 Angel Street, M4 4BQ (off Rochdale Rd)

☎ (0161) 833 4786

10 changing beers (sourced nationally) Ⓗ

The Angel is found huddled within a flurry of new development in what was a notorious slum area known as Angel Meadow. The busy junction on Rochdale Road makes it a hard place to reach at times, but it is worth making the effort, and in winter there is often a warming real fire. With a fine selection of beers and ciders adorning the 12 handpumps, usually including at least one dark beer, there is something for everyone.
❀❀≠(Victoria) 🚇(Shudehill) ●🅿❀🛜

Beatnikz Republic Bar

35 Dale Street, M1 2HF (corner of Dale St and Tariff St)

☎ 07761 800828 ● beatnikzrepublic.com

3 changing beers (often Beatnikz Republic)

Open since 2018 in part of a Grade II-listed former office block, the bar is less than a mile from the Beatnikz Republic Brewery. Entering up a number of steps reveals a long, narrow room with high tables to the left and

table and bench seating to the right, and the bar at the far end. There are four handpumps for the brewery's cask ales and a cider, plus 14 keg fonts on the back wall.
≠(Piccadilly) 🚇(Piccadilly Gardens) ●❀

Cafe Beermoth

40A Spring Gardens, M2 1EN (entrance is on Brown St)

☎ (0161) 835 2049 ● beermoth.co.uk/cafe

7 changing beers (sourced nationally) Ⓗ

Welcoming modern bar near Market Street, with a Belgian flavour and a relaxed and fun city-centre atmosphere. It serves an excellent range of beers from seven cask handpumps, plus 10 keg lines and a wide range of bottled ales. Attractions include regular tap takeover and Meet the Brewer events, plus food pop-ups and occasional live music at weekends. The outdoor seating area is great for watching the world go by. ♿&🚇(Market St) ❀🛜

Cask

29 Liverpool Road, M3 4NQ

☎ (0161) 832 2633

4 changing beers (sourced regionally; often Mallinsons, Pictish, Track) Ⓗ

A deceptively deep pub in the heart of Castlefield that consistently sells excellent cask ale. With beer on four handpumps, it usually offers a good range of flavours, including a dark. The selection of international beers is particularly impressive, both on fonts and in bottles. Although no food is provided, customers are permitted to bring their own, including takeouts from the excellent chippy next door.
❀≠(Deansgate) 🚇(Deansgate/Castlefield) ●🚍❀🛜

City Arms

46-48 Kennedy Street, M2 4BQ (near town hall, next door to Waterhouse pub)

☎ (0161) 236 4610

8 changing beers (sourced regionally; often Manchester, Titanic) Ⓗ

A compact pub, over 190 years old, with two traditional rooms and many original features. The room facing the street contains the bar and a few tables and is fairly basic. To the rear is a smarter, cosier room to relax in with good company. Eight handpulls offer a full range of beer styles in excellent condition, including a mild. The pub is often full and filled with groups of people conversing. ❀◗≠(Oxford Rd)🚇(St Peter's Sq)♣●🚍🛜

Gas Lamp

50A Bridge Street, M3 3BW

☎ (0161) 478 1224 ● thegaslamp.co.uk

4 changing beers (sourced nationally; often Pomona Island, Squawk) Ⓗ

An interesting pub housed in the former Manchester and Salford Children's Mission. It has an impressive frontage but the small doorway that leads down to the subterranean bar can easily be missed. The main bar area has Victorian glazed-brick walls and wooden flooring. A narrow passageway leads to a cosy back room with photos of the building's history. One of the beers is usually from the pub's own brewery in Salford, Pomona Island. ❀≠(Salford Central)🚇(St Peter's Sq)●🚍❀🛜

Grey Horse ✅

80 Portland Street, M1 4QX (jct with Princess St)

☎ (0161) 228 2595

Hydes Lowry, Original; 3 changing beers (sourced nationally) Ⓗ

Dispensing beer since 1851, this small, cosy pub is loved both by visitors and locals. It has a main circular bar serving an area that was originally two rooms. Especially busy on match days, it has a great ambience and you will

be made most welcome. The location is convenient for Chinatown and there are two other real ale pubs on this section of Portland Street. Well worth a visit.
≈(Piccadilly) ⊠(St Peter's Sq) 🚌(1) ❀ 🛜

Hare & Hounds ★

46 Shudehill, M4 4AA (opp bus station)
☎ (0161) 832 4737
Joseph Holt Bitter; Robinsons Dizzy Blonde Ⓗ
Fine beers and friendly staff help make the Hare & Hounds popular, especially with older customers. This Grade II-listed pub on CAMRA's National Inventory of Historic Pub Interiors dates back to about 1800 and was remodelled in 1925. The building's mottled tile frontage and an interior featuring a lot of attractive tiling make it a rare survivor of the period, particularly given its city-centre location. The entrance corridor leads to a lobby in front of the bar. There is a vault at the front and a comfortable lounge at the rear.
≈(Victoria) ⊠(Shudehill) 🚌❀🛜

Jack in the Box

1 Eagle Street, M4 5BU
7 changing beers (sourced nationally) Ⓗ
A lively bar in a modern market hall-style venue. Run by the team behind Blackjack and its sister venue in Altrincham market, the bar serves a good selection of quality cask and keg beers. With eight handpumps and 10 keg lines, it offers a changing range of local beers, plus some from further afield, in a relaxed atmosphere. Food can be obtained from vendors within the market, and bar customers can sit anywhere in the hall. Families and dogs are welcome.
🐕‍🦺♿≈(Victoria) ⊠(Shudehill) ●🛷❀🛜

Lass o' Gowrie ✔

36 Charles Street, M1 7DB (just off Princess St)
☎ (0161) 273 5822 ⊕ thelassogowrie.com
7 changing beers (sourced locally; often Greene King) Ⓗ
This pub is notable for its Victorian tiled frontage, and the interior is also traditionally decorated. It attracts a varied clientele, especially students in term time. Seven beers are served on handpump – a mixture of Greene King and local ales. There is a compact snug at the back and a small decked area over the River Medlock for outside drinking. Locally produced snacks and pub grub are offered, with many vegetarian and vegan options.
🐕◗≈(Oxford Road) ⊠(St Peters Sq) ♣●🚌(50,147) ❀🛜

Marble Arch Inn ★

73 Rochdale Road, Collyhurst, M4 4HY (corner Gould St)
☎ (0161) 832 5914 ⊕ marblebeers.com
Marble Pint, Manchester Bitter, Earl Grey IPA; 4 changing beers (sourced nationally; often Marble) Ⓗ
Marble Brewery's flagship establishment, this famous real ale pub is a 10-minute walk from the city centre. It serves five local Marble beers, three real ciders and a selection of craft keg ales. The interior's many interesting features include a sloping mosaic floor leading you to the bar. The impressive vaulted ceiling, frieze and walls are covered with Victorian tiles. There is also a plainer back room where food is served, and a beer yard at the rear.
Q🐕●◗≈(Victoria) ⊠(Shudehill) ●❀🛜

Peveril of the Peak ★

127 Great Bridgewater Street, M1 5JQ (jct of Great Bridgewater St and Chepstow St)
☎ (0161) 236 6364
Brightside Odin Blonde; Millstone Tiger Rut; Timothy Taylor Landlord; Titanic Plum Porter Ⓗ

The Pev's warm welcome for locals and visitors alike has long made it a favourite of Manchester ale lovers. The splendour of its exterior's green tiles is matched by the interior's wood and stained-glass panels. Four handpumps serve beer in the front room, with a blackboard displaying the choice. The snug is a cosy alternative to the liveliness often found on the other side. In 2021 it was the 50th anniversary of landlady Nancy's tenure.
Q❀≈(Oxford Rd) ⊠(St Peter's Sq) ♣🚌❀🛜

Port Street Beer House

39-41 Port Street, M1 2EQ (opp Brewer St)
☎ (0161) 237 9949 ⊕ portstreetbeerhouse.co.uk
7 changing beers (sourced nationally) Ⓗ
Vibrant pub split over two floors of a former shop in the Northern Quarter, its walls adorned with pictures of beer and beer festivals. It serves seven cask beers from a variety of breweries, alongside cider and a range of contrasting worldwide keg beers, bottles and cans. The pub hosts tap takeovers and beer festival fringe events. There is outside seating at the front and a courtyard at the rear.
🐕♿≈(Piccadilly) ⊠(Piccadilly Gardens) ♣●🚌❀🛜

Salisbury Ale House

2 Wakefield Street, M1 5NE
☎ (0161) 236 5590
Robinsons Trooper; Theakston Best Bitter, Old Peculier; 3 changing beers (sourced nationally) Ⓗ
The Salisbury is situated below Oxford Road station in one of the few remaining cottage streets from the canal-building era. It has the original exterior, covered in the glazed tiles that are synonymous with Manchester pubs. It is a rock pub in all the usual senses of the word and, although it attracts students, the clientele is extremely mixed and friendly. The beer range is a mixture of Theakston and other breweries.
🐕❀≈(Oxford Road) ⊠(St Peter's Sq) ♣🚌🛜

Smithfield Market Tavern

37 Swan Street, M4 5JZ (corner Coop Street)
☎ (0161) 839 1514
5 changing beers (sourced regionally) Ⓗ
One of the premier cask outlets in the Northern Quarter, the Smithfield was refurbished in 2020. A lively, modern take on a traditional pub, it is the flagship for Blackjack Brewery. It serves up to six cask ales, mostly from Blackjack, plus 10 keg beers and an interesting selection of bottled brews. A traditional bar billiards table and other pub games provide entertainment.
≈(Victoria) ⊠(Shudehill) ♣●🛷🚌❀🛜

Waterhouse Ⓛ ✔

67-71 Princess Street, M2 4EG (near St Peter's Square tram stop)
☎ (0161) 200 5380
Greene King Abbot; Hawkshead Windermere Pale; Phoenix Wobbly Bob; Sharp's Doom Bar; 6 changing beers (sourced nationally) Ⓗ
Standing adjacent to the town hall and named after the architect who designed it, Alfred Waterhouse, this Wetherspoon outlet is unusual for the chain in that it has a split interior with several areas for drinking and dining coming off a central corridor. To the left of the main bar is a separate room and this is where you will find the four regular beers alongside a varied range of six guest ales in different styles.
Q🐕❀◗♿≈(Oxford Rd) ⊠(St Peter's Sq) ●🚌🛜

Marple

Samuel Oldknow

22 Market Street, SK6 7AD
☎ 07766 301627
6 changing beers (sourced locally) Ⓗ
Named after a local mill owner who was responsible for much of the development of Marple and Mellor some 200 years ago, this is a somewhat quirky two-level bar in a converted shop. Six vintage-style handpulls dispense five changing real ales plus a real cider. The regular beers are from Brightside and Outstanding, complemented by guests from local micros. A range of bottled beers is also available to take away or to drink on the premises. Opening hours are subject to change. Q ☎ ⊛ ≠ ● ➡ ☺ ⏰

Traders

111-113 Stockport Road, SK6 6AF
3 changing beers (sourced regionally) Ⓗ
An interesting combined micropub and bottle shop, based in converted shop premises, which was called Beer Traders before its expansion in 2019. Three handpulls serve changing beers, normally from local micros. The aim is to have one traditional bitter, one darker beer and something hoppy. Three bag-in-box ciders are also available. Live music often features on Tuesday evening. Card payment only. ☎ ⊛ ≠ ● ➡ ☺

Marple Bridge

Northumberland Arms

64 Compstall Road, SK6 5HD
☎ (0161) 285 3755 ⊕ thenorthumberlandarms.com
Robinsons Unicorn; 3 changing beers (sourced locally; often Bank Top, Saltaire) Ⓗ
Former Robinsons house that reopened in 2017 as a pub owned and run by the local community. Used by numerous groups for meetings and activities, the place fulfils its role as a true local and a well-used hub of the area. Its small bar area serves three rooms, one of which is used for pub games. The traditional exterior is enhanced by a pleasant beer garden. Frequent buses stop outside. ☎ ⊛ ♣ P ➡ ☺ ⏰

Spring Gardens

89 Compstall Road, SK6 5HE
☎ (0161) 637 5950
4 changing beers (sourced locally; often Outstanding, Timothy Taylor) Ⓗ
Following a period of closure, The Spring Gardens reopened in 2016. It sells four or five rotating guest beers in addition to three real ciders. Smart, light and airy, this is a large pub with interconnected, but defined, spaces running off a large bar area. The bar counter features what may be called industrial chic fittings dispensing a wide range of keg and craft keg beers, in addition to having handpulls. Crown green bowling green is located on site. Motorhome stopovers are welcome.
☎ ⊛ ⏰ ♣ ● P ➡ (383,384) ☺ ⏰

Middleton

Ring o' Bells

St Leonards Square, M24 6DJ
☎ (0161) 654 9245
JW Lees Manchester Pale Ale, Bitter; 1 changing beer (sourced locally; often JW Lees) Ⓗ
The Ringers, a pub since 1831, enjoys a fine elevated location opposite the medieval parish church within a conservation area. Visitors can enjoy stunning views across to Oldham and beyond, especially at night. Lees' seasonal and Boilerhouse beers are served. Very much community focused, the pub hosts a unique Pace Egg

play on Easter Monday and a Maypole event on the May bank holiday Monday. Quizzes and monthly live music add to its attractions. The beer garden to the rear is a hidden bonus. ⊛ ♣ P ➡ (17,X63) ☺ ⏰

Tandle Hill Tavern

14 Thornham Lane, M24 2SD (1 mile on unmetalled road from either A664 or A627)
☎ (0161) 376 4492
JW Lees Bitter, Stout; house beer (by JW Lees); 1 changing beer (sourced locally; often JW Lees) Ⓗ
A one-mile walk from either end of a potholed lane rewards the drinker with the discovery of a neat little pub. A single bar serves the main lounge area and a separate quiet side room. Outside, there are benches to the front and side and a walled rear beer garden. The house beer, Bumpy Lane, is dry-hopped Lees Bitter; guest ales are from the Lees and Boilerhouse ranges. No food is served. In adverse weather, or in winter, phone ahead to check opening times. Q ⊛ P ☺

Milnrow

Waggon Inn

35 Butterworth Hall, OL16 3PE
☎ (01706) 648313 ⊕ waggoninnmilnrow.co.uk
Banks's Amber Ale; 2 changing beers (often Jennings, Marston's) Ⓗ
Built in 1782, this pub, locally known as the Back Waggon, has a traditional ambience. The building has been sympathetically refurbished, retaining many original features including mullioned windows. An excellent menu features tapas and a Sunday roast at reasonable prices. Fine dining is complemented by three beers from the Marston's range. Within easy walking distance of Milnrow's Metrolink stop and local bus services. ☎ ⊛ ⏰ ♿ P ➡ ☺ ⏰

Mossley

Britannia Inn

217 Manchester Road, OL5 9AJ
☎ 07548 716413 ⊕ thebritanniainnmossley.com
Marston's 61 Deep; 5 changing beers (sourced locally) Ⓗ
This fine gritstone building overlooks the station yard and car park. It was bought by Shaw and Bentley's Bardsley Brewery in 1887 before being passed to Rothwell's of Newton Heath in 1902 and then Marston's in 1961. Today The Brit belongs to a pubco. Outside, there is a covered seating area for drinkers and smokers. Within, one will find a semi open-plan pub with a games room, the bar and a cosy dining area. Meals are served until early evening. ☎ ⊛ ⏰ ≠ ♣ ➡ (343,350) ⏰

Rising Sun ⎣

235 Stockport Road, OL5 0RQ
☎ (01457) 238236 ⊕ risingsunmossley.co.uk
Millstone Tiger Rut, Stout; 6 changing beers (sourced locally; often Rising Sun, Saltaire, Thornbridge) Ⓗ
A former Wilsons pub but a free house for many years, a small brewery was added in 2016 by the current owner to augment the range of regular and guest beers. Pale, citrusy beers dominate, dispensed from eight handpumps, plus two reserved for cider. Open plan with log-burning fires, large TVs and music, mainly for City and United matches, and with bands playing some nights a boisterous atmosphere can be assured. There are fine views across the Tame Valley towards the Pennines beyond. ☎ ⊛ ● P ➡ (353) ⏰

New Windsor

Union Tavern

105 Liverpool Street, M5 4LG (corner Wilna Terrace opp West Charles St)
☎ (0161) 737 6831
Joseph Holt Bitter ⊞
A first-rate example of a traditional Victorian Salford street-corner local, this pub is one of the last survivors of its kind. It was extended into the adjoining property many decades ago, but otherwise remains almost unchanged. The surrounding area is undergoing extensive residential development. This tiled marvel comprises a lounge to the left and a vault, plus a pool room at the rear, all served from a central bar. The walls are adorned with photographs and memorabilia of Manchester United and the Munich Air Crash. There is also a collection of pictures of now closed and demolished local pubs. ❀⇌♣P🚋(79)❀🐾🛜

Oldham

Ashton Arms ℄

28-30 Clegg Street, OL1 1PL (opp Odeon cinema complex)
☎ (0161) 630 9709
Millstone Tiger Rut; Phoenix Arizona; Pictish Porter; 6 changing beers (often Elland, Stockport) ⊞
Traditional well-run town-centre free house, recently refurbished, with an open-plan interior on two levels. An excellent range of four to six handpulled beers is available, many from local microbreweries like Pictish and Millstone. The pub also offers a wide range of Belgian and German bottled beers, with often a real cider on handpump. Good-value home-cooked food is served weekdays, with sandwiches at weekends. Live sport is often shown on TV. Q⏚❀ℚ(Central)♣●🚋🛜

Carrion Crow ✅

271 Huddersfield Road, OL4 2RJ
☎ (0161) 633 4490
5 changing beers (often Banks's, Jennings, Marston's) ⊞
Located 20 minutes' walk from Oldham Mumps Metrolink stop, on the main Oldham to Huddersfield road, this thriving community local serves five cask ales from throughout Marston's extended family. It hosts cribbage, darts, dominoes, football and quiz teams, and there is usually live music on Saturday. Beer festivals are held on some bank holidays. A winner of several local CAMRA awards. ⏚❀⏚♣🚋(350)❀🛜

Cob & Coal Tap ℄

Units 12-14 Tommyfield Market, Albion Street, OL1 3BG
☎ (0161) 624 0446
6 changing beers (often Moorhouse's) ⊞
Opened in 2019, this micropub has rapidly become a firm favourite with Oldham's real ale lovers. A warm and friendly welcome is assured, along with excellently kept beer and ciders. Bijou inside, there is extra seating outside in the market hall, making it a convivial meeting place. There are six changing beers on handpump and a good selection of real ciders, plus foreign beers on tap and in bottles. CAMRA branch Cider Pub of the Year 2020 and Pub of the Year 2021. ℚ(Central)●🚋

Fox & Pine

18 Greaves Street, OL1 1AD
☎ (0161) 628 2475
10 changing beers (sourced regionally; often Donkeystone, Ossett) ⊞

This new pub opened in 2020 and is a valuable addition to the real ale scene in Oldham. The bar is downstairs and has an open seating area, upstairs are two linked rooms. Ten handpumps offer various beer styles, always including at least one dark beer, together with up to six real ciders on gravity. In addition there are five traditional Bavarian beers from ABK on tap. The beers are excellently kept, reflecting the dedication of the owners to real ale. Q⏚⏚ℚ(Central)●🚋❀🐾

Patricroft

Queen's Arms

Green Lane, M30 0SH (up ramp opp James Nasmyth Way)
☎ (0161) 789 2019
Sharp's Doom Bar ⊞
Traditional pub, Grade II listed at the instigation of the local CAMRA branch. Built in 1828 in as a refreshment stop in readiness for the opening of the Liverpool and Manchester Railway, it claims to be the world's first railway pub. It was renamed after Queen Victoria visited Salford in 1851. Recognised by CAMRA as a fine example of a traditional unspoilt pub, the bar serves a comfortable lounge to the rear, a vault and, across a lobby, a homely parlour. It is known locally as the Top House. Q⏚❀⇌♣P🚋(67,100)❀🛜

Prestwich

Crooked Man

7 Fairfax Road, M25 1AS
☎ 07738 670522 ⊕ thecrookedmanbar.com
3 changing beers (sourced locally; often Brightside) ⊞
The Crooked Man is a friendly bar in a renovated Victorian building, offering a changing selection of real ales and keg beers through three handpumps. Bar snacks are available as well as regular food pop-ups covering a range of styles. Guest DJs often provide music in the evenings. Upstairs, the large first floor has a variety of uses including displaying work by local artists and photographers and hosting live music. ⏚🚋🚋🛜

Ramsbottom

Irwell Works Brewery Tap ℄

Irwell Street, BL0 9YQ
☎ (01706) 825019 ⊕ irwellworksbrewery.co.uk
Irwell Works Lightweights, Breadcrumbs, Copper Plate, Costa Del Salford, Marshmallow Unicorn, Mad Dogs; 8 changing beers (often Irwell Works) ⊞
This small, characterful local is situated above the brewery itself and is decorated with photographs of old Ramsbottom. Eight handpumps usually offer the full range of Irwell Works beers. The beers are traditional in style, brewed with English hops and barley. Snack food is available at the weekend. Situated in the centre of Ramsbottom, a short walk from the East Lancashire Railway, a visit to the tap makes a pleasant day out. ❀⏚⇌(ELR)♣🚋(472,474)❀🛜

Northern Whisper Ramsbottom

59 Bridge Street, BL0 9HT
☎ (01706) 230082 ⊕ northernwhisperbrewingco.co.uk
Northern Whisper Blighty, Oppenchops, Yammerhouse, Beltie ⊞
The Northern Whisper Brewery Tap opened September 2020 and is another welcome addition to the already varied cask ale offering in this popular small market town. Situated at the traffic lights at the top of Bridge Street, the premises have been tastefully renovated,

with three separate drinking areas on different levels. There are four Northern Whisper cask ales on handpump, with a further eight craft keg taps selling Northern Whisper ales. ⍩�(ELR)🍺🐾🛜

Ramsbottom Royal British Legion

Central Street, BL0 9AF
☎ (01706) 822483
Fyne Ales Jarl; 1 changing beer (sourced locally) ℍ
Situated in a back street in the centre of Ramsbottom, this club could easily be missed, which would be a pity for it is a great little venue. The members and steward are more than welcoming, and there is no entry fee. Two handpumps are always in use, offering a variety of beers, often from local microbreweries. A short walk from the East Lancs Railway real ale trail, with street parking close by and on several bus routes. ⍩⟺(ELR)🍻🍺🐾🛜

Rochdale

Baum ⓛ

35 Toad Lane, OL12 0NU
☎ (01706) 352186 ⊕ thebaum.co.uk
6 changing beers (sourced nationally; often Pictish, Vocation) ℍ
A former CAMRA National Pub of the Year, the pub has never rested on its laurels and serves six excellently kept changing cask ales. The beers are often local. Food provision was reinvented in mid-2020 and the pub now serves a top-class menu at very reasonable prices. A beer garden and conservatory to the rear complement its heritage frontage and interior. Situated next door to the Rochdale Pioneers Museum. ⍩🎰◑🍴🍺🐾🛜

Bombay Brew

1 Drake Street, OL16 1LW
☎ (01706) 869502
House beer (by Vocation); 2 changing beers (sourced locally; often Bad Seed, Pictish) ℍ
The Bombay Brew is a unique concept – an Indian-style restaurant that serves cask ales, predominantly IPAs as you would expect, on three handpumps. Run by the team from the Flying Horse, the beer is very well kept and it is a pleasant change to enjoy a cask IPA with Indian food. There is usually also one real cider on sale. The excellent Indian-influenced menu is more inventive than the usual curry house staples. ◑⟺🍴🍺🐾🛜

Flying Horse Hotel ⓛ

37 Packer Street, OL16 1NJ
☎ (01706) 646412
10 changing beers (sourced locally; often Phoenix, Pictish, Serious) ℍ
Located opposite the magnificent Gothic-style town hall, the Flyer was built in 1691 and rebuilt in 1926. It retains some original features including fireplaces. Outdoor seating is available under cover in the town hall square. Ten cask ales are sold, often alongside two real ciders. There is an extensive home-made food menu. Live music features Thursday to Saturday. A regular winner of local CAMRA Pub of the Year and also Greater Manchester Pub of the Year 2019 and 2020. 🍴◑⟺🍴🅿🍺🐾🛜

Oxford ✅

662 Whitworth Road, OL12 0TB
☎ (01706) 345709 ⊕ theoxfordpub.com
Wainwright; 2 changing beers (sourced nationally; often Hawkshead, Timothy Taylor) ℍ
A family-run pub noted for its warm welcome, good food and well-kept, well-presented beers. It offers two regular real ales and one or two ever-changing guests, depending on demand. The island bar is surrounded by tables for drinking and dining, and there is a separate

dining room plus a good-sized beer garden. Situated on the A671 out of Rochdale toward Bacup and Burnley, it has a large car park. Q⍩🎰◑🅿🍺(486)🛜

Romiley

Jakes Ale House

27 Compstall Road, SK6 4BT
☎ 07927 076941
5 changing beers (sourced locally; often Poynton) ℍ
In just a few years this micropub in a former shop has established itself as a popular part of the Romiley pub scene. It has a cosy front bar with a relaxed atmosphere, and a smaller room at the rear. Many of the beers are from local microbreweries. It is close to the railway station and good bus routes, and the Peak Forest Canal is a short walk away. Opening hours may vary. Q⍩⟺🍻🍺🐾🛜

Royton

Puckersley Inn ✅

22 Narrowgate Brow, OL2 6YD (off A671 via Dogford Rd & Fir Lane)
☎ (0161) 652 2834
JW Lees Supernova, Manchester Pale Ale, Bitter; 1 changing beer (sourced locally; often JW Lees) ℍ
A detached, stone-fronted pub on the edge of the green belt, with panoramic views from the dining room and garden over Royton, Shaw and Oldham. It has a small vault, an open-plan lounge and a dining extension where children are welcome. An excellent range of meals is served lunchtimes and evenings. Four handpulled beers are available from the JW Lees range. The large garden runs alongside farmland. A popular local where conversation predominates. ⍩🎰◑🍴🅿🍺(408)🛜

Sale

JP Joule ⓛ

2A Northenden Road, M33 3BR
☎ (0161) 962 9889
Greene King Abbot; Ruddles Best Bitter; Sharp's Doom Bar; Wychwood Hobgoblin Gold; 5 changing beers (sourced nationally; often Hawkshead, Peerless, Titanic) ℍ
Named after the famous physicist who lived in Sale (and also worked in a brewery), this popular Wetherspoon is near the tram station and on several bus routes. It is set on two levels with a grand staircase leading to the upper floor. A total of 14 handpumps dispense nine real ales, with four duplicated upstairs. Five beers are constantly changing and sourced regionally. Real ale and cider and perry festivals are held twice a year. Q⍩🎰◑🍴🍺🐾🛜

Salford

Eagle Inn

18-19 Collier Street, M3 7DW (opp Rolla St)
☎ (0161) 819 5002 ⊕ eagleinn.info
Bootleg Fools Gold, Chorlton Pale Ale; Joseph Holt Bitter, Two Hoots ℍ
Hidden gem of a traditional back-street boozer, known to locals as the Lamp Oil. A Grade II-listed building dating from 1902, it features a fine terracotta plaque of an eagle above the door – for years this was the only pub sign. There are three small rooms off a central corridor with the bar in the middle. The cottage next door has been converted into a live music venue. Handily located for Manchester Arena. Q⍩🎰⟺ℝ(Victoria)🍻🍺🐾🛜

New Oxford 🅛

11 Bexley Square, M3 6DB (corner of Browning St)
☎ (0161) 832 7082 ⏺ thenewoxford.com
House beer (by Phoenix); 16 changing beers (sourced regionally; often Empire, Moorhouse's, Phoenix) 🅗
Two-roomed corner house dating from the 1830s with a recently refurbished interior. A winner of many awards, its bar features 20 handpumps and 24 fonts. The range of 17 cask ales is sourced regionally and usually include at least two dark beers. The remaining three handpumps are for cider or perry. There are also around 200 bottled Belgium beers. Good-value lunches are served Monday to Friday. ⏺⏺⏺⏺⏺⏺⏺⏺⏺

Stalybridge

Bridge Beers 🅛

55 Melbourne Street, SK15 2JJ
☎ 07948 617145 ⏺ bridgebeers.co.uk
4 changing beers (sourced locally) 🅖
A combined micropub and bottle shop on the main pedestrianised shopping street in Stalybridge. Originally a hairdresser's, the interior has been restyled to suit its new function. A small entrance area leads to the bar which sits in front of a row of stillaged casks, of which four are generally in use. The bottle display is opposite. Upstairs is a comfortable lounge. The four beers are constantly changing and all local. Last entry is one hour before closing. Q⏺⏺⏺⏺⏺⏺⏺

Cracking Pint

41 Melbourne Street, SK15 2JJ
☎ 07512 753554
4 changing beers 🅗
Microbar next to the canal in the main pedestrianised shopping street. It serves four changing real ales, mainly from local breweries but some from further afield. There is also a good selection of bottled beers, mainly from Germany. Board games are available. Children, dogs and their well-behaved owners are welcome. This is a bar where conversation dominates rather than piped music and TV screens. Q⏺⏺⏺⏺⏺

Society Rooms ⏺

49-51 Grosvenor Street, SK15 2JN
☎ (0161) 338 9740
Greene King Abbot; Ruddles Best Bitter; Sharp's Doom Bar; 5 changing beers (sourced nationally) 🅗
Popular split-level pub near the town-centre bus terminus, named after the former Co-op store it occupies. It was extended into adjacent premises in 2018, also adding a spacious beer garden, making it one of the largest Wetherspoons in the UK. Enthusiastic management and a strong focus on cask beers make this a favourite with local drinkers, with eight real ales and two real ciders on the bar. Two beer festivals are held a year, one including cider. ⏺⏺⏺⏺⏺⏺⏺⏺

Station Buffet Bar ★

Stalybridge Railway Station, Platform 4, Rassbottom Street, SK15 1RF (access from Platform 4)
☎ (0161) 303 0007
Changing beers (sourced regionally) 🅗
One of the few Victorian station buffet bars remaining and well worth missing a train for. A sympathetic refurbishment has allowed expansion of the food menu which includes home-cooked meals. Nine handpumps dispense a variety of beers, most of which are locally sourced, plus at least one real cider or perry. A good range of bottled beers is also available. Events include live music and Meet the Brewer nights. Monday is quiz night. On the Transpennine Real Ale Trail. Q⏺⏺⏺⏺⏺⏺

White House ⏺

1 Water Street, SK15 2AG
☎ (0161) 303 2154
Hydes Original; 5 changing beers 🅗
This popular pub, close to both bus and rail stations, is semi open plan but retains four distinct drinking areas. Up to five varying guest beers from microbreweries and Hydes Studio complement the Original. Up to three real ciders are also offered, and pies are available. A popular live music venue, folk night is every Thursday and bands play most Fridays and Saturdays. ⏺⏺⏺⏺⏺⏺⏺⏺

Standish

Albion Ale House 🅛 ⏺

12 High Street, WN6 0HL
☎ (01257) 367520 ⏺ albionalehouse.co.uk
8 changing beers 🅗
The first micropub in Standish, located in a former shop on the High Street. Now well established, it has a loyal clientele and has won local CAMRA Community Pub of the Year. At least five cask ales are on offer, sometimes more, including one dark beer. Snacks are also usually available. Attractions include occasional live music and beer festivals. Q⏺⏺⏺⏺(362,113)⏺

Foresters Arms 🅛

41 Shevington Moor, WN6 0SQ
☎ (01257) 472733 ⏺ foresters.pub
8 changing beers (sourced regionally) 🅗
Previously known as the Silver Tally, it is now a country pub serving traditional fare. It has three distinct areas – one for games, one for dining and another for drinking. Despite modern furnishings, the welcoming venue has an old-fashioned ambience. Q⏺⏺⏺⏺⏺⏺(113)⏺⏺

Standish Unity Club 🅛

Cross Street, WN6 0HQ
☎ (01257) 424007 ⏺ standishunityclub.com
Sharp's Doom Bar; 4 changing beers 🅗
In the centre of Standish but tucked away so a little tricky to find, this popular club offers five real ales including one dark beer, often Titanic Plum Porter. The club is divided in two – a large function room and a bar area including the games room, plus a quieter drinking area. A frequent winner of local CAMRA Club of the Year and a runner-up Regional Club of the Year.
Q⏺⏺⏺⏺⏺(362,113)⏺

Stockport

Angel Inn

20 Market Place, SK1 1EY (opp Market Hall)
☎ (0161) 429 0251
5 changing beers (sourced regionally) 🅗
After 67 years' closure, the Angel was reopened in 2018 by a consortium of locals. It is a vibrant combination of the traditional and new – stand-up drinking near the bar gives way to two seating areas behind, with a mix of wainscoted and rustic brick walls. The bar is dominated by an impressive array of German lager fonts, without detracting from its commitment to serving real ales and cider on handpump. A large selection of gins is also kept. A popular drop-in for the town's market customers. ⏺⏺⏺⏺⏺⏺⏺

Arden Arms ★

23 Millgate, SK1 2LX (jct Corporation St)
☎ (0161) 480 2185
Robinsons Wizard, Dizzy Blonde, Unicorn, Trooper 🅗**, Old Tom; 1 changing beer (often Robinsons)** 🅖

Grade II listed and on CAMRA's National Inventory of Historic Pub Interiors, this multi-room pub is just down the hill from Stockport's Market Place. Note the superb curved, glazed bar, the grandfather clock, and particularly the snug, which can only be accessed through the bar area itself (one of only four such in the UK). The building alone warrants a visit, but the food is also highly recommended. The large, attractive courtyard hosts live music on Saturday nights. A true gem.
👪❀⏰◐&♣🚌(384,383) ❀🌟📶

Bakers Vaults

Market Place, SK1 1ES (jct Vernon St)
☎ (0161) 480 9448
Robinsons Dizzy Blonde, Unicorn, Cascade IPA, Trooper, Old Tom; Titanic Plum Porter; 3 changing beers (sourced nationally) Ⓗ
Excellent market pub with a unique atmosphere that can be both cosy and relaxed as well as lively and vibrant. The Grade II-listed building was refurbished in 2014. Its gin palace-style interior's high ceilings and tall windows create a light and airy feel. This is one of the few Robinsons Brewery houses to serve guest beers from other brewers. Local CAMRA Pub of the Year 2019.
👪❀⏰◐≈♣●🚌❀🌟📶

Blossoms

2 Buxton Road, Heaviley, SK2 6NU (at A6/A5102 jct)
☎ (0161) 222 4150
Robinsons Dizzy Blonde, Unicorn, Trooper Ⓗ**, Old Tom; 1 changing beer (often Robinsons)** Ⓖ
Landmark street-corner local whose three rooms radiate off a traditional drinking lobby, served by the central bar. Many old features remain, particularly in the rear Smoke Room. The full Robinsons range is served, including a seasonal beer. A popular quiz is held on Wednesday night; the upstairs function room hosts live music on Friday night and at the weekend. Outside drinking is catered for in the cobbled alleyway. Q❀❀⏰◐≈♣P🚌❀🌟📶

Magnet

51 Wellington Road North, Heaton Norris, SK4 1HJ (jct Duke St)
☎ (0161) 429 6287 🌐 themagnetfreehouse.co.uk
Salopian Oracle; 13 changing beers (sourced nationally) Ⓗ
Popular, family-run pub that has been a free house for over a decade. It offers 14 cask ales alongside 12 craft keg beers, with digital boards displaying the available selection. On the left is a bustling vault leading to a lower pool room and a series of other rooms. Outside is a twin-storey beer terrace. A pizza vendor operates on Friday evening. Local CAMRA Pub of the Year 2020.
Q👪❀≈♣P🚌❀🌟📶

Olde Vic

1 Chatham Street, Edgeley, SK3 9ED (jct Shaw Heath)
🌐 yeoldevic.pub/en
5 changing beers (sourced nationally) Ⓗ
Now owned by its regulars, Ye Olde Vic continues to benefit from a programme of improvements, with more work carried out during the Covid lockdown. Bric-a-brac abounds, with something to catch your eye at every turn. The five changing guest beers come from small breweries around the UK and the pumpclips on the ceiling are a potted history of lost beers and brewers. Look for the sign over the bar describing the various forms of sparkler used in dispensing your beer.
Q❀≈♣🚌❀🌟📶

Petersgate Tap

19A St Petersgate, SK1 1EB (jct Etchells St)
☎ 07925 078426 🌐 petersgatetap.com

6 changing beers (sourced regionally) Ⓗ
This family-run bar on two floors is a dark-beer specialist and multiple award winner, notably for cider and perry. Downstairs, the decor is fairly modern with a continental feel to the bar area. Recycled oak-topped tables and a mix of seating are overlooked by interesting posters and breweriana on the walls. Upstairs is a bottle shop offering a wide range of British and foreign craft beers along with an additional drinking area which hosts regular events and tastings. Q❀&≈●🚌❀🌟📶

Project 53

22 Market Place, SK1 1EU (opp Market Hall)
☎ (0161) 969 1317 🌐 project53.bar
Mobberley Maori, Elysium; 1 changing beer (often Mobberley) Ⓗ
Sited in the town's burgeoning market area, this conversion of former retail premises by Mobberley Brewhouse has produced a rustic interior mixing grey decor and bare floorboards with a liberal spread of reclaimed planking adorning walls and forming the bar. The place has three prominently placed handpulls for cask, plus a wall with many craft keg taps. There is mostly a stand-up area in front of the bar, then to the rear are normal height tables and seating as befits a more relaxed environment. Food consists of pizzas only.
👪◐≈🚌❀🌟📶

Railway

1 Avenue Street, Portwood, SK1 2BZ (jct Gt Portwood St A560)
☎ (0161) 429 6062
Dunham Massey Dunham Porter; Outstanding UltraPale; Phoenix Arizona; Pictish Brewers Gold; Salopian Oracle; Thornbridge Jaipur IPA; 3 changing beers (sourced nationally) Ⓗ
Street-corner local popular with its crowd of regulars as well as shoppers from the Peel Centre. Its 11 handpumps showcase a range of beer styles, including three changing guests, one of which is a rotating mild. These are supplemented by a changing guest cider and a range of Belgian, German and other bottled beers. The bar billiards table is well used and the outside drinking area is a summer suntrap. Q❀♣●🚌❀🌟📶

Swan with Two Necks ★

36 Princes Street, SK1 1RY (jct Hatton St)
☎ (0161) 480 2341
Robinsons Unicorn, Old Tom; 1 changing beer (often Robinsons) Ⓗ
The pub was rebuilt in the 1920s and the interior remains pretty much unchanged since then – of particular note are the classic panelled drinking lobby and the top-lit middle room with mock-Tudor fireplace. The rear outside area has been stylishly reworked and is a lovely spot to enjoy a pint in the warmer months. Home-cooked food is recommended. Q👪❀⏰◐≈♣●🚌(325,330)❀

Swinton

Wobbly Stool

233 Manchester Road, M27 4TT
☎ 07764 621471
3 changing beers (sourced locally; often Beartown, Brightside)
Opened in 2019 on the main A6 road, this small, interesting bar has three handpumps offering a wide choice of beers, usually including a stout and often something from Beartown Brewery. There is also a fine selection of craft beer in KeyKeg, plus cider from Westons and bottled Belgium fruit beers. Tuesday is games night. There is a small garden at the rear and tables at the front. Sadly, none of the bar stools is wobbly. ❀◐♣🚌❀🌟📶

Tottington

Dungeon Hotel

9 Turton Road, BL8 4AW
☎ 07706 737753
Wainwright; house beer (by Thwaites); 4 changing beers ⊞

A traditional, family-friendly Thwaites pub. It has a quiet front lounge featuring an open fire in winter months, and a separate pool room off the main bar. To the rear is a suntrap beer garden. Six handpumps serve regular and guest ales. Live music is performed on Saturday evening. The pub is recognised by CAMRA as having a historic interior of regional importance. Dogs are welcome until 7.30pm. 눈⊛▶♣🚌(480,469)🐾🐾

Tyldesley

Mort Arms

235-237 Elliott Street, M29 8DG
☎ 07584 341099
Joseph Holt Bitter; 1 changing beer (sourced locally; often Bootleg) ⊞

From the façade to the interior, this 1930s pub is recognisable as a Holt's establishment. The entrance has two etched doors directing you into either the taproom or the lounge, with a central bar serving both. This is a community-based venue and supports and participates in the local darts and dominoes leagues. As well as the Bitter, there is often a guest beer from Joseph Holt or Bootleg. ⊛♣🚌(V2)🐾

Union Arms

83 Castle Street, M29 8EW
☎ (01942) 870645
2 changing beers (sourced locally; often Wainwright) ⊞

This family-friendly pub is part of the local community, with regular charity events and occasional theme nights including live music. The interior is divided into a number of separate connected areas. On the left side is the vault and on the right is a lounge used for dining. There are usually three real ales including Wainwright, with fresh home-cooked food served during the week and lunch on Sunday. Most sporting events are shown on TV. 눈⊛◑♣🚌(V2)🐾

Uppermill

Albion Tap ⅃

72 High Street, OL3 6AW
☎ (01457) 870770
Donkeystone Kaihe; Millstone Tiger Rut; Saltaire Blonde; 1 changing beer (often Marble, Thornbridge) ⊞

A stylish bar with entrances on High Street and Smithy Lane. It has a stainless steel bar, high wooden tables, exposed stonework and a mural of a Saddleworth snow scene. Bees adorn the ceiling, a tribute to the Manchester Arena victims. There are four handpumps usually offering Millstone and Donkeystone beers, and eight KeyKeg and keg fonts often featuring Cloudwater and Tiny Rebel ales. An interesting choice of UK and foreign bottles and cans is also kept, along with an extensive selection of gins and vodkas. 눈🖐🚌🐾

Cross Keys Inn ✅

Running Hill Gate, OL3 6LW (off A670 up Church Rd)
☎ (01457) 874626 ⊕ crosskeysinn.net
JW Lees Manchester Pale Ale, Bitter; 2 changing beers (sourced locally; often JW Lees) ⊞

Overlooking St Chad church and Saddleworth, this attractive 18th-century stone building is Grade II listed,

with exposed beams throughout. The public bar has a stone-flagged floor and a Yorkshire range. It was sympathetically refurbished in 2017. Home-cooked food includes daily specials. Outside, there is a small garden and children's play area to the rear, and an extended patio with a gazebo for smokers to the front. Situated in a popular walking area, ramblers and their dogs are welcome. Q눈⊛◑♣P🐾🐾🐾

Urmston

Barking Dog

9A Higher Road, M41 9AB
☎ (0161) 215 0858 ⊕ the-barking-dog.co.uk
House beer (by Marston's); 2 changing beers (sourced nationally) ⊞

Originally built in 1939, this conversion of an old post office has proved a welcome addition to the burgeoning Urmston beer scene. Its main room features high and low tables plus several settees, and a sizeable bar with five handpumps, four for ale and one serving cider. To the right is a comfortable snug where the building's post office past is most visible. A glass-fronted display cabinet in the corridor marks the former strongroom. Fresh meals are available using locally sourced ingredients where possible, including home-cooked pies and platters. 눈⊛◑🖐≠♣🚌🐾🐾

Flixton Conservative Club ✅

Abbotsfield, 193 Flixton Road, M41 5DF
☎ (0161) 748 2846 ⊕ flixtonconservativeclub.co.uk
6 changing beers (sourced nationally; often Dunham Massey, Elland, Pictish) ⊞

Former CAMRA Club of the Year set in its own grounds with an adjacent bowling green. The new stewards have maintained the high standards of their predecessors, with six handpumps offering a good choice of beers on the main bar. More handpumps in the large upstairs function room cater for a brewery tap takeover on the last Friday of each month. Attractions include four snooker tables, Saturday bingo and quizzes on Friday and the last Sunday of the month. 눈⊛≠♣P🚌(255)🐾

Lord Nelson

49 Stretford Road, M41 9LG
☎ 07827 850255
Joseph Holt Mild, Bitter; 1 changing beer (sourced locally; often Joseph Holt) ⊞

Big, classic community pub in a remarkable French-style building, with a 'best' room and a rather more basic vault. Draught beers form the main trade. The pub is quiet and relaxing by day, becoming lively when football is shown on TV. Tuesday is quiz night and the infamous Disco Erotica is hosted on Saturday night. The pub is known for charity fundraising and was voted local CAMRA Community Pub of the Year 2020. Children are not admitted. ⊛≠♣P🚌🐾🐾

Wardley

Morning Star

520 Manchester Road, M27 9QW (opp Bagot St)
☎ (0161) 727 8373
Joseph Holt Mild, Bitter, Two Hoots; 1 changing beer (sourced locally) ⊞

Built in 1890, this red-brick building is a popular community local with a modernised interior. As you enter, the vault is to the left with darts and TV. To the right is a small open front room leading to a much larger main lounge. The three rooms are served from a central bar. This is one of the few pubs still selling Holt's Mild. An extensive food menu is available. Wednesday is quiz night and live entertainment features at weekends. The front terrace beer garden is well used in summer. 🏃🐕🍴◐👌♿🍴♠P🛏🚆🛜

Westhoughton

Beer School 🅛

88 Market Street, BL5 3AZ
☎ (01942) 396280 ⊕ thebeerschool.co.uk
4 changing beers (sourced locally) 🄷
This micropub, decked out like a school, has developed into a lively and popular part of the Westhoughton community. Its 'cellar', on view behind the bar, supplies four handpumps serving beers of varied style and strength, some from local suppliers. Up to four bag-in-box real ciders are available, many from leading producers. Drinks can be sampled before ordering. Note that the toilets are upstairs. 🏠🚆●🍴🐾🛜

Brewery Tap 🅛

55 Market Street, BL5 3AG
7 changing beers (sourced locally; often Blackedge) 🄷
Opened in 2019, this is the second outlet for local award-winning Blackedge Brewery. It has the friendly, community feel of a micropub. The timber and brick decor is complemented by subdued lighting, creating a homely atmosphere. Seven handpumps serve the core range of Blackedge beers supplemented by its seasonal, occasional and one-off beers. There are also 10 modern keg fonts, mostly offering Blackedge beers but also one dedicated to nearby Rivington Brewery. 🏠🚆●🍴🛜

Whalley Range

Hillary Step 🅛

199 Upper Chorlton Road, M16 0BH
☎ (0161) 881 1978
5 changing beers (sourced regionally; often RedWillow, Squawk, Track) 🄷
Modern bar in a small strip of shops and bars a short walk north of Chorlton. Owned by The Unabombers and part of the Electrik group of bars, it is famous for its regular live music and DJ sessions. Five handpumps serve beers mostly from local and regional breweries such as Squawk, Track and Pomona Island, usually including a dark ale in winter. The eight keg fonts include a regular sour. Outside is a covered drinking area. Children are welcome until 7pm. 🏃🐕🚉(Firswood)♣🛏(86)🐾🛜

Wigan

Anvil 🅛 ✅

Dorning Street, WN1 1HE
☎ (01942) 239444
Banks's Mild; Brakspear Oxford Gold; Wainwright; 4 changing beers (sourced nationally) 🄷
Popular town-centre pub close to the bus station with seven handpumps offering various guest beers, two real ciders, six draught continental ales and a range of bottled beers. Several TV screens show sports action and the small snug contains the Wall of Fame displaying numerous award certificates. There is a garden at the rear. Over-18s only. 🏠🚆●🛏

Crooke Hall Inn 🅛

Crooke Road, WN6 8LR
☎ (01942) 236088 ⊕ crookepub.com
6 changing beers 🄷
Large, multi-roomed canalside pub in a picturesque location in Crooke village just outside Wigan. Popular with locals and visitors alike, dogs and children are

welcome until 9pm. Home-made food features locally sourced ingredients where possible. It has a separate cellar bar ideal for functions and a large beer garden. The pub is very much the hub of the village and was named local CAMRA Community Pub of the Year for 2019 and 2020. 🏃🐕◐●P🛏(635,635)🐾🛜

John Bull Chophouse

1 Coopers Row, Market Place, WN1 1PQ
☎ (01942) 242862 ⊕ johnbullchophousewigan.co.uk
House beer (by Thwaites); 10 changing beers 🄷
A vibrant and lively inn set over two floors in a town-centre building over 300 years old which has been cottages, stables and a slaughterhouse in the past. This quirky pub has been run by the same family for over 40 years and is reputed to have the best pub jukebox in the north-west. Six handpumps serve Thwaites beers. There is seating outside. The toilets are upstairs. Closed Monday and Tuesday in winter. The Hop House bar upstairs opens weekends only and serves six cask ales. 🏠🚆●🛏🐾

Raven 🅛 ✅

5 Wallgate, WN1 1LD
☎ (01942) 239764 ⊕ theravenwigan.com
5 changing beers (often Tetley) 🄷
An early 1900s commercial hotel, virtually derelict before a tasteful renovation in 2012 that retained and restored many original features including tiles, panelling and windows. The retro decor is typical of this small local pub chain, with cosy coal fires in winter and two unobtrusive TVs. It serves a varying range of real ales and cider on handpump, alongside good home-made pub food at reasonable prices. Loyalty cards are offered and Wednesday cask critics night gives discounts on real ale. 🏃🐕◐👌🚆●🛏🐾🛜

Real Crafty

9 Upper Dicconson Street, WN1 2AD
☎ (01942) 200364 ⊕ realcraftywigan.co.uk
Rat White Rat; 4 changing beers 🄷
A real ale and craft beer emporium in Wigan town centre on the former site of Bar Legion, just five minutes' walk from the bus station and 10 minutes from both the town's train stations. Expect to find up to five real ales dispensed via handpull, alongside craft beer, cider and perry served from 30 keg fonts. The Beer Atlas offers a collection of beers in bottles and cans from around the world. Real Crafty won Best New Cask Outlet and Cider Pub of the Year 2020. 🏃🐕👌🚆●P🛏🐾🛜

Sherrington's 🅛

57 Kenyon Road, WN1 2DU
☎ 07500 171114 ⊕ sherringtonsbar.com
6 changing beers (sourced locally; often Wily Fox) 🄷
An industrial-themed bar with six real ales on handpump, always including three from the Wily Fox stable and three varying guests. There are also 10 craft/lager/continental beer taps offering Peroni, Moretti and a Wily Fox along with seven varying guests. A selection of UK and continental bottled beers is also stocked, and there is an upper-floor gin bar. Tea, coffee and hot chocolate are available. Local CAMRA Best New Cask Outlet 2019/2020. Q🏃🐕👌●🛏🐾🛜

Swan & Railway 🅛 ✅

80 Wallgate, WN1 1BA
☎ (01942) 375817 ⊕ swanandrailwayhotelwigan.co.uk
Banks's Sunbeam; Courage Directors; Draught Bass; 4 changing beers (sourced locally) 🄷
Built in 1898 by WEV Crompton, this beautiful classic period pub features an impressive stained-glass window, and an interior adorned with historical photos of old Wigan, the railway and rugby league. It has seven

handpumps celebrating Draught Bass along with Banks's Sunbeam and Courage Directors. It also supports local breweries by regularly serving beers from Hophurst, Prospect, Wily Fox and Wigan Brewhouse.
🏠🛏🍴◖♿♣🚲❀☕🛜🛜

Tap 'n' Barrel Ⓛ ✔
16 Jaxon's Court, WN1 1LR
☎ (01942) 386966 ● tapnbarrelwigan.co.uk
4 changing beers (sourced regionally) Ⓗ
Located adjacent to the bus station in a narrow shopping mews, the main bar area is long and narrow, leading to a pleasant covered and heated garden, which hosts live music on Sunday afternoons. There is additional seating upstairs. Four real ciders are served from the fridge. Beer and cider are available in paddles of three third-pints. Occasional beer and sausage festivals are held.
Q≋●🚲❀☕🛜

Wigan Central Ⓛ
Arch No.1&2 Queen Street, WN3 4DY
☎ (01942) 246425 ● wigancentral.bar
House beer (by Prospect); 6 changing beers (sourced nationally) Ⓗ
This award-winning two-roomed pub has a railway-themed interior with a live feed displaying arrival and departure times from both railway stations. It sources real ales from all over, alongside continental bottled beers displayed in the 'library'. Live music plays on Sunday. Bar snacks are available. Local CAMRA Pub of the Year 2018/19 and Cider Pub of the Year 2019/20.
Q♿≋●🚲❀☕🛜

Withington

Victoria ✔
438 Wilmslow Road, M20 3BW (on B5093, jct Davenport Av)
☎ (0161) 434 2600
Hydes 1863, Original, Lowry; 5 changing beers (sourced nationally; often Hydes) Ⓗ
This friendly Hydes community pub attracts a convivial cross-section of Withington life, from seasoned locals to fresh-faced students. Its late 19th-century exterior

features etched windows. The refurbished interior has been opened out to create distinct drinking areas, each with its own atmosphere. Attractions include a pool table at the rear, an occasional quiz, sport on TV and live entertainment at the weekend. 🛏🍴◖♣●☕🛜🛜

Woodford

Davenport Arms (Thief's Neck)
550 Chester Road, SK7 1PS (on A5102, jct Church Lane)
☎ (0161) 439 2435 ● davenportarms.co.uk
Robinsons Wizard, Dizzy Blonde, Cumbria Way, Unicorn, Old Tom; 1 changing beer (often Robinsons) Ⓗ
Characterful red-brick farmhouse-style pub which has been smartly refurbished while retaining a multi-roomed feel, with real fires in winter. This is its 35th consecutive year in the Guide, and the licence has now been in the same family for a mammoth 89 years. Excellent food is mostly home made, with some adventurous specials. Outside, the spacious forecourt and attractive garden, set well away from the road, are popular in summer, boasting impressive floral displays.
🛏🏠🍴◖♣P🚌(42B)☕🛜

Worsley

Worsley Old Hall
Worsley Park, off Walkden Road, M28 2QT (next to Worsley Park Marriott Hotel)
☎ (0161) 703 8706
Brunning & Price Original; house beer (by Facer's); 4 changing beers (sourced regionally; often Howard Town, Moorhouse's) Ⓗ
Attractive 17th-century building set in extensive parkland, with a large beer garden to the rear. Refurbished in 2013, this Grade II-listed building has spacious, comfortably furnished drinking and dining rooms, and walls sporting many old and interesting pictures. Now run by Brunning & Price, the pub offers a good range of beers with at least six cask ales and an array of KeyKeg taps. Excellent food is served.
Q🛏🏠🍴◖♿♣P🚌(33,34)☕🛜

Angel Inn, Stockport (Photo: Lawrence Devaney)

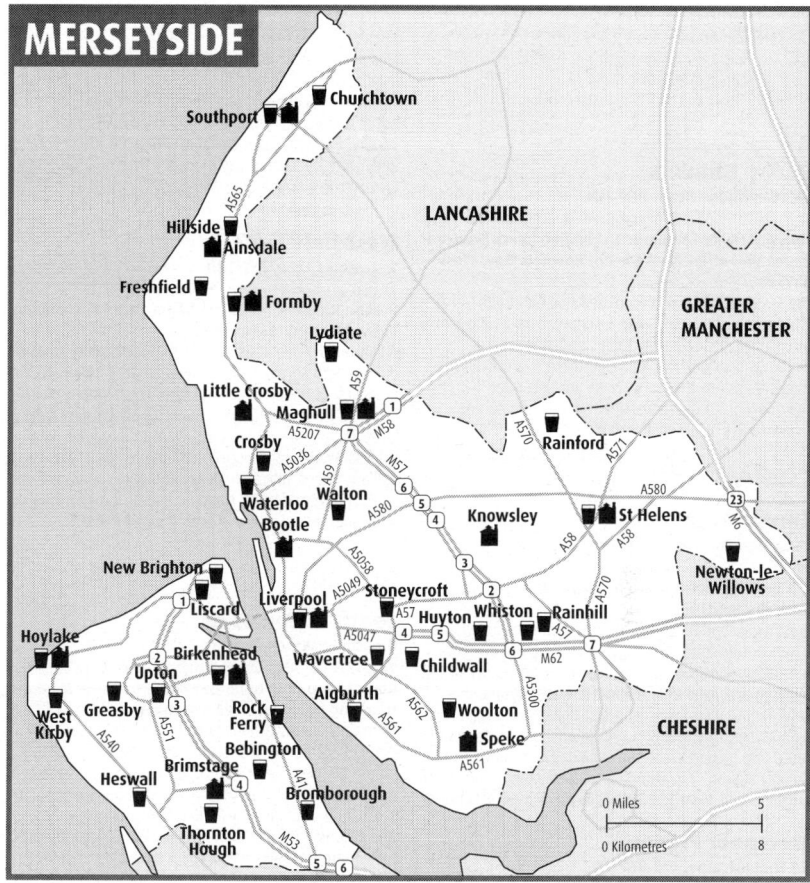

MERSEYSIDE

Southport · Churchtown

LANCASHIRE

Hillside · Ainsdale

Freshfield · Formby

Lydiate

GREATER MANCHESTER

Little Crosby
Maghull
Crosby
A5207
A5036
A565

Rainford

Waterloo · Walton
Bootle
A580

Knowsley · St Helens

Newton-le-Willows

New Brighton
Liscard
Liverpool
Stoneycroft
Huyton · Whiston · Rainhill

Hoylake
Birkenhead
Upton
Wavertree · Childwall

West Kirby · Greasby
Rock Ferry
Aigburth
Woolton

Bebington
Brimstage
Speke

CHESHIRE

Heswall · Bromborough

Thornton Hough

0 Miles 5
0 Kilometres 8

Bebington

Rose & Crown ✪

57 The Village, CH63 7PL

☎ (0151) 644 5829 ● roseandcrownbebington.co.uk

Thwaites Original, IPA, Gold, Amber; house beer (by Thwaites); 2 changing beers (sourced nationally) Ⓗ

A thriving, vibrant and friendly community pub that was once a coaching inn, built in 1732. It has a lounge, small bar and games room, with traditional decor and old photos of the area adorning the walls. Thwaites brews the house beer, Rose Gold, and some of the changing beers, with frequent guests from other breweries. Live music is hosted on Saturday nights with a quiz on Sunday. The pub is adjacent to Mayer Park and a short walk from Port Sunlight Village, which was founded by William Hesketh Lever in 1888 to house his soap factory workers and is the home of the Lady Lever Art Gallery.
Q ☺ ≈ (Port Sunlight) ♣ ☐ ☺ ☎

Traveller's Rest ✪

169 Mount Road, CH63 8PJ

☎ (0151) 608 2988 ● thetravsbebington.co.uk

Sharp's Doom Bar; Wainwright; 4 changing beers (sourced nationally; often Brimstage, Fuller's) Ⓗ

Reputedly over 300 years old, this former coaching inn is close to Storeton Woods. It has a cosy country-pub feel and is decorated throughout with brasses and bric-a-brac. The main bar area and two side rooms are served from a central bar. Guest ales are often from local microbreweries. At lunchtime the emphasis is on food,

but in the evening this is very much a traditional hostelry. No evening meals Monday and Tuesday.
Q ☺ ◑ ⅙ ♿ ☐ (464,487) ☺

Birkenhead

Gallaghers Traditional Pub Ⓛ

20 Chester Street, CH41 5DQ

☎ (0151) 649 9095

6 changing beers (sourced nationally; often Brimstage, Rat, Salopian) Ⓗ

Multiple award-winning free house close to the Mersey ferries, rescued after closure and refurbished in 2010. It is decorated with a fascinating range of military memorabilia and a collection of shipping images. Several ciders are always on offer. Meals are served daily except Monday. Live music plays every Sunday afternoon, and cheese night is the last Sunday of the month – bring your own cheese. The outside area at the rear has a retractable roof. ☺ ◑ ≈ (Hamilton Sq) ♣ ☐ ☺

Bromborough

Bow-Legged Beagle

11 Allport Lane, CH62 7HH

4 changing beers (sourced regionally) Ⓗ

This latest addition to the Bow-Legged Beagle chain of micropubs opened in March 2020. Its location – in a former shop in the main street, near the ancient market cross in the centre of Bromborough – is convenient for buses and a 10-minute walk from the railway station. The selection of cask ales usually includes a session pale and a stronger IPA, plus a bitter or amber brew and a stout or porter. Q♿🍽🚃♣

Churchtown

Peaky Blinders
145 Cambridge Road, PR9 7LN
☎ (01704) 808182 ⊕ peakyblinderschurchtown.com
Timothy Taylor Landlord; 3 changing beers (sourced nationally; often Black Sheep, Bowness Bay, Cross Bay) ⒣
The Peaky Blinders chain opened this pub in 2018 in what was once a bank. The L-shaped bar has modern furnishings, including tall tables and stools. Large windows overlook the road and there is a good-sized drinking area to the front. Walls are decorated with a reproduction of old newspaper adverts and cuttings.
🍽❄🚃♿🚃(47,X2) ♣🎵

Crosby

Corner Post Ⓛ
25 Bridge Road, L23 6SA
☎ 07587 177453
4 changing beers (sourced locally; often Peerless, Rock the Boat) ⒣
Crosby's second micropub, located in a former post office – hence the name – is easily spotted by the postbox outside. Interesting pictures depicting the history of the building and local area adorn the walls. Bottled continental beers, wine and soft drinks are available to complement the real ales and cider. Close to the 53 bus route and a short walk from Blundellsands and Crosby railway station, it is also near the Iron Men attraction on Crosby beach. Q⇌(Blundellsands & Crosby)♣●🚃(53)♣

Liverpool Pigeon Ⓛ
14 Endbutt Lane, L23 0TR
☎ 07766 480329 ⊕ liverpoolpigeon.co.uk
5 changing beers (sourced locally; often Bristol Beer Factory, Salopian) ⒣
Merseyside's pioneering micropub, named after a now extinct bird from Polynesia, is a fine example of the type, offering real ales, ciders and bottled beers but no spirits, alcopops, keg beers or music. The cask beers usually include a local brew and often a dark beer. Locally made pies are available at the bar. A former local CAMRA Pub of the Year. Q♿♣●🚃🐾♣

Formby

Cross House Inn ✓
Cross Green, L37 4BH
☎ (01704) 873775
Greene King IPA; 10 changing beers (sourced regionally) ⒣
The pub is divided into four rooms furnished with comfy sofas and chairs, and decorated with pictures of old Formby. Food is served all day from an extensive menu and a specials board. Up to 10 cask beers can be found, many from local breweries, as well as four ciders and a good selection of gin. Children are permitted up to 9pm if dining. Cask ale is discounted on a Monday.
Q🍽❄🌓♿⇌P🚃♣🎵

Freshfield

Beer Station
3 Victoria Buildings, L37 7DB (opp Freshfield station)
☎ (01704) 807450

3 changing beers (sourced locally; often Liverpool, Rock the Boat) ⒣
Freshfield's first micropub, with a focus on all things local. Beers are chosen to showcase the area's brewers, with the exception of one 'foreign' beer a month from out of the region. A fridge with bottled beers adds to the variety. Local pies are available. The walls are decorated with work by local artists. Dogs are welcome on a lead.
Q♿♿⇌♣●🚃♣🎵

Freshfield Ⓛ ✓
1 Massams Lane, L37 7BD
☎ (01704) 874871
Greene King IPA, Abbot; Oakham Citra; 11 changing beers (sourced regionally) ⒣
A community pub at its heart with three distinct areas – a dining room serving quality food, an area dominated by a bar full of handpumps, and 'the flags', where well-behaved dogs are welcome. Sport is shown on three large TVs and a real fire adds warmth in winter. Real cider is available on occasion during festivals. This is a place to meet, talk and spend time with friends old and new. A former CAMRA National Pub of the Year finalist and multi award-winner. 🍽❄🌓♿⇌♣P🚃♣🎵

Greasby

Coach & Horses ✓
Greasby Road, CH49 3NG
☎ (0151) 677 4509 ⊕ coachandhorsesgreasby.co.uk
Black Sheep Holy Grail; Butcombe Original; 2 changing beers (sourced nationally) ⒣
Charming whitewashed traditional street-corner local, dating back nearly 300 years. Formerly a farmhouse where ale was brewed and sold from 1725, it became a pub in the 1820s. The compact central bar space serves several discrete areas including two small cosy rooms, and warming fires in winter help create a country-pub feel. There is a folk/acoustic jam session every Monday.
Q🍽❄♣P🚃🎵

Irby Mill Ⓛ ✓
Mill Lane, CH49 3NT (on roundabout between Greasby and Irby)
☎ (0151) 604 0194 ⊕ irbymill.co.uk
Brains Rev James; Greene King Abbot; 6 changing beers (sourced nationally) ⒣

REAL ALE BREWERIES

Ad Hop Liverpool
Beer Station 🍽 Formby (NEW)
Big Bog ♣ Speke
Black Lodge ♣ Liverpool
Brimstage Brimstage
Brooks Hoylake
Carnival ♣ Liverpool
Connoisseur St Helens (brewing suspended)
Gibberish 🍽 Liverpool (brewing suspended)
Handyman 🍽 Liverpool
Howzat 🍽 St Helens
Liverpool Brewing Liverpool
Love Lane 🍽 Liverpool
Melwood Knowsley
Neptune ♣ Maghull
Peerless ♣ Birkenhead
Rock the Boat Little Crosby
Southport Southport
Stamps Liverpool: Bootle
Top Rope Liverpool
Tyton Ainsdale

A pub since 1982, the Irby Mill was previously a café and, originally, the house of the miller who worked the site's mill. It has thick sandstone walls, low beams and a real fire, and is divided into a small L-shaped, stone-floored bar plus a lounge that is used mainly by diners. It has an excellent reputation for its locally sourced home-made food, and offers a menu to suit most tastes.
Q♣⑳❀❶P🖵(82) ✿ 🛜

Heswall

Beer Lab 🅛
53 Telegraph Road, CH60 0AD
☎ (0151) 342 5475 ⏀ thebeerlab.co
Brimstage Trapper's Hat Bitter; 3 changing beers (sourced regionally; often Lister's, Purple Moose, RedWillow) 🖽
Heswall's first micropub opened in 2018 in what had been a cycle shop, an easy five minutes' walk from the main shopping area and the bus station. The relaxed and minimalist single-room bar is bright and airy, making the most of the available space. Four real ciders are always on tap together with Belgian bottled beers. Beer is served in pint, one-third and two-thirds measures only. Local CAMRA Cider Pub of the Year 2020.
Q♣❶🖵(22) ✿ 🛜

Jug & Bottle 🅛
13 Mount Avenue, CH60 4RH
☎ (0151) 342 5535 ⏀ the-jugandbottle.co.uk
Brains Rev James; Brimstage Trapper's Hat Bitter; 6 changing beers (sourced nationally; often Big Bog, Castle Rock, Peerless) 🖽
Built in the 1870s as a private house, this building was later offices, then in 1986 opened as the Mill House Hotel before becoming the Jug & Bottle in 1993. It is hidden behind the village hall and library, near the main shopping street. Inside, different cosy areas and open fires create a warm and friendly atmosphere. The decking outside gives views towards the River Dee and North Wales. Q♣❀❷⑳❺❶P🖵❀🛜

Hillside

Grasshopper ✅
70 Sandon Road, PR8 4QD
☎ (01704) 569794
8 changing beers (sourced regionally; often Cross Bay, Salopian, Slater's) 🖽
Micropub in a row of shops close to Hillside train station. It opened in 2016 in what was a Martins Bank branch until 1978; the Martins logo was a grasshopper. There is outdoor seating at the front and a secluded beer garden to the rear. Eight changing real ales and six real ciders are served. Local CAMRA Cider Pub of the Year 2021.
Q❀❺≠♣❶P🖵(47) ✿

Pines
3 Hillside Road, PR8 4QB
☎ 07454 453090
2 changing beers (sourced regionally) 🖽
An attractively decorated bar in what was once a hairdresser's in an area that previously had no pubs or bars but now has two award-winning outlets. Two handpumps offer a varied choice of beers, and a selection of bottled beers is also kept. An outside seating area at the front is popular in the warmer months. Sometimes the bar can be noisy and at others it can be quiet and relaxing, depending on the time of day.
🐦❀❺≠P🖵(47) ✿ 🛜

Hoylake

Black Toad
32 Market Street, CH47 2AF
☎ 07835 360691 ⏀ theblacktoad.co.uk
4 changing beers (sourced regionally; often Chapter, Neptune, Peerless) 🖽
Micropub that opened in 2019 in an abandoned unit on the main shopping street in central Hoylake. Its narrow main room and bar are attractively decorated with simple furniture. The owners offer a balanced selection of cask beers at all times. In 2020 the pub expanded into the next-door shop to create a new lounge area; the small rear room is now a bottle shop. Outside at the back is a pleasant beer garden. Q🐦❀≠❶🖵(38,407)✿ 🛜

Plasterers Arms ✅
35 Back Seaview, CH47 2DJ
☎ (0151) 345 0249
Purple Moose Cwrw Glaslyn/Glaslyn Ale; Rat White Rat; 2 changing beers (sourced nationally; often Black Sheep, Timothy Taylor) 🖽
Friendly, traditional two-room hostelry in a former fishing community, sadly long gone. A pub for over 250 years, it has fascinating decor – note the mirrored ceiling – with information about the inn and local history. Close to the beach, it is popular with walkers and birdwatchers, and a short walk to Market Street for shops, buses and the railway station. There is seating outside and a children's playground opposite. Regular entertainment features at weekends. Parking is on the street nearby.
Q🐦❀≠(Manor Rd)♣P🖵(38,407) ✿ 🛜

Huyton

Barkers Brewery 🅛 ✅
Archway Road, L36 9UJ
☎ (0151) 482 4500
Greene King Abbot; Ruddles Best Bitter; Sharp's Doom Bar; 4 changing beers 🖽
A large, airy Wetherspoon establishment with a traditional feel, popular with workers and families in the early evening. It serves a good selection of beers, including at least one local and one dark ale. The pub is on the site of the old Huyton Brewery, which was founded in 1825 and managed by four generations of the Barker family until 1925; the sculpture is of Richard Barker. The main dining area leads to a beer garden at the rear. Children are welcome until 9.30pm.
Q🐦❀❶❺≠P🖵(7,10B) 🛜

Liscard

Lazy Landlord Ale House
56 Mill Lane, CH44 5UG
☎ 07583 135616
Joseph Holt Bitter; Oakham Citra; 4 changing beers (sourced nationally; often Brimstage, Peerless, Rat) 🖽
Wirral's first micropub, opened in converted shop premises in 2014. It is run by cask ale enthusiasts the Henry brothers. The two small, cosy rooms, served from the front bar, feature breweriana, artworks and a small library. Two ciders are offered, usually from SeaCider and Snail Bank. It is a venue for meetings of local societies, and is mostly frequented by a mature, discerning clientele of regulars. Local CAMRA Pub of the Year 2017-19. Q🐦❀♣❶🖵(410,432)✿

Liverpool: Aigburth

Little Tap Room
278 Aigburth Road, L17 9PJ
🌐 aigburthtap.co.uk
5 changing beers (sourced locally; often Neptune) Ⓗ
This friendly two-room micropub opened in March 2020. It is close to Sefton Park, on a main road with excellent bus and Merseyrail services nearby. The front bar's handpulls serve both beer and cider. Bottled and canned ales are stocked, and the available spirits include the pub's own Sefton Park gin. Board games, a book club and background music are attractions but there is no TV or jukebox. Q♣🕭🖼(82)🛜

Liverpool: Childwall

Childwall Fiveways Ⓛ ✔
179 Queens Drive, L15 6XS
☎ (0151) 738 2100
Greene King Abbot; Ruddles Best Bitter; 6 changing beers (sourced nationally; often Robinsons) Ⓗ
A former Higson's tied house, this large single-roomed pub opened as a Wetherspoon in 2010. Located in a leafy suburb, it has good motorway and public transport links. The refurbished interior is decorated with wood panelling, and outside there is a beer garden. A popular establishment, it can get busy, especially at weekends. The site was used for a water tank during WWII.
🛏🏛🕽&🕭P🖼(79,81) 🛜

Liverpool: City Centre

Augustus John Ⓛ
Peach St, L3 5TX (off Brownlow Hill)
☎ (0151) 794 5507 🌐 the-augustus-john.business.site
5 changing beers (sourced nationally; often Peerless, Rock the Boat) Ⓗ
Opened in 1968 and run by the University of Liverpool, the Augustus John is an open-plan pub popular with students, lecturers and locals. Cask ales always come in a range of styles – light and dark – and there are two ciders on handpump and many more in the fridge. Pizza is served at all times, sport is shown and there is a jukebox. Closed over Christmas and New Year. A local and regional CAMRA Cider Pub of the Year. 🏛🕽&♣🕭🖼(79)🛜

Baltic Fleet Ⓛ
33A Wapping, L1 8DQ
☎ (0151) 709 3116 🌐 balticfleet.co.uk
Brimstage Trapper's Hat Bitter; Melwood Derby Stout; Robinsons Trooper; 3 changing beers (sourced locally; often Big Bog, Rock the Boat) Ⓗ
Grade II-listed building near the Albert Dock. It has a distinctive flat-iron shape and the interior is decorated on a nautical theme. The existence of tunnels in the cellar has led to speculation that the pub's history may involve smuggling. It also originally had many doors to allow customers to escape the press gangs. It can get busy when events are on at the nearby M&S Bank Arena. 🏛🕽🚄(James St) 🕭🖼(500) 🐕🛜

Bridewell Ⓛ
1 Campbell Square, L1 5FB
☎ (0151) 707 2372 🌐 thebridewellpub.co.uk
Kirkstall Pale Ale Ⓗ/Ⓖ**; house beer (by Ossett); 3 changing beers (sourced nationally; often Melwood)** Ⓗ
An imposing, Grade II-listed building that dates from the mid-19th century, when it was a police bridewell, or jail. The former cells are now seating areas and provide an unusual focus in the downstairs bar. Five cask beers are served, at least one local, alongside a range of craft keg

and continental ales. There is an outdoor patio at the front. The pub is close to the Liverpool One shopping area, the Albert Dock and the riverfront.
🏛🚄(Central) 🖼🛜

Coach House by the Angus Ⓛ
2B Maryland Street, L1 9DE
☎ 07595 588426
3 changing beers (sourced locally; often Ad Hop, Neptune) Ⓗ
A cosy bar on Maryland Street, next door to the shisha café and downhill from the Hope & Anchor, featuring a small upstairs room with seating. It dispenses three or four cask ales on gravity, often from microbreweries and local brewers, plus a selection of craft keg and bottled beers. The bar also specialises in artisanal gins and vodkas. Opening times may change during the year.
🏛🚄(Central) 🕭🖼(86) 🛜

Dispensary
87 Renshaw Street, L1 2SP
☎ (0151) 709 2160 🌐 dockleafbar.co.uk/thedispensary
Fernandes Malt Shovel Mild; Rat White Rat; Titanic Plum Porter; 4 changing beers (often Oakham, Ossett, Titanic) Ⓗ
Lively city pub that is a haven for real ale drinkers of all ages. It was formerly a Cains tied house but is now leased out as a free house. The attractive bar area has Victorian features, and there is a raised wood-panelled area to the rear. Originally The Grapes, the old sign is behind the bar. It can be busy when matches are shown on the big screens. There is a food stall outside.
🏛🕽🚄(Central) 🖼🛜

Doctor Duncan's
St Johns Lane, L1 1HF
☎ (0151) 709 5100 🌐 doctorduncansliverpool.com
House beer (by Rock the Boat); 4 changing beers (sourced nationally; often Salopian) Ⓗ
A former Cains Brewery flagship pub with an impressive Victorian interior featuring four distinctively different drinking areas – the green-tiled room is particularly handsome. The pub's name commemorates the first chief medical officer of Liverpool, a campaigner against poor living conditions in Victorian times; medical memorabilia is displayed throughout. The house beer is from Rock the Boat. 🏛🕽🚄(Lime St)♣🖼🛜

Excelsior Ⓛ ✔
121 123 Dale Street, L2 2JH (close to Birkenhead Tunnel entrance)
☎ (0151) 352 9544 🌐 excelsiorliverpool.co.uk
Salopian Oracle; Sharp's Doom Bar; Timothy Taylor Landlord; 3 changing beers (sourced regionally; often Big Bog, Salopian) Ⓗ
Large, comfortable corner pub on the edge of the business district. The main room has a three-sided bar and a series of distinct seating spaces. There is a large room off the main space with a raised seating area – this can be hired for meetings and functions. Three TVs show sports events, particularly football, but are generally silent otherwise. 🕽🚄(Moorfields)P🖼🛜

Fly in the Loaf ✔
13 Hardman Street, L1 9AS
☎ (0151) 708 0817
Okell's Bitter; 5 changing beers (sourced nationally; often Kirkstall, Okell's) Ⓗ
A former bakery, the name comes from the slogan 'no flies in the loaf'. Owned by Isle of Man brewer Okell's, it serves its own beers alongside a changing range of guests from around the country, many from microbreweries, and a good selection of foreign beers.

The spacious interior has a light, airy frontage with contrasting wood-panelled areas towards the rear. There is a small, attractive on-street drinking area at the front and a function room upstairs. ◑◗&≷(Central)🚌(86)🛜

Grapes 🅛

60 Roscoe Street, L1 9DW
☎ (0151) 709 3977
8 changing beers (often Ad Hop, Chapter) 🅗

A street-corner local that dates back to 1804 and has the original Mellors signage outside. The pub is known as the Little Grapes but was extended in a 2016 refurbishment. Stairs lead to a partly sheltered patio atop the added section. Most of the nine handpumps serve beers from smaller local and regional breweries, and one pump now regularly serves a real cider. An extensive selection of rums is also kept. Live jazz features every Sunday night. ❄≷(Central)🍴🚌(82) 🛜

Head of Steam

85-89 Hanover Street, L1 3DZ
☎ (0151) 708 6096
Camerons Strongarm; 6 changing beers (sourced locally; often Camerons, Neptune, Tiny Rebel) 🅗

Opened in 2017, with no connection to the Head of Steam previously on Lime Street, this is a large venue with plenty of seating in various arrangements. Most major sporting events are shown live so it can get busy, especially in the evening. Many foreign bottled and keg beers are on offer alongside the real ales. A private function area is available to hire. Handy for Liverpool One shops. ◑◗≷(Central)🍴🛜

Lion Tavern ★ 🅛 ✅

67 Moorfields, L2 2BP
⊕ theliontavernliverpool.co.uk
Wily Fox Crafty Fox; house beer (by Rock the Boat); 4 changing beers (sourced nationally; often Liverpool, Rock the Boat) 🅗

Named after the locomotive that worked the Liverpool and Manchester Railway (and is on display at the Liverpool museum), the Lion features mosaic floors, a tiled corridor plus intricately etched and stained glass. Refurbished in 2017, it retains Grade II-listed status and is on CAMRA's National Inventory of Historic Pub Interiors. Up to eight beers are from the SIBA list, usually including ales from local micros. Westons cider is regularly available and local gins are kept. Local CAMRA Pub of the Year. ◗≷(Moorfields)🍴🚌❄🛜

Pen Factory

13 Hope Street, L1 9BQ
☎ (0151) 709 7887 ⊕ pen-factory.co.uk
5 changing beers (sourced nationally; often Brimstage, Hawkshead, Titanic) 🅗

The Pen Factory opened in 2015, brought to you by the innovator of the original Everyman Bistro, entrepreneur Paddy Byrne. This large open-plan bistro-style establishment with a wood-burning stove and a small garden is a convivial place to drink and eat. At least five handpumps include beers from smaller breweries such as Brimstage. The food is excellent, not your average pub grub. The venue can be busy before or after productions at the nearby Everyman Theatre or Philharmonic Hall. ❄◑◗&≷(Central)🍴🚌(86) ❄🛜

Peter Kavanagh's ★ ✅

2-6 Egerton Street, L8 7LY (off Catharine Street)
☎ (0151) 709 3443
Greene King Abbot; 4 changing beers (sourced nationally; often Castle Rock) 🅗

A classic Grade II-listed pub on CAMRA's National Inventory of Historic Pub Interiors. The snugs display

murals by Eric Robinson and there are fine stained-glass windows with wooden shutters. The benches have carved armrests thought to be caricatures of Peter Kavanagh, the licensee for 53 years until 1950. These features were not adversely affected when the pub was expanded, firstly in 1964 into next door, then in 1977 into next door but one. Q🚌(86)❄🛜

Roscoe Head

24 Roscoe Street, L1 2SX
☎ (0151) 709 4365 ⊕ roscoehead.co.uk
Tetley Bitter; Timothy Taylor Landlord; 4 changing beers (sourced locally) 🅗

One of the Famous Five pubs that have featured in every edition of the Guide, this is a cosy four-roomed venue where conversation and the appreciation of real ale rule. Six handpumps serve beers from local and national breweries. Run by members of the same family for over 30 years, the pub commemorates William Roscoe, a leading campaigner against the slave trade. The freehold was sold to tenant Carol Ross in 2020, following a sustained Save the Roscoe Head campaign against the previous owners. Q❄◑◗≷(Central)♣🚌🛜

Ship & Mitre 🅛

133 Dale Street, L2 2JH (by Queensway Tunnel)
☎ (0151) 236 0859 ⊕ theshipandmitre.com
Flagship Lupa, Sublime, Silhouette; 5 changing beers (sourced nationally; often Big Bog, Flagship) 🅗

The name derives from two previous incarnations, the Flagship and the Mitre. The 1930s Art Deco pub is partly hidden by the Queensway Tunnel entrance. Fifteen handpulls offer an ever-changing array of beers and real ciders – friendly and knowledgeable staff are always willing to make a recommendation. There is also an impressive range of world beers. The pub now brews its own Flagship beers using the plant at Stamps Brewery in Crosby. ◑◗≷(Moorfields)♣🍴🚌❄🛜

Thomas Rigby's ✅

23-25 Dale Street, L2 2EZ
☎ (0151) 236 3269
Okell's Bitter, Dr Okell's IPA; 4 changing beers (often Kirkstall) 🅗

This multi-roomed, Grade II-listed building, bearing the name of a wine and spirit dealer, now supplies an extensive world beer range on draught and in bottles. The regular beers on handpump come from the pub's owner, Okell's. Good-value food including specials is served until early evening, with one room offering a friendly and efficient table service. The old coaching inn courtyard for outdoor drinking is shared with sister pub Lady of Mann. ❄◑≷(Moorfields)🚌🛜

Vernon Arms 🅛

69 Dale Street, L2 2HJ
☎ (0151) 236 6132 ⊕ vernonarms.co.uk
Brains Rev James; house beer (by Stamps); 3 changing beers 🅗

Situated close to the business district, the Vernon retains the feel of a street-corner local. The single long-roomed bar serves three drinking areas including a back room with frosted-glass windows advertising the Liverpool Brewing Company, which used to serve the pub. The main bar has wood panelling, several large columns and a small snug area. Real cider on handpull is unusual for the city centre. ◗≷(Moorfields)🍴🚌🛜

Liverpool: Stoneycroft

Cask 🅛

438 Queens Drive West Derby, L13 0AR (near jct of Queens Drive and Derby Lane)

☎ 07562 713967 ● caskmicropub.co.uk

4 changing beers (sourced nationally) 🅷

Comfortable, immaculate, one-roomed micropub that opened in 2015. An interesting collection of breweriana includes some from Higsons. There are usually four beers on Tuesday and Wednesday, five on Thursday and up to seven from Friday. Cider and perry are dispensed direct from taps at the rear of the bar. Bottled beers are stocked. Some roadside parking is available. A three-times former local CAMRA Pub of the Year.
Q✿♣●🖥🚃(60,81)

Liverpool: Walton

Jaxon's Micropub 🅛

21 Longmoor Lane, L9 0EA

☎ (0151) 524 2818 ● jaxonsmicropub.co.uk

4 changing beers (often Black Lodge, Neptune) 🅷

Opened in February 2020, this friendly micropub is a welcome addition to an area where real ale is, sadly, becoming increasingly scarce. This shop conversion has a modern but welcoming interior, and there is pavement seating in the summer. Real ale is dispensed from four handpulls, two of which are normally reserved for LocAles such as Neptune and Black Lodge. Real cider in a box is also available as well as a selection of bottled beer and craft cans. ≥(Orrell Park)●🖥🐾🗢

Raven 🅛 ✅

72-74 Walton Vale, L9 2BU

☎ (0151) 524 1255

Fuller's London Pride; Greene King Abbot; Ruddles Best Bitter; Sharp's Doom Bar; **5 changing beers** 🅷

This open-plan Wetherspoon pub is popular with locals, particularly at weekends. It is themed on Edgar Allan Poe's The Raven – local pavement artist James William Carling created illustrations for the famous poem in the late 19th century, and is buried nearby in Walton Cemetery. Aintree, home of horse racing's Grand National, is less than a mile away. Children are welcome until 9pm. 🛏🕭◑🕭≥(Orrell Park)🚃🗢

Liverpool: Wavertree

Willow Bank 🅛 ✅

329 Smithdown Road, L15 3JA

☎ (0151) 733 5782

Greene King IPA, Abbot; Tetley Bitter; house beer (by Greene King); **4 changing beers (sourced nationally; often Big Bog, Ossett)** 🅷

Vibrant, traditional, multi-room pub with the original public bar that dates back to when this was a Walkers house. It attracts a mixed clientele including shoppers, locals and students. Up to eight changing guest beers are on offer – real ale night is Tuesday – and there are occasional beer festivals. Westons Rosie is available. Good-value food is served including Sunday lunches. The attractive roadside patio is popular. Live sport is shown on large screens and a well-attended quiz night is hosted. 🛏🕭◑🕭◑🚃(60,86)🗢

Liverpool: Woolton

Gardeners Arms

101 Vale Road, L25 7RW

☎ (0151) 428 0775

Adnams Ghost Ship; Greene King IPA; Sharp's Doom Bar; Timothy Taylor Landlord; **2 changing beers (sourced regionally; often Big Bog)** 🅷

Friendly community village pub situated over the hill from Woolton village and separated from Menlove Avenue by blocks of flats. Guest ales regularly include a local Big Bog beer. A quiz is held on Tuesday evening. Woolton is famous as the home of the Beatles – their original name was The Quarrymen after Woolton quarry and they first met at the local St Peter's Church.
🛏🚃(76)🐾🗢

Lydiate

Scotch Piper ★ ✅

Southport Road, L31 4HD (800yds N of A5147/Moss Lane jct)

☎ (0151) 345 6399 ● scotchpiper.com

3 changing beers (sourced nationally; often Titanic) 🅷

The Scotch Piper is a whitewashed, thatched, medieval Grade II*-listed building just north of Lydiate. The doorway opens into a traditional bar with a servery on the left. A passage to the right leads to a further two rooms, the middle one with simple old woodwork. The end room, added later, is less rustic but retains some upholstered bench seating. The toilets are outside. Piper 1320 house beer is from Marston's.
Q🛏🕸◑▲♣🚃(300)🐾🗢

Maghull

Frank Hornby 🅛 ✅

38 Eastway, L31 6BR

☎ (0151) 520 4010

5 changing beers (often Brightside, Elland, Saltaire) 🅷

A Wetherspoon establishment named after the famed local man who invented the Hornby train set. Samples of his work are on display in the pub, including Meccano and Dinky Toys. Situated in a suburban street, the bar is spacious and light inside with a decked area outside at the front. It serves a varied selection of guest ales including some from local breweries. Q🛏🕸◑🕭🚃🗢

Maghull Cask Café

43 Liverpool Road South, L31 7BN

☎ (0151) 526 3877 ● maghull-cask.business.site

5 changing beers (sourced locally; often Neptune, Oakham) 🅷

This micropub is a hidden gem. Opened in 2018, it serves a good range of changing cask ales, continental bottles and gins. Beers are from regional brewers such as Oakham, Titanic and Salopian. Friendly, knowledgeable staff help to create a welcoming atmosphere where conversation prevails. The Liverpool to Leeds canal runs through Maghull and the pub makes an ideal base for a pleasant walk towards Burscough.
Q🕭●🖥🚃(300,310)🐾🗢

New Brighton

Bow-Legged Beagle 🅛

88 Victoria Road, CH45 2JF

☎ 07597 900114 ● thebowleggedbeagle.co.uk

5 changing beers (sourced regionally; often Beartown, Neptune) 🅷

Wirral's second micropub opened in 2017 in an old street-corner shop with a basic no-frills format and immediately proved popular with locals and visitors. It offers a friendly ambience and a regularly changing range of new and unusual local beers. There is seating

outside on the pavement in summer. The pub is close to the seafront and other local attractions, in an area that is being rejuvenated with attractive murals.
Q❀❄✦☒(410,432) ✿ ☞

Magazine Hotel L ✓

7 Magazine Brow, CH45 1HP (above Egremont Promenade)
☎ (0151) 630 3169 ⊕ the-magazine-hotel.co.uk
Brimstage Trapper's Hat Bitter; Draught Bass; 3 changing beers (sourced regionally; often Big Bog, Brimstage) Ⓗ
This unspoilt multi-roomed, low-beamed pub with an attractive black and white frontage, dating from 1759, suffered a fire in 2010 but has been restored without losing its unique character. It overlooks Egremont Promenade, with fine views across the River Mersey to Liverpool. Three rooms lead off the main central bar area with its open fireplace. The place is renowned for its Draught Bass and also serves ales from local microbreweries, plus one changing real cider. Local CAMRA Pub of the Year 2020.
Q✿❀✦✦●P☒(106,107) ✿ ☞

Newton-le-Willows

Kirkfield Hotel ✓

2-4 Church Street, WA12 9SU
☎ (01925) 222058 ⊕ thekirkfield.co.uk
4 changing beers (sourced locally) Ⓗ
Extensively renovated in 2018, the Kirkfield Hotel offers quality food and a good choice of real ales in the separate bar. Breakfast is served. Situated across the road from St Peter's Church and the Willow Park, this is a popular establishment. ✿❀✪◐✦❄✦P☒(34)✿ ☞

Rainford

Junction L

News Lane, WA11 7JU
☎ (01744) 882868 ⊕ junctionpubrainford.co.uk
5 changing beers Ⓗ
A community free house with a strong emphasis on showcasing local produce and local music. Beer festivals take place regularly, including one around the May Day bank holiday. A popular venue for local musicians, the pub hosts the Wooden Horse Folk Club on Sunday evening. Vintage car and motorcycle events also feature in the large space to the rear of the premises.
✿❀◐✦✦❄✦●P☒(38) ✿ ☞

Rainhill

Skew Bridge Alehouse L

5 Dane Court, L35 4LU
☎ (0151) 792 7906 ⊕ skewbridge.co.uk
Lister's Best Bitter; Outstanding 3.9; 5 changing beers (sourced locally; often Big Bog, Melwood, North Riding Brewery) Ⓗ
Quiet, atmospheric micropub serving a selection of up to six cask ales, four real ciders and three craft lagers. Local ales are complemented by beers from across the UK. The pub also stocks a range of wines, gins and single malt whiskies. Conversation is encouraged, with no TV or music to distract customers. Outdoor seating is available in summer. A folk, roots and acoustic night takes place on the first Tuesday of the month.
Q✿❀✦❄✦●P☒(10A,61) ☞

Rock Ferry

Refreshment Rooms L

2 Bedford Road East, CH42 1LS
☎ (0151) 644 5893 ⊕ refreshmentrooms.com
House beer (by JW Lees); 1 changing beer (sourced locally) Ⓗ
Refurbished and reopened in 2012 under its original name, the pub dates back to the 1880s when it was built for ferry passengers to Liverpool. The ferry terminal is long gone but fine views over the Mersey remain. A central bar services two rooms. The focus is on food, with excellent reasonably priced meals served daily until mid-evening. The house beer, HMS Conway, is from Lees; the real cider from Rosie's. Off the beaten track but well worth seeking out. ✿❀◐✦❄✦P☒ ☞

St Helens

Cowley Vaults L ✓

50 Cooper Street, WA10 2BH
☎ (01744) 750849
6 changing beers Ⓗ
Friendly local community venue a short distance from the town centre. Six handpulls serve cask ales on rotation, alongside two real ciders and a large range of whiskies and gins. The pub hosts pool teams and features live music on the last Saturday of the month. Quiz night on Thursday includes free half-time refreshments. There is a beer garden to the rear. Award-winning sister pub the Turk's Head is next door.
❀✦✦●❒❏✿ ☞

Cricketers Arms L

64 Peter Street, WA10 2EB
☎ (01744) 361846
12 changing beers (sourced locally; often Ossett) Ⓗ
A former CAMRA National Pub of the Year, this family-run establishment has 13 handpulls always offering at least one dark beer, plus 10 ciders and a range of spirits including over 100 gins. The traditional community pub has beer gardens, darts and pool leagues, quiz nights and fundraising events. An outside bar is used for beer festivals and private events. In 2020 the on-site Howzat brewery began production of house beers for this pub and others within the local area.
✿❀✦●P☒(10A,89) ✿ ☞

News Room

89 Duke Street, WA10 2JG
☎ (01744) 322129
2 changing beers (sourced nationally) Ⓗ
The music-themed News Room offers three handpulls, craft beers and a range of foreign bottled beers as well as gins, rums and malt whiskies. Set in stylish surroundings where conversation is encouraged, it has a warm, friendly, laid-back atmosphere, with music on film from the 60s, 70s and 80s playing on large screens. Themed music nights are hosted every six to eight weeks. ✦☒

Sefton ✓

1 Baldwin Street, WA10 1QA
☎ (01744) 22065
5 changing beers (sourced nationally) Ⓗ
A modern and comfortable town-centre venue that caters for everyone, whether you are looking for good pub food, live sport or just drinks with friends. The large room has a long bar down one side offering five regularly changing cask conditioned ales. There is a function room upstairs and a small beer garden to the rear. Live bands often play at the weekend. ✿❀◐✦❄(Central)☒ ☞

Turk's Head ⓛ

49 Morley Street, WA10 2DQ

☎ (01744) 751289

14 changing beers Ⓗ

Attractive Tudor-style 1870s pub near the town centre; the current local CAMRA Pub of the Year. It offers a rotating range of real ales on 14 handpulls, 15 draught ciders and a large whisky and gin bar. The upstairs Tower Lounge serves cocktails plus craft and continental beers, and hosts live music on Saturday evening. Excellent home-made food is available Wednesday to Sunday. Tuesday evening is smartphone quiz night with free half-time refreshments. There is a large beer garden to the side and rear. ⓈⓍ⊕⓪ⓖ♣♨🖵🚲🛜

Southport

Beer Den ⓛ

65-67 Duke Street, PR8 5BT

☎ (01704) 329007

2 changing beers (often) Ⓗ

Micropub set up in 2019 by The Parker Brewery, serving two of its own beers on rotation plus two guests. Two German lagers and an American IPA complement the range, alongside a carefully chosen spirit and wine selection. The pub is just around the corner from the famous British Lawnmower Museum. Q⊕ⓖ🖵🚲(46)

Guest House

16 Union Street, PR9 0QE

☎ (01704) 537660 🌐 guesthouse-southport.blogspot.com

Butcombe Adam Henson's Rare Breed; Ruddles Best Bitter; Theakston Best Bitter; house beer (by Caledonian); 2 changing beers (often Phoenix, Salopian, Southport) Ⓗ

Close to the station and Lord Street, this Grade II listed building has an impressive frontage and has been identified by CAMRA as having a regionally important pub interior, featuring three separate wood-panelled drinking areas. The bar has 11 handpumps, one serving a local microbrewery beer. A wide range of malt whiskies is also offered. This quiet, traditional pub attracts a mixed clientele. It hosts a quiz night on Thursday and an acoustic folk club on the first and third Mondays of the month. There is seating outside at the front and a courtyard to the rear. Q⊕⓪🚲♨🖵🛜

Phoenix ✪

4-6 Coronation Walk, PR8 1RF

☎ (01704) 513233

Sharp's Doom Bar; 3 changing beers (sourced regionally) Ⓗ

Popular sports pub at the south end of Lord Street, serving good food at reasonable prices. Family-run and free of tie, it is a favourite with real ale drinkers. The pub has plenty of traditional games and hosts a poker night on Monday and Wednesday, darts on Tuesday, and live music on Friday. Football is shown on TVs scattered about the pub. A great family-friendly establishment. Ⓢ⓪ⓖ🚲♣🖵❀🛜

Sir Henry Segrave ⓛ ✪

93-97 Lord Street, PR8 1RH (on A565, S end of Lord St)

☎ (01704) 530217

Greene King Abbot; Phoenix Wobbly Bob; Ruddles Best Bitter; Sharp's Doom Bar; Wainwright; 6 changing beers (sourced regionally; often Lytham, Robinsons, Saltaire) Ⓗ

Named after the former land speed world record holder who used to race on Southport flats, this is a spacious Wetherspoon pub with an attractive 19th-century exterior. The manager is a strong supporter of real ale

and runs regular beer festival trips and occasional Meet the Brewer evenings. Twelve handpumps offer the best all-round choice of microbrewery beers in Southport – regular orders are placed with Phoenix, Saltaire, Titanic and Hawkshead. There is outside seating on Lord Street. Q�Ⓧⓧ⓪ⓖ🚲♨🖵❀🛜

Tap & Bottles

19A Cambridge Walk, PR8 1EN

☎ (01704) 544322

4 changing beers Ⓗ

A micropub in the arcade between Chapel Street and Lord Street, next to the Atkinson Centre. It serves four real ales from a wide variety of sources, with a preference for North-West breweries. A huge range of bottles is also offered, not all of them real ale. The pub has stools and tables that use casks for support, alongside traditional benches and tables. There is also seating in the arcade. QⓈⓍⓖ♣🚲♨🖵❀🛜

Thornton Hough

Red Fox ⓛ

Neston Road, CH64 7TL

☎ (0151) 353 2920

Brightside Odin Blonde; house beer (by Phoenix); 8 changing beers (sourced locally) Ⓗ

An impressive sandstone building dating from the 1860s, set in extensive grounds. Refurbished in 2014, it is now a smart gastro-pub. The front bar area retains a pub feel, with the restaurant areas to either side. A smaller bar section at the back serves the terrace and large garden. Changing beers are usually from local microbreweries and the house beer by Phoenix is Brunning & Price Original Bitter. Up to 10 ciders are available. QⓈⓍ⊕⓪ⓖ♨🖵(487)❀🛜

Upton

Bow-Legged Beagle ⓛ

19 Arrowe Park Road, CH49 0UB

☎ 07989 392757 🌐 thebowleggedbeagle.co.uk

4 changing beers (sourced regionally; often Beartown, Neptune, Salopian) Ⓗ

This micropub opened in 2018 in a former bank on a busy row of shops near the centre of the village. The light, airy room has basic furnishings and a friendly ambience. Some of the old bank safes have been retained. This is the second Bow-Legged Beagle, following the success of the New Brighton micropub of the same name. QⓈ🖵(16,17)❀🛜

Waterloo

Four Ashes ⓛ

23 Crosby Road North, L22 0LD

6 changing beers (often Neptune, Rock the Boat, Wily Fox) Ⓗ

A family-run micropub owned by the Ashe family – hence the name. On the site of what was restaurant, it is a great addition to the vibrant real ale scene in and around Waterloo station. Beers are ordered direct from local microbreweries or through a wholesaler, resulting in a varied and interesting selection, always including at least one dark ale. Beers conditioning in the cellar are displayed on the wall. Qⓖ🚲♣♨🖵❀

Trap & Hatch

135 South Road, L22 0LT

☎ (0151) 928 5837 🌐 trapandhatch.co.uk

3 changing beers (sourced regionally) Ⓗ

Situated on a busy suburban street, this micropub has a modern and stylish interior featuring low lighting and long tables. Unobtrusive music plays but does not detract from good conversation. Live music features on Saturday evening. The bar has three handpulls offering a choice of interesting beers not often seen in this area. There is also a good range of bottle beers and real cider.
⊛&≠●🚋(53,47,X2) ♣ 🛜

Volunteer Canteen ★ 🄻

45 East Street, L22 8QR
☎ 07891 407464
4 changing beers (sourced nationally) Ⓗ

A cosy, traditional pub in a Grade II-listed terraced building. The Volly, as it is locally known, still provides table service. Nestling in the back streets of Waterloo, the pub dates from 1871. Until the 1980s it was owned by Higsons, evidence of which can be seen etched into its windows. Small breweries around Merseyside and north Wales often supply guest ales. Pies, pate, olives and nuts are served at all times. Q⊛≠♣🚋(53)♣🛜

Waterpudlian 🄻

99 South Road, L22 0LR (diagonally opp Waterloo station)
☎ (0151) 280 0035
5 changing beers (sourced locally; often Brimstage, Oakham, Salopian) Ⓗ

Previously Stamps Too, this past local CAMRA branch Pub of the Year was the area's first accredited LocAle pub. The friendly open-plan bar, where lively banter often prevails, is the haunt both of real ale enthusiasts and live music fans. Five handpumps serve mainly local beers, from Liverpool, Brimstage and Southport in particular, with occasional ales from further afield. A sixth handpump dispenses real cider. Bands and local musicians feature Thursday to Sunday.
&≠●🚋(53,133) ♣ 🛜

West Kirby

West Kirby Tap 🄻

Grange Road, CH48 4DY
☎ (0151) 625 0350 ⊕ westkirbytap.co.uk
Spitting Feathers Session Beer, Thirstquencher; 7 changing beers (sourced nationally; often Black Lodge, Oakham, Spitting Feathers) Ⓗ

A smart, modern, open-plan bar with plain wooden panelling, bare brick walls and a log-burning stove. Owned by Spitting Feathers brewery, it serves a wide range of beers, mainly from microbreweries, and one real cider. Food includes impressive platters of cheese, fish, cold meats and vegan snacks. Live music plays on Saturday night and the pub can get busy. Close to the shops and a short walk to the beach for those trekking to Hilbre Island, tides permitting.
🛏◑&≠●🚋(38,407) ♣ 🛜

White Lion 🄻

51 Grange Road, CH48 4EE
☎ (0151) 625 9037 ⊕ whitelionwestkirby.co.uk
Black Sheep Best Bitter; 4 changing beers (sourced locally) Ⓗ

A 200-year-old sandstone building close to the centre of West Kirby. This traditional pub is a little quirky and laid out on several different levels, with lots of cosy nooks to sit in, along with a real fire to keep you warm in winter. In summer months you can enjoy the lovely beer garden at the rear. Quiz night is Monday. ⊛≠🚋(80,81)♣

Whiston

Beer EnGin

9 Greenes Road, L35 3RE
☎ 07496 616132
5 changing beers Ⓗ

Set in a row of shops, this cosy single-room microbar is a delight from the moment you walk in. It serves five real ales from local breweries plus craft beers, wines and a variety of unusual gins. A selection of board games is available. Bank holiday hours may vary. A warm welcome is assured for all, including dogs.
&≠♣●P🚋♣

Cricketers Arms, St Helens (Photo: Steve Downing)

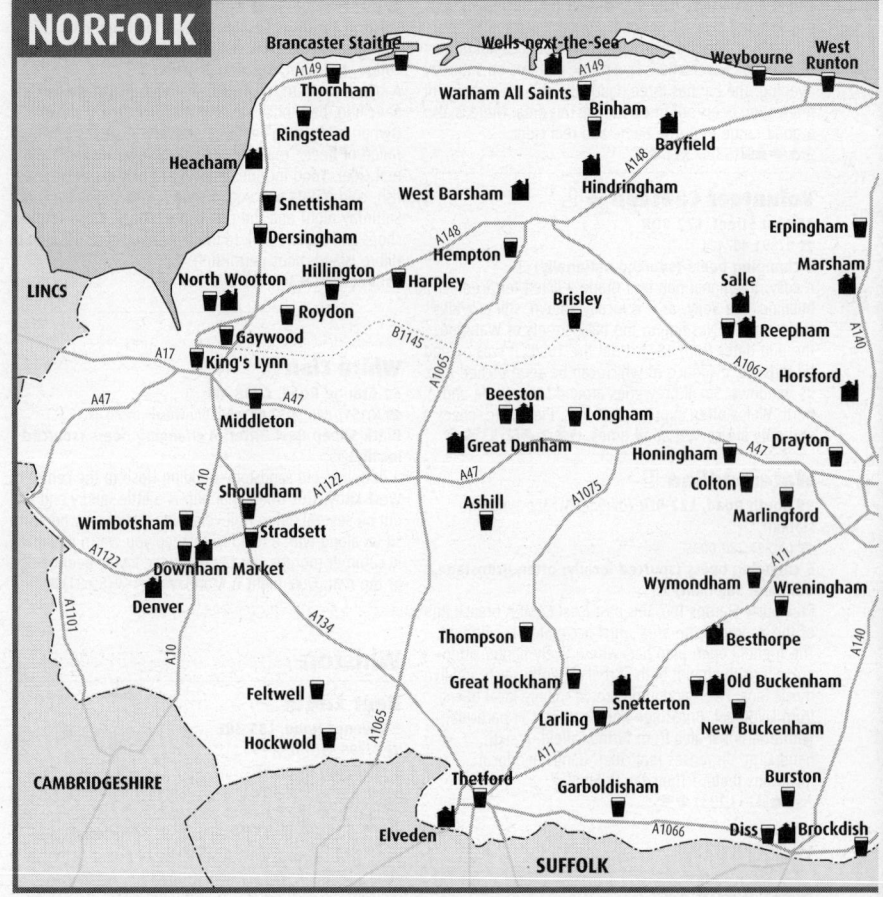

NORFOLK

Ashill

White Hart ◐

Church Street, IP25 7AW (100yds from St Nicholas' Church) TF885042

☎ (01760) 622190 ⊕ ashillwhitehart.co.uk

3 changing beers (sourced nationally; often Malden, Mighty Oak) Ⓗ

A building dating back to the 1800s and rebuilt following a fire in 1938, this pub reopened in late 2020 under its former name of the White Hart after a spell as McTaggarts. It has a warm and friendly atmosphere with a great choice of real ales and home-cooked foods. The pub is a hub for the local community as well as a good place for visitors to stay and enjoy the local area. There are four en-suite bedrooms. ⍟⊛⊨◑⚘AP⚘

Banningham

Crown Inn Ⓛ ◐

Colby Road, NR11 7DY (N of B1145, 1 mile E of A140)

☎ (01263) 733534 ⊕ banninghamcrown.co.uk

Greene King IPA, Abbot; 4 changing beers (sourced regionally) Ⓗ

Traditional 17th-century free house overlooking the village green. The original beamed bar interior has a warm atmosphere enhanced by a log fire in winter. Seven handpumps feature up to four guest beers from regionals and microbreweries, with an artisan cider from

nearby producers. Popular for fine cuisine using local produce, the restaurant is open to the kitchen and chefs. The patio, garden and barbecue areas are ideal for summer alfresco dining. The website has details of regular events, the annual music festival, and winter opening times. Q⊛◑&⚘A♣P⚘⊛

Beeston

Ploughshare

The Street, PE32 2NF

☎ (01328) 598995 ⊕ beestonploughshare.com

Beeston Worth the Wait; 3 changing beers (sourced locally; often Beeston) Ⓗ

This popular community-owned pub reopened in 2019 after extensive refurbishment. It has a comfortable bar with an inglenook fireplace and a log-burner, and a separate dining room with a small area off the bar that doubles as a café during the day. Additionally, there is another room off the end of the bar that houses a small shop providing day-to-day essentials. One Beeston beer is always available, and traditional English meals are served in the bar and dining room. Outside are a large patio and car park. Q⍟⊛◑⚘AP⚘⊛

Binham

Chequers Inn

Front Street, NR21 0AL

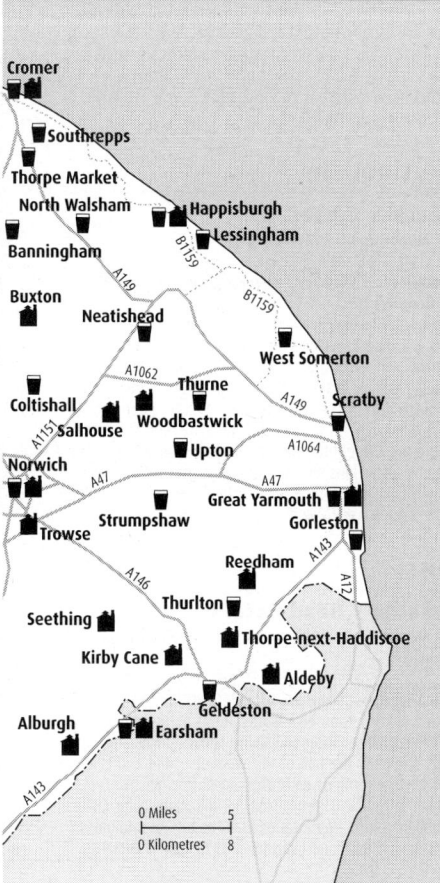

pizza. A beer and music festival is held every June and a cider festival in September. Coasthopper buses stop outside. Q✤⛽😀🐕🅿🌳♿🍴📶

Brisley

Brisley Bell Ⓛ ✔
The Green, NR20 5DW
☎ (01362) 705024 ⊕ thebrisleybell.co.uk
Adnams Ghost Ship; Woodforde's Wherry; 4 changing beers (sourced regionally) Ⓗ
A country pub with excellent views across a large open common. Remodelled in 2016, it retained its beams and brick interiors, with two large inglenook fireplaces, and has been much expanded, particularly at the rear, with a large patio and garden. The impression is one of space, with a warm welcome for diners, casual drinkers and dogs. An award-winning menu is locally sourced, as are most of the cask beers. Q✤⛽😀🐕🅿🍴📶

Brockdish

Old King's Head
50 The Street, IP21 4JY
☎ (01379) 668843 ⊕ kingsheadbrockdish.co.uk
2 changing beers Ⓗ
A 16th-century beamed community pub with a friendly atmosphere. The building reopened in 2015 with an

☎ (01328) 830297 ⊕ binhamchequersinn.co.uk
Adnams varies; Moon Gazer varies; Woodforde's varies; 1 changing beer (sourced locally) Ⓗ
A traditional brick-and-flint village free house, the Chequers is a tremendously popular place both with locals and visitors – a friendly establishment with strong support from the surrounding community. Guest beers are sourced regionally, often from Norfolk. The food menu comprises a range of good wholesome fare at reasonable prices; there is an additional specials menu and regular themed evenings. In addition to the bar area, there are benches and tables inside and out, plus a large garden to the rear. Q✤⛽😀🐕🅿🌳♿📶

Brancaster Staithe

Jolly Sailors
Main Road, PE31 8BJ
☎ (01485) 210314 ⊕ jollysailorsbrancaster.co.uk
Brancaster Best; Woodforde's Wherry; 2 changing beers (sourced nationally) Ⓗ
A cosy inn at the heart of village life with several small drinking sections and two dining rooms, convenient for the Norfolk coast path and Brancaster Staithe harbour. It has a garden and play area, an ice cream hut, and welcomes families and dogs. Brancaster beers are produced by a nearby brewery to the pub's recipes and at least one is always on the bar. Food is home-cooked and includes pub classics, local seafood and stone-baked

REAL ALE BREWERIES

All Day 🌿 Salle
Ampersand 🌿 Diss
Barsham West Barsham
Beeston Beeston
Birdhouse Downham Market
Blimey! Norwich
Bull of the Woods Kirby Cane
Chalk Hill 🍺 Norwich
Dancing Men 🍺 Happisburgh
Elmtree Snetterton
Fat Cat 🍺 Norwich
Fengate Marsham
Fox 🍺 Heacham
Golden Triangle Norwich
Grain Alburgh
Humpty Dumpty Reedham
Iceni Elveden
Lacons Great Yarmouth
Lynn North Wootton (NEW)
Malt Coast Wells-next-the-Sea
Moon Gazer Hindringham
Mr Winter's Norwich
Opa Hay's Aldeby
Panther Reepham
People's Thorpe-next-Haddiscoe
Poppyland Cromer
Redwell Norwich: Trowse
S&P Horsford
St Andrews Brewhouse 🍺 Norwich
Stumptail Great Dunham
Tindall Seething
Tipples Salhouse
Tombstone 🍺 Great Yarmouth
Two Rivers Denver
Wagtail Old Buckenham
Waveney 🍺 Earsham
Why Not Norwich
Wildcraft Buxton
Wolf Besthorpe
Woodforde's Woodbastwick
Yetman's Bayfield

added coffee shop, and sells delicious home-made cakes, plus bread at weekends. It offers family-friendly seating and a standing bar with a wood-burner, both serving imaginative Italian food in the afternoon. Gluten-free meals and cakes are also available. There are regular music events, usually on a Thursday, and a gin club adds to the mix with 150 gins. Local artists display work in the bars and gallery. ☞⊛◑&♣P🚃(581)☺

Burston

Crown Inn

Mill Road, IP22 5TW (by crossroads in middle of village, on green)

☎ (01379) 741257 ⊕ burstoncrown.com

Adnams Southwold Bitter H/G**; Greene King Abbot; 4 changing beers (often Adnams)** H

An attractive 16th-century Grade II-listed inn featuring exposed beams, deep sofas and a log fire in the inglenook fireplace. There are two bars, one with a pool table and darts. Boules is played in the garden in summer. A small restaurant serves a mixed cuisine of locally sourced freshly cooked food (no food Sun eve or Mon). Booking is advisable. Regular live music takes place on Thursday evenings and music and other entertainments are staged regularly throughout the year, including a beer festival. Q☞⊛◑♣P☺🎉

Coltishall

Red Lion L

77 Church Street, NR12 7DW

☎ (01603) 736644 ⊕ redlioncoltishall.co.uk

3 changing beers (sourced locally) H

Intricate two-level hostelry with a separate dining area, complemented by a café. It is warm, friendly and comfortable, and dates from the 16th century. The cosy lower bar has a log-burner and serves up to five real ales, some sourced from local or regional microbreweries. The varied food menu features specials and theme nights. Beer festivals are held at Easter and in late summer. ☞⊛♣P🚃☺🎉

Colton

Norfolk Lurcher L

High House Farm Lane, NR9 5DG (2 miles S of A47 Norwich southern bypass)

☎ (01603) 880794 ⊕ the-norfolklurcher.com

Beeston Worth the Wait; 3 changing beers (sourced regionally) H

Welcoming country pub in the heart of the Norfolk countryside yet only a short drive from Norwich. Family-owned and run, it has four handpumps serving quality ales from breweries in the area, alongside 60 single malts. Large comfortable bar areas are complemented by the excellent Ugly Bug restaurant serving locally produced food. The extensive beer garden is popular on warmer days. Monthly jazz and regular food and music evenings take place. There are eight en-suite bedrooms. Q☞⊛⇎◑&♣P🚃☺🎉

Cromer

Red Lion Hotel L

Brook Street, NR27 9HD (S of church on clifftop)

☎ (01263) 514964 ⊕ redlion-cromer.co.uk

10 changing beers H

Splendidly situated with views of Cromer pier and the sea, the 19th-century Red Lion has retained many original features including panelling, a Victorian tiled floor and open wood fires. The work of local artists

decorates the walls of the two bar areas. Up to six guest ales are usually served, often from nearby breweries such as Winter's and Green Jack. Beer festivals are held in the summer. The restaurant offers an extensive menu including breakfast. Accommodation is also available. Q☞⇎◑&♣🚃☺🎉

Dersingham

Coach & Horses

77 Manor Road, PE31 6LN

☎ (01485) 540391

Woodforde's Wherry; 3 changing beers (sourced nationally) H

Although the good-value home-cooked food is popular, this is at heart a village local rather than a gastro-pub. A former winner of the Norfolk CAMRA Pub of the Year, it offers cider alongside the beers on the bar. There is a pool table in the games room and a large garden with a play area. Live music and quiz nights are regular features. There are three letting rooms for those wishing to visit nearby attractions such as Sandringham or wanting to stay for the annual beer festival. Q☞⊛⇎◑Å♣P🚃☺🎉

Diss

Saracen's Head Hotel ✅

75 Mount Street, IP22 4QQ (at N end of town next to church)

☎ (01379) 652853 ⊕ saracensheaddiss.co.uk

Adnams Ghost Ship; Woodforde's Wherry H

A fine old two-roomed hostelry in this market town, with well-kept beers and good home-cooked food. The pub was originally the hall of the Weavers Guild and is a legacy that reminds us of the prosperous past of Diss, which in medieval times was an important commercial woollen centre. The interior features lots of original beams and mullioned windows. Q☞⊛⇎◑♣🚃P🚃

Downham Market

Crown Hotel

12 Bridge Street, PE38 9DH

☎ (01366) 382322 ⊕ crowncoachinginn.com

Adnams Southwold Bitter; Greene King IPA, Abbot; 2 changing beers (sourced nationally) H

An unspoilt 16th-century coaching inn at the heart of the town. Entering through a room with a lovely staircase brings you to the bar with a beamed ceiling, panelled walls and large fireplaces. A good selection of ales is served. There is a restaurant, plenty of outside seating, and a separate function room that caters for parties and weddings. Accommodation is provided in 18 rooms, including family suites. Q⊛⇎◑⇎P🚃🎉

Whalebone L ✅

58 Bridge Street, PE38 9DJ

☎ (01366) 381600

Adnams Ghost Ship; Greene King Abbot; Ruddles Best Bitter; Sharp's Doom Bar; 3 changing beers (sourced nationally) H

This listed building, formerly the White Hart, has been extensively modified but retains the original façade. This Wetherspoon pub has a large bar area that leads to the gardens at the rear and side. On the walls, heritage displays include whaling, drainage of the Fens, Horatio Nelson and replica whalebones. Look out for the unique carpet. Attractions include beer and cider festivals plus occasional tap takeovers. There is wheelchair access throughout. ☞⊛◑⇎♣P🚃🎉

Drayton

Bob Carter Centre 🅛

School Road, NR8 6DW
☎ (01603) 867102
6 changing beers (sourced regionally) Ⓗ

A sports and social club near the town centre, featuring a large single bar with plenty of comfortable seating. Up to five real ales are in stock at all times, including two from Greene King and three from smaller breweries in the area. Home-cooked food is served in the restaurant. The club was local CAMRA Club of the Year 2019 and is supportive of CAMRA aims. ◑ Ⓟ 🖳 🛜

Earsham

Queen's Head 🅛

Station Road, NR35 2TS
☎ (01986) 892623
Waveney East Coast Mild, Lightweight; 2 changing beers (often Nene Valley, Three Blind Mice) Ⓗ

Busy 17th-century locals' brewpub on the Norfolk-Suffolk border, just west of Bungay. Owned by the same landlord since 1998, and home to the Waveney Brewing Co, the pub usually dispenses four ales and at least one real cider. The main bar has a flagstone floor, wooden beams and a large fireplace with a roaring fire in winter. A separate dining area serves food at lunchtimes (not Mon & Tue). The large front garden overlooks the village green. A previous local CAMRA Pub of the Year.
Q ॐ ❀ ◑ & ♣ ● Ⓟ 🖳 (580) ❀ 🛜

Erpingham

Spread Eagle 🅛

The Street, NR11 7QA
☎ (01263) 761938
Adnams Ghost Ship; Grain ThreeOneSix; Woodforde's Wherry; 3 changing beers (sourced regionally) Ⓗ

Reopened in late 2019 after a period of closure, and once more with its original name, the pub traces its history back to the 1720s. It features a cosy main bar with wood-burning stoves, a function room and a large garden. The changing beer range always includes ales from both Adnams and Lacons, and there may be a real cider. There are plans for food service, but the emphasis is on real ale and a warm welcome. ॐ ❀ & ♣ ▲ Ⓟ 🖳 ❀ 🛜

Feltwell

Wellington 🅛

27-29 High Street, IP26 4AF
☎ (01842) 828224 ⊕ feltwellington.co.uk
3 changing beers (sourced nationally) Ⓗ

Wet-led pub that also serves award-winning food. It has a cosy lounge bar and a separate games room featuring pool and darts, plus a 36-seat restaurant to the rear. One real cider is always on handpump. There is plenty of interesting memorabilia relating to the pub's namesake WWII bomber. ॐ ❀ ◑ & ♣ ● Ⓟ 🛜

Garboldisham

Fox Inn 🅛

The Street, IP22 2RZ
☎ (01953) 688538 ⊕ garboldishamfox.co.uk
6 changing beers (sourced locally; often Boudicca, Cliff Quay, Elmtree) Ⓗ

A 17th-century coaching inn with a welcoming feel, near Bressingham Gardens and Banham Zoo. Bought by locals to operate as a community pub, it remains open while renovation continues. Ales come from breweries such as Blimey, Norfolk Brewhouse and Wolf. Rumour has it that one of the resident ghosts is a black labrador. The pub serves a roast on Sundays and sells locally made ice cream in tubs. Food including pizza and souvlaki is available on Saturday evenings from various street-food vendors. Q ॐ ❀ & ♣ ● Ⓟ ❀ 🛜

Gaywood

White Horse

9 Wootton Road, PE30 4EZ
☎ 07776 061934
Timothy Taylor Landlord Ⓗ

This local pub can be found near the Gaywood clock. Since refurbishment in 2017 it has an open-plan one-roomed bar, with a number of TVs showing various sporting events. There is also a sheltered seating and smoking area at the rear. Two beers are available, generally from breweries around the country. ❀ Ⓟ 🛜

Geldeston

Locks Inn 🅛

Locks Lane, NR34 0HS (around 800yds along track from Station Rd)
☎ (01508) 518414 ⊕ savethelocks.com
1 changing beer (sourced regionally) Ⓗ

The Locks Inn has recently been bought and refurbished by a local community group. It is on the River Waveney, at the end of a long track off Station Road in Geldeston. The original small main bar has low ceiling beams and a clay tile floor and is still lit by candlelight at night. The pub serves beer from at least three local breweries along with a guest ale. On either side of the main bar are a restaurant and a function room. Outside are large gardens and overnight moorings for boats.
Q ॐ ❀ & ▲ ♣ ❀

Gorleston

Dock Tavern 🅛

Dock Tavern Lane, NR31 6PY (opp N side of Morrisons)
☎ (01493) 442255 ⊕ thedocktavern.com
Adnams Broadside; 3 changing beers (sourced nationally) Ⓗ

As its name suggests, the Dock Tavern is close to the river, and not far from the main shopping area. This warm and welcoming venue has been subject to flood damage many times and the various flood levels can be seen by the front door. The outside drinking area at the front has views of the river and docks. There is live music most weekends, and curry and quiz nights monthly, plus an annual charity music day. ॐ ❀ ◑ ♣ ● 🖳 ❀ 🛜

New Entertainer 🅛

80 Pier Plain, NR31 6PG
☎ (01493) 300022
Greene King IPA; 9 changing beers (sourced nationally) Ⓗ

This unusual venue with a curved frontage, including original Lacons curved windows, has an interesting design and layout. There is a wide choice of beers on offer, including up to 10 guest real ales, many of which are locally brewed, as well as up to nine traditional ciders. The customers are as widely varied as the beers. The pub has pool and darts available, and holds a monthly quiz. This traditional free house is well worth seeking out; note that the main entrance is on Back Pier Plain. ❀ ⇌ ♣ ● 🖳 ❀ 🛜

Oddfellows Arms Ⓛ

43 Cliff Hill, NR31 6DG
☎ 07876 545982
Lacons Encore, Legacy; 2 changing beers (sourced nationally; often Lacons) Ⓗ
A cosy local, with two bars, a short distance from the harbour. Music and jam sessions are held on many Fridays, especially in summer. There are always four beers on offer, sometimes more, mainly from the multi award-winning Lacons Brewery in Great Yarmouth; the Oddfellows could almost be considered its brewery tap. There is a west-facing outdoor seating area and limited parking at the rear. The pub now stocks various bottled and canned craft ales from around the world. ♿❀&♦P❀🐾🛜

William Adams ✓

176-177 High Street, NR31 6RG
☎ (01493) 600295
Greene King Abbot; Ruddles Best Bitter; Sharp's Doom Bar; 6 changing beers (sourced nationally) Ⓗ
A new-build Wetherspoon named after William Adams, a famous Gorleston swimming instructor and lifesaver. It has a large open-room layout with all the usual Wetherspoon facilities, including a pleasant outside enclosed seated area with designated smoking section. Note that the outside area closes at 9pm. The decor depicts the famous local fishing industry and seaside themes. Six real ales are served with the chance of some real bag-in-box cider offerings. ♿❀🕙&♦🚃🛜

Great Hockham

Eagle Ⓛ ✓

Harling Road, IP24 1NP
☎ (01953) 498893 ⊕ hockhameagle.com
Black Sheep Best Bitter; Fuller's ESB; Greene King IPA; Morland Old Speckled Hen; Timothy Taylor Landlord; 2 changing beers (sourced nationally) Ⓗ
In 2019 the landlord celebrated 10 years at this large family-friendly pub, set in a picturesque village close to Thetford Forest. Two bars divided by an open fire serve five real ales on handpump. Outdoor seating is provided at the front and in an enclosed brick-weave courtyard at the rear. The pub is home to three pool teams and a darts team, and holds quiz and bingo nights on alternate Wednesdays, both preceded by fish & chips. There are also other regular events. ♿❀🕙&♣P❀🛜

Great Yarmouth

Blackfriars Tavern

94 Blackfriars Road, NR30 3BZ
☎ (01493) 331651 ⊕ blackfriarstavern.co.uk
4 changing beers (sourced regionally; often Milestone) Ⓗ
Run by an enthusiastic landlord, the Blackfriars Tavern is in a conservation area close to the most impressive section of Great Yarmouth's medieval town walls. Recently refurbished the pub has an outside covered area for drinking. An ever-changing range of real ales is served and food is planned. ❀&

King's Arms

229 Northgate Street, NR30 1BG (close to marketplace)
☎ (01493) 843736 ⊕ thekingsarmsgreatyarmouth.co.uk
Adnams Broadside; Woodforde's Wherry; 1 changing beer (sourced nationally) Ⓗ
This inn has one large room divided into drinking areas, and a comfortable seating section with a real fire at one end. The large well-kept garden is ideal for summer drinking and dining. Adnams Broadside and Woodforde's

Wherry are complemented by a more local offering. The friendly bar staff, landlord and landlady provide a welcoming atmosphere. It holds an annual August bank holiday beer festival. ♿❀🕙&♣♦P🚃🐾

Mariners Ⓛ

69 Howard Street South, NR30 1LN (between Palmers and Star Hotel)
☎ (01493) 331164
Greene King Abbot; 10 changing beers (sourced nationally) Ⓗ
Traditional two-bar flint-walled pub in the town centre which stocks up to 10 ales and several ciders or perries from all over the country. There is a maritime theme to the decor, with photos of different ships on the walls. In the winter you can enjoy your drinks while sitting next to a lovely open fire. Knowledgeable staff and a great choice of varying real ales make this place enjoyable. Local CAMRA Cider Pub of the Year 2019. ♿❀≈♦P🚃🚃🐾🛜

Red Herring Ⓛ

24-25 Havelock Road, NR30 3HQ (off St Peters St)
☎ 07876 644742
4 changing beers (sourced nationally) Ⓗ
The establishment gets its name from the fish that were smoked in the nearby but now-closed smokehouses. It offers four changing beers with two ciders on the handpumps, has a dartboard and pool table, and hosts a pool and darts team. The pub is close to the impressive medieval walls and the award-winning Time and Tide museum. There is always a relaxed and friendly atmosphere here along with a good regular following. Q❀♣♦🛎🚃

Tombstone Saloon Ⓛ

6 George Street, NR30 1HR (on NE corner of Hall Quay)
☎ 07584 504444 ⊕ tombstonebrewery.co.uk
10 changing beers (sourced nationally) Ⓖ
Western-style bar specialising in real ale and cider, operated by the Tombstone Brewery sited at the rear of the premises. Staff are friendly and knowledgeable about beer, and can usually serve you up to six Tombstone real ales plus four others from various breweries. The bar also has a stock of rare spirits from around the world as well as wines and a European bottled beer selection. Local CAMRA branch Pub and Cider Pub of the year 2020. Q≈♣♦🛎🚃🐾

Happisburgh

Hill House Ⓛ

The Hill, NR12 0PW (off B1159, behind church)
☎ (01692) 650004 ⊕ hillhouseinn.co.uk
6 changing beers (sourced regionally; often Lacons) Ⓗ
A Grade II-listed, 16th-century former coaching inn in an attractive coastal village. Sir Arthur Conan Doyle stayed at the pub in 1903, and the on-site brewery is named after a Sherlock Holmes story, the Dancing Men. Six real ales are served, with at least two brewed on-site, and usually one real cider or perry. A noteworthy beer festival is hosted each June offering over 120 real ales and ciders. ♿❀🛏🕙▲♣♦P🚃(34)🐾

Harpley

Rose & Crown

Nethergate Street, PE31 6TW
☎ (01485) 521807 ⊕ roseandcrownharpley.co.uk
Woodforde's Wherry; 4 changing beers (sourced nationally) Ⓗ

Just off the A148 King's Lynn to Fakenham Road, this attractive 17th-century pub offers guest ales from local breweries. It features open bar areas with a stylish and comfortable feel and has log fires in winter. Outside is an enclosed beer garden for summer drinking. There is an extensive menu serving excellent food, including one of the best Sunday roasts around. The unspoilt village provides pleasant walks and is close to Houghton Hall. Local CAMRA Pub of the Year 2019.
Q☆☺❊◑P🖵(X29) ❀ ☙

Hempton

Bell

24 The Green, NR21 7LG
☎ (01328) 864579 ⊕ hemptonbell.co.uk
Woodforde's Wherry; 3 changing beers (sourced regionally) 🅷
A popular family-run village inn with a relaxed, friendly atmosphere. It retains a two-bar layout little altered since the early 1970s. Pub games, including dominoes, cribbage and poker dice, are played – you will be welcome to get involved. Changing guest beers are from micros or independent breweries. Open mic folk sessions take place on the second Tuesday of the month and regular quizzes are held. Q☆☺❊Å♣P❀☙

Hillington

Ffolkes

Lynn Road, PE31 6BJ TF716255
☎ (01485) 600210 ⊕ ffolkes.org.uk
3 changing beers (sourced regionally) 🅷
This family-run 300-year-old former coaching inn was extensively refurbished in 2017. Located just six miles from King's Lynn and three miles from the Royal Sandringham Estate, it provides a perfect base for exploring North Norfolk. The Ffolkes has 25 bedrooms, an outdoor adventure play area and an indoor games room. There is an extensive menu and the popular street food events are now a fixture. There are always several real ales to choose from. The Ffolkes is part of the Norfolk Passport scheme and cardholders can get a discount from their bill. ☆☺❊◑♣P❀☙

Hockwold

Red Lion

114 Main Street, IP26 4NB
☎ (01842) 829728 ⊕ redlionhockwold.com
3 changing beers (sourced nationally) 🅷
Traditional, friendly village pub set on a green. The Red Lion was refurbished and reopened as a free house in 2012. It has a smart but comfortable interior – see how many toby jugs you can spot. A good selection of home-made food is served all week, with a carvery on Sunday and Tuesday lunchtime; Thursday evening is steak night. There are regular, well-supported quizzes and darts matches. Outside is a spacious garden with plenty of seating, a smoking shelter and a children's play area. ☆☺◑♣P❀

Honingham

Buck 🅛

29 The Street, NR9 5BL (centre of village)
☎ (01603) 880393 ⊕ thehoninghambuck.co.uk
Lacons Charter, Encore, Legacy; 1 changing beer (sourced locally) 🅷
Dating back to 1789, this traditional one-bar village pub has a separate restaurant area with an emphasis on home-cooked food. The excellent menu of unusual dishes is freshly cooked to order, making this a great venue for eating. The Buck has served Lacons real ales since the brewery bought it in 2015. Slate floors, oak beams, a large fireplace and period furniture enhance the image of a country inn. There is a large garden with plenty of seating. Accommodation is in eight en-suite rooms. Q☆☺❊◑◑♿P🖵❀☙

King's Lynn

Live & Let Live 🅛

18 Windsor Road, PE30 5PL (off London Rd nr Catholic church)
☎ (01553) 764990
5 changing beers (sourced nationally) 🅷
Popular back-street venue with two rooms, one a small cosy back bar and the other a larger area at the front with a TV. Five beers are served including a mild (rare for the locality). Cider drinkers have a wide choice, often including something from a local producer – the pub is the local CAMRA branch's Cider Pub of the Year for 2020. Live music sometimes features in the public bar. ☆●❀

Marriott's Warehouse

South Quay, PE30 5DT
☎ (01553) 818500 ⊕ marriottswarehouse.co.uk
Sharp's Doom Bar; 2 changing beers (sourced locally) 🅷
This 16th-century riverside building, originally a warehouse for corn, salt and wine, has been converted into a café/restaurant. There is a drinking area on the first floor with table service and views of the Minster. You will also find outdoor tables on the quayside. One of the guest ales is usually Moon Gazer. Pay parking is available on the quayside and behind the building. ☆◑≠(Kings Lynn) P☙

Stuart House Hotel

35 Goodwins Road, PE30 5QX (up gravel drive off Goodwins Rd)
☎ (01553) 772169 ⊕ stuart-house-hotel.co.uk
3 changing beers (sourced nationally) 🅷
The public bar of this hotel tucked away close to The Walks has featured in the Guide for around 25 years. Visitors will find a garden for summer and a real fire in the bar in winter. The annual beer festival coincides with the King's Lynn music festival. Beers are usually from larger regional producers. Note that the pub is open evenings only, unless by arrangement. ❊🏠≠(Kings Lynn) P❀☙

Wenn's Chop & Ale House

9 Saturday Market Place, PE30 5DQ
☎ (01553) 772077
4 changing beers (sourced nationally) 🅷
The Wenn's reverted to its former name after an extensive renovation in February 2020. The remodelled interior has a number of separate rooms and there are also tables outside on the edge of Saturday Market Place. Beers are from local breweries and, despite its name, the menu offers traditional pub food and does not major on chops. There is pay parking opposite and round the corner. Highly rated accommodation is available. Q☆🏠◑♿≠(Kings Lynn) ♣🛏❀☙

Larling

Angel

NR16 2QU (1 mile SW from Snetterton racetrack, just off A11)
☎ (01953) 717963 ⊕ angel-larling.co.uk

Adnams Southwold Bitter; 4 changing beers (sourced nationally) ⊞
Five real ales plus a real cider are on handpump here, always including a mild. Over 100 whiskies are stocked (one is featured each week), and there are 50 gins on the gin menu. The lounge and the bar have real open fires, and there is a dining room which boasts home-made fare in generous portions. A friendly atmosphere is enjoyed by locals, visitors, campers and rallyists who use the Angel's campsite. A popular long-running beer festival in August showcases over 80 real ales with live music. Q ⍿ ⌂ ≈ ◑ ◔ ↺ ⚲ ♣ ♠ P ⊞

Lessingham

Star Inn 🄻
Star Hill, NR12 0DN (just off main B1159, corner of High Rd and Star Hill)
☎ (01692) 580510 ⊕ thestarlessingham.co.uk
Fat Cat Norwich Bitter; Lacons Encore; 2 changing beers (sourced locally) Ⓖ
A rural gem with a friendly atmosphere, and a log fire in winter. Four ales, including one guest, are served from the cask, as are three ciders. The Star is popular for quality meals, with carefully sourced ingredients served in decent portions. Food may be enjoyed in the bar, in a separate restaurant or in the spacious beer garden. Two en-suite double B&B rooms make this the perfect base to explore the nearby coast and the Broads. Closing time may be early on Sunday winter evenings.
Q ⌂ ≈ ◑ ◔ ♣ ♠ P ⊟ 🚍 (34) ♥ 🛜

Longham

White Horse
Wendling Road, NR19 2RD
☎ (01362) 687464 ⊕ longhamwhitehorse.co.uk
Greene King Yardbird; 3 changing beers (sourced regionally) ⊞
An attractive and traditional village inn with a cosy feel and a high standard of decor. It has a main bar area with separate dining rooms off to the left and right, plus a large conservatory also used for dining at the rear, overlooking the garden. The real ale is generally from a brewery in the region, with one traditional cider also usually on the bar. The extensive menu caters for all tastes and requirements, with ingredients sourced locally. B&B is available. Q ⍿ ⌂ ≈ ◑ ◔ ↺ ♣ ♠ P ♥ 🛜

Marlingford

Marlingford Bell 🄻
Bawburgh Road, NR9 5HX
☎ (01603) 880263 ⊕ thebellatmarlingford.co.uk
4 changing beers (sourced regionally) ⊞
This extended country village pub has a refurbished front bar, with a wood-burning stove making it nice and cosy in winter. There are no regular beers – the changing ales come from Lacons, Winter's and Woodforde's, and occasionally other small Norfolk breweries, one dispensed on gravity. The large function and restaurant room with a separate bar at the rear opens onto a large garden. Quality, locally sourced food is prepared on the premises, and excellent bar menu dishes are served on biodegradable trays. Sunday roasts are popular (booking advised). Q ⍿ ⌂ ≈ ◑ ◔ ↺ ♠ P ♥ 🛜

Middleton

Gate
Hill Road, Fair Green, PE32 1RW (just N of A47; follow Fair Green signs)

☎ (01553) 840518 ⊕ thegatefairgreen.co.uk
Greene King Abbot; Woodforde's Wherry, Nog; 1 changing beer (sourced nationally) ⊞
Although there is a pleasant dining room, this friendly family-run place is still at heart a village local. The bar and semi-separate section with a jukebox and TV screen are used mainly by those who just want a drink. Food features seasonal produce and ingredients from suppliers in the area. The pretty garden is popular in summer. Note that the pub is closed on Mondays and there is no food on Tuesdays. Q ⍿ ⌂ ≈ ◑ ◔ ↺ ♣ ♠ A P ♥

Neatishead

White Horse 🄻
The Street, NR12 8AD
☎ (01692) 630828 ⊕ thewhitehorseinnneatishead.com
Woodforde's Wherry; 6 changing beers (sourced regionally) ⊞
Traditional Broadland village-centre pub, sympathetically modernised while retaining many original features, including three separate drinking areas and a log fireplace in the bar. Six of the seven real ales are mainly from microbreweries across the UK and change frequently. Up to seven craft keg beers are also dispensed. Beer festivals are held in spring and autumn. Meals are home-prepared with local produce and are reasonably priced, served in a comfortable split-level restaurant. Moorings are a short walk away.
Q ⍿ ⌂ ≈ ◑ ◔ ↺ ♣ ♠ A P ♥ 🛜

New Buckenham

King's Head
Market Place, NR16 2AN
☎ (01953) 861247
Adnams Southwold Bitter; Oakham Inferno; 1 changing beer (often Fuller's, Shepherd Neame) ⊞
Free house facing the village green in what was, in the 12th century, a new town. The hostelry served as a coaching inn between London and Norwich in the early part of the 16th century. It has a contemporary feel but still retains the inglenook fireplace and exposed beams in the original part of the building. There is a large restaurant extension at the rear. Q ⍿ ⌂ ≈ ◑ ◔ ↺ ♠ P 🛜

North Walsham

Hop In 🄻
2 Market Street, NR28 9BZ
☎ 07735 845983 ⊕ thehopin.co.uk
6 changing beers (sourced locally) Ⓖ
Owned by keen CAMRA members, this was Norfolk's first micropub, situated in a former taxi office just around the corner from the marketplace. Six changing ales are served on gravity dispense along with real cider, and there is usually one dark beer on. In keeping with the micropub tradition, there is no Wi-Fi, music or machines, just good conversation. There is a small seating area downstairs and more upstairs, plus a patio outside. Local CAMRA branch Pub of the Year 2020.
Q ⍿ ≈ ≋ ● ⊟ 🚍

North Wootton

Red Cat Hotel
Station Road, PE30 3QH (Station Rd is opp North Wootton Church of All Saints, at the jct of N end of Nursery Rd and W end of Manor Rd)
☎ (01553) 631244 ⊕ redcathotel.co.uk
Adnams Southwold Bitter; 1 changing beer (sourced nationally) ⊞

This traditional village local offers two real ales. Nicely decorated and in a quiet location, it has attractive gardens for summer drinks. Ask about the history of the namesake red cat – if you can believe it. The pub is near National Cycle Route 1, the Sandringham Estate and the West Norfolk coast. Q♿🏠♿P🚃(3)🐾🛜

Norwich

Alexandra Tavern
16 Stafford Street, NR2 3BB (on corner of Stafford St and Gladstone St, off Dereham Rd)
☎ (01603) 627772 ⊕ alexandratavern.co.uk
5 changing beers (sourced regionally) Ⓗ
Popular, bustling and friendly, this pub is a real gem sited just outside the city centre. The interior is brightly decorated, with the walls displaying pictures and articles of a nautical nature. The bar serves up to five changing beers from local breweries, and two real ciders. Food is served daily, with a good variety, including a soup menu. There is a dartboard, and plenty of board games to choose from. Children are welcome until early evening. Q♿🏠♿◗🐾♣🍴🚃🐾🛜

Artichoke
1 Magdalen Road, NR3 4LW
☎ (01603) 662807
8 changing beers (sourced nationally; often Golden Triangle) Ⓗ
A 1930s flint building, originally decorated in Brewers' Tudor style, with Young's, Crawshay & Young's windows, parquet flooring and a long solid-wood bar. Its two cone-shaped roofs give the pub its name. Sensitively refurbished by the owner of Golden Triangle Brewery in 2018, the bar now has eight handpumps offering two or three Golden Triangle beers, plus a great selection of craft ales and real cider. An eclectic menu is available from the kitchen, supplemented by pop-up caterers, and there's extensive seating outdoors. 🏠♿🍴P🚃🐾🛜

Beehive Ⓛ
30 Leopold Road, NR4 7PJ (between Unthank and Newmarket roads)
☎ (01603) 451628 ⊕ beehivepubnorwich.co.uk
5 changing beers (sourced regionally) Ⓗ
A friendly two-bar local with knowledgeable staff, featuring a comfortable lounge bar with sofas. The beer garden is used all year round and for charity barbecues during the summer months. A beer festival is held in late June with around 25 ales and ciders. There is a function room upstairs with a pool table (available to hire). The pub has hockey, korfball, golf, darts and pool teams, plus a regular quiz on Wednesdays, folk music nights and themed food evenings. Q♿🏠♿◗♣🍴P🚃🐾🛜

Coach & Horses
82 Thorpe Road, NR1 1BA
☎ (01603) 477077 ⊕ thecoachthorperoad.co.uk
Chalk Hill Tap Bitter, CHB, Gold, Dreadnought; 3 changing beers (sourced regionally) Ⓗ
Close to the station, this coaching inn, with its iconic balcony, is the home of the Chalk Hill Brewery, and serves its full range of beers. A tour of the brewery is available by appointment. Excellent-value food is served along with Burnards cider. Sport, especially rugby, is shown on big screens, and the large fire is welcome in winter. Not far from the football ground and busy before matches. 🏠◗♿🍴P🚃🐾🛜

Coach & Horses
51 Bethel Street, NR2 1NR
☎ (01603) 618522 ⊕ thecoachandhorsesbethelstreet.co.uk
6 changing beers (sourced regionally) Ⓗ

Historic city-centre outlet near the Theatre Royal, the Forum and City Hall. It has a bright, welcoming bar with several separate seating areas including in cosy alcoves, and a long narrow sun-trap patio. A Greene King house, it offers a good selection of beer styles from local breweries in a range that changes regularly. Food is based on an English tapas theme, which works well. Try some celeb spotting too, or a game of bar billiards. Q♿🏠◗♣🍴🐾🛜

Duke of Wellington Ⓛ
91-93 Waterloo Road, NR3 1EG
☎ (01603) 441182 ⊕ dukeofwellingtonnorwich.co.uk
Fuller's London Pride Ⓗ**; Oakham JHB, Bishops Farewell** Ⓖ**; Wolf Golden Jackal** Ⓗ**, Wolf in Sheep's Clothing; 15 changing beers (sourced nationally)** Ⓖ
A friendly pub with a changing range of guest ales to complement the permanent beers, the majority of which are served on gravity from a taproom behind the bar. The attractive award-winning enclosed rear garden/patio area accommodates a beer festival in late August plus regular barbecues at weekends in summer. Events include monthly quiz evenings. Customers can bring their own food or sample the filling and inexpensive pies and sausage rolls. 🏠♿♣P🚃🐾🛜

Fat Cat Ⓛ
49 West End Street, NR2 4NA
☎ (01603) 624364 ⊕ fatcatpub.co.uk
Crouch Vale Yakima Gold; Fat Cat Norwich Bitter Ⓗ**, Marmalade; Greene King Abbot; Oakham Bishops Farewell, Green Devil** Ⓖ**; 20 changing beers (sourced nationally)** Ⓗ/Ⓖ
An amazing range of brewery memorabilia is displayed around the walls and alcoves of this traditional hostelry, refurbished in 2018. Ales from the Fat Cat range are served, plus about 10 regular and 20 guest beers from all over the UK, real ciders, and several quality keg beers. Food is limited to good-value rolls and pies. A gem of a place – exactly what a real ale outlet should be, with excellent, friendly service. Twice voted CAMRA National Pub of the Year. Q🏠P🚃🐾🛜

Fat Cat & Canary Ⓛ
101 Thorpe Road, NR1 1TR
☎ (01603) 436925
Fat Cat Norwich Bitter, Hell Cat, Honey Ale, Wild Cat, Marmalade; 7 changing beers (sourced nationally) Ⓗ
Owned by the Norwich-based Fat Cat mini-chain and situated about a mile and a half from the centre of the city, the bar serves most of the Fat Cat's ales, and various guests from around the UK, together with continental beers and real ciders. There is a small TV towards the back of the main bar, a large car park and terraces to the front and rear, the latter being heated. Home-made rolls are available. Busy on Norwich City match days. 🏠◗♿🍴P🚃🐾🛜

Fat Cat Brewery Tap Ⓛ
98-100 Lawson Road, NR3 4LF
☎ (01603) 413153 ⊕ fatcattap.co.uk
Fat Cat Norwich Bitter Ⓗ**, Tom Cat** Ⓖ**, Honey Ale, Marmalade** Ⓗ**; Oakham Bishops Farewell; 20 changing beers (sourced regionally)** Ⓖ
Home of the Fat Cat Brewery, serving the Fat Cat range plus a huge choice of real ales, ciders and quality keg beers from across the country. Live music on Fridays and Sundays complements a variety of events including tap takeovers, themed beer evenings, a monthly cycling club, and a fortnightly quiz. Loaded chips and cheeseboards are available. A distinctive selection of breweriana adorns the ceiling beams and walls. Q🏠♿♣🍴P🚃(11,11A) 🐾🛜

Golden Star

57 Colegate, NR3 1DD
☎ (01603) 632447 ⊕ goldenstarnorwich.co.uk
Greene King IPA, Abbot; 3 changing beers (sourced nationally) ⓗ
A welcoming and relaxing pub with a main bar area and a second room to the left of the bar, hosting bar billiards and live music sessions. A quiz is held on Sunday evening. An excellent specials menu is served daily, including locally sourced meat. A wide selection of music is played, but unobtrusively. There is a small patio at the rear, and tables outside the front in summer. Handy for Norwich Playhouse and Norwich University of the Arts.
❀◖♣♠🖿🌢🗟

Jubilee ⓛ

26 St Leonards Road, NR1 4BL
☎ (01603) 618734
Hop Back Summer Lightning; Woodforde's Wherry; 4 changing beers (sourced nationally) ⓗ
Attractive Victorian corner pub with a warm welcome. There are two bars, a comfortable conservatory and an enclosed patio garden. Many of the well-kept ales and craft beers are from nearby. This popular venue, within easy reach of the city centre, is at the heart of the community and caters for all tastes, from sports fans to those who enjoy local history talks. There are regular Sunday roasts and occasional pop-up street-food fairs, and customers are welcome to bring in takeaway food.
Q🌣❀≉♣♠🖿🌢🗟

King's Arms

22 Hall Road, NR1 3HQ
☎ (01603) 477888 ⊕ kingsarmsnorwich.co.uk
Batemans Gold; 10 changing beers (sourced regionally) ⓗ
A friendly Batemans house just south of the city, serving a wide range of guest ales to complement the Batemans beers, usually including a stout or porter and a mild. Real ciders are also stocked. Customers can bring in their own food from various nearby takeaways, with plates and condiments provided. Monthly quiz nights, poker evenings and live music take place. The pub is a recipient of many Batemans cellar-keeping and floral display awards. It gets busy on football match days.
🌣❀♣♠🖿(39,40)🌢🗟

King's Head ⓛ

42 Magdalen Street, NR3 1JE
☎ (01603) 620468 ⊕ kingsheadnorwich.com
10 changing beers (sourced regionally) ⓗ
A welcoming traditional two-bar pub which offers no keg beer, but up to 10 quality real ales, mostly from the area but with a few from around the country, plus two ciders. Fresh eggs and honey are often available. No food is served except snacks, pork pies and pickled eggs, but customers can bring or order in their own, with plates and cutlery supplied. Bar billiards is well supported, with two teams in the local league. Q❀♣♠🞖🖿🌢🗟

Leopard ⓛ

98-100 Bull Close Road, NR3 1NQ
☎ (01603) 631111
6 changing beers (sourced regionally; often Lacons, S&P) ⓗ
Welcoming, traditional single-bar corner local with a variety of changing ales, many from smaller breweries. The pub has a clean and bright bar area which gives a spacious feel, plus a pleasant and quiet enclosed courtyard garden at the rear. Customers can bring in food and cutlery will be provided. There is a quiz night, usually on the third Tuesday of the month, and a live music night once a month on a Friday. ❀♣♠🖿🌢🗟

Lollards Pit ⓛ

69-71 Riverside Road, NR1 1SR
☎ (01603) 624675 ⊕ lollardspit.com
Woodforde's Wherry, Nelson's; 4 changing beers (sourced regionally) ⓗ
An attractive 17th-century inn, one of the first built outside the city walls, on the site of Lollards Pit - a place of execution for heretics for over 200 years. The pub is close to the river and yacht station moorings. Guest ales are from nearby breweries, and there are also interesting beers from further afield. Snacks include local pork pies and sausage rolls, with a more extensive food offering planned. Community groups, weekly quiz and bingo nights, and weekend parties are hosted here.
🌣❀♿≉♣🖿🌢🗟

Murderers

2-8 Timber Hill, NR1 3LB
☎ (01603) 621447 ⊕ themurderers.co.uk
Wolf Edith Cavell; 9 changing beers (sourced regionally) ⓗ
A busy city-centre pub that appeals to all sections of the public, with 10-12 real ales, including two permanent beers, one of which is the house Murderer's Ale (brewed by Wolf). Beer festivals feature in summer and autumn, with over 40 beers to choose from, including many from local brewers. The upper area has a large-screen TV, making it a popular venue for viewing sporting events. A traditional British menu is served in generous portions.
❀◖🖿🌢🗟

Plasterers Arms ⓛ

43 Cowgate, NR3 1SZ
☎ (01603) 440992 ⊕ theplasterersarms.co.uk
Adnams Mosaic; Moon Gazer Pintail; 8 changing beers (sourced nationally) ⓗ
This is a friendly corner local with a wide range of beers from around the country, specialising in new and exciting breweries. A variety of craft keg ales is also served, alongside a great range of bottled and canned brews. The pub offers tap takeovers, sport (with a big screen for more important events), music from DJs on Sundays, excellent pizzas, and breakfast at weekends. It also hosts a Fem.ale Festival celebrating great women in the brewing industry. Q◖🖿🌢🗟

Playhouse Bar

42-58 St George Street, NR3 1AB
☎ (01603) 598598
4 changing beers (sourced regionally) ⓗ
A bar serving the Norwich Playhouse theatre - it can be crowded before performances and at the interval - with a good-sized lounge across the foyer and a large tree-shaded patio by the river. It stocks three or four beers, often including an Adnams ale, and an eclectic and interesting selection of guests. The bar features a 3D cityscape on the ceiling and an unusual collection of objets d'art. There are regular DJ sessions at weekends.
❀♿🗟

Plough

58 St Benedict Street, NR2 4AR
☎ (01603) 661384
6 changing beers (sourced locally) ⓗ
A popular pub in one of the city's oldest areas, near the Norwich Arts Centre. It sells six ales, usually all from Grain Brewery. The two-bar interior is fairly small, with wooden chairs and tables, and has an open fire in winter. The large Mediterranean-style courtyard garden is a fine place to spend a summer's evening. Grain lager and craft beers are also served, along with Vic's special sausage pie, and there are barbecues in the summer. ❀♣🖿🌢🗟

Ribs of Beef L ✅

24 Wensum Street, NR3 1HY

☎ (01603) 619517 ⊕ ribsofbeef.co.uk

Adnams Ghost Ship; Oakham JHB; Wolf Golden Jackal; Woodforde's Wherry; 5 changing beers (sourced regionally) ⊞

Traditional and well-decorated pub overlooking the River Wensum. A welcoming row of nine handpumps dispenses four regular ales and a selection from quality microbreweries from outside the area. Foreign beers and real cider are also available. Good food is made with locally sourced ingredients. The atmosphere is relaxed and friendly, with a room downstairs, a small riverside terrace and several tables outside at the front and rear. There is a quiz every Thursday night and live music on Sunday evening. Sporting fixtures are shown live on TV. ⊛⊙♣♠➡🐶🛜

Rose Inn

235 Queens Road, NR1 3AE

☎ (01603) 623942 ⊕ theroseinnnorwich.co.uk

5 changing beers (sourced regionally) ⊞

Popular pub close to Carrow Road, the home of Norwich City FC. The owner's passion for beer shows in the selection of five regularly changing real ales and six craft ales from some of the most exciting breweries around the country, plus real ciders. Regular beer, cider and gin festivals and frequent tap takeovers are held. There is an in-house deli specialising in local foods, open the same hours as the pub, and home-cooked pizza is available. A bar billiards table has been installed. ⊛🚲♦⛓♣🅰♠➡🐶🛜

Rosebery

94 Rosebery Road, NR3 3AB

☎ (01603) 414284 ⊕ theroserypubnorwich.co.uk

4 changing beers (sourced regionally) ⊞

A busy Victorian corner pub that has been stylishly refurbished. Four real ales are dispensed on a rotational basis, most coming from local brewers. Several real ciders are also on sale. Food is served daily and the pub offers an excellent burger menu, as well as a Sunday roast. Regular live bands and reggae record nights make this a popular destination for music lovers. B&B accommodation is available. ⊛🚲♦⛓♣●P➡🐶🛜

St Andrew's Brewhouse

41 St Andrews Street, NR2 4TP

☎ (01603) 305995 ⊕ standrewsbrewhouse.com

6 changing beers (sourced locally) ⊞

A Grade II*-listed building refurbished during 2015 in distressed industrial style, now a brewhouse and restaurant with an eclectic food menu. The bar and microbrewery face St Andrews Street, and the restaurant has views of the ancient St Andrews Hall, home of the Norwich Beer Festival. Six handpumps dispense house beers for the most part. Wensum Ale (gluten-free) is served, with a couple of local guests or seasonal specials and sometimes a cider/perry, supplemented by a good range of craft beers. Upstairs rooms feature board games and have views of the brewery fermentation tanks. Q⊛⊛⊙⛓♣♠➡🐶🛜

Trafford Arms L ✅

61 Grove Road, NR1 3RL

☎ (01603) 628466 ⊕ traffordarms.co.uk

Adnams Southwold Bitter, Ghost Ship; 8 changing beers (sourced regionally) ⊞

Close to the city centre, this friendly local has a strong community feel and is open all day every day. It is a flagship for real ale in Norwich, offering regular and ever-changing guest beers, often including a dark ale. High-quality pub food is sold and there are special themed food evenings, and home-cooked Sunday roasts.

The February Valentine's beer festival is a major attraction, as is the regular quiz on the last Sunday of the month. ⊛⊛⊙P➡🐶🛜

Vine L

7 Dove Street, NR2 1DE

☎ (01603) 627362 ⊕ vinethai.co.uk

Fat Cat Tom Cat; Oakham JHB; 2 changing beers (sourced regionally) ⊞

One of Norwich's smallest pubs, located just off the marketplace. It serves up to four quality ales, mostly from local breweries, plus Thai cuisine in an award-winning combination. The pub has been in the same hands for over 10 years. The restaurant is upstairs, although customers often eat downstairs in the bar area. Functions are catered for outside normal opening hours on demand. Extra tables and chairs are set outside in the pedestrianised street. Occasionally open on a Sunday. Q⊛⊙♣●➡

White Lion

73 Oak Street, NR3 3AQ

☎ (01603) 632333

7 changing beers (sourced regionally) ⊞

A good changing range of real ales from breweries from the area and others is on sale here – often from Winter's, Bull of the Woods and Shortts. Eight to 10 ciders are also available plus, usually, at least one perry. Helpful and knowledgeable bar staff are on hand. Food is varied and excellent value, using local produce, with daily specials. Bar billiards, board games and darts are played. The traditional interior is split into three rooms, with a front and back bar and a games room to the side. Q⊛⊙♣●🖤🐶🛜

Wig & Pen L

6 St Martin at Palace Plain, NR3 1RN

☎ (01603) 625891 ⊕ thewigandpen.com

Adnams Southwold Bitter; 5 changing beers (sourced regionally) ⊞

Pretty, beamed 17th-century free house with a spacious patio, immediately opposite the Bishop's Palace, and with an impressive view of Norwich Cathedral spire. Six ales are always available, usually including two local beers. The small back room can be used for meetings. Good-quality food is served lunchtimes and evenings. The pub is a short walk from Tombland, where there are bus stands for several bus routes, and is an ideal starting or stopping place for a walk along the river. Q⊛🚲⊙⛓🛜

Old Buckenham

Ox & Plough

The Green, NR17 1RN (in centre of village)

☎ (01953) 860970

Adnams Southwold Bitter; Sharp's Doom Bar; 3 changing beers (often Hop Back, Oakham) ⊞

A family-friendly community pub on one of the largest village greens in England, at the heart of local life. It has two open-plan drinking areas, one of which is quiet, without TV or electronic game machines. The garden at the front overlooks the village green. Real ale is dispensed from three to five handpumps, and as a member of Oakham Academy the pub serves various changing Oakham ales (Oakham Green Devil is a regular keg beer). Bar snacks only. ⊛⊛♣♠P🐶🛜

Reepham

King's Arms L

Market Place, NR10 4JJ

☎ (01603) 870345 🌐 kingsarmsreepham.com
Adnams Southwold Bitter, Ghost Ship; Greene King Abbot; Panther Golden Panther; Woodforde's Wherry; 1 changing beer (sourced regionally) [H]
An old coaching inn dating back to 1667, in the picturesque square of this small market town, with original beams, Norfolk brickwork and open fires. There are several comfortable drinking and dining areas, and tables in front with views across the square. Five permanent real ales are on sale, including at least one from the local Panther Brewery, plus a guest. The comprehensive menu comes mostly from nearby suppliers. Jazz bands play in the rear courtyard on summer Sundays. Q🐎❀◐◑🚌🐾

Ringstead

Gin Trap Inn ✓
6 High Street, PE36 5JU
☎ (01485) 525264 🌐 thegintrapinn.co.uk
Adnams Southwold Bitter, Ghost Ship; Greene King IPA; Woodforde's Wherry; 1 changing beer (sourced nationally) [H]
This attractive, whitewashed 17th-century coaching inn has been operating since 1668. There is outside seating at the front and an enclosed garden to the rear. It has a split-level bar and a separate restaurant, although food is served throughout. Regular themed food evenings are hosted as well as live music nights. The main bar has a log-burning stove. The drinks menu also features a range of some 100 different gins, including the pub's own Gin Trap gin. ❀🛏◐◑♿P🐾📶

Roydon

Union Jack
30 Station Road, PE32 1AW (off A148)
☎ 07771 660439
Tydd Steam Piston Bob; 3 changing beers (sourced nationally) [H]
Popular with locals, this traditional village venue has twice been local CAMRA Pub of the Year. Four handpumps dispense one regular and three changing ales. Beer festivals are held over the Easter and August bank holidays, usually featuring local breweries. There are occasional food nights, live music each month, regular bingo and quizzes, and weekly support for darts, crib and dominoes. Outdoor seating is at the front. Q❀⛺♣🍎P🚌(48)🐾📶

Scratby

California Tavern
California Road, NR29 3QW
☎ (01493) 730340 🌐 californiatavern.co.uk
3 changing beers (sourced locally; often Wolf) [H]
A free house on top of the cliffs with a large child-friendly garden with up to three real ales on offer. Just the place after you have trudged up the steps from the beach. Food is served, with daily specials and a children's menu. Regular live music features. 🐎❀◐◑♣

Shouldham

King's Arms [L]
The Green, PE33 0BY
☎ (01366) 347410 🌐 kingsarmsshouldham.co.uk
2 changing beers (sourced nationally) [G]
Named the local CAMRA Pub of the Year for 2020, the King's Arms has now received this accolade four times in the last five years. This is a community-owned business that also includes a café. The beer is served in lined glasses straight from the cask and two or three choices are usually available. Cider is also frequently on offer. Many community activities take place, from poetry evenings and live music to quiz nights. Details are chalked up on a noticeboard. 🐎❀◐◑🍎P🚂🐾📶

Snettisham

Rose & Crown
Old Church Road, PE31 7LX (off B1440)
☎ (01485) 541382 🌐 roseandcrownsnettisham.co.uk
Adnams Broadside; Marston's Pedigree; Woodforde's Wherry; 2 changing beers (sourced nationally) [H]
The old front bar has been progressively added to, creating a more modern space mainly used by those enjoying the highly regarded food. Breakfast is served every day before the bar opens. There is a garden and play area for children, and accommodation is offered. This multi award-winning pub features in many guides and is popular, so you may need to book a table. Q🐎❀🛏◐◑♿♣P🚌🐾📶

Southrepps

Vernon Arms ✓
2 Church Street, NR11 8NP (NE of Thorpe Market off A149 Cromer-North Walsham road)
☎ (01263) 833355 🌐 vernonarms.com
Adnams Southwold Bitter; Fat Cat Norwich Bitter; Greene King Abbot; 1 changing beer (sourced regionally) [H]
A brick and flint village-centre establishment with a lively and welcoming atmosphere. The three regular ales are augmented by a variety of guest beers. The pub is popular for its fine food, prepared with locally sourced ingredients where possible. Takeaway fish & chips is available Tuesday to Saturday early evening. The front terrace includes a heated and covered smoking area and there is a garden at the rear. Various acoustic music sessions are held. Gunton station is just under 1½ miles. 🐎❀◐◑♿⛺♣P🚌(33,33A)🐾📶

Stradsett

Foldgate Inn
Downham Road, PE33 9HH (jct of A1122/A134)
☎ (01366) 347772 🌐 thefoldgateinn.co.uk
3 changing beers (sourced nationally) [H]
Once a Bagge Brewery pub, the Foldgate is situated at a busy crossroads close to the country estate where the family still reside. A popular destination for those looking for food, the pub is increasingly attracting drinkers in search of interesting ales. The original long bar has been extended with the addition of a modern conservatory used for dining. There is a large outdoor area with play facilities for children. Booking is recommended for those intending to dine. 🐎❀◐◑P🐾

Strumpshaw

Shoulder of Mutton [L]
9 Norwich Road, NR13 4NT (on Brundall-Lingwood road)
☎ (01603) 926530 🌐 themuttonstrumpshaw.co.uk
Adnams Ghost Ship; Sharp's Doom Bar; Timothy Taylor Landlord; 3 changing beers (sourced regionally) [H]
A traditional village pub with a friendly welcome. There are two main bar areas sharing the log-burner, and a separate dining room. Beers are from a variety of regional and micro breweries, complemented by three local ciders. Meals are freshly prepared from local

produce, with seafood and home-made pies prominent. Live music and events take place, and the rear patio overlooks the courtyard where pétanque is played. Close to the Broads and a nationally important RSPB site. ⊛🕪🕭🖐🗚♣🕪P🖵(15A) 🌸🛜

Thetford

Black Horse 🅛
64 Magdalen Street, IP24 2BP
☎ (01842) 762717
Adnams Southwold Bitter; Greene King IPA; Woodforde's Wherry; 2 changing beers (sourced nationally) Ⓗ
A good no-nonsense town pub offering a varying range of ales on five handpumps. It stages a popular annual St George's Day beer festival. The food is home-made and good both in quality and value – desserts are a feature – served in a small but pleasant eating area. Look for the changing murals on the end wall. ⊛🕪🖐P

Red Lion 🅛 ✅
Market Place, IP24 2AL
☎ (01842) 757210
Adnams Broadside; Greene King IPA, Abbot; 3 changing beers (sourced nationally) Ⓗ
On the market square, the Red Lion has had a varied history. It was opened by Lacons (the wall outside still retains its plaque), then it became a Portuguese restaurant, and finally a Wetherspoon establishment. The decor features information about local history and attractions. There is often a dark ale on the bar, and the pub has a variety of eating and drinking areas plus an outdoor space. 🌙⊛🕪🚮🖐🛜

Thompson

Chequers Inn
Griston Road, IP24 1PX
☎ (01953) 483360 ⊕ thompsonchequers.co.uk
Greene King IPA; Woodforde's Wherry; 1 changing beer (sourced nationally) Ⓗ
A 16th-century gem in this pretty village, featuring a steep thatched roof and timber-framed construction. Stooping to Tudor height will keep your head from the beams. There are two rooms for dining, and a small area and another small room for drinking. The pub has an excellent reputation for food. In fine weather the garden is popular, with plenty of tables. Guest beers are mostly from Woodforde's. 🌙⊛🏠🕪🖐P

Thornham

Lifeboat Inn ✅
Ship Lane, PE36 6LT (signed from A149 Coast Road)
☎ (01485) 512236 ⊕ lifeboatinnthornham.com
Greene King Abbot; Woodforde's Wherry; 2 changing beers (sourced nationally) Ⓗ
A busy pub just off the North Norfolk Coastal Path on the edge of the salt marshes. It has a wide range of drinking areas, from the dark and cosy bar to the light and airy conservatory. There is an enclosed garden at the rear. The interior has been tastefully renovated while retaining the atmosphere of the smugglers' inn it undoubtedly once was. Food is served throughout and there is also a large separate restaurant. Accommodation is available in 13 rooms. Q🌙⊛🏠🕪P🌸🛜

Thorpe Market

Gunton Arms 🅛 ✅
Cromer Road, NR11 8TZ (W of A149 Cromer to North Walsham road, SE of Thorpe Market; look for hanging sign, lit at night)
☎ (01263) 832010 ⊕ theguntonarms.co.uk
Adnams Broadside; Lacons Legacy; Woodforde's Wherry; 1 changing beer (sourced regionally) Ⓗ
A fine country inn with magical vistas of Gunton Park and its deer herd. It boasts tasteful decor with comfortable furnishings and a log fire in winter. East Anglian ales predominate, with regular guests. First-class cuisine is served in three restaurants; several dishes are cooked on an open range in the vaulted Elk Room. There is a beer garden for alfresco dining, and a food and music festival is held in summer. Sixteen rooms and suites are available. ⊛🏠🕪🖐P🖵(4)🌸🛜

Suffield Arms
Station Road, NR11 8UE
☎ (01263) 586858 ⊕ suffieldarms.com
4 changing beers (sourced regionally; often Grain, Lacons, Woodforde's) Ⓗ
Completely refurbished inside and out by the owner of the nearby Gunton Arms, there is a large bar at the front with a pool table, five handpumps and lots of bar stools. Out back is an impressive tapas bar with more seating and tables and a secluded area at the far end, plus another room off from the entrance. Upstairs is a smart cocktail lounge, and there's more seating outside. The pub is a minutes' walk from Gunton station, so is perfect for a trip out from the city. 🌙⊛🕪🚮🛤P🌸🛜

Thurlton

Queen's Head 🅛
Beccles Road, NR14 6RJ
☎ (01508) 548667 ⊕ queenshead-thurlton.co.uk
3 changing beers (sourced regionally; often People's) Ⓗ
A bustling community-owned pub with three real ales, including exclusive beers from the nearby People's Brewery. Other local and national ales are regularly available. The comfortable bar is on three levels, with a pool table at one end and a cosy log fire in the winter. Excellent locally sourced food is served, with themed menus and breakfast on Wednesdays. There is live music every weekend. Families, dogs and children are welcome. Q🌙⊛🕪🚮♣🖐P🖵(86)🌸🛜

Thurne

Lion Inn 🅛
The Street, NR29 3AP
☎ (01692) 671806 ⊕ thelionatthurne.com
6 changing beers (sourced regionally) Ⓖ
Large country pub in a remote village near the River Ant at the end of Thurne Dyke. Plenty of moorings are available nearby for passing Broads cruisers, and it has a large garden. Meals made from locally sourced produce are served in the large restaurant or bar area. The pub dispenses six changing real ales on handpump and there is a choice of up to 20 real ciders and 14 keg taps for craft offerings. Local CAMRA Pub of The Year 2019. Q🌙⊛🕪🖐🗚♣🖐🌸

Upton

White Horse 🅛
17 Chapel Road, NR13 6BT
☎ (01493) 750696 ⊕ whitehorseupton.com

Woodforde's Wherry; 3 changing beers (sourced regionally) ⊞
Traditional broadland venue dating from 1798, a 10-minute walk from Upton Dyke Staithe and moorings. It was renovated in 2012, and is now owned by the community. A shop caters for locals and holidaymakers alike. Beers are usually from nearby breweries. Genuine pub food features strongly, with noted Sunday roasts; fish & chip night is Friday. An annual beer, cider and perry festival takes place over the first full weekend in July.
ኄዼ◑ᵭ♣⚘♙Ქ❀⧈

Warham All Saints

Three Horseshoes
The Street, NR23 1NL (2 miles SE of Wells)
☎ (01328) 710547 ● warhamhorseshoes.co.uk
Woodforde's Wherry Ⓖ**; 3 changing beers (sourced regionally)** ⊞
A traditional brick and flint village pub with a warm atmosphere, log fires in winter and a unique serving hatch. Four cask beers include three from micros, and one cider is usually on sale. Food, including the famous pies, uses local ingredients. There is a separate dining room and a games room in the barn. The secluded garden is perfect for alfresco dining and has its own bar in summer. Q⊛☷◑ᵭ♣⚘♙Ქ❀⧈

West Runton

Village Inn
Water Lane, NR27 9QP
☎ (01263) 838000 ● villageinnwestrunton.co.uk
4 changing beers (sourced locally; often Adnams, Moon Gazer) ⊞
A large inn a short distance from the station and the beach, set in pleasant gardens in the centre of this quiet coastal village. Up to five well-kept and mostly local ales are stocked and rotated. Excellent home-cooked meals can be enjoyed in the dining areas or outside, where there is plenty of seating in the flint-walled garden. In the 1970s major rock bands including Deep Purple played secret gigs at the Pavilion which was at the rear of the pub, sadly now demolished.
Q❅⊛◑ᵭ⚘≈P➡❀⧈

West Somerton

Lion
Horsey Road, NR29 4DP
☎ (01493) 393861 ● thelionsomerton.co.uk
2 changing beers (sourced regionally) ⊞
Just a short walk from the Staithe, the Lion has a traditional, warm and welcoming feel. A local stalwart during the covid pandemic, it has recently been refurbished. The experienced licensees offer two real ales as well as home-made, locally sourced, freshly prepared food. Bed & Breakfast rooms are available.
ኄ⊛☷◑♣Ქ❀⧈

Weybourne

Ship Inn Ⓛ ✅
The Street, NR25 7SZ
☎ (01263) 588721 ● theshipinnweybourne.com
Woodforde's Wherry; 3 changing beers (sourced locally; often Moon Gazer) ⊞
In the heart of this attractive north Norfolk coastal village, the Ship dispenses up to four cask ales. It sells only local beers, including Woodforde's, Humpty Dumpty, Beeston, Moon Gazer, Wolf, Grain and Panther, plus a range of bottled craft brews. Home-cooked food is

served lunchtimes and evenings. A monthly quiz night is hosted. There is a pleasant enclosed garden for the summer, and the North Norfolk Railway and Muckleburgh Collection of military vehicles are close by. The Coasthopper bus stops outside.
Q❄⊛◑ᵭ♣⚘➡❀⧈

Wimbotsham

Chequers Inn ✅
7 Church Road, PE34 3QG
☎ (01366) 386768 ● thechequerswimbotsham.co.uk
Greene King IPA, Abbot; Woodforde's Wherry; 2 changing beers (sourced nationally) ⊞
A traditional English inn that dates back to the mid-17th century and overlooks the village green. There is a large bar and dining area with pub activities for the locals. An extensive food and drink menu is offered every day with the exception of Sunday evening. The pub has a separate function room and a car park to the rear. ኄ◑ᵭP⧈

Wreningham

Bird in Hand ✅
Church Road, NR16 1BJ
☎ (01508) 489438 ● birdinhandwreningham.com
Adnams Ghost Ship; Ruddles Best Bitter; Woodforde's Wherry; 1 changing beer (sourced regionally) ⊞
A friendly family-run Grade II-listed free house with conference and restaurant facilities, and Casque Mark cellar standards. The pub is close to Lotus Cars; the bar displays racing memorabilia alongside rural items and old photos of the village. Regular acoustic music nights and occasional quiz nights are held. There is a lovely garden plus a courtyard and large car park.
Q❄⊛❄◑ᵭ♣P➡(37A,805) ❀⧈

Wymondham

Feathers
13 Town Green, NR18 0PN
☎ (01953) 605675
Adnams Southwold Bitter, Ghost Ship; Fuller's London Pride; St Austell Tribute; 2 changing beers (sourced regionally) ⊞
The Feathers dates from the 18th century. Its interior has two main drinking areas and alcoves, served by a single bar. Walls are adorned with postcard collections, enamel signs, and farming and rural memorabilia, including an old bike. Good-value food is available lunchtime and evening. There is a large well-furnished patio garden at the rear. ኄ⊛◑≈♣➡⧈

Green Dragon Ⓛ ✅
6 Church Street, NR18 0PH (between Market St and Wymondham Abbey)
☎ (01953) 607907 ● greendragonnorfolk.co.uk
4 changing beers (sourced regionally) ⊞
A half-timbered inn recognised by CAMRA as having a historic interior of regional importance. On the road to Wymondham's beautiful abbey, this building dates back to 1371 and is reputed to be haunted. The interior has beamed timbers and carved stone, and shows evidence of medieval construction methods. One bar serves the downstairs area, a snug and the restaurant. The rotating real ales are mostly from nearby or East Anglian breweries. Excellent home-made food features locally sourced ingredients where possible. Beer festivals are held in May and August with live music. There is an attractive beer garden. Q❄⊛◑ᵭ≈♣⚘➡❀⧈

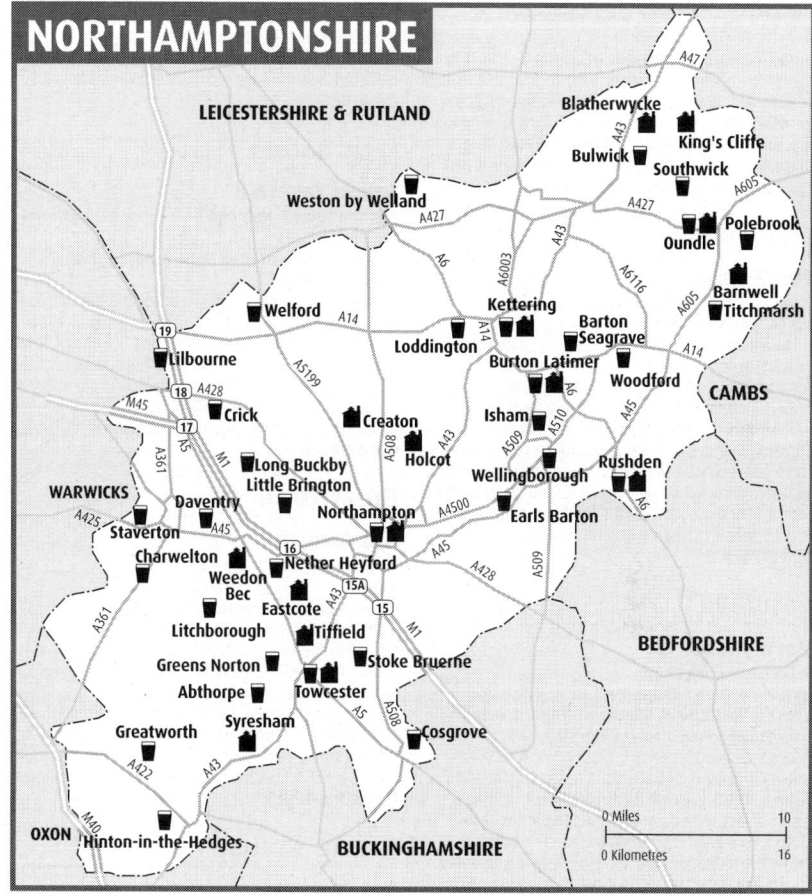

NORTHAMPTONSHIRE

LEICESTERSHIRE & RUTLAND

Blatherwycke
Bulwick
King's Cliffe
Southwick
Weston by Welland
Polebrook
Oundle
Barnwell
Titchmarsh
Welford
Kettering
Barton Seagrave
Loddington
Burton Latimer
Woodford
CAMBS
Lilbourne
Crick
Creaton
Isham
Long Buckby
Holcot
Rushden
Little Brington
Wellingborough
WARWICKS
Daventry
Northampton
Earls Barton
Staverton
Charwelton
Nether Heyford
Weedon Bec
Eastcote
BEDFORDSHIRE
Litchborough
Tiffield
Greens Norton
Stoke Bruerne
Abthorpe
Towcester
Greatworth
Syresham
Cosgrove
OXON
Hinton-in-the-Hedges
BUCKINGHAMSHIRE

0 Miles 10
0 Kilometres 16

Abthorpe

New Inn L

Silver Street, NN12 8QR (off Main St, left at church)
☎ (01327) 857306 ⊕ newinnabthorpe.uk
Hook Norton Hooky, Hooky Gold, Old Hooky; 1 changing beer (often Hook Norton) Ⓗ
A tranquil country hostelry tucked away close to the village green and church. It is a quintessentially English village pub built of local mellow sandstone, complete with low ceilings and an inglenook fireplace with seating. It serves good food including meats from the owner's farm, plus ales that are still brewed in the traditional way by Hook Norton – its seasonal beers feature as guests. Traditional pub games including darts and Northamptonshire skittles are played.
ॐ❀◑ᗢ♣P❀🕏

Barton Seagrave

Stirrup Cup L ✔

Woodland Avenue, NN15 6QR (off A14 jct 10)
☎ (01536) 722841 ⊕ thestirrupcupbartonseagrave.co.uk
Ruddles Best Bitter; 3 changing beers (sourced regionally; often Black Sheep, Potbelly) Ⓗ
Community-focused estate pub with two bar areas. The traditional sports bar features darts, pool and skittles; the lounge offers breakfast, lunch and afternoon tea from Monday to Friday. The pub has an emphasis on beer choice, usually stocking a local ale from Potbelly plus two

guests. Evening entertainment includes a quiz on Wednesday, jazz on Thursday and an open mic night on Sunday. Q ॐ❀◑ᗢ♣P🚐(A)❀🕏

Bulwick

Queen's Head L

Main Street, NN17 3DY
☎ (01780) 450272 ⊕ queensheadbulwick.com
Digfield Shacklebush; Grainstore Red Kite; 2 changing beers Ⓗ
Seventeenth-century stone pub with a Collyweston slate roof on the main street opposite the church. Access is through a small door via the patio and outside dining area at the rear. Inside, there is a single bar with four handpumps offering a range of changing beers, often from local micros. High-quality locally sourced food is served in a number of interconnecting dining areas and is thoroughly recommended (booking advisable). A former local CAMRA branch Pub of the Year. Open on some Mondays in summer. Q❀◑ᗢ♣P❀🕏

Burton Latimer

Duke's Arms L ✔

123 High Street, NN15 5RL (off A14 jct 10)
☎ (01536) 390874
3 changing beers (sourced nationally) Ⓗ

For many years keg only, this revitalised pub now features three handpumps for real ale and is the local outlet for Three Hills Brewing. A central U-shaped bar serves the opened-out rooms, with comfortable leather seating and more traditional seating in the small bay windows. The walls are adorned with vinyl LPs and there is a collection of books for customers to read. Tuesday is ukulele night. There is no parking but a free car park is just across the road. ▲★✿♠♣♥☷☺♥❄️

Charwelton

Fox & Hounds
Banbury Road, NN11 3YY (on A421)
☎ (01327) 260611 ⊕ foxandhoundscharwelton.co.uk
3 changing beers (sourced regionally; often North Cotswold) Ⓗ
An attractive stone-built pub, with parts dating from the 15th century. It was purchased by the local community following its closure in 2012, thus safeguarding its future. Comfortably furnished, it is a cosy place to enjoy the three beers on offer from local microbreweries. Food is available all week in the bar and restaurant. Note the Hunt Edmunds ceramic plaque by the entrance – the former Banbury brewery once owned the pub.
▲✿◖◗P☷❄️❄️⚡

Cosgrove

Barley Mow ⊘
7 The Stocks, MK19 7JD
☎ (01908) 562957 ⊕ thebarleymowcosgrove.co.uk
Everards Beacon Hill, Sunchaser, Tiger; 1 changing beer (sourced regionally; often Titanic) Ⓗ
A beautiful countryside pub backing on to the Grand Union Canal by Bridge 65. The 17th-century building's main bar and adjoining areas provide a charming environment, especially when the log fire is ablaze. Outside is a patio leading onto a lovely garden. The home-cooked food caters for all dietary requirements. Events are staged throughout the year, and may include a murder mystery evening as well as the monthly quiz.
Q▲★✿◖◗⚡♣P☷(90,90A) ❄️⚡

Crick

Wheatsheaf Ⓛ ⊘
15 Main Road, NN6 7TU (on main road through village)
☎ (01788) 823824 ⊕ wheatsheafcrick.com
Bombardier; house beer (by Banks's); 3 changing beers (sourced regionally; often Marston's, Phipps NBC, Potbelly) Ⓗ
An ironstone village local featuring a comfortable front bar area with exposed beams and a variety of seating areas. To the rear is a large restaurant and function room providing well-priced meals, with many ingredients sourced locally. The pub hosts frequent theme nights in the restaurant, with booking essential. Other attractions include occasional live music plus a quiz night on Tuesday. Good-value accommodation is available.
Q▲✿♠◖◗⚡♣P☷(96)❄️

Daventry

Early Doors Ⓛ
3 Prince William Walk, NN11 4AB
☎ 07944 649426 ⊕ earlydoorsdaventry.co.uk
Phipps NBC India Pale Ale; 5 changing beers (sourced locally; often Towcester Mill, Vale, XT) Ⓖ
Northamptonshire's first micropub is now run by a father-and-son team who took over from its founders. Tucked away down a narrow alley, this is a warm and

welcoming oasis in the heart of Daventry, with a real community feel. The bar is simply decorated. Ales, including a dark beer, are all on gravity, and locally produced cider is made within one mile of Welton.
Q&♥P☷❄️

Earls Barton

Saxon Tavern Ⓛ
25B The Square, NN6 0NA
☎ 07956 462352
6 changing beers (often Nene Valley, Potbelly, Towcester Mill) Ⓗ
A large, comfortable and relaxed single-room micropub with welcoming hosts. It has a central village location between the famous Barker Shoes and the historic Saxon tower and was previously the local headquarters of the Magic Circle. Six casks with cooling jackets are stillaged behind the bar. A wide selection of 130 gins is offered, along with bottled beers and box ciders from the fridge.
Q✿♣♥P☷❄️

Greatworth

Greatworth Inn Ⓛ
Chapel Road, OX17 2DT (off B4525)
☎ (01295) 521426 ⊕ thegreatworthinn.co.uk
4 changing beers (sourced regionally) Ⓗ
Stone-built free house dating from the 16th century, located in the centre of this attractive village. It was restored to its former glory by the owners on their return to the village, with numerous improvements undertaken while retaining a cosy and traditional pub atmosphere. The bar area features an inglenook fireplace with a log-burning stove; there is also a dining area. An annual soap box derby is held in June and a beer festival in August.
Q▲✿◖◗&♣P❄️❄️⚡

Greens Norton

Butchers Arms Ⓛ
10 High Street, NN12 8BA
☎ (01327) 358848 ⊕ thebutchersarms.pub
Great Oakley Wot's Occurring; St Austell Tribute; Silverstone Pitstop; 2 changing beers (sourced regionally; often Great Oakley) Ⓗ
A large pub at the centre of the village, with a modern rustic bar and relaxed dining area. It features wooden flooring and panelling throughout, complemented by bay window seating and a real wood-burning fire. It was

REAL ALE BREWERIES

Avalanche Burton Latimer
Boot Town Burton Latimer
Cotton End ☷ Northampton
Creaton Grange Creaton
Digfield Barnwell
Eastcote ☷ Eastcote
Great Oakley Tiffield
Holcot Hop-Craft Holcot
Hoppy Family Kettering
King's Cliffe King's Cliffe
Maule Northampton
Nene Valley (NVB) Oundle
Phipps Northampton
Potbelly Kettering
Rockingham Blatherwycke
Roman Way ✦ Weedon Bec
Silverstone Syresham
Towcester Mill ✦ Towcester
Weldon Rushden

listed as an asset of community value by the parish council, and the freehold was bought by a group of local investors keen to see it remain at the heart of the village. Q❄☆❀●❶⬤♣●P🖵 (86,87) ❀ 🛜

Hinton-in-the-Hedges

Crewe Arms 🅛
Sparrow Corner, NN13 5NF
☎ (01280) 705801 ⊕ crewearmshinton.co.uk
Hook Norton Hooky; Timothy Taylor Boltmaker; 1 changing beer (sourced nationally; often Vale) 🅗
Stone-built and situated in a gully in the village, the Crewe Arms can be hard to find – the entrance is through the rear gravel car park. Four comfortably furnished rooms provide a relaxed environment. The pub's cellar, located in the main dining area, may have been part of a tunnel between the village manor and the local church. Two real ales are served during the week and three at weekends. B&B is available in two rooms.
Q❄☆❀●❶⬤P🖵🛜

Isham

Lilacs 🅛
39 Church Street, NN14 1HD (off A509 at the church)
☎ (01536) 722348 ⊕ thelilacsisham.co.uk
Greene King IPA; 3 changing beers (sourced regionally; often Oakham, Potbelly) 🅗
Traditional inn in the heart of the village, named after a local breed of rabbit. Closed in 2018, the freehold was purchased by locals in order to preserve a pub in Isham. Now thriving again, it is popular with regulars, diners and drinkers alike. Inside are a small lounge, the former snug with a dartboard, and a large room to the rear. Quiz and live music nights are held regularly.
Q❄☆❀●❶⬤♣●P🖵 (X4) ❀ 🛜

Kettering

Alexandra Arms 🅛
39 Victoria Street, NN16 0BU
☎ (01536) 522730
Hop Back Summer Lightning; Marston's Pedigree; Wychwood Hobgoblin Gold; 11 changing beers (sourced nationally) 🅗
You will always find a beer from a little-known brewery in this classic street-corner local in the centre of town. The landlord continues to search out new and interesting ales, which are served through 14 handpumps. Two opened-out rooms feature a piano and settee, with the walls covered in breweriana and pumpclips. The rear bar has a TV and Northants skittles. A patio to the rear is a real suntrap. Q❀♣●❀

Piper 🅛
Windmill Avenue, NN15 6PS (near Wicksteed Park)
☎ (01536) 513870 ⊕ thepiper.net
Castle Rock Harvest Pale; Fuller's London Pride; 4 changing beers (sourced nationally; often Potbelly) 🅗
Popular 1950s two-roomed pub which has been run by an enthusiastic CAMRA member for over 30 years. It has a quiet lounge to the left. To the right is a more lively bar/games room where a quiz is held on Sunday night. A beer festival is held on the third weekend of August. There is an outdoor seating area across the road. Nearby Wicksteed Park was one of Britain's first theme parks, and Tresham College is opposite.
Q❄☆❀●❶⬤▲♣●P🖵❀🛜

Three Cocks 🅛
48 Lower Street, NN16 8DJ (opp Morrisons)
☎ 07909 698798
Full Mash Séance; Grainstore Ten Fifty; Oakham Inferno; 4 changing beers (sourced regionally; often Church End, Froth Blowers) 🅗
Popular locals' pub in the town centre. It has an L-shaped servery at the centre looking after the two main bar areas, and is furnished with comfortable armchairs and high-backed stools. Guest ales are on the main bar, the regulars to the side, always including a dark, a strong, a light and a citrus beer. On an upper level is a games area featuring Northants skittles and darts. The pub is home to three skittles teams and also hosts board games and monthly quiz evenings. Q❄☆⬤♣●🖵❀

Lilbourne

Head of Steam 🅛
10 Station Road, CV23 0SX (1 mile from A5, just off Rugby Rd)
☎ (01788) 860166
5 changing beers (sourced nationally; often Church End, Phipps NBC, Wye Valley) 🅗
Converted from a house in 2013, this thriving, railway-themed venue is the local CAMRA Country Pub of the Year. Friendly conversation dominates in this community free house, creating a welcoming atmosphere. Beers often come from Wye Valley. Locally sourced pork pies, cheeseboards and freshly made rolls are available. Sunday lunches are served, and there is a steak and cheese night every other Thursday. The large garden, with an outside bar throughout the summer, makes this a popular destination in warm weather.
Q❄☆❀❶⬤♣●P❀🛜

Litchborough

Old Red Lion 🅛
4 Banbury Road, NN12 8JF (opp church)
☎ (01327) 830064 ⊕ oldredlionlitchborough.co.uk
Great Oakley Wagtail; house beer (by Grainstore); 1 changing beer (sourced regionally) 🅗
A traditional four-roomed stone-built village pub that is well worth seeking out, popular with walkers and cyclists on the Knightly Way. The bar has flagstone flooring and seats inside the large inviting inglenook. The rear snug is a comfy casual room with double doors leading to a courtyard. The extension houses a restaurant and shop with local farm produce. Q❄☆❀❶⬤P🖵❀🛜

Little Brington

Saracen's Head 🅛 ✅
Main Street, NN7 4HS
☎ (01604) 770640 ⊕ thesaracensatbrington.co.uk
Timothy Taylor Landlord; 3 changing beers (sourced regionally; often Black Sheep, Grainstore) 🅗
Delightful ironstone building with old etched windows at the front, set in a pretty village. The bar is open plan but serves distinctly different areas of the pub. The floors are a mixture of flagstones and old wooden planking, and there is a large, attractive inglenook with wood-burner. Alongside the regular beers are three rotating guest ales, usually from local breweries. ❄☆❀●❶⬤P❀🛜

Loddington

Hare at Loddington
5 Main Street, NN14 1LA (on village loop)
☎ (01536) 710337 ⊕ thehareatloddington.com

Greene King Abbot; Sharp's Doom Bar; 2 changing beers (sourced regionally; often Church End, Phipps NBC) ⊞
The Hare is situated in a conservation area in a picturesque village built from local ironstone. It stands back in the middle of Main Street and has a pleasant front garden. Inside, it comprises four areas – two are spread around the central bar and two are for dining, serving good home-cooked food from local producers. The guest beers are from established breweries or local microbreweries. Q☕❀❍🚴♿🅿🚃(35)❀

Long Buckby

Badgers Arms 🗠
2 High Street, NN6 7RD
☎ (01327) 843003
4 changing beers (sourced regionally; often North Cotswold, Potbelly, XT) Ⓖ
Micropub that has been open since 2017 and has a reputation for quality local beers and ciders, plus an ambience and welcome second to none. Unusually, the bar is upstairs and has two distinct drinking areas. Downstairs is another small room, with table service for those unable to manage the stairs. Winner of CAMRA Regional Cider Pub of the Year in 2019 and a finalist in the National awards. Q☕●🚃(96,D4)❀

Nether Heyford

Foresters Arms 🗠
22 The Green, NN7 3LE
☎ (01327) 340729
2 changing beers (sourced locally) ⊞
Attractive, double bay-fronted ironstone pub that is the hub of village life. The many improvements under its current ownership include the introduction of two rotating beers, one always local. Real cider is available on gravity dispense behind the bar. The pub is predominantly for drinkers but offers simple bar meals and snacks. A mobile pizza van sets up shop in the forecourt on Thursday and Friday evenings.
❀❍♣●🅿🚃(D3) ❀ 🛜

Northampton

Albion Brewery Bar 🗠
54 Kingswell Street, NN1 1PR
☎ (01604) 946606 🌐 phipps-nbc.co.uk
Phipps NBC Red Star, Cobbler's Ale, India Pale Ale, Ratliffe's Celebrated Stout, Gold Star, Bison Brown; 1 changing beer (sourced nationally) ⊞
Phipps NBC returned to its roots in a Victorian brewery in the heart of Northampton in 2014, 40 years after Phipps' Bridge Street premises closed. The brewery bar subsequently opened, with an oak and glass partition between the bar and brewery enabling the equipment to be viewed. Almost all of the bar fittings are reclaimed, with many coming from closed Phipps NBC pubs. Much memorabilia is on display. Eight handpumps serve six in-house ales plus a rotating guest, with the final pump reserved for a Northamptonshire cider.
Q☕❍♿≠♣●🚃(7,X6)❀🛜

Cordwainer 🗠 ✅
The Ridings, NN1 2AQ (near jct with Fish St)
☎ (01604) 609000
Greene King Abbot; Phipps NBC Bison Brown, Gold Star; Ruddles Best Bitter; Sharp's Doom Bar; 7 changing beers (often Theakston) ⊞
Large town-centre Wetherspoon, particularly popular in fine weather due to its first-floor terrace and ground-

floor garden area. There is a large bar on each floor, with two sets of handpumps serving a wide choice of 12 real ales and an occasional real cider. Food is available throughout the day, including specials. The pub now only has one TV. Up to four beer festivals are held each year.
☕❀❍♿●🚃🛜

Kingsley Park Working Men's Club 🗠
120 Kingsley Park Terrace, NN2 7HJ
☎ (01604) 715514 🌐 kpwmc.co.uk
Fuller's London Pride, ESB; Greene King IPA; Shepherd Neame Spitfire; Tetley Bitter; 3 changing beers (sourced nationally; often Elgood's, Phipps NBC) ⊞
Long-established and thriving working men's club, founded in 1892 in a local street and now on the main road in a nearby residential area. Its eight handpumps serve five regular and three changing beers, overseen by an award-winning steward. Live music is hosted two nights a week and trips out are organised for members. A former local CAMRA Club of the Year. Q☕♿🚃🛜

Lamplighter 🗠
66 Overstone Road, NN1 3JS
☎ (01604) 631125 🌐 thelamplighter.co.uk
5 changing beers (sourced locally) ⊞
A traditional street-corner pub, just off the town centre, that is deservedly popular with young and old alike. It has an open fire in the bar and a heated courtyard. Five rotating beers come from established micros, including LocAles. Home-cooked food is served and children are welcome during mealtimes. The pub aims to support local industry by using nearby suppliers. It hosts weekly DJ nights, live music and quiz nights, and beer festivals throughout the year. ☕❀❍♿♣●🚃❀🛜

Malt Shovel Tavern 🗠
121 Bridge Street, NN1 1QF
☎ (01604) 234212 🌐 maltshoveltavern.com
Hook Norton Old Hooky; Oakham Bishops Farewell, JHB; Phipps NBC India Pale Ale; 10 changing beers (sourced nationally) ⊞
Popular award-winning pub close to the town centre and opposite the Carlsberg brewery. Breweriana features inside. The pub serves real cider, LocAle, Belgian draught and bottled beers, and offers home-made lunches all week. Two beer festivals with live bands are held each year on bank holidays. Blues bands play on Wednesday nights. The pub has a strong rugby following and is well worth a visit. ☕❀❍♿≠♣●🚃❀🛜

Olde England 🗠
199 Kettering Road, NN1 4BP (near racecourse)
☎ (01604) 603799
Digfield Chiffchaff; Jennings Cumberland Ale; Marston's Old Empire; Potbelly Beijing Black; Ringwood Fortyniner; Vale Gravitas ⊞; changing beers (sourced regionally; often Great Oakley, Phipps NBC) ⊞/Ⓖ
Converted end-of-terrace Victorian building on three floors. The ground and first floors have a medieval theme, with solid-fuel burners; the cellar has a contemporary style and is more intimate. Around 10 beers from local micros and regional breweries are served by handpump alongside 15 ciders. Various board games, cards and dominoes are provided. Live folk music plays on Thursday. A former local CAMRA Cider Pub of the Year and Northants Town Community Pub.
Q☕♣●🚃❀🛜

Pomfret Arms 🗠
10 Cotton End, NN4 8BS
☎ (01604) 555119 🌐 pomfretarms.co.uk

6 changing beers (sourced locally; often Great Oakley) 🄷
Town pub on the south-west side of the River Nene in Cotton End. Its small central bar has six handpumps serving both the front opened-out room and rear bar. The function room is in a separate building in the lovely beer garden. Seasonal opening hours vary. **🐎❀◐♿●🚌🐾📶**

Road to Morocco
Bridgwater Drive, NN3 3AG
☎ (01604) 632899
Greene King IPA; St Austell Tribute; Theakston Old Peculier; 3 changing beers (sourced nationally) 🄷
Run by a CAMRA member, this popular 1960s brick-built estate pub has a Moorish theme in some of its decor. There are two connected but distinctly different rooms. The bar area is quite lively, particularly when sporting events are shown on TV. This is also where darts and pool are played. The homely lounge is generally quieter. Quiz night is Tuesday. **🐎❀♿♣●P🚌**(5)**🐾📶**

St Giles Ale House Ⓛ
45 St Giles Street, NN1 1JF
☎ (01604) 636332
6 changing beers (sourced nationally; often Framework, Grainstore) 🄷
Northampton's first and only micropub is an ideal place for drinking and conversation, having no music or fruit machines. The one-room pub specialises in real ale and real cider, serving beers from around the country which tend to be new releases or from more obscure breweries. A beer club runs from Tuesday to Thursday teatime, offering a discount on ale and cider. A former local CAMRA Pub of the Year. **Q❀♿♣●🚌**(5)**🐾📶**

Oundle

Ship Inn Ⓛ
18 West Street, PE8 4EF
☎ (01832) 273918 🌐 theshipinnoundle.co.uk
Brewsters Hophead; Fuller's London Pride; 2 changing beers 🄷
This Grade II-listed pub is full of character with original beamed ceilings and the ghost of a former landlord. It has three bars with many small rooms adjoining, and a large function room available to hire for birthday celebrations and small weddings. Good food is served in all rooms. Accommodation is in two stone annexes and a small cottage at the back. The rear car park is accessed through an archway off West Street.
Q❀🛏◐♿▲♣P🚌(X4) **🐾📶**

Polebrook

King's Arms Ⓛ
Kings Arms Lane, PE8 5LW
☎ (01832) 272363 🌐 kingsarmspolebrook.co.uk
Digfield Fools Nook; 3 changing beers 🄷
Traditional stone-built thatched inn, accessible from doors at the front and rear off the car park. The pub is open plan with a main bar, three areas for diners, and an enclosed garden with a play area. Four beers are dispensed via handpump, always including at least one from the nearby Digfield Ales. Food is offered from an extensive menu and specials board. Third-pint glasses are available, giving the opportunity to taste a wider variety of beer. **Q❀◐♿♣P🚌🐾📶**

Rushden

Rushden Historical Transport Society Ⓛ
Station Approach, NN10 0AW (on ring road)
☎ (01933) 318988 🌐 rhts.co.uk
Phipps NBC India Pale Ale; 6 changing beers (sourced regionally; often Marston's, Woodforde's) 🄷
An award-winning club that occupies the former Midland Railway station. The ladies' waiting room is now the bar, with gas lighting and walls adorned with enamel advertising panels, railway photos and many CAMRA awards. On the platform, carriages house a meeting room, Northants skittles, and a buffet for the numerous open days held during the year when steam and diesel train rides are provided. A beer festival is held in September. Show a copy of the Guide to sign in.
Q🐎❀♿♣●🚌🐾

Southwick

Shuckburgh Arms Ⓛ
Main Street, PE8 5BL
☎ (01832) 272044 🌐 shuckburghpub.co.uk
Brewsters Hophead; Digfield Barnwell Bitter; 3 changing beers (sourced locally; often Fuller's, Grainstore) 🄷
Thatched stone-built pub in the village centre, serving five real ales. The bar area doubles as a restaurant and there is a small side room. To the rear is a covered outdoor area, car park, large garden and the village cricket pitch. The pub is run by the local community with shareholders and a small committee. It hosts the annual World Conker Championship in October. Popular well-priced food is available, including breakfast by arrangement. **Q❀◐▲♣P🚌🐾📶**

Staverton

Countryman Ⓛ ✔
Daventry Road, NN11 6JH (on A425)
☎ (01327) 311815 🌐 thecountrymanstaverton.co.uk
Bombardier; 2 changing beers (sourced locally; often Church End, Hook Norton) 🄷
A delightful 17th-century ironstone coaching inn that is the sole survivor of the three pubs that once used to thrive in this lovely village close to Daventry. The long wooden-beamed bar serves four areas, and an open hearth fire between the rooms provides some seclusion. The landlord offers a good choice of ales, always including one local brew. There is also a wide choice of reasonably priced food, sourced locally whenever possible. **Q🐎❀◐♿P🚌**(66)**🐾📶**

Stoke Bruerne

Boat Inn ✔
Bridge Road, NN12 7SB (on banks of Grand Union Canal)
☎ (01604) 862428 🌐 boatinn.co.uk
Banks's Amber Ale; Jennings Cumberland Ale; Marston's EPA, Old Empire; Ringwood Boondoggle; Wychwood Hobgoblin Ruby; 1 changing beer (sourced nationally) 🄷
The Boat Inn has been owned and run by the Woodward family since 1877. The delightful tap bar's interconnecting rooms have canal views, open fires, original stone floors and window seats; an adjoining room hosts Northants skittles. A large extension houses the lounge, plus the restaurant and bistro which are popular with diners. Additional beers are sold in summer. A canal boat is available to hire. Breakfast is served.
Q🐎❀◐♿▲♣P🐾📶

Titchmarsh

Wheatsheaf

1 North Street, NN14 3DH
☎ (01832) 732203 ⊕ the-wheatsheaf.pub
Butcombe Gold; Nene Valley Blonde Session Ale; 1 changing beer (often Nene Valley) Ⓗ
Nestled among the stone buildings of Titchmarsh's conservation area, the Wheatsheaf has a cosy bar area with beamed ceiling, comfy leather sofas, tub chairs, high tables, a fireplace and books. There is a separate restaurant area and, outside, a patio and beer garden. Three cask ales are on offer plus traditional cider. Northamptonshire skittles is played, with league matches on some Mondays. ⬤❀◑⬤P❀

Towcester

Towcester Mill Brewery Tap Ⓛ

Chantry Lane, NN12 6AD
☎ (01327) 437060 ⊕ towcestermillbrewery.co.uk
2 changing beers (sourced locally)
Popular and welcoming brewery tap in a historic Grade II-listed mill. The bar retains many original features including beams, stonework and a wooden floor. It serves two guest ales from other local breweries, and six ciders. There is a second room to cope with demand, and a large garden. Q⬤❀⬤P🖵❀🛜

Welford

Wharf Inn Ⓛ

On A5199, NN6 6JQ (on A5199 by canal basin)
☎ (01858) 575075 ⊕ wharfinnwelford.co.uk
Grainstore Ten Fifty; Marston's Pedigree; Oakham Bishops Farewell; 3 changing beers (sourced locally) Ⓗ
This original ironstone building dates from 1814 and is situated at the end of the Welford cut on the Grand Union Canal, a few yards from the border with Leicestershire. Inside, the main room is segregated by an open fireplace between the two rooms. A smaller snug and back bar is occasionally used. Guest beers are often sourced locally or regionally, and are served alongside good-value food. The pub is popular with walkers – ask for the leaflet with suggested routes. Q⬤❀⊟◑⬤P🖵(60)❀🛜

Wellingborough

Coach & Horses Ⓛ ✅

17 Oxford Street, NN8 4HY (800yds from Market Square)
☎ (01933) 441848
⊕ thecoachandhorseswellingborough.co.uk
12 changing beers (sourced nationally; often Castle Rock, Elland, Salopian) Ⓗ
A regular CAMRA award winner and long-standing Guide entry, this popular town-centre local is a former CAMRA East Midlands Leicestershire and Northamptonshire Pub of the Year. A constantly changing choice of 12 real ales and 15 ciders is always on offer. The central bar serves three drinking areas which are adorned with breweriana. Traditional home-cooked food is available including a wide choice of pies (no food Sun eve, Mon & Tue). A quiz is held on alternate Wednesdays, and a beer festival in August. Q⬤❀◑⬤♣⬤P❀🛜

Little Ale House Ⓛ

14A High Street, NN8 4JU
☎ 07870 392011
5 changing beers (sourced locally; often Castle Rock, Digfield, Oakham) Ⓗ/Ⓖ

Wonderfully friendly one-roomed micropub whose small size encourages interaction between guests and the landlady. Up to five rotating real ales are served on handpump and gravity, including a porter or stout. In addition, up to seven draught ciders and a good selection of gins, single malt whiskies, wines and soft drinks are stocked. A quiz is held on the first Tuesday of the month. Close to Jackson's Lane car park. Q⬤❀⬤P🖵❀🛜

Little R'Ale House Ⓛ

Midland Road, NN8 1NA
☎ 07711 928330 ⊕ thelittleralehouse-bar.business.site
4 changing beers (sourced locally; often Nene Valley, Potbelly) Ⓖ
Charming micropub on the station platform, occupying the former munitions building and filled with memorabilia. Up to four ales are served straight from the barrel, as well as two ciders and an interesting range of bottled beers and craft tins. Occasional music events and comedy nights are held. The patio area allows outdoor summer drinking. The pub is dog-friendly and popular with locals and commuters alike. Q⬤❀❀⇌⬤P🖵❀🛜

Queen's Head

49 Broad Green, NN8 4LH
☎ (01933) 224098 ⊕ queensheadwellingborough.co.uk
Timothy Taylor Boltmaker; 3 changing beers (sourced regionally) Ⓗ
A multi-roomed pub that was extended into the adjacent property many years ago. Its five drinking areas include the main L-shaped bar, which has a small brick-built servery and seating around the windows. To the left through an interconnecting room is a small snug complete with bookshelves and a Singer sewing machine. The rear bar serves the games rooms where bar billiards and darts are played. BT and Sky Sports are screened. ⬤❀◑♣🖵(X4)❀

Weston by Welland

Wheel & Compass

Valley Road, LE16 8HZ (off B664)
☎ (01858) 565864 ⊕ thewheelandcompass.co.uk
Banks's Amber Ale; Greene King Abbot; Marston's Pedigree; 2 changing beers (sourced nationally) Ⓗ
A popular rural pub in the picturesque Welland Valley. It has been refurbished to open up the entrance lobby and incorporate part of the former dining area, featuring flagstone floors and a wood-burner. Good-value food includes lunchtime specials. The outside drinking area offers views across the valley and is an ideal playground for children. This is a handy stopping-off place for walkers on the Jurassic Way which runs close by. ⬤❀◑♣⬤P❀🛜

Woodford

Dukes Ⓛ

83 High Street, NN14 4HE (off A510)
☎ (01832) 732224
Black Sheep Baa Baa; Fuller's London Pride; Greene King Abbot; 3 changing beers (sourced nationally; often Oakham, Phipps NBC, Digfield) Ⓗ
Every village should have a pub like this vibrant, community-focused inn overlooking the green. It was renamed in honour of the Duke of Wellington, a frequent visitor to Woodford. The interior includes a split main bar, lounge restaurant, rear room and an upstairs games room. The pub holds a May bank holiday beer festival and an August bank holiday music festival, plus regular open mic, disco, karaoke and acoustic music nights. Q⬤❀◑♣⬤P🖵(16X)❀🛜

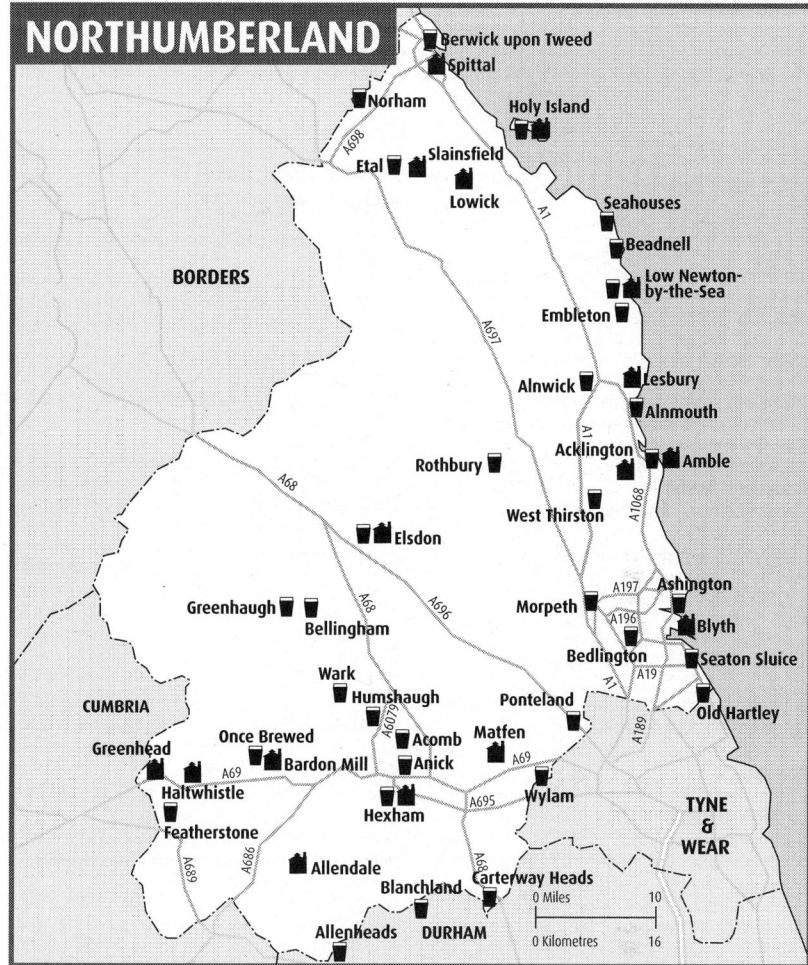

NORTHUMBERLAND

Berwick upon Tweed
Spittal
Norham
Holy Island
Etal Slainsfield
Lowick
BORDERS
Seahouses
Beadnell
Low Newton-by-the-Sea
Embleton
Alnwick Lesbury
Alnmouth
Acklington Amble
Rothbury
West Thirston
Elsdon
Greenhaugh
Bellingham
Morpeth Ashington
Blyth
Bedlington Seaton Sluice
Wark
Humshaugh Ponteland
Old Hartley
CUMBRIA
Greenhead
Once Brewed Acomb Matfen
Bardon Mill Anick
Haltwhistle Wylam
Featherstone Hexham TYNE & WEAR
Allendale
Blanchland Carterway Heads
Allenheads DURHAM

0 Miles 10
0 Kilometres 16

Acomb

Miners Arms

Main Street, NE46 4PW

☎ (01434) 603909 ⊕ theminersacomb.com

Hadrian Border Tyneside Blonde; 2 changing beers (sourced nationally) ⊞

Superb, family-run 1746 inn with an emphasis on real ale, which is served in oversized lined glasses. The bar is divided by a central staircase and has a cosy feel. Music and folk nights feature regularly. A traditional pub food menu offers home-made meals using locally sourced ingredients. ☎❀◑&♣🚲🚃(680)❀

Allenheads

Allenheads Inn 🗽

NE47 9HJ

☎ (01434) 685200 ⊕ allenheadsinn.co.uk

Anarchy Blonde Star; Hadrian Border Northern Pale; 3 changing beers (sourced nationally) ⊞

An 18th-century multi-room rural inn featuring a public bar with a log fire, a games room and dining room. The interior displays memorabilia and historical knick-knacks. Good bar meals are available at a decent price. On the Coast-to-Coast cycle route, the pub is welcoming to cyclists, ramblers and tourists. It will open early on request for coach parties and other groups.
☎❀🚪◑♣P🚃(688)❀

Alnmouth

Red Lion Inn 🗽 ✔

22 Northumberland Street, NE66 2RJ

☎ (01665) 830584 ⊕ redlionalnmouth.com

4 changing beers (sourced regionally) ⊞

A charming 18th-century coaching inn whose cosy lounge bar features attractive woodwork. Guest beers usually include one local ale and two interesting brews from further afield. The decked area at the bottom of the garden enjoys panoramic views across the Aln Estuary. Occasional live music plays – in the open air in summer. An annual beer festival is held in October. The pub opens early for breakfast. Excellent en-suite B&B accommodation is available.
Q☎❀🚪◑♣P🚃(X18)❀🛜

Alnwick

Ale Gate 🗽

25 Bondgate Without, NE66 1PR

☎ 07979 101332

6 changing beers (sourced locally) Ⓗ
Alnwick's first micropub opened in 2019 in a building that was once a shop unit, then an insurance office. It has a single open main room to the right, and a raised area to the rear. Six handpumps on the traditionally styled dark-wood bar offer a regularly changing range of beers from local breweries. ✦🚾♿

John Bull Inn ⒧
12 Howick Street, NE66 1UY
☎ (01665) 602055
4 changing beers (sourced nationally) Ⓗ
Frequently local CAMRA Pub of the Year, this 180-year-old inn thrives on its reputation as a back-street boozer. The landlord offers a wide range of cask-conditioned ales at varying ABVs, real cider, the widest range of bottled Belgian beers in the county and over 150 single malt whiskies. The darts team competes in the local league and the pub upholds the North-East tradition of an annual leek show. There is a cheese club on Saturday night. Q❀♣✦🚾♿

Tanners Arms ⒧
2-4 Hotspur Place, NE66 1QF
☎ (01665) 602553
5 changing beers (sourced nationally) Ⓗ
Ivy-covered stone-built pub just off Bondgate Without and a short distance from Alnwick Garden. The rustic single room has a flagstone floor and tree beer shelf. A large fireplace provides added warmth in winter. Acoustic music nights feature regularly, with open mic on the last Friday of the month. The varied real ales frequently come from North-East and Scottish Borders microbreweries. 🚆&♣✦🚾♿🎵⏹

Amble

Cock & Bull ⒧
Queen Street, NE65 0DQ
🌐 cockandbullpub.co.uk
4 changing beers (sourced locally) Ⓗ
Imaginatively run pub in a former tourist information office next to the town square. The interior has dark blue walls and an orange skylight in the ceiling, with bench seating around the walls and trestle tables. Four handpumps serve locally brewed ales. It features a local artist of the month, with works on display and for sale. There is some seating outside. ❀&🚾(X18,X20)♿⏹

Anick

Rat Inn
Anick, NE46 4LN (follow signpost at Hexham A69 roundabout)
☎ (01434) 602814 🌐 theratinn.com
Timothy Taylor Landlord; 4 changing beers (sourced locally) Ⓗ
Excellent 1750 country inn with spectacular views across the Tyne Valley. It has a reputation for good food prepared with locally sourced ingredients, and appears in several food guides. Half portions are available for children. Bottled beers are stocked. The first Thursday of the month is singers/poets night. Well worth the short taxi ride from Hexham rail station. Q🚆❀⏹♣✦P🚾(74)

Ashington

Hop 77
77 Station Road, NE63 8RS
3 changing beers (sourced nationally) Ⓗ
Ashington's first micropub opened in a former shop unit in 2019. It has a single room with a bar counter in one

corner. Furnishings are a mix of sofas and freestanding tables and chairs. It is on the main street just beyond the old railway station, and an easy walk from the bus station. 🚆✦🚾♿

Beadnell

Craster Arms Hotel ⒧
2-4 The Wynding, NE67 5AX
☎ (01665) 720272 🌐 crasterarms.co.uk
3 changing beers (sourced nationally; often Hadrian Border) Ⓗ
Vibrant pub in the centre of the village, welcoming to locals and tourists alike. The large bar is broken up into a couple of smaller areas, with a range of tables and chairs in each. At least two handpulls on the bar offer a rotation of well-known national beers. Many travel here for the splendid food, especially the Sunday roast. 🚆❀⏹&P🚾(X18,418)♿⏹

Bedlington

Box Wood Tap ⒧
40C Front Street, NE22 5UB
4 changing beers (sourced nationally) Ⓗ
Well-run venue in a small converted shop on the main street in the centre of town. The hand-built wooden bar has four handpumps for beer. A range of ciders is also available from bag-in-box in the fridge. There is some seating including a settee, and an extension into an adjoining former shop unit provides extra space. ✦🚾♿

Bellingham

Cheviot Hotel ⒧ ✅
Main Street, NE48 2AU
☎ (01434) 220696 🌐 thecheviothotel.co.uk
Hadrian Border Tyneside Blonde, Northern Pale; High House Farm Nel's Best; 1 changing beer (sourced nationally; often Hadrian Border) Ⓗ
Friendly hotel opposite the bus stop. A log-burning stove warms the bar area. Cask beer is available all year round including one varying ale from Hadrian Border Brewery. There is plenty of outside seating at the front. Regular theme nights are hosted. 🚆❀⏹&▲♣P🚾(680)♿⏹

Berwick upon Tweed

Atelier
41-43 Bridge Street, TD15 1ES
☎ (01289) 298180

3 changing beers (sourced nationally; often Hadrian Border) ⊞
Welcoming café bar with a shabby-chic interior. Three real ales are served, usually from Fyne Ales or Wylam, along with kegged craft beers. The food on offer is all locally sourced and a real highlight. Specialities include hot shortcrust pies with a variety of interesting fillings, and a locally sourced meat and cheese platter that rivals those served in continental cafés. ⏰≠❀🍴🞩

Curfew 🅛
46a Bridge Street, TD15 1AQ
☎ 07842 912268
4 changing beers (sourced nationally) ⊞
Berwick's first micropub opened six years ago, and is located up a small lane that opens out into a large courtyard off Bridge Street. It has a small bar area with a bottle fridge to one side, offering interesting local keg beers and foreign bottles. The courtyard makes a pleasant outdoor drinking area in summer. Excellent pork pies are available. A former local CAMRA Pub of the Year. Q⏰🞩≠♣🐾🞩

Pilot 🅛
31 Low Greens, TD15 1LZ
☎ (01289) 304214
3 changing beers (sourced nationally; often Hadrian Border, Firebrick) ⊞
Gem of a pub that is popular with locals and sought out by train trippers who have heard all about it. The friendly bar staff provide a warm welcome to all. This 19th century end-of-terrace pub is recognised by CAMRA as having a historic interior of regional importance. It retains the original small room layout and boasts several nautical artefacts over 100 years old. It is home to a darts team and hosts music nights. ⏰🞩🍴🛏♣🐾🐾🞩

Blanchland

Lord Crewe Arms
The Square, DH8 9SP
☎ (01434) 677100 ⊕ lordcrewearmsblanchland.co.uk
4 changing beers (sourced nationally; often Twice Brewed Brew House) ⊞
In the centre of the village, this ancient building is now a multi-roomed pub with the bar in a medieval vaulted room. Downstairs has flagstone floors and dogs are welcome. The restaurant upstairs has fine moorland views. Real fires give the stone rooms a welcoming warmth. ⏰🞩🍴🛏🞩&P

Carterway Heads

Manor House Inn ✅
DH8 9LX (on A68 S of Corbridge)
☎ (01207) 255268 ⊕ themanorhouseinn.com
Timothy Taylor Landlord; 3 changing beers (sourced nationally) ⊞
A warm and hospitable country inn with three open fires. A double-glazed window in the bar wall allows customers to view the well-maintained cellar. Good home-cooked food is on offer and popular both with tourists and locals. There are superb views over the valley from the rear beer garden. Derwent Reservoir is nearby. Excellent accommodation is available. ⏰🞩🍴🛏&♣P🞩🍴

Elsdon

Bird in Bush 🅛
Village Green, NE19 1AA
☎ (01830) 520804

4 changing beers (sourced locally) ⊞
Restored inn located in the north-west corner of the green in this quiet village. It offers beers from a wide range of sources including from the on-site brewery, so look out for First and Last ales at the bar. Food is served Friday to Sunday and accommodation is available. ⏰🞩🍴🛏♣P🞩

Embleton

Greys Inn 🅛 ✅
Stanley Terrace, NE66 3UZ
☎ (01665) 576983
5 changing beers (sourced locally) ⊞
Pleasant, traditional inn in a lovely seaside hamlet, just a short walk to a wonderful beach. It has three open fires, and a rare McLennan & Urquhart's Edinburgh Ales mirror on a chimney breast. It is home to a ladies' darts team, clay pigeon club and golf club. Winter hours may vary. ⏰🞩🍴🛏♣🚌(418,X18)🞩

Etal

Black Bull 🅛
TD12 4TL
☎ (01890) 820200 ⊕ theblackbulletal.co.uk
House beer (by Cheviot); 2 changing beers (sourced locally; often Cheviot) ⊞
Northumberland's only thatched pub has been restored in an attractive modern style, with an exposed roof structure that adds to its charm. Comfortable pale-wood furniture features throughout the spacious, open-plan interior. Three handpumps serve real ales exclusively from Cheviot Brewery, with a special dark bitter made for the pub. There is a function room and large outdoor seating area. 🞩🍴&P🚌(267)🞩

Featherstone

Wallace Arms 🅛
Rowfoot, NE49 0JF
☎ (01434) 298921
Allendale Pennine Pale; Great North Eastern Rivet Catcher; 2 changing beers (sourced nationally) ⊞
Cosy country pub warmed by real fires, with no jukebox or fruit machines. Split over two levels and three rooms, it has a traditional bar area and various spaces. The welcoming landlady is always prepared to open early for groups of walkers, preferably if arranged in advance. Opening hours are reduced in winter – check ahead. Q🞩🍴P🞩🍴

Greenhaugh

Holly Bush Inn 🅛 ✅
NE48 1PW
☎ (01434) 240391 ⊕ hollybushinn.net
High House Farm Nel's Best; 1 changing beer (sourced nationally) ⊞
Independently owned pub, over 300 years old and set in the heart of the Northumberland National Park and the Dark Sky Park, making it ideal for those with an interest in real ale and real stars. No TV and no mobile reception make for a peaceful drinking experience. The place hosts informal jam sessions – bring your instrument if you like. Q⏰🞩🍴&♣P🞩🍴

Hexham

Dipton Mill Inn 🅛
Dipton Mill Road, NE46 1YA
☎ (01434) 606577 ⊕ diptonmill.co.uk

Hexhamshire Devil's Elbow, Shire Bitter, Blackhall English Stout, Devil's Water, Whapweasel, Old Humbug ⊞
The tap for Hexhamshire Brewery, now located in the beer garden, this small inn is run by real ale enthusiasts who brew their own excellent ales. Blackhall English Stout has proved so popular with drinkers that it has ousted Guinness. To complement the beers there is great home-cooked food – Saturday is curry night. A cosy atmosphere and warm welcome make this pub well worth seeking out. Local CAMRA Pub of the Year 2020. Q❀❀◑●P

Heart of Northumberland ⓛ

5 Market Street, NE46 3NS
☎ (01434) 608013 ⊕ thehearthexham.com
Timothy Taylor Landlord; 4 changing beers (sourced locally) ⊞
Five handpumps, four selling local ales, adorn the bar in this renovated, Grade II-listed free house in the centre of Hexham. The single large room is divided almost in two near the end of the bar, with wooden floors throughout. A blazing fire in the six-foot open fireplace warms things nicely in the back room. Excellent food is served.
☎❀◑➔♣🖥❀

Platform Bar

Platform 2, Hexham Railway Station, Station Road, NE48 1ET
☎ (01434) 604997
5 changing beers (sourced locally; often High House Farm) ⊞
Single-room micropub that opened in 2019 in the former waiting room on the westbound platform of Hexham station. It features railway memorabilia on the walls and perimeter seating with freestanding tables. Opening hours are subject to review; currently alcohol is served from mid-morning, with tea, coffee and light snacks available earlier. Toilets are at the other end of the platform. Q➔●♦🖵

Holy Island

Crown & Anchor Hotel ⓛ

Market Place, TD15 2RX (check tidetable for causeway crossing times)
☎ (01289) 389215 ⊕ holyislandcrown.co.uk
Hadrian Border Tyneside Blonde, Secret Kingdom; 1 changing beer (sourced locally) ⊞
Exposed floorboards and wooden tables and benches provide seating in the cosy bar – note the Gothic carving of a local monk in the corner. There is a comfortable sitting room to the rear. The large beer garden provides scenic views to Lindisfarne Castle and the ruined priory to the rear of the pub. ❀🛏◑🖥(477)❀🖵

Humshaugh

Crown Inn ⓛ

NE46 4AG
☎ (01434) 681231
Hadrian Border Tyneside Blonde; 3 changing beers (sourced nationally) ⊞
Traditional village pub in the centre of beautiful Humshaugh, five miles north of the market town of Hexham. The Crown has a homely charm, with a wood-burning stove, cask ales and traditional home-cooked food. Simple guest accommodation is offered in comfortable rooms, ideal for those wishing to explore Hadrian's Wall. ❀🛏◑●🖥(680)

Low Newton-by-the-Sea

Ship Inn ⓛ

Newton Square, NE66 3EL
☎ (01665) 576262 ⊕ shipinnnewton.co.uk
Ship Inn Sea Coal, Sea Wheat; 4 changing beers (sourced nationally) ⊞
This small pub nestles in the corner of three sides of a square of former fishermen's cottages, a few yards from the beach. It attracts drinkers seeking ales from the in-house microbrewery, diners enjoying an excellent menu featuring fresh local ingredients, and walkers exploring the area's scenery. A public car park is close by at the top of the hill. Opening times may vary in winter; phone ahead if travelling. Q☎❀◑❀

Morpeth

Office ⓛ

Chantry Place, NE61 1PJ
☎ 07957 721066
8 changing beers (sourced locally) ⊞
A micropub with no music or games machines, it has a bar on the ground floor with further seating upstairs. It features eight handpulls and three craft keg beers, all of local origin, and three real ciders served on gravity from the glass-fronted fridge opposite the bar. It doesn't do food. Dogs are welcome. Local CAMRA Pub of the Year 2020. Q➔🖥❀

Tap & Spile ⓛ

23 Manchester Street, NE61 1BH
☎ (01670) 513894
Greene King Abbot; Hadrian Border Tyneside Blonde; Timothy Taylor Landlord; 5 changing beers (sourced nationally) ⊞
All are welcome at this popular locals' pub near the town bus station. It has eight handpulls offering a good choice of beers, with ales from Northumbrian breweries often available, alongside Westons Old Rosie cider. The bar area at the front of the building is usually busy. A quieter, cosy lounge to the rear is accessible from either side of the room. A traditional folk group plays at Sunday lunchtime. Q☎♣🖥❀🖵

Norham

Masons Arms

17 West Street, TD15 2LB
☎ (01289) 382326 ⊕ themasonsarmsnorham.co.uk
Allendale Wagtail Best Bitter; 3 changing beers (sourced nationally) ⊞
The cosy wood-panelled public bar, with a real fire at its heart, is the hub of this pub. Photos of bygone Norham adorn the walls, along with collections of fishing gear and joinery tools, and an old Younger's Brewery mirror. The area is popular with tourists – nearby are a ruined castle and the nearby former railway station is a museum. Close to the Tweed Cycle Way and bus stop. ❀🛏♣🖥(67)

Old Hartley

Delaval Arms ⓛ

NE26 4RL
☎ (0191) 237 0489 ⊕ thedelavalarms.co.uk
4 changing beers (sourced nationally) ⊞
Multi-roomed building dating from 1748, with a Grade II*-listed WWI water storage tower (part of Roberts Battery) behind the beer garden. It is the first pub in Northumberland for those following the coastal route. Good-quality, affordable meals complement the beer,

with guest ales coming from local micros. To the left as you enter is a room served through a hatch from the bar and to the right a room where children are welcome. Q✿🖤⏰🅿️�)(308,309) ❀

Once Brewed

Twice Brewed Inn 🄻 ✅
Miltary Road, Bardon Mill, NE47 7AN (on B6318 Military Road)
☎ (01434) 344534 🌐 twicebrewedinn.co.uk
6 changing beers (sourced nationally; often Twice Brewed Brew House) 🄷
Walkers and tourists are among those attracted to this excellent, remote inn on the Military Road, near to Hadrian's Wall, Steel Rigg and Vindolanda. Its bar area offers a wide range of bottled beers from around the world. The pub has full wheelchair access and welcomes dogs. B&B is offered in 18 en-suite bedrooms. The Twice Brewed Brew House started producing its own beers in 2017, using water from its own well.
Q✿🖤⏰🅿️❀

Ponteland

Pont Tap 🄻
10 West Road, NE20 9SU
☎ 07446 098501
4 changing beers (sourced nationally) 🄷
The Pont Tap opened in 2020 in what used to be an interior design shop. It serves a good range of – mostly local – cask and craft keg beers together with wine and spirits. The friendly welcome and comfortable surroundings make this pub a must-visit attraction if you're in the area. Q❀

Rothbury

Narrow Nick 🄻
High Street, NE65 7TB
☎ 07707 703182
6 changing beers (sourced locally) 🄷
Art Deco-style stained glass features in the front windows of this market-town micropub, located in a former clothes shop. The bar at one side of the single room has six handpumps, serving a range of beers from local breweries. A large range of gins is also kept. Winter opening times may vary. Q❀🚃❀

Seahouses

Olde Ship Inn 🄻
7-9 Main Street, NE68 7RD
☎ (01665) 720200 🌐 seahouses.co.uk
Black Sheep Best Bitter; Courage Directors; Hadrian Border Farne Island Pale Ale; Morland Old Speckled Hen; Ruddles County; Theakston Best Bitter; 4 changing beers (sourced nationally) 🄷
Originally a farmhouse, built in 1745, it became a pub in 1812 and is recognised by CAMRA as having a historic interior of regional importance. Family-owned since 1910, the pub has three quality bars displaying a treasure trove of 19th- and 20th-century maritime memorabilia. An interesting menu includes fish, fresh crab meals and snacks. Accommodation is available.
Q✿🖤⏰🅿️❀(418,X18)

Seaton Sluice

Melton Constable ✅
Beresford Road, NE26 4QL
☎ (0191) 237 7741 🌐 themeltonconstable.co.uk
Adnams Southwold Bitter, Broadside; Ossett Yorkshire Blonde; 2 changing beers (sourced nationally) 🄷
Large roadside pub a few minutes' walk from the beach and local history sights. It is named after the southern seat of Lord Hastings, a member of the Delaval family – Delaval Hall is close by. Tuesday is steak night, Wednesday is quiz night, and Sunday evening features live music. A fishing club meets here late at night and the BSA owners' club gets together on the first and third Thursdays of the month. 🖤⏰🅿️❀

Wark

Battlesteads Hotel 🄻 ✅
Wark on Tyne, NE48 3LS
☎ (01434) 230209 🌐 battlesteads.com
4 changing beers (sourced nationally) 🄷
Well-appointed 1747 converted farmhouse near Hexham with a superb rear walled garden, restaurant, large conservatory and accommodation. The five handpulls provide an excellent choice of beers, all in top condition. Ingredients for the quality menu come from within a 25-mile radius, including home-grown fruit and vegetables. Accommodation includes ground-floor rooms with wheelchair access. Handy for PlusBus via Hexham rail station. 🖤⏰🅿️(680)❀

West Thirston

Northumberland Arms 🄻 ✅
The Peth, NE65 9EE
☎ (01670) 787370 🌐 northumberlandarms-felton.co.uk
3 changing beers (sourced nationally; often Allendale) 🄷
Fine stone pub that was originally a coaching inn in the 1820s for Hugh Percy, third Duke of Northumberland. The building has been lovingly restored in an eclectic style while remaining warm, comfortable and welcoming. Bare stone walls and real fires add to the ambience. A large function room caters for groups of up to 30. The beer range is predominantly from local breweries. 🖤⏰🅿️(X15)

Wylam

Boathouse 🄻
Station Road, NE41 8HR
☎ (01661) 853431
12 changing beers (sourced nationally) 🄷
Superb two-roomed pub with 15 handpulls, most serving beers sourced locally and nationwide. Three are dedicated to cider, and there are more ciders in the cellar. Toasties and sandwiches are available during the day. The pub is a popular stopping-off point for Whistle Stops II travellers. Themed beer festivals are held on bank holidays. Alternate Tuesdays are buskers' nights. Fifteen CAMRA awards cover one wall including North-East Regional Pub of the Year. Q✿🖤🅿️❀

> Good ale is the true and proper drink of Englishmen. He is not deserving of the name of Englishman who speaketh against ale, that is good ale.
> **George Borrow, Lavengro**

NOTTINGHAMSHIRE

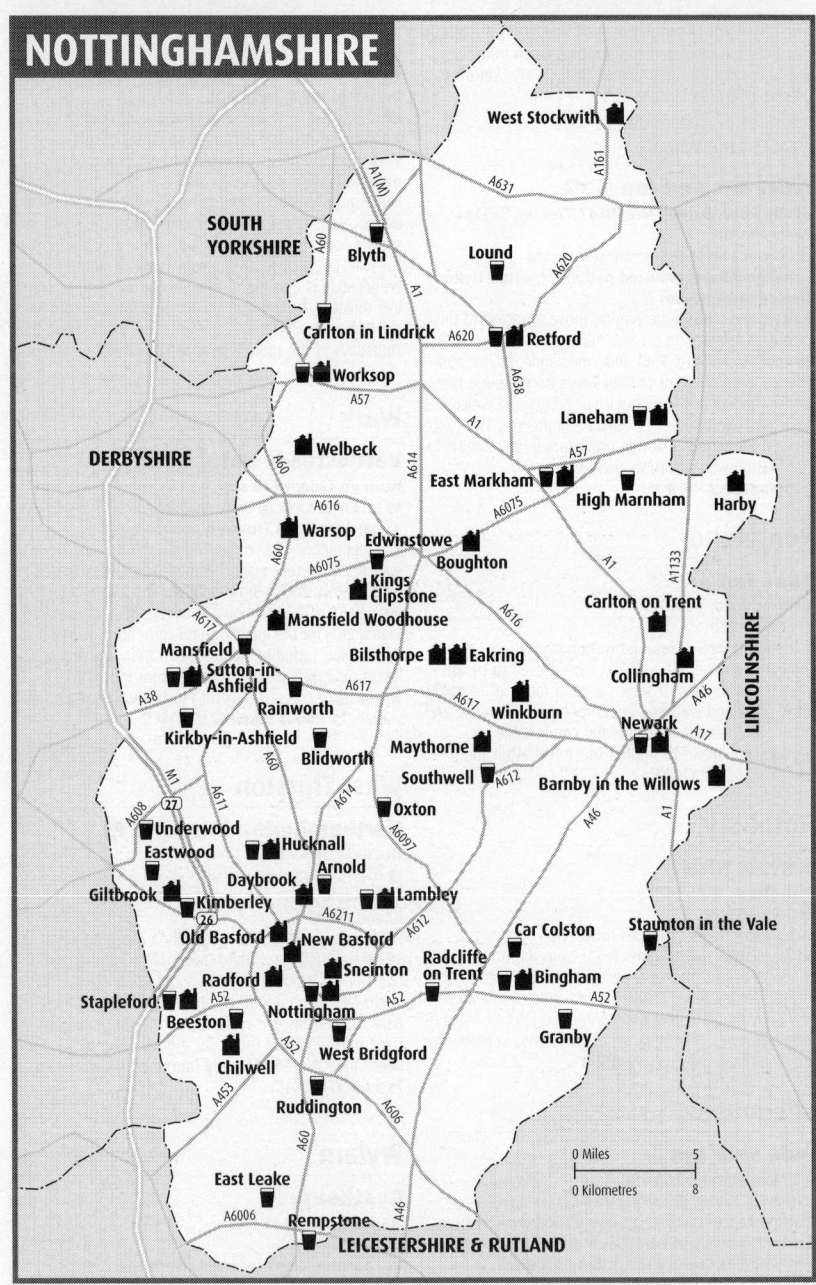

Arnold

Abdication 🄻

89 Mansfield Road, Daybrook, NG5 6BH (opp gates of former Home Brewery) ⊕ theabdication.co.uk

4 changing beers Ⓗ

Originally built in 1936/37, this modern, friendly micropub, opened in 2014, is part of the Home Brewery Coronation Buildings, opposite the gates of the former brewery, and was for many years a shop. The four changing cask ales, four craft beers and three ciders are from microbreweries, small producers or the on-site

Good Stuff nanobrewery, and come in a mix of styles. An archway divides the single room, giving an appearance of a much larger area. Q ➢ ৬ ♣ ♠ ♫ 🐾 ✿

Robin Hood & Little John 🄻 ✓

1 Church Street, NG5 8FD (on corner of Cross St)
☎ (0115) 920 1054 ⊕ therobinhoodandlittlejohn.co.uk

Everards Tiger; Lincoln Green Marion, Archer, Tuck; 10 changing beers Ⓗ

Former Home Brewery pub now operated by Lincoln Green and Everards breweries. The bar features Home Ales memorabilia, while the lounge has details of the pub's history and the local area, and there is a piano. The rear courtyard has outdoor seating and a covered skittles alley. Along with 10 real ale pumps in each bar offering microbrewery beers, the cider wall has four taps dispensing real ciders from small local producers and further afield. ♿🏠🍴♣⬤🚃🐾🛜

Beeston

Crown Inn ★ L

Church Street, NG9 1FY

☎ (0115) 967 8623

Blue Monkey BG Sips; Brewsters Hophead; Dancing Duck 22; Everards Tiger; Oakham Bishops Farewell; 6 changing beers Ⓗ

Nineteenth-century, Grade II-listed alehouse, acquired and sympathetically refurbished by Everards. Up to 11 ales and several real ciders and perries are served at this former East Midlands CAMRA Pub of the Year. An outside bar opens during the summer, extending the range to 22 beers. Inside, there are five distinct drinking areas including a snug and three-seat 'confessional', once used as a hideaway by the local vicar. Although busy, the pub retains a community feel, with a cosy atmosphere throughout. Substantial snacks are available.
Q♿🏠🍴🚃♣⬤🅿🚃🐾🛜

Star Inn L

22 Middle Street, NG9 1FX

☎ (0115) 854 5320 ⬤ starbeeston.co.uk

10 changing beers Ⓗ

Former Shipstone's pub still with branded windows, restored beyond its former glory. The decor is tasteful and minimal, with three separate rooms complemented by a permanent marquee and sports/games room and, outside, a spacious garden and patio. The bar featured in Boon and Auf Wiedersehen, Pet. Ten cask ales are on offer as well as a wide selection of whiskies, gins, rums and wines. Meals are served along with a range of traditional bar snacks. Families are welcome during the day. ♿🏠🍴🎭🅓♿🚃♣⬤🅿🚃🐾🛜

Victoria Hotel L

85 Dovecote Lane, NG9 1JG

☎ (0115) 925 4049 ⬤ vichotelbeeston.co.uk

Castle Rock Harvest Pale; Draught Bass; 14 changing beers Ⓗ

Located alongside the platform of Beeston railway station, this restored Victorian masterpiece has mass appeal. Thirteen real ales are joined by real ciders and perries, an extensive whisky and wine list, and a renowned food menu. Taster trays of three third-pints are offered. Two distinct bars joined by a dining room and a covered, smoke-free seating area outside. VicFest is hosted in July in addition to beer festivals throughout the year. Q🏠🅓♿🚃♣⬤🅿🚃🐾🛜

Bingham

Horse & Plough L

Long Acre, NG13 8AF

☎ (01949) 839313

Castle Rock Harvest Pale, Preservation; 7 changing beers Ⓗ

A former Methodist chapel in the heart of a busy market town, this small pub has a traditional interior and flagstone floor, with a terrace added in 2019. Up to nine cask ales and four ciders are served. Four times local CAMRA Pub of the Year, the pub always offers a wide range of styles and strengths of real ale and cider, showcasing smaller producers alongside Castle Rock and other established favourites. ♿🏠♿🚃♣⬤🚃🐾🛜

Wheatsheaf

Long Acre, NG13 8BG

☎ (01949) 837430 ⬤ thewheatsheafbingham.co.uk

Rufford Abbey Rufford Poacher; 6 changing beers Ⓗ

The Wheatsheaf reverted to its traditional name when it reopened in 2016 under new ownership. Ten handpumps offer a changing range of cask ales and ciders. Food is served lunchtimes and evenings both in the bar and the separate restaurant. The pub has a real fire in the bar, a fantastic outdoor terrace and hosts live music every week. A former local and regional CAMRA Cider Pub of the Year. ♿🏠🍴🅓♿🚃♣⬤🅿🚃🐾🛜

Blidworth

Black Bull

Main Street, NG21 0QH

☎ (01623) 490222 ⬤ blackbullblidworth.co.uk

5 changing beers (often Pheasantry, Stancill) Ⓗ

Refurbished, family-owned pub offering a warm welcome to locals and visitors. The large bar room serves up to five rotating guest beers, some of which are brewed in Nottinghamshire. The restaurant offers good

REAL ALE BREWERIES

Angel 🍺 ✦ Nottingham
Beermats Winkburn
Beeston Hop Nottingham: Sneinton
Black Iris ✦ Nottingham: New Basford
Black Market 🍺 Warsop
Blue Monkey Nottingham: Giltbrook
Brewhouse & Kitchen 🍺 Nottingham
Castle Rock Nottingham
Cat Asylum Collingham
Dukeries 🍺 Worksop
FireRock Sutton-in-Ashfield
Fish Key 🍺 Lambley
Full Mash Stapleford
Good Stuff 🍺 Nottingham: Daybrook
Grafton Worksop
Handley's 🍺 Barnby in the Willows
Harby 🍺 Harby
Harrison's Retford
Idle 🍺 West Stockwith
Kings Clipstone Kings Clipstone
Lazy Bay Nottingham
Lenton Lane Nottingham
Lincoln Green Nottingham: Hucknall
Linear Bingham
Liquid Light ✦ Nottingham
Lord Randalls Newark
Magpie ✦ Nottingham
Mallard Maythorne
Maypole Eakring
Milestone Newark
Navigation 🍺 Nottingham
Neon Raptor ✦ Nottingham
Newark Newark
Nottingham ✦ Nottingham: Radford
Pheasantry East Markham
Prior's Well ✦ Mansfield Woodhouse
Reality Nottingham: Chilwell
Reckless Dweeb Bilsthorpe (NEW)
Rufford Abbey Boughton
Scruffy Dog 🍺 Sutton-In-Ashfield
Shipstone's Nottingham: Old Basford
Springhead Laneham
Tom Herrick's Carlton on Trent
Totally Brewed Nottingham
Vaguely Bingham
Welbeck Abbey Welbeck

English food and more adventurous meals including vegetarian options, plus traditional roasts on Sundays. The menu changes reflecting seasonal availability, using ingredients freshly sourced from local suppliers. Dogs are allowed in the bar only. The pub opens early for breakfast, and B&B is available in four rooms. ♿❀✉◑♿P☷(141)❀

Blyth

Red Hart L
Bawtry Road, S81 8HG (opp church)
☎ (01909) 591221 ∰ redhart.co.uk
3 changing beers (sourced regionally) Ⓗ
An attractive village pub in the centre of Blyth with a lounge, a traditional taproom – with a pool table, darts and sports TV – an attractive dining room, and a spacious seating area outside. The walls in the lounge are decorated with photographs and paintings of nearby locations. Three changing beers are available and food is served daily. A former local CAMRA Pub of the Season. Q❀♿◑♿❀P☷(25,29)❀

Car Colston

Royal Oak ✓
The Green, NG13 8JE
☎ (01949) 20247 ∰ royaloakcarcolston.co.uk
Bombardier; Wainwright; 2 changing beers Ⓗ
This country inn – a former hosiery factory – is on one of England's largest village greens. The pub has a cosy bar with comfortable seating and a real fire, a separate, generously sized restaurant and a function room. Four beers, all from the Marston's range but often less-heralded brews, are available in the bar. Food is served lunchtimes and evenings. There is a skittle alley to the rear, a beer garden and camping facilities. ❀♿◑♿❀P❀❀

Carlton in Lindrick

Grey Horses Inn L
The Cross, S81 9EW (in centre of old village)
☎ (01909) 730252
Welbeck Abbey Henrietta, Portland Black; house beer (by Welbeck Abbey); 3 changing beers (sourced regionally) Ⓗ
The Grey Horses is situated at the heart of the village within the conservation area, and has a front bar accessible from the street, a spacious lounge bar where excellent food is served and a large beer garden. The pub is the tap for Welbeck Abbey Brewery, serving three or four of its beers plus two or three guests. It hosts an annual beer festival, usually in June. A warm welcome is assured at this local CAMRA award-winning hostelry. Q❀♿◑♿❀P☷(21,22)❀

East Leake

Round RobINN L
54 Main Street, LE12 6PG
☎ (0115) 778 8168
6 changing beers (sourced locally) Ⓖ
Micropub opened in 2015, serving six local beers on gravity, cooled on racks behind the bar. A range of ciders and continental bottled beers is also available. The single room accommodates up to 45 patrons – seating is a mixture of chairs, cushioned benches and high stools. A small outdoor area to the front offers alfresco drinking. Light bar snacks are served. Q❀♿❀♿☷(1)❀

East Markham

Queen's Hotel
High Street, NG22 0RE
☎ (01777) 870288
Adnams Southwold Bitter; Everards Beacon Hill, Tiger; 2 changing beers (sourced regionally) Ⓗ
Situated on the main street, this cosy pub has a warm, friendly atmosphere enhanced by an open fire in winter. A single bar with five handpumps serves the lounge and dining areas. Food ranges from hot and cold snacks to full home-cooked meals. There is a large garden area at the rear of the car park. The Queen's has received several local CAMRA awards. Q❀♿◑♿P☷(136,37)❀

Eastwood

Gamekeeper's L
136 Nottingham Road, NG16 3GD
5 changing beers Ⓗ
This micropub in the centre of Eastwood opened in 2017. It serves up to five ales, mainly local ones. The bar is at the back to the right; a seating area is at the front, along with an alcove section to the left. There is also an extensive garden/patio outside at the rear. Pub snacks are normally available. Q❀♿❀♿❀☷❀

Tap & Growler
209 Nottingham Road, Hill Top, NG16 3GS
∰ tapandgrowler.co.uk
8 changing beers (sourced locally) Ⓗ/Ⓖ
This welcoming micropub in a row of shops sells a range of real ales, most of them local, with five on handpump and up to five more on gravity. The pub gets its name not just from the growler beer jug – when the building was renovated a ceramic lion was found and it is now proudly on display as The Growler. A pub quiz is held on Monday. There is a fine hidden garden at the rear. A former winner of local CAMRA LocAle Pub of the Year. Q❀♿❀♿❀☷❀

Edwinstowe

Forest Lodge ✓
2-4 Church Street, NG21 9QA
☎ (01623) 824443 ∰ forestlodgehotel.co.uk
Bombardier; house beer (by Welbeck Abbey); 3 changing beers (often Acorn, St Austell) Ⓗ
Based in the heart of Sherwood Forest, this 18th-century coaching inn is a free house and offers a varying range of guest beers, including a house beer from Welbeck Abbey. The high-class restaurant serves a large selection of daily specials, and local produce is proudly used wherever possible. Private functions can be catered for. Accommodation is available in the AA four-star rated hotel. Q❀♿❀◑♿P❀☷❀

Granby

Marquis of Granby
Dragon Street, NG13 9PN
☎ (01949) 859517
Brewsters Hophead, Marquis; 4 changing beers Ⓗ
Believed to be the original Marquis of Granby, dating back to 1760 or earlier, this small two-roomed pub is the brewery tap for Brewsters – usually serving four, but up to six, cask ales. Guest beers mostly come from microbreweries, and include a mild, stout or porter. York stone floors complement the yew bar tops and wood-beamed rooms, period wallpaper features throughout and the lounge has a welcoming open fire in the winter months. Q❀♿❀♿P☷❀☷❀

High Marnham

Brownlow Arms

NG23 6SG (on edge of village)

☎ (01636) 822505 ⊕ thebrownlowarms.co.uk

Everards Tiger; Greene King Abbot; 1 changing beer (sourced locally) Ⓗ

A welcoming rural pub beside the River Trent, with an extensive food menu offering tasty and reasonably priced meals. The bar features two regular ales and one that changes, plus a varied selection of lagers, spirits and more. The pub has its own caravan park adjacent, which is family-friendly, and fishing is also available. It is within easy access of Retford, Lincoln and Newark. Q🏠🏵️🌃🅭🕭🆓️P🌸

Hucknall

Byron's Rest Ⓛ

8 Baker Street, NG15 7AS

Titanic Plum Porter; 8 changing beers (often Black Iris, Blue Monkey, Magpie, Shipstones) Ⓗ

Typical of a medieval burgage plot, this former sewing shop was converted into a micropub in 2018. While narrow, there is a snug just off the entrance and the pub extends considerably to the bar and comfortable bench seating at the rear, giving the illusion of separate drinking areas. Outside at the back, the garden area is covered providing a tranquil oasis in the heart of town. Up to eight real ales are served. Q🏵️🍺🆓🅭🌸🆓🔋🌸🛜

Kimberley

Roots Emporium

17 Nottingham Road, NG16 2NB

☎ 07864 572037

6 changing beers Ⓗ

Converted from a furniture and gift shop, much of this micropub's fixtures and fittings are made from the stock of the former business. The open-plan interior is small but reasonably spacious, with a patio at the front extending the drinking area further. Walls are adorned with interesting memorabilia including items relating to the former Kimberley Brewery. Beers are generally from microbreweries, always including at least one local brew. Q🏠🏵️🅭🆓🔋🌸

Kirkby-in-Ashfield

Dandy Cock Ale House

184A Victoria Road, NG17 8AT

☎ 07854 054060 ⊕ thedandycock.co.uk

4 changing beers (sourced locally; often Dancing Duck, Little Critters) Ⓗ

Micropub offering four real ales and up to six real ciders on tap. A range of wines and spirits including over 200 gins is also available. It has two small, comfortably furnished rooms, with views into the cellar from the bar. Acoustic nights are hosted on occasion. There is on-street parking and a bus stop outside the front door. Q🏠🅭🌸🔋🌸

Lambley

Woodlark Inn Ⓛ

Church Street, NG4 4QB

☎ (0115) 931 2535 ⊕ woodlarkinn.co.uk

Theakston Best Bitter; Timothy Taylor Landlord; 4 changing beers (often Fish Key) Ⓗ

Located in the quaint-sounding Upper Dumbles area of the village, this traditional pub dating back to the 19th century is the home of the Fish Key microbrewery. It is

popular both with locals and visitors from afar. There are two rooms – a bare red-brick bar with exposed beams serving four cask ales, and a lounge/restaurant which is popular for excellent home-cooked food. A music-free environment encourages the art of conversation. Two beer festivals are held each year. Q🏠🏵️🅭🌸🔋🆓🖵(46,47)🌸🛜

Laneham

Bees Knees Ⓛ

Springhead Brewery, Robin Hood Site, Main Street, DN22 0NA (centre of village)

☎ (01777) 228090 ⊕ springhead.co.uk

Abbeydale Daily Bread, Moonshine, Absolution; Oakham Citra; Pheasantry Dancing Dragonfly; 5 changing beers Ⓗ

A country pub with three small rooms converted from a shop on the Springhead Fine Ales brewery site and well supported by locals. It serves five regular ales and up to five rotating guests. Over 100 gins are also available. Excellent food is served (booking recommended). Quiz night is Wednesday and live jazz plays on the first Sunday of the month. There is an adequate outside seating area. A former local CAMRA award winner. Q🏠🅭🆓🅰️🔋🖵🌸🛜

Lound

Bluebell Inn

Town Street, DN22 8RN (on main road through village)

☎ (01777) 818457 ⊕ bluebellinnlound.co.uk

3 changing beers (sourced locally) Ⓗ

A traditional village inn with a lounge bar where food is served and a taproom with a pool table. The pub has a good reputation for the quality of its food and beers which rotate on demand. There is a large car park and a fenced seating area outside. French boules is played in the summer on Wednesday and Sunday. Wednesday is quiz night. Q🏠🏵️🍺🅭🆓🌸🖵🌸🛜

Mansfield

Bold Forester ✅

Botany Avenue, NG18 5NF

☎ (01623) 623970

Greene King IPA, Abbot; Hardys & Hansons Olde Trip; Morland Old Speckled Hen; 8 changing beers (often Little Critters, Pheasantry, Prior's Well) Ⓗ

Hungry Horse-branded pub and restaurant offering up to 12 real ales. Food is served daily. The open-plan interior has large-screen TVs showing most major sports. The beer garden is popular with families in the summer. Situated on the main road into Mansfield, it has a large car park, and regular bus services pass the door. 🏠🏵️🅭🆓🍺🌸🔋🖵🌸🛜

Brown Cow

31 Ratcliffe Gate, NG18 2JA

☎ (01623) 645854 ⊕ browncow-mansfield.co.uk

Everards Tiger; 9 changing beers Ⓗ

Owned by Everards Brewery and run by Silver Brewhouse as a Project William business. A range of up to 12 real ales is offered alongside ciders and international bottled beers. There are two separate bar areas and a function room upstairs. The pub is a short walk from the town centre. Q🏠🏵️🅭🍺🌸🔋🖵🌸🛜

Garrison

Leeming Street, NG18 1NA

☎ 07702 253235 ⊕ moodyfoxbrewery.com

Moody Fox Cub, Pale Tale; 4 changing beers Ⓗ

This is the brewery tap for the Moody Fox Brewery based nearby in Hilcote. It is inspired by the TV show Peaky Blinders, with some beer names reflecting the theme. Six real ales and a range of ciders are available. Located in the pedestrianised area of the town centre, it is a five-minute walk from public car parks. Q⇌♠🕯🖰🌸

Railway Inn
9 Station Street, NG18 1EF
☎ (01623) 623086
4 changing beers (often Dukeries, Full Mash, Pheasantry) Ⓗ
Close to the town centre bus and train stations, this community pub serves popular home-cooked meals. It has a main bar area and two separate rooms for diners or those looking for a quieter space. Up to four real ales and one or two real ciders are offered. The walled garden is popular in the summer. Q🕭🏵🌗⇌♠🖰🌸🗘

Redgate
189 Westfield Lane, NG19 6EH
☎ (01623) 624406 ⊕ redgateinn.co.uk
3 changing beers (sourced regionally; often Greene King, Prior's Well, Sharp's) Ⓗ
A community-focused pub with a spacious lounge, a separate restaurant area serving popular home-cooked food and a skittles alley. Darts and dominoes are also played. Sports memorabilia is on display in the main bar/ lounge. Three regularly changing real ales are offered from local and national breweries. Dogs are allowed in the bar area only. Q🕭🏵🌗&♣P🖰(6,23B)🌸🗘

Newark

Flying Circus Ⓛ
53 Castle Gate, NG24 1BE
☎ (01636) 302444 ⊕ flyingcircuspub.co.uk
4 changing beers (sourced nationally) Ⓗ
Reopened in its present incarnation in 2014, Monty Python quotes and brewery logos decorate the walls, and old aircraft are suspended from the ceiling. The four changing cask ales are complemented by a wide range of keg, bottled and canned craft beers. There is regular live music and a quiz night. The large outdoor courtyard is popular in the summer. 🕭🏵⇌🖰🌸🗘

Just Beer Micropub
32A Castle Gate, NG24 1BG (in Swan & Salmon Yard, off Castle Gate)
☎ (01636) 312047 ⊕ justbeermicropub.biz
4 changing beers (sourced nationally) Ⓗ
Friendly micropub offering a varied range of cask ale, craft beer from a tap wall, cider and perry, and world and unusual UK craft ales from the fridge. Several beer festivals are held throughout the year and there is a popular quiz night once a week. Snacks include local pork pies, cheeseboards and pork scratchings. Traditional pub games are played, with an annual cribbage tournament. Twice regional CAMRA Pub of the Year and a repeat local CAMRA Pub of the Year. Since opening in 2010 it has served more than 5,000 different cask ales.
Q&🅰⇌♣🕯🖰🌸🗘

Organ Grinder
21 Portland Street, NG24 4XF
☎ (01636) 671768
Blue Monkey BG Sips, Funky Gibbon, Infinity, Chocolate Guerrilla, Guerrilla, Ape Ale; 1 changing beer (sourced regionally) Ⓗ
Opened as the Organ Grinder in 2014, this no-nonsense beer-drinking pub offers six or seven real ales from Blue Monkey. Real cider and a range of bottled beers are also stocked. Bar snacks are served to accompany the ales. A

popular quiz is hosted every other Wednesday. The Monkey Room has a dartboard and a large TV screen. Books, games and a piano are available for customer use. A covered smoking area is to the rear.
⇌♣🕯🖰🌸🗘

Oscar's Inn
105 Balderton Gate, NG24 1RY
☎ (01636) 918130 ⊕ oscarsinn.co.uk
Thornbridge Jaipur IPA; 5 changing beers (sourced nationally) Ⓗ
Refurbished two-roomed pub a few minutes' walk from the town centre, named after the owner's dog. The Oscar Wilde room is open at all times, displaying quotes from the great man; the Oscar Peterson room opens at busier times and hosts music at the weekend. Six handpumps offer a varied selection of local and national beers. A food menu is available, specialising in generously sized pizzas. 🕭🏵🌗♦P🖰(3)🌸🗘

Prince Rupert Ⓛ
46 Stodman Street, NG24 1AW
☎ (01636) 918121 ⊕ kneadpubs.co.uk
Brains Rev James; Oakham Citra; 4 changing beers (sourced nationally) Ⓗ
Reopened in 2010, this historic pub dates back to around 1452. Multi-roomed on two separate levels, exposed beams are evident in several rooms and various interesting artefacts and brewery memorabilia decorate the walls and ceilings. There is a small but pleasant patio garden. An extensive lunchtime and evening menu featuring fresh local produce is available, with stone-baked pizzas a speciality. A former local CAMRA Pub of the Year, it has featured in the Guide for 11 consecutive years. Q🕭🏵🌗⇌🕯🖰🌸🗘

Nottingham: Central

Barrel Drop
7 Hurts Yard, NG1 6JD
☎ (0115) 924 3018
5 changing beers (often Magpie) Ⓗ
City-centre micropub opened in 2014 but taken over by the local Magpie Brewery in 2018. It is tucked away on Hurts Yard between Angel Row and close to Upper Parliament Street. Inside, there is a seating area to the right and steps leading down to the bar. More seating is available off the bar. Five beers are available from Magpie and other microbreweries around the country. There are also several taps dispensing keg beers and real ciders. Q🕭🖰♣🕯🖰🌸

BeerHeadZ
Cabman's Shelter, 1A Queens Road, NG2 3AS (adjoining Nottingham station)
☎ 07914 136055
5 changing beers Ⓗ
Small but sympathetically restored Edwardian cabman's shelter, adjacent to the main railway station entrance. It is run by BeerHeadZ, who operate similar outlets across the east Midlands. The single room has a central bar and retains period features including bench chests, wooden panelling, windows and coat hooks. There is a long table with stools opposite the bar, and beer barrels with wooden tops serve as seats. The five real ales change regularly and are seldom repeated. A large choice of bottles and cans is also available to enjoy in or take out. Q🏵⇌🅰🕯🖰🌸

Crafty Crow Ⓛ
102 Friar Lane, NG1 6EB
☎ (0115) 837 1992 ⊕ craftycrownotts.co.uk
8 changing beers (often Magpie) Ⓗ

Magpie Brewery's first pub. Twelve handpumps serve up to eight microbrewery beers, and up to four serve real ciders. Following on from the ethics of the brewery it features a green ethos throughout, the majority of fittings are recycled or home-made; the sinks are fashioned from beer casks with ex-keg fonts as taps. Snacks and light meals are served until 9pm, made from locally sourced produce. Situated on two levels, the side entrance leads directly to all facilities. Corvid birds feature strongly. ♿🏠🅿♿🚲🚃🚶♻🐕🍴☕🚭🛜

Fox & Grapes 🅛

21 Southwell Road, NG1 1DL
☎ (0115) 841 8970
Castle Rock Harvest Pale, Preservation, Elsie Mo; 4 changing beers 🅗
An impressive renovation of an Edwardian-fronted Victorian inn carried out by Castle Rock Brewery in 2017. The former two-room layout has been opened up into a single L-shaped room with raised areas on either side of the front door. A high ceiling and large windows give a light, airy feel. Sadly the fancy Edwardian window frames were lost in an earlier refit. The pub serves seven real ales, seven keg beers and ciders plus locally produced coffee, gin and artisan food.
♿🐾🏠🅿♿🚶🐕🍴☕🚭🛜

King William IV 🅛

6 Eyre Street, Sneinton, NG2 4PB
☎ (0115) 958 9864
Oakham Citra; house beer (by Black Iris); 7 changing beers 🅗
Known widely as the King Billy, this Victorian gem on the edge of the city centre is close to the Motorpoint Arena. A family-run free house that oozes charm and character, it is a haven for real ale drinkers, with a choice of up to eight microbrewery ales from near and far, as well as real cider. Folk music is popular on Thursday night. Look for the award-winning pub sign.
Q♿🐾🐕🍴🚃(43,44)☕🛜

Lincolnshire Poacher 🅛

161-163 Mansfield Road, NG1 3FR
☎ (0115) 941 1584
Castle Rock Harvest Pale, Sherwood Reserve, Elsie Mo, Screech Owl; 5 changing beers 🅗
Up to 13 handpumps offer a wide selection of guest ales, mainly from microbreweries. A mild, stout or porter is always available alongside real ciders and perries, continental bottled beers and a fine selection of whiskies. The food menu features locally sourced ingredients. The pub displays artwork celebrating its long-standing twinning with In de Wildeman bar in Amsterdam, as well as various memorabilia of local and international interest. Live music plays on Sunday and Wednesday. Q🐾🏠♿🚃🐕🍴☕🚭🛜

Newshouse 🅛

123 Canal Street, NG1 7HB
☎ (0115) 952 3061
Castle Rock Harvest Pale; Totally Brewed Slap in the Face; 3 changing beers (sourced locally) 🅗
In times past, newspapers would be read out here to inform the illiterate of elections at home and military victories overseas, hence the name. The walls are covered with framed front pages of local newspapers showing headlines going back over many years. The public bar has a large TV screen, dartboard, bar billiards and table skittles. The lounge has more comfortable seating. Light lunches are served and you can get snacks at all times. ♿🐾♿🚃🐕🍴🎱🚭🛜

Sir John Borlase Warren 🅛 ✅

1 Ilkeston Road, Canning Circus, NG7 3GD
☎ (0115) 988 1889 🌐 sirjohnborlasewarren.co.uk
Everards Tiger; 10 changing beers (often Lincoln Green) 🅗
An Everards Project William pub with Lincoln Green, this building is situated in the centre of Canning Circus. The lower bar area can be hired for private parties, and there is a small snug at the far end of the bar. Outside is a secluded, enclosed garden and a large rooftop patio – a quiet haven in the centre of a busy area. Tap takeovers often take place, when at least four handpumps feature a single brewery. Q♿🐾🏠🅿🐕🍴☕🚭🛜

Vat & Fiddle 🅛

Queens Bridge Road, NG2 1NB
☎ (0115) 985 0611
Castle Rock Harvest Pale, Session, Preservation, Elsie Mo, Screech Owl; 7 changing beers 🅗
This 1937 Art Deco gem is the brewery tap for the adjoining Castle Rock Brewery, two minutes' walk from Nottingham rail and tram station. Thirteen handpumps serve at least seven from the Castle Rock range, with guest beers including LocAles and others from further afield. It also sells up to 10 real ciders. Hot food is available throughout the week. The recently extended outside area to the rear overlooking the brewery yard features an impressive mural depicting Nottingham events. ♿🐾🏠♿🚃🐕🍴☕🚭🛜

Nottingham: East

Bread & Bitter 🅛

153-155 Woodthorpe Drive, Mapperley, NG3 5JL
☎ (0115) 960 7541
Castle Rock Harvest Pale, Preservation, Elsie Mo, Screech Owl; 7 changing beers 🅗
Castle Rock pub converted from the premises of an old bakery. The original baker's oven fronts are still embedded in an inside wall, giving the place a warm and welcoming feel. The pub started a revival of real ale outlets in Mapperley. Twelve handpumps serve Castle Rock beers, rotating guests and cider alongside an extensive bottled beer list. Food is home cooked and varies frequently. Q♿🐾🏠♿🐕🍴☕🚭🛜

Brickyard ✅

Standhill Road, Carlton, NG4 1JL
☎ (0115) 987 8707 🌐 brickyardcarlton.co.uk
5 changing beers (often Lincoln Green) 🅗
Formerly a social club, the building was renovated by Lincoln Green and reopened in April 2018. Although fairly small, there is plenty of seating and a snug at the back to the right of the bar. The pub contains a number of items of Hardys and Hansons memorabilia, including a scale model of the former brewery cleverly built into a table. Craft beers are also sold. 🐾🍴

Old Volunteer 🅛

35 Burton Road, Carlton, NG4 3DQ
☎ (0115) 987 2299
10 changing beers (often Flipside) 🅗
Refurbished by Flipside Brewing in 2014, the pub showcases four of the brewery's beers alongside several guests and a real cider. The interior is separated into distinct areas using unusual wooden dividing beams, with a raised corner and different types of flooring. Outside is a patio area with parasols leading to the main entrance. Food choices include speciality burgers with wedges, and snacks are always available. Beer festivals are held in a marquee in the car park.
🐾🏠♿🚶🐕🅿☕🛜

Nottingham: North

Doctor's Orders 🄻

351 Mansfield Road, Carrington, NG5 2DA
☎ (0115) 960 7985 ⊕ doctorsordersmicropub.co.uk
5 changing beers (sourced locally) 🄷
Compact beer emporium with two distinct sections. A small square lounge leads to a corridor flanked on one side by a narrow raised seating area with benches, with a small bar and serving area at the rear. Beer and cider are brought to your table from handpumps at the bar. While now owned by Magpie Brewery, the pub continues with its original ethos of providing a range of microbrewery beers in an intimate atmosphere.
Q🌣🅱♣♠♥🖵🌣🛜

Lion Inn 🄻

44 Mosley Street, New Basford, NG7 7FQ
☎ (0115) 970 3506 ⊕ thelionatbasford.co.uk
Draught Bass; 9 changing beers 🄷
A large, traditional free house with a horseshoe central bar and rustic bare-brick decor. The focus is on an ever-changing range of cask ales and traditional ciders from near and far. Outside has extensive covered and heated decking areas and a large garden with plenty of seating. Live music of all sorts features every weekend. It has won numerous dog-friendly pub awards.
🌣🕸🕪🅱♠♣♥🖵🌣🛜

Nottingham: West

Plough Inn 🄻

17 St Peter's Street, Radford, NG7 3EN
☎ 07972 094425
Nottingham Rock Ale Bitter Beer, Rock Ale Mild Beer, Legend, Extra Pale Ale; 2 changing beers 🄷
A traditional two-roomed public house, this is the brewery tap for the adjoining Nottingham Brewery and features a number of its ales with some changing guests. It has a wide clientele including university students from the extensive accommodation nearby. The cosy interior has two wood-burning stoves, and the garden area features a skittle alley. The pub hosts a popular quiz night once a week and frequent live music evenings.
Q🌣🕸🕪♣♥🖵🌣🛜

Oxton

Old Green Dragon 🄻 ✅

Blind Lane, NG25 0SS
☎ (0115) 965 2243
6 changing beers 🄷
This popular former local CAMRA Pub of the Year retains its traditional village-pub charm while also serving as a contemporary dining venue. It sells a varying selection of six real ales including at least three from local breweries, alongside offerings from further afield, as well as at least two real ciders. Outside there is a patio area and at the rear an enclosed garden. The car park has three electric car-charging points. 🌣🕸🕪🅱♥P🌣🛜

Radcliffe on Trent

Chestnut 🄻 ✅

Main Road, NG12 2BE
☎ (0115) 933 1994 ⊕ chestnutradcliffe.com
Bradfield Farmers Blonde; Timothy Taylor Boltmaker; 4 changing beers 🄷
Well-regarded, cask beer-led village pub. Originally the Cliffe Inn, following a major refurbishment in 2006 it became The Horse Chestnut and in 2015 simply The Chestnut. Seven reasonably priced real ales are served

including different guest beers, one always a local brew. Quality home-made food, ranging from stone-baked pizzas to classic British dishes, is served in a relaxed, casual atmosphere. 🌣🕸🕪🅱♥≈♥P🖵🌣🛜

Yard of Ale

1 Walkers Yard, NG12 2FF (off Main Rd, between Costa and public car park)
☎ (0115) 933 4888 ⊕ yard-of-ale.business.site
6 changing beers 🄷/🄶
A small, friendly micropub that opened in 2016 in a former café and chocolate shop in the centre of the village. The premises are narrow, with access from the side, and a step up to a small room. A variety of up to seven guest ales are on offer, always including at least one local brew and a dark ale. There is a separate gin bar known as Gin Within. Q≈♥P🖵🌣

Rainworth

Inkpot

Kirklington Road, NG21 0JY
☎ (01623) 230500
4 changing beers (often Batemans, Bradfield, Leatherbritches) 🄷
This micropub usually serves a range of up to four real ales and 11 real ciders. Based in what was once a betting shop, it is named after the octagonal building that used to stand nearby, now demolished, which was the toll house for the road to Mansfield. Local CAMRA Cider Pub of the Year 2019. Q🌣♥🖵(141,28)🌣

Rempstone

White Lion 🄻

Main Street, LE12 6RH
☎ (01509) 889111
Belvoir Dark Horse; Charnwood Vixen; Draught Bass; 1 changing beer 🄷
A small, welcoming village pub with a friendly clientele, saved from closure some years ago by four locals. It has just one room, warmed by a cosy fire in winter, and offers a choice of local and guest beers. Occasional themed events are held. Bar snacks are available.
Q🌣🕸🕪♠♥🖵🌣🛜

Retford

Beer under the Clock

3 Town Hall Yard, DN22 6DU (off Market Square, through arch to rear of 10 Green Bottles)
☎ 07985 102192 ⊕ beerundertheclock.com
5 changing beers (sourced nationally) 🄷
Formerly known as BeerheadZ, the bar offers five rotating guest beers, three ciders, a range of over 100 bottled beers and a limited choice of wines and spirits. The beers, often one-offs from near and far, are kept in excellent condition and served in oversized glasses so you can be sure of a full pint. The pub has won several CAMRA awards including Nottinghamshire Pub of the Year. Q🅱♥🗄🖵🌣🛜

Black Boy Inn 🄻

14 Moorgate, DN22 6RH (just off ring road)
☎ (01777) 7099
3 changing beers (sourced locally; often Pheasantry) 🄷
A friendly inn just off the town centre with a good regular trade. This cosy open-plan pub shows live sport on TV and has a dartboard, a comfortable smoking area and some outside seating. Cigarette card collections are displayed on the walls. Three changing beers are on

offer, reasonably priced and often from local breweries. Quiz night is Tuesday and the pub has a team in the local quiz league on Wednesday. Q✿🕿♣♠P🖵♻ ☕ 🛜

Brew Shed

104-106 Carolgate, DN22 6AS (on Carolgate bridge opp Masonic Hall)
Harrison's Vacant Gesture, Best Bitter, Pale Ale, Proof of Concept, Stout; 2 changing beers (sourced regionally) Ⓗ
The Brew Shed is the tap for Harrison's Brewery. The open-plan main room is at street level, with a smaller room downstairs leading to a large patio beside the canal. Five Harrison's Brewery beers, two rotating guests and a variety of kegs are on offer, alongside real cider and a good selection of gins, spirits and wines. Nottinghamshire CAMRA Pub of the Year 2019.
Q✿🕿♣♠P🖵♻ ☕ 🛜

Idle Valley Tap Ⓛ

Carolgate, DN22 6EF (at S end of main shopping area)
☎ (01777) 948586
House beer (by Welbeck Abbey); 6 changing beers (sourced regionally) Ⓗ
Originally the tap for Idle Valley Brewery, since its closure the beers are now sourced from elsewhere. Four (more when busy) rotating guest beers are on offer, along with gins, wines and spirits. The one-room pub has a pool table and dartboard away from the bar. The outside space has been put to good use, with plenty of seating attracting large numbers in fine weather.
🕿♣♠P🖵♻ ☕ 🛜

Ruddington

Frame Breakers Ⓛ

High Street, NG11 6DT
☎ (0115) 859 0060 ⊕ theframebreakers.co.uk
Nottingham Mild, Legend, Extra Pale Ale; house beer (by Nottingham); 3 changing beers (often Nottingham) Ⓗ
A large open-plan hostelry on a corner plot, with an L-shaped bar and seating on three sides. Run by Nottingham Brewery, it showcases the brewery's beers alongside a couple of changing guests – always including a dark beer – and four ciders on the cider wall. There is a large outdoor seating area. Live music features regularly. A yearly beer festival is held to coincide with the local annual Ruddfest. 🕿♣🌀♠P🖵 (3,10)☕ 🛜

Southwell

Final Whistle

Station Road, NG25 0ET
☎ (01636) 814953
Brewsters Hophead; Draught Bass; Everards Tiger; Salopian Oracle; 6 changing beers (sourced nationally; often Oakham) Ⓗ
Located at the end of the Southwell Trail, which runs along a disused railway line, this comfortable multi-roomed pub has a railway theme and is teeming with memorabilia. The courtyard garden is laid out like a mock station and has a separate bar and function room called The Locomotion. The main bar has 10 handpumps, with Bass and a stout or porter always available. Quiz nights are Sunday and Tuesday, folk club is on a Thursday. Quality bar snacks are available.
Q✿🕿♣♠P🖵 (28,100) ☕ 🛜

Old Coach House Ⓛ

69 Easthorpe, NG25 0HY
☎ (01636) 819526 ⊕ pubpeople.com

Sharp's Doom Bar; 6 changing beers (sourced nationally) Ⓗ
Traditional open-plan pub with five different drinking areas, oak beams and a large range fire. Six regularly changing real ales are on handpump from local and national breweries, often including Oakham JHB and Timothy Taylor Landlord. Live music features regularly on Saturday night, an open mic session is held on the last Sunday of the month, and a New Orleans pianist plays on the first Sunday. Outside to the rear is a well-kept patio garden. Q✿🕿♣Å♠P🖵☕ 🛜

Stapleford

Horse & Jockey Ⓛ

20 Nottingham Road, NG9 8AA
☎ (0115) 875 9655 ⊕ horseandjockeystapleford.co.uk
Full Mash Horse & Jockey; 12 changing beers Ⓗ
An open-plan bar with seating at the front and further seating up a couple of steps in an area that can also be used for functions. An array of 13 ales greets you, always including a house beer from the local Full Mash brewery, the rest always changing. Bar snacks are served – filled rolls, pork pies and sausage rolls. Some accommodation is available. Q✿🛏♣♠P🖵☕

Staunton in the Vale

Staunton Arms Ⓛ ✅

NG13 9PE
☎ (01400) 281218 ⊕ stauntonarms.co.uk
Castle Rock Harvest Pale; Draught Bass; 1 changing beer Ⓗ
Two hundred-year-old listed pub in the far north of the Vale of Belvoir, carefully restored to retain its original character. The large bar offers comfortable seating for drinkers and diners, with a further separate raised restaurant area. The pub serves freshly prepared meals lunchtimes and evenings, and has a deserved reputation for good food. The bar houses three cask beers, one always a LocAle. Mini festivals are held regularly, with upcoming events publicised on the website.
Q✿🛏◐♣P🛜

Sutton-in-Ashfield

Duke of Sussex

Alfreton Road, NG17 1JN
☎ (01623) 511469
5 changing beers (often Oakham, Pentrich, Welbeck Abbey) Ⓗ
Large open-plan pub with up to six real ales, owned by the Pub People Company of South Normanton. Sunday roasts and the Thursday steak club are popular. Jazz night is the first Thursday of the month and there is a quiz every Sunday. Live music features on some Saturday evenings. Q✿◐♣P🖵 (9.1)☕ 🛜

FireRock

24 Outram Street, NG17 4FS
☎ 07875 331898
3 changing beers (often Adnams, Oakham, FireRock) Ⓗ
Opened in 2018, this large open-plan bar is the tap for FireRock Brewing. Up to two real ales are on offer alongside a wide range of KeyKeg beers, bottles and cans. A good selection of (often rare) spirits is also available. Regular live music is hosted on the stage and there is a smaller snug space with a nautical decor. FireRock Brewery is now on-site in a room to the rear.
✿♣P🖵☕

Scruffy Dog

Station Road, NG17 5HF

☎ (01623) 550826 🌐 thescruffydog.co.uk

8 changing beers (often Abbeydale, Beartown, Thornbridge) Ⓗ

Comfy sofas and a real fire on colder days welcome visitors to this dog-friendly pub. Refurbished by the current owners, it has its own on-site Scruffy Dog microbrewery – the brew plant is visible from the end of the main seating area. Eight changing real ales are usually available from the brewery, plus up to five guest ales. Q🌣🕭🕏♿🐾P🚪😺🛜

Underwood

Ginger Giraffe Micro Pub & Gin Bar

14 Alfreton Road, NG16 5GB

☎ (01773) 533090

5 changing beers (often Castle Rock, Titanic) Ⓗ

This large micropub within an old factory unit has expanded several times to cope with demand. It offers five real ales, a range of real ciders and a wide choice of spirits, especially gin. There is a main bar area and a separate games room with a pool table and sports TV. Q🌣🕭♿♣🐾P🚪😺🛜

West Bridgford

Poppy & Pint Ⓛ

Pierrepont Road, NG2 5DX

☎ (0115) 981 9995

Castle Rock Harvest Pale, Preservation, Elsie Mo, Screech Owl; 8 changing beers Ⓗ

Former British Legion Club converted in 2011 by Castle Rock. It has a large main bar with a raised area and a family space with a café bar (children are welcome until 9pm). A large upstairs function room features a folk club and the beer garden overlooks tennis courts. Twelve handpumps dispense Castle Rock beers plus guests, often from new breweries. There are usually two real ciders, and excellent food is served. 🌣🕭🕪♿🐾P🚪😺🛜

Stratford Haven Ⓛ

2 Stratford Road, NG2 6BA

☎ (0115) 982 5981

Castle Rock Harvest Pale, Preservation, Elsie Mo, Screech Owl; 6 changing beers Ⓗ

A former pet shop, The Strat has a single central bar with extended seating at the back and a secluded snug to the right. Up to 12 cask ales plus a cider are available on handpump at any one time, including at least six from owner Castle Rock's portfolio. Guest ales are predominantly from microbreweries near and far. Food is served Wednesday to Sunday. Sunday is silent quiz night. Q🌣🕭🕪♿🐾🚪😺🛜

Worksop

Liquorice Gardens Ⓛ ✅

1A Newcastle Street, S80 2AS (just off town centre)

☎ (01909) 512220

Greene King Abbot; Ruddles Best Bitter; 5 changing beers (sourced nationally; often Little Critters, Milestone, Pheasantry) Ⓗ

The pub serves an excellent selection of ales, wines, spirits and craft beers. A good choice of food is available and there are ample seating areas as well as a covered garden/smoking area. Most of the real ales are local and the range changes weekly. There are occasional beer and cider festivals. 🌣🕭🕪♿🚲🐾🚪😺🛜

Mallard Ⓛ

Station Approach, S81 7AG (on station platform; entrance from main car park)

☎ 07973 521824

4 changing beers (sourced nationally) Ⓗ

Formerly the station buffet, this small pub offers a warm welcome. Four changing real ales are on sale, usually including three spards and a dark beer. Two ciders plus a selection of foreign bottled beers, country fruit wines and specialist gins are also available. There is a cosy main room plus a room downstairs used for special occasions. Four beer festivals are held each year. The recipient of many local CAMRA awards. Q🌣🚲♣🐾P🚪😺

Shireoaks Inn Ⓛ

Westgate, S80 1LT

☎ (01909) 472118 🌐 shireoaksinn.co.uk

3 changing beers (sourced regionally) Ⓗ

Warm, friendly pub converted from cottages. The public bar houses a pool table and large-screen TV, and the comfortable lounge bar has a separate dining area. Good-value home-cooked food is served. The three handpulls dispense regularly changing guest ales. A small outside area with tables is popular in the summer. The family owners also run the Station Hotel. 🌣🕪♿♣🐾P🚪

Station Hotel Ⓛ

Carlton Road, S80 1PS (opp railway station car park entrance)

☎ (01909) 474108 🌐 thestationhotelworksop.co.uk

5 changing beers (sourced regionally) Ⓗ

On the edge of the town centre, there is always a warm welcome at this pub. Up to five regularly changing real ales are available. The long bar serves a lounge drinking area with a separate dining room attached, and there is a further small room suitable for meetings. A spacious and well-maintained garden with seating is to the rear. Food is served lunchtimes and evenings and accommodation is offered. Q🌣🛏🕪🚲♣🐾P🚪(5)😺🛜

A short history of the Good Beer Guide

The Good Beer Guide was first published in 1972 and was just 18 pages long. Rather than a printed and bound edition, it was just a collection of sheets of paper stapled together and posted out to CAMRA members. The first printed edition was published in 1974 and contained a comment on Watney's brewery that was considered libellous, causing the first print run to be pulped and the description for the brewery to be revised. There are a few copies of the first print run out there but they change hands for a fair amount of money.

There has been a bound edition of the Guide printed annually since 1974, meaning it is now in its 49th year. The longest serving editor was Roger Protz, who edited the Guide from 1978–1983 and 2000–2018.

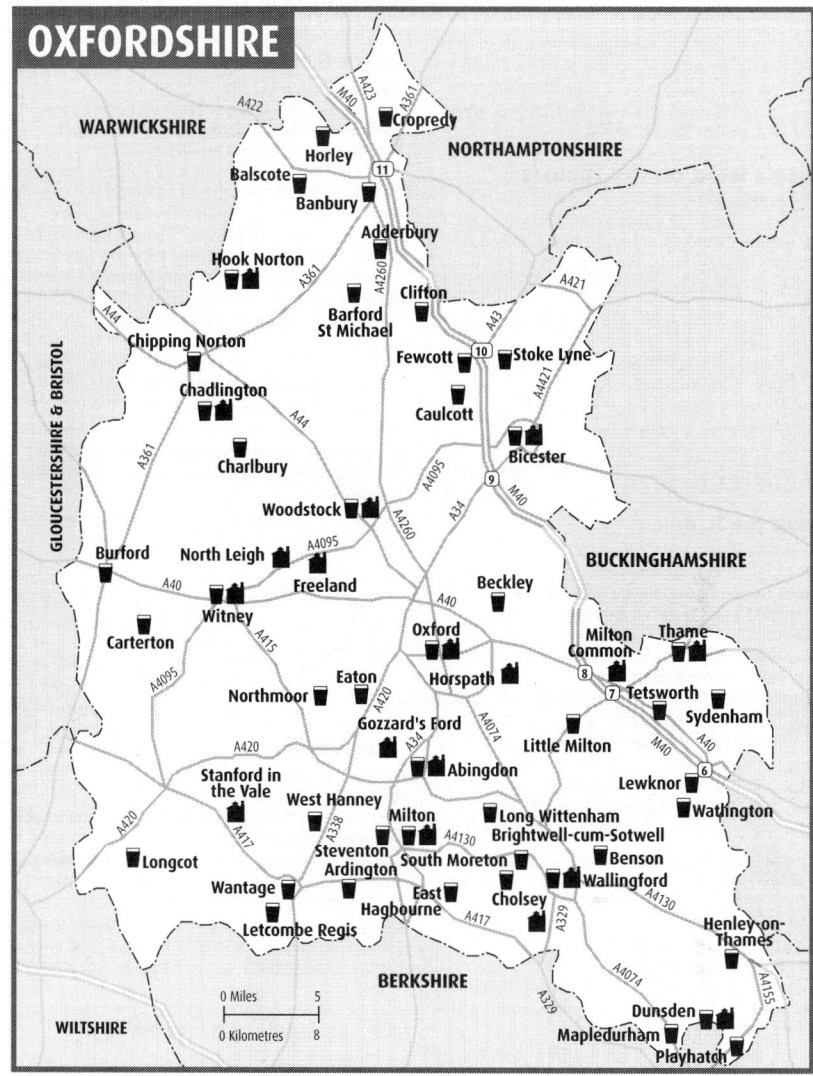

OXFORDSHIRE

Abingdon

Brewery Tap ⃝
40-42 Ock Street, OX14 5BZ
☎ (01235) 521655 ⊕ thebrewerytap.net
Loose Cannon Abingdon Bridge; 5 changing beers (sourced locally; often West Berkshire, White Horse, XT) ⊞
Morland created a tap for its brewery in 1993 from three Grade II-listed town houses. The brewery is no more but the pub, run by the same family since it opened, has thrived. It offers a diverse range of beers, all sourced locally, and hosts two or three beer festivals each year featuring ales from further afield. The pub has three rooms, two of them away from the bar, and a courtyard outside. Local CAMRA Town and Village Pub of the Year 2019 and 2020. Q✿🌭🏠🍴🍺👶♣🅿🖂🐶🛜

Broad Face ⃝ ✔
30-32 Bridge Street, OX14 3HR
☎ (01235) 538612 ⊕ broadfaceabingdon.co.uk

House beer (by Greene King); 7 changing beers (sourced nationally; often Dark Star, Loose Cannon, Morland) ⊞
Deceptively large, two-roomed, Grade II-listed pub near the river with a small outside seating area on Thames Street. The building was erected in 1840 but there are records of a pub on the site back to 1734, and possibly before that under a different name. Mystery surrounds the stories behind the pub's unique name, which are written on the outside wall, but omit the most likely explanation – that it was originally called the Saracen's Head and the sign was over-painted. Q✿🌭🍴🍺🖂🛜

King's Head & Bell ⃝
10 East St Helen Street, OX14 5EA
☎ (01235) 525362 ⊕ kingsheadandbell-abingdon.com
Loose Cannon Abingdon Bridge; 2 changing beers (sourced nationally; often Hook Norton, Loose Cannon, Sharp's) ⊞
In existence before 1554 as the Bell and for some time a coaching inn, in the 19th century it claimed to have stabling for nearly 100 horses and supplied the volunteer

fire brigade. Although with alterations and refurbishment carried out in 2019 by new management, the building still has historic traces. A number of rooms include two meeting rooms upstairs and a large conservatory for diners. The old courtyard is still the nicest beer garden in the town centre. ⊐※❀◑&♣무❀❀令

Nag's Head on the Thames 🅛
The Bridge, OX14 3HX
☎ (01235) 524516 ⊕ thenagsheadonthethames.co.uk
Brakspear Oxford Gold; Loose Cannon Abingdon Bridge; Timothy Taylor Landlord; 4 changing beers (sourced nationally; often Brakspear, Loddon, White Horse) 🅗
TSet on an island in the Thames, this Grade II-listed pub is split over two levels, with a large garden area next to the river and lovely views of the countryside and the town's historic buildings. Now owned by the Brakspear pubco, it offers a good choice of beers, often local. Live music is hosted. ⊐※❀◑&♣무❀❀令

Adderbury

Bell Inn 🅛 ✅
High Street, OX17 3LS (off A4260 in centre of village)
☎ (01295) 810338 ⊕ thebelladderbury.co.uk
Hook Norton Hooky, Hooky Gold, Old Hooky; 2 changing beers (sourced locally; often Hook Norton) 🅗
Well worth finding, this friendly village pub with its folkie roots is the spiritual home of the three village morris dancing teams. With a full range of Hook Norton ales and two bedrooms, it provides the ideal base for exploring the area. There are regular folk nights, and Aunt Sally is played in the summer. At the rear of the pub is a well-kept beer garden, ideal for enjoying your beer in the sunshine. Food is available at weekends. Closed weekday afternoons. Q⊐※❀☞◑&ᴧ♣●무(S4)❀令

Ardington

Boar's Head 🅛
Church Street, OX12 8QA
☎ (01235) 835466 ⊕ tbhardington.co.uk
Fuller's London Pride 🅗; North Cotswold Windrush Ale 🅗/🅖; 2 changing beers (sourced locally; often Loose Cannon) 🅗
The Boar's Head is owned by Lockinge Estates, like most of Ardington and Lockinge, and is an attractive timbered building in a side road between Ardington House and the church. The pub has been converted into a single bar, subdivided for diners and warmed by log fires in winter. It is a place to try home-cooked, seasonal food or sample the excellent beer range. Outside is a garden terrace for eating and drinking alfresco in summer. Closed afternoons. Q⊐※❀◑&♣무(X32,X33)❀令

Balscote

Butchers Arms ✅
Shutford Road, OX15 6JQ
☎ (01295) 730750 ⊕ butchers123.site123.me
Hook Norton Hooky; 2 changing beers (sourced nationally) 🅖
This cosy parlour pub dispenses Hook Norton ales plus a monthly guest straight from casks behind the bar. It has been a Hook Norton pub since 1878, but was once an abattoir and still has an ice house in the garden. Home-made food is served, including Sunday roasts. There is a monthly quiz on a Wednesday. In winter you can enjoy your pint by the roaring fire and for the summer there is a wonderful beer garden. Q⊐※❀◑♣무(270)❀

Banbury

Coach & Horses ✅
Butchers Row, OX16 5JH
☎ (01295) 266993 ⊕ thecoachandhorsesbanbury.com
Hook Norton Hooky, Hooky Gold, Old Hooky; 1 changing beer (sourced locally) 🅗
Town-centre pub popular with local shoppers and others as a place to relax and refresh in a vibrant and spacious environment. Three or four Hook Norton beers are available, along with ciders and home-made-to-order cocktails. The menu is frequently refreshed with locally sourced produce, including sharing and cheese platters. There is a small enclosed beer garden to the rear to enjoy alfresco drinking and dining. ※◑&≈●무

Olde Reine Deer Inn ✅
47 Parsons Street, OX16 5NA
☎ (01295) 270972 ⊕ ye-olde-reinedeer-inn-banbury.co.uk
Hook Norton Hooky Mild, Hooky, Hooky Gold, Old Hooky; 3 changing beers (sourced locally; often Hook Norton) 🅗
Traditional old English pub which first became an inn in 1570, featuring original wood panelling dating from the English Civil War. Cromwell's men are thought to have planned the Battle of Edge Hill and the siege of Banbury Castle from the Globe Room. A wide range of Hook Norton beers is served, along with food from a varied menu all day. There is an outside seating area with some cover. Identified by CAMRA as having a regionally important historic pub interior. Q※◑≈♣●무❀

White Horse 🅛
50-52 North Bar Street, OX16 0TH
☎ (01295) 277484 ⊕ whitehorsebanbury.com
Everards Tiger; Turpin Golden Citrus; 8 changing beers (sourced nationally) 🅗
The friendly landlords have turned the White Horse into a welcoming community pub. There are always at least four handpumps in use, offering a range of styles and strengths for the discerning drinker, along with several ciders. Friday nights are busy, with a local band often playing, and a monthly quiz on a Sunday. A beer festival is held at Easter. Outside is a small courtyard, partially covered, transformed into a haven, a lovely space for a drink. Closed Monday. Q⊐※❀◑&≈♣●무❀令

REAL ALE BREWERIES

Amwell Springs Cholsey
Barn Owl Gozzard's Ford
Bicester 🍺 Bicester
Brakspear 🖊 Witney
Brewery58 Wallingford
Chadlington Chadlington
Church Hanbrewery 🖊 North Leigh
Craftsman Abingdon (NEW)
Hook Norton 🖊 Hook Norton
Little Ox Freeland
Loddon 🖊 Dunsden
Loose Cannon 🖊 Abingdon
LoveBeer Milton
Oxford 🖊 Horspath
Philsters Milton Common
Tap Social Movement 🖊 Oxford
Thame 🍺 Thame
Turpin Hook Norton
White Horse Stanford in the Vale
Woodstock Woodstock (NEW)
Wriggly Monkey 🖊 Bicester
Wychwood 🖊 Witney

Barford St Michael

George Inn

Lower Street, OX15 0RH (off B4031)

☎ (01869) 338160 ⊕ thegeorgebarford.co.uk

3 changing beers (sourced nationally) ⊞

This charming 17th-century inn with a thatched roof is an interesting mix of village pub and relaxing getaway. A variety of ales, both local and from further afield, can be enjoyed in the flagstoned bar, by the fireplace or outside in the lovely garden with a covered terrace. A wide range of food is available, made with good local and sustainable ingredients. There are nine beautiful bedrooms for those who would like to stay.
Q✤☆🅰◑Ⅾ♿ＡＰ🖨🛜

Beckley

Abingdon Arms Ⓛ

High Street, OX3 9UU

☎ (01865) 655667 ⊕ theabingdonarms.co.uk

Ringwood Razorback; 3 changing beers (sourced locally; often Loddon, Oxford, Vale) ⊞

A lovely old pub with a fine garden affording great views across Otmoor. There is a small bar and separate dining area. The arms in question are of James Bertie (1653-1699) who was created 1st Earl of Abingdon in 1682. The Bertie family owned the village until 1919 when it was broken up and sold off in lots. The pub was put up for sale in 2016 and bought by a local community group after a community share offer. Q✤☆☆◑♣Ｐ🐾🛜

Benson

Crown Inn at Benson

52 High Street, OX10 6RP

☎ (01491) 528930 ⊕ thecrownatbenson.co.uk

Hook Norton Hooky, Hooky Gold, Old Hooky; 2 changing beers (sourced regionally; often Hook Norton) ⊞

This is Hook Norton Brewery's most southerly pub. A major refurbishment added six en-suite bedrooms. The building is a 17th-century, Grade II-listed, timber-framed former coaching inn, with a welcoming bar area and dining to the left and right. The two varying ales are from Hook Norton's hand-crafted ale range. The food menu comprises modern British classics, and there is a Smokehouse kitchen outside with a fully stocked bar with five real ale pumps. An on-site nanobrewery is planned. ☆☆◑Ｐ🖨🐾🛜

Bicester

Angel ✔

102 Sheep Street, OX26 6LP

☎ (01869) 360410 ⊕ theangelbicester.co.uk

Bicester Angelic Upstart; 5 changing beers (sourced regionally; often Chiltern, Rebellion, Vale) ⊞

Town-centre pub with a pleasant ambience and a welcoming bar area offering six real ales, often including a brew from the microbrewery behind the pub. A log fire adds extra comfort on chilly days. Bar snacks are limited but street food is available on summer weekends. There is a large seating area outside, a permanent marquee and an occasional cocktail bar. The microbrewery operates to seasonal demand.
Q✤☆♿⇌(North) Ｐ🐾🛜

Penny Black ✔

58 Sheep Street, OX26 6JW

☎ (01869) 321535

Greene King Abbot; Hook Norton Old Hooky; Ruddles Best Bitter; 8 changing beers (sourced nationally) ⊞

A popular town-centre Wetherspoon which was once Bicester's main post office and sorting office. Opened in 1997, it is situated in the town's pedestrianised area within walking distance of Bicester Village, bus and rail links. Up to 12 ales are usually on offer, and local beers are regularly promoted. The large single room has a long bar, and local information can be found on the walls. Outside there is seating at the front and a rear beer garden. Q✤☆☆◑♿⇌(North)●🖨🛜

Brightwell-cum-Sotwell

Red Lion Ⓛ

Brightwell Street, OX10 0RT (S off A4130)

☎ (01491) 837373 ⊕ redlionbrightwell.co.uk

Loddon Hoppit; West Berkshire Good Old Boy; 1 changing beer (sourced nationally) ⊞

A popular traditional Grade II-listed thatched inn dating from the 16th century in a quiet village. It has a cosy bar featuring exposed beams and an inglenook fireplace with log-burner, leading to a restaurant area, refurbished in early 2021. The rear courtyard garden is a summer suntrap. The beers and ciders are usually from local breweries and good-quality food is served, often with seasonal specials at weekends (no food Sun eve or Mon and Tue). Meat raffles and charity quiz nights are held regularly. Closed Monday and Tuesday.
☆☆◑♿♣●Ｐ🖨(33) 🐾🛜

Burford

Angel Inn ✔

14 Witney Street, OX18 4SN

☎ (01993) 822714 ⊕ theangelatburford.co.uk

Hook Norton Hooky, Old Hooky; 2 changing beers (sourced locally; often Hook Norton) ⊞

Small and cosy, warmed by a real fire, this 16th-century inn is just off the main High Street in picturesque Burford, the 'Gateway to the Cotswolds'. Comfortable mixed seating in front of the bar area caters for those wanting to enjoy the well-kept local Hook Norton ales, or locally sourced bar meals. The cosy restaurant is also filled with original features. Outside there is a lovely courtyard and walled garden with some covered seating. Families and dogs are welcome. Q✤☆☆🅰◑Ⅾ♿●🖨(233,853)🐾🛜

Carterton

Siege of Orleans Ⓛ

5 The Giles Centre, Alvescot Road, OX18 3DH (down passage next to cycle shop)

☎ (01993) 845663

4 changing beers (sourced regionally) ⊞

Not so much a pub as a self-styled micro-alehouse, set in a former record shop so on the small side. It has four handpumps dispensing mainly local ales from relatively unknown breweries alongside a selection of bottled and keg beers from around the world, and two real ciders. A gin bar opens upstairs Thursday to Saturday evenings. Regular retro games nights and competitions are hosted.
Q♿♣●Ｐ🖨🛜

Caulcott

Horse & Groom

Lower Heyford Road, OX25 4ND

☎ (01869) 343257 ⊕ horseandgroomcaulcott.co.uk

Black Sheep Best Bitter; Church End Goat's Milk; 3 changing beers (sourced nationally; often Church End, Goff's, Vale) ⊞

This lovely 16th-century coaching house provides a warm welcome along with three guest ales and two regulars. There is a roaring fire for winter and, outside, a small beer garden for the summer. Seasonal and locally sourced food is served by the French landlord/chef, including Sunday lunch (booking advised), and themed French evenings are hosted. The Bastille Day Beer Festival is an annual event. Dogs are allowed in the beer garden but not the bar. A repeat winner of Local CAMRA Pub of the Year. Closed Monday. Q✿⛲❶❷P🐾

Chadlington

Tite Inn
Mill End, OX7 3NY
☎ (01608) 676910 ⊕ thetiteinn.co.uk
Sharp's Doom Bar; 2 changing beers (sourced nationally; often Chadlington, Cotswold Lion, Sharp's) ℍ
A friendly welcome awaits at this cosy country pub in the Evenlode Valley. One regular and two guest ales are served along with a Westons cider on handpump. In winter there is a roaring fire, and for summer a beautiful hillside beer garden where a peaceful pint can be enjoyed, along with good reasonably priced food. Tite is old local dialect for spring – water runs under the pub and down the hill. Walkers are welcome.
Q✿⛲❶❷🅰🐾P🚆(S3,X9)🐾

Charlbury

Rose & Crown
Market Street, OX7 3PL
☎ (01608) 810103 ⊕ roseandcrown.charlbury.com
Hop Kettle Cricklade Ordinary Bitter; Salopian Oracle; 6 changing beers (sourced nationally; often Dark Star, Oakham, XT) ℍ
This ever-popular and welcoming traditional wet sales pub has been in the Guide for a well-deserved 35 consecutive years. It has a traditional pubby front bar plus a back bar and outside space. Eight real ales include changing guests, plus six traditional ciders and perries, giving a fantastic choice at the bar. Live music is hosted regularly. A former local and county CAMRA Pub of the Year. ✿🅰🚲♣🐾🚆(S3,X9)🐾

Chipping Norton

Chequers
Goddards Lane, OX7 5NP (next to theatre on corner of Spring St)
☎ (01608) 644717 ⊕ chequerschippingnorton.co.uk
Fuller's London Pride, ESB; Gale's Seafarers Ale, HSB; 3 changing beers (sourced nationally; often Dark Star, Fuller's, Gale's) ℍ
Traditional English pub with an emphasis on real ale and home-cooked food. Up to six ales from the Fuller's, Gale's and Dark Star ranges are available, and a cider served on gravity. The bar has three separate areas, all with flagstones and beams, and an airy restaurant and large function space to the rear. The cosy main bar area is warmed by a feature fireplace in winter, providing an excellent place to relax. Handy for the local theatre.
Q✿❶❷♣🐾🚆🐾

Clifton

Duke at Clifton Ⓛ
Main Street, OX15 0PE
☎ (01869) 226334 ⊕ thecliftonduke.co.uk
Hook Norton Hooky; Turpin Golden Citrus; 2 changing beers (often North Cotswold, Tring, XT) ℍ

This 17th-century Grade II-listed thatched country inn, originally named for Prince Rupert, is steeped in history, particularly from the Civil War. The roaring fire in the inglenook fireplace, and in good weather the superb garden, make this a perfect setting to sample the award-winning ales, whatever the season. Food is available from a locally sourced menu, and many of the ales are from local brewers. Walkers, dogs and wellies all welcome. There is a room for overnight stays and a fully serviced campsite. Q✿🛌❶❷🅰♣P🐾

Cropredy

Red Lion Ⓛ ✓
8 Red Lion Street, OX17 1PB
☎ (01295) 758680 ⊕ redlioncropredypub.co.uk
Butcombe Original; Purity Bunny Hop; 3 changing beers (sourced nationally; often Fuller's) ℍ
This part-thatched pub nestles in the middle of the village opposite the churchyard of St Mary the Virgin and the nearby Oxford Canal. It is a favourite both with boaters and walkers. Inside you will find a friendly welcome, a good choice of beer and well-cooked food, with themed food nights on occasion. There are three separate rooms within the pub and outside space to the rear. Take part in fun competitions such as pumpkin carving and enjoy the conversation.
Q✿❶❷🅰♣P🚆🐾

Dunsden

Loddon Tap Yard Ⓛ
Dunsden Green Farm, Church Lane, RG4 9QD
☎ (0118) 948 1111 ⊕ loddonbrewery.com/tapyard
Loddon Hullabaloo; 2 changing beers (sourced locally; often Loddon) ℍ
Opened in 2018 and adjoining the main brewhouse, this increasingly popular tap yard features three Loddon ales on handpump. With both indoor and outdoor seating, including covered decking, it is the perfect place to enjoy a pint in the beautiful countryside. A small range of home-made snacks is available. The shop offers a wide range of produce from within 40 miles of the brewery, including local wines, spirits, liqueurs and cider. The tap yard will stay open beyond the core hours if there is custom, and groups can visit at other times by arrangement. Closed Monday. ✿♣P🚆(800)🐾

East Hagbourne

Fleur de Lys Ⓛ
30 Main Road, OX11 9LN
☎ (01235) 813247 ⊕ thefleurdelyspub.co.uk
Morland Original Bitter; house beer (by LoveBeer); 4 changing beers (sourced nationally) ℍ
The Fleur de Lys is a family-friendly 17th-century pub in a rural village. It offers two regular beers – one a house beer (Wibbly Wobbly Whippet, 4.1% ABV) from nearby microbrewery LoveBeer – and up to four nationally sourced guests. The spacious bar and dining area are comfortable and cosy, warmed by an open fire. Live music evenings are hosted regularly, including two weekend music festivals in the summer. Aunt Sally is played in fine weather. The garden features a large semi-enclosed 'beer hall'. Local CAMRA and runner-up regional CAMRA Pub of the Year 2019. Closed Monday.
✿❶❷♣🐾🚆(94,94S)🐾

Eaton

Eight Bells Ⓛ
OX13 5PR

☎ (01865) 862261 🌐 8bells.co.uk
Loose Cannon Abingdon Bridge; 2 changing beers (sourced regionally) [H]
A cream-painted cottage-style brick building in the centre of the hamlet, to which extensions have been added over the years. Inside is a no-frills public bar with wooden benches and tables and a larger, simply furnished lounge bar, which leads on to the restaurant/function room. Three beers from breweries both local and further afield are sold. Closed Monday.
Q🐴❀◑♿P🚌🐾📶

Fewcott

White Lion [L] ✔
Fritwell Road, OX27 7NZ
☎ (01869) 346676
3 changing beers (sourced nationally) [H]
Step into this welcoming family-friendly free house with three varying real ales, and real cider in the summer, along with a good selection of whisky and gin. For sport lovers there are two large-screen TVs. The spacious beer garden is popular in summer and features a large pirate play ship. Aunt Sally can be played. A regular in the Guide, the pub is a former local CAMRA Pub of the Year and Cider Pub of the Year. Closed Monday and Tuesday.
🐴❀♿♣🍎P🐾📶

Henley-on-Thames

Bird in Hand
61 Greys Road, RG9 1SB
☎ (01491) 575775
Brakspear Gravity; Fuller's London Pride; 3 changing beers (sourced nationally; often Loddon, Rebellion, Tring) [H]
Celebrating 27 consecutive years in the Guide, the Bird has flourished under the stewardship of the same family throughout. Three guest beers complement the two regulars. TVs show sporting events, and the pub is home to darts and cribbage teams and hosts regular quiz nights. The family room leads to a delightful garden boasting a pond and aviary, and dogs on leads are welcome. Hot and cold snacks are available all day. A frequent winner of local CAMRA Pub of the Year including in 2020. Closed weekday afternoons.
Q🐴❀⛺🚆♣🚌🐾📶

Hook Norton

Pear Tree Inn [L] ✔
Scotland End, OX15 5NU (follow brown tourist signs to Hook Norton Brewery)
☎ (01608) 737482 🌐 peartreeinnhooknorton.co.uk
Hook Norton Hooky Mild, Hooky, Hooky Gold, Old Hooky; 2 changing beers (sourced locally; often Hook Norton) [H]
This managed house dispenses the full range of Hook Norton beers. Proper classic pub food is also served. The single bar is cosy in winter and the large child-friendly garden, with some covered seating, is popular for summer drinking. Aunt Sally is played here. With three bedrooms, the pub is a great base for a stopover before or after the popular brewery tours, or for discovering the surrounding local area.
Q🐴❀🛏◑♿⛺♣🍎P🚌(488)🐾📶

Horley

Red Lion [L]
Hornton Lane, OX15 6BQ
☎ (01295) 730427
Hook Norton Hooky; Purity Pure UBU; Sharp's Doom Bar; Turpin Golden Citrus [H]
This friendly local offers a warm welcome to all who enter – visitors, walkers and well-behaved dogs alike. A focal point of the village, its tranquil garden area is ideal for a summer evening tipple. There are three handpumped ales available year round, plus a fourth for special occasions. The St George's Day annual beer festival is a must for all. Aunt Sally, darts and dominoes are played here. Local CAMRA Pub of the Year 2020. Closed Monday. ❀♣P🐾📶

Letcombe Regis

Greyhound Inn [L]
Main Street, OX12 9JL
☎ (01235) 771969 🌐 thegreyhoundletcombe.co.uk
4 changing beers (sourced nationally; often North Cotswold, Ramsbury, Thornbridge) [H]
Large, welcoming pub in the centre of the village. Inside is a single bar with dining areas and a formerly hidden inglenook fireplace. Locally sourced home-cooked food and four constantly changing handpumped beers are served. The garden hosts alfresco dining during the summer months. There is parking at the side of the building, as well as secure bicycle storage. Within a couple of miles of the Ridgeway, the pub is a welcome place of refreshment for wayfarers. Accommodation is offered in eight boutique en-suite bedrooms.
Q🐴❀🛏◑♿⛺P🐾📶

Lewknor

Leathern Bottle
1 High Street, OX49 5TW (N off B4009 near M40 jct 6)
☎ (01844) 351482 🌐 theleathernbottle.co.uk
Brakspear Gravity; Marston's Pedigree; 1 changing beer (sourced nationally; often Young's) [H]
This traditional Grade II-listed country pub, run by two generations of the same family since 1980, has featured in all but one edition of the Guide. It serves good home-cooked pub food and has a family-friendly garden. The guest ale is usually Young's Bitter or London Special. The venue offers a warm welcome to all, including walkers from the nearby Ridgeway, with some of the best trails starting and finishing here. It is also a short walk from the Oxford Tube and the airline coach stop. Closed Monday. Q🐴❀◑♿♣P🚌🐾📶

Little Milton

Lamb
High Street, OX44 7PU (on A329)
☎ (01844) 279527 🌐 lambinnlittlemilton.co.uk
Brakspear Gravity; Courage Directors; 1 changing beer (sourced nationally) [H]
Thatched 16th-century stone pub on the main road through the village. The attractive, welcoming split-level bar in this Grade II-listed inn features original beams and has seating areas for those who just want a drink, as well as for diners enjoying the high-quality food. To the rear is a patio and a walled flower garden where a beer festival is held in July. Quiz night is the first Thursday of the month. 🐴❀◑P🐾📶

Long Wittenham

Plough [L]
24 High Street, OX14 4QH
☎ (01865) 407738 🌐 theploughinnlw.co.uk

Butcombe Original; 2 changing beers (sourced nationally; often Amwell Springs, Loose Cannon, West Berkshire) Ⓗ
A traditional Grade II-listed family-friendly pub built in the 17th century in this rural south Oxfordshire village. Its large garden stretches down to the River Thames and has ample outdoor seating and a children's play space. There are two bar areas and a separate restaurant. One regular and two changing beers are served, from breweries and microbreweries mainly in the South-East. The pub hosts many community events, notably Wittfest, a music festival each June that raises money for charities. A former local CAMRA Pub of the Season.
ﾋﾟ❀Ⓦ◑Å♣P⊟❀ ≷

Longcot

King & Queen Ⓛ
Shrivenham Road, SN7 7TL
☎ (01793) 784348 ⊕ kingandqueenlongcot.co.uk
3 changing beers (sourced nationally; often Loose Cannon, Ramsbury, Wychwood) Ⓗ
It is thought that the King & Queen was constructed about 200 years ago to cater for the navvies working on the Wilts & Berks Canal which passes nearby. From the pub, one may enjoy one of the best views of White Horse Hill and the famous 3000-year-old white horse. The layout inside comprises an extensive, open-plan drinking area and to one side, a restaurant serving substantial meals, while outside is a tranquil beer garden. The pub offers a good selection of beers from local breweries. Closed lunchtimes Monday-Tuesday.
Q ﾋﾟ❀Ⓦ◑�& ÅP⊟(66) ❀ ≷

Mapledurham

Pack Saddle at Mapledurham Ⓛ
Chazey Heath, RG4 7UD (off A4074)
☎ (0118) 946 3000 ⊕ thepacksaddle.com
Loddon Hoppit; 3 changing beers (sourced nationally; often Loddon, Rebellion, West Berkshire) Ⓗ
An independently owned country venue on the Mapledurham Estate, refurbished in summer 2020 to provide a welcoming main bar in the lower area, and an upstairs area for dining. Four of the five handpumps are normally in use at any one time, serving Loddon Hoppit as the regular ale and changing beers from other local breweries. An innovative modern British menu uses seasonal fresh ingredients, much from local producers. It also has a community garden, providing the freshest possible salad, fruit and vegetables for the pub kitchen.
Q ﾋﾟ❀◑♣P⊟❀ ≷

Milton

Plum Pudding Ⓛ
44 High Street, OX14 4EJ
☎ (01235) 834443 ⊕ theplumpuddingmilton.co.uk
Loose Cannon Abingdon Bridge; LoveBeer OG; 1 changing beer (sourced nationally) Ⓗ
Plum Pudding refers to the Oxford Sandy and Black pig, one of the older and rarer British breeds. The pub serves three real ales plus up to four real ciders. Regular live music is hosted, and beer festivals in April and October. Sitting in the pleasant walled garden, you wouldn't know it, but you are only a couple of minutes from the busy A34. En-suite accommodation is available. The place is a former local CAMRA Pub of the Year, repeat local Cider Pub of the Year, and was regional Cider Pub of the Year in 2019. ﾋﾟ❀Ⓦ◑♣♦P⊟❀ ≷

Northmoor

Red Lion Ⓛ ✓
Standlake Road, OX29 5SX
☎ (01865) 300301 ⊕ theredlionnorthmoor.com
Brakspear Gravity; Loose Cannon Abingdon Bridge; 2 changing beers (sourced locally; often Cotswold Lion, North Cotswold, Vale) Ⓗ
Traditional village inn with whitewashed stone walls, heavy oak beams, real fires and a large garden. Purchased by the local community from Greene King in 2014, the pub has gone from strength to strength. The focus is on local produce, with a changing menu of home-cooked food, some of which is grown in the pub's kitchen garden. A selection of three or four local beers is available in the small bar alongside locally made soft drinks from Samuelsons of Witney. Closed Monday.
Q ﾋﾟ❀Ⓦ◑♣P❀ ≷

Oxford

Bear Inn Ⓛ
6 Alfred Street, OX1 4EH
☎ (01865) 728164 ⊕ bearoxford.co.uk
Fuller's London Pride, ESB; Gale's HSB; Oxford Scholar; 2 changing beers (sourced regionally; often Fuller's, Gale's) Ⓗ
The Bear's precise age is open to debate but it is definitely old; the present building dates back to 1606 and has been identified by CAMRA as having a regionally important historic pub interior. Tucked away behind the town hall, it is a tied house in more ways than one, renowned for its collection of tie remnants taken from customers. A small pub popular with students and visitors, its main, low-ceilinged bar has two small rooms adjoining and gets crowded at times but there is more seating in a paved area to the rear. Q ﾋﾟ❀◑≷♣⊟ ≷

Butchers Arms
5 Wilberforce Street, Headington, OX3 7AN (from centre of Headington, past shark, first left, first right)
☎ (01865) 742470 ⊕ butchersarmsheadington.co.uk
Fuller's London Pride, ESB; Gale's Seafarers Ale; 2 changing beers (sourced regionally; often Fuller's) Ⓗ
A friendly back-street late-Victorian hostelry; this red-brick pub is a little hard to find but worth searching out. The long single room has the bar in the middle, and outside is a paved seating area. The pub offers a good range of Fuller's beers, traditional food and light lunch options. The inn sign, a parody of the arms of the Worshipful Company of Butchers, and the motto, which means 'God gives us everything', are both of unknown origin. Q ﾋﾟ❀◑♣♦❀ ≷

Chequers Ⓛ ✓
130A High Street, OX1 4DH
☎ (01865) 727463
St Austell Nicholson's Pale Ale; Sharp's Doom Bar; Thornbridge Jaipur IPA; 5 changing beers (sourced nationally; often Brakspear, Hook Norton) Ⓗ
Worth searching out down a passageway off the High Street, much of this Grade II-listed pub dates back to the early 16th century when it was converted from a moneylender's tenement to a tavern, hence the name. Note the fine carvings, windows and the ceiling in the lower bar. There is an upstairs bar with an additional three handpumps, and a cobbled courtyard provides an alfresco drinking, dining and smoking space.
Q ﾋﾟ❀◑&≷♦●❀ ≷

Fir Tree Ⓛ ✓
163 Iffley Road, OX4 1EJ
☎ (01865) 245290

5 changing beers (sourced nationally; often Greene King, Morland, Plain) [H]
Multi-level pub with a quiet snug at the back and a small patio garden and smoking area to the rear. There are some pavement tables at the front. The house speciality is pizza and a pop-up diner serves a vegan roast dinner on Sunday afternoon. The interior of this quirky pub still bears the scars of its days as a Morrell's Ale House, with a whole bank of handpumps and a variety of finishes, artefacts and pictures. ♿🏠🍴🌳🍺🚃(3)🐾♿

Gardeners Arms [L]
39 Plantation Road, Walton Manor, OX2 6JE
☎ (01865) 559814 ● thegarden-oxford.co.uk
4 changing beers (sourced locally; often Little Ox, Loose Cannon, XT) [H]
Established in the 1830s, this is a cosy pub down a narrow street off Woodstock Road. A popular and relaxing place to eat and drink, the small bar opens up to a spacious dining area, once two rooms, serving some of the finest vegetarian and vegan food in the city. At the rear is a large and pleasant garden, as well as the outside toilets. The famous weekly quiz is on Sunday evening.
Q♿🏠🍴🌳🍺🐾♿

Grapes [L]
7 George Street, OX1 2AT
☎ (01865) 793380 ● grapesoxford.co.uk
West Berkshire Mister Chubb's, Maggs' Mild, Good Old Boy, Maharaja IPA; 3 changing beers (sourced locally; often Amwell Springs, Loose Cannon, Siren Craft) [H]
First built in 1820 and rebuilt in 1879, this is a rare Victorian pub in the city centre. It has a single narrow panelled room with the bar on one side and seating on the other. Glazed timber screens separate some of the tables. In the entrance, original tiling and signs remain. The pub reopened under West Berkshire Brewery ownership in 2019 and offers a range of its beers plus others from local breweries, as well as 12 beers from kegs. Q🏠♿🚃🍺🐾♿

Mason's Arms [L] ✅
2 Quarry School Place, Headington Quarry, OX3 8LH
☎ (01865) 764579 ● themasonsarmshq.co.uk
Castle Rock Harvest Pale; Harvey's Sussex Best Bitter; 3 changing beers (sourced nationally; often Castle Rock, Oakham, Rebellion) [H]
Family-run community pub hosting many games leagues, including bar billiards and Aunt Sally. The guest ales are varied and turn over quickly, and a wide range of bottled beers is also stocked. The venue is home to the Headington beer festival in September. A heated decking area and garden lead to the function room, which hosts music and comedy nights. ♿🌳🍺🚃(H2)🐾♿

Plough at 38 [L]
38 Cornmarket Street, OX1 3HA
☎ (01865) 587159 ● ploughat38.com
XT Four, Animal; 1 changing beer (sourced locally; often XT) [H]
Two tenements were rebuilt as a hostelry and registered as the Plough Inn in 1656. It closed in 1924 and the building was changed to a shop, but some of the upper storeys are still original. It reopened as a pub in 2019. Three beers are served from casks and three local ales from kegs. Unfinished XT beer is delivered and conditioned in 1,000 litre copper tanks behind the bar before being served under pressure. Q♿🏠♿🚃🍺♿

Rose & Crown [L]
14 North Parade Avenue, OX2 6LX (½ mile N of city centre, off Banbury Rd)
☎ (01865) 510551 ● roseandcrownoxford.com

Adnams Southwold Bitter; Hook Norton Old Hooky; Oxford Scholar; 1 changing beer (sourced locally) [H]
Now a free house, this popular Victorian local on a vibrant north Oxford street is a time capsule with two small rooms and many original features. A friendly community pub, it has been run by the same landlords for over 30 years. No intrusive music or mobile phones are permitted. Its fame has even spread to Everest – see the photo on the wall. Identified by CAMRA as having a regionally important historic pub interior. Q🏠♿🍴🚃♿

Royal Blenheim [L]
13 St Ebbes Street, OX1 1PT
☎ (01865) 242355 ● royalblenheim.co.uk
Everards Tiger; Titanic Plum Porter; White Horse Bitter, Stable Genius, Village Idiot; 5 changing beers (sourced nationally) [H]
Single-room Victorian pub next to Modern Art Oxford – the building is all that is left of Hanley & Co Ltd, City Brewery. It was built in 1889 for Hanley's on the site of two alehouses, in what was then a very rough part of the city. The pub is owned by Everards but leased to Titanic, who run it in partnership with White Horse Brewery. Ten handpumps dispense a range of White Horse and Titanic beers, one from Everards, plus guests. Local CAMRA City Pub of the Year 2020. Q🏠♿🚃🍴🍺♿

St Aldate's Tavern [L]
108 St Aldate's, OX1 1BU
☎ (01865) 241185 ● staldatestavernoxford.co.uk
Hook Norton Hooky; XT Three; house beer (by West Berkshire); 3 changing beers (sourced regionally; often Box Steam, New Flying Monk, Siren Craft) [H]
Not the original St Aldate's Tavern - that was at no.61 and still has the Morland Artist plaque - but there was an inn recorded at this site in 1397. The pub has been rebuilt at least once since then and was a coaching inn in the 18th century. A friendly establishment opposite the town hall, it features up to seven well-kept real ales, with at least two from local breweries. Q🏠♿🚃🍴🍺♿

White Hart
12 St Andrew's Road, Headington, OX3 9DL (opp church in Old Headington village)
☎ (01865) 761737 ● thewhitehartheadington.com
Everards Tiger; 4 changing beers (sourced nationally; often Castle Rock, Everards, Oakham) [H]
Terraced stone-built pub offering a good selection of Everards ales, guest ales and two ciders. The interior is divided into three, with two small bars, and it has a large garden. Note the framed extract from a play, The Tragicomedy of Joan of Hedington, by Dr William King of Christ Church, written in 1712 about the proprietor of a dishonourable alehouse - thankfully the pub now has a much better reputation. The food is traditional and home-made, with pies a speciality. ♿🏠♿♿🚃🍴🐾♿

White Rabbit [L]
21 Friars Entry, OX1 2BY (alley between Magdalen St and Gloucester Green)
☎ (01865) 241177 ● whiterabbitoxford.co.uk
5 changing beers (sourced locally) [H]
The White Rabbit pub since 2012, this was previously the Gloucester Arms, which described itself as Oxford's premier rock pub. It has a small bar surrounded by three separate areas, and outside seating in a paved space with heated seats and parasols. Five local real ales are usually on offer, with one sometimes swapped for cider. Hand-made pizzas are a speciality, with gluten-free bases on request. The pub has been identified by CAMRA as having a historic interior of some regional importance. 🏠♿🚃♿🍺🐾♿

Playhatch

Flowing Spring

Henley Road, RG4 9RB (on A4155)
☎ (0118) 969 9878 ⊕ theflowingspringpub.co.uk
Tring Ridgeway, Colley's Dog; 4 changing beers (sourced nationally) ⊞
Sociable 18th-century country pub on the edge of the Chilterns. A free house owned by the former tenants, it features two regular plus three or four varying beers. It serves home-made food with award-winning gluten-free, dairy-free, vegetarian and vegan options. Events include monthly unplugged nights, classic car and bike meets, murder mysteries, and summer concerts in the large garden. The pleasant covered balcony and large riverside garden are ideal for summer. Closed Monday.
Ⴆⲱⴱ♣⊜P❀శ

South Moreton

Crown ⊞

High Street, OX11 9AG (in centre of village)
☎ (01235) 810005 ⊕ thecrown-southmoreton.co.uk
Loose Cannon Abingdon Bridge; house beer (by Amwell Springs); 2 changing beers (sourced nationally; often North Cotswold, West Berkshire, XT) ⊞
Previously a Wadworth pub and closed for several years, the Crown reopened in 2019 as a community pub. The current licensees have been in situ since July 2020, and have placed emphasis on showcasing local ales, including collaborating with Amwell Springs for a regular house beer. Food is sourced from fresh local produce and the menu refreshed regularly to reflect this. Closed Tuesday. QჄⲱⴱ♠♣P⊜(94S,D2)❀శ

Steventon

North Star ★ ⊞

2 Stocks Lane, OX13 6SG (at the end of The Causeway, off B4017)
Loddon Hullabaloo; 3 changing beers (sourced regionally; often Amwell Springs, Butts, Loose Cannon) Ꮐ
Identified by CAMRA as having a historic interior of outstanding national importance, the pub is situated next to the Causeway, a listed ancient monument. Popular with locals and visitors. It hosts many village clubs and social events. Inside are two bars, one with three settles around an open fireplace, and a separate function room. Three beers are served by gravity and presented through a stable door and hatch. Closed lunchtimes Monday-Thursday. Ⴆⲱ♣⊜P⊜(X2)❀శ

Stoke Lyne

Peyton Arms

School Lane, OX27 8SD
☎ 07546 066160
Hook Norton Hooky, Old Hooky Ꮐ; **1 changing beer (sourced locally; often Hook Norton)** ⊞
Entering this interesting pub is like stepping back in time. There are up to three Hooky ales served through a hatch, direct from the casks. A wealth of interesting memorabilia is all around and can be perused between conversations with other drinkers by the fire. Filled rolls are often available. The bar area is for adults only; however, children are welcome in the garden – but dogs are not allowed. Opening hours can vary so call to check. Identified by CAMRA as having a regionally important historic pub interior. QⲱP

Sydenham

Inn at Emmington ⊞

Sydenham Road, Emmington, OX39 4LD (on B4445)
☎ (01844) 351367 ⊕ theinnatemmington.co.uk
Rebellion IPA; 2 changing beers (sourced locally; often Chiltern, Loose Cannon, XT) ⊞
Situated on the edge of this delightful village, the Inn at Emmington is known for its cask ales – two plus one changing guest – convivial atmosphere and excellent home-cooking. Its prime location just off the M40 junction 6, close to the Chiltern Hills, is also a big draw. Those looking to explore the area should book a stay in one of the seven guest rooms, some of which boast views over the Oxfordshire countryside.
Qⲱ♫⊕♣⊜P⊜(40)❀శ

Tetsworth

Old Red Lion ⊞

40 High Street, OX9 7AS
☎ (01844) 281274 ⊕ theoldredliontetsworth.co.uk
XT Four; 1 changing beer (sourced locally) ⊞
The Old Red Lion has a warm and friendly atmosphere, with wood-burning stoves in the winter, and offers up to three well-kept real ales from local breweries. Traditional pub food is available in the bar all day. The place also serves as the village shop and offers B&B accommodation. It is a member of Brit Stops and allows motorhomes free overnight parking. Refurbished in early 2020, it is truly an Asset of Community Value.
QჄⲱ♫⊕Ġ♣⊜P⊜(275)❀శ

Thame

Cross Keys ⊞ ✓

East Street, OX9 3JS
☎ (01844) 218202 ⊕ crosskeysthame.co.uk
XT Four; 7 changing beers (sourced nationally; often Thame) ⊞
Once almost lost forever, the Cross Keys was saved by the current tenants, who have transformed it into a drinkers' local, serving a range of ales and ciders. The on-site Thame Brewery and other local breweries are often represented, along with microbreweries and small brewers around the country. On busy evenings it is not uncommon for several beers to change during the evening. It is home to local clubs and hosts community events such as comedy nights and live music. Local CAMRA Cider Pub of the Year 2019. Qⲱ♣⊜⊜❀శ

Wallingford

Royal Standard ⊞

32 St Marys Street, OX10 0ET
☎ (01491) 599105 ⊕ royalstandardwallingford.co.uk
Amwell Springs Chairman Dave, Easy Geez; 1 changing beer (sourced nationally; often Amwell Springs) ⊞
This much-loved 19th-century pub reopened in May 2019. It offers local ales from Amwell Springs and a great menu from a former Michelin-starred chef. On Tuesday to Friday it also serves as a coffee shop, with a soft play area for under-fives, but in the evening it has sports TV, quiz nights, entertainment and a warm atmosphere. The large beer garden has an 85-inch TV – perfect for those summer sports events.
Ⴆⲱ♫⊕Ġ♠⇌(Cholsey & Wallingford)⊜❀శ

Wantage

Lamb

59 Mill Street, OX12 9AB

☎ (01235) 766768 🌐 lambinnwantage.co.uk

Fuller's London Pride; Gale's Seafarers Ale; 1 changing beer (sourced nationally; often St Austell) Ⓗ

A 17th-century inn near the mill, this is the second oldest building in Wantage after the parish church, and the only thatched building in the town. It has never been sold and has had only two landlords in the last 50 years. The spacious interior has been extended at the rear and it serves an extensive range of pub food, freshly made using ingredients from local suppliers. This family venue extends a warm and friendly welcome to all.
😋🏵️🍺🕭♿️🅿️🚌🐾🛜

Royal Oak Ⓛ

Newbury Street, OX12 8DF (S of Market Sq)

☎ (01235) 763129 🌐 royaloakwantage.co.uk

Wadworth 6X; West Berkshire Maggs' Mild, Dr Hexter's Healer; 8 changing beers (sourced nationally) Ⓖ

This multi award-winning street-corner pub is a mecca for the discerning drinker. All beers are served by gravity, along with 30 or more ciders and perries. Photographs of ships bearing the pub's name are displayed. The lounge features wrought-iron trelliswork covered in pumpclips. Table football is played in the public bar. Awarded local CAMRA Pub of the Year and Cider Pub of the Year many times, including in 2020. Q😋🍺♣🍴🚌🐾🛜

Watlington

Spire & Spoke Ⓛ

21 Hill Road, OX49 5AD (E off B4009)

☎ (01491) 614956 🌐 theSpireandSpoke.co.uk

Timothy Taylor Landlord; 3 changing beers (sourced locally; often West Berkshire, XT) Ⓗ

Reopened in 2020, the former Carriers Arms was completely refurbished inside. Three or four local beers are available from breweries such as West Berkshire and XT. Coffee and home-made cakes are served with pizzas cooked in the external wood-fired oven. The Ridgeway crosses the road nearby, and from the garden there is a good view of the chalk triangle on Watlington Hill, originally cut to look like a spire on the parish church. Alcoholic drinks are served from 11am.
😋🏵️🍺🕭♿️🅿️🚌(11,137)🐾🛜

West Hanney

Plough Ⓛ ✅

Church Street, OX12 0LN

☎ (01235) 868987 🌐 theploughatwesthanney.co.uk

4 changing beers (sourced regionally; often Box Steam, Butts, White Horse) Ⓗ

Picturesque 16th-century thatched pub opposite the church. Sold in 2015 by Punch Taverns to a local community group, it has been refurbished and now serves four changing beers. The interior comprises a cosy beamed and alcoved split-level bar with an open fire and a separate dining room serving traditional British food. It is the hub of the village and most local clubs meet here from time to time. In summer Aunt Sally is played in the local league. Closed Monday. 😋🏵️🍺🕭♿️🅰️♣🅿️🐾🛜

Witney

Angel Inn Ⓛ ✅

42 Market Square, OX28 6AL

☎ (01993) 703238

Brakspear Oxford Gold; Wychwood Hobgoblin Gold, Hobgoblin Ruby; house beer (by Marston's) Ⓗ

A Grade II-listed free house at one time owned by Joseph Early of the blanket manufacturing dynasty and a brewer. It has a fine front bar with low beams and a bay window, with plenty of space for drinkers and diners beyond. Outside is a small paved and walled courtyard. The beer range is mostly from Marston's – its Wychwood Brewery is just around the corner, but the beer goes to Burton upon Trent to be casked. One of the regular beers is sometimes replaced by a guest. 🏵️🕭🍴🚌(S1,S2)🐾🛜

Drummer's Bar Ⓛ

8 Langdale Court, OX28 6FG (down passageway directly opp Blue Boar)

☎ (01608) 677717 🌐 drummersbar.co.uk

2 changing beers (sourced locally; often Church Hanbrewery, Goff's, Little Ox) Ⓗ

Witney's first micropub is a venture run by a father and son team. The pair started an eight-barrel brewery, Oxbrew, which has now merged with Little Ox Brewery. The pub, once a charity shop, serves the brewery's own beers alongside others from local small breweries via two handpulls from casks and six taps from kegs. Beers are kept in an air-conditioned cold room behind the bar. Closed Monday and Tuesday. Q🏵️🅿️🚌(S1,S2)🛜

Eagle Tavern Ⓛ ✅

22 Corn Street, OX28 6BL

☎ (01993) 700121

Hook Norton Hooky, Hooky Gold, Old Hooky; 1 changing beer (sourced locally; often Hook Norton) Ⓗ

This Grade II-listed building was bought by Hook Norton in 2001 and serves a range of the brewery's beers as well as malt whiskies, bourbons, gins and rums. The interior has three seating areas, lots of dark wood, and you can see the cellar through the window next to the bar. Closed Monday. Q🏵️🍺♣🍴🚌(S1,S2)🛜

Wychwood Brewery Tap Ⓛ

Eagle Maltings, The Crofts, OX28 4DP (down alleyway off Corn St just after Chequers)

☎ (01993) 890800

Wychwood Hobgoblin Gold, Hobgoblin Ruby; 2 changing beers (sourced nationally; often Brakspear, Ringwood, Wychwood) Ⓗ

The brewery now has a taproom open to the public five days a week with a small room containing a bar and a larger room with some comfortable seating. As well as the mainstream offerings, it sometimes serves beer in cask that would normally only go for bottling. Keg and bottled beers are also available. Closed Monday and Tuesday. Q😋🅿️🚌🛜

Woodstock

Black Prince

2 Manor Road, OX20 1XJ

☎ (01993) 811530 🌐 theblackprincewoodstock.com

Loddon Hullabaloo; St Austell Tribute; 2 changing beers (sourced nationally; often Chadlington, Vale) Ⓗ

This historic 16th-century riverside pub sits opposite the grounds of Blenheim Palace. Four ales – two regular and two changing, often locally sourced – are served, alongside fresh well-cooked meals and snacks at reasonable prices. Inside there are stone walls, two roaring log fires and even a suit of armour; outside there is a lovely riverside garden. Aunt Sally is played, and families, walkers and well-behaved dogs are all welcome. This is a lovely place to relax with a pint in summer and winter alike. Q😋🏵️🕭♣🅿️🚌🐾🛜

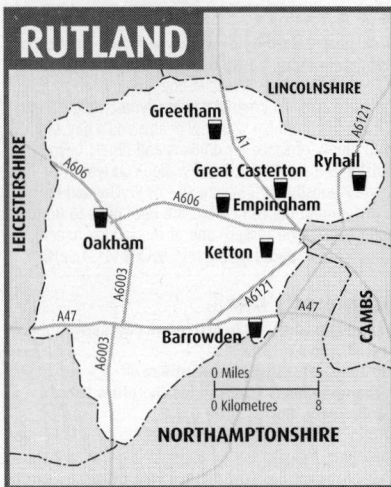

RUTLAND

LINCOLNSHIRE

LEICESTERSHIRE

Greetham

Great Casterton Ryhall

Empingham

Oakham Ketton

Barrowden

CAMBS

0 Miles 5
0 Kilometres 8

NORTHAMPTONSHIRE

Barrowden

Exeter Arms

28 Main Street, LE15 8EQ
☎ (01572) 747365 ⊕ exeterarmsbarrowden.co.uk
**Oakham JHB; Shepherd Neame Spitfire; Timothy
Taylor Landlord; 1 changing beer (often Grainstore)** ⊞
Collyweston slate-roofed building with a fine view over
the valley and village duck pond. This family-run pub
offers a warm welcome and serves highly regarded food
– Sunday roasts are especially popular (booking
essential). The interior was extensively refurbished in
2020, and the large, attractive garden features an
outdoor bar and kitchen providing high-quality barbecue
food at weekends. The Exeter Arms is popular with
walkers and is dog-friendly. Q❀🕸🕙👶🌳♣🅿🐾❤️📶

Empingham

Empingham Cricket & Social Club

Exton Road, LE15 8QB
☎ (01780) 460696 ⊕ empinghamcsc.org
**Magpie Best; 2 changing beers (often Greg's,
Stockport)** ⊞
Recently refurbished, the Cricket & Social Club is noted
for the quality and variety of the ales served, many from
microbreweries. It has limited hours, often extended
when sporting and other functions take place – check the
website for events. An annual beer festival is held to
coincide with the final matches of the Six Nations rugby.
A Rutland CAMRA award winner. Q❀🕸👶🅿🐾❤️📶

Great Casterton

Crown

Main Street, PE9 4AP
☎ (01780) 753838 ⊕ thecrowncasterton.co.uk
**Digfield Shacklebush; Oakham JHB; Sharp's Doom
Bar, Sea Fury** ⊞
This popular dog-friendly inn on the old Great North Road
serves the village and surrounding area. The former
Melbourns/Pubmaster pub has recently undergone a
major refurbishment and has four handpumps for regular
and guest ales. Food is now well established (booking
advised for Sunday lunch). Outside, there is a pétanque
area and an attractive beer garden.
Q❀🕸🕙👶🌳♣🅿🐾❤️📶

Greetham

Plough

23 Main Street, LE15 7NJ
☎ (01572) 813613 ⊕ theploughgreetham.co.uk
**Black Sheep Best Bitter; Marston's Pedigree;
Wainwright; 1 changing beer** ⊞
A Former Mann's pub dating back to the early 1900s, this
traditional country inn offers a decent beer range. Good-
value pub food is served daily featuring ingredients from
local suppliers and vegetables from the on-site
allotment. The community focused hostelry hosts pub
games and live music, and has undergone extensive
work to enlarge the outdoor seating area, adding an ice
cream parlour and tea room in the garden.
Q❀🕸🕙👶🌳🅿🚃📶

Ketton

Railway

Church Street, PE9 3TA
☎ (01780) 721050
Grainstore Rutland Osprey, Ten Fifty; Oakham JHB ⊞
A traditional village local situated in the shadow of the
impressive church, serving good beer and wine in a
welcoming and friendly atmosphere. The Grade II-listed
building is several hundred years old, with much
character and more than a little charm. Food is not
normally served but functions can be catered for. A
fourth beer can be added at busy times. Local CAMRA
Pub of the Year. Q❀🕸👶♣🅿🚃❤️

Oakham

Grainstore Brewery Tap

Station Approach, LE15 6EA
☎ (01572) 770065 ⊕ grainstorebrewery.com
**Grainstore Cooking, Daniel Lambert, Rutland Bitter,
Rutland Panther, Triple B, Ten Fifty; 3 changing beers
(often Grainstore)** ⊞
A pub and brewery in a cleverly converted small
warehouse over four floors, retaining some original
features. Brewery tours are available but must be
booked in advance. Ten handpumps offer a range of
beers, always including a mild. A range of bottle-
conditioned Belgian beers is also stocked. Home-made
food is served including breakfasts at the weekend. Live
bands feature regularly. Walkers and their dogs are
welcome. A Rutland CAMRA award winner.
Q❀🕙👶🚃♣👶🅿🐾❤️📶

Ryhall

Green Dragon

The Square, PE9 4HH
☎ (01780) 751999 ⊕ thegreendragonryhall.co.uk
Greene King IPA; 3 changing beers ⊞
A family-run, stone-built pub in the heart of the village.
The main building is Grade II listed and dates back to the
17th century, giving it a nice cosy feel with low ceilings
and nooks and crannies. Superb home-cooked meals are
served – pizzas are a speciality of the house, cooked in
the pizza oven and available every evening. A former
Rutland CAMRA Pub of the Year. Q❀🕸🕙👶♣🚃(202)🐾❤️

Bread is the staff of life,
but beer is life itself.
Traditional

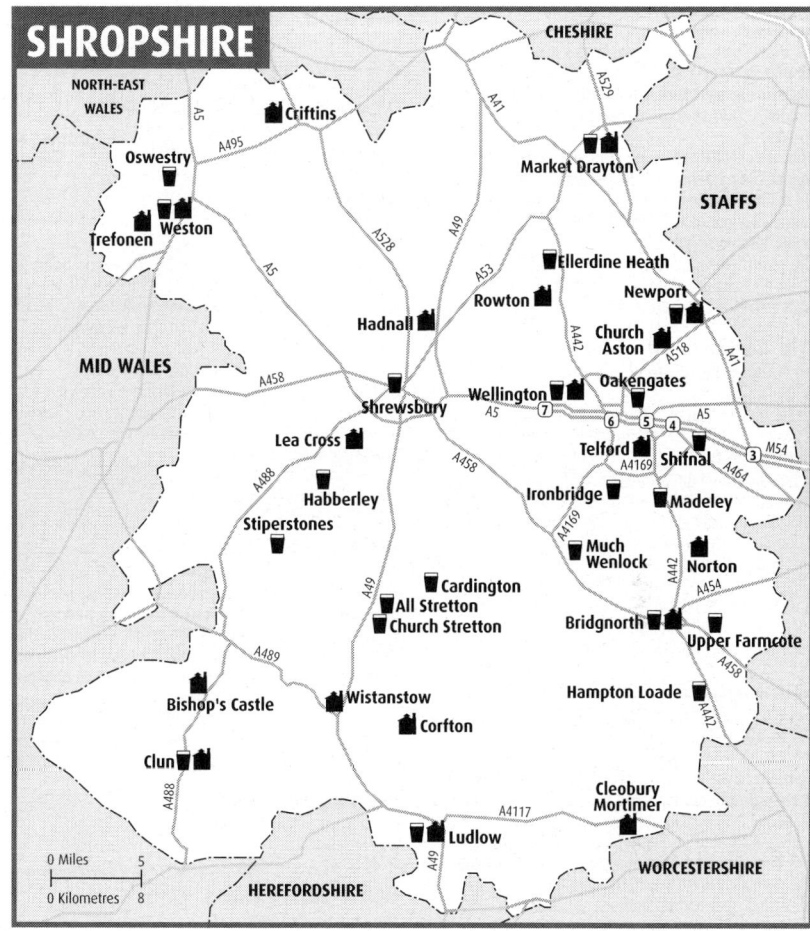

SHROPSHIRE

NORTH-EAST WALES
CHESHIRE
Criftins
Oswestry
Market Drayton
STAFFS
Trefonen Weston
Ellerdine Heath
Newport
Rowton
Hadnall
Church Aston
MID WALES
Oakengates
Shrewsbury Wellington
Lea Cross
Telford Shifnal
Habberley
Ironbridge Madeley
Stiperstones
Much Wenlock Norton
Cardington
All Stretton
Church Stretton
Bridgnorth
Upper Farmcote
Bishop's Castle Wistanstow
Hampton Loade
Corfton
Clun
Cleobury Mortimer
Ludlow
0 Miles 5
0 Kilometres 8
HEREFORDSHIRE
WORCESTERSHIRE

All Stretton

Yew Tree Inn 🄻
Shrewsbury Road, SY6 6HG
☎ (01694) 328953
Wye Valley HPA, Butty Bach; 2 changing beers (sourced locally) 🄷
A two-roomed local in a pretty village surrounded by the Shropshire Hills. The premises consist of a public bar and a separate lounge, each with its own character, but with an overall atmosphere of comfort, permanence and tradition. There are low exposed beams, log fires and masses of photographs, paintings and other ornaments adorning the walls. Traditional pub meals are offered, including a Sunday roast. There is a pleasant outdoor area by the main door. Q☎🝤🄻🌳🅿🝤(435)🌸

Bridgnorth

Black Boy 🄻
58 Cartway, WV16 4BG
☎ (01746) 769911
Hobsons Town Crier; Ludlow Blonde; 4 changing beers (sourced regionally) 🄷
Award-winning Grade II-listed alehouse, first licensed in 1790. It stands on the historic Cartway linking High Town with the quayside. Knowledgeable staff can advise on a range of ales from a selection of local brewers. Real

ciders and traditional bar snacks are also on sale. At the rear is a partially covered patio with views overlooking the River Severn. The Cliff Railway, England's oldest and steepest funicular railway, is nearby.
Q🝤🌳🏵🚋(SVR) 🍀🍺🖥🐾🛜

REAL ALE BREWERIES

All Nations 🍺 Telford
Chapel Criftins
Church Aston Church Aston
Clun 🍺 Clun
Corvedale 🍺 Corfton
Finney's Wellington
Hobsons 🍻 Cleobury Mortimer
Hop & Stagger Norton
Joule's Market Drayton
Ludlow 🍻 Ludlow
Offa's Dyke 🍺 Trefonen
Plan B Newport
Rowton Rowton/Wellington
Salopian Hadnall
Severn Valley Bridgnorth
St Annes Lea Cross
Stonehouse Weston
Three Tuns 🍺 Bishop's Castle
Wood Wistanstow

Golden Lion Ⓛ

83 High Street, High Town, WV16 4DS
☎ (01746) 762016 ⊕ goldenlionbridgnorth.co.uk
Holden's Black Country Mild, Black Country Bitter, Golden Glow, Special; 1 changing beer (sourced locally) Ⓗ
This 17th-century coaching inn has separate public and lounge bars. Extensively refurbished by Holden's, it offers a full range of the brewery's beers. Pictures on the walls of the two lounge bars reveal the history of the pub. The public bar has a TV and is the venue for sports teams. At the rear there is a covered smoking area leading to a patio drinking area. B&B accommodation is available.
Q ⛬ ❀ ♨ ⏜ ⇌ (SVR) ♣ ♠ P 🚲 ❀ 🛜

Old Castle Ⓛ ✅

10/11 West Castle Street, WV16 4AB (between SVR and town centre)
☎ (01746) 711420 ⊕ oldcastlebridgnorth.co.uk
Hobsons Town Crier; Sharp's Doom Bar; Wye Valley Butty Bach, HPA Ⓗ
A popular pub dating from the 1600s, just a short walk from the Severn Valley Railway. The bar in the middle has four handpumps offering local and regional ales. Good-quality meals are served lunchtime and evening in the front bar and the recently refurbished conservatory. Outside, the garden is full of flowers during the spring and summer months and has lovely views – an ideal spot for drinking and dining on a sunny day.
⛬ ❀ ⏜ ⇌ (SVR) 🚲 (436,890) ❀ 🛜

Railwayman's Arms Ⓛ ✅

Severn Valley Railway Station, Hollybush Road, WV16 5DT (follow signs for SVR)
☎ (01746) 760920 ⊕ svr.co.uk
Bathams Best Bitter; Hobsons Mild, Best, Town Crier; 4 changing beers (sourced locally; often Bewdley) Ⓗ
A unique and popular pub owned by the Severn Valley Railway. Located on Platform 1 at Bridgnorth station, it has been licensed since 1861 and is full of railway memorabilia. There are 10 handpumps, nine serving real ales from near and far and one for real cider. The platform drinking area is a great place to soak up the atmosphere of a steam railway. It gets busy at weekends and holidays. Cobs and pork pies are usually available.
Q ⛬ ❀ ♿ ⇌ (SVR) ♠ P 🚲 (9,436) ❀ 🛜

Shakespeare Inn Ⓛ

West Castle Street, WV16 4AD
☎ (01746) 768863 ⊕ theshakespearebrid.wixsite.com/website-1
Joule's Pure Blonde Ⓗ**, Pale Ale** Ⓗ/ℙ**, Slumbering Monk; 2 changing beers (sourced regionally; often Joule's)** Ⓗ
The pub is divided by a central bar serving both sides: the bar area has cosy corners and snugs warmed by a log-burner fire, while the smaller lounge, also with a log-burning stove, has French doors opening onto a covered courtyard. Off this is a function room decorated with reclaimed oak panelling. Up to four beers are on tap from Joule's plus a guest ale and a real cider. Home-cooked food is served every day. Q ⛬ ❀ 🕭 ♿ ⇌ ♣ ♠ 🚲 ❀ 🛜

White Lion Ⓛ

3 West Castle Street, WV16 4AB (between town centre and SVR)
☎ (01746) 763962 ⊕ hopandstaggerbrewery.co.uk
Hop & Stagger Shropshire Pale Ale, Golden Wander, Beckbury Bitter, Bridgnorth Porter; 3 changing beers (sourced regionally) Ⓗ
An 18th-century inn with an open fire, large beer garden and accommodation. The home of the Hop and Stagger Brewery, it has eight handpumps serving the pub's own

beers plus local and national brews. Home-made Scotch eggs and a wide range of hot and cold bar snacks are on offer all day. The pub is a venue for clubs, quizzes and musical nights. Dogs are welcome on leads.
Q ⛬ ❀ ♨ ♿ ⏜ ⇌ (SVR) ♣ ♠ 🚲 (436,890) ❀ 🛜

Cardington

Royal Oak

SY6 7JZ
☎ (01694) 771266 ⊕ at-the-oak.com
Ludlow Best; Sharp's Doom Bar; 2 changing beers Ⓗ
The Royal Oak, dating back to the 15th century, is reputedly Shropshire's oldest continually licensed pub, and is the archetypal country inn. The single room is multi-functional, with a bar, lounge and dining area, and has a relaxed ambience. It is low-beamed and dominated by a large inglenook fireplace which provides a home for various interesting artefacts. A good choice of beers includes a mix of local and regional brews.
Q ❀ 🕭 ▲ ♠ P 🚲 (540) ❀ 🛜

Church Stretton

Old Coppers Malt House

2 Shrewsbury Road, SY6 6DU
☎ (01694) 723336 ⊕ theoldcoppersmalthouse.co.uk
Draught Bass; Rat White Rat; 4 changing beers Ⓗ
Revitalised inn occupying a large corner building in the centre of town offering fine ales and good food. It has been freshly decorated while retaining a traditional pub feel. The beer selection changes frequently and includes a full range of styles. A Randall device has been incorporated into one pump, passing a base beer through additional dry hopping to add to the flavour. The pub has three rooms, one kept predominantly for dining.
⛬ ❀ 🕭 ⇌ ♠ 🚲 (435) ❀ 🛜

Clun

White Horse Inn Ⓛ ✅

The Square, SY7 8JA
☎ (01588) 640305 ⊕ whi-clun.co.uk
Clun Loophole, Clun Pale Ale, Citadel; Hobsons Best; Wye Valley Butty Bach; 2 changing beers (often Salopian) Ⓗ
Sixteenth-century inn and posthouse standing in the old market square, at the centre of a timeless town described by AE Housman as one of the quietest places under the sun. Inside is an L-shaped bar with low beams and adjoining dining room, which has been extended into the property next door, serving excellent, reasonably priced food. The pub is linked to the Clun Brewery and stocks its beers. Rotating real ciders are available. Outside is a secluded garden. Jam nights are held once a month. ⛬ ❀ ♨ 🕭 ▲ ♣ ♠ 🚲 ❀ 🛜

Ellerdine Heath

Royal Oak Ⓛ ✅

Hazles Road, TF6 6RL (midway between A442 and A53)
SJ603226
☎ (01939) 250300
Hobsons Best; Rowton Bitter; Wye Valley HPA; 3 changing beers (sourced locally; often Rowton, Salopian) Ⓗ
A long-standing Guide entry, known locally as the Tiddly. The heart of the local rural community, it is used by young farmers, shooting parties and French language classes. It has a pool table, dartboard, real fires in both main rooms, a smoking shed and a marquee used from Easter to October. Food is served in the dining room –

lunchtimes weekends only, evenings Wednesday to Sunday. A real gem, well worth the short detour from the main roads. Q❄☆❶◐↺Å♣♠P♨♥

Habberley

Mytton Arms L

SY5 0TP
☎ (01743) 792490
Hobsons Best; Three Tuns XXX; 2 changing beers (often Hobsons, Joule's) H
Situated in a small village on the edge of the South Shropshire Hills, somewhat off the beaten track, this popular pub is worth seeking out. There are four low-beamed rooms and a friendly rustic atmosphere – beer and conversation predominate. Outside are seats to the front and a paved area with a vine-covered pergola to the side. A well-known local character and pub regular features on the inn sign. The South Shropshire Hills shuttle bus provides transport in summer. Q☆♣♠P🚲♥

Hampton Loade

Unicorn Inn

WV16 6BN (1½ miles off B4555 at Chelmarsh)
☎ (01746) 861515 ⊕ unicornhamptonloade.co.uk
4 changing beers (sourced locally) H
A riverside pub featuring a large bar area with open fire, plus a separate dining room. The elevated patios with tables and umbrellas provide superb views towards the river and surrounding countryside. Four local real ales are served. Camping, B&B and self-catering accommodation are available. Hampton Loade station on the famous Severn Valley Railway is a short stroll from the pub and passing steam trains can often be heard.
☎☆🛏◐↺Å≩(SVR) ♣P♨♥

Ludlow

Charlton Arms

Ludford Bridge, SY8 1PJ
☎ (01584) 872813 ⊕ thecharltonarms.co.uk
Hobsons Best; Ludlow Gold, Stairway; Wye Valley Butty Bach; 1 changing beer (often Hobsons, Ludlow) H
This fine building overlooks the River Teme and is just across the historic Ludford Bridge, up towards Ludlow's last remaining fortified gate and the town centre. It has an attractive bar and a spacious lounge leading to a separate dining room with a terrace. The impressive function suite and roof bar offer fine views across the river towards the town. Accommodation is in 10 en-suite rooms. Dogs are allowed in the bar.
Q☎☆🛏◐↺P♥

Ludlow Brewing Co L

Station Drive, SY8 2PQ
☎ (01584) 873291 ⊕ theludlowbrewingcompany.co.uk
Ludlow Best, Blonde, Gold, Black Knight, Boiling Well, Stairway H
The Railway Shed is the brewery tap and visitor centre for the Ludlow Brewing Company. As the name suggests, the building was once a depot for railway goods. An imaginative conversion, it is built on two levels, with two huge mash tuns on the upper level, and comfortable seating and tables. On the ground floor there are hand-crafted timber tables and benches, together with a shop. Brewery visits are welcome and the centre is available for hire. Occasional beer festivals and events are hosted.
Q☎☆◐↺≩♠P🚲♥

Queen's L

113 Lower Galdeford, SY8 1RU (just off town centre, opp Co-op)
☎ (01584) 879177 ⊕ thequeensludlow.com
Hobsons Best; Ludlow Gold; Wye Valley Butty Bach; 1 changing beer (sourced locally; often Hobsons, Ludlow) H
Named after Queen Victoria, this is a popular pub and café bar with a decent range of local ales. Look out for the guest beer offered at a competitive price. The light and airy L-shaped bar has three distinct areas, with dining down a short flight of steps. Bar meals are available. The large enclosed patio garden has views toward Ludford. The monthly quiz is always well attended. ☆🛏◐↺♣🚲♥

Rose & Crown

8 Church Street, SY8 1AP
☎ (01584) 875726 ⊕ roseandcrowninnludlow.co.uk
Joule's Old No.6, Pale Ale, Pure Blonde, Slumbering Monk; 2 changing beers (often Hobsons, Hop Back) H
Hidden away in a courtyard, the Rose & Crown is probably Ludlow's oldest inn, possibly 12th century. Recent refurbishment has created a much larger pub with exposed beams and fireplace. The Sun Room is open to the elements on one side and there is a garden area. A private room is available upstairs for small groups. Food is good honest pub grub, such as bangers and mash or bubble and squeak. There is a carvery on Sunday. ☎☆◐↺♠🚲♥

Market Drayton

Hippodrome L ✓

Queen Street, TF9 1PS
☎ (01630) 650820
Greene King Abbot; Ruddles Best Bitter; 3 changing beers (sourced locally; often Lymestone, Slater's, Titanic) H
Originally Market Drayton's first cinema, which closed in 1966 having opened its doors to the public in 1927. After spells as a bingo hall and supermarket the pub was opened by Wetherspoon's in 2007, retaining some unique features of the original building. The usual food fayre is served but what makes this pub different is that it actively supports local breweries, regularly showcased on the bar. ☎☆◐↺♠🚲♥

Red Lion L

Great Hales Street, TF9 1JP
☎ (01630) 652602
Joule's Pure Blonde, Pale Ale, Slumbering Monk; 1 changing beer (sourced locally; often Joule's) H
A previous winner of the CAMRA Best Refurbishment award, this Joule's brewery tap is a former coaching inn built in 1623. Its unique features include the Mouse Room – a Robert Thompson-inspired function room featuring carved mice – and an illuminated well in the main bar. Log fires and oak beams create a comfortable atmosphere. Locally sourced food features on an extensive menu along with the Joule's range of beers produced in the adjacent brewery.
Q☎☆◐↺♠P🚲(64,164) ♥♥

Sandbrook Vaults L

4 Shropshire Street, TF9 3BY
☎ (01630) 478405
Joule's Pure Blonde, Pale Ale, Slumbering Monk; 1 changing beer (sourced locally; often Joule's) H
You are guaranteed a warm welcome at this Joule's pub, originally built in 1653. It has a familiar easy-on-the-eye Joule's interior and serves well-kept ales from the

brewery close by. The pub hosts high-quality live acoustic music nights on Thursday and Sunday featuring regional bands, and quiz nights in aid of charity.
❀♿♣🚌(64,164) 🐾📶

William Chester 🄻

20 Shropshire Street, TF9 3BY
☎ (01630) 652315
4 changing beers (sourced locally; often Facer's, Salopian, Slater's) 🄷
A small, comfortable bar in the centre of town offering three local beers on handpull, including a regular Slater's ale, as well as a cider. With a thoughtfully furnished interior, this pub is full of character and has a cosy atmosphere. Outside, there is a bright, terraced courtyard at the rear open until 10pm, which is a suntrap in the summer months. Q🐴❀♿♣🍎🚌(64,164)📶

Much Wenlock

George & Dragon 🄻

2 High Street, TF13 6AA
☎ (01952) 727009 🌐 thebestpubintheworld.com
Greene King Abbot; Hobsons Town Crier; Wye Valley HPA; 2 changing beers (sourced nationally) 🄷
Historic pub centrally located in this beautiful small market town and close to places of great interest like Wenlock Priory. Locals and visitors are all made welcome. The front bar has timber-backed settles, an original quarry-tiled floor and two open fireplaces. Whisky water jugs hang from the original beams, and interesting photographs are on the walls. The rear bar has an intimate atmosphere. A wide variety of food is served, with special offers most days (no food Mon or Sun eve). Dogs are welcome in the front bar.
Q🐴◐♿▲♣🚌(18,436) 🐾📶

Newport

New Inn 🄻

2 Stafford Road, TF10 7LX
☎ (01952) 812295 🌐 thenewinnnewport.co.uk
Joule's Pure Blonde, Pale Ale, Slumbering Monk; 2 changing beers (sourced locally; often Joule's, Ludlow, Wood) 🄷
Originally a coaching inn dating from 1792, the building has been extended and refurbished by Joule's and retains some old features. There is a Yorkist fireplace in the snug area plus a central wood-burner for winter comfort. The New Inn is friendly and lively, with helpful staff and good food including vegetarian options. Two beer festivals are held each year in the extensive garden. Live music plays every Sunday from 6pm. Wheelchair access is via the Stafford Road entrance.
Q🐴❀◐♿♣🍎🚌(5,519) 🐾📶

Oswestry

Bailey Head 🄻

Bailey Head, SY11 1PZ (in Market Square opp Guildhall)
☎ (01691) 570418 🌐 baileyhead.co.uk
6 changing beers (sourced nationally; often Salopian) 🄷
Award-winning free house in the market square, near the old castle. Seven constantly changing real ales, three KeyKeg beers and draught cider are on offer. Beers are sourced locally, regionally and nationally, usually from microbreweries, and served in thirds on request. Locally produced, traditional food is available, including vegan options. Events include Meet the Brewer and music and quiz nights. The market car park is close by.
🐴♿♣🍎▯🚌🐾📶

Black Lion 🄻

Salop Road, SY11 2RJ (500yds S of town centre on B4579)
☎ (01691) 652745
Salopian Oracle; 4 changing beers (sourced locally; often Hobsons, Salopian, Wood) 🄷
Just inside the town's conservation area, this establishment is a true community pub and has a warm and friendly atmosphere. It is home to sports teams and social groups, with plenty of TVs for sports fans and tasting boards for beer lovers. The central bar divides the pub into a comfortable lounge at the front and public bar at the rear. Well-kept ales from various local and regional brewers can be enjoyed. Q🐴❀♣🍎P🚌🐾📶

Shifnal

Anvil Inn 🄻

22 Aston Road, TF11 8DU
☎ (01952) 462686
Black Country Bradley's Finest Golden, Pig on the Wall, Fireside; 5 changing beers (sourced regionally) 🄷
Reopened in 2018 after extensive refurbishment by Black Country Ales, and thoroughly brought up to date, including accessible toilets. The interior has been expanded, but the original fireplace remains, with coal fires in winter. The dartboard is in an enclosed booth. The bar has 10 handpulls, three devoted to Black Country Ales, five for guests and two for real cider. Generous bar snacks are available. Dogs are welcome, and children until 7pm. The shortest route to and from the railway station is via the station car park. Q❀♿⇌♣🍎P🚌🐾📶

Plough Inn 🄻

26 Broadway, TF11 8AZ
☎ (01952) 463118 🌐 theploughinnshifnal.co.uk
Hobsons Mild, Best; 6 changing beers (sourced regionally; often Bathams, Sarah Hughes, Three Tuns) 🄷
Traditional, family-run free house dating back to the 17th century, with exposed beams and tiled floors. Ten handpulls offer an array of well-kept ales, always including one strong and one dark beer, as well as two draught ciders. Hearty home-cooked meals are served, with a popular roast on Sunday. The huge beer garden is a suntrap in the summer months, and a large function room is available to hire. The Wednesday night quiz is a must. Dogs are allowed in the garden.
Q🐴❀◐⇌♣🍎🚌🐾📶

Shrewsbury

Abbey 🄻 ✔

83 Monkmoor Road, Monkmoor, SY2 5AZ
☎ (01743) 236788
Bombardier; Sharp's Doom Bar; 6 changing beers 🄷
A large pub with several alcoves and multiple fireplaces, plus a beer garden with heated and covered areas. The publican is an ale enthusiast, running frequent Meet the Brewer sessions and several beer festivals a year. In between, he has expanded the range of guest ales and real ciders. Food is served every night. There are regular community events including quizzes and occasional live music. 🐴❀◐♿♣🍎P🚌(1)📶

Admiral Benbow 🄻

24 Swan Hill, SY1 1NF (just off Main Square)
☎ (01743) 244423
Ludlow Gold; 5 changing beers (sourced locally; often Hobsons, Salopian, Wye Valley) 🄷

Spacious free house serving a range of Shropshire and Herefordshire beers plus a selection of ciders from Rosie's including Black Bart and Wicked Wasp. A good choice of Belgian, American and other foreign beers is also offered. A small room off the bar can be used for private functions, and there is a seating and smoking area outside at the rear. Children are not permitted. The Admiral was a notorious 17th-century naval officer born in Shrewsbury. Q✿➘≠♣●❂❖

Anchor ◍
137 Frankwell, SY3 8JX
☎ (01743) 537169
Brains Rev James; Castle Rock Harvest Pale; Hobsons Town Crier; Wye Valley Butty Bach Ⓗ
Once owned by Wem Brewery, also by Wrekin Brewery of Wellington, the Anchor is a traditional one-roomed pub conveniently placed opposite Theatre Severn. There is a small but secluded smoking area to the rear. Wheelchair access is limited, but a ramp can be provided on request. A real cider is often available from the cellar. ☺✿◑◔≠♣●❂❀

Coach & Horses Ⓛ
23 Swan Hill, SY1 1NF
☎ (01743) 365661 ⊕ coachswanhill.co.uk
Salopian Shropshire Gold, Oracle; Stonehouse Station Bitter; 3 changing beers Ⓗ
Set in a quiet street off the main shopping area, the pub is a peaceful haven in which to enjoy great LocAle beers, with magnificent floral displays in summer. Victorian in style, it has a wood-panelled bar, a small side snug area and a large lounge where meals are served lunchtimes and evenings. Bar snacks are also available at lunchtimes. Cheddar Valley or Sweeney Mountain cider is dispensed on handpull. Q◑◔&≠♣●❂❖❀

Cross Foxes
27 Longden Coleham, SY3 7DE (close to River Severn in suburb of Longden Coleham)
☎ (01743) 355050
Draught Bass; Salopian Shropshire Gold; Three Tuns XXX; Wood Shropshire Lad Ⓗ
The pub has been a free house since its purchase from Mitchells & Butlers in the late 1980s, and run by the same family since 1985. It has one large, L-shaped room, with the bar and major drinking area on the large stroke, the smaller stroke occupied by the darts and another drinking area. The main part has an efficient wood-burner and the walls are adorned with sports trophies and a fine Bass mirror. Q&♣●❖

Loggerheads ★ Ⓛ ◍
1 Church Street, SY1 1UG
☎ (01743) 362398
Brakspear Oxford Gold; Marston's EPA, Pedigree; 2 changing beers (sourced nationally) Ⓗ
This 18th-century, Grade II-listed pub in the town centre has a nationally important historic interior, with a small bar, servery and three other rooms. The bar to the left is served from a hatch and was Gents Only until 1975. The rear room, served from the same hatch, has portraits of Shropshire poets. It hosts regular folk and acoustic music events. Q≠●❖❀

Montgomery's Tower Ⓛ ◍
Lower Claremont Bank, SY1 1RT
☎ (01743) 239080
Greene King IPA; Salopian Shropshire Gold; Wood Shropshire Lad; 4 changing beers (often Sharp's, Slater's) Ⓗ
Close to the Quarry Park and handy for Theatre Severn, this Lloyds No.1 offers a choice of two bars. To the left is

a large open area rich in natural light, with a smoking area to the rear. The bar to the right provides quieter surroundings and subdued lighting, except on Friday and Saturday when there is a DJ. The walls display prints illustrating local history and famous Salopians. ☺✿◑◔&≠●❂❖

Nags Head Ⓛ ◍
22 Wyle Cop, SY1 1XB
☎ (01743) 362455
Hobsons Best; Timothy Taylor Landlord; Wye Valley HPA; 2 changing beers (often Titanic) Ⓗ
A Grade II-listed, timber-framed building situated on the historic Wyle Cop. Its main architectural features are best appreciated externally – in particular the upper-storey jettying and, in the beer garden to the rear, the timber remnants of a 14th-century hall house including a screened passage which provided protection from draughts (and now offers shelter for smokers). The old-style interior has remained unaltered for many years. The pub is said to be haunted and features on the Shrewsbury Ghost Trail. ✿≠♣❀

Prince of Wales Ⓛ
30 Bynner Street, Belle Vue, SY3 7NZ
☎ (01743) 343301 ⊕ theprince.pub
Hobsons Mild, Twisted Spire; Salopian Golden Thread; St Austell Tribute; Wainwright; 1 changing beer (sourced locally; often Rowton, Stonehouse, Wood) Ⓗ
Welcoming two-roomed community pub with a heated smoking shelter and a large suntrap deck adjoining a bowling green overlooked by a 19th-century maltings. Darts, dominoes and bowls teams abound. Beer festivals take place in February and May. Shrewsbury Town FC memorabilia adorn the building, with some of the seating from the old Gay Meadow ground skirting the bowling green. Westons Rosie's Pig is on handpull. CAMRA West Midlands Regional Pub of the Year 2019. Q☺✿&♣●P❂❀

Salopian Bar Ⓛ ◍
Smithfield Road, SY1 1PW
☎ (01743) 351505
5 changing beers Ⓗ
A two-room pub, popular with all age groups, that was expanded and refurbished following flooding in 2020. The bar's management strives to vary the beer, cider and perry range to satisfy public demand. Regular cider and perry are provided by Westons and Thatchers, and an interesting and increasing range of bottled beers, including gluten-free ones, is also available. Largescreen TVs show coverage of major sporting events. Live music features on Friday evening. &≠●❂❀❖

Tap & Can
13 Castle Gates, SY1 2AB
☎ 07837 490495
4 changing beers Ⓗ
Opened in 2019, this single-room bar near the town railway station has its counter at the far end. Four handpumps offer a changing range of real ales, plus KeyKeg and keg craft beers. Cans are served from vast fridges near the bar, available to drink here or take away. The rear wall of the Gents is the exposed castle foundations and is over 900 years old. ≠●❂❀

Three Fishes Ⓛ
4 Fish Street, SY1 1UR
☎ (01743) 344793
Ludlow Best; Timothy Taylor Boltmaker; 3 changing beers (often Oakham, Salopian, Stonehouse) Ⓗ
Fifteenth-century building standing in the shadow of two churches, St Alkmund's and St Julian's, within the maze

of streets and passageways in the town's medieval quarter. Freshly prepared food is served lunchtimes and early evenings Monday to Saturday. The pub offers a range of up to five local and national ales, usually including some dark beers, and a choice of real ciders and perries. Although the lease has recently changed hands (to an active CAMRA member), cellar management has not. Q◑❀✦♣●🖵❄🛜

Woodman ⬭

32 Coton Hill, SY1 2DZ
☎ (01743) 351007
Salopian Shropshire Gold; Wye Valley Butty Bach; 3 changing beers (sourced regionally; often Abbeydale, Ossett) ⊞

Part-brick and part-timbered black and white corner pub, originally built in the 1800s, destroyed by fire in 1923, and rebuilt in 1925. The building is reputedly haunted by the ex-landlady who died in the fire. The wonderful oak-panelled lounge has two real log fires and traditional settles, and the separate bar has the original stone-tiled flooring, wooden seating, fire and leaded windows. The courtyard has a heated smoking area and seating. The bar specialises in pale, hoppy beers.
Q♿❀✦❀♣●🖵❄🛜

Stiperstones

Stiperstones Inn

SY5 0LZ
☎ (01743) 791327 ⊕ stiperstonesinn.co.uk
Three Tuns XXX; 1 changing beer (often Rowton, Stonehouse) ⊞

A delightful and homely pub tucked away under the Stiperstones range. The public bar is rather plain but the little lounge has its own charm. There are also two separate dining rooms. Whinberries – the local delicacy that grow wild in the area – are used here to make pies, home-made jam and as a gin flavouring. The pub is on the route of the Shropshire Hills shuttle bus during the summer months and welcomes walkers and their canine companions. ♿❀❤◑♿♣P🖵(552)❄🛜

Telford: Ironbridge

Coracle Micropub & Beer Shop

27 High Street, TF8 7AD
☎ (01952) 432664
5 changing beers (sourced nationally; often Salopian, Tiny Rebel) ⊞/🅐

Opened in 2018 by two beer enthusiasts, this is a quiet micropub with friendly and knowledgeable staff. The main room is semi-divided, creating two separate drinking areas and enhancing the cosy ambience. The well-stocked fridge contains up to 80 bottled and canned beers, listed on a beer menu, with more in the cellar. A good selection of locally sourced bar snacks is available, including a free cheeseboard on Sunday. Children are welcome until 7pm. The pub is central to Ironbridge, overlooking England's last coracle shed.
Q♿✦♣●🖵❄🛜

Telford: Madeley

All Nations ⬭

20 Coalport Road, TF7 5DP (signed off Legges Way, opp Blists Hill Museum)
☎ (01952) 585747

> I never drink water. I'm afraid it will become habit-forming. **W C Fields**

House beer (by All Nations); 2 changing beers (sourced regionally; often Hobsons, Ludlow) ⊞
Regulars and visitors love this pub for its cosy interior and friendliness. The historic 1852 brewhouse, an icon of home-brewing history, is still working at the back of the building. Four real ales are available, including the pub's own beers, plus cider or perry. Freshly prepared bar snacks are on offer – bacon and brie, black pudding and cheese baps are particular favourites. Visitors can browse books and newspapers by the fire. The TV is in use only for international Rugby Union matches. Monday is quiz night, and live bands play in the summer.
Q♿❀✦Å●P❄🛜

Foresters Arms

High Street, TF7 5AS
☎ 07889 843755
5 changing beers (sourced regionally; often Plan B) ⊞

Welcoming pub on the Halesfield side of Madeley, now under the Plan B Brewery banner. There are two rooms on different levels, offering three changing Plan B beers plus two guests. A range of bar snacks is available. Tuesday is poker night. There is wheelchair access through the top and lower bar, but toilet access is restricted. The pub has a large car park off Legges Way, the road to Blists Hill Museum. ♿❀♿♣●P🖵❄🛜

Telford: Oakengates

Crown Inn ⬭ ✅

Market Street, TF2 6EA
☎ (01952) 610888 ⊕ crown.oakengates.net
Hobsons Twisted Spire, Best; 10 changing beers (sourced nationally; often Backyard, Beartown, Rudgate) ⊞

Cosy, traditional, three-room town pub with real coal fires in the front and rear bars, close to Oakengates station. It has 14 cooled handpulls – with more for beer festivals in May and October, where some 18,000 beers have featured since 1995 – plus a large range of interesting continental bottled beers. There is a suntrap courtyard with wheelchair access, and a large municipal car park to the rear. The Crown hosts a comedy club, live music and traditional pub quizzes.
Q♿❀♿✦♣●P🖵❄🛜

Old Fighting Cocks ⬭

48 Market Street, TF2 6DU
☎ (01952) 615607
Everards Tiger; Rowton Ironbridge Gold, Area 51; 6 changing beers (sourced regionally) ⊞

Popular family-run Rowton Brewery pub with 12 handpulls, four for the brewery's own beers, plus five changing ales and three ciders. The building retains many period features including stained glass and a horse-feeding hatch in the accessible toilet. As well as the two main rooms the pub has a rear room and a snug. The large outside area has a covered space. Bar snacks are available. There are a number of car parks nearby.
Q♿❀♣●🖵❄🛜

Station Hotel ⬭

42 Market Street, TF2 6DU
☎ (01952) 612949
Bathams Best Bitter; 8 changing beers (sourced nationally; often Abbeydale, Pictish) ⊞

This multi-roomed local has been in the Guide for many years. It specialises in beers from Yorkshire, though local ales do appear now and then. Home-made rolls, pies and cheeses are available, and a curry night is held on Wednesday. An open fire warms the bar. The floor is level throughout and give easy wheelchair access to modern toilets. Three beer festivals are held a year – over the May and August bank holidays and in December. Outside is a patio and a covered and heated smoking area. Q♿🅿️♨️🚆🏧🚪🐾🛏️🛜

Telford: Wellington

Pheasant Inn 🅛

54 Market Street, TF1 1DT
☎ (01952) 260683

Everards Tiger; Rowton Ironbridge Gold; 5 changing beers (sourced nationally; often Finney's, Rowton) Ⓗ
Family-run Rowton Brewery tap, near the historic market. It has nine handpulls: three for Rowton's own beers, four for changing ales usually including a dark brew, and two for ciders. The large beer garden next to the brewery has a covered area. Home-made food is served Monday to Saturday during the day, with bar snacks at any time. A popular cheese night is held on the last Tuesday of the month. Q🌳🐕🏧🅿️🚆♿🐾🛏️🛜

William Withering 🅛 ✅

43-45 New Street, TF1 1LU
☎ (01952) 642800

Greene King Abbot; Ruddles Best Bitter; Sharp's Doom Bar; 3 changing beers (sourced nationally) Ⓗ
Named after a local physician who is best remembered for discovering and developing the drug Digitalis. This pub is a large single open-plan room with an interior styled as an 18th-century study. The regular beers are joined by three changing ales from local, regional and national breweries, with a focus on brews from the local area. Good-value food is served and the pub is busy at Saturday lunchtime with shoppers enjoying brunch. 🐕🐾🏧♿🚆🅿️🛜

Upper Farmcote

Lion o' Morfe 🅛

Upper Farmcote, WV15 5PS (½ mile from A458 signpost Claverley) SO770919
☎ (01746) 389935

Enville Ale; Hobsons Town Crier; Wye Valley HPA; 2 changing beers (sourced locally; often Bewdley, Ludlow, Three Tuns) Ⓗ
A Georgian farmhouse that became a pub in the early 1850s. After prolonged closure it has been extensively refurbished and the conservatory rebuilt. The doorway opens into the main bar with an open fire. At the rear is a snug in the former kitchen. To the left, a modern style lounge leads to a conservatory, which opens to a garden with picnic seating. Five ales and a local farm cider are on tap. Meals are served daily (no food Sun eve). Q🌳🐾🏧🅿️🛏️♿🐾🛏️

Weston

Stonehouse Brewery 🅛

Stonehouse, Weston Road, SY10 9ES (just off A483 Oswestry bypass)
☎ (01691) 676457 🌐 stonehousebrewery.co.uk

Stonehouse Sunlander, Station Bitter, Off the Rails; 1 changing beer Ⓗ
The family-run Stonehouse Brewery bar and shop is part of the brewery and is next to the preserved Cambrian Railway. The building has a pleasant rustic style and serves only Stonehouse products – at least four beers plus Sweeney Mountain Cider and Henstone spirits (whisky, gin, applejack, vodka and, sometimes, rum) distilled on-site. Bottles, gift packs and 'fill your own' are available. Food is served Wednesday to Sunday. Brewery tours are by appointment. Q🌳🐾🏧♿♣🐾🅿️🚆🛏️🛜

Coach & Horses, Shrewsbury (Photo: Reading Tom/Flickr CC BY 2.0)

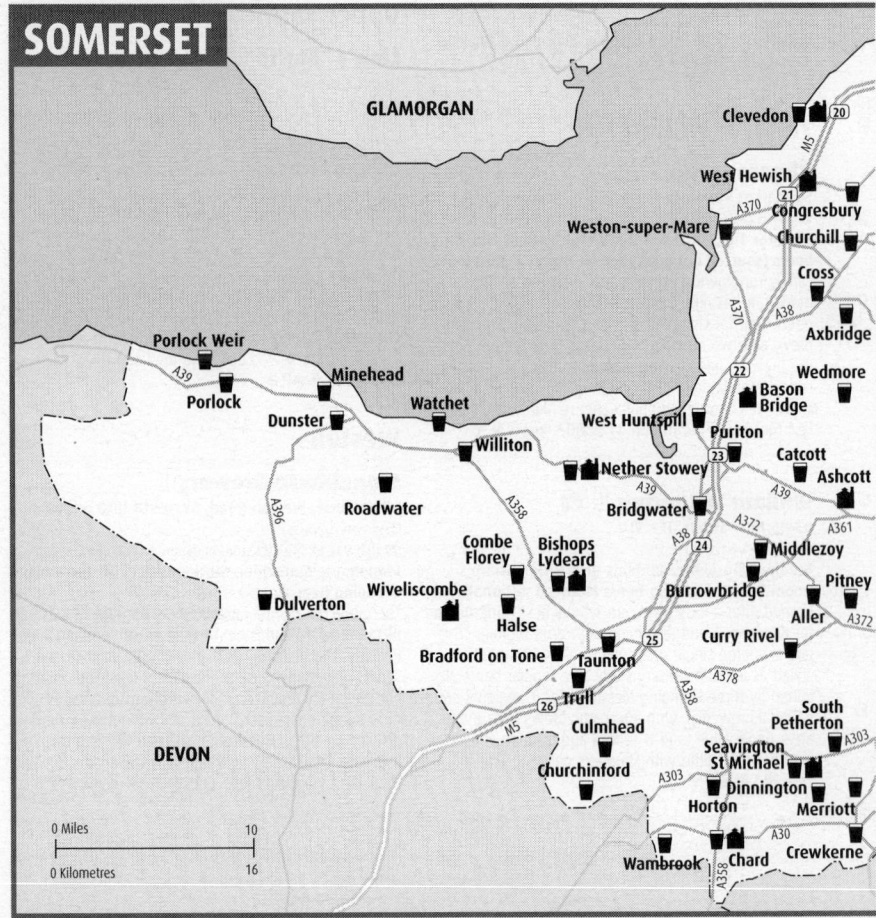

SOMERSET

GLAMORGAN

Clevedon

West Hewish

Weston-super-Mare

Congresbury

Churchill

Cross

Axbridge

Wedmore

Porlock Weir

Minehead

Watchet

West Huntspill

Bason Bridge

Puriton

Catcott

Ashcott

Porlock

Dunster

Williton

Nether Stowey

Bridgwater

Roadwater

Combe Florey

Bishops Lydeard

Middlezoy

Pitney

Dulverton

Wiveliscombe

Burrowbridge

Aller

Halse

Curry Rivel

Bradford on Tone

Taunton

Trull

South Petherton

Culmhead

Churchinford

Seavington St Michael

Dinnington

Merriott

Horton

Wambrook

Chard

Crewkerne

DEVON

0 Miles 10

0 Kilometres 16

Aller

Old Pound Inn

1 High Street, TA10 0RA (centre of village)
☎ (01458) 250469 🌐 oldpoundinn.com
Butcombe Original; Teignworthy Reel Ale; 1 changing beer (sourced regionally; often Exmoor, Otter) Ⓗ
This lovely 16th-century inn stands on the ground of the old village pound. A varying selection of three regional ales and a local cider is on handpump. A wonderful open Dutch fire is a feature in the centre of the bar. There is a separate restaurant/function room, a public lounge and a delightful snug. Excellent food, including a Sunday carvery, is served in the bar or restaurant.
ॐ❀ॐ◑🐾🅿🚆(16) 🌸🛜

Axbridge

Lamb ⊘

The Square, BS26 2AP
☎ (01934) 732253
Butcombe Original; 2 changing beers (sourced nationally; often Butcombe) Ⓗ
Lovely Butcombe-owned Grade II-listed coaching house in the village square. Inside is a large low-beamed bar area with several smaller, quieter areas leading off it, where traditional pub games can be played. Outside drinking spaces are to the front, as well as to the rear via the courtyard. Real cider is sold, and there is an

interesting food menu, including bar snacks. Directly opposite is the National Trust's medieval King John's Hunting Lodge, where Hanging Judge Jeffreys held court.
Q ॐ❀ॐ◑🐾🅿🚆(26,126) 🌸🛜

Batcombe

Three Horseshoes Inn

BA4 6HE (off Back Lane) ST69023908
☎ (01749) 850359
Butcombe Original; 3 changing beers Ⓗ
A 400-year-old country pub which has a spacious bar with an inglenook fireplace and beamed ceiling, a stunning dining room with a vaulted ceiling and a lawned garden overlooked by the church tower. Food is from suppliers in the area. Open to all, the pub welcomes drinkers, foodies, walkers, children (with colouring books and games, to keep them entertained) and dogs. Local cider is from Rich's. Q ॐ❀ॐ◑🐾🅿

Bath

Bath Brew House

14 James Street West, BA1 2BX
☎ (01225) 805609 🌐 thebathbrewhouse.com
Bath Brew House Gladiator, Carpe Noctem, Emperor; 3 changing beers (sourced regionally; often Bath Brew House, Bristol Beer Factory, Siren) Ⓗ

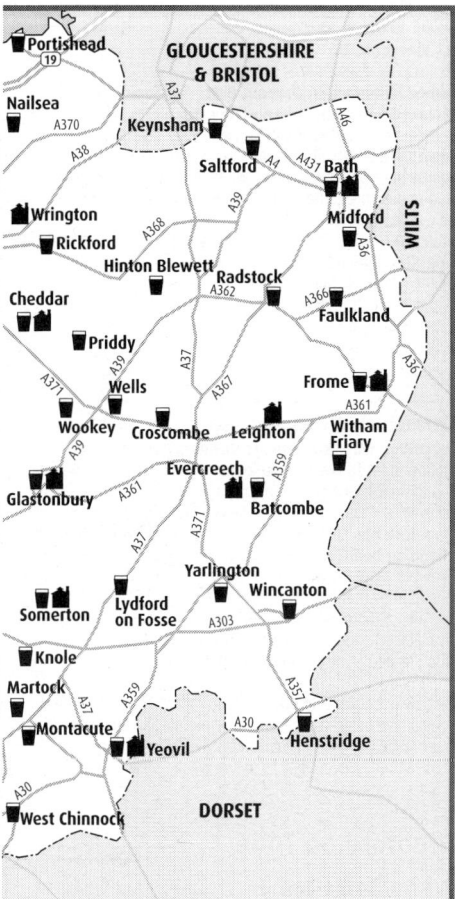

Coeur de Lion ✔

17 Northumberland Place, BA1 5AR
☎ (01225) 463568 ⊕ coeur-de-lion.co.uk
Abbey Bath Best, Bath Pale Ale; 2 changing beers (sourced nationally; often Abbey) Ⓗ
This pub in a passageway opposite the Guildhall in the centre of town claims to be the smallest in Bath. With just four tables in the small bar this may well be true. Traditional pub food is served at lunchtime. Seating capacity is increased in summer by placing tables outside. There is also an upstairs room used mainly for food. The building's most unique feature is the fine stained-glass window that forms the frontage. One guest beer is always from Abbey. Q ⠶ ⊛ ◑ ➜ (Spa) ♣ ● ⊟ ⠶ ⬳

Cross Keys ✔

Midford Road, Combe Down, BA2 5RZ
☎ (01225) 849180 ⊕ crosskeysbath.co.uk
Butcombe Original; Exmoor Ale; 2 changing beers (sourced locally) Ⓗ
A historic inn dating from 1718 on the southern outskirts of the city, close to the beautiful Midford valley and popular with walkers. It serves four ales, often including guests from a local Brewery of the Month range. Highly recommended gastro-standard home-made food is available at all sessions. The main bar on the left still has many original features and an open fire. The restaurant is on the right and split across three levels. Parking is a bit restricted. ⠶ ⊛ ◑ ⅙ ● P ⊟ (3,D2) ⠶ ⬳

Crystal Palace

10-11 Abbey Green, BA1 1NW
☎ (01225) 482666
Fuller's London Pride, ESB; 2 changing beers (often Butcombe, Wild Beer) Ⓗ
Set on the pretty Abbey Green and refurbished by Fuller's in 2014, this city-centre pub now has an upmarket feel. There are usually at least two Fuller's beers on plus a couple of guests ales, some from local brewers, others from further away but usually featuring interesting breweries. Full table service is available in the lounge. There is a glass-covered sitting area at the rear. ⠶ ⊛ ◑ ⅙ ➜ (Spa) ⊟ ⠶ ⬳

A 2013 refurbishment turned the Midland Hotel into a City Pub Company brewpub. The on-site James Street Brewery produces two regular beers, the malty Gladiator (3.9% ABV) and the hoppy, citrussy Emperor (4.4% ABV), plus rotating seasonal ales. Up to three, sometimes four, guests are also served, usually from nearby micros, and up to four craft beers. A large L-shaped bar leads to a dining area and a good-sized beer garden. The upstairs room hosts sports TV, quizzes, comedy and so on. ⊛ ◑ ⅙ ➜ (Spa) ● ⊟ ⠶ ⬳

Bell

103 Walcot Street, BA1 5BW
☎ (01225) 460426 ⊕ thebellinnbath.co.uk
Abbey Bellringer; Box Steam Golden Bolt; Butcombe Adam Henson's Rare Breed; Hop Back Summer Lightning; Otter Ale Ⓗ
Purchased by 536 of its regulars, fans and staff following a community buy-out in 2013, the Bell offers six regular ales plus three changing guests from local microbreweries. Live music is a mainstay, with bands playing Monday and Wednesday evenings and Sunday lunchtimes; in the separate Back Bar are open mic nights on Thursday evenings. The interior features a long main bar with a number of seating areas, while the wall space inside is taken up by posters for local events. There is also bar billiards, board games and even a tiny launderette. At the rear is a walled garden with covered seating. ⊛ ◑ ♣ ● ⊟ ⠶ ⬳

REAL ALE BREWERIES

Abbey Bath
Bason Bridge Bason Bridge
Bath Brewhouse ⊟ Bath
Black Bear ⊟ ⚲ Wiveliscombe
Blindmans Leighton
Butcombe Wrington
Cheddar ⚲ Cheddar
Clevedon ⚲ Clevedon
Electric Bear ⚲ Bath
Epic West Hewish
Exmoor Wiveliscombe
Fine Tuned Somerton
Frome Frome
Glastonbury Glastonbury
Isle of Avalon Ashcott
Parkway Somerton
Quantock ⚲ Bishops Lydeard
Ralph's Ruin ⊟ Bath
Stowey Nether Stowey
Tanners ⊟ Wiveliscombe
Tapstone ⚲ Chard
Twisted Oak Bristol: Wrington
Verse ⊟ Bath (NEW)
Wild Beer Evercreech
Windy ⊟ Seavington St Michael
Yeovil Yeovil

Old Green Tree ★

12 Green Street, BA1 2JZ

☎ (01225) 448259

Butcombe Original; Pitchfork Pitchfork; house beer (by Blindmans); 1 changing beer (sourced locally) Ⓗ

A classic, unspoilt pub in a 300-year-old building. The three oak-panelled rooms include a superb northern-style drinking lobby. Although it can get crowded, there is often space in the comfortable back bar. Guest beers generally come from microbreweries in the area, with a stout or porter usually on offer in the winter months. A local farmhouse cider is also available, along with a range of fine wines and malt whiskies. Winter Sunday hours may be extended. Q◖≢(Spa)●➡

Pulteney Arms ✔

37 Daniel Street, BA2 6ND (on corner of Daniel St and Sutton St)

☎ (01225) 463923 ● thepulteneyarms.co.uk

2 changing beers (sourced nationally) Ⓗ

Tucked away near the end of Great Pulteney Street, this establishment has been open since 1792. The cat symbol on the pub sign refers to the Pulteney coat of arms. There are five gas light fittings (now sadly condemned) above the bar. The decor shows an emphasis on sport, particularly rugby. The food menu is extensive and deservedly popular (no food Sun eves). The guest beers are usually from a national brewery. ⏴❀◖♣●➡❀☂

Raven

6-7 Queen Street, BA1 1HE

☎ (01225) 425045 ● theravenofbath.co.uk

House beer (by Blindmans); 4 changing beers (sourced regionally; often Gloucester, Moor Beer) Ⓗ

A busy 18th-century free house in the heart of Bath. Its six ales include two brewed exclusively by Blindmans; guest ales come from far and wide. The main bar and the quieter first-floor bar serve the same range of ales. Famous for its sausages and Pieminister pies, the Raven is one of the few pubs in Bath serving food on Sunday evening. It puts on several mini beer festivals each year. Q❀◖≢(Spa) ♣●➡❀☂

Royal Oak

Lower Bristol Road, Twerton, BA2 3BW (on A36 at intersection with road to Windsor Bridge)

☎ (01225) 481409 ● theroyaloakbath.co.uk

Ralph's Ruin Ivory Tower, Sirius, Dark Side of the Ralph; 2 changing beers (often Butts, Downton) Ⓗ

Up to three beers from the pub's own brewery, Ralph's Ruin, are served here alongside up to six guest ales from microbreweries near and far. An interesting range of ciders, perries and bottled British and Belgian beers is also on offer. The pub hosts regular quiz nights and occasional beer festivals, plus live music on Wednesday evenings and most weekends. Outside are a small secluded garden and a small car park. Local CAMRA Pub of the Year 2020. ❀≢(Oldfield Park)●P➡❀

Salamander

3 John Street, BA1 2JL

☎ (01225) 428889

Bath Ales Prophecy, Gem, Lansdown; 1 changing beer (sourced locally; often Bath Ales) Ⓗ

An 18th-century building, tucked away in a side street, that opened as a coffee bar in 1957 and got an on-licence five years later. Taken over by St Austell in 2017, it looks and feels like a pub that has been there for a century or more, with wooden floorboards, wood panelling and subdued lighting adding to the ambience of the ground-floor bar, created from several small rooms. A popular restaurant upstairs uses local ales in its cooking. ◖≢(Spa)♣●➡❀☂

Star Inn ★ ✔

23 Vineyards, BA1 5NA

☎ (01225) 425072

Abbey Bellringer Ⓖ; Draught Bass; 3 changing beers (sourced nationally; often Abbey, Titanic) Ⓗ

A main outlet for Abbey Ales, this classic town pub was fitted out by Gaskell & Chambers in 1928. Its four small rooms have benches around the walls, wood panelling and roaring fires. The smallest room has a single bench, called Death Row, and the place itself, which dates from around 1760, is coffin-shaped. Abbey Bellringer is served from the cask and complimentary snuff is available. Cheese night is Thursday and live music is played on Friday evening. Q♣●➡❀☂

Bishops Lydeard

Quantock Brewery Tap ⃒

Westridge Way, Broadgauge Business Park, TA4 3RU (follow signs to West Somerset Railway and shop can be found on left just before railway station)

☎ (01823) 433812 ● quantockbrewery.co.uk

Quantock Ale, QPA, Wills Neck, Plastered Pheasant; 1 changing beer (sourced locally; often Quantock) Ⓗ

Brewery taproom with up to six of its cask beers on handpump. There are two Quantock KeyKeg ales always on, plus a monthly small batch KeyKeg (subject to availability). One or two guest KeyKeg beers are also stocked (typically from Northern Monk, Salopian, Thornbridge, and Weird Beard). A brewery shop supplies takeaway bottles and other brewery gifts. There are regular live band, comedy and quiz nights, and an annual beer festival in July. Street food is available Friday and most Saturday evenings. ⏴❀♿≢●P➡(28)❀☂

Bradford on Tone

White Horse Inn ⃒

Regent Street, TA4 1HF (off A38 between Taunton and Wellington at World's End jct)

☎ (01823) 461239 ● whitehorseinn.pub

3 changing beers (sourced regionally; often Exeter, Otter, St Austell) Ⓗ

A friendly well-established and well-run free house with real fires in winter warming both the bar and restaurant. Three varying ales are either local or regional. Good home-cooked pub food is served at reasonable prices. The beautiful large garden hosts a barbecue in summer. Regular events include music, skittle matches, quiz nights and gatherings of local interest groups. ⏴❀◖▲♣P➡(22) ❀☂

Bridgwater

West India House

101 Durleigh Road, TA6 7JE (top of Durleigh Rd hill)

☎ (01278) 452533 ● westindiahouse.co.uk

Butcombe Original; Sharp's Doom Bar; 1 changing beer (sourced locally; often Cheddar Ales) Ⓗ

The building was constructed in 1936 and there has been a pub on the site for many years, the name derived from the days when Bridgwater was a bustling port. For a quiet drink in cosy surroundings there is the lounge bar complete with open log fire. For a more vibrant atmosphere try the saloon bar, which has been extended and refurbished with modern decor and has three good ales from Butcombe, Sharp's and, occasionally, Cheddar Ales. Q⏴❀◖♣P➡(14)☂

Burrowbridge

King Alfred Inn Ⓛ

Burrow Drove, TA7 0RB (on A361, 9 miles from Taunton)

☎ (01823) 698379 ● king-alfred.co.uk

Bristol Beer Factory Fortitude; Butcombe Original; Otter Amber Ⓗ

Welcoming free house with a friendly atmosphere, on the Somerset Levels between Taunton and Glastonbury, under Burrow Mump where King Alfred allegedly burnt the cakes. It is a perfect stopping-off point for walkers on the River Parrett Trail. The three cask ales rarely change but are always good quality, and the pub usually stocks a couple of local real ciders. It serves good home-made food, cooked to order and with many choices, including specialist burgers with a variety of fillings. The bus stops outside and there is a car park to the rear.

Q❀❀➊◑❀♣❀🅿️🚌(29)❀🐾🛜

Catcott

Crown Inn

1 The Nydon, TA7 9HQ

☎ (01278) 722288 ● thecrowncatcott.com

3 changing beers (sourced regionally; often Butcombe, Dartmoor, Exmoor) Ⓗ

Traditional freehold country pub in this Polden Hills village, which lies just off the A39 between Bridgwater and Street. The original part of the building is over 400 years old and has a log fire, original flagstone floors, cob walls and low-beamed ceilings. There is a large function room/skittle alley to the rear. Up to three cask ales are served, usually on handpump but sometimes on gravity.

❀❀➊Ⓐ♣❀🅿️❀🛜

Chard

Cerdic ✪

47 Fore Street, TA20 1PT (on A30 in centre of town)

☎ (01460) 260070

Greene King Abbot; Ruddles Best Bitter; Sharp's Doom Bar; 4 changing beers (sourced nationally; often Dorset, Exmoor, Otter) Ⓗ

A Wetherspoon that used to be a cinema with the same name before it closed in the 1960s. The well-kept guest beers are normally local and you may find a bigger selection at the weekend. In addition there are usually six real ciders. There is a bar area and a family eating section down some steps in a conservatory. A pleasant garden has been added at the rear.

❀❀➊&❀🚌(30,96)🛜

Cheddar

Cheddar Ales Tap Room

Winchester Farm, Draycott Raad, BS27 3RP

☎ (01934) 744193 ● cheddarales.co.uk

6 changing beers (often Cheddar Ales) Ⓗ

Newly opened taproom for Cheddar Ales Brewery, situated just outside the world famous village. The pub is a pleasant diversion from the tourist hotspot and serves up to six cask ales brewed on-site. Takeaway service is also available. Cider, gins and wines are served, along with wood-fired pizzas at weekends. There is indoor and outdoor seating, and occasional live music events take place. ❀❀▶&🅿️❀

Churchill

Crown Inn Ⓛ

The Batch, Skinners Lane, BS25 5PP (off A38, 400yds S of A368 jct)

☎ (01934) 852995 ● crowninnchurchill.co.uk

Bath Ales Gem; Butcombe Original; Exmoor Ale; Palmers IPA; St Austell Tribute; house beer (by St Austell); 1 changing beer Ⓖ

Long-time Guide regular and winner of many CAMRA awards, the Crown is tucked away down a small lane close to the village centre. Several cosy rooms with stone-flagged floors are warmed by two log fires, and offer an assortment of seating. Excellent food is produced at lunchtimes using local ingredients. Up to eight beers, usually from the area, are served on gravity. Outside drinking spaces are to the front and rear. Families are welcome away from the bar itself. An old, classic, unchanged pub. Q❀❀➊Ⓐ❀🅿️🚌(A2)❀🛜

Churchinford

York Inn ✪

Honiton Road, TA3 7RF

☎ (01823) 601333 ● yorkinn.co.uk

Otter Amber, Bitter; Sharp's Sea Fury; 1 changing beer (sourced regionally) Ⓗ

Sited in the Blackdown Hills, this is a traditional hostelry dating back, in some parts, to the 16th century. It has an open fireplace and oak beams, but at the same time offers contemporary facilities and a good range of four cask ales and one real cider. The menu features tasty home-cooked food which includes a specialist range of pies. ❀❀➊♣❀🅿️❀🛜

Clevedon

Fallen Tree Micropub Ⓛ

43 Hill Road, BS21 7PD

☎ (01934) 310515

5 changing beers (sourced locally; often Cheddar Ales, Pitchfork, Twisted Oak) Ⓖ

This micropub opened in 2018 in a shopping area up a hill from the Grade I-listed Clevedon Pier. Originally owned by Twisted Oak Brewery, it is now in private hands, but still sells Twisted Oak beers. Between five and eight ales, usually from local breweries such as Cheddar Ales, Pitchfork Ales, 3D Beers and Yeovil Ales, are served straight from casks in the wooden stillage behind the bar. The filled rolls provided at weekends come from Murrays deli on the same road. Q❀❀🚌❀

Royal Oak ✪

35 Copse Road, BS21 7QN (behind ice cream parlour nr pier; footpath along alley leads to pub)

☎ (01275) 563879 ● theroyaloakclevedon.co.uk

Butcombe Original; Fuller's London Pride; Sharp's Doom Bar, Atlantic Ⓗ

Lively, friendly, mid-terrace venue close to the seafront and connected via an alley. It has a large front window and an unexpectedly spacious interior with many rooms. This community hub is home to cribbage and cricket teams, with a quiz on Monday and acoustic music on Wednesday. The winner of various awards, it hosts many events, including a street party every two years. Food is served lunchtimes including daily specials and a range of salads. Q❀➊♣❀🚌❀🛜

Combe Florey

Farmers Arms 🅛

TA4 3HZ (on A358 between Bishops Lydeard and Williton)
☎ (01823) 432267 ⊕ farmersarmsatcombeflorey.co.uk
Exmoor Ale, Gold; Otter Ale; Quantock QPA Ⓗ
Thatched 14th-century Grade II-listed pub with cob walls, medieval chimney and fireplace and a restored staircase. The bar serves four cask ales and three real ciders plus some unusual keg brews, bottled beers and a large selection of gin and malt whisky. The restaurant does good-quality food with various special evening menus. During the summer months there is a splendid garden and a large pizza oven for key occasions.
Q🕭🐾🎕🕪🅰♿🅿🚐(28)🌸🐾

Congresbury

Plough 🅛

High Street, BS49 5JA (off A370 at jct with B3133)
☎ (01934) 877402 ⊕ the-plough-inn.net
Butcombe Original; St Austell Tribute Ⓗ/Ⓖ**; Twisted Oak Fallen Tree** Ⓖ**; 4 changing beers (sourced locally)** Ⓗ/Ⓖ
Characterful village inn with flagstone floors and many original features, decorated with interesting local artefacts. Four guest beers, mainly from nearby breweries, are delivered from a row of old cask heads behind the bar. Up to 16 ciders are also stocked. The Plough has a deserved reputation for the quality of its food, which is served lunchtimes and evenings except Sunday evening, which is quiz night. There are real fires and a large garden. Mendip morris men meet here.
Q🕭🎕🕪🅰♿🅿🚐(X1,X2)🌸🐾

Crewkerne

King William Inn

Barn Street, TA18 8BP (take A30 towards Chard and, at fringe of town, uphill Barn St is on left)
☎ (01460) 074492 ⊕ kingwilliamcrewkerne.com
3 changing beers (sourced nationally; often Bristol Beer Factory, Oakham, Tapstone) Ⓗ
A short walk from the town centre towards Chard takes you to this well-hidden traditional pub. There are three changing ales and two ciders, and the array of pumpclips adorning the beams indicates the huge range of beers that has been served. Twitter shows the beers that are being added. There is an early evening happy hour every Monday and Wednesday. For music lovers there is an acoustic night the last Wednesday of each month. Beer festivals are held in May and the end of September.
🕭🌸🕪🅿🚐(Y6,96)🌸

Croscombe

George Inn

Long Street, BA5 3QH (on A371 between Wells and Shepton Mallet)
☎ (01749) 342306 ⊕ thegeorgeinn.co.uk
House beer (by Blindmans); 3 changing beers (often Cotleigh, St Austell, Yeovil) Ⓗ
Attractive 17th-century inn, refurbished by the owner, serving at least four guest ales from West Country independents and hosting two beer festivals a year. Blindmans King George, and George and Dragon, are exclusively brewed for the pub. Four real ciders are on sale, with Hecks Kingston Black and Thatchers ciders as regulars. There is a large main bar plus a family room and a snug with a fireplace. A separate dining room serves food that is home-cooked using locally sourced

ingredients in a modern theatre kitchen. A skittle alley/meeting room is to the rear. Outside is a large garden with a covered terrace. Q🕭🌸🎕🕪🅰♿🅰♿🅿🚐🌸🐾

Cross

New Inn ✓

Old Coach Road, BS26 2EE (on A38/A361 jct)
☎ (01934) 732455 ⊕ newinncross.co.uk
Otter Bitter, Ale; 4 changing beers (often Box Steam, Bristol Beer Factory, Tiny Rebel) Ⓗ
A 17th-century roadside inn on the A38, close to the historic medieval town of Axbridge. It is popular for its extensive food menu served all day, and its beer festival at Easter. Four guest beers, often rare for the area, are usually on the bar. Families are welcome, and the large hillside garden with children's play facilities offers a fine view of the Mendip Hills and Somerset Levels. There is a small car park opposite. 🕭🎕🕪🅰♿🅿🚐(126)🌸🐾

White Hart

Old Coach Road, BS26 2EE
☎ (01934) 733108
Bath Ales Gem; St Austell Trelawny; 2 changing beers (often Bath Ales, St Austell) Ⓗ
One of Hanging Judge Jeffreys' victims is rumoured to haunt this 17th-century inn, which reopened in 2019 after refurbishment. Inside there is a games bar with pool and darts, and a door leading to a lounge-style area. Beers come from the St Austell stable. The kitchen opens for lunches, with evening meals available for groups by arrangement. The nearby bus stop is a Hail and Ride halt, and there is a large car park opposite.
🕭🎕🅰♿🅿🚐(491)🌸🐾

Culmhead

Holman Clavel Inn

TA3 7EA (¼ mile off B3170)
☎ (01823) 421070
Butcombe Gold; Fuller's London Pride; Hanlons Yellow Hammer; Otter Bitter, Amber, Ale Ⓗ
This is a real country pub set in the Blackdown Hills Area of Outstanding Natural Beauty. It offers six good ales straight from the barrel, Tricky cider, wine, food and good company. There are no TVs or machines but children, dogs, walkers, cyclists and muddy boots are welcome. Food is from local farmers, suppliers and businesses, and gluten-free diners and vegetarians are catered for. Local musicians play Irish-style sessions every first Thursday of the month. Q🕭🌸🎕🕪🅰♿🅿🌸

Curry Rivel

Firehouse 🅛

Church Street, TA10 0HE (off A378 Langport to Wrantage road)
☎ (01458) 887447 ⊕ thefirehousesomerset.co.uk
Butcombe Adam Henson's Rare Breed, Original; Fuller's London Pride; 1 changing beer (often Otter) Ⓗ
An enticing village hostelry that has been beautifully restored with a modern twist yet remains packed with traditional charm. On the left when entering is the house bar, which serves up to four real ales with one changing regularly. In addition there is real cider from local producers. There is a daily happy hour from late afternoon with £1 off a pint. Leading off the bar are five further sitting/dining areas arranged over three floors, with wood-burning stoves in abundance.
🕭🌸🎕♿🅿🚐(54)🐾

Dinnington

Dinnington Docks Inn ✪

TA17 8SX (approx 3 miles E of Ilminster off B3168)
☎ (01460) 52397 ⊕ dinningtondocks.com

Butcombe Original; Teignworthy Gun Dog; 3 changing beers (sourced locally; often Exmoor, Fine Tuned, Quantock) Ⓗ

A quirky gem, this traditional Somerset country pub has beautiful views from the large garden. It wears its heart on its sleeve, supports the community and offers a warm welcome to locals and visitors alike. There is a good selection of two permanent and three guest ales to suit all tastes, along with a wide range of wines and spirits. All this, combined with the renowned hearty meal menu, makes the pub a must-visit destination.
Q ☺ ❀ ◑ ♣ ● P 🖥 ❖ ♥

Dulverton

Bridge Inn 🄻

20 Bridge Street, TA22 9HJ
☎ (01398) 324130 ⊕ thebridgeinndulverton.com

Exmoor Ale; St Austell Tribute; 2 changing beers (sourced regionally; often Bath Ales, St Austell) Ⓗ

Warm, welcoming pub in this delightful small town, dating from 1845. As the name implies, it is close to a bridge crossing the River Barle upstream from its confluence with the River Exe. There is a cosy single-room bar with a wood-burning stove, plus an extended restaurant area. The pub serves an interesting choice of national cask ales and bottled beers, including a Belgian selection. Check on the website for restricted opening hours in winter. Q ☺ ❀ ◑ ▲ ♣ ● P 🖥 ❖ ♥

Dunster

Luttrell Arms Hotel

36 High Street, TA24 6SG
☎ (01643) 821555 ⊕ luttrellarms.co.uk

Exmoor Ale; Otter Amber; 2 changing beers (sourced locally; often Quantock) Ⓗ

The hotel, and its 28 beautiful bedrooms, is on the site of three ancient houses dating back to 1443. The back bar with its open log fire features some of the oldest glass windows in Somerset, and there is fine plasterwork on the lounge ceiling. You can dine in the à la carte restaurant or, if you prefer, order a bar snack. The view of Dunster Castle from the back garden is spectacular. Mini beer and cider festivals are held.
Q ☺ ❀ ◑ ▲ ♣ ● 🖥 (28,198) ❖ ♥

Faulkland

Tucker's Grave ★

BA3 5XF
☎ (01373) 834230 ⊕ tuckersgraveinn.co.uk

Butcombe Original Ⓖ

A gem from a bygone age, with a nationally important historic pub interior. This place was built in the mid-17th century and has changed little since. It was named after Tucker, who hanged himself close by and was buried at the crossroads outside; he featured in a song by The Stranglers. There is no bar – the beers and Thatchers cider are served from an alcove. Shove-ha'penny is played and there is a skittle alley. Next to the pub is a large 50-pitch campsite. Q ☺ ❀ ▲ ♣ ● P ♥

Frome

Griffin

Milk Street, BA11 3DB

☎ (01373) 228283 ⊕ griffinfrome.com

Frome Funky Monkey, Zig-Zag Stout; 2 changing beers (often Frome) Ⓗ

This venue, in the part of town known as Trinity, was formerly the brewery tap for Milk Street (now Frome) Brewery, selling up to four Frome ales or guests as well as a range of craft beers. Recently refurbished and under new management, the single bar retains some original features such as etched windows and a wooden floor. It serves burgers and street food from locally sourced ingredients and suppliers. Sunday lunch is popular.
☺ ❀ ◑ ♣ P 🖥 (184) ♥

Just Ales

10 Stony Street, BA11 1BU
☎ (01373) 462493 ⊕ Justalespart2.com

4 changing beers (sourced nationally) Ⓗ

Frome's first micropub opened in 2018 serving up to four real ales on handpump as well as a large range of local ciders. Set in what used to be a small café in the heart of Frome's vibrant St Catherine's District, Just Ales has a welcoming atmosphere and is run by the same team as Just Ales in Wells, including the friendly hound. Home-made Biltong is sold as a quick tasty snack. Outside seating is also available. Q ● 🖥 ❖ ♥

Glastonbury

Becket's Inn ✪

43 High Street, BA6 9DS (at top of High St in town centre)
☎ (01458) 832928 ⊕ becketspubglastonbury.co.uk

Wadworth Henry's IPA, 6X; 1 changing beer (sourced regionally) Ⓗ

A traditional town-centre hostelry named after Thomas Becket, with a pool room and three separate bar areas. Three well-kept Wadworth beers are on handpump. There is no food but customers are welcome to bring takeaways to eat in or for a picnic in the garden; plates and cutlery are provided and the Becket will even do the washing up. Children are welcome in daytime, but as there is a pub dog only assistance dogs are allowed.
☺ ❀ ♣ ● 🖥

George & Pilgrims

1 High Street, BA6 9DP (nr Market Cross)
☎ (01458) 831146

Otter Bitter; St Austell Tribute; 2 changing beers (sourced nationally; often Bristol Beer Factory, Quantock) Ⓗ

Three-storeyed stone-built gatehouse inn featuring a panelled embattled frontage with mullion windows. Walking through the stout doorway of this Grade I-listed building there is a corridor leading to the dining room and rear patio with several tabled alcoves on the right. The Pilgrims Bar on the left oozes old-world charm and displays medieval artefacts. Four well-kept real ales are served alongside a choice of ciders. The pub's history is worth reading about over a pint. A municipal car park is to the rear. Q ☺ ❀ ❀ ◑ ▲ ♣ P 🖥 ♥

Queen of Cups Restaurant & Freehouse

8-12 Northload Street, BA6 9JJ (at bottom of Glastonbury High St turn into Northload St at Market Cross)
☎ (01458) 831255

2 changing beers (often Fine Tuned, Moor Beer, Pitchfork) Ⓗ

Quirky hotel and bar in the centre of this historic town within walking distance of the Tor and abbey. It is a well-known music venue, with an open mic session on a

Tuesday, a blues jam on a Sunday and regular music on Friday nights. The pub is famous for serving authentic curries from around the world, and its Sunday carvery is popular. In May it hosts a well-supported beer festival with 20 ales and six ciders. ☺🅿🏠♿🅭🍴♣🅿🚪🐾🛜

Halse

New Inn
TA4 3AF
☎ (01823) 432352 🌐 newinnhalse.com
Exmoor Ale; Quantock QPA; 1 changing beer (often Exmoor) Ⓗ
Nestling between the Quantock Hills and Exmoor National Park, the New Inn is an 18th-century former coaching stop in this quaint village, five miles from Taunton on the A358 at Bishops Lydeard and only 40 minutes' walk from the famous West Somerset Railway. Reopened after a buy out and refurbishment by the Halse community, it dispenses beers from Exmoor and Quantock, with another pump providing a changing local ale. Attractions include a quiz, folk music and themed menu evenings, plus an annual beer festival in late May/early June. Q☺🅭🏠♿🅭♣🅿🐾🛜

Henstridge

Bird in Hand
Ash Walk, BA8 0QD
☎ (01963) 362255
Butcombe Original; 2 changing beers (often Sharp's) Ⓗ
Old stone village pub with low ceilings, beams, a fireplace at each end of an attractive long bar, and a games room housing a TV. There is an adjoining skittle alley. Excellent-quality ales and good-value snacks make a visit to this true community hub well worthwhile; it is at the heart of most village activities. Thatchers cider is served on handpump and there is more cider in boxes. Q🏠🅭♣♣🅿🚪(58)🛜

Hinton Blewett

Ring o' Bells
Upper Road, BS39 5AN (2 miles W of Temple Cloud from A37) ST594569
☎ (01761) 451245 🌐 ringobellshinton.co.uk
Butcombe Original; 3 changing beers (often Butcombe, Timothy Taylor) Ⓗ
Popular village pub dating from the 19th century, welcoming to cyclists, walkers, children and dogs. A dining/function room with its own garden was recently added, and blends nicely with the cosy bar and snug. Ashton Still, Cheddar Valley and other real ciders are served. Quality food is offered, using produce from the area when possible. Local sports clubs meet here and much memorabilia is on show, particularly cricket-related. Free boules is played on Tuesday evening. Open all day from June to September. Q☺🅭🏠♿🅭♣♣🅿🐾🛜

Horton

Five Dials Inn
Goose Lane, TA19 9QQ
☎ (01460) 55359 🌐 thefivedials.co.uk
Otter Bitter; Sharp's Doom Bar; 1 changing beer (often Otter) Ⓗ
An old coaching hostelry given a contemporary facelift. Three real ales and traditional local ciders from Perry's and Burrow Hill are on the bar, including the famous Somerset Cider Brandy. Fresh seasonal food is served, and there is a specials board that changes on a daily

basis. The inn offers six guest rooms with en-suite showers, and was awarded four stars by Enjoy England. There is also a self-contained studio apartment which includes kitchen and dining facilities. Open on bank holidays. ☺🅭🏠♿🅭🅿🐾🛜

Keynsham

Old Bank
20 High Street, BS31 1DQ
☎ (0117) 904 6356
3 changing beers (often Severn) Ⓗ
This Grade II-listed building was originally a coaching inn, then a branch of Westminster Bank, before becoming a pub again. It is a free house with one large room for drinking, and a covered, heated outdoor area at the back. The landlord tries to have at least one dark, often strong, beer on at all times. There is a large TV screen for sport and the place can sometimes get lively on late weekend openings. A small car park is to the rear. ♿♿🅭♣🅿🚪🐾🛜

Knole

Lime Kiln Inn ✅
TA10 9JH
☎ (01458) 241242 🌐 thelimekilninn.co.uk
Butcombe Original; 2 changing beers (often Butcombe) Ⓗ
Traditional inn that was first licensed in 1814, and has flagstoned flooring in the main bar area and a grand inglenook fireplace for winter warmth. Up to three real ales are dispensed. The adjoining, recently refurbished restaurant is modern and comfortable, with large doors leading onto the garden for summer use. It serves excellent food from the main menu and changing specials board. ☺🅭🏠♿🅭♣🅿🐾🛜

Lydford on Fosse

Cross Keys Inn Ⓛ
TA11 7HA (next to A37 between Yeovil and Shepton Mallet at traffic lights in village)
☎ (01963) 240473 🌐 crosskeysinn.info
House beer (by Otter); 1 changing beer (sourced regionally; often Bristol Beer Factory, Twisted Oak) Ⓖ
An 18th-century pub with flagstone floors, blue lias stonework and a wealth of beams. It has an open-plan bar with two fireplaces at each end and a snug. There are up to five ales on gravity, including the house beer. This community venue hots many attractions including live music, a beer festival, comedy nights and charitable events. Camping is available on-site with 29 pitches, a shower block and toilets. Q☺🅭🏠♿🅭♣♣🅿🚪(667)🐾🛜

Martock

White Hart Hotel Ⓛ
East Street, TA12 6JQ
☎ (01935) 822005 🌐 whitehartholmartock.co.uk
Otter Bitter; Sharp's Doom Bar; 1 changing beer (sourced regionally; often Exmoor, St Austell, Yeovil) Ⓗ
This hamstone Grade II-listed coaching inn at the centre of the village dates from 1735. The warm and welcoming establishment has a main bar for drinks, serving three real ales on handpulls, mainly from nearby breweries. The cosy restaurant offers great chef-cooked food with table service. Local music and film clubs use the pub as a meeting place. It has 10 en-suite letting rooms, including one for families. Q☺🅭🏠♿🅭♣🅿🚪(52)🐾🛜

Merriott

King's Head
Church Street, TA16 5PR
☎ (01460) 78912 ⊕ thekingsmerriott.com
Sharp's Doom Bar; 2 changing beers (sourced regionally; often Otter, Plain, Red Rock) �
A classical 17th-century inn with open-plan rooms and a mix of flagstones and wood flooring. A raised wood-burning stove in the flagstone area is welcoming in winter. As well as cask ales there is a selection of up to seven local ciders. The owner loves gin and there are more than 80 available. Outside is a large beer garden with a smoking section featuring a wood-burner. The inn is dog-friendly and popular with walkers.
Q☆❀◑♣👜P❀🐾📶

Middlezoy

George Inn 🄻
42 Main Road, TA7 0NN (off A372, 1 mile NW of Othery, 5 miles E of Bridgwater)
☎ (01823) 698215 ⊕ thegeorgeinnmiddlezoy.co.uk
House beer (by St Austell); 2 changing beers (sourced regionally; often Bath Ales, Cheddar Ales, Fine Tuned) ⌂
This pub, which has been in the Guide for over 20 years, is a 17th-century free house with stone-flagged floors, exposed beams and log fires. Excellent locally sourced food is served from Wednesday to Saturday evenings and at Saturday lunchtimes. A private dining room (seating 12) can be reserved. Farmer Jims and Orchard Pig ciders are served. Accommodation is provided, with three bedrooms. Live acoustic music takes place on the third Sunday each month and there is a monthly bingo night.
Q☆❀🛏Å♣👜P🚍(16)❀📶

Midford

Hope & Anchor
Midford Road, BA2 7DD
☎ (01225) 832296 ⊕ hopeandanchormidford.co.uk
2 changing beers (sourced regionally; often Otter, Three Daggers, Twisted) ⌂
An ivy-clad building dating back to the 17th century. Formerly owned by Courage Brewery, it became a free house in 1976 and has been run by the same family for over 25 years. The pub is close to the Two Tunnels cycle path leading to and from Bath, via the old S&D railway route. Beers served here are mostly from the West Country and vary according to the time of year. The cider is made at a local farm. ☆❀◑👜P🚍(D2)❀📶

Minehead

Kildare Lodge ✔
Townend Road, TA24 5RQ
☎ (01643) 702009 ⊕ kildarelodge.co.uk
St Austell Tribute; 3 changing beers (sourced regionally) ⌂
This cracking locals' venue is two minutes from the town centre. A Grade II-listed building in the Arts & Crafts style, it has a bar, two lounges and a dining room. There are 12 en-suite rooms including a bridal suite with a four-poster bed. Two beer festivals are held every year with up to 20 beers to choose from. The pub is in the local boules and quiz leagues. It is a great base for exploring Exmoor National Park, Dunster and the coast.
Q❀🛏◑👟Å🚆♣👜P🚍(28)❀

Montacute

Phelips Arms ✔
The Borough, TA15 6XB
☎ (01935) 822557 ⊕ phelipsarms.co.uk
Palmers Dorset Gold; 3 changing beers (sourced nationally; often Palmers) ⌂
Just 200 yards from the National Trust Montacute House, this lovely hamstone village pub offers a warm and friendly welcome. It has a selection of three or four Palmers cask ales, and the real cider on handpump is also from Palmers. Home-cooked meals and daily specials are made from locally sourced ingredients where possible. There is a walled garden. Open bank holiday Mondays.
☆❀◑♣👜P🚍(81)❀📶

Nailsea

Nailsea MicroPub
Unit 4, Ivy Court, 63A High Street, BS48 1AW
☎ 07496 428350
6 changing beers (sourced locally) 🄶
Nailsea's first micropub opened in 2019 in a former opticians'. It serves up to six ales straight from the cask, along with two real ciders. Beers of all styles come from up and down the country, as well as from local breweries. Bottled ciders, gins, wines and soft drinks are also available, as well as reasonably priced bar snacks, including filled rolls on busy weekends. There is no dedicated parking but there are ample public car parks nearby. Q❀♣👜🚍❀

Nether Stowey

George 🄻
1 St Mary Street, TA5 1LJ
☎ (01278) 732248 ⊕ georgestowey.com
2 changing beers (often Bays, St Austell, Stowey) ⌂
The George is the oldest pub in the village and can trace its history to 1616, although the original building dates back another century. It is a friendly multi-roomed place with a real fire, dark-wood interior, Tiffany lamps, and walls displaying historical photographs of the village. The pub serves as an outlet for the nearby Stowey Brewery. It hosts live music occasionally, and has a function room available upstairs. ☆❀🛏♣👜❀📶

Pitney

Halfway House 🄻
Pitney Hill, TA10 9AB (on B3153 between Langport and Somerton)
☎ (01458) 252513 ⊕ thehalfwayhouse.co.uk
Hop Back Crop Circle; Otter Bright; Teignworthy Reel Ale; 6 changing beers (sourced regionally; often Bristol Beer Factory, Pitchfork, Quantock) 🄶
An outstanding venue serving eight to 10 regional ales on gravity alongside many bottled beers and four real ciders. The inside is traditional, with flagstone flooring, old solid wooden tables and benches, and three real fires. This basic but busy place deserves its many accolades, including being in the Guide for over 25 years. It provides superb home-cooked food, and offers accommodation in a recent addition, the Hut.
Q❀🛏◑👜P🚍(54)❀📶

Porlock

Ship Inn 🄻 ✔
High Street, TA24 8QD
☎ (01643) 862507 ⊕ shipinnporlock.co.uk

Exmoor Beast; Otter Bitter; 6 changing beers (sourced regionally; often Cotleigh, Quantock, St Austell) Ⓗ
Known locally as the Top Ship, the bar is a gem with its flagstone floor, open fire and settle seating. It has changed little since featuring in RD Blackmore's novel Lorna Doone. The pub dates from the 13th century and sits at the bottom of the notorious Porlock Hill that takes you up to Exmoor. Eight ales and a cider from close by are available, and good food can be enjoyed either in the restaurant or, in fine weather, in the delightful three-tiered garden. Q♿️🏠⌂🕧🅮❤️⛺♣️🚶♿️P🚃(10)🐶

Porlock Weir

Ship Inn 🅛

TA24 8PB (take B3225 from Porlock)
☎ (01643) 863288 🌐 shipinnporlockweir.co.uk
Exmoor Ale, Stag; St Austell Tribute, Proper Job; 2 changing beers (sourced regionally; often Cotleigh, Otter) Ⓗ
This 400-year-old pub in Exmoor National Park offers fantastic views of the Bristol Channel and South Wales coast. It is set next to the small harbour and pebbled beach. As the Ship is on the South West Coast Path it is ideal for walkers. It gets busy in the summer but has a Pay & Display car park opposite. A beer festival is held in early July showcasing up to 50 ales. The pub offers accommodation, which is also dog-friendly.
Q🏠⌂🕧🅮❤️⛺♣️🚶♿️P🚃(10) 🐶🛜

Portishead

Ship

310 Down Road, BS20 8JT
☎ (01275) 848400
Draught Bass; Otter Bitter; 1 changing beer Ⓗ
A large hostelry with traditional opening hours on the coast road between Clevedon and Portishead. It enjoys views over the Severn Estuary from an award-winning garden. The landlord has been at the pub he built since 1973, and is a fount of local knowledge. Meals are served lunchtime only, but you can get pasties in the evening. There is a small library of books on-site with a particularly good selection on history of the area.
🏠🕧♣️P🚃🐶

Siren's Calling 🅛

315 Newfoundland Way, Portishead Marina, BS20 7PT
☎ (01275) 268278 🌐 sirenscalling.co.uk
5 changing beers Ⓗ
A modern single-room waterside bar, opened in 2018, serving up to six cask ales and nine craft keg beers in a variety of styles. Some are from breweries in the Bristol area, others from further afield. Still ciders are also sold. The pub is simply furnished, with large front windows overlooking the many boats moored in the marina. Food is always available but limited to cheese platters, Scotch eggs, pork pies and sausage rolls. Regular beer festivals are held. ♿️🏠🕧🅮❤️♣️🐶🛜

Windmill Inn 🅛

58 Nore Road, BS20 6JZ (next to municipal golf course above coastal path)
☎ (01275) 818483
Butcombe Original; Fuller's Oliver's Island, London Pride; 3 changing beers (often Fuller's) Ⓗ
Large split-level pub with a spacious patio to the rear, plus an extension enjoying panoramic views. It is above the coastal path on the edge of town; the Severn Estuary and both Severn bridges can be seen on clear days. The Windmill was acquired by Fuller's in 2014 but one guest ale comes from outside the brewery's stable. A varied

menu is served all day with table bookings available. Monday is quiz night. Dogs are allowed in the main bar area only. Q♿️🏠🕧🅮❤️⛺♣️P🚃🐶🛜

Priddy

Hunters' Lodge

Old Bristol Road, BA5 3AR (at isolated crossroads 1 mile from A39 close to TV mast) ST549500
☎ (01749) 672275
Butcombe Original; Cheddar Ales Potholer; 1 changing beer (often Butcombe) Ⓖ
The landlord of this timeless classic roadside inn has been in charge for over 50 years. Priddy is the highest village in Somerset, and popular with cavers and walkers. The pub's three rooms include one with a flagged floor. All beer is served direct from casks behind the bar; local cider is also on offer. Simple home-cooked food is excellent and exceptional value. A folk musicians' drop-in session is held on Tuesday evening. The garden is pleasant and secluded. Mobile phones are not welcome but dogs are. Q♿️🏠🕧🅮❤️♣️P🚃(683)🐶

Queen Victoria Inn ✅

Pelting Drove, BA5 3BA
☎ (01749) 676385 🌐 thequeenvicpriddy.co.uk
Butcombe Original; 2 changing beers (often Butcombe, Fuller's) Ⓗ
A creeper-clad inn, a pub since 1851, with four rooms that feature low ceilings, flagged floors and three log fires. It is a wonderfully warm and relaxing haven on cold winter nights, and is particularly popular during the Priddy Folk Festival in July. Reasonably priced home-cooked food is a speciality. Butcombe beers plus a guest are served, as well as real ciders. Children are welcome and there is a play area by the car park.
Q♿️🏠🕧⛺♣️P🐶🛜

Puriton

37 Club 🅛

1 West Approach Road, Woolavington Road, TA7 8AD (5 mins from jct 23 of M5 between Bridgwater and Wells)
☎ (01278) 685190 🌐 37club.co.uk
Otter Bitter, Ale; St Austell Tribute; 3 changing beers (sourced regionally; often Box Steam, Pitchfork, Quantock) Ⓗ
On the site of the former Royal Ordnance Factory, which was allocated the number 37, this is a large club offering a great many facilities to members and visitors. It has two bars, and its multi-roomed layout incorporates a concert room, two skittle alleys, a dining room and a snooker room with five tables. Outside are a beer garden, fishing lake and football pitch. CAMRA members are welcome with a membership card.
♿️🏠🕧⛺♣️P🚃(75)

Radstock

Fromeway

Frome Road, BA3 3LG
☎ (01761) 432116 🌐 fromeway.co.uk
Butcombe Original Ⓗ**; 2 changing beers (sourced nationally; often Otter, Twisted)** Ⓗ/Ⓐ
Friendly free house that is in its sixth generation of the same family. It serves a great, weekly changing selection of ales from all over the country. The food combines traditional classics with more contemporary dishes (booking essential). Outside is an award-winning garden. Regular charity events, quiz nights and walks take place from month to month. ♿️🏠⌂🕧🅮❤️♣️P🚃(768,178)🐶🛜

Rickford

Plume of Feathers

Leg Lane, BS40 7AH (off A368, 2 miles from A38; approaching from Churchill, left U-turn into Leg Lane is extremely tricky)
☎ (01761) 462682 ⊕ theplumeoffeathers.com
Butcombe Original; Cheddar Ales Potholer; 1 changing beer (often Butcombe, Cheddar Ales, Pitchfork) Ⓗ
This 17th-century building has been a pub since the 1800s. Its interior is divided into several areas, including a restaurant with a real fire. Beers are always from local breweries. There is a garden to the rear and a stream running along the front, leading to a ford. A popular charity duck race takes place in July. The pub provides a pleasant and convenient base from which to walk, fish or explore the Mendips. Car parking is limited.
Q ➰ ❀ ❆ ◑ ▲ ♣ ● P ▥ ➓ (791) ❀ 🛜

Roadwater

Valiant Soldier Ⓛ ✔

TA23 0QZ (off A39 at Washford)
☎ (01984) 640223 ⊕ thevaliantsoldier.co.uk
Dartmoor Jail Ale; 1 changing beer (sourced locally; often Exmoor) Ⓗ
The pub dates back to 1720 and has been run by the current landlord for over 30 years. It is ideal for country walks and exploring nearby Exmoor, the coast and Dunster. This vibrant locals' inn has quiz, pool, darts and nine skittles teams to see it through the winter months. It is by a small river where you can relax and watch the ducks and, if you are lucky, kingfishers. The food is of good quality and locally sourced. ➰ ❀ ❆ ◑ ♣ ● P ❀ 🛜

Saltford

Bird in Hand ✔

58 High Street, BS31 3EJ
☎ (01225) 873335 ⊕ birdinhandsaltford.co.uk
Butcombe Original; Sharp's Doom Bar; 2 changing beers (often Exmoor, Otter, Yeovil) Ⓗ
A convenient stopping-off point for cyclists on the Bristol to Bath Railway Path, this traditional 19th-century country inn is very close to the River Avon and only 400 yards from the A4. It has a long L-shaped bar and a pleasant conservatory with fine views across the garden to the hills beyond. Quality food is served lunchtimes and evenings, and all day at weekends, with gluten-free options. There is a pétanque piste in the garden.
➰ ❀ ◑ ♿ ♣ ● P ▥ ❀ 🛜

Seavington St Michael

Volunteer Inn Ⓛ

New Road, TA19 0QE (on old A303 between South Petherton and Ilminster)
☎ (01460) 240126 ⊕ thevolly.co.uk
Windy Drift, Tornado, Windward; 2 changing beers (sourced regionally) Ⓗ
Cosy three-roomed pub that has built a strong reputation with real ale enthusiasts for Windy Brewery beers, crafted on-site in the purpose-built structure to the rear. The owners wanted to form a true brewpub in Somerset and christened the brewery after the weather problems encountered by their builders. Even today all the brews are named after the wind and weather. This fine establishment is well worth a visit.
Q ➰ ❀ ❆ ◑ ♣ ● P ❀ 🛜

Somerton

Etsome Arms

6 West Street, TA11 7PS
☎ 07907 046213
4 changing beers (sourced locally; often Fine Tuned, Parkway, Yeovil) Ⓖ
A former café, this friendly and cosy micropub was among the first of the breed in Somerset. Its seating combines comfortable sofas with traditional tables and chairs. Between four and six ales are served on gravity, depending on the time of week and year, with all changing regularly. Quality cold bar snacks are sourced locally, and include a range of Scotch eggs and pies. Children and dogs are welcome. Runner-up for local CAMRA Pub of the Year 2020. ➰ ❀ ♣ ● ▥ (54,77) ❀ 🛜

White Hart Inn

Market Place, TA11 7LX (centre of village)
☎ (01458) 272273 ⊕ whitehartsomerton.com
Cheddar Ales Potholer; 2 changing beers (sourced regionally; often Gritchie, Otter) Ⓗ
The White Hart has been trading as an inn in Somerton's delightful market square since the 16th century; you cannot miss it as there is a large model of a white hart on the entrance porch. The pub is much larger inside than you might guess, and has plenty of tables for dining or enjoying coffee and cakes. A courtyard offers alfresco eating and drinking. Numerous awards and newspaper reviews can be found on the website.
➰ ❀ ❆ ◑ ♿ ● ▥ (54,77) ❀ 🛜

South Petherton

Brewers Arms Ⓛ

18-20 St James Street, TA13 5BW (½ mile off A303 in centre of village)
☎ (01460) 241887 ⊕ the-brewersarms.com
Otter Bitter; 3 changing beers (sourced nationally; often Butcombe, St Austell, Thornbridge) Ⓗ
This pub has appeared in more than 20 consecutive editions of the Guide. During this time around 3,000 different ales have been served and documented. The Brewers is a hub of village life, a true community pub that keenly supports local events and charities. Regular live music and quiz nights feature, and beer festivals are held over both spring and summer bank holiday weekends. The adjoining Old Bakehouse provides excellent quality food. ➰ ❀ ❆ ◑ ▲ ♣ ● ▥ (81) ❀ 🛜

Taunton

Bank

Middle Street, TA1 1SJ
☎ (01823) 257788 ⊕ thebanktaunton.co.uk
3 changing beers (sourced nationally; often Arbor, Moor Beer, Oakham) Ⓗ
Close to Somerset cricket ground, the Bank dispenses three varying cask ales from small breweries. It has two floors: the ground is a cosy bar, and upstairs is reserved for diners, with doors opening onto a terrace. A popular choice of keg beers and cans is served in addition to the cask ales. Quality food is on offer and can be described as modern British with an international influence. Bar meals reflect the quality of the main menu. Q ◑ ♿ ≷ ● ▥ ❀ 🛜

Coal Orchard Ⓛ ✔

30-32 Bridge Street, TA1 1UD (nr to River Tone bridge in town centre)
☎ (01823) 447330
Greene King Abbot; Ruddles Best Bitter; Sharp's Doom Bar; 4 changing beers (sourced regionally; often Dartmoor, Exmoor, Quantock) Ⓗ

North Town Wharf once stood behind this Wetherspoon house, next to the River Tone. Facing it was the Coal Orchard, the site of an orchard which became the landing place for Welsh coal. The pub was later converted from a former hardware store, and is one of the chain's smaller premises. Its frontage has Art Deco styling; seating is arranged over a single open-plan level. To the rear are a small garden and patio. Q

Ring of Bells L

16-17 St James Street, TA1 1JS
☎ (01823) 259480 ● theringofbellstaunton.com
5 changing beers (sourced nationally; often Dark Star, Oakham, Otter) Ⓗ
Close to Somerset cricket ground, this wooden-floored pub is a favourite haunt of cricket fans. It has two bars with open fires, plus a downstairs eating area, upstairs restaurant and large outside courtyard. The five cask beers are from local, regional and national breweries, or you may find some interesting keg ales if preferred. Excellent locally produced food is served, with booking recommended. Sporting events are shown on TV in the bar.

Wyvern Social Club L

Mountfields Road, TA1 3BJ (off South Rd, approx 1 mile from town centre)
☎ (01823) 284591 ● wyvernclub.co.uk
Exmoor Ale; 2 changing beers (sourced regionally; often Cotleigh, Exmoor, St Austell) Ⓗ
For over 30 years this has been a great venue in which to drink real ales and, now, real cider. A members-only club with a visitors' licence, it allows guests to be signed in on production of a CAMRA membership card. The club stages an annual beer festival in October, and is a hub for rugby, cricket and squash clubs who use the ajoining playing fields. Local CAMRA branch Club of the Year 2019. The bus routes listed apply only to Saturday daytime. (6,99)

Trull

Winchester Arms

Church Road, TA3 7LG
☎ (01823) 284723 ● winchesterarmstrull.co.uk
4 changing beers (sourced regionally; often Cotleigh, Otter, St Austell) Ⓗ
Thriving community free house on the outskirts of Taunton, near to the Blackdown Hills. A comfortable bar area is separated from the long dining area by a fireplace. The locally sourced home-cooked food is excellent (booking is advised at popular times). The streamside gardens, perfect for family and dogs, become the venue for entertainment and barbecues. A popular quiz takes place on Sunday nights and there is occasional live music. The pub offers good-value accommodation. Q (97)

Wambrook

Cotley Inn

TA20 3EN (from A30 W out of Chard, by toll house, take left fork and almost immediately left again; following signs for pub, continue for just over 1 mile on narrow lane)
☎ (01460) 62348 ● cotleyinnwambrook.co.uk
Otter Bitter; 1 changing beer (sourced regionally; often Exmoor, Tapstone, Teignworthy) Ⓖ
A traditional country pub that is well worth finding, in a wonderful rural setting where sitting outside is a delight. Inside the main entrance is a bar area with a welcoming wood-burning stove to greet you in the winter months.

To the right of the bar is a challenging skittle alley and to the left you will find dining spaces where you can sample the excellent food. Ales are served from gravity racking behind the bar. Q

Watchet

Esplanade Club L ✓

5 The Esplanade, TA23 0AJ (opp marina)
☎ (01984) 634518 ● esplanadeclub.net
House beer (by St Austell); 4 changing beers (sourced regionally; often Exmoor, Quantock, St Austell) Ⓗ
Built in the 1860s as a sailmaking factory, the Esplanade is now home to the Boat Owners Association. It is an archive of history and memorabilia of the area, with unique murals and even its own Tardis. There are great views over the marina and the Bristol Channel. The club is a busy music venue, hosting live acts every weekend, open mic on the first Tuesday of the month and folk every fourth Wednesday. Local CAMRA Club of the Year 2020. (28)

Pebbles Tavern

24 Market Street, TA23 0AN (in heart of town, nr museum)
☎ (01984) 634737
Timothy Taylor Boltmaker, Landlord Ⓗ**; 1 changing beer (sourced nationally)** Ⓗ/Ⓖ
Small and unique tavern that has won numerous CAMRA awards for Cider Pub of the Year, including in 2020. As well as the ales it serves up to 30 ciders, 60 gins, 24 rums and 64 whiskies. You are welcome to bring your fish & chips from the shop next door. Poetry night is on the first Tuesday of the month; regular music nights include folk, sea shanty, acoustic and jazz. (28)

Star Inn L

Mill Lane, TA23 0BZ
☎ (01984) 631367 ● starinnwatchet.co.uk
House beer (by Exmoor); 4 changing beers (often Butcombe, Dartmoor, Exmoor) Ⓗ
This two-time Somerset CAMRA Pub of the Year and runner-up in 2019 has been a Guide regular for two decades. Renowned for friendly staff and a congenial atmosphere, it has darts, quiz and boules teams, and hosts music nights in summer. It also holds port and cheese nights and is home to the Sunday night Bad Boys club. Mick's beer tours have run more than 100 trips. (28)

Wedmore

New Inn L

Combe Batch, BS28 4DU
☎ (01934) 712099
Butcombe Original; Timothy Taylor Landlord; 1 changing beer (sourced regionally; often Cheddar Ales, Exmoor, Fine Tuned) Ⓗ
This classic village inn is the centre for many local events including the famous annual turnip prize, spoof and penny chuffin'. The public bar, lounge and dining areas are complemented by a beer garden to the rear. A chalkboard lists forthcoming ales, mainly from the West Country, two dispensed from handpumps and two on gravity. Traditional and good-value home-cooked food is served. There is a skittle alley/function room, and winter skittles and darts provide a hive of activity. Q (67)

Wells

City Arms ✓
69 High Street, BA5 2AG
☎ (01749) 677768 ⊕ cityarmswells.co.uk
2 changing beers (sourced regionally; often Cheddar Ales, Timothy Taylor) Ⓗ
In 1810 the City of Wells jail closed and later became the City Arms. The main bar retains the small barred windows and low-vaulted ceilings of its former existence. The building encloses a courtyard on three sides, with outdoor seating. There is extensive food service in the bar, bistro and restaurant, made to order using fresh produce from the area. Between five and seven beers are normally available, mainly from local brewers. Q ᔕ ⊛ ⋈ ◑ ☖ ♣ ♠ ➋ ❀ 🐾 🛜

West Chinnock

Muddled Man Ⓛ ✓
Lower Street, TA18 7PT
☎ (01935) 881235 ⊕ themuddledmaninn.co.uk
3 changing beers (often Cheddar Ales, Quantock, Yeovil) Ⓗ
A popular traditional free house in a picturesque village. The family team gives a warm welcome to visitors and locals alike, serving good home-cooked food in a jovial way. The pub specialises in a variety of steaks, and Sunday lunch is so popular it must be pre-booked. A good range of three well-kept ales is served alongside a real cider. Outside is a large beer garden with exceptional flower boxes, troughs and baskets.
Q ᔕ ⊛ ⋈ ◑ ☖ ♣ ❀ 🐾 🛜

West Huntspill

Crossways Inn Ⓛ
Withy Road, TA9 3RA (on A38)
☎ (01278) 783756 ⊕ thecrosswaysinn.com
St Austell Trelawny; 9 changing beers (sourced nationally; often Bristol Beer Factory, Dartmoor, Yeovil) Ⓗ
Fabulous 17th-century character inn that has been a well-deserved winner of local CAMRA Pub of the Year for the last six years. It has several charming bar areas, a dining room and two log fires during winter plus an outside fireplace for smokers. A range of eight cask and two keg ales are on the bar, often all local but sometimes with a national brew to ensure a wide range of changing tastes. Six real ciders are also served, and good pub food is available. A beer festival is held in July.
ᔕ ⊛ ⋈ ◑ ☖ Å ♠ ➋ (21) 🐾 🛜

Weston-super-Mare

Black Cat Ⓛ
135 High Street, BS23 1HN
☎ 07735 880573
6 changing beers Ⓖ
Micropub that opened in 2018 in a former clothes shop, at the Playhouse Theatre end of the High Street. Five cask ales are served, chosen from local breweries and a few from further afield, plus a real cider. Food is available on Friday and Saturday evenings. Dogs are welcome, as are children until later in the evening. There is reasonable access for those of limited mobility. Look for the impressive Black Cat mural. Q ᔕ ◑ ♣ ♠ ➋ 🐾 🛜

Brit Bar Ⓛ ✓
118 High Street, BS23 1HP
☎ (01934) 632629
5 changing beers Ⓗ
Formerly the Britannia, this long-standing town-centre pub was bought by the current owners at auction after a period of closure and has now been given a bright, modern makeover while retaining the important traditional elements. Five changing beers are served, always including some dark brews. Bag-in-box real cider is usually sold too. Live music features at weekends and families are welcome at all hours in the covered courtyard, which is heated in cold weather.
ᔕ ⊛ ⋈ ◑ ☖ 🐾 🛜

Criterion
45 Upper Church Road, BS23 2DY
☎ 07538 753350
Courage Directors Ⓗ**; St Austell Tribute** Ⓖ**; 2 changing beers** Ⓗ
Genuine free house and traditional community venue, just off the seafront in the Knightstone area. Believed to be one of the oldest hostelries in town, it has interesting photos of the area on the walls. Pub games feature strongly, with darts, table skittles and a cribbage team. Bar snacks are available, with filled rolls served at lunchtime. Between two and four guest ales are sold, with all beer styles and local breweries well supported. Big on rugby and dogs. ☖ ♣ ❀ ➋ (1,4) 🐾

Duke of Oxford Ⓛ
27 Oxford Street, BS23 1TF
☎ (01934) 417762
3 changing beers (sourced locally) Ⓗ
Reopened in 2016 after a long period of closure, this pub is just outside the main shopping area and near the seafront. Refurbished as a café-style bar with accommodation, it has a grand piano and sometimes features jazz music. The beers are usually from local breweries and there is real cider. A small outdoor space is accessible via stairs. May close early during the off-season. ᔕ ⊛ ⋈ ◑ ☖ ⋈ ♣ ♠ ➋ ❀ 🐾 🛜

Fork & Ale Taproom & Kitchen
18 Walliscote Road, BS23 1UG
☎ (01934) 384044 ⊕ pitchforkales.com
6 changing beers (sourced locally; often 3D Beers, Pitchfork) Ⓗ
This pub opened in 2019, conveniently located in the town centre near the seafront and railway station. It has a modern look and feel, with an interior of wood, metal and brick, as well as a few comfy sofas. There is a big focus on the beer, with between four and six on at any one time, usually from Pitchfork and 3D. Food is a range of small plates of modern food. The toilets are upstairs. ◑ ⋈ ➋ 🐾 🛜

Regency
22-24 Lower Church Road, BS23 2AG
☎ (01934) 633406
Butcombe Original; Draught Bass; St Austell Tribute; Timothy Taylor Landlord; 2 changing beers (sourced nationally; often Dark Star) Ⓗ
Comfortable, friendly town-centre local, attracting a mixed clientele including students at lunchtime. It has pool, skittles and crib teams, but also offers a quiet refuge for conversation. The pool room with TV and jukebox is separate from the main bar area, and children are welcome here. Keenly priced home-cooked food is served lunchtimes, and there are curries on Wednesdays and grill evenings on Thursdays. Outside are front and rear patios. Pub outings feature, and live bands perform here occasionally. ᔕ ⊛ ◑ ☖ ♣ ➋

Williton

Masons Arms L

2 North Road, TA4 4SN
☎ (01984) 639200 🌐 themasonsarms.com
**Exmoor Ale; St Austell Tribute; 1 changing beer
(sourced regionally; often Dartmoor)** ⚏
Beautiful thatched 16th-century inn with oak beams
throughout and five en-suite rooms in an adjoining
annexe. The pub has a good reputation for food and for
the quality of its ales, and always offers Rich's cider. It
hosts quiz teams in the area league, and has a pleasant
beer garden where locals and visitors alike sit and relax.
Close to the Quantock Hills, West Somerset Railway and a
short drive away from Exmoor National Park.
Q ⏴ ❀ ⇚ ◑ ⅃ ❤ ▲ ❤ P ⊞ (28) ❀ ☎

Railway Inn L

55 Long Street, TA4 4QY
☎ (01984) 632508
**3 changing beers (sourced regionally; often
Butcombe, Exmoor)** ⚏
An old inn beside the A39 with two bars, a small lounge
and a games room. Internally, white walls are
interspersed with black beams and stone fireplaces. The
pub has teams in the local quiz, darts, skittles and pool
leagues, and also holds its own quiz on Monday nights.
By the skittle alley at the back is an outside seating area.
Close to the West Somerset Railway, the Quantock Hills
and Exmoor. ❀ ⇚ ◑ ⅃ ▲ ⇌ ❤ P ⊞ (28) ❀ ☎

Wincanton

Nog Inn

South Street, BA9 9DL
☎ (01963) 32998 🌐 thenoginn.com
**Otter Bitter; house beer (by Sharp's); 2 changing
beers (sourced regionally; often Cotleigh, Otter,
Sharp's)** ⚏
The striking Georgian façade of this attractive Grade II
listed inn fronts a long, narrow building with parts dating
back to the 16th century. Guest ales are often seasonal,
and there is always an extensive range of continental
beers on tap. The menu features home-cooked pub
classics, made with locally sourced and seasonal
ingredients where possible. At the far end of the
property is a secluded, sunny garden with covered
seating. ⏴ ❀ ◑ ❤ P ⊞ (58,667) ❀ ☎

Witham Friary

Seymour Arms ★

BA11 5HF
☎ (01749) 684280
Cheddar Ales Potholer ⚏
A hidden rural gem, this place looks to have changed
little over the last 50 or so years (apart from new loos!).
Built in the 1860s as a hotel to serve the nearby Mid-

Somerset GWR branch railway station, it was part of the
Duke of Somerset's estate. Sadly, in the 1960s Mr
Beeching closed the station, and the hotel became a
quiet country pub. One locally sourced beer and a cider
are served from a glass-panelled hatch in the central
hallway. Q ⏴ ❀ ♣ ❤ P ❀

Wookey

Ring o' Bells

High Street, BA5 1JZ
☎ (01749) 678079 🌐 ringobells.uk
**Butcombe Original; Cheddar Ales Potholer; 1
changing beer (sourced locally)** ⚏
Vibrant and handsome old pub in the village centre,
serving a good range of four beers and two ciders. It has
a pleasant terrace out front and a small courtyard garden
to the rear. Formerly a Wadworth outlet, it is now a free
house with ownership unchanged since 2016. It has a
large single bar with the bar itself made from old cider
barrels. There is a small dining room adjoining. The skittle
alley also acts as a function room. Food is sourced locally.
Q ⏴ ❀ ◑ ▲ ♣ ❤ ⊞ (67) ❀ ☎

Yarlington

Stag's Head

Pounds Lane, BA9 8DG ST65462923
☎ (01963) 440393 🌐 stagsheadinn.co.uk
**3 changing beers (often Bath Ales, Wriggle Valley,
Yeovil)** ⚏
Local ales, Somerset cider and food made using local
produce are just some of the attractions awaiting you as
you step over the threshold of this historic 18th-century
inn. It is set in a picturesque village with a beautiful
church and running stream, a working farm and circular
walks. Dogs are more than welcome in the bar area and
snug room. Q ⏴ ⇚ ◑ ❤ P ❀ ☎

Yeovil

Quicksilver Mail ✅

168 Hendford Hill, BA20 2RG (at jct of A30 and A37)
☎ (01935) 424721 🌐 quicksilvermail.com
**Butcombe Original; Dartmoor Jail Ale; St Austell
Tribute; 2 changing beers (sourced nationally)** ⚏
A roadside pub with a unique name commemorating a
high-speed mail coach. It has been run by the same
landlord since 2002 and has been almost ever-present in
this Guide. Alongside the large single bar is a separate
dining area serving excellent food and a well-priced
range of wines. The pub is a well-known live music
venue and also holds comedy, bingo and quiz nights in
the bar or function room. ⏴ ❀ ⇚ ◑ ▲ ♣ P ⊞ (6,96) ❀ ☎

Choosing pubs

CAMRA members and branches choose the pubs listed in The Good Beer Guide. There
is no payment for entry, and pubs are inspected on a regular basis by personal visits;
publicans are not sent a questionnaire once a year, as is the case with some pub guides.
CAMRA branches monitor all the pubs in their areas, and the choice of pubs for the
guide is often the result of democratic vote at branch meetings. However,
recommendations from readers are welcomed and will be passed on to the relevant
branch: write to Good Beer Guide, CAMRA, 230 Hatfield Road, St Albans, Hertfordshire,
AL1 4LW; or send an email to: **gbgeditor@camra.org.uk**

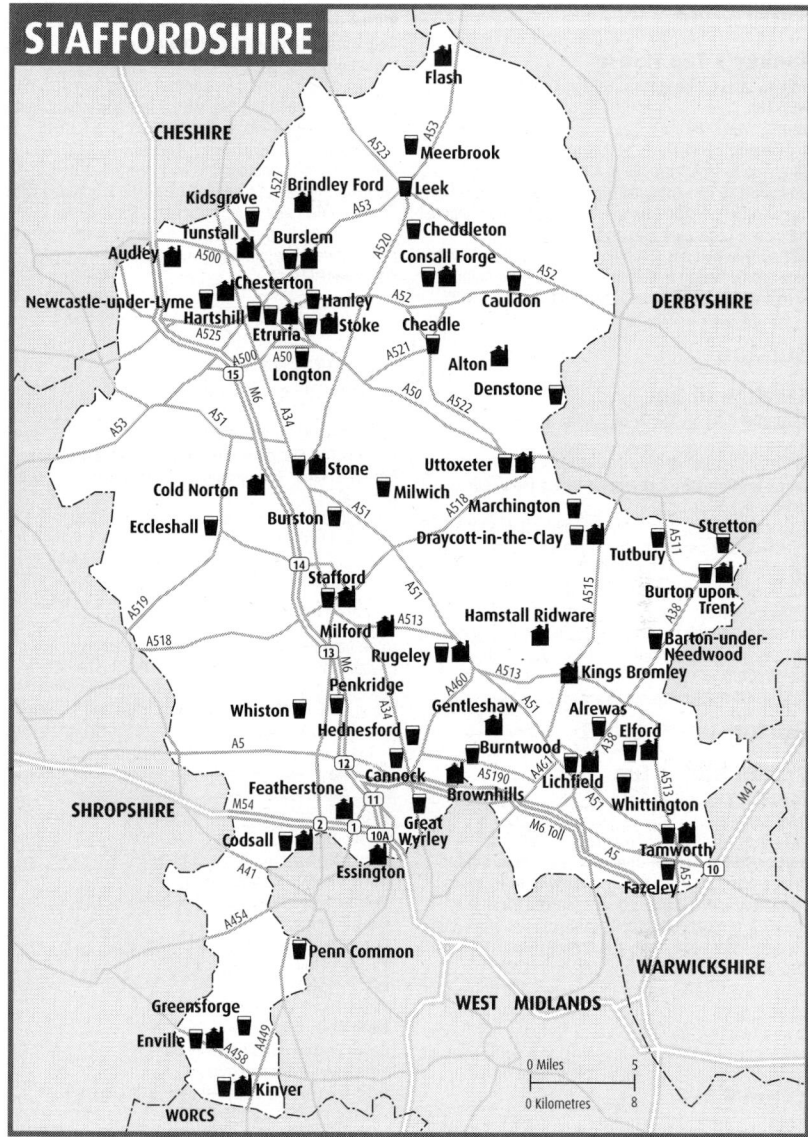

STAFFORDSHIRE

Alrewas

Swan Inn

Fradley Junction, DE13 7DN (by Trent & Mersey Canal, about 1 mile W of Fradley village) SK140140
☎ (01283) 790330 ⊕ swaninnfradley.co.uk
Everards Original, Sunchaser, Tiger; 1 changing beer (sourced regionally) ⊞
Known locally as the Mucky Duck, this 18th-century, Grade II-listed, mid-terrace pub overlooks the junction of the Trent & Mersey and Coventry canals. The cosy public bar, which retains an old-fashioned charm, and the smaller lounge are on opposite sides of a central serving area. There is also a cellar room, with vaulted brick ceiling. Guest beers are usually from Midlands micros (one available in winter, up to five in summer). No meals are served on Sunday evening. Boaters, walkers and gongoozlers welcome. Q❄️🐕🌳◐P🌸♿🛜

Barton-under-Needwood

Royal Oak ✅

74 The Green, DE13 8JD (½ mile S of B5016 via Wales Lane)
☎ (01283) 713852
Marston's Pedigree; 2 changing beers (sourced nationally) ⊞ /Ⓖ
Bustling community local on the southern edge of the village, home to many traditional pub games teams and a base for several local sports teams. Parts of the building date back to the 16th century and the pub has existed since the mid-1800s. Public bar and lounge customers are served from a central sunken bar below the level of the rest of the ground floor. A separate conservatory offers access to the garden. Beers are on handpump or by gravity, direct from the cask, on request.
Q❄️🐕🌳♣️🍴♿P🚃(12,12E) 🌸🛜

Burntwood

Sankey's Tap House

Unit 1, Lambourne House, Bridge Cross Road, WS7 2BX

☎ 07982 923744

4 changing beers 🄷

Burntwood's first micropub is a friendly place with no loud music or TVs, just good conversation and great beer. It serves four ales and six ciders from local and national breweries. Cobs, pork pies and the usual snacks are offered. The pub has recently been redeveloped, with both rooms having a welcoming feel. Closed Mondays, except on bank holidays. Q🚸♿♣🍏P🚌(60,61)🐾📶

Burston

Greyhound Inn

ST18 0DR (just off A51 N of Sandon and 3 miles S of Stone)

☎ (01889) 508263 🌐 greyhoundinn.info

Lancaster Bomber; 2 changing beers (sourced regionally) 🄷

A spacious and friendly family-owned establishment 15 minutes' walk from the Trent & Mersey Canal at Bridge 86, refurbished in 2017. It has a reputation for good food and beer, with a separate bar for those who just want a drink. The garden with farm animals helps make children welcome, and this is a dog-loving pub. Not to be missed on travels around Staffordshire. Local CAMRA Rural Pub of the Year runner-up in 2019. 🚸❀◐⛺♣P🐾📶

Burton upon Trent

Burton Bridge Inn

24 Bridge Street, DE14 1SY (on A511, at town end of Trent Bridge)

☎ (01283) 536596 🌐 burtonbridgeinn.co.uk

Burton Bridge Golden Delicious, Sovereign Gold, Bridge Bitter, Burton Porter, Stairway to Heaven, Festival Ale; 1 changing beer (sourced locally) 🄷

This 17th-century pub is the flagship of the Burton Bridge Brewery estate and fronts the brewery itself. It incorporates two rooms served from a central bar: a smaller front room, with wooden pews and displaying many awards, brewery memorabilia and framed old maps of Burton; and a back room featuring oak beams and panels. A small function room and a skittle alley are upstairs. Occasional live music takes place on Saturdays. Q❀♣🍏🚌🐾📶

Coopers Tavern ★

43 Cross Street, DE14 1EG (off Station St)

☎ (01283) 567246

Draught Bass 🄶**; Joule's Pale Ale, Slumbering Monk** 🄷**; 6 changing beers (sourced regionally)** 🄷/🄶

Classic 19th-century alehouse, once the Bass Brewery tap but currently part of the Joule's estate. Following a sympathetic refurbishment and expansion in 2017 the pub now incorporates five linked rooms. The intimate inner taproom has retained its barrel tables and bench seating, with the beer served from a small counter by the cask stillage. Fruit wines plus up to six ciders/perries (choice varies) are also available. Impromptu folk music regularly features on Tuesday evenings, and live music some Sunday afternoons. 🚸❀⇌🍏🚌🐾📶

Devonshire Arms

86 Station Street, DE14 1BT (on corner of jct with Milton St)

☎ (01283) 480022

Burton Bridge Bridge Bitter, Stairway to Heaven, Top Dog Stout; Draught Bass; 3 changing beers (sourced regionally) 🄷

Popular old pub, now a free house, dating from the 19th century and Grade II listed, with a recently refurbished public bar at the front. To the rear is a larger, more comfortable, split-level lounge featuring an 1853 map of Burton, old local photographs and unusual arched wooden ceilings. An extended rear patio is adorned with flower borders and hanging baskets. The Tuesday food evening has a theme such as fish, pies or steak. Football fans are welcome, including away supporters. ❀◗⇌♣🍏P🚌🐾📶

Old Royal Oak

11 Market Place, DE14 1HA (on N side of Market Place, off High St)

☎ (01283) 532202 🌐 oldroyaloak.co.uk

Fownes The Elephant Riders, Royal Oak Bitter, King Korvak's Saga; 2 changing beers (sourced regionally) 🄷

This half-timbered three-storey end-terrace pub is one of the oldest in the town, with parts dating back to the 17th century. It once incorporated a lockup for holding prisoners. After a recent chequered history, it was taken over by Fownes in 2020 and has become a convivial drinkers' hostelry. The single open-plan room features some partitioning, with a few old oak beams retained towards the rear. A TV screen near the the bar scrolls through the drinks menu. Meals are currently limited to pizzas on Thursday to Saturday evenings and weekend lunchtimes. Q❀◐♣🚌🐾

REAL ALE BREWERIES

Beowulf Brownhills
Blythe Hamstall Ridware
Brewhouse & Kitchen ⛁ Lichfield
Burton Bridge Burton upon Trent
Burton Town ◆ Burton upon Trent
Consall Forge Consall Forge
Crown Brewhouse ⛁ Elford
Enville Enville
Firs ⛁ Codsall
Flash Flash
Front Row Brindley Ford
Gates Burton Burton upon Trent
Gentlewood Gentleshaw
Grey Friars Featherstone (brewing suspended)
Heritage Burton upon Trent
Inadequate ⛁ Stoke-on-Trent: Etruria
Izaac Walton Cold Norton
Kickabo Stoke On Trent (NEW)
Kinver Kinver
Lymestone Stone
Marston's Burton upon Trent
Morton Essington
Peakstones Rock Alton
Quartz Kings Bromley
Roebuck Draycott-in-the-Clay
Shugborough Milford (brewing suspended)
Six Towns ⛁ Tunstall (brewing suspended)
Slater's Stafford
Tamworth ◆ Tamworth
Titanic Stoke-on-Trent: Burslem
Tower ◆ Burton upon Trent
Townhouse Audley
Trinity ◆ Lichfield (NEW)
Uttoxeter ◆ Uttoxeter
Vine Inn ⛁ Rugeley
Weal ◆ Chesterton

Roebuck Inn ✓

101 Station Street, DE14 1BT (on corner of jct with Mosley St)

☎ (01283) 511213 ⊕ roe-buck-inn.co.uk

Draught Bass; Greene King Abbot; Marston's Pedigree; Theakston Old Peculier; 2 changing beers (sourced regionally) ⊞

Friendly Victorian corner terrace pub near the railway station, once the Ind Coope Brewery tap, opposite the former brewery. The original classic Draught Burton Ale was launched here in 1976. Inside, there is a long narrow single room with dark wood panelling and the bar counter down one side. A small patio at the rear is available for outdoor drinking, plus a few tables and chairs outside at the front in summer. Live music is played early Sunday evenings.

✿⊿≹(Burton on Trent) ♣●✿✿ 🛜

Weighbridge Inn

Grain Warehouse Yard, Derby Street, DE14 2JJ (off S end of Derby St, A5121, one-way section)

☎ 07758 546922

4 changing beers (sourced regionally) ⊞/Ⓖ

Two-room micropub created in a late-Victorian former coal yard office in 2015 and now operated by the Muirhouse Brewery. It is close to the railway station and en route to Burton Albion's Pirelli Stadium, nearly a mile distant. The bar counter is in the main room, with the available beers and other offerings listed on a blackboard (two beers are usually from Muirhouse). A cosy smaller room is located through a doorway at the far end. Both rooms feature open fireplaces. Children welcome until early evening. Q⏱≹♣●🖥✿

Cannock

Linford Arms ✓

79 High Green, WS11 1BN

☎ (01543) 469360

Greene King Abbot; Ruddles Best Bitter; Sharp's Doom Bar; 5 changing beers (sourced nationally; often Backyard, Beowulf, Salopian) ⊞

Established town-centre Wetherspoon serving eight real ales and ciders. Its name derives from the builders' merchants that formerly occupied the premises. Food is served all day. There is a seating area on two floors, with quieter alcoves and a separate snug. The pub regularly features local breweries, hosts two ale festivals each year and has been a local CAMRA Pub of the Year finalist numerous times in recent years. It has good bus and rail links, and is not to be missed if visiting Cannock. ⏱🕯🕹🖥🛜

Newhall Arms

81 High Green, WS11 1BN

☎ 07852 573042

8 changing beers ⊞

Cannock's first micropub, owned and run by a father and son team. This friendly place in the town centre is a real gem, with no loud music or TVs, just good conversation and great beer. Its bar serves eight ales and two ciders. The beers change all the time, and include both local and national brews. Cobs are available alongside the usual snacks. Q✿🕹●P🖥✿🛜

Cauldon

Yew Tree Inn 🄻

ST10 3EJ (approx 1 mile from junction at Ye Old Crown hotel, Waterhouses)

☎ (01538) 309876 ⊕ yewtreeantiquepub.co.uk

Burton Bridge Bridge Bitter; Rudgate Ruby Mild; 1 changing beer (sourced nationally; often Blue Monkey, Dancing Duck, McMullen) ⊞

Situated halfway between Leek and Ashbourne, this is possibly one of the most famous pubs in the country and one of the few where even the local CAMRA committee would admit that the good real ale is the least of its attractions. The eponymous yew tree that dominates the entrance sets the scene for what lies inside – a step back in time with antiques, guns, pianos, penny farthings, a working pianola and much more period bric-a-brac. Q⏱✿🕹◗♣●P🖥(109)✿🛜

Cheadle

Bakers Arms

21 High Street, ST10 1AA

☎ (01538) 756237

Greene King Abbot; 5 changing beers (often Staffordshire) ⊞

Named after its former use as a bakery, the Bakers Arms opened in 2017. Three separate areas and a superbly set out rear yard make the most of the small space. A real fire, comfortable seating and outdoor suntrap seating make visiting the Bakers a real pleasure. A weekday evening quiz, Sunday evening live music, and regular nibbles on the tables and bar combine to make this place a lovely little boozer for locals and visitors. ✿🕯●P🖥✿🛜

Bird in Hand

117 Tape Street, ST10 1ER

☎ 07812 375407

Burton Bridge Bridge Bitter; Dancing Duck 22; 2 changing beers (often Brunswick, Burton Bridge) ⊞

A well-deserved entry into the Guide, this traditional, terraced street-corner pub occupies a main road position just outside the town centre. Two rooms have lovely coal fires. A large screen shows major sporting events, another room houses a dartboard, and a pool table is found in an ante-room. The cosy snug is quieter and also has a real fire. Outside is a patio for smokers. The licensees always give a warm welcome, as do the bar staff. Q♣🖥(32,32X)✿

Huntsman 🄻

The Green, ST10 1XS (at bottom of hill)

☎ (01538) 750502 ⊕ thehuntsmancheadle.com

Brains Rev James; Marston's Pedigree; Sharp's Doom Bar; 3 changing beers (sourced regionally; often Geeves, Peakstones Rock, Slater's) ⊞

A Guide regular on the edge of this market town, ideal for visiting Alton Towers, the Potteries or the Peak District. Family-friendly, it has a stylish interior and a welcoming atmosphere; guest beers are sourced locally and regionally. A beer and music festival is held at the end of May, with gin and cider festivals later in the year. The food is cooked from scratch, with the beef and lamb coming from the neighbouring farm. Highly recommended. ⏱✿⊿🕹🕯♣●P🖥(IN2)✿🛜

Cheddleton

Black Lion 🄻

12 Hollow Lane, ST13 7HP (turn off A520 into Hollow lane, opp Red Lion, and pub is approx 100yds up hill on right, next to church)

☎ (01538) 360620

Draught Bass; Timothy Taylor Landlord; 4 changing beers (often Salopian, Wincle) ⊞

A welcome new entry to the Guide, the Black Lion is a comfortable village local. Recently refurbished in a modern rustic style, it is warmed by real fires in the winter. An excellent range of well-kept beers is offered. Outside are a patio area to the front and an enclosed beer garden at the rear. The pub is close to the Flint Mill Museum and the Cauldon Canal, and beside the Grade II-listed St Edward's Church, which has a Wardle family connection and Arts and Crafts features. Q❁☺❀◖≠♣●P🚍(16) ☻🛜

Codsall

Codsall Station 🅛

Chapel Lane, WV8 2EJ
☎ (01902) 847061
Holden's Black Country Bitter, Golden Glow, Special; 3 changing beers (sourced regionally; often Holden's) 🅗

Sensitively converted from the waiting room, offices and stationmaster's house, the Grade II-listed building comprises a bar, lounge, snug and conservatory and displays worldwide railway memorabilia. Steps lead to the outside drinking area, with tables and benches overlooking the working platforms. Bar meals are served except Sunday and Monday and cobs and locally made pork pies are available all week. Beer festivals are held on the May and August bank holiday weekends. Q❁☺◖≠P🚍(5,10B) ☻🛜

Love & Liquor

1-3 Church Road, WV8 1EA
5 changing beers 🅗

Converted from a shop in 2019, this village-centre bar is an excellent addition to the real ale choice in Codsall. An upstairs room contains bench seating and a large TV showing sport. Downstairs is a bar area with comfortable seating, a wood-burning stove and another TV. Five varying ales are served, usually including a stout or porter. Tables on the pavement provide an outdoor drinking area. ☺☻≠🚍(5,10B)

Consall Forge

Black Lion 🅛

ST9 0AJ (off A522 follow signs to Consall Gardens, then Nature Reserve on hairpin bend; go straight on, ignore No Vehicular Access sign; at bottom of hill go left along track to car park)
☎ (01782) 550294
Peakstones Rock Black Hole; 3 changing beers (sourced regionally; often Consall Forge, Falstaff) 🅗

Walk, drive or travel by boat or train to visit this destination venue with its changing beer and cider selections. Regular beer festivals are held, normally to coincide with a steam gala on the neighbouring Churnet Valley Railway. Typical pub food is served; arrive hungry as the portions are large. Set in an area of outstanding natural beauty, this establishment is not easy to find by car but well worth the effort. Seek it out! Q❁☺◖À≠♣●P☻🛜

Denstone

Tavern 🅛

College Road, ST14 5HR
☎ (01889) 590847
Courage Directors; Marston's Pedigree; 2 changing beers (sourced nationally; often Brakspear, Marston's) 🅗

The Tavern is a recently refurbished 17th-century village inn offering fine food and good beers in comfortable surroundings. There is a bar area with darts, a comfortable lounge area and a conservatory for dining.

Quiz night is on Monday, when there is no food. Fresh wood-fired stone-baked pizzas are served Fridays and Saturday evenings, to eat in or take away. Booking tables in advance is advisable. Guest beers come from the Marston's range. Q❁☺❀◖À♣P🚍(32A,Swift)☻🛜

Draycott-in-the-Clay

Roebuck ✅

Toby's Hill, DE6 5BT (at Toby's Hill/A515 jct, 600yds N of village)
☎ (01283) 821135 ● theroebuckdraycott.co.uk
Roebuck Hopzester, Bitter, Blonde, IPA; 1 changing beer (sourced locally) 🅗

Welcoming early 19th-century family-owned free house, close to the A50/A515 junction and Staffordshire/Derbyshire boundary. The pub showcases beers from the associated Roebuck Brewery, which is in a splendid oak-framed building to the rear of the large car park. Traditional home-cooked food is served in the restaurant and cosy bar (no meals Sun eve). The Klondike Mill Steam Preservation Centre is nearby and the National Trust's Sudbury Hall and Museum of Childhood are within easy reach, as is the national football centre at St George's Park. ☺❀◖P🚍(402)☻🛜

Eccleshall

King's Arms Hotel ✅

17 Stafford Street, ST21 6BL
☎ (01785) 850294 ● kingsarmseccleshall.com
Marston's Pedigree; Wainwright; 4 changing beers (sourced nationally) 🅗

A former coaching inn and inland revenue office once known as the Unicorn. It was restored and refurbished in 2017; parts of the original building are still visible. Various rooms are served by a central bar. The pub is now a well run and friendly free house, warm and cosy in winter. It serves an interesting selection of beers, both local and national, often including those from the nearby Izaak Walton Brewery. A former local CAMRA Pub of the Season. ☺❀◖◖♿♣P🚍(23A,432)☻

Elford

Crown Inn 🅛

The Square, B79 9DB (600yds E of A513) SK189106
☎ (01827) 383602 ● thecrownelford.co.uk
Draught Bass; Purity Pure Gold; 2 changing beers (sourced locally; often Crown Brewhouse) 🅗

Grade II-listed village pub, with a simple but cosy bar room, a plush snug, two small dining rooms, and a quirky little space which was formerly the above-ground cellar. Solid fuel heating gives a rosy glow in winter. A changing ale from the in-house Crown Brewhouse is occasionally offered. Food is served Wednesday to Saturday evenings and Sunday lunchtime, with regular themed events. Children are welcome in a separate room on the car park side. ☺◖♣P☻🛜

Enville

Cat Inn 🅛

Bridgnorth Road, DY7 5HA (on A458)
☎ (01384) 872209 ● thecatinn.com
Enville Ale, Ginger Beer; Olde Swan Original; 4 changing beers (sourced nationally; often Enville, Froth Blowers, Skinner's) 🅗

Picturesque and impressive country retreat with multiple drinking and dining areas, all with their own real fires. The majority of the cask offering is made up of staple and seasonal Enville beers, but you will also find a number of guest beers and up to two real ciders. The attractive and spacious courtyard tempts many cyclists and ramblers, particularly in the warmer months. Q✿☺⌖◑⬤P✿✿🏠

Fazeley

Three Horseshoes

New Street, B78 3RD (nr jct of A4091 and B5404)
☎ (01827) 289754
Draught Bass; St Austell Tribute; 1 changing beer Ⓗ
This is very much a traditional local, with a friendly welcome for all. The single room features a quarry-tiled bar room, with a smaller, cosier area to the side. There are several TVs. Towards the rear is a large enclosed garden which proves popular in the summer. The guest ale changes frequently and is often from the area. Parking is usually available on nearby streets.
✿♣🚃(110) ✿🏠

Great Wyrley

Andys' Ale House

Unit 38, Quinton Court, WS6 6DS
☎ 07975 847318
5 changing beers (often Beowulf, Bristol Beer Factory, Sarah Hughes) Ⓗ
This venue is Great Wyrley's first micropub, owned and run by the two Andys and located in the Quinton Court Shopping Centre. It is a friendly place, with no loud music or TV, just good conversation and great beer. Its recently updated bar serves five ales and four ciders which change all the time, with both local and national beers offered. Cobs, pork pies and Scotch eggs are available alongside the usual snacks. ✿♿♣⬤P🚃(2)✿🏠

Greensforge

Navigation

Greensforge Lane, DY6 0AH
☎ (01384) 273721
Enville Ale; Three Tuns XXX; 2 changing beers (often Hobsons, Holden's, Olde Swan) Ⓗ
A food-oriented pub with an unspoilt interior which continues to command a loyal following of locals. On sunnier days drinkers can enjoy their beers on one of the many benches at the front of the premises, or on the numerous grass verges, which offer relaxing views. The Navigation sits on the Staffordshire and Worcestershire Canal towpath which connects Stourton and Hinksford. There is a large car park directly opposite. Drinkers may need to stand at busier times. Q✿☺◑P✿🏠

Hednesford

Bridge Inn

387 Cannock Road, WS11 5TD (on jct of Belt Rd and Cannock Rd)
☎ (01543) 423651
Banks's Amber Ale; 6 changing beers (sourced nationally) Ⓗ
Close to Cannock Chase, this is a real ale-focused pub that prides itself on a varied selection of beers, and also stocks real cider. Food is available Thursday to Sunday, all produced on-site using only fresh local produce. Pool and darts teams are based here and theme nights and live music take place most Saturday nights.
✿☺◑≢♣P🚃(25,26) ✿🏠

Cross Keys Hotel Ⓛ

42 Hill Street, WS12 2DN
☎ (01543) 879534
Draught Bass; Holden's Golden Glow; Salopian Oracle; Wye Valley HPA; 4 changing beers (sourced nationally; often Beowulf, Ludlow, Three Tuns) Ⓗ
A former coaching inn dating back to 1746, this traditionally styled establishment has historic and sporting photographs decorating its walls. Hednesford Town football club was originally based behind it; the licensee is an ex-player and current assistant manager. The pub serves up to eight real ales including several guests. Monthly quiz nights are held. It is rumoured that the infamous highwayman Dick Turpin stopped here on his legendary ride to York. Local CAMRA Pub of the Year many times. ✿≢♣P🚃🚃(33,60)✿🏠

Heddin's Ford

69 Market Street, WS12 1AD
Backyard The Hoard, Blonde; 2 changing beers (sourced nationally) Ⓗ
This venue is Hednesford's first micropub and is in the centre of the town. Recently redeveloped, its one room has a welcoming feel, with no loud music, just good conversation and great beer. It stocks four ales: two are permanent ones from Backyard and the others are selected from a variety of local and national breweries. Entertainment takes place at least once a month on Saturdays. Closed Monday except bank holidays, when Sunday opening times operate.
Q✿♿▲≢⬤P🚃(61,62) ✿🏠

Kidsgrove

Blue Bell

25 Hardingswood, ST7 1EG (off A50 nr Tesco, by canal bridge)
☎ (01782) 774052 ⊕ bluebellinnkidsgrove.com
Whim Arbor Light; 5 changing beers (sourced nationally) Ⓗ
Friendly traditional canalside venue offering six real ales and nine ciders, accompanied by a warm welcome from the hosts. The main bar has two separate areas off it and a smaller room to the rear. There is a beer garden at the back. The well-kept beer range features different styles, always including one dark ale. The pub holds an annual beer festival plus seasonal and charity events. Popular with locals, walkers and canal users.
Q✿✿♿≢⬤P🚃(3,4A) ✿🏠

Kinver

Cross Inn Ⓛ

Church Hill, DY7 6HZ
☎ (01384) 878481
Black Country Bradley's Finest Golden, Pig on the Wall, Fireside; 4 changing beers (sourced nationally; often Fixed Wheel, Oakham, Salopian) Ⓗ
A popular destination, with internal decor one would expect from a Black Country Ales outlet, including a real fire. Tasty and tempting food is served at the weekend including hot pork sandwiches. A small number of flatscreen TVs show football fixtures on match days. There is a large car park adjacent and Stourbridge buses stop nearby, but there is no service after 6pm or on Sunday.
✿♿♣⬤P🚃(228) ✿🏠

Leek

Blue Mugge Ⓛ

17 Osbourne Street, ST13 6LJ (off A53 Buxton Rd)
☎ (01538) 384450 ⊕ bluemugge.co.uk
Draught Bass; 4 changing beers (sourced nationally; often Coach House, Slater's) Ⓗ

Now an established entry in the Guide, just outside the town centre. Owned and run by the same family for over 40 years, this unassuming terraced street-corner local has several distinctly separate themed rooms, a result of three adjoining properties being knocked into one. The unique layout has bar service from a central octagonal pillar, with the beer pumps and taps behind the staff. Two handpulls are believed to be 120 years old. Constantly changing guest ales are listed on a blackboard. Good-value food is available lunchtimes. The bus station is nearby. Q ≅ ◁ ♣ ☗ ❀ ☎

Fountain Inn 🅛
14 Fountain Street, ST13 6JR
☎ (01538) 387205
Draught Bass; Exmoor Gold; Wye Valley Butty Bach; 5 changing beers (sourced nationally; often Exmoor, Front Row, Wincle) 🅗
A magnificent bank of 10 handpulls greets the eye on entering this smart town-centre local, a former CAMRA Regional Pub of the Year. Five real ales change regularly and always include a darker, stronger brew. Two real ciders are also on sale. Live music on Sunday plus a beer raffle help make this a real gem of a friendly community pub. Two well-appointed rooms upstairs offer accommodation, and there are plenty of places to eat nearby. Q ≅ ❀ ⇆ ♣ ☗ ☗ ❀ ☎

Roebuck 🅛
18 Derby Street, ST13 5AB (on main shopping street)
☎ (01538) 385602
Everards Tiger; Titanic Steerage, Iceberg, White Star, Plum Porter, Captain Smith's Strong Ale; 4 changing beers (sourced regionally; often Magic Rock, Salopian, Tiny Rebel) 🅗
A well-deserved new entry to the Guide, in the town centre. With its distinctive black and white wooden-framed frontage, this Titanic Brewery-owned former coaching inn dates back to 1626. It sells up to 13 ales at busier times, mainly from the Titanic range, including the award-winning Plum Porter, plus four guest ales, real cider and a range of craft beers. Award-winning food is served all day, including breakfast. Regular live music and outdoor events take place in the large rear beer garden. Close to the bus station. Q ≅ ❀ ◁ ♦ P ☗ ❀ ☎

Wilkes Head 🅛
15 St Edward Street, ST13 5DS
☎ 07976 592787
Whim Hartington Bitter, Hartington IPA, Flower Power; 2 changing beers (sourced nationally; often Broughton, Burton Bridge) 🅗
Reputedly the oldest licensed premises near the main market square, this Whim Brewery-owned local is the longest continuous Guide entry in the area and displays a range of past CAMRA awards over the bar. Live jam music is held on Monday evening hosted by the accomplished musician landlord, and several other all-day music events are staged throughout the year in the large back yard. The beers are from Whim, plus changing guests, usually including a darker, stronger brew. A good range of real cider is also available. Q ❀ ♣ ♦ ☗ ❀

Lichfield

Bitter-Suite 🅛
55 Upper St John Street, WS14 9DT
☎ 07852 179340 ⊕ bittersuite-micropub.co.uk
5 changing beers (sourced nationally) 🅖
Originally a micropub when it opened in 2017, this splendid venue has been so successful it is now a full-blown pub. It now has three comfortable rooms, with service to your table – make your choices from the board.

Five ales are available, usually alongside four real ciders. Gins, wines and bottled beers are also on offer, plus simple snacks. There is a large beer terrace to the rear with occasional live music. Children are welcome until early evening. Q ≅ ❀ ≈ ♦ ☗ ❀ ☎

Horse & Jockey 🅛
8-10 Sandford Street, WS13 6QA
☎ (01543) 410033
Holden's Golden Glow; Marston's Pedigree; Timothy Taylor Landlord; Wye Valley HPA; 4 changing beers (sourced nationally) 🅗
Lichfield's longest-serving Guide entry attracts locals as well as visitors from afar. The four guest ales are generally from microbreweries. Various comfy areas surround the central bar, and there is a suntrap beer terrace to the rear. Sports screenings are popular. Hot food is served Tuesday to Saturday lunchtimes, and a pork pie/cheeseboard selection is always available. A 21-plus age policy applies. ❀ ◁ ≈ ♣ ☗ ❀ ☎

Whippet Inn
21 Tamworth Street, WS13 6JP
☎ 07922 581468
4 changing beers (sourced nationally) 🅗
This former dress shop is an outstanding micropub with a proven record. It takes its name from a cheeky boozer in a Carry On film. Four well-chosen, varying ales are complemented by two changing real ciders and a selection of craft keg beers. With seating for around 25 and a capacity of up to 40, the pub offers a friendly intimacy. Q ≅ ≈ ♦ ☗ ❀ ☎

Marchington

Dog & Partridge
Church Lane, ST14 8LJ (250yds along Church Lane from High St)
☎ (01283) 820394 ⊕ dogandpartridgemarchington.co.uk
Draught Bass; 3 changing beers (sourced locally; often Abbeydale, Gates Burton, Uttoxeter) 🅗
A gem of a village inn with Bass always available, plus a selection of local guest ales on several handpumps. Formerly a restaurant, it is split into four main indoor areas with open fires. Food is served lunchtimes and evenings. A pleasant beer garden to the rear is popular in the summer months. The pub is renowned in the area for its weekly live music sessions and regular beer festivals. Parking is available to the side and close by at the church. Children are welcome. Q ≅ ❀ ◁ ▲ P ☗ (402) ❀ ☎

Meerbrook

Lazy Trout 🅛
ST13 8SN
☎ (01538) 300385
Greene King IPA; Morland Old Speckled Hen; 3 changing beers 🅗
A well-deserved new entry on the edge of the Peak District National Park and almost across the road from Tittesworth Water reservoir. Its position makes it a natural haunt for ramblers, cyclists, dog walkers and families, and wellies and walking boots are welcome! Five cask ales are stocked, with at least one from a local brewery. Food is served all day every day, with booking strongly advised at busier times. Ample outdoor seating at the front and rear with stunning views is complemented by a cosy real fire inside. ≅ ❀ ◁ ♦ P ❀

Milwich

Green Man

Sandon Lane, ST18 0EG (on B5027 in centre of village)
☎ (01889) 505310 ● greenmanmilwich.com
Draught Bass; 5 changing beers (sourced nationally) Ⓗ
A country pub well worth a visit, with 27 consecutive years in the Guide and a multiple local CAMRA Pub of the Year winner. The licensee has been in-situ since 1990 – he drinks Bass! There is also usually a dark beer available. The enormous luxurious beer garden is used to host an annual free music festival. This place is at the heart of a vibrant village community, and is popular with walkers and cyclists visiting the area. No food Mondays or Tuesdays. Q❀☆◑♣P❀♥🐾🛜

Newcastle-under-Lyme

Boat & Horses

2 Stubbs Gate, ST5 1LU (opp Morrisons supermarket, 500yds from bus station)
☎ (01782) 911528
Draught Bass; Facer's North Star Porter; Salopian Oracle; Thornbridge Jaipur IPA; 2 changing beers (sourced nationally) Ⓗ
Reopened in 2019 under an award-winning licensee, this pub has gone from strength to strength. It is a friendly and pleasant free house on the edge of the town centre, offering six real ales, up to six real ciders and a selection of craft beers in cans and bottles. No food is served but customers are welcome to bring their own and eat it with a purchased drink or two. Live music events take place on Sunday evenings, showcasing the best of local and regional talent. 🐾☆●🖵♥🛜

Bridge Street Ale House Ⓛ

31 Bridge Street, ST5 2RY
☎ (01782) 499394 ● bridgestreetalehouse.com
5 changing beers (sourced nationally; often Beartown, Facer's) Ⓗ
The first micropub in the area, this is a special place for regulars and newcomers alike, in the capable hands of the charismatic owner and his hospitable staff. The pub oozes charm and appeal, enhanced by the quirky décor. Five changing guest beers are on handpull from various breweries, with others occasionally available straight from the barrel. Nine real ciders and an extensive range of speciality rums add to the individuality of this fantastic hostelry – a Newcastle real ale institution. Q❀♣●🖵♥

Cask Bar

1-2 Andrew Place, ST5 1DL
☎ (01782) 870560
Sarah Hughes Dark Ruby Mild; 4 changing beers (sourced nationally) Ⓗ
An award-winning microbar just outside Newcastle town centre, open since 2017. One room houses a variety of different seating, from ordinary tables and chairs to the higher posing-style tables. Sarah Hughes Dark Ruby is the permanent cask beer along with four changing guests, two real ciders and a rotating craft keg selection, plus one of the best gin ranges in the area. Meals are served Wednesday to Sunday. Q◑●🖵♥🛜

Hopinn

102 Albert Street, ST5 1JR
☎ (01782) 711121 ● hopinn.net
Black Sheep Best Bitter; Draught Bass; Oakham Citra; 5 changing beers (sourced nationally; often Mallinsons, Northern Monk, Oakham) Ⓗ
Voted Pub of the Year four times by the local CAMRA branch, the Hopinn offers an outstanding range of quality national and regional beers. It serves eight cask ales, supplemented by five KeyKeg brews. Staff are ever-attentive and a warm welcome is extended to all. The pub's three rooms are comfortably furnished, with Art Deco features to admire, all contributing to a wonderful atmosphere. 🐾♿♣🖵♥

Hopwater Cellar Ⓛ

2 Bridge Street, ST5 2RY
☎ (01782) 713311
8 changing beers (sourced nationally) Ⓚ
This cellar bar, which opened in 2015, offers an amazing choice of beers and other drinks in such a small space. There are three drinking areas, two of them to the left and right of the main bar area. More than 400 bottles and cans from around the globe are accompanied by eight KeyKeg beers of different styles and strengths sourced countrywide, mainly from independent breweries. A range of premium whiskies, ciders and mead is also offered. Q❀♿🖵♥🛜

Lymestone Vaults Ⓛ

Pepper Street, ST5 1PR
☎ (01782) 615801
Lymestone Stone Cutter, Stone Faced, Foundation Stone, Stone the Crows; 4 changing beers (sourced regionally; often Lymestone) Ⓗ
A modern wine bar-type pub, the first to be owned by Lymestone Brewery of Stone. Accessed via an alleyway, it comprises one L-shaped room with a mixture of chairs and sofas, plus a piano in the corner contributing to an old-fashioned feel. Up to eight beers are available, including a choice of the pub's own Lymestone Brewery ales. At least eight real ciders are stocked, advertised on a tall pole. An excellent lunchtime menu includes the local delicacy of Staffordshire oatcakes, which are sold with a range of fillings and are highly recommended. 🐾◑♿♣●🖵♥🛜

Wellers Ⓛ

3 Pepper Street, ST5 1PR
☎ (01782) 698080
Weal Ales Weller Weal, Centwealial Milk Stout; 4 changing beers (sourced nationally; often Weal Ales) Ⓗ
Wellers is the taphouse for Weal Ales and showcases its national award-winning ales alongside three nationally sourced rotating guests. Two real ciders, two craft ales and speciality gins and vodkas are also sold. Just off the High Street, this is a modern, comfortable, family-friendly pub for a quality beer served by welcoming staff. Thursday is quiz night. No food is served but you can bring your own. Closed Mondays except bank holidays. 🐾●🖵♥🛜

Penkridge

Star Inn ✔

Market Place, ST19 5DJ
☎ (01785) 712513 ● thestarpenkridge.wixsite.com/home
Lancaster Bomber; Marston's Pedigree; Wainwright; 4 changing beers (sourced nationally) Ⓗ
A normally busy one-room venue with a welcoming feel. It has several distinct areas, plus a patio and seating area outside. The pub is in the old Market Place and first traded as an inn in 1830. It later closed and became a Co-op store, then a private residence, before being restored and converted back into a pub in 1981. Alongside the ales it serves the usual food and excellent Scotch eggs. 🐾❀◑🅰🚃●P🖵♥🛜

Penn Common

Barley Mow L ⊘

Pennwood Lane, WV4 5JN (follow signs to Penn Golf Club from A449) SO901949
☎ (01902) 333510
Greene King Abbot; Hobsons Town Crier; St Austell Tribute; Timothy Taylor Landlord; 2 changing beers (sourced regionally) ⊞

On the edge of Penn Common and sharing an access driveway with Penn Golf Club, this charming inn is worth seeking out. Built around 1630, it has low-beamed ceilings and steps leading down into the drinking and dining areas. It is rightly renowned for its steaks. The compact single bar has a display of drip mats and foreign banknotes, and serves a selection of six quality real ales. Thatchers Heritage cider is also on offer.
Q ✿ ☆ ◑ ● P ☀ ?

Rugeley

Plaza L ⊘

Horsefair, WS15 2EJ
☎ (01889) 586831
Greene King Abbot; Ruddles Best Bitter; Sharp's Doom Bar; 7 changing beers (sourced locally; often Beowulf, Blythe, Salopian) ⊞

Previously a cinema dating from the 1930s, this spacious Wetherspoon retains much of the cinematic atmosphere and Art Deco flourishes of the period. The light and airy interior allows for three widely separated levels, accentuated by a large window where the cinema screen once was. This leads to an outside drinking area, with balcony, terrace and lawned beer garden. Around seven guest ales are offered, with micros such as Salopian proving popular. The small car park is Pay & Display.
Q ✿ ☆ ◑ ◑ & ≠ ● P ▦ ?

Rusty Barrel

Fernwood Shopping Centre, Green Lane, WS15 2GS
⊕ therustybarrel.co.uk
Backyard Gold; Beowulf Dark Raven; Blythe Palmers Poison; Slater's 1 Hop; 4 changing beers (sourced locally; often Goff's, Leatherbritches, Titanic) ⊞

The first micropub in this town has one room and a friendly atmosphere. Its decor is simple painted brick, and the ceiling displays pumpclips showing the vast array of beers that have been sold. Four handpumps offer a changing selection of beers. At least five ciders are available alongside a good selection of wine, gin and whisky. Children are welcome until early evening.
Q ✿ & ♣ ● P ▦ (22,825) ❀

Vine Inn

Sheep Fair Close, WS15 2AT
☎ (01889) 574443
Vine Inn EPA, Vanilla Porter, Grapefruit IPA; 1 changing beer (sourced locally) ⊞

An old pub, one for the locals, on a quiet street, with its own brewery. It retains a traditional multi-room layout, with a spacious bar to the front, a small snug behind, plus a room to the rear offering pool. It also has a large function room upstairs. The venue feels pleasantly dated, with quarry tiles and an open log fire. There is a small beer yard at the front, underneath the sign.
Q ✿ ☆ & ♣ ▦ ❀ ?

Stafford

Bird in Hand

Victoria Square, ST16 2AQ (corner of Victoria Square)
☎ (01785) 252198 ⊕ birdinhandstafford.co.uk

Black Country Bradley's Finest Golden, Pig on the Wall, Fireside; 6 changing beers (sourced regionally) ⊞

Part of the Black Country Ales chain, refurbished in 2017. The pub has a traditional feel, with three rooms and open fires, and boasts the biggest beer garden in Stafford town centre. The Bird serves home-cooked food to complement its ales, and hosts live music every Sunday evening. Part of its history is as a Joule's of Stone outlet; the trademark cross can still be seen on the outside door frames. Over-18s only. ✿ ◑ ● ≠ ♣ ● ▦ ❀ ?

bod

57-59 Bodmin Avenue, ST17 0EF
☎ (01785) 661506
Titanic Iceberg, Plum Porter, Steerage; 3 changing beers (often Titanic) ⊞

The first of Titanic Brewery's bod chain of café bars opened in 2018, named after its location on Bodmin Avenue. It promises to provide breakfast, brunch, lunch, dinner, snacks and a well-deserved pint after a hard day's graft. Four Titanic beers are served on draught. The menu includes gluten-free and vegan options. The pub occupies a former Co-op shop; ironically, the new Co-op opposite is on the site of a former pub. Q ✿ ◑ & ▦ ❀ ?

Greyhound

12 County Road, ST16 2PU (off A34, opp jail)
☎ (01785) 222432
Bradfield Farmers Blonde; 7 changing beers (sourced nationally) ⊞

A short walk from the centre of Stafford, this two-room free house is well worth a visit. It dates from 1831 and a newspaper article from the day it opened can be seen above the bar. Today the pub offers a changing range of eight ales, and also stocks a variety of bottled ciders. It has won a number of CAMRA awards including Pub of the Year. Q ✿ ♣ ▦ ❀

Shrewsbury Arms

75 Eastgate Street, ST16 2NG
☎ (01785) 248240
Black Country Bradley's Finest Golden, Pig on the Wall, Fireside; 6 changing beers (sourced nationally) ⊞

Part of the Black Country Ales chain, this pub complements the firm's own range of beers with a choice from breweries both local and further afield. Two real ciders are also sold. Attractions include three open fires for cold weather, and a conservatory that can be booked for private functions. Light snacks are always available. It is said that the spirits in bottles are not the only ones around! Over-18s only. Q ✿ ☆ ≠ ♣ ● ▦ ❀ ?

Slater's Bar

28 Gaolgate Street, ST16 2NT
☎ 07977 982884 ⊕ slatersales.squarespace.com/slaters-bar
Slater's 1 Hop, Premium, Haka; 2 changing beers ⊞

A straightforward micropub with friendly staff; a good conversion from a former shop. It sells real ale, craft lager, ciders, speciality gins and spirits, wine, tea and coffee. A pavement drinking area has tables and chairs to enjoy the sun, and is in a pedestrianised area so there is little traffic. No food is served but customers are welcome to bring their own lunch. Evening attractions include open mic nights on Tuesday, a quiz on Thursday, live music on Saturday, and Drink and Draw on Sunday. Q ✿ & ≠ ● ▦

Spittal Brook

106 Lichfield Road, ST17 4LP
☎ (01785) 251343

St Austell Tribute; Wye Valley HPA; 2 changing beers (often Ringwood, Wye Valley) Ⓗ
A thriving traditional two-roomed alehouse within walking distance of the town centre down a cul-de-sac just before the railway bridge. There is a small front room with TV and dartboard and a larger rear room with a restaurant area. Food is locally sourced wherever possible. The beer range may vary. The pub hosts a cask ale club, darts, dominoes and cribbage on Monday, quiz night on Wednesday, poker night on Thursday, and live entertainment on most Saturdays. ≿❀◑♣P❀✿ᔑ

Sun
7 Lichfield Road, ST17 4JX
☎ (01785) 248361
Everards Tiger; Titanic Steerage, Anchor Bitter, Iceberg, White Star, Captain Smith's Strong Ale; 6 changing beers (sourced nationally) Ⓗ
One of Titanic Brewery's fleet, this multi-roomed, multi-level pub has 12 handpumps. Food is served throughout the day, using locally sourced ingredients. The Sunday menu includes a traditional roast. An outdoor drinking area with its own bar is ideal on warmer days. Beer festivals are held in spring and late summer in a large marquee at the rear of the building. Buses stop outside the front door. Q≿❀◑≈♣P❀✿ᔑ

Stoke-on-Trent: Burslem

Bull's Head Ⓛ
14 St John's Square, ST6 3AJ
☎ (01782) 834153
Titanic Steerage, Iceberg, White Star, Plum Porter; 6 changing beers (sourced nationally) Ⓗ
The Titanic Brewery tap offers 10 real ales, 10 ciders and perries served from the cellar, plus a selection of draught and bottled Belgian beers. Its large central bar gives customers a choice between the snug or the bar where bar billiards, a skittles table and jukebox can be found. A beer garden to the rear. The pub is close to Port Vale FC and opens early on match days – all fans are welcome. It is also a supporter of community events in the area.
Q≿❀♣●🖳(3,98)✿ᔑ

Bursley Ale House
Wedgwood Place, ST6 4ED
☎ (01782) 911393
5 changing beers (often Abbeydale, Blue Monkey, Charnwood) Ⓗ
A smallish pub on two floors, formerly run along the lines of a microbar. The cellar is on the ground floor to the right of the door, behind glass-fronted doors. Five constantly changing ales are served from handpump off the bar and can come from any brewery in the country. A couple of constantly rotating real ciders are also stocked, along with a selection of bottles. There is a large beer garden at the front. ❀≈♣●🖳(3,98)

Duke William Ⓛ
2 St John's Square, ST6 3AJ
☎ (01782) 814809 ∰ dukewilliamburslem.co.uk
Greene King Abbot; Oakham Citra; Sarah Hughes Dark Ruby Mild; 5 changing beers (sourced nationally; often Abbeydale, Acorn, Salopian) Ⓗ
This imposing mock-Tudor building is in the heart of the Potteries' mother town. Its friendly and relaxed atmosphere makes it a popular haunt both with diners and drinkers. The ground floor has a lounge and a snug, plus a large public bar. Original features abound, including the serving hatch and leaded windows, the horseshoe-shaped bar and its heated foot rail, plus bell pushes in the lounge. Eight beers are served, including five guest ales. ◑🖳&❀

Stoke-on-Trent: Etruria

Holy Inadequate Ⓛ
67 Etruria Old Road, ST1 5PE
☎ 07771 358238
Inadequate NZ Pale Ale, Roundhouse Stout; Joule's Pale Ale; 5 changing beers (sourced nationally; often Inadequate) Ⓗ
On the outskirts of Hanley, this popular establishment offers a warm welcome. An L-shaped lounge and bar area, a rear room – both with log-burners – and a covered beer garden provide a choice of places in which to enjoy the excellent variety of beer and real cider on offer. The in-house brewery goes from strength to strength. Scotch eggs and pork pies are available all day, and regular mini beer festivals are held. The pub is a regular recipient of local CAMRA awards, including Pub of the Year on four occasions. ❀●P🖳(4,4A)✿ᔑ

Stoke-on-Trent: Hanley

BottleCraft
33 Piccadilly, ST1 1EN (next to Regent Theatre)
☎ (01782) 911819 ∰ bottlecraft.beer
14 changing beers (sourced nationally)
Modern, comfortable, craft beer bar in the heart of the city centre, with two cask beers on handpull, 12 KeyKeg beers and up to two real ciders. There is also a huge range of both real ale and craft beer in bottles and cans. The friendly and experienced bar staff are more than happy to help. There is a larger seating area upstairs and an outdoor area at the front. Tasting events are run regularly. Q≿&●🖳✿ᔑ

Coachmakers Arms ★
65 Lichfield Street, ST1 3EA (opp Hanley bus station)
Draught Bass; 4 changing beers (sourced nationally) Ⓗ
A hidden gem of a historic Victorian corridor-style pub, comprising four rooms off a main passageway, with the bar accessible from the rear room, drinking corridor and the small snug. The front right-hand room is cosy, with a real fire. A fine selection of real ales on handpull is offered, with Draught Bass plus four guests, including many local and national favourites. A selection of bottles including lagers is also stocked, along with a significant range of real cider in the fridge. Q≿●P🖳✿

Unicorn Inn ✓
40 Piccadilly, ST1 1EG
Draught Bass; Fuller's London Pride; 4 changing beers (often Belhaven, Greene King) Ⓗ
A small, one-room city-centre pub opposite the Regent Theatre, popular with theatregoers both before and after a show. It comprises a comfortably furnished lounge and a popular snug at the rear. Bass and London Pride are supported by up to four changing beers from anywhere in the country. In the alley alongside is a narrow-gauge tram track, along which drayman used to deliver barrels. All this, plus the resident ghost! 🖳ᔑ

Victoria Lounge Bar Ⓛ
5 Adventure Place, ST1 3AF (next to Hanley bus station)
☎ (01782) 273530 ∰ victorialoungebar.co.uk
Salopian Oracle; 5 changing beers (sourced nationally) Ⓗ
Family run for close to 40 years, and with a well-established reputation for quality, it's no surprise this pub is popular with locals and travellers alike. It has a large split-level room with comfortable furnishings enhanced by the addition of chesterfield settees. The pub stocks up to six real ales from around the country, and serves good-value meals at lunchtime. It is conveniently close

to the theatres and main bus station, ideal for a pint or two before the show and for the bus home.
Q🌣🕙👤🍽☂

Woodman 🅛

3 Goodson Street, ST1 2AT
☎ (01782) 213996
6 changing beers (sourced nationally; often Facer's) 🄷

Large Caldmore Taverns pub in the city centre, reopened in 2018 after a long period of closure. Internally, it comprises four areas that extend around the bar in a lazy L-shape; two reach back towards the toilets, and there is a small snug behind the bar. A house beer is accompanied by five guest ales, including local brews and those from further afield. Two ciders are served for the apple enthusiast. A good, traditional hostelry for a neighbourhood severely lacking in such places.
Q♣👤🍽☂

Stoke-on-Trent: Hartshill

Artisan Tap

552 Hartshill Road, ST4 6AF
☎ (01782) 618378
4 changing beers (sourced nationally) 🄷

Converted from an old workshop in 2017, this popular venue on the Hartshill Mile soon established itself as a firm favourite with drinkers, serving four draught beers, three real ciders and several keg beers across all styles. The raised area in the main bar hosts regular live bands and a Tuesday quiz. The pub appears small but is bigger on the inside, with a long and quirky rear lounge plus outside seating at the front. Q🌣👤🍽❀☂

Greyhound 🅛

67 George Street, ST5 1JT
☎ (01782) 635814
Everards Tiger; Titanic Steerage, Iceberg, White Star, Plum Porter; 5 changing beers (sourced nationally; often Titanic) 🄷

The second pub in the Titanic fleet, this establishment holds its own in an area renowned for good beer. Nine handpulls showcase four Titanic beers plus five different guests from across the UK. Two real ciders are always on offer, along with a large selection of country wines and bottled beers. Three kegs are often used for tap takeovers. Tasty bar snacks are served. Entertainment includes regular live music from local bands and a quiz on Sunday evening. Q🌣🕙👤🍽☂

Sanctuary 🅛

493-495 Hartshill Road, ST4 6AA
☎ (01782) 437523 ⊕ sanctuaryhartshill.co.uk
4 changing beers (sourced locally) 🄷

This extremely popular micropub is a must-visit if you enjoy good conversation in a relaxed atmosphere with your drink. Cosy and eclectically furnished, the single-room bar is adorned with memorabilia and many intriguing ornaments. It has a real charm that makes you want to linger a little bit longer. The four handpull beers are well chosen and change all the time, and are joined by four traditional ciders plus an array of gins.
🌣♣👤🍽❀☂

Stoke-on-Trent: Longton

Congress Inn 🅛

14 Sutherland Road, ST3 1HJ (nr Longton police station)
☎ (01782) 763667 ⊕ congressinnlongton.co.uk

Adnams Broadside; Castle Rock Sheriff's Tipple; Townhouse Styrian Pale; 6 changing beers (sourced nationally; often Castle Rock, Townhouse) 🄷

A convivial, multi award-winning, two-roomed pub just outside the centre of Longton, dedicated to the dispense of good-quality real ale from a whole host of microbreweries. The left-hand room contains the bar, where the three permanent beers are joined by up to six guest ales. The right-hand room houses the dartboard, and is also used for meetings and the annual beer festival, held every May. It is hard for a real ale fan to go wrong in a place like this – four real ciders and a good selection of bottled beers are also available. ⇌♣🚌

Stoke-on-Trent: Stoke

Glebe 🅛

35 Glebe Street, ST4 1HG
☎ (01782) 860670
Joule's Pure Blonde, Pale Ale, Slumbering Monk; 1 changing beer (sourced nationally; often Joule's) 🄷

A short walk from Stoke railway station, this superb Joule's establishment has justifiably become one of the must-visit pubs in the city. Magnificent features, including beautifully restored stained-glass windows, along with the candlelit tables, all add to the welcoming atmosphere. Three mainstay Joule's ales are supplemented by one guest beer. Home-made meals are served at lunchtimes and early evenings and are of a high standard; there is also an extensive cheeseboard to choose from all day. 🕙⇌👤🍽❀

London Road Ale House 🅛

241 London Road, ST4 5AA
☎ (01782) 698070
6 changing beers (sourced nationally) 🄷

Enter through the telephone box door into this quirky one-room pub. The bar offers a choice of six ever-changing real ales and a selection of ciders. There are also bottles and cans, which can be selected by looking through windows into the cellar. Seating varies from high tables to church pews, and there is a chess table and a piano, both often in use. Large windows at the front depict scenes from the Potteries in years gone by.
Q♣👤🍽(21,21A)❀

Stone

Borehole

Unit 5 Mount Road Industrial Estate, Mount Road, ST15 8LL
☎ (01785) 813581 ⊕ lymestonebrewery.net
Lymestone Ein Stein, Stone Cutter, Stone Faced, Stone the Crows; 3 changing beers (often Lymestone) 🄷

A traditional pub that was once part of the Bent's Brewery site. It is small and friendly, with eight handpumps offering a range of Lymestone ales and the occasional guest beer, plus a range of bottled brews. Well-behaved children (to early evening) and dogs are welcomed. A light menu of pork pies, paninis, pickled eggs and home-made cakes is available to be enjoyed around a log-burner. There is a small, enclosed beer garden to the rear. Car parking is limited.
Q🌣🌼🕙⇌♣👤P❀☂

Royal Exchange

26 Radford Street, ST15 8DA (on corner of Northesk St and Radford St)
☎ (01785) 812685
Everards Tiger; Titanic Steerage, White Star, Captain Smith's Strong Ale, Plum Porter; 4 changing beers (sourced nationally; often Titanic) 🄷

A one-roomed pub, refurbished sympathetically to a high standard in 2015, with four distinct drinking areas and real fires at either end. Ten real ales and one real cider are always stocked, including three changing guest ales, usually including Titanic seasonal beers. There is no TV or piped music, just good conversation. Lunches are served Friday and Saturday, with totally local ingredients, and there is a set evening meal on Monday (except bank holidays). Acoustic music nights and monthly quiz nights are hosted, and many clubs meet here.
Q❄✿⏰❄♣♥🚌♿🐾🛜

Swan Inn

18 Stafford Street, ST15 8QW (on A520 nr Trent & Mersey Canal)
☎ (01785) 815570
House beer (by Coach House); 8 changing beers (sourced nationally) Ⓗ
A thriving free house where nine handpumps serve a range of beers and four real ciders on draught, plus bottled varieties. It comprises one long room, with coal fires at each end. It is a multiple local CAMRA award-winner whose themed beer festival each July is a mecca for beer lovers. Live, free music on Thursday and Saturday varies in style but often features rock, sometimes from national acts. Dogs are welcome. Over-18s only. ✿&♥🚌(101)🐾

Stretton

Junction

Unit 1A, 1 Main Street, DE13 0DZ (on corner of jct with Hillfield Lane, close to St Mary's Church)
☎ 07931 290879
Blythe Bagot's Bitter, Ridware Pale, Summer Breeze, Palmers Poison; 2 changing beers (sourced locally) Ⓗ
A former hairdressing salon converted into a single-room micropub by the owners of the Blythe Brewery in 2018 to showcase its beers; it is the brewery's only significant outlet in the area. Up to five real ciders, from Hurst View and Yoxall, are also sold. Unusual features include a slate-topped and metal-fronted bar counter, and some cinema-style folding seating. Children are welcome to early evening. There is no car park, but free public car parks and some street parking are nearby. Q❄&♥🚌🐾

Tamworth

King's Ditch Ⓛ

51 Lower Gungate, B79 7AS
☎ 07989 805828 ⊕ kingsditch.co.uk
Changing beers (sourced nationally) Ⓖ
Previously a cycle shop, this convivial micropub opened in 2014. Its primary focus is ale, with between four and six on offer. The pub is also well known for cider, serving up to 30 ciders and perries, and has been a finalist in CAMRA's national Cider Pub of the Year competition several times. The single ground-floor room is plainly decorated, and there is an additional small drinking area upstairs. Simple snacks are served. Children are welcome until 7pm. Occasional beer festivals are held.
Q❄✿❄♥🍴🚌🐾🛜

Sir Robert Peel Ⓛ

13-15 Lower Gungate, B79 7BA
☎ (01827) 300910
5 changing beers (often Church End, Salopian) Ⓗ
Busy town-centre free house celebrating its 18th consecutive year in the Guide. It is named after the former prime minister, known for his role in the creation of the police force and the Tamworth pig. Five changing ales are dispensed by friendly and knowledgeable staff.

Three or more real ciders also feature, plus a good selection of foreign bottled beers. A large and peaceful beer garden is to the rear, with ancient stone walls, overlooked by the historic St Editha's Church. ✿❄❄♥🚌🐾

Tamworth Tap Ⓛ ✅

29 Market Street, B79 7LR
☎ (01827) 319872 ⊕ tamworthbrewing.co.uk
8 changing beers (often Beowulf, Blythe, Tamworth) Ⓗ
This elegant building is home to Tamworth Brewing Company. The cosy upstairs rooms have Tudor features, the historic courtyard beer terrace to the rear offers striking views of Tamworth Castle, and there is café-style seating to the front. Eight handpulls usually feature two Tamworth ales, with the rest from near and far. Various snacks are offered, plus a wide range of gins, wines and bottled beers. Regular live music takes place. Winner of CAMRA Pub of the Year for Staffordshire in 2019.
✿❄♥🚌🐾🛜

Tutbury

Cross Keys ✅

39 Burton Street, DE13 9NR (E side of village, 300yds from A511)
☎ (01283) 813677
Burton Bridge Draught Burton Ale; 3 changing beers (sourced regionally) Ⓗ
Privately owned 19th-century free house, overlooking the Dove valley and providing a fine view of Tutbury Castle. The two split-level rooms – public bar and lounge – have a homely feel and are served from a similarly split-level bar. There is a separate large dining room to the rear just serving Sunday lunches. This is the only pub in the area that has offered Draught Burton Ale from its launch by Ind Coope in 1976 and through its 2015 reincarnation by Burton Bridge. ❄✿⏰&♣♥P🚌🐾🛜

Uttoxeter

Horse & Dove

21 Market Place, ST14 8HY
☎ (01889) 735942 ⊕ horsendove.co.uk
6 changing beers (sourced locally; often Heritage, Titanic, Uttoxeter) Ⓗ
A warm welcome awaits visitors to the town's first micropub, which has several other good pubs nearby. Traditional decor and plenty of soft furnishings give a cosy but vibrant atmosphere. All tastes are catered for with an excellent selection of up to six real ales, many from local breweries, plus a lengthy real cider list and a range of gins. Friendly staff and regulars ensure a pleasant and varied drinking experience. ❄♥🚌🐾🛜

Whiston, Penkridge

Swan at Whiston

Whiston Road, ST19 5QH (in Penkridge turn W off A449 at roundabout by Hodsons onto Bungham Lane, cross Cuttlestone Bridge and follow the signs to Whiston) SJ895144
☎ (01785) 716200 ⊕ swanwhiston.co.uk
Holden's Black Country Bitter, Golden Glow; Wye Valley Butty Bach, HPA; 4 changing beers (sourced nationally) Ⓗ
High-quality, well-kept ales and superb food make this a thriving pub despite its remote location. Built in 1593, it burnt down and was rebuilt in 1711. The oldest part today is the small bar housing an inglenook fireplace. The lounge features an intriguing central double-sided log fire. Six acres of grounds include a children's play

area, aviary and a large beer garden that gets busy on summer evenings. Open all day on bank holidays, except Christmas Day. Q ⑤ ✿ ◑ ♠ ♦ P ☒ (878,76) ❀ ☎

Whittington

Dog Inn ✓
2 Main Street, WS14 9JU
☎ (01543) 433091

Bass Draught; Marston's Pedigree; St Austell Proper Job, Tribute; 2 changing beers Ⓗ

Comfortable and spacious village inn with a long frontage. One or two guest ales are served, generally from well-known breweries. Food is on offer every day, including breakfasts from Friday to Sunday. Perhaps unsurprisingly, given its name, the pub is dog-friendly. Live music features occasionally, and Wednesday is quiz night. Bus services dry up in the early evening.
⑤ ✿ ◑ P ☒ (765) ❀ ☎

Barrel tables and bench seating in the Coopers Tavern, Burton upon Trent (Photo: The Roaming Picture Taker/Flickr CC BY 2.0)

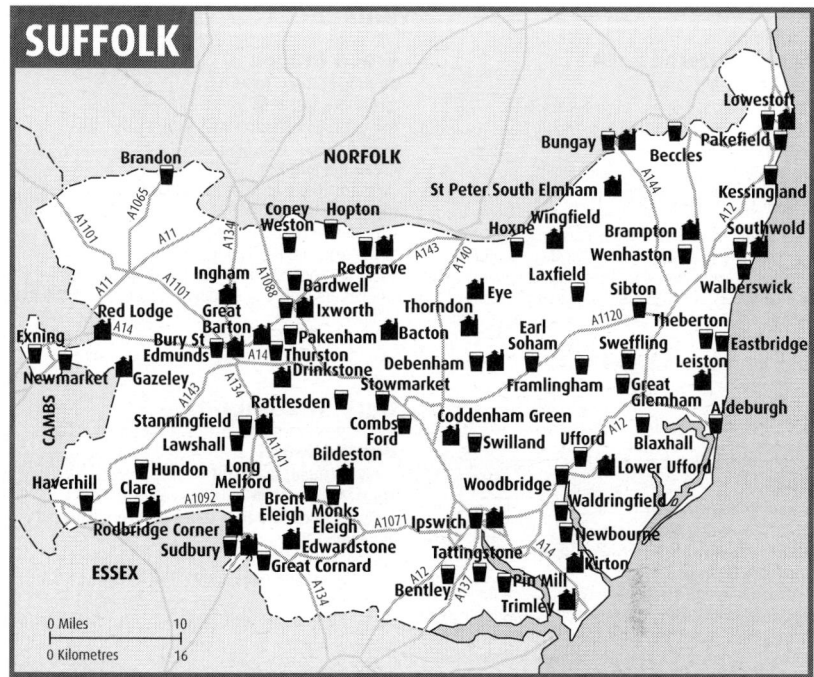

Aldeburgh

White Hart Ⓛ

222 High Street, IP15 5AJ (next to famous fish & chip shop)

☎ (01728) 453205 ⊕ whitehartaldeburgh.co.uk

Adnams Southwold Bitter, Ghost Ship, Broadside; 3 changing beers (often Adnams) Ⓗ

Friendly single bar, formerly used as a public reading room. Drinkers can buy fish & chips and eat them in the garden, when the weather permits, while enjoying a drink from the bar. Live music features on occasion. Families are welcome to use the garden in the summer months, with a covered barbecue and wood-fired pizza oven often in use Easter to mid-September. ❆⊛♣⊟❄❅

Bardwell

Grumpy Goat

Spring Road, IP31 1AB

4 changing beers (sourced locally) Ⓗ

Opened in 2007, this village club has always offered real ale. Part of the new cricket pavilion and open to the public, the bar in the new clubhouse usually has up to four real ales on, and a traditional cider in the cellar. Food is served on some evenings. The terrace is a great place to sit and watch the cricket on a sunny afternoon. ❅⊛◗&♣P

Beccles

Butchers Arms Ⓛ

51 London Road, NR34 9YT

☎ (01502) 712243 ⊕ mypub.org.uk

Woodforde's Nelson's; 5 changing beers (sourced regionally; often Bull of the Woods, Greene King, Woodforde's) Ⓗ

Just a 10-minute walk from the town centre, this friendly pub serves up to six real ales, mainly from local breweries. Live music, open mic evenings, charity and community-focused events are hosted. It initially had separate lounge and public bars, but the building has been extended and the interior is now open plan. The bar and real fire are in the original area, with more seating and pool tables in the extension. Pub grub is now available. ⊛♣◐P❄

Caxton Club Ⓛ

Gaol Lane, NR34 9SJ

☎ (01502) 712829

4 changing beers (sourced locally; often Green Jack, Greene King, Woodforde's) Ⓗ

Spacious club conveniently situated a short walk from the train and bus stations and close to the town centre. All members and guests receive a warm welcome (non-members pay a small fee to cover entertainment costs). It has a central bar, TV and darts room, and snooker room. There is also a large function room, garden with children's play area and a bowling green. Four real ales and a choice of real ciders are available. Only assistance dogs are allowed. ❅⊛&≈♣◐⊟❄

Ingate Ⓛ

108 Grove Road, NR34 9RE

☎ (01502) 712315 ⊕ theingatefreehouse.co.uk

4 changing beers (sourced locally; often Green Jack, Lacons) Ⓗ

Privately owned two-bar free house serving the local community, a short walk from the town centre and train station. The main bar, furnished with tables, bar stools and sofas, serves three real ales on handpump, and the front bar, with a dartboard and pool tables, has one handpump used only at weekends. Live sports and music are shown via plasma screen. Darts and pool are popular here and the pub's teams play in local leagues. ⊛≈♣◐P⊟❄❅

Bentley

Case is Altered L ✅

Capel Road, IP9 2DW
☎ (01473) 805575 ⊕ thecasepubbentley.co.uk
Adnams Southwold Bitter; 3 changing beers (sourced locally) Ⓗ
Owned and run by the local community, the pub has a single bar serving two drinking areas, a restaurant area with a wood-burning stove, and a pretty beer garden with plenty of seating. Various music evenings and themed food nights are hosted but there is no TV. Traditional pub games are played including darts, cards and dominoes. A quiz is held on the last Saturday of the month. Local artists' work is on display. Some of the produce used in the kitchen is grown at home by the locals themselves. ⑤❀◐◖♣Pᗣ❀☞

Blaxhall

Ship L

School Road, IP12 2DY
☎ (01728) 688316 ⊕ blaxhallshipinn.co.uk
Adnams Southwold Bitter; Woodforde's Wherry; 3 changing beers Ⓗ
A cosy two-roomed 16th-century inn with a traditional wood-beamed interior. The menu offers a wide choice of home-made dishes and daily specials using fresh locally sourced ingredients. Live entertainment includes folk music, bands and story-telling, and the pub hosts a Folk East stage during the festival weekend. Letting chalets are available beside the pub and there is camping at the nearby village hall by arrangement. ⑤❀❄◐◖▲♣●Pᗣ❀☞

Brandon

Ram

High Street, IP27 0AX
☎ (01842) 810275 ⊕ ramhotel.co.uk
Greene King Abbot; 6 changing beers (sourced nationally) Ⓗ
Said to be one of the oldest surviving buildings in Brandon, this attractive Grade II-listed inn dates back 500 years in parts. A wonderful log fire greets you on entering this friendly free house owned and run by the family. It is home to regular club nights for the Iceni Car Club, Classic Vehicle Club, Model Engineering Club, Brandon Speakers Club and the Champions Poker League. ⑤❀❄◐◖▲⇌♣Pᗣ(86)

Brent Eleigh

Cock ★

Lavenham Road, CO10 9PB
☎ (01787) 247371
Adnams Southwold Bitter; Greene King Abbot; 2 changing beers (sourced locally; often Bishop Nick, Mauldons) Ⓗ
An unspoilt gem, well worthy of its place on CAMRA's National Inventory of Historic Pub Interiors. With just two small bars, conversation with the regulars is assured. The public bar has an old wooden counter, a main table deeply etched with shove-ha'penny grooves and a settle with a 'pinch penny' cut into it. The snug bar is ideal for families. Good home-cooked food service does not intrude on the classic pub ambience. Q❀❄◐♣●Pᗣ❀☞

Bungay

Green Dragon L

29 Broad Street, NR35 1EE
☎ (01986) 892681 ⊕ greendragonbungay.co.uk
Green Dragon Chaucer Ale, Gold, Bridge Street Bitter, Strong Mild; 1 changing beer (sourced locally; often Green Dragon) Ⓗ
On the northern edge of town, this is Bungay's only brewpub and the home of the Green Dragon Brewery, with ales brewed in outbuildings adjacent to the car park at the rear. The pub is a regular in the Guide. It has a public bar and a spacious lounge with a side room where families are welcome, leading to an enclosed garden. In addition to the five Green Dragon ales, a range of KeyKegs and canned craft ales are served. Food is available Wednesday-Sunday. ⑤❀▲♣●Pᗣ❀☞

Bury St Edmunds

Beerhouse L

1 Tayfen Road, IP32 6BH
☎ (01284) 766415 ⊕ burybeerhouse.co.uk
Brewshed Best Bitter; 7 changing beers (sourced nationally) Ⓗ
Traditional beer house in an unusual semicircular Victorian building (previously called the Ipswich Arms), handy for the railway station, and refurbished with a modern feel. It serves its own beers from the Brewshed Brewery, which is located out of town and also supplies the company's four other local pubs. Seven beer engines provide an ever-changing selection of well-kept real ales. Three real ciders are also stocked. Regular beer

REAL ALE BREWERIES

Adnams Southwold
Artefact Ixworth (NEW)
Beccles Brampton
Biochemist Red Lodge (NEW)
Brewshed Ingham
Briarbank 🍺 Ipswich
Bruha 🍂 Eye
Cabin Bildeston
Calvors Coddenham Green
Cliff Quay Debenham
De Vossen Stanningfield (NEW)
Dove Street Ipswich
Drinkstone Drinkstone (NEW)
Earl Soham Debenham
Green Dragon 🍺 Bungay
Green Jack Lowestoft
Greene King Bury St Edmunds
Humber Doucy Bacton
Kings Head 🍺 Bildeston
Krafty Braumeister Leiston
Little Earth Project Edwardstone
Mauldons Sudbury
Mr Bees Trimley
Munson's 🍺 Gazeley
Nethergate 🍂 Rodbridge Corner
Old Cannon 🍺 Bury St Edmunds
Old Felixstowe Kirton (NEW)
Roughacre 🍂 Clare
Shortts Thorndon
St Judes 🍺 Ipswich
St Peter's 🍂 St Peter South Elmham
Star Wing 🍂 Redgrave
Stow Fen Bungay
Turnstone Wingfield
Uffa 🍺 Lower Ufford
Watts & Co Debenham (NEW)
Weird Sisters Great Barton

festivals and an annual cider festival are hosted. Major sporting events are shown on a big screen. An open fire adds warmth in winter. ♿⊛♒⇌⬤P🚃❀🛜

Dove 🅛

68 Hospital Road, IP33 3JU
☎ (01284) 702787 ⊕ thedovepub.co.uk
Woodforde's Wherry ℍ; changing beers ℍ/Ⓖ
This early-Victorian back-street community free house is just five minutes' walk from the town centre. It has six handpumps, plus jugged ales brought up direct from the cellar, and the staff are knowledgeable about the varying choice of local ales. A good selection of real ciders is also available. Truly traditional and basic, the Dove is just how pubs used to be – no lager, TVs, pool or gaming machines. A two-times winner of CAMRA Regional Pub of the Year. Q⊛♣⬤P🚃❀

Nutshell ★ ✅

17 The Traverse, IP33 1BJ
☎ (01284) 764867 ⊕ thenutshellpub.co.uk
Greene King IPA, Abbot ℍ
The Nutshell claims to be Britain's smallest pub, with an interior measuring only 15ft by 7ft, and is listed in the Guinness Book of Records. The main drinking area is crowded if more than six people are in it. The Grade II-listed building dates from the mid-19th century and is a popular tourist attraction in the town. Good-quality Greene King Abbot and IPA are regularly available. There is a function room upstairs. Q🚃

Oakes Barn

St Andrews Street South, IP33 3PH (opp Waitrose car park)
☎ (01284) 761592 ⊕ oakesbarn.co.uk
Oakham JHB; Woodforde's Wherry; 4 changing beers (sourced nationally) ℍ
A real ale free house and social hub near the town centre with some period features and historic links to the medieval town. Six real ales are always on the bar, including one dark beer alongside craft cider. Home-made food comprises lunchtime specials and snacks served all day, plus roasts on the first Sunday of the month. There is a covered smoking area outside and an open courtyard with seating. Regular events are held in the bar, and an upstairs function room can be hired. ♿⊛(🍴♣⬤🚃❀🛜

Old Cannon Brewery 🅛

86 Cannon Street, IP33 1JR
☎ (01284) 768769 ⊕ oldcannonbrewery.co.uk
Adnams Southwold Bitter; Old Cannon Best Bitter, Gunner's Daughter; 3 changing beers (sourced nationally; often Mauldons, Timothy Taylor, Old Cannon) ℍ
This excellent brewpub is on the site of the original Cannon Brewery. Both the brewpub and stable block date from the mid-19th century and are Grade II-listed. Now in private hands, this is a true free house. The beers are brewed on-site and tours of the microbrewery are available (book ahead). Brewing can often be seen taking place next to the bar on Mondays and Wednesdays. Good-quality food is served and comfortable accommodation is available. ⊛🛏(🍴⇌P🚃❀🛜

Clare

Globe

10 Callis Street, CO10 8PX
☎ (01787) 278122
Young's London Original; 3 changing beers (sourced nationally) ℍ

A phoenix risen from the ashes, the Globe reopened in 2013 after a two-year closure. Serving one well-kept regular beer and up to three changing guests, it is now a thriving local where beer and conversation dominate. Live music plays every other Saturday night and afternoon sessions every other Sunday. There is a separate pool room at the rear and a garden for summer drinking. No food is served. Q♿⊛♣P🚃❀🛜

Combs Ford

Gladstone Arms 🅛

2 Combs Road, IP14 2AP
☎ (01449) 771608 ⊕ gladstonearms.co.uk
Adnams Southwold Bitter, Broadside; Crouch Vale Brewers Gold; Fuller's London Pride; Sharp's Doom Bar; Woodforde's Wherry ℍ; 4 changing beers ℍ/Ⓖ
A large open-plan pub serving consistently good beer. The owners also run the Dove Street Inn in Ipswich. The two pubs share a similar beer range, with 12-14 ales, including house beers brewed in Ipswich. Four or five ciders and a wide range of craft lagers, imported foreign beers and whiskies are also available. Good-value snacks and meals are served, with vegetarian options. There are board games, sports TV and regular live music. A beer festival features over the Easter weekend. At the rear is the riverside garden. Q♿⊛(🍴🖱♣⬤P🚃(87,88)❀🛜

Coney Weston

Swan ✅

Thetford Road, IP31 1DN
☎ (01359) 221900 ⊕ swaninnconeyweston.com
Adnams Broadside; Greene King IPA; Wychwood Hobgoblin Ruby; 1 changing beer (often Adnams, Sharp's) ℍ
The current building is about a century old, though there has been an inn on this site for many more years – the original building burnt down. It serves a changing range of popular ales such as Draught Bass, Doom Bar and Hobgoblin. A full menu of traditional pub food is available. Regular events are hosted for charity, and the pub has its own bowling club. It is a camping and caravan stopover, and coaches are also welcome by arrangement. Q♿🖱🖱♣P🚃(338)❀

Debenham

Woolpack

49 High Street, IP14 6QN
☎ (01728) 860516
Earl Soham Victoria Bitter ℍ, Sir Roger's Porter Ⓖ; Fuller's London Pride; 1 changing beer (often Earl Soham) ℍ
Small one-bar wooden-floored pub with steps up from the road. Until recent years it was licensed as a beer house. Horse brasses, village photographs and miniature bottles decorate the bar area. Two TVs show terrestrial sport. Keenly priced home-cooked food is served. The pub is home to a darts team and hosts occasional live music, karaoke and quiz nights. There is a splendid view of the church from the patio – bell ringers meet here after practice on Tuesday. ♿⊛🖱♣❀🛜

Earl Soham

Victoria 🅛

The Street, IP13 7RL
☎ (01728) 685758
Earl Soham Victoria Bitter; 2 changing beers (often Cliff Quay, Earl Soham) ℍ

A popular, traditional pub that despite refurbishment has changed little over the years, with two small bars separated by a wood-burner, and the Gents' toilet outside. A varied menu with daily specials is offered lunchtimes and evenings, all home-cooked. The pub gets busy at weekends, especially on sunny days when even a seat in the garden can be hard to find. Dogs and children are welcome. The Earl Soham Brewery was originally behind the pub. Q ᗏ ✿ ◖ ♣ P ☷ ☺ 🥨

Eastbridge

Eel's Foot L

Leiston Road, IP16 4SN (close to entrance to Minsmere nature reserve)
☎ (01728) 830154 ⊕ theeelsfootinn.co.uk
Adnams Southwold Bitter, Ghost Ship, Broadside; 2 changing beers (often Adnams) Ⓗ
Much-improved pub adjacent to the famous nature reserve where avocets and otters are local success stories. Popular with ramblers and birdwatchers, it has a good reputation for locally sourced home-cooked food, with a small restaurant area leading to a large terraced space with seating for alfresco drinking and dining on summer days. There is an outdoor play area for children. Traditional music sessions feature on Thursday evenings and live bands monthly. En-suite accommodation is available. Q ᗏ ✿ 🛏 ◖ & ▲ ♣ P ☺ 🥨

Exning

White Horse ✅

23 Church Street, CB8 7EH
☎ (01638) 577323 ⊕ whitehorseexning.co.uk
3 changing beers Ⓗ
Mentioned in the Domesday Book and a pub for 300 years, this fine free house has been run by the same family since 1935. Still retaining much original character, it comprises a public bar, cosy lounge and separate restaurant. At least 10 changing real ales are on offer each week, plus cider on draught, and a good choice of home-cooked food is served. A private room can be hired. Q ✿ ◖ ♣ P ☷ (11) ☺

Framlingham

Station Hotel L

Station Road, IP13 9EE
☎ (01728) 723455 ⊕ thestationframlingham.com
Earl Soham Gannet Mild, Victoria Bitter, Brandeston Gold; 2 changing beers (often Earl Soham) Ⓗ
Cosy two-bar pub set in a former station buffet (the branch line closed in 1963). Beers and a guest cider are dispensed from a set of Edwardian German silver handpumps. The pub enjoys a good reputation for food, made with locally sourced ingredients and prepared on the premises – the ever-changing menu is displayed on chalkboards. On Sundays, brunch and beers are available. The garden bar has a wood-fired pizza oven. An annual beer festival is held in the summer. Children and dogs welcome. Q ᗏ ✿ ◖ ♣ P ☷ ☺ 🥨

Great Cornard

Brook Inn

241 Bures Road, CO10 0JQ
☎ 07759 960051
5 changing beers (sourced nationally) Ⓗ
Friendly, welcoming, locals' pub, formerly owned by Greene King and now independent. Set in the country near the Suffolk/Essex border, it has a beer garden and a good-sized car park. There are two bars, one with low-key TV for sports events. Bar billiards and pool are played, with teams in local leagues. An open-mic music session is held on the third Sunday of each month. A good range of up to five real ales is served on handpump. ᗏ ✿ & ♣ P ☷ ☺ 🥨

Great Glemham

Crown L

The Street, IP17 2DA
☎ (01728) 663693 ⊕ thecrowninnglemham.co.uk
6 changing beers (sourced locally) Ⓗ
Furnished to a high standard, this multi-roomed pub has wood-burners, traditionally tiled floors and many lovely seating areas. Up to six beers are on offer during the busy summer months and at least four during quieter periods. Acoustic music sessions feature regularly. The pub hosts a local community lunch once a month and caters for private parties. All food is cooked on the premises, from bar snacks to an à la carte menu (no food Tue). ᗏ ✿ ◖ ♣ P ☷ ☺ 🥨

Haverhill

Royal Exchange ✅

69 High Street, CB9 8AH
☎ (01440) 702155
Greene King IPA; Nethergate Suffolk County Best Bitter; 3 changing beers (sourced nationally; often Nethergate) Ⓗ
Friendly town-centre local in a classic street-corner location. The Greene King-managed house has had the full refurb treatment, with scrubbed floors and traditional furniture. It can be boisterous with sports fans watching the five TVs – glasses are available for those wishing to watch in 3D. A swift turnover on the beer helps sustain its high quality. There is a large public car park behind the Arts Centre opposite. ᗏ & ♣ ☷ ☺

Hopton

Vine

High Street, IP22 2QX
☎ (01953) 688581
Adnams Southwold Bitter; Greene King IPA, Abbot; Timothy Taylor Landlord; 5 changing beers (sourced locally; often Colchester, Lacons, Mauldons) Ⓗ
On the main road near the church, this village local has been revitalised since it was taken over by the current landlord in 2013. Nine ales including a selection of local and regional guests are offered at reasonable prices. A variety of ciders is also available. This welcoming pub, popular with locals and visitors, is a regular winner of local CAMRA Pub of the Year. ᗏ ✿ & ♣ P ☷ (100) ☺ 🥨

Hoxne

Swan Inn of Hoxne

Low Street, IP21 5AS
☎ (01379) 668275 ⊕ theswaninnofhoxne.co.uk
Adnams Southwold Bitter, Ghost Ship, Broadside; Timothy Taylor Landlord Ⓖ
The Swan reopened in 2016 after temporary closure and is once again a thriving village local. The 15th-century building has a colourful history – it claims to be both the former home of the Bishop of Norwich and later a brothel. There is a large open fire in the main bar and a wood-burner in the adjacent bar. The restaurant serves excellent home-cooked food, with an emphasis on local produce. To the rear is a large garden. An annual beer festival features in August. Buskers' night is Thursday. ᗏ ✿ ◖ & ♣ P ☷ ☺ 🥨

Hundon

Rose & Crown

20 North Street, CO10 8ED (in centre of village)

☎ (01440) 786261 ⊕ hundon-village.co.uk/
roseandcrown.html

Sharp's Doom Bar; 3 changing beers (sourced nationally; often Fuller's, Mauldons, St Austell) Ⓗ

A traditional country pub comprising two bars with open fires. Home-cooked food is available Thursday to Sunday, with the Sunday lunchtime roasts ever-popular. The deceptively large beer garden has a patio for alfresco dining leading to a lawned area with a stage. The outside bar is used for weddings, parties, an annual community music festival over the August bank holiday and other events. The morris men gathering on St George's Day is enjoyed by all. A proud former winner of local CAMRA Community Pub of the Year. ☎✿ⓓ&♣P❀?

Ipswich

Arcade Street Tavern

Arcade Street, IP1 1EX (behind Corn Exchange)

☎ (01473) 805454 ⊕ arcadetavern.co.uk

2 changing beers (sourced regionally) Ⓗ

A stylish and highly popular multi-roomed café bar with a traditional wooden interior, and an emphasis on craft and imported beers. Two handpumps dispense a variety of beers, mainly from East Anglia. There is no food in-house but the bar regularly hosts Street-Food Friday in conjunction with local food traders. There are heated seating areas outside and two function rooms – one used for product launches and tasting evenings. Artisan coffee is available. ✿🖵?

Dove Street Inn Ⓛ ✓

76 St Helen's Street, IP4 2LA

☎ (01473) 211270 ⊕ dovestreetinn.co.uk

Adnams Broadside; Crouch Vale Brewers Gold; Fuller's London Pride; Greene King Abbot Ⓗ**; changing beers (often Dove Street)** Ⓗ/Ⓖ

Popular inn with a wide selection of ales, continental beers and ciders. Some ales are from its own Dove Street Brewery. There is also a gin bar. Home-cooked food and bar snacks are served at all times. Sports TV is shown in the conservatory. A covered and heated seating area outside hosts various events including three beer festivals. Well-behaved dogs and children are welcome. A sister pub to The Gladstone Arms in Combs Ford. Last admission is 10.45pm. ☎✿🛏ⓓ&♣●🖵(66)❀?

Duke Ⓛ

212 Woodbridge Road, IP4 2QP

☎ (01473) 216007 ⊕ thegrandolddukeofyork.co.uk

6 changing beers Ⓗ

The Duke has a single large bar with various seating areas and a pool table, plus a large raised patio area outside to the rear of the small car park. It offers a good selection of real ales from a variety of local brewers, including three mystery house beers. Bottled beers and draught craft beer are also available. Live music sessions feature at weekends. Food is provided by local street concessions. ☎✿ⓓ&♣P🖵(11,66)❀?

Fat Cat

288 Spring Road, IP4 5NL

☎ (01473) 726524 ⊕ fatcatipswich.co.uk

Adnams Southwold Bitter Ⓗ**; Crouch Vale Amarillo; 14 changing beers** Ⓖ

A small, multi-roomed drinking bar, free from background music and games machines. Up to 14 beers and five ciders are dispensed from the taproom. Bar snacks include Scotch eggs and pasties cooked on the

premises. An airy conservatory behind the main bar leads to the pretty garden, providing extra space on sunny afternoons, with the occasional barbecue. A quiz is held monthly. Often voted the best pub in town by local CAMRA branch members. No under-16s. Q✿ⓓ●🖵❀?

Greyhound

9 Henley Road, IP1 3SE

☎ (01473) 252862 ⊕ thegreyhoundipswich.co.uk

Adnams Southwold Bitter, Ghost Ship, Broadside; 3 changing beers (often Adnams) Ⓗ

This tied house has a small bar at the front and a larger, more modern drinking and dining room to the side and rear. The recently expanded outside drinking space can be busy during the summer months and hosts occasional barbecues. A new kitchen offers freshly prepared food and various daily specials, with vegetarian options. On Sunday, breakfast is available. Quizzes take place twice a month on Sunday evenings. The TVs are only turned on for sporting events. Q☎✿ⓓ&♣P🖵(116)?

Lord Nelson

81 Fore Street, IP4 1JZ

☎ (01473) 407510 ⊕ thenelsonipswich.co.uk

Adnams Southwold Bitter, Ghost Ship Ⓖ**; 3 changing beers (often Adnams)** Ⓗ

Timber-framed building dating from the 17th century, just a short walk from the historic waterfront. An unusual gravity dispense system incorporates a row of wooden casks to good effect and guarantees temperature-controlled real ales. Freshly prepared food is served including daily specials. Outside is a small enclosed patio area to the rear where families and dogs are welcome. Quiz nights are held twice a month. A sister pub to the Red Lion in Manningtree and Marlborough in Dedham. ☎✿ⓓ&♣P❀?

Ixworth

Greyhound ✓

49 High Street, IP31 2HJ

☎ (01359) 230887

Greene King IPA, Abbot; 3 changing beers (sourced nationally) Ⓗ

Situated on the village's attractive high street, this welcoming traditional inn has three bars, one a lovely central snug. The heart of the building dates back to Tudor times. Good-value lunches and early evening meals are served in the restaurant, including a daily special. Dominoes, crib, darts and pool are played in leagues and for charity fundraising. Dogs and children are welcome. Q☎✿ⓓ▲♣P🖵(304,338)❀

Kessingland

Sailors Home Ⓛ

302 Church Road, NR33 7SB

☎ (01502) 740245 ⊕ sailorshome.co.uk

Adnams Southwold Bitter Ⓗ**; 6 changing beers (sourced nationally; often Green Jack, Lacons, Wolf)** Ⓗ/Ⓖ

On the sea front, with coastal views, the pub is popular in summer with holidaymakers from nearby caravan parks and guest houses. The interior has a mock-Tudor design with four adjoining rooms – one for diners serving value-for-money food, a large central bar area with a TV screen, a games room and a side room. Four handpulls are available and up to three on gravity, plus a changing real cider. ☎✿ⓓ▲♣●🖵(99)❀?

Lawshall

Swan

The Street, IP29 4QA
☎ (01284) 828477 ⊕ swaninnlawshall.com
5 changing beers (sourced nationally; often Adnams, Colchester, Woodforde's) Ⓗ
Set in a village in the heart of rural Suffolk, the Swan is a classic Suffolk country pub. The beautiful 18th-century thatched building with a low-beamed bar and an inglenook fireplace has been lovingly restored and is crammed full of period features. On the menu you will find all the traditional pub classics and a few extra culinary delights. The large garden encourages children to play. Q☎❀❀◑❀P❀❀

Laxfield

King's Head (Low House) ★

Gorams Mill Lane, IP13 8DW (walk through churchyard and exit via lower street gate; pub is on your right)
☎ (01986) 798395 ⊕ laxfieldkingshead.co.uk
Green Jack Golden Best; Shortts Skiffle; Timothy Taylor Landlord; 4 changing beers (sourced locally; often Shortts) Ⓖ
Community pub also known as the Low House, bought from Adnams in 2018. This timeless thatched inn is a classic and always worth a visit. The main room features high-back settles set around a small fireplace, and the beer is served on gravity from a small taproom to the rear. The separate dining room offers an interesting menu of locally sourced food, including roast lunch on Sunday. There is an enclosed garden and patio to the rear. Accommodation is available in an outbuilding.
❀❀❀❀❀P❀❀

Long Melford

Crown Inn

Hall Street, CO10 9JL
☎ (01787) 377666 ⊕ thecrownhotelmelford.co.uk
Adnams Southwold Bitter, Ghost Ship; 2 changing beers (sourced nationally) Ⓗ
A busy family-run free house and cosy hotel set in this popular antiques centre. Two regular ales and two changing guests, together with real cider, are on handpump. A high-quality home-cooked menu is served in the spacious bar and separate restaurant. There is a large, attractive patio garden for summer dining and drinking. Eleven comfortable bedrooms are available for those wishing to stay and explore this picturesque area.
Q☎❀❀◑❀❀P❀❀❀

Nethergate Brewery Tap

Rodbridge Corner, CO10 9HJ
☎ (01787) 377087 ⊕ nethergate.co.uk
8 changing beers (sourced locally; often Nethergate) Ⓗ
Nethergate Brewery was founded in 1986 and its new visitor centre and taproom opened in 2017. The taproom has a bar offering a range of Nethergate ales on draught, and a shop selling bottled beers, wines and spirits. There is a window to view the brewery and tours can be booked. The members' club hosts regular events including beer festivals. Q❀❀P❀

Lowestoft

Norman Warrior Ⓛ

Fir Lane, NR32 2RB
☎ (01502) 561982 ⊕ thenormanwarrior.co.uk

Greene King IPA; 4 changing beers (sourced nationally; often Greene King, Lacons, Wolf) Ⓗ
Large estate pub on the northern side of town with ample parking, close to the bus stop and a 20-minute walk from Oulton Broad North train station. It comprises a public bar where pool and darts are played and a comfortable lounge leading to a spacious restaurant serving home-cooked food daily. Outside is a terrace and the garden where a beer and cider festival featuring live music is held over the August bank holiday weekend. A popular quiz takes place weekly.
Q☎❀◑❀❀P❀(102)❀❀

Triangle Tavern Ⓛ

29 St Peters Street, NR32 1QA
☎ (01502) 582711 ⊕ green-jack.com
Green Jack Golden Best, Trawlerboys Best Bitter, Lurcher Stout, Gone Fishing ESB, Ripper Tripel; 2 changing beers (sourced locally; often Crouch Vale, Green Jack, Oakham) Ⓗ/Ⓖ
This lively family-friendly town-centre tavern is the brewery tap for Green Jack Brewery. The cosy parlour-style front bar is heated with a wood-burner in winter months and hosts live music every Friday evening and a monthly quiz night. A corridor leads to the back bar with a central pool table and a jukebox. Alongside the full Green Jack range are guest ales, real ciders and continental beers. Customers are welcome to bring in their own food. ❀❀❀❀❀❀❀

Monks Eleigh

Swan

The Street, IP7 7AU
☎ (01449) 744544 ⊕ swaninnmonkseleigh.co.uk
Greene King Abbot; Mighty Oak Oscar Wilde; 2 changing beers (sourced regionally) Ⓗ
A welcoming, traditional country pub in the heart of Suffolk. Food and drink come from small and artisan producers, bringing a range of Suffolk ingredients to the table and bar, including cask ales on handpump. The uppermost restaurant area has a large inglenook fireplace and there is a smaller real fire in the bar area. Events include comedy and quiz nights. Closed Monday but available to hire. ❀◑❀(111)❀

Newbourne

Fox Inn ✔

The Street, IP12 4NY
☎ (01473) 736307
Adnams Southwold Bitter; 3 changing beers Ⓗ
This picturesque timber-framed, two-bar village local is becoming increasingly popular, not just with ramblers and cyclists, but also with discerning diners. The refurbished kitchen offers a wide range of locally-sourced food, all home cooked from an à la carte menu, with vegetarian and gluten-free options plus daily specials. The large garden has a pond and shed which houses an old skittle alley – the only one in Suffolk. The restaurant has recently been extended in sympathy with the existing building. Extra car parking is available in summer. Q☎❀◑❀❀▲❀P❀(179)❀❀

Newmarket

Golden Lion ✔

44 High Street, CB8 8LB
☎ (01638) 672040
Adnams Ghost Ship; Greene King Abbot; 7 changing beers Ⓗ

A large, bustling, 18th-century Wetherspoon on the main street. The name is thought to have come from King Henry I, who was known as the Lion of Justice. Knowledgeable and efficient staff serve up to seven real ales at any one time, including up to four guest ales. Real cider is also available. The pub is popular with the local horse-racing community. Children are welcome until 9pm in the family area. ♿🕮🕖🌙�;⩴♿P🖵🛜

Pakefield

Oddfellows 🅛

6 Nightingale Road, NR33 7AU
☎ (01502) 538415
Adnams Southwold Bitter; house beer (by Green Jack); 3 changing beers (sourced locally; often Green Jack, Lacons, Woodforde's) 🅗
Close to the cliff top, this pub is popular with local drinkers, holidaymakers and walkers on the heritage coastal path. The interior comprises three open-plan areas including one for diners, and has wooden flooring and panelling throughout. Sporting events are shown on TV screens. Up to five ales are available from local breweries. In summer, a popular beer festival is hosted on the green opposite and, in January, a small winter festival is held, with the Old Glory Molly Dancers performing. ♿🕮🕖🖵🌙🛜

Pakenham

Fox

The Street, IP31 2JU
☎ (01359) 230194 ⊕ pakenhamfox.co.uk
Mighty Oak Kings; 3 changing beers (sourced locally; often Elmtree, Shortts, Star Wing) 🅗
Traditional 18th-century pub in a picturesque village, beautifully restored with a handcrafted central bar. A free house, the Fox serves four well-chosen ales from local breweries and two real ciders on draught. The chef prepares lunches Wednesday to Sunday and evening meals Wednesday, Thursday and Saturday using local ingredients. Friday is home-made pizza night. The spacious beer garden, smokers' shelter and pétanque pitch overlook a wildflower meadow. Every second Tuesday is quiz night. Q♿🕮🕖🖒♣⩴♿P🖵(304,338)🌙🛜

Pin Mill

Butt & Oyster ✅

Pin Mill Road, IP9 1JW
☎ (01473) 780764
Adnams Southwold Bitter, Ghost Ship, Broadside; 1 changing beer (often Adnams) 🅖
Dating from the 17th century, this pub enjoys a famous setting, with magnificent views of the River Orwell from the main bar and patio. Inside, it has three separate rooms connected via a flagstoned corridor. High-backed settles and a wood-burner in the main room help to create an old-world charm on cold winter days. The patio at the front is often used by diners during busy sessions. Breakfast is served on weekends only. Q♿🕮🕖🖒♣P🖵(97,202)🌙🛜

Rattlesden

Five Bells

High Street, IP30 0RA
☎ (01449) 737373
3 changing beers (sourced locally; often Earl Soham, Elgood's, Woodforde's) 🅗
Set on the high road through a picturesque village, this is a good old Suffolk drinking house – few of its kind still survive. Three well-chosen ales on the bar usually come direct from the breweries, often including a mild. The cosy single-room interior has a games area on a lower level and there is occasional live music. Pub games include shut-the-box and shove-ha'penny, plus pétanque in the garden in summer. Q♿♣🖵🌙

Redgrave

Cross Keys

The Street, IP22 1RW
☎ (01379) 779822 ⊕ crosskeysredgrave.co.uk
Earl Soham Victoria Bitter; 3 changing beers (sourced locally) 🅗
The building dates from the late-16th or early-17th century, with later extensions. It was bought by the community and reopened in 2018, run by a mixture of paid staff and volunteers. Earl Soham Bitter is the regular beer, complemented by three changing ales. Numerous events are held – see Facebook for details. Please check food service times ahead of your visit as they may vary. ♿🕮🖒♣P🖵(304)🌙🛜

Star Wing Tap Room 🅛

Hall Farm, Church Road, IP22 1RJ
☎ (01379) 890586 ⊕ starwingbrewery.com
Star Wing Dawn on the Border, Gospel Oak, Spire Light, Red at Night, Four Acre Arcadia, Stain Glass Blue; 1 changing beer 🅗
The Tap Room opened in 2019 and has developed a reputation as an excellent place to enjoy Star Wing and guest ales. Based in an old sawmill, the bar retains many original features and has an on-site bakery. As well as the core range of six Star Wing craft ales on tap, it offers a full bar featuring local suppliers including Finningham-based Betty's Gin. There is also a fine keg wall. 🕖🖒⩴P🌙🛜

Sibton

White Horse

Halesworth Road, IP17 2JJ
☎ (01728) 660337 ⊕ sibtonwhitehorseinn.co.uk
Adnams Southwold Bitter; 2 changing beers 🅗
A characterful 16th-century inn with lots of exposed beams and a large fireplace with a wood-burner. A raised galley is on one side of the main bar area. The spacious garden to the rear has a children's play area and a barbecue in summer. Much of the kitchen produce is grown in the pub's own garden. Various themed food evenings are held. There is a separate annexe for accommodation and it has a registered Caravan and Motorhome Club site. ♿🕮🚪🕖🖒♣P🌙🛜

Southwold

Lord Nelson 🅛 ✅

42 East Street, IP18 6EJ
☎ (01502) 722079 ⊕ thelordnelsonsouthwold.co.uk
Adnams Southwold Bitter, Ghost Ship, Broadside; 2 changing beers (sourced locally; often Adnams) 🅗
There is no shortage of outlets selling Adnams beer in Southwold and they all have their merits, but this is a special place in which to drink the full range of Adnams ales, including its seasonal beers. A stone's throw from the sea and Southwold Sailors' Reading Room, the pub is always busy and lively. The central bar has a flagstone floor and open fireplace and is decorated with naval memorabilia. Children are welcome in a side room and there is a heated patio to the rear. ♿🕖🖒🅐🖵🌙🛜

Sole Bay Inn [L]
7 East Green, IP18 6JN
☎ (01502) 723736 🌐 solebayinn.co.uk
Adnams Southwold Bitter, Mosaic, Ghost Ship, Broadside; 1 changing beer [H]
This single-room street-corner pub, built in about 1835, stands in the shadow of the lighthouse and is very close to Adnams brewery. The interior was significantly modernised in 2003 as Adnams sought to create a number of bistro-style pubs. It still retains a few bits of nautical bric-a-brac and offers five Adnams real ales along with other beers of theirs and spirits. There is also a small number of tables outside the pub. 👶◐◑🚌🐾📶

Stanningfield

Red House
Bury Road, IP29 4RR
☎ (01284) 828330 🌐 theredhousesuffolk.co.uk
Greene King IPA; 2 changing beers [H]
Red brick in construction and displaying the red dress uniform of the Suffolk Regiment on its sign, the Red House is a family-run free house at the heart of the village. Good-value lunches and early evening meals are home cooked. The pub supports darts, cribbage and bar billiards teams and hosts regular entertainment nights.
👶❀◐◑♣P🚌(750,753) 🐾📶

Stowmarket

Royal William [L]
53 Union Street East, IP14 1HP
☎ (01449) 674553
Greene King IPA; 10 changing beers [G]
An end-of-terrace back-street bar tucked away down a narrow side street, a short walk from the town centre and railway station, and well worth seeking out. Ales are dispensed on gravity from the cellar behind the bar, and it has up to 10 beers and five ciders. There is a games room, home to dominoes, darts and crib matches, and a smoking area outside. Sport is shown on TV and traditional music hosted monthly. Home-made bar snacks are available. A winner of many local CAMRA awards. 👶❀◐◑♿🚆♣🍎🚌🐾📶

Walnut
39 Violet Hill Road, IP14 1NE
☎ (01449) 401 6769 🌐 the-walnut.square.site
6 changing beers [H]
Refurbished by the landlord and landlady in early 2019, this much-improved back-street venue offers a changing selection of real ales on handpump, along with ciders and craft beers listed on a large blackboard. The beer menu regularly features some unusual choices for the area. Good-value snacks are available. The pub holds regular quiz and vinyl nights. There are two beer gardens, with children welcome until 8pm. Local CAMRA Pub of the Year 2020. 👶❀♿🚆🍎🚌🐾📶

Sudbury

Brewery Tap [L]
21-23 East Street, CO10 2TP (200yds from marketplace)
☎ (01787) 370876 🌐 thebrewerytapsudbury.co.uk
Mauldons Moletrap Bitter, Suffolk Pride, Black Adder [H]; 7 changing beers (sourced nationally) [H]/[G]
The Mauldons Brewery tap is a haven for ale lovers. A good selection of the brewery's beers is always stocked, complemented by a range of national and locally sourced ales, up to 10 at any one time, on both handpump and gravity. Hearty snacks are served at lunchtime including pies and sandwiches. Beer festivals are held in April and October, and quiz, music and comedy nights are regular attractions in a pub where conversation dominates.
Q❀♿🚆♣🍎📺🚌🐾

Sweffling

White Horse [L]
Low Road, IP17 2BB
☎ (01728) 664178 🌐 swefflingwhitehorse.co.uk
3 changing beers [G]
A cosy two-room pub, warmed by a wood-burner and wood-fired range. Beers from local brewers are dispensed on gravity, served through a taproom door. Cider is also available, as well as fairtrade, organic and locally produced bottled beers. Hot and cold bar snacks are sold. Pub games include bar billiards, darts, crib and board games, and live music features twice a month. A former CAMRA East Anglian Pub of the Year with a small beer garden and an award-winning campsite.
Q👶❀🛏◑⛺♣🍎P🐾📶

Swilland

Moon & Mushroom
High Road, IP6 9LR
☎ (01473) 785320 🌐 themoonandmushroom.co.uk
4 changing beers (sourced locally) [H]
A comfortable and cosy single-bar pub, attractively decorated throughout, with local pictures, tiled floors and scrubbed tables. A good selection of beers on gravity is always available from the taproom, and home-cooked food including some game dishes is served both in the bar and an adjoining dining room. It has occasional live music on Sunday and special themed nights. Outside, there is seating in the pretty patio garden.
👶❀◐◑♿P🐾📶

Tattingstone

Wheatsheaf [L]
Church Road, IP9 2LY
☎ (01473) 805470 🌐 wheatsheaftattingstone.com
3 changing beers (sourced locally) [G]
Comfortable open-plan single-bar pub, refurbished by the current owners. It is on the outskirts of a small village divided by the Alton Water Park reservoir. There is a large garden to the side – home to the annual charity music and beer festival in June. An interesting beer selection includes many from local brewers. Live music and quiz nights are always popular, as are themed food evenings and Sunday roasts. It hosts local cribbage league matches and caters for private parties.
👶❀◐◑⛺♣P🚌(94,96) 🐾📶

Theberton

Lion [L]
The Street, IP16 4RU
☎ (01728) 830185 🌐 thebertonlion.co.uk
Woodforde's Wherry; 2 changing beers (sourced locally) [H]
Lively old village bar with patio seating outside at the front, various seating areas inside and a central fireplace. Many pictures of the area decorate the walls. The local beer club meets in the bar. Real ciders in bottle (BiB) are now available all year round including Giggler and Thistly Cross Traditional. The outdoor toilets have been retained. Two log cabins are available to let. Opening hours vary depending on the time of year. 👶❀🛏◐◑♿♣🍎P🐾📶

Thurston

Fox & Hounds

Barton Road, IP31 3QT

☎ (01359) 232228 🌐 thurstonfoxandhounds.co.uk

Greene King IPA; 5 changing beers (sourced nationally; often Cliff Quay, Green Jack, Tring) ⊞

A listed building, this popular local sits in the middle of the village a short walk from the railway station. The restaurant, serving good home-cooked food, is in a separate space within the public bar area, and there is a bar for pool and darts. The pub holds regular quiz nights and bingo, and live music on bank holidays and special occasions. It has its own golf society. ⅀❀🛏👌🅰🚆🅿🐾🛜

Ufford

White Lion 🅛

Lower Street, IP13 6DW

☎ (01394) 460770 🌐 uffordwhitelion.co.uk

Adnams Southwold Bitter; 3 changing beers (often Uffa) Ⓖ

Cosy single-bar pub with a quarry-tiled floor offering various beers including home-brewed ales on a gravity stillage. Food is all locally sourced and freshly prepared on the premises. The large garden leads to the River Deben and includes a substantial marquee used for different occasions on summer days including car rallies, an annual beer festival over the August bank holiday, quiz nights, hog roasts and various private events. Camping is available by arrangement. Q⅀❀🛏🅿🐾

Walberswick

Anchor 🅛 ✅

The Street, IP18 6UA

☎ (01502) 722112 🌐 anchoratwalberswick.com

Adnams Southwold Bitter, Ghost Ship; 1 changing beer (sourced locally; often Adnams) ⊞

Situated in an idyllic coastal village, this hotel caters for holidaymakers and locals alike. It has two cosy alcove areas heated by a real fire on both sides and a side room for families. Real ales from Adnams and a large selection of global craft bottled beers are on offer. A spacious restaurant to the rear serves high-quality local produce. Accommodation is available in the main building and in chalet rooms in the garden. Q⅀❀🛏👌🅰🅿🐾🛜

Waldringfield

Maybush ✅

Cliff Road, IP12 4QL

☎ (01473) 736215

Adnams Southwold Bitter; Greene King IPA ⊞

A popular riverside restaurant and pub operated by Deben Inns. The interior is well furnished and has been divided into various areas primarily used for dining, although drinkers are also very welcome. A wide-ranging food menu is available, with fresh fish dishes a popular choice. There is a large garden with fine views of the River Deben from the terrace. ⅀❀👌👌♣🅿🛜

Wenhaston

Star Inn 🅛

Hall Road, IP19 9HF

☎ (01502) 478240 🌐 wenhastonstar.co.uk

Adnams Southwold Bitter; Green Jack Golden Best; 4 changing beers (sourced locally; often Colchester, Green Jack, Wolf) ⊞

Free house on the outskirts of the village, with fine views of the Blyth Valley from the lawned garden. It has three small public rooms – the front bar is full of character with old enamel advertising signs and an open fire in winter. Good food is all home-cooked using local produce (no food Sun). Beer festivals are held over the late May and August bank holiday weekends. Camping is available by prior arrangement. Q⅀❀🛏👌🅰♣👌🅿(99A)🐾🛜

Woodbridge

Angel 🅛

2 Theatre Street, IP12 4NE

☎ (01394) 382660 🌐 theangelwoodbridge.co.uk

Adnams Southwold Bitter; 5 changing beers ⊞

A traditional two-bar drinking pub with beams and tiled floors. The regularly changing range of real ales is complemented by a selection of over 270 gins. There is seating outside and a former stables to the rear. No meals are served but there is a wood-fired oven in the garden for pizza. Open mic is hosted on the second and fourth Wednesday of the month plus a DJ every Saturday evening and more live music. ⅀❀🚆♣👌🅿🐾🛜

Cherry Tree

73 Cumberland Street, IP12 4AG

☎ (01394) 384627 🌐 thecherrytreepub.co.uk

Adnams Southwold Bitter, Ghost Ship, Broadside; Elgood's Black Dog; 5 changing beers (often Adnams) ⊞

Spacious family-friendly lounge bar/diner with a central servery and several distinct seating areas. Up to nine beers are usually on offer and an annual summer beer festival is hosted. The new kitchen provides home-cooked food all day every day, starting with breakfast, including vegetarian and gluten-free options. Board games and cards are available and a quiz is held on Thursday. The large garden has children's play equipment. Accommodation is in a converted barn. ⅀❀🛏👌🚆♣🅿🐾🛜

Olde Bell & Steelyard ✅

103 New Street, IP12 1DZ

☎ (01394) 382933 🌐 yeoldebellandsteelyard.co.uk

Greene King IPA, Abbot; 2 changing beers (often Greene King) ⊞

Large family-friendly pub with oak beams in two bars and a separate function room. The steelyard – a former cart weighbridge that still worked until hit by a lorry in 2018 – dates from 1650 and was on show at the Great Exhibition in 1851. Good home-cooked food is served. Traditional games include bar billiards, chess and bar skittles. Live rugby is shown on TVs in the side bar area. To the rear of the building is a heated and covered patio area and wheelchair access. ⅀❀👌🚆👌♣🅿🐾🛜

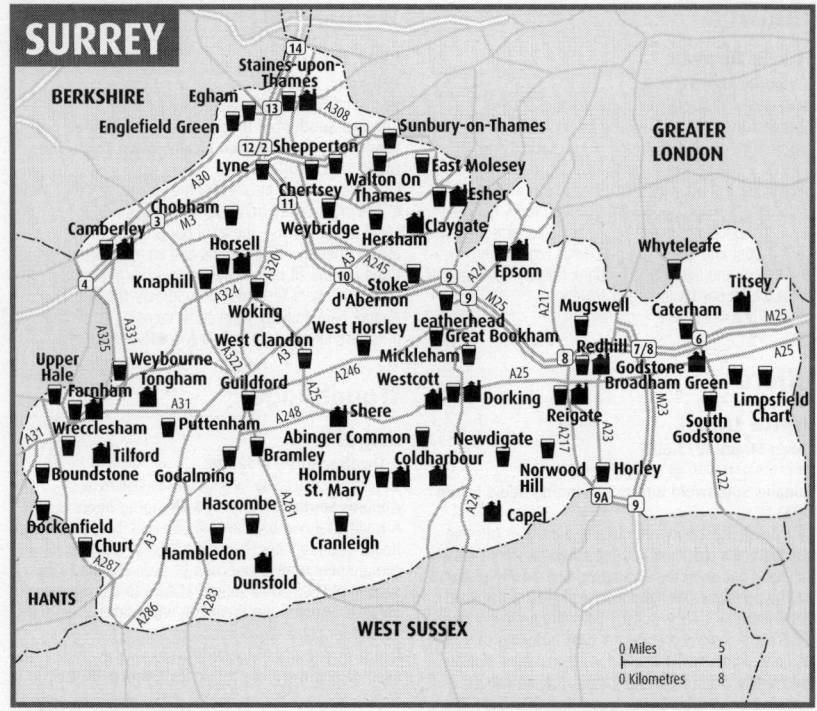

SURREY

(Map of Surrey showing towns including: Staines-upon-Thames, Egham, Englefield Green, Sunbury-on-Thames, Shepperton, Lyne, Chertsey, Walton On Thames, East Molesey, Esher, Chobham, Weybridge, Hersham, Claygate, Camberley, Horsell, Knaphill, Woking, Stoke d'Abernon, Epsom, Leatherhead, Mugswell, Caterham, Whyteleafe, Titsey, West Horsley, Great Bookham, Redhill, Godstone, West Clandon, Mickleham, Broadham Green, Limpsfield Chart, Upper Hale, Weybourne, Tongham, Guildford, Westcott, Dorking, Reigate, South Godstone, Farnham, Wrecclesham, Puttenham, Shere, Abinger Common, Newdigate, Coldharbour, Norwood Hill, Horley, Tilford, Bramley, Holmbury St. Mary, Capel, Boundstone, Godalming, Hascombe, Bockenfield, Churt, Hambledon, Cranleigh, Dunsfold. Neighbouring counties: BERKSHIRE, GREATER LONDON, HANTS, WEST SUSSEX)

```
0 Miles          5
0 Kilometres     8
```

Abinger Common

Abinger Hatch 🅛

Abinger Lane, RH5 6HZ TQ11574596
☎ (01306) 730737 ⊕ theabingerhatch.com
Ringwood Razorback; 3 changing beers 🅗
Dating from the 17th century this inn is situated opposite the village church in the lovely Surrey Hills. The recently refurbished interior rambles over three levels, all served from a beautiful English oak bar. The lowest level has a flagstone floor and there are wooden beams and posts throughout. Good food is a feature, with a varied menu on offer. There is a large garden at the rear. The beer range changes frequently. Q⌂❀❀◐▶P🚌(22)❀�🛜

Boundstone

Bat & Ball 🅛

15 Bat & Ball Lane, GU10 4SA (off Sandrock Hill Rd via Upper Bourne Lane) SU833444
☎ (01252) 792108 ⊕ thebatandball.co.uk
Adnams Ghost Ship; Dark Star Hophead; Hop Back Summer Lightning; house beer (by Itchen Valley); 2 changing beers (sourced locally) 🅗
A traditional country free house dating back 150 years, set in the Bourne Valley. It has been run by the same family for two generations. The pub has several different rooms, with an open log fire, panelled walls and oak beams. The attractive garden has a children's play area and is popular with families. There is an annual beer festival, a weekly quiz on Tuesday and live music once a month. An afternoon menu is served at weekends. Q⌂❀◐▶&P🚌(16,17)❀☀🛜

Bramley

Jolly Farmer 🅛

High Street, GU5 0HB

☎ (01483) 893355 ⊕ jollyfarmer.co.uk
Greene King IPA; 7 changing beers (sourced nationally; often Crafty, Firebird) 🅗
A stagecoach inn that seems almost unchanged from yesteryear, with accommodation available in four en-suite rooms and a three bedroom flat. A privately owned free house, it is full of character and has a cosy, welcoming atmosphere. Dark-wood beams hint of its upgrade long-ago from an entirely timber-framed construction. The decor is a celebration of the countryside and beer, featuring many historic beer mats and a large selection of pumpclips. The L-shaped bar offers a diverse range of up to eight real ales, plus real ciders in summer. ⌂❀❀⇛◐♣●P🚌(53,63)❀☀🛜

Broadham Green

Haycutter 🅛

69 Tanhouse Road, RH8 9PE
☎ (01883) 776955 ⊕ haycutter.co.uk
Harvey's Sussex Best Bitter; 3 changing beers 🅗
This smart Brunning & Price pub has been much extended at the back yet retains a cosy feel due to its many small areas. Food is extremely popular but the main bar area is maintained as a community hub for locals. The guest beers are often from local breweries and the house beer is from Westerham. Outside there is seating for diners in the summer and a separate large garden for drinkers, with a children's play area. Q⌂❀◐&♣●P❀🛜

Camberley

Claude du Vall 🅛 ✓

77-81 High Street, GU15 3RB
☎ (01276) 672910

Greene King Abbot; Ruddles Best Bitter; Sharp's Doom Bar; 4 changing beers (often Ascot, Tillingbourne, Windsor & Eton) Ⓗ
The Claude du Vall is conveniently close to the station and bus stops, at the end of the High Street. The large, modern interior is divided into a number of different areas. The long bar offers three regular beers, four guests including at least one LocAle, and a real cider. Wetherspoon's reputation for good-value food and drinks attracts customers throughout the day, from breakfast onwards. Silent TVs generally show news programmes.
🐴❀◑♿⇌●🚌📶

Caterham

King & Queen 𝕃
34 High Street, CR3 5UA (on B2030)
☎ (01883) 345438 🌐 kingandqueencaterham.co.uk
Fuller's London Pride, ESB; 1 changing beer Ⓗ
Traditional community pub that was originally three cottages dating back 400 years - as is evident from the inglenook fireplace and exposed beams. It became an inn in the 1840s. It now has three distinct areas in which to drink the superb beer. One bar is overlooked by portraits of King William and Queen Mary; another contains a dartboard. Live music features once a month.
🐴❀◑♣P🚌🐾📶

Chertsey

Coach & Horses 𝕃 ✔
14 St Ann's Road, KT16 9DG (on B375)
☎ (01932) 563085 🌐 thecoachandhorseschertsey.co.uk
Fuller's London Pride, ESB Ⓗ
An attractive, tile-hung Fuller's community local with linked drinking areas, built in 1860 as a school. Good-value food is served Tuesday to Friday but the landlady likes to keep a 'proper pub' for beer and conversation at weekends. It hosts league darts and has a sports TV. Outside, there is a garden to the rear and seating at the front. Abbeyfields park and Chertsey's cricket and football clubs are within walking distance and Thorpe Park is a short bus or car journey.
❀🛏◑♣●P🚌(446,456) 📶

Olde Swan
27 Windsor Street, KT16 8AY
☎ (01932) 562129 🌐 theoldeswanhotel.co.uk
Sharp's Doom Bar; Timothy Taylor Landlord; Tring Side Pocket for a Toad; 1 changing beer (sourced nationally; often Dorking, Thames Side) Ⓗ
Refurbished when acquired by Mclean Inns, without spoiling its charm, the Olde Swan gives drinkers and diners a mellow experience with its shabby-chic decor. Four ales are usually on offer. The menu features stone-baked pizza, home-made burgers and sizzling steaks, with Mexican night on Friday. Accommodation includes double, twin and family rooms. Chertsey is handy for the M3 and Thorpe Park. 🐴❀🛏◑⇌●P🚌(446,456)📶

Chobham

Horse & Groom
30 High Street, GU24 8AA
☎ 07785 283573
🌐 horse-and-groom-micropub.business.site
4 changing beers (sourced locally; often Thurstons) Ⓗ
New to the Guide, this micropub is on the site of an old hairdresser's; however, long before that, it was part of the original Horse & Groom inn that closed in 1960. The new micro describes itself as 'a village pub but smaller' - an apt description as it has the feel of a local, with conversation a key part of the ambience. Beers are from the area and all come direct from the brewery. A range of snacks is available. Q●🚌(39A,73)

White Hart 𝕃
58 High Street, GU24 8AA
☎ (01276) 857580 🌐 whitehart-chobham.co.uk
House beer (by St Austell); 4 changing beers (sourced locally) Ⓗ
A lovely rambling building with interesting nooks and crannies, next to the village church on an attractive and historic High Street with a cricket pitch behind the pub. Five ales are served in a range of strengths and styles. Brunning & Price Original is always available; guests could come from any of many local breweries, with the distance from the pub prominently displayed. There are two restaurant areas and a less formal space for drinkers as you enter. Brunch is offered at weekends.
Q🐴❀◑♿P🚌(39A,73) 🐾📶

Churt

Crossways Inn 𝕃
Churt Road, GU10 2JS
☎ (01428) 714323 🌐 weydonian.net/crossways
Arundel Sussex IPA; Hop Back Crop Circle; Loose Cannon Abingdon Bridge Ⓗ**; 4 changing beers** Ⓖ
Friendly two-bar pub with a homely ambience. At the centre of village life, it is popular with local groups as well as customers from further afield including ramblers and cyclists. Guest beers are fetched from their casks in the cellar, usually including local ales and a stout or porter. Good-value food is served lunchtimes, plus fish & chips on Wednesday night (no food Sun).
❀◐♣●P🚌(19) 🐾

Cranleigh

Three Horseshoes 𝕃 ✔
4 High Street, GU6 8AE (on B2128)
☎ (01483) 276978 🌐 threehorseshoescranleigh.co.uk
5 changing beers Ⓗ
This two-bar 17th-century inn features an inglenook fireplace with a roaring wood fire in winter. The long-gone Brufords Brewery used to stand behind the pub and some photos in the lounge bar show the building. Good home-made food is served daily except Sunday evening. The elaborate walled garden boasts a spectacular

REAL ALE BREWERIES

Antoine's Westcott
Ascot Camberley
Big Smoke ✦ Esher
Brightwater Claygate
By the Horns Redhill
Craft Brews Farnham
Crafty Brewing Dunsfold
Dorking ✦ Capel
Felday ▤ Holmbury St Mary
Fuzzchat ▤ Epsom
Godstone ✦ Godstone
Hogs Back ✦ Tongham
Leith Hill ▤ Coldharbour
Pilgrim ✦ Reigate
Surrey Hills ✦ Dorking
Thames Side ✦ Staines-upon-Thames
Thurstons Horsell
Tilford ▤ Tilford
Tillingbourne Shere
Titsey Titsey
Trailhead ✦ Dorking (NEW)

children's playhouse and the patio is covered against the weather. Five constantly changing guest beers are sold, mostly from local brewers. ☺✿❍◗❤♣◆P🖵❀✿🛜

Dockenfield

Bluebell 🅛

Batts Corner, GU10 4EX (½ mile N of Dockenfield village) SU820410
☎ (01252) 792801 ⊕ bluebell-dockenfield.com
Langham Hip Hop; Triple fff Moondance; 2 changing beers (sourced locally; often Crafty, Hogs Back) Ⓗ
A 150-year-old hidden gem tucked away in a rural setting. The Bluebell has a large garden, plenty of parking and is a truly independent family-run pub. The open-plan interior has a light, contemporary feel with three different seating areas for both formal and informal dining as well as drinking, with a real fire in winter. Beers are usually obtained directly from breweries within 15 miles. Q☺✿❍◗❤♣AP❀✿🛜

Dorking

Cobbett's 🅛

23 West Street, RH4 1BY (on A25 one-way system eastbound)
☎ (01306) 879877 ⊕ cobbettsrealales.com
6 changing beers Ⓗ/Ⓖ
In an old part of town, this excellent micropub and real ale off-licence was once a dolls' house shop. It offers the largest choice of beer in Surrey, constantly changing and served by knowledgeable staff. Up to six cask ales are available alongside six from KeyKeg and 200 bottles and cans from Britain and beyond. The tiny pub is in a back room (open from noon) with its own garden, and is a great place to chat. Q☺✿❀≉(West)◆🖵❀🛜

Cricketers 🅛 ✅

81 South Street, RH4 2JU (on A25 one-way system westbound)
☎ (01306) 889938 ⊕ cricketersdorking.co.uk
Dark Star Hophead; Fuller's London Pride, ESB; 2 changing beers Ⓗ
Small, comfortable pub that has a single L-shaped bar, with old mirrors, photographs and adverts on the walls. This is a big rugby pub with all Six Nations matches and other internationals covered, and other terrestrial sport may be screened. The guest beers usually come from Dark Star or Fuller's but sometimes from a different brewery on the list. There is a wide selection of board games, and darts is played. Two beer festivals are usually held each year in the garden. ☺✿❍◗♣🖵❀🛜

Old House ✅

24 West Street, RH4 1BY (on A25 eastbound)
☎ (01306) 889664 ⊕ oldhousedorking.co.uk
Young's Bitter; 3 changing beers Ⓗ
Attractive 15th-century inn situated in the Dorking Conservation Area. It is a successful blend of old and modern, with a single bar serving a number of distinct areas. The beer range will always include a selection from Dorking and SlyBeast. Very good home-made food ranging from bar snacks to daily specials is available each day. Outside, the surprisingly large patio garden can be quite a suntrap. ✿❍◗≉(West)🖵

East Molesey

Bell 🅛 ✅

4 Bell Road, KT8 0SS (off B369)
☎ (020) 8941 0400

Greene King Abbot; Morland Old Speckled Hen; 4 changing beers (often Hogs Back, Twickenham, Wimbledon) Ⓗ
A quirky, welcoming back-street inn, a short walk from the main shopping street. Several separate drinking areas make it ideal for a quiet pint or a larger gathering. The pub dates from 1460 and was later East Molesey's first post office. The 18th-century highwayman Claude Duvalier hid from the Bow Street Runners here. The large garden has a children's play area. Various TV screens show sport, which can be avoided if preferred. Quiz night is Tuesday. ☺✿❍◗♣P🖵(411)❀🛜

Egham

Egham United Services Club 🅛

111 Spring Rise, TW20 9PE (close to A30 Egham Hill)
☎ (01784) 435120 ⊕ eusc.club
Rebellion IPA; 3 changing beers (sourced nationally; often Burning Sky, Surrey Hills, Thames Side) Ⓗ
Local CAMRA Club of the Year and a former National Club of the Year finalist. A changing range of guest ales includes something dark, and a wide choice of ciders is available from the cellar. Three beer festivals a year showcase an eclectic range of ales, mostly from the newest micros around. The club is comfortably furnished with sports TV, and hosts live music most Saturday evenings. Show a CAMRA membership card to be signed in. ☺✿❀≉♣◆P🖵(8,441)🛜

Englefield Green

Happy Man 🅛 ✅

12 Harvest Road, TW20 0QS (off A30)
☎ (01784) 433265 ⊕ thehappyman.co.uk
Hop Back Summer Lightning; 3 changing beers (sourced nationally; often Crouch Vale, Purity, Whitstable) Ⓗ
In Victorian times two houses were converted to a pub serving workers building Royal Holloway College. Refurbished but virtually unchanged, this local CAMRA Pub of the Year is a popular haunt for students and locals. Alongside regular ale Summer Lightning from Hop Back, it serves three changing guests from local and national breweries. Beer festivals are held on the rear patio, which has a heated marquee. Darts and quiz nights are hosted and food is available every day.
✿❍◗♣◆🖵(8,441)❀

Epsom

Assembly Rooms ✅

147-153 High Street, KT19 8EH (on A24 Northbound)
☎ (01372) 737290
Fuller's London Pride; Greene King IPA, Abbot; Sharp's Doom Bar; 6 changing beers Ⓗ
A large, attractive building at one end of the marketplace in the centre of Epsom. Originally built as the town assembly rooms in the early 18th century, it became a Wetherspoon in 2002. The open-plan interior is broken up by dividing walls, with a long bar running across the rear facing stone-paved and carpeted seating areas that drop down on slightly different levels. Alcoholic drinks are served from 9am. Q☺✿❍◗❤≉🖵🛜

Jolly Coopers 🅛

84 Wheelers Lane, KT18 7SD (off B280 via Stamford Green Rd)
☎ (01372) 723222 ⊕ jollycoopers.co.uk
Surrey Hills Ranmore; 3 changing beers (sourced regionally; often Fuzzchat) Ⓗ

Close to Epsom Common, this pub is more than 200 years old. The interior is divided into two – a carpeted bar area to the left, and another larger area with polished parquet flooring to the right used more for dining, although not exclusively so. The decor is modern, with painted walls. There is a large paved garden at the rear. It can get busy at weekends but is quieter during the week. The Fuzzchat Brewery is in an outbuilding at the back. Various ciders are sold in summer. Q❄️👍🏴🅿️🚪(E9,E10) 😺 📶

Rifleman 🅛
5 East Street, KT17 1BB (on A24)
☎ (01372) 721244 🌐 therifleman.co.uk
Greene King London Glory; house beer (by Hardys & Hansons); 3 changing beers (sourced locally; often Dorking, Hogs Back, Windsor & Eton) 🅗
Small corner pub in the shadow of a bridge carrying the railway to and from London. It is decorated in a traditional style featuring two fireplaces and dark-green wood panelling, but also has some modern features such as bare brickwork and high tables at the front. There is a pleasant garden to the rear, an oasis of calm close to central Epsom. The name comes from the Surrey Rifle Volunteers who trained nearby to meet the threat of French invasion. Children welcome until 6pm. 🕒👍🏴🚪😺📶

Esher

Albert Arms
82 High Street, KT10 9QS (on A307)
☎ (01372) 877117 🌐 thealbertarmsesher.co.uk
Dark Star Hophead; Fuller's London Pride; 1 changing beer (sourced regionally; often Fuller's) 🅗
A welcoming late 19th-century street-corner pub in the centre of Esher. It was named after Prince Albert, who at one time lived nearby. There is a large, wood-panelled bar area plus a smaller dining space where drinkers are also welcome. The TV is for major sporting occasions only. Two dining rooms upstairs can be hired for special events. Open for breakfast, with alcoholic drinks available from 11am. 🕒🍴👍🚪😺📶

Wheatsheaf 🅛
40 The Green, KT10 8AG
☎ (01372) 464014 🌐 wheatsheafesher.co.uk
Surrey Hills Shere Drop; Young's Bitter; 1 changing beer (sourced locally) 🅗
Imposing inn in about 200 years old opposite Esher Green. This is a smart, popular local with a vibrant atmosphere. Its spacious and modern interior comprises a large central bar and several seating areas. Drinkers and diners are equally welcome, with high-quality food available all day. The bar area has an open fire. A bicycle rack is provided at the rear. Changing guest beers include local ales. A former local CAMRA Pub of the Year. 🕒👍🏴🅿️🚪😺📶

Farnham

Hop Blossom
50 Long Garden Walk, GU9 7HX (between Waitrose and Castle St) SU838469
☎ (01252) 710770 🌐 hopblossom.co.uk
Fuller's London Pride, ESB; Gale's Seafarers Ale; 2 changing beers (often Dark Star, Fuller's, St Austell) 🅗
A hidden gem in the heart of Farnham, with a lovely welcoming feel and a log fire in winter. It has three distinct areas – the main bar, a conservatory and a back room. Seating includes some old pews, with traditional

floorboards underfoot. The pub can be crowded during events in the town. Dogs are welcome, as are children during the day and early evening. 🕒♿🏴🚪(4)😺📶

Nelson Arms 🅛 ✅
50-52 Castle Street, GU9 7JQ
☎ (01252) 727222 🌐 thenelsonarmsfarnham.co.uk
Andwell Gold Muddler; Hogs Back TEA; Timothy Taylor Boltmaker; 1 changing beer (sourced nationally) 🅗
Originally three farm cottages belonging to the Bishop of Winchester's estate, this pub has plenty of history. Horatio Nelson is reputed to have stayed here while visiting Lady Hamilton, who lived nearby. There are many original dark beams and some exposed brickwork, with a log fire between the two main seating areas. The guest beer pump usually features a traditional amber bitter, or a golden ale in summer. Alongside the excellent beer, the pub serves good food, including at its grill night on Tuesday. 🕒👍🍴♿🚪(4)😺📶

Godalming

Star Inn ✅
17 Church Street, GU7 1EL
☎ (01483) 417717 🌐 starinngodalming.co.uk
Hardys & Hansons Olde Trip 🅗**; 9 changing beers (sourced nationally; often Greene King)** 🅗/🅖
Dating from around 1830, the Star has a small public bar at the front and a main room to the side that leads to a patio garden and smoking area. There is a separate lounge with a bespoke cider bar, open Thursday to Sunday. Up to 10 real ales are stocked. Beer festivals are held at Easter and Halloween. The pub is a regular winner of CAMRA cider awards. 🕒👍🍴♿🏴🚪😺📶

Great Bookham

Anchor ✅
161 Lower Road, KT23 4AH (off A246 via Eastwick Rd)
☎ (01372) 452429
Fuller's London Pride; Young's London Original 🅗
Historic Grade II-listed inn dating from the 15th century. Low-beamed ceilings, wooden floors, exposed brickwork and inglenook with a real fire in winter give the pub a very traditional and homely feel. A charity quiz night is held every Tuesday (book ahead) and a meat raffle on Sunday. There is a patio garden with a pond and heated smoking area at the front. Children are not allowed in the bar. Q👍🍴🏴🅿️🚪(479)😺📶

Guildford

King's Head
27 King's Road, GU1 4JW (on A320 Stoke Rd)
☎ (01483) 568957 🌐 kingsheadguildford.co.uk
Dark Star Hophead; Fuller's London Pride, ESB; 1 changing beer (sourced nationally) 🅗
Originally two cottages dating back to 1860, then a beer house. The interior is deceptively spacious and now much enlarged. Service is from both sides of a central bar, with the full range of Fuller's beers available, including seasonals, complemented by a draught cider. TV sport is screened in most areas. Acoustic music features on Tuesday, quiz night is Wednesday, and open mic night is Thursday. The pub is noted for its attractive hanging baskets. 🕒👍🍴♿♿(London Rd)🚪🅿️😺📶

Rodboro Buildings 🅛 ✅
1-10 Bridge Street, GU1 4SB (opp Friary Centre)
☎ (01483) 306366
Greene King Abbot, IPA; Sharp's Doom Bar; 7 changing beers 🅗

This Wetherspoon maintains a range of up to 10 real ales, often from local breweries. It is spread over three levels in a Grade II-listed former industrial building that was the original home of the Dennis car (later truck) company. The community noticeboard publicises a range of local events. The pub also hosts occasional Meet the Brewer nights and brewery battles. 🏠🖤🍴🕹🛇❤🍷

Royal Oak

Trinity Churchyard, GU1 3RR (behind Trinity church)
☎ (01483) 457144 ⊕ royaloakguildford.co.uk
Fuller's London Pride; Gale's HSB; 3 changing beers (sourced nationally; often Dark Star, Fuller's, Windsor & Eton) Ⓗ
This pub has been serving real ale since 1870. It was built as an extension to the rectory next door, with a hall upstairs and rooms at ground level. These rooms are now the bar area and show the building's heavily beamed structure. Outside there is a patio area on one side and a couple of tables overlooking Trinity churchyard on the other. A takeaway service is available, including for real ale. 🏠🕷🕹➕🅿🛒❤🍷

Hambledon

Merry Harriers 🅛 ✅

Hambledon Road, GU8 4DR SU967391
☎ (01428) 682883 ⊕ merryharriers.com
Surrey Hills Shere Drop; 3 changing beers (sourced locally; often Crafty, Dorking, Greyhound) Ⓗ
This impressive 16th-century country inn, popular with walkers and cyclists, takes you back in time. It is in the heart of a picturesque village, set against the backdrop of the Surrey Hills, surrounded by open fields, in a designated area of outstanding natural beauty. The free house is owned by local resident Peter de Savary. An open field at the rear is home to the pub's llamas.
Q🏠🕷🚪🕹➕❤🅿(503)❤🍷

Hascombe

White Horse ✅

The Street, GU8 4JA (at S end of village, by jct of The St and Church Rd)
☎ (01483) 208258 ⊕ whitehorsepub.net
Harvey's Sussex Best Bitter; Hogs Back TEA; Otter Bitter; Surrey Hills Shere Drop; 1 changing beer (sourced locally) Ⓗ
A coaching inn dating from the 16th century, the White Horse has traditional adults-only public bar, decorated with sporting photos and old agricultural tools. Several other rooms, where families are welcome, lead to the garden. The guest beer is usually from a local brewery. Food is served daily, lunchtimes and evenings, featuring locally sourced meat and game. The pub is on the Greensand Way and convenient for other local attractions. Q🏠🕷🕹🅿(42)❤🍷

Hersham

Bricklayers Arms

6-8 Queens Road, KT12 5LS (off A317)
☎ (01932) 220936
Hogs Back TEA; Hop Back Crop Circle; Shepherd Neame Spitfire Ⓗ
This two-bar Victorian pub, just off the green, has built up a fine reputation. It is divided into a spacious public bar and comfortable saloon. Excellent food is served in the lounge, including daily specials. Features include wonderful external floral displays and a secluded rear garden. Two letting rooms are available. Parking can be difficult. 🕷🚪🕹🛇➕🅿(458,515)❤🍷

Holmbury St Mary

Royal Oak 🅛

The Glade, Felday Road, RH5 6PF
☎ (01306) 898010 ⊕ theroyaloakholmbury.co.uk
Felday Legacy; 4 changing beers Ⓗ
This 17th-century pub by the picturesque church and village green is a popular destination for walkers and cyclists. The main bar, warmed by an attractive fire, has a few steps up to a back dining room, and there are some tables in the small entrance porch. Outside, there is a small fenced garden at the back and more seats at the front. The Felday Brewery is custom built on-site. Guest beers often come from local breweries.
🏠🕷🕹➕🅿🛇❤🍷

Horley

Jack Fairman ✅

30 Victoria Road, RH6 7PZ (on main shopping street near Waitrose)
☎ (01293) 827910
Greene King Abbot; Ruddles Best Bitter; Sharp's Doom Bar; 4 changing beers Ⓗ
After a period as a Kwik-Fit tyre centre, this building reopened as a Wetherspoon pub in the centre of town, and is conveniently close to the station and bus stops. The 1930s building was formerly a garage used by local motor racing driver Jack Fairman, and historical racing-related items can be found on the walls of the industrial-look interior. Food is available all day. Televised news and sport are shown on three screens (usually silently with subtitles). Q🏠🕷🕹🛇♿🅿🍷

Horsell

Crown 🅛

104 High Street, GU21 4ST
☎ (01483) 771719
6 changing beers (sourced locally; often Surrey Hills, Thurstons) Ⓗ
Welcoming two-bar community local with six real ales in the saloon bar. Three beers are from Thurstons, who started brewing in the Crown and are now located next door. Other ales come from independent local or regional breweries. Behind the pub is a sturdy smokers' shelter and beyond that a large garden with two pétanque pistes. Real cider is available occasionally, more often in summer. It hosts at least one beer festival a year. Local CAMRA Pub of the Year 2019. 🏠🕷➕🅿(48)❤🍷

Knaphill

Garibaldi ✅

134 High Street, GU21 2QH
☎ (01483) 473374 ⊕ thegaribaldiknaphill.co.uk
2 changing beers (sourced regionally) Ⓗ
Enterprising pub on the edge of Knaphill. Its compact interior has exposed beams and wooden floors. Two or three changing cask ales are served, with regional beers favoured. A real cider is available direct from the cellar. Monday is real ale club night, with beers sold at reduced prices. It hosts a Sunday evening quiz, a Tuesday curry night and a Thursday steak night. A beer festival is held over Easter. 🏠🕷🕹➕🅿(39A,48)❤🍷

Royal Oak 🅛

Anchor Hill, GU21 2JH
☎ (01483) 473330
5 changing beers (often Exmoor, Ringwood, St Austell) Ⓗ

An attractive 17th-century building set back from the road at the bottom of the hill. Up to seven ciders are served alongside the beers. Food is available Wednesday to Sunday, with a roast on Sunday. Behind the pub is a superb garden with a barbecue and children's play equipment. An outside bar opens at the weekend in summer. Live music is hosted twice a month, plus an annual beer festival and two cider festivals.
👪❀🕏◑♣♠P🚆(48,91) ❀ 🌐

Leatherhead

Running Horse 🅛
38 Bridge Street, KT22 8BZ (off B2122)
☎ (01372) 372081 🌐 running-horse.co.uk
Shepherd Neame Spitfire; Surrey Hills Ranmore; 1 changing beer (sourced regionally; often Shepherd Neame) 🅗
Overlooking the River Mole, this Grade II*-listed two-room pub, dating from 1403, features a real log fire, home-made food, a courtyard seating area plus a large back garden. Elizabeth I apparently spent the night here. The public bar has TV, a pool table and dartboard, and the cosy lounge bar features low ceilings and exposed beams. Quiz night is Tuesday. Live jazz plays on Sunday lunchtime and live bands monthly, with a charity music event on May Day. Children are welcome until 9pm.
Q👪❀🕏◑≠♣P🚆❀🌐

Limpsfield Chart

Carpenters Arms 🅛
12 Tally Road, RH8 0TG (off B269)
☎ (01883) 722209 🌐 carpenterslimpsfield.co.uk
Westerham Summer Perle, British Bulldog, 1965 – Special Bitter Ale; 2 changing beers 🅗
This former Westerham Brewery tied house is adjacent to the National Trust's Limpsfield Common and attracts both walkers and horse-riders. The L-shaped bar has parquet flooring and the walls are adorned with an interesting collection of old photos and artwork. One side of the bar caters for diners enjoying the good food on offer. There is also a separate function room. 👪❀🕏◑♣P🚆(594)❀🌐

Lyne

Royal Marine
Lyne Lane, KT16 0AN
☎ (01932) 873900 🌐 royalmarinelyne.co.uk
Ruddles Best Bitter; 1 changing beer (sourced nationally; often Shepherd Neame) 🅗
The name of this cosy rural inn commemorates Queen Victoria's review of her troops in 1853 on nearby Chobham Common. Royal Marine memorabilia, a collection of drinking jugs and other bric-a-brac are on display. Generous portions of home-cooked food are served Monday to Friday and Sunday lunchtime. Friday is bingo quiz night. There is an extensive garden to the rear. Note that the pub is closed on Saturday.
Q👪❀🕏◑♣P❀🌐

Mickleham

King William IV 🅛
4 Byttom Hill, RH5 6EL (off A24 southbound behind Frascati Restaurant)
☎ (01372) 372590 🌐 thekingwilliamiv.com
Fuller's London Pride; Surrey Hills Shere Drop; 1 changing beer (sourced locally; often Crafty Brewing) 🅗
A quaint, welcoming country pub, nestled on a hillside and dating from 1790. The main bar is homely with a log fire and there is a smaller bar to the front. An attractive outside terrace, with some tables under cover, enjoys stunning views over the Mole Valley. Good home-made food is served – book ahead for lunch, especially on summer weekends. Steep steps can make access difficult. A shared car park is on the A24 southbound.
Q👪❀🕏◑P🚆(465) ❀ 🌐

Mugswell

Well House Inn 🅛 ✅
Chipstead Lane, CR5 3SQ (off A217) TQ25845526
☎ (01737) 830640 🌐 thewellhouseinn.co.uk
Fuller's London Pride; Hogs Back TEA; Surrey Hills Shere Drop; 2 changing beers 🅗
This Grade II-listed building has been a pub since the 1950s. It has three small bars – a snug to the left with a dartboard, a dining room to the right and a conservatory. Food is a feature here. The guest beers may include a local ale. The pleasant garden contains St Margaret's Well or Mag's Well, which is reputedly mentioned in the Domesday Book and gives the area its name.
👪❀🕏◑♣P❀🌐

Newdigate

Surrey Oaks 🅛
Parkgate Road, Parkgate, RH5 5DZ (between Newdigate and Leigh) TQ20524363
☎ (01306) 631200 🌐 thesurreyoaks.com
Surrey Hills Ranmore, Shere Drop; 4 changing beers 🅗
The 'Soaks' is a multi award-winning 16th-century free house serving a changing range of six cask beers including a dark ale, 12 keg beers from a beer wall and 16 ciders. The interior has a number of distinct areas with low beams, flagstones and an inglenook fireplace with log-burning stove. Good home-made food includes daily specials. The excellent garden is nearly an acre in size and benefits from many tables plus a children's play area in one corner. Popular beer festivals are held over the late May and August bank holidays.
Q👪❀🕏◑♣🚶P🚆(21) ❀ 🌐

Norwood Hill

Fox Revived 🅛
RH6 0ET
☎ (01293) 229270 🌐 foxrevived.co.uk
Surrey Hills Shere Drop; 4 changing beers 🅗
Fully refurbished and extended in 2017, this stylish country pub, dating back to the 19th century, focuses on dining, with good food served all day. Situated at a crossroads at the top of a hill, it enjoys views towards Box Hill and the North Downs. An attractive garden room looks out over the stone terrace and makes the most of the delightful vista. The guest beers are usually local.
👪❀◑♿🚶P🚆(22) ❀ 🌐

Puttenham

Good Intent
60-62 The Street, GU3 1AR
☎ (01483) 923434 🌐 goodintentputtenham.co.uk
Hogs Back TEA; Sharp's Doom Bar; Timothy Taylor Landlord; 1 changing beer (sourced nationally) 🅗
Attractive, welcoming village pub. Classic red carpets and contrasting dark varnished woodwork contribute to a warm, comfortable ambiance. During winter an even greater warmth comes from the massive inglenook fireplace. The layout and bar are L-shaped with the handpumps split between the long and short sides of the bar. Low partitions break up the floor space creating

separate areas. The North Downs Way is at the other end of the village as is one of Surrey's few remaining hop growers. Q☼☸⬤◗⬤⟁AP☀✿🛜

Redhill

Garibaldi ⓛ
29 Mill Street, RH1 6PA
☎ (01737) 773094 ⬤ thegaribaldiredhill.co.uk
4 changing beers Ⓗ
The Garibaldi, which can be found alongside Redhill Common, has been a pub for over 150 years and is now not-for-profit and community-owned. The single compact room has a central bar with TV screens at each end for sporting events, and a small side area with a dartboard. The large garden has views across Redhill. The place hosts a variety of social events including two beer festivals each year. Beers are primarily local and usually include at least one from Pilgrim Brewery.
☙☼☸≈(Earlswood) ♣🛒✿🛜

Sun ⓛ ✔
17-21 London Road, RH1 1LY (on A25 in town centre)
☎ (01737) 766886
Greene King Abbot; Ruddles Best Bitter; Sharp's Doom Bar; 5 changing beers Ⓗ
This purpose-built Wetherspoon comprises a single large room with one long bar, a raised dining space at one end and an area for families until 6pm. Up to six guest beers are served, usually including several from local microbreweries. It serves the chain's typical food menu all day. Several TV screens show major sporting events with the sound turned off. Its name commemorates the astronomer Richard Carrington, who built an observatory in Redhill in 1853 and made observations of sunspots.
Q☙☼◗⬤≈♣🛒✿🛜

Reigate

Bell Inn ⓛ ✔
21 Bell Street, RH2 7AD (on A217)
☎ (01737) 244438 ⬤ thebellreigate.co.uk
Greene King IPA; Morland Old Speckled Hen; 4 changing beers Ⓗ
One of the oldest pubs in Reigate, from the front it looks tiny but inside it opens into a long, narrow bar with a low ceiling and wooden floor. To the rear is a heated patio garden. The menu includes more than a dozen speciality burgers made with locally sourced meat. The guest beers change frequently and are usually from local breweries plus Greene King seasonals. Note the old Ordnance Survey map on the ceiling. ☙☼◗≈🛒✿🛜

Hop Stop Bar
73 Bell Street, RH2 7AN (on A217 S of town centre)
☎ (01737) 221781 ⬤ hopstopbeers.co.uk
2 changing beers Ⓗ
Comfortable continental-style bar with modern furnishings and several different seating areas. Specialising in beer, wine and spirits from small suppliers, it has around 10 draught beers in a variety of styles, served from handpump, KeyKeg and keg, all beautifully kept with individual temperature control. The fridge contains around 80 changing bottles and cans. The owners also have a bottle shop by Oxted Station.
☙🛒✿🛜

Pilgrim Brewery Tap Room ⓛ
11 West Street, RH2 9BL (off A25 towards Dorking)
☎ (01737) 222651 ⬤ pilgrim.co.uk
Pilgrim Surrey, Session IPA, Progress, Quest; 2 changing beers Ⓖ

Surrey's oldest brewery is hidden in a yard just off the town centre in an old Victorian bakery, with the cosy taproom in a converted office. Outside is a pleasant area overlooking Reigate Priory cricket ground. There are usually six cask ales on sale along with around six keg (some of which will be experimental). No food is served but you are welcome to bring in a pizza from across the road. Closed Monday and Tuesday. Q☙☼☸≈♣P🛒✿🛜

Shepperton

Barley Mow ⓛ
67 Watersplash Road, TW17 0EE (off B376 in Shepperton Green)
☎ (01932) 225326
Hogs Back TEA; Hop Back Summer Lightning; 3 changing beers (sourced locally; often Thames Side, Tillingbourne, Twickenham) Ⓗ
Friendly community local in Shepperton Green to the west of the main village centre. Five handpumps serve two regular beers plus up to three – usually local – guest ales. Many pumpclips adorn the bar and beams. Entertainment includes jazz on Wednesday, a quiz night on Thursday, live rock or blues bands on Friday or Saturday night, and a traditional charity meat raffle on Sunday afternoon. Outside is a covered, heated patio at the rear. ☼♣⬤P🛒(458,574)✿🛜

South Godstone

Fox & Hounds ⓛ ✔
Tilburstow Hill Road, RH9 8LY
☎ (01342) 893474 ⬤ foxandhounds.org.uk
Greene King Abbot; St Austell Tribute; 3 changing beers Ⓗ
This attractive building, with parts dating back to 1368, became a pub in 1601. There are original beams throughout and a large inglenook in the restaurant. The bar area is low-ceilinged and very cosy, with high-back settles and a fire. The pleasant garden at the rear has a children's play area. Guest beers usually include offerings from Hogs Back and Pilgrim. With good-quality food also available, this is a pub well worth seeking out.
☙☼◗♣P✿🛜

Staines-upon-Thames

Old Red Lion ✔
Leacroft, TW18 4PB
☎ (01784) 453355
Bombardier; Courage Best Bitter; Fuller's London Pride; 1 changing beer (sourced nationally) Ⓗ
Cosy community local dating back to 1610 – look out for the low beams. In a quiet location facing a green and a small wood, it is only a couple of minutes' walk from the railway station. There is decking at the front and a garden and benches for alfresco drinking. Food is available lunchtimes and evenings except Monday, including popular Sunday roasts and steak nights. Quiz nights and occasional live music are hosted.
☼◗≈P🛒(117,216) ✿

Swan Hotel
The Hythe, TW18 3JB (overlooking Thames by Staines Bridge)
☎ (01784) 452494 ⬤ swanstaines.co.uk
Fuller's London Pride, ESB; 2 changing beers (often Dark Star, Fuller's) Ⓗ
Rambling 18th-century hotel a short walk from the town centre, much enlarged and refurbished over the years. Its warren of rooms includes two bars, a restaurant open every day, and 15 bedrooms. The walls display evocative

pictures of Thames life, including local rowing events. The long riverside terrace by the hotel's moorings is ideally placed to watch the boats go by.
ॐ❀⌖◑P🖵❀🛜

Thames Side Brewery & Tap Room Ⓛ
Bridge Street, TW18 4TG (on Thames towpath by Bridge Street car park)
☎ 07749 204242 ⊕ thamessidebrewery.co.uk
Thames Side Heron Ale, White Swan Pale Ale, Egyptian Goose India Pale Ale; 2 changing beers (sourced locally; often Thames Side) Ⓗ
Interesting views are guaranteed at this former Sea Cadets headquarters on the riverbank. Its downstairs taproom, which serves five real ales and a cider, overlooks the brewery. Historic Staines Bridge can be seen from the upstairs lounge, and from tables placed alongside the towpath in summer. Food includes artisan pies and bar snacks from local producers. The bar opens at noon on brewing days – check the website for details.
ॐ❀◑⅄●P🖵❀

Wheatsheaf & Pigeon Ⓛ ✅
Penton Road, TW18 2LL (corner of Wheatsheaf Lane and Penton Rd)
☎ (01784) 452922 ⊕ wheatsheafandpigeon.co.uk
Bombardier; Fuller's London Pride; Otter Ale; 2 changing beers (sourced regionally; often Robinsons, Thames Side) Ⓗ
Community local situated between Staines and Laleham, a short signposted walk from the Thames Path, with Staines Town FC also nearby. Ales often include local micro or West Country guests. Good-value, interesting food is served every day, excluding Sunday and Monday evenings. The pub is dog-friendly, with water bowls provided. Outside seating is available at the front and back, plus a covered area. ॐ❀◑⅄♣P🖵(458,570)❀🛜

Stoke d'Abernon

Old Plough Ⓛ
2 Station Road, KT11 3BN (off A245)
☎ (01932) 862244 ⊕ oldploughcobham.co.uk
Fuller's London Pride; Surrey Hills Shere Drop Ⓗ
Dating from the late 16th century, this listed building was once a courthouse with the gallows outside, and the stables were used for hansom cab trade. The interior has been opened out but retains much of its original character, particularly at the front. An extension houses a dining area to the rear. The decor is a mix of bare brick, wood panelling and painted walls. There is a pleasant garden area to the side and rear. The pub has a good reputation for food, which makes it busy at times.
Q ॐ❀◑⅄⇌P🖵❀🛜

Sunbury-on-Thames

Admiral Hawke
81 Green Street, TW16 6RD
☎ (01932) 781326
Courage Best Bitter; Ringwood Razorback; Sharp's Doom Bar; Timothy Taylor Landlord Ⓗ
Traditional community local close to Hawke House, home of the 18th-century seafarer who gave the pub its current name. It was originally called the Railway when built in 1862, but the line ended up running some way to the north. There is a rear garden and additional seating out at the front. This is the closest pub to London Irish rugby club's headquarters, and five minutes' walk from the Thames towpath. Food is served evenings only in winter.
ॐ❀◑P🖵❀

Upper Hale

Alfred Free House
9 Bishops Road, GU9 0JA
☎ (01252) 820385 ⊕ thealfredfreehouse.co.uk
4 changing beers (sourced nationally) Ⓗ
This friendly local pub, tucked away down a residential road, features a bar area and a restaurant/function room. Three or four guest ales are available, usually including a dark beer. Fresh home-made food, using locally sourced ingredients, is served Wednesday to Saturday evenings and Sunday lunchtime. The pub hosts events including charity quiz nights and two beer festivals each year, at Easter and in October. Q ॐ❀◑⅄♣●P🖵(5)❀🛜

Walton on Thames

Walton Village
29-31 High Street, KT12 1DG
☎ (01932) 254431 ⊕ thewaltonvillage.com
Big Smoke Solaris Session Pale Ale; 1 changing beer (sourced locally) Ⓗ
Modern high-street pub in a converted shop premises, featuring exposed brickwork and wood panels. The large front bar has a raised seating area and there is a room to the rear for private events. A wide range of food is served all day, which includes vegan and gluten-free choices. Breakfast is available at the weekend. Quiz night is Thursday. Attractions include a table-tennis table, and a mini dog bar with water and treats on offer.
ॐ❀◑⅄♣🖵❀🛜

West Clandon

Bull's Head Ⓛ
The Street, GU4 7ST
☎ (01483) 222444 ⊕ bullsheadwestclandon.co.uk
Hogs Back TEA; Surrey Hills Shere Drop; Young's London Original Ⓗ
Sixteenth-century village inn with several areas on different levels – beware of the low ceilings and oak beams. Food is an important part of the pub's trade and the focus is on traditional British cooking at reasonable prices (no food Sun eve). To the rear is a hedged garden where you can while away a secluded couple of hours enjoying the three regular beers.
Q ॐ❀◑P🖵(463) ❀🛜

West Horsley

Barley Mow
181 The Street, KT24 6HR
☎ (01483) 282693 ⊕ barleymowhorsley.com
Dark Star Hophead; Fuller's London Pride; Surrey Hills Ranmore, Shere Drop; 1 changing beer Ⓗ
A traditional pub in the heart of the Surrey Hills with a cosy mix of carpet and flagstone floors, low beams, and a variety of dining and lounge furniture. The large building incorporates the Malting House to the rear, which is available for functions. Thai food is served lunchtimes and evenings, except Sunday, and traditional English meals at lunchtime. The garden has plenty of seating dotted around and a substantial open grassed area which is great for dogs. ॐ❀◑♣P🖵(478)❀🛜

Weybourne

Running Stream ✅
66 Weybourne Road, GU9 9HE
☎ (01252) 323750
Greene King IPA, Abbot; Hardys & Hansons Bitter; Morland Old Speckled Hen; 1 changing beer Ⓗ

A good old-fashioned friendly locals' pub. A horseshoe-shaped room surrounds the central bar, with basic tables dotted around the outer perimeter and stools at the bar. The handpumps dispense Greene King beers plus one free of tie, usually including a mild. Attractions include a quiz on Wednesday and Sunday plus occasional live music. There is a pleasant garden at the rear. ⊛◖P☕☙᎗

Weybridge

Jolly Farmer
41 Princes Road, KT13 9BN (off A317)
☎ (01932) 856873
5 changing beers ⊞
Friendly back-street mid-Victorian pub situated in a residential area. The single comfortable L-shaped room has a low-beamed ceiling, with upholstered bench seats opposite the small bar. Photos of old Weybridge are displayed on the walls. Guest beers are often from local brewers. A large garden is available and the orangery at the back can be booked for private functions. Sunday lunches are popular (make a reservation in advance). Q⊝⊛◖☷(436,515) ☙᎗

Whyteleafe

Radius Arms
205 Godstone Road, CR3 0EL (on A22)
☎ 07514 916172
4 changing beers ⊞/Ⓖ
This friendly and popular micropub thrives on eccentricity and its excellent, ever-changing selection of beer and cider. At least four cask ales, four KeyKegs and around 15 ciders are always available. A pickled onion competition, ceiling of beer mats and furniture recycled from the Olympic Park in London are some of its quirky features. There is also a small library and some seats outside for smokers. Local CAMRA Cider Pub of the Year. Closed Monday. Q⊛⇌☙☷☙

Woking

Herbert Wells Ⓛ ⊘
51-57 Chertsey Road, GU21 5AJ

☎ (01483) 722818
Courage Best Bitter; Greene King Abbot; Hogs Back TEA; Sharp's Doom Bar; 7 changing beers (sourced nationally) ⊞
A varied range of up to seven guest beers, plus six ciders and perries, are served at this popular town-centre Wetherspoon, which is close to bus stops and the railway station. The large open-plan bar is decorated with HG Wells-inspired features including an invisible man sitting in the window and its own time machine. A wealth of information about local history covers the walls of both the main bar and the smaller side room. Q⊝◖&⇌☙☷᎗

Woking Railway Athletic Club
Goldsworth Road, GU21 6JT (behind offices at E end of Goldsworth Rd) TQ003585
☎ (01483) 598499
3 changing beers ⊞
Lively social club tucked away near Victoria Arch, serving three or four beers. One side of the bar is sports-oriented with darts, free-to-play pool and Sky Sports; the other side is quieter. Filled rolls are available on Saturday afternoon. Children are welcome at all times. Show a CAMRA membership card or copy of this Guide for entry. Local CAMRA Club of the Year 2019 and 2020. ⊝⇌♣☷᎗

Wrecclesham

Sandrock Ⓛ
Sandrock Hill Road, GU10 4NS
☎ (01252) 447289 ⊕ sandrockwrecclesham.co.uk
Bowman Swift One; Exmoor Gold; Fuller's London Pride; Hop Back Summer Lightning; Timothy Taylor Landlord; Triple fff Moondance; 1 changing beer (often Hogs Back, St Austell, Surrey Hills) ⊞
Traditional pub with a contemporary feel, benefiting from a refurbishment in 2018. The focus here is on quality real ale and Thai food, served in the separate restaurant, with a take-away service available. Families and dogs are welcome. Outside is a patio garden and a small car park. Q⊝⊛◖&♣P☷(16,17)☙᎗

Cricketers, Dorking (Photo: Jim Linwood/Flickr CC BY 2.0)

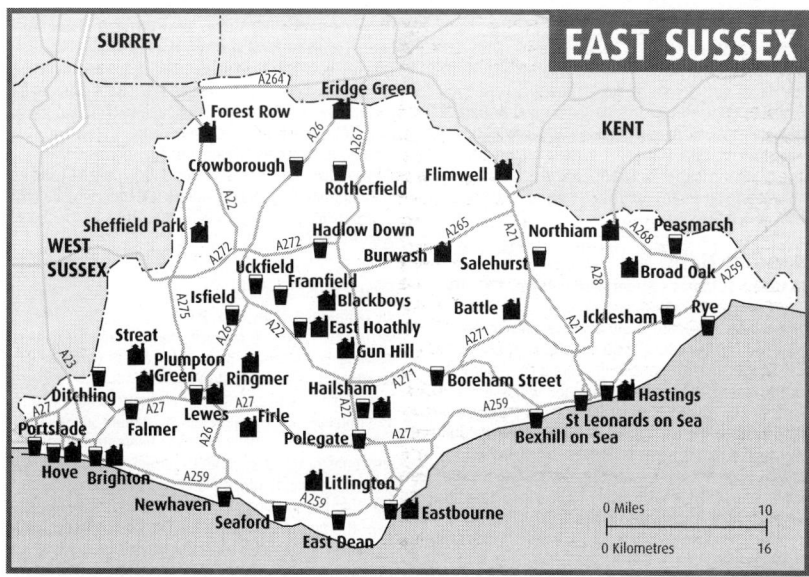

Bexhill on Sea

Albatross Club (RAFA) L

15 Marina Arcade, TN40 1JS (on seafront 200yds E of De
La Warr Pavilion)
☎ (01424) 212916 ⊕ bexhillrafa.co.uk
5 changing beers (sourced locally) Ⓗ
Many times local CAMRA branch Club of the Year, this
popular and friendly Royal Air Forces Association
establishment has five handpumps dispensing ales both
from the area and further afield. Four real ciders are
usually available. Beer festivals are held in June and
November along with quizzes, jazz, ukulele and vinyl
nights, notably on Fridays. Lunchtime food is served
weekdays except Monday (the club is closed Sun and
Mon eves). CAMRA members are welcome.
Q ➣ ◑ &⇌ ● ⬇ ♦ (98,99) ❀ 🖤

Brickmaker's Alehouse

27 Sea Road, TN40 1EE
☎ (01424) 602778 ⊕ brickmakersalehouse.co.uk
5 changing beers Ⓖ
Bexhill's first micropub opened in November 2019,
owned and run by two local CAMRA members. It is
conveniently close to the town centre, seafront, bus
routes and Bexhill station. Five real ales and three real
ciders are served by gravity dispense from a chilled
cabinet behind the bar, with other drinks available. The
pub is furnished with high chairs at the bar and low
chairs at tables, with a couple of tables outside on the
pavement at the front. ⇌ ● ⬇ (98,99) 🖤

Boreham Street

Bull's Head L

The Strait, BN27 4SG
☎ (01323) 831981 ⊕ bullsheadborehamstreet.com
**Harvey's Sussex Best Bitter; house beer (by
Harvey's); 2 changing beers** Ⓗ
On the main road, this traditional country inn boasts
large grounds, including a beer garden, ample parking
and a campsite. Charity events are often held here.
Traditional English pub food is offered; the pub is
renowned for its pies. Harvey's Sussex Best Bitter is
always on tap, along with the exclusive Bull's Head
Bitter, a seasonal and an occasional beer. Closing times
may sometimes be a little earlier in the winter,
especially if it's quiet Monday to Wednesday.
Q ➣ 🐾 ◑ ▲ ● P ⬇ (98) 🖤

Brighton

Basketmakers Arms L

12 Gloucester Road, BN1 4AD
☎ (01273) 689006
**Dark Star Hophead; Fuller's London Pride, ESB; Gale's
Seafarers Ale, HSB; 4 changing beers (sourced
nationally; often Butcombe, Fuller's)** Ⓗ
A much-loved Brighton institution, now under new
management. It is a busy two-room street-corner pub,
popular with young and old alike, located on the edge of
Brighton's famous bohemian North Laines. Eight
handpumps serve a selection of the Fuller's range plus
guests. Locally sourced home-made food is available
every day including for Seafood Saturday and the popular
traditional Sunday roasts. The walls are adorned with old
metal signs and tobacco tins. Live jazz music features on
the first Sunday of every month. Q ➣ ◑ ⇌ ⬇ 🖤 🛜

Brighton Bierhaus L

161 Edward Street, BN2 0JB
☎ (01273) 686386 ⊕ brightonbierhaus.pub
**Brighton Bier West Pier; 4 changing beers (sourced
locally; often Brighton Bier)** Ⓗ
This single-bar outlet is the Brighton Bier Brewery tap
and is centrally situated near the Royal Pavilion and
Brighton Pier. It serves up to five changing beers and two
ciders on handpump along with keg and bottled beers.
An extensive pizza range can be ordered from a nearby
takeaway to eat in the bar. There is a free cheeseboard
on Sundays. A muted TV screen shows BT sport. Local
CAMRA Pub of the Year 2019. ◑ ● ⬇ 🖤 🛜

Evening Star L

55-56 Surrey Street, BN1 3PB (200yds S of station)
☎ (01273) 328931
**7 changing beers (sourced regionally; often Dark Star,
Pig & Porter)** Ⓗ

A classic, compact Brighton pub/alehouse five minutes from the station, majoring in good real ale and craft beers. Fairly basic in decor, it has window seats and a few tables outside on the street, and there are board games to choose from. It is no longer tied to Dark Star Brewery as it was when it had the brewery in the cellar. Nevertheless, Dark Star beers may be on, together with several interesting brews from around Britain. The Trollburger van serves food Thursdays to Saturdays. 🏠🅿♿️⌂♣🚆🐾⏸🐾🎵📶

Hand in Hand ⓛ

33 Upper St James's Street, Kemp Town, BN2 1JN
☎ (01273) 699595 ⊕ handbrewpub.com
House beer (by Hand Brew Co); 1 changing beer (sourced locally; often Franklins, Hand Brew Co) Ⓗ
One of the smallest pubs in the country still finds room for the smallest tower brewery in the world. Kemptown beers are brewed on-site by Brighton Bier and are sold exclusively in the bar, together with beers from other micros. The pub is home to cricket and volleyball teams and hosts jazz sessions every Sunday. Note the one-armed bandit. Food is available from a local café and pizza outlet at lunchtimes. 🚆♣🍴🚆(37,47)🐾📶

Hanover ⓛ

242 Queens Park Road, Hanover, BN2 9ZB
☎ (01273) 679902 ⊕ hanoverbrighton.co.uk
Sharp's Doom Bar; 4 changing beers (sourced locally) Ⓗ
An estate pub dating from the late 1920s, since opened out but retaining its well-used function/meeting room. Although the place is quite large there are discrete areas with a variety of seating and tables. Part of the Indigo chain, it stocks a range of Sussex ales plus a local cider on handpump. Food, including Sunday roasts, is served from about midday, a feature of the bar being the pizza oven. There is a quiz night on Tuesdays and occasional live music. 🚆🏠⏸♣🍴🚆(21,23)🐾📶

Haus on the Hill ⓛ

58 Southover Street, Hanover, BN2 9UF
☎ (01273) 601419 ⊕ hausonthehill.pub
Brighton Bier West Pier; 3 changing beers (sourced locally; often Brighton Bier, Hand Brew Co) Ⓗ
This pub, previously the Southover, is now operated by Brighton Bier. Being at the top of a steep hill it is probably best approached by bus. There are two function rooms upstairs and a covered patio for smokers. Conversation is the norm here and there is no TV or jukebox. A guest beer is always sold, along with three from Brighton Bier plus a cider. A number of bottled ales and keg brews, both British and foreign, complete the range. Q🚆🏠⏸♣🍴🚆(18,23)🐾📶

Lord Nelson Inn ⓛ ✅

36 Trafalgar Street, BN1 4ED
☎ (01273) 695872 ⊕ lordnelsonbrighton.co.uk
Harvey's Sussex Best Bitter; 5 changing beers (often Harvey's) Ⓗ
Flagship Harvey's pub just down Trafalgar Street from the station. It remains cosy and traditional despite benefiting from a recent makeover, and having taken over the shop next door. There are separate drinking areas based on the original layout, with bare wood floors and the occasional rug. This is the place to sample Harvey's beer range, including its craft brews. Food is available until mid-evening. The pub is on a gently sloping road, so the levels vary a bit. 🏠⏸🚆🚆🐾📶

Mitre Tavern ⓛ ✅

13 Baker Street, BN1 4JN
☎ (01273) 622759

Harvey's Dark Mild, Sussex Best Bitter; 3 changing beers (sourced locally; often Harvey's) Ⓗ
Situated between the London road shops and the Level park, this is a good old-fashioned side-street pub that has hardly changed in decades. Subdued background music does not detract from the lively banter in this two-roomed Harvey's establishment. The regular beers are Harvey's XX Mild and Sussex Best bitter, joined by Old Ale in winter and Olympia during the summer, when a cider is also available. A small rear patio caters for smokers. 🏠🚆♣🚆🐾📶

Prince Albert ⓛ

48 Trafalgar Street, BN1 4ED
☎ (01273) 730499 ⊕ princealbertbrighton.co.uk
Burning Sky Plateau; 5 changing beers (sourced locally; often Burning Sky) Ⓗ
Large multi-roomed Victorian free house originally built as a hotel serving Brighton railway station. Six constantly used handpumps chiefly dispense beers from local breweries or guest beers from further afield. The clientele is mainly office workers during the day and mixed in the evening, when there is either live music or a DJ. The pub is famous for the Kissing Coppers artwork by Banksy on the pub wall. The kitchen facility was withdrawn in summer 2019, and customers may now arrange meal deliveries or bring in food from establishments nearby. 🚆🏠🚆♣🍴🚆🐾📶

Crowborough

Cooper's Arms ⓛ

Coopers Lane, TN6 1SN
☎ (01892) 654796
Harvey's Sussex Best Bitter; 3 changing beers (sourced nationally) Ⓗ
This friendly local drinkers' pub has been a regular Guide entry for many years. It serves changing beers, often from the area and always served in top condition, and

REAL ALE BREWERIES

1648 🍺	East Hoathly
360 Degree	Sheffield Park
Battle ♦	Battle
Beak ♦	Lewes
Bedlam	Plumpton Green
Beer Me 🍺	Eastbourne
Benchmark	Eridge Green (NEW)
Brewery at the Watchmaker's Arms 🍺	Hove
Brewing Brothers 🍺	Hastings
Brighton Bier	Brighton
BRZN	Brighton
Burning Sky	Firle
Cellar Head ♦	Flimwell
FILO	Hastings
Franklins	Ringmer
Furnace Brook	Hailsham (NEW)
Gun	Gun Hill
Hand 🍺	Brighton
Harvey's	Lewes
High Weald	Forest Row
Laine 🍺	Brighton
Lakedown ♦	Burwash (NEW)
Long Man ♦	Litlington
Loud Shirt ♦	Brighton
Old Tree	Brighton
Rectory	Streat
Rother Valley	Northiam
Three Acre	Blackboys
Three Legs ♦	Broad Oak
Unbarred ♦	Brighton

offers brews from further afield at the regular beer festivals, when all 12 handpumps are put to good use. A real cider is also sold. Food may be available Sunday lunchtimes but it is best to enquire first. There is a secluded rear garden. Q❄️☺️♿️●P�🐾🐱🛜

Wheatsheaf L ✓

Mount Pleasant, TN6 2NF
☎ (01892) 663756 🌐 wheatsheafcrowborough.co.uk
Harvey's Dark Mild, IPA, Sussex Best Bitter; 1 changing beer (often Harvey's) Ⓗ

This quintessential 18th-century inn is in the quiet outskirts of Crowborough. Harvey's beers are served from the three-sided bar. Log fires are to be found in each of the seating areas, where photos of the pub's history are displayed. Regular live music events are staged and the well-attended annual beer festival at the end of May is held in a marquee. The outside seating space features many colourful hanging baskets.
Q❄️☺️♿️●➡️♣️P🚋(228,229)🐾🛜

Ditchling

White Horse L

16 West Street, BN6 8TS
☎ (01273) 842006 🌐 whitehorseditchling.com
Harvey's Sussex Best Bitter; Long Man Long Blonde; 3 changing beers (sourced locally) Ⓗ

This inn, which dates back to the 12th century, lies below the parish church in this picturesque, historic village. The venue can cater for weddings and birthday parties, or as a stopover while walking the South Downs Way. Log fires in winter, excellent food and constantly changing quality guest beers are certain to fortify the traveller.
Q❄️☺️♿️●➡️P🚋(167,168)🐾🛜

East Dean

Tiger Inn L ✓

The Green, BN20 0DA
☎ (01323) 423209 🌐 beachyhead.org.uk/the-tiger-inn
Harvey's Sussex Best Bitter; Long Man Long Blonde; St Austell Tribute; 3 changing beers (sourced locally) Ⓗ

Situated by the village green, with plenty of outside seating, this 15th-century inn is an ideal place to relax after a Downland walk. It features wooden beams and stone flooring, and serves good-quality food. The bar area is in the centre and has a log fire, the lower area has wheelchair access including for the toilets, and the snug is used for dining. At least one real cider is available. Several times winner of local CAMRA Country Pub of the Year. Q❄️☺️♿️●➡️♿️●P🚋🐾🛜

East Hoathly

King's Head L

1 High Street, BN8 6DR
☎ (01825) 840238 🌐 thekingshead.org
1648 Signature, Triple Champion; Harvey's Sussex Best Bitter; 1 changing beer (often 1648) Ⓗ

A long-established family-run free house which has been a pub for over 250 years. The 1648 Brewing Company was established in 2003 in the old stables next door; two of its beers are always stocked, usually including a dark ale, as well as a changing cider. An extensive range of home-cooked food is available every day. There is a walled garden to the rear and additional outside seating at the front. Local CAMRA Pub of the year 2019.
Q❄️☺️♿️●Å●P🚋(54)🐾🛜

Eastbourne

Crown L

22 Crown Street, Old Town, BN21 1PB
☎ (01323) 724654
Gun Scaramanga Extra Pale; Harvey's Sussex Best Bitter; Shepherd Neame Spitfire Ⓗ**; Young's London Special** Ⓗ/Ⓖ**; 1 changing beer** Ⓖ

Traditional pub in the Motcombe area of Eastbourne's Old Town, featuring a comfortable interior and log fires in winter. Popular with locals and visitors, it has separate public and saloon bars serving well-kept beer, plus a separate pool room. Home-made bar snacks are served. Regular events include quiz nights, Sunday lunchtime competitions, three annual beer festivals and occasional live music. An enclosed rear garden has children's play equipment and is the setting for summer barbecues.
❄️☺️♣️♿️P🚋🐾🛜

Hurst Arms L ✓

76 Willingdon Road, Ocklynge, BN21 1TW
☎ (01323) 419440 🌐 thehurstarms.pub
Harvey's Sussex Best Bitter; house beer (by Harvey's); 2 changing beers (sourced locally; often Harvey's) Ⓗ

This Harvey's tied house is a thriving drinkers' pub – Sussex Best is always available and usually four others according to the season. It has two bars: a smaller, comfortable lounge bar, and a larger public bar with pool table, jukebox, dartboard and a TV showing BT Sport. There is outside seating under cover to the rear and in the front garden. Music events feature approximately fortnightly. No food is served, and on-site parking is limited to four spaces. ❄️☺️♿️♣️P🚋🐾🛜

Lamb Inn L ✓

36 High Street, Old Town, BN21 1HH
☎ (01323) 720545 🌐 thelambeastbourne.co.uk
Harvey's Sussex Best Bitter, Armada Ale; 1 changing beer (sourced locally; often Harvey's) Ⓗ

Many period features remain at this Harvey's inn in the Old Town, which dates back to 1180. Tours of the crypt (beer cellar) can be arranged. There are two bars serving Harvey's regular and seasonal ales. Food is available throughout the day, including vegetarian and vegan dishes. Live music, theatrical productions and comedy nights are regular events. The pub has a function room for private parties as well as accommodation.
Q❄️☺️♿️●♿️♣️●P🚋🐾🛜

London & County L ✓

46 Terminus Road, BN21 3LX
☎ (01323) 746310
Greene King Abbot; Ruddles Best Bitter; Sharp's Doom Bar; 3 changing beers (sourced nationally) Ⓗ

A Wetherspoon Lloyds No.1 bar occupying the former London & County Bank, arranged over two floors, each with a bar; the upstairs can be hired for functions. It is close to bus stops and the railway station. Varying guest beers are on offer, including at least one LocAle. Food is served all day. Muted TV screens display news, and music is played in the evening. There is a DJ on Friday/Saturday evenings, when a smart-casual dress code applies.
❄️●♿️➡️●🚋🛜

Falmer

Swan Inn L ✓

Middle Street, BN1 9PD (just off A27 in N of village)
☎ (01273) 681842
Palmers Tally Ho!; 5 changing beers (sourced regionally; often Downlands, Long Man, Palmers) Ⓗ

A traditional family-run free house near the universities, with three bars and a barn available for functions. Food is served but check for times. The place gets busy when Brighton & Hove Albion play at home. It opens at varying times on match days, including for Monday evening games. There is a small courtyard area at the side. Local CAMRA Rural Pub of the Year 2021.
Q ᗰ ⊛ ◑ & ⇌ ♣ P ⊟ (28,29) ❀ 🛜

Framfield

Hare & Hounds L
The Street, TN22 5NJ
☎ (01825) 890118 ⊕ hareandhounds.net
Harvey's Sussex Best Bitter Ⓗ
Cosy and welcoming village pub dating from 1428. Recently refurbished, it offers separate dining, bar and snug sections with an inglenook fireplace and comfy chairs. It has a reputation for its food, especially Sunday roasts, and has a busy programme of community events, quiz nights and live music. Child- and dog-friendly, with a good sized garden with kiddie area, it offers something for all ages. No food on Mondays. Q ᗰ ⊛ ◑ & ▲ P ❀ 🛜

Hadlow Down

New Inn ★ L
Main Road, TN22 4HJ (on A272)
Harvey's IPA, Sussex Best Bitter; 1 changing beer (often Harvey's) Ⓗ
This quirky but welcoming village inn has been identified by CAMRA as having a nationally important historic pub interior on account of the back bar fittings, ceramic spirit casks and panelled counter. These date from 1885 when the premises were rebuilt following a fire. There is another bar at the back and a function room. The no-frills environment is more than compensated for by the conviviality and excellently kept beer. No food is available other than bar snacks. Q ᗰ ⊛ ♣ P ⊟ (248) ❀

Hailsham

George Hotel L ✓
3 George Street, BN27 1AD
☎ (01323) 445120
Greene King Abbot; Ruddles Best Bitter; Sharp's Doom Bar; 2 changing beers (sourced nationally) Ⓗ
Busy town-centre Wetherspoon that delivers the chain's model to a high standard. It is popular with locals and handy for visitors to Hailsham Pavilion cinema opposite. At least five real ales, including one LocAle, are on the bar alongside up to 11 real ciders and perries. There is a quiet enclosed patio to the rear and an outdoor terrace at the side. Local branch Cider & Perry Pub of the Year in 2019 and runner-up in 2020. Q ᗰ ⊛ ◑ & ● ⊟ 🛜

King's Head L ✓
146 South Road, Cacklebury, BN27 3NJ
☎ (01323) 440447 ⊕ kingsheadcacklebury.co.uk
Harvey's Sussex Best Bitter; 1 changing beer (often Harvey's) Ⓗ
Expect a warm welcome at this traditional community local which has been a tied Harvey's house since 1841. Inside are a quiet snug and two separate bars featuring exposed beams and a log fire. Outside is a large garden with a covered seated smoking area. A variety of traditional pub games and board games is available, and live music events take place throughout the year, including monthly open mic nights. Home-made food is served on Friday, Saturday and Sunday.
Q ᗰ ⊛ ◑ ♣ ● P ⊟ ⊟ ❀ 🛜

Hastings

Albion L
33 George Street, Old Town, TN34 3EA
☎ (01424) 439156 ⊕ albionhastings.com
Harvey's Sussex Best Bitter; 3 changing beers (often Bedlam, Three Legs) Ⓗ
A spacious refurbished former hotel with a drinks licence dating from 1730, featuring beautiful metal bar tops and stylish furniture, plus a stage for live music. The separate bar can be used as a function room. Previously a Younger's of Edinburgh outlet, the pub retains original 1940s wood panelling in the main bar, incorporating many clan tartans. Excellent food is served including home-made pies with unusual fillings. There is a large paved seating area on Marine Parade.
Q ᗰ ⊛ ◑ ♣ ● ⊟ ❀ 🛜

Crown L
64-66 All Saints Street, Old Town, TN34 3BN
☎ (01424) 465100 ⊕ thecrownhastings.co.uk
4 changing beers (sourced locally) Ⓗ
This award-winning pub, with its vast crown sculpture above the door, is just below the East Hill Country Park. Drinkers and diners can feel equally at home, with four real ales from breweries in Sussex and Kent and a regularly changing food menu using locally sourced produce. The wooden floor, subdued paintwork and hand-made furniture, together with two open fires (one in a small snug) help to create a relaxed atmosphere for all. Cider is usually from Seacider. ᗰ ◑ ♣ ● ⊟ ❀ 🛜

Dolphin L ✓
11-12 Rock-A-Nore Road, Old Town, TN34 3DW
☎ (01424) 434326 ⊕ thedolphinpub.co.uk
Dark Star Hophead; Harvey's Sussex Best Bitter; Young's London Special; 3 changing beers (sourced nationally) Ⓗ
Traditional family-run pub next to Hastings' famous fishing huts and close to Europe's largest beach-launched fleet. The interior features memorabilia and old photographs of the Hastings fishing community. There is a wood-burning stove, and a front terrace that is popular in summer. Six cask beers are dispensed, including three regularly changing guests. Fish & chip suppers are served on Monday evening. Live music, showcasing local bands, takes place on Tuesday, Friday and Saturday.
Q ᗰ ⊛ ◑ ♣ ● ⊟ ❀ 🛜

First In Last Out L
14-15 High Street, Old Town, TN34 3EY (nr Stables Theatre)
☎ (01424) 425079 ⊕ thefilo.co.uk
FILO Brewery Crofters, Churches Pale Ale, Old Town Tom, Gold; 1 changing beer (sourced regionally) Ⓗ
The FILO is a traditional pub, with a fireplace in the middle adding warmth during the winter months. A selection of six ales from its own FILO brewery is offered, plus a guest. The hostelry has very strong community ties, with many regular patrons as well as visitors contributing to a convivial atmosphere in which to enjoy local beer. Good food is served daily. Live music features regularly (check website for details). Q ᗰ ◑ ♣ ⊟ ⊟ ❀ 🛜

Jenny Lind L ✓
69 High Street, Old Town, TN34 3EW
☎ (01424) 421392 ⊕ jennylindhastings.co.uk
Courage Directors; Old Dairy Uber Brew; Theakston Old Peculier; 5 changing beers (sourced nationally) Ⓗ
This traditional Old Town pub is named after the Swedish opera singer who, it is reputed, stayed in Hastings in the 1880s. There are eight real ales, including up to five nationally sourced guests, and four traditional ciders.

Free music events take place Friday to Sunday on a stage overlooked by a large mermaid figurehead. There is a separate cosy back bar with an open log fire and bar billiards. Upstairs to the rear is a terraced garden. ⯁⌖⊨♣♦⊟❀☂

Jolly Fisherman
3 East Beach Street, Old Town, TN34 3AR
☎ (01424) 428811 ⊕ jollyfishermanhastings.com
3 changing beers ⊞
A pub until the 1950s, then a café and now Hastings' first micropub. At least three changing cask beers, together with six real ciders and perries and keg beers, are supplemented by a large range of canned and bottled beers of UK and foreign origin. Home-made bar snacks are available Wednesdays to Saturdays, with free cheese on Sunday afternoons. The rustic furniture is arranged to help create a friendly atmosphere. Toad in the hole and shove-ha'penny can be played. ⯁◑♣♦⊟❀

Twelve Hundred Postcards
80 Queens Road, TN34 1RL
☎ 07883 408909
3 changing beers (sourced locally) Ⓖ
A one-room micropub incorporating benches and high stools on both sides, with novel ceiling lights made from green beer bottles in baskets. At the rear is a cool room for the ales, cask and keg, with a large viewing window. Two or three real ciders are offered. The pub's name references a former sweet shop owner, who 100 years ago sold illegal French postcards, resulting in his imprisonment and destruction of the postcards. ⯁⇌♦⊟❀

White Rock Hotel Ⓛ
White Rock, TN34 1JU
☎ (01424) 422240 ⊕ thewhiterockhotel.com
4 changing beers (sourced locally) ⊞
The hotel is on the seafront next to the White Rock Theatre, opposite the pier. Its bar overlooks the sea, with a terrace outside, a superb vantage point in good weather. Four changing ales are served, all from Sussex, and at least one LocAle. Plenty of sofas and easy chairs provide a relaxing and comfortable seating area; there is restaurant-style seating for table service. Light snacks are available all day and a dinner menu in the evening. Q⯁⊨◑⇌P⊟❀☂

Hove

Foghorn Ⓛ
55 Boundary Road, BN3 4EF
☎ (01273) 419362
5 changing beers (sourced regionally; often Brighton Bier, Burning Sky) Ⓖ
The Foghorn is on the busy corner of New Church Road and Boundary Road, offering a quiet haven within for drinkers. Opened in 2018, this enterprise has soon become a go-to venue with its wide-ranging selection of beers. The cellar sits just behind the bar and can be viewed through the glass partition. Furniture and décor is best described as minimalist, and the toilets are well maintained. Local branch Pub of the Year 2021. Q⯁&⇌♦⊟❀☂

Neptune Inn Ⓛ
10 Victoria Terrace, BN3 2WB (on coast road E of King Alfred leisure complex)
☎ (01273) 736390 ⊕ theneptunelivemusicbar.co.uk
Dark Star Hophead; Greene King Abbot; Harvey's Sussex Best Bitter; 2 changing beers (sourced regionally) ⊞

A no-frills single-bar Victorian pub close to the King Alfred centre and Hove seafront. A reclining figure of Neptune rests above the old Courage signage at the front. Five beers are on the bar including two changing guests. Children are welcome until early evening. Live music features strongly, with blues or rock every Friday and jazz on Sundays (see website for details). ⊟(700) ❀☂

Watchmaker's Arms Ⓛ
84 Goldstone Villas, BN3 3RU
☎ (01273) 776307 ⊕ thewatchmakersarms.co.uk
5 changing beers (sourced regionally; often Brighton Bier, Downlands) Ⓖ
This micro is handy for Hove station. The clock theme is recognised with old watches and timepieces on the wall – not always correct! Tall tables and benches line the walls, and pizzas from a local takeaway can be ordered; otherwise, sausage rolls and scratchings are the fare. Beercraft, a small on-site brewery, is now in full swing and the output can be sampled here. Q⇌♦⊟(7,21)❀

Icklesham

Queen's Head Ⓛ
Parsonage Lane, TN36 4BL (opp village hall)
☎ (01424) 814552 ⊕ queenshead.com
Greene King Abbot; Harvey's Sussex Best Bitter; 4 changing beers (sourced locally; often Hardys & Hansons) ⊞
Delightful 17th-century inn that has been in the Guide for over 30 years. Three changing ales, often local, are normally on tap alongside two ciders. Open fires and good-value home-made food make the place popular with visitors, regulars and walkers on the 1066 Country Walk. Live music features on Sunday and also at the mini beer festivals held on bank holidays. The large garden has sweeping views over the Brede Valley. There is a pétanque piste behind the pub. ⯁⌖◑♣♦P⊟(100) ❀☂

Isfield

Laughing Fish Ⓛ ✔
Station Road, TN22 5XB (off A26 between Lewes and Uckfield)
☎ (01825) 750349 ⊕ laughingfishisfield.com
Greene King IPA; Hardys & Hansons Olde Trip; Long Man Best Bitter; 3 changing beers (sourced locally; often Burning Sky, Gun) ⊞
Formerly the Half Moon, then the Station Hotel, this 1860s building is next to the preserved Lavender Line. WWII brought the custom of Canadian troops, not without incident. In the 1950s this was the HQ of the District Angling Club, the probable origin of the present name. The pub offers the Greene King portfolio plus guest beers from other Sussex breweries. It serves good pub food and hosts a range of games including bar billiards. A quiz is held on the first Sunday of each month. ⯁⌖◑&▲♣♦P⊟(29,29B) ❀☂

Lewes

Black Horse Ⓛ ✔
55 Western Road, BN7 1RS
☎ (01273) 473653 ⊕ theblackhorselewes.co.uk
Burning Sky Plateau; Greene King Abbot; Harvey's Sussex Best Bitter; Morland Old Speckled Hen; 3 changing beers (sourced regionally; often Dark Star, Greene King, Old Dairy) ⊞
A Greene King Local Heroes establishment that allows the licensee to sell Sussex ales and produce. This

traditional community venue in the western end of the town has feature bay windows and a large main bar with a real fire, together with a quieter back bar. Two TVs show most sporting events. Home-made food includes vegan options. The pub's teams play a wide variety of games including toad in the hole and crib.
🏖🏠🅰🌡🚍♿♣🍴🚪(28,29)🐾🅿🛜

Brewers Arms 🄻

91 High Street, BN7 1XN (nr Lewes Castle)
☎ (01273) 475524 ⊕ thebrewersarmslewes.com
Harvey's Sussex Best Bitter; 4 changing beers (sourced regionally; often Burning Sky, Gun, Tring) Ⓗ
A two-bar pub with separate characteristics, the front bar being quiet and more food-oriented, and the back bar offering sports TV, darts and pool. The exterior features an original plaque advertising the former owners, Page and Overton's Croydon Ales. Food, including traditional breakfasts, is served until early evening. The pub has a dwyle flunking team, and is popular on match days with Lewes FC, Brighton & Hove Albion and away fans. It hosts an annual beer festival. 🏠🅰🌡🚋♣🍴🚍(28,29)🐾🛜

Dorset 🄻 ✅

22 Malling Street, BN7 2RD
☎ (01273) 474823 ⊕ thedorsetlewes.co.uk
Harvey's Sussex Best Bitter; 3 changing beers (sourced locally) Ⓗ
Refurbished in 2006, this Harvey's tied house has several drinking and dining areas, a large patio and six reasonably priced en-suite bedrooms. It serves at least four ales on handpump. An extensive menu features traditional home-cooked dishes and an ever-changing fish menu using ingredients fresh from Newhaven. The pub is the home of the Cliffe Bonfire Society – the largest of the five Lewes bonfire societies. Closing times may vary in winter so it is advisable to check beforehand. 🏠🏖🅰🌡♿🚋♣🍴🚍(28,29)

Gardener's Arms 🄻

46 Cliffe High Street, BN7 2AN
☎ (01273) 474808
Harvey's Sussex Best Bitter; 5 changing beers (sourced regionally; often Harvey's, Parkway, Rother Valley) Ⓗ
A traditional, genuine free house near Harvey's Brewery. It is a one-roomed pub with a wooden floor and a central bar. Five changing guest ales are dispensed, generally from small breweries across the country, and a real cider is always available. Snacks include locally made pies and pasties. The pub is popular with Lewes and Brighton FC fans on match days. It hosts a dark beer festival in March. Dogs are especially welcome but children are not allowed. 🌡♣🍴🚪(28,29)🐾🛜

John Harvey Tavern 🄻 ✅

1 Bear Yard, Cliffe High Street, BN7 2AN (opp Harvey's Brewery)
☎ (01273) 479880 ⊕ johnharveytavern.co.uk
Harvey's Dark Mild, IPA Ⓗ**, Sussex Best Bitter** Ⓖ**, Armada Ale** Ⓗ**; 2 changing beers (sourced locally; often Harvey's)** Ⓗ/Ⓖ
This tavern is housed in a former stable block of the Bear Inn, next to the River Ouse. The bar boasts wooden beams, a slate floor, a log-burner and two large wine vats, providing cosy seating areas. Children are allowed in the restaurant until mid-evening. Upstairs is a large function/dining room. The outside tables are a suntrap in summer and therefore popular. There is a folk night on Tuesday and music on Sunday.
Q🏖🏠🌡🚋♣🍴🚪(28,29)🐾🛜

Lansdown Arms 🄻

36 Lansdown Place, BN7 2JU
☎ (01273) 470711
Gun Base Ejection Smoked Rye; Harvey's Sussex Best Bitter; Timothy Taylor Boltmaker; 1 changing beer (sourced locally; often Long Man, Timothy Taylor) Ⓗ
Close to the railway station at the foot of a steep hill, this smallish corner pub is dark and cosy, and popular with fans and visitors to both Lewes FC and Brighton & Hove Albion on match days. It was built in 1827, before the arrival of the railway in the town and was, at one time, a Whitbread house. It hosts popular live music, regularly featuring bands from the area, and has a free jukebox. Local artists display their work on the walls. It has some outdoor seating by the pavement at the front.
🏖🌡🚋♣🍴🚪🐾🛜

Rights of Man 🄻 ✅

179 High Street, BN7 1YE
☎ (01273) 486894 ⊕ rightsofmanlewes.com
Harvey's IPA, Sussex Best Bitter; 5 changing beers (sourced locally; often Harvey's) Ⓗ
A small two-bar pub near the law courts. The front bar has two tall tables near the front windows, wonderful for having a pint and watching the world go by. It sports dark oak-panelled walls and etched-glass screens to form booths. The small Martyr's bar has pictures of each local bonfire society on the wall and more seating. Good-quality food is served, lunch and evening. The Astroturf-covered roof terrace is a real suntrap in the summer.
🏠🌡🚋♣🍴🚪(28,29)🐾🛜

Royal Oak 🄻

3 Station Street, BN7 2DA
☎ (01273) 474803 ⊕ royaloaklewes.co.uk
Harvey's Sussex Best Bitter; St Austell Tribute; 2 changing beers (sourced locally; often Bedlam, Five Points, Gun) Ⓗ
This single-room pub at the top of the station hill is the birthplace of Lewes FC (1875) and home to the Waterloo Bonfire Society. Good food is complemented by a range of five beers, usually at least one coming from Bedlam. The upstairs function room has its own bar and hosts regular live music sessions. There is a DJ in the bar on Friday nights, and sometimes karaoke. To the rear of the pub is a secret garden. 🏠🌡🚋♣🍴🚪🐾🛜

Snowdrop Inn 🄻 ✅

119 South Street, BN7 2BU
☎ (01273) 471018
Harvey's Sussex Best Bitter; 3 changing beers (sourced locally; often Burning Sky, Cellar Head, Gun) Ⓗ
On the outer edge of the Cliffe area of this historic town, the Snowdrop is a popular and welcoming free house serving four cask ales (five in summer), one cider and four beers on KeyKeg. The pub has a central bar, with additional seating upstairs and two outside drinking spaces. It is family-friendly and serves good home-cooked food all day. It hosts a jazz night every Monday and music most Saturdays, and a beer festival in October.
🏖🏠🌡🚋♣🍴🚪(28,29)🐾🛜

Newhaven

Prince of Wales 🄻

49 South Road, BN9 9QL
☎ (01273) 513364
Long Man Best Bitter, Old Man Ⓗ
A former United Ales outlet with a beautiful tiled exterior. This two-room pub has been run by the same couple for 20 years on traditional lines. There is therefore

no TV, jukebox or food. The two handpumps serve, usually, Long Man beers. The pub has a pool table, and darts and toad in the hole are played in the public bar. It is now only open on a part-time basis. Q❄️🍴♣️🚪

Peasmarsh

Horse & Cart Inn
School Lane, TN31 6UW
☎ (01797) 230034 ⊕ thehorseandcart.co.uk
House beer (by Romney Marsh); 2 changing beers (sourced locally; often Three Legs) Ⓗ
A traditional country village inn with oak-beamed rooms, a single bar, a large restaurant area and a south-facing garden with plenty of seating at the rear. As well as the house beer from Romney Marsh Brewery, Horse and Cart Best, there is always a Three Legs Brewery ale on offer. An extensive menu features home-cooked pub favourites, including pizza, using local and seasonal produce where possible. Breakfast is served at weekends. Q🕰️🐕🏠🌙👜♣️P🚪(344)🏵️📶

Polegate

Dinkum Ⓛ
54 High Street, BN26 6AG
☎ (01323) 482106
Harvey's Sussex Best Bitter; 2 changing beers (sourced locally; often Harvey's) Ⓗ
This Harvey's tied house is a lively, friendly pub with a loyal core of locals happy to welcome visitors. Patrons regularly organise card games in one of the two spacious bars, while in the other all the important sports events are shown, alongside the playing of darts, pool and toad in the hole. Pizzas, warm flatbread and nachos are on offer as well as typical bar snacks throughout opening hours. Nearby public transport is excellent. 🕰️🐕❄️♣️👜P🚪🏵️📶

Portslade

Railway Inn Ⓛ ✅
2 Station Road, BN41 1GA
☎ (01273) 271220 ⊕ therailwayinnportslade.co.uk
Harvey's Sussex Best Bitter; 3 changing beers (sourced regionally) Ⓗ
Following a full refurbishment, the former Whistlestop has reverted to its old name. Four handpumps dispense Harvey's Sussex Best and three changing guest ales. The pub also serves a real cider and a perry. It welcomes families and dogs and, located close to Portslade station, is aiming to be a focal point of the community; all are encouraged to come for a drink or a bite to eat. There is an extensive menu served all day plus a gelato bar. 🕰️🐕🌙❄️👜🚪🏵️📶

Stag's Head Inn Ⓛ
35 High Street, Old Portslade, BN41 2LH
☎ (01273) 416058
Harvey's Sussex Best Bitter; Long Man American Pale Ale; 3 changing beers (sourced nationally; often Brains, Goddards) Ⓗ
Former tap for the Dudney Brewery (closed 1930) which still stands nearby, this friendly two-bar community venue offers four beers. The regular ales are from Sussex, with guests mainly from outside the county. The old Watney's decor behind each bar is of interest. The pub hosts regular quiz nights and live music events, together with TV sport and bar billiards, and is home to the local golf society. 🕰️❄️♣️🚪(1,1A)🏵️📶

Stanley Arms Ⓛ
47 Wolseley Road, BN41 1SS (on corner of Wolseley Rd and Stanley Rd)
☎ (01273) 701738 ⊕ thestanley.com
Harvey's Sussex Best Bitter; 4 changing beers (sourced regionally; often Downlands, Harvey's, Long Man) Ⓗ
A welcoming no-frills back-street pub, the hub of the local community, with a changing range of guest beers from Sussex and beyond. Cellar Night is a feature every second Monday of the month, when you can visit the cellar and get reduced prices on beer, together with free nibbles at the bar. TV sport is regularly shown. There are Quiz Wednesdays and occasional beer festivals. Q🕰️🐕🏵️❄️♣️👜🚪(2,46)🏵️📶

Rotherfield

King's Arms Ⓛ
High Street, TN6 3LJ
☎ (01892) 853441
Harvey's Sussex Best Bitter; 3 changing beers (sourced locally) Ⓗ
A 17th-century timber-framed tile-hung pub with exposed beams, set in the heart of the village. This is a friendly community hostelry known for its range of beers from the surrounding area and for its good food, most of which is locally sourced. Open fires make the pub cosy in winter. In summer it offers extensive views from the large beer garden, where a number of music events are held. Q🕰️🐕🌙👜♣️P🚪(252)🏵️📶

Rye

Standard Inn Ⓛ
The Mint, TN31 7EN
☎ (01797) 225231 ⊕ thestandardinnrye.co.uk
House beer (by Old Dairy); 3 changing beers (often Romney Marsh, Three Legs) Ⓗ
Close to the town centre and riverside area, the Standard has recently been refurbished, revealing beautifully carved beams dating back to its 15th-century pub origins. Quarry-tiled floors, exposed brick, stone walls and open fires adorn the quaint interior. High-quality food from the area is served, notably Rye Bay scallops. The house beer, Farmers Ale, is from Old Dairy, supplemented by LocAle from Three Legs and Romney Marsh. Five en-suite rooms are available. A recent local CAMRA branch Pub of the Year. Q🕰️🐕🏠🌙❄️♣️🚪(100,101)🏵️📶

Waterworks Ⓛ
Tower Street, TN31 7AT
☎ (01797) 224110 ⊕ ryewaterworks.co.uk
House beer (by Three Legs); 7 changing beers (sourced locally) Ⓖ
This place is steeped in history. For 300 years it was a water pumphouse, then in the 1800s a soup kitchen, which has now been opened up as a feature. The building then served as the town's public toilets before becoming the first micropub in the area. It is now a family business serving eight real ales, including its own uRYEnal Best Bitter. There is also a choice of 12 ciders, all coming from within 30 miles. Pork pies and Scotch eggs are popular snacks. Current local CAMRA Pub of the Year. Q🕰️🐕🏵️♿❄️♣️🚪🏵️📶

Ypres Castle Inn Ⓛ
Gun Garden, TN31 7HH (can be accessed from A259 up a flight of steps, for fewer steps approach from Church Sq)
☎ (01797) 223248 ⊕ yprescastleinn.co.uk

House beer (by Rother Valley); 3 changing beers (sourced locally) Ⓗ
An attractive weatherboarded pub, set just below the Rye Castle Museum and above the A259. The adjacent Gun Gardens give superb views across Romney Marsh, as do the outside drinking areas. There is one large bar with a log fire, and a smaller adjoining room. Quality bar snacks are offered alongside a simple menu centred around gourmet sandwiches. The house beer from Rother Valley Brewery is Ypres Castle Bitter (ABV 3.8%). Real cider is from Nightingale's. 🛏★♣◑≠🍴🐾☀🛜

St Leonards on Sea

Tower
251 London Road, Bohemia, TN37 6NB
☎ (01424) 721773
Dark Star Hophead, American Pale Ale; 4 changing beers (sourced nationally) Ⓗ
Popular community pub with a lively, convivial atmosphere, offering six ales and up to seven ciders. All the main football, cricket and rugby matches are shown on HD screens. There is a pool table and a wood-burning stove. An annual beer festival is held in February, and occasional trips are arranged to breweries and sporting events. Local CAMRA branch Pub of the Year in 2019, and runner-up in 2020. 🛏★♣◑🍴🐾☀🛜

Salehurst

Salehurst Halt Ⓛ
Church Lane, TN32 5PH (by church)
☎ (01580) 880620 ⊕ salehursthalt.co.uk
Harvey's Sussex Best Bitter; 2 changing beers (sourced locally) Ⓗ
This delightful community village pub welcomes locals and visitors alike. Established in 1867, it was saved from closure by local families some years ago. Three real ales and a cider from the area are normally on offer, together with a varied menu of excellent fresh home-cooked food (booking advisable). Pizza is cooked on an outdoor wood-fired oven every Wednesday in summer. Upstairs is a function room for up to 20 people. The lovely garden has views over the tranquil Rother Valley. Q🛏★◑🚲&♣🐾☀🛜

Seaford

Old Boot Inn Ⓛ
16 South Street, BN25 1PE
☎ (01323) 895454
Harvey's Sussex Best Bitter; 4 changing beers (sourced regionally; often Dark Star, Pitchfork, Thornbridge) Ⓗ
This deceptively large pub, under the same ownership as the Gardener's Arms in Lewes, has entrances in both South Street and the High Street. Wheelchair access is possible. There are plenty of tables, and the food served includes a wide range of roasts on Sundays. Harvey's Best Bitter is always on one of the six handpumps, along with Old Ale in season. Four changing guests and six bag-in-box ciders complete the range. 🛏★◑🚲&♣🍴🐾☀🛜

Steamworks Ⓛ
Cafe Unit, Seaford Station, Station Approach, BN25 2AR
☎ 07541 858996
3 changing beers (sourced locally; often 360 Degree, Bedlam, Downlands) Ⓖ
Right on the station platform, the Steamworks is a two-room buffet bar which is busy with coffee service to the early morning commuters. It then becomes a micropub

with three interesting, normally local, beers dispensed by an unusual gravity system plus a selection of craft keg beers. The decor and furniture is best described as distressed industrial sanded-down woodwork, as if the Ragged-Trousered Philanthropists had only recently left! Food is pasties. Q&≠🍴🐾♣

Uckfield

Alma Arms Ⓛ ✓
65 Framfield Road, TN22 5AJ (on B2102 from jct with High Street)
☎ (01825) 762232 ⊕ almaarmsuckfield.co.uk
Harvey's Dark Mild, Sussex Best Bitter; 2 changing beers (often Harvey's) Ⓗ
Within 10 minutes' walk of the town centre, railway and bus stations, this traditional pub has two separate bars and a large function room with its own facilities. It dates from 1851 and was named after the 1854 Crimean War battle. The regular draught cider has recently changed and is now Westons Family Reserve. A quiz is held every Thursday and various other events take place from time to time. No food is served on Monday or Tuesday. Q🛏★◑&≠♣🅿🚌(231)🐾☀🛜

SUSSEX (WEST)

Amberley

Bridge Inn Ⓛ ✓
Houghton Bridge, BN18 9LR (on B2139 just W of railway bridge at Amberley station)
☎ (01798) 831619 ⊕ bridgeinnamberley.com
Harvey's Sussex Best Bitter; Long Man Long Blonde; 1 changing beer (sourced nationally; often Timothy Taylor) Ⓗ
Grade II-listed inn close to Amberley Working Museum and Heritage Centre, the South Downs Way and Amberley railway station. It has a single cosy bar, and open log fires in winter. Three real ales are dispensed. A large dining area to the side serves mainly locally sourced home-cooked produce. There is a patio at the front and an attractive gated beer garden to the side. Q🛏★◑≠🅿🚌(73)🐾☀🛜

Balcombe

Half Moon
Haywards Heath Road, RH17 6PA
☎ (01444) 811582 ⊕ halfmoonbalcombe.com
Harvey's Sussex Best Bitter; 2 changing beers (sourced locally; often Dark Star, Long Man) Ⓗ
A small outlet with tables in the lower part as you enter, and the bar beyond up a couple of steps. The venue is food-led, serving a varied range of locally sourced and seasonal meals. This is north Sussex's first community-owned pub, since January 2017, with four handpumps. One normally has Harvey's Sussex Best, the other three dispense rotating guests, which are mainly from the area, with one from Balcombe Brewery. 🛏◑≠🍴🅿☀🛜

Barns Green

Queen's Head Ⓛ
Chapel Road, RH13 0PS
☎ (01403) 730436 ⊕ thequeensheadbarnsgreen.co.uk
Fuller's London Pride; Long Man Best Bitter; 2 changing beers (sourced regionally) Ⓗ
A cosy 17th-century village pub, with old timber beams and a large inglenook fireplace used in winter. It is mainly open plan, with three seating areas and a small

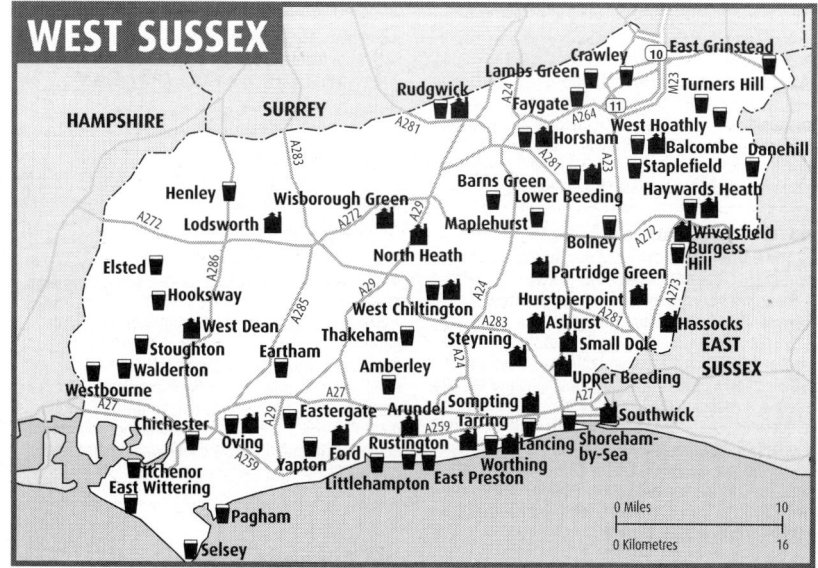

separate room. A garden with some covered seating is at the back. Originally known as the Bricklayer's Arms in the early 19th century. Q ⏚ ❀ ⏍ ▶ A P ❀ ☂

Bolney

Bolney Stage ⓛ
London Road, RH17 5RL
☎ (01444) 881200
6 changing beers ⓗ
This pub dates back to the 16th century, and is situated on the old A23 coaching route. It has a large bar area with three separate dining areas and a beer garden. The rooms feature huge inglenook fireplaces, ancient flagstones, open-timbered ceilings and crooked beams, together with comfy old furniture. A blackboard by the bar gives tasting notes on the four regularly changing beers, mainly from Sussex breweries.
⏚ ❀ ⏍ ♿ P 🚌 (273) ❀ ☂

Burgess Hill

Quench Bar & Kitchen ⓛ
2-4 Church Road, RH15 9AE
☎ (01444) 253332 ⊕ quenchbar.co.uk
Harvey's Sussex Best Bitter; 2 changing beers (sourced regionally) ⓗ
Close to the railway station and bus stops, this bar is at the top end of the town's original shopping street. It comprises a bar area together with a comfortable lounge. In addition to cask ales there is a varied range of bottled beers, spirits, teas and espresso coffees. There are old clocks above the bar and a display case of old cameras in the lounge. A limited number of tables and chairs is provided outside. ⏍ ≉ 🚌 ☂

Watermill Inn ⓛ
1 Leylands Road, RH15 0QF
☎ (01444) 235517
Harvey's Sussex Best Bitter; 3 changing beers (sourced regionally) ⓗ
This recently refurbished community local opened around 1850 in the Worlds End area, and was named after the nearby Valebridge water mill (no longer working). There are up to three changing beers on

handpump. The popular pub tends to get busy on Thursday night when a quiz is held. The enclosed garden provides a safe space for families. Thatchers Heritage is the real cider. ❀ ♿ ≉ ♣ ⏍ 🚌 ☂

Chichester

Chichester Inn ⓛ
38 West Street, PO19 1RP (at Westgate roundabout)
☎ (01243) 783185 ⊕ chichesterinn.co.uk
Harvey's Sussex Best Bitter; 3 changing beers (sourced regionally; often Bedlam, Vibrant Forest) ⓗ
Pleasant two-bar pub featuring a real fire in the front bar surrounded by comfortable chairs, with a mix of seating and table types elsewhere. The larger public bar to the rear hosts regular live music on Wednesday, Friday and Saturday evenings. There is a strong emphasis on LocAles, and food includes Sunday lunches. Outside is an attractive walled garden with a heated and covered smoking area. Four B&B rooms are available.
❀ 🛏 ⏍ ≉ ♣ ⏍ P 🚌 ❀ ☂

Eastgate ✓
4 The Hornet, PO19 7JG (500yds E of Market Cross)
☎ (01243) 774877
Dark Star Hophead; Fuller's London Pride; Gale's Seafarers Ale, HSB; 1 changing beer (sourced nationally; often Dark Star, Fuller's) ⓗ
Welcoming town outlet with an open-plan bar, and tables for diners where good-quality traditional pub meals are served daily. There is a heated patio garden to the rear, which is the venue for a beer festival in July. The pub attracts locals, holidaymakers and shoppers from the nearby market, with a warm welcome and traditional games such as darts, cribbage and pool. Music is turned up on Friday and Saturday late evenings, and live bands perform once a month. ⏚ ❀ ⏍ ♣ 🚌 (51,700) ❀ ☂

Hole in the Wall
1A St Martins Street, PO19 1NP (just off East St, almost opp back door to Marks & Spencer)
☎ (01243) 788877 ⊕ theholeinthewall-pub.co.uk
Big Smoke Solaris Session Pale Ale; 7 changing beers (sourced nationally; often Bristol Beer Factory, Gun, Harvey's) ⓗ

This old pub building is believed to have started as an 18th-century debtors' prison. Now operated by Big Smoke Brewing Company, it has been knocked through so the bar wraps round to form three areas. The interior features brick pillars and half-height painted wood panelling, which creates a cosy, friendly atmosphere. There are 12 handpumps, including four for real cider, plus 20 craft keg beers. Food is served all day. Quiz night is Sunday. ☕😋🍴♿🛏️P🚲🐾🛜

Hornet Alehouse

23 The Hornet, PO19 7JL (from market cross head due E)
☎ (01243) 696387 🌐 thehornetalehouse.co.uk
5 changing beers (sourced nationally; often Downlands, Elusive, Vibrant Forest) Ⓖ
Busy split-level micropub with plenty of standing room at the bar in addition to seating both downstairs and upstairs. This venue is a wonderful addition to the city, offering a changing range of cask ales served from a temperature-controlled cool room. The staff are friendly and knowledgeable, and offer tasters if you're unsure. Four ciders are always on the bar as well as four craft keg taps. The upstairs room has board games and hosts twice-monthly quiz nights and monthly Meet the Brewer events. Q☕♣🐾🛏️🚲(700)🐾🛜

Crawley

Brewery Shades Ⓛ

85 High Street, RH10 1BA
☎ (01293) 514255 🌐 breweryshades.co.uk
Dark Star Revelation; Greene King Abbot; 8 changing beers Ⓗ
Possibly the oldest building in Crawley High Street, the pub dates back to the 1400s and comes complete with two active ghosts. It is wet-sales led. The licensee has a true passion for the trade, demonstrated by the inspired range of guest ales and ciders which are always in excellent condition. The haunted upstairs room is now available for meetings. Good food is served during the day and evening – check the specials board.
☕😋🍴♿🛜

Danehill

Coach & Horses Ⓛ

School Lane, RH17 7JF
☎ (01825) 740369 🌐 coachandhorses.co
Harvey's Sussex Best Bitter; 1 changing beer (sourced locally; often 360 Degree, Cellar Head, Franklins) Ⓗ
A traditional country pub dating from 1847 and retaining many original features. The public and saloon bars have real fires and simple farmhouse-style furniture. There is always a cider from Black Pig on the bar, and occasionally its perry too. The separate restaurant section serves locally sourced, high-quality food. The large garden is a delight in summer and includes a children's play area. Q😋🍴♣🐾P🚲(270)🐾🛜

Eartham

George Ⓛ ✔

PO18 0LT (turn N off A27 at Crockerhill or W of Fontwell and proceed 2 miles to centre of village)
☎ (01243) 814340 🌐 thegeorgeeartham.com
House beer (by Otter); 3 changing beers (sourced locally; often Dorking, Greyhound, Langham) Ⓗ
A tastefully refurbished old village pub whose landlord's passion for the best of English, and especially Sussex, extends to the entire drinks and food menu. All changing beers are LocAle and always include one from Langham. Usually one is a hoppy golden ale and another a porter,

old ale or mild. The food menu features locally-sourced ingredients. The pub holds a beer festival in its garden each April featuring LocAles and live music. Popular with walkers and cyclists. Q☕😋🍴♿🛏️AP🚲(99)🐾🛜

East Grinstead

Engine Room Ⓛ

The Old Mill, 45 London Road, RH19 1AW
☎ (01342) 327145 🌐 theengineroomeg.com
5 changing beers (sourced locally; often Long Man, Titsey) Ⓖ
A bar serving all its real ales on gravity, up a path between the shops close to Whitehall bus stop in London Road. It is a downstairs labyrinth of small seating areas, good for small groups to hold conversations. There is live music on Thursday evening; other attractions include a dartboard and a selection of board games. Due to the downstairs location, access is not wheelchair-friendly. Q♿🐾🛏️🚲🛜

Old Dunnings Mill ✔

Dunnings Road, RH19 4AT
☎ (01342) 821080 🌐 olddunningsmill.co.uk
Harvey's Sussex Best Bitter; 4 changing beers (often Harvey's) Ⓗ
Large pub on the edge of town, based in an old watermill. Separate bar and restaurant sections are on various levels but the main areas are wheelchair-friendly. A heated, covered space to the rear has a working water wheel. Two beer festivals a year are planned. The bar is basically a quiet place, although music plays on appropriate occasions. Families and pets are welcome. Q☕😋🍴♿P🚲(84)🐾

REAL ALE BREWERIES

81 Artisan West Dean
Adur Steyning
Arundel Ford
Balcombe 🍺 Balcombe (NEW)
Brew Studio Sompting
Brewhouse & Kitchen 🍺 Horsham
Brolly 🍺 Wisborough Green
Chapeau Horsham
Dark Star Partridge Green
Downlands Small Dole
Firebird 🍺 Rudgwick
Goldmark Arundel
Greyhound West Chiltington
Gribble 🍺 Oving
Hairy Dog 🍺 Wivelsfield
Hand Worthing
Heathen Haywards Heath
Hepworth North Heath
Horsham Horsham (NEW)
Hurst Hurstpierpoint
Kissingate 🍺 Lower Beeding
Langham Lodsworth
Lister's Ford
Pin-Up Southwick
Polarity Worthing
Ridgeway North Heath
Riverside Upper Beeding
Silver Rocket Hassocks (NEW)
Top-Notch Haywards Heath
Vine 🍺 Tarring
Wingtip Ashurst

ENGLAND

East Preston

SP Alehouse

23 Sea Road, BN16 1JN
☎ 07736 928347
House beer (by Langham) [G]; 3 changing beers (often Bedlam, Firebird) [H]
This micropub opened in 2020 selling a varied selection of cask ales; usually four are on offer, including the house beer, and come mainly from Sussex and Hampshire breweries. Four good-quality craft keg beers are also stocked, again changing constantly. Real cider is available along with wines, gin, soft drinks and a traditional mead. Bar snacks are served and there is a free cheeseboard on a Sunday. ●🚌(700)🐾

East Wittering

Shore [L]

Shore Road, PO20 8DZ (50yds from sea)
☎ (01243) 674454 🌐 theshorepub.co.uk
Hop Back Summer Lightning; Langham Hip Hop; Palmers Copper Ale, Dorset Gold; Sharp's Doom Bar; 1 changing beer (sourced regionally) [H]
Friendly beachside pub popular with the locals (particularly dog owners) and the many summer visitors. Outside seating affords splendid sea views. There are two main bars offering good-value beers, a children's area and a fair-sized space for outside drinking as well as smoking. The good-quality lunchtime menu can be enjoyed either in the bar or restaurant, when extremely inviting dishes are on offer at fair prices (the selection is on a blackboard). Occasional live music is hosted; see website for details. Q❀◐♿♣P▯🚌(52,53)🐾

Eastergate

Wilkes' Head [L] ✔

Church Lane, PO20 3UT (off A29 in old village, 350yds S of B2233 roundabout, 1¼ miles W of Barnham station) SU943053
☎ (01243) 543380
Adnams Southwold Bitter; 5 changing beers (sourced nationally; often Bedlam, Downlands, Langham) [H]
A small Grade II-listed red-brick pub, built in 1803 and named after the 18th-century radical John Wilkes. It has a cosy lounge left of the central bar, and to the right a larger room with an inglenook fireplace, flagstones and low beams, plus a separate restaurant. Five well-chosen changing beers are served. To the rear are a large garden, a permanent marquee with seating and a heated smokers' shelter. Regular beer festivals are held. Q❀◐♿♣●P🚌🐾📶

Elsted

Three Horseshoes

GU29 0JY (at E end of village)
☎ (01730) 825746 🌐 3hs.co.uk
Bowman Wallops Wood; Flower Pots Bitter; Young's London Original; 2 changing beers (sourced locally; often Hop Back, Langham, Red Cat) [G]
Old and cosy rural inn divided into small rooms, including one reserved for dining and one with a blazing wood-burning stove in winter. Outside, the large, pleasant garden enjoys superb views of the South Downs. Five beers are available in summer (mainly from local micros) and three in winter, all served by gravity from a stillage alongside the bar. Meals are substantial and of high quality. This is a popular and homely pub that you will be reluctant to leave. Q❀◐♣P🐾

Faygate

Frog & Nightgown [L]

Wimlands Lane, RH12 4SS
☎ (01293) 852764 🌐 thefrogandnightgown.co.uk
Fuller's London Pride; 3 changing beers (sourced regionally; often Dark Star, Harvey's) [H]
A vibrant establishment that was comprehensively refurbished after changing hands in 2015 and also doubles as a tea room. It is known as the fastest pub in West Sussex due to its motorsport connections. Regular events include classic car meets, quiz nights, live music and open mic evenings. Street food is often available on a Friday night. Q❀◐P🚌🐾📶

Haywards Heath

Lockhart Tavern [L]

41 The Broadway, RH16 3AS
☎ (01444) 440696 🌐 thelockharttavern.co.uk
6 changing beers (sourced nationally; often Franklins, Heathen) [H]
This is a centrally located free house conversion of retail premises. It has two distinct areas, with drinkers catered for at the front with high tables and matching seating; towards the rear is a wood-panelled dining area. There are also picnic tables outside on the patio. Good food is served lunchtimes and evenings, with regular menu changes. In addition, the pub serves a choice of wines, spirits, keg, canned and bottled beers. Q❀◐≥🚌🐾📶

Henley

Duke of Cumberland [L]

Henley Village, GU27 3HQ (off A286, 2 miles N of Midhurst) SU894258
☎ (01428) 652280 🌐 dukeofcumberland.com
Harvey's Sussex Best Bitter; Langham Hip Hop; Timothy Taylor Landlord; 1 changing beer (sourced locally; often Langham) [G]
Stunning 15th-century inn nestling against the hillside in over three acres of terraced gardens with extensive views. The rustic front bar has scrubbed-top tables and benches, plus log fires at both ends. To the rear is a dining extension that blends in perfectly with the original pub and offers much-needed additional space. Outside is a smokers' shelter with its own wood-burner. This rural gem is a former local CAMRA Pub of the Year. May close winter Sunday evenings. Q❀◐♣P🚌(70)🐾📶

Hooksway

Royal Oak

PO18 9JZ SU815163
☎ (01243) 535257 🌐 royaloakhooksway.co.uk
Langham Hip Hop; 3 changing beers (sourced nationally; often Hepworth, Langham) [H]
An idyllic country inn, unspoilt and with great country walks, close to the South Downs Way and perfect for getting away from it all. In winter two lovely log fires greet you. Three permanent real ales and a regular guest are on offer, most from local breweries. An extensive food offering caters for all tastes and includes a varied children's menu. The pub is popular with hikers, horse riders and people with young families; the large garden has a play area for children. Q❀◐P🐾

Horsham

King's Arms [L]

64 Bishopric, RH12 1QN
☎ (01403) 451468 🌐 kingsarmshorsham.com

St Austell Tribute; 3 changing beers (sourced locally; often Chapeau, Hepworth, Horsham) Ⓗ
Near the town centre, this 18th-century coaching inn is close to the site of the former King & Barnes Brewery. A comfortable two-bar pub, it has long been popular with regulars, and shows sports on TV at the weekend. There are five handpulls with at least three rotating local ales, and also a keg line that serves Brolly ale. ✿◖🚃🛜

Malt Shovel Ⓛ
15 Springfield Road, RH12 2PG
☎ (01403) 252302
Surrey Hills Shere Drop; 4 changing beers (sourced regionally) Ⓗ
Close to the town centre, this pub has six handpumps in use all year round, plus two ciders and a mix of bottles and canned ales. The landlord and his friendly staff take great pride in the real ale. They do not stock any regular beers, but focus on local brews and usually offer at least one dark ale. The bar is warmed by a real fire in winter. Live music is hosted every Saturday night, and there are regular open mic and jam events. Parking is good bearing in mind the location. ✿◖🕭♣🅿🚃🛜

Piries Bar Ⓛ
Piries Alley, The Carfax, RH12 1NY
☎ (01403) 267846
Gun Scaramanga Extra Pale; Timothy Taylor Landlord; 1 changing beer (sourced locally; often Gun) Ⓗ
In a building dating from the 15th century with exposed original timber beams, the pub is tucked away down a narrow alley adjoining Horsham's Carfax. It comprises a small downstairs room, an upstairs lounge bar, and a small modern extension in character with the building. Regular charity events are organised. Evenings here can be lively, with karaoke on Sundays, quiz nights on Tuesdays and occasional live music. With two cask ales always on the go, this bar is well worth a visit. ⟲◖≋🚃🛜

Itchenor

Ship
The Street, PO20 7AH (on main street, 100yds from waterfront)
☎ (01243) 512284 ⊕ theshipinnitchenor.co.uk
Arundel Castle; Langham Hip Hop, Best; 1 changing beer (often Itchen Valley) Ⓗ
Popular venue in the main street of an attractive village on the shore of picturesque Chichester harbour. The cosy bar decorated with yachting memorabilia adds to the pub's character and is complemented by a pleasant patio, a suntrap in summer. The separate restaurant area offers a wide range, including local seafood. Accommodation is available in a two-bedroom apartment and a three-bedroom cottage. Q⟲✿🛏◖🕭♣🐾🛜

Lambs Green

Lamb Inn Ⓛ
RH12 4RG (2 miles north of A264)
☎ (01293) 871336 ⊕ thelambinn.org
Dark Star Hophead; Gales HSB; 1 changing beer (sourced locally) Ⓗ
Lovely old pub with a mixture of flagstones and wooden floors, with wrought-iron work, low-beamed ceilings and exposed brick walls. Furnishings include high-backed settles and soft sofas, and a real fire in winter. There is outside seating with a woodfired pizza oven during warmer months. The friendly landlord and staff make this a welcoming hostelry, with lunchtime and evening

quality homemade meals served daily, from locally sourced ingredients. Normally two real ciders are available. Q⟲✿🕭◖🕭♣🐾🅿🐾🛜

Lancing

Stanley Ale House Ⓛ
5 Queensway, BN15 9AY (200yds N of Lancing railway station and nr local shops)
☎ (01903) 366820 ⊕ thestanleyalehouse.com
Langham Arapaho; 3 changing beers (sourced regionally; often Downlands, Franklins) Ⓗ
This former launderette opened as a family-run micropub/ale house in 2014. It offers several changing ales, plus ciders, wine and gin. The owners have listened to customers and now have both keg and cask beers. There is ample seating inside and outside, and bar snacks are available. The pub has variety of board games and holds a weekly quiz, regular music nights, takeaway night and other events. Q⟲🛏◖♣≋🐾🚃🐾🛜

Littlehampton

New Inn ✅
5 Norfolk Road, BN17 5PL (N from Sea Road)
☎ (01903) 713112 ⊕ newinnla.co.uk
3 changing beers (sourced nationally) Ⓗ
A friendly community pub, offering three regularly changing ales, just a short walk from the beach. This traditional inn has two bar areas. The front bar has ample seating, a real fire and hosts weekly quizzes and regular charity events. The rear bar has a pool table and dartboard, and shows live sport. A free jukebox is a feature of Monday nights. There is a heated courtyard at the back. ⟲✿♣🚃🐾🛜

Steam Packet Ⓛ
54 River Road, BN17 5BZ
☎ (01903) 715994 ⊕ the-steam-packet.com
Fallen Acorn Pompey Royal; 3 changing beers (sourced locally; often Bedlam, Franklins, Vibrant Forest) Ⓗ
This one-bar pub has a pleasing seating area which makes good use of the available floor space. It overlooks the harbour and is near the river footbridge, and is a short distance from where a cross-Channel steam packet ferry service operated from Littlehampton to Honfleur. All ales are from independent microbreweries, mainly local. Real ciders plus craft beer in cans are available, fresh food is prepared on the premises, and vegetarians, vegans and those with allergies are catered for. ✿🛏◖≋🐾🚃(700)🐾

Lower Beeding

Kissingate Brewery
RH13 6LU (Pole Barn, Church Lane Farm Estate, Church Lane)
☎ (01403) 891335 ⊕ kissingate.co.uk
Kissingate Black Cherry Mild, Pernickety Pale, Chennai, Powder Blue; 8 changing beers (sourced locally) Ⓖ
This is the taproom for the renowned Kissingate Brewery. You will find a selection of beers from the Kissingate range served on gravity, plus cider and perry from Black Pig and JB Cider. On the last Friday of the month the bar opens later into the evening. Events including curry nights are held, and there is a function area upstairs. ✿♿🅰♣🅿🐾🛜

Maplehurst

White Horse Ⓛ
Park Lane, RH13 6LL
☎ (01403) 891208 ⊕ whitehorsemaplehurst.co.uk
4 changing beers (often Harvey's, Hepworth, Kissingate) Ⓗ
Under the same ownership for 39 years, this splendid and welcoming country pub has appeared in the Guide 36 times, and is popular with locals, cyclists and walkers. The cosy interior, with its unusually wide wooden bar, boasts real fires and many interesting artefacts and bric-a-brac. Good honest fare is provided, with the emphasis on beer and conversation. Many ales from the area feature, with a good selection of dark brews. JB Cider from nearby is also available. Q🕏❀❶🎵🍴❀P❀🐾🗢

Oving

Gribble Inn Ⓛ
Gribble Lane, PO20 2BP (at W end of village)
☎ (01243) 786893 ⊕ gribbleinn.co.uk
Gribble Flint's Full Glory, Ale, Fuzzy Duck, Reg's Tipple, Pig's Ear, Wobbler; 1 changing beer (often Gribble) Ⓗ
Once home to a Miss Gribble, this attractive thatched cottage has been a traditional village pub for over 30 years and shares the premises with the Gribble Brewery. The full range of regular Gribble beers complemented by seasonals is always on the go. It is cosy, with log fires in winter, and serves home-made food in the bar/restaurant. In summer a large attractive garden offers occasional weekend barbecues, and the skittle alley is also available for functions. Q🕏❀❶🎵🍴P🖳(85,85A)❀🗢

Pagham

Inglenook Ⓛ
255 Pagham Road, PO21 3QB SZ892986
☎ (01243) 262495 ⊕ the-inglenook.com
Fuller's London Pride; Young's London Special; 4 changing beers (sourced nationally; often Brighton Bier, Dark Star, Vibrant Forest) Ⓗ
A 16th-century Grade II-listed hotel, restaurant and free house, owned and run by the Honour family for over 40 years. It always offers a selection of excellent well-hopped real ales from highly regarded microbreweries, alongside local ciders. The cosy bar has real fires. There is a large garden to the rear and a patio at the front. Q🕏❀❶🎵🍴❀P🖳🖳(600)❀🗢

Rudgwick

King's Head Ⓛ ✔
Church Street, RH12 3EB
☎ (01403) 822200 ⊕ kingsheadrudgwick.co.uk
Crafty Brewing Crafty One; 2 changing beers (often Harvey's) Ⓗ
This 17th-century low-beamed pub can be found at the northern end of the village. It is opposite the Norman church and in a conservation area. There is a bar with a wood-burning stove and leather sofas at one end, and a restaurant at the other. Food is freshly prepared for the Italian menu. The Downslink footpath passes nearby. Q🕏❀❶🎵🍴P🖳❀

Rustington

Georgi Fin Rustington
106 The Street, BN16 3NJ
☎ (01903) 785743 ⊕ thegeorgifin.co.uk
4 changing beers (sourced locally; often Greyhound, Oakham) Ⓗ
This micropub opened in August 2020 at one end of a busy shopping street. It has the same name as the owner's other micropub in West Worthing, and the premises have been fully refitted with a similar theme. Ales, including several from local brewers, are served by gravity direct from casks in a cool room, with KeyKeg beers from fonts on the bar. Wine, gin, bottled and canned beers and other drinks are available. There is outside seating. 🕏❀❀🖳(700,9)❀

Selsey

Crab Pot
153 High Street, PO20 0QB
☎ 07834 226751 ⊕ crabpotmicropub.co.uk
3 changing beers (sourced regionally) Ⓗ
After two years in a former tea shop, the Crab Pot's popularity has led to a move down the street to larger premises, where a bigger cool room allows a wide range of real ciders to complement the three changing real ales. One of these is often from Brew Studio. The mixture of high and low seating makes for a relaxed and friendly atmosphere; a warm welcome is assured for visitors and locals alike. There is a function room behind the bar where televised sport, especially rugby, can be watched. ▲❀❀🖳(51)❀🗢

Shoreham-by-Sea

Duke of Wellington Ⓛ
368 Brighton Road, BN43 6RE (on A259)
☎ (01273) 441297 ⊕ dukeofwellingtonbrewhouse.co.uk
7 changing beers (sourced regionally) Ⓗ
A pub of contrasts: on some nights it is a quiet drinking emporium, on others it is packed to the gills with a ukulele band, the Wellington Wailers or a local group. What is consistent is the former Dark Star outlet's beer quality and range. The original brewer has a small shrine of certificates together with copies of all the Good Beer Guides in a display case. There are original Kemp Town Brewery windows. 🕏❀❀❀🖳(2,700)❀🗢

Old Star Ale & Cider House Ⓛ
Church Street, BN43 5DQ
☎ 07999 915242 ⊕ oldstarshoreham.co.uk
3 changing beers (sourced regionally; often Brighton Bier, Burning Sky, Gun) Ⓖ
A well-run micropub just off the High Street. Three beers are on tap through the week, with up to five on Saturdays, most from Sussex microbreweries and almost always including one dark ale. They are served direct from the casks on stillage behind the bar. There is a range of real and craft ciders and perries. A cider festival is held over the autumn bank holiday. A complimentary cheese board is on offer every Saturday evening. Q❀❀❀🖳(2,700)❀🗢

Staplefield

Jolly Tanners Ⓛ ✔
Handcross Road, RH17 6EF
☎ (01444) 400335
Fuller's London Pride; Harvey's Sussex Best Bitter; 4 changing beers (sourced locally; often Dark Star, Tring, Wimbledon) Ⓗ
On the north corner of the village green, this welcoming venue combines all the best elements of a village inn. The spacious bar is divided into two distinct areas, with two log fires adding to the cosy feel. There is an extensive range of guest beers, always including a mild,

and real cider is also sold. A good range of tasty food is served at all sessions. This is a friendly place and still very much a locals' pub. Q❄☆❀◑↻&▲♣●P⊒(271)❀♥❡

Stoughton

Hare & Hounds 🅛

PO18 9JQ (off B2146, through Walderton) SU803115
☎ (023) 9263 1433 ● hareandhoundspub.co.uk
Dark Star Hophead; Long Man Best Bitter; Otter Amber; 2 changing beers (sourced locally; often Fallen Acorn) ⓗ

Traditional country pub in a beautiful setting that makes it an ideal base for walking. The large dining room serves fresh produce from the area in comfortable surroundings, with an open fire in winter. A separate public bar has pictures of vintage racing cars and its own open fire, which attracts locals. The fires, stone-flagged floors and simple furniture create a wonderful atmosphere. Outside, the paved patio complements a rear garden for dining and drinking. Two ciders are stocked.
Q❄◑♣●P❀♥❡

Thakeham

White Lion Inn

The Street, RH20 3EP (turn right, 300 yards N of village, on B2139)
☎ (01798) 813141 ● whitelion-thakeham.co.uk
Harvey's Sussex Best Bitter; St Austell Tribute; 2 changing beers (sourced nationally; often Greyhound) ⓗ

A 16th-century inn in the atmospheric conservation area, with stone steps leading up to the door. Inside is a delightful country pub interior, with an ornamental white lion on the bar. There are three separate bar spaces and a room that doubles as a function room or restaurant. The inn is renowned for its food (not served Sun eve), with one of the fireplaces used to smoke local ham. Outside are a garden and large south-facing patio.
Q❄◑●P⊒(72) ❀♥❡

Turners Hill

Red Lion 🅛 ✅

Lion Lane, RH10 4NU
☎ (01342) 715416 ● redlionturnershill.com
Harvey's Dark Mild, IPA, Sussex Best Bitter; 2 changing beers (sourced locally; often Harvey's) ⓗ

A regular entry in the Guide, this place is still very much a village local, offering a warm welcome to all who enter. It has a split-level layout and features a large inglenook fireplace. There is a popular fortnightly quiz on a Wednesday. The local CAMRA branch held its first meeting here in 1974. Children and dogs are welcome, and newspapers are provided for customers.
Q❄☆◑&♣P⊒(84,272) ❀♥❡

Walderton

Barley Mow

Breakneck Lane, PO18 9ED
☎ (023) 9263 1321 ● thebarleymow.pub
Dark Star Hophead; Harvey's Sussex Best Bitter; Otter Amber; Ringwood Fortyniner; 1 changing beer (sourced locally; often Harvey's) ⓗ

An attractive free house in the centre of this picturesque village, popular with walkers and visitors to the South Downs National Park. Much of this cosy traditional pub caters for diners but drinkers are most welcome in the large bar area. There are usually five handpumps in use featuring two beers from Harvey's. There are log fires in

winter and the pretty garden alongside the River Ems is popular in summer. The skittle alley can double as a function room. Q❄☆◑&P⊒(54)❀♥❡

West Chiltington

Five Bells 🅛

Smock Alley, RH20 2QX (approx 1 mile S of old village centre) TQ092171
☎ (01798) 812143 ● thefivebellsinn.com
5 changing beers (sourced nationally; often Harvey's, Jennings, Palmers) ⓗ

A friendly village free house that is a Guide regular. Dating from 1935, this former King & Barnes pub has been run by the same couple since 1983. Five handpumps sit on what is probably Sussex's longest copper-top counter. Local and regional ales are on offer, one of them usually dark. There is a copper-hooded open fire. Locally sourced home-cooked meals are served in the bar and large conservatory (no food Sun eve). Q❄☆⇄◑●P⊒(1,74)❀♥❡

West Hoathly

Cat 🅛

Queen's Square, North Lane, RH19 4PP
☎ (01342) 810369 ● catinn.co.uk
Firebird Parody; Harvey's Sussex Best Bitter; Larkins Traditional Ale; 2 changing beers (often Bedlam, Dark Star, Harvey's) ⓗ

Set in a picturesque hilltop village in the heart of the Sussex countryside, this 16th-century free house is within reach of several attractions. It retains oak beams and two inglenook fireplaces. There is an outside terrace, where food and drink can be consumed in the summer months. Five local ales are on the bar and good-quality food is cooked to order, most of the time using ingredients sourced from suppliers from the area. This cosy pub has four letting rooms.
Q❄☆⇄◑&▲P⊒(84) ❀♥❡

Westbourne

Cricketers ✅

Commonside, PO10 8TA (N from The Square, turn E at Chidham Garage)
☎ (01243) 372647
Flack Manor Flack's Double Drop; Flower Pots Perridge Pale; Harvey's Sussex Best Bitter; 2 changing beers (sourced locally; often Itchen Valley, Langham) ⓗ

This 300-year-old local is the only true free house in the village. Situated on the northern outskirts, it is hard to find but well worth the effort. Conversation abounds in the single L-shaped, half-panelled bar. Up to two guest beers come mostly from Hampshire and Sussex micros. The beer range may vary a little from that shown. There is a suntrap garden to the side, with a covered and heated smoking area. Q❄♣P❀♥❡

Worthing

Anchored in Worthing 🅛

27 West Buildings, BN11 3BS (close to seafront)
☎ (01903) 529100 ● anchoredinworthing.co.uk
3 changing beers (sourced locally; often Gun, Hand, Rother Valley) Ⓖ

Look for the Tardis-style entrance to Sussex's original micropub, where you are assured of a warm welcome. High wooden tables are arranged so customers face each other and conversation quickly flows. The ceiling is adorned with pumpclips of many previous ales sold. The walls have maps showing breweries and micropubs, plus CAMRA and local event information. All ale, cider, wine, gin and soft drinks are from Sussex producers. There is a free cheeseboard on Sundays. Q♣●⊟🐾ᯤ

Brewhouse & Kitchen 🄻

14 Wykeham Road, BN11 4JD

☎ (01903) 948222

Brewhouse & Kitchen Swiss Cottage, Stormtrooper, Scombrini; 2 changing beers (sourced locally) 🄷

The former Beechwood Hall Hotel was taken over by Brewhouse & Kitchen and opened in May 2021. The original building has been refurbished and extended sympathetically. This is the first Brewhouse & Kitchen site to offer accommodation, so is described as a 'BrewTel'. It serves in-house brewed ales and keg beers alongside a good food menu. There is a large garden with seating areas including covered pods. Some ales and rooms are named using the former names of the building. ❀⛟◐♿●P🐾ᯤ

Brooksteed Alehouse 🄻

38 South Farm Road, BN14 7AE (100yds N of South Farm Rd level crossing, 5 mins walk from Worthing station)

☎ 07484 840103 🌐 brooksteedalehouse.co.uk

House beer (by Arundel); 4 changing beers (sourced nationally; often Brighton Bier, Goldmark, Gun) 🄶

Worthing's second micropub opened in 2014, with a change of ownership in 2017. It has a stylish and interesting décor, with high tables and comfortable seating inside plus outside seating areas at the front and rear. This popular pub has a strong community spirit and organises events that include other local businesses. It serves a good selection of regularly changing cask ales, KeyKeg and cider/perry from local and national brewers, plus a range of bottled beers, wines and gin. There is a cheeseboard on Sundays. Q♉❀⇌●P⊟(16)🐾ᯤ

Corner House 🄻 ✔

80 High Street, BN11 1DJ (opp Waitrose)

☎ (01903) 216463 🌐 cornerhouseworthing.co.uk

4 changing beers (sourced regionally; often Goldmark, Harvey's, Shepherd Neame) 🄷

This venue occupies a prominent position at the town centre's eastern edge. The original pub, the Anchor, dated back to 1805 and was one of Worthing's oldest, but was rebuilt in 1895. After several different names, it reopened in 2015 under new ownership and with a new name, quickly becoming popular. There is an emphasis on local suppliers for both food and drink, including for the Sunday roasts. The large heated beer garden is well used all year round. ♉❀◐⇌⊟🐾ᯤ

Cricketers 🄻 ✔

66 Broadwater Street West, Broadwater, BN14 9DE (at S end of Broadwater Green on A24)

☎ (01903) 233369 🌐 cricketersworthing.co.uk

Arundel Sussex IPA; Fuller's London Pride; Long Man Best Bitter; 2 changing beers 🄷

The current site had a much older building dating from the 1700s and there has been a pub here since the 1800s. This traditional hostelry has a single bar with a number of rooms, including one where food is served. There is a large beer garden and children's area. Ales are from regional and national brewers, with changing guest brews. There is a popular beer festival in July coinciding with the local carnival. ♉❀◐♣P⊟🐾ᯤ

Fox & Finch Alehouse 🄻

8 Littlehampton Road, BN13 1QE (on N side of A259 across from Thomas a Becket) 🌐 thefoxandfinch.co.uk

4 changing beers (often Arundel, Dark Star, Fallen Acorn) 🄷

Worthing's fifth micropub opened in 2019 and quickly became popular, offering a warm welcome to all. The premises are decorated in a homely, traditional pub style with high and low tables and comfortable seating. A cold room behind the bar houses the ale served directly from the cask; the keg range is from taps on the bar. The pub also offers a range of Belgian beers, plus fine wine and a small selection of spirits. It has limited outside seating. Local CAMRA branch Pub of the Year 2020. ♉♿●⊟🐾ᯤ

Georgi Fin 🄻

54 Goring Road, BN12 4AD (on A259, N side, in Goring Rd shops)

☎ (01903) 249224 🌐 thegeorgifin.co.uk

4 changing beers (sourced regionally; often Franklins, Gun, Thornbridge) 🄶

Named after the owner's children, this popular micropub opened in 2017 in a busy shopping parade. It has a selection of high and low tables and seating, and both ladies' and gents' toilets (unusual at this kind of small venue). The drinks are served from a purpose-built cold room. They include ales from local and national brewers, KeyKeg brews and a selection of English, Belgian and German bottled beers, plus wines and traditional ciders. A cheeseboard is available on Sundays. Q⇌●⊟🐾

Green Man Ale & Cider House 🄻

17 South Street, Tarring, BN14 7LG (40yds N of West Worthing railway crossing)

☎ 07984 793877

5 changing beers (sourced regionally; often Goldmark, Gun, Wantsum) 🄶

Worthing's third micropub opened in 2016 in a former café and is known for its friendly atmosphere. The temperature-controlled cellar is visible from the bar, which is furnished with high-level tables, benches and stools arranged to encourage interaction and chat. Typically, a selection of ales is dispensed on gravity, plus ciders/perries, a whisky and a number of gins, wines and soft drinks. Local CAMRA Pub of the Year and Cider Pub of the Year 2019. Q⇌♣●⊟🐾

Park View

Salvington Road, BN13 2JR (corner of Salvington Rd and Durrington Lane)

☎ (01903) 521397 🌐 parkview-worthing.co.uk

Bath Ales Gem; 2 changing beers (sourced regionally; often Dark Star, St Austell) 🄷

Formerly the Lamb, the Park View reopened in 2018 as a community pub and kitchen in the Durrington and Salvington area of Worthing. It has a sports bar showing Sky Sports and BT Sport, an informal lounge bar and an extensive garden. The pub serves a changing selection of real ales from local and national breweries, along with freshly prepared, locally sourced food. Regular events include a weekly quiz on Thursdays and live music on Saturday nights. ♉❀◐♿♣⊟(5,6)🐾ᯤ

Parsonage Bar & Restaurant 🄻 ✔

6-10 High Street, Tarring, BN14 7NN (at S end of Tarring High St - not to be confused with High St Worthing)

☎ (01903) 820140 🌐 theparsonage.co.uk

Burning Sky Plateau; Harvey's Sussex Best Bitter 🄷; 2 changing beers (sourced locally; often Downlands, Harvey's, Lister's) 🄷/🄶

This lovely Grade II-listed 15th-century building in the heart of the village was originally three cottages. It has been a quality restaurant since 1987 but the bar now has several well-kept local ales, two of which change regularly and always include a dark brew. Customers are welcome to drink without having a meal, although the bar menu is good value. The courtyard garden is great for warmer weather. Q🏠🍴◖≉⏰🚌(6,16)🐾📶

Selden Arms 🅛

41 Lyndhurst Road, BN11 2DB (about 5 mins from centre of town and 2 mins from Worthing Hospital)
☎ (01903) 523361 🌐 seldenarms.co.uk
6 changing beers (sourced nationally; often Gun, Pilgrim, Vibrant Forest) 🅷
Welcoming 19th-century free house that has been in the Guide for 22 years. Six handpumps serve a changing selection of local and national ales, one of which is always dark. There is also a selection of craft beers, both keg and in cans and bottles, plus an extensive range of bottled Belgian brews. A blackboard displays upcoming ales. Lunchtime food is available Monday to Saturday, with curry Friday and Saturday evenings. A winter beer festival is held in January. ◖≉♣🍴🚌🐾📶

Yapton

Maypole 🅛

Maypole Lane, BN18 0DP (off B2132 ½ mile N of village; pedestrian access is across railway from Lake Lane, 1¼ miles E of Barnham station) SU978042
☎ (01243) 551417
Bedlam Phoenix IPA; Lister's Best Bitter; 3 changing beers (sourced locally; often Bedlam, Cellar Head, Greyhound) 🅷
A small 18th-century flint-built free house of great character. It is hidden away from the village centre, down a narrow lane that ends in a pedestrian crossing over the railway. The cosy, often lively lounge boasts a log-burner and a row of six handpumps that dispense beers from local micros. There is also a traditional public bar with pool and darts, plus a skittle alley/function room with bar billiards. Real cider is served from the cellar. Fresh filled rolls are available at lunchtimes. Dogs are welcome. Q🏡🐕🏠♿🅐♣🍴P🚌🐾📶

Brewers Arms, Lewes, East Sussex (Photo: Matthew Black/Flickr CC BY-SA 2.0)

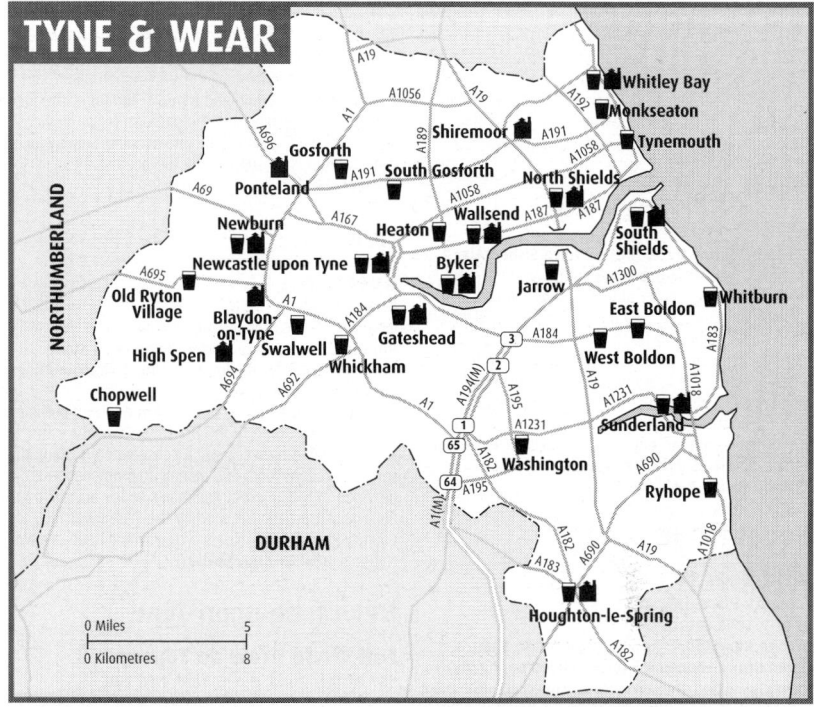

Chopwell

Red House

1 Millfield Terrace, NE17 7LL

☎ (01207) 560065 ⊕ the-red-house-bar.business.site

3 changing beers (sourced nationally) Ⓗ

This micropub is on the main street in the centre of the village and is a welcome addition to the real ale scene. Run by a fireman with a passion for real ales and ciders, the friendly community establishment is well worth a visit. Open Thursday to Sunday.

East Boldon

Grey Horse ✪

Front Street, NE36 0SJ

☎ (0191) 519 1796

6 changing beers (sourced nationally) Ⓗ

A distinctive-fronted building with a separate bar and lounge area. Up to six handpulls dispense changing beers. There is seating out front and a beer garden at the rear. A large-screen TV in the bar shows sporting events and regular quizzes are held, with prizes for the winning table. There is a function room upstairs which can be hired. Food is served, with regular specials throughout the week. Q☎✿◑🏵&♿P🚃❀🐾 ⚹ 🛜

Gateshead

Central ★ Ⓛ

Half Moon Lane, NE8 2AN

☎ (0191) 478 2543

8 changing beers (sourced nationally) Ⓗ

A mid-19th century four-storey wedge-shaped building. It has a revamped public bar, two function rooms and a rooftop terrace, and hosts regular live music. However, the Grade II-listed premises' main attraction is the magnificently restored Buffet (closed when quiet; ask to

view), designated by CAMRA as an interior of special historic interest. It remains as fitted out circa 1900 with a carved U-shaped counter and bar-back, plasterwork frieze and panelling. ☎◑&♿♣♿🚃❀🐾 ⚹ 🛜

Old Fox Ⓛ

10-14 Carlisle Street, Felling, NE10 0HQ

☎ (0191) 447 1980

5 changing beers (sourced nationally) Ⓗ

The Fox is a traditional community single-room venue with a roaring fire in the winter months, only a short walk from Felling Metro station. Ales are drawn both from national and local breweries. Snacks and Sunday lunches are available. There is live music over the weekend, and the dartboard is in frequent use. A friendly and welcoming pub with a beer garden at the rear. ☎✿♿≠🚇(Felling) ♣🚃🐾 ⚹ 🛜

Schooner Ⓛ

South Shore Road, NE8 3AF (vehicular access only from E end of South Shore Rd)

☎ (0191) 477 7404 ⊕ theschooner.co.uk

Rat White Rat; 5 changing beers (sourced nationally) Ⓗ

On the banks of the Tyne, the Schooner currently has six handpumps for cask ales and one for cask cider. The selection changes regularly to showcase the best local and national ales and ciders. Great-value home-cooked food is served throughout the week, with traditional roasts on Sunday. Live music plays every Sunday afternoon, some Saturday nights, and on many other occasions. ☎✿◑&♣🚃P🚃(93,94)🐾 ⚹ 🛜

Station East Ⓛ

Hills Street, NE8 2AS

☎ (0191) 435 3389

Hadrian Border Tyneside Blonde, Farne Island Pale Ale, Grainger Ale; 3 changing beers (sourced nationally; often Hadrian Border) Ⓗ

Occupying the site of the former Gateshead East station and Railway Hotel, the building is now stripped back and enlarged with much structural work. Formerly a small pub, it is now open and spacious. There is a pleasant mezzanine floor above the main room and a further arched room to the rear below another railway bridge. A back room is available for functions. Q&♿🚫

Wheat Sheaf ㄴ

26 Carlisle Street, Felling, NE10 0HQ
☎ (0191) 597 2981
Big Lamp Sunny Daze, Bitter, Prince Bishop Ale; 2 changing beers (sourced nationally) Ⓗ
Welcoming street-corner pub owned by Big Lamp Brewery and patronised by a loyal band of regulars who often travel quite a distance to drink here. The pub features some original details, mismatched furniture and, when needed, real coal fires. There is a fortnightly Monday night quiz, traditional folk music featuring keen local musicians on Tuesday night and dominoes on Wednesday night. An original CAMRA clock keeps time behind the bar. Snacks are available.
🕭≠Q(Felling) ♣♦🚍😺🐾🎵

Houghton le Spring

Wild Boar ✓

Frederick Place, DH4 4BN
☎ (0191) 512 8050
Greene King Abbot; Ruddles Best Bitter; Sharp's Doom Bar; 4 changing beers (sourced nationally) Ⓗ
Previously a club, the Wild Boar is named after the black sabre boar on the crest of the former rector of Houghton. This open-plan Wetherspoon was opened in 2011 and offers well-priced ales and has a good-value food menu. Its 10 handpulls offer a selection of regular, national and local beers. Note the old photographs and paintings that adorn the walls and staircase. Two beer festivals are usually held every year. Q🕭😺🕓◗&P🚍🎵

Jarrow

Albion Gin & Ale House

Walter Street, NE32 3PQ (behind town hall)
☎ (0191) 489 7222
4 changing beers (sourced nationally) Ⓗ
Old-style pub with a single room and a beer garden at the back. There are four real ales and a large selection of gins on sale in the bar, which is decorated with local items around the walls. Live music is always on at weekends, with quizzes and karaoke taking place during the week. The landlord also makes extra efforts to celebrate occasions such as Halloween, St George's Day, St Patrick's day and other notable dates. &🚍P🚍🎵

Monkseaton

Front Street Tap House

17B Front Street, NE25 8AQ
4 changing beers (sourced locally; often Cullercoats) Ⓗ
The latest addition to the local micropub scene opened in 2018 in a former florist's shop on the main street. It has one main room including the bar, with a smaller raised area to the rear. Four handpumps and four keg taps feature beers from local breweries. Card payments only at present. 🚍🚍😺

Left Luggage Room ㄴ

Unit 6, Monkseaton Train Station, Norham Road, NE26 3NR
🌐 leftluggageroom.co.uk

6 changing beers (sourced nationally) Ⓗ
Situated in the former parcel and left luggage room of Monkseaton Metro station, access is directly from the southbound platform side. The single open-plan room has the bar at one end and a mix of furniture. The area between the building and the platform fence provides covered outdoor seating until mid-evening. Sunday lunch can sometimes be supplied by the nearby café.
Q🕭😺&♿🚍●🚍🐾😺

Newburn

Keelman ㄴ

Grange Road, NE15 8NL
☎ (0191) 267 1689 🌐 biglampbrewers.co.uk
Big Lamp Sunny Daze, Bitter, Summerhill Stout, Prince Bishop Ale, Keelman Brown; 1 changing beer (sourced nationally) Ⓗ
This tastefully converted, Grade II-listed former pumping station is now home to the Big Lamp Brewery – the Keelman is the brewery tap. A conservatory restaurant serves excellent food, and quality accommodation is provided in the adjacent Keelman's Lodge and Salmon Cottage. Attractively situated by the Tyne Riverside Country Park, Coast-to-Coast cycleway and Hadrian's Wall National Trail. 🕭😺🏨◗&P🚍(22,71)🎵

Newcastle upon Tyne

Full Circle Brew Co Taproom ㄴ

167 Walker Road, Hoults Yard, NE6 2HL
☎ (0191) 481 4114 🌐 fullcirclebrew.co.uk
4 changing beers (sourced locally; often Full Circle) Ⓐ
Brewing started here in 2020. The taproom is on a glass-fronted balcony overlooking the brewery. A small range of cask ales and a large range of craft keg beers are available from Full Circle, plus collaborations and seasonal beers from other small brewers. Pizzas are made to order. The new beer garden has space for up to 60 people. ◗&P

REAL ALE BREWERIES

Almasty ⚡ Shiremoor
Anarchy ⚡ Newcastle upon Tyne
Big Lamp Newburn
Brinkburn Street ⚡ Newcastle upon Tyne: Byker
Cullercoats Wallsend
Darwin Sunderland
Dog & Rabbit 🍺 Whitley Bay
Errant Newcastle upon Tyne
Firebrick Blaydon-on-Tyne
Flash House North Shields
Flying Gang ⚡ Ponteland (NEW)
Full Circle ⚡ Newcastle upon Tyne
Great North Eastern ⚡ Gateshead
Hadrian Border Newburn
Maxim Houghton le Spring
Metalhead North Shields
Newcastle Newcastle upon Tyne
Northern Alchemy ⚡ Newcastle upon Tyne: Byker
One More Than Two ⚡ South Shields (NEW)
Out There Newcastle-upon-Tyne
Stu Brew Newcastle upon Tyne
Tavernale 🍺 Newcastle upon Tyne
Three Kings North Shields
TOPS High Spen
Two by Two Wallsend
Tyne Bank ⚡ Newcastle upon Tyne
Vaux Sunderland (NEW)
Whitley Bay 🍺 Whitley Bay
Wylam ⚡ Newcastle upon Tyne

Newcastle upon Tyne: Byker

Brinkburn Street Brewery Bar & Kitchen 🄻

Unit 1B, Ford Street, Ouseburn, NE6 1NW
☎ (0191) 338 9039 ⊕ brinkburnbrewery.co.uk
8 changing beers (sourced locally) 🄷
The main attraction here is the range and quality of beers available. Most ales are brewed on-site, alongside a couple of guests, often from Steam Machine. Food is also a major feature, with a kitchen that uses locally sourced ingredients and serves traditional local dishes. The hall is used as a venue for occasional beer festivals and other events. The quirky bar features a collection of armoury and objets d'art. ◖◗ᘒ♣

Cluny 🄻

36 Lime Street, NE1 2PQ
☎ (0191) 230 4474 ⊕ thecluny.com
7 changing beers (sourced nationally) 🄷
Large industrial building converted into a pub, art gallery and live music venue. The pub runs frequent themed beer festivals and always has a good selection of British and foreign draught and bottled products available. The art gallery puts on work of all kinds, from final degree shows to local independent established artists in all media, with the displays changing monthly. Live music sessions are held most evenings and include a wide range of British, European and American musicians.
ᘒ◖◗ᕃᘒ♠ᕀ☎

Cumberland Arms 🄻

James Place Street, NE6 1LD
☎ (0191) 265 1725 ⊕ thecumberlandarms.co.uk
6 changing beers (sourced nationally) 🄷
Three-storey venue rebuilt over 100 years ago and relatively little changed since, standing in a prominent position overlooking the lower Ouseburn Valley. The pub is home to traditional dance and music groups. A multiple winner of CAMRA regional Cider Pub of the Year awards, it generally offers up to 12 ciders and perries. Winter and summer beer festivals are held each year. Closing time may vary. Accommodation is in four en-suite rooms. ᘒᔆ❀ᕂᘒ(Byker)♣♠P❀☎

Free Trade Inn 🄻

St Lawrence Road, NE6 1AP
☎ (0191) 265 5764
7 changing beers (sourced nationally) 🄷
Unique former Scottish & Newcastle pub with wonderful views of the Tyne bridges and Newcastle and Gateshead quaysides. Up to nine beers and five ciders are available on the bar. Interesting ales come from far and wide, with regular tap takeovers and an extensive range of foreign bottled beers. The jukebox is classic and free, and the beer garden is excellent. It hosts regular pop-up food vendors. A former local CAMRA Pub of the Year and Cider Pub of the Year. ᘒᔆ❀ᘒ(Byker)♣♠ᘒ(Q3)❀☎

Tyne Bank Tap Room 🄻

375 Walker Road, NE6 2BS
☎ (0191) 265 2828
14 changing beers (sourced nationally; often Tyne Bank) 🄷
Tyne Bank's tap house has an industrial feel, with views into the working brewery. Open steel roof trusses are on display, the bar is constructed from scaffolding planks, and corrugated iron continues the theme. Downward-facing gas heaters are an interesting feature. Live music and events are held on the corner stage. Eight handpumps provide ales alongside a range of keg beers. The huge steel pipe keg fonts are unusual. ᕃᘒ(Q3)☎

Newcastle upon Tyne: City Centre

Beer Street 🄻

Arch 10, Forth Street, NE1 3NZ
5 changing beers (sourced nationally) 🄷
Sited in a railway arch, this micropub with seating for 50 people opened in 2018. There is a main bar area with five handpumps. Stairs at the rear give access to a mezzanine floor above, with pump badges from former beers adorning the staircase. Interesting artwork covers the walls, apparently inspired by the famous Hogarth paintings Beer Street and Gin Lane. ⇌ᘒ(Central)♠❀

Lady Greys 🄻 ✅

20 Shakespeare Street, NE1 6AQ
☎ (0191) 232 3606 ⊕ ladygreys.co.uk
House beer (by Ridgeside); 7 changing beers (sourced nationally) 🄷
Close to the historic Theatre Royal and busy shopping areas, it is nice to see this pub, formerly The Adelphi, adding itself to the city-centre real ale scene. Beers are mainly from local brewers Hadrian Border, Allendale and Wylam, with guests from all over the country. Refurbishment has added two more handpumps for beer and two for real cider. Food is served all day.
◖◗⇌ᘒ(Monument) ♠ᕀ

Mean-Eyed Cat

1 St Thomas Street, NE1 4LE
☎ (0191) 222 0952
Rat White Rat; house beer (by Almasty); 4 changing beers (sourced nationally) 🄷
Situated in a former newsagent's in the street opposite Haymarket bus station, this one-room micropub opened in 2018 with six handpumps. It serves beers from local, national and international suppliers, alongside a range of eight craft keg beers. A good selection of up to six ciders is available – traditional still and served from the 'cellar'. Mexican spirits are also on offer. There are street food pop-ups on occasion. ᘒ(Haymarket)♠ᘒ

Newcastle Tap

Ground Floor, Baron House, 4 Neville Street, NE1 5EN
☎ (0191) 261 6636 ⊕ tapnewcastle.com
8 changing beers (sourced nationally) 🄿
Opened in 2017 on the ground floor of a former office block next to Head of Steam and opposite Royal Station Hotel and Newcastle Central station. The Tap has a single open-plan room with beer casks and kegs displayed behind glass on a mezzanine above the bar. Cask beers are delivered through taps in the bar-back rather than handpumps – there are no dispensers on the bar counter itself. Gravity dispense is assisted by FloJet pumps. A pizza menu is available all day. ◖◗⇌ᘒ(Central)ᘒ

Split Chimp 🄻

Arch 7, Westgate Road, NE1 1SA
⊕ splitchimp.pub
House beer (by Three Kings); 4 changing beers (sourced nationally) 🄷
Newcastle's first micropub opened in 2015 in a refurbished railway arch behind Central station opposite the site of the former Federation Brewery. It relocated to this larger arch on Westgate Road in 2016. More spacious than some micropubs and split over two levels, it has six handpumps serving a wide selection of real ales, with one dedicated to the house beer, Clever Chimp 2, from nearby Errant Brewery. A selection of real ciders is also available, as well as foreign bottled beers. Winter opening hours may vary. ᔆ⇌ᘒ(Central)♣♠❀☎

Strawberry 🅛

7 Strawberry Place, NE1 4SF
☎ (0191) 232 6865 ⊕ thestrawberrypub.co.uk
Caledonian Deuchars IPA; 4 changing beers (sourced nationally) 🅗
A single-room pub directly opposite St James' Park, the Strawberry gets busy on match days. The walls are covered in Newcastle United memorabilia, and silent TV screens show sporting events. A new roof terrace with canopies and heaters overlooks the city centre. Two guest beers are available, and above-average food at below-average prices is served all day. Check out the giant filled Yorkshire puddings.
👶🍴🕐♿≠♀(St James)♣P🕏

Town Mouse Ale House 🅛

Basement, 11 St Mary's Place, NE1 7PG
⊕ townmousealehouse.co.uk
6 changing beers (sourced nationally) 🅗
This well-designed micropub is in the basement of what was a coffee shop and has space for around 50 people. The bar area is to the front with more seating to the rear. A large blackboard gives details of the four cask beers and a larger range of keg and bottled beers. Local CAMRA branch Pub of the Year 2019. ✿♀(Haymarket)♣●🐾

Newcastle upon Tyne: Gosforth

County 🅛 ✅

High Street, NE3 1HB
☎ (0191) 285 6919
Draught Bass; Great North Eastern Rivet Catcher; Greene King IPA, Yardbird; Hadrian Border Farne Island Pale Ale; Sharp's Doom Bar; 8 changing beers (sourced nationally) 🅗
A large L-shaped bar with pleasant stained-glass windows on the main road frontage. It attracts a variety of visitors, from office workers to students, and can get busy, especially at weekends. A separate quiet room at the back offers respite from the hustle and bustle of the main bar, and also doubles as a small meeting or function room. Several guest beers are available.
✿●P🚘🐾🕏

Gosforth Hotel 🅛 ✅

High Street, NE3 1HQ
☎ (0191) 285 6617 ⊕ gosforthhotelnewcastle.co.uk
Anarchy Blonde Star; 7 changing beers (sourced nationally) 🅗
Located on the corner of a busy junction at the top of the High Street, this is a stalwart of the lively Gosforth pub scene. Popular with a wide clientele, from nearby office workers to locals and students, the place often gets busy. The rear bar opens at 5pm Monday to Thursday and midday Friday to Sunday. A good range of local ales is always available. 🕐♿♀(Regent Centre)🚘🕏

Newcastle upon Tyne: Heaton

Heaton Tap 🅛

41A Warton Terrace, NE6 5LS
4 changing beers (sourced locally) 🅗
Micropub and bottle shop just off Chillingham Road in Heaton with a newly refurbished lounge area, bar area and outside drinking area. Four real ales are served including some from the wood as well as local ales. The front room has the bottle shop offering a very good range of premium bottled beers.

Newcastle upon Tyne: South Gosforth

Millstone 🅛

Haddricks Mill Road, NE3 1QL
☎ (0191) 285 3429
Allendale Pennine Pale; Anarchy Blonde Star; Draught Bass; 4 changing beers (sourced nationally) 🅗
A modern, stylish two-roomed pub with a lounge to the front and a small public bar to the rear, offering beers from local microbreweries as well as national favourites. Bass has been popular with the regulars for many years. The free-to-hire function room upstairs hosts CAMRA events. Complimentary bar nibbles are served every Sunday from noon. 👶✿🕐P🚘(55)🕏

Victory ✅

43 Killingworth Road, NE3 1SY
☎ (0191) 285 1254 ⊕ victorysouthgosforth.co.uk
Timothy Taylor Landlord; Wainwright; 4 changing beers (sourced nationally) 🅗
Established on this site since 1861, the pub takes its name from Nelson's flagship and once served the local mining community. It is essentially a single room, with two lounge areas each side of the entrance and some seating near the bar. A rear lounge overlooks the Ouseburn river. Food is served daily using locally sourced, fresh ingredients. ✿🕐♿♀P🚘🐾🕏

North Shields

Enigma Tap

60 Bedford Street, NE29 0AR
☎ 07792 822063
4 changing beers (sourced nationally) 🅗
Micropub in a former shop unit just off the main Northumberland Square. There is a seating area near the entrance and a narrower raised area towards the rear incorporating the photograph-covered bar and craft beer tap board. Outside, there is a small patio in the back yard.
👶✿♀♣🚘🐾

Old Ryton Village

Olde Cross

Burnmoor Lane, NE40 3QP
☎ (0191) 447 3460 ⊕ yeoldecross.co.uk
Timothy Taylor Landlord; 3 changing beers (sourced locally; often Firebrick) 🅗
This community-owned inn in the Tyne Valley is an attractive Edwardian half-timbered local in a lovely setting by the village green and the cross it is named after. The original Cross Inn dates from the mid-19th century and was partly rebuilt in 1909. The pub is a centre for the local community, hosting entertainment and activities. Two community events – the hirings, which take place in spring and autumn, and the annual carols at Christmas – are held on the village green. Winner of a CAMRA Pub Saving Award in 2020.
👶♿♣🐾🕏

Ryhope

Guide Post 🅛 ✅

Ryhope Street South, SR2 0RN
☎ (0191) 523 5735 ⊕ theguidepost.co.uk
Maxim Double Maxim; Timothy Taylor Landlord; 2 changing beers (sourced nationally) 🅗
This friendly and popular street-corner local is run by an enthusiastic landlord. There are three handpulls. With a cask ale club, sports TV, a pool table, a Thursday quiz, regular weekend entertainment, dominoes and poker on

Sunday, there is something for everyone. Bar snacks are available. A brewhouse was added to the pub in 2021. At the rear is a pleasant enclosed garden. ⏻❀♣🚪☙♿🛜

South Shields

Cask Lounge 🅛

Charlotte Terrace, NE33 1QQ
☎ 07513 906703
4 changing beers (sourced nationally) Ⓗ
This micropub, a former housing office opposite the town hall, has taken over a coffee shop next door, nearly doubling in size. It is run by an experienced couple who value the principle of the micropub, encouraging conversation by not having TVs or gambling machines. There are five handpulls dispensing changing real ales. The place is light and airy and includes a comfortable sofa, soft carpeting and background music to complete the experience. Close to the public transport interchange. ♿🚃🚪🛜

Marine 🅛

230 Ocean Road, NE33 2JQ
☎ (0191) 455 0280
Allendale Golden Plover; 7 changing beers (sourced nationally) Ⓗ
Large 1840s pub opposite Marine Park, near the seafront. This family-run free house serves eight changing real ales and four real ciders. To the left of the bar are raised areas with plenty of seating, and to the right is a games area. Upstairs is a function room. Unobtrusive background music plays. Pub food is served daily. Local CAMRA Pub of the Year 2021. ◖🚃♣🚪(E1,516)❀🛜

Steamboat 🅛 ✅

Mill Dam, NE33 1EQ (follow signs for Customs House)
☎ (0191) 454 0134
9 changing beers (sourced nationally) Ⓗ
The only pub in the North-East to receive a Golden Award as part of CAMRA's 50th anniversary celebrations, the Steamboat is full of character. The split-level bar and small lounge are decorated with a nautical theme. There is a large selection of cask ales, and 13 handpumps dispense real ales from local and national breweries as well as real ciders. Meet the Brewer events and beer festivals are held, in addition to regular music nights. Q🚃❀❀🛜

Wouldhave ✅

16 Mile End Road, NE33 1TA
☎ (0191) 427 6014
Greene King Abbot; Ruddles Best Bitter; 3 changing beers (sourced nationally) Ⓗ
Named after local boat builder William Wouldhave, co-inventor of the self righting lifeboat, this town-centre Wetherspoon has had a major refit, extending the customer area and creating a new garden. The pub offers well-priced bar meals all day and a selection of real ales from 12 handpumps, with three regular beers and a rotation of guest ales. There are twice-yearly beer festivals. Five minutes from the town-centre public transport interchange. Q⏻◖♿🚪🛜

Sunderland: City Centre

Chaplins

40 Stockton Road, SR1 3NR
☎ (0191) 565 3964
6 changing beers (sourced nationally) Ⓗ
A city-centre pub with six real ale handpulls and one for real cider. The house beer, Happy Chappy, is brewed at nearby Darwin Brewery. Good-value food is served every day. A quiz is held on Thursday evening. There is plenty of seating either side of the main entrance, as well as outside. Some tabletops depict scenes of Sunderland's industrial heritage. Handy for public transport, with Park Lane Interchange two minutes away. ❀◖♿🚃🚪🛜

Chesters 🅛 ✅

Chester Road, SR4 7DR
☎ (0191) 565 9952
6 changing beers (sourced nationally) Ⓗ
This popular pub just outside the city centre has a smart and comfortable interior which had a major refurbishment in 2020. There is a large main bar and a more intimate area at the back. Real ale is dispensed from up to six handpulls, invariably offering an ale from a local brewery. Meals are served all day. Outside there is a large car park and beer garden. A function room with private bar is available upstairs. ⏻❀◖♿🚃(Millfield)🚪🛜

Dun Cow ★ 🅛

High Street West, SR1 3HA
☎ (0191) 567 2262
5 changing beers (sourced nationally) Ⓗ
This Grade II-listed building is an architectural gem and features on CAMRA's National Inventory of Historic Pub Interiors. It was a winner of two CAMRA/Historic England awards for restoration and conservation following a refurbishment in 2014. Since then it has had a major external makeover. Real ale and cider feature on eight handpulls. The pub is next to the Sunderland Empire and can get busy around performance times. There is a Tuesday buskers' night and a Thursday quiz. A function room is available upstairs. Q♿🚃(Park Lane)❀🚪🛜

Fitzgeralds 🅛

12-14 Green Terrace, SR1 3PZ
☎ (0191) 567 0852
Titanic Plum Porter; 8 changing beers (sourced nationally) Ⓗ
A Grade II-listed pub that has been in the Good Beer Guide since 1983. It serves two regular beers complemented by up to six guest beers. The pub comprises a large main bar offering a number of seating areas and a smaller, quieter nautically themed Chart Room. Meals are served daily until early evening. Now owned by the Ladhur Group, the pub has retained its old name. Also known as Fitzies. ⏻❀◖🚃🚪🛜

Ivy House

7A Worcester Terrace, SR2 7AW
☎ (0191) 567 3399 🌐 ivyhousesunderland.co.uk
6 changing beers (sourced nationally) Ⓗ
Tucked away and close to Park Lane public transport interchange, the Ivy House is well worth seeking out. Six changing guest ales feature, plus an extensive range of international bottled beers. Home-made pizzas and burgers are prepared in an open kitchen. It has a weekday happy hour from 5pm, themed meal nights and a Wednesday night quiz. Live music features on the second Saturday and last Sunday of the month. Recipient of a CAMRA Lockdown Hero Award. ❀◖♿🚃(Park Lane) 🚪❀🛜

Ship Isis 🅛

26 Silksworth Row, SR1 3QJ
☎ (0191) 514 7684
9 changing beers (sourced nationally) Ⓗ
The Ship Isis was restored to its original Victorian splendour by the former Jarrow Brewery in 2011. With knowledgeable staff, the pub has seven handpumps offering five cask beers and two real ciders. An extensive selection of bottled beers and craft gins means there is something for everyone. Opposite the main bar is a

quieter lounge, with extra seating upstairs at weekends. There is live music on Sundays, a Monday quiz and Wednesday is buskers' night. ♿≠ଛ(Millfield)●🖳🌺🛜

Sunderland: North

Avenue

Zetland Street, SR6 0EQ (just off Roker Avenue)
☎ (0191) 567 7412
6 changing beers (sourced nationally) Ⓗ
Fifteen minutes' walk from the Stadium of Light, this local pub is tucked away just off Roker Avenue. There are up to six varying real ale handpulls, both local and national. Several real ciders are also available. Themed nights include Wednesday pool, a popular Thursday night quiz, and a Sunday domino handicap. The former upstairs games room is now a restaurant. The Avenue was the regional CAMRA Cider Pub for 2020.
🌺🌘♣●P🖳(E1)🌺🛜

Harbour View

SR6 0NU
☎ (0191) 567 1402
6 changing beers (sourced nationally) Ⓗ
The Harbour View is a modern local pub with six handpulls whose beers change frequently. The cask ales are chosen by some of the regulars and a tally of beers to date from 1 January is displayed behind the bar; the aim is to have in excess of 600 ales in one year. The cask ale club meets every Wednesday evening. This is a relaxing place with additional seating outside to take in the sun.
🌺🖳(E1,18)🌺

Lighthouse Ⓛ

7 Sea Road, Fulwell, SR6 9BP
Maxim Double Maxim; 2 changing beers (sourced nationally) Ⓗ
Sunderland's first micropub is in the centre of Fulwell. A former café, the place has been transformed into a small but comfortable bar. It has three handpulls and three keg fonts. There is an outdoor drinking area at the rear and a small room upstairs. It features no TV, no gaming machines and no music, just conversation. There are frequent buses nearby to Sunderland and South Shields. Seaburn Metro is 10 minutes' walk. Q🌺🌺ଛ(Seaburn)🖳🌺

Swalwell

Owa the Road

Unit 1, Spencer House, Market Lane, NE16 3DS
4 changing beers (sourced nationally) Ⓗ
Situated within the old Co-op building directly opposite the Sun Inn, this micropub has no music and no TV. It does have four changing beers on handpull though, two of which are generally beers from the wood. The owner is working with a number of breweries to bring beers to the pub that are not normally found in wooden casks. Real ciders are served from boxes. Local CAMRA branch Cider Pub of the Year 2020. Q●P🌺

Sun Inn ✅

Market Lane, NE16 3AL
6 changing beers (sourced nationally) Ⓗ
A hostelry in the heart of the historic village that spawned many internationally renowned engineers and industrialists, and of course the famous Swalwell cabbage. This truly no-nonsense community pub provides good company for locals and strangers alike. Sword dancers, darts, dominoes handicaps, a monthly pie competition and a buskers' night all feature. Bar food and snacks are available, free on Sunday. There is a regular bus service from Newcastle. 🕭🌺♣●🖳🌺

Tynemouth

Tynemouth Lodge Hotel Ⓛ

Tynemouth Road, NE30 4AA
☎ (0191) 257 7565 ⊕ tynemouthlodgehotel.co.uk
Caledonian Deuchars IPA; Draught Bass; Hadrian Border Tyneside Blonde; Marston's Pedigree; 1 changing beer (sourced locally) Ⓗ
This externally tiled 1799 free house, next to a former house of correction, has featured in every issue of the Guide since 1983. The comfortable one-room pub has a U-shaped lounge with the bar on one side and a serving hatch on the other, and is noted in the area for its Draught Bass. It's a pub with no TV, no music and no gaming machines. An ideal stopping-off point for those completing the Coast-to-Coast cycle route.
Q🌺🌺ଛP🖳(1,1A)🛜

Tynemouth Social Club Ⓛ

15/16 Front Street, NE30 4DX
☎ (0191) 257 7542
2 changing beers (sourced nationally) Ⓗ
Formerly a Co-op, this well-established social club at the heart of Tynemouth has a full pub licence and welcomes visitors. After several attempts to sell real ale, the club now has a rotating guest beer policy which has stimulated demand. The ale is well kept by the bar/cellarman and the club is well worth a visit. Local CAMRA Club of the Year 2019. ଛ●🖳🛜

Wallsend

Ritz Ⓛ ✅

87/93 High Street West, NE28 8JD
☎ (0191) 296 9600
Greene King Abbot; Ruddles Best Bitter; Sharp's Doom Bar; 4 changing beers (sourced nationally) Ⓗ
A welcome addition to Wallsend High Street, this pub opened in 2015. The building was originally the Ritz cinema and later a bingo hall before Wetherspoon took it over. Entering from the High Street, the original period decoration can be seen. Quiz night is Monday. There is a large car park at the rear. 🕭🌺🌘♿●🛜

Washington

Courtyard Ⓛ

Biddick Lane, NE38 8AB
☎ (0191) 417 0445 ⊕ artscentrewashington.co.uk/courtyard.aspx
8 changing beers (sourced nationally) Ⓗ
Located within the Washington Arts Centre, this light and airy café/bar offers a warm welcome to drinkers and food lovers alike. Up to eight changing handpulls serve real ales from local, regional and national brewers. An extensive range of food is served from noon up to early evening. Outdoor seating is available within the spacious courtyard which includes a large marquee. Popular beer festivals are usually held over the Easter and August bank holidays. 🕭🌺🌘♿P🖳🌺🛜

Sir William de Wessyngton ✅

2-3 Victoria Road, NE37 2SY
☎ (0191) 418 0100
Greene King Abbot; Maxim Maximus; Ruddles Best Bitter; Sharp's Doom Bar; 4 changing beers (sourced nationally) Ⓗ
This large open-plan Wetherspoon used to be a snooker hall and ice cream parlour. It is named after a Norman knight and lord of the manor whose descendants later emigrated to the United States. The pub offers value-for-money beer and the usual well-priced Wetherspoon menu. The regular ales are complemented by at least

four guests. Twice-yearly beer festivals are held. A large selection of local and international bottled beers is available. Recipient of a CAMRA Lockdown Hero Recognition Award. Q⏱❀◗&P☷♿

Steps
47 Spout Lane, NE38 7HP
☎ (0191) 415 0733
5 changing beers (sourced nationally) Ⓗ
In part of the Washington Village conservation area and opened in 1894 as the Spout Lane Inn, the pub was renamed the Steps in 1976. The small, comfortable and friendly single-room lounge bar is divided into two drinking areas, with pictures of old Washington decorating the walls. Five varying beers are on tap, often selected by the regulars, with some from local microbreweries. A quiz is held on Tuesday night, and live entertainment features every first and last Saturday of the month. Opening hours may vary. Q❀♣P☷(84)♿

West Boldon

Black Horse
Rectory Bank, NE36 0QQ (off A184)
☎ (0191) 536 1814
Harviestoun Bitter & Twisted; 1 changing beer (sourced nationally) Ⓗ
Iconic coaching inn-style pub which has recently had a covered seating area added to the frontage, the pub can trace its history back at least to the early 1700s. The inside is split between a bar/lounge and restaurant, with the walls decorated with bric-a-brac and photos taken by the owner. Normally on sale is Harviestoun Bitter and Twisted plus a guest. Meals can also be taken in the bar and outside for customers with dogs; there is also a take-away service available. ◗&P☷

Whickham

One Eyed Stag 🅛
5 The Square, NE16 4JB
☎ 07811 261924
5 changing beers (sourced nationally) Ⓗ
A fairly recent addition to the pubs in Whickham, this micropub has a tile-topped bar with four handpumps serving beer from local microbreweries. Blackboards adorn the wall behind the bar giving details of the beers

and other drinks available. There is an interesting light fitting covering most of the ceiling and an electric stove in an alcove to the right. &P❀♿

Whitburn

Blues Micropub 🅛
Percy Terrace, SR6 7EW
4 changing beers (sourced nationally) Ⓗ
This micropub opened in 2020. There are four cask handpulls, often featuring local beers. Real cider is available. The room above is a bottle shop and there is an outdoor seating area. A cask club is held very Wednesday, Thursday is Pie and a Pint night, and there is a free cheeseboard every Sunday. This is a small, friendly place encouraging conversation, with no TVs or gaming machines. Q●☷❀

Whitley Bay

Dog & Rabbit 🅛
36 Park View, NE26 2TH
☎ 07944 552716
4 changing beers (sourced nationally) Ⓗ
This bar and brewery, converted from a women's clothing shop, adds to a number of pubs in the area. The corner bar has four handpumps, for most of the time serving local beers. The owner's microbrewery has been installed in the pub brewing Dog & Rabbit beers. With no music, Wi-Fi or sports TV, conversation is encouraged among visitors. Local CAMRA Pub of the Year 2020.
Q⏱♿(Monkseaton) ●☷❀

Split Chimp 🅛
Unit 1, Ground Floor, Spanish City Dome, Marine Avenue, NE26 1BG
⊕ splitchimp.pub
House beer (by Errant); 4 changing beers (sourced nationally) Ⓗ
Opened in early 2019, this micropub occupies one of the external units of the recently refurbished Spanish City and overlooks the promenade along the North Sea coast. The single room has a long bar counter facing the entrance, with seating around the periphery. The house beer from Three Kings is supplemented by a changing range of four beers from near and far. Winter opening hours vary – check ahead of your visit. ⏱❀&●☷❀♿

Reading the runes

There are terms and expressions used in the pub trade that need to be translated into a language understood by consumers.

Wet pub doesn't mean the roof leaks but indicates that beer and other alcohols are the main feature, rather than food.

Stillage is a cradle or platform in the pub cellar where casks of beer are stored horizontally while a secondary fermentation takes place.

Barrel behind the bar is a widely-used description but usually inappropriate as a barrel is a large 36-gallon container, too big to store at bar level. The correct term for a container for real ale is cask and casks come in several sizes: 4 and a half gallon pins; nine-gallon firkin; 18-gallon kilderkin; 36-gallon barrels; and 54-gallon hogshead. Hogsheads are rare. Most pubs use firkins and kilderkins these days. If a cask is used at bar level to serve a seasonal beer such as winter ale, it's likely to be a pin.

Beer **served by gravity** means it comes straight from the cask and is not drawn by a beer engine and handpump.

Tight sparkler is a small device containing a mesh that's screwed to the nozzle of a beer engine operated by a handpump on the bar. The sparkler agitates the beer as it enters the glass and creates the tight, thick head of foam preferred by northern drinkers.

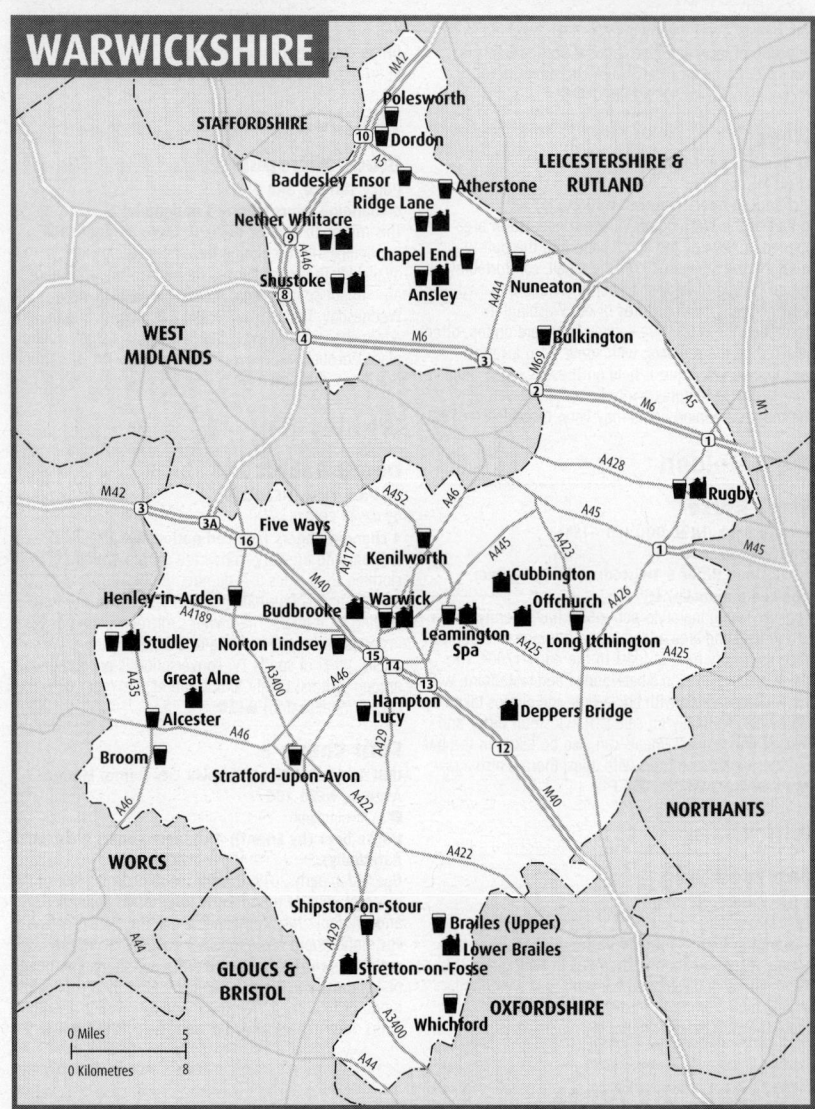

WARWICKSHIRE

STAFFORDSHIRE

Polesworth
Dordon
10
Baddesley Ensor
Ridge Lane
Atherstone
Nether Whitacre
9
Chapel End
Shustoke
8
Ansley
Nuneaton

LEICESTERSHIRE & RUTLAND

WEST MIDLANDS

Bulkington

Rugby

Five Ways
16
Kenilworth
Henley-in-Arden
Budbrooke
Warwick
Cubbington
Offchurch
Studley
Norton Lindsey
Leamington Spa
Long Itchington
Great Alne
15 14
Alcester
13
Hampton Lucy
Deppers Bridge
Broom
12
Stratford-upon-Avon

NORTHANTS

WORCS

Shipston-on-Stour
Brailes (Upper)
Lower Brailes
Stretton-on-Fosse
Whichford

GLOUCS & BRISTOL

OXFORDSHIRE

0 Miles 5
0 Kilometres 8

Alcester

Turk's Head
4 High Street, B49 5AD
☎ (01789) 765948 ⊕ theturkshead.net
**Wye Valley HPA; 3 changing beers (sourced
nationally; often Purity, Salopian, Skinner's)** Ⓗ
Central to the town, this busy pub is dedicated to real ale
and is well worth a visit, with its bare wood floors,
exposed beams and roaring log fires. Beers served are
from local breweries as well as Shropshire, Yorkshire and
south Wales. Good food is a daily feature; there is a
separate dining room as well as a quiet garden. It
provides a street bar during annual town festivals.
Q❄️🛏️🍴🐕♿🍺🚗♣️🎵🛜

Ansley

Lord Nelson Inn Ⓛ ✅
Birmingham Road, CV10 9PQ

☎ (024) 7639 2305 ⊕ thelordnelsoninnansley.co.uk
**Sperrin Ansley Mild, Head Hunter, Band of Brothers,
Third Party, Thick as Thieves; 3 changing beers** Ⓗ
This nautically themed inn has been run by the Sperrin
family since 1974, incorporating a brewery at the rear of
the building since 2012. Nine handpulls dispense its own
Sperrin brews plus guests. There is an extensive food
menu with meal nights and tribute nights hosted. A
monthly quiz is held in the Victory restaurant. The
suntrap courtyard garden is a venue for a beer festival
and barbecue in August. 🛏️❄️🍴🐕♿🅿️🚗♣️🛜

Atherstone

Angel Ale House Ⓛ
24 Church Street, CV9 1HA
☎ 07525 183056
**Leatherbritches Mad Ruby; Oakham Citra; 4 changing
beers** Ⓗ

This attractive pub on the market square is a frequent local CAMRA Pub of the Year winner. Its interior features an inglenook fireplace with log-burning stove. The pub offers six real ales, often local and always including a dark beer, plus up to 10 real ciders. Music is via customer select-and-play from a large vinyl LP collection. There is a large free council car park to the rear. ⊛≠⊛P🛏️⌖

Baddesley Ensor

Red Lion

The Common, CV9 2BT (from Grendon roundabout on A5 go S up Boot Hill) SP273983
☎ (01827) 718186
Draught Bass; Greene King Abbot; Marston's Pedigree; 3 changing beers Ⓗ
Popular village pub where food does not feature, just ale and conversation. The landlord has been here for more than 20 years. Comfy seating and a log fire are enhanced by a music-free environment. Three guest ales are served, often from major concerns such as Greene King and Everards, but sometimes from small local breweries. The sparkler is willingly removed on request. Off-road parking is available opposite. Lunchtime opening is weekends only. Q♣⊛🛏️⌖

Brailes (Upper)

Gate Inn Ⓛ

OX15 5AX (on B4035, 3 miles from Shipston towards Banbury)
☎ 07973 853149
3 changing beers (sourced locally) Ⓗ
Traditional rustic free house with immense character. Well regarded and busy, it features a log fire in winter and a huge garden. Three cask ales are always served, along with Napton Recipe No.3 cask cider. Food is limited to crisps and nuts served at the bar, but customers are welcome to bring their own – the landlord will supply plates and cutlery. Q⊛♣⊛P🛏️(3A)⌖🤶

Broom

Broom Tavern Ⓛ

32 High Street, B50 4HL
☎ (01789) 778199 ⊕ broomtavern.co.uk
Purity Pure UBU; Wye Valley HPA; 2 changing beers Ⓗ
A lovely brick and timber multi-room building retaining a great amount of character. It has been tastefully made over while keeping the cosy snug and log fire in winter. It serves great food lunchtimes and evenings, made with local ingredients. Local beers are frequently found here along with at least one real cider. There is a choice of beer gardens. Q⊛◑♣⌖

Bulkington

Weavers' Arms

12 Long Street, CV12 9JZ
☎ (024) 7631 4415 ⊕ weaversarms.co.uk
Draught Bass; 1 changing beer Ⓗ
Family-owned, two-roomed village pub converted from weavers' cottages. It has a wood-panelled games room, log-burning fireplace and slate floor. Outside, the extensive, well-kept beer garden hosts barbecues in the summer. Children are welcome and private functions can be catered for. The Pork Pie Club, Weavers Walkers and Hillbilly Golf Society hold regular meetings here. 🛏️⊛♣🛏️(56)⌖⌖

Chapel End

Salutation

Chancery Lane, CV10 0PB
☎ (024) 7704 7573
Draught Bass; 2 changing beers Ⓗ
Chapel End used to have five pubs but now only the Sally remains. A popular, sports-oriented inn, it shows major football, rugby and boxing matches on TV. Quizzes and other events take place in this community award-winning establishment as well as traditional pub games. Live bands perform regularly, usually on Saturday night or Sunday late afternoon. Bass is always available, along with guest beers from all over. 🛏️♣P⊛⌖⌖

Dordon

Mini Miner

13 Browns Lane, B78 1TR
☎ 07455 242415
3 changing beers (often Church End) Ⓗ
Now the only pub in Dordon, this small, single-roomed bar in a parade of shops and takeaways provides much-needed refreshment for local drinkers. Its name refers to a former pub in the village, the Merrie Miner, later renamed the Cuckoo's Rest before closing for good. The arty wall decor themes are a curious mix of mining and the classic film, The Italian Job. Two or three ales are served, typically including a local beer and a well-known brew. 🛏️♣P🛏️(65)⌖

Five Ways

Case is Altered Ⓛ

Case Lane, Five Ways, Haseley, CV35 7JD (off Five Ways Rd near A4141/A4177 jnct) SP225701
☎ (01926) 484206 ⊕ caseisaltered.com
Old Pie Factory Pie in the Sky; Wye Valley Butty Bach; 3 changing beers (sourced locally) Ⓗ
A classic unspoilt country pub with a bar and separate snug, identified by CAMRA as having a historic pub interior of regional importance. The current landlady has been here for more than 30 years, after taking over from her grandmother. The traditional bar billiards table still takes old sixpences, which have to be bought from the bar. Monday is cribbage night. A propeller from a World War I fighter plane is on the ceiling. Q⊛&♣P

Hampton Lucy

Boar's Head Ⓛ ✅

Church Street, CV35 8BE
☎ (01789) 840533 ⊕ theboarsheadhamptonlucy.com

Ringwood Razorback; 4 changing beers (sourced locally; often Church End, North Cotswold, Slaughterhouse) ⓗ
A friendly, popular village pub dating back to the 17th century. Situated on a Sustrans route and close to the River Avon, the pub is frequented by cyclists, walkers and visitors to nearby Charlecote Park. Five real ales are served including at least two LocAles. The menu offers fresh, locally sourced, home-made food. The walled rear garden is popular in good weather. An annual themed beer festival is held in late May. ⏰🕙🅿🍴🐾⛶

Henley-in-Arden

Three Tuns
103 High Street, B95 5AT
☎ (01564) 792723
Church End Goat's Milk; Fuller's London Pride; Sharp's Doom Bar, Atlantic; Wye Valley Butty Bach ⓗ
A small, unpretentious 16th-century inn with a single bar serving two rooms. Popular with locals, this drinkers' pub is usually busy and the atmosphere is always friendly. Five real ales are served in consistently good condition. Pub snacks plus home-made cobs and sausage rolls are usually available. Parking is on the main street.
Q🌳🛇♿🚭🚌(X20) 🐾⛶

White Swan ✪
100 High Street, B95 5BY
☎ (01564) 792623 🌐 thewhiteswanhotel.com
St Austell Tribute; Sharp's Doom Bar; Wadworth Horizon; 1 changing beer (often Purity) ⓗ
An inn has existed on this site since 1352 – the current building was erected between 1550 and 1565. Locals claim to have seen a ghostly child roaming around. The main bar is a cosy, attractive space with many exposed original beams and a real fire. Good-quality, home-cooked food is served to complement the excellently kept ales. The rear area is now a Stoneaged Steakhouse restaurant, serving food Monday to Saturday.
Q🌳🌸🛏🕙♿🚭🅿🚌(X20) ⛶

Kenilworth

Ale Rooms & Gin Bar ⓛ
7 Smalley Place, CV8 1QG (opp clock tower)
☎ (01926) 854585
5 changing beers (sourced regionally; often Church End, Silhill) ⓗ
A small pub located in what was once a shop opposite the clock at the end of Warwick Road, the town's main street. A relatively new edition to the Kenilworth pub scene, it has become deservedly popular not only for the variety of real ales on offer, but also for real cider in summer, craft keg beers and gins. There is an upstairs chill-out lounge and a comfortable patio seating area at the front. 🌳♿🚭🍴🚌(11,X17)⛶

Gauntlet ✪
8 Oaks Precinct, Caesar Road, CV8 1DP
☎ (01926) 852110 🌐 gauntletkenilworth.co.uk
Robinsons Trooper; St Austell Proper Job; Sharp's Sea Fury; 1 changing beer (sourced regionally) ⓗ
A recently updated 1960s estate pub with a contemporary feel, set in a quiet part of town. It is believed to be the only English pub with this name. The licensee has extensive local experience in the trade and the pub is inclusive and welcoming of the local community and beyond. The quality home-cooked food, served daily, is particularly popular at weekends when it is available all day. Not far from the Talisman Theatre.
🌳🕙🕙♿🅿🐾⛶

Old Bakery ⓛ
12 High Street, CV8 1LZ (near A429/A452 jct)
☎ (01926) 864111 🌐 theoldbakerykenilworth.co.uk
Wye Valley HPA; 3 changing beers (sourced regionally) ⓗ
In the heart of the old town, this small two-roomed former bakery is cosy and welcoming, with beams and rustic furniture. It has a good mix of locals and visitors, with conversation the main entertainment. The owners plan to broaden the variety of beer styles and strengths further, and to extend the opening hours and offer lunchtime snacks and afternoon teas. Wheelchair access is to the rear. Accommodation is offered in 14 en-suite rooms. Q🌸🛏♿🅿🚌(11)🐾⛶

Leamington Spa

Benjamin Satchwell ✪
112/114 The Parade, CV32 4AQ (almost opp town hall)
☎ (01926) 883733
Greene King Abbot; Ruddles Best Bitter; Sharp's Doom Bar; 4 changing beers ⓗ
Named after a renowned local benefactor who discovered Leamington's second spa spring in 1784, this pub bears all the hallmarks of the Wetherspoon style. Converted from two shops, it is large, stretching back to Bedford Street. The building's split levels have been used well to create comfortable seating areas. The upper level hosts an impressively long bar. Wall panels depict local history and personalities. 🌳🕙♿🚭🍴🚌⛶

New Inn ✪
197 Leam Terrace, CV31 1DW
☎ (01926) 422861 🌐 thenewinnleamington.co.uk
Eagle IPA; Sharp's Doom Bar, Atlantic, Sea Fury; 2 changing beers (often Byatt's) ⓗ
A traditional pub in a wide Victorian terrace on the outskirts of town. The original pub has been extended into the next-door property. A central door opens directly onto the bar, with a seating area to the left and a games area to the right leading to an extension at the rear. Outside is a good-sized walled garden. Quality home-cooked food is served. A quiz is hosted fortnightly on a Wednesday as well as other events including hosting local bands and entertainment.
🌳🕙🕙♿♣🚌(63,64) 🐾⛶

White Horse ⓛ ✪
4-6 Clarendon Avenue, CV32 5PZ
☎ (01926) 426892 🌐 thewhitehorseleamingtonspa.co.uk
Purity Pure UBU; Sharp's Doom Bar; 4 changing beers ⓗ
Popular town pub that dates back to the 1830s and has been enlarged and modified over the years. The extended section now holds the main bar, serving a large selection of cask, craft and continental beers, while the original bar area is reserved for private functions. An arched stable entrance featuring a full-sized white horse leads to a courtyard and beer garden with covered and heated seating. 🌳🕙🕙♿♣🍴⛶

Woodland Tavern ⓛ
3 Regent Street, CV32 5HW
☎ (01926) 425868
Slaughterhouse Saddleback Best Bitter; Timothy Taylor Landlord; 2 changing beers ⓗ
A traditional Victorian street-corner pub situated close to the centre of Leamington Spa and enjoyed by locals and visitors alike. It has a public bar and a separate lounge, also used as a function room. The unique partially covered courtyard features murals depicting local references and jokes. On the side of the building is a

large, colourful mural showing a dray and horses delivering ale to the pub. Real cider is from Napton Cidery. ✿&≒♣♠☕😺🐾🛜

Long Itchington

Harvester L

6 Church Road, CV47 9PE (off A423 at village pond then first left)

☎ (01926) 812698 ⊕ theharvesterinn.co.uk

3 changing beers Ⓗ

White-fronted pub near the village pond, on the corner of the square. Inside is a main bar, a small drinking area and a restaurant specialising in good-value steaks. The ale range changes frequently, usually supporting smaller breweries. Real cider and a Belgian fruit beer are also stocked. It hosts a beer festival each May bank holiday. A large walled courtyard garden to the rear has a wood-fired pizza oven. ঌ❀⊛◑&▲♠🛒(64)😺🛜

Nether Whitacre

Dog Inn

Dog Lane, B46 2DU SP232930

☎ (01675) 481318

Castle Rock Harvest Pale; Sharp's Doom Bar; Wye Valley Butty Bach; 1 changing beer (sourced nationally; often Castle Rock) Ⓗ

A well-hidden black and white country pub, popular both with drinkers and diners. Its characterful interior features two intimate dining rooms. Brass knick-knacks abound, and there are two hefty log fires in winter. Occasional ales from the tiny on-site Whitacre Brewing Company disappear quickly. Half pints are sold at a premium – try-before-you-buy is offered on all ales. Free bar nibbles are provided Sunday lunchtimes. The peaceful beer garden includes a pets' corner. ঌ❀◑P😺🛜

Norton Lindsey

New Inn L ✔

Main Street, CV35 8JA

☎ (01926) 258411 ⊕ thenewinn.pub

Greene King IPA; Timothy Taylor Landlord; 2 changing beers (sourced locally; often Church End, M&B, Slaughterhouse) Ⓗ

Warwickshire's first community-owned pub opened in 2017 after fundraising resulted in it being saved from closure; it was purchased by a collective of more than 200 people. Located on a street corner in the heart of the village, it features an open-plan interior with a wooden floor that gives a light and airy feel. Food is locally sourced, with many specials on offer. Circular walks start and end here. Q঍❀◑P😺

Nuneaton

Felix Holt L ✔

3 Stratford Street, CV11 5BS

☎ (024) 7634 7785

Byatt's Regal Blond; Greene King Abbot; Oakham Citra; Ruddles Best Bitter; Sharp's Doom Bar; changing beers Ⓗ

Large Wetherspoon outlet in the town centre. The pub takes its name from a novel by George Eliot and the literary theme is reflected in the decor of books and pictures of local history. Look out for the comical metal sculptures on the walls. A good range of guest beers includes local ales. Food is served throughout the day. Outside are tables and chairs for alfresco drinking and eating, plus a heated area for smokers. Q঍❀◑&≒🛒🛜

Lord Hop L

38 Queens Road, CV11 5JX

☎ (024) 7798 1869 ⊕ lordhopnuneaton.co.uk

4 changing beers Ⓗ

Town-centre micropub on two levels, the upper one boasting settees, a small library and board games. Four or more real ales are served on handpull or straight from the cask, both from local and national breweries, alongside up to eight ciders or perries in the chiller, plus up to four KeyKeg lines. Wine, gins, bottled lager and soft drinks are also sold. Snacks are available, or bring your own takeaway. CAMRA magazines are provided for reading. No under-18s, and assistance dogs only. Local CAMRA Pub of the Year and Cider Pub of the Year. Q≒🛒🛜

Rose Inn

Coton Road, CV11 5TW (opp Our Lady of the Angels Catholic church)

☎ (024) 7674 2991

Banks's Amber Ale; Marston's Pedigree Ⓗ

This is the pub CAMRA chose as the venue for its first AGM. The L-shaped lounge houses a pool table and the front bar has a dartboard. Outside at the rear is a paved, partially covered and heated area for alfresco drinkers and smokers, with a border planted with roses and shrubs. Across the road is Riversley Park and Nuneaton Museum. Q঍❀◑♣P🛒(41,48)😺

Polesworth

Bull's Head

Tamworth Road, B78 1JH (by canal bridge on B5000)

☎ (01827) 898990

3 changing beers (sourced nationally) Ⓗ

Welcoming community local attracting boaters from the nearby canal. It comprises a traditional bar and a small lounge featuring unusual arches. Drinks served in the lounge usually include two or three real ales plus one real cider. With no music, the pub is a conversational hub except now and again when sport is screened. Games, quizzes and raffles are popular. Snacks are offered on darts nights and other occasions. ♣♠P🛒😺🛜

Ridge Lane

Church End Brewery Tap L

CV10 0RD (2 miles SW of Atherstone)

☎ (01827) 713080 ⊕ churchendbrewery.co.uk

Church End Goat's Milk, Gravediggers Ale, What the Fox's Hat, Fallen Angel; 4 changing beers Ⓗ

This brewery tap is hidden from the road, with access opposite Tom Piper Close. The brewery is visible from the bar area. Eight handpulls serve the bar and vestry, with a mild always among the beers. Ciders are dispensed direct from the barrel. Children are allowed in the vestry until 6pm, and are welcome in the meadow garden. Events include a monthly quiz night. Q✿&AP🛒😺🛜

Rugby

Merchants Inn L

5-6 Little Church Street, CV21 3AW

☎ (01788) 571119

Nethergate Venture; Oakham Bishops Farewell; Purity Mad Goose Ⓗ**; 6 changing beers (sourced nationally)** Ⓗ/Ⓖ

Busy town-centre pub frequented by a varied local clientele. Flagstone floors and an open fire greet you on entering – the interior is a museum of brewery memorabilia. Food is served Monday to Saturday, and traditional roasts on Sunday. Rugby and cricket are popular on the TV. Activities held around the calendar include Belgian and German nights, beer festivals and gin and cider weekends. ☺⊛⊙⊛♣●🗑🖳🐾🛈 🛜

Rugby Tap Room Ⓛ

4 St Matthews Street, CV21 3BY (close to town centre adjacent to A426 gyratory)
☎ 07540 490377 ⊕ rugbytap.com
Changing beers (sourced locally; often Byatt's, Church End, Phipps NBC) Ⓖ
Micropub featuring a long room with a large selection of gravity-served draught ales and ciders racked at the far end. The atmosphere promotes conversation and there is no electronic entertainment, although acoustic music is performed on Thursday evening. The pub serves up to six LocAles plus canned craft beers. Traditional pub snacks are available. There is outside seating at the front.
Q☺≂♣●🖳🐾🛈 🛜

Seven Stars

40 Albert Square, CV21 2SH
☎ (01788) 535478 ⊕ sevenstarsrugby.co.uk
Byatt's Platinum Blonde; Everards Tiger; 7 changing beers (sourced nationally) Ⓗ
The 14 handpumps here dispense ales including milds, stouts and porters, plus four ciders. Food features an impressive selection of pub-made Scotch eggs, which sell out quickly, plus filled rolls and locally produced pork pies. All can be enjoyed in the rear courtyard garden. Rugby is popular on the bar's TV. A frequent winner of local CAMRA Pub of the Year. No children after 7pm.
Q☺≂⊛≈♣●🖳🐾🛈 🛜

Squirrel Inn Ⓛ

33 Church Street, CV21 3PU
☎ (01788) 578527
4 changing beers (sourced nationally; often Dow Bridge, Marston's, Pitchfork) Ⓗ
A warm welcome is guaranteed at this historic free house, Rugby's jewel in the town. A real fire and pictures of old Rugby contribute to the intimate ambience. Ales from Dow Bridge, Cotleigh, Pitchfork and 3D breweries are frequently served alongside Marston's beers and four ciders. Live music is a regular attraction, with various genres performed on Saturday evening and an open mic night on Wednesday. Poetry features on the last Sunday of the month. ♣●🖳🐾🛈 🛜

Town & County Ⓛ

12 Henry Street, CV21 2QA
☎ 07487 413960
Church End Gravediggers Ale; Greene King IPA; 2 changing beers (sourced nationally; often Donnington, Otter, Timothy Taylor) Ⓗ
Small town-centre club which has been trading since 1933 and is making its fourth appearance in this Guide. Its four handpumps include two dispensing changing guest ales from breweries near and far. The club hosts dominoes and skittles teams, and holds regular events including Tuesday bingo and monthly quizzes, plus occasional live music and coach trips. CAMRA members are welcome and guests may be signed in. Q☺♣🖳🐾

Victoria Inn Ⓛ

1 Lower Hillmorton Road, CV21 3ST
☎ (01788) 544374
Atomic Strike; Hook Norton Hooky; 5 changing beers (sourced nationally; often Abbeydale, Atomic, Titanic) Ⓗ
A beautiful Victorian pub just outside the town centre – a true gem and the last of its kind in the town. Built in a wedge shape, the multi-roomed local features a traditional bar, larger lounge and two relatively new

snugs. Owned by the town's Atomic Brewery, the pub offers two of its beers plus five rotating guests. It shows sport on TV and hosts quiz nights on Wednesday and Sunday. ☺⊛♣🖳🐾🛈 🛜

Windmill Inn

1 North Street, CV21 2AB (town centre near clock tower)
☎ (01788) 547142
Black Country Bradley's Finest Golden, Pig on the Wall, Fireside; 9 changing beers (sourced nationally) Ⓗ
The Windmill is a 19th-century coaching inn reopened by Black Country Ales after a decade of closure. The interior has been completely refurbished but has the appearance of a long-established traditional pub. There is a small courtyard at the rear. Bar snacks consist of fresh cobs, pork pie and sausage rolls. Four beers from Black Country Ales, eight guest ales, and three changing ciders or perries are served on handpump. ☺⊛≈♣●🖳🐾🛈 🛜

Shipston-on-Stour

Black Horse Inn Ⓛ

Station Road, CV36 4BT
☎ (01608) 238489 ⊕ blackhorseshipston.co.uk
Prescott Hill Climb; Wye Valley Butty Bach; 3 changing beers (sourced regionally; often Courage, Uley, Young's) Ⓗ
This stone-built 15th-century inn is the oldest pub and only thatched building in Shipston, with a licence dating back to 1540. Its cosy lounge has a friendly feel with a large inglenook log fire. Traditional pub games are popular in the left-hand bar, and sport is shown on TV. The excellent Thai restaurant operates a take-away service. The enclosed rear garden has a large decking area, welcomes both children and dogs, and hosts live music in summer. Q☺⊛⊙♣●P🖳🐾🛈 🛜

Thirst Edition

46B Church Street, CV36 4AS
☎ (01608) 664974 ⊕ thirstedition.co.uk
4 changing beers (sourced regionally; often Burton Bridge, Byatt's, Iron Pier) Ⓖ
A micropub in this small market town serving up to four real ales, mostly local or regional, straight from the cask. Real ciders, craft beers, wines and six gins are also available. Since opening in 2018 the pub has offered well over 350 real ales. It hosts regular live music including a singalong on the last Sunday of the month. The free-to-enter Thursday quiz has raised more than £3,000 for local causes. Bus 50 from Stratford stops outside.
Q♿♣●🖳(50) 🐾🛜

Shustoke

Griffin Inn Ⓛ

Church Road, B46 2LB (on B4116 on sharp bend)
☎ (01675) 481205
Freestyle Griffin Dark; Oakham Citra; Theakston Old Peculier; Wye Valley Butty Bach; 8 changing beers (sourced nationally; often Freestyle, Oakham) Ⓗ
A renowned real ale venue with more than 25 consecutive years in this Guide. Its interior features a stone bar, inglenook fireplaces and beams decorated with old beer mats. No music is played. The pub serves up to eight guest beers, usually including Freestyle ales from the adjacent brewery. There is always one real cider, and up to four in summer. Children are welcome on the beer terrace and in the conservatory and meadow-style garden. Home-cooked lunches are served (no food Sun). Q☺⊛⊙Å●P🐾🛜

Stratford-upon-Avon

Bear Freehouse L ✅

Swan's Nest Lane, CV37 7LT (S end of Clopton Bridge)
☎ (01789) 265540 ⊕ thebearfreehouse.co.uk
Hook Norton Old Hooky; North Cotswold Shagweaver; Silhill Blonde Star; Wye Valley Butty Bach; house beer (by North Cotswold); 3 changing beers (sourced regionally; often Church End, Purity) Ⓗ
Welcoming and delightful pub on the waterside, five minutes' walk from the town centre. Refurbished with a quiet room and a snug, it features a wood-panelled interior and pewter bar. It dispenses up to eight real ales, some seasonal, with a focus on local and regional brewers. High-quality traditional pub cuisine is served in a friendly atmosphere. Board games are available.
🌞🚪🕪🔥🅿🚪🐶🐾🛜

Garrick ✅

25 High Street, CV37 6AU (opp town hall)
☎ (01789) 292186
Greene King IPA, Abbot; house beer (by Hardys & Hansons); 1 changing beer (sourced regionally; often Greene King, Prescott) Ⓗ
Reputedly the oldest pub in Stratford-upon-Avon, there has been an inn on this site since medieval times. It is Grade II listed with a fine timbered frontage. The interior retains its authentic old-world charm, with irregularly sized rooms, wooden beams and flagstone floors. The cosy front bar is a haunt for locals as well as theatregoers. Well-kept Greene King ales are complemented by regular guests.
Q🌞🕪🔥🌲🔥🚪🐶🐾🛜

Stratford Alehouse L

12B Greenhill Street, CV37 6LF
☎ 07746 807966 ⊕ thestratfordalehouse.com
4 changing beers (sourced nationally; often Byatt's, North Cotswold, Wye Valley) Ⓖ
A family-run, one-bar micropub offering the finest real ales, ciders and wines. There are no gaming machines to distract you here, just a friendly welcome in a relaxing environment for drinking, chatting, making new friends or reading the newspapers. More than 1,380 different beers have been served since the pub opened in 2013. Snacks are available. Occasional TV sport is shown and there may be live music events including the regular Stratford Folk Club – check the website for details.
Q🌲🔥🚪🐶

Studley

Weatheroak Tap House L

21A High Street, B80 7HN
☎ (01527) 854433 ⊕ weatheroakbrewery.co.uk
Weatheroak Bees Knees, Victoria Works, Keystone Hops; 3 changing beers (sourced locally; often Beowulf, Church End, Weatheroak) Ⓗ
This popular and welcoming micropub with two small, cosy rooms opened in 2016 and is an outlet for the nearby Weatheroak Brewery. Basic snacks and sweets are available and there is a chip shop next door – you are welcome to bring in food. Off-sales from Weatheroak in various sizes are also sold. Q🌞🔥🚪🅿🚪🐶🛜

Warwick

Cape of Good Hope L

66 Lower Cape, CV34 5DP (off Cape Rd)
☎ (01926) 498138 ⊕ thecapeofgoodhopepub.com
Church Farm Harry's Heifer; Hook Norton Hooky; Wye Valley Butty Bach; 3 changing beers Ⓗ

On the Grand Union Canal, this historic alehouse, built in 1798, welcomes canal users and locals alike. The original building on the waterside is now the front bar, with a modern extension to the rear. Three permanent real ales are offered along with three locally sourced guest beers. The friendly staff are knowledgeable, and proud to serve local ales and food. There is outside seating alongside the water next to a double lock that can get busy.
🌞🚪🕪🔥🌲🅿🚪(G1)🐶🛜

Fourpenny Pub

27/29 Crompton Street, CV34 6HJ (near racecourse, between A429 and A4189)
☎ (01926) 491360 ⊕ 4pennyhotel.co.uk
6 changing beers Ⓗ
The pub is part of a Georgian building dating from around 1800, a short distance from the town centre, close to the racecourse and castle. Its name derives from the price of a cup of coffee and tot of rum that was charged to workers building the nearby Grand Union Canal in the early 1800s. The single, split-level room has a contemporary feel and a relaxed atmosphere, enhanced by the absence of machines or loud music.
Q🌞🚪🕪🌲🚪🅿🚪🐶🛜

Old Post Office L

12 West Street, CV34 6AN
☎ 07765 896155 ⊕ oldpostofficewarwick.com
Slaughterhouse Saddleback Best Bitter Ⓗ**; 3 changing beers** Ⓗ/Ⓖ
Warwick's first alehouse offers a friendly, relaxed atmosphere and traditional beers served both on handpump and straight from the cask. Popular with real ale enthusiasts and local residents, the small bar is housed in a former shop just below the West Gate and within easy walking distance of the castle. It is decorated with a large collection of pub memorabilia. A good selection of ciders is also available. No food is served but you are welcome to bring your own. 🌞🌲🚪🐶🐾

Wild Boar L

27 Lakin Road, CV34 5BU
☎ (01926) 499968 ⊕ thewildboarwarwick.co.uk
Slaughterhouse Saddleback Best Bitter; 9 changing beers (often Everards, Slaughterhouse) Ⓗ
Award-winning Project William community pub, close to the railway station. An end-of-terrace Victorian building, it has a bar, snug and separate beer hall which was previously a skittle alley. It is the taphouse for Slaughterhouse Brewery. Ten handpumps deliver Slaughterhouse, Everards and guest ales, with two real ciders also available. Outside is an attractive patio hop garden – the hops are used for Slaughterhouse's annual brew, the Green Hopper. Q🌞🚪🕪🌲🚪🐶🚪(X17)🐶🛜

Whichford

Norman Knight L

CV36 5PE (2 miles E of A3400 at Long Compton, facing village green)
☎ (01608) 684621 ⊕ thenormanknight.co.uk
Hook Norton Hooky; Prescott Hill Climb; house beer (by Goff's); 2 changing beers (sourced regionally; often Purity, Timothy Taylor) Ⓗ
A friendly pub in the centre of this picturesque village, well worth seeking out. Popular with locals and visitors, its attractive decor and stone-flagged floor contribute to a cosy and comfortable ambience. High-quality food features locally sourced ingredients where possible. It holds monthly music nights, and in summer hosts classic car meetings on the third Thursday of the month. Accommodation is available in high-spec glamping pods behind the garden. Q🌞🚪🕪🌲🔥🅿🚪🐶🛜

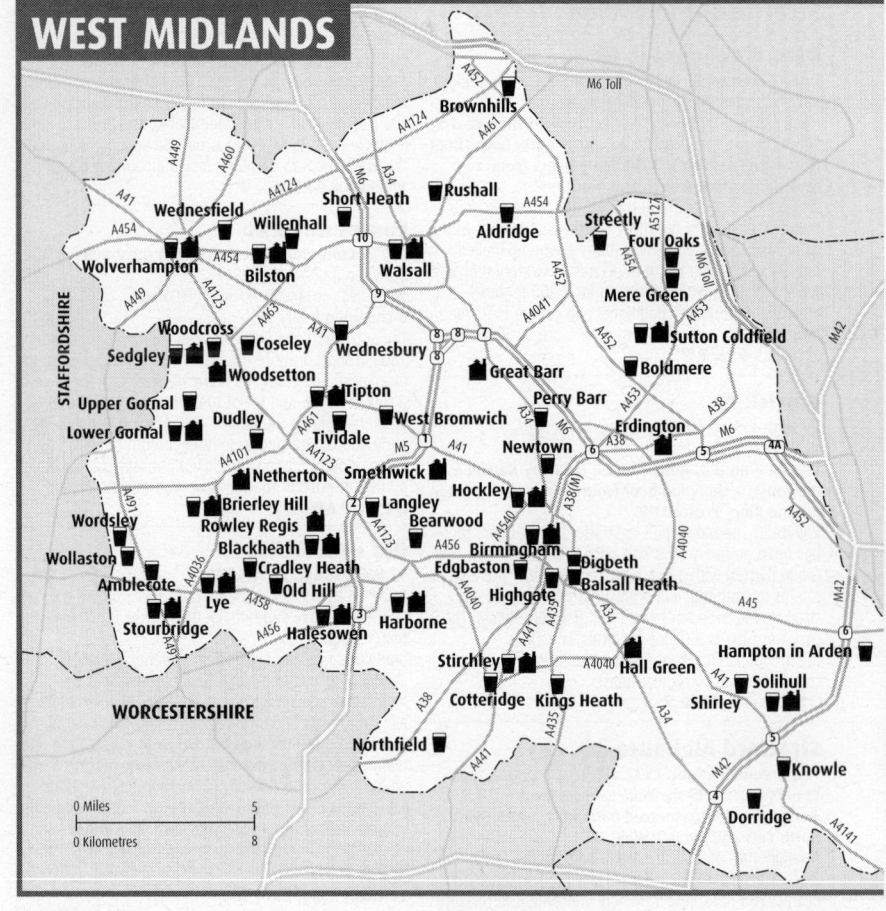

WEST MIDLANDS

Aldridge

Turtle's Head L
14 Croft Parade, WS9 8LY
☎ (01922) 325635 ⊕ theturtleshead.co.uk
4 changing beers (sourced locally; often Backyard, Bristol Beer Factory, Dancing Duck) H
Micropub with a warm welcome, opened in 2015 in the centre of Aldridge. The establishment has four handpulls serving a range of ales from throughout the United Kingdom. Bar food includes freshly made rolls and bar snacks, with complimentary cheese and pâté on a Sunday. You can bring your own food if you are drinking. Closed on Mondays except bank holidays. Discounts are offered on a Tuesday. ☼🏠👷♿🖳🐾🌢

Amblecote

Robin Hood L
196 Collis Street, DY8 4EQ (on A4102 one-way street off Brettell Lane, A461)
☎ 07436 793462
Bathams Best Bitter; Holden's Golden Glow; St Austell Proper Job; Sarah Hughes Dark Ruby Mild; Titanic Plum Porter; Wye Valley HPA; 4 changing beers H
Fine ales, quality food and a warm welcome – a great traditional Black Country local. In 2015 it celebrated 160 years as a licensed house. The front rooms hold a wonderful beer bottle collection including international

and historic brews. Some national guest ales are served but the LocAle scheme is emphasised, with more local beers on permanent sale. Food is available at weekends and the pub hosts occasional themed culinary nights.
Q☼🏠👷♿🖳🚃🖳🌢

Bearwood

Bear Tavern ✅
500 Bearwood Road, B66 4BX
☎ (0121) 429 1184
Greene King IPA; 5 changing beers (sourced nationally; often Fixed Wheel, Purity, Titanic) H
Busy open-plan community local dominated by a central bar, with sports screens scattered throughout – live matches are often shown. Attentive staff serve an interesting range of nationally sourced real ales and up to two bag-in-box real ciders. There is a large wooden-floored function room upstairs, available to hire. Affordable classic pub food is served. The diverse clientele spans all age groups. ☼🏠🕤♿♣🖳🌢

Midland
526-528 Bearwood Road, B66 4BE
☎ (0121) 429 6958
Black Country Bradley's Finest Golden, Pig on the Wall, Fireside; changing beers (sourced nationally; often Blue Monkey, Downton, Magpie) H

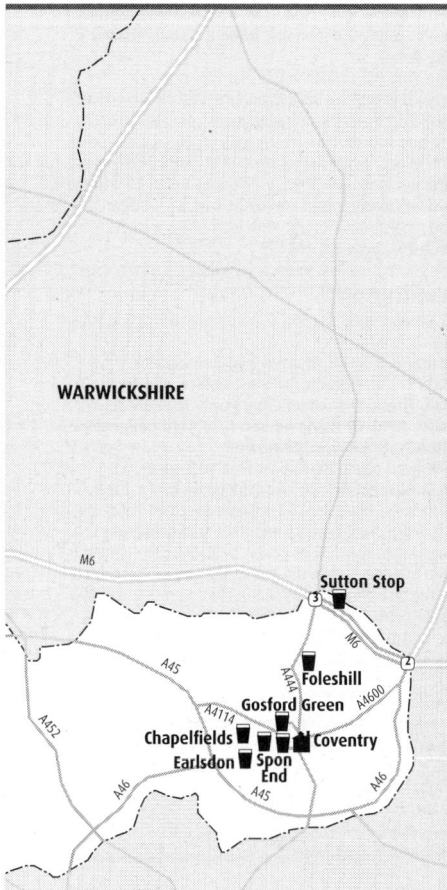

A former HSBC bank, the single-room, open-plan pub began trading in 2014 following a thorough refurbishment, and is now decorated in accordance with the established Black Country Ales theme to a high standard. It serves up to 13 real ales and three still ciders. It has a beer cellar on the same floor which can be viewed through a glass inspection panel. Standard bar snacks including crusty cobs can be purchased. Q❄️♿♣♠☂🚌🛜

Bilston

Cafe Metro 🄻

46 Church Street, WV14 0AH (opp St Leonards Church, close to town hall)
☎ (01902) 498888
Thornbridge Jaipur IPA; Wye Valley Butty Bach; 4 changing beers (sourced nationally) Ⓗ
Friendly, busy high-street venue near both bus and Metro stations, operating more as a café in the mornings and afternoons and as a bar in the evenings. The small welcoming bar area at the front leads to a further room with seating. There is a large function room at the rear where regular beer festivals are held and which is also available for hire. Q◑♿♠♣🅿️🚌🛜

Trumpet 🄻

58 High Street, WV14 0EP
☎ (01902) 493723 ⊕ thetrumpet-bilston.com

Holden's Black Country Mild, Black Country Bitter, Golden Glow, Special Ⓗ
Welcoming one-room local with jazz (mainly trad) featured seven nights per week and Sunday lunchtimes – a collection plate for the band is handed around when live music is being played. Holden's award-winning ales and the music draw in customers from around the area. Music memorabilia of all styles and eras line the walls. Around a 10-minute walk from the bus and Metro stations. ❄️🍺(Central)🚌

Birmingham: Balsall Heath

Old Moseley Arms 🄻

53 Tindal Street, B12 9QU (400yds off Moseley Rd)
☎ (0121) 440 1954 ⊕ oldmoseleyarms.co.uk
Church End Goat's Milk; Enville Ale; Wye Valley Butty Bach, HPA; 1 changing beer (sourced nationally) Ⓗ
Another of Birmingham's hidden gems. The left bar has an 80-inch screen for sport, the right bar has a jukebox. Upstairs is for functions, and there are comfy sofas in the newly extended garden/smoking area. A superb tandoori menu is served in the evening and all day Sunday. Regular beer festivals feature 12 ales and two ciders. Live music showcases local talent upstairs or outside every Sunday evening. The bar gets busy when international and T20 cricket matches are played at Edgbaston (10 minutes' walk away). ☂❄️♣🚌(50)🛜

Birmingham: City Centre

Bull

1 Price Street, B4 6JU (off St Chads Queensway)
☎ (0121) 333 6757
Hook Norton Old Hooky; Oakham Citra; 2 changing beers (sourced nationally) Ⓗ
A country pub in the city centre located near Aston University, this friendly and popular back-street local is one of Birmingham's oldest and has a snug, comfortable and homely feel. Two distinct drinking areas surround a U-shaped bar, with a smaller back room for more privacy. A small garden area occupies the rear. Guest beers change regularly. A large collection of jugs abounds alongside a number of old pictures and memorabilia. Traditional, hearty pub food is served. Eleven en-suite letting bedrooms are available at affordable rates. Q❄️🛏️◑♿☂🚌🛜🐾🛜

Colmore

116 Colmore Row, B3 3BD
☎ (0121) 238 1041 ⊕ colmoretap.co.uk
9 changing beers (often Thornbridge) Ⓗ
Thornbridge Brewery has joined forces with Pivovar to convert and refurbish a former Lloyds bank as a bar. It offers a combination of Thornbridge beers on handpump, in draught and in bottle, with additional craft beers from Pivovar. This welcoming, stylish venue is family-friendly and serves fresh pizza made with Jaipur IPA. A range of craft beers is also available alongside wines and spirits, including no fewer than 20 gins. There is a pool table downstairs. ☂◑🚌🚌

Craven Arms 🄻

47 Upper Gough Street, B1 1JG (in side street near the Mailbox)
☎ (0121) 643 2852
Black Country Bradley's Finest Golden, Pig on the Wall, Fireside; 8 changing beers (sourced nationally) Ⓗ
This early 19th-century former Holder's outlet, restored by Black Country Ales, sports an attractive blue-tiled exterior and a cosy interior. In addition to three

permanent Black Country beers the pub serves between six and eight changing guest casks, often from breweries new to Birmingham. ⏚≹(New St)●P✿ ?

Gunmakers Arms ⬙

93 Bath Street, B4 6HG

☎ (0121) 236 8486 ⊕ gunmakersarms.com

Two Towers Baskerville Bitter, Hockley Gold, Complete Muppetry, Chamberlain Pale Ale; 5 changing beers (sourced regionally; often Lincoln Green, Millstone, Stockport) Ⓗ

Small, pleasant, back-street pub just off the inner ring road, five minutes' walk from Snow Hill station. This Grade II-listed Regency building, the Two Towers brewery taphouse, was tastefully refurbished in 2017, and has five Two Towers beers and up to three guests on handpump. There is a large bar at the front, snug seating areas and a smaller room behind leading to a rear courtyard with access to the brewery. Cobs are served, plus pies on Tuesday evening. Various events are hosted (details on website, Twitter and Facebook). B&B is available at reasonable rates. ✿⇵⬙≹Ⓡ♣❀

Head of Steam ⬙

Somerset House, 36 Temple Street, B2 5DP

☎ (0121) 643 6824

House beer (by Camerons); 9 changing beers (sourced regionally) Ⓗ

The Birmingham addition to the Camerons Head of Steam chain, it features a large and spacious interior decorated in a steampunk style, with plenty of seating and booths for people to enjoy a wide variety of food and drinks. Ten handpulls showcase Camerons' own beers and offerings from local breweries. Keg lines include international beers such as Delirium and La Chouffe. Tends to close early if quiet.

⬙&≹(New St) Ⓡ❀

Post Office Vaults ⬙

84 New Street, B2 4BA (entrances are on both New St and Pinfold St)

☎ (0121) 643 7354 ⊕ postofficevaults.co.uk

Hobsons Mild; house beer (by Kinver Brewery); 6 changing beers (sourced nationally) Ⓗ

A two-minute walk from the Stephenson Street entrance to New Street station and close to Victoria Square, this subterranean bar offers a range of eight traditional beers in excellent condition. It always stocks at least 350 different bottled beers from all over the world – one of the largest ranges in the country – and serves 14 ciders and perries. The extremely knowledgeable staff will make your visit a pleasure. Q≹(New St)Ⓡ♣●Ⓡ ?

Prince of Wales ⬙

84 Cambridge Street, B1 2NP (behind ICC/NIA and Rep Theatre)

☎ (0121) 413 4180

5 changing beers (sourced nationally) Ⓗ

Tastefully restored Victorian back-street venue that is always popular with locals, visitors from the Symphony Hall and fans of live music. Its one-roomed interior is a quirky blend of modern and traditional, with an L-shaped bar where eight handpulls take prominence. The toilets are interesting too! You will find freshly cooked pub favourites on the menu, with curry nights on Wednesdays. Live music takes place every Sunday afternoon/evening, and open-mic on Thursdays, when the place can get busy. ⬙●Ⓡ❀

Pure Craft Bar & Kitchen ⬙

30 Waterloo Street, B2 5TJ (5 mins from New St and Snow Hill stations)

☎ (0121) 237 5666 ⊕ purecraftbars.com

Purity Bunny Hop, Pure Gold, Mad Goose; 3 changing beers (sourced nationally; often Kirkstall, Rooster's, Tiny Rebel) Ⓗ

Pure Craft Bar & Kitchen was the first in the chain to open. It is set in a traditional building with an industrial interior in the centre of the business district, its walls adorned with modern art. The pub serves six cask and 16 craft beer lines, plus a selection of 60 bottled craft beers. Gourmet food is on offer, with the menu matched to the beers available; meals can be booked online. There is also a cellar bar. Popular with local office workers. ✿⬙≹Ⓡ(Snow Hill) ♣Ⓡ ?

Wellington ⬙

37 Bennetts Hill, B2 5SN (5 mins from New St and Snow Hill stations)

☎ (0121) 200 3115 ⊕ thewellingtonrealale.co.uk

Black Country Bradley's Finest Golden, Pig on the Wall, Fireside; Oakham Citra; Purity Mad Goose; Wye Valley HPA; 10 changing beers (sourced nationally; often Froth Blowers, Titanic) Ⓗ

A stalwart of the Birmingham real ale scene, the Wellington has the feel of a community local in the heart of the city. There are 27 handpulls over two floors, dispensing well-kept ale and three traditional ciders. A huge range of whiskies is also available - the ground floor offering Scotch, the rest of the world represented on the first-floor bar. The suntrap roof terrace is a hidden urban gem. Regular quizzes, folk nights and cheese nights are held. There is no food but you can bring your own - plates, cutlery and condiments are provided.

Q✿&≹♣●Ⓡ ?

REAL ALE BREWERIES

AJ's Walsall
Angel Ales Halesowen
Attic ✦ Birmingham
Backyard ✦ Walsall
Banks's Wolverhampton
Bathams Brierley Hill
Beat ✦ Lye
Birmingham Birmingham
Black Country ⬛ Lower Gornal
Brewhouse & Kitchen ⬛ Sutton Coldfield
Burning Soul Birmingham: Hockley
Byatt's ✦ Coventry
Craddock's ⬛ Stourbridge
Davenports Smethwick
Dhillon's ✦ Coventry
Dig Birmingham
Fixed Wheel Blackheath
Fownes Brierley Hill
Froth Blowers Erdington
Glasshouse Stirchley
Green Duck ✦ Stourbridge
Halton Turner Birmingham: Hall Green
Holden's Woodsetton
Indian Great Barr
Leviathan ✦ Sutton Coldfield
Mashionistas Coventry
Newbridge Bilston
Olde Swan ⬛ Netherton
Ostlers ⬛ Harborne
Pig Iron Rowley Regis
Printworks ⬛ ✦ Stourbridge
Rock & Roll Birmingham
Sarah Hughes ⬛ Sedgley
Silhill Solihull
Toll End ⬛ Tipton
Triumph Coventry
Twisted Barrel Coventry
Two Towers Birmingham

Birmingham: Cotteridge

Red Beer'd

1891 Pershore Road, B30 3DJ
4 changing beers (often Fownes) ℍ
This nice addition to the Cotteridge and Stirchley pub scene is a micropub with four cask and up to 10 keg taps. There is seating for about 12 downstairs and a few more upstairs. The staff are friendly, knowledgeable and passionate about beers. It is close to Kings Norton railway station. ➡️🅿️

Birmingham: Digbeth

Spotted Dog 🄻

104 Warwick Street, B12 0NH
☎ (0121) 772 3822 🌐 spotteddog.co.uk
Castle Rock Harvest Pale; 4 changing beers (sourced nationally) ℍ
A traditional multi-roomed pub of Irish character, family owned and with the same landlord since the 1980s. Rugby and Irish sports are shown on large-screen TVs. Outside is an extensive covered patio garden and smoking area with heaters, a large real fireplace, a barbecue, a projection screen and eclectic adornments. A traditional Irish music night takes place on alternate Mondays, a jazz night on Tuesdays, and the venue is the home of Na Madrai golf society and the Digbeth O'lympics. There is usually a cask mild on the bar. Often busy when Birmingham City play at home.
🌟🍴🚃🅿️🛜

Woodman ★ 🄻

New Canal Street, B5 5LG (opp old Curzon St station by Millennium Point)
☎ (0121) 643 4960 🌐 thewoodmanbirmingham.co.uk
Castle Rock Black Gold, Harvest Pale; 3 changing beers (sourced nationally) ℍ
Lovingly restored Victorian-era hostelry with original features preserved, including a gilded and etched mirror at the centre of the bar, period tiles and the old smoke room with (now no longer functioning) bell pushes in the wall for table service. Hearty pub food is served every day until the evening. The roof terrace overlooks Eastside Park, popular with local students and skateboarders. Regular live music showcases varied talent from the adjacent Royal Birmingham Conservatoire in the well-appointed function room. Student groups sit cheek by jowl with older regulars to create a lively and vibrant atmosphere. 🌟🍴🚃(Moor St)🅿️🛜

Birmingham: Edgbaston

Physician

Harborne Road, B15 3DH
☎ (0121) 272 5900
Brunning & Price Original; Purity Mad Goose; Timothy Taylor Landlord; 3 changing beers (sourced regionally) ℍ
Large historic former BMI building used to house the vast Sampson Gamgee Library for the History of Medicine, recently converted into a pub. It is an upmarket establishment with several drinking and dining areas. A range of ales is served, often featuring numerous local brews, alongside a good selection of wines, gins and whiskies. 🌟🍴🅿️

Birmingham: Harborne

Hop Garden

19 Metchley Lane, B17 0HT (100yds from High St, at back of M&S)

☎ (0121) 427 7904
5 changing beers (sourced nationally) ℍ
A small pub serious about craft beer, with few mainstream products. It serves five real ales from small and local breweries, seven craft beers and five craft ciders, as well as real cider. There is also an interesting selection of bottled beers. The decor is original and eclectic, and there really are hops growing in the garden! 🌟🍴🅿️

White Horse 🄻 ✅

2 York Street, B17 0HG
☎ (0121) 608 7641 🌐 whitehorseharborne.com
Greene King Abbot; Ostlers Terry's Gold; 7 changing beers (sourced regionally; often Bathams, Church End, Wye Valley) ℍ
Traditional community local just off the High Street, a former Festival Alehouse with a long history of real ale. It brews on the premises as Ostlers Ales. There are four rotating craft beers on KeyKeg – check what beers are on in real time via the website beerboard. Entertainment includes live music at the weekend, quizzes on Tuesday and Thursday, and BT/Sky sport on TV. 🌟🍴🅿️🛜

Birmingham: Highgate

Lamp Tavern 🄻

157 Barford Street, B5 6AH (500yds from A441 Pershore Rd nr bottom of Hurst St)
☎ (0121) 688 1220
Hobsons Mild; 4 changing beers (sourced nationally) ℍ
Hidden gem in close proximity to Digbeth and the Arcadian areas of Birmingham that serves one permanent real ale and four changing guests, often including one from Stanway as well as local breweries. The pub has been run by the friendly licensee for over 27 years and has a proper homely feel, with a folk club on Fridays and a jazz club some Tuesdays. There is road parking only, but good bus routes nearby. Closes early if quiet. Q🅿️

Birmingham: Hockley

1000 Trades

16 Frederick Street, B1 3HE
☎ (0121) 233 6291 🌐 1000trades.org.uk
House beer (by Rock); 3 changing beers (sourced nationally; often Titanic) ℍ
This independent craft beer bar is a delightful addition to the Jewellery Quarter. It has bare boards and brickwork, with full-width doors opening onto the pavement, giving a distinctive atmosphere. Four handpumps serve a changing range of beers, usually with at least one from a local micro. The cask offering is supported by five KeyKeg taps and an interesting range of bottled beers. The bar is a music venue showcasing independent labels. It also operates kitchen residencies, so the menu is characterised by evolving variety, often street food in style. 🍴🚃🅿️

Burning Soul Brewery 🄻

Unit 1, Mott Street Industrial Estate, B19 3HE
☎ (0121) 439 7253 🌐 burningsoulbrewing.com
11 changing beers (sourced locally; often Burning Soul) ℍ
A changing list of smaller, experimental pilot brews is available here, so the brewery can capture at first-hand what people think of the beers – the favourites are rebrewed and sold outside the brewery. There is one handpump for cask ale plus 10 KeyKeg taps, with all Burning Soul beers meeting the CAMRA definition of real

ale. Bottled mead is also sold. Brewery tours can be arranged. Card payment is preferred.
≥₩(St Paul's) ♣P₩

Jewellers Arms
23 Hockley Street, B18 6BW
☎ (0121) 212 0347
Black Country Bradley's Finest Golden, Pig on the Wall, Fireside; 7 changing beers ⊞
Refurbished and reopened by Black Country Ales in 2017, this pub serves 10 real ales and two ciders, and gets busy in the evenings. Food is limited to freshly made cobs. The interior is now all open plan, with a real fire at one end lit daily in winter. There is just one fruit machine. A function room is available upstairs.
Q⏴≥₩(Jewellery Quarter) ●₩(8A,8C) ☀

Rock & Roll Brewhouse ⓛ
19 Hall Street, B18 6BS
☎ 07969 759649
Rock & Roll Brew Springsteen, Thirst Aid Kit, Voodoo Mild ⊞
A quirky brewery taproom where the excellent bar staff have a great knowledge of beer. The brewery's other shared love is music and music memorabilia; a playlist of what you are hearing is on the wall. There is usually a choice of three vegan-friendly ales, always including a dark beer. Hogan's cider is also available. Open Thursday and Friday evenings and Saturday afternoons only. Check Facebook before visiting as the taproom is occasionally closed for music festivals. ≥₩

Birmingham: Kings Heath

Hop & Scotch
9 Institute Road, B14 7EG
☎ (0121) 679 8807 ● hopscotchbrum.com
4 changing beers (sourced locally; often Green Duck, Kinver Brewery) ⊞
Friendly and welcoming microbar with three to four cask beers, often from local producers Green Duck and Kinver, together with an interesting range of KeyKeg beers from breweries near by, some of which are vegan-friendly. Bottled and canned ales are also sold. Beers currently on offer are displayed on torn-off paper strips stuck on a side wall. There are various seating areas in differing styles. The bar attracts a wide age range and can get busy in the evening. Dogs are welcome, with snacks offered. Opening hours can change – see the website for up-to-date times. ₩☀

Birmingham: Newtown

Bartons Arms ★
144 High Street, B6 4UP
☎ (0121) 333 5988 ● thebartonsarms.com
Oakham JHB, Inferno, Citra, Bishops Farewell; 2 changing beers (sourced nationally; often Oakham) ⊞
This Grade II*-listed building is a classic example of late-Victorian splendour. From the main bar the superb original stained-glass windows can be viewed, with the M&B logo as it was in 1901. There are ornate Minton tiles and a fancy tiled staircase. At least one guest ale is usually served alongside the regular Oakham beers and seasonals. The restaurant is well known for its excellent Thai cuisine. The pub can get busy when Aston Villa are at home. ⅁⏴●P₩奈

Birmingham: Northfield

Black Horse ★ ⓛ ✔
Bristol Road South, B31 2QT (opp Sainsbury's)
☎ (0121) 477 1800
Greene King Abbot; Ruddles Best Bitter; Sharp's Doom Bar; changing beers (sourced nationally; often Adnams, Fuller's, Purity) ⊞
Large inter-war mock-Tudor roadhouse offering the only extensive real ale choice in this part of the city. It has been transformed from being an undesirable local into a popular pub serving consistently good quality beer. Unusually for Wetherspoon's, this place has a multi-room layout and bars on two levels. It still retains the original baronial hall entrance but the bar has been tastefully refurbished with an etched-glass entrance door. There is a bowling green with original outbuildings to the rear.
Q⅁⏴●₻≥●P₩奈

Birmingham: Perry Barr

Arthur Robertson ✔
51-53 One Stop Retail Park, Walsall Road, B42 1AA
☎ (0121) 332 5910
Greene King Abbot; Ruddles Best Bitter; 3 changing beers ⊞
A Wetherspoon at the One Stop shopping centre in Perry Barr, named after Birchfield Harriers' first ever Olympian and medal winner. The manager tries to keep three local guests available when possible, and the pub serves the standard Wetherspoon's food menu. It can get busy when Aston Villa are playing at home. ⅁⏴≥●P₩奈

Birmingham: Stirchley

Wildcat Tap
1381-1383 Pershore Road, B30 2JR
● stirchleywildcat.co.uk
5 changing beers (sourced nationally) ⊞
This bar is much changed from the original Wildcat just down the road. It is spacious for a micropub, with adequate seating, although it attracts all ages and does get busy at weekends. The beer range of cask and keg is adventurous and interesting. There are five casks on handpump plus a real cider and eight craft keg lines, complemented by a selection of bottled craft beers, gin, whisky and soft drinks. ≥●₩

Blackheath

Britannia ✔
124 Halesowen Street, B65 0ES
☎ (0121) 559 0010
Exmoor Gold; Greene King Abbot; Ruddles Best Bitter; 6 changing beers (sourced nationally; often Backyard, Kinver Brewery, Slater's) ⊞
An L-shaped Wetherspoon outlet at the very heart of Blackheath. The garden at the rear of the property provides a pleasant space away from the main A4099. The exposed brick façade is often decorated with hanging baskets in the warmer seasons. Six changing beers are accompanied by three permanent ales. Pictures placed throughout the pub depict local monuments and historic characters. Food is served all day, every day. A small car park for customers can be accessed via Cross Street. ⅁❀⏴⅁≥♣●P₩奈

Boldmere

Bishop Vesey ⓛ
63 Boldmere Road, B73 5XA
☎ (0121) 355 5077

Backyard Blonde; Greene King Abbot; Oakham Citra; Ruddles Best Bitter; Sharp's Doom Bar; 11 changing beers (sourced nationally; often Oakham) ⊞
A busy Wetherspoon whose consistent performance has earned it over 20 consecutive years in the Guide. Named after the area's Tudor benefactor, who is credited with gaining royal status for Sutton Coldfield, it features a carved wooden pulpit by the entrance. Up to 11 interesting guest beers are offered, many from local microbreweries, plus a changing real cider. As well as extensive seating areas upstairs and down, there is a spacious rooftop garden, and a smaller beer garden downstairs. ⏾❀◑↻≈♣●🖺🛜

Cask & Craft
56 Boldmere Road, B73 5TJ
☎ 07497 828911
2 changing beers (sourced nationally) ℗
Friendly micropub that opened in 2019 serving craft beers, usually along with two real ales. There are no handpulls – the ales come through a keg tap but are fed by an electric pump. Wines, gins and cocktails also feature. The bar area is on the small side but a larger room upstairs offers more seating. A well-stocked fridge stocks a range of craft beers, mostly canned. ≈🖺🛜

Brierley Hill

Rose & Crown ℒ
161 Bank Street, DY5 3DD (on B4179)
☎ (01384) 936166
Holden's Black Country Bitter, Golden Glow, Special; 1 changing beer (often Holden's) ⊞
This traditional pub was originally two terraced properties. One end of the bar is dominated by a dartboard. A conservatory provides extra space and is used as a function room, opening onto a small garden with tables and benches. There is a bus stop outside, or a five-minute walk takes you to Brierley Hill High Street, which is served by several bus routes. Holden's seasonal beers are rotated. Q⏾❀♣🖺🛜❀🛜

Vine
10 Delph Road, DY5 2TN
☎ (01384) 78293
Bathams Best Bitter, Mild Ale ⊞
Unspoilt brewery tap with an ornately decorated façade proclaiming the Shakespearian quotation, 'Blessing of your heart, you brew good ale'. It is an elongated pub with a labyrinthine feel. The front bar is staunchly traditional, and the larger rear room has its own servery, leather seating and a dartboard. The homely lounge was partly converted from former brewery offices. Black Country lunches, such as faggots and home-made pies, are served weekdays, with generously filled rolls and pork pies at all times. Q⏾❀◑♣🖺(8)❀🛜

Waterfront Inn ⊘
6-7 The Waterfront, Level Street, DY5 1XE (between A461 and A4036)
☎ (01384) 262096
Greene King Abbot; 3 changing beers (sourced nationally; often Exmoor, Sharp's, Shepherd Neame) ⊞
Comparatively small single-room Wetherspoon outlet in an attractive location overlooking the Dudley Number One Canal basin, with a patio and garden enjoying a sunny aspect. The guest beers typically feature well-known national brands; bag-in-box real cider comes from the fridge. Food is served from the standard menu all day. The pub now benefits from a recent resurgence in entertainment and drinks venues across the Waterfront Business Park. Q⏾❀◑↻&●🖺(8,81)🛜

Brownhills

Jiggers Whistle ℒ
5-7 Brownhills High Street, WS8 6ED
☎ 07854 356976
House beer (by Green Duck); 3 changing beers (sourced nationally; often AJ's, Backyard, Green Duck) ⊞
Friendly micropub that opened in 2017. Its one room is split into three interconnected drinking areas. The pub serves a wide range of cask and craft keg ales plus around eight real ciders, and offers bar snacks at weekends. It has grown hugely in popularity and now boasts its own darts team. The owners offer customers a warm welcome and are keen to support local events. Q⏾♣●🖺(10)❀🛜

Coseley

Old Chainyard ℒ
63 Castle Street, WV14 9DW
2 changing beers (sourced regionally; often Church End, Salopian) ⊞
Lively single-roomed community pub serving two rotating cask beers, at least one from Salopian Brewery. The handpulls not in use advertise beers that are currently resting in the cellar and coming soon. A number of beer festivals are hosted throughout the year. The pub is a five-minute walk from Coseley train station and a three-minute walk from the A4123 – both of which offer direct links to Birmingham and Wolverhampton. ⏾❀≈♣🖺❀🛜

Coventry: Chapelfields

Hearsall Inn ℒ
45 Craven Street, CV5 8DS (1 mile W of city centre, off Allesley Old Rd)
☎ (024) 7671 5729 🌐 hearsallinn.com
Church End Goat's Milk; Draught Bass; 2 changing beers (sourced locally; often Byatt's) ⊞
Built in the 1850s to serve Chapelfields' historic watchmaking district, this free house has been run by the same family for 23 years. It has separate bar and lounge areas, with a paved patio to the front. Four handpumps dispense local and regional beers. Freshly made batches are available throughout the day. The pub is home to darts, dominoes and football teams and hosts traditional Irish music on Tuesday nights. The building has an externally mounted defibrillator. ⏾❀♣🖺❀🛜

Coventry: City Centre

Earl of Mercia ⊘
18 High Street, CV1 5RE
☎ (024) 7643 3990
Greene King Abbot; Ruddles Best Bitter; Sharp's Doom Bar; 5 changing beers (sourced nationally) ⊞
A popular city-centre Wetherspoon housed in a former bank near to the imposing Council House. It is named after Leofric, Earl of Mercia who, along with his wife Godiva, founded Coventry's St Mary's Priory in 1043. A good selection of ales is on offer, with local brands regularly featured. The pub has seating split across ground floor and mezzanine levels, plus a small front patio area. It is ideally situated for exploring the nearby cathedrals and other attractions. ⏾❀◑↻&≈●🖺🛜

Gatehouse Tavern ℒ
44-46 Hill Street, CV1 4AN (close to Belgrade Theatre and Spon St, nr jct 8 of ring road)
☎ (024) 7663 0140

Draught Bass; Fuller's London Pride; 4 changing beers (sourced locally; often Byatt's, Church End, Purity) ⊞
A single-roomed local which, although not particularly spacious, does boast a large garden and covered outdoor area. The building was converted by the landlord from the former gatehouse of the now demolished Leigh Mill. The stained-glass windows depicting the six nations are an indication of the pub's sporting leanings, with sports events shown on several screens. Good-value home-cooked food complements the high-quality ales and real cider. ⌂❀❶◗●☘☂

Golden Cross 🅛 ✓

8 Hay Lane, CV1 5RF (nr old cathedral ruins)
☎ (024) 7655 1855 ⊕ thegoldencrosscoventry.co.uk
House beer (by Ringwood); 3 changing beers (sourced locally; often Adnams, Byatt's, Church End) ⊞
This imposing medieval building was once a mint and now claims to be the oldest pub in Coventry, although this is disputed. It was marred by an unsympathetic refurbishment in the 1960s but great efforts have been made to right the wrongs. There is a small courtyard at the rear and an upstairs bar providing more space. A particularly handy place to recharge the batteries after visiting the nearby cathedrals. ❀❶●☘☂

Old Windmill 🅛 ✓

22-23 Spon Street, CV1 3BA (behind IKEA)
☎ (024) 7625 1717
Morland Old Speckled Hen; Theakston Old Peculier; Timothy Taylor Landlord; 4 changing beers (sourced locally; often North Cotswold) ⊞
A stunning 15th-century building in a medieval street in the centre of the city. It contains a number of rooms that still hold clues to their former uses, such as a stove within a large fireplace with adjacent priest hole, plus a Victorian brewhouse. The pub is still known in the area as Ma Brown's in memory of an early 20th-century landlady. Locally produced pork pies are available and recommended. Two beer festivals are held annually. ♣●☘❀☂

Town Crier ✓

Corporation Street, CV1 1PB (close to medieval Spon St)
☎ (024) 7663 2317
Marston's Saddle Tank; 3 changing beers (sourced nationally; often Marston's) ⊞
Built in the late 1980s by Banks's with a single bar serving a large room. Close to historic Spon Street and the city centre, it is well placed to enjoy the UK City of Culture 2021 and is popular with shoppers and workers, giving it a mix of clientele. Recently refurbished, the pub is bright and welcoming inside – the illuminated clock in the alcove one of many features. Real ale is supplemented by up to four real ciders. ❀❶●☘☂

Town Wall Tavern ✓

Bond Street, CV1 4AH
☎ (024) 7622 0963
Brains Rev James; Draught Bass; Theakston Best Bitter, Old Peculier; Wye Valley HPA; 3 changing beers (sourced nationally; often North Cotswold) ⊞
Hidden away behind the Belgrade Theatre and crowded in by modern structures, this is a rare city-centre example of a traditional boozer. Two bars are supplemented by a tiny third one, the Donkey Box, so named since someone proved that it was big enough to hold a donkey – just. In the lounge a window depicting the long defunct Atkinsons Brewery marks the original external wall of the building. Understandably popular with theatregoers and those seeking out the excellent food. ❀❶●☘❀

Coventry: Earlsdon

City Arms 🅛 ✓

1 Earlsdon Street, CV5 6EP (on roundabout at centre of Earlsdon)
☎ (024) 7671 8170
Greene King Abbot; Ruddles Best Bitter; Sharp's Doom Bar; 7 changing beers (sourced nationally; often Byatt's, Grainstore, Purity) ⊞
A large mock-Tudor building housing a popular Wetherspoon in the heart of the bustling Earlsdon suburb, named after the Coventry coat of arms. With excellent transport links to the city centre and local universities, it appeals to a mixed clientele and can get busy on weekend evenings. It has a large open-plan main room with a quieter smaller room, plus an attractive outdoor drinking area to the side. Good-value food is served and there are regular beer and gin festivals. ⌂❀❶◗⌗●☘(5,11)☂

Coventry: Foleshill

Byatt's Brewhouse Bar 🅛

Unit 7-8 Lythalls Lane Industrial Estate, Lythalls Lane, CV6 6FL
☎ (024) 7663 7996 ⊕ byattsbrewery.co.uk
6 changing beers (sourced locally; often Byatt's) ⊞
A contemporary brewery taproom on a small industrial estate, consisting of a ground-floor bar area plus a mezzanine with various commissioned artworks, some celebrating the history of Coventry. Up to six changing beers with some seasonal variations are served. Three gravity ciders and Byatt's bottle-conditioned beers and carry-out containers can be purchased. There are occasional quiz and music nights plus bookable brewery tours and tastings. The bar opens some Sundays if a fixture is being played at the nearby Coventry Arena. ⌂⌗●☘❀❀☂

Coventry: Gosford Green

Twisted Barrel Brewery & Tap House 🅛

Fargo Village, Far Gosford Street, CV1 5ED
☎ (024) 7610 1701 ⊕ twistedbarrelale.co.uk
Twisted Barrel Beast of a Midlands Mild, Detroit Sour City, God's Twisted Sister, Sine Qua Non, Naido; 18 changing beers (sourced nationally) ⊞ /ℙ
Popular with a range of drinkers, the taphouse is in Fargo Village, an area of independent craft, food and arts units in an old industrial site which will play a key role in Coventry's City of Culture programme in 2021/2022. The building comprises the brewery, a bar which can offer over 20 beers on KeyKeg, and a spacious seating area. A core range is supplemented with seasonal and pilot beers and guests from elsewhere. All beers are vegan-friendly. ⌂⌗●☘❀❀☂

Coventry: Spon End

Broomfield Tavern 🅛

14-16 Broomfield Place, CV5 6GY (adjacent to rugby ground but hidden from main road)
☎ (024) 7663 0969
Church End Fallen Angel; Froth Blowers Piffle Snonker; 8 changing beers (sourced locally) ⊞
This multi award-winning pub is in the midst of refurbishments as the owners strive to return it to its original Victorian (1853) incarnation. The character and cosiness will remain when the work is complete. A genuine free house, it hosts beer from near and far as well as an impressive range of expertly curated ciders.

The knowledgeable staff ensure a memorable experience. It can get busy when rugby is being played at the adjacent Butts Park Arena. Q🍺♣♨🖳🌸

Coventry: Sutton Stop

Greyhound Inn

Hawkesbury Junction, CV6 6DF (off Grange Rd at jct of Coventry and Oxford canals)

☎ (024) 7636 3046 ⊕ thegreyhoundlongford.co.uk

Draught Bass; Greene King Abbot; 3 changing beers (sourced nationally) ⊞

Traditional award-winning pub that dates from the 1830s, and is popular with regulars and visitors alike. The canalside patio is an idyllic setting for summertime narrowboat watching. In the winter drinkers and diners can enjoy a real fire in the cosy bar area. At the rear there is a separate bar and garden for summer events. A wide range of food is served in the bar and restaurant. 🍺🌸◑♣♨P🌸?

Cradley Heath

Plough & Harrow

82 Corngreaves Road, B64 7BT

☎ (01384) 638351

Banks's Mild; Wye Valley Butty Bach, HPA; 3 changing beers (sourced nationally; often Abbeydale, Bristol Beer Factory, Mallinsons) ⊞

An easy-going and homely venue that is a mecca for beer lovers. It specialises in strong and hoppy pale beers; the guest ales are typically 5% ABV or above. There is a strong community focus, with women's darts among various sports teams hosted. At the rear is an enclosed outdoor seating area, some of which is sheltered. The pub regularly raises money for a variety of charities and good causes. Q🍺🌸♣♨P🖳(18,14A)🌸?

Dorridge

Knowle & Dorridge Cricket Club ✔

Station Road, B93 8ET (corner of Station Rd and Grove Rd)

☎ (01564) 774338 ⊕ kdcc.play-cricket.com/home

3 changing beers (sourced nationally) ⊞

This established cricket club, inaugurated in 1896, is set in an upmarket residential area. Visitors are welcome to try the changing range of up to three cask-conditioned ales, always in excellent condition and often from interesting breweries. There are no entry restrictions, but club members are able to purchase drinks at a reduced price. There is outside seating to watch high-class cricket in the Birmingham league. Bar snacks and filled rolls are usually available. Local CAMRA Club of the Year three years in succession. 🍺🌸◑&♣♨P🖳(S2,S3)🌸?

Dudley

Malt Shovel

46 Tower Street, DY1 1NB (off the Broadway, A459, opp Dudley College Evolve campus)

☎ (01384) 252735

Holden's Golden Glow; 4 changing beers (sourced nationally; often Neepsend, Oakham, Pictish) ⊞

Originally known as the Lord Wellington in the 19th century, this exciting and trendy town-centre establishment is now part of the Red Pub Co portfolio. It has a popular balance of locally produced cask beers and modern, nationally-sourced brews on the bar; Yorkshire breweries are often showcased. The mixture of seating styles includes classic benches, which contrast nicely with the high stools. There are a small number of gaming

and betting machines and live entertainment and Sky Sports are screened. A cosy beer garden with decking is at the rear. 🍺&P🖳🌸?

Four Oaks

Butlers Arms ✔

444 Lichfield Road, B74 4BL

☎ (0121) 308 0765 ⊕ butlersarms.co.uk

4 changing beers ⊞

Family-run pub geared towards dining, though drinkers are always made welcome. The décor has an engagingly eccentric style, with mirrors, lamps, curiosities and colourful seating. The four guest ales change and often come from well-known breweries. The food menu is excellent and wide ranging, with fish-lovers looked after particularly well. Live music is hosted on the last Friday of the month. A small beer terrace is to the front. Car parking is free but requires registration number entry at the bar. Q🍺🌸◑&♨P🌸

Halesowen

Crafty Pint H'ales'owen 🅛

8 Wassell Road, B63 4JU

☎ 07823 880240

Wye Valley Butty Bach; 5 changing beers (sourced nationally) ⊞

A micropub, now occupying the adjacent building as well, run by a local resident. It offers traditional ale, cider, wines and beverages plus pork pies. Coffee is generally available during the week, along with crusty cobs and sausage rolls. Children are not allowed in the evening. Closes early on Saturday night. Q🍺♨P🖳🌸?

Hawne Tavern 🅛

76 Attwood Street, B63 3UG (just off Stourbridge Rd, down Short St opp Tesco Express)

☎ (0121) 602 6743

Bathams Best Bitter; Oakham Citra; Wye Valley HPA; 6 changing beers ⊞

A back-street locals' pub just off the main bus route. It has a large bar with a pool table and a TV showing sports (not Sky), with separate seating areas plus a smaller cosy lounge. There are three regular and up to six guest ales, many from microbreweries, with northern beers a speciality. Real cider is also sold. Baguettes are available in the evenings, hot sandwiches and chips at weekends. The enclosed rear garden has a smoking shelter. Q🌸♣♨🖳🌸

Shell-ter 🅛

1A Nimmings Road, B62 9JJ

Enville Ale; Wye Valley HPA; 1 changing beer (sourced regionally) ⊞

A micropub near Shell Corner, open since 2017, featuring a large single room big enough for up to 50 customers. Three real ales are always on, usually from local breweries, as well as a box of real cider. Cold snacks are served (cobs, samosas, etc). The comfortable interior decor is military-themed, with a gas mask, German hand grenade, ammo box and replica plane in the roof space. There is no car park but plenty of street parking is available in the vicinity. &♨♨P🖳(14)🌸?

Hampton in Arden

White Lion

10 High Street, B92 0AA

☎ (01675) 442833 ⊕ thewhitelioninn.com

Banks's Mild; Hobsons Best; Holden's Golden Glow; M&B Brew XI; Skinner's Betty Stogs; Wye Valley HPA ⊞
A charming 17th-century timber-framed building with Grade II status, the White Lion has been licensed since 1838. It has an L-shaped lounge and dining area plus a separate public bar, with lovely real fires. The quality of the real ales is always of the highest level; the pub looks to rotate two beers every five to six months. The dining area is light, airy and open plan. It serves excellent British pub food, with a French accent, at lunchtimes and evenings. Q☯♿⌂◀)◐&≉P🚪(82)☙🞄

Knowle

Ale Rooms
1592 High Street, B93 0LF
☎ (01564) 400040
7 changing beers (sourced nationally; often Church End, Silhill) ⊞
This micropub in a converted shop (formerly a funeral parlour) is a welcome addition to the Knowle pub scene. It stocks at least one real ale from the local Silhill brewery, along with one from Church End and guests, and also offers real cider, wines and spirits, including speciality gins. There is free Wi-Fi, and the usual snacks are available. CAMRA branch Pub of the Year 2019, and West Midlands County Pub of the Year 2019.
◐🚪(S3)☙🞄

Langley

Old Dispensary
Causeway Green Road, B68 8LS (turn right off Wolverhampton Rd, A4123, if heading S towards Harborne)
Wye Valley Butty Bach; 3 changing beers (sourced nationally; often New Bristol, Tiny Rebel, Vocation) ⊞
In a shop unit that was previously a pharmacy, this intimate microbar now serves progressive and adventurous real ales. Small in size but big in ideas, the venue offers high-quality cask, craft, and ciders. A range of themed and fun events are run on a rotating basis, including bingo nights. You can observe how many beers have previously been on sale by scrutinising the many pumpclips on display overhead. Q☯♿&◐🚪(49,126)🞄

Lower Gornal

Fountain Inn
8 Temple Street, DY3 2PE (on B4157 5 mins from Gornal Wood bus station)
☎ (01384) 596317
Church End Fallen Angel; Greene King Abbot; Hobsons Town Crier; Wye Valley HPA, Butty Bach; 7 changing beers (sourced nationally; often Abbeydale, Oakham, Salopian) ⊞
Under new management since 2018, this pub has reinstated itself as a destination both for quality real ales and food. To the rear, the courtyard has recently been extended and refurbished to a high standard. The beers conditioning in the cellar are listed on a board opposite the main bar. There is an elevated, separate restaurant to the rear. ☯♿&♿🚪(17/A,27/A)🞄

Old Bull's Head
1 Redhall Road, DY3 2NU (at jct with Temple St, B4175)
☎ (01384) 231616
Black Country Bradley's Finest Golden, Pig on the Wall, Fireside; Hobsons Town Crier; 4 changing beers (often Fixed Wheel, Oakham, Salopian) ⊞

The brewery tap for Black Country Ales, offering a choice of eight beers. The rear lounge has a sports focus and is also used to host celebrations; the front bar has a dartboard adjacent to the real fire. Large crusty cobs are a popular accompaniment to the ales. Customers can view a variety of CAMRA reading material. Regular beer festivals are held in the garden, where there is additional seating. ☯♣♿P🚪(17/A,27/A)☙🞄

Lye

Windsor Castle L ✅
7 Stourbridge Road, DY9 7DG (at Lye Cross)
☎ (01384) 897809 ⊕ windsorcastleinn.co.uk
6 changing beers (sourced locally) ⊞
Formerly the taphouse and brewery for Sadler's Ales, the Windsor Castle now offers its own Printworks Brewery beers. The modern yet cosy interior has an atmosphere that is relaxed during the week and livelier at weekends. Home-made food is served daily, including breakfast on Saturday. Ale can be provided to take away by those frequenting one of the local curry houses. The adjoining brewery offers brewery tours. Accommodation is available. Q☯⌂◀)&≉♿P🚪(9,7)☙🞄

Mere Green

Mare Pool L ✅
294 Lichfield Road, B74 2UG (behind shops on E side of Lichfield Rd)
☎ (0121) 323 1070
Greene King IPA, Abbot; Sharp's Doom Bar; 5 changing beers ⊞
This is a busy Wetherspoon that works hard to keep its ale choices interesting. Local and national beers are featured, with an emphasis on change. The Mare pool was one of many pools that used to surround Sutton Coldfield, and the watery theme is reflected in the decor, with hundreds of hanging glass droplets. The comfortable interior is complemented by café-style seating outside at the front, plus a beer terrace to the side. Q☯♿◀)&≉P🚪🞄

Old Hill

Wheelie Thirsty L
215 Halesowen Road, B64 6HE
Fixed Wheel Wheelie Pale; Oakham Inferno; 4 changing beers (often Fixed Wheel, Titanic) ⊞
The second establishment operated by Fixed Wheel Brewery, joining the Brewery Tap in Blackheath. This single-room micropub opened in May 2019 and was previously a Mediterranean café. In addition to the cask ales, there is a range of rotating craft keg beers and eight ciders. Quiz/cheese/pizza nights take place monthly, with music on alternate Sunday afternoons. Street parking is free and unconstrained after 6pm.
☯♿♿(19,X10)☙🞄

Rushall

Manor Arms ★ L ✅
Park Road, off Daw End Lane, WS4 1LG (off B4154 at Canal Bridge)
☎ (01922) 642333
Banks's Amber Ale, Sunbeam; Bombardier; Wainwright; 1 changing beer (often Young's) ⊞
A canalside venue built around 1105, thought to have held a licence for ale since 1248, and one of the oldest hostelries in the country. It retains features of exposed beams and open fires in both bars. Beer pulls come straight out of the wall, resulting in the place being

known locally as the pub with no bar. It is next to a country park and nature reserve and, although a little off the beaten track, is well worth a visit. Q♉❀P🚌🐾

Sedgley

Beacon Hotel ★ 🄻

129 Bilston Street, DY3 1JE (on A463)
☎ (01902) 883380 🌐 sarahhughesbrewery.co.uk
Sarah Hughes Pale Amber, Sedgley Surprise, Dark Ruby Mild; 3 changing beers (sourced nationally; often Bristol Beer Factory, Shiny, Team Toxic) 🄷
A unique destination brewery tap for Sarah Hughes, also offering progressive guest beers. It is a popular Grade II-listed pub brimming with character – queues have been known to assemble ahead of opening time. The biggest-selling beer by some margin is the award-winning Sarah Hughes Dark Ruby Mild. The large garden has children's play facilities at the rear and is used to host various annual events such as Black Country Day.
Q♉❀P🚌(229,224)

Clifton ✔

Bull Ring, DY3 1RX (on A459)
☎ (01902) 677448
Greene King Abbot; Ruddles Best Bitter; changing beers (sourced nationally; often Beowulf, Oakham, Salopian) 🄷
Multi-level Wetherspoon outlet at the heart of Sedgley. Popular with drinkers and diners of all ages, it gets exceptionally busy at peak weekend times. The building opened as a cinema back in 1937 before becoming a bingo hall in the 1970s. A taxi rank is located immediately outside the premises and a Pay & Display car park can be accessed via Townsend Avenue.
Q♉❀◑♿●P🚌📶

Mount Pleasant

144 High Street, DY3 1RH (on A459)
☎ 07950 195652
9 changing beers (sourced nationally; often Enville, Oakham, Wychwood) 🄷
Known locally as the Stump, this popular free house serves a selection of nine beers. It has a mock-Tudor frontage and a Tardis-like interior. The front bar is the first room off a long corridor. The lounge areas have an intimate feel, with two rooms on different levels housing various nooks and crannies, both with a real coal stove. The pub is on the main number 1 bus route, or a five-minute walk from the centre of Sedgley. Q❀♣P🚌(1)🐾

White Lion Inn

104 Bilston Street, DY3 1JF
☎ (01902) 685232
Oakham Bishops Farewell; 3 changing beers (often Olde Swan, Salopian, Thornbridge) 🄷
Large wet-only establishment serving a range of pale and often hoppy beers, popular for spectators of sport, which is shown on TVs. The former restaurant is now a quieter drinking lounge and can be used for meetings and functions. There is a small garden with benches at the rear. The pub is served by a large car park next door, accessed via Claremont Road. ❀P🚌(229,224)📶

Shirley

Shaking Hand

Unit 24 Parkgate, Stratford Road, B90 3GG
☎ (0121) 733 1176 🌐 theshakinghand.co.uk
4 changing beers (sourced nationally) 🄷
Friendly, light and airy venue, though small, in the Parkgate shopping centre. It is a single-room premises serving four regularly changing guest ales, two usually from local breweries and two from further afield. With all of the feel of a micropub, it has however embraced some of the needs of the modern clientele, such as sports television. You will always get a warm welcome and excellent quality ale and cider.
Q♉♿●P🚌📶

Short Heath

Duke of Cambridge 🄻

82 Coltham Road, WV12 5QD
☎ (01922) 712038
Black Country Bradley's Finest Golden, Pig on the Wall, Fireside; 3 changing beers (sourced nationally) 🄷
A traditional homely, welcoming pub converted from 17th-century cottages. The public bar has a solid fuel wood-burner and wooden beams. The quieter lounge has been tastefully refurbished. A rear room caters for darts and pool and is also used for functions and beer festivals. A quiz is held every other Wednesday. There is a beer garden at the rear. Q♉❀♿♣●🚌(41,69)🐾

Solihull

Fieldhouse ✔

10 Knightcote Drive, B91 3JU
☎ (0121) 703 9209
Purity Pure UBU; St Austell Proper Job; house beer (by Brakspear); 3 changing beers (sourced nationally; often Black Sheep) 🄷
Part of the Ember Inns chain, this large, modern venue is tastefully decorated and comfortably furnished. It features three large fires (one real, two coal-effect) and pleasant patio areas. Six ales are normally served, with three guest ales from across the country, often unusual ones, changing frequently. The pub is frequently busy and attracts a wide age range. Quiz nights are Sundays and Tuesdays; on Mondays cask ales are discounted. Monthly tribute acts and occasional Meet the Brewer events are hosted. ♉❀◑♿P🚌(S15,5)📶

Pup & Duckling

1 Hatchford Brook Road, B92 9AG
☎ (0121) 247 8358 🌐 pupandduckling.co.uk
6 changing beers (sourced nationally; often Fixed Wheel) 🄷
Solihull's first micropub, opened in 2016 in a vacant shop on the corner of Old Lode Lane and Hatchford Brook Road. Family run, it has added a garden area and another room to the initial two-room layout. Six rapidly changing real ales are on handpull, along with six ciders. The latest ales are listed on Facebook, but they can sell out in an evening. Bar snacks are served and customers are welcome to bring in their own food from the nearby Chinese, Indian and fish & chip takeaways. Local CAMRA Pub of the Year 2020. Q❀●🚌(73,957)🐾📶

Stourbridge

Queen's Head 🄻

111 Enville Street, DY8 3TQ
☎ (01384) 396283
Black Country Bradley's Finest Golden, Pig on the Wall, Fireside; 7 changing beers (sourced nationally) 🄷
Purchased by Black Country Ales in 2018, this is a real ale-centric outlet with 12 handpulls, just a short walk from Stourbridge town centre. At the rear there is a comfortable heated smoking shelter, and a separate function room with a newly renovated skittle alley, ideal

for events and private functions. Regular live music and comedy events now feature. Bar snacks are available. Former local CAMRA Pub of the Year. ✿♣🍴🚇😺❄

Red House Boutique 🄻

21-26 Foster Street East, DY8 1EL
☎ (01384) 936430
Enville Ale; Holden's Golden Glow; 6 changing beers (sourced nationally) Ⓗ
Large, single-bar free house near to Stourbridge Interchange. Originally part of the Hogshead chain, this refurbished venue has returned to being an alehouse. Beers from Enville, Fixed Wheel and Three Tuns will usually be on the bar, but may change from those listed. A range of KeyKegs is also on sale. Gourmet snacks can be enjoyed at all times including Scotch eggs and flavoured scratchings. Fridges behind the bar are stocked with many bottles from around the world.
✿👶❄🍴🚇😺❄

Waggon & Horses 🄻

31 Worcester Street, DY8 1AT
☎ (01384) 395398
Church End Goat's Milk; Enville Ale; Holden's Golden Glow; 4 changing beers Ⓗ
Recent refurbishment has created a comfortable, welcoming alehouse. There is a small cask ale bar to the front, with a narrow passageway leading to a larger rear bar. To the side is a cider bar with a small serving hatchway, offering two or more real ciders. Parking can be difficult in the surrounding narrow streets.
✿👶❄🍴🚇😺❄

Streetly

Brew House

49 Boundary Road, B74 2JR
☎ (0121) 353 3358
4 changing beers Ⓗ
This basic micropub, opened in 2018, sits at the end of a parade of suburban shops and is an ale oasis in an area dominated by chain pubs. Up to four brews are served, with a growing array of pumpclips showing those you've missed. Craft beers, real ciders and spirits are also offered. Car parking is available at the front in the area shared by the row of shops. 🚶✿👶🍴P🚇😺❄

Sutton Coldfield

Station ✅

44 Station Street, B73 6AT (nr Sutton station southbound platform)
☎ (0121) 362 4961 ⊕ craft-pubs.co.uk/thestationsuttoncoldfield
Sharp's Doom Bar; Timothy Taylor Landlord; 6 changing beers Ⓗ
Traditional rail-themed pub right next to the station, ideal for commuters, with a view of the departures board from the bar. Up to eight ales are offered on handpulls in both front and back bars – check the board for what is available. Note the ceiling-level model railway in the rear room. Quizzes, live music and comedy nights are among the entertainment. In summertime the multi-level beer terrace to the rear hosts DJs and live music.
🚶✿🕪👶❄🚇😺❄

Tipton

Fountain ✅

51 Owen Street, DY4 8HE
☎ (0121) 522 3606 ⊕ thefountaintipton.co.uk

Greene King Abbot; Wye Valley HPA; 4 changing beers (often Salopian, Wadworth, Wye Valley) Ⓗ
Canalside pub with two beer gardens attracting gongoozlers, boaters, families and lovers of real ale. Changing beers include national brands, namely Wadworth and Wye Valley, but also core range beers from Salopian and Hobsons. Lunchtime meals, such as beef and onion pie, are served Monday to Friday. Snacks are available all week, including cobs and pork pies. The Fountain became a Grade II listed building in 1982. A small car park can be accessed from Factory Road.
🚶✿🕪❄♣P🚇😺❄

Rising Sun 🄻

116 Horseley Road, DY4 7NH (off B4517)
☎ (0121) 557 1940
Black Country Bradley's Finest Golden, Pig on the Wall, Fireside; 7 changing beers (sourced nationally; often Coach House, Froth Blowers, Malvern Hills) Ⓗ
A former CAMRA National Pub of the Year which reopened in 2013 following refurbishment by Black Country Ales. This imposing Victorian hostelry has two distinct rooms warmed by open fires, and a large yard at the rear with patio heaters and an outbuilding. There are seven changing guest beers plus the three Black Country Ales core beers and five traditional ciders. Cobs are served. Great Bridge is a 10-minute walk, with frequent services to Dudley, West Bromwich and Birmingham.
✿♣🍴🚇(22) 😺❄

Tame Bridge

45 Tame Road, DY4 7JA (off A461)
☎ (0121) 557 2496
Wye Valley HPA; 3 changing beers (sourced nationally; often Abbeydale, Ossett, Rat) Ⓗ
A back-street local offering a varying range of guest beers, advertised in advance on a blackboard near the bar. The rear White Room is used for occasional live entertainment and can also be hired for events and meetings. Live sporting fixtures are shown on a flatscreen TV, below which is a real fire. The pub is part of the popular Red Pub Co regional portfolio. An adjacent public footpath leads to Sheepwash Nature Reserve.
🚶✿❄🚇(74) 😺❄

Tividale

Tivi Ale

45-47 Regent Road, B69 1TL
Holden's Golden Glow; 3 changing beers (sourced nationally; often Enville, Mad Squirrel, Salopian) Ⓗ
A popular microbar that opened in 2018 in a former convenience store. One of the guest beers is from a local brewery, the other two are national ales. Fresh cakes are available daily and afternoon tea can be served (book ahead). Regular family-friendly events are held throughout the year and often spill out on to the front terrace. An array of interesting gins and tonics is also on sale. 🚶✿👶🚇❄

Upper Gornal

Britannia ★ 🄻

109 Kent Street, DY3 1UX (on A459)
☎ (01902) 883253
Bathams Best Bitter Ⓗ
Dating to the early 19th century, this inn has a nationally important historic pub interior because of the taproom at the rear with its wall-mounted handpulls. Service can be obtained from the front bar, itself a comfortable place to be. There is also a family/games room with a TV. Behind the building is the former brewhouse and the garden.

Large cobs and pork pies are sold. It is on the main bus route between Wolverhampton and Dudley.
🛇❀♠🖳(1) ☺🛜

Walsall

Black Country Arms 🅛
High Street, WS1 1QW (in market, opp Asda)
☎ (01922) 640588 🌐 blackcountryarms.co.uk
Black Country Bradley's Finest Golden, Pig on the Wall, Fireside; 13 changing beers (sourced nationally; often Fixed Wheel, Mallinsons, Salopian) Ⓗ
A short walk from the train and bus station, this pub has an unrivalled selection of constantly changing real ales and ciders. It is open plan, with comfortable seating and various quieter areas. The staff offer a warm welcome to all, even during the busier periods. Food is served during the day. Entertainment is held regularly on Saturday nights and there are sports TVs spread around the pub. Dogs are welcome in all areas. 🛇❀◑≉♣🖳☺🛜

Butts Tavern 🅛
44 Butts Street, WS4 2BJ (200yds from the arboretum's Lichfield St entrance)
☎ (01922) 629332 🌐 buttstavern.co.uk
Holden's Golden Glow; Wye Valley Butty Bach; 2 changing beers (often Castle Rock, Church End, Marston's) Ⓗ
A warm welcome is assured from the staff in this large community-based local, which has a spacious main bar containing a stage and sports TV. A smaller bar is at the rear with pool table and darts facilities, and outside is a patio area for smokers and summer drinking. Dominoes and crib teams are based here. There is often entertainment on Friday or Saturday nights.
🛇❀&♣🖳🛜

Fountain Inn 🅛
49 Lower Forster Street, WS1 1XB (off A4148 ring road)
☎ (01922) 633307
Backyard The Hoard, Blonde; 6 changing beers (sourced regionally; often Green Duck, Salopian, Titanic) Ⓗ
A family-run backyard brewery tap serving up to eight real ales plus cider, with friendly staff and great atmosphere. There are two comfortable rooms with log fires. It is a rare example of a lively wet-led pub, with bar snacks available (cobs, pork pies, crisps and nuts). There are regular music nights including vinyl, indie classic rock and reggae, as well as monthly drawing classes. A superb back-street boozer within easy walking distance of the town centre. 🛇≉♣🖳☺

Lyndon House Hotel 🅛
9-10 Upper Rushall Street, WS1 2HA (below St Matthew's Church)
☎ (01922) 612511 🌐 lyndonhousehotel.co.uk
Bathams Best Bitter; Burton Bridge XL Mild, Stairway to Heaven; Caledonian Deuchars IPA; Greene King Abbot; Holden's Golden Glow Ⓗ
The old Royal Exchange pub at the top of the Walsall market was incorporated into an adjoining Salvation Army hostel and former leather works in 1995, and now forms the luxurious Lyndon House Hotel. The comfortable bar has an island counter, cosy corners and old wood and brick, giving it a traditional feel. With its function room, and outdoor terraces, it is unexpectedly spacious. Live music takes place on Sunday afternoon and Monday evening. Lunchtime hot club sandwiches are a delicious bargain. Q❀≉◑&🖳(7,51)🛜

Pretty Bricks 🅛
5 John Street, WS2 8AF (near magistrates court, off B4210)
☎ (01922) 612553
Black Country Bradley's Finest Golden, Pig on the Wall, Fireside; 6 changing beers (sourced nationally) Ⓗ
This small, friendly, cosy pub on the edge of town dates from 1845 and has a front bar with a wood fire, a lounge, an upstairs function room and a small blue brick courtyard. It was originally called the New Inn; the current name derives from a part-glazed frontage. Great cobs and pork pies provide sustenance alongside the great range of ales. A folk night is held every second Thursday of the month. Q❀≉♣🖳☺🛜

St Matthew's Hall ✪
Lichfield Street, WS1 1SX (adjacent to Town Hall)
☎ (01922) 700820
Greene King Abbot; Ruddles Best Bitter; Sharp's Doom Bar; 4 changing beers (sourced regionally; often AJ's, Backyard, Salopian) Ⓗ
A stunning Grade II-listed Wetherspoon outlet in the centre of Walsall town, easily accessible by public transport and with plenty of parking nearby. Regular beer festivals feature throughout the year as well as entertainment every Friday and Saturday night until late. A large beer garden at the side sells a selection of national guest ales, supplementing the three regular beers. 🛇❀◑&≉♣🖳☺🛜

Victoria 🅛
23 Lower Rushall Street, WS1 2AA
☎ (01922) 635866
Backyard Bitter; Banks's Sunbeam; Church End Gravediggers Ale; Wye Valley Butty Bach; 3 changing beers (sourced regionally; often AJ's, Fixed Wheel, Salopian) Ⓗ
Popular two-roomed pub close to the town centre, dating from 1845. It has a former brewhouse, a pleasant garden and smoking facilities at the back. A large Pay & Display car park is also to the rear. Bar snacks are available along with Sunday lunches. Open mic and quiz nights are held regularly, Sunday evening has live entertainment, and retro games nights are on a monthly cycle. A pool table is located upstairs. One real cider is permanently available. 🛇❀◑≉♣🖳☺🛜

Walsall Arms 🅛
17 Bank Street, WS1 2EP (behind Royal Hotel, off A34)
☎ (01922) 649839
Wye Valley Bitter, Butty Bach, HPA; 3 changing beers (sourced locally; often Salopian) Ⓗ
Refurbished back-street hostelry with one large, carpeted comfy bar area. The location is just a short walk from Walsall town centre. There is a small bar access via the passageway. The pub features an open fire, old Walsall photographs and two TV screens. A refurbished patio painted in an Italianate fashion is at the rear. There is a quiz on the first Monday of the month, themed food every Thursday, and regular jazz nights. ❀◑&♣🖳(51,377)☺🛜

Walsall Cricket Club
Gorway Road, WS1 3BE (off A34, by university campus)
☎ (01922) 622094 🌐 walsall.play-cricket.com
Wye Valley HPA; 1 changing beer (sourced regionally; often Backyard, Castle Rock) Ⓗ
On a fine summer day, the click of bat on ball welcomes you to a green oasis on the outskirts of town. The club room has had a major renovation and now provides a luxurious setting with a panoramic view of the field. The club contains local cricket memorabilia and two large

441

sporting screens. There is occasional entertainment and the venue is popular for function hire. Non-members' entry is by CAMRA membership card. Sunday hours are reduced in winter. ♿🏛♿♣🅿�(51)🐾📶

Wednesbury

Bellwether ✅
3-4 Walsall Street, WS10 9BZ
☎ (0121) 502 6404
Greene King Abbot; Oakham JHB; Ruddles Best Bitter; 7 changing beers (sourced nationally) Ⓗ
Near the main shopping area and market, this pub attracts a wide clientele. It has a large L-shaped room on two levels, with open-plan tables and chairs in front of the bar. More intimate seating at the rear leads on to a tranquil, split-level garden area. The pub is decorated with images of historic events and characters associated with the town. Ten handpulls serve a large selection of guest ales. Q♿🏛🍴🍺♿♣🅿🚾📶

Olde Leathern Bottel ✅
40 Vicarage Road, WS10 9DW (just off A461; bus 311 from Walsall is 5 mins' walk)
☎ (0121) 505 0230
4 changing beers (sourced nationally; often Marston's, Wye Valley) Ⓗ
The front areas of the bar and snug are set in cottages dating from 1510; a later extension contains a comfy lounge. The small snug is often used as a function room. The four rooms have many old photos and the bar displays a picture of the pub from 1887 and a map of Wednesbury from 1846. The friendly staff are happy to help. Entertainment takes place on Saturday nights. ♿🏛🍴♣🅿🚾(11)🐾📶

Wednesfield

Royal Tiger Ⓛ ✅
41-43 High Street, WV11 1ST
☎ (01902) 307816
Greene King Abbot; Sharp's Doom Bar; changing beers Ⓗ
A typical Wetherspoon, built on the site of a former bakery. It gets its name from an earlier pub which stood next door. The staff and management are enthusiastic and knowledgeable about their ale, and keen to showcase local microbreweries. Food is served well into the evening, with families welcome. The pub has no car park, but is on the main number 59 bus route and is also approachable from the canal towpath at the rear. 🏛🍴♿♣🚾📶

Vine ★ Ⓛ
35 Lichfield Road, WV11 1TN
☎ (01902) 733529
Black Country Bradley's Finest Golden, Pig on the Wall, Fireside; 6 changing beers (sourced nationally) Ⓗ
Built in 1938, this Grade II-listed community local is a rare intact example of a simple inter-war working-class hostelry. It has been identified by CAMRA as having a nationally important historic pub interior, which has retained its original bar, lounge and snug. Cobs and pork pies are available at all times. Darts and dominoes are played and there are TVs showing sport and horse racing. A covered smokers'; shelter and a beer garden provide outdoor areas. ♿🏛♣♿🅿🚾(59,60)🐾📶

West Bromwich

Crown & Cushion ✅
2 Lloyd Street, B71 4AT
☎ (0121) 553 4493
Castle Rock Harvest Pale; St Austell Tribute; 1 changing beer (sourced nationally; often Harviestoun) Ⓗ
Family-friendly hostelry on the outskirts of town run by staff who make you feel at home. It has an L-shaped single room and is popular in the summer with visitors to the nearby park. It is within easy walking distance of West Bromwich Albion's ground and so gets busy on match days. Away supporters are always welcome. A quiz night is held on Thursdays. ♿🏛♿♣♿🅿🚾(47)🐾📶

Royal Oak Ⓛ ✅
14 Newton Street, B71 3RQ (down side road off Hollyhedge Rd)
☎ (0121) 532 5692
St Austell Proper Job; Wye Valley HPA; 2 changing beers (sourced nationally) Ⓗ
Traditional back-street local with two small rooms, both showing TV sport. The bar on the left is adorned with West Bromwich Albion memorabilia, and on the right is the quieter lounge. There is a terrace in the rear yard for smokers, and two benches outside the front to bask on in the summer. Bar snacks are on offer. Parking is available in the street. ♿🏛♣♿🐾📶

Three Horseshoes Ⓛ
86 Witton Lane, B71 2AQ
☎ (0121) 502 1693
Black Country Bradley's Finest Golden, Pig on the Wall, Fireside; 4 changing beers (sourced nationally) Ⓗ
This refurbished one-roomed pub was taken on by Black Country ales in 2016, with 10 handpulls added. The spacious interior is furnished in a traditional style, with TVs showing live sport. The warm welcome provided by the staff makes you feel right at home in the large expansive hostelry. There are bar snacks available and a beer garden for fine weather enjoyment. ♿🏛♿♣♿🅿🚾(79,49)🐾📶

Willenhall

Falcon
77 Gomer Street West, WV13 2NR (off B4464, behind flats)
☎ (01902) 633378
Hobsons Town Crier; 3 changing beers (sourced regionally; often Castle Rock) Ⓗ
A two-roomed establishment with a lively public bar and quieter lounge at the rear, a short walk from the town centre. Dating back to 1936, the Falcon has been in the same family for over 30 years. Old pub memorabilia adorn both rooms, where keenly priced beers are served. There is a beer garden at the rear. On-street parking is plentiful. ♿🏛♣♿🚾🚾(529)🐾📶

Wollaston

Foresters Arms Ⓛ ✅
Bridgnorth Road, DY8 3PL (on A458 towards Bridgnorth)
☎ (01384) 394476 🌐 foresterswollaston.co.uk
Enville Ale; Ludlow Gold; Wye Valley HPA; 1 changing beer Ⓗ
Located on the ridge, ideal for ramblers, this warm, cosy and friendly traditional local is situated on the outskirts of Wollaston next to the countryside. The L-shaped room provides a convenient area where diners can sample

food of good quality and value. Quizzes are usually held on the first and third Sunday of each month, with regular themed evenings also hosted. There is a heated and covered smoking area, and in summer a large, furnished marquee, available for hire. 🔥❀◑P🚌(8,227,228)🐾📶

Unicorn Ⓛ

145 Bridgnorth Road, DY8 3NX (on A458 towards Bridgnorth)

☎ (01384) 394823

Bathams Best Bitter, Mild Ale Ⓗ

A former brewhouse purchased by Bathams, the Unicorn has barely altered in appearance since the Billingham family sold up in the early 1990s. It is a traditional two-bar drinking house, with a small back room popular with all age groups (children are welcome), and where conversation is the order of the day. The brewhouse remains but is no longer in use. Fresh cobs – with hot pork and stuffing on Saturday lunchtimes – are available on request. Bathams XXX is sold in the winter only. Q🔥❀♿P🚌🐾📶

Wolverhampton

Chindit Ⓛ ✔

113 Merridale Road, WV3 9SE

☎ 07986 773487

Rat White Rat; Wye Valley HPA; 3 changing beers (sourced regionally) Ⓗ

The Chindit was built in the 1950s as an off-licence. Its first pub landlord had served in the British and Indian armies' Chindit special forces division in Burma in WWII and named it after his comrades. It is thought to be the only pub in the country honouring Major General Orde Wingate's Chindits; their history is displayed in the lounge. The two-roomed venue consists of a small lounge and a bar featuring an original Wurlitzer jukebox stocking 45rpm records from the 60s and 70s. There is live music every Friday and an open mic night on Sunday. 🔥❀♣P🚌(3,15) 📶

Combermere Arms

90 Chapel Ash, WV3 0TY (on A41 Tettenhall Rd)

☎ (01902) 421880

5 changing beers (sourced nationally) Ⓗ

A Grade II-listed building with original sash windows. A short walk or bus ride from the city centre, the pub comprises three charming rooms with cosy fireplaces replete with classic adverts. The renowned tree in the Gents is still growing despite being trimmed. One locally brewed beer, four from the Greene King portfolio, and a varying cider are on sale. Pie, sausage and cheese-tasting festivals are held annually and there is occasional live entertainment. To the rear are a courtyard and beer garden. Q🔥❀●P🚌🐾

Hail to the Ale Ⓛ

2 Pendeford Avenue, Claregate, WV6 9EF (at Claregate island)

☎ 07846 562910 🌐 mortonbrewery.co.uk/httahome.htm

6 changing beers (sourced locally; often Morton) Ⓗ

The West Midlands' first micropub is a welcoming one-room venue that was opened in 2013 by Morton brewery, with a focus on beer and conversation. Six handpulls dispense at least two Morton beers alongside guest ales that are usually from microbreweries in the area. Four ciders or perries are also available, along with 10 fruit wines. Locally sourced pies, cheese, sausage rolls and Scotch eggs are served. Local CAMRA branch Pub of the Year five years running from 2015-2019. Q🔥❀♿♣●P🚌(5,6) 🐾

Hogshead Ⓛ ✔

186 Stafford Street, WV1 1NA

☎ (01902) 717955 🌐 craft-pubs.co.uk/hogsheadwolverhampton

10 changing beers (sourced nationally) Ⓗ

A traditional 19th-century city-centre building with an attractive brick terracotta exterior. A stained-glass window above the entrance displays the original name, the Vine. The large interior single room is divided into separate areas, with TVs showing sport throughout the pub. It serves a range of 10 guest ales, with regular brewery tap takeovers, and a large number of ciders, mostly from Lilley's. The pub is popular with all age groups. It hosts a quiz on Wednesday evenings, and a DJ on Saturday evenings. 🔥❀◑♿≹🚉♣●🚌📶

Keg & Comfort Ⓛ

474 Stafford Road, Oxley, WV10 6AN

☎ 07952 631032 🌐 kegandcomfort.co.uk

4 changing beers (sourced locally) Ⓗ

The city's second micropub opened in 2018 in a former bank. The main contemporary room has a striking bar custom-built using coloured bottles, seating for around 40, and old barrels as tables for customers who prefer to stand. A small side room houses a large sofa and a games cupboard. Four changing ales (one dark), five ciders or perries and a selection of fruit wines are served. Live music features on the first Wednesday of the month. Local CAMRA Cider Pub of the Year 2020. Q🔥♿♣●P🚌(3) 🐾

Posada Ⓛ

48 Lichfield Street, WV1 1DG

Hobsons Town Crier; Sharp's Doom Bar; 3 changing beers Ⓗ

Victorian Grade II-listed city-centre pub with tiled walls and original bar fittings – including rare snob screens – little altered since 1900. It attracts a varied clientele and is quiet during the day but busy in the evening and weekends, especially when Wolverhampton Wanderers are at home. There is a courtyard to the rear with a smoking area. Cobs are served and Westons Old Rosie is on handpump. 🔥❀≹🚉●🚌📶

Royal Oak Ⓛ ✔

70 Compton Road, WV3 9PH

☎ (01902) 422845 🌐 theoakchapelash.com

Banks's Mild, Amber Ale, Sunbeam; Wainwright; Wychwood Hobgoblin Gold; 3 changing beers (sourced nationally) Ⓗ

A friendly hostelry, a short walk or bus ride from the city centre, that serves a wide range of real ales from the Marston's portfolio. The bustling bar hosts jam nights on Tuesdays, open mic evenings on Wednesdays, and live bands on Fridays and Saturdays (also summer Sunday afternoons). Part of the community, it raises money for regional and national charities, and is the headquarters of Old Wulfrunians Hockey Club. Pub and local history and maps are displayed on a wall. Cobs are served. 🔥❀♿♣P🚌(10,9) 🐾📶

Starting Gate Ⓛ

134 Birches Barn Road, Penn Fields, WV3 7BG

5 changing beers (sourced regionally; often Ludlow, Sarah Hughes, Wye Valley) Ⓗ

Opened in 2018, this small outlet occupies a former bank branch and retains the original counter and wings. The impressive rear door to the garden also reflects its previous use. The small bar area leads to a cosy lounge, with another lounge upstairs reached by an open spiral staircase. Paintings, silks and other memorabilia signal the owner's brother's interest in horse racing, hence the name of the pub. Q❀♿●🚌(2)🐾📶

Stile Inn 𝕃 ✔

3 Harrow Street, Whitmore Reans, WV1 4PB (off Newhampton Rd East/Fawdry St)
☎ (01902) 425336
Banks's Mild, Amber Ale, Sunbeam; 1 changing beer (sourced locally) ⊞
A typical late-Victorian street-corner pub built in 1900, featuring a public bar, smoke room and snug. It is a true community local with an emphasis on sports – darts and dominoes feature inside, crown green bowls on the unusual L-shaped green outside, and it is busy with Wolverhampton Wanderers' fans on match days. Excellent-value food, including Polish dishes, is served all day. Friday is disco night and Saturday is karaoke. Sky Sports and BT Sport are shown in all rooms.
♘❀◑♣🚌(5,6)🐾ᯤ

Swan 𝕃

Bridgnorth Road, Compton, WV6 8AE (at Compton Island, A454)
☎ (01902) 754736
Banks's Mild, Amber Ale, Sunbeam; Marston's Old Empire; Wainwright; 1 changing beer (sourced nationally) ⊞
Built around 1780, this Grade II-listed former coaching inn is popular with locals, boaters, ramblers and cyclists, as it is close to the Staffordshire & Worcestershire Canal and Smestow Valley Nature Reserve. It comprises a lively bar with banter, plus a games room and a more sedate snug. Quizzes are held on Tuesdays and a darts team plays on Wednesdays. The pub hosts charity dog shows and, weekly, the area's pigeon flyers' club.
Q♘❀♣P🚌🐾ᯤ

Woodcross

Horse & Jockey 𝕃

Robert Wynd, WV14 9SB
☎ (01902) 662268
Hobsons Twisted Spire, Town Crier; St Austell Tribute; 3 changing beers (sourced locally) ⊞
Run by two CAMRA members, this friendly and thriving community pub comprises a bar, a large contemporary lounge with a seasonal open fire, a rear beer garden and a small smoking shelter at the front. Good-value home-cooked food, including vegetarian options, is served daily until early evening. Under-18s are allowed in the lounge area and newly refurbished garden during the day.
Q♘❀◑♣●P🚌🐾ᯤ

Wordsley

Bird in Hand

57 John Street, DY8 4AZ
☎ (01384) 865809
Enville Ale; Hobsons Town Crier; Holden's Golden Glow; 3 changing beers (sourced nationally; often Fixed Wheel, Tiny Rebel, Titanic) ⊞
An ambitious and inviting back-street local which ticks all the boxes on a CAMRA member's wish list. With a high turnover on the permanent cask range and a changing trio of national guest beers, there is always a tipple to please. Multiple teams and community groups meet here. The venue is part of the popular Red Pub Co regional portfolio. The homely garden at the rear has some sheltered seating. Flatscreen TVs show sports fixtures in the bar area only. Q♘❀♣●🚌🐾ᯤ

New Inn 𝕃

117 High Street, DY8 5QR (on A491)
☎ (01384) 295614
Bathams Best Bitter, Mild Ale ⊞
Acquired by Daniel Batham Ltd in 2008, this L-shaped bar serves a single room with a small annexe at one end, plus a patio area and pleasant garden outside. The beer choice includes Bathams Mild Ale, which is only available in certain pubs across the Bathams estate. Various cobs are on offer. Children are welcome in the garden but not in the pub. ♘❀♣P🚌🐾ᯤ

Bartons Arms, Birmingham: Newtown (Photo: Tony Hisgett/Flickr CC BY 2.0)

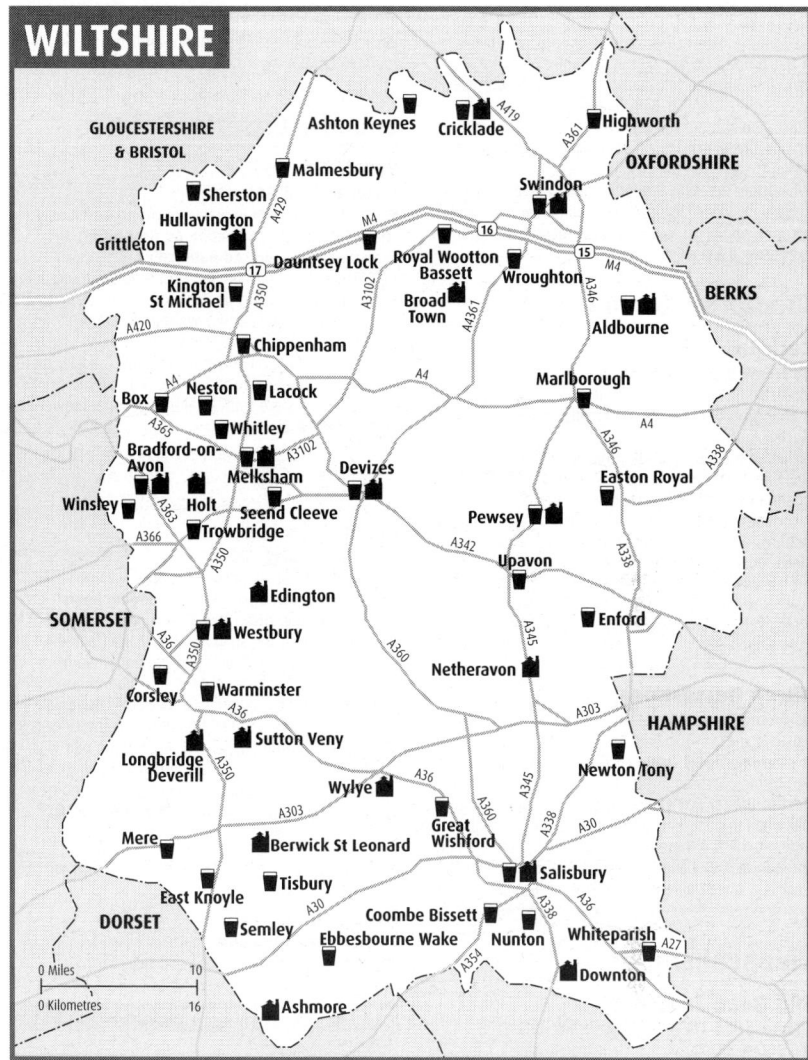

WILTSHIRE

Aldbourne

Crown ✓

The Square, SN8 2DU
☎ (01672) 540214 ⊕ thecrownaldbourne.co.uk
Sharp's Doom Bar; Timothy Taylor Landlord; 1
changing beer (sourced nationally) Ⓗ

The Crown is set in the middle of the village opposite the duck pond, with a Dalek standing guard outside. It is near the historic market towns of Marlborough and Hungerford, and a stone's throw from the ancient Avebury Rings, Silbury Hill and Stonehenge. At the heart of the local community, it has a relaxed and pleasant atmosphere. The main bar is stylishly refurbished with a welcoming fire in winter. The smaller bar shows films on Monday night. There is a Sunday carvery, a meat draw on Saturday afternoon and quiz night on Tuesday. All food is cooked to order and made from local produce whenever possible, catering for a range of dietary needs. Accommodation is in five spacious en-suite bedrooms. An ideal base for walkers, the famous Roman Ridgeway is nearby. ⊛🛏🌙🅰♣🚲(46,48)🐾🐾📶

Ashton Keynes

White Hart 🅛 ✓

High Road, SN6 6NX
☎ (01285) 861247 ⊕ thewhitehartashtonkeynes.com
Ramsbury Gold; house beer (by Stroud); 2 changing
beers (sourced nationally; often Fuller's, Timothy
Taylor) Ⓗ

Set next to one of the four village crosses, the pub is a community hub for beautiful Ashton Keynes. Its interior features plenty of bare stone and is divided into three: the main bar, a restaurant and a small bar with games and television. There is a separate function room, plus a secluded garden. Four real ales are served, two of them constantly changing guests. The good-quality food uses locally sourced ingredients. 🛏⊛🌙♣🅿🚲(93A)🐾📶

Box

Quarryman's Arms 🅛

Box Hill, SN13 8HN (signed from A4)
☎ (01225) 743569

Butcombe Original, Gold; 3 changing beers (sourced nationally; often Liberation, Oakham, VOG) ⊞
A Butcombe Brewery pub in a hamlet off the A4 near Box. This 300-year-old former miners' inn, with views over Bath, is popular with locals and visitors. The Butcombe ales are complemented by different nationally and locally sourced guest ales. A high-quality varied menu is served in the restaurant, bar and garden. Wheelchair access is limited although assistance is happily provided. The pub has a large car park, and accommodation in four rooms for those wishing to stay. Q⏱❀⛵⟋◑Å♣●P🐾

Bradford-on-Avon

Lock Inn
48 Frome Road, BA15 1LE
☎ (01225) 868068 ⊕ thelockinn.co.uk
2 changing beers (sourced locally; often Kettlesmith) ⊞
Although essentially a café, this popular venue sells two real ales from local brewers. Food, including the hearty boatman's breakfast, is served and is highly recommended. Originally a canalside cottage, the pub features an interior decorated with bric-a-brac and old signs. Outside, there are tables in the garden alongside the Kennet & Avon and two enclosed dining rooms, as well as a narrowboat. The café closes about an hour earlier on weekdays in autumn and winter.
Q⏱❀◑⟋≈●🐾

Three Horseshoes
55 Frome Road, BA15 1LA
☎ (01225) 865876
3 changing beers (sourced regionally) ⊞
A nice old coaching inn on the edge of the town centre next to the railway station. It comes complete with the old wooden door where the horses went through to the yard. At the bar there are usually three changing beers, often local. Live bands play at weekends. Outside at the back is a small garden and terrace with seating. Parking is at the rear and is a bit limited. ❀≈♣P🚃(D1)🐾🛜

Chippenham

Old Road Tavern ✔
Old Rd, SN15 1JA (over bridge from station)
☎ (01249) 247080
Bath Ales Gem; Hop Back Summer Lightning; Otter Bitter; Wye Valley HPA; 2 changing beers (sourced nationally) ⊞
A traditional community venue since 1842. The pub has a large garden with plenty of seating and a smoking shelter. A diverse mix of locals ensures lively and friendly conversation. Four regular ales are supplemented with two varying guest beers. Bar snacks are available. There is frequent live music and a monthly comedy club in the refurbished adjoining hall, which is available for hire. Well-behaved dogs are welcome in the pub and garden. ⏱❀≈♣🚃🐾🛜

Three Crowns ⑬
18 The Causeway, SN15 3DB (S of town)
☎ (01249) 449029 ⊕ threecrownschippenham.co.uk
7 changing beers (sourced nationally; often Arbor, Slater's, XT) ⊞
A welcoming 18th-century waggoners' inn with a main bar warmed by a real fire and a cider/snug bar. A proper pub without noisy distractions, it hosts quizzes, darts and a cheese club, and is popular with visitors and locals. Beers include local ales and dark beers, alongside four ciders or perries. Filled rolls and pork pies are served. The

quarterly beer festivals feature 12 ales and eight ciders/perries plus more substantial hot and cold snacks. A multiple CAMRA award winner. Q❀≈♣●P🚃🐾🛜

Coombe Bissett

Fox & Goose ⑬
Blandford Road, SP5 4LE
☎ (01722) 718437 ⊕ foxandgoose-coombebissett.co.uk
Sharp's Doom Bar; Sixpenny 6d Best Bitter; 1 changing beer (sourced nationally) ⊞
An 18th-century coaching inn on the A354, three miles south of Salisbury. This popular community pub has a loyal village clientele and a welcoming atmosphere. Divided into a bar and restaurant, it offers an extensive food menu with ever-changing specials. Outside, there are pleasant gardens to the rear and a covered smoking area. Guest ales are from local and national breweries. Q⏱❀◑P🚃🐾🛜

Corsley

Cross Keys Inn
Lye's Green, BA12 7PB
☎ (01373) 832406 ⊕ crosskeyscorsley.co.uk
Three Daggers Daggers Ale; 3 changing beers (sourced locally; often Box Steam, Moles, Twisted) ⊞
This rural gem in the shadow of Cley Hill (famed for its UFO sightings) has a large open fire and a warm, welcoming atmosphere. A good selection of guest ales, mainly from local breweries, is available, along with excellent bar food and restaurant meals. The cider is Cheddar Valley from Thatchers. In 2016 the pub was taken over by a village consortium. It is in an excellent walking area, close to the Somerset border, and near Longleat House and Safari Park. ⏱❀◑Å♣●P🐾🛜

Cricklade

Red Lion ⑬
74 High Street, SN6 6DD
☎ (01793) 750776 ⊕ theredlioncricklade.co.uk

REAL ALE BREWERIES

Arkell's Swindon
Blonde Brothers Wylye
Box Steam 🚲 Holt
BrightBeer Swindon (brewing suspended)
Broadtown 🚲 Broad Town
Dark Revolution 🚲 Salisbury
Downton 🚲 Downton
Flying Monk Hullavington
Gritchie Ashmore
Hop Back Downton
Hop Kettle 🍺 🚲 Cricklade/Swindon
Kettlesmith Bradford-On-Avon
Keystone Berwick St Leonard
Plain 🚲 Sutton Veny
Ramsbury Aldbourne
Rusty Garage Swindon (NEW)
Shed Pewsey
Stealth Melksham
Stonehenge Netheravon
Three Castles Pewsey
Three Daggers Edington
Twisted Westbury
Wadworth 🚲 Devizes
Wessex Longbridge Deverill
World's End 🚲 Pewsey

Hop Kettle Cricklade Ordinary Bitter, North Wall; St Austell Tribute, Proper Job; 6 changing beers (sourced nationally; often St Austell, Hop Kettle) Ⓗ
A popular and comfortable pub that features part of the old Saxon town wall in the building. It is home to the original Hop Kettle brewery and this remains despite the pub having been acquired by St Austell. There are 10 real ales on offer – three from Hop Kettle and four from St Austell, plus three guests. Excellent food is served and there are five rooms for B&B. Outside at the back is a large garden. Q❀🛏🍴🕭🚆(51,53)🐾🛜

Dauntsey Lock

Peterborough Arms Ⓛ

SN15 4HD (on the B4069)
☎ (01249) 247833 ⏛ peterborougharms.com
3 changing beers (sourced nationally; often Box Steam, Plain, Three Castles) Ⓗ
Saved by the Wilts & Berks Canal Trust and restored by its volunteers, this place reopened in 2018 offering three real ales including a dark beer, plus real cider and good pub food. It is home to both skittles and darts teams and hosts regular quiz nights. There is a beer garden for the summer and a log-burner for the winter. The pub is alongside the old canal, which is under restoration by the WBCT. Q🚳❀🍴🕭♣🍺PⓊ🛜

Devizes

British Lion ✅

9 Estcourt Street, SN10 1LQ (on A361 opp Kwik Fit)
☎ (01380) 720665 ⏛ britishliondevizes.co.uk
4 changing beers (sourced nationally; often Palmers, Plain, Stonehenge) Ⓗ
The British has featured in every edition of the Guide for over 26 years. An unpretentious free house with wooden floors, cosy settles and an eclectic group of talkative regulars, it is an essential port of call in town. There are four handpumps and the beers change frequently throughout the week - time it right and you can savour eight different ales. The knowledgeable landlord is always pleased to offer his advice. The cider is often Cheddar Valley or Black Rat. ❀🍺PⓊ🚆🛜

Southgate Inn

Potterne Road, SN10 5BY
☎ (01380) 722872
Hop Back GFB, Crop Circle, Summer Lightning; 3 changing beers (sourced nationally) Ⓖ
The five-minute walk from the town centre is well worth while for the welcome you will receive here. The cosy, friendly pub has three separate bar areas, lots of nooks and crannies and a large courtyard. It usually offers six ales - mainly from Hop Back but often a guest too - plus still ciders and a perry, all served straight from the cask. Attractions include live music throughout the weekend, an acoustic jam session on Wednesday and a Friday afternoon ukulele group. Well-behaved dogs are positively encouraged. 🚳♣🍺PⓊ(49)🐾🛜

Vaults

28A St John's Street, SN10 1BN (opp town hall)
☎ (01380) 721443 ⏛ thevaultsdevizes.com
5 changing beers (sourced nationally; often Stealth) Ⓗ
The Vaults maintains its high standards, with a long, galley-style bar usually offering at least two ales from Stealth Brew Co, normally at least one dark beer, plus up to three still ciders. Beer paddles are available and a selection of bottles and cans from around the world is also stocked. Conversation rules here – there are no fruit machines or loud music, just a great atmosphere. The large cellar is used for events ranging from quizzes to a poetry club and a Christmas story evening. ♦PⓊ🐾🛜

White Bear ✅

33 Monday Market Street, SN10 1DN
☎ (01380) 727588 ⏛ whitebeardevizes.co.uk
Wadworth Henry's IPA; 5 changing beers (sourced nationally; often Wadworth) Ⓗ
Recently refurbished throughout, this old coaching inn with original beams and wood-burning stoves dates from the 1500s. It offers six real ales, two from Wadworth – IPA and a varying beer - plus four guests. A dark ale is usually among the selection, plus a changing still cider. Food is served all week. The pub does not have a car park but there are public car parks adjacent, plus plenty of on-street parking. 🛏🍴♦🐾🛜

East Knoyle

Fox & Hounds

Wise Lane, The Green, SP3 6BN ST87113135
☎ (01747) 830573 ⏛ foxandhounds-eastknoyle.co.uk
3 changing beers Ⓗ
Attractive old thatched black and white pub situated high on a hillside with extensive panoramic rural views, especially from the beer garden. Comfortable and cosy inside, it provides a warm welcome that is enhanced in winter by a blazing log fire in a huge inglenook fireplace. Three ales are always available, encompassing a wide range of strengths and varying continuously, with local beers given prominence. The cider is Harry's. Food is served at all sessions. An adjacent skittle alley doubles as a function room. Q🚳❀🍴♦P🐾

Easton Royal

Bruce Arms ★ Ⓛ

Easton Road, SN9 5LR
☎ (01672) 810216
Sharp's Atlantic; Stonehenge Pigswill; Wadworth 6X; 2 changing beers (sourced regionally) Ⓗ
Located in the heart of rural Wiltshire, this mid-19th century local has been identified by CAMRA as having a nationally important historic pub interior. It has a cosy bar with furniture that probably goes back to the 1850s, a small lounge with easy chairs and a piano, and a larger dining/function room at the back. The pub exists in splendid isolation, so its campsite with full facilities is an asset that makes it a good venue for meetings and rallies. Q🚳❀Å♣🍺P🚆(103)🐾🛜

Ebbesbourne Wake

Horseshoe

The Cross, SP5 5JF
☎ (01722) 780474 ⏛ thehorseshoe-inn.co.uk
Bowman Swift One; Gritchie English Lore; Otter Bitter; 1 changing beer (sourced nationally) Ⓖ
Unspoilt 18th-century inn in a remote rural setting at the foot of an old ox drove. This friendly pub has two small bars displaying an impressive collection of old farm implements, tools and lamps, plus a restaurant, conservatory and pleasant garden. Good local food is available Tuesday to Sunday and beers are poured direct from casks behind the bar. The original serving hatch just inside the front door is still in use. Real cider is usually available, often Orchard Pig Reveller or Wessex. Local CAMRA Country Pub of the Year 2019 and 2020. Q🚳❀🛏🍴Å♦P🚆🐾

Enford

Swan [L] ✔

Long Street, SN9 6DD

☎ (01980) 670338 🌐 theswanenford.co.uk

5 changing beers (sourced locally; often Stonehenge, Three Daggers) [H]

Everyone is welcome at this 16th-century, Grade II-listed pub, which was purchased by villagers for the community in 1998. It is one of only a handful of pubs in the country with the inn sign hanging on a gantry over the road. Old beams, an inglenook fireplace, sloping walls and quiet nooks and crannies add to its character. Flights of three third-pints help you sample a selection of mainly local ales. 🐴❀◐♣🍏P🚌🐾📶

Great Wishford

Royal Oak

Langford Road, SP2 0PD

☎ (01722) 790613 🌐 royaloakgreatwishford.com

Shepherd Neame Master Brew; 4 changing beers (sourced regionally) [H]

17th-century, ivy-clad traditional village pub with a changing selection of real ales. A comfortable main bar area with large restaurant is to the rear, with good, freshly prepared food including a Sunday carvery. Popular with horse riders, cyclists (route 24) and walkers. Regular music events and quizzes are held and it is heavily involved in the village celebrations on Oak Apple Day (29 May). Q🐴❀◐♣P🚌(2)🐾📶

Grittleton

Neeld Arms

The Street, SN14 6AP

☎ (01249) 782470 🌐 neeldarms.co.uk

St Austell Tribute; Wadworth 6X; 1 changing beer (sourced locally; often Plain) [H]

Its motto 'Proud to be a proper pub' sums up this 17th-century, Grade II-listed inn with its four handpumps, beamed ceiling, two stoves and bench tables in the bar. A reasonably priced lunch and evening menu includes an interesting specials board. An annexe can also be used for private functions. The owners of 20 years plan an event each month. Ample roadside parking is available. Accommodation is in six en-suite rooms.
Q🐴❀🛏◐P🐾📶

Highworth

Rose & Crown

19 The Green, SN6 7DB

☎ (01793) 764699

5 changing beers (sourced nationally; often Sharp's) [H]

Now a free house, this is one of the oldest pubs in Highworth. The interior features wooden beams decorated with hops, and an efficient wood-burner. There are five handpumps serving changing ales, with a Sharp's beer always on at some point in the week. The lunch menu offers good quality and value. Cheerful, friendly staff add to the pleasant atmosphere. Occasional open mic and folk sessions are hosted. Outside is a boules pitch in the garden. 🐴❀◐♣🍏P🚌(7)🐾📶

Kington St Michael

Jolly Huntsman [L]

SN14 6JB (signposted from A350)

☎ (01249) 750305 🌐 jollyhuntsman.com

Moles Best; 2 changing beers (sourced locally; often Goff's, Ramsbury) [H]

A former brewery situated on the village high street, this free house offers a warm and friendly welcome, with a large open fire in winter. It serves a selection of locally brewed real ales and a choice of ciders, usually from regional suppliers. An excellent menu is available lunchtimes and evenings, featuring a range of traditional fare and chef's specials, and there are occasional themed evenings. Accommodation is en-suite.
Q🐴🛏◐♿🍏P🚌(99)

Lacock

Bell Inn [L]

The Wharf, SN15 2PJ

☎ (01249) 730308 🌐 thebellatlacock.co.uk

House beer (by Great Western); 3 changing beers (sourced regionally; often Butts, Great Western, Plain) [H]

Popular free house just out of Lacock towards Bowden Hill. A regular local CAMRA Pub of the Year, it has two house beers, Beau Bell and Arlo's, as well as up to three guest ales. A wholesome and varied food menu is served in the restaurant, bar, conservatory and the spacious garden. A substantial new covered outdoor dining and drinking area was added in 2021. Two beer festivals are held each year. Q🐴❀◐♣🍏P🚆🐾📶

Malmesbury

Whole Hog [L]

8 Market Cross, SN16 9AS

☎ (01666) 825845 🌐 wholehogmalmesbury.co.uk

Ramsbury Same Again; Stonehenge Pigswill; Wadworth 6X; 2 changing beers (sourced regionally; often Hook Norton) [H]

A very welcoming town-centre pub adjacent to the market cross and abbey, offering local ales and good-quality food in its restaurant. Sit on the stools at the large feature window to watch what is going on in town. This community pub has won local CAMRA awards and has had the same landlord for over 20 years. It is conveniently situated, close to the bus stop in the Cross Hayes and with plenty of car parking nearby.
Q◐♣🍏🚌📶

Marlborough

Wellington Arms [L] ✔

46 High Street, SN8 1HQ

☎ (01672) 516697 🌐 thewellingtonarmsmarlborough.co.uk

Ramsbury Farmer's Best, Gold; 2 changing beers (sourced nationally; often Ramsbury) [H]

This friendly 18th-century pub with an open fire is the tap for Ramsbury Brewery. Pieminister pies are served. Entertainment includes a vinyl evening on Tuesday – bring your own records and get a discount on drinks – a weekly pub quiz and regular live music. To the rear is the garden which has a covered area.
🐴❀◐♣🍏🚌(X5,80)🐾📶

Melksham

Hiding Place Micropub

15 High Street, SN12 6JY

☎ (01225) 899022

4 changing beers (often Stealth) [H]

As Melksham's only micropub this innovative venue is much appreciated by those looking for interesting and diverse ales and ciders. It mostly features local Stealth cask beers, supplemented by guest keg craft beers and lager, plus locally produced spirits. An open-plan design encourages conversation. Downstairs is bright and welcoming while upstairs offers more comfortable seating. Note: cashless payment only. ⬤🚪🛜

Mere

Butt of Sherry
Castle Street, BA12 6JE
☎ (07765 072796)
Wriggle Valley Desert Nomad; 1 changing beer (sourced regionally) 🅗
This single-bar pub is well supported by locals and visitors alike. The Grade II-listed building in the centre of Mere dates from the late 18th century and features coursed limestone rubble walls and a plain tile mansard roof. A small rear courtyard adds to the facilities. Parking is available on-street and in the free public car park opposite. Q🏴‍☠️🛏️◑🚪

Neston

Neston Country Inn 🄻
25 Pool Green, SN13 9SN
☎ (01225) 811694 ⊕ theneston.com
Stonehenge Pigswill; 1 changing beer (sourced locally) 🅗
This classic, cosy and welcoming village pub with well-kept cask ales and real cider dates back to 1820. It has been in the safe hands of the current landlords for more than 10 years, and the pub is thriving in their care. Excellent traditional food uses high quality ingredients with some interesting twists. Visitors can enjoy the monthly quiz nights, darts and live music. The garden is a great size for families and leads to the local park. Q🏴‍☠️🎇🛏️◑♣⬤P🚪(10)🐾🛜

Newton Tony

Malet Arms 🄻
SP4 0HF
☎ (01980) 629279 ⊕ maletarms.co.uk
4 changing beers (sourced locally; often Plain, Ramsbury, Stonehenge) 🅗
Charming and historic pub, with a restaurant extension, in the conservation area of the village and with the River Bourne flowing past in winter. The window in the larger bar is reputed to come from a galleon. Celebrating 21 years at the pub, the landlord is as enthusiastic and proud of his high-quality food as he is of his ales. Four mainly local beers change weekly and Old Rosie cider is served. The pub welcomes walkers and dogs. Closed Sunday evenings except summer bank holidays. Q🏴‍☠️🎇◑⬤P🚪🐾

Nunton

Radnor Arms 🄻 ✅
SP5 4HS
☎ (01722) 329722 ⊕ theradnor.com
Downton New Forest Ale; 3 changing beers (sourced locally) 🅗
A popular, spacious pub dating from 1853 and named after the local landowner. The landlady and her staff offer a warm welcome to all, including families, children and dogs. Three dining areas adjoin the main bar and an extensive and regularly changing menu is provided to suit all tastes. The large open garden extends to the river and has a secure children's playground. The pub hosts an annual summer festival. Q🏴‍☠️🎇◑♿P🚪🐾🛜

Pewsey

Coopers Arms 🄻
37-39 Ball Road, SN9 5BL
☎ (01672) 562495
Ramsbury Gold; Wadworth 6X; 3 changing beers (sourced nationally; often Box Steam, St Austell, Skinner's) 🅗
Worth seeking out, this down-to-earth thatched pub on the eastern edge of Pewsey has a historic interior with an open-plan bar, two side rooms and a warming fire in winter. Five real ales are served: two local regulars plus three changing guests, usually from the South-West. Real cider is available in summer. The pub hosts live music monthly on a Friday night and a quiz on the first Sunday of the month. No food, but snacks are available. Q🎇🛏️♣⬤P🚪(X5)🐾🛜

Crown Inn 🄻
60 Wilcot Road, SN9 5EL
☎ (01672) 562653 ⊕ thecrowninnpewsey.com
5 changing beers (sourced locally; often Stonehenge, Three Castles, World's End) 🅗
This traditional local is the tap for World's End Brewing, which is behind the pub. At least two of the brewery's own beers are always among the five on offer. The small bar has an attractive stone and brick fireplace in its centre. Poetry and live music are hosted every Thursday, with a ukulele night on the last Thursday of the month. Food is generally only served on theme nights, Friday evenings and Sunday lunchtimes. Q🏴‍☠️🎇♿🛒♣⬤P🚪(X5)🐾🛜

Royal Wootton Bassett

Five Bells 🄻 ✅
Wood Street, SN4 7BD
☎ (01793) 849422
Black Sheep Special Ale; Fuller's London Porter; 5 changing beers (sourced nationally; often Sharp's, Timothy Taylor) 🅗
Dating from before 1841, this is a busy and cosy traditional thatched local with a beamed ceiling and open fires. It has been run by the same couple for over 20 years. The bar has seven handpumps for two regular beers, four guests and Old Rosie cider. Food is served lunchtimes and Tuesday and Wednesday evenings (booking recommended). The pub has darts and crib teams. Local CAMRA Pub of the Year. Q🎇◑♣⬤P🚪(31,55)🐾🛜

Salisbury

Deacons 🄻 ✅
118 Fisherton Street, SP2 7QT
☎ (01722) 322866 ⊕ deaconssalisbury.com
Hop Back GFB, Summer Lightning; Sharp's Doom Bar; 1 changing beer (sourced regionally) 🅗
A friendly, independently owned free house a stone's throw from Salisbury railway station and a short walk from the cathedral. The landlord collaborates with local breweries to showcase quality real ale. Sport is shown on TV in one room; the front room has a regal jukebox. The pub hosts live music, quiz nights and beer festivals. Local CAMRA Pub of the Year 2020. 🏴‍☠️🛏️🛒♣🚪🐾🛜

Duke of York 🄻
34 York Road, SP2 7AS
☎ 07881 812218
Hop Back GFB; Sixpenny 6d Best Bitter; 5 changing beers (sourced locally; often Downton, Plain, Stonehenge) 🅗

A popular free house sporting local beers and two changing traditional ciders. The focus is on the community, with an informal Sunday night quiz, wine club, whisky club and thriving conversation. The pub is home to the Fisherton History Society who meet on the second Wednesday of the month and host occasional events. Live music plays every other Saturday. Barbecues are held at weekends during the summer.
🏠≉♣♠🚍👹🕭🛜

Haunch of Venison ★ 🅛

1 Minster Street, SP1 1TB
☎ (01722) 411313 🌐 haunchpub.co.uk
Courage Best Bitter; Hop Back GFB, Summer Lightning; 1 changing beer (sourced regionally) Ⓗ
A fine old inn, identified by CAMRA as having a nationally important historic interior. The main bar, the Commons, is timber-panelled and has a rare pewter-topped bar. A tiny second bar features original spirit taps and floor tiles recovered long ago from a refurbishment of the cathedral. On the mezzanine floor, the House of Lords area contains the mummified hand of a card cheat. Upstairs again, there are two separate dining rooms, one with an old fireplace dating back to 1588.
🛏🕭≉♣🚍👹🛜

Rai d'Or 🅛

69 Brown Street, SP1 2AS
☎ (01722) 327137 🌐 raidor.co.uk
2 changing beers (sourced locally) Ⓗ
Characterful 13th-century free house near the cathedral, with a fascinating history highlighted by a blue plaque recalling a 14th-century landlady. An inglenook fireplace and low ceilings make for an appealing ambience. Excellent, reasonably priced Thai food is complemented by two changing, usually local, beers, and Wessex Dry cider. The pub can be busy at mealtimes but drinkers are always welcome. There is a discount on food if you eat early. A former local CAMRA Town Pub of the Year, with 20 years in the Guide. 🛏🕭♣♠🚍👹🛜

Rugby Club 🅛

Castle Road, SP1 3SA
☎ (01722) 325317 🌐 salisburyrfc.org
Hop Back GFB, Crop Circle, Summer Lightning; 1 changing beer (sourced locally) Ⓗ
Occupying a corner of the large club house, this cosy, refurbished lounge bar is open to the public. Retaining its sporting roots, the bar features rugby memorabilia. Two TVs generally show rugby or other sport. The function room bar is open at busy times such as match days. The three Hop Back ales are often joined by a Hop Back or Downton seasonal brew. Quiz night is Wednesday. A beer festival is held in May. There are camping facilities close by. 🛏🏠P♠👹🛜

Village Freehouse 🅛

33 Wilton Road, SP2 7EF
☎ (01722) 329707
Downton Quadhop; 4 changing beers (sourced nationally) Ⓗ
A lively pub near the train station. Microbrewery beers come from near and far, with customer requests welcome. There is always at least one dark brew – stout, porter or mild. Teams are fielded in the local crib, cricket and football leagues, and a TV shows BT Sport, with the sound off much of the time. Filled rolls are available or you are welcome to bring your own food. Local CAMRA Pub of the Year three times. ≉🚍👹🛜

Winchester Gate 🅛

113-117 Rampart Road, SP1 1JA
☎ (01722) 503362

4 changing beers (sourced regionally; often Downton, Plain, Red Cat) Ⓗ
Characterful free house, an inn since the 17th century, which once provided for travellers at the city's east tollgate. Four handpumps offer changing ales and often real ciders from across the country. Beer and cider festivals are held, sometimes in association with a live music event. A small lawned garden offers a pleasant area to sit out, particularly during the summer. The pub is renowned for live music every Friday and Saturday, and frequently on Thursday too. 🏠♣♠P👹🛜

Wyndham Arms 🅛

27 Estcourt Road, SP1 3AS
☎ (01722) 331026
Hop Back GFB, Citra, Crop Circle, Summer Lightning; 2 changing beers (sourced locally; often Hop Back) Ⓗ
The birthplace of the Hop Back Brewery, the pub is now celebrating 35 consecutive years in the Guide. A traditional ale house, it has a single bar serving a selection of Hop Back ales – normally Taiphoon in summer and Entire Stout in winter – alongside seasonal offerings and a fine selection of bottled beers and wines. Two small rooms off the main bar area provide quiet spaces and more seating. This is a pub for conversation, good-natured banter and fine ales. Local CAMRA Pub of the Year 2019. 🛏♣🚍👹

Seend Cleeve

Brewery Inn

SN12 6PX
☎ (01380) 828463
2 changing beers (often Plain, Ramsbury)
Popular, well-run community pub that has been much improved, particularly for outdoor dining. Indoors there is a separate dining area, and the large garden features enclosed dining pods with heaters to keep out bad weather. Several real ciders are sold. Pool and TV are in a separate room. Owned by the Banwell House group and now a free house. Q🛏🏠🕭♣♠P👹🛜

Semley

Benett Arms

Village Green, SP7 9AS (1 mile E of A350) ST891270
☎ (01747) 830221 🌐 thebenettarms-semley.co.uk
Exmoor Ale; 2 changing beers Ⓗ
A genuine free house sitting by the green and pond in a quiet village, with a single small bar and separate dining areas. The beer choice varies but there are usually three to choose from, either on handpump or direct from the cellar. Excellent home-cooked food is available at all sessions. A warm welcome is extended to all, including families and dogs, in an area popular with walkers. There are three letting rooms. Twice local CAMRA Pub of the Year. Q🛏🏠🛏🕭♣🚍(84,247)👹🛜

Sherston

Rattlebone Inn 🅛

Church Street, SN16 0LR
☎ (01666) 840871 🌐 therattlebone.co.uk
New Flying Monk Elmers; St Austell Tribute; 1 changing beer (sourced nationally; often Butcombe) Ⓗ
A well-managed classic old Cotswold village pub, with rambling rooms, perfectly conditioned ales and a warm welcome. Popular with locals and visitors alike, the building dates from the 17th century and the comfortable decor with lots of cosy nooks gives it a relaxed ambience. The traditional pub food is sourced

locally. Of special note are the double garden and terrace with boules pitches as well as a skittle alley and other pub games. Q🐴❀◑♣P🚌🐾📶

Swindon

Beehive ✔

55 Prospect Hill, SN1 3JS

☎ (01793) 523187 🌐 bee-hive.co.uk

Hardys & Hansons Olde Trip; house beer (by Hardys & Hansons); 4 changing beers (sourced regionally; often Greene King) [H]

This pub dates from 1871 and is built on a corner on a hill, giving a nearly triangular layout on five different levels. It serves six real ales including four changing guests, with a regional focus. A popular live music venue, it hosts performances on most Thursday and Friday nights, and a world music club on the last Wednesday of the month. The walls display pictures and other art for sale. Locally sourced pies are available lunchtime until early evening. ◑♣🚌🐾📶

Blunsdon Arms ✔

Lady Lane, SN25 2NA

☎ (01793) 729801

St Austell Tribute; house beer (by Black Sheep); 6 changing beers (sourced nationally; often Bath Ales, Butcombe) [H]

Opened in 2006 and owned by Ember Inns, the Blunsdon Arms is a large, open-plan, popular pub with friendly, pleasant staff. It features an 18-plus area, where no children are allowed. The six guest beers rotate from a selection of 12 ales, which change quarterly. Three real ciders are also available. Food is served every day. There is a quiz on Wednesday and Sunday, poker on Monday and live music the last Saturday of the month.
🐴❀◑♿♣🍎P🚌📶

Glue Pot

5 Emlyn Square, SN1 5BP

☎ (01793) 497420

Hop Back Citra, Fuggle Stone, Crop Circle, Entire Stout, Summer Lightning; 3 changing beers (sourced nationally; often Downton, Hop Back) [H]

An unspoilt inn, the last remaining pub in the historic stone-built Railway Village built in the 1840s. An Allsopp's Brewery logo adorns one window. Seven Hop Back or Downton ales are joined by one guest. Local CAMRA Cider Pub of the Year, it stocks 11 real ciders. A range of sandwiches, wraps and subs is available. Busy at weekends, the pub has a quiz on Wednesday, a price reduction on Monday and a beer festival at Easter.
Q❀🚆🍎🚌🐾

Goddard Arms ✔

1 High Street Old Town, SN1 3EG

☎ (01793) 619090

Ringwood Fortyniner; St Austell Tribute; Sharp's Doom Bar; 2 changing beers (sourced nationally; often Prescott, Timothy Taylor) [H]

This Grade II-listed building was the home of the magistrates' court until 1852. The smart interior is spacious with comfortable seating. The bar features five real ales, two of them changing guests, and Lilley's cider. Good-value food is available all day, making the pub busy most of the time. Sports TV is screened in the background. There is accommodation and a separate function room upstairs. 🐴❀🛏◑♿🍎P🚌(12)📶

Hop Inn [L]

8 Devizes Road, Old Town, SN1 4BH

☎ (01793) 976833 🌐 hopinnswindon.co.uk

House beer (by Ramsbury); 6 changing beers (sourced regionally; often Arbor) [H]

The pub that began the Devizes Road real ale boom, the Hop Inn moved two doors down from its original location to larger premises in 2019. This free house now has eight handpumps serving six changing guest ales and Hop Inn Bitter brewed by Ramsbury. Two ciders from Hungerford Park are also sold. The interior is decorated in an eclectic style, including tables and chairs made from reclaimed wood. Wings and burgers are available.
Q🐴❀◗🍎🚌(11,22)🐾📶

Tap & Brew [L]

51 Devizes Road, SN1 4BG

Hop Kettle Cricklade Ordinary Bitter, North Wall; 4 changing beers (often Hop Kettle) [H]

The Tap & Brew is latest addition to the Old Town beer scene and features its own microbrewery. The inside is plain and functional with a variety of seating options. The six handpumps and 14 keg taps sell a full range of beers from both the Cricklade and Swindon Hop Kettle breweries as well as its own experimental and limited run beers. You can also purchase Hop Kettle merchandise and beers to takeaway. Q❀🍎🚌(12,9)📶

Wyvern Tavern ✔

49-50 Bridge Street, SN1 1BL

☎ (01793) 484924

Butcombe Original; 5 changing beers (sourced nationally) [H]

Large town-centre chain pub which unusually has a better-than-average interest in and sale of real ales and ciders, offering one regular and five changing guest beers alongside Lilley's cider. It can be very lively, especially later in the week and at the weekend. Essentially a sports bar, it has a number of TV screens showing various sports and news. Refurbished in 2019 with more seating, facilities are all on one level.
🐴❀◑♿🚆♣🍎🚌(1,8)🐾📶

Tisbury

Boot Inn [L]

High Street, SP3 6PS

☎ (01747) 870363

3 changing beers (sourced locally) [G]

Fine village free house, licensed since 1768 and run by the same family since 1976. A traditional, Chilmark stone building, it has a relaxed, friendly atmosphere and offers a cordial welcome to locals and visitors alike. Join in the conversation at the bar or find a quiet table at which to enjoy well-kept, mostly local ales served from casks behind the bar. The beer range may increase at weekends and in summer. Excellent food is served and there is a spacious garden. The third Tuesday of the month is quiz night. Q❀◑🚆♣P🚌(25)🐾📶

Trowbridge

King's Arms

5 Castle Street, BA14 8AN

☎ (01225) 751310 🌐 thekingsarmstrowbridge.co.uk

Butcombe Original; Sharp's Doom Bar; 2 changing beers (sourced regionally; often Dark Star, St Austell, Wye Valley) [H]

Following an extensive refurbishment, this town-centre pub is now a smart, welcoming free house. Its single drinking area, served by a central bar, has partitions creating a number of snug-like areas. The patio at the back, with its listed tree, makes a pleasant spot for an alfresco drink. An interesting and varied food menu is offered. Four beers are usually available – including guest

ales from larger micros in Wiltshire, Somerset or Devon – alongside a varied choice of real ciders.
Q☺☕🍴♿🅿️♿🚪📶

Upavon

Ship 🅛

10 High Street, SN9 6EA
☎ (01980) 630313 ⊕ theshipatupavon.co.uk

Butcombe Original, Gold; 4 changing beers (sourced locally; often Plain, Stonehenge, Three Castles) Ⓗ
This popular village pub is now locally owned and run. Parts of the Grade II-listed building date from the 15th century. Inside, it combines traditional wooden beams with a light, open decor. The dining room has a huge model of the Cutty Sark. There are six real ales, four of them locally sourced. An extensive food menu makes use of local ingredients when available, with various theme nights. Live music features on occasion.
☺🍴♿🅰♣🚪(X5) 🐾📶

Warminster

Fox & Hounds

6 Deverill Road, BA12 9QP
☎ (01985) 216711

Wessex Warminster Warrior; house beer (by Wessex); 2 changing beers (sourced regionally; often Bath Ales, Palmers) Ⓗ
A friendly two-bar local – the main bar with a pool table and sports TV is at the rear, and a quiet snug bar is to the right of the entrance. There is a large skittle alley and function room at the back. Guest real ales are usually from local and regional breweries. Regular ciders are from Thatchers and Rich's, plus up to five guests. Closing time may be later than 11pm. A local CAMRA multiple award-winning pub. Q☺♿♣🚪🐾📶

Westbury

Angel

3 Church Street, BA13 3BY
☎ (01373) 822648

4 changing beers (often Irving, Twisted) Ⓗ
A traditional, welcoming pub whose several rooms include a library for customers. At least four beers are served, always including one from local brewer Twisted. Others come from the south and the West Country. A couple of ciders are also available. There are plans to offer food in the future. ☺🍽♣🚪(D1)🐾📶

Horse & Groom

18 Alfred Street, BA13 3DY
☎ (01373) 859433 ⊕ horseandgroomwestbury.co.uk

Sharp's Doom Bar; 2 changing beers (sourced regionally; often Twisted) Ⓗ
A large pub on the north-eastern edge of the town centre. There are two separate bars – one is essentially a restaurant. The pub has an attractive patio-style drinking area at the front, which can be a suntrap in the summer, as well as a large garden with plenty of seating and a good-sized car park. Opposite is a skittle alley that can be used as a function room. ☺🍽♿♣🚪🐾📶

Whiteparish

Parish Lantern 🅛

Romsey Road, SP5 2SA
☎ (01794) 884392 ⊕ theparishlantern.co.uk

Flack Manor Flack's Double Drop; Hop Back Citra; St Austell Cornish Best Bitter, Tribute, Proper Job; 2 changing beers (sourced locally; often Downton, Hop Back) Ⓗ
A welcoming pub run by the same couple since 1991. Its single bar has a central fireplace and areas for dining, pool and darts. Guest beers are from Hop Back, Downton or other local breweries. Food is served lunchtimes and evenings, and there are regular themed dining nights. A spacious garden with play equipment for children leads to a camping area with space for five caravans. The pub hosts family events on bank holidays and occasional beer festivals. ☺🍴♿🅰♣🚪🐾📶

Whitley

Pear Tree Inn 🅛

Top Lane, SN12 8QX (off B3353 on Purlpit/Atworth road)
☎ (01225) 704966 ⊕ peartreewhitley.co.uk

Bath Ales Gem; 2 changing beers (sourced locally) Ⓗ
Following a sympathetic refurbishment this place, a farm in the 17th-century, is now a pub restaurant. Its small, rustic bar features a large open fire, stone walls and flagstone floors. Three local ales and a local real cider are available. Restaurant areas are to the rear, where a wide range of food is served, with an emphasis on locally sourced, seasonal ingredients. In the extensive gardens is a vegetable plot that supplies the pub.
Q☺☕🍴♿🅰🅿️🚪(D3)🐾📶

Winsley

Seven Stars ✅

Bradford Rd, BA15 2LQ
☎ (01225) 722204 ⊕ sevenstarswinsley.co.uk

Palmers IPA; 3 changing beers (sourced regionally; often Exmoor, Plain, Three Daggers) Ⓗ
A fine old village pub, part of which dates back to the early 1700s. It serves four beers including three changing guests, usually from the West Country. The home-made food comes highly recommended and can be ordered gluten-free; booking is recommended. There is a peaceful garden and spacious car park. The D1 bus from Bath to Salisbury and Warminster stops right outside.
☺🍴♿🅰🅿️🚪(D1)🐾📶

Wroughton

Carters Rest 🅛

57 High Street, SN4 9JU
☎ 07816 134966

Ramsbury Deerstalker; 6 changing beers (sourced regionally) Ⓗ
First mentioned in 1671, this popular real ale pub was extensively altered around 1912 to give its current Victorian appearance, and was refurbished in 2017. There are 12 handpumps but currently the beer range is seven, with eight at the weekend. Ales are mainly from small independent breweries within a 50-mile radius, although occasionally they may be from further afield. Poker night is Tuesday and quiz night Thursday.
Q☺☕♿♣🚪(9,49) 🐾📶

Not all chemicals are bad. Without chemicals such as hydrogen and oxygen, for example, there would be no way to make water, a vital ingredient in beer. **Dave Barry**

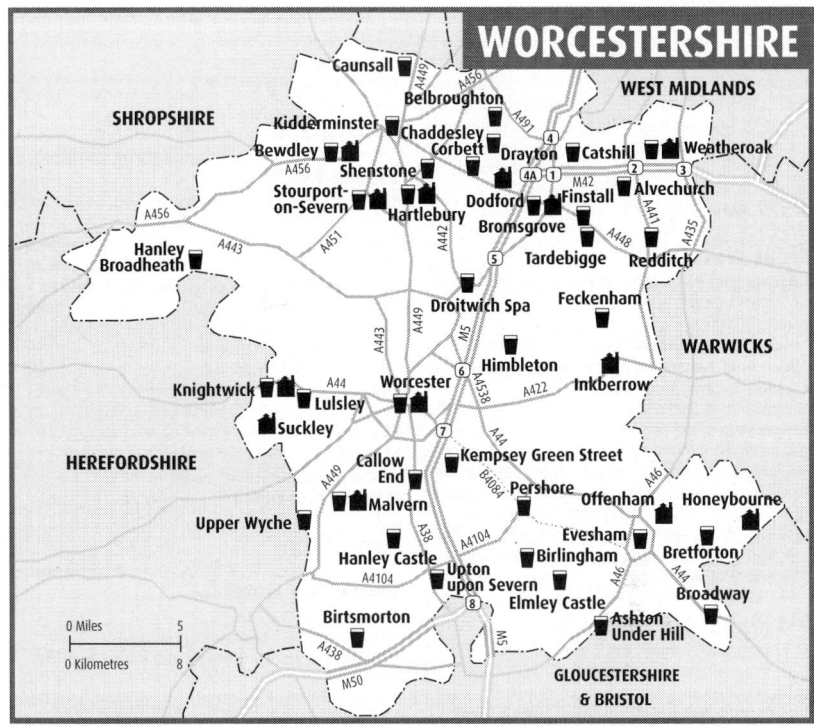

WORCESTERSHIRE

ENGLAND

Alvechurch

Weighbridge 🄻

Scarfield Wharf, Scarfield Hill, B48 7SQ (follow signs to marina from village) SP022721

☎ (0121) 445 5111 ⊕ the-weighbridge.co.uk

Kinver Light Railway; 5 changing beers (sourced locally; often Hobsons, Kinver, Wye Valley) 🄷

This cosy canalside pub has received many CAMRA awards. It has two small lounges, a public bar and a pleasant garden. Good-value, home-cooked food is served lunchtimes and evenings, with excellent Sunday lunches (no food Tue and Wed). A covered area outside can be used for functions. There are changing beers from Kinver, Weatheroak and Wye Valley, plus three changing guests from other breweries, one of which is a mild, as well as a real cider. Spring and autumn beer festivals are held. Q🛏🕸🌓◑⇌🌢P🛜

Ashton under Hill

Star Inn ✅

Elmley Road, WR11 7SN

☎ (01386) 881325 ⊕ thestar-ashtonunderhill.co.uk

3 changing beers 🄷

A delightful pub on the edge of Bredon Hill, welcoming walkers for a pint and a meal. The menu offers good home-made country food prepared using local produce, including veg from the Vale and meat from the pub's own family farm. Food is served in the bar, which is warmed by an open fire, and the separate restaurant. The large garden is family-friendly. 🕸◑P🌢

Belbroughton

Holly Bush Inn

Stourbridge Road, DY9 9UG (set back from A491 Stourbridge Rd)

☎ (01562) 730207

Hobsons Mild, Twisted Spire, Town Crier; 1 changing beer (sourced regionally; often Hobsons) 🄷

This traditional inn was originally terraced cottages built in 1845. Beers from the Hobsons range are served, along with a real Westons cider. The pub menu includes good-value steak and fish dishes. Full of character, it has a lounge/dining area, central bar section and a small raised restaurant. Cards and dominoes are frequently played. A winner of CAMRA awards including branch Pub of the Year. Q🛏🕸◑◐&🌢P🛒(318)🌢

Bewdley

Bewdley Brewery Tap

Bewdley Craft Centre, Lax Lane, DY12 2DZ

☎ (01299) 405148 ⊕ bewdleybrewery.co.uk/visit-bar

Bewdley Worcestershire Way, Sir Keith Park, Worcestershire Sway; 2 changing beers (sourced locally; often Bewdley) 🄷

Bewdley Brewery produces a range of six regular cask ales and a greater number of bottled beers, some for the Severn Valley Railway. The spacious taproom, to the rear of a former school building, is adorned with railway and brewery memorabilia, and has an old-fashioned feel. Five of the brewery's cask ales are served through half-pint pulls, giving each pint a perfectly clear dispense, and the full range of bottled beers is available. Open on bank holidays; winter hours may vary. 🛏🛒

Black Boy 🄻

50 Wyre Hill, DY12 2UE (up Sandy Bank from Cleobury Rd at Welch Gate)

☎ (01299) 400088 ⊕ theblackboybewdley.co.uk

Bewdley Worcestershire Way; Hobsons Town Crier; Three Tuns XXX; Wye Valley Bitter; 1 changing beer (sourced locally; often Swan) 🄷

Up a hill from the town centre, this friendly, ancient inn is worth the climb. The attractive, half-timbered building is the oldest pub in Bewdley, with a beamed interior and an open fire in winter. Up to five beers are served, plus a cider or two. Cobs and pork pies are always on offer, with hot meals available four evenings a week, plus Sunday. Attractions include bar skittles, bagatelle, board games and shove-ha'penny. A folk session is hosted on the second Monday of each month.
Q ☺ ☼ ❀ ♣ ♠ 🚃 (8,292) ☻ 🖢

Great Western 🄻

Kidderminster Road, DY12 1BY (near SVR station – walk past signal box and under viaduct)
☎ (01299) 488828
Bewdley 2857, Worcestershire Way; Morland Old Golden Hen; 2 changing beers (sourced locally; often Hobsons, Ludlow, Three Tuns) Ⓗ
Conveniently located a short way from the Severn Valley Railway station, the pub has a traditional interior with a railway theme reminiscent of an earlier age. Overlooking the bar is an upper level from which to admire the fine glazed decorative tiling. Snacks such as cobs and tasty local pork pies are in keeping with the traditional ambience. On the bar are five real ales, including the house beer 2857 from Bewdley, and two Westons ciders.
Q ☺ ☼ ❀ ≉ (SVR) ♣ ♠ P 🚃 ☻ 🖢

Old Waggon & Horses 🄻

91 Kidderminster Road, DY12 1DG (on Bewdley to Kidderminster road at Catchem's End)
☎ (01299) 403170
Banks's Mild; Bathams Best Bitter; Ludlow Gold; Wainwright; 1 changing beer (sourced locally; often Enville, Hobsons, Holden's) Ⓗ
Popular locals' and visitors' pub with a central bar serving three distinct areas. The small wooden-floored snug has a dartboard, the larger room a wood-burner and a roll-down screen for major sporting events, but at most times conversation prevails. An old kitchen range adds to the cottagey feel. Guest ales come from local independents. Pub food is available, plus a pie night and a tapas night held once a month, and a carvery on Sunday. The attractive terraced flower garden is on many levels.
☼ ☼ ❀ ≉ (SVR) ♣ ♠ P 🚃 ☻ 🖢

Birlingham

Swan

Church Street, WR10 3AQ
☎ (01386) 750485 ● theswaninn.co.uk
2 changing beers (often Goff's, Purity) Ⓗ
A pretty, thatched, food-oriented free house tucked away at the end of a lane in a quiet village. It has a separate bar and conservatory overlooking the fine garden, where food is served. The menu features fresh fish specials. The pub has been modernised inside but in a sympathetic manner in keeping with the age of the building. Q ☼ ◑ P 🚃 (382) ☻ 🖢

Birtsmorton

Farmers Arms

Birts Street, WR13 6AP (off B4208) SO790363
☎ (01684) 833308 ● farmersarmsbirtsmorton.co.uk
Hook Norton Hooky, Old Hooky; 2 changing beers (sourced locally) Ⓗ
Grade II-listed black and white village pub dating from 1480, found down a quiet country lane. The large bar area features a splendid inglenook fireplace while the cosy lounge has old settles and low beams. Good-value, home-made food is on offer daily. A beer from a small

local independent brewer is often available. The spacious garden, complete with swings, provides fine views of the Malvern Hills. A caravan site is nearby.
Q ☼ ☺ ◑ ❀ ♣ ♠ P 🚃 (577) ☻ 🖢

Bretforton

Fleece Inn ★ 🄻

The Cross, WR11 7JE (near church)
☎ (01386) 831173 ● thefleeceinn.co.uk
Purity Mad Goose; Uley Pig's Ear Strong Beer; Wye Valley Bitter; 3 changing beers (sourced regionally; often Marston's, North Cotswold, Wye Valley) Ⓗ
Originally a farmhouse in the 15th century, the timber-framed Fleece was owned by the Taplin family until 1977 when the last Miss Taplin died in the bar. It was then bequeathed to the National Trust. The interior is filled with low wooden beams and open fires. The famous pewter collection was saved by locals from a fire in 2004. Its medieval barn hosts events. Serving six cask ales alongside local and home-made ciders, the pub is definitely worth a visit if you are in the area.
Q ☼ ☺ ☼ ◑ ❀ ♣ ♠ P 🚃 ☻ 🖢

Broadway

Broadway Hotel 🄻

The Green, WR12 7AA
☎ (01386) 852401 ● broadway-hotel.co.uk
Hook Norton Hooky, Hooky Gold; house beer (by Goff's) Ⓗ
This opulent, refurbished 16th-century hotel, partly black and white, is a former coaching inn that once belonged to Pershore Abbey. A countryside ambience blends with cosy home furnishings and quirky decor, featuring comfy armchairs, a minstrels' gallery and a huge inglenook with log fire. Real ale and bar meals are served in the racing-themed Jockey Club Bar, seasonal food in the elegant award-winning brasserie. ☼ ☺ ☼ ◑ ❀ ♣ ♠

Crown & Trumpet Inn 🄻 ✅

14 Church Street, WR12 7AE
☎ (01386) 853202 ● crownandtrumpet.co.uk
North Cotswold Green Man IPA, Shagweaver; Timothy Taylor Landlord; 1 changing beer (sourced locally; often North Cotswold) Ⓗ
Picturesque 17th-century Cotswold-stone inn, just off the village green, with friendly staff and run by a landlord with more than 35 years' experience as a Guide licensee. This hostelry has an abundance of character, with oak beams, a log fire and Flowers Brewery memorabilia. Good honest home-made local dishes are offered at

---

REAL ALE BREWERIES

Ambridge Inkberrow
Bewdley ✦ Bewdley
BOA (Brothers of Ale) ✦ Stourport-on-Severn
Boat Lane ✦ Offenham
Brew61 Bromsgrove (NEW)
Friday Beer Malvern
Hartlebury Hartlebury
Hop Shed Suckley
Lakehouse Malvern
Malvern Hills Malvern
Sociable ✦ Worcester
Teme Valley 🍺 ✦ Knightwick
Weatheroak Hill Weatheroak
White Rabbit Honeybourne
Wintrip Worcester
Woodcote Dodford
Worcester Worcester

reasonable prices alongside regular ales and guests plus ciders and perries. Entertainment includes midweek live jazz and blues nights. Q✿✿🛏🕪♣🐾P🔊

Bromsgrove

Golden Cross Hotel 🅛 ✅
20 High Street, B61 8HH (S end of High St)
☎ (01527) 870005
Greene King Abbot; Ruddles Best Bitter; Sharp's Doom Bar; 9 changing beers Ⓗ
A busy town-centre pub set in a former hotel and coachhouse. This split-level Wetherspoon has 12 booths with stained-glass surrounds and an open fire. Daily themed food deals and manager's specials are always on offer. Three regular core beers are served plus nine various guests, many from local breweries. The licensee asks for suggestions on beer choices and reacts to feedback. During seasonal festivals cask ales from across the UK are promoted. ♿✿🕪♿P🖂🔊

Little Ale House
21 Worcester Road, B61 7DL (on corner of Station St)
☎ 07791 698641
6 changing beers (often Hobsons, Malvern Hills, Wye Valley) Ⓖ
A micropub with a cosy atmosphere. Up to six ales are served straight from the cask, from Hobsons, Malvern Hills, Wye Valley and Woodcote. A range of ciders and perries is also stocked and takeaways are available. Snacks include fresh cobs. A council car park is nearby and the bus station is parallel with the high street. Q♿♣🖂🐾🔊

Callow End

Old Bush 🅛
Upton Road, WR2 4TE (small lane off B4424) SO835497
☎ (01905) 830792 ⊕ old-bush.com
Butcombe Original; Hobsons Twisted Spire; Wye Valley HPA; 1 changing beer (sourced locally) Ⓗ
Village local down a quiet lane off the main road with a pretty black and white exterior and a cosy interior with log-burner. One or, occasionally, two guest beers, often locally sourced, are available, and a guest cider in summer. Good home-made food is served in the separate dining area, though you can also eat in the bar. The large and attractively laid-out garden has country views and a play area for children with a chicken run. The pub hosts regular live music and an annual blues festival. There is a camping and caravan site in the grounds. ♿✿🕪Å♣🖂P🖂🐾🔊

Catshill

Royal Oak ✅
41 Barley Mow Lane, B61 0LU
☎ (01527) 870141 ⊕ theroyaloakbromsgrove.com
4 changing beers (sourced regionally; often Enville, Timothy Taylor) Ⓗ
Popular local situated just off the main A38. The front bar incorporates a pool room and the larger lounge/restaurant to the rear extends into a sunny conservatory. The food menu offers excellent-value traditional English fare, and the beer menu normally includes up to four ales. The pub is close to the start of the three Royal Hunters' Walks around the local villages of Bournheath and Dodford. ♿✿🕪♿♣P🖂🐾🔊

Caunsall

Anchor Inn 🅛
DY11 5YL (off A449 Kidderminster to Wolverhampton road)
☎ (01562) 850254 ⊕ theanchorinncaunsall.co.uk
Hobsons Best, Town Crier; Wye Valley Butty Bach, HPA; 1 changing beer (sourced regionally; often Hobsons, Three Tuns) Ⓗ
Friendly village inn renowned for its five real ales, traditional ciders and, especially, its well-filled cobs. A central doorway leads into the bar with its original 1920s furniture and horse-racing memorabilia. Outside, the garden is a suntrap in summer, and this popular pub can get busy, especially at lunchtimes and weekends. Easily reached from the nearby canal, this gem is well worth stopping off for. A winner of many local CAMRA awards, most recently Silver Pub of the Year 2020.
Q♿✿🕪♣P🖂(9A,9C)🐾🔊

Chaddesley Corbett

Swan 🅛
High Street, DY10 4SD (along High St from A448)
SO892737
☎ (01562) 777302 ⊕ theswanchaddesleycorbett.co.uk
Bathams Best Bitter, Mild Ale Ⓗ
Dating from 1606, this traditional inn sits at the heart of the village, featuring a public bar, side room with a real fire and an impressive lounge with a raised area for entertainment. Filled rolls and pies are available. Quiz night is held every Wednesday and jazz night every Thursday. There is a large garden and children's play area at the rear overlooking beautiful countryside. The pub is popular with walkers and cyclists alike. Bathams XXX is available in December. Q♿✿♿Å♣🖂P🖂(42)🐾🔊

Drayton

Robin Hood
Drayton Road, DY9 0BW (on Chaddesley Corbett to Belbroughton road) SO905758
☎ (01562) 730526 ⊕ robinhoodinn-drayton.co.uk
Enville Ale, Ginger Beer; Purity Pure Gold; Wye Valley Butty Bach, HPA Ⓗ
A welcoming country pub, refurbished while retaining the ambience of a rural retreat. Quality, freshly prepared food is served in the traditional bar as well as in the cosy lounge, ranging from snacks to full main meals. Six real ales plus Thatchers Heritage real cider are available. Outside there is a large car park, paved patio, a spacious garden and a play area for children. Barbecues are held regularly in the summer months, with drinks served from an outside bar. ♿✿🕪♿♣P🔊

Droitwich Spa

Hop Pole 🅛
40 Friar Street, WR9 8ED (100yds from Norbury Theatre)
☎ (01905) 770155
Wye Valley Butty Bach, HPA, Wholesome Stout; 1 changing beer (often Ambridge) Ⓗ
Popular 18th-century inn located in the old part of Droitwich between the Norbury Theatre and the fire station. There is a separate pool room adjoining the bar and a recently refurbished patio area at the rear. Three locally sourced beers are usually available as well as an occasional guest. Good-value food is served at lunchtimes. Pub games and live music on some weekends add to the convivial atmosphere. ♿✿🕪≈♣🖂🐾🔊

Elmley Castle

Queen Elizabeth L
Main Street, WR10 3HS
☎ (01386) 710251 ⊕ elmleycastle.com
Purity Mad Goose; Wye Valley Bitter; 2 changing beers (sourced nationally; often Goff's, North Cotswold) ⊞
An old inn with a fresh, modern feel inside, named in honour of Elizabeth I's visit to the village in August 1575. This is a community pub, owned by a group of local residents who rescued it from closure. The bar has a flagstone floor, timber beams and a roaring fire, and normally serves one local beer. There is a comfortable lounge and a separate dining room. Regular themed food evenings are held and there are beer festivals on the May and August bank holidays. The café is open during the day Tuesday to Friday, and on Saturday for breakfast. Q❀☺◐▶●P🚲🐾🐾🛜

Evesham

BCM
6 Bridge Court, 64 Bridge Street, WR11 4RY (courtyard off Bridge St 10yds from Mill St)
☎ 07703 753064
3 changing beers (sourced locally; often Wye Valley) ⊞
At the end of a gated courtyard, this 16th-century, Grade II-listed building houses a single bar room with tables and perimeter seating, decorated in a contemporary style with lots of natural wood and exposed beams. The family-run pub offers three real ales including a house beer from Green Duck Brewery and a regular Wye Valley special, together with craft beers. Quality bar food comes from a local butcher. Open Thursday to Sunday only.
❀☺&▲╪♣🚲🐾🐾🛜

Red Lion L
6 Market Place, WR11 4RE
☎ (01386) 761688
Cannon Royall Arrowhead Bitter; White Rabbit Elwood's Dark; 3 changing beers (sourced locally) ⊞
Community pub tucked away in the corner of Evesham's Market Square. It has a main bar, seating areas at the front and side, and a smaller snug at the rear with its own bar and an inglenook fireplace. The pub is now the sole stockist of Cannon Royall and White Rabbit beers. One real cider is always available, two in summer. Live music plays Friday evenings and Sunday afternoons. There is no TV or piped music, no alcopops and no food – but you are welcome to bring in your own.
Q❀☺╪♣●🚲🐾🐾🛜

Feckenham

Rose & Crown ✅
High Street, B96 6HS
☎ (01527) 892188 ⊕ roseandcrownfeckenham.co.uk
Banks's Amber Ale; Brakspear Oxford Gold; 2 changing beers (often Ambridge, Marston's) ⊞
A welcoming family-run Grade II-listed venue in this old village. Its traditional bar offers up to four real ales, plus at least one real cider. A wide menu of pub classics is served in the cosy lounge, with wooden settles for seating. There is a large enclosed beer garden at the rear. An annual beer festival is held over the August bank holiday. Parking is limited but there is a free car park 200 yards away. Q❀☺◐▶&♣●🐾🛜

Finstall

Cross Inn L
34 Alcester Road, B60 1EW (on B4184 Finstall corner)
☎ (01527) 577328
Black Country Bradley's Finest Golden ⊞, Pig on the Wall ⊞/🄶, Fireside; 4 changing beers ⊞
Black Country Ales pub that features its portfolio of beers as well as guest beers and ciders. Nine handpumps dispense beers (including a dedicated dark ale) and ciders. These are displayed on electronic screens. Cobs, pork pies and local Scotch eggs are served. It holds charity and other events, crib and dominoes are played here, and it has a small garden area with a heated shelter. Branch Pub of the Year 2021 and County Pub of the Year 2019 winner. ❀☺&♣●P🚲(43,42)🐾🛜

Hanley Broadheath

Fox Inn L
WR15 8QS (on B4204 E of Tenbury Wells) SO671652
☎ (01886) 853189
Bathams Best Bitter; Brakspear Oxford Gold; 1 changing beer ⊞
The main bar of this spacious 16th-century black and white timbered free house is decorated with hops and has a large fireplace with a wood-burning stove. The panelled dining area is separated from the bar by wood beams. The games room has a pool table, TV and darts. Home-made food, including Sunday lunch, is available, with bar snacks at any time. Q❀☺◐▶▲♣P🚲(309)🐾🛜

Tally Ho! L
WR15 8QX (on B4204 road E of Tenbury Wells) SO662655
☎ (01886) 853241
Ludlow Gold; Wye Valley HPA; 3 changing beers (sourced nationally; often Malvern Hills, Wye Valley) ⊞
An inviting, cosy, 14th-century inn with an abundance of beams and stonework, featuring local beers on the bar. The separate restaurant in the conservatory has grand views of the countryside. A carvery is served on Sunday lunchtime (book ahead for food on Sun eve). The garden enjoys more panoramic views of Titterstone Clee Hill and the Teme Valley, and has a children's playground. Pool and darts are popular. ☺⇦◐▶&▲♣●P🚲(309)🛜🐾

Hanley Castle

Three Kings ★ L
Church End, WR8 0BL (signed off B4211) SO838420
☎ (01684) 592686
Butcombe Original; Hobsons Best; 3 changing beers (often Beowulf, Malvern Hills, Slater's) ⊞
On CAMRA's National Inventory of Historic Pub Interiors, this unspoilt 15th-century country pub on the village green near the church has been run by the Roberts family since 1911. The three-room interior comprises a small snug with large inglenook, serving hatch and settle wall, a small side room, and Nell's Lounge with another inglenook, beams and its own entrance. Three guest ales are on offer, often from local breweries, plus Westons Old Rosie draught cider. Live music sessions feature regularly and a beer festival is held in November. Q❀☺♣●P🚲(363)🐾

Hartlebury

Tap House L
Station Road, DY11 7YJ
☎ (01299) 253275 ⊕ thetaphousehartlebury.co.uk

Hartlebury Hooker, Off the Rails, Rambo Mango, APA; **4 changing beers (sourced regionally; often Hobsons, St Austell, Wye Valley)** Ⓗ
A modern conversion of the old Hartlebury railway station that backs onto the station platform. The lounge bar has comfortable bench seating reminiscent of old railway days, a large fireplace with wood-burner and railway-style signs. Outside, tables on the terrace overlook the valley. Food is served all day (except Sun eve) including specials. Eight real ales are available from national and local breweries including the adjacent Hartlebury Brewery. ⭐⊛⏰ᵰⅅ≠Pᵰ❀🖤

Himbleton

Galton Arms Ⓛ

Harrow Lane, WR9 7LQ
☎ (01905) 391672 ⊕ thegaltonarms.co.uk
Banks's Amber Ale; Bathams Best Bitter; Wye Valley HPA Ⓗ
Splendid rural pub situated on the edge of the village with a friendly welcome, attracting locals and visitors alike. Its unspoilt interior is warmed by open fires and retains the original beams that divide up the space. The bar area shows sports TV. Good-value food is served in two separate dining areas. The beer garden is suitable for children. Q⭐⊛⏰ᵰⅅP🚃(356)❀

Kempsey Green Street

Huntsman Inn Ⓛ

Green Street, WR5 3QB (from A38 at Kempsey via Post Office Lane) SO868490
☎ (01905) 820336
Bathams Best Bitter; Greene King IPA; Morland Original Bitter Ⓗ
This cosy and friendly multi-roomed local inhabits a 300-year-old farmhouse and still has the exposed wood beams. There is a small main bar with a real fire to the front and a larger bar down steps. A separate restaurant serves reasonably priced home-cooked food. There is also a skittle alley with its own bar, an attractive garden and a large car park. The pub is closed at lunchtimes during the week. Dogs are welcome in the bar and lounge. ⭐⊛⏰♣P❀

Kidderminster

Bear & Wolf Ⓛ

11-17 Worcester Street, DY10 1EA
☎ (01562) 227150
House beer (by Fixed Wheel); 5 changing beers (sourced regionally; often Wye Valley) Ⓗ
This modern town-centre pub opened in 2019, specialising in real ales. A range of six beers is offered from local and regional breweries, always including a dark ale and often more unusual beers, as well as up to four ciders. A variety of canned craft beers is also available, and crusty cobs to eat. The interior is deceptively spacious, with a mix of sofas, tables and high stools. Quiet background music encourages conversation, and on some Saturdays there is live music. ᵰ≠●🚃❀🖤

Beer Emporium & Cider House

Oxford Street, DY10 1AR
☎ (01562) 752852
4 changing beers (sourced nationally) Ⓖ
Micropub close to the station and the town centre. There is plenty of conversation around the room and table service is the norm. A chalkboard shows four changing real ales from around the country, usually including a dark one. Four ciders and two perries, a

selection of foreign bottled beers, craft KeyKeg beers, wines and soft drinks ensure there is something for everyone. Local CAMRA Gold Cider Pub of the Year 2019 and 2020. Q⭐⭐ᵰ≠●Pᵰ🚃🖤❀

Weavers at Park Lane Ⓛ

40 Park Lane, DY11 6TG (canalside opp Tesco)
☎ (01562) 742717
Wye Valley Butty Bach; house beer (by Woodcote Manor); 4 changing beers (sourced regionally; often Bathams, Ludlow, Swan) Ⓗ
Canalside inn with a beer garden overlooking the water – moorings are on the towpath a short walk from the nearby bridge. The pub offers cobs, pork pies and an impressive range of six well-kept real ales, including local and unusual beers from further afield, and six ciders and perries. Live music features at weekends throughout the year, outside during the warmer months. Last orders are 20 minutes before closing time. Opening hours vary November to Easter. Q⭐⊛⏰♣●P❀🖤

Weavers Real Ale House Ⓛ

98 Comberton Hill, DY10 1QH (300yds downhill from railway station)
☎ (01562) 229413
Three Tuns XXX; Wye Valley Butty Bach; house beer (by Britt); 5 changing beers (sourced nationally; often Church End, Fixed Wheel, Fownes) Ⓗ
One-room conversational pub serving eight interesting and changing real ales, always including at least one dark ale, along with six craft beers on tap. Four ciders are also on handpump, often including a perry. Cobs are served. Close to the railway station, the pub is convenient for a pint and a chat on the way into town. Local CAMRA Pub of the Year 2018, Silver Cider Pub of the Year 2019. Q⭐⭐≠●🚃🖤❀

Ye Olde Seven Stars ✅

13-14 Coventry Street, DY10 2BG (not far from upper end of High St facing Swan Centre)
☎ (01562) 228641
4 changing beers (often Draught Bass, Wye Valley) Ⓗ
With four changing real ales and a draught cider, this historic town-centre pub is well worth visiting. The front and rear bars display many features from previous ages. Snacks include pork pies, and customers can bring their own food (there are plenty of takeaways nearby), with tableware and condiments provided. Live music plays on the last Friday of the month. Families are welcome and the rear garden is popular in summer. The pub's friendly atmosphere and excellent ales won it local CAMRA Bronze Pub of the Year 2019. ⭐⊛♣●🚃🖤❀

Knightwick

Talbot Ⓛ

WR6 5PH (on B4197, 400yds from A44 jct)
☎ (01886) 821235 ⊕ the-talbot.co.uk
Teme Valley T'Other, This, That Ⓗ**; changing beers (often Teme Valley)** Ⓖ
This was a coaching inn and dates from the 14th century. It has a large lounge bar divided into two by a fireplace, a separate taproom and a conservatory. The small wood-panelled restaurant serves an imaginative evening menu using local ingredients. The bar usually offers three or four beers from the Teme Valley Brewery behind the pub. There is a farmers' market outside on the second Sunday of the month. Beer festivals are held in April, June and early October (for green-hopped beers). Dogs and walkers are welcome.
Q⭐⊛ᵰ⏰ᵰⅅ♣P🚃(420)🖤❀

Lulsley

Fox & Hounds 𝕃

WR6 5QT

☎ (01886) 821228 🌐 foxandhoundslulsley.com

Hop Shed Sebright Golden Ale; Wye Valley Butty Bach; 2 changing beers (often Ambridge, Ledbury) Ⓗ

Originally a Victorian pub with two bars, now with a dining area and a conservatory added. The two guest beers are usually locally sourced, as is the food. There is an extensive garden and children's play area at the back, with the River Teme beyond. A beer festival is held over the spring bank holiday. Q🐴❀◑♿●P🐾ᯤ

Malvern

Great Malvern Hotel 𝕃

Graham Road, WR14 2HN (by crossroads with Church St)

☎ (01684) 563411 🌐 great-malvern-hotel.com

Malvern Hills Black Pear; Wye Valley HPA, Butty Bach; 2 changing beers (often Draught Bass, Friday Beer, Lakehouse) Ⓗ

Popular hotel public bar, a short walk from the Malvern Theatres complex, ideal for pre- and post-performance refreshment. Meals are served in the bar and the adjoining brasserie, including breakfast and Sunday lunch. There is a comfortable lounge with lots of sofas, fresh coffee and daily newspapers. Live music sessions are hosted during the week. The Great Shakes cellar bar features sports TV and is available for hire. Parking is limited. 🐴❀🛏◑⇌(Great Malvern)P🚌🐾ᯤ

Morgan 𝕃 ✔

52 Clarence Road, WR14 3EQ

☎ (01684) 578575

Wye Valley Bitter, HPA, Butty Bach; 2 changing beers (sourced locally) Ⓗ

Named after the town's Morgan car factory, this Wye Valley Brewery-owned premises has an open-plan interior divided into a games area for darts, a drinking space and a slightly raised seating section with comfy settees. The landscaped patio has ample seating, a fish pond and 'Them Organ' gates. Activities include a monthly book club and weekly quizzes. The TV is only turned on for major sporting events. Up to two guest beers come from the Wye Valley range, often the stout. 🐴❀◑⇌(Great Malvern) ♣🚌🐾ᯤ

Nag's Head 𝕃

19-21 Bank Street, WR14 2JG (off Graham Rd at Link Top common)

☎ (01684) 574373 🌐 nagsheadmalvern.co.uk

Banks's Amber Ale; Bathams Best Bitter; Wood Shropshire Lad; 5 changing beers (often Otter) Ⓗ

A free house where the permanent beers are joined by guests from all over the county plus two draught ciders. Mismatched furniture, nooks and crannies, newspapers and foliage create a homely environment, attracting visitors throughout the week. Quality food is served in the bar and separate restaurant. Outside is a large covered and heated area to the front and a garden to the rear. The small car park is backed up by ample street parking. Dogs are welcome and numerous. ❀◑♣●P🚌(44) 🐾ᯤ

Pershore

Pickled Plum 𝕃

135 High Street, WR10 1EQ

☎ (01386) 556645 🌐 pickledplum.co.uk

Brakspear Gravity; Wye Valley Butty Bach; 4 changing beers (often Purity, Salopian) Ⓗ

A large, smart pub with a modern, airy interior, divided into several areas, with exposed beams and real fires creating a cosy old-world charm. The bar serves up to six real ales plus six real ciders. A three third-pints tasting option is offered. Food is available lunchtimes and evenings. The pub hosts a regular Sunday night quiz and an acoustic jam on the first Monday of the month. There is seating outside on the patio at the rear. 🐴❀◑♿●P🚌

Redditch

Black Tap 𝕃

Church Green East, B98 8BP (near top of Church Green East opp fountain)

☎ (01527) 585969 🌐 blacktapredditch.co.uk

Backyard Blonde; 3 changing beers (sourced locally; often Church End, Oakham) Ⓗ

A converted office building and former brewpub. The main bar has a roaring fire, which adds to the friendly atmosphere among regulars. Conveniently located near the town centre, a good mix of beer styles is usually available along with cider. A small side room can also be booked and live music usually features at weekends. The nearby Quadrant car park is free after 7pm. 🐴❀⇌♣●P🚌(57,58) 🐾ᯤ

Rising Sun 𝕃 ✔

4 Alcester Street, B98 8AE (opp town hall)

☎ (01527) 62452

Greene King Abbot; Ruddles Best Bitter; Sharp's Doom Bar; 6 changing beers (sourced regionally; often Morland, Purity, Salopian) Ⓗ

Large open-plan town-centre pub in the Wetherspoon style with a raised seating area and booths, serving up to 10 cask ales and two ciders on handpull. Local histories of Redditch's manufacturing industries adorn the walls, and a large metal horse and rider stands in the centre. Outside, a glass canopy and café-style seating are ideal for people-watching. Screens at both ends of the pub show news and sports on terrestrial TV. 🐴◑♿⇌●P🚌ᯤ

Shenstone

Plough 𝕃

DY10 4DL (off A450/A448) SO865735

☎ (01562) 777340

Bathams Best Bitter, Mild Ale Ⓗ

This traditional pub has been at the heart of the village since 1840. The long single bar serves both the public bar and the lounge, which has a real fire and memorabilia of the Parachute Regiment and the Falklands War. Bathams Mild and Bitter are on tap all year while the stronger XXX is available in December. Snacks include cobs and pork pies. A large enclosed courtyard acts as an overflow, and there is a small patio to the front. Q🐴❀♿♣P🐾ᯤ

Stourport-on-Severn

Black Star 𝕃 ✔

Mitton Street, DY13 8YP (just off top end of High St next to canal)

☎ (01299) 488838

Wye Valley The Hopfather, HPA, Butty Bach, Wholesome Stout; 5 changing beers (sourced regionally; often Enville, Hobsons, Ludlow) Ⓗ

Situated next to the canal, there are moorings just through the bridge towards the basins. An attractive beer garden with a shelter, tables and raised flowerbeds overlooks the water. A changing selection of excellent quality beers is available from Wye Valley and other local breweries, and two ciders. The varied food menu includes vegan options, doorstep sandwiches, baguettes and home-cooked meals. Local CAMRA Gold Pub of the Year 2020. ➘✿❶❶🍴🖵🕏🏵🛜

Swan

56 High Street, DY13 8BX
☎ (01299) 877832
Bewdley Worcestershire Way; Brains Rev James; 4 changing beers (sourced regionally) Ⓗ

A pub by day and music venue by night, this former hotel has a large lounge bar decorated with vinyl LPs. Six ales grace the bar, along with a gin menu. At the back there is a tranquil, secluded garden. The integral Mimi's Bistro serves food and Mediterranean specialities from a wood-fired oven during the day. Live music on most evenings has a loyal following. An interesting and unusual venue, well worth a visit. ➘✿❶❶🖵🏵🛜

Tardebigge

Alestones

Unit 23 Tardebigge Court, B97 6QW
☎ (01527) 275254 ⊕ alestones.co.uk
Woodcote Manor SSS; 3 changing beers Ⓗ

A well-maintained micropub, opened in 2016, which sits in a courtyard alongside several small independent shops and businesses. There are usually four beers, including a golden ale, a dark beer and a best bitter, plus real cider and perry. Although opened out, it retains its cosy, convivial atmosphere. Local musicians play monthly on a Sunday. Pub snacks are usually available.
Q➘✿●P🖵(43,42) 🛜

Upper Wyche

Wyche Inn Ⓛ

Wyche Road, WR14 4EQ (on B4218, follow signs from Malvern to Colwall)
☎ (01684) 575396 ⊕ thewycheinn.co.uk
Wye Valley HPA; 3 changing beers (sourced regionally) Ⓗ

The highest pub in Worcestershire, this free house has panoramic views towards the Cotswolds and is ideally situated for hill walkers. It offers two bars – one with pool and darts, the other dedicated to drinking and dining. A range of real ales is available, sourced from small and micro breweries, including some locals. Green-hop beers are available throughout October. Home-cooked food is served lunchtimes and evenings, with themed nights Tuesday to Saturday. B&B, self-contained flats and a cottage provide accommodation.
Q✿🚪❶♣P🖵(675) 🏵🛜

Upton upon Severn

Olde Anchor Inn Ⓛ ✔

5 High Street, WR8 0HQ
☎ (01684) 593735 ⊕ anchorupton.co.uk
Hobsons Best; St Austell Tribute; Sharp's Doom Bar; 2 changing beers (often Timothy Taylor) Ⓗ

Authentic old oak-beamed inn with low ceilings, built in 1601 and mentioned in Cromwell's dispatches. The bar features a large fireplace and range, and a bar billiards table, and there is a separate restaurant area. An additional wood-panelled function room is available for meetings and parties. The remains of the Old Brew House, once used by the defunct Jolly Roger Brewery, are at the rear. Q✿❶❶🖵🏵🛜

Weatheroak

Coach & Horses Ⓛ

Weatheroak Hill, B48 7EA (on Alvechurch to Wythall road) SP057740
☎ (01564) 823386 ⊕ coachandhorsesinn.co.uk
Holden's Golden Glow; Hook Norton Old Hooky; Weatheroak Hill IPA, Impossible IPA, Gold, Cofton Common; 4 changing beers (sourced nationally; often St Austell, Weatheroak Hill, Wood) Ⓗ

Traditional rural coaching inn with an idyllic beer garden. The bar remains untouched, with a log fire, tiled floor and old church pews, while a modern lounge offers comfy sofas and a restaurant. Four beers are usually stocked from the on-site brewery housed in the former stables, alongside a wider selection from regional independents. Freshly made rolls are always available. Sunday evening opening hours may vary in winter. The pub is adjacent to Icknield Street, the old Roman road. ➘✿❶❶♿♣P🏵🛜

Worcester

Bull Baiters Inn

43-49 St Johns, WR2 5AG
☎ (01905) 427601 ⊕ bullbaiters.com
6 changing beers (sourced locally) Ⓗ

A small bar housed in a medieval building with an interesting history, previously a hall house. A high beamed ceiling and a large stone fireplace add to the old-world ambience, conducive to conversation. A small room upstairs provides additional seating and features an original painted wall and a mummified cat. Ever-changing beers – up to six – are usually local, and complemented by eight ciders and perries. Simple snacks are available. Q✿♣●🖵🏵🛜

Cardinal's Hat Ⓛ

31 Friar Street, WR1 2NA
☎ (01905) 724006 ⊕ the-cardinals-hat.co.uk
Purity Mad Goose; 4 changing beers (sourced locally) Ⓗ

Worcester's oldest pub is a period building set in the heart of the city centre. The main bar at the front has a scrubbed wooden floor, beams and leaded windows. A stone-flagged, panelled passageway leads to a patio at the rear. The atmospheric back room features wood panelling, more stone-flagged flooring, a serving hatch and impressive fireplace with wood-burner and dribbly candles. A small snug has views of the bustling old street outside. Folk night is the first Tuesday of the month. Imaginative bar snacks are available.
➘✿🚪❶🚆(Foregate St) ●🖵🏵🛜

Dragon Inn

51 The Tything, WR1 1JT (on A449, 300yds N of Foregate St station)
☎ (01905) 25845 ⊕ thedragoninnworcester.co.uk
Church End Goat's Milk, Gravediggers Ale, What the Fox's Hat, Fallen Angel; 4 changing beers (often Church End) Ⓗ

A Georgian building on the edge of the city centre run by Church End Brewery. The bar is towards the back of the smart interior, while the front space offers the opportunity to watch the world go by on the busy street outside. Behind the pub is a large, quiet patio with a covered area in the old side passage. A changing variety of Church End beers is on the bar plus two guest ales from other small breweries. Pork pies and sausage rolls are always available. Q✿♿🚆(Foregate St)♣●🖵🏵🛜

Oil Basin Brewhouse

7 Copenhagen Street, WR1 2HB

☎ 07964 196194 ⊕ wintripbrew.co

Wintrip Butchers Beastly Best; 3 changing beers (often Salopian, Teme Valley, Tiny Rebel) Ⓗ

A cosy, dimly lit bar with comfy chairs, wood-beamed ceiling, bare boards and a small brewery out the back. It serves a variety of interesting real ales, mostly local, and craft keg. A good selection of craft beers and ciders is also kept in the fridge. The pub is centrally located, just off the High Street, with Chad's Smashery occupying the second floor, offering Italian and vegetarian food including pizzas cooked in a wood-fired oven. There is level access to the bar and toilets.

Q◑≓(Foregate St)♣🚃🐾❀

Plough Ⓛ

23 Fish Street, WR1 2HN (on Deansway)

☎ (01905) 21381

Hobsons Best; Malvern Hills Black Pear; 4 changing beers (sourced regionally; often Salopian) Ⓗ

A Grade II-listed pub near the cathedral. There is a short flight of steps leading to a tiny bar with rooms to either side. The beers usually come from breweries in

Worcestershire and surrounding counties, but occasionally from small breweries further afield. Draught cider and perry are from Barbourne in the city. There is also a wide range of whiskies. Outside is a small patio area. Rolls are available at weekends and when the cricket is on, with cooked meals Friday to Sunday lunchtimes only. ᐃ❀◑≓(Foregate St)♣🚃❀

Postal Order ✅

18 Foregate Street, WR1 1DN

☎ (01905) 22373

Greene King Abbot; Ruddles Best Bitter; 10 changing beers (sourced nationally; often Bespoke, Lakehouse) Ⓗ

A Wetherspoon pub, formerly the old Worcester telephone exchange. It offers a wide range of ales of different styles and strengths, some from local breweries. Beer festivals throughout the year add more variety. A cider from local producer Barbourne and Old Rosie from Westons are always on the bar, plus two others. Good-value food is served from 8am daily (alcoholic drinks from 9am). The volume on the TV may be turned up for important games.

Q ᐃ◑&≓(Foregate St)🚃🛜

Plough, Shenstone (Photo: Andy Checketts Consultancy)

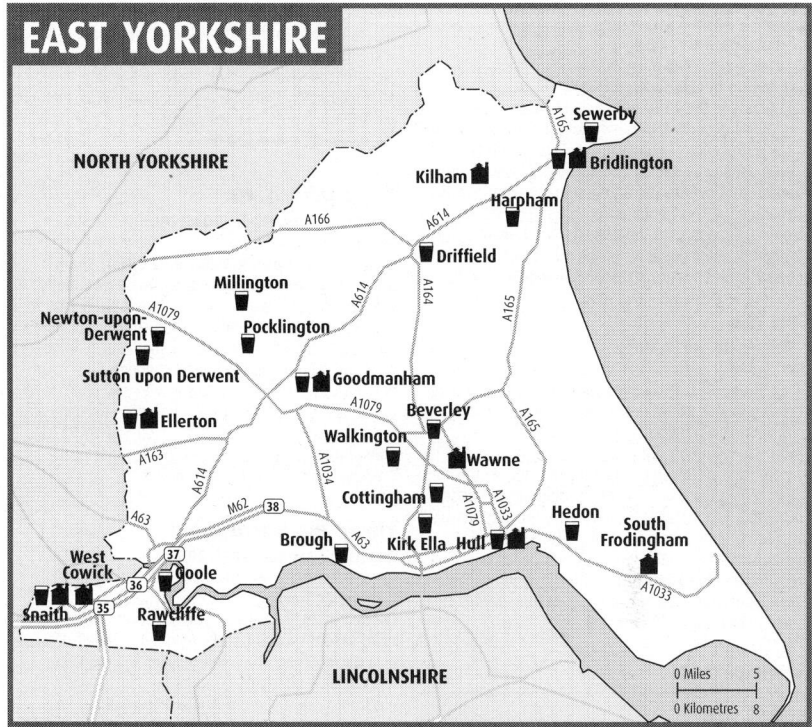

EAST YORKSHIRE

YORKSHIRE (EAST)

Beverley

Chequers Micropub 🅛

15 Swaby's Yard, Dyer Lane, HU17 9BZ (off Saturday Market)

☎ 07964 227906

5 changing beers (sourced regionally; often Brass Castle, North Riding Brewery) Ⓗ

Yorkshire's first micropub is in a former baker's shop, near the bus station. Local breweries are well represented on the bar plus micros from throughout the UK. Several ciders/perries are sold and there are three KeyKeg lines. Typically for this kind of establishment, no lager is available, and there is no TV or loud music, making it a place for real conversation, like pubs used to be. Customers can choose from a selection of board games. CAMRA branch Cider Pub of the Year 2019.

Q❀≷♣🍺🚌♿

Cross Keys 🅛 ✓

8 Lairgate, HU17 8EE

☎ (01482) 880388

Greene King Abbot; Ruddles Best Bitter; Sharp's Doom Bar; 5 changing beers (sourced nationally) Ⓗ

One of Beverley's historic pubs, saved from long-term closure. The main building dates from the mid 18th century and has been fully renovated with respect to its period features, although given a split-level layout with a large central area and smaller rooms off. Some areas can be used by groups by arrangement. Spacious outdoor areas at the rear further extend its capacity. The usual Wetherspoon menu and offers are available.

Q🛏🐕🍴◐≷🍺♿📶

Dog & Duck 🅛

33 Ladygate, HU17 8BH (off Saturday Market adjacent to Brown's store and close to the bus station)

☎ (01482) 862419 ⊕ bedandbreakfastbeverley.com

Black Sheep Best Bitter; John Smith's Bitter; Ossett Yorkshire Blonde; Timothy Taylor Boltmaker; 1 changing beer (sourced regionally; often Great Newsome) Ⓗ

Situated in the historic Beverley town centre, the pub was built in the 1930s and has been run by the same family for 45 years. It comprises three areas: a bar with a period brick fireplace and bentwood seating, a front lounge with an open fire, and a rear snug. Good-value, home-cooked lunches are popular. Bed and breakfast guest accommodation is in six purpose-built self-contained rooms to the rear. Dogs are welcome outside food service times. 🛏◐≷♣🍺🚌♿📶

Green Dragon ✓

51 Saturday Market, HU17 8AA

☎ (01482) 889801 ⊕ thegreendragonbeverley.co.uk

Black Sheep Best Bitter; Sharp's Doom Bar; Timothy Taylor Landlord; Wainwright; 6 changing beers (sourced nationally; often Adnams, Purity, Rudgate) Ⓗ

A historic narrow-fronted Tudor timber-style inn accessed down a side passageway, with a further rear entrance off Lairgate. Renamed the Green Dragon in 1765, it was refurbished in 2018 and updated to increase its appeal to family diners. It opens early for breakfast and serves meals throughout the day. Sports fans are catered for with several large-screen TVs. A wide range of beer styles is delivered from the nine or 10 handpumps and further KeyKegs. Quiz nights are held on Tuesday and Thursday. 🐕◐≷🍺♿📶

Monks Walk [L]

19 Highgate, HU17 0DN
☎ (01482) 864972 🌐 monkswalkinn.com
6 changing beers (sourced locally) [H]/[G]
Dating back to the 13th century and built as a merchant's warehouse, records show there was a brewery attached in the 19th century. Access to the Minster Bar is by an open passageway, plus a dining room which features exposed roof beams and an open fire. Conversation is encouraged at this genuine free house (known as the George & Dragon until the 1980s). The sheltered beer garden has splendid views of the Minster. Access to the car park is off Eastgate. Q🐴❀◐♿🚆♣🍎P▯🚌🐾📶

Sun Inn

1 Flemingate, HU17 0NP
☎ 07541 456215 🌐 suninnbeverley.co.uk
Black Sheep Best Bitter; Morland Old Speckled Hen; Timothy Taylor Boltmaker; York Guzzler; 1 changing beer (sourced nationally; often Robinsons) [H]
This medieval timber-framed building is set opposite the eastern front of Beverley's famous minster, so the view from the courtyard beer garden should not be missed. Formerly a Tap & Spile establishment, the stripped-back interior featuring bare brick walls reflects that style. It is a live music venue, with blues and rock bands on a weekend and folk sessions on Saturday teatimes; among other events there is a popular quiz on Thursdays. Sunday lunches are served. ❀◐🚆♣🚌🐾

Bridlington

Board Inn

62 High Street, YO16 4QA
☎ (01262) 672087
Adnams Ghost Ship; Fuller's ESB; St Austell Proper Job; Titanic Plum Porter; 3 changing beers (sourced nationally; often Tetley) [H]
Located in Bridlington's Old Town, this lovingly restored historic inn dates back to the 18th century, and has wood panelling, flagged and timber floors and four open fires. It has a multi-roomed interior, with three comfortably furnished rooms and a snug upstairs – a real gem, not to be missed. Music nights take place at weekends. To the rear a new tap has been established selling 10 craft-brewed beers in converted stables, and there are also open fires here. Recognised by CAMRA for the restoration undertaken. Q❀P🚌🐾

Marine Bar [L]

North Marine Drive, YO15 2LS (1 mile NE of centre)
☎ (01262) 675347
Theakston Best Bitter; Timothy Taylor Landlord; 2 changing beers (sourced regionally; often Daleside, Rooster's, Wold Top) [H]
A large open-plan bar, part of the Expanse Hotel. Spectacular sea views are the perfect accompaniment to enjoying the home-cooked food served here daily. Attracting a good mix of regulars, a warm welcome also awaits the influx of summer visitors. Two regional guest beers complement the three regular ales, with real cider also available. There is ample parking along the promenade, where a land train operates during the summer. 🐴❀🛏◐◑⛺♣🍎P🚌(512,513)

Old Ship Inn ✔

90 St John Street, YO16 7JS
☎ (01262) 401906
Bridgehouse Porter; 6 changing beers (sourced regionally) [H]
A multi-roomed pub including a large, cosy and comfortable lounge (used for functions) with a smaller front bar to the right of the entrance and another smaller separate room to the left. It serves six changing ales, with Bridgehouse Porter as a regular. The lounge has a plentiful collection of Frank Meadow Sutcliffe photographs of Whitby and a smaller number featuring Bridlington. It puts on a full programme of events during the week. 🐴❀🚆♣🚌🐾📶

Prior John [L] ✔

34-36 The Promenade, YO15 2QD (nr bus station)
☎ (01262) 674256
Greene King Abbot; Ruddles Best Bitter; Sharp's Doom Bar; 6 changing beers (sourced nationally) [H]
This venue was extended in 2019 and refurbished to provide an enlarged dining section suitable for families. Internal features include a spiral staircase to an upper floor and a dome with original artwork by the main entrance. An outside area to the side and rear allows customers to enjoy the sea air. It is close to many of the seaside attractions Bridlington is well known for, and is named after John de Tweng, a former prior of the local medieval monastery. Q❀◐◑♿🍎🚌📶

Three B's Micropub [L]

2 Marshall Avenue, YO15 2DS
☎ (01262) 604235 🌐 threebspubbrid.co.uk
4 changing beers (sourced regionally) [H]
Opened in 2020, in a side street just off one of the town's main shopping thoroughfares. It is self-described as a micropub and therefore applies the Micropub Association's principles of no keg products, spirits or electronic entertainment. There is a small outdoor seating area to complement the two indoor areas, one of which is accessed by stairs. Beers are available to take away and social media is used to promote the range. Food is available occasionally. Q🐴❀🚆🍎🚌🐾📶

Brough

Centurion Arms [L]

39 Skillings Lane, HU15 1BA
4 changing beers (sourced regionally; often Great Newsome, Half Moon, Wold Top) [H]
A converted shop unit, among a number of small businesses supporting the community. This is unlike any other pub in the village, with a changing variety of real ale and cider, evidenced by the extensive collection of pump badges which add to the eclectic variety of paraphernalia decorating the place. Locally produced artwork is also on show. Social interaction and conversation (helped by sound-absorbing clouds) is encouraged among regulars and strangers. Dog snacks provided. 🐴❀♿🚆♣🍎P🚌(158)🐾

REAL ALE BREWERIES

Aitcheson's Wawne
All Hallows 🛢 Goodmanham
Atom Hull
Bone Machine ◆ Hull
Bricknell Hull
Bridbrewer 🛢 Bridlington (NEW)
Great Newsome South Frodingham
Half Moon ◆ Ellerton
Old Mill Snaith
Raven Hill Kilham
Spotlight West Cowick
Vittles Hull
Woolybutt Hull
Yorkshire Brewhouse Hull
Yorkshire Coast 🛢 Bridlington

Cottingham

Hugh Fitz-Baldric

144 Hallgate, HU16 4BB
Salopian Lemon Dream; Titanic Plum Porter; house beer (by Marston's); 3 changing beers (sourced nationally) ⓗ

A one-room pub with quiet corners, converted from a shop in the busy main street. It is furnished with repurposed items and a log-burner adds cosiness in winter. This is a quaint and peaceful place to enjoy a good range of real ales, complemented by real ciders and gins, and other drinks following trends in changing tastes. CAMRA branch Village Pub of the Year 2019.
Q⇄♠☐♨

King William IV

152 Hallgate, HU16 4DB
☎ (01482) 875996
Banks's Sunbeam; Jennings Cumberland Ale; Marston's Pedigree; Wainwright; Wychwood Hobgoblin Ruby; 2 changing beers (sourced nationally; often Brakspear, Ringwood, Wychwood) ⓗ

A village-centre pub with a traditional bar and quiet lounge. It hosts weekly quiz nights and is a venue for Cottingham's annual music festival. At the rear a former brewery has been converted into a function room offering live music and special events. The beer garden and side courtyard have covered smoking areas. Excellent-value meals are served in large and small portions, and Thatchers cider is on handpump. Local CAMRA Village Pub of the Year runner-up for the last two years. Q❀❀◑⇄♣♠☐♨🛜

Driffield

Benjamin Fawcett Ⓛ ⊘

Middle Street North, YO25 6SW
☎ (01377) 249130
Greene King Abbot; Ruddles Best Bitter; changing beers ⓗ

Like most Wetherspoons, this is now a spacious one-room venue, and is a conversion from previous licensed premises on the site. There are both quiet areas and others that seem livelier, decorated with artefacts that pay tribute to members of the armed forces stationed nearby during World War II. Family diners are welcome. Its name comes from the local printer who was one of the first to print in colour; framed examples are on display. ❀◑♿⇄♠☐(121)🛜

Ellerton

Boot & Shoe

Main Street, YO42 4PB
☎ (01757) 288346
House beer (by Dark Horse); 2 changing beers (sourced nationally; often Dark Horse) ⓗ

A welcoming country village inn of character dating from the 17th century. The building wraps around a large tree and features low-beamed ceilings. There is a cosy bar area with exposed brick and an open fire, plus two intimate separate dining rooms. Three real ales are on offer in this free house, including two from Dark Horse brewery. Food is served Friday and Saturday evenings and Sunday lunchtimes (booking advisable). Q◑▸♣P♨

Goodmanham

Goodmanham Arms Ⓛ

Main Street, YO43 3JA

☎ (01430) 873849
All Hallows Peg Fyfe Dark Mild; Hambleton Stallion Amber; Theakston Best Bitter; 3 changing beers (sourced regionally; often All Hallows, Oakham, Wold Top) ⓗ

Unique village inn with the All Hallows Brewery attached, close to the Wolds Way footpath. There are three log fires warming the bar, dining room and kitchen, and candlelight during dark winter nights. An extension decorated with vintage artefacts has been added to meet demand for space. Hearty meals are served and events are organised on bank holidays. Local CAMRA Village Pub of the Year winner many times, and runner-up in 2019. Q❀❀◑▸♣P

Goole

Tom Pudding

20 Pasture Road, DN14 6EZ (2 mins' walk from Goole station)
☎ 07762 525114
4 changing beers (sourced regionally; often Hambleton, Wold Top) ⓗ

This micropub was once a newsagents' and was opened in 2017 by two CAMRA members with an enthusiasm for real ale. It can accommodate up to 50 people, and is often sought out by travelling football fans on their way to Hull and Doncaster. It always sells a gluten-free beer and up to four real ciders, often from Henry Weston and Gwynt y Ddraig. It has interesting internal brickwork and an exposed wooden-beamed ceiling.
⇄♣♠☐(155,X55)♨

Harpham

St Quintin Arms Ⓛ

Main Street, YO25 4QY (¾ mile off A614 Driffield-Bridlington road)
☎ (01262) 490329 ⊕ stquintinarms.com
Theakston Best Bitter; Wold Top Wold Gold ⓗ

This 13th-century village establishment, with a long history as a hostelry and coaching inn, is tucked away off the beaten track. The licensee offers good food including locally bred lamb to complement the locally sourced real ales. There are several areas both inside and out to enjoy the cosy open fires in winter and sunshine in summer. Accommodation is available. ❀❀◄◑▸P🛜

Hedon

Hed'On Inn

7 Watmaughs Arcade, St Augustine Gate, HU12 8EZ
☎ (01964) 601100
Black Sheep Best Bitter; 4 changing beers (sourced nationally) ⓗ

A micropub adjacent to a car park at the end of a shopping arcade in the centre of this old market town, converted from a disused carpet shop office. The premises are tastefully decorated with recycled fittings. There are two regular and four changing beers covering the full spectrum of styles, together with real ciders, bottled beers and a range of spirits and wines. Acoustic music sessions are held on Tuesday nights and Sunday afternoons, and quizzes and games on Wednesday nights. Q♣♠P☐

Hull

Admiral of the Humber Ⓛ ⊘

5-7 Anlaby Road, HU1 2NT
☎ (01482) 381850

Greene King Abbot; Ruddles Best Bitter; Sharp's Doom Bar; 6 changing beers (sourced nationally) ⊞
This is a Wetherspoon hotel, and was formerly a paint and wallpaper shop. Previous to that, the site was connected to Hull's seafaring past. Now a large single room, mostly on one level, the building is ideally suited to those finding steps or stairs a problem. There is a large open-air roof-top garden for smokers and non-smokers alike (closes 10pm nightly). A designated area is set aside for diners during the day, and children are welcome until 6pm. Q✩⚲⊛❧◑🐾⬲●P🚃 ⏃

Alexandra Hotel 🅛

69 Hessle Road, HU3 2AB
☎ 07768 781277 ⊕ alexandrahotelhull.co.uk
Yorkshire Brewhouse EYPA; 7 changing beers (often Yorkshire Brewhouse) ⊞
Known as the 'Alex', this Grade II-listed building is slowly being given new life by the current owners through its restoration. It is located on one of Hull's main thoroughfares, Hessle Road, easily accessible on foot. The pub has many architectural features that make it stand out; a glazed brick frontage and the old gas lighting, now electrified, give a traditional appearance outside, while inside plush seating and interesting historic pub artefacts add to the atmosphere.
✩🏠🐾●P🚩 .

Furley & Co 🅛

18-20 Princes Dock Street, HU1 2LP (opp dockside entrance to Princes Quay shopping centre)
☎ (01482) 229649
5 changing beers (sourced nationally; often Atom, Half Moon, North Riding Brewery) ⊞
A popular family-friendly bar, offering local and regional cask and craft beers and overlooking the waterfront of the former Princes Dock. Historically, the premises were warehousing and offices for a shipping company and the first bottled gas merchant in Hull; the decor is now neo-industrial, portraying music and film iconography on the walls. Varied events include occasional live music and monthly visits from the chess society. Additional seating upstairs can be used for functions. ✩⚲◑♿🐾●🚃❤

George Hotel ✅

Land of Green Ginger, HU1 2EA
☎ (01482) 226373
Abbeydale Deception; Bradfield Farmers Blonde; Theakston Old Peculier; 3 changing beers (sourced regionally) ⊞
This pub, in the heart of the old town on Hull's most famous street, was totally refurbished in early 2020. The downstairs real ale bar, with wood-panelled walls and ceiling beams, still has its period fittings. Features of historic interest such as the fine glazed leaded windows have been retained - of note is reputedly the smallest pub window in England, dating from the building's former coaching days. Upstairs, a second bar has TVs for sporting events. A former CAMRA branch City Pub of the Year. 🐾🚃

Head of Steam 🅛

1Q King Street, HU1 2JJ
☎ (01482) 217236
6 changing beers (sourced regionally; often Atom, Camerons) ⊞
This is a single-roomed pub decorated with beer-related artefacts, whose large picture windows overlook Hull Minster and Trinity Square. An outdoor seating area to the front provides an ideal location to watch the world go by. The cask ales, which constantly vary, often promote new breweries, and are complemented by an extensive selection of craft products, which reflect the

passion of the management team. The food offered includes a wide range of vegan products.
✩⚲◑⬲●🚃❤

Hop & Vine 🅛

24 Albion Street, HU1 3TG (250yds from Hull New Theatre and Central Library)
☎ 07507 719259
3 changing beers (sourced nationally; often Great Newsome, Isaac Poad, Wold Top) ⊞
An atmospheric basement bar free house serving three changing guest beers largely from Yorkshire's independent breweries. Unusual still ciders and perries are also stocked and some continental bottled beers; a variety of other drinks is always on offer. Oversized lined glasses are used. A selection of freshly prepared food including home-baked bread is served until 9pm. Shove-ha'penny, cribbage and shut the box games are played. Former CAMRA National Cider Pub of the Year and four times Yorkshire regional winner. ✩◑⏃⬲♣●🚃❤

Kingston Hotel

25 Trinity House Lane, HU1 2JA
☎ (01482) 223635
Jennings Cumberland Ale; Marston's EPA; Ringwood Boondoggle; 1 changing beer (often Marston's) ⊞
A traditional street-corner pub with a curved frontage. Outdoor pavement seating allows drinkers to enjoy the sunshine and views of the adjacent Hull Minster. Inside, there are two rooms, one decorated with carved prow heads and the other with paraphernalia of Hull's fishing history. The wooden carved bar-back dates from Victorian times and is of historical interest. ⚲⬲♣

Minerva Hotel 🅛

Nelson Street, HU1 1XE
☎ (01482) 210025 ⊕ minerva-hull.co.uk
Tetley Bitter; 5 changing beers (sourced regionally; often Bone Machine) ⊞
Looking out over the Humber estuary and Victoria Pier, this famous pub, built in 1829, is a great place to watch the ships go by. Photos and memorabilia are a reminder of the area's maritime past. The central bar serves various rooms including a tiny three-seat snug. The former brewhouse was converted to provide additional drinking space and is available for functions. The building is connected to The Deep visitor attraction by a footbridge at the mouth of the River Hull.
✩⚲◑🚃(16) ⏃

Olde White Harte ★ ✅

25 Silver Street, HU1 1JG (in alley between Silver St and Bowlalley Lane)
☎ (01482) 326363 ⊕ yeoldewhiteharte.com
Caledonian Deuchars IPA; Theakston Best Bitter, Old Peculier; 3 changing beers (sourced nationally) ⊞
A historic pub in a 17th-century merchant's house, with strong connections to the English Civil War, hidden down an alley near Hull's Old Town. The existing ground-floor interior dates back to a major refurbishment in 1881, which was an idealised re-creation of an old English inn, complete with massive inglenook fireplaces and stained-glass windows. The first floor features the Plotting Parlour and restaurant facilities, while a courtyard provides an outdoor drinking area. ⚲♣🚃❤

Pave 🅛 ✅

16-20 Princes Avenue, HU5 3QA
☎ (01482) 333181 ⊕ pavebar.co.uk
Tetley Gold; Theakston Best Bitter; 3 changing beers (sourced regionally; often Great Yorkshire, Saltaire, Scarborough) ⊞

The original pavement café in this popular area of the city, this lively continental-style bar attracts a diverse range of customers. Independent and locally-owned it has a relaxed, friendly atmosphere. As well as the regular ales there are three guests, usually sourced regionally and including one stout, and a varied range of European draught and bottled beers. A changing Westons cider is also sold. Home-cooked food including vegetarian and gluten-free options is served daily. Live music is free on Tuesday evenings and Sunday afternoons. ▷❀❶৬⇋♠🖶🐾🛜

St John's Hotel
10 Queens Road, HU5 2PY
☎ (01482) 341013
Marston's 61 Deep; Wainwright; 3 changing beers (sourced nationally) Ⓗ
A Grade II-listed classic street-corner hostelry that boasts one of the least altered interiors in the city, recognised by CAMRA as having a regionally important historic pub interior. The front corner public bar complements a quiet back room, with original bench seating. A basic larger room accommodates the pool table and is home to regular beer festivals. A community local, it has two darts teams, a football team and the Oddfellows cricket league which hosts quiz nights in the winter. Open mic night is on Tuesday. Q▷❀৬♣🖶🐾🛜

Taphouse ⓛ
70 Humber Street, HU1 1TU
☎ (01482) 618000 ● taphousehull.co.uk
5 changing beers (sourced regionally; often Bone Machine) Ⓗ
The bar is a single spacious room, with an on-site brewery transformed from the previous brewhouse, which in turn was formerly a fruit merchant's warehouse. The original on-site brewery (Yorkshire Brewery, now closed) was one of the first businesses in the area responsible for its early regeneration. Consequently this place is now at the heart of Hull's thriving fruit market. Meals are provided by street-food vendors on a regularly changing basis, and bar snacks are available when the kitchen is closed. ▷❀❶৬♠🛜

Three John Scotts ⓛ ✅
Lowgate, HU1 1AA
☎ (01482) 381910
Greene King Abbot; Ruddles Best Bitter; Sharp's Doom Bar; 7 changing beers (sourced regionally; often Great Newsome) Ⓗ
Originally an Edwardian post office, this open-plan Wetherspoon features modern decor and works of art. The name derives from the three successive 19th-century vicars of St Mary's church opposite. The pub has established a broad customer base and appeals to all types. Up to 10 real ales and two real ciders are served. Children are welcome until 9pm. There is a large rear courtyard seating area which is a suntrap in the summer. ▷❀❶৬♣🖶🐾🛜

Whalebone ⓛ
165 Wincolmlee, HU2 0PA
☎ 07506 868461
Half Moon Old Forge Bitter; Rudgate Viking; 5 changing beers (sourced regionally; often Abbeydale, North Riding Brewery, Rat) Ⓗ
A rare gem sited within the old Greenland whaling trading area. Licensed since 1791, the current building dates from 1890, and has been a free house since 2002. Photos celebrating the city's sporting heritage and bygone Hull pubs adorn the walls. Artefacts showcasing the whaling industry can be viewed in the quiet room, once the pub's brewery. Hung outside from a bygone

year is a Moors' & Robson's brewery sign. CAMRA branch City Pub of the Year 2019, and many times previously. Q▷❀♣♠🐾🛜

White Hart ★ ⓛ
109 Alfred Gelder Street, HU1 1EP
☎ 07793 710160 ● whiteharthullpub.co.uk
5 changing beers (sourced regionally; often Crafty Little, North Riding Brewery, Revolutions) Ⓗ
Reopened in 2018 after many years of closure, this hostelry is on the edge of Hull's Old Town. It has a nationally important historic pub interior, with a rare bar front and many other original features. It is largely the brewery tap for Crafty Little Brewery, whose beers are usually featured, but it also showcases the more progressive breweries regionally and has a number of craft and KeyKeg beers as well. Runner-up local CAMRA Pub of the Year 2019. Q▷❀♣🖶P🖶🐾🛜

Kirk Ella

Beech Tree
South Ella Way, HU10 7LS
☎ (01482) 654350
Brakspear Gravity; Tetley Bitter; house beer (by Black Sheep); 5 changing beers (sourced nationally) Ⓗ
Open-plan inn on the western outskirts of Hull, owned by a pub company committed to cask ale. Up to eight real ales are available including at least one dark beer – try-before-you-buy is encouraged. Food is served every day, all day. Monday and Wednesday are quiz nights, and families with children are welcome throughout. A real fire makes for a hospitable winter feel. Buses stop close by until early evening, and later on a 10-minute walk away. ▷❀❶৬P🖶(154,180)🛜

Millington

Gait
Main Street, YO42 1TX
☎ (01759) 302045 ● gait-inn-millington.co.uk
Black Sheep Best Bitter; Tetley Bitter; Theakston Best Bitter; 2 changing beers (sourced locally; often Great Yorkshire, Half Moon, Wold Top) Ⓗ
A delightful Yorkshire Wolds pub that provides a warm welcome, both to locals and to the many walkers enjoying the attractions of Millington Woods and Pastures. It has an idiosyncratic bar with a wood-burning stove in winter, filled with a range of ornaments and local pictures. Sit at kitchen-style tables to enjoy hearty, home-made food served from an extensive menu. Three regular beers are stocked plus at least one guest, often all from Yorkshire. The pub stages an annual beer festival with up to 35 beers. ▷❀🍴❶♣P🐾🛜

Newton-upon-Derwent

Half Moon
Main Street, YO41 4DB
☎ (01904) 608883 ● thehalfmoonnewton.co.uk
Ainsty Flummoxed Farmer; Old Mill Traditional Bitter, Blonde Bombshell; Timothy Taylor Landlord; 1 changing beer Ⓗ
This free house has served the community here since 1743. Originally a single storey thatched-roof building, it had taken on its present guise by 1904, and then underwent some refurbishment in the 1930s. In the 1800s inquests were conducted here and from 1852 the Newton agricultural shows were held in the grounds, ending the day with a wonderful village dinner and many toasts. ▷❀❶P🐾🛜

Pocklington

Feathers Hotel
56 Market Place, YO42 2AH
☎ (01759) 303155 ⊕ thefeathers-hotel.co.uk
Theakston Best Bitter; York Guzzler; 3 changing beers (sourced locally) ℍ
Steeped in history, this is an old posting and market inn in the centre of town, dating back to Elizabethan times. It underwent extensive reconstruction in the early 19th century, while still retaining some of its original features, and has benefited from refurbishment over the past couple of years under the present ownership. With a busy public bar, it offers a choice of five real ales, including three guest beers usually from Yorkshire breweries. ⇦◖P

Rawcliffe

Jemmy Hirst at the Rose & Crown
26 Riverside, DN14 8RN (from village green turn N on Chapel Lane)
☎ (01405) 837902
Timothy Taylor Landlord; 5 changing beers (sourced locally; often Bradfield, Brown Cow, Little Critters) ℍ
A free house in the heart of the village, well-established and recognised as an award-winning real ale local pub. The new owners have kept this hostelry in its traditional style while investing in modernising the cellar and redecorating to give it a fresh, cared-for and loved atmosphere. Customers old and new are assured of a warm and friendly greeting – families and dogs welcome. Q⏰❀➤♣P⏾(401)❀

Sewerby

Ship Inn ✓
Cliff Road, YO15 1EW
☎ (01262) 672374 ⊕ shipinnsewerby.co.uk
Jennings Cumberland Ale; Mansfield Cask Ale; 3 changing beers (sourced nationally; often Banks's, Ringwood, Wychwood) ℍ
Village-centre pub featuring a wood-panelled bar with a beamed ceiling, a separate dining room and lounge. Popular with both locals and holidaymakers, it has a beer garden with a children's play area overlooking the sea. The restaurant serves traditional pub food – booking is recommended for the popular Sunday carvery (no food winter Mon). Nearby is a model village and Sewerby Hall, along with clifftop walks. A land train terminates not far away. ⏰❀◖▲♣P⏾(502,510)❀≈

Snaith

Yorkshire Ales Beer Café Bar
Selby Road, DN14 9HT (on edge of marketplace)
☎ (01405) 860603
Bad Seed Session IPA; Brown Cow White Dragon; 4 changing beers (sourced regionally) ℍ
The Yorkshire Ales bar promotes beers brewed by small, independent Yorkshire microbreweries. The building dates back to 1750 and has seating for 80 over two floors, and a beer garden. Food is snacks only, but artisan chefs and street-food vendors are booked regularly. Music plays at background volume and there are no TVs, helping to promote the art of conversation. Local cycling and photography clubs meet here regularly, and the weekly general knowledge quiz is popular. Q⏰❀≈♣●⏾(401) ❀≈

Sutton upon Derwent

St Vincent Arms ℒ
Main Street, YO41 4BN
☎ (01904) 608349 ⊕ stvincentarms.co.uk
Fuller's London Pride; Greene King IPA; Theakston Old Peculier; Timothy Taylor Landlord; York Guzzler; 1 changing beer (sourced nationally) ℍ
A former winner of many area CAMRA awards, this pretty white-painted village free house on a bend in the road has been family owned and well run for generations. It has a consistent but large beer range – the changing beer is usually from an independent brewer nearby. The cosy bar to the right, featuring a large Fuller, Smith & Turner mirror, is popular with locals. Another small bar to the left, with a serving hatch, leads to the dining rooms. Excellent food is served, beyond the usual pub fare, catering for a variety of tastes. Q⏰❀◖P

Walkington

Barrel Inn
35 East End, HU17 8RX
☎ 07550 078833
Thwaites IPA; Wainwright ℍ
A friendly drinkers' local in a quiet village, one of only a handful of Thwaites pubs in East Yorkshire. The front bar, with a log fire and a beamed ceiling, has a step leading to a connecting lounge, also with a log fire. To the rear is a secluded cottage garden. Families and dogs are welcome. Although the pub is essentially quiet, major Premier League football matches and some other sporting events are shown. Thursday is quiz night. ⏰❀♣⏾❀

YORKSHIRE (NORTH)

Aldwark

Aldwark Arms ℒ
YO61 1UB
☎ (01347) 838324 ⊕ aldwarkarms.co.uk
House beer (by Daleside); 3 changing beers (sourced locally) ℍ
With its riverside setting and rural location, this family-owned dining pub caters for all – from locals and ramblers to cyclists and horse riders (it has a hitching rail and water buckets) – and offers a warm and friendly welcome. Although two of the three rooms are set out for dining, the bar/lounge area has comfy leather chairs and sofas to relax in, plus a small number of tables that can be pressed into service for diners at peak times. Beer and music festivals feature regularly. The beer range comes from Yorkshire breweries. ⏰❀◖P⏾(29)❀≈

Appleton Wiske

Lord Nelson
High Street, DL6 2AD
☎ (01609) 881351 ⊕ lordnelsoninn.org.uk
Theakston Black Bull Bitter; 1 changing beer (sourced nationally) ℍ
A true locals' pub in the centre of this picturesque award-winning village near Northallerton, facing the beautiful village green. It is divided into two rooms, one set out for meals and the other a welcoming bar for drinkers. Food is served Thursday and Friday evening and Sunday lunchtime. Two beers are always on – a traditional house bitter and a rotating local lighter beer. There is themed dining on Thursdays – check the website for details. ❀◖P❀

Appletreewick

Craven Arms L
BD23 6DA
☎ (01756) 720270 ⊕ craven-cruckbarn.co.uk
Dark Horse Craven Bitter, Hetton Pale Ale, Night Jar;
Theakston Old Peculier; Wharfedale Blonde; 2
changing beers (sourced regionally) ⊞
Dating from 1548, this multi-roomed free house has
stone-flagged floors, oak beams and gas lighting. The bar
features an original Yorkshire range while the cosy
taproom has an open fire and the game of ring the bull.
A snug behind the bar leads to the cruck barn, added in
2006 using traditional techniques. This can be hired for
functions and hosts occasional events including music
and a beer festival in October. Two additional guest beers
are added in summer. Accommodation is in three
shepherd's huts. Q⟲⟲❀⇄❀❀◑⟲⅄▲♣●P➝(74A)❀❖

Askrigg

Crown Inn L ✅
Main Street, DL8 3HJ
☎ (01969) 650387 ⊕ crowninnaskrigg.co.uk
Black Sheep Best Bitter; John Smith's Bitter; 2
changing beers ⊞
A three-roomed family-run pub at the top of the main
street of the village. This busy, friendly Dales inn attracts
a good mix of regulars and visitors, and is particularly
popular for its bar meals sourced from local suppliers. The
interior has been partly opened out but retains much of
its traditional character, with an impressive range in the
cosy snug, and open fires to warm cold walkers seeking
shelter from the fells. ⟲◑▲P➝❀❖

King's Arms L
Main Street, DL8 3HQ
☎ (01969) 650113 ⊕ kingsarmsaskrigg.com
3 changing beers ⊞
This characterful Grade II-listed Dales free house starred
as The Drover's Arms in All Creatures Great and Small. A
huge open fireplace and a painting of the local friendly
society add charm to the stone-flagged bar. There are
separate dining rooms plus a vaulted games room to the
rear and a small outdoor courtyard. Three house beers
are from the Yorkshire Dales Brewery, a few hundred
yards away. ⟲❀◑▲⇄❀❖

Austwick

Game Cock
LA2 8BB (on road to Horton)
☎ (015242) 51226 ⊕ gamecockinn.co.uk
Thwaites Mild, Original, IPA, Gold; 1 changing beer ⊞
Cosy, multi-roomed pub with the emphasis on good
food. The old-fashioned bar, used mainly for drinking,
has a warming real fire and is decorated with cartoons
and old photos. Popular with locals, hikers and cyclists, it
can be quite intimate, with conversation involving the
whole room. One beer will be a guest from Thwaites.
There are two cosy snugs behind the bar, and the dining
rooms extend into the small south-facing conservatory.
Food specials include French night Wednesday, Steak
night Thursday, Fish & Chips Friday and Sunday roasts.
Q❀⇄◑▲♣P➝(581)❀❖

Beck Hole

Birch Hall Inn ★ L
YO22 5LE (approx 1 mile N of Goathland)
☎ (01947) 896245 ⊕ beckhole.info

Black Sheep Best Bitter; North Yorkshire Beckwater;
1 changing beer (sourced locally) ⊞
Unspoilt, family-run rural gem, resting among a hamlet
of cottages, run by a licensee, an accomplished fine
artist, now celebrating 42 years of continuous service in
the trade. It comprises the Big Bar and the Small Bar,
which sandwich a sweet shop. Pleasant outdoor drinking
facilities overlook the Murk Esk. The house beer,
Beckwater, is brewed organically by North Yorkshire
Brewery. Sandwiches, pies, beer cake and traditional
sweets are always available. Hours change during
winter. Q⟲❀⅄♣●❀

Beckwithshaw

Smiths Arms L ✅
Church Row, HG3 1QW
☎ (01423) 504871
Black Sheep Best Bitter; Greene King IPA; Timothy
Taylor Boltmaker; 2 changing beers ⊞
A Chef & Brewer food-led venue in an 18th-century
building that, as the name suggests, was formerly a
blacksmith's forge. Set in a quiet hamlet to the south-
west of Harrogate, the pub comprises an L-shaped bar
area and a separate restaurant. An excellent menu with
many seasonal dishes is offered throughout the day in
both the restaurant and bar. The five handpumps serve
three permanent beers and two widely sourced guest
ales. Boxed ciders may also be available.
⟲❀◑⅄P❀❖

Bishopthorpe

Bishopthorpe Sports & Social Club L
12 Main Street, YO23 2RB
☎ (01904) 707185 ⊕ bishopthorpeclub.co.uk
John Smith's Bitter; York Guzzler; 2 changing beers
(sourced regionally) ⊞
Over the past two decades, the stewards have
established this club as a popular destination, and it has
been voted CAMRA branch Club the Year on multiple
occasions. It has three handpulls with one rotating guest
– mainly from the region. The annual St Patrick's beer
festival, held in the refurbished function room,
encourages non-members to enjoy an extended range of
real ales and ciders, and to raise money for local
community sports teams. Close to the river, you can
arrive by boat. ⅄▲♣P➝❀❖

Marcia L
29 Main Street, YO23 2RA
☎ (01904) 706185 ⊕ themarciayork.co.uk
Leeds Pale; Rooster's Yankee; 3 changing beers
(sourced locally; often Atom, Half Moon, Treboom) ⊞
This popular village community venue has a landlord
who is passionate about real ale, with five handpumps
serving mainly LocAle. An annual beer and cider festival
is held in the large rear garden, which has a children's
play area. A good range of food is served every day. The
pub has a relaxed and friendly atmosphere, traditional
games, a Wednesday quiz night and support for local
clubs and teams. Q⟲❀◑⅄▲♣P➝(11)❀❖

Bradley

Slaters Arms L ✅
Crag Lane, BD20 9DE (SE corner of village on back road
to Kildwick)
☎ (01535) 632179
Timothy Taylor Boltmaker, Golden Best; 1 changing
beer (sourced locally; often Saltaire) ⊞

NORTH YORKSHIRE

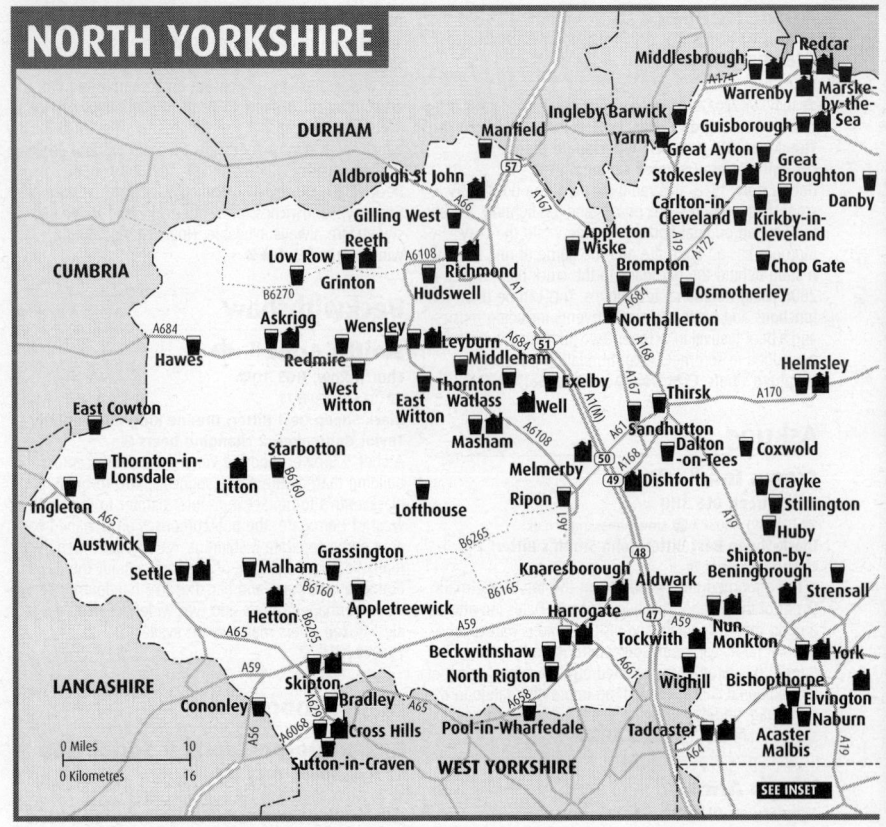

Two-roomed local, half a mile from the canal. The large outdoor area has extensive views of the Aire Valley. The main 'horse brass and wooden beam' style lounge has an open fireplace and real fire. The separate cosy back room is adorned with sporting photos, mainly of the local cricket teams which are based at the pub. Well-behaved children are permitted early doors or if eating. Quiz last Wednesday of the month. A Timothy Taylor Champion Club member. ⚲❀◑♣P🚍(71,78A)❀↺

Brompton

Green Tree ᴸ

Stokesley Road, DL6 2UA (on main A684, not in village centre)

☎ (01609) 780251 ⬚ greentreeinn.co.uk

3 changing beers (sourced locally) Ⓗ

Situated on the edge of the village on the main Northallerton-Osmotherley road, this traditional single-room free house retains the feel of a friendly community local. There are two distinct drinking areas either side of a central bar, with real fires at both ends of the room. To the rear, a sheltered beer garden includes a quoits pitch and is a suntrap on a good day. Guest beers are usually from Yorkshire microbreweries. ⚲❀◑♣P🚍❀❀⬚

Burn

Wheatsheaf ᴸ

Main Road, YO8 8LJ

☎ (01757) 270614 ⬚ wheatsheafburn.co.uk

6 changing beers (often Brown Cow, Ossett, Timothy Taylor) Ⓗ

A traditional country pub serving a varied range of guest beers mainly from Yorkshire breweries, and popular for its excellent, reasonably priced food. There is a collection of artefacts from bygone days and memorabilia of 578 and 431 Squadrons stationed at Burn in World War II. It stages regular beer festivals, quiz nights and many other activities. Q⚲❀◑♣P🚍(476,405)❀❀

Burythorpe

Bay Horse

Main Street, YO17 9LH

☎ (01653) 658700 ⬚ bayhorsepub.co.uk

All Hallows Peg Fyfe Dark Mild, Ragged Robyn, No Notion Porter; 3 changing beers (sourced locally; often Hambleton, Ossett, Theakston) Ⓗ

Nestled in the Yorkshire Wolds, the multi-roomed Bay Horse is a homely place, with farming paraphernalia, low lighting, multiple real fires, traditional furniture and a tiled floor. The choice of beers includes three from the All Hallows Brewery based at its sister pub in Goodmanham. The menu is wide ranging and adventurous, using locally sourced ingredients and priced attractively, with steak and pie nights on Tuesdays. The pub reopened following an extensive renovation in 2016 after a previously uncertain future. Q⚲❀◑♣●P🚍❀❀

Carlton-in-Cleveland

Blackwell Ox Inn

TS9 7DJ (800yds E of A172)

☎ (01642) 712287 ⬚ blackwellox.co.uk

4 changing beers Ⓗ

3 changing beers H

Set amid a walkers' paradise, and close to the route of Wainwright's Coast-to-Coast path, this picturesque family-run village pub offers a truly Yorkshire/Teutonic twist. Three locally sourced beers and seven especially imported draught lagers, brewed under the 505-year-old German Purity Laws, are served, together with real home-made food, again half-Yorkshire, half-German. There are six en-suite bedrooms, some designated dog-friendly, while free camping is offered to those who also choose to dine here. Check winter opening hours. Q ⬤♿🅿️ ⬤(M4) 🐕 📶

Church Fenton

Fenton Flyer L ✅

Main Street, LS24 9RF

☎ (01937) 558137

Rat White Rat; 4 changing beers (sourced regionally; often Ilkley, Leeds, Ossett) H

Friendly village pub with pictures of the nearby WWII airbase that is now a commercial airport. The beers are chosen from the SIBA list and are often LocAle. Live music features on the first Friday of each month, there is a monthly Saturday disco with karaoke, and a quiz night on Wednesday raising money for local charities. Sky and BT Sports TV are in the main bar, and there is an adjacent games room with a pool table and darts. Beer festivals are held in June and November. ⬤♿🅿️(492)🐕📶

Cliffe

New Inn L

York Road, YO8 6NN

☎ (01757) 633888

Theakston Best Bitter; 6 changing beers (sourced regionally; often Half Moon, Small World, Sunbeam) H

This cosy, welcoming, two-roomed country inn close to the A63 offers seven real ales, mostly local and certainly from Yorkshire. There are regular quiz and dominoes nights, and the pub is home to the village football teams. With a real fire in winter and a welcoming beer garden in summer, you will always feel at home. Watch out for the annual late-August charity beer festival with an even more eclectic choice of ales. ⬤♿ Å ♣🅿️ 🐕 📶

Cloughton

Bryherstones Country Inn

Newlands Road, YO13 0AR (½ mile up Newlands Rd off A171 at Cloughton)

☎ (01723) 870744 ⊕ bryherstonescountryinn.co.uk

Timothy Taylor Landlord; 1 changing beer (sourced regionally; often York) H

A stone-built pub nestling between the North York Moors and the coast, just outside the village of Cloughton. Now back in the hands of the Shipley family, it has been restored to its former glory. Its many rooms are full of features, and there is a separate games room. An extensive locally sourced food menu is offered (booking advised for evenings and Sunday lunchtimes). The pub welcomes children and dogs, and there is a play area in the spacious beer garden, as well as a large car park. ⬤♣🅿️(115) 🐕📶

Hayburn Wyke Hotel L

Newlands Road, YO13 0AU (off Ravenscar road, 1½ miles N of jct with A171)

☎ (01723) 870202 ⊕ hayburnwykeinn.co.uk

Black Sheep Special Ale; Theakston Old Peculier; 2 changing beers (sourced regionally) H

Set in beautiful surroundings on the northern edge of the North York Moors, with the same licensee for over 30 years, this popular, multi-roomed village inn is as renowned for its fine beers as it is for its authentic Thai food. Look out for the lunchtime and early-doors food offers. But you do not have to eat; four handpumps provide an eclectic range of beers in various styles. The garden has an extensive well-designed children's play area. Q ⬤♿🅿️(89)

Cawood

Ferry Inn L

2 King Street, YO8 3TL

☎ (01757) 268515

Leeds Pale; Timothy Taylor Landlord; 3 changing beers (sourced regionally; often Bradfield, Theakston, Wold Top) H

Wooden-beamed, 16th-century inn, with a homely ambience and two open fires to welcome visitors on winter days. During summer months, enjoy a picturesque backdrop of river views, open countryside and the adjacent swing bridge from the vantage point of the popular outside terrace. Regular games, pub games, live music and extended opening hours ensure this establishment keeps both visitors and the local community well satisfied. ⬤♿🅿️(42)🐕📶

Chop Gate

Buck Inn L

TS9 7JL (on B1257, between Stokesley and Helmsley)

☎ (01642) 778334 ⊕ the-buck-inn.co.uk

An 18th-century coaching inn in woodland next to the disused Scarborough to Whitby railway, and only minutes away from the Cleveland Way coastal path and rocky beach. It is popular with cyclists and walkers. Home-made food is served lunchtimes and evenings (no food Mon eves), with the Sunday carvery a local favourite. En-suite accommodation is available. Outside is a well-provisioned children's play space and a sizeable heated smoking area. ☺❀🛏◐Å♣P🚌(115)🐾📶

Cononley

New Inn 🄻

Main Street, BD20 8NR

☎ (01535) 636302

Timothy Taylor Golden Best, Boltmaker, Knowle Spring, Landlord; 1 changing beer (often Timothy Taylor) 🄷

A real local community pub with mullioned windows and low-beamed ceilings. The bar area is warmed by a wood-burning stove in a huge stone fireplace. Pot plants and china animals adorn the shelves and windowsills. The Archives room has a pool table and TV. Quiz night is on Tuesday. A short walk from Cononley railway station. ☺❀Å⇌♣🚌(78A)🐾

Coxwold

Fauconberg 🄻

YO61 4AD (leave A19, travel through Husthwaite, and at crossroads in centre of Coxwold village turn left, pub is on right)

☎ (01347) 868214 🌐 fauconbergarms.com

Isaac Poad No.84 India Pale Ale; John Smith's Bitter; Theakston Best Bitter; 1 changing beer (sourced locally) 🄷

Smart village venue well known for food but ably catering for drinkers as well. A family connection to the Isaac Poad brewery means there are always two Poad beers on tap. Convenient for local attractions such as the White Horse, Mouseman and Shandy Hall (home to English novelist Laurence Sterne). The small shop at the back supplies the village with essentials, which is a nice touch. Q☺❀🛏◐♣●P🚌(31X)🐾📶

Crayke

Durham Ox

Westway, YO61 4TE

☎ (01347) 821506 🌐 thedurhamox.com

Black Sheep Best Bitter; Timothy Taylor Boltmaker; York Guzzler; 1 changing beer 🄷

Set in a picturesque village, this inn is renowned for its fine dining, but remains the community local, providing three real ales. The drinking area is used for bar meals at peak times but also hosts a fine selection of board games. Live music is hosted – mainly jazz and folk – as well as various specialist nights ranging from cooking to antiques. The pub boasts some fantastic views of the Hambleton Hills and over the Vale of York. Q☺❀🛏◐♿P🚌🐾📶

Cross Hills

Gallagher's Ale House 🄻

1-3 East Keltus, BD20 8TD (in village centre)

☎ (01535) 957270

5 changing beers (sourced nationally) 🄷

This popular micropub is in what used to be Gallagher's bookmaker's shop. The five changing ales usually include a dark beer, a pale bitter and a strong or speciality beer. The cellar can be viewed through a window to the left of the bar. No electronic music or TV disturb the conversation. Parking is available adjacent to the Co-op store round the corner. Q♣●🚌(M4,66)🐾📶

Dalton-on-Tees

Chequers Inn

The Green, DL2 2NT

☎ (01325) 721213

Bombardier; Ringwood Boondoggle; 1 changing beer (sourced nationally) 🄷

An inn dating back to the 1840s, comprising a bar, lounge and restaurant, with friendly and welcoming staff. It combines both the atmosphere of a traditional pub and a contemporary restaurant. Up to three of the beers are Marston's mainstays. Good food is available every day, and traditional roast lunches on Sundays. Overnight accommodation comprises five rooms overlooking the green and its pump. Handy for Croft Circuit. Q☺❀🛏◐♣P🚌(X27)🐾📶

Danby

Duke of Wellington 🄻

West Lane, YO21 2LY (300yds N of railway station)

☎ (01287) 660351 🌐 dukeofwellingtondanby.co.uk

Daleside Bitter; Whitby Saltwick Nab; 1 changing beer 🄷

This 18th-century inn is set in idyllic countryside, close to the Moors National Park Centre and a traditional baker's shop. The venue was used as a recruiting post during the Napoleonic Wars, and a cast-iron plaque of the first Duke of Wellington, unearthed during restorations, hangs above the fireplace. All beers are from Yorkshire. At lunchtime, sandwiches can be brought into the pub. During the evening, the kitchen offers traditional British home-cooked meals at their best, using local produce. Q☺🛏◑⇌♣●🚌🐾

Drax

Drax Sports & Social Club 🄻

Main Road, YO8 8PJ

☎ (01757) 618041 🌐 draxsandsclub.co.uk

2 changing beers (sourced regionally) 🄷

Nestled in the shadow of the giant Drax power station, this club is full of life and enthusiasm. A lively bar area is supplemented by a huge function room which is often the venue for beer festivals and similar events. The club takes a little effort to get to but there are some buses from nearby Selby. A well-deserved local CAMRA branch Club of the Year in 2020. ☺Å♣●P🐾

East Cowton

Beeswing

Main Road, DL7 0BD

☎ (01325) 378349 🌐 thebeeswing.weebly.com

3 changing beers (sourced nationally) 🄷

Traditional country village inn with two bars, a pool room and a highly rated restaurant. Named after a locally bred champion racehorse, there are numerous racing references inside. Up to three changing ales are served from breweries countrywide and one craft beer. The staff are supportive and welcoming, and real fires create a relaxing atmosphere. The pub supports the local community with regular music events, quizzes and a pool table. Q☺❀◐♿♣P🐾📶

East Witton

Cover Bridge Inn 🔟
DL8 4SQ (½ mile N of village on A6108)
☎ (01969) 623250 🌐 thecoverbridgeinn.co.uk
5 changing beers (sourced locally) Ⓗ
A splendidly traditional Dales inn where numerous
CAMRA awards tell their tale. The River Cover runs along
the foot of the attractive garden and play area, near its
confluence with the River Ure. Fathom out the door latch
and you'll be able to enjoy the warm welcome in the
unspoilt public bar, with its eight beer pumps and giant
hearth, or sit in the tiny lounge or pleasant beer garden.
There is a choice of locally brewed beers and guests from
further afield, plus two real ciders and perry.
Q❀☺🏠🍴◑🕯♣🅿🚲(159)🐾🛜

Egton

Wheatsheaf Inn 🔟
YO21 1TZ
☎ (01947) 895271 🌐 wheatsheafegton.com
**Black Sheep Best Bitter; Helmsley Striding the Riding;
Timothy Taylor Landlord; 1 changing beer** Ⓗ
Winner of many industry and CAMRA awards, this Grade
II-listed 19th-century hostelry only serves Yorkshire
beers. The pub is now in its 22nd year in the Guide, and
remains under the stewardship of a licensee with over
30 years of continuous Guide recognition. Church pews,
country collectables and a roaring range add to the
ambience. The grassy areas are ideal for lazy summer
drinking, while the renowned first-class restaurant
always features local meat, fish and game.
Q❀🏠◑🕯♣🅿🚲(95)🐾

Exelby

Exelby Green Dragon 🔟
High Row, DL8 2HA
☎ (01677) 427715 🌐 exelbygreendragonpub.co.uk
2 changing beers (sourced nationally) Ⓗ
Reopened in 2018 following a community buyout and
renovations. The knocked-through interior provides a
number of discrete areas and a separate deli, and
features two real fires. A spacious restaurant opens onto
the decked terraced beer garden. The slightly altered
new name distinguishes the pub from the Green Dragon
in nearby Bedale. Music events include the twice-
monthly folk club and weekly Wednesday sing-alongs,
and numerous village activities include book, art and
gardening clubs. ☺❀🏠◑🕯🅿🐾🛜

Filey

Bonhomme's Bar
Royal Crescent Court, The Crescent, YO14 9JH
☎ (01723) 515325
**Rudgate Ruby Mild; house beer (by Isaac Poad); 1
changing beer (sourced nationally)** Ⓗ
Located just off the fine Victorian Royal Crescent Hotel
complex, the bar's name celebrates John Paul Jones,
father of the American Navy. His ship, the Bonhomme
Richard, was involved in a battle off nearby Flamborough
Head during the War of Independence. Up to five
handpumps dispense ale in summer, reducing to three in
winter. Food is served daily except Monday. A quiz is
held on Thursday evening and Saturday afternoon each
week. ☺🅰🚋♣🚲(12,13)🐾🛜

Gilling West

White Swan 🔟
51 High Street, DL10 5JG (1 mile W of Scotch Corner, off
A66)
☎ (01748) 825122 🌐 thewhiteswan.co
**House beer (by Mithril); 2 changing beers (sourced
nationally)** Ⓗ
A historic coaching inn, recently modernised, with a bar,
restaurant and rooms. An open fire, a courtyard garden
and wooden beams continue the tradition, while a
granite bar, tin tables and modern rooms bring this
charming village pub into the present. Real ales come
from a local microbrewery, Mithril, who brew the house
beer, The Swan, and there are also craft lagers and an
extensive wine and gin menu. The kitchen specialises in
steaks, seafood and Yorkshire tapas. It does all its own
butchery in-house and gets its famous steaks from a local
Yorkshire farm. There is regular live music, and a modern
gym. Q❀☺🏠◑🕯🅰♣🅿🚲(29)🐾🛜

3 Non Beards 🍴 ♦ York
Ainsty ♦ Acaster Malbis
BAD Dishforth
Bad Seed Malton
Black Sheep Masham
Brass Castle Malton
Brew York ♦ York
Brown Cow Barlow
C'84 Cropton
Captain Cook Stokesley
Copper Dragon Skipton
Crooked ♦ Church Fenton
Daleside Harrogate
Dark Horse Hetton
Great British Breworks Kirkbymoorside
Guisborough Guisborough
Hambleton Melmerby
Harrogate ♦ Harrogate
Helmsley ♦ Helmsley
Hop Studio ♦ Elvington
Jolly Sailor 🍴 ♦ Selby
Lady Luck 🍴 Whitby
LAMB Litton
Little Black Dog Carlton
Live Reeth
Malton Malton (NEW)
Mithril Aldbrough St John
Naylor's ♦ Cross Hills (brewing suspended)
North Riding (Brewery) Snainton
North Riding (Brewpub) 🍴 Scarborough
North Yorkshire Warrenby
Pennine Well
Play Brew ♦ Middlesbrough
Redscar 🍴 Redcar
Richmond Richmond
Rooster's ♦ Harrogate
Rudgate Tockwith
Ryedale Sinnington
Samuel Smith Tadcaster
Scarborough Scarborough
Settle Settle
Theakston ♦ Masham
Treboom Shipton-by-Beningbrough
Turning Point ♦ Knaresborough
Wensleydale ♦ Leyburn
Whitby ♦ Whitby
Wold Top Wold Newton
Yorkshire Dales ♦ Askrigg
Yorkshire Heart Nun Monkton

Grassington

Foresters Arms 🅛 ✅

20 Main Street, BD23 5AA

☎ (01756) 752349 ⊕ forestersarmsgrassington.co.uk

Black Sheep Best Bitter, Riggwelter; Tetley Bitter; Timothy Taylor Landlord; 2 changing beers (sourced locally; often Tetley, Timothy Taylor) Ⓗ

Just off the cobbled town square, the Foresters is a lively inn, popular with locals and visitors alike, which has been run by the same family for decades. The main bar and pool/TV area are to the left, and further seating to the right leads to a separate dining room. Accommodation is available in seven en-suite rooms, fishing permits for the River Wharfe nearby can be bought at the pub, and secure cycle storage is available for staying guests. A quiz is held on Mondays. ⛲😄🛏️🕐♣🚲(72,72B)🌮🎵♿

Great Ayton

Royal Oak Hotel 🅛 ✅

123 High Street, TS9 6BW (in centre of village opp High Green)

☎ (01642) 722361 ⊕ royaloakgreatayton.co.uk

Theakston Old Peculier; Timothy Taylor Landlord; Wainwright; 1 changing beer Ⓗ

A warm welcome is assured at this family-run 18th-century Grade II-listed building, situated at the heart of the community. Always busy, the pub is equally famed for its four beers as for its food menu – breakfast, lunch and dinner are served, with various offers throughout the week, including seniors' specials on Monday. An enclosed courtyard to the rear, a function room and four en-suite bedrooms are available. Q⛲😄🛏️🕐🚲(28,81)

Tannery

The Arcade, High Street, TS9 6BW (50yds through archway next to baker's shop)

☎ (01642) 909030 ⊕ thetanneryayton.co.uk

4 changing beers Ⓗ

This former hairdressers' has been tastefully refurbished and is now the village micropub. Opened in 2018 by experienced licensees, it has always attracted a discerning clientele. Four rotating guest beers, several craft beers and an extensive gin menu are served by enthusiastic and knowledgeable bar staff, with third-pint beer bats available. A free cheese and biscuit evening is hosted on Wednesday, with donations going to charity. ♿🚲(28A,81)🌮

Great Broughton

Bay Horse 🅛

88 High Street, TS9 7HA (at S end of village)

☎ (01642) 712319 ⊕ thebayhorse-greatbroughton.co.uk

Camerons Strongarm; 3 changing beers Ⓗ

Visitors and locals alike enjoy the welcoming hospitality offered by the friendly bar staff at this spacious village country inn, situated beneath one of the northern entrances to the North York Moors. Always busy, with an emphasis on good-value, freshly prepared, home-cooked meals, it also caters well for drinkers. In addition to Strongarm, which the pub is renowned for having served for many years, three changing guest beers from the Marston's stable are also on the bar. Q⛲😄🕐🚲(89)

Grinton

Bridge Inn

DL11 6HH (on B6270, 1 mile E of Reeth)

☎ (01748) 884224

3 changing beers (sourced nationally) Ⓗ

A friendly, well-run historic inn close to a crossing of the River Swale, as its name suggests, and lying beneath the towering hills of Fremington Edge and Harkerside. It has a comfortable lounge, a wood-panelled bar and two restaurant rooms offering home-made food, and is a haven for walkers and cyclists on the Coast-to-Coast and Inn Way walks and Dales Cycle Way; a youth hostel is half a mile up the hill. Guest beers are from the Marston's range. May close early at quiet times. Q⛲😄🛏️🕐♣🚲P🚲(30)🌮🎵

Grosmont

Crossing Club

Co-operative Building, Front Street, YO22 5QE (opp NYMR car park – ring front door bell for entry)

☎ 07766 197744

4 changing beers Ⓗ

Set amid beautiful scenery in the Esk Valley, this former local CAMRA branch Club of the Year is opposite the NYMR/Esk Valley railway stations in what was the village Co-op's delivery bay. Converted by dedicated villagers 23 years ago, a warm welcome always awaits CAMRA members. Over 1,400 different beers have been served during the club's history. Railway enthusiasts will enjoy both the steam and diesel memorabilia adorning the walls. Opens every evening in summer; hours may vary during winter. Q🚆♣🕐🌮

Guisborough

Monk 🅛

27 Church Street, TS14 6HG (at E end of Westgate)

☎ (01287) 205058

Timothy Taylor Landlord; 4 changing beers Ⓗ

This contemporary venue is an upmarket addition to the town's social life and attracts a discerning clientele. It is opposite Gisborough Priory, which was razed to the ground by King Henry VIII in 1540, and is aptly named as, legend has it, the 12th-century Black Monk made use of a tunnel, discovered during recent renovations, for his nefarious night-time activities. The tunnel's access steps are now on view. Five beers and a real cider are served. Better-value four-drink paddles are available. ♿🚲(5,X93)🌮🎵

Harrogate

Blues Café Bar 🅛

4 Montpellier Parade, HG1 2TJ

☎ (01423) 566881 ⊕ bluesbar.co.uk

4 changing beers (often Daleside, Ossett, Rooster's) Ⓗ

A small, single-room café bar in the town centre overlooking the lovely Montpellier gardens, modelled on an Amsterdam café bar, which has been going for more than 30 years. Noted for live music seven days a week, with three sessions on a Sunday, it is popular with music lovers and can get busy. Upstairs is the Gin Bar and Yorkshire Tapas restaurant, a room with seating in large booths where customers can watch the band on a TV screen while dining or drinking. 🕐🚆🎵🎵♿

Devonshire Tap House 🅛

10 Devonshire Place, HG1 4AA

☎ (01423) 568702 ⊕ devonshiretaphouse.business.site

Timothy Taylor Boltmaker; 7 changing beers (often Brass Castle, Harrogate, Wilde Child) Ⓗ

A cosy old pub, rescued, restored and renovated in 2014, then refurbished and reopened again by new independent operators in 2019. It retains its original semicircular counter and stained-glass canopy, has wood flooring throughout, and a mix of wooden benches, tables and chairs. Four handpumps on each side of the bar dispense a largely changing selection of beers from Yorkshire and northern breweries, and there are 12 keg lines and a beer fridge. Food offering is pizzas, including gluten-free and vegan options. ♿🏠🚂🚌🐾

Disappearing Chin

38 Beulah Street, HG1 1QH (opp bus station)
☎ 07539 942344 ⏚ thedisappearingchin.co.uk
3 changing beers ⓗ
This small bar, opened in 2019 in a shop unit opposite the bus station, is accessible from either Beulah Street or Station Parade. Long and narrow, it has soft seating at both ends in the windows, and stools at the bar, with some standing room. There are tables and chairs for outside drinking on Beulah Street. Three handpumps serve three changing cask ales, always including a dark beer, and there are eight craft keg fonts. Tap takeovers are sometimes organised. Card payments only.
♿♻🚂🚌🐾🛜

Harrogate Tap ⓛ

Station Parade, HG1 1TE
☎ (01423) 501644 ⏚ harrogatetap.co.uk
11 changing beers (often Brew York, Harrogate, Rooster's) ⓗ
Overlooking Harrogate station is this impressive transformation of a neglected railway building. The pub is of similar style to the Tapped Brew Company's other bars in York and Sheffield. It comprises a long bar room and a separate snug; the décor features dark-wood panelling, a tiled floor and tasteful Victorian-style fittings. A diverse range of cask ales is available on 12 handpumps, with one devoted to cider. The cask ales are complemented by craft kegs and bottled world beers. Bar snacks are served. ♿♻🚂🚌🐾🛜

Inn at Cheltenham Parade ⓛ ✔

26-30 Cheltenham Parade, HG1 1DB
☎ (01423) 505041 ⏚ innatcheltenhamparade.co.uk
Timothy Taylor Golden Best, Boltmaker, Knowle Spring, Landlord, Landlord Dark ⓗ
Timothy Taylor purchased the former Harrogate Brasserie in 2017 and continued to run it as a restaurant and boutique hotel under the same name until September 2019, when it was refurbished and renamed, now operating with more emphasis towards drinkers. The main bar area is in the centre with high tables and stools, and low tables in the window. There is a restaurant to the left, and a separate raised carpeted section to the right. Open for breakfast daily. ♿🏠🛏🍴🚂🚌🐾

Little Ale House

7 Cheltenham Crescent, HG1 1DH
☎ (01423) 391996 ⏚ alehouseharrogate.co.uk
5 changing beers ⓗ
Harrogate's first micropub, comprising one room with the counter at the back, and a downstairs cellar room. As with many micropubs, the beers are kept cool in a glass cabinet to one side. Five handpumps dispense cask ales, usually including a dark beer, and there is always at least one real cider. KeyKeg beer and local artisan gins are also sold. There is an outside seated area at the front as well as a pleasant covered yard with bench seating at the rear, with service at the window in summer. Card payments preferred. Q🏠🚂🍴🐾🛜

Major Tom's Social ⓛ

The Ginnel, HG1 2RB
☎ (01423) 566984 ⏚ majortomssocial.co.uk
4 changing beers (often Rooster's, Turning Point) ⓗ

A café bar housed above a vintage shop in a former antiques emporium, providing real ale, craft keg, pizza, music and art. It is simply furnished with wooden tables and chairs and some bench seating. The décor is in a mix of styles to suit its eclectic customers, including artwork for sale. Four handpumps dispense a variety of ales, usually from a range of smaller breweries, often including the local Rooster's brewery, as well as Turning Point from nearby Knaresborough. ♿🍴🚂🚌🐾🛜

Old Bell ⓛ

6 Royal Parade, HG1 2SZ
☎ (01423) 507930
Ilkley Mary Jane; Timothy Taylor Boltmaker; 6 changing beers (often Ilkley, Okell's, Rooster's) ⓗ
A Market Town Taverns establishment, the Old Bell opened in 1999 on the site of the Blue Bell Inn, which closed in 1815 and was later demolished. President Bill Clinton came to the inn during a visit to Harrogate in 2001. Later the same year the pub expanded into the former Farrah's toffee shop, where there is a collection of Farrah's memorabilia. The interior was refurbished in 2017, with new leather armchairs and updated decor. Eight handpumps serve beers from local Yorkshire breweries, often including at least one dark beer. ♿🍴🚂🐾🛜

Starling Independent Bar Café Kitchen ⓛ

47 Oxford Street, HG1 1PW
☎ (01423) 531310 ⏚ murmurationbars.co.uk
Kirkstall Three Swords; 4 changing beers (often Rooster's) ⓗ
A relaxed café bar with a contemporary feel and stripped-back brickwork throughout. A downstairs wall features a mural of a murmuration of starlings. The pallet-fronted counter holds six handpulls offering a well-chosen range of mainly Yorkshire beers in a good mix of styles and strengths, usually including a dark beer. The sixth pump is devoted to real cider. A large blackboard on the bar-back lists the current beers and is updated regularly. Stone-baked pizzas are a favourite here. Card payments preferred. ♿🏠🍴🚂🚌🐾🛜

Tap on Tower Street ⓛ ✔

Tower Street, HG1 1HS
☎ (01423) 565600 ⏚ thetapontowerstreet.co.uk
6 changing beers (often Rooster's, Timothy Taylor) ⓗ
Completely refurbished in modern style by new operators in 2017, however the three-room layout is unchanged. Food is available all day, mainly in the form of hot and cold snacks rather than formal cooked meals. Take away bottles and cans are available from fridges in the public bar and the rear room has a selection of more than 300 board games. There are four handpumps in each of the front bars with up to six changing beers. ♿🏠🍴🚂🚌🐾🛜

Winter Gardens ⓛ ✔

4 Royal Baths, HG1 2WH
☎ (01423) 877010
Daleside Blonde; Greene King Abbot; Ruddles Best Bitter; Sharp's Doom Bar; 5 changing beers ⓗ
Converted from part of the Royal Baths complex in 2002, this magnificent building has a spacious interior reached from the Parliament Street entrance by a sweeping Hollywood-style double stone staircase. Wheelchair access is from the entrance in The Ginnel. In addition to the usual core Wetherspoon range of beers, numerous locally sourced guests are always dispensed across three sets of handpumps. The pub can get busy due to its location near Harrogate's conference and exhibition centre. ♿🏠🍴♿🚂🐾🛜

Hawes

Board Inn ✓
Market Place, DL8 3RD
☎ (01969) 667223 ● theboardinn.co.uk
1 changing beer (sourced nationally) ⓗ
A comfortable and traditional pub located in the heart of this busy Dales town, popular with walkers and other visitors. The main front bar has a warming coal fire in winter and there is also a pleasant dining room, plus an outdoor seating area at the front. Home-cooked food is served all day during the summer, but not during winter afternoons. There are five en-suite letting rooms.
🛏🍴🕪▲♣🖵🐱🛜

Helmsley

Helmsley Brewing Co
18 Bridge Street, YO62 5DX
☎ (01439) 771014 ● helmsleybrewingco.co.uk
Helmsley Yorkshire Legend, Striding the Riding, Howardian Gold; 4 changing beers (sourced locally; often Helmsley) ⓗ
Brewery tap for the Helmsley Brewing Company, close to the market square in this picturesque village, the only market town in the North York Moors National Park and the perfect base for enjoying the wider area. It serves four changing beers from its own range. Brewery tours and the on-site shop complete the full beer experience.
🚌

Hinderwell

Brown Cow
55 High Street, TS13 5ET (on A174)
☎ (01947) 840694
2 changing beers (sourced regionally) ⓗ
Real inns like this are hard to find. Wedged between the moors and the coast, this recently refurbished establishment, still retaining an interior reminiscent of a 1960s front parlour, welcomes visitors and locals alike. Two more interesting rotating guest beers are served, as are good-value home-cooked meals. The pub supports darts teams, charity nights and dominoes drives, while quiz night is on Sunday. Children and dogs are welcome, and smokers are well provided for. Reasonably priced accommodation is in four bedrooms.
Q🛏🐱🍴🕪க♣🅿🚽🖵(X4)🐱

Huby

Mended Drum Ⓛ
Tollerton Road, YO61 1HT
☎ (01347) 810264 ● themendeddrum.com
Tetley Bitter; 4 changing beers (sourced locally; often Brass Castle) ⓗ
With a Terry Pratchett connection, this large open-plan venue is bigger than it looks. Welcoming to families and cyclists, it is the lively centre of this rural community. Known for its interesting range of frequently changing beers from the area and knowledgeable staff, it also offers classic pub food with a modern twist, including vegan, vegetarian and gluten-free dishes. Voted local CAMRA branch Pub of the Year 2019, it holds three beer festivals per year, and is well worth seeking out.
🛏🕪க▲♣🅿🖵(40) 🐱🛜

Hudswell

George & Dragon Ⓛ
DL11 6BL
☎ (01748) 518373 ● georgeanddragonhudswell.co.uk

4 changing beers (sourced locally) ⓗ
Rescued from closure by the local community in 2010, this homely, two-roomed village inn became CAMRA's National Pub of the Year just six years later. It now features its own library, shop, allotments and other facilities, as well as great food, Yorkshire-brewed beers and a selection of nearly 70 whiskies. A large beer terrace to the rear offers stunning panoramic views over the Swale valley, and it is a pleasant hike from Richmond, so long as you do not mind the 300-plus steps. Open all day bank holidays.
Q🛏🕪▲♣🅿🖵(32) 🐱🛜

Ingleby Barwick

Beckfields ✓
Beckfields Avenue, TS17 0QA (W off A1045, along Ingleby Way, then first left along Beckfields Ave)
☎ (01642) 766263
4 changing beers ⓗ
If your passion is for well-known and stronger best and premium beers, then this popular and uniquely named community venue will serve you well. It is at the heart of one of the six villages that make up what is reputedly Europe's largest private housing estate. Under the stewardship of a licensee with many years service to the trade, four handpulls operate on a rotating guest basis. An extensive pub grub menu is also served.
🛏🕪க♣🅿🖵(15) 🐱🛜

Ingleton

Masons
New Road, LA6 3HL
☎ (015242) 42040 ● masonsismoran.co.uk
Sharp's Doom Bar; 4 changing beers ⓗ
An early-Victorian building on the busy main road away from the centre of this popular tourist village. Extensively refurbished in 2016, it is now a true family-run free house. A small bar counter serves a long drinking space of linked areas with light and airy decor. Live music takes place, but not regularly. There is a patio with a glazed roof and heating. 🍴🕪▲🅿🖵(80)🐱🛜

Kirk Smeaton

Shoulder of Mutton
Main Street, WF8 3JY (follow signs from A1)
☎ (01977) 620348
Black Sheep Best Bitter; 1 changing beer (sourced regionally; often Bradfield, Stancill) ⓗ
Convenient for the Went Valley and Brockadale Nature Reserve, this welcoming and traditional village pub is popular with walkers and the local community. The beer comes direct from the brewery and the quality is superb. It is an award-winning free house and comprises a large lounge with open fires and a cosy, dark-panelled snug. The spacious pub garden has a covered and heated shelter for smokers, and there is ample parking. Quiz night is Tuesday. Q🛏♣🅿🖵(409)🐱🛜

Kirkby-in-Cleveland

Black Swan
Busby Lane, TS9 7AW (800yds W of B1257) NZ539060
☎ (01642) 712512 ● theblackswankirkby.co.uk
Bradfield Farmers Blonde; Sharp's Doom Bar; Timothy Taylor Landlord; Wainwright; 1 changing beer ⓗ
Nestling at the foot of the Cleveland Hills, at the crossroads of this ancient village, this warm and cosy free house is under the stewardship of a licensee of 25 years' standing, and is a place where a genuine welcome is

always afforded from the friendly staff. It comprises a bar, an adjacent pool room, a lounge/restaurant, a conservatory and a patio seating area. Four regular beers and a guest are available, while good-value meals are served, including daily specials and bar meals. ♿❀◑🕭♣️P🖱️🚃(89) 🐾🍴🛜

Knaresborough

Blind Jack's 🅛

19 Market Place, HG5 8AL

☎ (01423) 860475

Black Sheep Best Bitter; 6 changing beers (sourced nationally) 🅷

An entry in this Guide for 30 consecutive years, this is a Georgian listed building with bare-brick walls and wooden floorboards, comprising two small rooms on the ground floor and two similar rooms up a steep staircase. It provides a focal point both for locals and for the many visitors who appreciate the excellent selection of ales, the cosy ambience and lively banter. The diverse beer range includes at least one dark and one gluten-free choice, as well as a range of craft kegs. A trompe l'oeil painting on the exterior features the pub's namesake, Blind Jack Metcalf. Q🚃🖱️🐾🛜

Cross Keys ✔

17 Cheapside, HG5 8AX

☎ (01423) 863562

Ossett Yorkshire Blonde, Silver King, White Rat, Butterley Bitter; 3 changing beers (sourced regionally; often Ossett, Rudgate) 🅷

A former Tetley's house, refurbished by Ossett Brewery in its trademark style, with stone-flagged floors, bare-brick walls and stained glass. This traditional pub serves up to seven cask ales, mostly from the Ossett stable, which also includes Fernandes, Rat, Riverhead and Salt breweries. A guest beer is sometimes on the bar, and there is always a dark beer served. Boxed ciders, eg Lilley's, are sometimes available. Thursday is quiz night and a live band often plays on Saturday nights. ♿❀🚃🖱️🐾🛜♪

Half Moon 🅛

1 Abbey Road, HG5 8HY

☎ (01423) 313461 ⊕ thehalfmoonfreehouse.com

Rooster's Yorkshire Pale Ale; 3 changing beers (sourced locally) 🅷

A lovingly restored independent free house, down by Low Bridge, providing a warm and welcoming atmosphere, with a real fire and a wood-burning stove. There is a small, attractive, enclosed outdoor space, with tables and chairs and some benches under heated awnings. Four handpumps dispense a varying range of beers, mostly from Yorkshire breweries. A grazing menu of meat and cheese boards complements the beers, served every day; you can order pizzas on weekday evenings. Coffee and home-made cakes are also available. Dogs are welcome in the outside area. ♿❀◑🚃🖱️(22)🛜

Mitre 🅛 ✔

4 Station Road, HG5 9AA

☎ (01423) 868948

Ilkley Mary Jane; Timothy Taylor Boltmaker; 3 changing beers (often Rooster's) 🅷

Opposite Knaresborough's Grade II-listed railway station and signal box, this Market Town Taverns pub offers a modern split-level bar with wooden flooring throughout. There is a side room mostly used for dining, a function room in the basement, and a sunny terrace at the back with views of the local church. The six handpumps dispense a range of Yorkshire ales and occasional beers from smaller national breweries. Food is served every day and well-behaved dogs and children are welcome. ♿❀🥘◑🕭♿🚃🖱️(1)🐾🛜

Lastingham

Blacksmith's Arms

Anserdale Lane, YO62 6TN

☎ (01751) 417247 ⊕ blacksmithsarmslastingham.co.uk

Saltaire Blonde; Theakston Best Bitter, Old Peculier; 1 changing beer (sourced regionally; often Daleside, Rudgate) 🅷

A pretty stone inn in a conservation village, opposite St Mary's church, famous for its 11th-century crypt. The interior comprises a cosy bar with a York range lit in winter, a snug, and two dining rooms. Excellent-quality food including local game dishes is served alongside interesting guest beers and a changing guest cider, often Thistly Cross. A secluded beer garden is to the rear which now includes a pizza oven. This remote pub is popular with regulars, walkers and shooting parties. Dogs welcome outside only. Q♿❀🥘◑🍴

Leavening

Jolly Farmers 🅛

Main Street, YO17 9SA

☎ (01653) 658276

Timothy Taylor Landlord; York Guzzler; 2 changing beers (sourced locally; often Great Newsome, Half Moon) 🅷

A 17th-century hostelry on the edge of the Yorkshire Wolds between York and Malton. The pub is homely and welcoming, with low ceilings, tile flagged floors and an intriguing series of rooms. Serving locally sourced food and a range of ales from near and far, it is a popular stopping-off point for ramblers as well as locals. Annual beer and gin festivals are hosted. The outside drinking area has table football and a cask of drinking water for dogs complete with handpump. Q♿❀🥘◑🕭♣️P🖱️🐾🛜

Leyburn

Golden Lion 🅛

Market Place, DL8 5AS

☎ (01969) 622161 ⊕ goldenlionleyburn.co.uk

1 changing beer (sourced locally) 🅷

Facing the main square of this busy and attractive Dales centre, this traditional market town pub is a short walk from the revived Wensleydale Railway with its steam trains in summer. The comfortable main bar area is opened out and largely wood-panelled, with a real fire at each end, and there is a separate dining room to the rear, particularly popular for the Sunday carvery. There are tables outside for eating and drinking in fine weather. ♿❀🥘◑🕭🚃♣🔥🐾🛜

King's Head 🅛

Grove Square, DL8 5AE

☎ (01969) 622798

Changing beers

Set off the main marketplace, at the junction of the moor road and the Richmond road, this locals' pub is a rare example of a wet-led house in this tourist area, offering a selection of well-kept cask ales at attractive prices. It is an enthusiastic provider of sports TV, especially football, which is well supported, and also hosts regular live music. The rooms have been knocked through, but the bar, lounge and games room have the feel of separate areas. Attractions include a pool table, two dartboards, fruit machines, open fires, and the only jukebox in town. ♿♿🚃♣🖱️🐾🛜

Lofthouse

Crown Hotel L

Thorpe Lane, HG3 5RZ

☎ (01423) 755206

Black Sheep Best Bitter; Dark Horse Hetton Pale Ale; Theakston Best Bitter ⊞

A traditional Dales pub and hotel in the Nidderdale Area of Outstanding Natural Beauty, a short way uphill from the main part of the village on a road with spectacular views. There is an unusual panelled entrance corridor leading to a traditionally furnished, comfortable bar decorated with local pictures, maps and brassware; a more formal dining room is reached through the bar. There is also a rack of walking sticks for sale if required. No mobile phone coverage indoors. Q✿⏸❁▲◗▲♣P❀

Low Row

Punch Bowl Inn L

DL11 6PF

☎ 0333 700 0779 ⊕ pbinn.co.uk

1 changing beer ⊞

A smart two-room 17th-century inn with a focus on food, owned by the same people as the CB Inn at nearby Langthwaite. The bar area is pleasant, featuring a Mouseman Thompson counter, bare floorboards and old pine tables, with comfortable leather settees around the stove. The pub offers welcome rest and recreation for walkers (provided muddy boots are removed). The guest beer is often from Rudgate. Q✿⏸❁▲♣P❀⬤

Malham

Lister Arms L ✅

Gordale Scar Road, BD23 4DB

☎ (01729) 830444 ⊕ listerarms.co.uk

Thwaites Gold, IPA, Original; 3 changing beers (sourced locally; often Dark Horse, Settle, Thwaites) ⊞

Substantial stone-built Grade II listed inn dating from 1723 or earlier, overlooking the green. The tiled entrance hall opens to the stone-flagged main bar, with separate areas to left and right and a dining room/restaurant beyond. The large secluded garden at the rear has ample comfortable seating. Food is served all day, with breakfast and brunch on offer in the morning, and the main menu thereafter. Home-made cakes and cream teas are also available. Malham can get busy on weekends and school holidays. ✿❁▲◗▲P❅❀⬤

Malton

Blue Ball

14 Newbiggin, YO17 7JF

☎ (01653) 690692

Tetley Bitter; Timothy Taylor Landlord; 1 changing beer (sourced locally) ⊞

Called the Blue Ball since 1823, this Grade II-listed pub dating from the 16th century is recognised by CAMRA as having a historic interior of regional importance. The low front elevation hides a maze-like interior, with the frontward cosy bar, compact servery and linking corridor retaining most of the historical flavour. A smoking area is at the rear. Home-cooked food is served daily (except Wed). The Blue Ball Folk Club meets here on the second Tuesday of each month. Q✿⏸❁♣P❅(843)❀⬤

Brass Castle Brewery Tap House L

10 Yorkersgate, YO17 7AB

☎ (01653) 698683 ⊕ brasscastle.co.uk

3 changing beers (sourced locally; often Brass Castle) ⊞

Formerly a town-centre temperance hotel, Malton's newest hostelry is a short walk from the railway station. The single-roomed bar is tastefully designed in a rustic style, with one wall partially adorned with barrel staves. Three regularly changing cask ales are offered and six craft keg ales, alongside an extensive range of bottled beers. Snacks may be purchased at the bar. There is a smoking/drinking area to the rear of the premises and an upstairs seating section. Q✿♿❁♣❅(843)❀⬤

New Malton

4 Market Place, YO17 7LX

☎ (01653) 693998 ⊕ thenewmalton.co.uk

3 changing beers (sourced regionally) ⊞

Situated in the busy marketplace, this Grade II-listed building, formerly tea rooms, has been sensitively renovated. The large single-room interior is divided into three distinct drinking and dining areas, and three handpumps here deliver varying beers mainly originating from Yorkshire breweries. Meals are served from midday throughout the week, all locally sourced and prepared on-site. There is a small space at the front for alfresco drinking. Children and dogs are welcome. Q✿⏸♿❅(843)❀

Manfield

Crown Inn

Vicars Lane, DL2 2RF (500yds from B6275)

☎ (01325) 374243

Draught Bass; Village White Boar; 5 changing beers (sourced nationally; often) ⊞

This 18th-century inn in a quiet village has been local CAMRA Country Pub of the Year 16 times, and previously Yorkshire Pub of the Year. It has two bars, a games room, a real log fire in the main bar, and an extensive beer garden. A mix of locals and visitors creates a friendly atmosphere. Up to six quest beers are sourced from microbreweries, alongside five ciders or a perry. Two seasonal beer festivals are held. Q✿❁⏸♣♣P❅(29)❀❀

Marske-by-the-Sea

Clarendon L

88-90 High Street, TS11 7BA

☎ (01642) 490005

Black Sheep Best Bitter; Camerons Strongarm; Copper Dragon Golden Pippin; Theakston Best Bitter, Old Peculier; 1 changing beer ⊞

The Middle House, as it is also known, is a popular one-room locals' pub, where little has changed since the 1960s. Six beers are served from the mahogany island bar, a rarity on Teesside. The walls are adorned with interesting photographs of yesteryear. There is no TV, no pool table, no children or teenagers, just regulars indulging in convivial conversation. There is no catering either, but tea and coffee are always available. Local CAMRA branch 2020 award winner. Q❁❅P❅(X3,X4) ❀

Masham

White Bear L ✅

Wellgarth, HG4 4EN

☎ (01765) 689319 ⊕ thewhitebearhotel.co.uk

Theakston Best Bitter, Lightfoot, Old Peculier ⊞

Theakston's only pub, an award-winning venue and a great favourite with the locals as well as directors and staff from the brewery. A large dining area to the left and

a cosy taproom to the right offers exclusively Theakston's beers. Unusually for the Yorkshire Dales, this building was a victim of wartime bombing, following which it was derelict for many years before it was rescued and renovated to a high standard. A popular beer festival is hosted in June showcasing over 30 beers.
ॐ⊛⌺◑♿♣⇄Pॿ❀≋

Middleham

Richard III Hotel ⅃
Market Place, DL8 4NP
☎ (01969) 623240 ⊕ richard111hotel.co.uk
1 changing beer Ⓗ
A comfortable and small 17th-century hotel in this horse-racing centre, with an opened out front bar, carpeted and decorated with flock wallpaper. There is a real fire and a separate dining room and snug to the rear, and a warm welcome from the local owners. Tables are set out on cobbles at the front – the ideal spot to enjoy breakfast while racehorses trot by. ॐ⌺◑ॿ(159,859)❀

Middlesbrough

Bottled Note ⅃
55-57 Borough Road, TS1 3AA (just N of university campus)
☎ (01642) 644214
4 changing beers (sourced nationally) Ⓗ
One of several micropubs located in a series of parallel streets just south of the Cleveland Centre, now in its sixth year of operation. Half of this double-fronted Victorian terrace is a micropub. The other half, which opens at weekends, is a cocktail and wine bar. Four handpumps generally include a beer from Three Brothers, while a stout or a porter is also usually served. A wide selection of bottled beers is also available. ⊛♿⇄ॿ≋

Infant Hercules ⅃
84 Grange Road, TS1 2LS (just S of Cleveland Centre and N of university campus)
☎ 07980 321626
4 changing beers Ⓗ
This regular CAMRA branch award-winner is one of several micropubs in the town's original solicitors' quarter, all located in a series of parallel streets close to the law courts. It is named after Gladstone's description of the town in 1862, after he had witnessed the rapid expansion of the area's steel furnaces and shipbuilding industries. Third-pint tasting bats are available. Teesside University's Real Ale Society (TURAS) continues to meet here on Thursdays.
Qॐ⊛⇄♥ॿ❀≋

Isaac Wilson ⅃
61 Wilson Street, TS1 1SF (at N end of town, close to railway station)
☎ (01642) 247708
Camerons Strongarm; Sharp's Atlantic; 3 changing beers Ⓗ
Popular pub named after a 19th-century railway industry magnate and company director of the world's first railway, the Stockton and Darlington. The Isaac, a former Wetherspoon's conversion of the old law courts, has recently gained new owners and continues to follow, more or less, the chain's formula. Two regular beers, three local guests and several ciders, together with good-value food, are served. The single room interior has walls adorned with photographs of old Middlesbrough. Third-pint glasses are available. ॐ◑♿⇄♥ॿ≋

Naburn

Blacksmith's Arms
Main Street, YO19 4PN
☎ (01904) 623464 ⊕ blacksmithsarmsnaburn.com
Marston's EPA; Ringwood Razorback; Wychwood Hobgoblin Gold; 2 changing beers (sourced nationally; often Marston's) Ⓗ
A fantastic riverside village inn, with a selection of real ales, excellent food and a great community ethos. It is the hub for much local life, often coordinating village events. There is a pleasant, fairly new outdoor area, and the pub is easily accessible by road, river or the York to Selby cycle path. There are camping facilities nearby and a holiday cottage in the grounds. Children are welcome – there is even a large pick-and-mix sweet stand.
ॐ⊛⌺◑♿Å♣ॿ❀≋

North Rigton

Square & Compass ⅃ ✅
Rigton Hill, LS17 0DJ
☎ (01423) 733031 ⊕ thesquareandcompass.com
Leeds Pale; Ossett Yorkshire Blonde; Theakston Best Bitter; Timothy Taylor Landlord; 2 changing beers (often Rooster's) Ⓗ
A large, elegant, open-plan pub with multiple sections laid out for dining, although the main bar at the front is a pleasant space for drinking, furnished with tables and leather armchairs and overlooking a large sunny terrace. One area to the side of the bar features a large chandelier, and there is a bookshelf with second-hand books for sale. Six handpumps dispense beers from Yorkshire breweries, including one from the local Rooster's Brewery. ॐ⊛◑♿Pॿ(747,X52)❀≋

Northallerton

Oddfellows Arms ⅃
251 High Street, DL7 8DJ (off main part of High St)
☎ (01609) 259107
2 changing beers (sourced locally) Ⓗ
Hidden behind the parish church by the cemetery gates, the Oddies does not appear to be on the high street, despite its address. A thriving back-street community pub, it handles a mainly local trade and is popular with darts players, TV football fans and church bell ringers. Refurbished in a simple but traditional style with an open-plan interior, there is a games room upstairs and a secluded beer garden to the rear. ॐ⊛◑♣ॿॿ❀≋

Standard ⅃ ✅
24 High Street, DL7 8EE (at N end of High St)
☎ (01609) 772719
Hambleton Stallion Amber; Timothy Taylor Landlord; 2 changing beers Ⓗ
Half a mile north of the town centre, opposite Sainsbury's supermarket on the A167 Darlington road, this community local takes it name from the English defeat of the Scots at the nearby Battle of the Standard in 1138. The interior decor is old world-style with bare stone, brickwork and old photographs, and the three distinct drinking areas offer good-value and wholesome food. The large beer garden to the rear features a Jet Provost aircraft. ॐ⊛◑⇄♣ॿ❀≋

Stumble Inn ⅃
4 Garthway Arcade, DL7 8NS (in pedestrian arcade off High St next to Grovers shop)
☎ 07817 568042
5 changing beers (sourced locally) Ⓗ
This friendly and cosy micropub is hidden away near the Applegarth car park. It serves a selection of local ales,

craft beers and up to 20 real ciders, and staff are keen to offer tasting advice and guidance. With no music, gaming machines, Wi-Fi, children or sports TV, there is just good old-fashioned chat here, plus a quiz on the last Sunday of each month and seasonal beer and cider festivals. The beer choice always includes a dark one. Q🍴🚑♿

Nun Monkton

Alice Hawthorn
The Green, YO26 8EW
☎ (01423) 330303 🌐 thealicehawthorn.com
Changing beers (often Yorkshire Heart) Ⓗ
Originally called the Bluebell Inn, the Alice has been a pub since 1787, overlooking the green in this picturesque village. Kate and Richard Harpin bought the premises in 2013 with a will to make it a cracking little place and to secure its future. It serves good-quality food, made with local produce, and cask ales from Yorkshire Heart, based just outside the village. Accommodation is available in 12 rooms. 🏠🛏◐

Osgodby

Wadkin Arms Ⓛ
Cliffe Road, YO8 5HU
☎ (01757) 702391
Brown Cow White Dragon; Ossett Yorkshire Blonde; Timothy Taylor Landlord; 1 changing beer (sourced nationally; often Marston's) Ⓗ
A true community pub at the heart of the village, with five handpumps dispensing ales largely sourced from Yorkshire breweries. The Wadkin has a homely feel, with open fires and a friendly welcome, and is home to regulars and visitors alike. The nearby Transpennine Cycle Trail sees cyclist and walkers visiting in the summer months, and a local bus service passes too. You will see much evidence of CAMRA sympathies on display. 🚑🏠♿🅿🚌(4)♿🎵

Osmotherley

Golden Lion Ⓛ
6 West End, DL6 3AA (in village centre, 1 mile E of A19)
☎ (01609) 883526 🌐 goldenlionosmotherley.co.uk
2 changing beers (sourced locally) Ⓗ
Set in the centre of a picturesque village on the edge of the North York Moors National Park and at the start of the long-distance Lyke Wake Walk, this old inn is a favourite with hikers, casual visitors and regulars. Much of the focus is on high-quality locally sourced food, but drinkers are always welcome, and the view from the outside drinking tables is an attraction on fine days. Regularly changing beers are from breweries nearby and there is a beer festival each November. Dogs are welcome. Q🏠🛏◐🅰🚌(80,89)♿🎵

Pickering

Black Swan Ⓛ
18 Birdgate, YO18 7AL
☎ (01751) 798209 🌐 blackswan-pickering.co.uk
Great British Breworks Coal Porter, Great Scot, Istanbul; 3 changing beers (sourced regionally; often Yorkshire Heart) Ⓗ
Grade II-listed, 18th-century former coaching inn, located in the heart of Pickering. There is a large main bar with timber-beamed ceiling, divided into drinking and dining areas. Three beers from its own brewery, Great British Breworks, are available at all times. Meals are served lunchtimes and evenings. To the rear is a smoking/drinking area adjacent to the car park. Live

entertainment features at weekends. Children and dogs are welcome and accommodation is available. Q🚑🏠◐🍴♿(N Yorkshire Moors)🅿🚌(128)♿🎵

Sun Inn Ⓛ
136 Westgate, YO18 8BB (on A170, 400yds W of traffic lights in town centre)
☎ (01751) 473661 🌐 thesuninn-pickering.co.uk
Tetley Bitter; 5 changing beers (sourced regionally) Ⓗ
Friendly local CAMRA Rural Pub of the Year, close to the steam railway. Six real ales are served, often from Yorkshire micros, and several traditional ciders. A cosy bar with a real fire leads to a separate room, ideal for families and special occasions, where artists from the area display their work. The large beer garden is used for the annual beer festival in September. Regular events include fortnightly acoustic music, charity quizzes and monthly vinyl nights. Dogs (on leads), children and walkers are welcome. 🚑🏠♿♣🚌(128)♿

Pool-in-Wharfedale

Hunters Inn Ⓛ
Harrogate Road, LS21 2PS
Abbeydale Moonshine; Black Sheep Best Bitter; Morland Old Speckled Hen; 6 changing beers (often Bradfield, Ossett) Ⓗ
A single-storey building on the main Harrogate to Bradford road with views across lower Wharfedale. The large open-plan interior incorporates a raised area at one end, with a warming real fire during colder months. Nine handpumps dispense a varying selection of ales, mainly sourced from Yorkshire breweries. There is a pool table and video jukebox at one end, and a small games room with fruit and pinball machines. Children are allowed during the day. 🚑🏠♣🅿🚌♿🎵↻

Redcar

Rita's Pantry Ⓛ
1 Esplanade, TS10 3AA (opp Beacon)
☎ 07730 445483
3 changing beers Ⓗ
A former amusement arcade is now the town's first micropub. Situated on the seafront, from where the petrified forest can be seen at low tide, a warm welcome is extended to CAMRA members, locals and visitors alike. Three interesting beers are served, as well as real cider, and third-pint glasses are available. The amiable licensee hosts various social events, including a music quiz on Sunday and occasional Belgian beer nights. 🏠◐♿🅰♿🚌(X3,X4)♿🎵

Redmire

Bolton Arms Ⓛ
DL8 4EA
☎ (01969) 624336 🌐 boltonarmsredmire.co.uk
1 changing beer (sourced nationally) Ⓗ
This attractive village lies at the western terminus of the revived Wensleydale Railway and less than a mile from the historic Bolton Castle. The stone-built pub is a 10-minute walk from the station and trains provide a good way to travel as parking can be limited. Inside, lunchtime and evening meals are available in the large dining area, as well as snacks served all day, as well as four real ales, usually locally brewed. 🚑🏠🛏◐♿🅰♿♣🅿🚌♿🎵

Richmond

Castle Tavern ✅
Market Place, DL10 4HU

☎ (01748) 823187 ⊕ castletavernrichmond.com
3 changing beers (sourced nationally) ⊞
Near the foot of the market square, the Castle is a
friendly place serving up to four real ales, one real cider
and good-value food in a long knocked-through main
room with a separate side room. Run by Richmond
Brewing Co, whose brewery is down the hill in the old
station, it is the company's only pub in the town and
always serves at least one of its beers. Accommodation is
upstairs, and live music sometimes features. 🛏️◑🍴🍽️

Holly Hill Inn ⃝
Sleegill, DL10 4RJ
☎ (01748) 822192 ⊕ holly-hill-inn.co.uk
1 changing beer ⊞
A pleasant but strenuous walk half a mile south from the
town centre, this popular pub lies beyond the castle,
across the River Swale and high above it. The main bar is
split into two levels separated by a stone chimney breast
with a cast-iron stove, while a large extension in the
style of a baronial hall with an impressive fireplace is
used as a restaurant and function room. Quiz nights are
on Wednesdays. Q🛏️🌳🍴◑🚶♿♣🅿️🚏(30)🐾🛜

No.29 Alehouse & Gin Bar
29 Frenchgate, DL10 4HZ
☎ (01748) 850491
⊕ number-29-alehouse-gin-bar.business.site
3 changing beers (sourced locally) ⊞
This real ale, craft beer, gin, wine and tapas bar opened
in 2018. It is just off the foot of Richmond's market place,
on the road down to the former station complex. The
single small bar has a wooden floor and simple decor.
The beers are usually local or regional. Food such as
cured meat and cheese sharing boards, ploughman's and
various tapas dishes are on sale. May close early if quiet.
◑🚏

Ripon

One Eyed Rat ⃝
51 Allhallowgate, HG4 1LQ
☎ (01765) 607704
**Saltaire Blonde; Timothy Taylor Landlord; 5 changing
beers** ⊞
A real ale destination in Ripon over many decades, the
One Eyed Rat was refurbished and re-opened under new
management in the summer of 2020. A Grade II listed
building set within a terrace of 200-year-old houses, its
narrow frontage leads to a warm and welcoming
hostelry. The pub has a long, narrow interior with
traditional seating and an open fire, and there is a large
garden at the rear, including a sizeable covered area. Up
to seven cask ales, mainly from Yorkshire, are served.
Q🛏️🌳🚏🐾🕯️

Royal Oak ⃝
36 Kirkgate, HG4 1PB
☎ (01765) 602284 ⊕ royaloakripon.co.uk
**Saltaire Blonde; Timothy Taylor Golden Best,
Boltmaker, Landlord, Landlord Dark; 1 changing beer
(often Timothy Taylor)** ⊞
This venue is in what was an 18th-century coaching inn,
now beautifully renovated in a modern idiom, in the
centre of historic Ripon between the cathedral and the
Market Square. Timothy Taylor's most northerly tied
house, the Royal Oak serves a top-quality range of the
brewery's beers alongside a regular Saltaire Blonde. The
pub is separated into relaxed dining areas with log-
burning stoves and comfortable seating, and offers a
first-class locally sourced menu. You can stay in one of
the six stylish and comfortable bedrooms, and a hearty
English breakfast is included. 🛏️🌳🍴◑🚶🅿️🚏(36)🐾🛜

Robin Hood's Bay

Bay Hotel ⃝
The Dock, YO22 4SJ (at end of very steep road, down
towards bay from top car park)
☎ (01947) 880278 ⊕ bayhotel.info
**Leeds Pale; Theakston Best Bitter, Lightfoot;
Wainwright** ⊞
This magnificent Grade II-listed 1822 building is the finish
line for Wainwright's Coast-to-Coast 192-mile walk. The
bottom bar, named in his honour, gives access to the
Dock patio, situated at the seawater's edge and
providing superb panoramic views. With a licensee of
more than 20 years' service, a friendly welcome awaits
regulars, visitors, their children and their dogs. An
extensive good-value home-cooked menu is served.
Access to this part of the village is not easy for the less
mobile. 🛏️🌳🍴◑🚏(X93)🐾

Rosedale Abbey

Coach House Inn
YO18 8SD
☎ (01751) 417208 ⊕ coachhouseinn.co.uk
**Black Sheep Best Bitter; Theakston Best Bitter; York
Guzzler; 3 changing beers (sourced locally; often
Wold Top)** ⊞
A country inn and restaurant in this beautiful moorland
village in the heart of the North York Moors National
Park. There is a great choice of real ales from dark and
amber to blonde or IPA, and the overall quality is good.
The bar staff are friendly and helpful.
Q🛏️🌳◑🚶♿🅿️🚏🐾🛜

Saltburn-by-the-Sea

Saltburn Cricket, Bowls & Tennis Club ⃝
Marske Mill Lane, TS12 1HJ (next to leisure centre)
☎ (01287) 622761 ⊕ saltburn.play-cricket.com
3 changing beers ⊞
Visitors are made most welcome at this local CAMRA
multi-award winner, well supported by the community
and now celebrating 25 years of continuous Guide
recognition. Three interesting beers are served, often not
lasting the evening. An enthusiastic steward hosts a
variety of events, including a monthly blues club. The
balcony, ideal for those lazy summer afternoons,
overlooks the cricket field. On Saturday and Sunday
match days the club opens at 12pm. Please check winter
opening hours. ♿🚶♣🅿️🚏(X3,X4)🐾

Sandhutton

King's Arms ⃝
YO7 4RW
☎ (01845) 587887 ⊕ thekingsarmssandhutton.co.uk
**Black Sheep Best Bitter; 2 changing beers (sourced
locally)** ⊞
A well-appointed 200-year-old roadside inn in a small
village, focusing largely on food served to a high
standard featuring locally-sourced ingredients and
organic vegetables, although it retains a popular public
bar. Three beers are usually on, often including an ale
from Rudgate, and the licensee is an enthusiastic
supporter of LocAle. Outside, an honesty box shop sells
produce from the area and also offers bicycle spares and
storage, gels and free air. 🛏️◑🅿️

Scarborough

Hole in the Wall
26-32 Vernon Road, YO11 2PS
☎ (01723) 379329
4 changing beers (sourced nationally; often Titanic) Ⓗ
Built in the 1840s, the pub has a split-level interior with three seating areas. This friendly, conversational local is handy for the town centre and spa complex. Formerly a Marston's establishment but now privately owned, it matches its former status as a real ale mecca. Up to seven guest beers are offered at weekends. Sky and BT satellite TV may be enjoyed. There is an outside covered smoking space to the side. ❀⌖≠♣🚗❀

North Riding Brew Pub Ⓛ
161-163 North Marine Road, YO12 7HU
☎ (01723) 370004 ⊕ northridingbrewpub.com
6 changing beers (sourced nationally; often North Riding Brewery, North Riding Brewpub) Ⓗ
Scarborough's only brewpub, serving at least six continually changing beers from local breweries and microbreweries around the UK. It always has one or more North Riding beers together with some brewed on the premises. These are complemented by three craft keg beers from around the world, and an extensive range of craft bottled beers. There is a public bar and quiet lounge, both with real fires. Quiz night is Thursday. Q⌖❀♣●🚗(9,9A)❀🖤

Scarborough Borough Council Employees Welfare Club Ⓛ
Dean Road, YO12 7QS
☎ (01723) 364593
3 changing beers (sourced locally; often Great Newsome, North Riding Brewery) Ⓗ
Close to the town centre, this club comprises a large bar area with an adjacent snooker room and a 200-capacity function room upstairs. Three changing guest cask ales are offered. Club teams participate in local snooker, darts and dominoes leagues. The place is family friendly, and CAMRA members are welcome subject to signing in. An outdoor drinking/smoking space is at the side. Local CAMRA Club of the Year. Q⌖≠♣🚗(8,8A)❀

Scholars Bar Ⓛ
6 Somerset Terrace, YO11 2PA
☎ (01723) 372826
Hambleton Nightmare Porter; 5 changing beers (sourced regionally; often North Riding Brewery, Ossett) Ⓗ
A warm, friendly atmosphere prevails at this town-centre pub at the rear of the main shopping centre. The large front bar is dominated by TV screens showing major sporting events, and there is a smaller games area to the rear. Five rotating guest beers, usually from Yorkshire microbreweries, are offered, plus numerous ciders and perries. The Thursday night quiz is popular, with a first prize of 28 pints. ⌖≠♣●🚗❀🖤

Stumble Inn
59 Westborough, YO11 1TS (approx 200yds SW of railway station) ⊕ stumbleinnmicropub.weebly.com
6 changing beers (sourced nationally) Ⓗ
The first micropub in Scarborough, this was a welcome addition to the local real ale scene, quickly gaining a positive reputation for its beer and cider. A former solicitors' office, it is a single-roomed venue offering six rotating guest ales, with the area's breweries always represented. Up to 26 ciders and perries are also stocked. An ideal place for a cosy chat and chillout, where dogs are welcome. ⌖≠●🚗❀

Valley Bar Ⓛ
51 Valley Road, YO11 2LX
☎ (01723) 372593 ⊕ valleybar.co.uk
Dark Star Hophead; 4 changing beers (sourced nationally; often Scarborough) Ⓗ
The bar, recently relocated adjacent to the original cellar bar, is a large room divided into several drinking areas. There is also a pool room and a separate function room. Of note is the remarkable decor utilising antique furniture. Four guest beers are offered, usually including one or more from Scarborough Brewery. Up to 10 real ciders and perries are also sold, together with a selection of Belgian bottled beers. Accommodation is available. ⌖❀⌖♣●🚗❀🖤🛜

Wilsons
West Sandgate, YO11 1QL
☎ 07544 775051
8 changing beers (sourced nationally) Ⓗ
The Grade II-listed Wilsons (formerly the Leeds Hotel) is close to the seafront and offers a warm welcome to regulars and visitors. This is a single-roomed venue with a horseshoe bar adorned with numerous photographs relating to the region's fishing industry. Up to eight cask ales are offered. Teams participate in the local darts league, and there is live music on Sunday afternoon. En-suite accommodation is available in five letting rooms. 🛏⌖≠♣🚗❀🛜

Selby

Doghouse Ⓛ
8 Park Street, YO8 4PW
☎ 07495 026173
3 changing beers (often Little Black Dog) Ⓗ
Selby's first craft beer café, the Doghouse features six draught beers from its own brewery based at Carlton, together with four ciders and a large range of keg beers. The upstairs room is a meeting place for many local groups and there is a weekly quiz night, regular live music and occasional guest food suppliers. You can be sure of a warm welcome at this family-run bar. ❀≠●

Giant Bellflower Ⓛ ✅
47A Gowthorpe, YO8 4HF
☎ (01757) 293020
Greene King IPA, Abbot; Sharp's Doom Bar; 4 changing beers (sourced nationally; often Adnams, Rudgate, Sharp's) Ⓗ
Busy town-centre Wetherspoon, named after the flower which was found on the banks of the town's river. It is a modern, spacious pub, converted from a furniture showroom, displaying artefacts and pictures of Selby's past. It offers typical Wetherspoon fare, a range of keenly-priced beers, real ciders and LocAles. ⌖❀🖤♿≠●🚗🛜

Settle

Golden Lion Ⓛ ✅
Duke Street, BD24 9DU
☎ (01729) 822203 ⊕ goldenlionsettle.co.uk
Thwaites Mild, Original, IPA, Gold, Amber; 1 changing beer (sourced locally; often Dark Horse, Kirkby Lonsdale, Settle) Ⓗ
Built around 1670, this former coaching inn has two comfortable high-ceilinged rooms for drinking. The main bar has wood panelling, a grand staircase and a huge fireplace. The Lion's Den is accessed from the bar or via a low door off the street. There is a separate bright and colourful dining area. Outside seating is in the yard to the side of the pub. ⌖❀🛏🕭Å≠♣●🚗❀🛜

Talbot Arms Ⓛ ✓

High Street, BD24 9EX

☎ (01729) 823924 🌐 talbotsettle.co.uk

Settle Mainline; Theakston Best Bitter; 3 changing beers (sourced regionally; often Saltaire, Wishbone) Ⓗ

Just off the square, this family-run free house, claiming to be the oldest pub in town, offers a welcoming and friendly atmosphere. In winter a stove glows in the large stone feature fireplace to the left, with a pool table and a dartboard beyond providing a base for teams in local leagues. A pleasant, terraced beer garden is at the rear. The guest beers are usually from Cumbria, Lancashire or Yorkshire. Good-value food is served until 8pm all week. Live music plays most Fridays. 🏠🕮🌜🎵🅰️🍴🅿️♿💷🛜

Skipton

Beer Engine Ⓛ

1 Albert Street, BD23 1JD

☎ 07930 810763

6 changing beers (sourced nationally) Ⓗ

A well-established micropub in a tiny street between the town centre and the canal. Six handpumps dispense varying beers, always including one blonde or pale ale and one dark beer, plus a character beer. A still cider and a fruit cider are also on tap alongside a selection of canned and bottled beers and wines. The beers are stored in refrigerated cabinets behind the bar. The ambience is friendly and welcoming. Q🏠🚲🍴🖨💷🛜

Boat House Ⓛ

19 Coach Street, BD23 1LH

☎ (01756) 701660

5 changing beers (sourced regionally) Ⓗ

Tucked out of the way, access is through an arch from Coach Street or via the canalside path. The bar is light and airy with picture windows looking onto the canal basin, and the decor has a canal theme. A cobbled outdoor drinking area offers the opportunity to enjoy a beer while watching the boats go by. An old-style stove keeps the bar warm in winter. One dark cask ale and keg craft beers are usually sold. 🏠🕮🍴🖨💷🛜

Narrow Boat Ⓛ

36-38 Victoria Street, BD23 1JE (alleyway off Coach St nr canal bridge)

☎ (01756) 797922

Ilkley Mary Jane; Okell's Bitter; Timothy Taylor Landlord; 5 changing beers Ⓗ

A long-standing Guide entry and, with eight handpulls dispensing an eclectic selection of cask ales, there should always be a beer to suit most tastes. Bottled and keg continental and craft beers and up to three ciders or perries complement this offering. Two separate rooms downstairs and an upstairs gallery and function room plus a drinking/smoking area at the front provide ample space. Note the unusual interpretation of the Leeds-Liverpool canal map on the wall. Children are welcome if eating. 🕮🌜🍴🖨💷🛜

Starbotton

Fox & Hounds Ⓛ

BD23 5HY

☎ (01756) 760269 🌐 foxandhoundsstarbotton.co.uk

Timothy Taylor Boltmaker; Wharfedale Blonde; 2 changing beers (often Naylor's, Wensleydale, Yorkshire Dales) Ⓗ

A family-run, whitewashed 17th-century inn, divided into two cosy rooms, with flagstone floors and a large stone fireplace enhancing the atmosphere. In fine weather the sheltered patio at the front provides additional seating. A locally brewed golden ale and dark beer are dispensed alongside the regular beers. Lunch is available daily and evening meals are served Wednesday to Sunday. There is a piano in the bar which visitors are encouraged to play. The daytime community-run bus stops outside. 🏠🕮🏨🌜♣🅿️🖨(72B,874)💷

Stillington

White Bear Ⓛ

Main Street, YO61 1JU

☎ (01347) 810338 🌐 thewhitebearinn-york.co.uk

Leeds Pale; house beer (by Rudgate); 3 changing beers (sourced regionally) Ⓗ

You will always get a warm welcome in this traditional venue. To the left is a gem of a restaurant (booking advised), and to the right is a classic pub bar. The Autovac system is put to good use so beer is always fresh and lively, and the staff are helpful and friendly. It is definitely worth making the effort to visit if you are not already a regular. 🏠🕮🏨🌜♣🅿️(40)💷🛜🔄

Stokesley

White Swan Ⓛ ✓

1 West End, TS9 5BL (150yds beyond shops)

☎ (01642) 714985 🌐 whiteswanstokesley.co.uk

Captain Cook Sunset, Slipway, Endeavour; 5 changing beers Ⓗ

Home of the Captain Cook Brewery, this friendly 18th-century pub is at the west end of the pretty market town. Eight handpulls serve six beers from the Captain Cook portfolio of 10 beers, together with two interesting guest ales, while two real ciders are also always available. Beer festivals are held at Easter and in October. Open mic night is Tuesday, quiz night is Wednesday, while music night is Thursday. The sheltered outdoor drinking area overlooks the brewery. Over-18s only, please. 🕮♣🍴🖨💷🛜

Strensall

Ship

23 The Village, YO32 5XS

☎ (01904) 490302 🌐 theshipinn-strensall.co.uk

Timothy Taylor Landlord; 3 changing beers (sourced regionally) Ⓗ

Popular family-run village pub near the River Foss, offering four real ales, one real cider and restaurant food. Open all day and late at the weekend, it attracts walkers, cyclists and caravanners in summer, with outside seating and a children's play area at the rear. Although well known for its food, it has a dedicated area for people just wanting a quiet drink. Regular events are held including music and quiz nights, and an annual spring beer festival. The bus stop from York is just across the road. 🏠🕮🌜♿🅰️🅿️🖨💷🛜

Sutton-in-Craven

King's Arms Ⓛ ✓

High Street, BD20 7LP (near the jct with Main St)

☎ (01535) 636854

3 changing beers (often Moorhouse's, Saltaire, Tetley) Ⓗ

The King's is a friendly, homely pub. The main bar has two distinct areas: a smart carpeted room with high-backed settles, a fish tank and a real fire and a smaller games area with darts. Note the interesting collection of clocks. The bar has three handpumps with a rotating beer selection. There is a separate pool room at the rear, bookable for meetings, a covered patio and upgraded beer garden out back. A good range of malt whiskies is available. Regular jam sessions. ⏱☸♣🚲(66,78A)🐾🛜

Tadcaster

Angel & White Horse

23 Bridge Street, LS24 9AW
☎ (01937) 835470
Samuel Smith Old Brewery Bitter Ⓗ

An old coaching inn in the centre of town and next to the Samuel Smith Brewery, making it the brewery tap. It has a large wood-panelled interior with two huge log fires in winter. A rear door leads to a courtyard, the brewery and the stables for the grey dray Shire horses used to deliver the beer to local pubs. All cask beer is served from wooden casks. Only assistance dogs are permitted.
Q☸🚲

Thirsk

Little 3 Ⓛ ✅

13 Finkle Street, YO7 1DA
☎ (01845) 523782 🌐 littlethree.co.uk
5 changing beers (sourced nationally) Ⓗ

Just off the Market Place, this old, low-beamed and characterful pub claims a history from 1214. It is a warren of nooks and crannies, all decorated in mock half-timbering, with an impressive fireplace in the main bar. Formerly the Old Three Tuns, it was renamed to avoid confusion with the nearby Three Tuns. Regularly changing guest beers are from local and national brewers and there is a happy hour daily except Saturday. Food is served in the upstairs bistro and live music plays every Thursday and Saturday. ⏱☸◐🅿🚲🐾🛜

Thornton le Dale

New Inn ✅

The Square, YO18 7LF
☎ (01751) 474226 🌐 the-new-inn.com
Theakston Best Bitter; 2 changing beers (sourced nationally) Ⓗ

Family-owned Grade II-listed inn, restored to create the feel of yesteryear. Dating to around 1720, this former coaching inn overlooks the medieval village stocks and market cross, and is an ideal touring base for the North Yorkshire Moors, Dalby Forest, Ryedale and the coast. The pub prides itself on freshly cooked food, with a wide range of specials available. The large main room is separated into a drinking and a dining area. Outside, there is a smoking/drinking space at the rear. Dogs are welcome away from dining areas. En-suite accommodation is available in six rooms plus a self-catering holiday cottage. Q⏱☸🛏◐🅿🚲(128,840) 🐾🛜

Thornton Watlass

Buck Inn Ⓛ ✅

Village Green, HG4 4AH
☎ (01677) 422461 🌐 buckwatlass.co.uk
Black Sheep Best Bitter; Theakston Best Bitter; Timothy Taylor Landlord; Wensleydale Falconer; 1 changing beer Ⓗ

Overlooking the village green, this traditional country inn, with five letting rooms, features a cosy bar room with a real fire, a lounge/dining room and a large function room known as the Long Room. The building has been refurbished throughout by the owners, while retaining a village pub atmosphere. Excellent meals are available and four regular Yorkshire beers are served,

with a changing ale added in summer. Live trad jazz music is hosted on Sunday lunchtimes once a month. ☸🛏◐🅿🚲🐾

Thornton-in-Lonsdale

Marton Arms

LA6 3PB (¼ mile from A65/A687 jct)
☎ (015242) 42204 🌐 martonarms.co.uk
Black Sheep Best Bitter; 5 changing beers (sourced regionally; often Farm Yard, Timothy Taylor) Ⓗ

In a hamlet with a parish church, old stocks and little else, you will come across this independently owned free house. Behind the 1679 date stone and old oak door, a flagged passage leads to a modern bar refurbished in 2017. Alongside the beers there are 56 gins. The pub has an attractive little garden with a view of Ingleborough, and is 10 minutes' walk from the start of the Waterfalls Walk. ☸🛏◐▲♣🅿🚲(80,581)🐾🛜

Ugthorpe

Black Bull Inn Ⓛ

Postgate Way, YO21 2BQ
☎ (01947) 840286 🌐 blackbullwhitby.co.uk
Theakston Old Peculier; 1 changing beer Ⓗ

A warm welcome is assured at this traditional Grade II-listed, pantiled country inn, where photographs of yesteryear adorn the walls. A comfortable, family-run establishment, it comprises a main bar, snug, restaurant and games room. The guest beers complement the Old Peculier and change weekly. Portions of home-cooked food are such that going home hungry is not an option. Diners travel from far and wide for the impressive Sunday lunch carvery (booking in advance is advised). Q⏱◐♿♣🅿

Wensley

Three Horseshoes Ⓛ

DL8 4HJ (on A684)
☎ (01969) 622327 🌐 thethreehorseshoeswensley.co.uk
2 changing beers (sourced nationally) Ⓗ

This traditional country pub is full of atmosphere, with its small bar and dining room both featuring low beams and real fires. Outside, there is a terraced beer garden offering glorious views across Wensleydale – a real suntrap on fine days. Wholesome and reasonably priced lunchtime and evening meals are served daily (no food Mon). Guest beers in busier months are usually from the Marston's range. Q⏱☸◐♿♣🍴🅿🚲🐾🛜

West Heslerton

Dawnay Arms

Church Street, YO17 8RQ
☎ (01944) 728507 🌐 dawnayarms.co.uk
Theakston Best Bitter; 2 changing beers (sourced regionally; often Wold Top) Ⓗ

This village inn just off the A64 has a main bar divided into drinking, eating and games areas, together with a separate restaurant. One regular beer is offered in addition to two guests from Yorkshire microbreweries. High-quality, locally sourced, home-cooked meals are served. Teams participate in local pool, darts and dominoes leagues. At the rear is a spacious beer garden and a partially covered smoking/drinking area. Two en-suite rooms are available.
⏱☸🛏◐♿▲♣🅿🚲(843)🐾🛜

West Witton

Fox & Hounds 🅛

DL8 4LP (on A684)
☎ (01969) 623650 ⊕ foxwitton.com
3 changing beers (sourced locally) Ⓗ
This welcoming Grade II-listed family-run free house is full of character. A real community hostelry, it has a down-to-earth bar and games room popular with locals and visitors alike. Good-value meals are served all week with a roast on Sundays, and the dining room boasts an inglenook fireplace with quaint stone oven. Once a rest house for 15th-century Jervaulx Abbey monks, it has a pleasant patio at the rear. Beware the tight entry to the car park. Ꮟ❀◑Å♣♠Ｐ🐾❀ ᗧ

Whitby

Arch & Abbey

2-4 Skinner Street, YO21 3AJ (at S end of Skinner St, towards St Hilda's Terrace)
4 changing beers (sourced nationally) Ⓗ
Recently opened micropub, close to Botham's Bakery, operated by enthusiastic licensees who strive to adhere to the original micropub norms. This successful crowd-funded start-up is in what was a truly old-fashioned ladies' dress shop that would not have looked out of place in a heritage museum. Four interesting beers, several real ciders, and light bites and snacks are served. Check ahead for winter opening hours. Children are allowed until 9pm. Q Ꮟ ⇌ ♠ ♣ (X93,840) ❀ ᗧ

Black Horse 🅛 ✅

91 Church Street, YO22 4BH (on E side of swing bridge on way to Abbey steps, close to marketplace)
☎ (01947) 602906 ⊕ the-black-horse.com
5 changing beers Ⓗ
This little multi-roomed gem, dating from the 1600s, offers a warm welcome. The frontage, with its frosted glass, together with one of Europe's oldest public serving bars, was built in the 1880s and remains largely unchanged. Beer is poured from five handpumps, and the cider is Westons Rosie's Pig. Snuff, tapas, olives, Yorkshire cheeses and hot drinks are always available, while hot lunches are served during the winter months. Accommodation is in four bedrooms.
Q Ꮟ Ꮟ ◑ ◐ ⇌ ♣ ♠ (X93,840) ❀ ᗧ

Little Angel ✅

18 Flowergate, YO21 3BA (200yds W of swing bridge, 200yds N of rail and bus stations)
☎ (01947) 820475 ⊕ littleangelwhitby.co.uk
5 changing beers (sourced regionally) Ⓗ
Now the home of Lady Luck Brewery, locals and visitors alike are afforded a genuine friendly welcome at this extremely popular venue where, it is rumoured, the remains of the castle form part of the structure. Large-screen sports TVs, live music, an outdoor beer terrace, and even a horse mount for those requiring this feature, complement the five beers and real cider served to three separate rooms from a central bar. Local CAMRA branch Best Town Pub for three years' running.
Ꮟ❀⇌♣♠ (X93,840) ❀ ᗧ

Station Inn 🅛

New Quay Road, YO21 1DH
☎ (01947) 600498 ⊕ stationinnwhitby.co.uk
Black Sheep Best Bitter; Ossett Yorkshire Blonde; Silver King; Theakston Old Peculiar; Timothy Taylor Boltmaker; Whitby Jet Black; 2 changing beers (sourced nationally) Ⓗ
Next to the harbour and marina, this popular multi-roomed inn is under the proud stewardship of an enthusiastic licensee who ensures that the eight beers, including two guests, always encompass an eclectic range of varying beer styles, while real cider is also served. Situated opposite the bus station and the NYMR/Esk Valley Railway station, this pub has become the discerning travellers' waiting room. Live music features on three evenings a week. There are four letting bedrooms. ᗏ⇌♠♣ (X93,840) ❀ ᗧ

Waiting Room 🅛

2 Whitby Station, Langborne Road, YO21 1YN (by main entrance to NYMR/EVR station)
☎ (01947) 821640
5 changing beers Ⓗ
Located on the platform that the North York Moors Railway steam trains use, the friendly owners of Whitby's first micropub strive to adhere to the original micropub values – no keg beers or lagers, no spirits, no jukebox, no TV. Five handpumps and a dozen or more ciders add to a pleasant atmosphere and lots of convivial conversation. The six-yards-square establishment gets busy at times, so don't be disappointed if there's no room inside. Local CAMRA branch Cider Pub of the Year. Q♿⇌♠♣ (X93,840) ❀ ᗧ

Whitby Brewery Tap 🅛

East Cliff, YO22 4JR (at top of 199 steps)
☎ (01947) 228871 ⊕ whitby-brewery.com
Whitby Abbey Blonde, Jet Black, Saltwick Nab, Whitby Whaler, Black Death Ⓗ
Away from the hustle and bustle of the town, perched on the cliff edge and in the shadow of the abbey, these new and larger premises now include space for a small bar that serves up to five of the brewery's seven beers together with an occasional guest. When the bar area is full, drinkers overflow into the brewery itself, or outside if the weather isn't too inclement. Brewery tours are available (book ahead), including sampling the beers.
Q❀♿Å⇌Ｐ♠ (840,X93)

Wighill

White Swan 🅛 ✅

Main Street, LS24 8BQ
☎ (01937) 832217 ⊕ thewhiteswanwighill.co.uk
3 changing beers (sourced locally) Ⓗ
A cosy, friendly and well-decorated pub with a roaring fire in the winter. The cask ales are in good condition and excellent locally sourced food is served from the renovated kitchen, where you can observe the chefs creating your meals. Walkers and cyclists are welcome. There is a large car park at the rear, accessed by a lane to the left-hand side. Q Ꮟ❀◑◐♿Ｐ♠ (37) ❀

Yarm

Ketton Ox 🅛 ✅

98-100 High Street, TS15 9AU (at N end of High St)
☎ (01642) 788311
Draught Bass; Timothy Taylor Landlord; 4 changing beers Ⓗ
A historic 17th-century Grade II-listed inn, once renowned for its illegal cock fighting and its upstairs morgue. It is named after a famous shorthorn ox, Comet, born in nearby Ketton Hall in 1796, who established the standards by which the breed has become defined. Recently refurbished, this contemporary outlet ticks all the boxes, including friendly staff, six handpulls, and reasonably priced pub food. The large upstairs function room can be used for private parties. Third-pint glasses are available. Ꮟ❀◑◐♿♣♠ (7,17) ❀ ᗧ

York

Ackhorne ⃞

9 St Martins Lane, YO1 6LN

☎ (01904) 671421

Rudgate Jorvik Blonde; 4 changing beers (often Ainsty, Bad Seed, Half Moon) ⃞

This traditional 18th-century inn, with six cask ales, is hidden off the beaten track down a narrow cobbled lane at the bottom of Micklegate. It is partially open plan, with separate areas up a couple of steps or through an archway. There is a pleasant beer garden at the back. The pub's friendly family atmosphere appeals to all age groups, and there is a regular evening quiz as well as lunch on Sunday. ⃞⃞⃞⃞⃞⃞⃞⃞

Blue Bell ★ ⃞ ⃞

53 Fossgate, YO1 9TF

☎ (01904) 654904

Bradfield Farmers Blonde; Kelham Island Best Bitter; Rudgate Ruby Mild; Timothy Taylor Landlord; 4 changing beers (sourced locally; often Bad Seed, Half Moon, Rooster's) ⃞

This very small Edwardian pub is full of character and has a nationally important Grade II* historic interior (from 1903), with its central bar supplying two small rooms and a side corridor. With a charismatic landlord and a welcoming atmosphere, it can get full so entry may be restricted at busy times. It has enforced house rules and a strict no-groups policy. Permanent beers are complemented by a great range of rotating guests through eight handpulls. Bar snacks and pork pies are available. Q⃞⃞⃞⃞⃞⃞⃞

Brew York Tap Room ⃞

Unit 6, Enterprise Complex, Walmgate, YO1 9TT

☎ (01904) 848448

Brew York JARSA, Maris the Otter, Viking DNA; changing beers (sourced locally; often Brew York) ⃞

Brew York's taproom is inside the brewery and the beer hall in the adjacent old maltings. Over 50 regular, seasonal, experimental and collaboration real ales (including gluten-free ones) from the multiple award-winning brewery, served via 10 handpulls and 50 KeyKeg pumps, offer a different taste on each visit. There is plentiful seating in the beer hall, in the taproom by the brew tanks and outside in the beer garden by the River Foss. Innovative fresh food is available including a good vegan range. ⃞⃞⃞⃞⃞⃞⃞⃞⃞

Fox ⃞

168 Holgate Road, Holgate, YO24 4DQ

☎ (01904) 787722

Ossett Yorkshire Blonde, Silver King, Excelsius; Rat White Rat; Tetley Bitter; 4 changing beers (sourced regionally; often Fernandes, Rat, Riverhead) ⃞

Set in the Holgate district of York, the Fox is a venue whose history is linked to the golden age of rail. Sympathetically restored by Ossett Brewery, it is recognised by CAMRA as having a historic interior of regional importance. It offers a good range of Ossett beers plus real cider and interesting guest ales. It also has a large, popular beer garden. ⃞⃞⃞⃞P⃞(1,5)⃞⃞

Golden Ball ★ ⃞

2 Cromwell Road, YO1 6DU

☎ (01904) 849040 ⃞ goldenballyork.co.uk

Acorn Barnsley Bitter; Ainsty Assassin; Timothy Taylor Golden Best; 3 changing beers (sourced regionally; often Salamander, Salopian, Whitby) ⃞

A Victorian street-corner community-run hostelry. It has an impressive glazed-brick exterior and was extensively refurbished by John Smith's in 1929. Grade II listed, it has

four very different rooms: a main bar, a back room, a comfortable lounge and a snug. Outside is a large south-facing beer garden. Seven handpumps dispense three permanent ales plus three changing guests. Local produce is on sale in the bar in addition to Scotch eggs, pork pies and nuts. The pub hosts bar billiards games and community meetings, as well as music and quiz nights and exhibitions by local artists. Q⃞⃞⃞⃞⃞⃞⃞

House of the Trembling Madness

14 Lendal, YO1 8AA

☎ (01904) 848998 ⃞ tremblingmadness.co.uk/lendal.html

3 changing beers (often Tiny Rebel) ⃞

This establishment is set in a historic building that was until recently an old saddlery and harness maker – the conversion was a joint winner in the York Restoration Design awards 2018. It boasts a wide selection of guest ales on tap. The building comprises five floors: Basement (craft beer shop selling beers, meads and ciders to drink in or take away); Ground Floor (bar with 11 kegs and three casks, and serving Yorkshire-inspired pintxos and a full food menu); First Floor (bar with a further 11 kegs, a large range of spirits, plus a full food menu including specials); Second Floor (toilets and kitchen); Third Floor (private hire rooms and events). ⃞⃞

Maltings ⃞

Tanners Moat, YO1 6HU

☎ (01904) 655387 ⃞ maltings.co.uk

Black Sheep Best Bitter; Treboom Yorkshire Sparkle; York Guzzler; 4 changing beers (sourced nationally; often Bad Seed, Hop Studio, Wilde Child) ⃞

A popular pub close to the station. Customers can choose from seven real ales and four traditional ciders. The four changing beers always include one from Rooster's alongside various ales from microbreweries both local and further afield. There is also a good selection of bottled and craft beer. An extension has provided more seating and a small outside area, while maintaining the original character. Local CAMRA Cider Pub of the Year 2020. ⃞⃞⃞⃞⃞⃞

Market Cat

6 Jubbergate, YO1 8RT

☎ (01904) 637023 ⃞ marketcatyork.co.uk

Thornbridge Lord Marples, Jaipur IPA; 6 changing beers (often Hawkshead, Tapped (Sheffield), Thornbridge) ⃞

A bar operated by Thornbridge and Pivovar UK which opened in 2018. The three-storey building has seating on all three floors, with excellent views across the Shambles market and towards the minster from the upper two. It offers a range of cask ales and pizza. A changing selection of real ales is served from eight handpumps, with a mixture of beers from Thornbridge, Tapped and other breweries. ⃞⃞

Phoenix

75 George Street, YO1 9PT

☎ (01904) 656401 ⃞ phoenixinnyork.co.uk

Timothy Taylor Landlord; Wold Top Anglers Reward; 3 changing beers (sourced regionally) ⃞

An independently run free house with a regionally important historic pub interior, where a friendly pub welcome awaits visitors and locals. It is close to the city walls, and Dick Turpin's grave is in the garden nearby. Relax in a traditional hostelry with no noisy gaming machines, TV or jukebox, and sip your beer while reading a newspaper or just chatting with fellow drinkers. In the colder months an open fire can be enjoyed in the front parlour. The rear room boasts bar games and weekly music events. A true gem and not to be missed. Q⃞⃞⃞⃞⃞⃞⃞

Pivni

6 Patrick Pool, YO1 8BB

☎ (01904) 635464 ● pivni.co.uk

5 changing beers (sourced nationally; often Tapped Sheffield) Ⓗ

The founding bar of the Pivovar group, in a beautiful three-storey timber-framed building dating back to 1190. It serves five regularly rotating cask ales from across the UK, usually including one from its brewery, Tapped Brew Co in Sheffield. There is also a changing range of seven craft keg beers, mostly from Europe, the US and the UK, four real ciders and over 40 varied bottled beers. There are bar games available, fresh coffee and a jukebox, and children and dogs are welcome. Bar snacks, including local pork pies, are on offer. ●♣

Rook & Gaskill Ⓛ

12 Lawrence Street, YO10 3WP

☎ (01904) 674067 ● rookandgaskillyork.co.uk

Castle Rock Harvest Pale; 21 changing beers (sourced nationally; often Bad Seed, Brass Castle, Brew York) Ⓗ

Many could make the mistake of walking past this little gem, with an unassuming exterior hiding a thriving pub that is home to locals, students and beer aficionados. There is always a wide range of ales, many of which are from the area, dark to light and very reasonably priced. Real ciders are available and multiple KeyKeg taps ensure all tastes are catered for. A menu of fresh cooked foods features generous portions and reasonable prices. ֎❶♣♠⊟♣✿

Slip Inn Ⓛ

Clementhorpe, YO23 1AN

☎ (01904) 621793

Leeds Pale; Rudgate Ruby Mild; Timothy Taylor Boltmaker; 5 changing beers (sourced regionally; often Revolutions, Ridgeside) Ⓗ

Local CAMRA Pub of the Year 2020, this independent free house is a thriving community local, with two bars, a snug and a sheltered courtyard beer garden. A big scheme of investment in the buildings in 2019 has doubled the beer range on the bar and created a dedicated outside festival bar. The Slip hosts regular beer festivals and events each year, including one jointly run with the Swan just up the road. It supports traditional games including darts, dominoes and cribbage. ֍֎♣⊟(11) ✿♥

Swan ★ Ⓛ

16 Bishopgate Street, YO23 1JH

☎ (01904) 634968 ● theswanyork.co.uk

Tetley Bitter; Timothy Taylor Landlord; house beer (by Treboom); 4 changing beers (sourced regionally; often Half Moon, Revolutions, Salamander) Ⓗ

A thriving street-corner local, within sight of the city walls, which has been free of tie since 2017. Grade II listed, the traditional West Riding-style drinking lobby and two bars have a friendly and comfortable feel; the pub has been identified by CAMRA as having a nationally important historic interior. To the back is a heated and partially covered beer garden where an annual beer festival is hosted jointly with the nearby Slip Inn. ֎♣♠⊟(11) ✿

Three-Legged Mare

16 High Petergate, YO1 7EN

☎ (01904) 638246

Black Sheep Special Ale, Riggwelter; York Guzzler; Yorkshire Terrier, Centurion's Ghost Ale; 5 changing beers (sourced regionally) Ⓗ

A modest frontage gives way to a roomy interior with plenty of seating, and there are views of the minster

from the seats by the door. The pub has been owned since 2018 by Black Sheep Brewery, who now produce the York Brewery beers. The regular beers are supplemented by an interesting choice of guests in both cask and keg. A wide range of real ciders and perries is served direct from the box. A spiral staircase leads down to the toilets. ♿➹♠⊟♣✿♥

Volunteer Arms Ⓛ

5 Watson Street, YO24 4BH

☎ (01904) 541945

Black Sheep Best Bitter; Brown Cow Mrs Simpson's Thriller in Vanilla Porter; Leeds Yorkshire Gold; Saltaire Blonde; Timothy Taylor Dark Mild; 3 changing beers (sourced locally) Ⓗ

An independent free house just off Holgate Road, close to the centre of York. The venue has a real community feel and is welcoming to all. It offers an excellent beer range for a suburban pub, with loyalties firmly with local breweries, emphasising its commitment to LocAle. There are five permanent beers and two changing guests. Entertainment include live blues every Saturday night and a quiz every Sunday night. Q֎➹♠⊟(1,10)✿♥

Waggon & Horses

19 Lawrence Street, YO10 3BP

☎ (01904) 637478 ● waggonandhorsesyork.com

Batemans XB, XXXB; Oakham Citra; 5 changing beers (sourced nationally; often Bad Seed, Rat, Revolutions) Ⓗ

Run by a landlord who loves real ale, this family-run pub, owned by Batemans, has eight handpulls. Beers from the wood are occasionally available. The multi-roomed interior includes the bar area and front room with screens showing BT Sport. Two rooms at the back are quieter and are used by various local groups for meetings. There is free bar billiards, board games, and good-value accommodation. A former local CAMRA Pub of the Year. ֎⌂♿♣♠⊟♣✿♥

York Tap

Railway Station, Station Road, YO24 1AB

☎ (01904) 659009 ● yorktap.com

Timothy Taylor Golden Best, Boltmaker, Knowle Spring; Landlord; 18 changing beers (sourced nationally; often Anarchy, Tapped Sheffield, Thornbridge) Ⓗ

This pub, opened in 2010, is a conversion of the former Victorian tearooms on York station. The ornate ceiling, Art Deco stained-glass windows, terrazzo floors and stained-glass ceiling domes create an award-winning backdrop to the central bar. Twenty handpumps offer 18 cask beers plus two ciders or perries. There is also a large range of keg and bottled beers. The parent company, Pivovar, sources the beers from many of Britain's finest breweries, and all styles and strengths are represented. No meals are provided, although pies are available at the bar. ֎♿➹♠⊟✿

YORKSHIRE (SOUTH)

Armthorpe

Wheatsheaf

Church Street, DN3 3AG

☎ (01302) 835868

Purity Pure UBU; 2 changing beers (often Black Sheep, Woodforde's) Ⓗ

A roadside pub serving excellent beers and a variety of good-quality food. You are assured of a warm welcome here, and there is plenty of entertainment including darts, dominoes and pool. Food is served Tuesday to

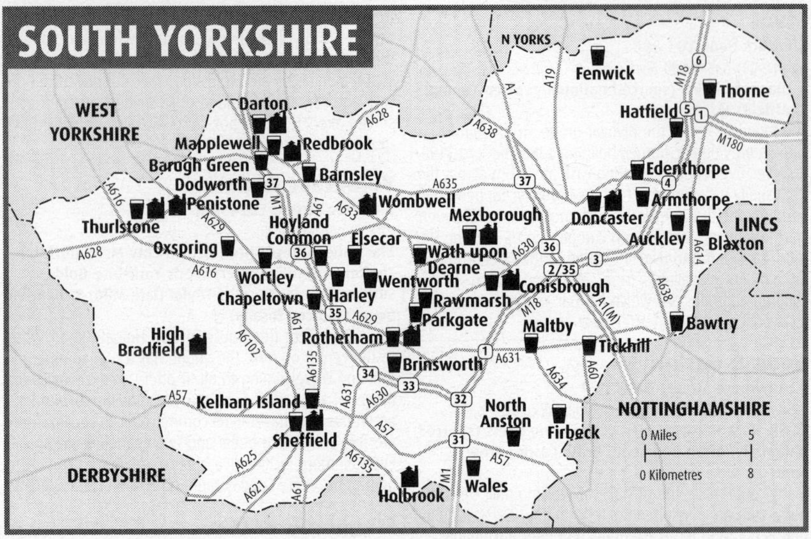
SOUTH YORKSHIRE
N YORKS
WEST YORKSHIRE
LINCS
NOTTINGHAMSHIRE
DERBYSHIRE
Fenwick
Thorne
Hatfield
Edenthorpe
Armthorpe
Doncaster
Auckley
Blaxton
Bawtry
Tickhill
Maltby
Conisbrough
Firbeck
North Anston
Wales
Holbrook
Sheffield
Kelham Island
Brinsworth
Rotherham
Parkgate
Rawmarsh
Wath upon Dearne
Mexborough
Wombwell
Wentworth
Harley
Chapeltown
Elsecar
Hoyland Common
Wortley
Oxspring
Penistone
Thurlstone
Dodworth
Barugh Green
Mapplewell
Darton
Redbrook
Barnsley
High Bradfield
A628
A638
A635
A633
A629
A616
A61
A19
A1
M18
M180
A630
A1(M)
A614
A631
A634
A60
A6102
A6135
A57
A625
A621
A6135
M1
0 Miles 5
0 Kilometres 8

Saturday, lunchtimes and evenings, with a popular carvery on Sunday. There is a good-sized outside drinking area at the front. Q🔥❀◑♿♣🍎P🚌(81)🐾📶

Auckley

Eagle & Child ✔

24 Main Street, DN9 3HS

☎ (01302) 770406 🌐 eagleandchildauckley.co.uk

Acorn Barnsley Bitter; Black Sheep Best Bitter; Timothy Taylor Landlord; 2 changing beers (sourced regionally; often Milestone, Welbeck Abbey) [H]

A much-loved pub, on the main road in the village, and winner of numerous CAMRA awards. Dating from the early 19th century, it has real character. There are two bars, one with a TV, the other quieter, with tables for bar meals. The separate restaurant is decorated with photographs of local historic interest, and home-cooked meals have a deserved reputation. There is an outside seating area and beer garden. Robin Hood Airport is a mile away. Q🔥❀◑♣P🚌(57f)🐾📶

Barnsley

Jolly Tap on the Arcade [L]

31 The Arcade, S70 2QP

Jolly Boys Blonde; 3 changing beers (sourced locally; often Hilltop, Jolly Boys, Outhouse Barnsley) [H]

Barnsley's first micropub, a tiny one-up one-down place, was opened in 2017 by Two Roses Brewery and is now owned by the Jolly Boys Brewery. The bar serves up to five real ales alongside a choice of craft beers, all sourced locally. It is in the lovely Victorian Arcade and was a cake shop before. The staff are welcoming and knowledgeable on the cask and craft beers on offer. Q🚆🚌🐾📶

Old No.7 [L]

7 Market Hill, S70 2PX

☎ (01226) 244735 🌐 oldno7barnsley.co.uk

Acorn Barnsley Bitter, Blonde; 6 changing beers (sourced regionally; often Acorn) [H]

This is the Acorn Brewery tap, now in its 10th consecutive year in the Guide, with up to six Acorn beers alongside two changing guest beers. A choice of real ciders and perry as well as a wide range of craft and continental beers are also on offer. The downstairs bar is available for functions, meetings and events, and opens on match days and busy Friday and Saturday evenings. Regular live music takes place. 🚆♣🍎🚌🐾📶

Tipsy Cow [L]

Unit 2B, Gateway Plaza, Saville Street, S70 2RD

4 changing beers (sourced regionally) [H]

This micropub near the entrance to the Gateway Plaza complex opened in 2018. Ideally located on the edge of the town centre, close to the Lamproom Theatre. It is split over two levels, with a mezzanine floor looking over part of the ground floor. A café bar outdoor drinking area was added in 2019 and is popular in the summer months. Four changing real ales, craft beers and cider are on offer, and a wide gin selection. No under-12s or dogs allowed. Q❀♿🚆P🚌📶

Barugh Green

Crown & Anchor [L]

Barugh Lane, S75 1LL (on B6428)

☎ (01226) 387200 🌐 thecrownandanchor.com

5 changing beers (sourced regionally; often Acorn, Bradfield, True North) [H]

Known locally as The Whitehouse, this large pub is the Barnsley outpost of the True North portfolio. Seven handpulls (three always serving True North beers, the others beer from anywhere in the country) ensure that there are styles to suit all drinkers, along with a good selection of bottled world beers and a lengthy list of gins. The food menu changes often. The garden has a shipping container as an external bar. 🔥❀◑♿♣🍎P🚌🐾📶

Bawtry

Ship ✔

Gainsborough Road, DN10 6HT (on A631 nr traffic lights)

☎ (01302) 710275 🌐 theship-bawtry.com

Marston's 61 Deep; 4 changing beers (sourced nationally) [H]

One of the local CAMRA area's success stories, this previously run-down roadside pub was taken over in 2007 by the family of the present licensees. Extensively refurbished inside and out, it has gained an enviable reputation for high-quality food and beer, has won several food awards, and holds beer festivals. Two ales are always available, selected from the Marston's range. ⌂⊛❍ᗗ♣●P➟(21,25) ❀☆

Blaxton

Station ⎵

Station Road, DN9 3AA
☎ (01302) 770055
3 changing beers (often Black Sheep, Navigation Brewery, Theakston) Ⓗ

A popular village local which in 2018 underwent a refurbishment under new owners, and was reopened and relaunched later that year. It has since gained a reputation for good food and cask ales, the ales coming from a range of breweries. Beers from Navigation Brewery have proved especially popular. It now offers accommodation and is handy for users of Robin Hood airport. ⌂⊛➟❍ᗺP❀☆

Brinsworth

Phoenix Sports & Social Club ⎵ ✓

Pavilion Lane, S60 5PA (off A631 Bawtry Rd, 1½ miles from M1 jct 33 – look for sign)
☎ (01709) 363788 ⊕ phoenixssc.co.uk
3 changing beers (sourced regionally) Ⓗ

Extensively refurbished in 2017, the bar here offers a warm welcome to all. It also serves as the clubhouse for the adjoining Phoenix Golf Club. The comfortable lounge serves three cask ales, often from local breweries, and lunchtime and evening meals are available. It also boasts a family room, TV room, snooker room and function room. A wide variety of outdoor and indoor sports is played and the patio overlooks the cricket pitch. Dances, music and quiz nights are regularly held. Local CAMRA branch Club of the Year 2020. ⌂⊛❍ᗺ♣P➟

Stop Inn Time ⎵

17 Brinsworth Lane, S60 5BS
4 changing beers (sourced locally; often Dukeries, Little Critters) Ⓗ

This micropub, opened in March 2019 in a former hardware shop in the centre of the village, provides a contrast with the nearby Three Magpies hotel. A friendly welcome and warm atmosphere are guaranteed within. The four changing real ales are often, but not exclusively, from local breweries, and are a mixture of light and dark styles. The decor is themed on timepieces – note the interesting ceiling and wall clocks. Handy for events at the Centre and playing fields. Q⊛ᗺP➟❀

Conisbrough

Hilltop ⎵

Sheffield Road, DN12 2AY (on main A630)
☎ (01709) 868811
Hilltop Classic Bitter, Blonde, Porter, Stout Ⓗ

A traditional family-run free house standing alone on the Rotherham road, offering a relaxed and friendly atmosphere. The interior is divided into a public bar and lounge area. A wall of old Conisbrough photos includes pictures of a trolleybus. Four real ales are served, all from the on-site brewery. Quiz night is on a Wednesday and includes supper. The Hilltop has won several local CAMRA awards, has been in the Guide since 2014, and is District Pub of the Year 2020. Q⌂⊛❍♣●P➟(X78)❀☆

Darton

Anvil Arms ⎵

28 Church Street, S75 5HG
☎ (01226) 805225
6 changing beers (sourced locally; often Nailmaker) Ⓗ

Formerly the Old Co-op Ale House, this welcoming micropub in the heart of Darton is now under the ownership of the Nailmaker Brewery, serving six real ales and three ciders on handpull, with a 12-tap beer wall. During lockdown sympathetic improvements have been made, from new seating to outdoor drinking areas to the front and side of the building, while keeping the features customers have come to love, like the bare brick walls and log fire. The pub prides itself on the art of conversation. Various events are hosted, including a quiz and a games evening. This venue has definitely become a permanent feature on the Mapplewell and Darton real ale corridor. Qᗺ⇌♣●➟❀

Darton Tap ⎵

70 Church Street, S75 5HQ
☎ (01226) 383444 ⊕ dartontap.co.uk
Rat White Rat; house beer (by Nailmaker); 2 changing beers (sourced locally) Ⓗ

This stylish micropub has now extended into next door and become a pub, and is positioned along the increasingly popular Darton and Mapplewell real ale corridor. It has four cask lines, several draught lines and a large spirits selection. Drinkers can enjoy a beer in a modern and comfortable environment, close to transport links. Dogs are welcome, with doggie treats and paw towels provided. Strictly over-18s only. ᗺ⇌P➟☆

REAL ALE BREWERIES

1086 ✦ Doncaster
Abbeydale Sheffield
Acorn Wombwell
Blue Bee Sheffield
Bradfield High Bradfield
Chantry Rotherham
Dead Parrot Sheffield
Doncaster ✦ Doncaster
Exit 33 Sheffield
Fuggle Bunny Holbrook
Gorilla ✦ Mexborough
Grizzly Grains Sheffield
Heist ✦ Sheffield
Hilltop 🍺 Conisbrough
Imperial 🍺 Mexborough
Jolly Boys ✦ Redbrook
Kelham Island Sheffield
Kibble 🍺 Thurlstone (NEW)
Little Critters Sheffield
Little Mesters ✦ Sheffield (NEW)
Lost Industry Sheffield
Loxley 🍺 Sheffield
Nailmaker ✦ Darton
Neepsend ✦ Sheffield
On the Edge Sheffield
Sheffield ✦ Sheffield
St Mars of the Desert ✦ Sheffield
Stancill Sheffield
Tapped 🍺 Sheffield
Toolmakers ✦ Sheffield
Triple Point ✦ Sheffield
True North Sheffield
White Rose Mexborough
Whitefaced Penistone

Dodworth

Dodworth Tap
Station Road, S75 3JA
House beer (by Nailmaker); 3 changing beers (sourced regionally; often Nailmaker, Rat) ⌂
Close to Dodworth railway station, this pub was brought back from the brink in 2020 by the people who run the Darton Tap, and they have lovingly restored the place to its former glory. It now serves up to four real ales including a house beer, and has an extensive spirit collection and a good selection of craft beers. A huge open fireplace lost until the recent renovations has been brought back into service. Work to fully refurbish the upper parts of the building and create a function room with a separate bar was completed in early 2021. The huge beer garden has been revamped.
🌳❀&≠♣P🚃(21A,22) ☙ 奈

Doncaster

Doncaster Brewery Tap L
7 Young Street, DN1 3EL
☎ (01302) 376436
Doncaster Cheswold, Sand House; 4 changing beers (sourced locally; often Doncaster) ⌂
Doncaster Brewery Tap opened in 2014 with the brewery moving into the same building in the same year. The bar offers six cask beers served in lined glasses, two of which are guests. Also on handpull are six traditional ciders and perries. Food is served Friday to Sunday. There is an outside seating area. This is a welcoming place and always has something different going on. Local CAMRA Pub of the Year 2020. Q≠♣●🚍🚃☙奈

Draughtsman Alehouse
Station Court, DN1 1PE
☎ 07999 874660 ⊕ thedraughtsmanalehouse.co.uk
3 changing beers (sourced regionally; often Allendale, Northern Monkey, Thornbridge) ⌂
This venue, on platform 3b of Doncaster station and opened in 2017, was highly commended in CAMRA's Pub Design Awards. The former Victorian buffet bar had stood empty for 18 years before being restored. Be sure to inspect the Victorian tiles and mounted plan drawings of steam locomotives. Real ales on offer mainly come from regional brewers, with occasional collaborations and exclusives. Snacks include locally made pies. Regular tap takeovers and special events take place here.
Q&≠🚃(21) 奈

Hallcross
33-34 Hall Gate, DN1 3NL
⊕ hallcrossdoncaster.co.uk
Tetley Bitter; 2 changing beers (sourced nationally; often Dancing Duck, Elland, Welbeck Abbey) ⌂
This venue has been recently refurbished, with real ale and cider reinstated after many years' absence. It has a front bar playing background music, and showing sports but with sound only for major events. There is a separate soundproofed function room for live music at weekends, and a patio area, with a snug at the back. Hallcross is the home of the resurrected Stocks Beers (brewed at Welbeck Abbey), which were previously brewed on the premises 20 years ago. ❀&≠●🚃(21,25)奈

Leopard ●
2 West Street, DN1 3AA (less than 5 mins' walk from station)
☎ (01302) 739460
4 changing beers (sourced regionally; often Acorn, Stancill, Titanic) ⌂

This street-corner pub, close to the town centre and railway station, has been a regular CAMRA award winner over the years. It has a superb tiled frontage, recalling its days as a Warwicks & Richardson's house. There are two rooms downstairs, and a large one upstairs that regularly hosts live music at weekends. The pub is owned by Doncaster Culture and Leisure Trust, and one of the five real ales on offer is from its own 1086 brewery.
❀◐&≠♣●P🚃(71,72) ☙ 奈

Little Plough ★ L
8 West Laith Gate, DN1 1SF (close to Frenchgate shopping centre)
☎ (01302) 738310
Acorn Barnsley Bitter; Bradfield Farmers Blonde; 2 changing beers (sourced regionally; often Brains, Fuller's, Titanic) ⌂
A friendly haven for anyone wishing to escape the town-centre bustle. Three real ales are served, and there are beer festivals twice yearly. The interior, with a public bar at the front and a lounge to the rear, dates from 1934 and is on CAMRA's National Inventory of Historic Pub Interiors. The walls are adorned with pictures of old agricultural scenes. A winner of many local CAMRA awards. Q❀≠♣🚃☙奈

Queen Crafthouse & Kitchen
1 Sunny Bar, DN1 1LY (on corner of Sunny Bar and Market Place)
☎ (01302) 562908
5 changing beers (sourced nationally) ⌂
An old established market place pub, recently renovated under new ownership. An interior created out of unusual boarding sets the scene, attracting customers young and old to sample the real ales, atmosphere, and live music at weekends. Close by the historic Corn Exchange and market, this is a welcome addition to the town's real ale scene. Five changing beers are on the bar, usually from regional breweries, and two real ciders.
Q&≠●🚃(15) ☙ 奈

Edenthorpe

Eden Arms ●
Eden Field Road, DN3 2QR (adjacent to Tesco)
☎ (01302) 888682
Abbeydale Moonshine; Thornbridge Kipling; house beer (by Sharp's); 3 changing beers (sourced nationally; often Black Sheep, Marston's, Thornbridge) ⌂
A fine, modern and busy estate pub, built in the late 1980s. Attractive and comfortable, it is one of the area's most CAMRA-friendly venues. On Monday all cask ales are generously discounted all day. Five real ales are usually on offer, with a display at the entrance informing customers about present and future cask beers. There is a large outside drinking area, and a pleasant gas-flamed fire indoors. Meet the Brewer evenings are popular. The pub is notable for its good-quality classic meals.
Q🌳❀◐&P🚃(87,8) 奈

Elsecar

Crown Inn L ●
22 Hill Street, S74 8EL
☎ (01226) 361488
3 changing beers (sourced regionally; often Abbeydale, Ossett) ⌂
A stone-built roadside pub in a picturesque village. Its two rooms are quite different, with the front room having the community feel and the lounge to the back being a little more formal, its conservatory adding a

warm atmosphere. The family-friendly garden has a children's play area. Guest beers here are all local, as is its one changing beer. ♿️🏠🍴👶♿️♣🚲P🚊(66)🐾🛜

Maison du Biere 🅛

Wath Road, S74 8HJ (in Elsecar Heritage Centre, Unit 15)
☎ (01226) 805255 🌐 maisondubiere.com
Changing beers (sourced nationally)
This popular beer shop and tap is in the heart of the heritage centre, serving up over 400 bottled, canned and draught beers and ciders (many of them real cider), including 10 lines of craft/draught beers. The knowledgeable staff can navigate you on a taste journey. The tap is visited by locals and visitors alike, and lots of monthly events take place here.
♿️🏠♿️🚲♣♠P🏠🚊(66,227) 🐾🛜

Fenwick

Baxter Arms

Fenwick Lane, DN6 0HA (between Askern and Moss)
☎ (01302) 702671
House beer (by Theakston) 🅗
An award-winning free house that is truly a rural gem. It has been run by the same family for nearly 30 years, and you can be sure of a warm welcome. Three real ales from small independent breweries are always available, and reasonably priced fresh food sourced locally is served all day. Outside is a drinking area with seating and ample parking. Quiz night is Wednesday. Q♿️🏠🍴👶♠🚲P🐾🛜

Firbeck

Black Lion 🅛

9 New Road, S81 8JY (opp village hall)
☎ (01709) 812575
Chantry New York Pale; Timothy Taylor Landlord; 2 changing beers (sourced locally; often Abbeydale, Bradfield, Pheasantry) 🅗
Traditional free house, reopened in 2017 after a period of closure, attracting drinkers, diners, walkers and the local community. Four real ales are offered and the two changing beers come from microbreweries in the area, especially Pheasantry. The food is freshly cooked to order. Pictures of the old village adorn the walls of the snug. Firbeck was the birthplace of the horse race that led to the St Leger, and it is handy for the ruins of Roche Abbey and countryside walks. The No.20 bus only serves the village Monday-Saturday daytime.
Q♿️🏠🍴♿️♠P🚊(20) 🐾

Harley

Horseshoe 🅛

9 Harley Road, S62 7UD (off A6135 on B6090, 1 mile from Wentworth)
☎ (01226) 742204 🌐 thehorseshoeharley.co.uk
Neepsend Blonde; 2 changing beers (often Acorn, Greene King, Little Critters) 🅗
A cosy village local, in the same family for many years, and a community hub for well over a century. Real ales change frequently and often come from local breweries. Food is served Friday and Saturday evenings, with a carvery on Sunday afternoons. The location is handy for the nearby Wentworth estate, Needles Eye and Elsecar Heritage Centre. The pub is home to sports teams and gets busy when the pool team are playing and when the village gala is held in July. There is some seating out front and a small outside area to the rear. 🏠🍴♠P🚊(44)🐾

Hatfield

Jack Hawley at the Grange

Manor Road, DN7 6SB
☎ 07769 927603
Timothy Taylor Landlord; 4 changing beers (sourced regionally; often Kelham Island, Welbeck Abbey, York) 🅗
This micro is the project of a real ale enthusiast who was previously landlord of the Black Swan in Asselby, and was local CAMRA District Pub of the Year 2020. Access is via a staircase to the first floor. There is a long, narrow lounge with mixed seating; one wall has four guitars and the other has the story of Jack Hawley, a local character from the 19th century who was renowned for his hospitality. 🏠♠P🚊(84,87A)

Hoyland Common

Tap & Brew 🅛

9 Hoyland Road, S74 0LT
☎ (01226) 824614
6 changing beers (sourced regionally) 🅗
A popular micropub converted from a tea room in 2017. New owners in 2019 have kept it pretty much how the regulars like it. It offers a fine selection of cask ales as well as a good range of bottled beers and artisan spirits. No meals are served but there is a wide choice of bar snacks, pies and pastries. The pub also hosts weekly quiz and music nights, and a popular open mic night, all adding to a great atmosphere. 🏠♣🚊🐾🛜

Maltby

Queen's Hotel ✅

Tickhill Road, S66 7NQ
☎ (01709) 812494
Greene King Abbot; Ruddles Best Bitter; Sharp's Doom Bar; 3 changing beers (sourced regionally) 🅗
A former residential hotel on a busy crossroads, completely refurbished and reopened by Wetherspoon after a lengthy period of closure, leading to a much-needed raising of the profile of real ale in Maltby. Now firmly established, this spacious pub has an attractive family dining area offering typical Wetherspoon value-for-money food and drink. Regular Meet the Brewer nights are held. Next to Coronation Park and handy for Maltby Crags and Roche Abbey. ♿️🏠🍴♿️♠P🚊🛜

Mapplewell

Talbot Inn 🅛 ✅

Towngate, S75 6AS
☎ (01226) 385629 🌐 thetalbotmapplewell.co.uk
Nailmaker Anvil Porter; 3 changing beers (sourced locally) 🅗
The first and original tap for Nailmaker Brewery, this pub spearheaded the real ale revival in the area, with four rotating beers from the brewery and occasional guests, as well as tap takeovers from the likes of Magic Rock and North Brewing. This place is a favourite with locals for a quick pint and a meal, or for the ever-popular Speed Quiz. During 2021 the pub had an extensive refurbishment, from new roof windows and internal decoration to increased seating in the upper part of the downstairs bar. There is a restaurant upstairs, and food is also served at all tables daily.
Q♿️🏠🍴♠P🚊(1,X10) 🐾🛜

Wentworth Arms 🅛 ✅

Greenside, S75 6AU
☎ (01226) 390702 🌐 wentwortharms.co.uk

4 changing beers (sourced regionally; often Nailmaker) Ⓗ

Sister pub to the Talbot, this popular chilled-out establishment is well known for its excellent and changing array of real ale and craft-on-draught beers. It has a cared-for beer garden with lovely festoon lighting. During 2020 refurbishment work to the upstairs area created a new bar called The Loft to host private events or just as a great place to chill and relax with a beer with friends. This venue has firmly positioned itself as a prominent participant in the real ale triangle of Mapplewell, Darton and Barugh Green.
✿⬤◗&🄿🖵(1,x10) ✿ ✿ 🛜

Mexborough

Imperial Brewery Tap Ⓛ

Cliff Street, S64 9HU (opp bus station)
☎ (01709) 584000
Imperial Classical Bitter, Platinum Blonde, Bees Knees, Nah Then; 3 changing beers (sourced locally) Ⓗ

A friendly brewery tap with a lot to offer. It has a main bar where all the entertainments are held, a cosy lounge area, plus a games/function room. The eight handpumps only dispense quality ale: two permanent Imperial beers, with six rotating from the brewery itself as well from a plethora of excellent breweries around the country. Entertainment ranges from karaoke on Wednesday to an award-winning acoustic night on Thursday and a wide range of live music Friday/Saturday.
🕭✿&≉♣🖵(220,221) ✿ 🛜

North Anston

Little Mester Ⓛ ✅

Nursery Road, S25 4BZ
☎ (01909) 562484
Greene King IPA; 4 changing beers (sourced locally; often Stancill, Welbeck Abbey) Ⓗ

A modern estate pub, built in the 1960s, reopened following refurbishment in 2016 and now emphasising real ale. Beers may be from far and wide but local breweries often feature strongly among up to five guests. There is a Cask Ale Club with a free pint offered for every seven purchased. The venue gets lively at the weekend, when a DJ and live entertainment feature. It is handily sited for visiting the nearby Butterfly Farm and walks around Anston Stones. 🕭✿⬤◗&🄿🖵

Oxspring

Smithy Arms Ⓛ

Bower Hill, S36 8YA
☎ 07712 929011
3 changing beers (often Abbeydale, Acorn, Chantry) Ⓗ

This popular micropub was opened in 2017 in the extended garage of the owner's house, so named as it is on the site of a former blacksmith's. Opening four days a week, the pub hosts three changing real ales, usually from breweries in the area. It has a wood-burning fire for cosy winter nights and a small beer garden to the rear. Quiz night is Thursday. Q🕭✿&🄿🖵✿

Parkgate

Little Haven Micro Bar Ⓛ

96 Broad Street, S62 6EN
☎ (01709) 710134
🌐 the-little-haven-micro-bar.business.site

Chantry New York Pale; 3 changing beers (sourced locally) Ⓗ

Friendly micropub, opened in 2018 in a former post office and hair salon, with four handpumps plus four craft taps, favouring local breweries. Real cider is also sometimes stocked. Compact and welcoming, it serves nibbles plus pie and peas on Wednesdays and breakfast on Sunday mornings. Board games are available and musicians play on Tuesday and Saturday evenings. A little snug was recently added, and outside seating is accessed via the pub. It comes as a welcome break from Parkgate Retail World and is 10-15 minutes' walk from the tram/train stop there. Q✿♣🖵✿ 🛜

Rawmarsh

Something Brew Inn Ⓛ

2 Stocks Lane, S62 6NL
Bradfield Farmers Blonde; Chantry New York Pale; Sharp's Doom Bar; 3 changing beers (often Abbeydale, Bradfield, Chantry) Ⓗ

Micropub and coffee house in a former office building behind the Star pub, opened in 2018 in an area not renowned for selling real ale. The four changing real ales are often from Chantry and other local breweries. Craft keg and bottled beers are also stocked, as is a selection of real ciders. It is tastefully decorated inside, with a long bar, and has outside seating at the front and rear, including deckchairs in the rear yard. A Sunday jam session and a Wednesday night quiz are held.
Q✿♣🖵✿ 🛜

Rotherham

Bluecoat Ⓛ ✅

The Crofts, S60 2DJ (behind town hall, off Moorgate Rd, A618)
☎ (01709) 539500
Greene King Abbot; Ruddles Best Bitter; Welbeck Abbey Cavendish; 7 changing beers (sourced locally) Ⓗ

Former charity school, opened in 1776 by the Ffeofees of Rotherham, which became a pub named Ffeofees in 1981 and a Wetherspoon in 2001. Up to 10 handpulled beers are listed on a screen behind the bar, with preference given to nearby microbreweries. Up to three real ciders or perries are served from boxes behind the bar. Regular Meet the Brewer nights are held, and special beers are brewed for the pub four times a year. It is a Guide regular, and winner of numerous local CAMRA branch awards. 🕭✿⬤◗&≉(Central)♣◗🄿🖵 🛜

Cutlers Arms Ⓛ

29 Westgate, S60 1BQ
☎ (01709) 382581 🌐 cutlersarms.co.uk
Chantry New York Pale, Iron and Steel Bitter, Diamond Black Stout; house beer (by Chantry); 2 changing beers (sourced locally; often Chantry) Ⓗ

Rebuilt for Stones Brewery of Sheffield in 1907 to the design of R Wigfull, with an impressive façade. Recognised by CAMRA as having a historic interior of regional importance, the pub was saved from demolition in 2004 following statutory listing and restored to Edwardian splendour by Chantry Brewery, reopening in 2014. The original Art Nouveau windows, tiling and curved bar counter with its dividing screen have been retained. The full range of Chantry beers, two real ciders and quality craft beers are sold. There is live music Friday to Sunday, and student night on Thursday. Snacks are available. Q✿⬤◗≉(Central)◗🖵✿ 🛜

Dragon's Tap 🄻

477 Herringthorpe Valley Road, Broom, S65 3AD
☎ 07864 680301 ⊕ dragontaps.com
Chantry New York Pale; 5 changing beers (sourced locally; often Elland, Little Critters, Magic Rock) Ⓗ
A micropub on two floors opened in 2018 in a former DIY shop, simply but tastefully decorated with modern art prints. The six changing beers are from local and national microbreweries. Four craft keg beers and real ciders are also sold, plus bottled beers. No food is served, save for snacks, but you can bring in food from nearby takeaways. There are tables at the front. A general knowledge quiz is held on Wednesday evening and live acoustic music on the third Sunday of the month.
Q☸🕭♿♣P🖺🐾

New York Tavern 🄻

84 Westgate, S60 1BD (jct of Coke Lane)
☎ (01709) 371155 ⊕ newyorktavern.co.uk
Chantry New York Pale, Iron and Steel Bitter, Diamond Black Stout; house beer (by Chantry); 2 changing beers (sourced locally; often Chantry) Ⓗ
This wedge-shaped house became a licensed premises in 1856. Previously called the Prince of Wales Feathers, it was reopened by Chantry Brewery in 2013 and renamed after a pub that was demolished when the nearby ring road was built. At least six Chantry beers and two real ciders or perries on offer at competitive prices, alongside a large selection of foreign bottled beers. Bar snacks are available. The pub is handy for New York Stadium, and has Rotherham United memorabilia on display. Occasional live entertainment features. Local CAMRA branch Town Pub of the Year, most recently in 2020.
➔(Central)♦🖺🐾

Sheffield: Central

Bath Hotel ★ 🄻 ✅

66-68 Victoria Street, S3 7QL
☎ (0114) 249 5151 ⊕ beerinthebath.co.uk
Thornbridge Lord Marples; 5 changing beers (sourced regionally; often Thornbridge) Ⓗ
A careful restoration of the 1930s interior gave this two-roomed venue a conservation award and a listing on CAMRA's National Inventory of Historic Pub Interiors. The bar lies between the tiled lounge, a small corridor drinking area and the cosy well-upholstered snug. Three Thornbridge beers and three guests are usually on tap. There is regular live music and a weekly quiz on Thursdays. Light snacks are served. Q🞄♣♦🖺🐾

Dog & Partridge 🄻 ✅

56 Trippet Lane, S1 4EL
☎ (0114) 270 6156 ⊕ thedogsheffield.co.uk
4 changing beers (sourced locally; often Bad Seed, Blue Bee, Stancill) Ⓗ
Behind an impressive Gilmour's Brewery frontage lies a comfortable multi-roomed pub served by a central bar. To the right of the entrance is a spacious taproom with dartboard, and on the left a smaller seating area. Behind the servery is a cosy snug with a hatch for service and, at the rear, the lounge often features live music. The four changing beers are usually sourced from local breweries.
🏃☸🕭🚆(City Hall)♣🖺🐾🛜

Fagans 🄻

69 Broad Lane, S1 4BS
☎ (0114) 272 8430
Abbeydale Moonshine; Tetley Bitter Ⓗ
With no significant changes in over 60 years, this traditional local comprises a main bar area, a smaller room to the rear and a tiny snug at the front. Fagans is

named after former landlord Joe Fagan, who previously served as a pilot in Bomber Command, and the walls are decorated with pictures of bombers in tribute. The pub is noted for its folk music and the challenging Thursday night quiz. 🏃☸🕭♣🖺🐾

Head of Steam 🄻

103-107 Norfolk Street, S1 2JE
☎ (0114) 272 2128
6 changing beers (sourced regionally; often Abbeydale, Magic Rock) Ⓗ
A pub for some 20 years, this former bank was acquired by Camerons Brewery in 2015 and after extensive refurbishment reopened as part of its Head of Steam chain. Behind the imposing frontage, the large single room is served by a central island bar, with a separate seating section at the rear leading to an outside drinking area in Tudor Square. In addition to the brewer's own ales, beers from independents in Yorkshire and the North-East are usually on handpump.
☸🕭🕭♿➔🚆(Cathedral)♦P🖺🐾🛜

Old Queen's Head 🄻 ✅

40 Pond Hill, S1 2BG
☎ (0114) 327 0704 ⊕ theoldqueenshead.co.uk
Thwaites Mild, IPA, Gold, Amber; 3 changing beers (sourced locally; often Abbeydale, Marston's) Ⓗ
Dating from Tudor times, when it was originally the hunting lodge for the nearby Sheffield Castle, the inn is the oldest surviving domestic building in Sheffield, but now adjoins the transport interchange. The central bar serves a U-shaped lounge and is adjacent to a superb beamed dining room in the oldest part of the building. The pub is the meeting place for history groups, and is included on popular ghost tours. The food menu includes Czech specials alongside the usual pub fare.
🏃☸🕭🕭➔🚆(Fitzalan Square)♣♦🖺🐾🛜

Rutland Arms 🄻

86 Brown Street, S1 2BS
☎ (0114) 272 9003 ⊕ rutlandarmssheffield.co.uk
Blue Bee Reet Pale; 6 changing beers (sourced regionally; often Blue Bee) Ⓗ
Occupying a corner site in the Cultural Industries Quarter and near Sheffield's main railway station, the pub has operated as a free house since 2009. The comfortable interior provides ample seating either side of the central entrance, and the walls are covered in the pumpclips and font badges of the huge number of guest beers that have featured over the years. The beers are mostly from local and regional microbreweries. Food is served throughout the day till late. 🏃☸🕭➔🚆(Sheffield Station)♦🖺🐾🛜

Sheffield Tap ★ 🄻

Platform 1b, Sheffield Station, Sheaf Street, S1 2BP
☎ (0114) 273 7558
Thornbridge Jaipur IPA; 9 changing beers (sourced nationally; often Tapped Sheffield) Ⓗ
Opened in 2009, this was originally the First Class refreshment room for Sheffield Midland Station, built in 1904. After years of neglect the main bar area has been subject to an award-winning restoration, retaining many original features. Further seating has been provided in the entrance corridor and to the right of the bar. Three beers are usually from the on-site Tapped Brewery, opened in 2013 in the impressive former dining room, and visible behind a glass screen.
Q🏃☸🕭♿🚆(Sheffield Station)♦🖺🐾🛜

Sheffield: Chapeltown

Commercial 🄻

107 Station Road, S35 2XF

☎ (0114) 246 9066

Abbeydale Moonshine; 7 changing beers (sourced nationally; often Durham, Neepsend, White Rose) Ⓗ
Built in 1890 by the long-closed Strout's Brewery of Neepsend, this friendly well-established free house provides six guest beers, including a porter or stout, together with at least one real cider. A central island bar serves the games room, lounge and taproom. There is a rear outdoor area, and an upstairs function room with regular folk sessions. Beer festivals are held in May and November. Monthly tutored whisky tastings take advantage of the extensive range stocked. No meals Sunday evening. ♿🏵🕙▶🚭(Chapeltown)♣🍴P🚃🐾🛜

Sheffield: East

Chantry Inn Ⓛ
400 Handsworth Road, Handsworth, S13 9BZ
☎ (0114) 288 9117
Chantry New York Pale, Iron and Steel Bitter, Diamond Black Stout; 2 changing beers (sourced regionally; often Chantry) Ⓗ
Housed in what was an ecclesiastical building dating from the 13th century, in the churchyard of St Mary's Church, this is believed to be one of only four UK pubs set in consecrated ground. Becoming a pub in 1804 as the Cross Keys, it acquired its present name in 2019 when it was taken over by the Chantry Brewery of Rotherham. The three rooms – taproom, lounge and snug at the rear – are served from a central bar. 🏵🍴🚃🐾🛜

Sheffield: Kelham Island

Bar Stewards
163 Gibraltar Street, S3 8UB
☎ (0114) 327 3580 ⊕ thebarstewards.uk
4 changing beers (sourced nationally; often Abbeydale, Blue Bee, North Riding Brewery) Ⓗ
Opened in a shop unit in 2017, the Bar Stewards is a modern-style bar and bottle shop, and is a welcome addition to the Kelham Island circuit. The four well-chosen cask beers often include a local ale, and there is also a good range of keg beers, bottles and cans from independent breweries. The venue can be hired for private functions and a mobile bar service is available. 🏵🚃🚗🐾🛜

Crow Inn Ⓛ
35 Scotland Street, S3 7BS
☎ (0114) 201 0096
Abbeydale Heathen; 4 changing beers (sourced nationally; often Abbeydale, Arbor) Ⓗ
The former Old Crown Inn, after several years as a hotel, reopened in summer 2019 as a free house under its new name. The old pub layout is still discernible, with two comfortably furnished seating spaces either side of the entrance corridor which leads to the bar area. A wide range of cask and craft beers is served, with five handpumps and 11 keg lines, together with a large choice of spirits including 40 malt whiskies. There are seven ensuite hotel rooms. 🏵🛏♿🅿(Cathedral)🍴🚃🐾🛜

Fat Cat Ⓛ
23 Alma Street, S3 8SA
☎ (0114) 249 4801 ⊕ thefatcat.co.uk
Kelham Island Best Bitter, Pale Rider; Timothy Taylor Landlord; 8 changing beers (sourced nationally; often Kelham Island) Ⓗ
Opened in 1981, this is the place that started the real ale revolution in the area. Beers from around the country are served alongside those from the adjacent Kelham Island Brewery. The walls are covered with many awards

presented to the pub and brewery. An anniversary beer festival is held in August. Vegetarian and gluten-free dishes feature on the menu, and Monday is curry and quiz night. Q♿🏵🕙▶🍴♿🚪🍴P🚃🐾

Harlequin Ⓛ
108 Nursery Street, S3 8GG
☎ 07794 156916 ⊕ theharlequinpub.wordpress.com
Exit 33 Northern Best, Citra Smash; 8 changing beers (often Exit 33, North Riding Brewery) Ⓗ
Run by the owners of Exit 33 Brewing, the Harlequin takes its name from another former Ward's pub just around the corner, now demolished. The large open-plan interior features a central bar with seating on two levels. There are two regular beers from Exit 33, as well as guests from far and wide, with the emphasis on microbreweries. A large range of real ciders is also available. Wednesday is quiz night and there is live music at weekends. ♿🏵🕙▶🍴♣🍴🚃🐾

Kelham Island Tavern Ⓛ
62 Russell Street, S3 8RW
☎ (0114) 272 2482
Acorn Barnsley Bitter; Blue Bee Triple Hop; Pictish Brewers Gold; 10 changing beers (sourced nationally; often Abbeydale, Blue Bee, North Riding Brewery) Ⓗ
Twice CAMRA National Pub of the Year and a regular regional and local winner, this small gem was rescued from dereliction in 2002. Thirteen handpumps dispense an impressive range of beers, always including a mild, a porter and a stout. In the warmer months you can relax in the multi award-winning beer garden. Regular folk music features on Sunday evenings and quiz night is Monday. No meals Sunday. Q♿🏵🕙▶🍴♣🍴🚃🐾

Shakespeare's Ale & Cider House Ⓛ
146-148 Gibraltar Street, S3 8UB
☎ (0114) 275 5959 ⊕ shakespeares-sheffield.co.uk
Abbeydale Deception; Stancill Barnsley Bitter; 7 changing beers (sourced nationally; often Bad Seed, Blue Bee, North Riding Brewery) Ⓗ
Dating back to 1821, the building reopened as a free house in 2011 following a refurbishment that included incorporation of the archway to the rear yard into the pub. A central bar serves three rooms including the extension, and there is a further room across the corridor. The eight handpumps have featured over 5,000 different beers over the last 10 years, and over 100 whiskies are also stocked. There is regular live music, and beer festivals twice a year. Q🏵🍴♣🍴🚃🐾🛜

Wellington Ⓛ
1 Henry Street, S3 7EQ
☎ (0114) 249 2295
Neepsend Blonde; 6 changing beers (sourced regionally; often Neepsend) Ⓗ
A traditional two-roomed local opened as a free house in 1993. Now part of the small Sheaf Inns group of pubs, it is the tap for the nearby Neepsend Brewery. Sympathetically refurbished, the rooms are comfortably furnished and welcoming. The seven handpumps feature at least three Neepsend beers and up to three changing guests mainly from micros, together with a real cider. An extensive range of malt whiskies is also on offer. Q🏵🍴(Shalesmoor) ♣🍴🚃🐾

Sheffield: North

Blake Hotel Ⓛ
53 Blake Street, Upperthorpe, S6 3JQ
☎ (0114) 233 9336
Neepsend Blonde; 5 changing beers (sourced regionally; often Blue Bee, Neepsend) Ⓗ

This community hostelry at the top of a steep hill (pedestrian handrails provided) reopened in 2010 after being closed for seven years. Although extensively restored, it retains many Victorian features, including etched windows and mirrors. There is a large decked garden to the rear. The pub has probably the largest selection of whiskies in Sheffield and a growing range of rums and other spirits. It has no electronic games, TV or jukebox. Part of the local Sheaf Inns chain, along with the Sheaf View and the Wellington.
Q❀🜂🚃(Langsett) ♣🍴🚃(135) ❀

Gardeners Rest 🅛 ✅

105 Neepsend Lane, Neepsend, S3 8AT
☎ (0114) 272 4978 ⊕ gardenerscomsoc.wordpress.com
Sheffield Crucible Best, Five Rivers, Blanco Blonde; 6 changing beers (sourced locally) �🅷
Taken over by the Gardeners Rest Community Society in 2017, this friendly pub acts as the brewery tap for the nearby Sheffield Brewery. There are also at least six guest beers sourced nationwide from independent breweries. The cosy Dram Shop includes a bar billiards table and, to the rear, a conservatory leads to an eclectically decorated beer garden overlooking the River Don. It stages live music at weekends and regular beer festivals. Local CAMRA Pub of the Year 2019.
Q❀&🜂♣🍴🛈🚃❀

New Barrack Tavern 🅛

601 Penistone Road, Hillsborough, S6 2GA
☎ (0114) 232 4225 ⊕ newbarracktavern.com
Bradfield Farmers Bitter; Castle Rock Harvest Pale, Screech Owl; 6 changing beers (often Castle Rock) �🅷
A multi-roomed pub with an original 1936 floor plan, including a Gilmours-branded doorstep and distinctive colourful exterior tiles. In 2018 a new bottle/cider room was converted from a kitchen. The snug has a local sports theme while the lounge features live bands at weekends and a monthly comedy club on the first Sunday. The function room has three handpumps. Outside is an award-winning heated and covered patio garden. CAMRA Yorkshire Cider Pub of the Year 2019.
Q🛆❀🜂♣🍴🚃❀🛜

Wisewood Inn 🅛 ✅

539 Loxley Road, Loxley, S6 6RR
☎ (0114) 233 4310 ⊕ wisewoodinn.co.uk
8 changing beers (often Acorn, Bradfield, Stancill) ⅃🅷
The main bar has three rooms (including one for pool) and below is the cellar bar, which is available for hire. A large garden to the rear overlooks the Loxley Valley. Loxley Brewery, which commenced production in 2018, is adjacent to the cellar bar. In addition to its own Loxley ales, other local beers are invariably available on the five handpumps. There are also eight keg taps, often featuring brews from Beavertown and Thornbridge. The extensive food menu includes continental sausages, pizzas and tapas. 🛆❀🍴♣🚃❀🛜

Sheffield: South

Beer Engine 🅛

17 Cemetery Road, Highfield, S11 8FJ
☎ (0114) 272 1356 ⊕ beerenginesheffield.com
Neepsend Blonde; 5 changing beers (sourced nationally; often Bristol Beer Factory, Manchester) ⅃🅷
This traditional multi-roomed pub, cosy and with a great atmosphere, reopened as a free house in 2015 following a sympathetic refurbishment. A generous choice of high-quality drinks is provided for its wide clientele. The five changing handpulled beers come from an interesting mix of microbreweries from Sheffield and across the country. Excellent mainly tapas-style food is served in the

evenings and on Friday and Saturday lunchtimes, and a traditional roast on Sunday lunchtimes. The large beer garden has a heated, covered area. ❀🍴🚃❀🛜

Broadfield 🅛

452 Abbeydale Road, Nether Edge, S7 1FR
☎ (0114) 255 0200 ⊕ thebroadfield.co.uk
Abbeydale Moonshine; True North Blonde; 7 changing beers (sourced nationally; often Abbeydale, Ilkley, True North) 🅷
Dating from 1896, the Broadfield has established a deserved reputation for quality food served until late, with an extensive menu including hearty meat pies and home-made sausages. There are nine cask ales including some from owners True North, and a large range of bottled beers and whiskies. The pub has a great atmosphere and, located in the city's Antiques Quarter, is now a leading player in the local social scene.
🛆❀🍴&🍴🚃❀🛜

Brothers Arms 🅛

106 Well Road, Heeley, S8 9TZ
☎ (0114) 258 3544
Abbeydale Deception; house beer (by Abbeydale); 6 changing beers (sourced nationally) 🅷
A classic, traditional local; although the interior is open plan, it is designed so the various areas of seating and games all feel individual and cosy. The pub's name reflects its association with locally well-known parody ukulele band, The Everly Pregnant Brothers, and live music is hosted every Thursday evening, supplemented by folk sessions on the third Sunday. The bar features eight real ales – two regular beers and six changing guests – together with a real cider. 🛆❀♣🍴🚃❀🛜

Sheaf View 🅛

25 Gleadless Road, Heeley, S2 3AA
☎ (0114) 249 6455
Neepsend Blonde; 7 changing beers (sourced regionally; often Neepsend, Pictish, Saltaire) 🅷
A 19th-century pub near Heeley City Farm, the Sheaf experienced a chequered history before becoming a real ale oasis since reopening as a free house in 2000. The walls and shelves are adorned with assorted breweriana and provide an ideal background for good drinking and conversation. A wide range of international beers, together with malt whiskies and a real cider, complement the eight reasonably priced real ales. It gets busy, especially on Wednesday quiz night and Sheffield United match days. Q❀&♣🍴🚃❀

White Lion 🅛 ✅

615 London Road, Heeley, S2 4HT
☎ (0114) 255 1500 ⊕ whitelionsheffield.co.uk
Abbeydale Moonshine; Tetley Bitter; Wychwood Hobgoblin Ruby; 9 changing beers (sourced nationally) 🅷
This Grade II-listed inn has been respectfully refurbished over the years. A tiled central corridor links a number of delightful small rooms and leads to the larger rear concert room. The wide selection of cask-conditioned beers always includes a vegan option, and the pub also proudly offers a good range of whiskies. Many community events are hosted and there is live music every night except Wednesday, which is quiz night.
🛆❀♣🍴🚃❀🛜

Sheffield: West

Ale Club 🅛

429 Ecclesall Road, Sharrow, S11 8PG
☎ (0114) 453 6818

5 changing beers (sourced regionally; often Bad Seed, Brew Foundation, Don Valley) [H]
A busy micropub in the heart of the Ecclesall Road social scene, but only a stone's throw from the tranquil botanical gardens. It is comfortably furnished and has a cosy atmosphere, in contrast to the sometimes spartan decor of some of these establishments. Owned by the Brew Foundation, the brewer is often on hand to answer questions about the beers and advise on home brewing. In addition to the cask ales there is an extensive range of craft keg beers, bottles and cans from independent brewers. Q🎠❀♣🍎🚌🐾

Beer House [L]
623 Ecclesall Road, Sharrow, S11 8PT
🌐 the-beer-house-172.mytoggle.io
6 changing beers (sourced nationally; often Abbeydale, Blue Bee, Exit 33) [H]
Sheffield's first micropub opened in a small former shop unit in 2014. The front of two rooms has level access from the street and contains the bar, with its bank of six handpumps displaying a changing range of beers mainly from microbreweries, often including local breweries. The rear room has seating focused around the fireplace, and there is a quiz on Wednesday evening. Q🎠❀♣🚌🐾

Itchy Pig Ale House [L]
495 Glossop Road, Broomhill, S10 2QE
☎ (0114) 327 0780 🌐 theitchypig.co.uk
5 changing beers (sourced regionally; often Abbeydale, Exit 33) [H]
A cosy, friendly micropub with a relaxed atmosphere and a continental feel. The whitewashed walls are decorated with porcine-themed artwork, hop sacks and dried hops. There is quality carpentry in evidence, including a bar formed from Victorian era doors with a glass-covered top made with two pence coins set in resin. A wide range of pork scratchings is available. Q🎠♣🍎🚌(120)🐾

Rising Sun [L] ✔
471 Fulwood Road, Nether Green, S10 3QA
☎ (0114) 230 3855 🌐 risingsunsheffield.co.uk
Abbeydale Daily Bread, Deception, Moonshine, Absolution; 7 changing beers (sourced nationally; often Abbeydale, Saltaire, Welbeck Abbey) [H]
A large suburban roadhouse operated by local brewer Abbeydale. There are two comfortably furnished rooms with a log-burning fire between the main bar and the glass-roofed extension, which also has glass panels in the end wall. A range of Abbeydale beers is always served, with up to six guests, mainly from micros, dispensed from the impressive bank of 13 handpumps. Quizzes are on Sunday and Wednesday evenings. The Sunfest beer festival is in July.
Q🎠❀🍴♿♣🍎P🚌(120,83A)🐾📶

University Arms [L]
197 Brook Hill, Broomhall, S3 7HG
☎ (0114) 222 8969
Kelham Island Pale Rider [H]**; Welbeck Abbey Red Feather** [H]/[G]**; house beer (by Acorn); 5 changing beers (sourced regionally)** [H]
Owned by the University of Sheffield, this former staff club has an open-plan lounge with a bar at one end adjacent to a small alcove seating area, and a conservatory leading to the large garden. There is additional seating upstairs with separate rooms for snooker and darts. The guest beers are mostly local, and there are regular beer festivals. Entertainment includes a quiz on Tuesdays and open mic night on Wednesdays (during term time).
Q🎠❀🍴♿🚊(University of Sheffield)♣🍎🚌🐾📶

Thorne

Windmill ✔
19 Queen Street, DN8 5AA
☎ (01405) 812866
Kelham Island Pale Rider; Stancill Barnsley Bitter; 3 changing beers (sourced regionally; often Thornbridge, York) [H]
Friendly community pub close to the town centre on a street parallel with the main road. Four real ales from small independent breweries are sold, and good-natured conversation with staff and clientele is assured. The interior comprises a smart lounge with a conservatory at the side, linked by an archway to another room with a pool table. Outside is a large garden with play equipment, and ample parking. Sunday is quiz night.
🎠❀🚆(North)♣🍎P🚌(87,88a)🐾📶

Thurlstone

Huntsman [L]
136 Manchester Road, S36 9QW (on main A628 through village)
☎ (01226) 764892 🌐 huntsmanthurlstone.co.uk
Black Sheep Best Bitter; Timothy Taylor Landlord; 4 changing beers (sourced nationally) [H]
The location of this village local on the main East-West Pennine route provides an interesting mixture of customers from both regular and passing trade. Genuine and friendly drinking and talking are this pub's lifeblood. Throw in old-fashioned pub games, LocAle, and a seriously dog-friendly attitude, and you have a venue that just should not be passed by. The choice of six real ales has contributed to the Huntsman being in the Guide now for 12 consecutive years. Food is served Tuesday evening and Sunday lunchtime only. There is no jukebox or TV, but live music features on Wednesday evening.
Q🎠❀🍴♣🍎🚌🐾📶

Tickhill

Scarbrough Arms [L]
Sunderland Street, DN11 9QJ (on A631 near Buttercross)
☎ (01302) 742977
Greene King Abbot; John Smith's Bitter; Timothy Taylor Landlord; 2 changing beers (sourced locally; often Abbeydale, Bradfield, Welbeck Abbey) [H]
A regular in the Guide since 1990, this stone-built pub originally dates back to the 16th century. There is a taproom at the rear that features darts and sports TV, while a spacious lounge can be found at the front. Between the two is a Barrel Room snug with barrel-shaped furniture. Outside is a covered smoking area and a large attractive beer garden. Quiz nights are Monday and Thursday. Beer festivals feature in the summer.
Q🎠❀♣🍎P🚌(22,205)🐾📶

Wales

Duke of Leeds [L] ✔
16 Church Street, S26 5LQ (off A618 into School Rd, opp parish church)
☎ (01909) 515490
Bradfield Farmers Blonde; 3 changing beers (sourced regionally; often Abbeydale, Box Steam, Theakston) [H]
Three hundred years old, this is the former coaching inn of the Duke of Leeds, extensively refurbished and reopened in 2015 under new ownership. The bar area leads to three other spaces where drinks and meals can be consumed. Outdoor seats afford views of the village,

and the upstairs function room can hold 60 people. Changing beers are sourced both locally and from further afield, and food is freshly cooked to order. The pub is on the Five Churches Walk and popular with walkers. ♿🐕🍴♣️🅿️🚃🐾

Wath upon Dearne

Church House 🅛 ✅
Montgomery Square, S63 7RZ
☎ (01709) 879518
Greene King Abbot; Ruddles Best Bitter; 4 changing beers (often Acorn, Elland) Ⓗ
A large pub with an impressive frontage set in a pedestrianised square in the town centre, with excellent access to local bus services (across the square). It was built in about 1810 and consecrated by the nearby church in 1912. It became a pub in the 1980s and a Wetherspoon in 2000. Handy for exploring the RSPB Old Moor Wetlands Centre and for Manvers Commercial Park, it serves a wide variety of beers from both national and local brewers. Real ciders or perries are also on handpull. ♿🐕🍴👶♣️🅿️🚃🛜

Wath Tap 🅛
49 High Street, S63 7QB
☎ (01709) 872150
6 changing beers (sourced locally; often Fernandes, Geeves, Ossett) Ⓗ
The local CAMRA branch's first micropub, opened in a former butcher's shop in 2016, where a warm welcome is guaranteed. Six changing real ales are sold, mostly from breweries in the vicinity, and five real ciders. These are listed on chalkboards by the bar. The former walk-in cold store is now the cellar. Seats out front are protected from the rain by the original shop canopy. Jam sessions are sometimes held and board games are available. Food may be brought in from the surrounding takeaways. Local CAMRA Pub of the Year 2017-2020. Q♿♣️👶🚃🐾🛜

Wentworth

George & Dragon 🅛
85 Main Street, S62 7TN (stands back from road on B6090)
☎ (01226) 742440 ⊕ georgeanddragonwentworth.Com
Theakston Old Peculier; 7 changing beers (often Bradfield, Chantry, Geeves) Ⓗ
A village free house, licensed since 1804, offering eight changing real ales from local and national brewers. It has a front patio with a large garden and children's adventure playground at the rear, as well as a craft shop and the Hoober Room, available for hire. Home-cooked food from an extensive menu is served, and a pop-up pie shop opens every Saturday and Sunday afternoon. The pub is a Guide regular, winner of numerous local CAMRA branch awards, and is handy for historic Wentworth Woodhouse, Needle's Eye and Hoober Stand. It is accessible from the parish church via the garden. Q♿🐕🍴🅿️🚃(44,136)🐾🛜

Wortley

Wortley Men's Club 🅛 ✅
Reading Room Lane, S35 7DB (in centre of village at back of Wortley Arms public house)
☎ (0114) 288 2066 ⊕ wortleymensclub.co.uk
Timothy Taylor Landlord; 2 changing beers (sourced nationally) Ⓗ
A club that has won many CAMRA awards including regional, national and local club of the year; this is the 10th consecutive year it has been in the Guide. It is

situated in a pretty rural village near to Wortley Hall and gardens. The opulent interior and exterior feature exposed timber frames, ornate ceilings, wooden panelling and a real fire. Guest ales are from local and national breweries, and a guest cider is also served. The club runs an annual beer festival in July. Show your CAMRA membership card or a copy of this Guide on entry. Q🐕♿♣️👶🅿️🚃(23,23A)

YORKSHIRE (WEST)
Ackworth

Masons Arms 🅛
Bell Lane, WF7 7JD (a turning off A628 by disused railway bridge)
☎ 07966 501827
Bradfield Farmers Blonde, Farmers Brown Cow; 2 changing beers (sourced regionally) Ⓗ
Grade II listed coaching house dating from 1682, built of locally quarried stone. A unique display of old photographs portrays the local social and industrial heritage. The central bar serves the main room, pool room and smaller lounge. Log-burning fireplaces in both the main rooms were discovered 15 years ago during a sensitive refurbishment. Live music takes place on Saturday and Sunday, bingo on Tuesday and a quiz on Thursday night, all well attended by locals and visitors alike. ♿🐕♿♣️🅿️🚃🛜

Altofts

Robin Hood 🅛
10 Church Road, WF6 2NJ (from Normanton town centre take road over railway into Altofts, continue through Lee Brigg, then High Green Rd and left on to Church Rd)
☎ (01924) 892911 ⊕ robinhoodaltofts.co.uk
Acorn Barnsley Bitter; 5 changing beers (sourced locally; often Tarn 51) Ⓗ
Locally owned free house and brewpub at the top end of the village, which now has a large new patio seating 70 people. Tarn 51 microbrewery has moved into a new brewhouse next door. It is within easy reach of the Pennine Trail and Aire & Calder Navigation, and only a mile from Stanley Ferry Marina. ♿🐕♣️🅿️🚃🐾🛜

Armitage Bridge

Armitage Bridge Monkey Club 🅛
Dean Brook Road, HD4 7PB
☎ (01484) 522370
Goose Eye Bitter; 2 changing beers (sourced nationally; often Empire) Ⓗ
Refurbished and air conditioned, this thriving and friendly little club in the hamlet of Armitage Bridge serves two guest beers. It is a regular local CAMRA Club of the Year, well worth seeking out and a great place to relax with a pint on an evening. There are plans for an annual one-day beer festival in September. ♿🐕♿🅿️🚃🐾🛜↻

Baildon

Bull's Head Inn 🅛
6 Westgate, BD17 5ES
☎ (01274) 976416
Goose Eye Chinook Blonde; Saltaire Blonde; Sharp's Doom Bar; Tetley Bitter; 2 changing beers (sourced nationally; often Nightjar) Ⓗ
A traditional two-roomed pub with log fires and a warming and friendly atmosphere. It is a popular village venue, frequented by a wide range of customers, where

WEST YORKSHIRE

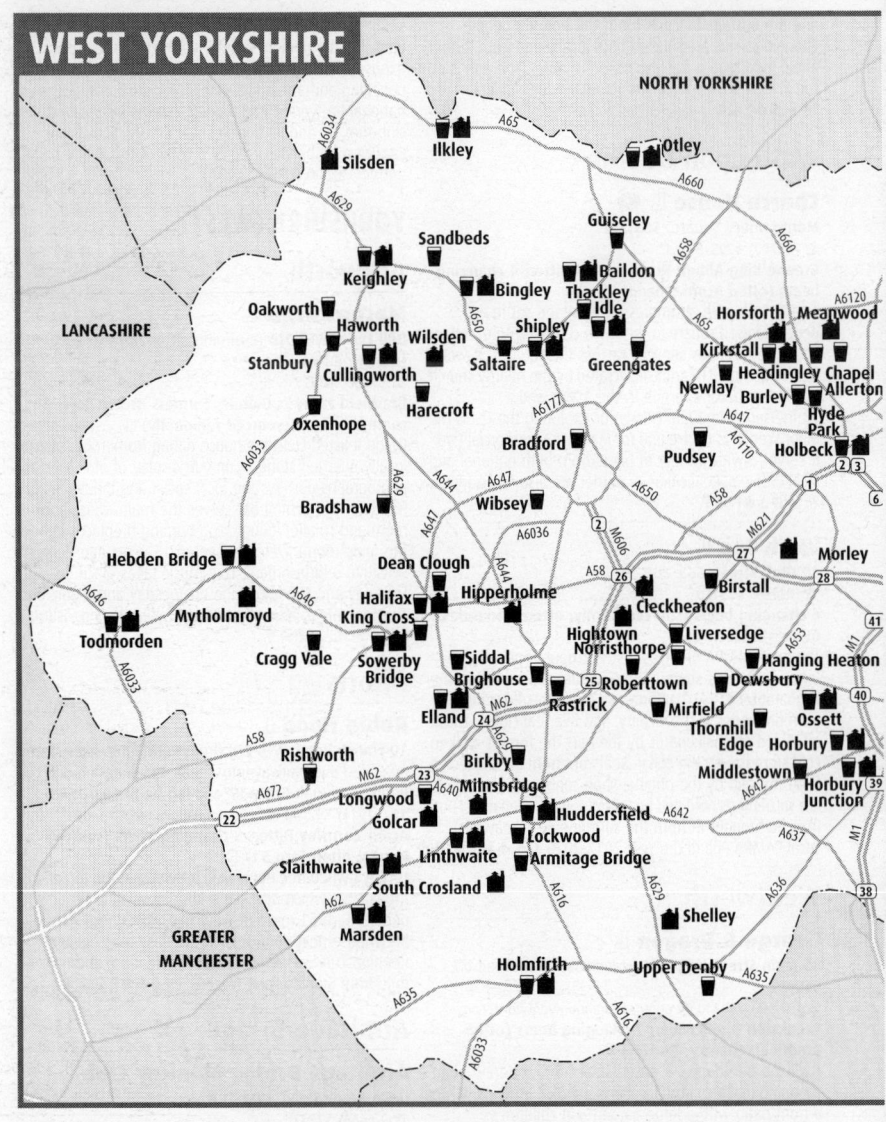

NORTH YORKSHIRE

Ilkley

Otley

Silsden

Guiseley

Sandbeds

Baildon

Keighley

Bingley

Thackley

Oakworth

Haworth

Shipley

Idle

Horsforth

Meanwood

Stanbury

Wilsden

Saltaire

Greengates

Kirkstall

Cullingworth

Newlay

Headingley

Chapel Allerton

Oxenhope

Harecroft

Burley

Hyde Park

Bradford

Pudsey

Holbeck

LANCASTER

Bradshaw

Wibsey

Morley

Hebden Bridge

Dean Clough

Birstall

Mytholmroyd

Halifax

Hipperholme

Cleckheaton

King Cross

Hightown

Liversedge

Hanging Heaton

Todmorden

Cragg Vale

Sowerby Bridge

Siddal

Norristhorpe

Dewsbury

Brighouse

Robertown

Rishworth

Elland

Rastrick

Mirfield

Thornhill Edge

Ossett

Longwood

Birkby

Milnsbridge

Horbury

Golcar

Huddersfield

Middlestown

Horbury Junction

Slaithwaite

Linthwaite

Lockwood

Armitage Bridge

South Crosland

Shelley

GREATER MANCHESTER

Marsden

Holmfirth

Upper Denby

visitors and well-behaved dogs are always welcome. Photos of Baildon adorn the walls. As well as the four regular ales from local and national brewers, a varying guest beer, usually of a darker style, is also offered. The separate taproom houses darts and dominoes.

Junction

1 Baildon Road, BD17 6AB (on A6038/B6151 jct)
☎ (01274) 582009
Junction Blonde; Timothy Taylor Landlord; 4 changing beers (sourced nationally; often Acorn, Junction, Rudgate)
Popular, multi-award-winning, three-roomed traditional local comprising a lounge, public bar and a games area. Three regularly available beers, usually including at least one from the in-house Junction Brewery, are complemented by three guest ales. Bottled ciders and foreign beers are also sold. Sports events are shown on TV, quiz nights hosted on Tuesdays and Thursdays, and

there is a piano for those wanting to join in with impromptu live music and sing-alongs. A regular beer festival is held at the end of July. The pub is the 'headquarters' of Shipley Town FC.

Bingley

Chip N Ern

73 Main Street, BD16 2JA
☎ (01274) 985501
7 changing beers (sourced locally; often Bridgehouse, Goose Eye, Revolutions)
This traditionally styled micropub is a popular destination on the local real ale scene. The wood-panelled ground-floor bar has a distinctive and eclectic range of decorations, and there is additional seating in the upstairs room. Seven cask ales include a varying range from Bridgehouse, Goose Eye and other guest breweries. A selection of ciders is also offered. A musician's jam night is held early on Tuesday evenings, while a folk jam

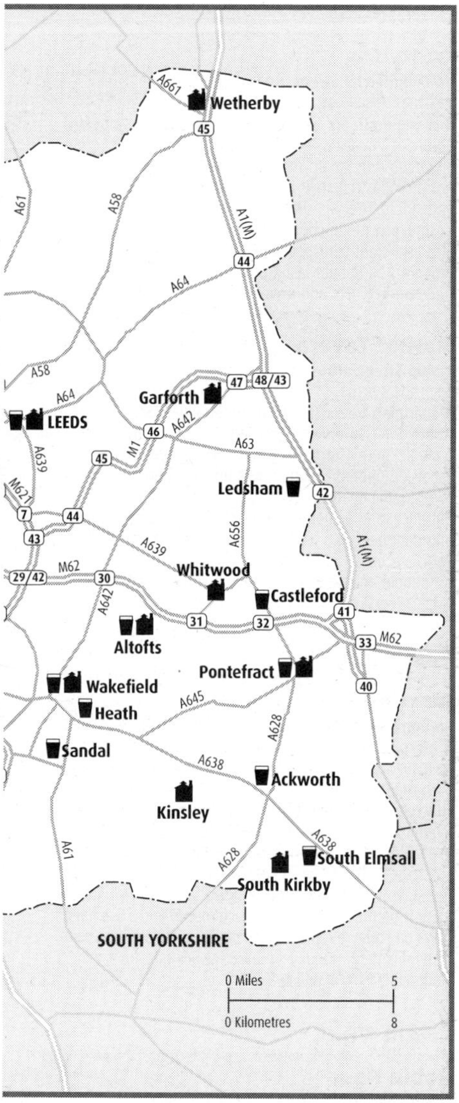

night takes place the first Mondy of the month. The pub is close to the railway station and handy for exploring the famous Five Rise Locks on the adjacent Leeds-Liverpool Canal. 🐴♿🚆🍎🚌🐾📶↺

Birkby

Magic Rock Brewery Tap [L]

Willow Park Business Centre, Willow Lane, HD1 5EB
☎ (01484) 649823 🌐 magicrockbrewing.com
Magic Rock Dark Arts, Hat Trick, Ringmaster; 3 changing beers (sourced locally; often Magic Rock) [H]
Following relocation from Quarmby, the brewery's meteoric rise has been mirrored by the tap. Open every day, five cask beers always include a dark one. Lower strength beers double up on match days. On the back wall there are views into the brewery and barrel-ageing beers to one side. There is plenty of undercover seating outside. Exhibitions, festivals and Saturday tours are staged, and street-food outlets and other caterers attend every weekend. The venue is less than 10 minutes' walk from the town centre, and has a good bus service.
🐴❀◐◑♿P🚌🐾📶

Birstall

Black Bull

5 Kirkgate, WF17 9PB (off A652 near jct of A643)
☎ (01274) 865609 🌐 theblackbullinnbirstall.co.uk
Black Sheep Best Bitter; Saltaire Blonde; 1 changing beer (sourced nationally; often Bradfield, York) [H]
A stone-built 17th-century community pub important through the centuries. The upper room, used as a local magistrate's court in times gone by, remains preserved and is used for functions. On the ground floor is a snug, main bar area and a piano room. There is an open fire in the winter amid comfortable, traditional surroundings. To the rear is a car park and a tidy beer garden. Board games are played. 🐴❀♣🍎P🚌(200,283)🐾📶↺

Bradford

Corn Dolly [L]

110 Bolton Road, BD1 4DE
☎ (01274) 720219 🌐 thecorndollypub.co.uk
Everards Tiger; Moorhouse's White Witch; Timothy Taylor Boltmaker; 5 changing beers (sourced regionally; often Abbeydale, Pictish, Wishbone) [H]
A traditional award-winning free house run by the same family for over 25 years, close to the city centre and within easy reach of Forster Square railway station. Previously called the Wharfe due to its location near the former Bradford canal, it first opened its doors in 1834. An open-plan layout incorporates a games area to one end. Good-value food is served weekday lunchtimes. The pub has a friendly atmosphere and is popular before Bradford City matches. A collection of pumpclips adorns the beams and the jukebox is worth checking out if you like rock and 80s tunes.
❀◐♿🚆(Forster Square) ♣🍎P🚌(640,641) ↺

Exchange Craft Beer House [L]

14 Market Street, BD1 1LH
☎ (01274) 306078
5 changing beers (sourced regionally; often Nightjar, Nomadic, Stod Fold) [H]
This establishment is located beneath the Victorian splendour that is the Wool Exchange building. Despite being a cellar bar, it has a light and airy feel. It is open plan, with a large seating area and bar under a brick barrel ceiling, and a smaller raised seating area near the entrance. A real ale from the owner, Nightjar Brewery, is usually available, alongside others from smaller regional breweries and sometimes further afield, in a variety of beer styles from light to dark.
🐴🚆(Forster Square) ♣🚌🐾📶

Fighting Cock [L]

21-23 Preston Street, BD7 1JE (close to Grattans, off Thornton Rd)
☎ (01274) 726907
Ilkley Mary Jane; Theakston Old Peculier; Timothy Taylor Golden Best, Boltmaker, Landlord; 7 changing beers (sourced nationally; often Millstone, Oakham, Vocation) [H]
A drinkers' paradise in an industrial area, this multi award-winning and traditionally-styled free house is 20 minutes' walk from the city centre and close to bus routes along Thornton Road and Legrams Lane. Twelve real ales are usually available including at least one dark beer. A variety of real ciders is also sold along with foreign bottled beers. Good-value lunches are served

Monday to Saturday. The large beer garden is opposite the pub. Twice-yearly beer festivals take place. ⊛⓿❶◐🖵❀❖🛜↺

Jacobs Well 🅛

14 Kent Street, BD1 5RL (by Jacobs Well roundabout at end of Hall Ings)
☎ (01274) 395628
Abbeydale Deception; Half Moon Dark Masquerade; 6 changing beers (sourced regionally; often Bingley, Spotlight, Sunbeam) 🅷
Traditionally styled real ale and cider free house dating from 1811. The interior is open plan but with a rustic feel, and there is a snug to the side of the bar. Nine handpulls offer a varying range of beers from local and regional independents, and always feature some darker ales. Numerous ciders are always stocked, together with a good range of foreign bottled beers. Sit outside and watch the city bustle while enjoying good ale.
⊛≂(Interchange) ●🖵❖🛜↺

Peacock Bar

25 North Parade, BD1 3JL
☎ 07979 182599 ∰ peacockbar.co.uk
Bradfield Farmers Blonde; Thornbridge Jaipur IPA; 2 changing beers (sourced regionally; often Nook, Saltaire) 🅷
Opened in 2016, this Indian-themed bar offers real ale and Indian street food with a twist. Four handpumps serve real ale (two permanent beers and varying regional guests) while a further pump serves cider. Indian street food is prepared and served on the ground floor. The upstairs room, with a large TV showing sports, can be hired. The Peacock is popular with football fans, especially when Bradford City are at home, and it can be busy on weekend evenings.
⛟◑≂(Forster Square) ●🖵🛜↺

Record Café

45-47 North Parade, BD1 3JH
☎ (01274) 723143 ∰ therecordcafe.co.uk
4 changing beers (sourced regionally; often Brass Castle, North Riding Brewery, Wilde Child) 🅷
A modern award-winning café bar located in the city's independent quarter selling ale, vinyl and ham. Four handpulls serve real ales, sourced regionally, in varying styles, usually including a dark beer. Real cider and perry are also offered and there are seven craft keg beers from independent brewers on tap. A charcuterie-style food menu specialises in hams and cheeses from Spain. Vinyl records are sold in the upstairs mezzanine area. Local CAMRA branch Pub of the Year 2020.
⛟⊛◑ₐ≂(Forster Square) ●🖵❖🛜↺

Bradshaw

Golden Fleece 🅛 ✅

1 Bradshaw Lane, HX2 9UZ
☎ 07522 190990 ∰ goldenfleecebradshaw.co.uk
Saltaire Blonde; Tetley Bitter; 2 changing beers (sourced regionally; often Fuzzy Duck, Stod Fold) 🅷
Set in the heart of this picturesque village, the pub has a spacious, comfortable lounge and a separate room at the rear. A small snug leads out to a large beer garden with tables and chairs. Barbecues are held during the summer to take advantage of the scenic views. Local pool and dominoes teams are supported, quiz night is on a Wednesday and there is a themed music night every Saturday. ⛟⊛♣ₐ♣🖵🛜↺

Brighouse

Crafty Fox

44 Commercial Street, HD6 1AQ
☎ 07847 205425 ∰ craftyfox.bar
6 changing beers (sourced regionally; often Salopian, Squawk, Vocation) 🅷
Situated on the main shopping street, this family-run bar has an industrial-style interior with several pallet tables and stools. There is similar seating upstairs, ideal for hosting private functions and meetings. Six changing real ales and eight craft beers are served. The owner organises blind beer tastings once a month and there are frequent live acts and a weekly quiz. ⛟≂●🖵❖🛜

Market Tavern 🅛

2 Ship Street, HD6 1JX
☎ 07908 698360
6 changing beers (sourced regionally; often Abbeydale, Salopian, Squawk) 🅷
A single-storey former pork pie factory next to the canalside open-air market, this micropub has comfortable seating in the bar, a small snug by the entrance, and a sheltered outside drinking area. At least one dark beer and one real cider, Thistly Cross Whisky Cask, are on sale at all times. Snacks are available both for people and dogs. Open bank holiday Mondays.
Q⛟⊛≂●🖵❖🛜

Castleford

Junction 🅛

Carlton Street, WF10 1EE (enter Castleford on A655; pub is on corner of Carlton St at top of town centre)
☎ (01977) 277750 ∰ thejunctionpubcastleford.com
5 changing beers 🅷
This rejuvenated pub specialises in beers from the landlord's own wooden casks. Up to six guest ales are available in the wood from enterprising local brewers. The large L-shaped bar is kept warm with open fires, and the stove-heated snug can be used for functions. Folk night is on the last Sunday of each month and a live band plays on Friday evening. An annual Easter Woodfest beer festival is held. Handily situated for bus and train stations. Q⛟≂♣●🖵❖🛜

Cragg Vale

Robin Hood 🅛

Cragg Road, HX7 5SQ (on B6138 1½ miles S of Mytholmroyd)
☎ (01422) 885899
Timothy Taylor Boltmaker, Landlord; 3 changing beers (sourced regionally; often Goose Eye, Millstone, Oakham) 🅷
A warm welcome is assured at this friendly, two-roomed, split-level local in a beautiful wooded valley popular with walkers and cyclists. On entering, the cosy bar – with a real fire in winter – is to the right, while the larger dining room is to the left. Food is served Thursday to Sunday (times vary). Two Timothy Taylor beers are complemented by up to three guests from regional breweries (often Goose Eye, Millstone and Oakham). Real cider is sometimes available.
Q⛟⊛◑ₐ🖵(900,901) ❖🛜↺

Cullingworth

George 🅛

Station Road, BD13 5HN
☎ (01535) 275566

Old Spot Light But Dark, OSB, Spot Light, Spot o' Bother; 3 changing beers (often Great Newsome, Old Spot) Ⓗ

Rescued from oblivion in 2011 by local brewery owners, this lovely old-fashioned village pub has a pleasant setting near the church. The emphasis is primarily on food from an extensive and imaginative menu, but there is also an attractive bar area to the front. The taphouse for Old Spot, the brewery's beers are sold over the majority of the seven handpulls. Guest ales from regional breweries are also offered. Dogs are permitted in the bar area only. ❧✿①&P🚪✿🗖🔌🏷️

Dewsbury

Shepherd's Boy Ⓛ ✅

157 Huddersfield Road, WF13 2RP (on A644 about ½ mile W of town)
☎ (01924) 454116

Ossett Yorkshire Blonde, Silver King; Rat White Rat; Riverhead Butterley Bitter; 2 changing beers (sourced regionally; often Rat, Thornbridge, Vocation) Ⓗ

A fine Ossett Brewery reconstruction of a former Webster's outlet, it features four distinct and separate comfortable drinking areas, with a trademark brick arch separating the front from the rear of the pub. The hidden beer garden behind and below the building provides shade on summer days. Thursday is quiz night. Tasty home-made snacks are often available, while guest ales usually include a renowned IPA and a dark ale. ✿🌸🍺P🚪✿🔌🏷️

West Riding Refreshment Rooms Ⓛ

Dewsbury Railway Station, Wellington Road, WF13 1HF
☎ (01924) 459193 ⊕ beerhouses.co.uk/the-west-riding

Black Sheep Best Bitter; Timothy Taylor Landlord; 7 changing beers (sourced nationally; often Brass Castle, Magic Rock, Vocation) Ⓗ

This multi award-winning pub in a Grade II-listed station building has celebrated over 25 years in the Guide. Situated in the original waiting room on platform 2 of Dewsbury train station, it has nine handpumps dispensing a range of beer styles and strengths; a 10th is reserved for real cider. Good food is served daily including a range of pizzas. There are monthly Meet the Brewer sessions, occasional beer festivals, and live music outside in summer. The pub gets busy on Saturdays due to its prominent position on the Transpennine Rail Ale Trail. ✿①&≈🌸🍺🚪✿🔌🏷️

Elland

Elland Craft & Tap Ⓛ

102 Southgate, HX5 0EP
☎ (01422) 370630 ⊕ craftandtap.co.uk

Elland Blonde; 4 changing beers (sourced regionally) Ⓗ

On the main street in town, this bar has been busy since opening in 2018, and has made a good impression on local CAMRA members. It used to be a bank, and the main room still has the original ornamental features.

REAL ALE BREWERIES

Anthology ⚭ Leeds
Barker's South Crosland
Beer Ink ⚭ Huddersfield
BEEspoke ≣ Shipley
Bingley ⚭ Wilsden
Bini Ilkley (NEW)
Bone Idle Idle
Bosun's Huddersfield
Bridgehouse Keighley
Briscoe's Otley
Burley Street ≣ Leeds (brewing suspended)
Chevin Otley
Chin Chin South Kirkby
Cobbydale ≣ Silsden
Concept ≣ Horsforth
Cooper Hill Leeds
Darkland Halifax
Eagles Crag ⚭ Todmorden
Elland Elland
Empire Slaithwaite
Fernandes ≣ ⚭ Wakefield
Five Towns Wakefield
Frisky Bear ⚭ Leeds: Morley
Ghost Baildon
Goose Eye ⚭ Bingley
Halifax Steam ≣ Hipperholme
Haworth Steam ≣ Cleckheaton
Henry Smith ≣ Pontefract
Hogs Head ≣ Sowerby Bridge
Horbury ≣ Horbury
Horsforth ⚭ Leeds: Horsforth
Ilkley Ilkley
Junction ≣ Baildon
Kirkstall Leeds: Kirkstall
Lazy Turtle Holmfirth
Leeds Leeds
Linfit ≣ Linthwaite
Little Valley Hebden Bridge
Lord's ⚭ Golcar

Luddite ≣ Horbury Junction
Magic Rock ⚭ Huddersfield
Mallinsons Huddersfield
Meanwood ⚭ Leeds
Mill Valley ⚭ Hightown
Milltown Milnsbridge
Morton Collins ≣ Wakefield
Nightjar Mytholmroyd
Nomadic ⚭ Leeds
Nook ≣ Holmfirth
North ⚭ Leeds
Northern Monk ⚭ Leeds: Holbeck
Old Spot Cullingworth
Ossett ⚭ Ossett
Outgang ≣ Kinsley
Piglove ⚭ Leeds
Quirky ⚭ Leeds: Garforth
Rat ≣ Huddersfield
Revolutions Whitwood
Ridgeside ⚭ Leeds: Meanwood
Riverhead ≣ Huddersfield: Marsden
Salt ⚭ Shipley
Saltaire ⚭ Shipley
Shadow Otley
Small World Shelley
Stod Fold Halifax
Sunbeam Leeds
Tapped Leeds
Tarn 51 ≣ Altofts
Tartarus Horsforth (NEW)
Three Fiends Holmfirth
Tigertops Wakefield
Timothy Taylor Keighley
Truth Hurts ⚭ Leeds: Morley
Vocation Hebden Bridge
Wetherby ≣ ⚭ Wetherby
Wharfedale ≣ Ilkley
Wilde Child ⚭ Leeds
Wishbone ⚭ Keighley
Zapato ⚭ Marsden

There are stairs to a second room where you will find the bar. The pub supports various community groups and has a room upstairs for private meetings. Quiz night is every Wednesday. Q ⬤ ♿ & 🐕 🚌 (501,503) 🌸 📶

Greengates

Cracker Barrel
832 Harrogate Road, BD10 0RA
Tetley Bitter; 4 changing beers (sourced regionally; often Abbeydale, Saltaire, Wishbone) 🅷
Opened in 2017, this friendly, popular, family-run micropub has a cosy, homely feel. The bar is at the rear of the single room. Tetley Cask Bitter is the regular beer. The other four handpulls serve a varying range of real ales, often including a dark beer, from regional breweries. The pub welcomes families and dogs. It has a small beer garden at the back, and outside seating to the front next to a busy main road. ⬤ ♿ 🐕 🚌 🌸 📶

New Line 🅛
60 New Line, BD10 9AP
☎ (01274) 613855 🌐 thenewline.co.uk
Timothy Taylor Landlord; 3 changing beers (sourced nationally; often Abbeydale, Oakham) 🅷
Opened in 2018, this is an impressive, high-quality conversion of a former 1800s residential property. The downstairs room contains the bar, and there is an additional upstairs seating area with a TV and a wood-burning stove. The original stonework and roof beams have been exposed and restored, and the furnishings are luxurious. One regular and three guest real ales are served from the handpulls. A waitress service to the upstairs room is offered on a weekend. ⬤ 🚌 📶

Guiseley

Coopers 🅛 ✅
4-6 Otley Road, LS20 8AH
☎ (01943) 878835
Ilkley Blonde; Rooster's Yorkshire Pale Ale; Timothy Taylor Landlord; 5 changing beers (sourced regionally; often Brass Castle, Hawkshead, Thornbridge) 🅷
The name of this modern pub comes from its former existence as a Co-operative store. There is a bar and separate dining area downstairs, and a function room upstairs. A good range of cask beers is served, generally from Yorkshire or northern breweries, with a dedicated dark beer pump and a large selection of other beers on tap and in bottles and cans. The upstairs room is used for events and also serves as an extra dining space. Q ⬤ ♿ ◑ & 🚌 🌸 📶

Guiseley Factory Workers Club 🅛
6 Town Street, LS20 9DT
☎ (01943) 874793 🌐 guiseleyfactoryworkersclub.co.uk
Tetley Bitter; 3 changing beers (sourced locally; often Goose Eye, Mallinsons, Rudgate) 🅷
Award-winning three-roomed club founded over 100 years ago by the Yeadon and Guiseley Factory Workers Union. The two-sided bar serves both the lounge and the concert room, and has guest ales sourced both locally and nationally. There is also a snooker room and a large beer garden. The concert room has a stage for bands, who play on some weekend evenings, and hosts many clubs and organisations. CAMRA members are welcome on production of this Guide or a membership card. ♿ ≠ ♣ P 🚌 🌸 📶

Halifax: Dean Clough

Stod Fold Dean Clough 🅛
HX3 5AH
☎ (01422) 355600 🌐 stodfolddeanclough.co.uk
3 changing beers (sourced nationally; often Stod Fold) 🅷
A sympathetically restored industrial-chic bar tucked just inside Gate One of the architecturally significant Dean Clough Mills. The bar has seven handpumps, mostly serving the core Stod Fold range, plus guest beers. Food is provided by the Stod Fold Yorkshire Kitchen, run by a local Halifax chef, offering a range of core meals as well as small plates and bar snacks using locally sourced, sustainable and seasonal ingredients. The Stod Fold beer range is used in many of the dishes. ⬤ ♿ ◑ & 🐕 🚌 🌸 📶

Halifax: King Cross

Wainhouse Tavern 🅛 ✅
Upper Washer Lane, Pye Nest, HX2 7DR (take Edwards Rd off Pye Nest Rd)
☎ (01422) 339998 🌐 wainhousetavern.co.uk
Wychwood Hobgoblin Gold; house beer (by Stod Fold); 5 changing beers (sourced regionally; often Elland, Mallinsons, Rudgate) 🅷
Former home to industrialist JFE Wainhouse, most famous for his nearby tower. The building was converted to a public house in the 1960s and saved from an uncertain future by the present owners. No two windows are alike in this Grade II-listed Gothic-fronted building. A small lounge at the front opens up to a much larger bar at the rear. Private functions, live music and games nights take place here. Traditional home-cooked food is served in the evenings and at weekends. ⬤ ♿ ◑ ♣ P 🚌 (579,560) 🌸 📶

Halifax: Siddal

Cross Keys 🅛
3 Whitegate, HX3 9AE
☎ (01422) 300348 🌐 crosskeyshalifax.co.uk
8 changing beers (sourced regionally; often Abbeydale, Salopian, Squawk) 🅷
This 17th-century tavern has a real traditional feel. There is a snug adjacent to the bar with an inglenook fireplace dividing the remaining area, and a small taproom to the rear. Walkers and cyclists are welcome. The walls display various beer mats from many now-closed breweries. Live music is featured on Sunday afternoon. Outside is a spacious, sheltered beer garden. Q ⬤ ♿ ♣ 🐕 🚌 (542,555) 🌸 📶

Halifax: Town Centre

Alex
17 Alexandra Street, HX1 1BS
☎ (01422) 341003 🌐 alexandrabeerhouse.co.uk
3 changing beers (sourced regionally; often Nightjar, Salopian, Squawk) 🅷
Extensively refurbished and extended in 2021, this town centre pub is modern and contemporary. The bar is on the ground floor with open plan seating, with additional seating upstairs. The jewel in the crown is the large rooftop terrace with stunning views of the architectural features of Halifax and Beacon Hill beyond. Three cask ales are served and eight craft beers. Q ♿ ≠ 🚌 🌸 📶

Grayston Unity 🅛
1-3 Wesley Court, HX1 1UH
☎ 07807 136520 🌐 thegraystonunity.co.uk

3 changing beers (sourced regionally; often Five Points, Northern Alechemy, Wilde Child) ⓗ
This bar is opposite Halifax's town hall in a Grade II listed building. It consists of a single room with a mixture of seating, leading to a covered backyard area with benches. Seating is available on the Town Hall terrace at weekends. The UK's smallest music venue, it hosts gigs, quizzes, talks and more. A bitter and a dark ale are always on tap, and it works hard to bring different breweries to the bar. Bring your own food or purchase its own pies and samosas. ⏰❀≉♣🖵❀🐾🎵

Kobenhavn ⓛ
6 Westgate Arcade, HX1 1DJ
9 changing beers (sourced nationally; often Brew York, Kirkstall, Vocation) ⓗ
This spacious, minimalistic, Scandinavian-style micropub opened in 2019. It has three tiered seating sections, a covered outdoor drinking area in the arcade itself. Six microbrewery beers are served and there are also 24 keg lines. A dark beer is always available on handpump, with several others, in a wide range of different beer styles, on keg. ≉🖵

Meandering Bear ⓛ
21-23 Union Street, HX1 1PR
☎ 07807 136520
Hawkshead Windermere Pale; 4 changing beers (sourced regionally; often Fallen, Goose Eye, Pig & Porter) ⓗ
Located close to Halifax Piece Hall and Westgate Arcade, this modern and tastefully decorated bar opened in 2019. Its name is derived from a time in 1913 when a large grizzly bear escaped from Halifax zoo and then wandered around the city before being caught. The classy room is split-level and incorporates comfortable seating, with the bar at the back on a higher level. Five beers are provided on handpump, and there are seven keg lines. Locally sourced bar food is available. ◖≉🖵🖵

Three Pigeons ★ ⓛ ✅
1 Sun Fold, HX1 2LX
☎ (01422) 347001
Ossett Yorkshire Brunette, Yorkshire Blonde; Rat White Rat; house beer (by Ossett); 4 changing beers (sourced nationally; often Fernandes, Jennings) ⓗ
A striking octagonal drinking lobby forms the hub from which five distinctive rooms radiate in this Art Deco pub, built in 1932 by Websters Brewery. Sensitively refurbished and maintained by Ossett Brewery, this venue attracts a variety of local groups and societies along with football and rugby enthusiasts. Three Ossett beers are always on, the fourth on a rota basis. Three guest beers also feature along with a stout or porter. Q❀≉♣🖵🖵❀🎵🔊

Victorian Craft Beer Café ⓛ
18-22 Powell Street, HX1 1LN
🌐 victorian.beer
10 changing beers (sourced nationally; often Squawk, Vocation) ⓗ
A popular award-winning pub behind the Victoria Theatre, opened in 2014 after a complete refurbishment of a once-popular Italian restaurant. It offers eight rotating real ales from nationally sourced microbreweries alongside 18 keg lines, a choice of world bottled beers, and two draught ciders. The main seating area has wooden floors and a tiled bar; to the left is a more secluded area and steps to an upper level with further seating. Many beer-themed events and tap takeovers take place (see website for details). ⏰≉🖵🎵🔊

Hanging Heaton

Hanging Heaton Cricket Club
Bennett Lane, WF17 6DB
☎ (01924) 461804 🌐 hangingheaton.play-cricket.com
Bradfield Farmers Ale; 3 changing beers ⓗ
A long-established, welcoming community sports and social club, twice local CAMRA Club of the Year and 2019 Yorkshire runner-up. The successful cricket team plays in the local league, and snooker is taken seriously, with two well-used snooker tables and frequent celebrity appearances. Four handpumps are cared for by the knowledgeable steward, who is enthusiastic about real ale. Well-chosen guest beers are mainly from Yorkshire breweries. There are no regular meals but pizzas are available (Fri-Sun 4-7pm). ⏰❀◐♣🖵(202)🎵🔊

Harecroft

Station Hotel ⓛ
122 Lane Side, BD15 0BP (on B6144)
☎ (01535) 272430
Timothy Taylor Landlord; 2 changing beers (sourced locally; often Bingley, Copper Dragon) ⓗ
Located in the heart of the small village of Harecroft on the B6144 between Bradford and Haworth, this traditional homely community pub is named after a station on the long-gone Great Northern Railway. It comprises two linked rooms with real fires and a games room, and is home to the local pool team. A jazz/swing band plays on Monday night. The local bus only runs until early evening and not at all on Sunday. ⏰❀♣🖵(K17)🐾🔊

Haworth

Fleece Inn ⓛ ✅
67 Main Street, BD22 8DA
☎ (01535) 642172 🌐 fleeceinnhaworth.co.uk
Timothy Taylor Boltmaker, Golden Best, Knowle Spring, Landlord, Landlord Dark; 1 changing beer (often Timothy Taylor) ⓗ
A stone-built coaching inn on Haworth's famous cobbled Main Street, with spectacular views over the Worth Valley and close to the Keighley & Worth Valley historic heritage railway. A cosy room to the right and a lower-level dining area offer quiet alternatives to the busy bar. Locally sourced food and accommodation are offered, and breakfast is available to all. The beer garden is three storeys up from the bar, on the roof. A Timothy Taylor tied house, popular with tourists and locals alike. ⏰❀🛏◐🚪♿▲≉(Keighley & Worth Valley)♣🖵🐾🎵

Heath

King's Arms ★ ⓛ ✅
Heath Common, WF1 5SL (at edge of village off A655 Wakefield-Normanton road)
☎ (01924) 377527 🌐 thekingsarmsheath.co.uk
Ossett Yorkshire Brunette, Yorkshire Blonde, Silver King; Rat White Rat; 3 changing beers ⓗ
The King's Arms, acquired by Clark's Brewery in 1989, is now leased to Ossett Brewery. Built in the early 1700s and converted into a public house in 1841, it has three oak-panelled rooms with gas lighting plus a conservatory and gardens to the rear. In the summer months you can sit outside and relax peacefully amid the acres of common grassland surrounding the area. A quiz is held on Tuesdays. Time may be called early on quieter evenings. Q⏰❀🛏◐♿♣🖵(188)🐾🎵

Hebden Bridge

Fox & Goose ⓛ ✓

7 Heptonstall Road, HX7 6AZ (at traffic lights on jct of A646 and Heptonstall Rd)

☎ (01422) 648052 ⊕ foxandgoose.org

Pictish Brewers Gold; 4 changing beers (sourced nationally; often Burton Bridge, Darkland, Eagles Crag) Ⓗ

West Yorkshire's first community co-operative pub extends a warm welcome to locals and visitors alike. A single bar serves three different rooms and an upstairs beer garden. The main bar is warmed by a roaring coal fire in winter, while the room to the left exhibits the work of artists from the area and often hosts live music. The room to the right has a dartboard. At least one vegan beer and one dark beer are always on tap. Do not miss the hillside beer garden with its great views. Monday is quiz night. Q❀♣●⋆☷🖵(590,592)🐾🐾🛜

Nightjar ⓛ

New Road, HX7 8AD

☎ (01422) 713015 ⊕ nightjarhebden.co.uk

House beer (by Nightjar); 2 changing beers (sourced nationally) Ⓗ

Opened in 2017 next door to the Picture House in Hebden Bridge, this is the tap for Nightjar Brew Co, the Mytholmroyd-based brewery. It serves three real ales, often two from its own brewery and a third usually from one of the many other small independent breweries. It is furnished in a flood-proof style, sensible after the recent floods, and is notable for its commitment to real ale and its friendly environment. Q➹♣●☷🖵(590,592)🐾🛜

Old Gate Bar & Restaurant ⓛ

1-5 Old Gate, HX7 8JP

☎ (01422) 843993 ⊕ oldgatehebden.co.uk

Vocation varies; 5 changing beers (sourced nationally) Ⓗ

A smart, modern downstairs bar and upstairs restaurant. The downstairs room has an impressive long copper-topped bar with 11 handpumps, one of which always dispenses a dark beer. Quality food is served all day. The bar area is furnished with a mixture of tables and chairs, benches and comfy sofas. The big picture windows and outside patio are great for people-watching. There is a comedy club on Friday evenings and occasional live music at weekends. Q🚳❀⓪➹●🐾🛜🖰

Holmfirth

Nook ⓛ ✓

7 Victoria Square, HD9 2DN (down alley behind Barclays bank)

☎ (01484) 682373 ⊕ thenookbrewhouse.co.uk

Nook Baby Blond, Best, Blond, Oat Stout; 2 changing beers (often Nook) Ⓗ

The Nook, properly the Rose & Crown, dates from 1754, and is a well-known real ale pub in the village. It has been dispensing beers from its own adjacent brewhouse since 2009, alongside occasional guest beers and Pure North ciders. Home-cooked food is served daily. There is a popular folk evening every Sunday, and real ale festivals both on the weekend before Easter and on the August bank holiday. The log fire is particularly warming on cold winter nights. 🚳❀⊠⓪♣●🖵🐾🛜🖰

Horbury

Boons Horbury ⓛ ✓

6 Queen Street, WF4 6LP (off B6128 Horbury-Ossett road, opp Co-op)

☎ (01924) 280442

Timothy Taylor Landlord; 7 changing beers (sourced regionally) Ⓗ

A popular community pub in the centre of town just off the High Street attracting people of all ages. The interior is based on a traditional layout around a central bar, with Rugby League memorabilia on the walls. Outside, there is a sizeable drinking area that is well used in summer. A guest cider is stocked. The pub has held a beer festival on the first weekend in June for many years. 🐾♣●🖵🛜

Cherry Tree Inn

Church Street, WF4 6LT

☎ (01924) 262916

House beer (by Horbury); 2 changing beers (sourced locally) Ⓗ

The Cherry Tree is home to the Horbury Ales Brewery, and as well as being a great place for cask ale it has a superb range of craft beers, fine wines, artisan gins, spirits and great coffee. It also serves fantastic chef-prepared food, from classic pub favourites to seasonal à la carte specials. 🐾⊠⓪🅿🖵🐾🛜🖰

Cricketers Arms ⓛ ✓

22 Cluntergate, WF4 5AG (a right fork off High St at its lower end)

☎ (01924) 267032

Timothy Taylor Landlord; house beer (by Elland); 6 changing beers (sourced regionally) Ⓗ

On the edge of the town centre, this former Melbourne/Tetley's pub is now a genuine free house, also stocking a range of craft and keg beers. It has a poker night on Monday, a quiz night on Wednesday and a meat raffle on Friday. Music is provided by way of an open mic night on the second Sunday and live music on the last Sunday of each month. The pub has won many awards including local CAMRA Pub of the Year. 🐾♣🅿🐾🛜

Horbury Junction

Calder Vale Hotel ⓛ

Millfield Road, WF4 5EB (from main A642 road follow signs through housing estate to Horbury jct industrial area; also walkable from canalside via tubular bridge)

6 changing beers (sourced locally; often Bad Seed, North Riding Brewery, Revolutions) Ⓗ

Established in 1874, this lovingly restored Victorian commercial hotel is steeped in local industrial history. Reopened in 2019, it is home to the Luddite Brewery. It boasts Yorkshire stone floors and log-burning fires, and has a delightful garden and nearby canal walks. Street-food weekends are held and occasional entertainment takes place in an upstairs room. Voted Yorkshire's most dog-friendly pub. Q🚳⓪🅵♣●🅿🖵🐾

Huddersfield

Cherry Tree ✓

14-18 John William Street, HD1 1BG

☎ (01484) 448190

Elland 1872 Porter; Greene King Abbot; Ruddles Best Bitter; 7 changing beers (sourced nationally; often Acorn, Saltaire, Sharp's) Ⓗ

Converted in 2001, this former bed shop is now a modern town-centre Wetherspoon outlet. The prosaic architecture is outshone by the range and quality of the ales. Alongside the permanent beers are seven changing guests, regularly from Saltaire, Leeds, Adnams, Naylor's, Acorn and Moorhouses's breweries. American craft beers on cask are an occasional feature at beer festivals. Three real ciders and one perry are always available. Food is served all day and alcoholic drinks from 9am. 🚳⓪🅵➹●🖵🛜

Grove 🅛

2 Spring Grove Street, HD1 4BP
☎ (01484) 430113 ⊕ thegrove.pub
16 changing beers (often Hawkshead, Mallinsons, Northern Monk) ⓗ

This establishment is the antithesis of everything mass market, with artwork, a snack range and live music that are unusual, to say the least. However, it is the array of 31 beers, lagers and a real cider that sets the place apart, including a confusion-inducing 19 handpulled ales. Ranging from table beers through IPAs to imperial stouts, there is something for all. In addition, there is a superb menu of 200-plus bottled beers and a comprehensive spirits range. The Grove is the area's must-visit pub.
Q🌑☆✿♣♠🍴🖵🐾🕯🛜

King's Head

St George's Square, HD1 1JF (in station buildings, on left when exiting station)
☎ (01484) 511058
Bradfield Farmers Blonde; Magic Rock Ringmaster; Timothy Taylor Golden Best, Landlord; 6 changing beers (sourced regionally; often Abbeydale, Oakham, Pictish) ⓗ

A friendly welcome always awaits at this award-winning pub. Situated in the Grade I-listed station and winner of a railway heritage award, the King's Head has been carefully restored, with features including a beautiful tiled floor, wood panelling and wood-burning stoves. It dispenses beers from breweries near and far, four of them permanent and six rotating. A mild and a dark beer are always on tap, as is one real cider. There is live music on Sunday afternoon, and hot food is served on match days. ◖✤♠🍴🖵🐾🛜🕯⏱

Rat & Ratchet 🅛 ✅

40 Chapel Hill, HD1 3EB (on A616 just off ring road; car park is at rear)
☎ (01484) 542400
Ossett Yorkshire Blonde, Silver King; Rat White Rat; King Rat; 9 changing beers (sourced regionally; often Acorn, Fernandes, Riverhead) ⓗ

A multi award-winning outlet owned by Ossett, with an on-site Rat microbrewery. Eleven handpumps offer beers from a range of breweries including its own, in addition to two permanent darks, alongside a good range of ciders and perries. The large main open-plan area still retains the feel of separate rooms. A further room at the back leads to the outside drinking area. There is a dartboard and a pinball machine. Live music is hosted on Tuesdays, Fridays and the first and third Sundays of the month, plus a quiz on Wednesdays, and regular beer festivals. 🌑☆✿♣♠🍴P🖵🐾🛜⏱

Sportsman ★ 🅛 ✅

1 St John's Road, HD1 5AY
☎ (01484) 421929
Timothy Taylor Boltmaker; 7 changing beers (sourced regionally; often Anthology, Three Blind Mice, Wilde Child) ⓗ

This 1930s pub, with a 1950s refit by Hammond's (note the windows), is a previous winner of the CAMRA/ English Heritage Conservation Award. The superb curved central bar has a parquet floor and an interesting wooden entrance. Eight ales are arranged in strength order. A dark beer is always available, along with two real ciders. Two rooms off are regularly used for meetings, such as poker, poetry and music clubs. A Meet the Brewer night is on the last Tuesday of the month.
🌑☆◖✤♠🍴🖵🐾🛜⏱

Idle

Idle Draper

28 The Green, BD10 9PX
☎ 07525 751574
3 changing beers (sourced regionally; often Bingley, Bone Idle, Parkway) ⓗ

Situated in the centre of Idle, this modern microbar is housed within the former Briggs draper's. A single room contains the bar on the ground floor with an additional lounge area above. The in-house Bone Idle Brewery is located in a converted barn to the rear, next to which is a beer garden. Three handpulls offer a varying range of real ales. The upstairs room and barn can be hired. The Bone Idle Men's Club meets every Wednesday evening.
🌑☆🖵

Ilkley

Flying Duck 🅛 ✅

16 Church Street, LS29 9DS (on A65)
☎ (01943) 609587 ⊕ theflyingduck.co.uk
Dark Horse Hetton Pale Ale; Rooster's Yankee; Wharfedale Black, Blonde, Best; 4 changing beers (sourced regionally; often Goose Eye, Ilkley, Rooster's) ⓗ

A beautifully refurbished Grade II-listed traditional inn close to the town centre. Originally constructed as a farmhouse in 1709, this it is reputed to be Ilkley's oldest pub building. It retains many original features including York stone and oak flooring, beamed ceilings, internal stonework and mullioned windows. Up to eight real ales, including four regulars, and two real ciders, are available. Wharfedale Brewery is located to the rear. Food is served Tuesday to Sunday and also on bank holiday Mondays.
🌑☆◖✤♠🍴🖵🐾🛜⏱

Keighley

Boltmakers Arms 🅛

117 East Parade, BD21 5HX
Timothy Taylor Boltmaker, Dark Mild, Golden Best, Knowle Spring, Landlord, Landlord Dark; 2 changing beers ⓗ

This classic town-centre pub remains the de facto Taylor's Brewery Tap. The tiny split-level layout adds to the character of the place. Brewery memorabilia adorn the walls. The panorama of the old Taylor's brewery above the bar is taken from an original kept at the brewery, and the mural in the upper level features the brewery's last cooper. The entire Taylor's core range is normally on offer. There is a fine selection of single malt and gins. Dominoes and playing cards are available on request behind the bar. Children welcome until 8pm.
☆✤♣🖵(662,60) 🐾🛜

Brown Cow 🅛

5 Cross Leeds Street, BD21 2LQ
☎ (01535) 382423
Timothy Taylor Boltmaker, Landlord; 5 changing beers ⓗ

A short walk from the town centre, this family-run free house is about quality, choice and the comfort of customers. Five guest beers come mainly from nearby micros, including at least one session beer, a strong one and a dark one. A quiz takes place on the second and last Wednesday of the month. A no bad language policy is in place. Local CAMRA Pub of the Year 2021.
Q🌑☆✿♠🍴P🖵🐾🛜

Ledsham

Chequers Inn L
Claypit Lane, LS25 5LP SE455297
☎ (01977) 683135 ⊕ thechequersinn.com
Leeds Best; Theakston Best Bitter; Timothy Taylor Landlord; house beer (by Brown Cow); 1 changing beer (sourced locally; often Brown Cow, Stod Fold) ⊞
Dating from the 16th century, this family-run pub is at the heart of the village close to All Saints church. It is handy for the Fairburn Ings RSPB reserve and walkers and dogs are welcome. The range of cask beers is mainly from Yorkshire breweries. Various low-beamed rooms lead off from the passageway, with real fires and cosy alcoves. The walls are decorated with old photographs. In the garden is a marquee used for events in the summer months. Q✿❀◑P🖪(175)♣✿🎐

Leeds: Burley

Cardigan Arms ★ L
364 Kirkstall Road, LS4 2HQ
☎ (0113) 226 3154 ⊕ cardiganarms.co.uk
Kirkstall Pale Ale, Three Swords, Dissolution IPA, Black Band Porter; 2 changing beers (sourced regionally; often Kirkstall, Track, Wylam) ⊞
Built in 1896 and named after the Cardigan family who owned land locally, this is a classic Grade II-listed Victorian pub, with four rooms off an L-shaped bar area. It reopened in 2017 as a Kirkstall Brewery outlet after an award-winning refurbishment; its fine woodwork, etched glass and ornamented ceilings are now revealed in their full glory. The refurb included the addition of period furniture and fittings including some splendid brewery mirrors and antique chandeliers. There is a first-floor function room. Q✿🍴◑❀👶♣🚆🖪✿🎐

Leeds: Chapel Allerton

Further North L
194 Harrogate Road, LS7 4NZ (200yds N of centre of Chapel Allerton)
☎ (0113) 237 0962
1 changing beer (sourced locally; often Kirkstall, North, Rooster's)
With a quirky retro look and feel, this is one of Leeds' first microbars. It is a welcoming, family-friendly, conversation-focused establishment with no TVs. There is an upstairs room free to hire for functions. Alongside the cask ale there are seven UK and continental draught beers and a fridge stocked with quality world beers. The food is a choice of cheeseboard or pies. During the summer the whole frontage can be opened up to give an alfresco vibe. 🍴👶♣✿🎐

Leeds: City Centre

Assembly Underground
Civic Court, Calverley Street, LS1 3AB
Vocation Bread & Butter; 3 changing beers (sourced locally; often Kirkstall, Vocation) ⊞
A clever refurbishment of the basement of a Grade II-listed building has created a food and drink hall in the heart of Leeds, which features a Vocation Brewery bar with 50 taps, street-food stalls, and a coffee bar. Bench seating is provided in the main area. The cask beers are from the taps at the right of the bar. There is a separate gin bar, the Staff Room, which is available for functions. Wheelchair access is at the rear on Alexander Street. 🍴◑👶🚆♥🖪✿🎐

Bankers Cat
29 Boar Lane, LS1 5DA
☎ (0113) 440 7998 ⊕ bankerscat.co.uk
Thornbridge Lord Marples, Jaipur IPA; house beer (by Thornbridge); 3 changing beers (often Buxton, Thornbridge, Wild Beer) ⊞
This Thornbridge Brewery bar opened in 2019. There is a variety of seating surrounding the central bar. To the right-hand side is a stained-glass window and a small library of books. Downstairs has additional seating in the old bank vault, which still has the vault door. Normally three regular and two changing Thornbridge beers are on tap plus a guest beer and at least one dark beer. 🚆🖪

Brunswick L
82 North Street, LS2 7PN
☎ (0113) 247 0546 ⊕ thebrunswick.co.uk
5 changing beers (sourced locally; often Kirkstall, Saltaire) ⊞
Approaching the Brunswick you can see its eyecatching exterior mural, and the modern vibe continues inside with handmade furniture, bare boards, an upstairs gallery/dining area, a function room in the loft and sometimes a DJ. Alongside the six handpumps, one of which dispenses cider, is a range of other beers on keg, and cans and bottles in the fridges. Coffee is available, and burgers, dirty fries, brunch and mega Sunday lunches are all on the menu. ◑👶🚆🖪✿🎐

Duck & Drake L
43 Kirkgate, LS2 7DR
☎ (0113) 245 5432 ⊕ duckndrake.co.uk
Brains Bitter; Bridgehouse Blonde; Rooster's Yankee; Theakston Old Peculier; Timothy Taylor Landlord; 10 changing beers (sourced locally; often Elland, Saltaire) ⊞
A fine example of a two-roomed Victorian corner pub, retaining some original features and traditional wooden flooring. The central bar sits in between both rooms. There is live music most nights from a small stage in the corner of the front room. On the back wall is a mural depicting many blues and rock legends, and there is music memorabilia throughout. ❀◑🚆🖪✿🎐🔊↻

Friends of Ham L
4-8 New Station Street, LS1 5DL
☎ (0113) 242 0275 ⊕ friendsofham.co.uk
Kirkstall Pale Ale; 1 changing beer (sourced locally) ⊞
Since opening in 2012 this bar and charcuterie has featured a wide range of interesting beers perfect for all tastes on its modern scaffolded bar. A large blackboard provides information on the current beers both in cask and keg. A three or six sampling tray of third pints is available, and two ciders are usually sold. Around the bar is a contemporary shabby-chic interior with diners and drinkers sharing the same space. The downstairs area hosts events such as beer tastings. ◑🚆♥🖪✿🎐 .

Head of Steam L
13 Mill Hill, LS1 5DQ
☎ (0113) 243 6618
Camerons Strongarm; Timothy Taylor Boltmaker; 6 changing beers (sourced locally; often Camerons, Ilkley, Wilde Child) ⊞
The central island bar is surrounded by a number of semi-separate seating areas. The handpumps on the bar dispense a range of cask beers, one of which is normally dark. There is also usually a cider on handpump, as well as many keg fonts serving beers from around the world. In the large fridges behind the bar there is an extensive range of bottles and cans. The walls are decorated with various beer-related paraphernalia. Regular live jazz sessions are staged. 🚆♥🖪✿🎐

Hop 🅛 ✅

Granary Wharf, Dark Neville Street, LS1 4BR
☎ (0113) 243 9854 ⊕ thehopleeds.co.uk
Ossett Yorkshire Blonde, Silver King, Excelsius; 6 changing beers (sourced locally; often Ilkley, Rat, Thornbridge) Ⓗ

Beneath the arches of Leeds station's platform 17, the Hop serves a range of cask ales, mainly from the Ossett family of brewers, together with several guest beers and also cider. The bar is surrounded by comfortable seating with bare brick walls decorated with murals and pictures depicting rock bands. The stairs on either side of the bar lead to another seating area which hosts regular live music. An unusual feature is the ground-floor cellar.
🏮🌑◗≠●🛋😸🎵🛜

North Bar 🅛

24 New Briggate, LS1 6NU
☎ (0113) 242 4540
3 changing beers (sourced locally; often Kirkstall, North) Ⓗ

A long, narrow bar which was one of the first in Leeds to showcase a wide range of both local and worldwide beers. Near the door there is a display area for artists' work and some seating. Further back is the bar along one wall with an array of beer fonts and fridges packed with bottles and cans from all over the world, while opposite it is more seating. Themed beer festivals are held at various times of the year. 🏮🌑◗≠●🛋🛜

Reliance 🅛

76-78 North Street, LS2 7PN
☎ (0113) 295 6060 ⊕ the-reliance.co.uk
House beer (by Acorn); 3 changing beers (sourced locally; often Magic Rock, Rooster's, Sunbeam) Ⓗ

Just outside the city centre, the Reliance is on a street corner, offering two bare-boarded rooms and a third on the mezzanine level predominantly for diners. It is simply furnished throughout, with local artists' and photographers' exhibitions adding to the informal drinking and dining experience. Food includes home-made charcuterie. Along with the cask ales and cider there is a great selection of traditional and modern bottled and canned beers and a range of fine wines.
🌳🏮🌑◗●🛋🛜

Scarbrough Hotel 🅛 ✅

Bishopgate Street, LS1 5DY
☎ (0113) 243 4590
St Austell Nicholson's Pale Ale; Tetley Bitter; 3 changing beers (sourced nationally; often Black Sheep, Sharp's, Wainwright) Ⓗ

A thriving ale house, the Scarbrough is possibly the most misspelt place in Leeds as it is named after its first owner, Henry Scarbrough, rather than the seaside town. The building, with its impressive tiled frontage, dates from 1765, becoming a pub in 1826. It provides a convenient place to wait for a train from Leeds station across the road. On the long bar facing the entrance is a range of cask ales from across the UK. 🏮🌑◗♿≠●🛋🛜

Tapped Leeds 🅛

51 Boar Lane, LS1 5EL
☎ (0113) 244 1953
10 changing beers (sourced nationally; often Kirkstall, Tapped Sheffield, Wild Beer) Ⓗ

A modern bar with large windows that open onto the street and a small seating area outside. To one side of the room is a microbrewery – two or three of the beers come either from here or the brewery at its sister pub on Sheffield station. A real-time online beer list shows details of the wide range available. Under-18s are welcome until 8pm, football shirts and scarves are not allowed, and there is a dress code for Friday and Saturday nights – no shorts or tracksuit bottoms.
🌳🏮🌑◗♿≠●🛋🛜

Templar 🅛 ✅

2 Templar Street, LS2 7NU
☎ (0113) 243 0318
House beer (by Tetley); 6 changing beers (sourced locally; often Bradfield, Greene King, Kirkstall) Ⓗ

Grade II listed, with fine wood panelling from 1928 and a splendid exterior with green and cream Burmantofts tiling, this is a traditional city-centre locals' pub. The bowing courtier logo can be seen in the leaded window panes that date from when it was a Melbourne Brewery establishment. The cask beers are mainly from Yorkshire, with one or two from the Greene King stable. The landlord and many of the staff have served here for over 30 years. League darts and dominoes are played.
≠♣🛋🛜

Town Hall Tavern 🅛 ✅

17 Westgate, LS1 2RA
☎ (0113) 244 0765
Timothy Taylor Dark Mild, Golden Best, Boltmaker, Knowle Spring, Landlord, Landlord Dark Ⓗ

Small, traditional inter-war pub dating from 1926 with a full range and a good reputation for its food menu. The single room has open alcoves to the left and right of the door and a semicircular bar along the left-hand wall. The decor includes circular copper-topped tables and old photographs of Leeds. Tables for dining can get booked up early on busy days, although the pub may close early if quiet, especially on Mondays. ◗≠●🛋🛜

Wapentake 🅛

92 Kirkgate, LS2 7DJ
☎ (0113) 243 6248 ⊕ wapentakeleeds.co.uk
4 changing beers (sourced locally; often Kirkstall, Nomadic, Sunbeam) Ⓗ

Wapentakes used to be the administrative subdivisions of the Yorkshire ridings. This bar, describing itself as a little piece of Yorkshire that welcomes grumpy old men, children and dogs, effortlessly attracts a wide age range and has generated a community feel. The beers are usually from smaller breweries in the area and normally include a dark brew. Eclectic framed prints and beer mats adorn the walls and there is a TV for sports events upstairs. Home-made food and cakes use locally sourced ingredients. 🌳🏮🌑≠●🛋😸🛜

Whitelock's Ale House ★ 🅛

Turk's Head Yard, LS1 6HB (off Briggate)
☎ (0113) 245 3950 ⊕ whitelocksleeds.com
Five Points Pale; Kirkstall Pale Ale; Theakston Old Peculier; Timothy Taylor Landlord; 1 changing beer (sourced locally; often Acorn, North) Ⓗ

Described by John Betjeman as the very heart of Leeds, Whitelock's dates from 1715 and occupies a long narrow yard. The interior is largely unchanged since 1895 and is a feast of mirrors, polished metal and woodwork, stained glass, iron pillars, and faience tiling. On the long, copper-topped bar is a well-chosen mixture of classic local beers and interesting ales from quality brewers further afield. The outside yard is shared with the Turk's Head bar.
🏮🌑≠🛋😸🛜

Leeds: Headingley

Arcadia Ale House 🅛

34 Arndale Centre, Otley Road, LS6 2UE (corner of Alma Rd)
☎ (0113) 274 5599

Timothy Taylor Boltmaker; 7 changing beers (sourced locally; often Kirkstall, Ridgeside) Ⓗ
An award-winning bar which is an important part of the beer scene in Headingley, with two ground-floor rooms and an upstairs mezzanine level. A mural of local landmarks features above the bar. Eight real ales are on handpull along with a range of canned, bottled and draught beers. There are always several vegan beer options. Also available is a wide selection of gins, some locally produced. Those under 18, large groups and fancy dress are not permitted. Dogs are positively encouraged. Q&⬤🖫🌢🤶🛜

Leeds: Holbeck

Grove Inn ⓛ
Back Row, LS11 5PL
☎ (0113) 244 2085 ⊕ thegroveinnleeds.co.uk
Daleside Blonde; 5 changing beers (sourced regionally; often Acorn, Moorhouse's, Settle) Ⓗ
A traditional West Yorkshire pub nestled among modern office blocks and a short walk from the city centre. Cask beers from both local and regional breweries are served to the public bar and the corridor. There are two small side rooms providing quiet away from the busier taproom. To the rear of the building is the Concert Room where a wide range of live music is performed and which has been, since 1962, the home of reputedly the oldest folk club in the country. ⬤🌢♣⬤🖫🤶🛜

Leeds: Hyde Park

Brudenell Social Club ⓛ
33 Queen's Road, LS6 1NY
☎ (0113) 275 2411 ⊕ brudenellsocialclub.co.uk
3 changing beers (sourced locally; often Kirkstall, Ossett) Ⓗ
A legendary gig venue which retains the feel of a working mens' club, the no-frills look belying a community-centred, family-friendly local with a lively atmosphere. The Brudenell hosts two live music rooms, a large lounge showing televised sports and a wood-panelled snooker and pool room with multiple tables. The menu comprises pies with all the trimmings and is frequently supplemented with food trucks in the car park. An annual beer festival is held in January. ⧖🌢⬤&♣⬤🖫(56)🤶🛜

Leeds: Kirkstall

Kirkstall Bridge Inn ⓛ
12 Bridge Road, LS5 3BW
☎ (0113) 278 4044 ⊕ kirkstallbridge.co.uk
Kirkstall Pale Ale, Three Swords, Dissolution IPA, Black Band Porter Ⓗ
A stone-built roadside pub with two floors and an extensive riverside beer garden. On the bars there is a range of Kirkstall Brewery cask ales and changing guests, with a selection of continental lagers and other beers on keg. Food is served every day, with booking advised for dining on a weekend. Frequent events include the annual Kirkstapalooza music and beer festival and a hugely popular bonfire night. A selection of board games is available. Dogs are welcome in the downstairs bar. ⬤🌢⬤♣P🖫🤶🛜

West End House ⓛ
26 Abbey Road, LS5 3HS
☎ (0113) 278 6332 ⊕ thewestendhouse.co.uk
3 changing beers (sourced nationally; often Brains, Marston's, Timothy Taylor) Ⓗ

First listed as a beer house in 1867, this busy local is just down the road from Kirkstall Abbey and the museum. The bar room shows sports TV, and food is served in the large lounge. On the bar there are four handpumps dispensing frequently changing cask ales and cider, along with foreign beers and drinks from a well-stocked fridge and wine rack. A small smoking area and drinking patio is outside. Regular quiz nights are held. ⬤🌢⧖⬤🖫🤶🛜

Leeds: Newlay

Abbey Inn ⓛ
99 Pollard Lane, LS13 1EQ (vehicle access from B6157 only)
☎ (0113) 258 1248
Leeds Pale; 8 changing beers (sourced locally; often Kirkstall, Ossett) Ⓗ
A stone-built former farmhouse dating from 1714, nestling between the River Aire and the Leeds-Liverpool canal. A local community pub, the Abbey showcases a selection of ales predominantly from the area, with pumps dedicated to dark ale and real cider. Also sold is a range of keg beers, wines and whiskies. Events include live music and quizzes. Ample seating outside attracts dog walkers and cyclists. Access is either by road from Pollard Lane, on foot over Pollard Bridge or along the canal from Kirkstall Forge station. ⧖🌢⬤&⧖♣⬤P🤶🛜

Linthwaite

Sair ⓛ ✓
139 Lane Top, HD7 5SG (top of Hoyle Ing, off A62)
☎ (01484) 842370
Linfit Bitter, Gold Medal, Special, Swift, Autumn Gold, Old Eli Ⓗ
Home of the Linfit Brewery, this traditional multi-roomed stone-built brewpub stands overlooking the Colne Valley. It represents the ultimate in LocAle, with up to 10 different beers brewed on-site, including three dark beers and a cider from Pure North. A central bar serves four rooms, each with a real fire, providing a popular meeting place for locals and visitors. It supports community events and is dog-friendly. A former National Pub of the Year. Q⬤♣⬤🖫🤶🛜↻

Liversedge

Black Bull ⓛ ✓
37 Halifax Road, WF15 6JR (on A649, close to A62)
☎ (01924) 403779
Ossett Yorkshire Blonde, Silver King, Excelsius; house beer (by Ossett); 5 changing beers (sourced nationally; often Goose Eye, Riverhead, Saltaire) Ⓗ
Ossett Brewery's first pub. The five rooms each have a unique style, including one dubbed the Chapel which has a high ceiling and reminders of local industrial heritage. Nine handpumps always offer a dark ale, plus guest beers from the group and wide-ranging independents. A regular Guide entry, the Black Bull is a popular, sociable community local with a warm welcome. Quiz night is on Tuesday, with darts and dominoes on Monday in the local league. A fine sheltered beer garden sits by a stream. Q⧖🌢&♣P🖫(254,254A)🤶🛜↻

Lockwood

Shoulder of Mutton
11 Neale Road, HD1 3TN
☎ (01484) 302838
6 changing beers (sourced nationally; often Abbeydale, Beartown, Oakham) Ⓗ

A well-run back-street local offering a decent selection of real ales from brewers including Abbeydale, Beartown and Oakham. It has a medium-sized bar with two snug rooms either side and a pool room upstairs. A CAMRA award winner, it is recognised as having a historic interior of regional importance, being little-changed since 1927. Easily reached by a regular bus service and close to Lockwood train station. Q☺▷✿≢♣♠P☐☼☕🔊

Longwood

Dusty Miller Inn Ⓛ ✅

2 Gilead Road, HD3 4XH

☎ 07946 589645 🌐 dustymillerlongwood.com

Milltown Weaver's Bitter, Platinum Blonde, Black Jack Porter; Timothy Taylor Landlord; 3 changing beers (often Brunswick, Milltown, Newby Wyke) Ⓗ

Local historic photographs adorn the walls and stone floors dominate at this pub, the Milltown Brewery tap. The cosy interior is open plan but has three distinct areas. From the benches outside there are great views up the Colne Valley. Seven real ales are served, showcasing the Milltown brews, alongside two changing guests, always including a dark beer, plus a permanent real cider. Locally made pies from Brosters Farm at Lindley Moor are served. Q☺▷♣♠☐(356)☼☕🔊

Marsden

Riverhead Brewery Tap Ⓛ ✅

Peel Street, HD7 6BR

☎ (01484) 844324 🌐 theriverheadmarsden.co.uk

Ossett Yorkshire Blonde, Silver King; Riverhead Butterley Bitter, March Haigh, Redbrook Premium; 5 changing beers Ⓗ

A modern brewpub owned by the Ossett Brewery, with the microbrewery visible from the main bar. Ten beers are served in all: up to six regular Riverhead beers and occasional specials, plus two from Ossett as well as guests. A dark beer and a real cider are also on offer. Upstairs there is a restaurant and another bar with comfy seating. Outside is a riverside terrace for alfresco drinking. A popular venue for locals and visitors, it gets busy on Saturdays. On the Real Ale Rail Trail. ☺✿▷❍♿≢♠P☐(185)☼☕🔊

Middlestown

Little Bull Ⓛ

72 New Road, WF4 4NR (on A642 at crossroads in centre of village)

☎ (01924) 726142 🌐 thelittlebull.co.uk

Abbeydale Deception; 2 changing beers (sourced locally) Ⓗ

This free house has been established since 1814. A single bar services a number of smaller rooms, with an open fire in colder weather. There is a gin bar on the last Saturday of the month. Meals are served throughout the week but times vary – Monday is fish night and Wednesday is pie night. All food is locally sourced and home cooked. A beer festival is held on the last weekend in July. The National Coal Mining Museum is nearby. ☺✿❍▷P☐(232,128)☼☕

Mirfield

Flowerpot Ⓛ ✅

65 Calder Road, WF14 8NN (over river, 400yds S of railway station)

☎ (01924) 496939

Ossett Yorkshire Blonde, Silver King, Excelsius; Rat White Rat; Riverhead Butterley Bitter; 4 changing beers (often Acorn, Fernandes, Riverhead) Ⓗ

An award-winning 1807 local with a typically sensitive, tasteful restoration by Ossett Brewery featuring an impressive tiled flowerpot as the centrepiece. It boasts four separate drinking areas and a real fire. There is a terrace and a fine riverside beer garden. Quiz night is Tuesday. Nine ales are offered from Ossett's five breweries and independents, usually including a mild or stout, plus a cider. It is on the Transpennine Real Ale Trail and holds occasional beer and cider festivals. Q✿❍≢♣♠P☐(261)☼☕🔊

Knowl Club Ⓛ ✅

17 Knowl Road, WF14 8DQ

☎ (01924) 493301 🌐 knowlclub.co.uk

Acorn Barnsley Bitter; Saltaire Blonde; 2 changing beers (sourced nationally) Ⓗ

The former Mirfield Liberal Club has been established for more that 130 years. It is an ideal place for a quiet pint and extends a friendly welcome both to its members and the public, holding both club and public house licences. A long well-furnished room houses the single bar, which offers up to four beers. There is also a private function room and a pool table downstairs, and a snooker room upstairs. The small car park at the rear is accessed down an adjacent narrow alley. ▷♿≢♣♠P☐☼☕🔊

Navigation Tavern Ⓛ ✅

6 Station Road, WF14 8NL (next to Mirfield railway station)

☎ (01924) 492476 🌐 navigationtavern.co.uk

Magic Rock High Wire, Ringmaster; Theakston Best Bitter, Lightfoot, Old Peculier; 3 changing beers (sourced nationally) Ⓗ

A family-run canalside free house, popular for its Theakston beers plus guests, all at keen prices. It features on the Transpennine Rail Ale Trail and hosts occasional fundraising events plus weekend live entertainment, and has active sports teams. Winter comfort is aided by a large wood-burning fire. Outside is a large, sheltered canalside beer garden with an open fire for cool days. Gourmet hotdogs are available plus sandwiches and pastries in the morning. ☺✿❍♿≢♣♠P☐☕🔊

Old Colonial

Dunbottle Lane, WF14 9JJ (off A644 up Church Lane, 1 mile NE of station)

☎ (01924) 496920

Copper Dragon Best Bitter; 3 changing beers (sourced regionally; often Stancill) Ⓗ

A former club offering a cosy retreat, with sofas around the fire and fascinating colonial memorabilia. A Royal British Legion memorial is in the prize-winning garden and local charities are well supported. The spacious conservatory is used for functions and meetings. Up to three guest beers come from a range of brewers and usually include a dark ale. High-quality and good-value meals are served Thursday to Saturday plus Sunday lunchtime. Opening times vary so ring ahead. ☺✿❍♿♠P☐(202,205)☕🔊

Norristhorpe

Rising Sun Ⓛ

254 Norristhorpe Lane, WF15 7AN (½ mile off A62)

☎ (01924) 400190

Abbeydale Moonshine; Acorn Barnsley Bitter; Saltaire Blonde; Timothy Taylor Landlord; 3 changing beers (sourced locally; often Bradfield, Copper Dragon, Hawkshead) Ⓗ

This village hostelry, under family ownership, is tastefully decorated, featuring a light and spacious bar and cosy lounge areas with exposed brickwork and real fires. The beer range is mainly from Yorkshire but with guests from local and national sources. Every Tuesday there is a popular quiz with prizes, also occasional live music, advertised on Facebook. The large well-maintained beer garden has plenty of seating and extensive views over the valley towards Mirfield and Emley Moor.
⏰✿♣🅿🚍(261) 🌟🛜🕒

Oakworth

Oakworth Social Club 🛇
Chapel Lane, BD22 7HY
☎ (01535) 643931
Goose Eye Chinook; Timothy Taylor Golden Best; 1 changing beer (sourced locally; often Saltaire) 🅗
Friendly and welcoming, this imposing Victorian building on the main thoroughfare was originally built as the Liberal Club in the late 19th century. Now a social club with a thriving membership, it has a comfortable front lounge and a back bar with traditional games and a TV. Upstairs, a third room caters for functions and meetings. Quiz night is Monday, and regular live music events are staged (see Facebook). Local CAMRA Club of the Year 2021. ⏰✿🅰🚶≈♣🅿🚍(K7,K10)🌟🛜🕒

Ossett

Bier Huis 🛇
17 Towngate, WF5 9BL (in shopping parade which backs onto bus station)
☎ (01924) 565121 🌐 bierhuis.co.uk
3 changing beers (sourced locally) 🅗
A specialist beer shop stocking over 500 bottled beers from many Yorkshire breweries and an extensive selection of foreign bottled beers, with an emphasis on Belgian and German beers. It has three changing draught beers and a wide range of draught ciders. Bottled beers can also be drunk on the premises. CAMRA branch Cider Pub of the Year in 2019. Q⏰🚶♿🍴🅿🍴🚍🛜

Brewers Pride 🛇 ✔
Low Mill Road, Healey, WF5 8ND (down Healey Rd from The Green, by Dimple Well Lodge hotel, and left at Matthews Foods)
☎ (01924) 273865
Ossett Yorkshire Blonde; Rat White Rat; Rudgate Ruby Mild; 6 changing beers (often Ossett) 🅗
Once found never forgotten, in what is now largely the Healey Mills industrial area on the outskirts of the town beside the River Calder. One of the best free houses around for many years, it was sold to Ossett Brewery in 2018 and is finding its feet after the transition from free to tied house. Good-value meals are served.
Q⏰✿🕭♣🍴🍴🚍(102,121) 🌟🛜

Otley

Black Horse 🛇
2 Westgate, LS21 3AS
☎ (01943) 466383 🌐 blackhorseotley.co.uk
Kirkstall Pale Ale, Three Swords, Dissolution IPA, Black Band Porter; 4 changing beers (sourced nationally; often Five Points, Hawkshead, Vocation) 🅗
An impressive corner building dating from the start of the 20th century with a Victorian-style interior. Refurbished in early 2019 with quality furniture, fittings and brewery mirrors, it is run as a partnership between Kirkstall Brewery and the Brudenell Social Club. The ornate

wooden bar has a range of Kirkstall beers, changing guest cask ales, and a good selection of keg beers on draught. There is a large covered outside seating area. Q⏰✿🕭🕭♿🍴🌟🛜

Old Cock 🛇
11-13 Crossgate, LS21 1AA
☎ (01943) 464424
Ilkley Mary Jane; Theakston Best Bitter; Timothy Taylor Landlord; 6 changing beers (sourced locally; often Brass Castle, Briscoe's, Five Towns) 🅗
An award-winning and genuine free house which has been cleverly converted from a former café in such a way that you would think it had been a pub for many years. There are two low-ceilinged rooms downstairs with stone-flagged floors and a further room upstairs. The guest ales are mostly from local breweries. At least two real ciders are also served, plus a good range of foreign beers. Frequent beer festivals are held. No admittance to under-18s. Q✿♿🍴🍴🌟🛜

Oxenhope

Bay Horse 🛇 ✔
20 Uppertown, BD22 9LN (on A6033)
☎ (01535) 642921
Moorhouse's White Witch, Pride of Pendle; Timothy Taylor Landlord; 4 changing beers (sourced regionally) 🅗
A friendly village inn that welcomes families and dogs. It has a pleasant single-bar setup with a real fire, a cosy room to the rear, and a separate seating area up a flight of steps. The guest beers come from local breweries such as Bowland, Goose Eye and Wishbone. Traditional ciders from Lilley's and Gwynt y Ddraig are also served. The pub is one of the main stopping points for the annual village charity Straw Race. Regular live music is a feature.
⏰✿≈♣🍴🅿🌟🛜

Dog & Gun Inn 🛇
Denholme Road, BD22 9SN
☎ (01535) 643159 🌐 dogandgunoxenhope.co.uk
Timothy Taylor Boltmaker, Golden Best, Knowle Spring, Landlord, Landlord Dark 🅗
One of the highest 17th century coaching inns in West Yorkshire. This traditional stone building has been sympathectially extended over the years. The emphasis is on food, but locals also support the pub for its real ale, warming open fire and good service. The pub hosts numerous charity events throughout the year. Private parties can be booked in the separate restaurant areas. In the Wells Restaurant to the right of the bar, you can see the original well through a glass floor panel.
⏰🍴🕭♿🅰🅿🚍(915) 🛜

Pontefract

Old Grocers 🛇
26 Beastfair, WF8 1AL
5 changing beers 🅗
A new micropub converted from a hair and beauty salon into a craft ale and gin bar, spread over the ground and first floor with seats for around 60 customers. The proprietor seeks to fill a niche market not currently served in the town with a good range of cask ales, cask cider and gins. It was also previously a grocery shop, hence the name. Q✿≈(Tanshelf)🍴🚍

Robin Hood 🛇
4 Wakefield Road, WF8 4HN (at town end jct of A645 Wakefield Rd with roads to Barnsley and Doncaster)
☎ (01977) 702231

Timothy Taylor Landlord; 9 changing beers (sourced regionally; often Henry Smith, Revolutions) Ⓗ Recently bought and totally refurbished by a local landlord, the Robin has been a pub since 1791 when it was owned by the Duchy of Lancaster. It is the home of the Henry Smith Brewery, named after the son of the present owner. A folk session is held on Sunday and live music on Thursday. The regulars are invited to choose the guest beers. There are two outside drinking areas. Q❀★&♣♠🖳❀

Pudsey

Fleece ⓁⓋ
100 Fartown, LS28 8LU
☎ (0113) 236 2748 ● fleecepudsey.co.uk
Tetley Bitter; Timothy Taylor Golden Best, Landlord; house beer (by Sunbeam); 1 changing beer (sourced locally; often Elland, North Riding Brewery, Stod Fold) Ⓗ
This community focused pub on the outskirts of Pudsey is a regular winner of CAMRA awards, which are proudly displayed in the entranceway. To the left of the front door is a small and basic taproom with a flagged floor, known as the Snug. To the right is the relatively large lounge with plenty of comfy settles around the perimeter. Look around and see how many film stars can you name or Laurels and Hardys you can spot! ❀♣P🖳❀

Manor Inn Ⓛ
Manor House Street, LS28 7BJ
Saltaire Blonde; 3 changing beers (sourced locally; often Brew York, North, Wishbone) Ⓗ
A modern, community-focused alehouse round the back of the town hall, this little pub packs a lot into its small proportions. The wooden-boarded single room has cushioned benches along one side and a bar along the other, with four pumps dispensing local and interesting ales. The fridge is packed with quality beverages, the walls have large (but only occasionally noisy) TVs for music and sport, sometimes there is live music, and all the time dogs are welcome. 🖳❀❀

Rastrick

Roundhill Inn ⓁⓋ
75 Clough Lane, HD6 3QL (400yds from A643/A6107 jct towards M62 motorway bridge)
☎ (01484) 713418 ● roundhillinn.co.uk
Bradfield Farmers Blonde; Sharp's Doom Bar; Timothy Taylor Golden Best, Landlord; house beer (by Ashover); 2 changing beers (sourced nationally) Ⓗ
A two-roomed genuine free house and locals' pub lying on the edge of Rastrick, easily reached by bus from Brighouse or Huddersfield. In daytimes during the week it operates as a private function venue, often hosting wakes as the crematorium in neighbouring Kirklees is nearby. Separate wheelchair access is provided (though staff need to be alerted) and accessible toilets are available through two doors. Q♣P🖳(547,549)❀❀

Rishworth

Booth Wood Inn Ⓛ
Oldham Road, HX6 4QU (on A672 towards Jct 22 of M62) SE034170
☎ (01422) 825600 ● boothwoodinn.co.uk
Bradfield Farmers Blonde; Joseph Holt Bitter; 3 changing beers (sourced locally; often Bradfield, Pennine, Salopian) Ⓗ
A traditional country pub and restaurant close to the scenic Yorkshire moors, on the A672. It has three rooms;

a ain bar, a restaurant and a snug. The bar area has stone floors with elevated barrel seating. All food is freshly prepared each day, with frequently changing daily specials and a value for money retro menu. The outside space is on three levels, the top two tiers covered and heated. ❀❀◑&P🖳(560)❀

Roberttown

New Inn ⓁⓋ
Roberttown Lane, WF15 7NP
☎ (01924) 500483 ● newinnroberttown.co.uk
Abbeydale Moonshine; Bradfield Farmers Blonde; Leeds Best; 3 changing beers (sourced nationally; often Sharp's) Ⓗ
A free house centrally located in Roberttown, originally a beer house. The talented licensees ensure that the inn sits at the heart of the local community. There is a main bar area, a cosy snug and a room suitable for functions. Outside is a sunny seating space and a covered smoking shelter. A popular quiz is hosted on Wednesdays, occasional live music at weekends, and an annual charity fundraising mini beer and cider festival. ❀❀♣♠P🖳(229,228)❀❀❀❀

Saltaire

Cap & Collar Ⓛ
4 Queens Road, BD18 4SJ
4 changing beers (sourced nationally; often Ilkley, Saltaire, Thornbridge) Ⓗ
Popular modern micropub with an open-plan café-style layout accommodating up to 35 customers. A beer garden with smoking area is at the rear. Four handpulls serve a varied range of real ales, many of them from local breweries, although some are from further afield. Real cider is dispensed on draught and there is a good selection of bottle-conditioned ales. Tap takeover events are held regularly and a homebrew club also meets here. Live music plays on Sunday afternoons and occasional evenings. Pub snacks are available. Dogs are permitted unless the pub is busy. Q❀❀❀≠♠🖳❀❀

Salt Cellar Ⓛ
192 Saltaire Road, BD18 3JF (on A657)
☎ (01274) 955051
House beer (by Bingley); 5 changing beers (sourced regionally; often Oaks, Small World, Stod Fold) Ⓗ
Traditional inn on the edge of the World Heritage Site of Saltaire village with a friendly, cosy feel. The two-roomed pub has a Victorian character, with comfortable seating, stained-glass partitions and bookshelves. Numerous pictures of old Saltaire adorn the walls. Six handpulls deliver a varying range of real ales from local and regional breweries, usually two blondes, two ambers and two dark beers. Closing time on Friday and Saturday may vary. ❀❀&≠P🖳❀❀❀

Sandal

Star Ⓥ
Standbridge Lane, WF2 7DY (nr Asda on A6186 which links A61 and A636)
☎ (01924) 255254
6 changing beers (sourced regionally; often Morton Collins) Ⓗ
A cosy pub dating from 1821 with a streamside beer garden, leased from Enterprise Inns by the Morton Collins Brewery, which has moved to the premises. Half the beers it serves come from Morton Collins, while most of the guests come from local breweries. It is a welcoming place with an open-plan layout and open fires in winter.

There is a function room for hire. Quiz night is on Tuesday, and a beer festival is held annually. Q👪❀◑♿♣P🚌(110)🐾📶

Sandbeds

Airedale Heifer [L] ✔

Bradford Road, BD20 5LY

☎ (01274) 515870 🌐 airedaleheifer.co.uk

Bridgehouse Blonde, Aired Ale, Porter, Holy Cow; 2 changing beers (often Bridgehouse) [H]

An extensive roadside hostelry with a substantial food presence, many dishes featuring the brewery's beers. It is the tap for Bridgehouse Brewery, situated in the car park behind. The pub is named after a famous heifer of the early 1800s, the heaviest cow in the UK (see the statue at the front). The open-plan layout has a single L-shaped bar and a sizeable south-facing garden with patio heaters. Children are welcome during the day, later if dining. 👪❀◑♿P🚌(662,K17)🐾📶

Shipley

Beehive

1 Saltaire Road, BD18 3HH (on A657)

☎ 07738 098330

6 changing beers (sourced regionally; often Abbeydale, North Riding Brewery) [H]

A stone-built former Hammond's outlet, built in 1870, reopened under new ownership in 2018. A traditional establishment, it comprises two semi open-plan ground-floor rooms, divided by a central bar, and a snug to the rear. Up to nine real ales and 11 local ciders are sold. It has a large beer garden to the rear, and a basement room that can be hired for functions and events. Closed for the first two weeks of January. Local CAMRA branch Cider Pub of the Year 2020. ❀🚆🍎P🚌🐾📶↺

Fox [L]

41 Briggate, BD17 7BP

☎ (01274) 594826 🌐 thefoxshipley.co.uk

BEEspoke Plan Bee, Shipley Stout; 4 changing beers (sourced regionally) [H]

A friendly independent café-bar with a single-room interior, simply but smartly furnished and featuring recycled church pews. Six handpulled ales include some from the in-house BEEspoke microbrewery. Real ciders, often from a local producer, are available, as is a wide range of international bottled beers. Live music takes place on Tuesday and Wednesday evenings, and frequently on Saturday nights, when the bar can get busy. A handy place to wait for a train as the station is close by. 👪❀♿🚆🍎🚌🐾📶

Hullabaloo

37-41 Westgate, BD18 3QX

☎ 07974 910838

4 changing beers (sourced regionally; often Magic Rock, Northern Monk, Wilde Child) [H]

A popular modern bar close to Shipley town centre and the bus interchange. Launched in 2017, it is mostly open plan but with four distinct areas in a variety of styles over split levels. Four handpumps serve a range of real ales, usually from regional brewers and often different from what you might find in other local pubs. A further handpump is dedicated to cider. Artisan craft beers are also available on six keg taps. Children are welcome. 👪◑🚆🍎🚌📶

Sir Norman Rae [L] ✔

Victoria House, Market Place, BD18 3QB

☎ (01274) 535290

Elland 1872 Porter; Greene King Abbot; Ruddles Best Bitter; 7 changing beers (sourced nationally; often Goose Eye, Wychwood) [H]

A typical conversion by Wetherspoon from a former Co-op department store, this large, open-plan pub is a popular feature in the town centre. Ten handpumps dispense real ale, comprising three regular beers and seven guests, often focusing on local breweries. Meet the Brewer nights are occasionally held. The good-value food on offer is from the usual Wetherspoon menu. The pub is nicknamed the Waiting Room due to its proximity to Shipley bus interchange; the railway station is also nearby. 👪◑♿🚆🚌📶

Slaithwaite

Commercial [L]

1 Carr Lane, HD7 5AN (village centre, off A62)

☎ (01484) 846258

Empire Moonrakers Mild; house beer (by Empire); 5 changing beers [H]

Since reopening in 2009, this free house has enjoyed deserved success. Nine handpumps provide ample variety; the keenly priced house beers are supplied by Empire Brewery and there are five rotating guest ales and a rotating guest cider. The Commercial is an essential stop for Transpennine Rail Ale Trailers and welcomes ramblers and dogs. Downstairs is an open-plan drinking area with the feel of separate rooms, and upstairs there is a pool room. Live sports are screened in the bar. ❀🚆♣🍎🚌🐾↺

South Elmsall

Barnsley Oak ✔

Mill Lane, Minsthorpe, WF9 2DT (on B6474, off A638)

☎ (01977) 643427

Black Sheep Best Bitter; 1 changing beer [H]

About a mile from the village centre, this is a thriving community pub run to high standards. Built in 1970 by the Barnsley Brewery Co, it has been smartly refurbished. Excellent-value food is served daily using locally sourced produce and is freshly prepared. There are good views of the Elm Valley from the conservatory. Quiz nights and TV sport are popular. Guest ales are usually from Yorkshire breweries. 👪❀◑♿P🚌

Sowerby Bridge

Hogs Head Brew House & Bar [L]

1 Stanley Street, HX6 2AH

☎ (01422) 836585 🌐 hogsheadbrewhouse.co.uk

Hogs Head Maltings Ale, 6 To 8 Weeks, White Hog, Hoppy Valley, Old Schnozzler; 3 changing beers (sourced regionally; often Goose Eye, Phoenix, Vocation) [H]

Close to the centre of Sowerby Bridge, this is is a former 18th-century malthouse which has been extensively renovated. The brewery is at the back of the building and can be viewed from the bar. Five core Hogs Head beers are on tap as well as guest ales. There is plenty of seating in the huge, sprawling bar area where snacks are also served. Additional seating is provided upstairs at weekends and there is an extensive covered outdoor area across from the pub. Q❀♿🚆🚌🐾📶↺

Hollins Mill [L]

12 Hollins Mill Lane, HX6 2QG

☎ (01422) 647410

Phoenix Hopsack; Timothy Taylor Golden Best, Boltmaker, Landlord; 6 changing beers (sourced regionally; often Oakham, Phoenix, Vocation) [H]

Converted from what used to be a joinery, this spacious open-plan local, beside the Rochdale Canal on the western side of the town centre, features exposed beams and floorboards. The main room is large and has an L-shaped bar. There is a small room in one corner used to host live folk music monthly on a Thursday. Upstairs is a smaller bar and a room available to book for meetings and entertainment. Q⊛&≢P🖳❀🎵🗢ʊ

Stanbury

Wuthering Heights Inn 🕒 ✪
Main Street, BD22 0HB (in village centre)
☎ (01535) 643332 ⊕ thewutheringheights.co.uk
Moorhouse's White Witch; Theakston Best Bitter; Timothy Taylor Landlord; 2 changing beers (sourced regionally; often Abbeydale, Bradfield) Ⓗ
Set in a farming village, this popular and friendly inn dates from 1763. Warmed by log-burners, the traditional main bar displays photographs showing the history of Stanbury. The cosy dining room has a Bronte theme, and there is a third room that can be booked for parties and meetings. The rear garden has spectacular views down the Worth Valley and a separate camping area (no caravans). There is a quiz every Thursday. Well-behaved dogs and children are welcome. ⊱⊛🏠🌗A♣P🖳❀🗢

Thackley

Black Rat 🕒
530 Leeds Road, BD10 8JH
☎ 07920 061671
4 changing beers (sourced regionally; often Millstone, Samuel Smith, Settle) Ⓗ
Previously a florists', this micropub (it has capacity for approximately 15 people) opened in 2016. A friendly welcome is assured and there is a cosy atmosphere. There is no music, TV or games machines – conversation and banter is key. The pub offers a varying selection of four real ales, primarily from Yorkshire breweries. Also stocked are two craft keg ciders, four boxed ciders and two craft lagers, along with a range of artisanal gins. Q🌗❀🖳❀

Thornhill Edge

Flatt Top 🕒
29 Albion Road, WF12 0HD (off B6117)
☎ (01924) 462883
Abbeydale Moonshine; Tetley Bitter; Wychwood Hobgoblin Ruby Ⓗ
An unusual castle-like building on the edge of a steep slope, affording excellent views. It is a free house, popular with locals and welcoming to visitors. Two ground-floor rooms serve as a public bar and a cosy lounge with character, while occasional functions are held on the lower ground floors. There is a large south-facing patio for enjoyment of the vista. The beer range may vary according to customer demand.
⊱⊛&♣P🖳(280) ❀🗢ʊ

Todmorden

Alehouse 🕒
52 Patmos, Burnley Road, OL14 5EY
☎ 07407 747956
Eagles Crag Pale Eagle; 3 changing beers (sourced locally) Ⓗ
Welcoming micropub with a community feel, in a row of shops set back from the road; the River Calder is culverted under the broad patio area. A wooden bar is at the rear of the single room, which features exposed brickwork. Food may be ordered from the neighbouring businesses. Four changing ales always include a dark option on the right-hand pump. ⊛≢❀🖳❀🗢

Pub
3 Brook Street, OL14 5AJ
☎ (01706) 812145
6 changing beers (sourced nationally) Ⓗ
Todmorden's first micropub opened in 2017 in a former café close to the market. The décor – exposed stone walls, reclaimed wood bar – enhances the simple layout, making the most of the limited space. There are 20 seats downstairs, and a flight of steep stone steps leads to another small seating area, as well as the toilets. Six handpumps serve a constantly changing range of beers, with full tasting notes on a chalkboard by the stairs. More than 30 UK distilled gins are stocked. Q≢🖳❀🗢

Upper Denby

George Inn 🕒 ✪
114 Denby Lane, HD8 8UE
☎ (01484) 861347 ⊕ thegeorgeinn-upperdenby.co.uk
Tetley Bitter; Timothy Taylor Landlord; 1 changing beer (often Acorn, Empire, Small World) Ⓗ
This family-run village inn is going from strength to strength since becoming a free house in late 2012, and is former winner of the local CAMRA Rural Pub of the Year. The pub hosts regular pie and pea walks, with a reward of home-made food at the end. Other entertainment includes jazz on a Thursday and folk on the first and third Mondays. Walkers and dogs are welcome, and families until early evening. Q⊱⊛🌗A♣P🖳❀🗢

Wakefield

Black Rock ✪
19 Cross Square, WF1 1PQ (between Bull Ring and top of Westgate)
☎ (01924) 375550
Oakham Citra; Tetley Bitter; 4 changing beers (sourced regionally) Ⓗ
An arched, tiled façade leads into this compact city-centre local, where a warm welcome is assured. The comfy interior includes photographs of old Wakefield. The Rock stands as one of the few proper pubs left in the middle of the clubs and bars of Westgate, and is popular with drinkers of all ages looking for a real pint. Customers are encouraged to suggest beers to try, with four regularly changing guest ales on the bar. There is a free function room for private use. Q≢(Westgate)🖳ʊ

Fernandes Brewery Tap & Bier Keller 🕒
5 Avison Yard, Kirkgate, WF1 1UA (turn right approx 100yds S of George St/Kirkgate jct nr Scartop Pine)
☎ (01924) 386348
Fernandes Polaris, Black Voodoo; Ossett Yorkshire Brunette, Yorkshire Blonde; 4 changing beers (sourced regionally; often Fernandes) Ⓗ
An Ossett Brewery tied house with Fernandes Brewery in the cellar. Eight handpulls dispense four Fernandes beers, two from Ossett, and two guest beers, and there are two bag-in-box ciders. The Bier Keller, which opens Friday and Saturday evenings, has premier foreign beers on keg plus a draught Ossett beer and one bag-in-box cider. There is a quiz on Wednesday evening, and folk music on the first Sunday of each month.
Q🌗≢(Kirkgate)❀🖳❀🗢ʊ

Harry's Bar 🄻

107B Westgate, WF1 1EL (turn right from Westgate station, cross road at traffic lights, and pub is at back of car park on right)

☎ (01924) 373773

House beer (by Five Towns); 7 changing beers (often North Riding Brewery) 🄷

This small, one-roomed pub is set in an alleyway just off Westgate. A bare-brick and wood interior and a real fire enhance the cosy establishment. In addition to the draught ales, a selection of bottled Belgian beers adds to the temptation. An extensive decking area has been added to the side. There is also a fantastic view of Wakefield's famous 99-arch viaduct – if only steam trains were a regular feature. Q✿&≷(Westgate)●P🖫🛜

Henry Boons 🄻 ✅

130 Westgate, WF2 9SR (200yds below railway bridge on Westgate)

☎ (01924) 378126

Rat White Rat; Timothy Taylor Boltmaker, Landlord; 3 changing beers (sourced regionally; often Blue Bee, Five Towns, Nook) 🄷

Quiet in the daytime, this pub gets busy in the evenings as it is on the Westgate run. It is the brewery tap for Clark's, which is behind the building. Hogsheads are used as tables, and there many items of breweriana, plus a thatched bar. The pub caters for drinkers of all ages and features live music. Two function rooms are available for hire. Most bus routes to the west of the city pass the door. &≷(Westgate)♣🖫🐾🛜

Wakefield Labour Club 🄻

18 Vicarage Street, WF1 1QX (at top of Kirkgate, round corner from Wakey Tavern)

☎ (01924) 215626 ⊕ theredshed.org.uk

5 changing beers (sourced regionally) 🄷

The Red Shed, as the club building is known, is a secondhand army hut that has been extensively refurbished, and is home to many union, community and charity groups. It has three rooms, two available to hire for functions. Quiz night is on Wednesday, there is occasional live music on the second Saturday, and open mic folk music night on the last Saturday of each month. There is an extensive collection of union plates and badges over the bar, as well as numerous CAMRA awards adorning the walls. Q🌣&≷(Kirkgate)♣P🖫🐾

Wibsey

Hooper Micropub 🄻

209 High Street, BD6 1JU

⊕ thehoopermicropub.co.uk

5 changing beers (sourced regionally; often Goose Eye, Moorhouse's, Salopian) 🄷

A cosy and friendly split-level micropub that has quickly established itself with local people in this urban village. The bar is on the upper level and there is comfortable seating in the lower part. Five handpulls offer a varying selection of beers, primarily from the Yorkshire region but also occasionally from further afield. Photographs of old Wibsey provide interest in an otherwise minimalist décor. Closing time may vary depending upon demand. Q🌣♣🖫🐾🛜

Broadfield, Sheffield: South, South Yorkshire (Photo: Dave Pickersgill)

NORTHERN ISLES

SHETLAND

HIGHLANDS & WESTERN ISLES

ABERDEEN & GRAMPIAN

TAYSIDE

LOCH LOMOND STIRLING & THE TROSSACHS

FIFE

ARGYLL & THE ISLES

GREATER GLASGOW & CLYDE

EDINBURGH & LOTHIANS

BORDERS

AYRSHIRE & ARRAN

DUMFRIES & GALLOWAY

NORTHUMBERLAND

TYNE & WEAR

NORTHERN IRELAND

CUMBRIA

DURHAM

ISLE OF MAN

NORTH YORKSHIRE

LANCASHIRE

EAST YORKS

WEST YORKS

MERSEYSIDE

GREATER MANCHESTER

SOUTH YORKS

CHESHIRE

DERBYSHIRE

NOTTINGHAM-SHIRE

LINCOLNSHIRE

NW WALES

NE WALES

SHROPSHIRE

STAFFORD-SHIRE

LEICESTERSHIRE

NORFOLK

MID WALES

HEREFORD-SHIRE

WEST MIDLANDS

WARWICK-SHIRE

NORTHAMPTON-SHIRE

CAMBRIDGE-SHIRE

SUFFOLK

WEST WALES

WORCESTER-SHIRE

BEDFORD-SHIRE

GLAMORGAN

GWENT

GLOUCS & BRISTOL

OXFORD-SHIRE

HERTFORD-SHIRE

ESSEX

WILTSHIRE

BERKSHIRE

GREATER LONDON

SURREY

KENT

SOMERSET

HAMPSHIRE

WEST SUSSEX

EAST SUSSEX

CHANNEL ISLANDS

DEVON

DORSET

ISLE OF WIGHT

CORNWALL

Wales

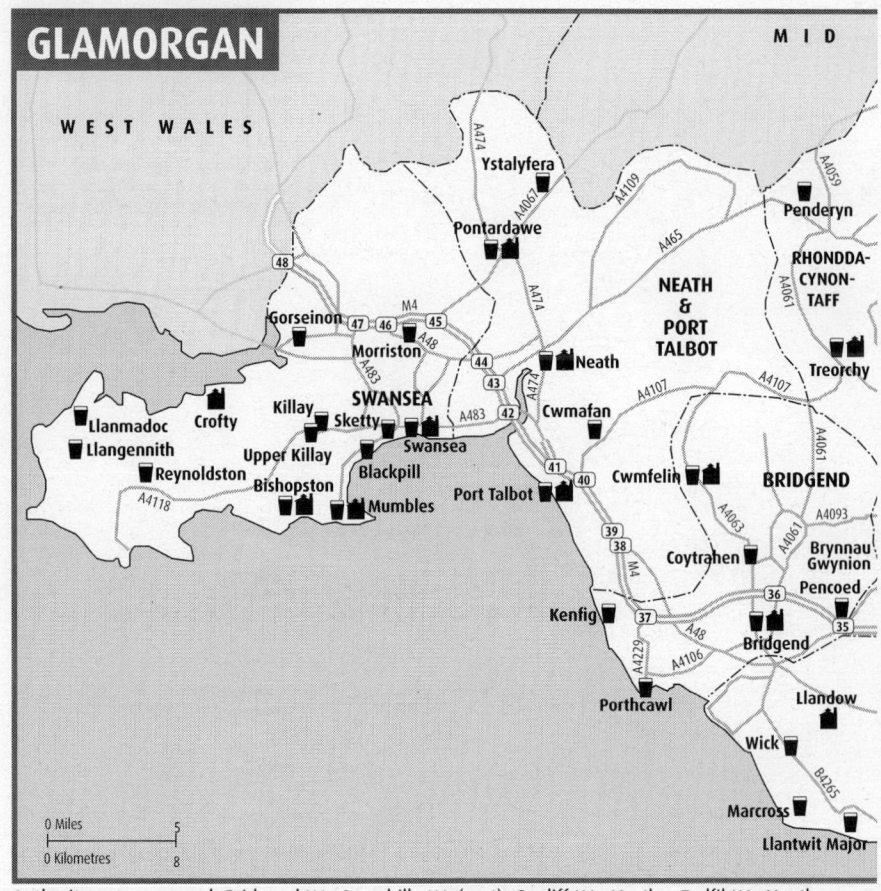

GLAMORGAN

MID

WEST WALES

Ystalyfera
Penderyn
Pontardawe
RHONDDA-
CYNON-
TAFF
NEATH
&
PORT
TALBOT
Gorseinon
Morriston
Neath
Treorchy
Killay
SWANSEA
Sketty
Crofty
Cwmafan
Llanmadoc
Swansea
Llangennith
Upper Killay
Cwmfelin
BRIDGEND
Reynoldston
Blackpill
Bishopston
Port Talbot
Mumbles
Coytrahen
Brynnau
Gwynion
Kenfig
Pencoed
Bridgend
Porthcawl
Llandow
Wick
Marcross
Llantwit Major

0 Miles   5
0 Kilometres   8

Authority areas covered: Bridgend UA, Caerphilly UA (part), Cardiff UA, Merthyr Tydfil UA, Neath & Port Talbot UA, Rhondda, Cynon & Taff UA, Swansea UA, Vale of Glamorgan UA

Aberdare

Ieuan ap Iago ✅
6 High Street, CF44 7AA
☎ (01685) 880080
Greene King Abbot; Ruddles Best Bitter; Sharp's Doom Bar; 4 changing beers (sourced nationally) Ⓗ
Popular edge of town Wetherspoon, formerly the main post office. Ieuan ap Iago (Evan James) is the author of the words of the Welsh national anthem Hen Wlad Fy Nhadau. Opposite stands a plaque comemorating his son Iago ap Ieuan, who wrote the music. Real cider is always available, together with a varied selection of national guest ales. Food is available daily. The pub is a modest stroll from the Dare Valley Country Park.
Ꝺ❀ⅅ&♿♠Ᵽ🖼🐾🛜

National Tap Ⓛ
Cross Street, CF44 7EG
☎ (01685) 267310 ⊕ greytreesbrewery.com
Grey Trees Caradog, Diggers Gold, Mosaic Pale Ale, Afghan Pale; 3 changing beers (sourced regionally; often Grey Trees, Purple Moose, Salopian) Ⓗ
New town micropub established in 2019. The first pub outlet for the award-winning Grey Trees Brewery, it has gained an excellent reputation for outstanding ales and value for money. Budweiser Budvar is stocked, plus a range of craft beer. One wall features a superbly detailed 1950s image of the bustling street outside, in tribute to the former National School the building once was.
Q❀≉♠🖼🐾🛜

Whitcombe Inn
Whitcombe Street, CF44 7DA
☎ (01685) 875106
Wye Valley Butty Bach; 2 changing beers (sourced nationally; often Sharp's) Ⓗ
Traditional and friendly street-corner local, close to the town centre. The single bar backs on to a pool area at the rear. Sport often plays on TV screens but is rarely obtrusive except on rugby international days. Children are welcome until 9pm. Live music is hosted occasionally. The pub is approximately one mile from the picturesque Dare Valley Country Park, offering great walks and also pitches for campers and touring vans.
Å≉♣♿🖼🐾🛜

Aberthin

Hare & Hounds
Aberthin Road, CF71 7LG
☎ (01446) 774892 ⊕ hareandhoundsaberthin.com
Hancocks HB; Wye Valley HPA; 2 changing beers (sourced regionally; often Glamorgan) Ⓗ
A characterful village pub with a cosy public bar with thick stone walls, wooden beams and log fire where the

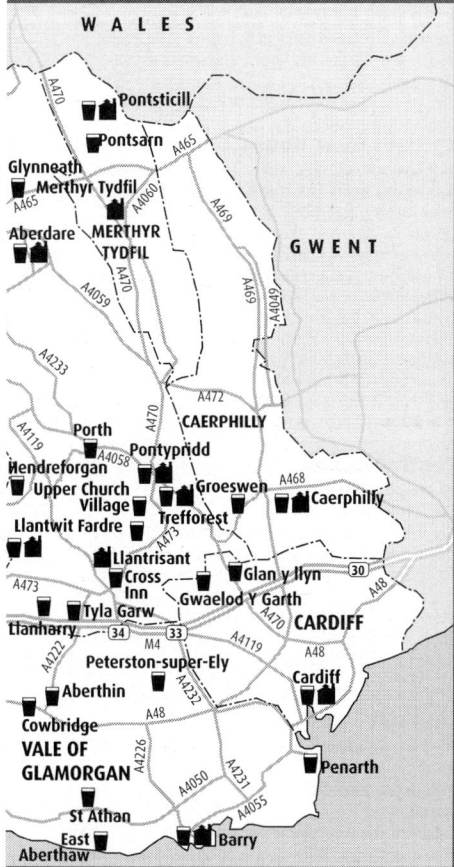

10 changing beers (sourced nationally; often Box Steam, Grey Trees, Mumbles) G
Formerly a shop, converted in 2017, this is a single room with no bar – customers are served at their tables, with blackboards showing what's on offer. Up to eight predominantly Welsh cask ales on gravity, two craft keg beers and more than a dozen real ciders are available. The licensee is a fan of The Jam – the pub is named after one of the band's songs – and memorabilia includes a series of tiles in the toilet. Winner of SME National Business Awards Pub of the Year in 2019.
Q&♿➔(Docks) ●🚆🐾🐾🛜

Bishopston

Joiners Arms L
50 Bishopston Road, SA3 3EJ
☎ (01792) 232658 ⊕ thejoiners.info
Courage Best Bitter; Marston's Pedigree; Swansea Bishopswood Bitter, Three Cliffs Gold, Original Wood; 1 changing beer (sourced nationally) H
Situated in the heart of the village, this 1860s free house remains popular with locals and visitors. Home of the Swansea Brewing Company, the six cask handpumps are in the rear area of the bar. Good-value food is served lunchtimes and evenings (no food Mon and Sun eve) and there are occasional music events, usually around public holidays. Major sporting fixtures are shown on large screens. There is a small car park. ᗺ🍴🕙➤♣🅿🚆(14)🐾🛜

Blackpill

Woodman ✪
120 Mumbles Road, SA3 5AS (near turn-off for B4436, opp Blackpill Lido)
☎ (01792) 402700

locals gather. The rustic dining area serves award-winning high-quality fare, with some ingredients grown by the chef. A full menu is also available in the bar. The guest ales are mainly local, the ciders are from Llanblethian Orchards. Outside, the beer garden has its own bar shack and occasionally hosts live music. There is limited parking at the front of pub.
Q᠅🕙❀♿♣●🅿🚆(321) 🐾🛜

Barry

Barry West End Club L
54 St Nicholas Road, CF62 6QY
☎ (01446) 735739 ⊕ barrywestendclub.webs.com
Sharp's Doom Bar; Wye Valley HPA; 2 changing beers H
Frequent local CAMRA branch Club of the Year, housed in a large multi-floored red-brick building overlooking the old harbour. Visitors are welcome and CAMRA members treated as honorary club members. Home to cricket, football, snooker and skittles teams as well as chess, scuba diving and fishing clubs, among others, there is always something going on here. Two beer festivals a year, live music at the weekend, pub grub and a friendly atmosphere makes this club an essential visit.
Q᠅🕙❀♿➔♣●🚆🛜

Butterfly Collector
50A Holton Road, CF63 4HE
☎ 07542 673794

REAL ALE BREWERIES

Bang-On ✦ Bridgend
Borough Arms 🍺 Neath
Boss ✦ Swansea
Brains Cardiff
Brew Monster ✦ Caerphilly
Brewhouse & Kitchen 🍺 Cardiff
Cerddin 🍺 Cwmfelin
Coach 🍺 Bridgend
Cold Black Label Bridgend
Crafty Dragon Pontsticill
Cwm Rhondda Treorchy (brewing suspended)
Dog's Window Bridgend
Freetime Swansea
Glamorgan Llantrisant
Gower Crofty
Grey Trees Aberdare
Little Goat Pontardawe
Mabby 🍺 Trefforest
Mountain Hare 🍺 Brynnau Gwynion
Mumbles Swansea
Neath Port Talbot
Pilot Brewery 🍺 Mumbles
Pipes Cardiff
Swansea 🍺 Swansea: Bishopston
Tomos a Lilford Llandow
Tomos Watkin ✦ Swansea
Twin Taff Merthyr Tydfil (brewing suspended)
Twt Lol Pontypridd
VOG Barry
Well Drawn ✦ Caerphilly
Zepto Caerphilly (brewing suspended)
Zerodegrees 🍺 Cardiff

Greene King IPA, Abbot; 3 changing beers (sourced nationally; often Greene King, Mumbles, Tomos Watkin) ⊞

Historic pub and restaurant dating back to 1819 and attractively refurbished. The deceptively spacious establishment, with its various nooks and alcoves, is on the main seafront road by the entrance to the beautiful Clyne Gardens. Popular with families and diners, the pub also welcomes those seeking only liquid refreshment. A changing range of ales is offered, including at least one from a local brewery. There are three outside seating areas including a small beer garden.
ᐁ❀◑♿P☐(2,2A) ♣🐾

Bridgend

Coach
37 Cowbridge Road, CF31 3DH
Coach Bridgend Pale Ale ⊞**; 5 changing beers (often Grey Trees, New Bristol, Thornbridge)** ⊞/🄶

An incredible commitment to real ale, cider and independent producers has been the basis for the running of this pub since the current owners took it on. Basically furnished but comfortable, there is an art wall for local artists to display their work. Events include open mic nights, outings and two beer festivals a year. The owners began brewing in 2018 – the brewery is visible from inside the pub – and one Coach cask beer is usually on handpump. Q ᐁ❀🐾≉♣●☐(303,X2)♣🐾

Brynnau Gwynion

Mountain Hare
Brynna Road, CF35 6PG
☎ (01656) 860453
Wickwar BOB; 3 changing beers (sourced nationally; often Glamorgan, St Austell, Salopian) ⊞

This typical Welsh village inn has featured in the Guide for more than 10 years. It is also a brewpub – the licensee began brewing on-site in 2014 and conjures up some tasty treats. The inn has been owned by the same family for over 40 years and has a traditional public bar, games room and a lovely old stone-walled lounge. Sport is often on TV in this rugby lovers' venue. Staff and locals are most welcoming to visitors.
Q ᐁ❀◑♿♣●P☐(64,404) ♣🐾

Caerphilly

Malcolm Uphill ✅
89-91 Cardiff Road, CF83 1FQ
☎ (029) 2076 0720
Greene King Abbot; Ruddles Best Bitter; Sharp's Doom Bar; 2 changing beers (sourced nationally) ⊞

Popular Wetherspoon at the top of the town, close to the main transport hub. It usually has one or two guest beers, particularly at the weekend, and up to two ciders, often including Gwynt y Ddraig Black Dragon. The pub can be crowded towards the weekend, and hosts a popular quiz on quieter Sundays. Ring the main entrance doorbell if the separate accessible entrance is needed.
Q ᐁ◑♿≉●☐🐾

Cardiff

Andrew Buchan
29 Albany Road, Roath, CF24 3LH
Rhymney Hobby Horse, Dark, Bitter, Export; 1 changing beer (sourced locally; often Rhymney) ⊞

The only regular outlet in Cardiff for the award-winning Rhymney Brewery. This converted shop on the corner of a busy suburban street has a long, narrow bar. The front area is a cosy lounge with sofas and an open fire, while the rear space hosts frequent live acoustic sessions. Since its opening, the pub has forged strong links with the local community, and supplied a take-away service through the pandemic lockdowns. ❀♿≉(Cathays)●☐🐾🐾

Cathays Beer House
109 Crwys Road, CF24 4NF
4 changing beers (sourced nationally; often Bristol Beer Factory, Liverpool) 🄶

Now in its third year, this quirky family-run micropub, with a welcoming, friendly atmosphere, has developed a loyal following among locals and students. A former post office, the decor and seating are no-frills, with tractor-style seats at the bar and a tank of exotic fish. The bar offers ever-changing beers served on gravity plus around 100 bottled and canned beers. A range of harder-to-find bag-in-box ciders has earned it a local CAMRA branch Cider Pub of the Year award.
Q ᐁ❀♿≉(Cathays) ●☐🐾🐾

Central Bar ✅
39 Windsor Place, CF10 3BW
☎ (029) 2078 0260
Greene King Abbot; Ruddles Best Bitter; Sharp's Doom Bar; 5 changing beers (sourced nationally) ⊞

A popular Wetherspoon pub just off Queen Street near its eastern end. This former night club has an upper storey used as an additional bar, open most times. There is an outdoor drinking area at the rear. The bar usually has the full range of up to five guest beers, as well as a number of real ciders or perries. ᐁ❀◑♿≉(Queen St)●☐🐾

Deri ✅
Heol-y-Deri, Rhiwbina, CF14 6UH
☎ (029) 2062 6237
4 changing beers (often Fuller's, Greene King, St Austell) ⊞

Suburban pub with a large car park and pleasant outside area, popular and often busy around mealtimes. The internal space is divided into distinct areas. Quizzes are hosted, when no restrictions apply, twice a week. It has an outside covered smoking area. The beer range may increase when trade justifies it. There is background music and a TV in the bar area. Q ᐁ❀◑♿P☐🐾

Flute & Tankard
4 Windsor Place, CF10 3BX
☎ (029) 2039 8315 ⊕ thefluteandtankard.com
4 changing beers (sourced nationally; often Grey Trees) ⊞

You will find this quiet and comfortable pub just off the eastern end of Queen Street. It is just the ticket for anyone wanting a break from the hustle-bustle of city-centre activity. The range of four regularly changing real ales can come from anywhere within the UK, with beers from west Wales often featured. Enjoy the live events in the upstairs function room most weekday evenings.
Q ❀≉(Queen St) ●

Grange
134 Penarth Road, CF11 6NJ
☎ (029) 2025 0669
4 changing beers (sourced nationally; often Brecon, Grey Trees) ⊞

Welcoming community establishment run by the same management team that runs the Lansdowne, both award-winning outlets. The emphasis is on quality real ales and home-made food, and the pub seeks to provide an outlet for new small breweries. The interior is divided into two rooms with simple and functional decor, both served from a central bar. A traditional skittle alley adds to the attraction. Q ᐁ❀◑≉(Grangetown)♣●☐

Head of Steam

18-19 Church Street, CF10 1BG
☎ (029) 2037 2582
Camerons Strongarm; 5 changing beers (sourced nationally; often Castle Rock, Hydes) H
Only a few minutes' walk from the main Central railway station. Now established as part of Cardiff's 'pub mile', it offers a good range of cask and craft ales, with a range of Belgian/German beers providing further choice. It has a central island bar with seating around it, booths down one side and tables down the other. There is more seating in an area upstairs. ◆◆≠(Central)◆◆◆

Heathcock

58-60 Bridge Street, Llandaff, CF5 2EN
☎ (029) 2115 2290 ⊕ heathcockcardiff.com
Glamorgan Cwrw Gorslas/Bluestone Bitter; Wye Valley HPA; 3 changing beers (sourced regionally) H
Revived roadside pub on the northern approach to Llandaff City with its cathedral and medieval ruins of the former bishop's palace. A central bar serves an adjoining public bar, lounge and pleasant outdoor area at the rear. The bar is cosy and traditional, with a small fireplace and a mix of furniture. The lounge is spacious and doubles as a dining room, albeit with a TV. ◆◆◆(25)◆◆

Lansdowne

71 Beda Road, CF5 1LX
☎ (029) 2022 1312
5 changing beers (sourced regionally; often Grey Trees) H
An award-winning community pub with an open-plan layout and a central bar area, divided into three distinct areas. Five handpumps serve one dark beer and one local ale, with the remainder dedicated to independent brewers, often rare for the area. At least one keg beer from a local craft brewery is also offered, along with a traditional cider. A beer festival is held in mid-June. The pub is popular with families and serves good-quality food including Sunday lunches.
◆◆◆◆≠(Ninian Park) ◆◆◆(96,X2) ◆

Pen & Wig ✓

1 Park Grove, CF10 3BJ
☎ (029) 2037 1217
8 changing beers (sourced nationally; often Bristol Beer Factory, Grey Trees, Mumbles) H
Converted large Victorian terraced residence, just off the city centre and near the university and National Museum. The clientele is typically professionals and office workers during the day, students in the evening. The beer range comes from local, regional and national breweries. Monthly Meet the Brewer events and brewery takeovers are held. The large garden includes a covered section and a smokers' area. Prices are at the higher end for the area. ◆◆◆≠(Queen St) ◆◆◆◆

Queen's Vaults

29 Westgate Street, CF10 1EH
☎ (029) 2022 7966
Felinfoel Double Dragon; 5 changing beers H
Busy city-centre pub offering good-value drinks and food. It has a raised lounge/dining area at the front, pool tables and darts towards the rear. Sport shown on several TVs is occasionally noisy but can be muted or replaced by music at times. Real cider is featured, and the place has been a cider pub award-winner in recent years. ◆◆◆≠◆◆◆

Romilly L ✓

69-71 Romilly Crescent, CF11 9NQ
☎ (029) 2025 6345

Brains Bitter, SA, Rev James; 1 changing beer (sourced nationally; often Brains, Marston's) H
A comfortable locals' haunt with a variety of interconnecting rooms served by a single bar, with a darts area towards the front. Antique-style prints adorn the walls. Outside, there is a front forecourt and a larger garden at the rear. Live music is hosted on Tuesday, a quiz on Sunday. Now run by Marston's following its deal with Brains, the pub's lessees recently celebrated their 20th anniversary. It is CAMRA-accredited for serving consistently well-kept real ales. ◆◆◆◆◆◆(61)

St Canna's Ale House

42 Llandaff Road, CF11 9NJ
☎ 07890 106449
6 changing beers (sourced nationally; often Grey Trees, Tiny Rebel, Untapped) G
Micropub just off Cowbridge Road East, with two distinct rooms and a recently enhanced outdoor area. It serves up to six real ales on cooled gravity stillage, and four real ciders. The pub is community-focused and hosts regular activities such as tap takeovers, open mic nights and street food events. It has a piano and traditional board games to play. The yard, reached via a second room, has a covered smoking area. A take-away service was provided throughout the lockdowns.
Q◆◆◆◆≠(Ninian Park) ◆◆◆(17,18) ◆

Tiny Rebel

26 Westgate Street, CF10 1DD
☎ (029) 2039 9557 ⊕ tinyrebel.co.uk/bars/cardiff
Tiny Rebel Cwtch, Fubar, Juicy, Stay Puft; 4 changing beers (sourced nationally; often Bristol Beer Factory, Thornbridge) H
Multi-room city-centre pub in a historic building opposite the Principality Stadium. It is the Cardiff outlet for Tiny Rebel beers in cask and keg form, along with guest beers. Four further handpumps offer ciders and perries. There are several rooms upstairs and downstairs, decorated in Tiny Rebel's unique style – some available for private hire. The pub holds regular quiz nights, bring your own vinyl nights and board game nights, as well as occasional brewery tap takeovers.
◆◆◆≠(Central) ◆◆◆

Cowbridge

1 Town Hall Square

1 Town Hall Square, CF71 7DD
⊕ 1townhallsquare.com
Wye Valley Butty Bach H**; 3 changing beers (sourced nationally; often Coach, Grey Trees, Thornbridge)** H/G
This 2017 addition to the local beer scene is aimed squarely at real ale enthusiasts. The small bar has seating off it while upstairs are another two rooms. The decor is traditional, with exposed stonework, tiled and wooden floors, and low beams. The entrance courtyard is a suntrap. No food is served but customers are welcome to bring their own. Butty Bach may be substituted by a beer from the Coach brewpub in Bridgend, which is under the same ownership. ◆◆◆◆(X2,321)◆◆

Vale of Glamorgan Inn

51 High Street, CF71 7AE
☎ (01446) 772252
Glamorgan Jemimas Pitchfork; Hancocks HB; Wye Valley HPA, Butty Bach; 2 changing beers (sourced nationally; often Grey Trees, Salopian, VOG) H
Popular single-room pub where conversation is the main entertainment. The wooden-floored bar has a warming range fire; to the rear is a flagstone-floored area with another stove. Photographs and pictures of local interest

adorn the walls. Outside is an attractive enclosed garden with a separate covered and heated smoking area. A now well-established annual beer festival coincides with the town's food and drink festival in May. Good-value home-made food is served at lunchtime (no food Sun). Real cider may sometimes be available. Q ► ✿ ◑ ● ☷ (X2,321) ☙ ☎

Coytrahen

Nicholls Arms
Nicholls Road, CF32 0ED
☎ (01656) 724680
1 changing beer (often Sharp's, Wye Valley) ⊞

Grade II-listed building on the Bridgend to Maesteg road. The truly stunning interior features wood-panelled and exposed stone walls, brass, paintings, a superb collection of Spode plates, and photographs commemorating the area's mining history. Seating includes luxurious old leather armchairs and settees. There is no music, games or TV. A friendly group of locals regularly enjoys the quality meals served in the dining room. Beers may change. Q ► ✿ ◑ ♠ P ☷ (70,71) ☙ ☎

Cross Inn

Cross Inn Hotel ⊘
Main Road, CF72 8AZ
☎ (01443) 223431
Hancocks HB; Wye Valley HPA; 2 changing beers (sourced nationally) ⊞

A welcoming, traditional pub which is popular with locals and visitors alike. Immaculately maintained throughout, the large single room is divided into a bar area and a comfortable lounge in which home-prepared meals are served. Sunday lunches are popular, as are themed food nights including cheese and grazing board evenings (booking recommended). There is a large car park at the rear. Q ✿ ◑ ♿ ♠ P ☷ ☙ ☎

Cwmafan

Brit ⫩ ⊘
London Row, SA12 9AH
☎ (01639) 680247 ⊕ thebrit.wales
3 changing beers (sourced regionally; often Grey Trees, Cold Black Label) ⊞

Built in 1845 and formerly known as Britannia Inn, this cosy, dog-friendly establishment was local CAMRA Pub of the Year 2019. It has a relaxed atmosphere with rustic, quirky surroundings. It serves three rotating ales, often sourced locally, plus a real cider. The pub hosts summer and winter beer festivals and is also noted for its good food. Accommodation includes three bunk rooms plus a double en-suite, ideal for the Afan Valley mountain bikers. May occasionally close on a Monday in January and February. Q ► ✿ ⇌ ◑ ♿ ● P ☷ (81) ☙ ☎

Cwmfelin

Cross Inn
Maesteg Road, CF34 9LB
☎ (01656) 732476
Cerddin Solar, Cascade; 3 changing beers (often Cerddin) ⊞

Multiple local CAMRA Pub of the Year winner and home to the Cerddin Brewery, this is a must-visit pub. The traditional two-roomed Valleys inn offers a warm welcome, with friendly locals and knowledgeable staff. Alongside the five cask beers, a range of bottle-conditioned beers is also available. There is a patio area outside the brewery. The Tuesday night quiz raises

money for the local food bank. Two-times winner of CAMRA South Wales Regional Pub of the Year. Q ✿ ⇌ (Garth) ♠ ● ♿ ☷ (71) ☙ ☎

East Aberthaw

Blue Anchor
CF62 3DD
☎ (01446) 750329 ⊕ blueanchoraberthaw.com
Brains Bitter; Theakston Old Peculier; Wadworth 6X; Wye Valley HPA; 1 changing beer (often Tomos Watkin) ⊞

Dating from 1380, this attractive thatched pub has been in the same family for over 75 years. Its thick stone walls house a labyrinth of rooms, with stone floors, wooden beams and open fires adding to the character and making the pub a popular stop-off for visitors to the area. Up to five ales and award-winning food are served in the bar and upstairs restaurant. The guest beer and cider are often locally produced. Q ► ✿ ◑ ● P ☷ (303) ☙

Glan y llyn

Fagins Craft Beer House & Art Café ⫩
9 Cardiff Road, CF15 7QD
☎ (029) 2081 1800
3 changing beers (sourced regionally; often Grey Trees, Twt Lol) ⊞

Quiet pub with a warm, friendly atmosphere enhanced by a log-burner and the buzz of pleasant chat. Handpulled beers come from several local suppliers including Grey Trees and nearby Twt Lol, as well as nationals. Two handpumps serve real cider. A selection of craft keg and bottled ciders is also stocked. Good-value meals are available in the bar and rear dining area. A popular destination for dog walkers. Q ► ✿ ◑ ● ♿ ☷ (26,132) ☙ ☎

Glynneath

Dinas Rock Hotel ⫩
High Street, SA11 5AP
☎ (01639) 720105
2 changing beers (sourced regionally; often Evan Evans, Glamorgan, Tomos Watkin) ⊞

Traditional local in the centre of the village and a welcome refuge in an area where real ale is hard to find. Two wood-burning stoves and original stone walls make for a cosy atmosphere. Live televised rugby, especially Six Nations and Ospreys games, is always popular. Real cider hand-produced by one of the regulars is available seasonally. Live music often features at weekends. Q ► ✿ ♿ ♠ ● ☷ (8,X7) ☎

Gorseinon

Mardy Inn ⊘
117 High Street, SA4 4BR
☎ (01792) 890600
Greene King Abbot; Ruddles Best Bitter; Sharp's Doom Bar; 4 changing beers ⊞

This Wetherspoon establishment was formerly a traditional high-street pub. It is now modern in style, with a large single bar with several TVs for news and sport, and an adjoining airy extension overlooking the furnished patio area. Some interesting pictures of old Gorseinon are on the walls, depicting the town and its inhabitants in years gone by. A good selection of local and national beers can be enjoyed in the beer garden. ► ✿ ◑ ♿ ● P ☷ (110,111) ☎

Groeswen

White Cross Inn

CF15 7UT (overlooking Groeswen chapel)
☎ (029) 2085 1332
4 changing beers (sourced nationally) Ⓗ
Friendly little pub well worth finding, offering excellent choice and value. Six handpumps serve four changing beers and two ciders from local producer Williams Brothers. Four guest beers come in a diverse range of styles and strengths, with one always a dark brew. New and local breweries often feature, many making their debut in the area. The back room hosts meetings including the popular monthly Beer Bellies gathering, with visiting brewers and beer industry speakers. Beer festivals are held on bank holidays. The road access is narrow. ⏴❀♣☗❀☂

Gwaelod Y Garth

Gwaelod y Garth Inn

Main Road, CF15 9HH
☎ (029) 2081 0408 ⊕ gwaelodygarthinn.co.uk
Wye Valley Bitter; 5 changing beers (sourced nationally; often Thornbridge) Ⓗ
A characterful, stone-built, multi-award winning village venue on the edge of Cardiff and on the lower slope of the Garth mountain. Frequented by regulars, walkers and cyclists, it is the focus of the village. The bar offers a range of real ales along with two traditional ciders. There is a separate games room next to the main bar area and a dining room upstairs. The pub supported the local community with a shop during the pandemic. Local CAMRA Pub of the Year 2020.
Q⏴❀🛏◑♣☗(26B)❀☂

Hendreforgan

Griffin Inn Ⓛ

CF39 8YL
☎ (01443) 670379
Glamorgan Cwrw Gorslas/Bluestone Bitter; Jemimas Pitchfork Ⓗ
A warm welcome is assured at the Griffin (locally known as the Bog), a pub that has been in the same family for generations. Recognised by CAMRA as a Real Heritage Pub of Wales, the immaculate decor features oak furniture, gleaming brasses and a Victorian counter with an 1870 till. It is a little difficult to find, but you will be rewarded by its quirky character and superbly kept beers.
Q⏴❀Å☗(150,172)❀

Kenfig

Prince of Wales

CF33 4PR
☎ (01656) 740356 ⊕ princeofwalesinn.co.uk
Draught Bass; Gower Gold; Worthington's Bitter; 1 changing beer (sourced regionally) Ⓖ
A heritage award-winning inn dating from the 15th century and steeped in local history. Visitors can expect three quality ales on gravity, good locally sourced food and a warm welcome. Family-friendly and popular with dog walkers, the pub is comfortable and cosy. Outside there is a stunning view over Kenfig Nature Reserve. The Draught Bass is renowned throughout the local area and outsells all the pub's lagers combined. Guest beers and cider are occasionally available.
Q⏴❀◑♣☗(63B)❀☂

Killay

Village Bar Café

5-6 Swan Court, The Precinct, SA2 7BA
☎ (01792) 203311
Sharp's Doom Bar; 2 changing beers Ⓗ
Situated in a small shopping precinct in Killay on the gateway to Gower, the Village has changed its focus from a traditional pub to a café bar. It retains a single, split-level bar, offering three real ales. There is a quiz on Sunday and Tuesday nights. The food menu is varied and offers plenty of choice including vegetarian and vegan options. The kitchen is closed on Sunday and Monday, but the café/bar is open for coffee, cake and drinks.
⏴◑&♣☗(20,21)❀☂

Llangennith

King's Head Ⓛ

SA3 1HX
☎ (01792) 386212 ⊕ kingsheadgower.co.uk
Gower Gold; 5 changing beers (sourced regionally; often Evan Evans, Mumbles, Tomos Watkin) Ⓗ
A row of three 17th-century stone-built cottages, this large pub has two separate bars and a variety of rooms for drinking and dining. Ales from nearby breweries are on the bar (up to five in summer, fewer in winter). An impressive variety of home-made food is served, with dishes inspired by fresh local produce. It is at the western end of the Gower Peninsular, a short distance from the sandy stretches of Llangennith Beach.
⏴❀🛏◑Å♣☗(116)❀☂

Llanharry

Fox & Hounds

Llanharan Road, CF72 9LL
☎ (01443) 222124 ⊕ foxandhoundsllanharry.co.uk
Courage Directors; 4 changing beers (sourced nationally; often Glamorgan, Oakham, Salopian) Ⓗ
Stone-built traditional pub with an enviable reputation for choice and quality. The lounge has an open fire and comfortable settees, and there is a games room and separate restaurant. Guest beers are often modern and progressive in style, and attract a keen following. The pub also has a growing reputation for serving good food. Live bands play on Saturday evenings. There is a large car park to the side and a beer garden at the rear.
⏴❀◑&♣☗(64,404)❀☂

Llanmadoc

Britannia Inn

SA3 1DB
☎ (01792) 386624 ⊕ britanniagower.com
Gower Gold; Sharp's Doom Bar; 1 changing beer (sourced nationally) Ⓗ
Timbers from ships wrecked on the nearby coast were used in the construction of this pretty and popular 17th-century pub in a quiet corner of Gower. A cosy bar at the entrance serves good food and beer; the back bar area has been converted into a fine-dining restaurant. Beer gardens to the front and rear offer stunning views over the nearby estuary, with an aviary and pet area popular with children. ⏴❀◑Å♣☗(30)❀☂

Llantwit Fardre

Bush Inn

Main Road, CF38 2EP
☎ (01443) 203958

Hancocks HB; 2 changing beers (sourced regionally) Ⓗ
Bustling pub in the centre of the village. The interior is semi open plan, with exposed stone walls and timber. Guest beers can be from national brewers, but are more often from independents, particularly larger Welsh providers. There is a quiz on Tuesday and Wednesday, plus a jam session on Thursday. A band often plays on Saturday, when the pub can get quite busy.
✿♿♣️P🚌(100,400) ❀🐾📶

Ship Inn

Crown Hill, CF38 1BH (100yds from A473, signposted Llantwit Fardre)
☎ (01443) 202341
Greene King Abbot; Wickwar BOB Ⓗ
Traditional one-bar pub in a semi-rural location, convenient for the local foot and cycle path. Outside, there is a large, partly sheltered terrace with seating, and a children's play area. The pub is popular for its classic pub food, served in the bar and separate restaurant (booking recommended, particularly for Sunday lunch). The menu includes vegetarian options. ✿🕽♣️P🚌(90)

Llantwit Major

Llantwit Major Rugby Club

Old Market, Boverton Road, CF61 1XZ
☎ (01446) 792276 🌐 llantwitmajor.rfc.wales
Sharp's Doom Bar; 2 changing beers (often Brains, Wye Valley) Ⓗ
A friendly community club, proud of its rugby history, which welcomes visitors. The regular beer and two changing guest ales are all excellent value for money. There is a cosy, well-appointed lounge bar and a function room which hosts frequent live music and is available for hire. A small patio is popular in summer and there is a covered smoking area. Dogs are welcome in the players' bar. ⅏♿🅰️🚈P🚌(303,321)❀📶

White Hart Inn ✅

Wine Street, CF61 1RZ
☎ (01446) 796956 🌐 oldwhitehartllantwitmajor.co.uk
Ringwood Fortyniner; Wadworth Horizon; 1 changing beer (often Wainwright) Ⓗ
A recent winner of the local CAMRA branch's County Community Pub of the Year, rewarding the licensees' participation in town events. Dating back to the 15th century, the pub is set in the picturesque town square. The cosy public bar has a large log-burner, two TVs and three ales on sale. There is a separate restaurant offering a range of traditional food. A large beer garden at the back hosts popular music events and small beer festivals.
⅏✿🍴🕽🅰️♣️P(303,95) ❀📶

Marcross

Horseshoe Inn

CF61 1ZG
☎ (01656) 890568 🌐 theshoesmarcross.co.uk
Sharp's Atlantic; Wye Valley Butty Bach; 2 changing beers (often Gower, VOG) Ⓗ
The Shoes is a beautiful 19th-century inn set in the hamlet of Marcross. It usually has a range of three ales, one a Welsh brew. An extensive food menu offers a choice of good pub fare. The bar is cosy on winter nights with a log-burner; the beer garden is delightful in summer. With its friendly staff, the place is popular with students from the local international college. It is convenient for spectacular coastal walks, taking in the nearby Nash Point cliffs and lighthouse.
Q⅏✿🕽♣️P(303)

Morriston

Red Lion Inn ✅

49 Sway Road, SA6 6JA (near Morriston Cross opp fire station)
☎ (01792) 761870
Greene King Abbot; Ruddles Best Bitter; 6 changing beers (sourced nationally; often Draught Bass, Mumbles, Sharp's) Ⓗ
Deceptively spacious Wetherspoon pub with a large, comfortable, open-plan room featuring an open log fire at the front and high bar stools at the back. On the walls are a number of pictures depicting the long-gone industrial history of the area. A community board advertises trips to breweries and other events in the area. At least one guest ale comes from a local brewery.
⅏✿🕽♿♣️P🚌(4,X6) 📶

Mumbles

Beaufort Arms Ⓛ

1 Castle Road, Norton, SA3 5TF
☎ (01792) 514246
Draught Bass; Glamorgan Jemimas Pitchfork; 2 changing beers (often Brains, Gower) Ⓗ
Charming 18th-century village local with a welcoming atmosphere. Previously closed by its owning pub group, it was bought by a private couple in 2017 and attractively renovated. There is a traditional main bar with a TV and dartboard, and a small, comfortable lounge. Both rooms have real fires, and outside there is a small beer garden to the rear. A quiz is held on Tuesday. An increase in the range of beers has added to the its popularity.
Q✿♣️🚌(2A,3A) ❀📶

Mumbles Ale House

21 Westbourne Place, SA3 4DB
☎ 07917 100508
4 changing beers (sourced nationally; often Bristol Beer Factory, Glamorgan, Mantle) Ⓗ/Ⓖ
Traditional back-street corner local in the heart of Mumbles, dating from the 1860s and now specialising as an alehouse. Decorated in a traditional and comfortable style, it retains some original features of historic interest including a well in the bar area – the source of water in the days when the pub brewed its own beer. Live music plays most Sunday evenings. There is often a pop-up kitchen on a Monday evening. Q⅏✿🚌(2A,3A)❀

Park Inn Ⓛ

23 Park Street, SA3 4DA
☎ (01792) 366738
5 changing beers (sourced regionally; often Evan Evans, Mumbles, Tiny Rebel) Ⓗ
The convivial atmosphere in this small establishment in a village side street attracts discerning drinkers of all ages. Five handpumps dispense a varying range of beers, with particular emphasis on independent breweries from Wales and the west of England. Alongside a fine display of pumpclips are pictures of old Mumbles and its pioneering railway. A popular quiz is held on Thursday, with occasional music at weekends.
Q⅏✿❀♣️🚌(2A,3A) ❀📶

Pilot Inn Ⓛ

726 Mumbles Road, SA3 4EL
☎ 07897 895511 🌐 thepilotofmumbles.co.uk
Draught Bass; 6 changing beers (sourced nationally; often Pilot) Ⓗ
Welcoming and friendly local on the seafront at Mumbles and home to the Pilot Brewery. Seven ales are available, usually including up to three rotating beers brewed on-site. A wide range of bottled ciders is also kept and hot

drinks are served. This historic pub, built in 1849, is next to the coastal path and popular with lifeboatmen, locals, walkers and cyclists. A former Welsh CAMRA Pub of the Year. Q❧✿♣●🖳(2B)🐾☔

Ty Cwrw

650 Mumbles Road, SA3 4EA (next to Mumbles Carlton Hotel)

☎ 07488 298344

4 changing beers (sourced nationally; often Tenby, Tiny Rebel, Tomos Watkin) Ⓗ

Small and friendly independently owned pub – the name Ty Cwrw is Welsh for beer house. It serves four real ales and six craft keg beers, all from a variety of Welsh breweries and listed on a large blackboard. Although the frontage appears to be narrow from the outside, there is a second room behind the front room and the long wooden bar. Both rooms have a light, modern decor and feature paintings from local artists. ❧♣●🖳(2A,3A)🐾☔

Neath

Borough Arms Ⓛ

2 New Henry Street, SA11 1PH (off Briton Ferry road, near Stockhams Corner roundabout)

☎ (01639) 644902

House beer (by Draught Bass); 4 changing beers (sourced regionally; often Glamorgan, Grey Trees) Ⓗ

The emphasis in this welcoming local is very much on ales and conversation. The landlord and brewer occasionally has his own ales on tap, but there is always a good choice from regional breweries. The pub holds an annual GlastonBorough festival in May featuring live music, plus a beer festival over the August bank holiday. Live acoustic music plays every Wednesday. Well worth the 10-minute walk from the town centre. Q✿≠🖳☔

David Protheroe Ⓛ ✅

7 Windsor Road, SA11 1LS (opp railway station)

☎ (01639) 622130

Greene King Abbot; Ruddles Best Bitter; Sharp's Doom Bar; 5 changing beers (sourced regionally; often Brains, Evan Evans, Grey Trees) Ⓗ

A former police station and courthouse, the David Protheroe is named after the first policeman to be posted in Neath. A Wetherspoon pub, it is ideally positioned in the centre of town, directly opposite the railway station and a short walk from the bus terminus. It has three permanent and up to five changing beers, often including a locally brewed ale. Ciders are also available. ❧✿◐♿≠●🖳☔

Greyhound

11 Water Street, SA11 3EP

☎ 07896 418110

2 changing beers (sourced regionally) Ⓗ

Around 400 years old, the pub has been attractively modernised, with an open-plan layout served by an L-shaped bar. It has a strong local following and is home to three darts teams. The choice of ales reflects customer preferences and usually includes a dark ale or stout. Live music features on Saturday and Sunday, karaoke on Friday. TV screens show live sport at an acceptable volume. The pub holds many charity events. Well worth visiting if in Neath town centre. ❧✿≠🖳

Penarth

Golden Lion

69 Glebe Street, CF64 1EF

☎ (029) 2070 1574

4 changing beers (often Glamorgan, Grey Trees, VOG) Ⓗ

A genuine back street locals' pub with a reputation for serving some of the best-kept quality real ale in the area. Three or four beers from Welsh breweries are usually on offer, along with good-value home-made food. It can sometimes be loud and lively with its popular jukebox and numerous sports TVs, and football and darts teams are among the regular customers. The small beer garden is a delight in warmer weather, with artificial grass and wall paintings depicting Penarth. ✿◐♿≠(Dingle Rd)♣🖳☔

Pilot

67 Queen's Road, CF64 1DJ

☎ (029) 2071 0615

4 changing beers (often Grey Trees, Saltaire, VOG) Ⓗ

The Pilot has established a reputation for high-quality beer, wine and food. Its ales are chosen from some of the best Welsh breweries, alongside more unusual offerings from around the country. The four handpumps usually serve up to three beers and often one real cider. The front bar is dog-friendly, there is pleasant seating outside at the front for warm weather, and the rear restaurant area with its log-fired stove is comfortable on winter days. Because of its popularity, booking is recommended for meals at peak times. Q❧◐♿≠(Dingle Rd)●🖳🐾☔

Windsor Ⓛ ✅

95 Windsor Road, CF64 1JE

☎ (029) 2070 8675

Brains Bitter, SA, Rev James; 3 changing beers (sourced nationally; often Brains) Ⓗ

Refurbished a few years ago to a high standard, the Windsor has an emphasis on quality dining. It serves a selection of ales mainly from the core Brains range. The pub offers a relaxing environment, with a cosy front area with comfortable seating, a long dining/drinking space opposite the bar, and further tables to the rear. It is popular with families for Sunday lunch and lively on weekend evenings with live music acts. Q❧◐♿≠(Dingle Rd)🖳🐾☔

Pencoed

Little Penybont Arms

11 Penybont Road, CF35 5PY

☎ 07734 767937

3 changing beers Ⓖ

Since opening, this cosy micropub has built up a strong local following. It offers a choice of changing beers on gravity, craft keg beer, 10 ciders and more than 15 single malt whiskies and gins. The nearby Steak & Stamp restaurant is under the same ownership and serves the same range of drinks. The pub itself has excellent bar snacks include pork pies, nuts and home-made pork scratchings. A quiz and pizza night is held on Wednesday. Q❧✿◐≠♣●🖳🐾☔

Penderyn

Red Lion

Church Road, CF44 9JR

☎ (01685) 811914 ⊕ redlionpenderyn.com

Brains Rev James; Draught Bass; Fuller's ESB; Gower Gold; 1 changing beer (sourced nationally) Ⓖ

Family-owned drovers inn on the edge of the Brecon Beacons National Park. Parts date back to the 12th century – at one time it was a Welsh longhouse. Much renovated over the last 40 years, there are two log fires in the small but delightfully cosy bar. Darker, traditional ales predominate, with Fuller's ESB a stalwart for many years. Two or more local ciders and perries are always available. High-quality food is served (booking advised as it can get busy). Q❀◑🕭🐾●P🐾〽

Peterston-super-Ely

Sportsman's Rest 🅛
CF5 6LH

☎ (01446) 760675 🌐 thesportsmansrest.co.uk

Otter Ale; Wye Valley HPA; 2 changing beers (sourced nationally) Ⓗ

Attractive village pub with outdoor seating front and rear and a children's play area. The comfortable interior includes a bar area for drinkers and a larger split-level dining section. An emphasis on quality food – with special deals and themed food evenings – is balanced by a good range of real ales, some unusual for the area. Community and charity events are well supported, including an annual beer festival to coincide with the village duck race in May. 🐾❀◑🕭🐾●P🚲(320)🐾〽

Pontardawe

Pontardawe Inn 🅛
123 Herbert Street, SA8 4ED

☎ (01792) 447562 🌐 pontardaweinnpub.co.uk

Ringwood Fortyniner; 3 changing beers (sourced nationally; often Marston's, Mumbles) Ⓗ

Former Welsh longhouse later converted to a drovers' pub. A side room and stable were added in 1850 as a sorting depot for the Royal Mail. The central bar serves one regular and up to three changing ales, as well as a range of real ciders. Good food is available daily. Seasonal beer festivals and music festivals are held, and live music features at weekends. The award-winning pub is situated alongside the River Tawe and local cycle path. Its landscaped beer garden is pleasant in fine weather and proved especially popular during lockdown restrictions. 🐾❀◑🕭🐾●P🚲(56,X6)〽

Pontsarn

Aberglais Inn
CF48 2TS (between Trefechan and Pontsticill) SO043098

☎ (01685) 377344 🌐 aberglais.com

Wye Valley Bitter, Butty Bach; 3 changing beers (sourced nationally; often Cold Black Label, Grey Trees) Ⓗ

Located on the way to Pontsticill Reservoir, the pub has a pleasant and relaxing main bar with a light decor and a cosy wood stove, and an adjoining restaurant area. It is popular with families, hikers, holidaymakers and cyclists on the nearby trails. Dogs are welcome in the bar and beer garden. Good food is served and booking is essential on Saturday and recommended at other times. 🐾❀◑P🚲🐾

Pontsticill

Butchers Arms Restaurant, Bunkhouse & Brewpub
CF48 2UE

☎ (01685) 723544 🌐 butchersbunkhouse.com

3 changing beers (sourced regionally; often Crafty Dragon, Grey Trees, Twin Taff) Ⓗ

Located on the southern edge of the Brecon Beacons with spectacular views. A roaring log fire and traditional pub decor add to the cosy welcome. Food is served throughout the day. Bunkhouse accommodation is available, as well as bike hire to explore the many nearby trails. In-house Crafty Dragon beers are

sometimes on offer, along with well-kept and varied guest beers. There is seating outside and a large car park. Q🐾❀🕭◑🍴🐾●P🐾〽

Red Cow
Main Road, CF48 2UN

☎ (01685) 387775 🌐 redcow.wales

Wye Valley Bitter; house beer (by Grey Trees); 1 changing beer (sourced regionally; often Boss, Cotleigh, Twt Lol) Ⓗ

A handsome and tranquil pub in the middle of Pontsticill with views of the Brecon Beacons. Warm, friendly and inviting, the interior is open plan and comfortably furnished, with a log fire in the cosy snug. Permanent beers are from Grey Trees and Wye Valley; the rotating guest is often from Twt Lol or Cotleigh. Popular for meals, food is served until 9pm. There is a garden and a large car park. Q🐾❀◑P🐾〽

Pontypridd

Bunch of Grapes 🅛 ✔
Ynysangharad Road, CF37 4DA (off A4054)

☎ (01443) 402934 🌐 bunchofgrapes.org.uk

Grey Trees Diggers Gold; 9 changing beers (sourced nationally; often Oakham, Salopian, Tiny Rebel) Ⓗ

A short walk from the town centre, this popular pub has won multiple awards. The guest ales range always changes and includes at least one local beer. Two ciders are also sold. Events include beer, cider and food festivals. A popular quiz is held on Tuesday evening. The separate highly acclaimed restaurant serves locally sourced produce. Q🐾❀◑🕭●P🚲🐾

Llanover Arms 🅛
Bridge Street, CF37 4PE (opp N entrance to Ynysangharad Park)

☎ (01443) 403215

3 changing beers (sourced nationally; often Salopian) Ⓗ

Built around 1794 to serve thirsty boatmen on the newly opened Glamorganshire Canal, this historic free house has been owned by the same family for over a century. It has three rooms linked by passageways – all with their own distinct character and atmosphere. Nearby is the famous old town bridge and Ynysangharad Park with its restored National Lido of Wales. The Taff Trail passes close by. Q🐾❀🕭●P🚲🐾

Patriot Bar 🅛
25B Taff Street, CF37 4UA

☎ (01443) 407915

Rhymney Bevans Bitter, Bitter, Export; 2 changing beers (often Rhymney) Ⓗ

A Rhymney Brewery tied pub, near the bus station and a short walk from the railway station. Its well-kept beers include two guests from the Rhymney range. Trade is brisk, with beers turning over quickly, helped by the keen prices. Real cider is sometimes stocked. The pub is easy to find, located in a former shop in Taff Street. It is fondly known as the Wonky Bar, recalling its former twisted entrance. It can be loud and bustling but is a gem. 🕭🚲🐾〽

Tumble Inn ✔
4-9 Broadway, CF37 1BA

☎ (01443) 484390

Greene King Abbot; Ruddles Best Bitter; Sharp's Doom Bar; 3 changing beers (sourced regionally; often Boss, Glamorgan, Rhymney) Ⓗ

A long single bar serves this large open-plan single-level Wetherspoon/Lloyds No.1 Bar. The food service is varied and available throughout the day. Monday is poker night,

Wednesday is quiz night. The patio outside is divided into smoking and no-smoking areas. Handy for the town centre and railway station, with several main bus routes close by. ⏶⛾⬤⬤&⇌⬤🖳⏧

Port Talbot

Lord Caradoc 🅛 ⊘
69-73 Station Road, SA13 1NW
☎ (01639) 896007
Greene King Abbot; Ruddles Best Bitter; Sharp's Doom Bar; 5 changing beers (sourced regionally; often Glamorgan, Rhymney, Tomos Watkin) Ⓗ
On the main shopping street, this Wetherspoon Lloyds bar with a varied clientele has a relaxed atmosphere, with a spacious open-plan layout and family-friendly area. The choice of beers is open to suggestion from customers, with a wide range always available, frequently including a locally brewed ale. The walls are adorned with historic photographs of the town and famous local people. The pub has been recognised by Wetherspoon for its high standard of catering on several occasions. ⏶⛾⬤⬤&⇌⬤🖳⏧

Porth

Rheola
Rheola Road, CF39 0LF
☎ (01443) 682633
Rhymney Bevans Bitter, Bitter, Export Ⓗ
A Rhymney Brewery house since 2015, this friendly local sells a range of the brewery's beers. The large, detached building is situated at the confluence of the two Rhondda rivers, and is well served by both rail and bus. The bar features a jukebox, pool table and dartboard, and is often quite lively. The comfortable lounge generally provides a quiet haven and tends only to get busy at weekends. Activities include a quiz, whist and a monthly open mic night. ⛾⇌♣P🖳(120,132)⏧

Porthcawl

Lorelei Hotel
36-38 Esplanade Avenue, CF36 3YU
☎ (01656) 788342 ⊕ loreleihotel.co.uk
Draught Bass Ⓖ; Rhymney Export; 2 changing beers Ⓗ
Near the seafront, the town centre and the Grand Pavilion, this is the 23rd year the Lorelei has been in this Guide. Good-quality and value-for-money food is served evenings (no food Mon) and Sunday lunchtime. Four draught beers are available plus cider in summer. Beer festivals are held twice a year on Grand National and Halloween weekends. Built around the end of the 19th century, during World War I it was two separate buildings – one used as a hospice for injured soldiers. Q⏶⛾⬤♣⬤🖳⏧

Reynoldston

King Arthur Hotel
Higher Green, SA3 1AD (on village green)
☎ (01792) 390775 ⊕ kingarthurhotel.co.uk
Gower Gold; Sharp's Doom Bar; 2 changing beers (sourced nationally; often Glamorgan, Tenby, Tiny Rebel) Ⓗ
Traditional family-owned hotel and acclaimed wedding venue, situated at the foot of Cefn Bryn in beautiful Gower, overlooking the village green. There is covered outdoor seating by the pub entrance and a large seating area on the green itself. The cosy, atmospheric main and rear bars are welcoming to drinkers and diners, serving home-cooked food made with local produce. Main meals and bar snacks are available all day, as well as breakfasts for non-residents. ⏶⛾⬤⬤&⬤P🖳(118,119)⏧

St Athan

Roost
Rock Road, CF62 4PG
☎ (01446) 753715 ⊕ theroostonrockroad.com
Hancocks HB; Wye Valley HPA; 1 changing beer (often Glamorgan) Ⓗ
Formerly the Four Bells, the pub is now more modern in style following a major refurbishment, but some original features remain – the old floorboards now form the bar front. Food is of a high standard and the menu is varied. Beer is always in top condition. Outdoor events are hosted on the patio and a grass area in summer. Accommodation is in five rooms. Q⏶⛾⬤⬤P🖳(304) ⏧

Sketty

Vivian Arms ⊘
106 Gower Road, SA2 9BT (jct of A4118 and A4216)
☎ (01792) 516194
Brains Bitter, SA, SA Gold, Rev James; 1 changing beer Ⓗ
On the main crossroads in Sketty and known locally as the Vivs, it is a spacious pub that attracts a wide range of customers, young and old. It has a mixture of seating areas and plenty of TV screens throughout showing live sport. There is a small meeting room. A popular carvery is held on Sunday. Live music features on Friday and occasionally Saturday, a general knowledge quiz on Sunday and a music quiz on Wednesday. The beer range may include an ale from the Marston's stable. ⏶⛾⬤🖳(20,21) ⬤⏧

Swansea

Bank Statement ⊘
57-58 Wind Street, SA1 1EP
☎ (01792) 455477
Sharp's Doom Bar; 5 changing beers (sourced nationally; often Exmoor, Fuller's, Jennings) Ⓗ
A former Midland Bank, sympathetically transformed by Wetherspoon while retaining its original ornate interior. Trading as a Lloyds No.1, the pub is at the heart of the city's popular bar quarter and has a large ground floor with plenty of seating. Attracting all ages, it is busy throughout the week. Sport is shown on its many screens. The bottled beer selection includes real ales. ⏶⬤&⇌⬤🖳⏧

Brunswick Arms
3 Duke Street, SA1 4HS (between St Helens Rd and Walter Rd)
☎ (01792) 465676 ⊕ brunswickswansea.com
Butcombe Original; Courage Directors; Wye Valley Butty Bach Ⓗ**; 2 changing beers (sourced nationally)** Ⓗ/Ⓖ
A side-street pub with the air of a country inn in the city. Wooden beams and comfortable seating create a traditional, relaxing atmosphere, and a local artist's work is displayed for sale. Up to six beers are usually available – one of the changing beers is dispensed on gravity, often from a local microbrewery. A popular quiz is held on Monday, live music on Thursday and Saturday, and an open mic session on the second Tuesday of the month. ⬤&⬤🖳(200) ⏧

No Sign Bar

56 Wind Street, SA1 1EG

☎ (01792) 465300 ⊕ nosignwinebar.com

Gower Gold; 3 changing beers (sourced nationally; often Butcombe, Mumbles, Tiny Rebel) ℍ

Historic narrow bar established in 1690, formerly Mundays Wine Bar and reputedly a regular haunt of Dylan Thomas. The interior is divided into separate areas, with architectural remains from various periods of the pub's past still in evidence. Quality food and wine are available, and up to five real ciders. Live music features in the bar on Friday, Saturday and often Sunday evenings. Bands also play in the Vault basement later at night. ❖❀◖❶✿≠➡➡🖴♠

Potters Wheel

85-86 The Kingsway, SA1 5JE

☎ (01792) 465113

Adnams Broadside; Fuller's London Pride; Ruddles Best Bitter; Sharp's Doom Bar; 6 changing beers (sourced nationally) ℍ

City-centre Wetherspoon outlet with a long sprawling bar area offering various seating arrangements, attracting customers of all ages and backgrounds. An interesting selection of guest beers is kept, with a commitment to local breweries. Real cider is always available. Photographs on the walls feature local dignitaries associated with the area's industrial past, particularly the ceramics and pottery industries. Look for the CAMRA board and beer suggestion box. ❖◖❶✿➡🖴♠

Queen's Hotel

Gloucester Place, SA1 1TY (near Waterfront Museum)

☎ (01792) 521531

Theakston Best Bitter, Old Peculier; 2 changing beers (sourced nationally; often Bristol Beer Factory, Fuller's, Glamorgan) ℍ

Vibrant free house near the Dylan Thomas Theatre, City Museum, National Waterfront Museum and marina. The walls display photographs depicting Swansea's rich maritime heritage. The pub enjoys strong local support, and home-cooked lunches are popular. Evening entertainment includes a Sunday quiz, bingo on Wednesday and live music on Saturday. This is a rare local outlet for Theakston Old Peculier, in addition to a seasonal guest beer, often from a local microbrewery. A former local CAMRA Pub of the Year. ◖🖴♣♠

Uplands Tavern ✔

42 Uplands Crescent, Uplands, SA2 0PG

☎ (01792) 458242

Greene King IPA, Abbot; 2 changing beers (sourced locally) ℍ

Situated in the heart of Swansea's student quarter, the Tav attracts regulars from all walks of life. The large single-room pub is a former haunt of Dylan Thomas, who is commemorated in a separate snug area. The pub has a reputation for the quality and variety of its live music at weekends and open mic nights on Mondays. Quiz night is Tuesday. Shufl board (shuffleboard with a concave playing surface) is a popular game here. There is a large heated outdoor drinking area. ❀✿♣🖴♠

Westbourne

1 Brynymor Road, SA1 4JQ

☎ (01792) 476637 ⊕ westbourneswansea.com

> Beer is proof that God loves us and wants us to be happy.
> **Benjamin Franklin**

Greene King Abbot; Sharp's Doom Bar; 2 changing beers ℍ

Located on the western fringe of the city centre, this family-run street-corner pub has a single split-level bar with various drinking areas; outside there is a heated terrace. Popular with diners, the menu includes vegan options (it is advisable to book for Sunday lunch). A quiz is held on Tuesday evening. The pub does not subscribe to sports TV channels but will show major sporting events on Freeview. ❀◖♣🖴(2,3)♠

Trefforest

Otley Arms Ⓛ

Forest Road, CF37 1SY (on gyratory system)

☎ (01443) 402033

Mabby Blue, Red, Green, Black; 3 changing beers (sourced regionally; often Grey Trees, Salopian, Tiny Rebel) ℍ

Hospitable and informal pub, a haven for students from the nearby university and locals alike. The open-plan bar has a log fire and leather sofas. A wide variety of guest and craft ales is on offer along with Mabby Brewing Co beers brewed on-site. Traditional food is of a high standard, and the service and atmosphere are always friendly. Board games are available and a quiz is held on Monday. The pub is well served by train and bus. ❖❀◖≠♣🖴(90,100)🐾♠

Rickards Arms Ⓛ

61 Park Street, CF37 1SN

☎ (01443) 402305

3 changing beers (sourced nationally; often Grey Trees) ℍ

Close to Trefforest railway station and backing onto the railway line, the pub is popular with students at the nearby University of South Wales. It is divided into four areas, all served by a single bar. Three guest beers are available, one usually local and two national. Food is good value, especially the famous cooked breakfasts. The pub hosts regular quiz and music nights. ❀◖≠♣🖴(90,100)🐾♠

Treorchy

Pencelli Hotel

Pencae Terrace, CF42 6HL

☎ (01443) 775181

5 changing beers (sourced nationally; often Glamorgan, Salopian, Tiny Rebel) ℍ

Two large rooms are served by a central bar offering a range of beer styles. A log fire adds warmth in winter. The pub has a strong musical following and hosts live bands on Thursdays, Saturdays and bank holidays. It is easily reached by bus or train and has ample car parking opposite. A winner of many local CAMRA awards, and Wales CAMRA Cider and Perry Pub of the Year in 2020. ❖❀◖≠♣🖴

Tyla Garw

Boar's Head

Coedcae Lane, CF72 9EZ (600yds from A473 over level crossing)

☎ (01443) 225400

Glamorgan Jemimas Pitchfork; 3 changing beers (sourced regionally; often Oakham, Salopian) ℍ

This award-winning pub includes a bar, two dining areas, a gin bar and Piglets lounge, which is a coffee bar during the day. The zero waste shop (selling local produce and organic, vegan and gluten-free foods) is in keeping with the pub's role as a community hub. Classic pub meals include Sunday lunch (booking advisable). Quiz night is every other Tuesday. Pontyclun railway station is a 10-minute walk. ⚒☀◑❿♿≉(Pontyclun)♠P

Upper Church Village

Farmers Arms ✅
St Illtyd Road, CF38 1EB
☎ (01443) 205766
Brains Rev James; 2 changing beers (sourced regionally) Ⓗ
Comfortable village local with one large bar and an attractive split-level garden and patio. The changing beers can include national brands but are more often unusual ales for the area. A popular quiz night is hosted on Tuesday, but beer and conversation are the main attractions. Traditional pub food is available most days except Sunday. ☀◑P🚆(90)🌼

Upper Killay

Railway Inn Ⓛ
553 Gower Road, SA2 7DS
☎ (01792) 203946
Swansea Deep Slade Dark, Bishopswood Bitter, Three Cliffs Gold, Original Wood; 1 changing beer Ⓗ
Classic locals' pub set in woodlands in the Clyne Valley. The adjacent former railway line forms part of Route 4 of the National Cycle Network. There are two small rooms at the front – one the main bar and snug – and a larger lounge at the rear. In winter the fire in the lounge provides welcome warmth and cheer. At least one guest ale is kept alongside the Swansea Brewing Company beers. A large area outside hosts occasional barbecues and music events. Q☀♣♠P🚆(118)🌼

Wick

Star Inn
Ewenny Road, CF71 7QA
☎ (01656) 890080 ⊕ thestarinnwick.co.uk
Glamorgan Welsh Pale Ale; 2 changing beers (often Glamorgan) Ⓗ
Originally three farm cottages, the interior comprises a traditional bar with pew seating, a lounge/diner with flagstone flooring – both warmed by log-burning fires – and an upstairs pool/function room. The friendly landlady, staff and locals help make this a pleasant place to visit. Good food is available – the meat is supplied by an award-winning farm butcher a short distance away. Dogs are welcome in the bar. Local CAMRA Pub of the Year 2020. Q⚒☀◑♣♠P🚆(303)🌼🛜

Ystalyfera

Wern Fawr Ⓛ
47 Wern Road, SA9 2LX (on main road through Ystalyfera)
☎ (01639) 843625
9 Lives Brewing Amber, Dark, Gold; 1 changing beer (sourced nationally) Ⓗ
Entering this quirky pub feels like stepping back in time. Run by the same family for three generations, the two-roomed inn is full of industrial memorabilia from the local area. It has a cosy lounge and a friendly locals' bar with an old-fashioned stove that keeps the room toasty in wintertime. The beers are brewed locally by 9 Lives Brewing, accompanied by one changing guest ale. The newly landscaped beer garden with a spectacular view is a delight in fine weather and proved especially popular during lockdown restrictions. Q♣♠🚆(X6)🌼

Queen's Vaults, Cardiff (Photo: Elliott Brown/Flickr CC BY-SA 2.0)

GWENT

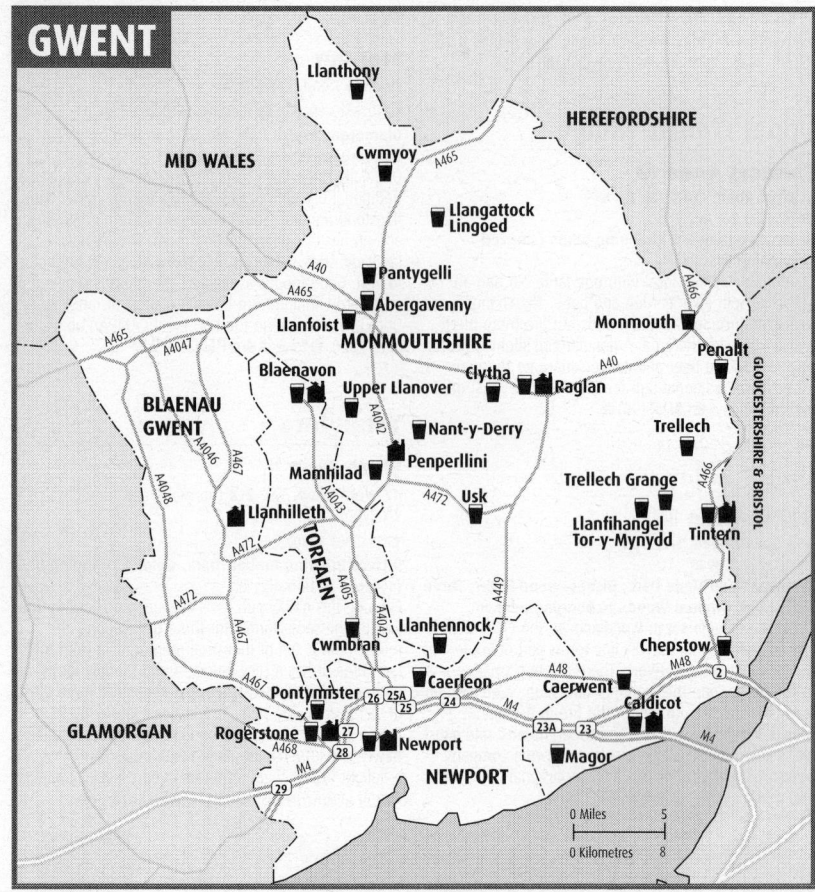

Authority areas covered: Blaenau Gwent UA, Caerphilly UA (part), Monmouthshire UA, Newport UA, Torfaen UA

Abergavenny

Cantreff Inn

61 Brecon Road, NP7 7RA
☎ (01873) 855888
Grey Trees Diggers Gold; Wye Valley Butty Bach; 1 changing beer (often Grey Trees) Ⓗ
There is a homely atmosphere in this pub on the main road to Brecon, near the hospital. It has separate rooms for drinking and dining, with a central servery and is well-known for its good quality meals. The comfortable bar has a light decor and features a settee, large mirror, antique clock and wood-burning stove, all of which contribute to the pleasant ambience. There is outdoor seating at the front and in the attractive rear garden.
☕🕮❀◑Pᕈ(X4) ❀ 🤟

Grofield Ⓛ

Baker Street, NP7 5BB
☎ (01873) 858939 ⊕ grofield.com
Rhymney Bevans Bitter; Sharp's Doom Bar; 1 changing beer (sourced nationally; often Kingstone, Untapped) Ⓗ
Family-run free house whose licensee's long experience is reflected in the quality of beers, warmth of welcome, level of service and general ambience. The bar is horseshoe-shaped around a central counter and is often busy throughout the day, especially when food is

available. The well-maintained garden is a town-centre haven of greenery, lovely on warm days.
☕🕮❀◑♣ᕈ(47) ❀

Blaenavon

Lion Hotel

41 Broad Street, NP4 9NH
☎ (01495) 792516 ⊕ thelionhotelblaenavon.co.uk
House beer (by Tomos a Lilford); 1 changing beer (sourced regionally; often Glamorgan, Tudor) Ⓗ
A quality hotel for visitors to the local world heritage sites as well as a place for regulars to enjoy. Its interior features contemporary artwork and is attractively

REAL ALE BREWERIES

Anglo Oregon Newport
Kingstone Tintern
Mad Dog 🍺 Penperllini
Rhymney Blaenavon
Tiny Rebel Rogerstone
Tudor 🍺 Llanhilleth
Untapped Raglan
Weird Dad 🍺 Newport (NEW)
Wye Valley Meadery Caldicot (NEW)
Zulu Alpha Caldicot

decorated with light wood and soft furnishing. The guest beer is usually from a Welsh brewery. The restaurant has an excellent reputation. ♿❀⚅◖➘(High Level) P🚶(X24,30) 🛜

Caerleon

Hanbury Arms 🅛 ✅

Uskside, High Street, NP18 1AA
☎ (01633) 420361
Brains Rev James; 2 changing beers (often Brains, Marston's) Ⓗ

You can understand why Alfred, Lord Tennyson, who penned his Idylls of the King there, found this 16th-century inn to his liking. It has a rambling, characterful interior with ample room for drinkers and diners, plus plenty of outdoor space to sit and relax while watching the ebb and flow of the tidal River Usk. The real ale range may include a beer from the Marston's stable alongside the Rev James. Diners can choose from an extensive menu. Q♿❀◖P🚶❀🛜

Caerwent

Coach & Horses

Green Lane, NP26 5AX
☎ (01291) 420352 🌐 caerwent-coachandhorses.co.uk
Brains Rev James; Wye Valley Butty Bach, HPA; 1 changing beer (sourced regionally; often Gower) Ⓗ

Popular two-bar inn in a village with Roman fortress remains all around. A smart, dog-friendly public bar at the front links to a lounge behind, with plentiful comfortable space in the large dining area. Conversation rules and this thriving pub is well established as the centre of village life. Three B&B rooms are available. ♿❀⚅◖♣P🚶(73) ❀🛜

Caldicot

Cross Inn

1 Newport Road, NP26 4BG
☎ (01291) 409042 🌐 crossinncaldicot.co.uk
Sharp's Doom Bar; 2 changing beers (sourced nationally) Ⓗ

In the pedestrianised centre of Caldicot, this pub has a large bar that is lively from late afternoon and at weekends. A central wall with a TV above a fireplace separates the open-plan bar area from a secluded seating space. A large clock fixed to a pillar is useful if you have a bus to catch outside. A second, smaller bar has a pool table. ♿❀♿♣P🚶(62,74)❀🛜

Chepstow

Chepstow Athletic Club 🅛

Mathern Road, Bulwark, NP16 5JJ (off Bulwark Rd)
☎ (01291) 622126 🌐 chepstowac.co.uk
St Austell Cornish Best Bitter; Wye Valley Butty Bach; 2 changing beers (sourced regionally) Ⓗ

Friendly club, now in its eighth decade, with an enduring appeal to the local community. Four real ales, all keenly priced, provide the focal point of the comfortable bar, where conversation rules and two muted TV screens keep sports fans happy. An upstairs function room also serves real ale. On sunny summer weekends the patio provides an opportunity to sit with a pint and watch cricketers on the club's own pitch. Visiting CAMRA members are welcome. ♿❀♣P🚶(74)

Queen's Head 🅛

Moor Street, NP16 5DD
☎ 07793 889613

8 changing beers (sourced regionally; often Gower, Grey Trees, Untapped) Ⓗ

A classic, basic and welcoming micropub where high-quality, mainly local beers – usually including a stout or porter – and ciders are the centre of attention. Although Welsh brews predominate, other nations' beers are periodically served. With no TV or games machines, the only regular entertainment is conversation. Pub crawls and outings to beer festivals are often arranged. A multiple local CAMRA Pub of the Year. Q➘♿P🚶(73,74)❀

Three Tuns Inn 🅛

32 Bridge Street, NP16 5EY
☎ (01291) 645797
5 changing beers (sourced regionally; often Kingstone, Wadworth, Wye Valley) Ⓗ

A pleasant walk from the town centre and close to the River Wye, this fine old inn sits in the shadow of the stunning Chepstow Castle, where open-air plays and concerts take place in the summer. The interior is split-level, with a pleasant rustic charm. Local beers are attractively priced, and locally sourced food is served at lunchtime. ♿❀⚅◖➘♿P🚶❀

Clytha

Clytha Arms 🅛

Groesonen Road, NP7 9BW (on B4598 old road between Abergavenny and Raglan)
☎ (01873) 840206 🌐 clytha-arms.com
Uley Bitter; Untapped UPA, Whoosh; 3 changing beers (sourced nationally) Ⓗ

This multi CAMRA award-winning pub has been in the Guide for well over a quarter of a century. Set in extensive grounds, the building started out as a dower house. It has a single bar, a separate dining area and good-quality accommodation. Beers from the nearby Untapped Brewing are always available, together with a wide and eclectic mix of regularly changing ales from around the country. Q♿❀⚅◖▲♣P🚶(83)❀

Cwmbran

Bush Inn 🅛

Graig Road, Upper Cwmbran, NP44 5AN
☎ (01633) 483764 🌐 thebushuppercwmbran.co.uk
2 changing beers (sourced regionally; often Tudor) Ⓗ

A cosy nook tucked into the slopes of Mynydd Maen, the traditionally styled split-level interior giving a clue that the pub was originally two cottages. Pictures of the inn and its formerly industrial locality are on display. There is nearly always an interesting selection of two or three guest ales plus a choice of ciders to help slake thirsts. Food features curry, pizza or steak on different evenings, with booking advisable. ♿❀◖♣♿P🚶(8,1)❀🛜

Mount Pleasant 🅛

Wesley Street, Old Cwmbran, NP44 3LX
☎ (01633) 712176
2 changing beers (sourced locally; often Kingstone, Mumbles, Rhymney) Ⓗ

The Mount is conveniently placed both for town centre shopping and for worship of many denominations – or as a welcome alternative. It is a traditional community hub where conversation is the main theme. The compact three-zone interior is complemented by a partially covered terrace and other outdoor seating. Beer is generally local and from independent breweries. Home-cooked food is served, with booking recommended for the Sunday roast. ♿❀◖♣♿P🚶(6)❀🛜

Queen Inn
Upper Cwmbran Road, Upper Cwmbran, NP44 5AX
☎ (01633) 484252
2 changing beers (sourced regionally) Ⓗ
A youthful-looking Queen Victoria on the pub sign
beckons you to enjoy the hospitality at this popular
venue with its attractive countryside backdrop. It was
formerly three dwellings before becoming a pub.
Separate sections cater for drinkers and diners, and there
are extensive outdoor facilities. Regularly changing ales
and a choice of ciders help to wash down the tasty food.
🌑☕◑♣♠P🚃(1,8)🌸

Cwmyoy

Queen's Head
NP7 7NE (from centre of village take lane signed to
Llanthony; pub is about 1 mile on right) SO311221
☎ (01873) 890241
Kingstone Classic Ⓗ
A venerable institution in the beautiful Llanthony valley,
known locally as Billy's in honour of the landlord of over
40 years' standing. Only a couple of miles off the main
A465 at Llanvihangel Crucorney, yet in a truly rural spot,
the pub looks over the River Honddu and up to the open
hills beyond. Thick walls, heavy beams and flagstone
floors reflect the building's ancient origins. Q❀P

Llanfihangel Tor-y-Mynydd

Star on the Hill
NP15 1DT (near Llansoy)
☎ (01291) 650256 ⊕ thestaronthehill.co.uk
**Kingstone Gold; Tiny Rebel Cwtch; Wye Valley Butty
Bach; 1 changing beer (sourced regionally; often Wye
Valley)** Ⓗ
The public bar is comfortably furnished with sofas and a
large wood-burning stove, and has a Great Britain theme
with Union Jack memorabilia. The bar has a separate
entrance to the restaurant side where home-cooked food
is made to order. It extends into a large conservatory and
has three more fireplaces. Wheelchair access is at the
back through the conservatory. Well worth seeking out.
🌑☕◑♿🅰♠P🌸

Llanfoist

Bridge Inn
Merthyr Road, NP7 9LH
☎ (01873) 854831 ⊕ bridgellanfoist.com
**Glamorgan Jemimas Pitchfork; Wye Valley Bitter,
Butty Bach** Ⓗ
Attractive roadside pub at the end of the old bridge
across the River Usk. Its large grassed garden has views
over the river to Abergavenny and the hills behind. The
owners have upgraded the facilities, including kitchens
and accommodation. Large TVs show sport. The pub
hosts beer festivals featuring local breweries. Guest ales
sometimes come from national breweries, including
some rarely seen locally. 🌑☕◑♨◑♠P🚃(X4)🌸🛜

Llangattock Lingoed

Hunter's Moon Inn
NP7 8RR (two miles off B4521 Abergavenny to Ross old
road) SO361201
☎ (01873) 821499 ⊕ hunters-moon-inn.co.uk
Wye Valley Butty Bach Ⓗ**, HPA; 1 changing beer
(sourced regionally)** Ⓗ/Ⓖ
Family-run free house in a quiet hamlet on the Offa's
Dyke Path. The interior retains rustic charm as befits such

an ancient building. The pub has improved its already
lovely gardens, making it a wonderful place to enjoy
alfresco drinking and eating. Visitors travel some distance
to join the small local population in celebrating this
wonderful venue. It offers accommodation to walkers
and others who enjoy Monmouthshire's rolling, unspoilt
countryside. Q🌑☕◑♨◑♣P🌸🛜

Llanhennock

Wheatsheaf
NP18 1LT ST353927
☎ (01633) 420468
**Fuller's London Pride; 2 changing beers (sourced
regionally)** Ⓗ
A fixture in this Guide for more than 30 years, the pub
has remained almost unchanged over that time. The
main bar is to the right, with a slightly smaller, cosier bar
to the left. The walls are festooned with old photographs,
bric-a-brac and memorabilia. There are views of the hills
miles away from front and back, plus a secluded garden.
Boules is played seriously in the car park. There is usually
a beer from a local brewery on the bar. 🌑☕🅰♣P🌸🛜

Llanthony

Half Moon
NP7 7NN SO286279
☎ (01873) 890611 ⊕ halfmoon-llanthony.co.uk
**Wye Valley Butty Bach; 1 changing beer (sourced
regionally; often Wye Valley)** Ⓗ
Originally built as two cottages in the 1700s, this
traditional pub is set in remote and romantic countryside
in the heart of the Black Mountains. The ruins of the
medieval abbey are nearby along the lane, and soaring
ridges on both sides of the valley draw visitors who want
to get away from it all. The recently developed beer
garden is a lovely place to sample the home-produced
food while enjoying a pint in these stunning
surroundings. Q🌑☕◑🅰♣P🌸🛜

Magor

Wheatsheaf Ⓛ ✅
The Square, NP26 3HN
☎ (01633) 880608 ⊕ wheatsheafinn.webeden.co.uk
**4 changing beers (sourced regionally; often
Rhymney, Tiny Rebel)** Ⓗ
Village pub with a sense of longevity within its
whitewashed walls and old wooden beams. It has a
taproom, public bar, lounge and restaurant. The regulars
tend to gather somewhere near the handpumps in the
lounge. An enthusiastic management team ensures
there is an interesting choice of ales from breweries near
and far. The partly covered garden/patio is a pleasant
spot on warm days. 🌑☕◑♿♣P🚃(62,X74)🌸🛜

Mamhilad

Horseshoe Inn ✅
Old Abergavenny Road, NP4 8QZ
☎ (01633) 880542 ⊕ horseshoe.wales
**House beer (by Sharp's); 2 changing beers (sourced
regionally; often Tiny Rebel, Tomos a Lilford)** Ⓗ
Pleasant country pub, ideal for those looking for a good
pint of ale or cider accompanied by top-quality food. Its
traditional, spacious interior features a main bar/dining
room plus a separate restaurant area. A locally brewed
house ale is served alongside two guests and a range of
ciders. Q🌑☕◑🅰♣P🌸🛜

WALES

Monmouth

Punch House ✓
4 Agincourt Square, NP25 3BT
☎ (01600) 713855
Brains Dark, Rev James Gold, Rev James Ⓗ
Imposing Grade II-listed former coaching inn with a distinctive white exterior that stands out when approached from Monnow Street. The traditional interior displays interesting artefacts including the door of the old town gaol. Food is very much to the fore, starting with breakfast/brunch, but drinkers are well catered for. Letting rooms are available, and live entertainment features on Friday evening. The family-friendly pub, well-loved for generations, welcomes children until mid-evening. ❀🖂◑&🏵🗚(69)❦🛜

Nant-y-Derry

Foxhunter Inn
NP7 9DN
☎ (01873) 881101 ⊕ foxhunterinn.com
Felinfoel Double Dragon; Untapped Whoosh; Wye Valley Butty Bach; 1 changing beer (sourced regionally; often Wadworth) Ⓗ
This fine old building once used to serve as the tea rooms for Nant-y-Derry station, which was opposite. It has been a popular bar and restaurant for many years. The current licensee reopened the pub in 2015 and offers good food and drink plus occasional entertainment. Curry night is Tuesday, seniors' specials are served on Thursday lunchtime (booking advisable). Accommodation is available in two adjoining cottages. ➽➚❀🖂◑&P❦

Newport

Cellar Door
5 Clytha Park Road, NP20 4NZ
☎ 07930 857897
3 changing beers Ⓗ
Newport's only micropub opened in 2017 and is just five minutes' walk from the railway station. Regularly changing artwork is displayed on the walls. Three ales from microbreweries are augmented by up to eight ciders from local producers. Chilled bottled ales from Newport's own Anglo-Oregon Brewing Company are always on sale. Following on from the 2019 addition of an overspill room, 2020 saw the completion of an outside drinking area at the rear. Q❀➽♣●🗚❦

Godfrey Morgan Ⓛ ✓
158 Chepstow Road, Maindee, NP19 8EG
☎ (01633) 221928
Brains SA; Greene King Abbot; Ruddles Best Bitter; Sharp's Doom Bar; 2 changing beers (sourced nationally; often Rhymney) Ⓗ
Taking its name from the 1st Viscount Tredegar, a survivor of the Charge of the Light Brigade, this large, open-plan Wetherspoon pub was once a cinema, and displays photos of film stars from a bygone-age with local connections. It stocks the usual range of national and regional ales, plus one or two more interesting options. The pub has a small car park at the rear, with some or all of the charge refundable when you buy your pint. Q➽❀◑&P🗚(8,73)🛜

Olde Murenger House
52-53 High Street, NP20 1GA
☎ (01633) 263977
Samuel Smith Old Brewery Bitter Ⓗ
No pub crawl of Newport is complete without calling in to savour the atmosphere of this Victorian-style Samuel Smith establishment. Note the wood panelling, high-

back settles and memorabilia of local history, commemorating iconic buildings and celebrities past and present. The building dates back to the 16th century and served several purposes before becoming a pub. Now offering keenly priced ale and tasty food, it has become something of a local institution. ◑➚🗚❦

Pen & Wig Ⓛ
22-24 Stow Hill, NP20 1JD
☎ (01633) 666818
Draught Bass; 5 changing beers (sourced regionally; often Boss, Gloucester, Tudor) Ⓗ
Popular city-centre pub with several linked sections, some for dining, and most within sight of a TV for sport. The food offering is appetising and substantial; just the job to complement the interesting range of ales. The pub prides itself on showcasing Welsh and West Country beers alongside the Bass. A large upstairs function room is available for hire, and a deck patio at the rear is popular in fine weather. ❀◑➽♣P🗚(151)❦

St Julian Inn
Caerleon Road, NP18 1QA
☎ (01633) 243548 ⊕ stjulian.co.uk
Bath Ales Gem; Fuller's London Pride; 1 changing beer (sourced regionally; often Ludlow, Quantock, Wye Valley) Ⓗ
Well-run pub in a scenic location, perched on a bend overlooking the River Usk with views towards the Roman attractions of Caerleon. Several areas are arranged around a central bar, including a lounge lined with wood panelling recovered from a former ocean liner. The regular beers are usually joined by a light, hoppy guest ale. The riverside balcony is popular for outdoor supping with a countryside view. ➽❀◑♣P🗚❦🛜

Tiny Rebel
22-23 High Street, NP20 1FX
☎ (01633) 252538
Tiny Rebel Cwtch; 4 changing beers (sourced nationally; often Tiny Rebel) Ⓗ
Modern bar showcasing the innovative products of one of the UK's most progressive breweries. Beers of all types appear here, attracting drinkers who enjoy both traditional and more experimental ales. The bar displays Tiny Rebel's quirky decor; downstairs are a lounge and games area. Food includes pizza and pasta, and you can watch your meal being cooked through a window at the back of the bar counter. ❀◑&➚♣●❦🛜

Pantygelli

Crown Inn Ⓛ
Old Hereford Road, NP7 7HR
☎ (01873) 853314 ⊕ thecrownatpantygelli.com
Draught Bass; Rhymney Bevans Bitter; Wye Valley HPA; 1 changing beer (sourced regionally; often Evan Evans, Grey Trees, Tomos Watkin) Ⓗ
Set in rolling countryside two miles north of Abergavenny, with fine views across fields to the Skirrid mountain, this CAMRA award-winning gastropub is renowned for its high-quality ale and food. Booking is recommended for meals. The well-balanced portfolio of beers includes a frequently changing guest. Outside is a lovely flower-decked patio, popular on sunny days. ➽❀◑♣P

Penallt

Boat Inn
Lone Lane, NP25 4AJ
☎ (01600) 712615 ⊕ theboatpenallt.co.uk

Kingstone Gold ⊞; Wye Valley Butty Bach; 1 changing beer (sourced regionally; often Wickwar) ⊞/Ⓖ
Pub locations do not come much more idyllic than this, set amid wondrous Wye Valley scenery. Easiest access is across the old railway footbridge from Redbrook in England. One Wye Valley ale is always available alongside two varying guest beers, with at least 12 draught ciders providing fulsome choice. The home-cooked food is particularly popular.
🛌🌣🖪◗♣🍴P🚏(69) ♣

Pontymister

Commercial Inn ✪
Commercial Street, NP11 6BA
☎ (01633) 612608 ⊕ thecommercialpontymister.com
3 changing beers (sourced nationally) ⊞
Busy locals' pub on the main road through the village, popular for reasonably priced and varied meals plus a wide range of cask and craft keg ales. The room is somewhat dominated by TV sets on most walls, though these are mercifully muted unless there is a match on. A pool table is in one corner and there is a decent jukebox near the bar. The outside area is inviting in summer.
🛌🌣◗♿⇌(Risca & Pontymister) ♣🚏(151,56) 🛜

Raglan

Beaufort Arms
High Street, NP15 2DY
☎ (01291) 690412 ⊕ beaufortraglan.co.uk
Untapped Border Bitter, UPA, Whoosh ⊞
Former coaching inn with a cosy feel and good-quality accommodation, diagonally opposite the large parish church. The bar has a hunting and fishing theme and the larger lounge offers a relaxing atmosphere; the elegant brasserie is modern but sympathetic to the older fabric of the building. Beers from the local Untapped Brewing Company find favour as it's almost the brewery tap. The Mediterranean-inspired menu features locally sourced produce, with themed nights including pie Tuesday, curry Wednesday and seafood Thursday. 🌣🖪◗P🚏(60,83)🛜

Rogerstone

Tiny Rebel Brewery Bar
Wern Industrial Estate, Wern Terrace, NP10 9FQ (off Chartist Drive for vehicles)
☎ (01633) 547378
Tiny Rebel Cwtch; 2 changing beers (sourced locally; often Tiny Rebel) ⊞
Modern, trendy barn of a place, with an upstairs balcony and views of the brewery through windows at the back. There is an impressive array of handpulls on the bar, though with some duplication. A huge screen and quality sound system mean the pub can get noisy during sporting events. The veranda with its comfortable seating is a suntrap in summer.
🛌🌣◗♿♣P🅿🚏(151,56) ♣🛜

Tintern

Wye Valley Hotel
Monmouth Road, NP16 6SQ
☎ (01291) 689441 ⊕ thewyevalleyhotel.co.uk
Wye Valley Bitter; 1 changing beer (sourced locally; often Kingstone) ⊞
Set in a beautiful valley, here is a fine place to pause, drink and stay. A Wye Valley beer is always on offer along with something from the nearby Kingstone Brewery. The comfortable single bar has a multi-angled shape matching the distinctive 1920s pub itself. An array

of commemorative beer bottles lines a shelf around the room. Generous home-cooked meals are available in the bar and traditional restaurant. Opening times are extended in summer. 🛌🌣🖪◗♿▲P🚏(69)♣🛜

Trellech

Lion Inn ✪
Church Street, NP25 4PA
☎ (01600) 860322 ⊕ lioninn.co.uk
3 changing beers (often Kingstone, Wye Valley) ⊞
Traditional country inn located in a history-steeped village that is well worth exploring. The charming bar is centred around a fireplace. On a slightly higher level is a cosy lounge and dining area where good food is served from an interesting menu. Ales are from breweries in south Wales and the West Country. The pub hosts beer and cider festivals featuring live music.
Q🛌🌣🖪◗♣P🚏(65) ♣🛜

Trellech Grange

Fountain Inn
NP16 6QW SO503011
☎ (01291) 689303 ⊕ fountaininntrellech.co.uk
Glamorgan Brewing Co Cwrw Gorslas/Bluestone Bitter; Wye Valley Butty Bach; 1 changing beer (sourced locally; often Kingstone) ⊞
A fine 17th-century drovers' inn, in the countryside a few miles from Tintern Abbey, somewhat off the beaten track but worth seeking out. Three well-kept ales are always available alongside one local cider. In winter two real fires keep you cosy; in summer the garden with its own brook is welcoming. Hours may vary so check ahead.
🛌🌣◗▲♣P♣

Upper Llanover

Goose & Cuckoo Ⓛ
NP7 9ER (follow handwritten signs to pub) SO292073
☎ (01873) 880277 ⊕ gooseandcuckooinn.wales
Rhymney Bitter; Untapped Monnow; 2 changing beers (sourced regionally; often Felinfoel, Wye Valley) ⊞
Step back in time at this remote hilltop pub situated at the end of a winding single-track lane above Llanover, with lovely views across the Vale of Usk from its garden. The building, with its flagstoned floor and large wood-burning stove, has remained unchanged for many years. Popular with walkers, cyclists and visitors to the area, it is also a local for those living on these hillsides in the Brecon Beacons National Park. Local CAMRA Country Pub of the Year 2020. Q🛌🌣🖪◗♣P♣

Usk

New Court Inn
62 Maryport Street, NP15 1AD
☎ (01291) 671319 ⊕ thenewcourtinn.co.uk
Draught Bass; Glamorgan Welsh Pale Ale; Wye Valley Butty Bach; 2 changing beers (sourced regionally) ⊞
Tastefully restored by the present owners, this is an established dining venue with a pleasant bar in which to enjoy a choice of real ales and ciders. The beer range includes popular house ales plus guests; the food menu has an excellent choice of lip-smacking dishes. At the rear is a suntrap garden for when the weather is fine. Good-quality accommodation makes this a handy base from which to explore the local area.
Q🛌🌣🖪◗♣🍴🚏(60,63) ♣🛜

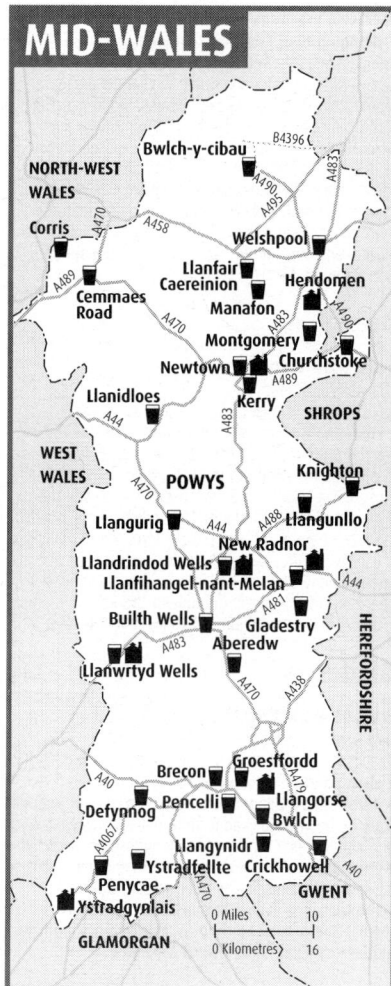

MID-WALES

NORTH-WEST WALES

Bwlch-y-cibau
B4396
A483
A490
A495
Corris
A470
A458
Welshpool
Llanfair Caereinion
Hendomen
Cemmaes Road
Manafon
A470
A483
A490
Montgomery
Newtown
Churchstoke
A489
Llanidloes
Kerry
A44
A483
SHROPS

WEST WALES

POWYS
Knighton

Llangurig
A44
A488
Llangunllo
New Radnor
Llandrindod Wells
Llanfihangel-nant-Melan
A481
A44
Builth Wells
Gladestry
Aberedw
A483
Llanwrtyd Wells
A470
A438
HEREFORDSHIRE

Brecon
Groesffordd
Defynnog
Pencelli
Llangorse
A40
A4067
Bwlch
Llangynidr
Ystradfellte
Crickhowell
A40
Penycae
GWENT
Ystradgynlais
GLAMORGAN

0 Miles 10
0 Kilometres 16

Authority area covered: Powys UA

Aberedw

Seven Stars Inn

LD2 3UW (next to church)
☎ (01982) 560762 ⊕ sevenstarsaberedw.co.uk
Changing beers
Nestled in the centre of the village of Aberedw this historic inn is close to the ancient church, a castle mound and scenic river gorge. A recent community buyout saved the Seven Stars for the village. Its large main bar has low beams, exposed stonework and a wood-burning stove. Food is served daily with home-made desserts a speciality. B&B accommodation is available in three en-suite rooms. Phone for opening hours and food times before travelling. Q⟡🛏️◑&🅰️♿P🐾🌐

Brecon

Brecon Tap

6 Bulwark, LD3 7LB
☎ (01874) 622353
4 changing beers (sourced regionally) 🅷
In a prime town-centre location, this contemporary bar has a light and airy feel, with comfortable seating

throughout and walls lined with bottle-filled shelves. Three or four varying guest ales are served, often from Welsh breweries. There is also an interesting range of international and UK craft ales, plus simple food including sandwiches and pies. Bottled beers, wines, craft spirits and local artisan produce are available for off-sales. Q⟡◑♿🛏️🚌(T4,X43) 🐾🌐

Clarence

25 The Watton, LD3 7ED
☎ (01874) 622810 ⊕ clarenceinn.co.uk
1 changing beer 🅷
Two-roomed town-centre community pub with a contemporary, welcoming and relaxed atmosphere. The front bar tends to be frequented by locals; the larger back bar is more popular with diners. Guest beers are generally from local breweries. A large-screen TV shows big sporting events. The spacious garden is a major attraction, especially during the annual Brecon Jazz Festival. ⟡🐾🛏️◑♿🚌(T4, X43)🐾

George Hotel ✓

1 George Street, LD3 7LD (just off The Struet)
☎ (01874) 620250
2 changing beers 🅷
Former 16th-century inn, now a Wetherspoon house, bringing additional choice to the town centre. The expanded interior incorporates a large bar area at the back with numerous rooms leading off it. Up to six ales are served, with national brews supplemented by beers from smaller breweries. Food is available all day and there are four letting bedrooms. ⟡🐾🛏️◑&🚌(T4,X43) 🌐

Builth Wells

Fountain Inn ✓

7-9 Broad Street, LD2 3DT
☎ (01982) 553888
3 changing beers 🅷
Town-centre pub that is popular with locals. Decorated in a modern style, it retains a traditional feel with stonework, exposed floorboards and a wood-burner. The pub serves up to four regularly changing real ales plus a real cider. Pool and darts are played in the bar, and sports TVs show major events. Next door is a café area and an upstairs terrace with a view of the River Wye. ◑♣♿P🛏️

Bwlch

New Inn

Brecon Road, LD3 7RQ (on A40 between Brecon and Crickhowell)
☎ (01874) 730215 ⊕ beaconsbackpackers.co.uk
2 changing beers (sourced regionally) 🅷
Lively and cosy village pub popular both with locals and visitors. A comfortable dining area sits to the side of the stone-flagged bar, with armchairs around a huge fireplace. Two interesting guest beers supplement the regular ale, and good-value home-cooked food is available at weekends – the pies are deservedly popular. It is an excellent base for exploring the surrounding

Brecon Beacons and Black Mountains, with bunkhouse accommodation available. Local CAMRA Pub of the Year 2017-2020. Q ✤ 🐕 ⛽ ◑ ♣ ● P 🚆 (X43,43) 🌳 🛜

Bwlch-y-cibau

Stumble Inn

SY22 5LL

☎ (01691) 648860 ⊕ thestumble.co.uk

2 changing beers ⊞ /ℙ

The Stumble was established in the 16th century. It was originally called the Cross Keys but changed its name to avoid confusion with another local pub. On the right as you enter is a wooden-beamed public bar, and on the left a well-appointed 50-seat restaurant, which serves award-winning food. The beers are rotated on a regular basis, with at least one from a local brewery. Seasonal hours may operate so it's best to phone ahead if travelling. Q ✤ 🐕 ◑ ♣ ● P 🚆 (Tanat Valley 76) 🌳 🛜

Cemmaes Road

Dovey Valley Hotel ★

SY20 8JZ

☎ (01650) 511335 ⊕ doveyvalleyhotel.com

2 changing beers (sourced locally; often Evan Evans, Monty's) ⊞

A gem of a pub built to serve the nearby railway. Boasting a nationally important historic interior, it comprises a cosy main bar and snug with features from the 1870s, including original slate floors and an Edwardian tiled fireplace, with log fire in winter. The pub is furnished with mirrors and brewery memorabilia. Spontaneous live music sessions occasionally take place. Q ✤ 🐕 ⛽ ◑ ▲ ♣ ● P 🚆 (T12) 🌳 🛜

Churchstoke

Horse & Jockey

SY15 6AE

☎ (01588) 620060

2 changing beers (sourced regionally) ⊞

A prominent stone-built pub on the edge of the village. It serves a changing range of guest ales, plus up to nine real ciders and perries during the summer. The wood-beamed public bar hosts pool, darts and bar billiards. The carpeted lounge features comfortable armchairs and wall seating, and leads to a large, smart restaurant. A stone fireplace with wood-burning stove provides winter warmth. ✤ 🐕 ◑ ♿ ▲ ♣ ● P 🚆 (81) 🌳 🛜

Corris

Slaters Arms

Bridge Street, SY20 9SP

☎ (01654) 761324 ⊕ slatersarmscorris.co.uk

3 changing beers (sourced nationally; often Big Bog, Conwy, Cwrw Ogwen) ⊞

Named after what was once the main trade in Corris, this Grade II-listed, three-roomed village pub is popular with locals and visitors staying nearby. Its main bar has traditional slate flooring and a decorative mantelshelf above a large inglenook fireplace. The pub offers a third-pint platter for the price of a pint. There is a dining room to the left and a room for pub games at the rear. Walkers, families and well-behaved dogs are welcome. Take-away food is available. ✤ ◑ ▲ ♣ ● P 🚆 (34) 🌳 🛜

Crickhowell

Bear Hotel

High Street, NP8 1BW

☎ (01873) 810408 ⊕ bearhotel.co.uk

1 changing beer (sourced regionally) ⊞

Originally a 15th-century coaching inn, this is now an award-winning hotel and Guide regular. Its grand, multi-roomed bar features exposed beams, wood panelling, settles and an eclectic selection of furnishings and decorations. The two bar rooms have exposed fireplaces, as does one of the side rooms. Four ales are usually served, often including guests from smaller Welsh breweries. Food is excellent and the menu features much local produce. An excellent base for exploring the Black Mountains and Brecon Beacons National Park. Q ✤ 🐕 ◑ ♿ ▲ P 🚆 (X43,43) 🌳

Defynnog

Tanners Arms

LD3 8SF (on A4067)

☎ (01874) 638032 ⊕ tannersarmspub.com

2 changing beers (sourced locally) ⊞ /🄶

Family-run country pub known for its warm welcome, set in a delightful village in the Brecon Beacons National Park. It has traded continuously since 1870 and the original buildings – cottages for workers at the nearby tannery – date from circa 1806. A selection of real ciders is usually on offer alongside home-cooked food. The pub opens all day on bank holidays, and holds a number of beer and cider festivals throughout the year. A multiple local CAMRA award winner. ✤ 🐕 ◑ ▲ ♣ ● P 🚆 🌳 🛜

Gladestry

Royal Oak Inn

HR5 3NR

☎ (01544) 370586 ⊕ theroyaloakgladestry.co.uk

2 changing beers (sourced regionally) ⊞

A 17th-century village inn on Offa's Dyke Path National Trail, in the wilds of Radnorshire between Hay-on-Wye and Kington. It is run by a couple whose previous pubs were Guide regulars with excellent reputations. Dogs on leads are welcome in the beer garden. B&B accommodation is available in two en-suite rooms. Opens most lunchtimes and evenings, but check before travelling. Q ✤ 🐕 ◑ ▲ ♣ P 🌳 🛜

Groesffordd

Three Horseshoes

LD3 7SN (just off B4558 in centre of village)

☎ (01874) 665672 ⊕ threehorseshoesgroesffordd.com

2 changing beers (sourced regionally) ⊞

Busy village-centre venue in the heart of the Brecon Beacons, boasting superb views from its outdoor seating areas. The pub is only a 10-minute walk from the Brynich lock on the Monmouthshire & Brecon Canal and is a popular stop for boaters and other visitors. The emphasis here is on the excellent food but the ales are always varied and interesting. Brynich caravan site and the Brecon YHA are nearby. ✤ ◑ ♿ ▲ ♣ ● 🌳 🛜

Kerry

Kerry Lamb

SY16 4NP

☎ (01686) 670226 ⊕ thekerrylambpowys.co.uk

Wye Valley Butty Bach; 2 changing beers (often Three Tuns, Tudor, Purple Moose) ⊞

Prominent red-bricked pub on the edge of the village, named after the Kerry Hill sheep. Locally owned, it seamlessly flits between its role as a community pub and restaurant, offering something for all tastes. It consists of a large lounge/bar, a games room and dining room. The

St Michael and All Angels church backs on to the rear, giving a picturesque view from the beer garden during warmer weather. 🏃😋🍷🚫♿♣♠P🚃(81)😺🛜

Knighton

Watsons Ale House
24 High Street, LD7 1AT
☎ (01547) 740017
3 changing beers Ⓗ
A former tea room and butcher's shop near the clock tower, this is the home of Watson's Real Powys Farmhouse Cider. The pub is next to a chip shop, where food can be ordered to eat with your beers. It welcomes walkers and dogs, and has become a regular post-lockdown drinking place for CAMRA members. Phone for opening times before travelling. Q😋🍷≠♠🚃(46)😺🛜

Llandrindod Wells

Middleton Arms
Tremont Road, LD1 5EB (corner of Trefonen Lane)
☎ (01597) 822066
1 changing beer (sourced regionally) Ⓗ
A friendly street-corner local at the north end of town on the A483 road to Newtown, named after one of the town's Victorian developers. The guest beer changes weekly. It supports four darts teams as well as pool and dominoes teams, and screens sports channels on TV. There is an enclosed drinking area outside. Families and dogs are welcome.
Q🏃😋♿≠(Llandrindod)♣🚃(461,T4)😺🛜

Llanfair Caereinion

Goat Hotel
High Street, SY21 0QS (off A485)
☎ (01938) 810428 ⊕ thegoathotel.co.uk
3 changing beers (sourced locally; often Stonehouse, Wood) Ⓗ
An excellent 300-year-old beamed coaching inn whose welcoming atmosphere attracts both locals and tourists. The plush lounge, dominated by a large inglenook with open fire, features comfortable leather armchairs and sofas. The real ale selection usually includes a beer from the Wood Brewery. Home-cooked food is served in the dining room, and there is a games room at the rear. Beware the low-beamed entrance to the Gents.
Q🏃😋🍷≠(Welshpool & Llanfair LR)♣🚃(87)😺🛜

Llanfihangel-nant-Melan

Fforest Inn
LD8 2TN (jct of A44 and A481)
☎ (01544) 350526 ⊕ thefforest.co.uk
2 changing beers (sourced nationally) Ⓗ
One of Wales' oldest pubs and built in the 16th century as a drovers' inn it is steeped in history and retains many original features. It has gained a good reputation for quality beers over many years. The menu highlights fresh local produce. Well-behaved dogs are welcome in the bar. Phone before travelling. Q🏃😋🍷P🚃(461)😺

Llangunllo

Greyhound Ⓛ
LD7 1SP (in village centre on B4356)
☎ (01547) 550400
2 changing beers (sourced nationally) Ⓗ
This unique 16th-century inn, set in picturesque countryside, is the first stop on the Glyndwr's Way long-distance trail. Its regular beers are usually from regional

breweries, with guest ales often different and interesting. The pub's owners have always taken great care to ensure the beers are in good condition. The cider is Westons Family Reserve. There are regular open mic music sessions on the first Saturday of the month. Phone to check opening times before travelling.
Q🏃😋♿≠(Llangynllo)♣😺🛜

Llangurig

Black Lion Hotel
SY18 6SG
☎ (01686) 440223
Three Tuns Best; 1 changing beer (sourced locally; often Three Tuns) Ⓗ
Originally a shooting lodge, the Black Lion was first licensed in 1633 and rebuilt as a hotel in the late 19th century. It has low ceilings and wooden beams, and is divided into two bars and a conservatory. The first bar acts as a games area, with pool and table skittles. The lounge/dining area has a stone fireplace, wall seating and settles. There is also a side room with comfortable armchairs. Q🏃😋🍷🍷♿♣P🚃(X75,525)😺🛜

Llangynidr

Red Lion
Duffryn Road, NP8 1NT (off B4558)
☎ (01874) 730223 ⊕ theredlion1.vpweb.co.uk
2 changing beers (sourced regionally) Ⓗ
Popular village local, situated away from the main road, with a warm welcome for families, dogs, walkers and boaters – the Monmouthshire & Brecon Canal is a short walk away. The beer range changes regularly and good-value home-cooked food is served in the bar. A separate games area, outside seating and children's play area make this a pub for all. Regular quiz nights and live music also feature. 🏃😋🍷🍷♣P🚃😺🛜

Llanidloes

Crown & Anchor ★
41 Long Bridge Street, SY18 6EF
☎ (01686) 412398 ⊕ crown-anchor-inn-pub.business.site
Wye Valley Butty Bach; 2 changing beers (sourced regionally; often Purple Moose, Wye Valley) Ⓗ
A Grade II-listed pub affectionately nicknamed Ruby's after its long-serving landlady, who has now retired. It comprises five unspoilt rooms, one of which was a haberdasher's shop before becoming part of the pub in 1948. A small corridor links the rooms, one displaying guitars that visiting musicians are welcome to play. A middle room and snug are connected to the bar by glass serving hatches. Q🏃😋♣🚃(X75,525)😺🛜

Llanwrtyd Wells

Neuadd Arms Hotel Ⓛ
The Square, LD5 4RB
☎ (01591) 610236 ⊕ neuaddarmshotel.co.uk
4 changing beers (sourced locally) Ⓗ
This large Victorian hotel is the tap for the Heart of Wales Brewery. The Bells Bar features a large fireplace and an eclectic mix of furniture. The bells, formerly used to summon servants, remain on one wall, along with the winners' boards from some of the town's unusual and famous competitions. The lounge bar is more formal. A good range of real cider is served alongside the ales. The hotel takes part in local events, including a beer festival over two weekends in November.
Q😋🍷🍷≠(Llanwrtyd)♣😋P😺

Manafon

Beehive Inn
SY21 8BL
☎ (01686) 651007
**Salopian Shropshire Gold; Stonehouse Station
Bitter** Ⓗ
A timbered black-and-white Rhiw Valley local in the
heart of the village. Established in the 1650s as a drovers'
inn, it has original beams and settles throughout. The
pub was originally much smaller; other rooms have been
incorporated over the years, including one on the right
which was once a butcher's. There is a caravan park at
the rear with the river running beside the large beer
garden. The adjacent church creates a peaceful backdrop
amid pleasant scenery. Q ☺ ❀ ♣ ♠P 🎄

Montgomery

Dragon Hotel
Market Square, SY15 6PA
☎ (01686) 668359 ⊕ dragonhotel.com
**4 changing beers (sourced regionally; often
Monty's)** Ⓗ
Dating from the mid-1600s, this former coaching inn has
a distinctive Tudor black-and-white half-timbered
frontage. The bar has been relocated to the rear of the
hotel, giving more space to the clientele. There are patio
areas outside to the front and rear for alfresco drinking.
The hotel boasts an indoor swimming pool and a large
function room. Q ☺ ❀ ⇆ ⏃ ⏃ ♠P🚌 (T12,81)❀ 🎄

Newtown

Railway Tavern
Old Kerry Road, SY16 1BH (off A483)
☎ (01686) 626156
2 changing beers (sourced regionally) Ⓗ
A return to the Guide for this establishment. The Railway
consists of two areas, a lower bar and a rear space with
benches and tables. Darts and dominoes are hosted; the
pub gets crowded on match nights. Two guest beers are
usually on tap, often from regional or small breweries.
Note the poster listing more than 50 pubs that once
operated in Newtown. Outside toilets are located
through the passageway. ❀🍺♣🚌 (X75,X81)

Sportsman Ⓛ
17 Severn Street, SY16 2AQ (off A483)
☎ (01686) 623978
**Monty's Sunshine; Salopian Oracle; Wye Valley Butty
Bach, HPA; 2 changing beers (sourced nationally)** Ⓗ
Free house that was formerly Monty's taphouse. The pub
is divided into three areas – a snug with comfortable wall
seating, a main bar area with a wood-burning stove and
a rear tiled games area with pool table, TV and darts.
There is a patio at the rear for summer drinking. A former
local CAMRA Pub of the Year and Welsh Cider Pub of the
Year. Q❀♿⇆♣♠🚌🎄

Pencelli

Royal Oak
LD3 7LX
☎ (01874) 665396 ⊕ theroyaloakpencelli.com
3 changing beers (sourced regionally) Ⓗ
Friendly family-run pub in a quiet village alongside the
Monmouthshire & Brecon Canal. Its extended opening
hours are welcome in this part of the Brecon Beacons.
The regular ale is supplemented with two or three
others, usually from independent Welsh breweries. The
pretty garden next to the canal is a delight on a sunny

day. Popular with walkers, cyclists and boaters, with
moorings adjacent to the garden.
Q❀❀⏃♿Å♣♠P🚌(X43)❀🎄

Penycae

Ancient Briton
Brecon Road, SA9 1YY (on A4067 Swansea to Brecon
road)
☎ (01639) 730273 ⊕ ancientbriton.co.uk
**Wye Valley Butty Bach; 6 changing beers (sourced
nationally; often Oakham, Pitchfork, Salopian)** Ⓗ
Warm and friendly pub in the Brecon Beacons National
Park. Up to seven ales and six ciders are served regularly.
The pub welcomes children, campers and walkers. It is
close to the famous Dan yr Ogof show caves and Craig y
Nos castle. There is plenty of car parking on-site, and
accommodation in four en-suite rooms. A former local
CAMRA Pub of the Year on numerous occasions for both
its ales and ciders. ☺❀⇆⏃♣♠P🚌(T6)❀🎄

Welshpool

Angel
12 Berriew Street, SY21 7SQ
☎ (01938) 553473 ⊕ angelwelshpool.com
**3 changing beers (sourced locally; often Hobsons,
Salopian, Three Tuns)** Ⓗ
Modernised town-centre pub with a small, comfortable
snug near the main door as a reminder of how it once
was. The long main bar leads to a rear section featuring a
pool table and numerous TVs showing sport – there is
even a TV in the Gents. The three ales come from
Shropshire breweries. Outside to the rear is an area for
drinking and smoking. Happy hour is 4-8pm during the
week. ☺❀⏃♿⇆♣🚌🎄

Pheasant Inn
43 High Street, SY21 7JQ
☎ (01938) 553104 ⊕ pheasantwelshpool.co.uk
**3 changing beers (sourced locally; often Ludlow,
Salopian, Three Tuns)** Ⓗ
Vibrant pub in a terrace of what were 18th-century town
houses. The Grade II-listed building is much modified
internally, featuring a long room with wooden floor, pool
table and dartboard, and comfortable seating at the far
end. A rear door leads to the outside drinking area. Ales
are usually from small or regional breweries, with a third
guest beer often served at weekends. ❀⇆♣🚌🎄

Ystradfellte

New Inn
CF44 9JE
☎ (01639) 721014 ⊕ waterfallways.co.uk
2 changing beers (sourced locally) Ⓗ
A 16th-century village pub in the middle of Waterfall
Country, a popular walking area in the Brecon Beacons.
With two log fires and a small beer garden, it offers a
welcome whatever the weather. Two local ales are kept
on tap, usually from Glamorgan and Grey Trees
breweries. There is a strong focus on local produce,
including spirits from nearby Penderyn Distillery. Home-
cooked food includes the popular Boozy Cow Pie, made
fresh with the ale on tap. Q☺❀⏃Å♠P❀

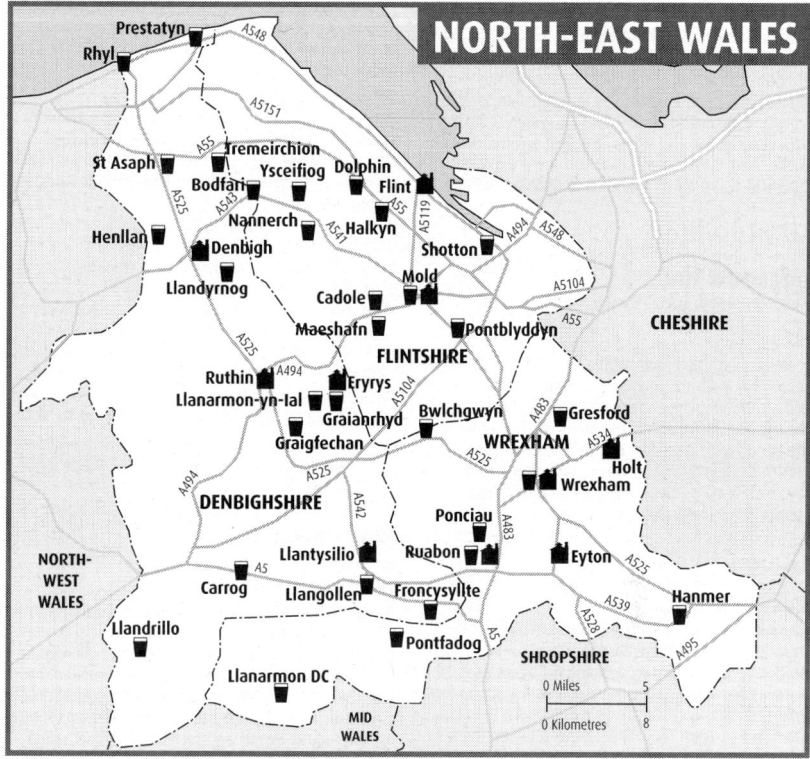

NORTH-EAST WALES

WALES

Authority areas covered: Denbighshire UA, Flintshire UA, Wrexham UA

Bodfari

Dinorben Arms ⓁL

B5429, LL16 4DA SJ092701

☎ (01745) 775090

Brunning & Price Original; Facer's North Star Porter; Timothy Taylor Boltmaker; 4 changing beers (sourced locally) ⒽH

Reputedly established in 1640, the building was derelict for eight years before it was acquired by Brunning & Price. Its elevated position by the 16th-century church and tower offers fine views across the Vale of Clwyd. Primarily a destination pub popular for meals, the spacious interior has several dining areas in typical B&P style. Food is served all day, as well as a good selection of real ales including three regular beers and four guests usually from local micros. 坐⊛◑ & P♫ (14)♣ 🡪

Bwlchgwyn

King's Head Inn ⓁL

Ruthin Road, LL11 5UT (on A525)

☎ (01978) 753089

2 changing beers (sourced locally; often Big Hand) ⒽH

Friendly locals' free house standing on the main road through one of Wales' highest villages. It reopened in 2017 after an impressive and modern refurbishment. Entrance is through a neat and tidy room warmed by a large wood-burner, with the bar facing you. To the side is another comfortable room with banquette seating. The pub offers hearty meals to accompany two local beers on handpump, usually from Big Hand. Bus services are limited. 坐⊛◑♫□(X51)♣ 🡪

Cadole

Colomendy Arms

Village Road, CH7 5LL (off A494 Mold-Ruthin road)

☎ (01352) 810217

6 changing beers ⒽH

A wonderful pub in the middle of the village, run by the same family for more than 30 years and featuring in the Guide for most of that time. It has two cosy rooms with real fires, festooned with local history and photographs. Conversation is king here. Its six changing beers come from far and wide. A popular stop-off for walkers, with the Loggerheads Country Park close by. Q⊛♣P♫♣

Carrog

Grouse Inn

LL21 9AT (on B5437, off A5 at Llidiart Y Parc)

☎ (01490) 430272 ⊕ thegrouseinncarrog.co.uk

JW Lees Bitter, Founder's; 1 changing beer (often JW Lees) ⒽH

Originally a farm and brewhouse, this friendly family-run inn has a single bar serving several rooms. It was refurbished in 2020 without losing its fabulous character. Generous home-cooked food is served in most areas of the pub. The large covered patio offers splendid views of the Dee Valley, Berwyn Mountains and 1660 Carrog Bridge. Carrog station on the Llangollen Railway is a short walk away. Q坐⊛◑♫ ♣♫□♣ 🡪

Dolphin

Glan yr Afon Inn ⓁL

Milwr, CH8 8HE

☎ (01352) 710052 ⊕ glanyrafoninn.com

Facer's Dave's Hoppy Beer, Landslide ⊞
You can expect a warm welcome at this popular pub. It first opened in the 16th century and is in an elevated position with views of the Dee Estuary and the Wirral Peninsula. A central bar serves four separate seating areas and the dining room, while the games room has its own bar. The inn also offers food and accommodation. Walkers and dogs are welcome and there is a real fire to keep you warm on cold days. Q⏱♿✉⏸◖⏹&♣♠P🍴🐕🛜

Froncysyllte

Aqueduct Inn
Holyhead Road, LL20 7PY (on A5)
☎ (01691) 777118
4 changing beers (sourced nationally) ⊞
A welcoming free house on the busy A5. The small central bar leads to a games room with a TV to the right and a comfortable lounge with a wood-burning stove to the left. Outside, the veranda offers panoramic views of the Pontcysyllte Aqueduct on the Llangollen Canal. Up to four changing ales are available, with Bathams a favourite. Food is served daily, with a traditional roast on Sunday. ⏱♿◖⏹♣♠P🍴(64)🐕🛜

Graianrhyd

Rose & Crown
Llanarmon Road, CH7 4QW (on B5430 off A5104)
☎ (01824) 780727 ⊕ theroseandcrownpub.co.uk
Black Sheep Best Bitter; 2 changing beers ⊞
A traditional early 19th-century pub with a strong local following. The long bar serves two rooms – the main room has an open fire, copper-topped tables and a vast array of pumpclips. Guest beers are usually from local breweries. The pub is popular with tourists, walkers, cyclists and fell runners keen to fuel up on post-race chip baps following the local Dash in the Dark. Q⏱♿✉◖A♣♠P🍴(2)🐕

Graigfechan

Three Pigeons Inn 🄻
LL15 2EU (on B5429 about 3 miles from Ruthin)
☎ (01824) 703178 ⊕ threepigeonsinn.co.uk
4 changing beers ⊞
Fine old drovers' inn with parts originating from the 12th century. The interior is tastefully decorated, retaining original features and open log fires. There is an extensive lounge area with a sports room to one side and a large dining space to the other. Cellars are ideal for keeping the cask ales that are still, on occasion, served in jugs. An outdoor area to the rear has great views over the Vale of Clwyd. Two self-catering apartments are available and a campsite is adjacent. ⏱♿✉◖A♣♠P🍴(76)🐕🛜

Gresford

Griffin Inn
Church Green, LL12 8RG
☎ (01978) 855280
Courage Best Bitter; 1 changing beer (sourced nationally; often Moorhouse's, Weetwood) ⊞
Friendly community pub with an irregular, open-plan layout adorned with many interesting pictures. Lively conversation at the bar does not impinge on the quieter corners. Sited where pilgrims came to drink in the Middle Ages, opposite is All Saints Church, whose bells are one of the Seven Wonders of Wales. There is a lawned area to the side with seating. Bus No.1 (Chester-Wrexham) stops in the village half a mile away. The landlady has been running the pub since 1973. Q⏱♿♠P🍴(1)🛜

Pant-yr-Ochain 🄻
Old Wrexham Road, LL12 8TY (off A5156, E from A483; follow signs to The Flash)
☎ (01978) 853525
Purple Moose Cwrw Eryri/Snowdonia Ale; Timothy Taylor Landlord; Titanic Plum Porter; Weetwood Eastgate; house beer (by Phoenix); 4 changing beers (sourced regionally; often Big Hand, Castle Rock, Mobberley) ⊞
Impressive 16th-century dower house that retains many historic features, situated beside a small lake within extensive gardens. The central room, dominated by a large double-fronted bar, leads to a variety of seating areas including a garden room, a snug behind a period inglenook fireplace, and the patio and lawn outside. Although hugely popular, the pub retains a quiet feel. Food is served all day and five regular beers are supplemented by four guests and often a draught cider. Happy hour is 5-7pm midweek. Q⏱♿◖&♣♠P🍴🐕🛜

Halkyn

Blue Bell Inn 🄻
Rhosesmor Road, CH8 8DL (on B5123)
☎ (01352) 780309 ⊕ bluebell.uk.eu.org
JW Lees Bitter; 3 changing beers (sourced locally) ⊞
Situated on Halkyn Mountain, the Blue Bell is a traditional rural inn and a good base for exploring the local countryside, with free guided walks around the area. Built in the 1700s and named after a local privateer's boat, the pub has a strong community focus, hosting regular events and societies. The beer range usually includes ales from north Wales breweries, often Facer's or Cwrw Llyn. A wide selection of real ciders is also available. Q⏱♿&A♣♠P🍴🐕🛜

Hanmer

Hanmer Arms
SY13 3DE (just off A495 1 mile from jct with A525)
☎ (01948) 830458 ⊕ hanmerarms.com
4 changing beers (sourced nationally) ⊞
This attractive hotel/restaurant just off the main Wrexham to Whitchurch road makes an ideal base for exploring the north Welsh borderlands, Shropshire and Cheshire. It is a short stroll from the picturesque Hanmer Mere and adjacent to the charming 12th-century St Chad's church. Hook Norton ales are usually on the bar, complemented by beers from Purple Moose and other changing guests. Lunchtime and evening meals are served plus a popular Sunday carvery. Accommodation is provided in 11 en-suite bedrooms. Q⏱♿✉◖&♣♠P🍴(146)🐕🛜

REAL ALE BREWERIES

Beech Avenue Holt (NEW)
Big Hand Wrexham
Denbigh Denbigh
Dovecote Denbigh
Facer's Flint
Hafod ⚘ Mold
Iâl Eryrys
Llangollen 🍺 Llantysilio
Magic Dragon Eyton
McGivern 🍺 Ruabon
Reaction Ruthin
Sandstone Wrexham

Henllan

Llindir Inn L

Llindir Street, LL16 5BH

☎ (01745) 812188

5 changing beers (sourced locally) H

Thirteenth-century Grade II-listed thatched inn. On entry you are welcomed into a room with a long copper bar and an inglenook fireplace, with a comfortable TV lounge offset. Three steps take you up to another bar and a further three steps to a pleasant restaurant. The interior retains its original character with old beams, tiled floors, copper and brassware. Up to five guest beers are available. Q☺�❀◑♣P🖵(6)�⚘ 🗢

Llanarmon DC

Hand at Llanarmon

LL20 7LD (at end of B4500 from Chirk)

☎ (01691) 600666 ⊕ thehandhotel.co.uk

2 changing beers (sourced locally; often Big Hand, Stonehouse, Weetwood) H

Cosy free house in a very scenic location at the head of the stunning Ceiriog Valley. Look for the giant wooden carved hand outside. Two – usually local – real ales are always available. The bar is dog-friendly, with an open fire. Walkers, cyclists and tourists are all welcome. Book ahead if dining at busy times. Both food and accommodation are of a very high standard, and the hotel has a spa. Q☺�❀◑✦⚘♣P🖵(64)⚘ 🗢

West Arms

LL20 7LD (at end of B4500)

☎ (01691) 600665 ⊕ thewestarms.com

4 changing beers (sourced nationally; often Big Hand, Timothy Taylor) H

Historic hotel in a scenic location at the end of the Ceiriog Valley. The garden runs down to the infant River Ceiriog and offers excellent views. The lounge features settles and an inglenook while the narrow bar is frequented by locals, dogs and walkers. Four changing ales often come from local breweries. Good-quality food is served lunchtimes and evenings (all day Sun), plus breakfast from early on and sandwiches in the afternoon. Q☺�❀◑✦♣P🖵(64) ⚘ 🗢

Llanarmon-yn-Ial

Raven Inn L

Ffordd-Rhiw-Ial, CH7 4QE (signed 500yds W of B5430)

☎ (01824) 780833 ⊕ raveninn.co.uk

Purple Moose Cwrw Eryri/Snowdonia Ale; 2 changing beers (sourced locally) H

Community-run by volunteers since 2009, this delightful old pub continues to go from strength to strength, with all profits used to benefit the community. There is a friendly and inviting ambience from the moment you enter. The bar serves two separate carpeted areas and a tiled area to one side. The three guest beers are from local breweries. Excellent locally sourced home-cooked food is served Thursday to Sunday. It has three self-catering bedrooms. Q☺�❀◑✦♣P🖵(2)⚘ 🗢

Llandrillo

Dudley Arms Hotel L

High Street, LL21 0TL

☎ (01490) 440223 ⊕ dudleyarms.wales

Stonehouse Station Bitter; 1 changing beer (sourced locally) H

Traditional Welsh village inn nestling within the Berwyn mountains. The owners have carried out an extensive

refurbishment to create a pub full of charm, with many period features and exposed oak beams. There are several discrete areas including a lounge, dining area and pool room, with stone walls, tiled floors and cosy fires. The guest beer is always from a local brewery. B&B accommodation is available upstairs and in an adjacent refurbished cottage. ☺�❀◑♣P🖵(T3)⚘ 🗢

Llandyrnog

Kinmel Arms L

Waen, LL16 4HN

☎ (01824) 790291 ⊕ kinmelarms.com

Marston's Saddle Tank; Young's London Special; 3 changing beers (often Big Hand) H

A warm and traditional pub on the edge of the Clwydian Range and close to Offa's Dyke path and Moel Arthur hill fort. The front bar area features a large wood-burner. There is a separate dining space, children's play area and games room. The guest beers are usually from local breweries Cwrw Ial, Big Hand and Wild Horse. Opening times are subject to change so check before visiting. Q☺�❀◑&✦♣P🖵(76) ⚘ 🗢

Llangollen

Chainbridge Hotel L

Berwyn, LL20 8BS (off B5103)

☎ (01978) 860215 ⊕ chainbridgehotel.com

Stonehouse Station Bitter; 2 changing beers (sourced locally; often Purple Moose, Stonehouse) H

Near the Horseshoe Falls, this comfortable hotel with a cosy bar and dining areas is set beside the turbulent River Dee with its chain bridge. Outside seating, bedecked in summer with colourful hanging baskets, makes the most of the dramatic location. White water thrill-seekers and puffing steam locomotives on the Llangollen Railway provide further entertainment. Llangollen itself is a short train ride from Berwyn station opposite, or a pleasant 30-minute stroll along the canalside towpath. ☺�❀◑&➔(Berwyn)P🖵(T3)⚘ 🗢

Three Eagles

Bridge Street, LL20 8PF

☎ (01978) 869595 ⊕ thethreeeagles.co.uk

Sharp's Doom Bar; house beer (by Big Hand); 1 changing beer (sourced locally; often Purple Moose) H

Formerly the Wynnstay Arms, this historic coaching inn is now a gastro-restaurant. The bar and main dining area are on the ground floor, with further dining areas on the upper two floors. The house beer is by Big Hand and the changing beer usually comes from a small local brewery. There is seating in the bar for those not dining. Features include a well by the entrance and a glass floor above the wine cellar. Q☺�❀◑&➔🖵(5,T3)⚘ 🗢

Maeshafn

Miners Arms L

Village Road, CH7 5LR (off A494 in village centre)

☎ (01352) 810464 ⊕ miners-arms-maeshafn.com

Facer's Flintshire Bitter; Theakston Old Peculier; Timothy Taylor Landlord; Wainwright H

Originally built in the 1820s as part of the development of lead mining in the area. Located in a small hamlet, the pub is surrounded by scenic countryside and is popular with hikers. Under new management, it has been refurbished, and has a central bar area divided from the dining section by a double-sided wood-burning stove, creating a warm atmosphere throughout. There is pleasant seating outside at the front. ☺❀P🖵(2)⚘ 🗢

Mold

Fat Boar 🄻

17 Chester Street, CH7 1EG
☎ (01352) 759890 ⊕ thefatboar.co.uk
2 changing beers (sourced locally) Ⓗ
Formerly called the Boar's Head and closed for several years, the pub reopened as the Fat Boar following renovation. Predominantly food-led, it has two local real ales on handpump. Two floors provide seating for around 80 people, and there is an additional outside space at the back of the building. The rear dining room has a TV for sports fans. Centrally situated in this market town, the pub is handy for local transport to and from surrounding areas. 🌑🎜🍽🍴🛢🚪🛜

Gold Cape ✅

8-8A Wrexham Street, CH7 1ES (next to Market Square crossroads)
☎ (01352) 705920
Greene King Abbot; Ruddles Best Bitter; Sharp's Doom Bar; 4 changing beers Ⓗ
Wetherspoon pub named after a 4,000-year-old solid gold ceremonial cape found near Mold in 1831. The original is now displayed in the British Museum in London and there is a copy in Mold Library. The walls display pictures of the town's past, including local poet and novelist Daniel Owen. The familiar range of drinks and food are available and annual beer and cider festivals hosted. Q🌑🍽🅰🍴🚪🛜

Mold Alehouse 🄻

Unit 2, Earl Chambers, Earl Road, CH7 1AL
☎ (01352) 218188 ⊕ moldalehouse.co.uk
4 changing beers (sourced locally; often Cwrw Ial, Facer's, Hafod) Ⓗ
Since opening in 2016, this micropub has won many CAMRA awards and gained a strong following based on sound principles of good beer, fellowship and conversation. It is centrally situated in a Grade II-listed building opposite the town hall and near Daniel Owen Square, named after the renowned Welsh writer, and home to Mold Library & Museum. The four cask ales include a dark beer, and there are also five KeyKeg lines and four ciders. Q🍴🚪🐾🛜

Nannerch

Cross Foxes 🄻

Village Road, CH7 5RD
☎ (01352) 741464 ⊕ cross-foxes.co.uk
3 changing beers (sourced locally; often Big Hand, Cwrw Ial) Ⓗ
This delightful village pub close to the church was built in 1780 and originally doubled up as a butcher's – the meat hooks still remain over the bar. The entrance leads into a main bar with a large fireplace. Off this is another small bar, a lounge and a function room. Three pumps serve changing beers, usually from local brewers including Big Hand and Cwrw Ial. Beer festivals are held in March and October. 🌑🍽🅰🍴🚪🛜

Ponciau

Colliers Arms

Chapel Street, LL14 1SE (off B5426)
3 changing beers (sourced regionally) Ⓗ
Splendid free house on a narrow terraced street with a convivial atmosphere. A rare cask ale outlet for the locality, guest ales are often from local microbreweries. The front room has a slate floor, comfortable bench seating and cast-iron tables. There is also a small snug and a back room with a pool table. To the rear is a

pleasant decked area and lawn. Public parking is available nearby. A former local CAMRA Pub of the Year. 🌑🎜🛢🍴🚪(3) 🐾🛜

Pontblyddyn

Bridge Inn

Wrexham Road, CH7 4HN (on A541 3 miles S of Mold)
☎ (01352) 770087
2 changing beers Ⓗ
Fine old building situated at a crossroads, with the River Alyn at the rear. The unspoilt interior has a warm and cosy front bar with a real fire, with another room leading off to the right and a separate restaurant to the left. There is also a courtyard area to the front and an extensive riverside beer garden and children's play area out the back. Q🌑🎜🍽🍴🚪🐾🛜

Pontfadog

Swan Inn

Llanarmon Road, LL20 7AR (on B4500 next to post office)
☎ (01691) 718273 ⊕ theswaninnpontfadog.com
2 changing beers (sourced locally; often Stonehouse) Ⓗ
Welcoming village free house in the scenic Ceiriog Valley. The cosy red-tiled bar, where the locals tend to congregate, features a central fireplace which separates the TV and darts area from the servery. The separate dining room leads to the outdoor area, which now has a terrace offering good views. On the bar are two changing ales from local breweries, often Stonehouse. Q🌑🎜🍽🍴🛢🚪(64) 🐾🛜

Prestatyn

Bar 236 🄻

236 High Street, LL19 9BP
☎ (01745) 850084 ⊕ bar236.co.uk
4 changing beers (sourced locally; often Cwrw Ial) Ⓗ
This refurbished café bar at the top of the High Street opened in 2010. The L-shaped room has a minimalist but pleasant feel with a wood-boarded floor and blue-tiled bar front. Glass-fronted on two sides, if offers open views inside and outside. TV sport is well catered for and there is live music at weekends, when it can be quite noisy. 🌑🍴🚪🐾🛜

Halcyon Quest Hotel 🄻

17 Gronant Road, LL19 9DT (on A547 just E of town centre)
☎ (01745) 852442 ⊕ halcyonquest-hotel.com
Facer's Flintshire Bitter; 3 changing beers (sourced nationally) Ⓗ
A longstanding supporter of cask beer, the HQ, as it is known, is at the southern end of town. It has just one room packed with sporting and other memorabilia, including a rowing boat suspended from the ceiling dedicated to JR Hartley of fly fishing fame. The extensive garden patio at the rear has a covered area and is popular in the summer months. 🌑🎜🛏🅰🚆🍴🚪(35,36) 🐾

Rhyl

Cob & Pen 🄻

143 High Street, LL18 1UF
☎ (01745) 350446
Facer's Mountain Mild, Flintshire Bitter; 3 changing beers Ⓗ

A fine traditional town-centre pub close to the railway and bus stations with three separate areas to suit all tastes, served from a central bar. It hosts darts, pool and dominoes teams and shows televised sports events, all adding to its popularity. Interesting novelty clocks are displayed in a side bar. The beers are usually from microbreweries including a cask mild – a rarity for these parts. Guest ales change every other day or so, giving customers more choice. ♿🕮🛈⌑🍴🚃🚆🅿🛜

Dove at Rhyl L

2 St Margarets Buildings, St Margarets Drive, LL18 2HT (on A525, half mile from centre)
☎ 07908 957116
4 changing beers (sourced locally; often Dovecote) Ⓗ
Situated on the outskirts of town, this welcome addition to the local pub landscape is the first in a small chain of pubs operated by Dovecote Brewery under the Dove umbrella. The interior is bright and airy, featuring a mural of Rhyl High Street, and the atmosphere is relaxed and friendly. The cask beer range includes at least two from Dovecote plus two guests from a local microbrewery. Closed Monday except bank holidays. Q♿🛀🚆(51)✪

Ruabon

Bridge End Inn L

5 Bridge Street, LL14 6DA
☎ (01978) 810881 ● bridgeendruabon.co.uk
8 changing beers (sourced nationally; often Ossett, Rat, Salopian) Ⓗ
Welcoming, traditional, community-focused local, close to Ruabon station, with three low-ceilinged rooms and a covered outside drinking area. It has deservedly won numerous awards since its revitalisation by the McGivern family, including CAMRA UK and Welsh National Pub of the Year. The changing range of eight cask ales may include a brew from the on-site McGivern Brewery, plus porter and a stout. There is usually a real cider. Families and well-behaved dogs are welcome in the lounge. Q♿🛀🚃🍴🚆🅿🚆✪🛜

St Asaph

New Inn ✓

Lower Denbigh Road, LL17 0EF
☎ (01745) 584600
JW Lees Bitter; 2 changing beers (often JW Lees) Ⓗ
The pub has a main lounge bar leading to a games room with pool and darts. The separate back bar has a real open fire and another dartboard. Outside, there is a raised seating area with a large landscaped garden below. The pub backs on to the River Elwy, with easy access for dog walkers. There is a large car park. Q♿🕮🛈🅿🚆(51)✪🛜

Shotton

Central Hotel ✓

2-4 Chester Road West, CH5 1BX
☎ (01244) 845510
Greene King IPA, Abbot; Ruddles County; 3 changing beers (sourced nationally; often Big Hand, Hafod) Ⓗ
Built in 1943, this formerly run-down premises was refurbished by Wetherspoon in 2008. The interior is typical Wetherspoon mock-Edwardian, with the very large bar partially separated into three similarly furnished areas. There is an outdoor seating space to the front. Two or three guest beers come from local microbreweries such as Hafod or Big Hand. Occasional Meet the Brewer evenings are held. ♿🛀🕮🛈🚃🚆🅿🚆🛜

Tremeirchion

Salusbury L

LL17 0UN (one mile S of A55 from jct 30)
☎ (01745) 710532
2 changing beers (often Cwrw Ial, Dovecote) Ⓗ
Traditional old village pub with parts reputed to date back to the time of the Magna Carta. It is now under the ownership of the nearby Dovecote Brewery. The interior divides into several areas including dining rooms, a snug and a meeting room. Outside, there is a large space with a children's play area. Beers from other microbreweries are usually on the bar alongside the Dovecote range. ♿🕮🛈🚃🛀🅿🚆🛜

Wrexham

Elihu Yale ✓

44-46 Regent Street, LL11 1RR
☎ (01978) 366646
Greene King Abbot; Ruddles Best Bitter; Sharp's Doom Bar; 5 changing beers (sourced nationally) Ⓗ
Formerly a cinema, this Wetherspoon town-centre pub is within walking distance of both railway and bus stations. It serves three regular beers plus at least five guest ales, one from a north Wales brewery, and up to two real ciders. There are various seating areas in the large room, with a quieter section near the front. Families are welcome until 10pm. Quiz night is Wednesday, poker on Sunday. Q♿🕮🛈🚃🚆🅿🚆🛜

Fat Boar L

11 Yorke Street, LL13 8LW
☎ (01978) 354201 ● thefatboarwrecsam.co.uk
4 changing beers (sourced locally; often Big Hand, Hafod) Ⓗ
A sister venue to the one of the same name in Mold, this stripped-down pub has a clean, bright feel with ceiling beams and exposed brick walls. It comprises a large L-shaped bar/lounge downstairs and a restaurant upstairs. Up to four handpumps usually feature beers from local microbreweries. There is a large beer garden at the rear. 🛈🚃🚆🛜

Magic Dragon Brewery Tap L ✓

13 Charles Street, LL13 8BT
☎ (01978) 365156
Magic Dragon Eyton Gold, Ice Dragon; 4 changing beers (sourced regionally; often Salopian, Magic Dragon) Ⓗ
The tap for the Magic Dragon Brewery, this single-roomed pub is just outside Wrexham, on the edge of what was known as the Beast Market (the brewery is based a few miles away at Eyton). The building was originally the Elephant & Castle and after several changes of use is now pleasingly a pub once more. The compact interior has bare brick walls and a wood-panelled bar. Six handpumps dispense at least three Magic Dragon beers including a dark ale. Q🚃🛀🚆✪🛜

Ysceifiog

Fox ★

Ysceifiog Village Road, CH8 8NJ (signed from B5121)
☎ (01352) 720241 ● foxinnysceifiog.co.uk
Tetley Bitter; 2 changing beers Ⓗ
Built around 1730, the Fox is well worth seeking out. The interior comprises four small rooms, two of them for dining. The bar has a sliding door that takes you back to the 1930s. There is a choice of four beers. A children's playground is adjacent to the outside drinking area. Identified by CAMRA as having a nationally important historic interior, this is a rare classic. Q♿🕮🛈🅿✪🛜

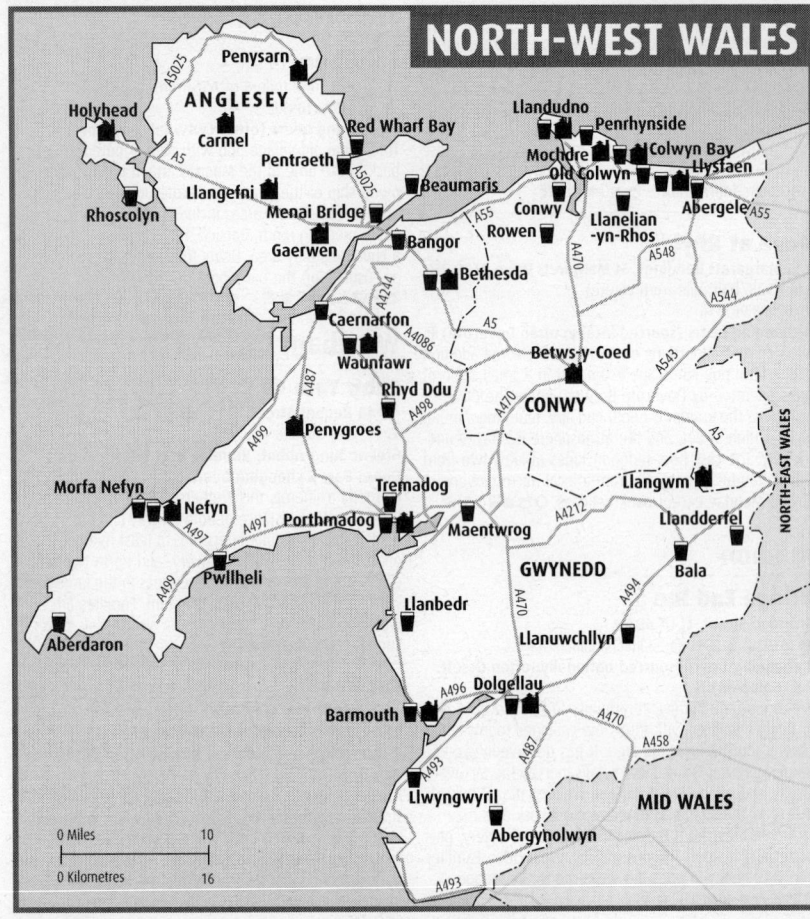

NORTH-WEST WALES

Authority areas covered: Anglesey UA, Conwy UA, Gwynedd UA

Aberdaron

Ty Newydd
LL53 8BE

☎ (01758) 760207 ⊕ gwesty-tynewydd.co.uk
Purple Moose Calon Lan; 2 changing beers (sourced locally) Ⓗ
The hotel is at the centre of a picturesque and historic village at the end of the Llyn Peninsula. Beers are from two local breweries. Freshly caught Bardsey lobster and crab are on the menu, as well as afternoon teas. Eleven en-suite bedrooms are available, with stunning sea views. The Wales coastal footpath passes through the village. Bus services run from Pwllheli. Dogs are welcome in the Yellow Room and on the terrace, but are not permitted in the bar/restaurant. Q🏠🛏️◑🅿️🅐🚆🛜

Abergele

Hoptimist Ⓛ
32 Market Street, LL22 7AA
3 changing beers (sourced locally; often Cwrw Ial, Dovecote) Ⓗ
An innovative conversion of a former building society, Abergele's first micropub – originally a joint venture between Cwrw Ial and Dovecote breweries – opened in 2018. Information regarding the beers and ciders, along with their prices and strengths, is clearly displayed on a large blackboard on the back wall. The bank of 13 taps dispenses five cask, five keg beers and three ciders, served in third-pint glasses on request. The large rear courtyard offers views into the small cellar.
Q🏠❄️🚆🅿️🚋(12,13) ♿

Abergynolwyn

Railway Inn
Lichfield Terrace, LL36 9YW (on B4405)
☎ (01654) 782744
3 changing beers Ⓗ
Hospitable community local in the centre of the village not far from the Talyllyn Railway. You can still see the remains of the incline that brought goods down from the railway station to the village. Excellent food is served along with a choice of three draught beers and the occasional cider. The pub has stunning views of the nearby hills and there are wonderful walks in the valley.
Q🏠❄️◑🅐♿🚆(Tallylyn) P🅿️♿

Bala

Stori Ⓛ
101 High Street, LL23 7AE (on A494 in town centre opp Old Bull's Head and Co-op)
☎ (01678) 520501 ⊕ storibeers.wales

3 changing beers (sourced locally) G
A bottle shop and taproom centrally situated in this popular town close to the lake and other attractions. The shop offers a wide range of beers and beer-related merchandise, with the emphasis on local products, and to the rear is the taproom. Cask and craft keg beers are available to either take away or enjoy in the cosy tasting room. Opening hours may be subject to seasonal variation. Q✿🖫(T3)❀ 🛜

Bangor

Blue Sky Bar & Café
236 High Street, LL57 1PA
☎ 07415 845599
2 changing beers (sourced locally) H
Established in 2019, this taproom/microbar has a contemporary layout. It offers two draught beers from local breweries, up to 10 craft ales, plus a large range of predominantly Welsh bottled and canned beers. Drinks can be taken up to the café upstairs where food is served until mid-afternoon every day. Live music is performed upstairs on a monthly basis. Dogs are welcome downstairs in the taproom. ◖🖙🖫❀

Patrick's
59 Holyhead Road, LL57 2HE
☎ (01248) 353062 🌐 patricksbar.com
4 changing beers (sourced regionally) H
Situated in upper Bangor, this lively Irish-themed bar is popular both with the locals and students at Bangor University. Numerous TVs display sporting events. There are usually two local ales and one regional beer on the bar. Opening hours are extended for sports and late-night drinking. On the bus route towards the Menai Straits and near the railway station. ◖🖙🖫

Barmouth

Royal Hotel
LL42 1AB
☎ (01341) 406214
4 changing beers H
Located beneath the main hotel with access from the main road, the pub is on two levels, with the main bar next to the entrance, and the lower level primarily for playing pool. There is a beer garden to the rear. Beers are usually from Welsh breweries but occasionally come from just over the border. 🛏◖🖙Å🖙♣🖫❀🛜

Beaumaris

Castle Court Hotel ✅
Castle Square, LL58 8DA
☎ (01248) 810078 🌐 castlecourtbeaumaris.co.uk
Facer's This Splendid Ale; 1 changing beer (sourced regionally) H
In the centre of this historic town and overlooking the castle, this guesthouse was originally the White Lion Hotel. The owners have renovated the reception and dining areas. There is a small beer garden to the rear, and in spring and summer the courtyard outside the main door provides more seating. Facer's Splendid Ale is always available alongside one guest beer from a small independent brewery. Lunchtime meals are served during school holidays only. 🛏🌣🛏Å🖫🛜

Bethesda

Y Sior
35-37 Carneddi Road, LL57 3SE
☎ (01248) 600072

4 changing beers (sourced locally) H
A friendly locals in the village of Carneddi, just outside Bethesda. Free of tie, it serves a variety of ales from the Marston's range as well as locally brewed beers. There are views across the valley to the local slate quarry, which has the longest zip wire in Europe. The pub is a short drive from the A5 and has plenty of parking nearby. Q🖙🖫❀

Caernarfon

Bar Bach
Tan y Bont/Greengate Street, LL55 2NF (just off square behind Caffi Maes)
☎ (01286) 673111
2 changing beers (sourced locally) H
Under the looming shadow of Caernarfon's imposing castle lies the self-proclaimed smallest bar in Wales. It is part of Caffi Maes on Castle Square, with a narrow entrance just around the corner. This charmingly intimate place does indeed occupy a small area but it is deceptive in that the bar leads to another longer room on a lower level. It has a lived-in feel, with a small fireplace, exposed stonework and a mix of dark-wood furniture. Q◖🖙(WHR)❀🛜

Black Boy Inn ✅
Northgate Street, LL55 1RW
☎ (01286) 673604 🌐 black-boy-inn.com
Draught Bass; 5 changing beers (sourced regionally) H
Characterful pub set within the town walls between the marina and castle. This historic town, a World Heritage Site, is well worth a visit, ending with a welcome pint at the Black Boy. The public bar and small lounge are warmed by roaring fires. Good-value food is served and a guest beer usually comes from Purple Moose. There is a drinking area outside on the traffic-free street. Former local CAMRA Pub of the Year. 🛏🌣🛏◖🖙♿🖙(WHR)♣🖫(5C,S4)🛜

Colwyn Bay

Bay Hop 🅛
17 Penrhyn Road, LL29 8LG
🌐 thebayhop.co.uk
5 changing beers (sourced regionally) H
A multi award-winning micropub with a welcoming and friendly atmosphere. Furnishings include wooden settles and comfy chairs around larger tables, plus tall barrel tables for those who prefer to stand. Five ciders and

---

REAL ALE BREWERIES

Anglesey Brewhouse Llangefni
Anglesey Brewing Carmel (brewing suspended)
Black Cloak 🍺 Colwyn Bay
Cader Dolgellau
Conwy 🍺 Llysfaen
Cybi Holyhead
Druid Penysarn (brewing suspended)
Geipel Llangwm
Lleu Penygroes
Llyn Nefyn
Mona Anglesey: Gaerwen
Myrddins Barmouth
Nant Betws-y-Coed (NEW)
Ogwen Bethesda
Purple Moose Porthmadog
Snowdon Craft Mochdre
Snowdonia Parc 🍺 Waunfawr
Wild Horse 🍺 Llandudno

perries are available from a fridge in addition to an extensive range of beers in bottles and cans for drinking in or taking out. Thursday is cheese night. Recently voted local CAMRA Pub of the Year for four successive years, plus Cider Pub of the Year and North Wales Pub of the Year. ☞≉✚🚪(12,13)🐾🛜

Black Cloak Taproom 🅛

71 Abergele Road, LL29 7RU

☎ (01492) 330274

3 changing beers (sourced locally) 🅗

Brewpub opened in 2018 by two former employees of Heavy Industry Brewing, who are now producing their own beer on-site using a one-barrel plant. Beers are available on cask, keg and direct from a brite tank, and served in thirds, halves, two-thirds or pint measures. Guest beers are from quality breweries throughout the UK and bottled beers are also on offer. The taproom has comfortable seating and a convivial atmosphere. ☞🌞≉🚪(12,13)🐾🛜

Pen-y-Bryn 🅛

Pen-y-Bryn Road, LL29 6DD

☎ (01492) 533360 ⊕ penybryn-colwynbay.co.uk

House beer (by Phoenix); 3 changing beers (sourced regionally; often Purple Moose, Timothy Taylor) 🅗

Large open-plan pub with bookcases, old furniture and real fires during the winter. The walls are decorated with old photographs and memorabilia from the local area. Panoramic views of the Bay of Colwyn and the Great Orme can be admired from the terrace and garden. The food menu changes daily and is served throughout the day. A boardroom-style function room for celebrations and meetings has been created in the cellar, opening onto the garden. Q☞🌞🕽🛆P🚪(23)🐾🛜

Conwy

Albion Ale House ★ 🅛

Upper Gate Street, LL32 8RF

☎ (01492) 582484 ⊕ albionalehouse.weebly.com

6 changing beers (sourced locally) 🅗

Multi-room pub on CAMRA's National Inventory of Historic Pub Interiors, superbly refurbished by the current owners – each room retains original 1920s features and several have interesting fireplaces. There is no music or TV, just pleasant conversation. The pub is managed by three local brewers – Conwy, Purple Moose and Snowdon Craft – and showcases their beers as well as guests. There are up to 10 ciders and a good selection of wines and malt whiskies. CAMRA awards include local and Welsh Pub of the Year. Q🌞≉♣●🚪(5,19)🐾🛜

Bank of Conwy 🅛

1 Lancaster Square, LL32 8HT

☎ (01492) 573741 ⊕ thebankofconwy.wales

4 changing beers (sourced regionally) 🅗

Craft beer bar in a Grade II-listed former bank. It uses many fittings from the original building – the counter, manager's office and vault. Food is served daily. There is a wide selection of beers, with four cask and 13 keg pumps. An extensive selection of bottled beers, wines and gins is also available. Dogs are welcome, with free sausages. Attractions include music on Wednesday and Friday, and an open mic night on Tuesday. ☞🕽≉🚪(5,19)🐾🛜

Erskine Arms 🅛

Rosehill Street, LL32 8LD

☎ (01492) 593535 ⊕ erskinearms.co.uk

Black Sheep Best Bitter; Conwy Clogwyn Gold; Timothy Taylor Boltmaker; 2 changing beers (sourced regionally; often Purple Moose) 🅗

Reopened in 2017 following a major refurbishment, the pub's name was changed back to the Erskine Arms – the family name of the owners. It was previously the Malt Loaf, in keeping with its sister pub the Cottage Loaf in Llandudno. The inn has two distinct dining areas, one on an upper floor, and there is a snug to the left and an outside drinking area. The decor includes traditional wooden features, open fires and pictures on the walls portraying local history. 🌞🍴🕽≉●🚪(5,19)🐾🛜

Mulberry

Conwy Marina, Morfa Drive, LL32 8GU

☎ (01492) 583350 ⊕ mulberryconwy.pub

Robinsons Dizzy Blonde, Cumbria Way, Unicorn; 1 changing beer (often Robinsons) 🅗

A nautically-themed Robinsons pub on the marina that opened again in 2016 following renovation. Its spacious ground-floor area features a rowing boat in the ceiling, and an open stairwell leading to the first-floor bar and restaurant. The front patio overlooks the marina and the Conwy estuary across to Deganwy. It has a pirate ship that is a children's play area. ☞🌞🕽🛆≉P🚪(27)🐾🛜

Dolgellau

Torrent Walk Hotel 🅛

Smithfield Street, LL40 1AA

☎ (01341) 422858

Purple Moose Cwrw Eryri/Snowdonia Ale; Wychwood Hobgoblin Ruby; 3 changing beers (sourced nationally) 🅗

An 18th-century hotel in the narrow streets of the town centre, retaining most of its multi-roomed interior and old fireplaces, although the bar fittings date from circa 1970. Note the Coffee Room etched panel in the door from the lobby to the room on the right. A real cider is always served alongside up to five ales, mostly from local breweries. An ideal base for walking in the Cader Idris area. 🍴🕽♣●🚪🐾🛜

Llanbedr

Ty Mawr Hotel

LL45 2HH

☎ (01341) 241440 ⊕ tymawrhotel.com

4 changing beers 🅗

Small country hotel set in its own grounds. The modern lounge bar has a slate-flagged floor and cosy wood-burning stove. Unusual flying memorabilia reflect connections with the local airfield. French windows open out onto a veranda and landscaped terrace with seating. An annual beer festival is held in a marquee on the lawn. The hotel welcomes children and dogs, and is popular with locals and walkers. Meals are served all day. Q🍴🕽🅰♣🚪🐾

Llandderfel

Bryntirion Inn 🅛

B4401, LL23 7RA (on B4401 4 miles E of Bala)

☎ (01678) 530205 ⊕ bryntirioninn.co.uk

Purple Moose Cwrw Eryri/Snowdonia Ale; 1 changing beer (sourced locally) 🅗

Dating back to 1695, this former hunting lodge and coaching inn overlooks the Dee Valley. The cosy and comfortable bar area with a log fire is open all day. There are a number of other rooms to accommodate diners and families including a large function room for special events. There is also a small covered and heated courtyard at the rear. The guest beer varies and may be from a local or national brewer. Two en-suite guest rooms are available upstairs. Q☞🌞🍴🕽♣P🚪(T3)🐾🛜

Llandudno

Albert 🄻

56 Madoc Street, LL30 2TW
☎ (01492) 877188
Conwy Clogwyn Gold; Timothy Taylor Landlord; 2 changing beers (sourced regionally) 🄷
Pub-restaurant just off the town centre and close to the railway station, featuring modern decor with interesting photographs and pictures on display. It serves five handpulled ales from local and independent breweries, plus a range of meals throughout the day. Current beers are displayed on blackboards above and beside the L-shaped bar. Third-pint glasses are available. At the front is a heated and covered veranda with seating.
�}⛲🍽️🛗♿🚲🚃(5,12)♣🐾🛜

Cottage Loaf 🄻

Market Street, LL30 2SR
☎ (01492) 870762 🌐 the-cottageloaf.co.uk
Conwy Welsh Pride; Courage Directors; Timothy Taylor Landlord; 2 changing beers (sourced regionally) 🄷
Popular pub in a former bakery, hence the name. Its interior features stone-flagged floors and an impressive fireplace. Much of the wood used in the raised timber-floored area came from the Flying Foam, a schooner shipwrecked on Llandudno's West Shore. Excellent home-cooked food is served all day, every day. There is a conservatory-style restaurant and an enclosed outdoor terrace. 🌞⛲🍽️🚃🚲🚃(5,12)🛜

Palladium 🄻 ✅

7 Gloddaeth Street, LL30 2DD
☎ (01492) 863920
Greene King Abbot; Ruddles Best Bitter; Sharp's Doom Bar; 5 changing beers (sourced regionally) 🄷
When this huge Wetherspoon venue opened in 2001 it was the largest pub in the UK. It was converted from a theatre originally built in 1920 on the site of the Market Hall; the boxes and upper seating remain but are not in use. The walls display theatrical memorabilia including original programmes bearing the names of the stars of the day. There are spacious areas on split levels including a family dining room. A lift is available.
🌞🍽️🛗♿🚲🚃(5,12) 🛜

Snowdon

11 Tudno Street, LL30 2HB
☎ (01492) 872166 🌐 thesnowdon.co.uk
Draught Bass; house beer (by Coach House); 4 changing beers (sourced regionally) 🄷
One of the oldest pubs in Llandudno, the Snowdon features a large main drinking area with an attractive mirror above the fireplace. It serves six real ales including the house beer, Coach House Blue Sky. The raised pavement garden gives a fine view of the Great Orme and the goats, if you are lucky. The pub is a repeat winner of the annual Llandudno in Bloom award for its floral displays. 🌞⛲🍽️🚲🚃(5,12)♣🛜

Tapps 🄻

35 Madoc Street, LL30 2TL
☎ (01492) 870956
Conwy Welsh Pride; 4 changing beers (sourced regionally) 🄷
Micropub in what used to be a cake shop, featuring an open-plan bar at the front and a small snug to the rear. Welsh beer is to the fore and there is a large bottled beer selection. Vinyl music is played on an old record player. One of the tables is a chessboard that transforms into a backgammon or card table. Other board games are provided and there are books to borrow.
🌞⛲🚃♣🚲🚃(5,12)♣🛜

Llanelian-yn-Rhos

White Lion Inn ✅

LL29 8YA
☎ (01492) 515807 🌐 whitelioninn.co.uk
Marston's Saddle Tank; 2 changing beers (sourced regionally) 🄷
A regular in the Guide for 30 years, this 16th-century inn in the hills above Old Colwyn, next to St Elian's Church, offers a warm welcome. Gracing the entrance are two white stone lions, leading into the bar area with slate-flagged flooring and large comfortable chairs around the log fires. Decorative stained glass is mounted above the bar in the tiny snug. The restaurant serves home-cooked food. Jazz night is Tuesday and quiz night Thursday.
Q🌞⛲🍽️♣🚲P🚃🛜

Llanuwchllyn

Eagles Inn (Tafarn Yr Eryrod) 🄻

LL23 7UB
☎ (01678) 540278 🌐 yr-eagles.co.uk
4 changing beers (sourced locally; often Purple Moose) 🄷
An old stone-built village local opposite the church, this little gem offers a friendly welcome to all. Its bar area doubles as a shop and is open all day. The pub retains plenty of historic features including a wonderful stone floor. The adjacent restaurant serves excellent locally produced food. There are fine mountain views from the patio garden. Llanuwchllyn station on the Bala Lake Railway is a 10-minute walk away. The opening times and beer range are reduced in winter.
🌞⛲🍽️🅰🚃♣P🚃(T3)♣🛜

Llwyngwril

Garthangharad Hotel

LL37 2UZ
☎ (01341) 251255 🌐 thegarthangharad.co.uk
3 changing beers (sourced regionally) 🄷
This hotel in the centre of the village is the only pub for miles around. Built circa 1736 and extended in 1840, it has a front lounge, rear bar and outside courtyard/beer garden. Pub food and accommodation are available. The railway halt on the beautiful Cambrian Coast line is a 10-minute walk, and bus service 28 stops nearby. Opening hours are extended in summer – check the website.
⛲🛏️🍽️🚃P🚃(28) 🛜

Llysfaen

MASH 🄻

Unit 2 Ty Mawr Enterprise Park, off Tan Y Graig Road, LL29 8UE
☎ (01492) 514305 🌐 conwybrewery.co.uk
Conwy Rampart, Welsh Pride; 1 changing beer (sourced locally) 🄷
Micropub and Conwy Brewery tap that has become a community hub since opening in 2018. It serves a good range of ales, lagers, wines and spirits, with coffee, tea and soft drinks also available. Innovative use is made of old seating casks as lampshades in the bar and at the tables outside. Following the public footpath finger post at the front corner of the brewery leads to views over the bay of Colwyn towards the Great Orme. Third-pint glasses are available. 🌞⛲♣P🚃♣🛜

Maentwrog

Grapes Hotel 🄻

LL41 4HN (on A496 near A487 jct)

☎ (01766) 590365 🌐 grapeshotelsnowdonia.co.uk
Purple Moose Cwrw Eryri/Snowdonia Ale; Sharp's Doom Bar; 1 changing beer (sourced locally) Ⓗ
Former coaching inn that dates back to the 17th century and overlooks the Vale of Ffestiniog. Its interior comprises a lounge, public bar, veranda and large dining room; outside to the rear is a sheltered beer garden. Most of the beers are local. Plas Halt railway station nearby is on the scenic Ffestiniog line. The village is an ideal base for visiting this beautiful area.
Q❄❀🚭🌛♿♠⋈(Plas Halt)♣●P🚃

Menai Bridge

Liverpool Arms ✅
St George's Pier, LL59 5EY
☎ (01248) 712453
Facer's Flintshire Bitter; Purple Moose Cwrw Eryri/ Snowdonia Ale Ⓗ/Ⓖ**, Ochr Dywyll y Mws/Dark Side of the Moose; 1 changing beer** Ⓗ
Nautically themed pub frequented by locals, students in term time and the local sailing fraternity. The Livvy has four cask ales on offer and serves good-quality home-cooked food. A short walk takes you beneath the famous Grade I-listed suspension bridge, and the pub is close to the quay for seasonal tourist boats. The Anglesey and Welsh Coast footpaths are nearby. 🌛🌜♿🚃🛜

Morfa Nefyn

Ty Coch Inn
Porthdinllaen, LL53 6DB (access by foot only)
☎ (01758) 720498 🌐 tycoch.co.uk
Cwrw Llyn Brenin Enlli; Purple Moose Cwrw Ysgawen/ Elderflower Ale; 1 changing beer (sourced regionally) Ⓗ
The Ty Coch opened as a pub in 1842 to serve local fishermen, and more recently was named as one of the top 10 beach bars in the world. Set in an iconic position in this beautiful village, it can only be reached on foot either along the beach or across the golf course. The single open-plan room is served by a central bar. Parking is available at the National Trust car park or the golf clubhouse. Check for out-of-season opening times. 🌛🌜❀

Nefyn

Bragdy Llyn
Ffordd Dewi Sant, LL53 6EG
☎ (01758) 721981 🌐 cwrwllyn.cymru
Cwrw Llyn Brenin Enlli, Cwrw Glyndwr, Seithenyn; 1 changing beer (sourced locally) Ⓗ
A friendly bar located within the Cwrw Llyn Brewery, open to the public all year round. Closing time may be later on Friday and Saturday depending on customer demand. Brewery tours are available on request, and include a short film plus tasters of the core range of ales. Near the coast and the National Trust village of Porthdinllean. ♿P

Old Colwyn

Crafty Fox Ⓛ
355 Abergele Road, LL29 9PL
☎ 07733 531766
5 changing beers (sourced regionally) Ⓗ
Previously two shops – a tattoo parlour and a butcher's – this welcoming micropub opened in 2018. The main entrance leads to the bar, with hops draped across the ceiling. The lounge is furnished with a mixture of leather sofas and stools. On the bar wall is an interesting set of photographs comparing the present street scene with a century ago. Loyalty cards are available for regular drinkers. Q🌛♣●🚃(12,13)❀🛜

Red Lion
385 Abergele Road, LL29 9PL
☎ (01492) 515042
Courage Best Bitter; 6 changing beers (sourced nationally) Ⓗ
In the Guide for 27 consecutive years, this free house serves up to six guest ales from independent and national brewers. It has an L-shaped lounge featuring antique brewery mirrors, local photographs and other memorabilia. There is a traditional public bar with a pool table, dartboard and several TVs. To the rear is a Victorian-style covered and heated smoking conservatory. Take a look at the pub sign on your way in. Q❀♣●🚃(12,13)❀🛜

Penrhynside

Penrhyn Arms Ⓛ
Pendre Road, LL30 3BY
☎ (01492) 549060
Banks's Amber Ale; 4 changing beers (sourced regionally) Ⓗ
Welcoming free house offering up to four guest ales, concentrating on new breweries and new beers, as well as local ciders and perries. The spacious single room has an L-shaped bar, comfortable seating, real fires and a widescreen TV. Food highlights include Wednesday pie and pint night and Thursday cheese night. Pizza is available on Friday and Saturday. The rear conservatory leads to a raised landscaped garden terrace with extensive views of the coastline. 🌛❀🌛●🚃(14,15)❀

Pentraeth

Panton Arms
The Square, LL75 8AZ
☎ (01248) 450959
Purple Moose Cwrw Glaslyn/Glaslyn Ale; 2 changing beers Ⓗ
Spacious 18th-century coaching inn with a long lounge bar and separate taproom, popular with locals and tourists alike. Purple Moose Glaslyn is available all year round. The pub's location is ideal for walks in the nearby forest and it is served by a frequent bus service from the coast. Midweek opening times can vary in winter. Q🌛❀🌛♿P🚃(62)❀🛜

Porthmadog

Australia
31-35 High Street, LL49 9LR
☎ (01766) 515957
Purple Moose Cwrw Eryri/Snowdonia Ale, Cwrw Ysgawen/Elderflower Ale, Ochr Dywyll y Mws/Dark Side of the Moose; 2 changing beers (sourced locally; often Purple Moose) Ⓗ
A pub since 1864, the Australia was taken over by the Purple Moose Brewery in 2017 and serves as its taphouse. Most of the core real ale range is available as well as seasonal and special beers. Two rooms are served by a long wooden bar with eight handpumps. There is a small outdoor seating area at the back. It is situated in the centre of town next to the bus stops and near the Ffestiniog & Welsh Highland Railways station. A former local CAMRA Pub of the Year. 🌛🌜♿⋈●🚃❀🛜

Pwllheli

Pen Cob ✔

Station Square, LL53 5HG

☎ (01758) 704970

Greene King Abbot; Ruddles Best Bitter; 4 changing beers [H]

Wetherspoon pub opposite the railway station at the start of the scenic Cambrian Coast Line. Previously a clothing store, it is now a light and airy venue patronised by young and old. It gets busy with locals and tourists at weekends and during the holiday season. The area is popular for sailing. 👪🍴♿🚆🚌📶

Red Wharf Bay

Ship Inn ✔

LL75 8RJ (off A5025 between Pentraeth and Benllech)

☎ (01248) 852568 🌐 shipinnredwharfbay.co.uk

Adnams Broadside; Brains SA; 2 changing beers [H]

Red Wharf Bay was once a busy port exporting coal and fertilisers in the 18th and 19th centuries. Previously known as the Quay, the Ship enjoys an excellent reputation for its bar and restaurant, with meals served lunchtimes and evenings. It gets busy with locals and visitors in summer. The garden has panoramic views across the bay to south-east Anglesey. The resort town of Benllech is two miles away and the coastal path passes the front door. Q👪❀🍴♿P

Rhoscolyn

White Eagle

LL65 2NJ (off B4545 signed Traeth Beach)

☎ (01407) 860267 🌐 white-eagle.co.uk

Marston's 61 Deep, Pedigree; Weetwood Best Bitter; 2 changing beers [H]

Saved from closure by its owners, this pub has been renovated and rebuilt with an airy, brasserie-style ambience. It has a fine patio enjoying superb views over Caernarfon Bay and the Llyn Peninsula to Bardsey Island. The nearby beach offers safe swimming with a warden on duty in summer. The pub is also close to the coastal footpath. Excellent food is available lunchtimes and evenings, all day during the school holidays.
Q👪🍴♿⛺♣P

Rhyd Ddu

Cwellyn Arms

LL54 6TL

☎ (01766) 890321 🌐 snowdoninn.co.uk

Conwy Welsh Pride; 5 changing beers (sourced regionally) [H]

Traditional Welsh country inn in a fabulous scenic location in this village at the foot of Snowdon. The pub's boast that it has nine real ales nine days a week is only slightly exaggerated. There are usually four handpulls in operation serving ales from local breweries. The lovely log fire makes the pub cosy and welcoming after a walk on Snowdon, or after a ride on the nearby Welsh Highland Railway. ❀🛏🍴♿⛺🚆(WHR)P🚌🐾

Rowen

Ty Gwyn

High Street, LL32 8YU

☎ (01492) 650232

JW Lees Bitter; 2 changing beers (sourced regionally) [H]

Community village inn in an idyllic setting with a warm welcome for locals and visitors alike. The comfortable lounge has horse brasses and old pictures on the walls, and there is a small restaurant area serving good food made with locally sourced ingredients. Traditional Welsh singing features on Friday evenings, live entertainment most Saturdays and charity quiz nights on occasion. There are two walled gardens, one with a stream running by. Opening times may vary seasonally.
👪❀🍴⛺♣P🚌(19A)🐾📶

Tremadog

Union Inn ✔

7 Market Square, LL49 9RB

☎ (01766) 512748 🌐 union-inn.com

Big Bog Bog Standard Bitter; Purple Moose Cwrw Eryri/Snowdonia Ale; 1 changing beer [H]

Friendly venue in the village square, with two separate cosy bars and a restaurant at the rear. The pub has a policy of using locally sourced produce, and the ale range mainly features local beers. Children are welcome and there are board games available. Excellent food is served in the bar and restaurant. Tremadog was the birthplace of Thomas Edward Lawrence (Lawrence of Arabia) in 1888. Frequent bus services pass nearby, and Porthmadog is within walking distance.
Q👪❀🍴♿⛺🚆🍎📺🚌(1A,T2)

Waunfawr

Snowdonia Park

Beddgelert Road, LL55 4AQ

☎ (01286) 650409 🌐 snowdonia-park.co.uk

House beer (by Snowdonia Parc); 5 changing beers [H]

Home of the Snowdonia Brewery, this is a popular pub for walkers, climbers and families, with children's play areas inside and out. Meals are served all day. The pub adjoins Waunfawr station on the Welsh Highland Railway – stop off here before continuing on one of the most scenic sections of narrow-gauge railway in Britain. There is a large campsite adjacent on the riverside. A former local CAMRA Pub of the Year.
Q👪❀🍴♿⛺🚆♣🍎P🚌🐾📶

Choosing pubs

CAMRA members and branches choose the pubs listed in The Good Beer Guide. There is no payment for entry, and pubs are inspected on a regular basis by personal visits; publicans are not sent a questionnaire once a year, as is the case with some pub guides. CAMRA branches monitor all the pubs in their areas, and the choice of pubs for the guide is often the result of democratic vote at branch meetings. However, recommendations from readers are welcomed and will be passed on to the relevant branch: write to Good Beer Guide, CAMRA, 230 Hatfield Road, St Albans, Hertfordshire, AL1 4LW; or send an email to: **gbgeditor@camra.org.uk**

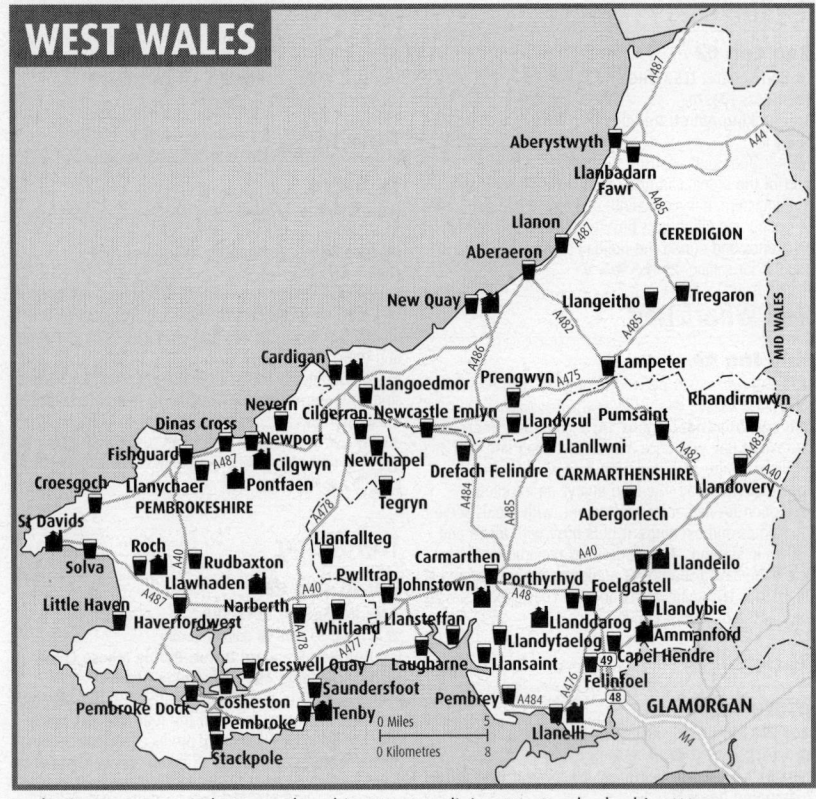

WEST WALES

Authority areas covered: Carmarthenshire UA, Ceredigion UA, Pembrokeshire UA

Aberaeron

Cadwgan Inn
10 Market Street, SA46 0AU (off A487, overlooking harbour)
☎ (01545) 570149
Hancocks HB; 2 changing beers (sourced nationally; often Bluestone, Mantle, Tenby) Ⓗ
Named after the last ship to be built in this attractive Regency town, this old-fashioned single-bar pub offers a friendly welcome and lively conversation. It is popular for its sports coverage. The guest beers are chosen from a wide range of small and regional breweries. Gwynt y Ddraig bottled ciders are available. There is a colourful hidden garden at the rear, and the small pavement drinking area at the front is a suntrap. Opposite is a free but busy harbourside public car park. ❀♿🚲🚍(T1,T5)❀🛜

Abergorlech

Black Lion
Abergorlech Road, SA32 7SN
☎ (01558) 685271 ⊕ blion.co.uk
Evan Evans Warrior; 2 changing beers (sourced regionally; often Bluestone, Evan Evans, Tenby) Ⓗ
Traditional village pub as well as a restaurant/coffee shop serving home-made food produced and sourced locally in Wales wherever possible. All the cakes are home-made as well. Just a few steps from the pub you can take advantage of signposted walks in the Brechfa Forest or the thrilling Brechfa Mountain Bike Trails. Bike locking facilities are provided in the car park and muddy bikers are always welcome, as the 300-year-old stone floor in the bar is easily cleaned! ☕❀🍴♿🅿🚍❀🛜

Aberystwyth

Glengower Hotel Ⓛ
3 Victoria Terrace, SY23 2DH (on seafront at N end of promenade)
☎ (01970) 626191 ⊕ glengower.co.uk
Mantle Rock Steady; Wye Valley Butty Bach; 3 changing beers (sourced regionally; often Evan Evans, Purple Moose, Timothy Taylor) Ⓗ
Excellent coastal views of Cardigan Bay can be enjoyed from the suntrap front terrace at this seafront hotel. The central front bar is the main drinking area, with a log-burner for the winter months. Up to five ciders from Gwynt y Ddraig are served alongside regional guests. There is also a quieter dining area and a large rear games room. Food is locally sourced wherever possible. Q♿❀🏠🍴♿🅿🚍(03) ❀🛜

Hen Orsaf ✅
Station Buildings, Alexandra Road, SY23 1LH
☎ (01970) 636080
Greene King Abbot; Ruddles Best Bitter; Sharp's Doom Bar; 6 changing beers (sourced nationally; often Evan Evans, Glamorgan, Purple Moose) Ⓗ
An award-winning conversion of Aberystwyth's former GWR railway station, which dates from 1924. This excellent Wetherspoon pub offers up to six guest ales, usually including light and dark beers, and with a Purple Moose brew always available. Ciders are from Westons and Gwynt y Ddraig. Drinks can be enjoyed outdoors on the old station concourse, which has access to the railway station. Convenient for trains, buses and taxis. ♿❀🍴♿🚲≠♿🚍🛜

Ship & Castle

1 High Street, SY23 1JG
☎ 07773 778785
Wye Valley HPA, Butty Bach; 3 changing beers (sourced nationally; often Oakham, Salopian, Tiny Rebel) Ⓗ

Aberystwyth's flagship pub offers microbrewery guest ales from the UK and Ireland. Small amounts of excellent beer in other formats are also served, including craft keg, bottles (eg Wild Beer, Polly's) and cans, plus cider and perry from Gwynt y Ddraig. A five-pump platter of third-pint measures is available. Beer festivals in spring and autumn offer extended choice. The well-considered decor reflects the pub's name and history. The venue can be busy on rugby days, but is welcoming at all times.
⚴≋♣♠Ⓟ🖳🐾♿🛜

Capel Hendre

King's Head Hotel Ⓛ

Waterloo Road, SA18 3SF
☎ (01269) 842377
2 changing beers (sourced regionally; often Boss, Gower) Ⓗ

A village pub tucked away just three miles from junction 49 of the M4, and a couple of miles from the former mining town of Ammanford. It has a main bar and dining room, with a sliding door leading to a separate snug. The pub serves two or sometimes three real ales from Wales, with Glamorgan, Bluestone and Neath breweries often represented. Outside are a garden and large car park.
🛏️❀🖚🌗♿♠Ⓟ🖳(128,129)♿🛜

Cardigan

Black Lion Hotel

High Street, SA43 1HJ
☎ (01239) 612532 ⊕ blacklionhotelcardigan.com
Mantle Cwrw Teifi; Wadworth 6X; 1 changing beer (sourced locally) Ⓗ

Dating from 1105, the Black Lion is said to be the oldest coaching inn in Wales. Originally known as a Grogg Shope, it is an ideal stopping point for visitors and locals. There are three separate rooms – a traditional bar with real fire, a relaxing coffee room, and a restaurant. The pub serves ales from the local Mantle Brewery alongside guests. Opening times vary in winter. 🖚🌗♣🖳🛜

Grosvenor

Bridge Street, SA43 1HY SN177459
☎ (01239) 613792
Greene King Abbot; Sharp's Doom Bar; 1 changing beer (sourced nationally) Ⓗ

Large pub on the edge of the town centre, next to Cardigan Castle and the River Teifi. It offers a good choice of ales, including a selection of bottled beers. The large open-plan bar/lounge provides various areas to relax, eat and drink, and there is an extra room upstairs for dining and functions. Good-value food is served lunchtimes and evenings every day. An outdoor patio area overlooks the river and the revamped quay.
🛏️❀🌗♿♣♠🖳♿🛜

Carmarthen

Coracle Tavern

1 Cambrian Place, SA31 1QG
☎ (01267) 468180
2 changing beers (sourced regionally; often Glamorgan) Ⓗ

In the centre of town, close to the main shopping area, this friendly free house offers a warm welcome to locals

and visitors alike. The large open-plan bar area has comfy sofas, and there is a separate restaurant upstairs. Breakfast is served Tuesday to Saturday. Darts is popular and a number of teams play here. 🌗♣🖳

Friends Arms

Old St Clears Road, SA31 3HH (W of town centre at bottom of Monument Hill)
☎ (01267) 234073
Mantle MOHO; Thornbridge Jaipur IPA; 2 changing beers (sourced locally; often Tiny Rebel) Ⓗ

Excellent hostelry half a mile from the town centre with a cosy and friendly atmosphere and a warm welcome, enhanced by two open fires. Popular with sports fans, it hosts darts and shows the main sports channels on TV. The pub has its own microbrewery which regularly produces good beer. An outbuilding on two floors has function rooms for meetings and parties. The local CAMRA branch meets here occasionally.
🛏️❀♣♠🖳(222,322)♿🛜

Stag & Pheasant

34 Spilman Street, SA31 1LQ
☎ (01267) 232040
2 changing beers (sourced nationally; often Glamorgan, Ringwood) Ⓗ

Busy pub on Carmarthen's main thoroughfare, with a warm and friendly atmosphere that is enjoyed both by locals and tourists. The landlady has the freedom to serve a selection of excellent ales. Two TVs make this a popular venue for watching sport. The pleasant rear beer garden has heaters for cold weather. ❀♿≋♣🖳🛜

Yr Hen Dderwen

47-48 King Street, SA31 1BH
☎ (01267) 242050
Glamorgan Jemimas Pitchfork; Greene King Abbot; Ruddles Best Bitter; 7 changing beers (sourced nationally; often Exmoor, Gower, Kelham Island) Ⓗ

Terraced town-centre pub named after the local legend of Merlin and an ancient oak which is depicted throughout the premises. Local Welsh ales are always available alongside a good selection of beers from around the world, including bottled and canned craft ale. There are beer festivals in the spring and autumn and a cider festival in the summer. Meet the Brewer sessions feature throughout the year. Food is served all day.
🛏️🌗♿🖳🛜

Cilgerran

Masons Arms

Cwnce, SA43 2SR
☎ 07989 990461

Hancocks HB; Sharp's Doom Bar; 1 changing beer (often Mantle) ⊞

Also known as the Rampin, this venue is thought to have opened in 1836. It is a small, cosy and friendly village pub with an open fire (an old kitchen range). Many local characters can be found here, contributing to an excellent atmosphere. Three real ales are on offer, one changing regularly, usually from a local brewery. Various charity events are held during the year along with an occasional musical evening. Winter opening times may vary – check ahead. ⌂✿⌷♣P❀

Cosheston

Brewery Inn
SA72 4UD
☎ (01646) 686678 ⊕ thebreweryinn.com
Brains Rev James; Coles Family Cwrw Blasus; 1 changing beer ⊞

This Grade II-listed free house was once accommodation for monks, with its own brewhouse in outbuildings behind (brewing ceased in 1889). The light and airy stone-built inn has a traditional slate floor and beamed ceiling. To one side is a cosy area for drinkers to enjoy a chat in front of the log fire. The pub has a reputation for fine ales and food. Ingredients for its extensive menu are sourced locally, including fresh fish.
Q⌂✿⌷⊕⌷&⌷♣P❀❀⊛

Cresswell Quay

Cresselly Arms 🄻
SA68 0TE
☎ (01646) 651210
Sharp's Doom Bar ⊞**; Worthington's Bitter** ⌷**; house beer (by Caffle); 2 changing beers (sourced locally; often Bluestone, Mantle)** ⊞

Situated on the Cresswell River, this 250-year-old ivy-covered hostelry is a throwback to the Victorian age. Its homely farm kitchen interior, where a roaring fire burns in the hearth, is a haven for locals and visitors alike. The house beer from Caffle is complemented by Worthington's Bitter dispensed from the barrel by jug. The pub is on several interesting walking routes, and at high tide is accessible by boat from the Milford Haven estuary. Q⌂✿&⌷♣P❀(361)

Croesgoch

Artramont Arms
SA62 5JP (on A487)
☎ (01348) 831309
2 changing beers (often Shepherd Neame) ⊞

Friendly, family-run village local that has been licensed premises since the 1700s; in the past it also sold petrol and incorporated a post office. It now features a large public bar with tiled floor plus a lounge with dining area. There is also a small library for customers, and a pleasant garden outside. Good food is available from an interesting and varied menu. Check winter opening times before travelling. ⌂✿⌷♣P❀(T11)❀

Dinas Cross

Freemasons Arms
Spencer Buildings, SA42 0UW (on A487 coast road midway between Fishguard and Newport)
☎ (01348) 811674
Gower Gold; 1 changing beer (often Coles Family) ⊞

Traditional sea captains' meeting place in the Pembrokeshire Coast National Park. This pub is conveniently placed for those who enjoy sailing or like to

visit attractive beaches and walk the coastal path. It also has the advantage of being on a principal bus route. The main bar, tastefully refurbished while retaining its original character, features a cosy open fire and a dining area at the side. Check winter opening times before venturing forth. Q⌂✿⊛⌷&⌷♣P❀(T5)❀⊛

Drefach Felindre

John y Gwas
SA44 5XG SN354383
☎ (01559) 370469
2 changing beers (sourced nationally; often Brains, Courage, Marston's) ⊞

Early 19th-century village tavern with a striking yellow and black livery. It attracts locals and tourists alike with snugs, a wood-burning stove, quality beer and cider, and a warm welcome, especially for dogs. Two ales are generally offered, alongside a wide variety of bottled beers and ciders. A beer festival, showcasing more than 10 different ales, is held over the August bank holiday weekend. ⌂✿⌷♣P❀(460)❀⊛

Felinfoel

White Lion Inn
Parkview, SA14 8BH (on main A476 in Felinfoel)
☎ (01554) 776644
Gower Gold; 4 changing beers (sourced nationally) ⊞

A family-friendly split-level hostelry with defined drinking and dining spaces plus a function room. There are covered and open drinking areas outside. A selection of well-kept real ales is available, and a good-value carvery. Quiz nights are Sunday and Wednesday. National cycle and walking paths to the Swiss Valley and beyond are nearby. There is ample parking on the roadside. ⌂✿⌷♣P❀⊛

Fishguard

Royal Oak Inn
Market Square, SA65 9HA
☎ (01348) 218632
Brains Rev James; Glamorgan Jemimas Pitchfork; 1 changing beer (sourced locally; often Bluestone) ⊞

This Grade II-listed building has a place in history: a French invasion attempt on the west coast of Wales in 1797 was thwarted by locals in the Battle of Fishguard, regarded as the last invasion attempt on Britain. A peace treaty was signed between the British and French in the Royal Oak's bar area. The interior is sparingly decorated with exposed stone and wooden beams, but with little reference to its historic past. Q⌂✿⌷⌷&⌷♣⊟

Foelgastell

Smiths Arms
Heol y Foel, SA14 7EL
☎ (01269) 842213 ⊕ thesmithsarms.co.uk
2 changing beers (sourced nationally; often Boss, Marston's, Rhymney) ⊞ /⌷

A friendly locals' pub that also provides a handy stopping-off point for travellers on the A48, and visitors to the nearby National Botanic Garden of Wales. The beer selection varies and usually includes one or two real ales from local and national breweries. Real cider is often available. Food is served lunchtimes and evenings except Sunday evening, with a choice of bar or restaurant menus. ⌂✿⌷⌷&⌷♣P❀(166)❀⊛

Haverfordwest

William Owen ⓛ ✓
6 Quay Street, SA61 1BG
☎ (01437) 771900
Greene King IPA, Abbot; Sharp's Doom Bar; 5 changing beers (sourced regionally; often Bluestone, Boss, Caffle) ⊞
Pembrokeshire's first and only Wetherspoon pub occupies a handsome 19th-century building, formerly a shop, hotel and restaurant, with a spacious extension to the rear. It was reputedly built in 1856 for Joseph Thomas, a corn and manure merchant, by local architect William Owen. It has also been a saddler's and, more recently, the Wilton House Hotel. Beer from one of the county's breweries is regularly available. The pub offers the chain's standard menu and promotional deals, and opens early for breakfast. Q🟢🐕🏛️♿🚌🍴🅿️🚃🛏️🛜

Lampeter

Nag's Head
14 Bridge Street, SA48 7HG
☎ (01570) 218517
2 changing beers ⊞
Town-centre pub featuring a modern and bright horseshoe-shaped bar area. Friendly and fun, it attracts a good mix of customers – locals, students and tourists. Most major sports events are screened, and live music often features. The pub also offers B&B, evening and lunchtime meals, and a function room.
🏛️🛏️🍴▲♿🚌🐾🛜

Laugharne

New Three Mariners Inn ⓛ
Victoria Street, SA33 4SE
☎ (01994) 427426
1 changing beer (sourced locally; often Evan Evans) ⊞
The building is in the centre of this historic town and only yards from its early 11th-century castle. Dylan Thomas lived in Laugharne for a number of years and he and his wife Caitlin are laid to rest in the graveyard of St Martin's Church. The pub moved to its current site when the original ale house opposite was converted to a carpentry shop. Popular with locals, it serves evening meals and hosts a weekly quiz night. 🟢🏛️🛏️♿▲🅿️🐾🛜

Little Haven

Saint Brides Inn ⓛ
St Brides Road, SA62 3UN
☎ (01437) 781266 ⊕ saintbridesinn.co.uk
Brains Rev James; Hancocks HB; 2 changing beers (sourced locally; often Bluestone, Caffle) ⊞
A quaint old fishing village in a conservation area of the Pembrokeshire Coast National Park. This family-run pub in the centre of Little Haven is open all year round, selling a range of Welsh ales and often local Pembrokeshire ones. It is noted for the ancient well in the cellar. The attractive interior includes a separate dining area, and there are heaters on the patio in the pretty suntrap garden. Q🟢🏛️▲🅿️🚌(311,400)🛜

Llanbadarn Fawr

Black Lion
SY23 3RA
☎ (01970) 636632
Wye Valley Butty Bach; 3 changing beers (sourced nationally; often Banks's) ⊞
Modernised pub in the village centre, a mile from Aberystwyth, popular with locals and students. Its spacious main bar has seating at one end, darts and pool at the other, plus a second bar and a function room at the rear. Local darts, pool and poker teams meet here regularly. The pub hosts a monthly karaoke night and a quiz every other Friday. The large rear garden, next to the village's ancient church, has a delightful air of rural seclusion. Q🟢🏛️🐕🅿️🚌(526,X47)🛜

Llandeilo

Salutation Inn
33 New Road, SA19 6DF
☎ (01558) 824255
Sharp's Doom Bar; Timothy Taylor Landlord; Titanic Plum Porter; Wye Valley Butty Bach; 1 changing beer (sourced regionally; often Gower) ⊞
A locals' pub near the town centre. Friendly staff dispense five well-kept ales. The interior is divided into two areas, with a pool table on one side and a wood fire on the other. Live music often features at weekends. There is a garden and function area to the rear. The pub hosts a beer festival in the summer. 🏛️♿▲🅿️🐾🛜

Yr Hen Vic
82 New Road, SA19 6DF
☎ (01558) 822596
3 changing beers (sourced regionally; often Mumbles, Oakham) ⊞
A lively venue with a warm welcome for all who pass through its doors. Originally a sports club, it has been a pub for more than a decade. Three well-kept, constantly changing beers are always available. Several large TVs show sport in the bar, and there is a separate pool room. To the front is a refurbished dining area.
🟢▲🅿️🚌(X13,281)🐾🛜

Llandovery

Whitehall
1 High Street, SA20 0PU
☎ (01550) 721139
Coles Family Llanddarog; 2 changing beers (often Mantle) ⊞
A 17th-century pub in the town centre and one of the oldest in town. A friendly place to visit, with cosy log fires in the winter. It is the home of the Llandovery Vintage Tractor Club, quiz nights and darts. There is seating at the front and a beer garden to the rear.
🟢🏛️🛏️▲🅿️🐾🛜

Llandybie

Ivy Bush
18 Church Street, SA18 3HZ (100yds from church)
☎ (01269) 850272
Timothy Taylor Landlord; 1 changing beer (sourced regionally; often Exmoor) ⊞
This friendly local, modernised several years ago, contains a single bar with two comfortable seating areas. It usually serves Timothy Taylor's Landlord alongside at least one regularly changing guest ale. The pub hosts weekly games and quizzes, and shows sport on TV. The local birdwatching group meets here. The nearby railway station is on the scenic Heart of Wales line.
🟢🏛️▲🅿️🚌(103,X13) 🛜

Llandyfaelog

Red Lion
SA17 5PP (300yds off A484)

☎ (01267) 267530 ⊕ redlionllandyfaelog.co.uk
3 changing beers (sourced regionally; often Butcombe, Evan Evans, Glamorgan) �

A family-run village hostelry that can truly be described as being at the heart of the community – it has an annexe that hosts the local choir's practice evenings and stages concerts and functions for the surrounding area. The large public bar, featuring darts and a pool table, is complemented by a restaurant and a family room. Food is served in both the bar and restaurant.
Q ☼ ⌂ ◑ ⅃ ▲ ♣ ⇊ (198,X12) 🖰

Llandysul

Porth Hotel

Church Street, SA44 4QS SN418407
☎ (01559) 362202 ⊕ porthhotel.co.uk
2 changing beers (sourced locally) ⌁

Set on the banks of the River Teifi, this former 17th-century coaching inn is now a family-run village hotel with a bar, restaurant and function room. The public rooms still retain the original oak beams and panels. Food and drink is sourced locally, where possible. At the rear of the hotel is a car park and lawned garden beside the river, with access to walks and fishing. Accommodation is in seven en-suite bedrooms.
☼ ⊛ ⌂ ◑ ♣ ⇊ P 🖰 🖰 🖰

Llanelli

Stradey Arms ✔

1 Stradey Road, SA15 4ET
☎ (01554) 753332
Brains Bitter, Rev James, SA; 1 changing beer (sourced nationally) ⌁

A busy Brains pub on the outskirts of the town, with a comfortable bar and separate restaurant. Real ale is poured from up to four handpumps. A varied menu of freshly prepared food is served all day except on Sunday, when there is a lunchtime carvery. Friendly and welcoming staff add to the pleasant ambience here. It is a popular venue for sporting events, especially rugby internationals. ☼ ⊛ ⌂ ◑ ⅃ P 🖰 🖰 🖰

York Palace ✔

51 Stepney Street, SA15 3YA (opp Town Hall Square Gardens)
☎ (01554) 758609
Greene King Abbot; Ruddles Best Bitter; 8 changing beers (often Glamorgan, Gower, Tomos Watkin) ⌁

A refurbished former picture palace retaining much of the original decor, offering a good selection of beers from around the world including bottled and canned craft ales. It also boasts a varied selection of boxed and bottled real ciders, occasionally also on handpull. There are beer festivals in the spring and autumn, and a cider festival in summer. The pub hosts Meet the Brewer sessions throughout the year. Food is served all day.
Q ◑ ⅃ ⅃ ⇊ 🖰 🖰

Llanfallteg

Plash

SA34 0UN (off A40 at Llanddewi Velfrey)
☎ (01437) 563472 ⊕ theplashinn.co.uk
Wye Valley Butty Bach; 2 changing beers ⌁

At the centre of village life, this terrace-style cottage pub has been an inn for more than 180 years. Its guest beers are usually from small, independent breweries. It serves home-made food using locally sourced ingredients, with specials on Wednesday, Friday and Saturday. It holds a quiz night on Tuesday, a regular monthly folk night and

other entertainment. An accessible entrance is to the rear. A former local CAMRA Pub of the Year.
Q ☼ ⊛ ⌂ ◑ ⅃ ▲ ♣ ⇊ P 🖰 🖰

Llangeitho

Three Horseshoe 🅛

SY25 6TW
☎ (01974) 821244
2 changing beers (sourced regionally; often Gower, Mantle, Wye Valley) ⌁

A traditional, family-run pub in this historic village. It has a main bar, dining area, function room and sunny outside seating. The friendly landlord is a keen supporter of real ale and offers a constantly changing range, with three beers alongside two or three bag-in-box ciders from Welsh producers including Gethins and Marcherman. Excellent-value, home-cooked meals are served, with a popular special offer menu on Wednesday. Pool and darts are played, and there is a big screen for sporting events. ☼ ⊛ ⌂ ◑ ♣ ⇊ 🖰 (585) 🖰 🖰

Llangoedmor

Penllwyndu

SA43 2LY (on B4570 4½ miles from Cardigan) SN240458
☎ (01239) 682533
Hancocks HB; 2 changing beers (sourced regionally; often Brains) ⌁

Old-fashioned alehouse standing at an isolated crossroads where Cardigan's evildoers were once hanged – the pub sign is worthy of close inspection. The cheerful and welcoming public bar retains its quaintness, with a slate floor and inglenook with wood-burning stove. Good home-cooked food including traditional favourites is available all day in the bar and the separate restaurant. Free live music plays on the third Thursday evening of the month. ☼ ⊛ ◑ ♣ P 🖰

Llanllwni

Talardd Arms

SA39 9DX (on A485) SN487392
☎ (01559) 395633 ⊕ talardd.co.uk
1 changing beer (sourced regionally) ⌁

There are records of this old drover's inn dating back to 1626. Drovers would stop for refreshments for man and beast before driving their livestock over Llanllwni Mountain on their way to markets over the border. Though sympathetically modernised, Tafarn Y Talardd still offers a traditional warm and friendly welcome, with a bar, lounge and separate restaurant. ☼ ⊛ ◑ ♣ P 🖰 🖰 🖰

Llanon

Rhos yr Hafod Inn 🅛

Cross Inn, SY23 5NB (at B4337/B4577 crossroads)
☎ (01974) 272644
2 changing beers (sourced regionally; often Bluestone, Evan Evans, Mantle) ⌁

A warm welcome and a varied range of guest ales await at this family-run pub. Its choice of drinking areas includes the front bar, popular in the early evening with lively locals, and the comfortable rear bar. For sunny days there is a large rear garden and a roadside drinking space. A selection of vinyl, a turntable and vinyl collection are available for customers' use. Various events are held throughout the year. A former local CAMRA Pub of the Year. ☼ ⊛ ♣ ⇊ P 🖰

Llansaint

King's Arms

13 Maes yr Eglwys, SA17 5JE
☎ (01267) 267487
Glamorgan Jemimas Pitchfork; Young's London Special; 1 changing beer (sourced nationally) Ⓗ
Friendly village hostelry that has been a pub for over 200 years. Situated near an 11th-century church, it is reputedly built from stone recovered from the lost village of St Ishmaels. Attractions include live music every Thursday and a TV for major sporting events. Good-value home-cooked food is served (book ahead, especially Sunday). Carmarthen Bay Holiday Park is a few miles away. A former local CAMRA Pub of the Year.
(198)

Llansteffan

Castle Inn

The Square, SA33 5JG
☎ (01267) 241225 thecastleinnpub.com
Sharp's Doom Bar; house beer (by Evan Evans); 2 changing beers (often Evan Evans) Ⓗ
The Castle is a traditional inn committed to real ale, with a welcoming atmosphere and friendly staff. The interior has been completely redecorated. It has an open-plan layout but also plenty of cosy corners for customers to relax and unwind in relative peace and quiet. The pub hosts a number of local community groups. It offers bar snacks from an uncomplicated menu. There is an outside seating area overlooking the village square where locals and tourists mingle. Q (227)

Llanychaer

Bridge End Inn

SA65 9TB (on B4313, 2 miles SW of Fishguard)
☎ (01348) 872545
Mantle Rock Steady, Cwrw Teifi, Dark Heart Ⓗ**; 1 changing beer (sourced locally; often Bluestone, Evan Evans)** Ⓗ/Ⓖ
Known locally as the Bont, this friendly country pub, over 150 years old, nestles in the beautiful Gwaun Valley at a bridging point across the river. The cosy bars with log fires serve, mainly, local real ales. The dining room is housed in the smithy, once run as a complementary business to the inn, and features an external water wheel. Home-made food includes popular Sunday lunches. Check ahead for winter hours and food service.
Q (345)

Narberth

Dingle Inn

Jesse Road, SA67 7DP
☎ (01834) 869979 dinglecaravanparknarberth.co.uk
3 changing beers (sourced regionally) Ⓗ
Friendly local next to a caravan and camping site, offering plenty of Narberth's distinctive community spirit. Having only one handpump the beer changes frequently – with customers' preferences guiding the selection of ales from the local area and further afield. The town boasts a range of specialist shops and attractions, including an award-winning museum, that would be the envy of many larger places. P (381)

Nevern

Trewern Arms

SA42 0NB (off A487, 2 miles N of Newport)
☎ (01239) 820395 trewernarms.com
3 changing beers (sourced nationally; often Bluestone, Harbwr, Mantle) Ⓗ
A picturesque 16th-century pub deep within a secluded valley astride the banks of the River Nevern. The village of Nevern is less than a mile from the beautiful fishing town of Newport. This multi-roomed pub caters for all, from those who just want a drink to large parties and wedding receptions. A great place to stay to experience some of the best walks in West Wales.
Q P (T5)

New Quay

Black Lion

Glanmor Terrace, SA45 9PT
☎ (01545) 560122 blacklionnewquay.co.uk
2 changing beers (sourced locally; often Mantle, Purple Moose, Sharp's) Ⓗ
Perched atop a steep street, this striking pub has Dylan Thomas connections. Refurbished in a contemporary style, it has separate dining areas and a main bar that gets busy when big games are screened on TV. The large garden has a play area and stunning sea views (dogs welcome in the garden). Up to three, mostly Welsh, beers are served alongside bottled cider from Gwynt y Ddraig. Excellent food is on offer. Live music is hosted during New Quay's August festival. Accommodation is available in nine bedrooms.

Newcastle Emlyn

Bunch of Grapes

Bridge Street, SA38 9DU
☎ (01239) 711185
2 changing beers Ⓗ
A Grade II*-listed building dating back to the 17th century, reputed to have been built from the ruins of the nearby 13th-century castle. Set in the heart of the community, the pub offers a warm and welcoming place to eat, drink and relax. Its enclosed rear garden features a children's play area and a covered smoking shelter.
P (460)

Newchapel

Ffynnone Arms

SA37 0EH
☎ (01239) 841800 ffynnonearms.co.uk
Hancocks HB; Wye Valley Butty Bach; 1 changing beer (sourced locally; often Mantle) Ⓗ
This charming and traditional 18th-century pub has recently been attractively refurbished. Local ales are often available alongside the regional and national beers, and Welsh cider Gwynt y Ddraig is also sold. The landlady prides herself on serving good food using locally sourced ingredients where possible, with gluten-free, dairy-free and sugar-free options. Fish & chips night is Wednesday, and on Sunday there is a carvery. The pub is on the borders of three counties – Pembrokeshire, Carmarthenshire and Ceredigion. Welsh and English are spoken. Q P

Newport

Royal Oak

West Street, SA42 0TA
☎ (01239) 820632 theroyaloaknewport.co.uk
Felinfoel Best Bitter; Gower Gold; 1 changing beer (sourced nationally) Ⓗ
A warm welcome awaits at this traditional Welsh country pub, which retains all the charm and atmosphere of its roots, with oak beams, a tiled bar area and many original

features. As well as offering quality real ales, the pub is renowned for its good home-made food, notably curries and fish & chips. A pensioners' lunch is served on Tuesday. Q🐴◑♿P🚌📶

Pembrey

Ship Aground Inn

Ashburnham Road, SA16 0TL

☎ (01554) 835724

4 changing beers (often Sharp's, Tiny Rebel) 🄷

A friendly husband and wife team offer a warm welcome to all at this popular pub on the road between Pembrey and Burry Port. Now refurbished, it has an open-plan bar area plus a separate restaurant space. Real ale provision is a cornerstone of the premises, with four changing beers served. The pub also offers a wide range of locally sourced home-cooked food. 🐴❀◑P

Pembroke

Old King's Arms 𝕃

Main Street, SA71 4JS

☎ (01646) 683611 🌐 oldkingsarmshotel.co.uk

Felinfoel Double Dragon; Marston's Old Empire; 2 changing beers (sourced locally; often Bluestone, Evan Evans) 🄷

This former coaching inn is allegedly the oldest inn in Pembroke, dating from around 1520. The hotel's King's Bar is a small room with exposed stone walls, beams and a real fire. It has four handpumps serving local, regional and national beers. There is a separate lounge with a dining area, and a restaurant with room for larger groups. Locally sourced meat and fish products are a feature of the menu. Q🐴❀🛏◑♿P🚌🐾📶

Pembroke Dock

First & Last

London Road, SA72 6TX (on A477)

☎ (01646) 682687

Brains Rev James; Worthington's White Shield; 1 changing beer (sourced nationally; often Skinner's) 🄷

Friendly single-bar local run by the same family for more than 50 years. Formerly the Commercial, it acquired its more distinctive name in 1991 to reflect its edge-of-town location. The walls display an eclectic mix of photos and prints. The food is good pub fare. There is a popular quirky Sunday evening quiz. It is handy for the Cleddau Bridge, giving easy access to Haverfordwest, and close to the historic naval dockyard and Irish Ferries. Q🐴❀◑🚆P🚌📶

Porthyrhyd

Mansel Arms 𝕃 ✔

Banc y Mansel, SA32 8BS (on B4310 between Porthyrhyd and Drefach)

☎ (01267) 275305

Marston's Pedigree 🄷**; 5 changing beers (sourced nationally; often Courage, Evan Evans, Glamorgan)** 🄷/🄶

Welcoming 18th-century coaching inn with plenty of traditional character, featuring wood fires in both bars. The landlord is passionate about real ale and encourages customers to experience a variety of flavours, with third-pints available. Beers are varied, and selected from local and national brewers, with a new ale every couple of days. The pub's cask ale members' club offers regular brewery visits. Excellent home-cooked food is served. A former CAMRA Wales national Pub of the Year. 🐴❀◑🍏P🚌(129) 🐾📶

Prengwyn

Gwarcefel Arms

SA44 4LU (on A475/B4476 crossroads) SN424442

☎ (01559) 363126 🌐 gwarcefelarms.co.uk

Sharp's Doom Bar; 1 changing beer (sourced nationally) 🄷

A traditional country inn with a friendly atmosphere where everyone is welcome, including families and dogs. Situated at the junction of five roads in Prengwyn, three miles north of Llandysul, the pub has a main bar with a wood-burning stove, cosy seating, a pool table and dartboard. A separate restaurant area, which caters for functions and parties, offers evening meals and Sunday lunches. The beer garden and ample car park are to the rear. 🐴❀◗♣P🐾

Pumsaint

Dolaucothi Arms

SA19 8UW (on A482 midway between Llanwrda and Lampeter)

☎ (01558) 650237

2 changing beers (sourced regionally; often Evan Evans, Purple Moose, Wye Valley) 🄷

A substantial stone-built inn with a friendly welcome, owned by the National Trust and tastefully restored in traditional style. Real cider and real ales are offered, usually including two beers from Welsh breweries. An excellent menu features seasonal ingredients. The large beer garden provides views over the valley and the Rivers Cothi and Twrch. Winner of the BBC Countryfile Pub of the Year in 2019. The Dolaucothi Gold Mines are nearby. 🐴❀🛏◑♿⛺♣🍏P🚌🐾📶

Pwlltrap

White Lion

SA33 4AT

☎ (01994) 230370 🌐 whitelion-pwlltrap.co.uk/home

Courage Directors; Greene King Abbot; Shepherd Neame Bishops Finger; Young's London Original; 1 changing beer (sourced locally) 🄷

This roadside pub, just outside St Clears on the road to Whitland, is warm and welcoming, with a real fire in winter. It has an old-world charm, with oak beams and panelled walls, and boasts a large annexe restaurant serving good food. Two cask beers are available in winter, four in summer. Pool and darts are played and a large-screen TV shows sporting fixtures. The pub organises a range of events throughout the year. Q◑♿♣P🚌(224,322) 🐾📶

Rhandirmwyn

Towy Bridge Inn

SA20 0PE

☎ (01550) 760370

2 changing beers (sourced locally; often Glamorgan Brewing Co) 🄷

In a delightful rural riverside location, the interior here is a single room with table seating in one part and a bar. Real ales come from local Welsh breweries. It offers a very extensive home-cooked menu using locally sourced ingredients. There is a large outdoor seating area with views across the river. It is popular with walkers, bikers and cyclists, and dogs are welcome. Q🐴❀◑⛺🍏P🐾📶

Roch

Victoria Inn

SA62 6AW (on A487)

☎ (01437) 710426 ⊕ thevictoriainnroch.com
Victoria Inn NewgAle, Fine & Dandy, WOW; 1 changing beer (sourced locally; often Victoria Inn) Ⓗ
A little gem of a brewpub, with views across St Brides Bay, offering a warm welcome. The inn was established in 1851, although parts are older, and has retained much of its 19th-century appeal, with beamed ceilings and low doorways. The home-brewed house bitter is Fine & Dandy. Food is available every day except Monday; curry and a pint night is Friday. For those in a hurry there is a beer carry-out service. Live music features occasionally. Q ➤ ❀ ⏾ ◑ ▲ ♠ P ❑ (T11) ☎

Rudbaxton

Corner Piece Inn

SA62 5PG (on A40)
☎ (01437) 742185
Caffle Drop Squint; Gwaun Valley Pembrokeshire Best Bitter Ⓗ
This is the first pub for two miles from Haverfordwest in one direction and Wolfs Castle in the other. A cosy three-roomed hostelry serving good beer and food, the owners are enthusiastic about their real ale. Pie night is Wednesday and fish night Friday. There is seating and children's play equipment outside but the location on the busy A40 can be noisy. Q ➤ ❀ ⏾ ◑ ▲ ⇌ P ❑ (T5)

Saundersfoot

Harbwr Bar & Kitchen

1 High Street, SA69 9EJ
☎ (01834) 811413 ⊕ harbwrbarandkitchen.wales
Harbwr MV Enterprise, North Star, RFA Sir Galahad; 1 changing beer (often Harbwr) Ⓗ
A modern pub and restaurant in the centre of this popular village, set in the Pembrokeshire Coast National Park and just a short walk from the long, sandy beach. The modern, spacious interior features upstairs seating giving superb views, and the outlook from the patio stretches across the bay to Tenby. The pub serves the full range of Harbwr Tenby Harbour Brewery beers alongside a good selection of gins. It can get a little noisy when busy but is well worth a visit when in Saundersfoot. ➤ ❀ ⏾ ◑ ⏣ P ❑

Solva

Cambrian Inn Ⓛ

SA62 6UU
☎ (01437) 721210 ⊕ thecambrianinn.co.uk
Gwaun Valley Blodwen; 2 changing beers (sourced locally) Ⓗ
Situated in a popular coastal village, renowned as one of the most delightful places in Pembrokeshire, this sympathetically restored local pub has a reputation for good beer and food. The bar area is decorated with local paintings, creating a cosy atmosphere enjoyed by village residents and visitors alike. Guest beers are from local breweries. Q ❀ ⏾ ◑ ▲ P ❀ ☎

Royal George

13 High Street, SA62 6TF
☎ (01437) 720002 ⊕ theroyalgeorgesolva.co.uk
Felinfoel Double Dragon; Sharp's Doom Bar; Wye Valley Butty Bach Ⓗ
Set on the main road to St David's in Upper Solva, this friendly, imposing community pub commands stunning views over St Brides Bay. The one-roomed bar has a busy, homely feel, with rugby pictures on the walls. The furniture is both rustic and eclectic, which adds to the ambience. In winter a guest beer is only available on big

occasions. A beer festival is held at least once a year. Chinese food is cooked to order at weekends. ➤ ❀ ❤ ⏾ ◑ ▲ ♠ P ❑ (T11) ❀ ☎

Stackpole

Stackpole Inn

Jasons Corner, SA71 5DF (on B4319)
☎ (01646) 672324 ⊕ stackpoleinn.co.uk
Brains Rev James; Felinfoel Best Bitter, Double Dragon; 1 changing beer (sourced regionally; often Mantle) Ⓗ
A multi award-winning pub three miles south of the historic town of Pembroke in the Pembrokeshire Coast National Park. The inn has a restaurant that focuses on local seafood dishes, and offers superb B&B accommodation. It is a short walk to the beautiful Pembrokeshire Coast Path, and when visiting you can also explore the Stackpole Estate, Bosherston Lily Ponds and the amazing Barafundle Bay and Broad Haven beach. ➤ ❀ ❤ ⏾ ◑ ▲ ♠ P ❀ ☎

Tegryn

Butchers Arms

SA35 0BL
☎ (01239) 698680
Gower Gold Ⓗ**; Morland Old Speckled Hen** Ⓖ**; Sharp's Doom Bar** Ⓗ
A rural pub with a great atmosphere, well off the beaten track in a hard-to-find location, but on the National Cycle Network Route 47. It has been attractively refurbished using local slate on the walls and floor. There is a games room featuring a mobile skittle alley plus other traditional pub games. A beer festival is held here every July. Q ➤ ◑ ⏣ ♠ P ❀ ☎

Tenby

Hope & Anchor Ⓛ

St Julian Street, SA70 7AS
☎ (01834) 842186
Felinfoel Double Dragon; Harbwr MV Enterprise, North Star Ⓗ**, Caldey Lollipop** Ⓖ**; Sharp's Atlantic; 2 changing beers (sourced nationally; often Bluestone, Mantle)** Ⓗ
Welcoming pub set in the old town on the way down to the harbour and close to the beaches, catering for locals and tourists alike. The convivial atmosphere and interesting local decor make this an excellent place to relax over a beer. It serves up to four guest ales, mainly from Welsh breweries including Evan Evans, Mantle and Purple Moose, although Wye Valley sometimes makes an appearance. Ciders include Westons Old Rosie and Somerset Tree Shaker West Country Cider. Food is important and specials supplement the standard menu. The medieval town walks can be seen nearby. ➤ ❀ ⏾ ◑ ▲ ⇌ ❤ ⏣ ❑ ❀ ☎

Tenby Harbour Brewery Tap & Kitchen Ⓛ

St Julian Street, SA70 7AS (on street linking town square to harbour)
☎ (01834) 842273
Harbwr MV Enterprise, Caldey Lollipop, RFA Sir Galahad; 1 changing beer (sourced locally; often Harbwr) Ⓗ
Situated in a quaint street that links the town square to the harbour and beaches. The bar area is large but has a cosy feel with beams, stove and Tenby memorabilia adorning the walls. A sunny walled beer garden is to the rear. The pub is the brewery tap for the adjacent Tenby

Harbour Brewery and showcases its full range of beers. Food is served all day with locally sourced produce, including fresh fish, featuring on the menu.
🕭✿◑人⇌●🖵♻🛜

circus elephant reputedly buried here. Accommodation is available with dogs welcome.
Q🕭✿📥◑&♣●P🖵(585,588) ♻🛜

Tregaron

Talbot 🗌
The Square, SY25 6JL
☎ (01974) 298208 ⊕ ytalbot.com
2 changing beers (sourced regionally; often Evan Evans, Ludlow, Mantle) Ⓗ

A former drovers' inn of immense character in an unspoilt town on the edge of the Cambrian Mountains. It has a cosy front bar with a real fire, a beamed and flagstoned snug with an inglenook fireplace, a rear bar with TV and a restaurant. Two real ales are available in winter, three in summer, and three real ciders. Quality food includes locally reared meat and tempting desserts. The beautiful garden has fine views and a memorial to a

Whitland

Station House Hotel
St Johns Street, SA34 0AP
☎ (01994) 240556 ⊕ stationhousewhitland.co.uk
5 changing beers (often Sharp's, Wye Valley, Young's) Ⓗ

A smile and a warm welcome are always on tap at this friendly hostelry. It is very much a locals' pub for all ages and offers something for everyone, including pool and darts teams, and bingo on Sunday evening. A small room is available for people looking for a quiet corner. The outside drinking area is partly under cover. Car parking is to the rear and the railway station is close by.
✿◑⇌♣●P🖵♻🛜

Ship & Castle, Aberystwyth (Photo: Tom Bastin/Flickr CC BY 2.0)

Scotland

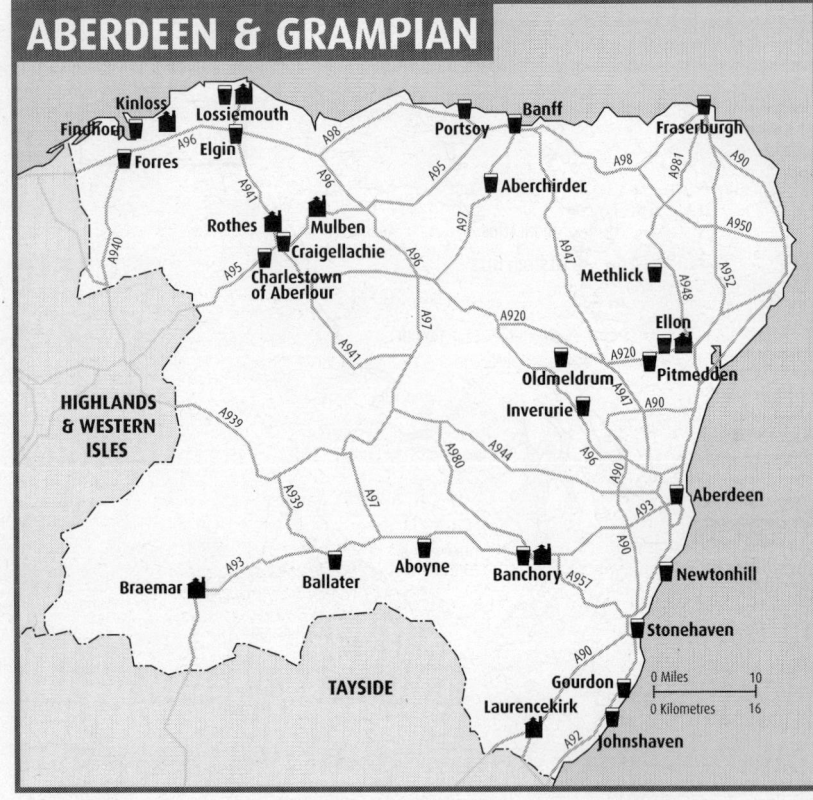

ABERDEEN & GRAMPIAN

Authority areas covered: Aberdeenshire UA, City of Aberdeen UA, Moray UA

Aberchirder

New Inn

79 Main Street, AB54 7TB

☎ (01466) 780633 ⊕ newinnaberchirder.co.uk

Windswept Wolf; 4 changing beers (sourced nationally; often Caledonian, Hambleton, Orkney) Ⓗ

Extensively refurbished during the recent Covid lockdowns, this traditional, friendly inn has wood-burning stoves, candlelit areas and a vintage atmosphere. It offers a changing selection of five quality ales from local and national breweries. A separate dining area provides home-made food prepared by the owner/chef using locally sourced produce with the pork pies highly recommended. Families are welcome in the dining room until early evening (booking recommended). Dogs are permitted in the bar but should be kept on a lead at busy times. Planning permission has been granted for a microbrewery to brew beers exclusively for the pub. Q❄❀⚪◗&P🚍(301,303)❀🛜

Aberdeen

Archibald Simpson ✓

5 Castle Street, AB11 5BQ (E end of Union St)

☎ (01224) 621365

Caledonian Deuchars IPA; Greene King Abbot; 9 changing beers (sourced nationally; often Orkney, Redcastle, Stewart) Ⓗ

The former headquarters of Clydesdale Bank, this Wetherspoon has a pillared entrance and retains many original features – the main room is a central hall with a high ceiling and additional seating

areas to the side. Twelve handpumps offer beers from various Scottish breweries. There is a narrow outside drinking space on the pavement. Beer festivals are held several times a year. ❄◗&🚍🛜

Blue Lamp

121 Gallowgate, AB25 1BU

☎ (01224) 647472 ⊕ thebluelampaberdeen.com

Cromarty Happy Chappy; 1 changing beer (often Cromarty) Ⓟ

Time has stood still in the small public bar here, where little has changed since the 1960s. In the same family for more than 70 years, it is now run by the grandson of the late Sandy Brown. The cavernous converted warehouse next door is a popular music venue and usually hosts the Aberdeen Jazz Festival each March, plus other jazz events and a Wednesday blues jam. Various styles of band play at weekends for which there may be a charge. One beer is served in both bars, occasionally with a second in the

REAL ALE BREWERIES

Braemar Braemar (NEW)
Brewdog Ellon
Burnside Laurencekirk
Deeside Banchory
Keith Mulben
Quiet 🖫 Banchory
Rothes Rothes
Six ° North Laurencekirk
Spey Valley Mulben
Windswept Lossiemouth
WooHa Kinloss

lounge. The small, dimly lit upstairs lounge is available for private functions. Opening times may vary; the big lounge stays open till the small hours at weekends. ♿🍴

Ferryhill House Hotel

169 Bon Accord Street, AB11 6UA (10 mins' walk from Union St)

☎ (01224) 590867 ⊕ ferryhillhousehotel.co.uk

Caledonian Deuchars IPA; Orkney Corncrake, Dark Island; Timothy Taylor Landlord Ⓗ

A small city-centre hotel in a quiet residential area, with tables and chairs in the extensive garden featuring a children's play area. There is a large, modern, lounge bar with a selection of more than 60 malt whiskies, a large restaurant and a conservatory. A wheelchair access ramp leads to the front door. The Dark Island pump may serve a varying beer. ☆🏨🚪◑♿➘P🚌(17,17A)🛜

Globe Inn

13-15 North Silver Street, AB10 1RJ (off Golden Square)

☎ (01224) 641171 ⊕ the-globe-inn.com

3 changing beers (sourced regionally; often Cromarty, Swannay, Windswept) Ⓗ

Convivial open-plan venue that is now in private ownership, having previously been run by Belhaven. Its three Angram pumps serve beers from a variety of Scottish breweries. Live music plays on Friday and Saturday, ranging from pop and rock covers to acoustic blues. A quiz is held on Monday evening. The pub is convenient for nearby entertainment venues His Majesty's Theatre and Music Hall, and offers reasonably priced en-suite accommodation. The beer garden can be partially covered in inclement weather.
☆🏨🚪◑♿➘❄🛜

Grill ★

213 Union Street, AB11 6BA

☎ (01224) 583563 ⊕ thegrillaberdeen.co.uk

Fyne Ales Jarl; 4 changing beers (sourced regionally; often Cromarty, Orkney, Windswept) Ⓗ

With an exquisite interior redesigned in 1926, this is the only pub in the area listed on CAMRA's National Inventory of Historic Pub Interiors. It has been part of the McGinty's Group since 2019. Centrally positioned ale pumps offer guest beers from various Scottish breweries. The large selection of whiskies has won numerous awards. Bar snacks are available. Musicians appearing at the Music Hall opposite often visit during concert breaks. A former CAMRA branch Pub of the Year. ➘🚌🛜

Krakatoa

2 Trinity Quay, AB11 5AA (facing quayside at bottom of Market St)

☎ (01224) 587602 ⊕ krakatoa.bar

Changing beers (sourced regionally; often Cromarty, Spey Valley, Windswept) Ⓟ

This historic harbourside bar, formerly the Moorings, changes character from a friendly, laid-back local to a raucous rock bar on weekend evenings, when there may be a cover charge. The eclectic jukebox is popular with the varied clientele. A wide selection of Scottish ales is served on up to 12 American-style fonts to the far left of the bar, and a varied selection of Belgian beers and ciders is also available. Local CAMRA City Pub of the Year 2019. ♿➘♣🍴🎲🚌❄🛜

Number 10 Bar & Restaurant

10 Queens Terrace, AB10 1XL (10 mins' walk from W end of Union St)

☎ (01224) 631928 ⊕ no10aberdeen.co.uk

Caledonian Deuchars IPA; Timothy Taylor Landlord; 2 changing beers (sourced regionally; often Stewart) Ⓗ

A basement bar close to the West End, featuring a contemporary interior with exposed granite walls, traditional herringbone floors and dark-wood furnishings. It has two seating areas to the right and left as you come in, with several TV screens showing sport. The bar along the back wall has four handpumps. A wide choice of meals is available in the restaurant in the former Number 9, with an additional separate menu in the bar. ◑🚌🍴🛜

Prince of Wales ✅

7 St Nicholas Lane, AB10 1HF (in lane opp Marks & Spencer)

☎ (01224) 640597 ⊕ princeofwales-aberdeen.co.uk

Greene King IPA, Abbot; 6 changing beers (sourced nationally; often Cromarty, Swannay, Windswept) Ⓗ

One of the oldest bars in Aberdeen, the Prince of Wales has possibly the longest bar counter in the city, a large following of regulars and a friendly atmosphere buzzing with conversation. It is listed among CAMRA Scotland's True Heritage Pubs, and offers a varied selection of ales, mostly from Scottish breweries, with tasters for the undecided. Good-value food is served daily including filled rolls. Folk music features on Sunday evening.
Q☆🍴◑🚌🛜

Queen Vic

126 Rosemount Place, AB25 2YU (approx 10 mins' walk up Rose St from W end of Union St)

☎ (01224) 638500 ⊕ queenvicaberdeen.co.uk

Timothy Taylor Landlord; 3 changing beers (sourced nationally; often Burnside, Spey Valley, Windswept) Ⓗ

A cosy one-room locals' lounge bar slightly off the beaten track in a converted shop in the residential area of Rosemount. Sporting events are frequently shown, when the pub can get busy and noisy. The cask ales are complemented by an extensive range of locally brewed bottled beers. A popular quiz featuring a Play Your Cards Right jackpot is held on Monday evening and live bands play occasionally at weekends, with live jazz on one Sunday a month. A variety of sandwiches are available daily with occasional additional snacks/specials. Local CAMRA Pub of the Year 2020. 🚌(3,3A)❄🛜

St Machar Bar

97 High Street, Old Aberdeen, AB24 3EN

☎ (01224) 483079

Stewart Pentland IPA; 2 changing beers (sourced regionally; often Inveralmond, Orkney, Stewart) Ⓗ

Located in the photogenic Old Aberdeen conservation area amid the university buildings and close to King's College, this friendly and historic bar is frequented by academics and locals alike. The bar features a splendid mirror from the long-gone local Thomson Marshall Aulton Brewery, and there is another from the original Devanha Brewery at the rear beside the toilets. Alongside the ales is a comprehensive selection of whiskies and gins. The bar is home to a darts team, university football team and rugby team. The tiny kitchen serves traditional pub grub. ❄◑♣🚌(20)🛜

Aboyne

Boat Inn

Charleston Road, AB34 5EL (N bank of River Dee next to Aboyne Bridge)

☎ (01339) 886137 ⊕ theboatinnaboyne.co.uk

2 changing beers (sourced nationally; often Belhaven, Cairngorm) Ⓗ

Popular riverside inn with a food-oriented lounge. Junior diners (and adults) may request to see the model train, complete with sound effects, traverse the entire pub at picture-rail height upon completion of their meal. The

Shed public bar has a recess at the back used for live music nights. Three ales are served in summer, two in winter, usually at least one from Belhaven and another from a local brewery. Breakfast is available. It has 15 twin rooms and a family room for overnight stays.
Q❄🛏️◑♿🅰️P🐾🛜

Ballater

Alexandra Hotel

12 Bridge Square, AB35 5QJ
☎ (01339) 755376 ⊕ alexandrahotelballater.co.uk
Cairngorm Trade Winds; 2 changing beers (sourced regionally; often Cairngorm) Ⓗ
Originally built as a private home in 1800, this friendly, family-owned lounge bar became the Alexandra Hotel in 1915. It is popular both with locals and those visiting for bar suppers. Three Cairngorm ales are available in summer, generally just two in winter. It has a beer garden to the rear for alfresco drinking. A handy stop-off on your way to Braemar for the Highland Games or on a visit with the royals at Balmoral. ❄🛏️◑♿🅰️P🚲🐾🛜

Glenaden Hotel

6 Church Square, AB35 5NE
☎ (01339) 755488
3 changing beers (sourced regionally; often Windswept) Ⓗ
Situated on the far side of the picturesque town square, this small hotel displays a prominent external sign for its Barrel Lounge. It normally serves three beers in busy periods, usually Scottish, mostly from Windswept. Darker ales are apparently favoured by the locals. There is a large function suite and a beer garden at the rear of the hotel. Q❄🅿️🛏️◑♿🐾P🚲🐾🛜

Banchory

Douglas Arms Hotel

22 High Street, AB31 5SR (opp West Church)
☎ (01330) 822547 ⊕ douglasarms.co.uk
Cairngorm Trade Winds; 1 changing beer (sourced nationally) Ⓗ
The former public bar to the front of this hotel has remained virtually unchanged over the last century, and is a classic Scottish long bar with etched windows and vintage mirrors. It is one of CAMRA Scotland's True Heritage Pubs but it now operates as the Coffee Bothy. The ales are served in the redesigned, refurbished lounge bar, with two real ales at peak times. To the rear is a large, south-facing exterior decking area, ideal for alfresco drinking. Q❄🅿️🛏️◑♿🅰️🐾🛜

Ravenswood Club (Royal British Legion)

25 Ramsay Road, AB31 5TS
☎ (01330) 822347 ⊕ banchorylegion.co.uk
2 changing beers (sourced nationally) Ⓗ
Large British Legion club with a comfortable lounge adjoining the pool and TV room and a spacious function room frequently used by local clubs and societies as well as members. Darts and snooker are popular and played most evenings. The two handpumps offer excellent value and the beer choice is constantly changing, with ales consistently the best quality in the village. An elevated terrace has fine views of the Deeside hills. Show a copy of this Guide or your CAMRA membership card for entry. ❄🅿️🛏️◑♿🅰️P🛜

Banff

Market Arms

5 High Shore, AB45 1DB
☎ (01261) 818616
1 changing beer (sourced nationally; often Morland, Ruddles, Timothy Taylor) Ⓗ
This fine building is one of the oldest in historic Banff, dating back to 1585. The courtyard at the back retains many original features. The long public bar has several fine examples of historic brewery and distillery mirrors. One of the two handpumps always serves a changing beer - two beers are on at weekends and holidays. The impressive upstairs lounge is used mainly for meals.
🛏️◑♿🅰️🐾🛜

Charlestown of Aberlour

Mash Tun

8 Broomfield Square, AB38 9QP (signposted from village square)
☎ (01340) 881771 ⊕ mashtun-aberlour.com
2 changing beers (sourced locally; often Cairngorm) Ⓗ
A busy traditional bar promoted as a whisky bar, offering the world's only full collection of Glenfarclas whisky plus more than 100 other malts. The Speyside Way and Alice Littler Park are close by, as is the River Spey itself which makes the pub popular with anglers. When it opened in 1896 as the Station Bar, a pledge in the title deeds allowed a name change if the railway closed - but it must revert to the Station Bar if a train ever pulls up again outside. Food is served all day at weekends.
❄🅿️🛏️◑🅰️P🚲(36)🐾🛜

Craigellachie

Highlander Inn

10 Victoria Street, AB38 9SR (on A95, opp post office)
☎ (01340) 881446 ⊕ whiskyinn.com
3 changing beers Ⓗ
Picturesque whisky and cask ale bar on Speyside's Whisky Trail, close to the Speyside Way. Popular with tourists, walkers and anglers, it is busy during whisky festivals and the tourist season. Twinned with the Highlander Whisky Bar in Tokyo, it offers a fine selection of malts including many from Japan. Up to three ales are served alongside locally sourced food from the hotel kitchen. CRAC (Craigellachie Real Ale Club) meets on the first Wednesday of the month and its members help to choose the guest ales. An outside decked area is a delight on a sunny afternoon. ❄🅿️🛏️◑🅰️P🚲(36)🛜

Elgin

Muckle Cross ⊘

34 High Street, IV30 1BU
☎ (01343) 559030
Caledonian Deuchars IPA; Greene King Abbot; Sharp's Doom Bar; 4 changing beers (sourced regionally; often Windswept) Ⓗ
A typical small Wetherspoon pub converted from what was once a bicycle repair shop. The pleasant long room has ample seating, a family area and a long bar. Deservedly popular, it can be busy, particularly at weekends. Eight handpumps offer a wide range of beers from national and Scottish microbreweries, and ciders are available during the annual cider fest. Two beer festivals are held annually. Q❄◑♿🎋🐾🛜

Ellon

Tolbooth

21-23 Station Road, AB41 9AE
☎ (01358) 721308
3 changing beers (sourced nationally; often Cromarty, Orkney) Ⓗ

A large pub, popular with all ages, close to the centre of the town and just a short walk from the bus stops on Market Street. There are separate seating areas on split levels as well as an airy conservatory with barrel tables. One Scottish and one English guest ale are usually available. Several National Trust Scotland properties are nearby. No food is served but carry in is allowed if required. ⊛ⓀⅬ♣🖵🐾 🖤🕏

Findhorn

Kimberley Inn

94 Findhorn, IV36 3YG
☎ (01309) 690492 🌐 kimberleyinn.com
2 changing beers (sourced regionally; often Cairngorm, Orkney) Ⓗ

The inn is situated on the shore of Findhorn Bay in a charming seaside village with a fine stretch of beach. It has three areas – a family room with wood-panelled walls, a snug with splendid views of the hills across the Moray Firth, and the bar, with an excellent log fire. Two ales are available, one in winter, mainly from Scottish micros. The extensive food menu features home-cooked meals, with local seafood the speciality, and local ice cream. Q🕏⊛Ⅼ🍺ⓀⅬ♣🖵(31)🐾

Forres

Mosset Tavern Ⓛ

Gordon Street, IV36 1DY
☎ (01309) 672981 🌐 mossettavern.com
5 changing beers (sourced locally; often Spey Valley, Swannay, Windswept) Ⓗ

Described as 'the country pub in the heart of Forres', this smart, popular Scottish lounge bar/restaurant is situated next to the Mosset burn and pond. Friendly, efficient staff serve ale from a single handpump in the lounge and up to five in the spacious, comfortable public bar, where there are pool tables and large screens showing sport. A large function room is also available, home to the Foot Tapper beer festival in April. Live music plays on Friday evening, and there is a pub quiz every Tuesday. 🕏⊛🍺Ⓚ🍺♣🖵(10) 🐾🕏

Red Lion

2-6 Tollboth Street, IV36 1PH
☎ (01309) 672716
2 changing beers (sourced nationally) Ⓗ

Dating from 1838 and known locally as the Beastie, this popular venue is one of the oldest real ale outlets in the north of Scotland. Its smart, modern lounge offers two beers from the Belhaven list. The public bar has a pool table and features a rare mirror from Campbell & Co's Argyle Brewery. Live music plays on Saturday night. 🕏🍺Ⓚ♣🖵(10,19A)🐾

Fraserburgh

Elizabethan Bar & Lounge

36 Union Grove, AB43 9PH (near Academy)
☎ (01346) 510464
3 changing beers (sourced regionally; often Kelburn, Windswept) Ⓗ

Set in the middle of a housing estate, with a mock-Tudor exterior, the pub has a public bar, games room with four dartboards and two pool tables, and a lounge bar with a large-screen TV usually featuring sport. The bar has a formidable reputation for offering a wide range of quality ales sourced from throughout the country, and also features well over 200 malts, the largest collection in the area. The beach, harbour and lighthouse museum are a mile away. A former CAMRA branch Pub of the Year. 🕏ⓀⅬ♣🖵🐾🕏

Saltoun Inn ⊘

Saltoun Square, AB43 9DA
☎ (01346) 519548
Greene King Abbot; Sharp's Doom Bar; 5 changing beers (sourced nationally) Ⓗ

A Wetherspoon renovation of the historic Saltoun Arms Hotel, built in 1801. It comprises several interconnecting low-ceilinged rooms, including a lounge area to the left of the entrance. There is a garden area to the rear. Accommodation is offered in 11 rooms, with reduced rates at weekends. The Scottish Lighthouse Museum and main fishing harbour are nearby, and the main surfing beach is one mile south. Q🕏⊛🍺Ⓚ🍺Ⓚ🖵🕏

Gourdon

Harbour Bar

William Street, DD10 0LW
☎ (01561) 361337
1 changing beer (often Strathbraan) Ⓗ

Traditional seafaring decor abounds in this harbourside howff. It has a public bar, a smaller tap room, and a separate pool room with more seating. Nationally sourced beers are offered in winter and local ales during the summer season. The locally renowned Quayside Restaurant & Fish Bar is next door and the Maggie Law Maritime Museum nearby. Food is available daily at lunchtimes (Thu-Mon eves). 🕏⊛🍺ⓀⅬ♣🖵(747)🐾🕏

Inverurie

Gordon Highlander ⊘

West High Street, AB51 3QQ
☎ (01467) 626780
Sharp's Doom Bar; 4 changing beers (sourced nationally; often Cairngorm, Inveralmond, Strathaven) Ⓗ

A fine Wetherspoon conversion of a splendid Art Deco building which used to be the Victoria Cinema. The name refers to a locomotive built at the now defunct Inverurie Locomotive Works and there are many references to this throughout the pub. The famous Gordon Highlander Regiment also features prominently, with displays and a large mural. The books on the shelves are free to read and take home, with donations welcome. There are at least three guest ales and three real ciders, and the usual Wetherspoon beer festivals are staged. 🕏🍺Ⓚ🖵(10,37) 🕏

Johnshaven

Ship Inn

3 CastleStreet, DD10 0ER
☎ (01561) 362257
1 changing beer (often Strathbraan) Ⓗ

While it may appear to be closed, check for a small light in the window near the door or just do battle with the door latch to the public bar. First licensed in 1763, this well-worn howff offers a warming welcome and beers from the Strathbraan range. The public bar has a traditional coastal decor complete with mixed fuel stove and bar counter water fonts. Children are allowed in the adjacent lounge, which has a pool table. The local knitting club meets here every Wednesday and the pub is a proud sponsor of the local shipwreck charity walk. ⬧A♣🖪(747) ❀ 🛜

Lossiemouth

Windswept Tap Room
13 Coulardbank Industrial Estate, IV31 6NG
☎ (01343) 814310 ⊕ windsweptbrewing.com/tap-room
2 changing beers (sourced locally; often Windswept) ℗
This small industrial/office unit, converted to a taproom for the brewery next door, is now the only outlet for real ale in Lossiemouth. It has an industrial chic decor, with furniture fashioned from pallets. A large adjacent marquee is used on busy nights. Two varying ales on cask are supplemented by eight KeyKeg beers. Coffee, tea, soft drinks, cakes and snacks are sold, as well as a range of bottled beers and brewery merchandise. The bar is available for private hire and may host the occasional weekend beer festival. Closed Sunday and from 5pm Monday-Thursday. ❀℗🖪(33A,33C)🛜

Methlick

Ythanview Hotel
Main Street, AB41 7DT
☎ (01651) 806235 ⊕ ythanviewhotel.co.uk
2 changing beers (sourced regionally; often Fyne Ales, Swannay) ℍ
Traditional inn in the village centre, home to the Methlick Cricket Club at nearby Lairds. Log fires warm both the lounge bar at the front and the friendly sports-themed public bar at the rear. Beers are exclusively from Scottish micros. The restaurant is renowned for the owner's special chicken curry, and steak night on Thursday is popular. Meals are served all day at weekends. Live music and quiz nights take place on most Saturdays. Haddo House, Tolquhon Castle and Pitmedden Garden are nearby. Closed Monday-Friday afternoons. ⬧❀🖾◑♣P🖪(290,291) ❀🛜

Newtonhill

Newton Arms
10 Old Mill Road, AB39 3TZ
☎ (01569) 730227
1 changing beer (sourced regionally; often Cromarty, Orkney) ℍ
Traditional village local with a classic, dark-wood panelled public bar featuring 1950s bar counters, intriguing under-counter shelves for drinks and an original Devanha Brewery mirror. The lounge at the side has light-wood panelling and tables; you are welcome to bring in a curry from the Tandoori next door. Up to two beers are available in the public bar only, but usually just one. There is an east-facing patio to the rear for alfresco drinking. ⬧❀♣🖪❀🛜

Oldmeldrum

Redgarth
Kirk Brae, AB51 0DJ (signed off A947)
☎ (01651) 872353 ⊕ redgarth.com
3 changing beers (sourced locally; often Cromarty, Fyne Ales, Swannay) 🄶
Offering a warm welcome and excellent views of the eastern Grampian mountains, the Redgarth celebrated 31 years under the same ownership in 2021. The emphasis is on excellent beers served on gravity, with three handpumps on the bar to show which ales are available. Extra choice is offered during occasional

Brewer in Residence evenings. Meals are served in the bar, and it has a restaurant area. A winner of many CAMRA awards, the pub retains a strong reputation for its imaginative choice of Scottish beers. Closed Monday-Saturday afternoons. ⬧❀🖾◑A♣P🖪(35,X35)🛜

Pitmedden

Craft Bar
Tarves Road, AB41 7NX
☎ (01651) 842049 ⊕ thecraftpitmedden.wordpress.com
2 changing beers (sourced regionally; often Orkney, Spey Valley, Windswept) ℍ
A one-room corner pub run by a local CAMRA member. Old church pews provide seating for some of the tables around the walls; other tables have bench seating. Two handpumps serve ales from Scottish breweries, supplemented by a wide variety of KeyKeg beers. There is also a comprehensive range of bottled and canned beer in the fridge. Occasional Brewer in Residence evenings are held. Snacks are available. ⬧A♣P🖪❀🛜

Portsoy

Shore Inn
Church Street, AB45 2QR (overlooking harbour)
☎ (01261) 842831
2 changing beers (sourced regionally; often Kelburn, Spey Valley, Windswept) ℍ
Cosy, comfortable, coastal howff with a warm welcome in winter and scenic outdoor views in summer. The pub overlooks the oldest harbour on the Moray coast, which was a location for the remake of Whisky Galore. The L-shaped room with low ceilings is a fine example of a nautical bar. Expect the pub to be busy each June during the Scottish Traditional Boat Festival. ⬧❀A♣❀🛜

Stonehaven

Marine Hotel
9-10 Shorehead, AB39 2JY (overlooking harbour)
☎ (01569) 762155 ⊕ marinehotelstonehaven.co.uk
Timothy Taylor Landlord; house beer (by Six Degrees North); 4 changing beers (sourced regionally; often Cairngorm, Cromarty, Windswept) ℍ
Now the only outlet in the Six Degrees North empire that serves real ale, this is a former Scottish CAMRA Pub of the Year and a multiple branch award winner. The small harbourside hotel features simple wood panelling in the bar and a rustic lounge with an open fireplace. Seating outside offers a splendid view of the harbour. Ales from Six Degrees North are served plus numerous Belgian beers and up to 18 craft keg beers. Historic Dunnottar Castle is one mile south and an open-air bathing pool one mile north. ⬧❀🖾◑A🖳🖪(747,X7)❀🛜

Ship Inn
5 Shorehead, AB39 2JY
☎ (01569) 762617 ⊕ shipinnstonehaven.com
2 changing beers (sourced regionally; often Harviestoun, Strathaven, Strathbraan) ℍ
Built in 1771, this harbour-front hotel has a maritime-themed, wood-panelled bar and a small seating area outside overlooking the water. The long, narrow bar features a mirror from the defunct Devanha Brewery. Two beers are offered, at least one from Strathbraan, and an extensive range of malt whiskies is stocked. A modern restaurant with panoramic harbour views is adjacent to the bar – fish is the speciality and food is served all day at the weekend. Accommodation is available in 11 guest rooms. ⬧❀🖾◑&A🖳(747,X7)❀🛜

ARGYLL & THE ISLES

HIGHLANDS & WESTERN ISLES

Isle of Tiree
Tobermory
MULL
Isle of Colonsay
COLONSAY
JURA
ISLAY
Bridgend
Ellenabeich
Oban
Bridge of Orchy
Cairndow
Inveraray
Kilmartin
Cairnbaan
Strachur
Innellan
BUTE
KINTYRE
TAYSIDE
LOCH LOMOND, STIRLING & THE TROSSACHS
GREATER GLASGOW & CLYDE VALLEY
AYRSHIRE & ARRAN
SCOTLAND

0 Miles 20
0 Kilometres 32

Authority area covered: Argyll & Bute UA

Bridge of Orchy

Bridge of Orchy Hotel
PA36 4AD
☎ (01838) 400208 ⊕ bridgeoforchy.co.uk
**Harviestoun Bitter & Twisted; 1 changing beer
(sourced regionally; often Harviestoun)** ⊞
On the A82 that leads north to Glencoe, Fort William and
Skye, and with a railway station not far away, this
remote hotel is surprisingly accessible. With mountains
and glens nearby it is popular with walkers, climbers and
other outdoor types. The bar faces the road and features
an iron stove, as does the comfortable lounge. The
restaurant offers a panoramic view of the mountains.
Local produce is well represented on the menu.
⬥❀⊞◗⊃⇌P➲(915) ❀ 🛜

Cairnbaan

Cairnbaan Hotel
PA31 8SQ (on B841 by canal bridge)
☎ (01546) 603668 ⊕ cairnbaan.com
**3 changing beers (sourced regionally; often Fyne
Ales)** ⊞
The hotel was built in 1815 as a coaching inn to serve
users of the Crinan Canal – at its midpoint beside Lock 5 –
and has been accommodating travellers ever since. The
dark-painted bar and restaurant are housed in a more

recent addition to one side. The bar opens onto a
conservatory furnished with comfortable sofas; outside
there is a small seating area offering views of the canal.
Usually only two beers are available in winter.
Q⬥❀⊞◗⊃P➲❀🛜

Cairndow

Fyne Ales Brewery Tap 🅛
Achadunan, PA26 8BJ (up side road at head of Loch
Fyne)
☎ (01499) 600120 ⊕ fyneales.com/visit
**Fyne Ales Jarl; 4 changing beers (sourced locally;
often Fyne Ales)** ⊞
Brewery tap and shop, open since 2012 in what was
originally a farm building. The bar, with its fine polished
granite front, supports five handpumps selling a range of
ales from the brewery along with a varied selection of
bottled beers. Meat produced on the farm is available to

REAL ALE BREWERIES
Argyll Tobermory: Isle of Mull
Bun Dubh 🍺 Sandaig: Isle of Tiree
Colonsay Scalasaig: Isle of Colonsay
Fyne ✎ Cairndow
Islay ✎ Bridgend: Isle of Islay

buy and is also used to fill the excellent pies, which can be enjoyed in the bar or the courtyard looking across to the brewery. Q🕏🌣🍴P🐾🤶🛜

Ellenabeich

Oyster Bar & Restaurant 🗒

PA34 4RQ

☎ (01852) 300121 🌐 oysterbareasdale.com

2 changing beers (often Fyne Ales, Orkney, Williams Bros) 🅗

Pub by the harbour at the end of a row of low whitewashed cottages, which were once occupied by workers at the nearby slate quarries. Ales are generally from Scottish micros, often more unusual brews. The small lounge bar opens out to a rear decking area that offers views of Scarba and Jura. It is hard to believe that the remains of a flooded slate quarry could look so good! Q🌣🍴🤶🖨(418) 🐾🛜

Innellan

Osborne

44 Shore Road, PA23 7TJ

☎ (01369) 830820 🌐 theosborneinnellan.co.uk

St Austell Tribute; 2 changing beers (sourced nationally) 🅗

This whitewashed seafront hotel a few miles south of Dunoon was built in 1869 and has been completely refurbished in the past few years. The comfortable bar has a pool table to one side and a cosy lounge with a log fire. At the front a conservatory acts as the dining room and provides excellent views across the Firth of Clyde. Any good weather can be enjoyed in a small outdoor area to one side. 🕏🌣🍴🍽🖨(489)🛜

Inveraray

George Hotel

Main Street East, PA32 8TT

☎ (01499) 302111 🌐 thegeorgehotel.co.uk

3 changing beers (sourced regionally; often Caledonian, Fyne Ales, Inveralmond) 🅗

Attractive hotel developed from two private houses in 1860 by the Clark family, who still own it. The restaurants and bars have been completely restored but retain the original ambience with an abundance of dark wood, flagstone floors throughout and four roaring log and peat fires. Food has an emphasis on quality local produce, and the beers are mainly local too, served both in the main restaurant and the lively public bar alongside. Q🕏🌣🍴🍽♿P🖨(926,976) 🐾🛜

Kilmartin

Kilmartin Hotel

PA31 8RQ (on A816 10 miles N of Lochgilphead)

☎ (01546) 510250 🌐 kilmartin-hotel.com

3 changing beers (sourced regionally; often Fyne Ales, Loch Lomond, Orkney) 🅗

Whitewashed hotel on a promontory overlooking Kilmartin Glen and many sites of historic and religious significance. The small public bar to one side provides a cosy fireside nook and offers a good selection of whiskies to complement the real ale. To the rear, a pool and games room leads to a beer garden and smoking shed. Good home-made food is available in the evenings and some lunchtimes in the adjacent dining room, or in the garden in summer. 🕏🌣🍴🍽♿P🖨(423)🐾🛜

Oban

Corryvreckan 🗸

The Waterfront Centre, Railway Pier, PA34 4LW

☎ (01631) 568910

Caledonian Deuchars IPA; Greene King Abbot; Sharp's Doom Bar; 6 changing beers (sourced nationally) 🅗

Excellently located Wetherspoon named after the famous whirlpool between Jura and Scarba. It lies alongside the fishing boat berth, next door to both the rail station and ferry terminal and with views across Oban Bay. The interior has a wood-panelled roof and is open and spacious. The pub is enlivened by much nautical ephemera including a casting of a sea eagle. 🕏🌣🍴♿🍽🖨🛜

Oban Inn

1 Stafford Street, PA34 5NJ

☎ (01631) 567441

3 changing beers (often Fyne Ales) 🅗

This traditional corner local by the old harbour pier was shut for many years before reopening in 2016. The public bar remains unspoilt and retains its dark-wood panelling and stone floors of Easdale slate. Maritime artefacts decorate the walls, and banknotes from many nations cover the wooden beams. Real ale is only occasionally available in the comfortable lounge upstairs but it is still possible to admire the stained-glass panels acquired from an Irish monastery. 🍴≒🍽🛜

Strachur

Creggans Inn 🗒

PA27 8BX (on A815 at N end of village)

☎ (01369) 860279 🌐 creggans-inn.co.uk

2 changing beers (sourced locally; often Fyne Ales) 🅗

Convenient stopping place along Loch Fyne. MacPhunn's bar, named after a half-hung sheep rustler of yore, is comfortable with a real fire and plenty of room for dining. Two handpumps offer a changing selection of beers from Fyne Ales. Drinks may be taken to other lounges, the restaurant or games room, or enjoyed in the garden overlooking the loch. The games room and toilets are decorated with charts of the sea around Scotland and elsewhere. Q🕏🌣🍴🍽P🖨(484,486)🐾🛜

A quart a day keeps the doctor away

A judicious labourer would probably always have some ale in his house, and have small beer for the general drink. There is no reason why he should not keep Christmas as well as the farmer; and when he is mowing, reaping, or is at any other hard work, a quart, or three pints, of really good fat ale a-day is by no means too much.

William Cobbett, Cottage Economy, 1822

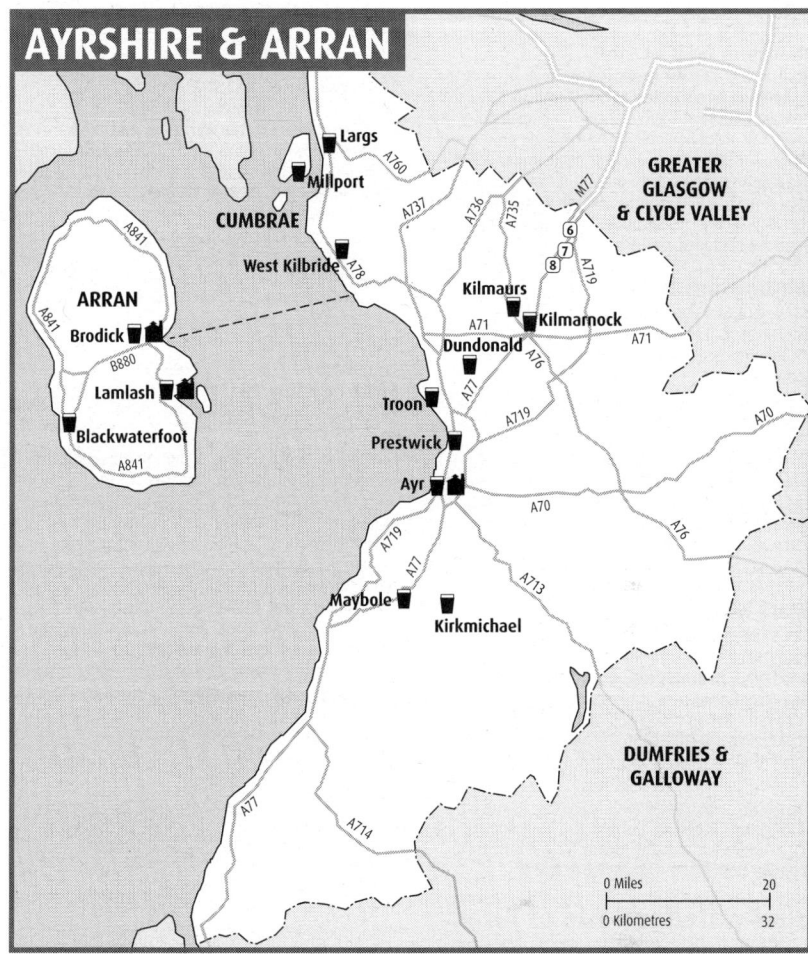

AYRSHIRE & ARRAN

Largs
Millport
CUMBRAE
West Kilbride
GREATER GLASGOW & CLYDE VALLEY
ARRAN
Brodick
Lamlash
Blackwaterfoot
Kilmaurs
Kilmarnock
Dundonald
Troon
Prestwick
Ayr
Maybole
Kirkmichael
DUMFRIES & GALLOWAY

0 Miles 20
0 Kilometres 32

SCOTLAND

Authority areas covered: East Ayrshire UA, North Ayrshire UA, South Ayrshire UA

Ayr

Abbotsford Hotel

14 Corsehill Road, KA7 2ST

☎ (01292) 261506 ⊕ abbotsfordhotel.co.uk

2 changing beers (often Fyne Ales, Wainwright) Ⓗ

Just under a mile south of Ayr town centre and a 20-minute walk from the rail station, this fine Scottish baronial-style building has been under the same ownership since 1966. The delightful and aptly named Copper Bar has the real ale. There is a pleasant dining room and a games room with TV showing sports. Book ahead for meals. The pub is close to the seafront, with golf courses, parks and Burns attractions nearby.

ᵬ✿🛏️◑♿🅰♣🅿🚲 (57,361) 🐾 🛜

Chestnuts Hotel

52 Racecourse Road, KA7 2UZ (on A719, 1 mile S of centre)

☎ (01292) 264393 ⊕ chestnutshotel.com

3 changing beers Ⓗ

This family-run hotel attracts both locals and visitors. Three changing real ales from a range of breweries are available in The 19th Hole, a delightful oak-beamed hall with an interesting history and a huge collection of whisky water jugs. Excellent food is served in the bar and

separate restaurant. Open log fires add to the comfortable atmosphere in winter and a pleasant beer garden is popular when the weather allows.

ᵬ✿🛏️◑♿🅰🅿🚲 (9) 🛜

Glen Park Hotel Ⓛ

5 Racecourse Road, KA7 2DG

☎ (01292) 263891 ⊕ theglenparkhotel.co.uk

Ayr Leezie Lundie, Jolly Beggars; 2 changing beers (often Ayr) Ⓗ

This comfortable lounge bar, in an attractive 1860s B-listed Victorian building, is the tap for Ayr Brewing Company, who operate in the rear of the building. The guest ales often include a seasonal from the brewery. Beers are usually also available to take away from a shop/bar at the rear of the dining room. Bar and restaurant meals are served daily except Monday.

ᵬ✿🛏️◑♿🅿🚲 (9) 🐾 🛜

REAL ALE BREWERIES

Arran ✏ Brodick: Isle of Arran
Ayr 🍺 Ayr
Seagate Lamlash: Isle of Arran

563

Smoking Goat

2A Academy Street, KA7 1HS
☎ (01292) 857137 ⊕ thesmokinggoat.com
2 changing beers (often Ayr, Fyne Ales) ⊞
A basement bar at the entrance to a lane opposite Ayr Town Hall, identified only by a small sign on the wall next to the door. There are two handpumps, which dispense changing beers from Ayr Brewing Co and Fyne Ales. It hosts a quiz night on Tuesdays and DJ nights Thursday, Friday and Saturday. The outside drinking area has been upgraded. 🌳🚃🛜

Wellingtons Bar

17 Wellington Square, KA7 1EZ
☎ (01292) 262794 ⊕ welliesbar.weebly.com
3 changing beers (often Born, Kelburn, Loch Lomond) ⊞
A large wellington boot advertises the location of this basement bar. Close to the seafront, bus station and local government offices, it attracts tourists and office workers alike. The Wednesday evening quiz is popular and at the weekend there may be live music, or a DJ on Saturday and an acoustic session on Sunday. Three changing ales vary constantly between brewers. Bar food is served, with daily specials on the menu. Local CAMRA Pub of the Year 2019. Q🍽️🍴◁🍺🚃🏀🛜

West Kirk ⊘

58A Sandgate, KA7 1BX (close to bus station)
☎ (01292) 880416
Caledonian Deuchars IPA; Greene King Abbot; 5 changing beers ⊞
This Wetherspoon conversion of a former church retains many original features – the toilets are reached via the pulpit (there is an accessible toilet downstairs). Up to five changing guest ales are offered and local microbreweries are usually well represented. Meals are served all day, starting with breakfast. Outside, the front drinking area has a shelter for smokers. Handy for Ayr bus station. Licensed from 10am. Q🍽️🌳🍴◁🛜🚃🏀🚃🛜

Blackwaterfoot: Isle of Arran

Kinloch Hotel

KA27 8ET
☎ (01770) 860444 ⊕ bw-kinlochhotel.co.uk
Ayr Uisge Dubh; 1 changing beer (often Ayr, Belhaven, Greene King) ⊞
A hidden gem in a quiet rural village on the west coast of Arran, offering coastal comfort and spectacular scenery. The family hotel has 37 bedrooms, a restaurant and three refurbished bars, and facilities including a heated indoor swimming pool, squash court and a fitness room and sauna. Fabulous local produce is served including fish and seafood. A beer festival is held in August. 🍴🌳🏨◁🛏️🍴♣♠P🏀🛜

Brodick: Isle of Arran

Ormidale Hotel

Knowe Road, KA27 8BY (off A841 at W end of village)
☎ (01770) 302293 ⊕ ormidale-hotel.co.uk
3 changing beers (often Arran) ⊞
This large red sandstone hotel with a small bar and spacious conservatory is set in seven acres of grounds. Beers are now served from handpumps rather than founts on the boat-shaped bar, although one original fount remains. Three ales are available in summer, often including Arran Blonde. Home-cooked meals are recommended. Entertainment includes discos and folk nights, and the attractive beer garden has views across Brodick Bay. 🍴🌳🏨◁♣P🚌(322,324)🏀🛜

Dundonald

Auchans

29-31 Main Street, KA2 9HH (on B730)
☎ (01563) 851472 ⊕ theauchans.co.uk
2 changing beers (often Ayr, Fyne Ales, Kelburn) ⊞
Friendly family-run restaurant bar with a varied food menu including tapas and pizzas appealing to all tastes. The restaurant is to the rear and the comfortable lounge bar has views of the historic 14th-century castle. Up to two beers on handpump change regularly and tend to come from local and regional breweries. Dundonald is a pleasant village at the end of the historic smugglers' trail from Troon. Q🍴🌳◁🛴♿P🚌(10,110)🏀🛜

Kilmarnock

First Edition ⊘

50-54 Bank Street, KA1 1ER
☎ (01563) 528833
Caledonian Deuchars IPA; 3 changing beers (often Inveralmond, Strathaven, Wychwood) ⊞
Large town-centre pub in a former furniture shop in the historic core of Kilmarnock. Four ales are usually available including two from Scottish regional brewers. The large modern pub serves food all day in bright surroundings. The revamped beer garden has table tennis and pool tables under cover. Numerous TV screens inside and three outside show sports, and a DJ plays Friday to Sunday evenings. 🌳🍴◁♿🚃🚃🏀🛜

Wheatsheaf Inn ⊘

70 Portland Street, KA1 1JG
☎ (01563) 572483
Greene King Abbot; Sharp's Doom Bar; 6 changing beers ⊞
This sizeable town-centre Lloyds No.1 bar, originally the historic Wheatsheaf Hotel, is famous for its links to Robert Burns, who was first published in Kilmarnock. The bar is divided into various seating areas, with booths, sofas and a raised dining space. Six handpumps dispense a range of ales plus real cider; food is standard Wetherspoon fare. DJs entertain on Friday and Saturday, with karaoke early Friday evening, but otherwise conversation dominates. Licensed from 11am. 🌳🍴◁♿🚃🏀🛜

Kilmaurs

Weston Tavern

27 Main Street, KA3 2RQ
☎ (01563) 538805 ⊕ westontavern.co.uk
2 changing beers (often Cairngorm, Theakston) ⊞
Housed in the former manse of reformist minister David Smeaton, a contemporary of Robert Burns, this fully refurbished country pub and restaurant has a tiled floor, stone walls and a wood-burning fire. It sits beside the Jougs, a former jailhouse and tollbooth. Two handpumps serve ales from a rotating list of local breweries. The place holds regular live music and quiz nights. Local CAMRA Pub of the Year 2019. 🍴🌳◁♿🚃♣P🏀🛜

Kirkmichael

Kirkmichael Arms

3-5 Straiton Road, KA19 7PH
☎ (01655) 750200 ⊕ kirkmichaelarms.co.uk
2 changing beers (often Ayr) ⊞
A friendly country pub at the heart of the community with a lounge bar, separate dining room and a small private dining room/function room. Two handpumps dispense an Ayr Brewing Co beer plus a guest. It serves

excellent meals, using locally sourced ingredients where possible. Walkers and dogs are welcome, and small functions are catered for. Q✿ᗒ❄ⓓ❖♣🚍(358,361)✿🍴🛜

Lamlash: Isle of Arran

Pierhead Tavern
Shore Road, KA27 8JN
☎ (01770) 600418 ⊕ thepht.co.uk
3 changing beers (often Ayr, Fyne Ales, Kelburn) Ⓗ
This famous village local was saved by new owners from conversion into flats. Handpumps serve a choice of three rotating ales from breweries such as Kelburn, Ayr and Fyne Ales in summer, reduced to two in winter. The pub grub is all home made and chef's specials change weekly. Live music features on Saturday and Sunday afternoon, and a quiz on Wednesday. The views from the roof terrace across to Holy Isle are spectacular.
ᗒ❄ⓓ❖♿♣🚍(323)✿🍴🛜

Largs

Three Reasons
14 Gallowgate Street, KA30 8LX (on A78)
☎ (01475) 672330
1 changing beer (often Greene King, Kelburn, Orkney) Ⓗ
This friendly one-roomed pub is situated on the seafront near the pier and Cumbrae ferry terminal, close to the railway station and handy for the Waverley paddle steamer in summer. It is popular for food, and children are welcome when dining. A single handpump offers one changing real ale, so beers may occasionally be unavailable while switching casks. ᗒⓓ❖♿🚂♣🚍🍴🛜

Maybole

Maybole Arms
37 Whitehall, KA19 7DS
☎ (01655) 883173
1 changing beer (often Ayr, Caledonian, Sulwath) Ⓗ
A welcome watering hole for those visiting an area which has few real ale pubs. This small, established local inn has a friendly clientele and offers good food from a family-friendly menu. Dogs are permitted, with water and biscuits supplied. A handy stop-off for nearby Culzean Castle & Country Park.
ᗒⓓ❖🚂♣P🚍(58,60)🍴🛜

Millport: Isle of Cumbrae

Fraser's Bar Ⓛ
9 Cardiff Street, KA28 0AS
☎ (01475) 530518
2 changing beers (often Jaw, Kelburn, Redcastle) Ⓗ
Well maintained and tidy, this place caters for visitors to the island as well as locals. Buses meet every ferry from Largs and terminate just across the road. Two handpumps serve mostly light-coloured ales, usually including one from a local brewery. Good-value pub food is available lunchtime and early evening. The main bar has an open fire and a fine display of old Clyde steamer photographs. Children are welcome in the rear lounge until 8pm. Q✿ᗒ❄ⓓ❖♣🚍(320)🛜

Prestwick

Prestwick Pioneer ✓
87 Main Street, KA9 1JS
☎ (01292) 473210
Greene King Abbot; Sharp's Doom Bar; 8 changing beers Ⓗ
Modern Wetherspoon outlet in a former Woolworths store, named after the first Scottish Aviation Pioneer light aircraft, built in 1947 at the nearby international airport. The pub has an airy feel with a light-wood decor, and features photographs of early Open Championship golf at Prestwick, and of Elvis at the airport – the only place in the UK he set foot on. Ten handpumps serve local and national ales and food is available. Licensed from 10am.
ᗒⓓ❖♿🚂♥🚍🛜

Troon

McKay's
69 Portland Street, KA10 6QU
☎ (01292) 737372
3 changing beers (often Fyne Ales, Greene King, Harviestoun) Ⓗ
A welcoming single-room town-centre bar with a large CAMRA award-winning beer garden, which is popular on sunny days. The bar hosts local dominoes competitions and shows live sports on TV. Dogs are permitted in the garden only. A longstanding stalwart of the local real ale scene and former local CAMRA Regional Pub of the Year.
ᗒ❄ⓓ❖🚂🚍🍴🛜

Number Forty Seven
47 Templehill, KA10 6BQ
☎ (01292) 312814
Cairngorm Wildcat; Morland Old Speckled Hen; 3 changing beers (often Belhaven) Ⓗ
A long single-room bar which has been refurbished. Five handpulls dispense real ales from Scottish and English breweries, with a discount for over-60s on request. Quiz night is Thursday. There is a pool table, jukebox and several TVs showing live sport. The gantry has a well-stocked variety of spirits. On Friday and Saturday nights a DJ plays from 10pm and the bar moves into nightclub mode. 🚂♣🚍🍴🛜

West Kilbride

Twa Dugs
71 Main Street, KA23 9AW
☎ (01294) 822524
2 changing beers (often Ayr, Five Kingdoms, Kelburn) Ⓗ
Popular venue refurbished to a high standard and patronised by all age groups. Two handpulls dispense ales mostly from local breweries, and bar food is available Thursday to Sunday. There is a pool table, live music at the weekend and a regular quiz. Ziggy's restaurant next door is linked to the pub and serves meals Thursday to Sunday (booking advised). There is a bus stop opposite and the railway station is five minutes away. Local CAMRA Pub of the Year 2019.
ⓓ🚂♣🚍(585,585A)🍴🛜

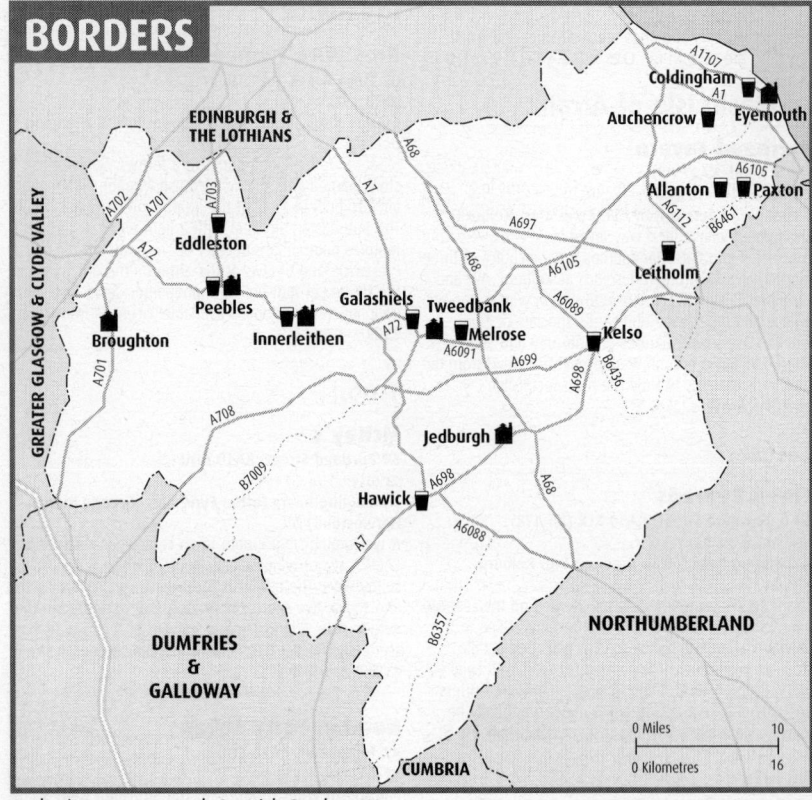

BORDERS

Authority area covered: Scottish Borders UA

Allanton

Allanton Inn

TD11 3JZ
☎ (01890) 818260 ⊕ allantoninn.co.uk
**2 changing beers (sourced nationally; often Born,
Fyne Ales, Timothy Taylor)** Ⓗ
An old coaching inn dating back to the 18th century with
a bright, airy feel. Quality food is served in the dining
room at the front. The small bar area, which overlooks
the superb beer garden with views of the countryside
beyond, may also be used for dining. It has an attractive
decor with artworks and comfortable cushioned benches.
Families are welcome – a children's menu and games are
provided. A large covered dining area has been created
in the beer garden. With good quality accommodation,
this is an ideal base for exploring Berwickshire and north
Northumberland. Q ⌂ ⏡ ✿ ☕ ◗ ♣ P ⊟ (260) ⟟

Auchencrow

Craw Inn

TD14 5LS (well signed from A1)
☎ (01890) 761253 ⊕ thecrawinn.co.uk
**Timothy Taylor Landlord; 2 changing beers (sourced
nationally; often Fyne Ales, Tempest)** Ⓗ
A friendly 18th-century Grade C-listed country inn. The
real ales are usually from smaller breweries, as can be
seen from the numerous pumpclips on show. The bar has
a wood-burning stove and tables for dining and drinking.
Excellent home-cooked food is served (all day Sun) in
both the bar and well-appointed restaurant. There is also
an attractive rear area with comfy furniture and a

separate games room with a pool table. Local CAMRA
Pub of the Year 2020. Likely to be closed all day Monday
and mid-afternoons Tuesday to Friday. Winter hours may
vary. Q ⌂ ⏡ ✿ ⏡ ◗ ♣ P ⊟ (34) ⟟

Coldingham

New Inn

1 Bridge Street, TD14 5NG (by village square)
☎ (01890) 771315
**2 changing beers (sourced regionally; often Hadrian
Border, Orkney, Fyne Ales)** Ⓗ
Recently refurbished to give a lighter feel, this is a cosy
little pub in the village centre with a corner bar, wooden
floor and real fire. Steps lead up to a dining area. A
second bar, reached by a separate entrance, opens at
busy times and for functions. The two real ales are
usually from Scottish or Northumbrian breweries. Meals
are served all day in summer including a children's
menu. Handy for the beach and St Abb's Head. Opening
times can vary depending on custom, especially in
winter. Likely to be closed mid-afternoons Monday to
Thursday. ⌂ ✿ ◗ ⅄ ▲ ⊟ (235) ❀

REAL ALE BREWERIES

Aye Been Eyemouth
Born ⚲ Jedburgh
Broughton Broughton
Freewheelin' Peebles
Tempest ⚲ Tweedbank
Traquair House Innerleithen

Eddleston

Horseshoe Inn

EH45 8QP

☎ (01721) 730225 ⊕ horseshoeinn.co.uk

3 changing beers (sourced nationally; often Broughton, Orkney, Stewart) Ⓗ

A large and welcoming free house with a separate dining room and snug, plus eight luxury B&B rooms in an annexe. The bar and snug feature original flagstone floors, exposed beams and characterful old timber furniture; the quiet dining room has a more elaborate decor. The menu offers a wide choice of dishes including many pub classics, and there are also light bites at lunchtime. The TV in one corner of the bar is just for major sporting events.

Q ⏰ ❀ 🛏 ◑ & ♣ P ☷ (X62,X70) ● 🌣

Galashiels

Hunters Hall ●

56 High Street, TD1 1SE

☎ (01896) 759795

Caledonian Deuchars IPA; Greene King Abbot; 3 changing beers (sourced nationally; often Broughton, Sharp's, Stewart) Ⓗ

Extensively refurbished and extended in 2019, this original Presbyterian Church and School has been sympathetically restored to expose much of the original stonework, high ceiling and the skylight roof panels. Historical photographs of Galashiels decorate the walls. It offers typical Wetherspoon fare, and caters for families, locals and students. Meals are available all day. Real cider is generally only available during festivals. Alcoholic drinks are served from 11am. Q ⏰ ❀ ◑ & A ≈ ♣ P ☷ 🌣

Ladhope Inn ●

33 High Buckholmside, TD1 2HR (A7, ⅓ mile N of centre)

☎ (01896) 752446

1 changing beer (sourced regionally; often Black Sheep, Born, York) Ⓗ

A comfortable, friendly local with a vibrant Borders atmosphere. Originating circa 1792, the place has been altered considerably over the years and comprises one long single room, decorated with a large inked map of the area. One real ale is served, sometimes two at weekends. Three TVs ensure the bar is busy during sporting events, and live music is hosted on occasion. The pub is a community hub for golf, horse-racing and fishing trips. Children are not allowed. Likely to be closed until 4pm Monday to Friday. ❀ A ≈ ♣ 🛏 (X95) ● 🌣

Hawick

Bourtree ●

22 Bourtree Place, TD9 9HL (NE edge of town centre)

☎ (01450) 360450

Caledonian Deuchars IPA; Greene King Abbot; 3 changing beers (sourced nationally; often Sharp's, Stewart, Wychwood) Ⓗ

Built as the Hawick Conservative Club in 1897, this listed building has been stunningly transformed into a Wetherspoon pub. The original badminton and snooker halls form the main area, while there are three other spaces for quieter or private use. Photographs depict a history of Hawick life, including mills, railways, common riding and motorcycling. There are regular festivals, and bingo or a quiz on Wednesday evening. Real cider is generally only available during festivals. Alcoholic drinks are served from 11am. Q ⏰ ❀ ◑ & ♣ 🛏 P ☷ 🌣

Exchange Bar (Dalton's)

1 Silver Street, TD9 0AD (off SW end of High St)

☎ (01450) 376067

2 changing beers (sourced regionally; often Belhaven, Born, Orkney) Ⓗ

Tucked away near St Mary's Kirk, the 19th-century building used to overlook the Corn Exchange. However, a previous owner was called Dalton and that name has stuck ever since. Popular with locals, the bar is a Victorian gem featuring original dark-wood panelling and ornate cornice work. There is a comfy back lounge used for parties, occasional karaoke and Sunday folk sessions. Children are not admitted. A CAMRA Borders Real Ale Quality Award runner-up. ❀ A ♣ P ☷ ● 🌣

Innerleithen

St Ronan's Hotel

High Street, EH44 6HF

☎ (01896) 831487 ⊕ stronanshotel.co.uk

2 changing beers (sourced regionally; often Born, Orkney, Traquair House) Ⓗ

A village hotel with a prominent blue and white exterior, named after a local saint. The public bar is long and narrow with a wood-burning stove. Two alcoves in differing styles offer extra seating and a darts area. There is also a pool room and a restaurant where meals are served in the evening. A pick-up service and packed lunches are available for Southern Upland Way walkers. For children, there is a garden play area and indoor games. ⏰ ❀ 🛏 ◑ A ♣ P ☷ (X62) ● 🌣

Traquair Arms Hotel

Traquair Road, EH44 6PD (B709, off A72)

☎ (01896) 830229 ⊕ traquairarmshotel.co.uk

3 changing beers (sourced nationally; often Stewart, Tempest, Traquair House) Ⓗ

Elegant 18th-century hotel in the scenic Tweed Valley offering accommodation in 16 en-suite rooms and two self-catering cottages. The comfortable lounge bar features a welcoming real fire, and a flagstoned sports bar with log-burner provides an ideal thawing-out space for mountain bikers, walkers and anglers. A bistro area and separate restaurant offer plenty of room for diners. Meals are served all day at weekends and there is a menu for children. One of the few outlets for draught real ale from Traquair House. The bar may close earlier if quiet. ⏰ ❀ 🛏 ◑ & A ♣ P ☷ (X62) ● 🌣

Kelso

1905

Crawford Street, TD5 7DP (off N corner of town square)

☎ (01573) 225556

3 changing beers (sourced regionally; often Firebrick, Hybrid, Stewart) Ⓗ

This bar, formerly the Red Lion, has a pleasant, peaceful ambience, although it can get lively when entertainment is hosted. The main room has a fine wood and plaster vaulted ceiling, wooden panelling and mosaic flooring, and there are two more rooms featuring striking wall coverings. Brewery mirrors adorn the walls and are inlaid into the bar gantry. Children are not admitted, except for some functions. There are plans to serve food. Likely to be closed Monday and on winter afternoons Tuesday to Thursday. Q ⏰ ❀ 🛏 ♣ 🛏 ☷ 🌣

Cobbles Freehouse & Dining

7 Bowmont Street, TD5 7JH (off N corner of town square)

☎ (01573) 223548 ⊕ cobbleskelso.co.uk

1 changing beer (sourced locally; often Tempest)

This popular, long-established gastro-pub is essentially operating as a restaurant with a bar, though drinkers are welcome. The bar is on the right, featuring a real fire at the far end. The dining area is on the left, but food is served throughout, and is available all day. Both areas are bright and welcoming and there is a menu to suit all tastes, including children's options. The handpumps are dedicated solely to Tempest beers – some lined glasses are available. Likely to be closed Mondays and Tuesdays. ♿🕮🏮⏸️🚲🛗🚪🐱🛜

Leitholm

Plough Inn

Main Street, TD12 4JN

☎ (01890) 840408 ⊕ theploughinnleitholm.co.uk

House beer (by Born); 1 changing beer (sourced nationally; often Cheviot, Greene King, Hetton Law) ℍ

Set in the main street of a quiet village, this formerly closed pub has been transformed into a charming and friendly family-run inn. The wooden-floored bar is decorated and furnished to create a bright, modern and welcoming ambience. A massive clock dominates the fireplace area. Children are welcome until 9pm. The beer garden overlooks fields. Opening hours may be extended in summer. Real cider is generally only available during summer. Likely to be closed all day Monday and Tuesday, and mid-afternoons Wednesday to Saturday. ♿🕮🏮⏸️🌳🍴🚪🐱🛜

Melrose

Burts Hotel

Market Square, TD6 9PL

☎ (01896) 822285 ⊕ burtshotel.co.uk

Born Amber; Timothy Taylor Landlord; 1 changing beer ℍ

An elegant family-run hotel with colourful window boxes adding to the building's attractive appearance in summer. The lounge bar décor reflects the country sports interests of many of its clientele. The focus is unashamedly on fine dining, with excellent food served in both the bar and restaurant. Those visiting solely for a drink may find space limited. Closed mid-afternoons. Q♿🕮🏮⏸️🛗🌲🚪🐱🛜

George & Abbotsford Hotel

High Street, TD6 9PD (NW of Market Sq)

☎ (01896) 822308 ⊕ georgeandabbotsfordmelrose.co.uk

Fyne Ales Jarl; Tempest Armadillo; 2 changing beers (sourced regionally; often Greene King) ℍ

A spacious family-run hotel with a comfortable bar and lounges, offering a warm welcome to locals and visitors alike. The real ales come from both sides of the border.

Food features prominently and is served all day, including various specials and children's options. The enclosed suntrap beer garden has plenty of seating and an outdoor play area. A pleasant walk from the rail terminus at Tweedbank, the bar is popular with walkers, cyclists and, naturally, Melrose rugby supporters. Q♿🕮🏮⏸️🌲🚲🚪🐱🛜

King's Arms Hotel

High Street, TD6 9PB (NW of Market Sq)

☎ (01896) 820101 ⊕ kingsarmsmelrose.com

House beer (by Laine); 2 changing beers (sourced nationally; often Born, Timothy Taylor) ℍ

Historic old coaching inn dating from 1793. The bar has a wooden floor, church pew seating and a TV for sporting events. It is decorated with rugby memorabilia and local photographs. The quieter lounges and conservatory, where families are welcome, are comfortably furnished – one has a lovely old carved door set into the ceiling. Food is served all day from 7.30am. Alcoholic drinks are served from 11am (noon Sun). Q♿🕮🏮⏸️🌲🚲🚪🐱🛜

Paxton

Cross Inn

TD15 1TE (off B6461)

☎ (01289) 384877 ⊕ thecrossinn.co.uk

Timothy Taylor Landlord; 2 changing beers (sourced regionally; often Hadrian Border) ℍ

A rejuvenated 19th-century village local with friendly staff. Its small, welcoming bar is stone-floored; the larger dining and function area has floorboards and carpeting. At the front is a raised area for outside drinking and eating. Food is served all day; the menu, along with daily specials, children's options and Sunday roasts, should appeal to most tastes. Occasionally there may be a real cider. It is likely to be closed Mondays and Tuesdays. ♿🏮⏸️🛗🌲🚲🚪🐱🛜

Peebles

Bridge Inn (Trust)

Portbrae, EH45 8AW

☎ (01721) 720589 ⊕ thebridgeinnpeebles.co.uk

Fyne Ales Jarl; 3 changing beers (sourced nationally; often Born, Stewart, Tempest) ℍ

Cheerful, welcoming pub also known as the Trust and once called the Tweedside Inn. The bright, comfortable bar is decorated with jugs, bottles, pictures of old Peebles and displays relating to outdoor pursuits. There is a cosy corner with a log-burner, and a small room to the rear with a dartboard. The suntrap patio overlooks the river and hills beyond. Children are not admitted. CAMRA Scotland and N Ireland Pub of the Year 2019. 🏮🌲🚲🚪🐱🛜

Fishing for beer

Ah! My beloved brother of the rod, do you know the taste of beer – of bitter beer – cooled in the flowing river? Take your bottle of beer, sink it deep, deep in the shady water, where the cooling springs and fishes are. Then, the day being very hot and bright, and the sun blazing on your devoted head, consider it a matter of duty to have to fish that long, wide stream. An hour or so of good hammering will bring you to the end of it, and then – let me ask you avec impressement – how about that beer? Is it cool? Is it refreshing? Does it gurgle, gurgle and 'go down glug' as they say in Devonshire? Is it heavenly? Is it Paradise and all the Peris to boot? Ah! If you have never tasted beer under these or similar circumstance, you have, believe me, never tasted it at all.

Francis Francis, By Lake and River, 19th century

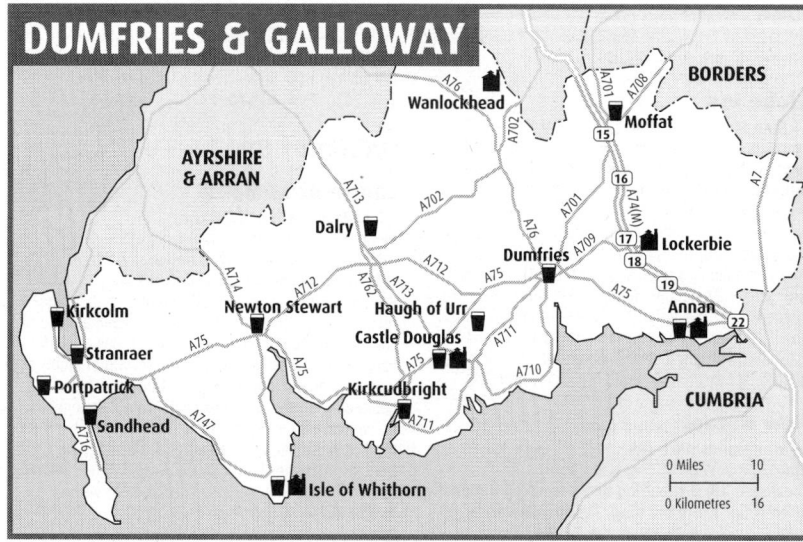

Authority area covered: Dumfries & Galloway UA

Annan

Blue Bell Inn

10 High Street, DG12 6AG

☎ (01461) 202385

Caledonian Deuchars IPA; 4 changing beers (sourced nationally; often Carlisle, Kelburn, Strathaven) Ⓗ

Former coaching inn dating from 1770 where Hans Christian Andersen is said to have stayed. It was part of the Gretna State Management Scheme from 1917 to 1972 when pubs were nationalised. The red sandstone building retains some traditional features, notably the panelled interior and rear stables. The Gents has a panelled ante-room, tiled inner room and original Shanks urinals. The inn is home to many community activities along with annual beer and cider festivals. Motte & Bailey beers, brewed on-site, are only available here. Local CAMRA Pub of the Year 2020.

✿☼Å⇄♣♠P🚌(79,383) 🐾🐕📶

Castle Douglas

Sulwath Brewery Tap Room Ⓛ

209 King Street, DG7 1DT

☎ (01556) 504525 ⊕ sulwathbrewers.co.uk

Sulwath Black Galloway; 5 changing beers (sourced locally; often Sulwath) Ⓗ

The visitor centre for Sulwath Brewery is a showcase for the brewery's beers (including its prize-winning Black Galloway) although not all are cask-conditioned. At times there may be guest beers from elsewhere. One draught cider, usually from Westons, is also available. Dried hop bines decorate the walls, and old wooden casks of various sizes provide some of the furniture. Brewery tours are available and there is an annual beer festival. Local CAMRA Cider Pub of the Year 2020.

Q✿Å♠P🚌🐾📶

Dalry

Clachan Inn

8-10 Main Street, DG7 3UW

☎ (01644) 430241 ⊕ theclachaninn.co.uk

2 changing beers (sourced regionally; often Ayr, Fallen, Fyne Ales) Ⓗ

The Clachan has a reputation for excellent food, cosy, well-equipped bedrooms and a welcoming atmosphere. The menu is varied with excellent daily specials, and the kitchen makes good use of local produce. The pub has an attractive traditional main bar, a relaxing lounge bar and a separate restaurant – both bars have wonderfully warming open log fires in winter. A handy stop for walkers on the Southern Upland Way. Two-times winner of local CAMRA Pub of the Year. Winter opening hours may vary. Q✿☼☀⇄◑♿Å♣♠P🚌(520,521)🐾📶

Dumfries

Cavens Arms

20 Buccleuch Street, DG1 2AH

☎ (01387) 252896 ⊕ cavensarms.com

Fyne Ales Jarl; Greene King Yardbird, Abbot; Morland Old Speckled Hen; Swannay Orkney IPA; 4 changing beers (sourced nationally) Ⓗ

Busy food-oriented pub, popular with diners for its range of good-value meals. A separate restaurant area has been created to cope with demand at peak times. Drinkers are welcome in the bar but seating can be limited during food service times. Guest ales are from a wide range of breweries, including some rarely seen in this locality. There are regular charity quizzes and other theme nights. ◑♿🚌📶

Coach & Horses

66 Whitesands, DG1 2RS

☎ 07746 675349

Draught Bass Ⓗ

A small, lively former coaching inn overlooking the River Nith. Situated next to the tourist information centre, the pub is handy for local attractions. The bar is small but service is always quick. The room features a flagstone floor with a warming open fire during the colder months.

SCOTLAND

There is a great atmosphere in this gem of a pub, enhanced by regular live music sessions. Winter opening times may vary. ❀⬤♣P🖫♨

Globe Inn

56 High Street, DG1 2JA

☎ (013873) 23010 🌐 globeinndumfries.co.uk

Lowland Twa Dugs, Dryfe Blonde; 1 changing beer (often Lowland) 🅷

The Globe dates from 1610 and is the oldest inn in Dumfries. A busy town-centre pub steeped in tradition, it is up a close off the High Street, with a public bar, dining area and adjoining small snug. It has a close association with Scotland's national bard, Robert Burns, who was a frequent visitor, is home to the world-famous Burns Howff Club, and holds much memorabilia; rooms associated with the poet can be visited by arrangement. Occasional functions are held here. Q❀⬤❶⬆🖫♨

New Bazaar

39 Whitesands, DG1 2RS

☎ (01387) 268776

Theakston XB; 3 changing beers (sourced nationally; often Fuller's, Greene King, Timothy Taylor) 🅷

Former coaching inn beside the River Nith with an attractive airy bar featuring a splendid Victorian gantry that displays an impressive malt whisky collection. The cosy lounge provides a quiet retreat and has a warming coal fire in winter. A small room is available for meetings. The pub is a favourite with football supporters attending nearby Palmerston Park and is ideally situated for car parking, local buses and tourist attractions. Winter opening times may vary. ❀♣P🖫♨

Riverside Bar

Dock Park, DG1 2RY

☎ (01387) 254477

Morland Old Speckled Hen; 3 changing beers (sourced nationally) 🅷

The Riverside Bar is an established venue on the Dumfries real ale scene. Comfortable and friendly, it has seating on two levels and a large conservatory. Two outside seating areas include a terrace with open views over the Dock Park and down to the River Nith. The pub is accessible from the St Michaels area near the Robert Burns Mausoleum or from Dock Park. Guest beers can be from local brewers as well as from further afield. ⬤❀♣🖫♨

Robert the Bruce ✅

81 Buccleuch Street, DG1 2AB

☎ (01387) 270320

Caledonian Deuchars IPA; Greene King Abbot; Sharp's Doom Bar; 4 changing beers (sourced nationally) 🅷

This former Methodist church, sensitively converted by Wetherspoon, has a relaxed atmosphere and is a popular meeting place in the town centre. There is a pleasant outside seating area to the rear. The pub stands near the site where Robert the Bruce killed John Comyn in 1306 in an incident linked to Scotland's fight for independence. The food menu offers a range of good-value meals all day, every day. Alcoholic drinks are served from 11am. ⬤❀❶♿⬆♣🏠P🖫♨

Tam o' Shanter

113-117 Queensberry Street, DG1 1BH

☎ (01387) 267880

Broughton Clipper IPA; 4 changing beers (sourced nationally; often Broughton, Sulwath) 🅷

Established in 1630, this 17th-century coaching inn with a connection to Robert Burns has been a mainstay of the Dumfries beer scene for many years. It is small and traditional, with a main bar and a couple of quiet cosy

rooms including a games area behind. There are always guest beers from local breweries. An upstairs room hosts live music and other functions. The pub is well positioned just off the High Street. Local CAMRA Town Pub of the Year 2020. ⬤⬤♣P🖫♨♨

Haugh of Urr

Laurie Arms Hotel

11-13 Main Street, DG7 3YA

☎ (01556) 660246 🌐 haugh-of-urr.co.uk

4 changing beers (sourced nationally; often Caledonian, Fyne Ales, Strathaven) 🅷

Welcoming family-run establishment in a charming, quiet village, popular for its range of beers and freshly cooked food featuring local produce. It has a good village-pub atmosphere, enhanced on winter nights by a warming log fire in the bar. Up to four beers are available depending on the season, mainly from independent breweries. National Cycle Route 7 passes nearby. It is on the bus route between Dumfries, Dalbeattie and Castle Douglas. A former local CAMRA award winner. Winter opening times may vary, so check before visiting. ⬤❀❶♣P🖫(501)♨♨

Isle of Whithorn

Steam Packet Inn ✅

Harbour Row, DG8 8LL (on B7004 from Whithorn)

☎ (01988) 500334 🌐 thesteampacketinn.biz

Morland Old Speckled Hen; 7 changing beers (often Five Kingdoms, Fyne Ales, Kelburn) 🅷

Traditional and historic family-run hotel overlooking the harbour, welcoming to all including families and pets. The public bar has stone walls and a multi-fuel stove, and there are pictures of the village and maritime events throughout. Four guest ales from a wide variety of breweries, along with up to four beers from in-house brewery Five Kingdoms, are available in both bars. Bottle-conditioned ales are also stocked. The extensive food menu features local produce. Local CAMRA Pub of the Year 2020. Q⬤❀🛏❶♣🏠P🖫(415,416)♨♨

Kirkcolm

Blue Peter Hotel

23 Main Street, DG9 0NL (on A718 5 miles N of Stranraer)

☎ (01776) 853221 🌐 bluepeterhotel.com

2 changing beers (often Ayr, Born) 🅷

A small family-run hotel with two bars packed with memorabilia. Two handpumps dispense a constantly changing range of ales. Home-cooked food is served using fresh local produce, with takeaways available. Outside, the decked patio has views of abundant wildlife including red squirrels. The hotel is popular with real ale enthusiasts as well as walkers and wildlife watchers. It opens on Wednesday and Thursday evenings if darts or dominoes matches are held. Good-value Bed & Breakfast accommodation is available in three en-suite rooms. Q⬤❀🛏Å♣🖫(408)♨

Kirkcudbright

Masonic Arms

19 Castle Street, DG6 4JA

☎ (01557) 330517 🌐 masonic-arms.co.uk

2 changing beers (sourced nationally) 🅷

This friendly pub in the town has been a firm favourite with real ale enthusiasts for many years. There is a smaller back bar, and a beer garden to the rear with a smoking area. One real ale is available all year round, two in the summer months. A selection of more than 50 malt whiskies and over 230 gins is available, as well as a good range of world beers. Q✿&APᗺ❀ 🛜

Selkirk Arms Hotel ✓

High Street, DG6 4JG
☎ (01557) 330402 ● selkirkarmshotel.co.uk
2 changing beers (sourced nationally; often Sulwath) Ⓗ
Refurbished 18th-century hotel with a restaurant, bistro and lounge bar, renowned for locally sourced food, highlighted by the menus and photos of suppliers on the walls. The large garden area with tables is popular in summer. Two real ales are served, sometimes three in summer, as well as a good selection of malt whiskies and gins. Robert Burns wrote his famous Selkirk Grace at the hotel in 1794. Kirkcudbright is notable for its artistic heritage and houses a number of interesting galleries and museums. Q⏁✿🖾◑&APᗺ❀🛜

Moffat

Star Hotel

44 High Street, DG10 9EF
☎ (01683) 220156 ● famousstarhotel.co.uk
2 changing beers (sourced regionally; often Greene King, Sulwath) Ⓗ
The Famous Star Hotel is recognised in the Guinness Book of Records as the narrowest detached hotel in the world. The building is 20 feet wide and 162 feet long but feels much bigger due to the clever use of internal space. There is a large public bar at the rear and a smaller lounge accessed from the front. It has been run by the same family for over 30 years and offers excellent service. At least one beer is available all year round. Moffat is a good base for exploring the Southern Uplands. ⏁✿🖾◑&APᗺ❀🛜

Newton Stewart

Crown Hotel

102 Queen Street, DG8 6JW
☎ (01671) 402727 ● the-crown-hotel.com
1 changing beer (often Belhaven, Greene King) Ⓗ
A well-established hotel on the outskirts of town, popular with a wide mix of visitors and locals. Real ale is available from the Belhaven list, changing weekly. The interior is spacious and modern – the bar area has sports and seating areas. The restaurant offers good-value Scottish and traditional fare, from bar meals to an à la carte menu, plus a Sunday carvery. To the rear are a patio, decked area and beer garden. ⏁✿🖾◑&Å♣Pᗺ(359,500) ❀🛜

Portpatrick

Crown Hotel

9 North Crescent, DG9 8SX (facing harbour)
☎ (01776) 810261 ● crownhotelportpatrick.com
2 changing beers (often Ayr, Five Kingdoms, Sulwath) Ⓗ
Hotel overlooking the picturesque harbour with views on a clear day across to Ireland. The large, comfortable bar area at the front is adorned with pictures and ornaments, and warmed by an open fire. Two regularly changing ales come from breweries across the UK, including the nearby Five Kingdoms. Live music plays on Friday and Saturday nights. ⏁✿🖾◑&Å♣(367)❀🛜

Sandhead

Tigh-na-Mara Hotel

Main Street, DG9 9JF (8 miles S of Stranraer on A716)
☎ (01776) 830210 ● tighnamarahotel.co.uk
1 changing beer (often Five Kingdoms, Hadrian Border) Ⓗ
Village hotel close to a beautiful stretch of unspoilt, sandy beach on the east side of the Rhins of Galloway. It has a traditional bar and a comfortable lounge/restaurant with an excellent reputation for quality food using local produce. Early bird, à la carte and table d'hote menus are available. To the rear is a well-furnished outdoor area with lovely views across to the Machars peninsular. ⏁✿🖾◑&♣Pᗺ(407)❀🛜

Stranraer

Grapes

4-6 Bridge Street, DG9 7HY
☎ (01776) 703386
2 changing beers (often Ayr) Ⓗ
Popular historic public bar, with an impressive mirror and gantry, which has altered little in over 50 years. It has a refurbished snug bar downstairs, an upstairs Art Deco lounge/function room, and a courtyard area with seating. Local musicians play in the public bar most Friday evenings, and touring American-style bands often perform upstairs. There is a strong commitment to real ales, sourced both locally and from all over the UK. Mini beer festivals are held twice yearly. ⏁✿≠♣ᗺ❀🛜

Spores for thought

Yeast is a fungus, a single cell plant that can convert a sugary liquid into equal proportions of alcohol and carbon dioxide. There are two basic types of yeast used in brewing, one for ale and one for lager. (The yeasts used to make the Belgian beers known as gueuze and lambic are wild spores in the atmosphere). It is often said that ale is produced by 'top fermentation' and lager by 'bottom fermentation'. While it is true that during ale fermentation a thick blanket of yeast head and protein is created on top of the liquid while only a thin slick appears on top of fermenting lager, the descriptions are seriously misleading. Yeast works at all levels of the sugar-rich liquid in order to turn malt sugars into alcohol. If yeast worked only at the top or bottom of the liquid, a substantial proportion of sugar would not be fermented. Ale is fermented at a high temperature, lager at a much lower one. The furious speed of ale fermentation creates the yeast head and with it the rich, fruity aromas and flavours that are typical of the style. It is more accurate to describe the ale method as 'warm fermentation' and the lager one as 'cold fermentation'.

EDINBURGH & THE LOTHIANS

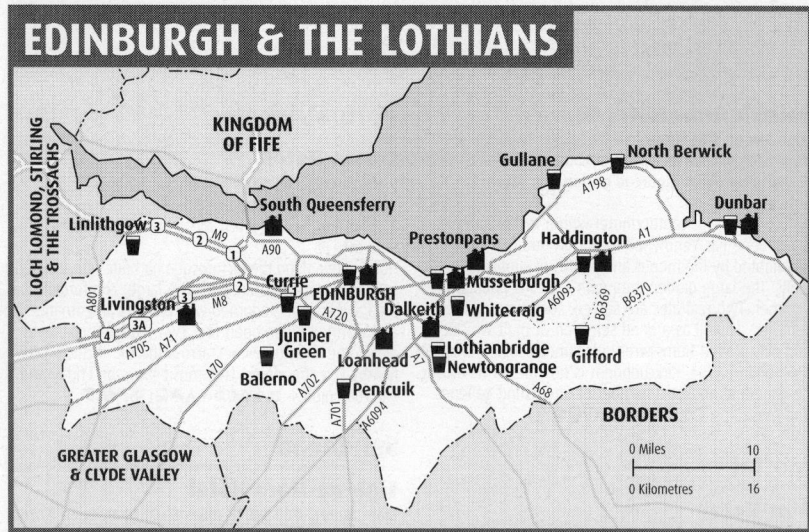

Authority areas covered: City of Edinburgh UA, East Lothian UA, Midlothian UA, West Lothian UA

Balerno

Grey Horse

20 Main Street, EH14 7EH (off A70, in pedestrian area)
☎ (0131) 449 2888 ⊕ greyhorsebalerno.com
4 changing beers (sourced regionally; often Alechemy, Orkney, Stewart) Ⓗ
Traditional stone-built village pub dating from the 18th century. The cosy public bar retains original features including wood panelling and a fine Bernard's mirror. A varied food menu is offered in the pleasant lounge and restaurant, with lighter options at lunchtime, a children's menu and Chinese specials (no food Mon). A folk session takes place one Tuesday evening a month. Dogs are allowed in the bar, with biscuits and water provided.
Q ⑂ ✿ ◑ & 🚫 (44) ✿

Currie

Riccarton Inn

198 Lanark Road West, EH14 5NX
☎ (0131) 449 2230 ⊕ riccartoninn.co.uk
4 changing beers (sourced nationally; often Inveralmond, Stewart, Timothy Taylor) Ⓗ
Originally a coaching inn, the comfortable pub has a long central bar with half-timbered walls and contemporary exposed stonework. There are attractive seating areas including booths next to the bar and a separate restaurant space. Meals are served all day including a children's menu. The decking at the front has southerly views to the Pentland Hills and the inn is handy for the Water of Leith Walkway. Alcoholic drinks are served from 12.30pm on Sunday. ⑂ ✿ ✚ ◑ 🅿 🚫 (44,45) ✿ 🛜

Dunbar

Volunteer Arms

17 Victoria Street, EH42 1HP
☎ (01368) 862278 ⊕ volunteerarmsdunbar.co.uk
2 changing beers (sourced nationally; often Cairngorm, Harviestoun, Stewart) Ⓗ
Close to Dunbar's harbour and swimming pool, this is a friendly traditional locals' pub. The cosy wood-panelled bar is decorated with lots of fishing and lifeboat-oriented memorabilia, interesting photos and a good selection of old pumpclip badges on the ceiling. The two real ales are often from smaller breweries. Upstairs is a restaurant serving an excellent good-value menu all day (also available downstairs), with an emphasis on seafood. A menu and games are provided for children.
⑂ ✿ ◑ A ✚ ♣ 🚫 🚆 ✿ 🛜 Ʊ

Edinburgh: Central

Abbotsford Bar & Restaurant ★

3-5 Rose Street, EH2 2PR
☎ (0131) 225 5276 ⊕ theabbotsford.com
6 changing beers (sourced regionally; often Cromarty, Fyne Ales, Swannay) Ⓗ / Ⓐ
The Abbotsford was named after novelist Sir Walter Scott's baronial mansion in Roxburghshire. This traditional Scottish bar features a magnificent island bar and gantry in dark mahogany that have been fixtures since 1902. The ornate plasterwork and corniced ceiling are outstanding. The room is predominantly furnished with large tables and wooden bench seating. An extensive food menu is available all day in the bar. The separate restaurant is upstairs – real ale can be ordered from downstairs – and children over five are permitted here. Q ⑂ ✿ ◑ 🚆 (Waverley) 🚫 ✿ 🛜 Ʊ

REAL ALE BREWERIES

Alechemy Livingston
Barney's Edinburgh
Belhaven Dunbar
Bellfield ✦ Edinburgh
Black Metal Loanhead
Caledonian Edinburgh
Campervan ✦ Edinburgh
Cross Borders ✦ Dalkeith
Faking Bad 🍺 Prestonpans
Ferry Brewery ✦ South Queensferry
Hanging Bat 🍺 Edinburgh
Hurly Burly Musselburgh
Pilot Beer Edinburgh
Stewart ✦ Loanhead
Tartan Shark Edinburgh (NEW)
Top Out Loanhead
Winton ✦ Haddington

Blue Blazer

2 Spittal Street, EH3 9DX (SW side of centre)

☎ (0131) 229 5030

7 changing beers (sourced regionally; often Kelburn, Stewart) ⓗ

Two-roomed pub with wooden floors, high ceilings and old brewery window panels giving an old-fashioned feel, complemented by candles in the evening. Named after a local school uniform, it features a tiled blue blazer inlaid on the floor. The pub specialises in real ales from smaller Scottish breweries. The cider varies and may not be real. Snacks are available all day. Close to theatres and cinemas, it stays open later during August and December. Children are not admitted. ●🏠😾🛜🕙

Caley Picture House ⊘

31 Lothian Road, EH1 2DJ (W edge of centre)

☎ (0131) 656 0752

Caledonian Deuchars IPA; Greene King Abbot; Sharp's Doom Bar; 9 changing beers (sourced nationally) ⓗ

A stunning Wetherspoon renovation of a Grade B-listed former cinema, originally opened in 1923. The main bar has a superb screen-style backdrop and is complemented by a smaller bar 35ft higher in the 'gods', complete with plush cinema-style seating. Meals are served all day and there is a children's menu. Highly commended in the CAMRA Pub Design Awards. Alcoholic drinks are served from 9am (11am Sun). 🛏️◑👩‍🦽🏠(West End-Princes St) 🏠🛜

Guildford Arms

1 West Register Street, EH2 2AA (off E end of Princes St)

☎ (0131) 556 4312 ∰ guildfordarms.com

Fyne Ales Jarl; Orkney Dark Island; Stewart Pentland IPA; Swannay Orkney IPA; 5 changing beers (sourced nationally; often Black Sheep, Loch Lomond, Timothy Taylor) ⓗ

A large establishment built in the golden age of Victorian pub design. The high ceiling, cornices, friezes, window arches and screens are spectacular. There is a large standing area around the canopied bar plus extensive seating areas. The diverse range of real ales includes many from Scottish micros. Simple bar snacks are available all day. Children over five are only allowed in the noteworthy upstairs gallery restaurant. 🛏️◑≡(Waverley) 🏠(St Andrew Square)🏠😾🛜🕙

Haymarket ⊘

11-14A West Maitland Street, EH12 5DS (W edge of centre)

☎ (0131) 228 2537

St Austell Nicholson's Pale Ale; Timothy Taylor Landlord; 5 changing beers (sourced nationally; often St Austell, Stewart, Timothy Taylor) ⓗ

This large, busy establishment has a comfortable interior refurbished in 2020 and is decorated with historic prints of the pub, the locality and local sports teams. The bar overlooks the large central area, with a raised mezzanine floor to one side and arches leading through to a restaurant. Sports events are shown on several TV screens. Food is served all day from the Nicholson's and Pie House menus. Children are allowed until 9pm for meals. May close early if quiet. 🛏️😾◑👩‍🦽≡(Haymarket)🏠😾🛜

Jolly Judge

7 James Court, 493 Lawnmarket, EH1 2PB (Old Town)

☎ (0131) 225 2669

3 changing beers (sourced nationally; often Cromarty, Cross Borders, Tempest) ⓗ

Comfortable bar with an attractive painted ceiling just off the Royal Mile down an Old Town close. There are steps down to the entrance, as was common in the past. This is

a welcome spot for refreshment after visiting the castle. The real ales are usually from smaller breweries UK-wide. A varying selection of six real ciders is also available. Dogs are permitted after 3pm, but no children inside. CAMRA Scottish Cider Pub of the Year 2019. Q😾◑≡(Waverley) 🏠●🏠😾🛜

Monty's

185 Morrison Street, EH3 8DZ (W edge of centre)

☎ (0131) 629 1104 ∰ montys.bar

Cross Borders Session Pale; 6 changing beers (sourced nationally; often Mallinsons, Oakham, Two by Two) ⓗ

Busy street-corner bar favoured by a younger clientele and keen to promote real ale. Cask ale is featured on the bar counter with keg beer on the back wall. The wood-panelled interior has large windows and a varied range of comfortable seating. There is also a cosy upstairs area with more seating. Bar snacks, including cheese, charcuterie, toasties and pizzas brought in from a nearby restaurant, are served all day. Children are not allowed. Closing time may be later for national rugby matches. 😾◑≡🏠🏠😾🛜🕙

Teuchters Bar & Bunker

26 William Street, EH3 7NH (W edge of centre)

☎ (0131) 225 2973 ∰ teuchtersbar.co.uk

Fyne Ales Jarl; Stewart Pentland IPA; Swannay Dark Munro; Timothy Taylor Landlord; 1 changing beer (sourced regionally; often Fyne Ales, Inveralmond) ⓗ

A cosy but deceptively roomy bar with a rustic feel, wooden beams and original stone walls. Seating includes chunky sofas and chairs around wooden tables. Small placename plates from Teuchterland create a frieze along the walls. Real ales are usually from Scottish micros. The gantry has an impressive range of single malt whiskies and an explanation of the pub's name. Meals are served all day. 🛏️◑👩‍🦽≡🏠🏠😾🛜

Edinburgh: East

Bellfield Brewery Tap Room

46 Stanley Place, EH7 5TB (1 mile E of centre)

☎ (0131) 656 9390 ∰ bellfieldbrewery.com

1 changing beer (often Bellfield)

The taproom is on the brewery site and tours and tastings are available. It has an excellent beer garden, adjacent to the East Coast mainline, with covered booths. The one cask ale is usually from the standard range but some new pilot brews appear at times. Bellfield was the UK's first craft brewery dedicated to gluten-free beers, and all are certified gluten-free. Food is available while open and is provided on a pop-up basis, with the choice changing every few days (see website for schedule). 🛏️😾◑👩‍🦽🏠😾🛜

Regent ⊘

2 Montrose Terrace, EH7 5DL (1 mile E of centre)

☎ (0131) 661 8198 ∰ theregentbar.co.uk

Caledonian Deuchars IPA; 2 changing beers (sourced nationally; often Harviestoun, Stewart, Timothy Taylor) ⓗ

Large brightly decorated tenement bar with two rooms, popular with LGBT real ale drinkers. The comfortable seating includes banquettes, leather sofas and armchairs. Real ales are served without sparklers on request. Bar snacks and simple meals, including good vegetarian and vegan options, are available all day. A novel slant on pub games is the gymnastic pommel horse. Children over five are permitted until 8pm. 🛏️◑●🏠😾🛜

SCOTLAND

Edinburgh: North

Dreadnought

72 North Fort Street, Leith, EH6 4HL (2 miles N of centre)

☎ 07876 351535 ⊕ dreadnoughtpub.com

4 changing beers (sourced nationally; often Brass Castle, Cromarty, Dark Revolution) Ⓗ

A welcoming one-roomed pub with big picture windows, a high ceiling with plaster cornicing, an attractive old-fashioned bar gantry and sports TV screens. A large photograph of HMS Dreadnought hangs on the wall along with other nautical items. The Brass Castle beers are all vegan. No food is prepared on-site, but pizza and burgers can be ordered from local outlets. A wheelchair ramp is available but there are no accessible toilets. Children are not admitted. Local CAMRA Edinburgh Pub of the Year 2020. Closed Monday-Thursday afternoons, open from 2pm Friday-Sunday. ❀❶♣♠➡❤❄☏

Henry Hall's Carriers Quarters

42 Bernard Street, Leith, EH6 6PR (2 miles N of centre)

☎ (0131) 554 4122 ⊕ carriersquarters.co.uk

2 changing beers (sourced regionally; often Fallen, Fyne Ales, Stewart) Ⓗ

Popular with locals, this cosy two-roomed bar is said to be the oldest pub in the area. It has a small front bar with a panelled counter and an alcove displaying a series of historical prints depicting life in Leith. The rear room has exposed stone walls, bare boards and a large fireplace with a welcoming gas fire in winter. The real ales are from Scottish breweries and there is a good selection of malt whiskies. Children are not admitted. ♣➡❤❄☏

Kay's Bar

39 Jamaica Street West, EH3 6HF (New Town, off India St)

☎ (0131) 225 1858 ⊕ kaysbar.co.uk

Caledonian Deuchars IPA; Fyne Ales Jarl; Theakston Best Bitter; Timothy Taylor Landlord; 3 changing beers (sourced nationally; often Cross Borders, Fallen, Stewart) Ⓗ

A cosy and convivial pub that retains many features from its days as a Victorian wine merchant and decorated with whisky barrels. Considering its size, it offers an impressive range of real ales. It also specialises in malt whisky, with a large selection behind the bar. If the front bar is busy, try the small room at the back. Lunches are mainly traditional Scottish fare. Children are not admitted. Dogs welcome outside food service hours. Q❶♣➡❤❄☏Ⓤ

Malt & Hops

45 The Shore, Leith, EH6 6QU (1½ miles N of centre)

☎ (0131) 555 0083

Hadrian Border Tyneside Blonde; 7 changing beers (sourced nationally; often Fyne Ales, Swannay) Ⓗ

Single-roomed, old-fashioned bar by the Water of Leith dating from 1747. It has a real fire and the walls are bedecked with mirrors, prints and beer-related artefacts. A large selection of pumpclips, many from long-lost breweries and distilleries, hangs from the ceiling along with hop bines renewed every harvest. The wide variety of real ales has an emphasis towards smaller breweries – beers are listed on the mirror behind the bar. Children are permitted until 6pm. ➳❀➡❤❄☏Ⓤ

Stockbridge Tap

2-4 Raeburn Place, Stockbridge, EH4 1HN (¾ mile N of centre)

☎ (0131) 343 3000

Swannay Island Hopping; 5 changing beers (sourced nationally; often Alechemy, Cromarty, Cross Borders) Ⓗ

A multi CAMRA award-winning specialist real ale house, offering unusual and interesting ales from all over the UK and holding occasional beer festivals. The L-shaped room, with a bright bar area, boasts mirrors from lost breweries including Murray's and Campbell's. There is plenty of seating and also ample space for vertical drinking. A handy stop for those walking the Water of Leith path. Children are not admitted. ♿♣➡❤❄

Teuchters Landing

1c Dock Place, Leith, EH6 6LU (2 miles N of centre)

☎ (0131) 554 7427 ⊕ aroomin.co.uk/teuchters-landing-bar-edinburgh

Fyne Ales Jarl; Inveralmond Ossian; Timothy Taylor Landlord; 2 changing beers (sourced regionally; often Fallen, Stewart, Tryst) Ⓗ

Once the waiting room for the Leith to Aberdeen ferry, the attractive front bar has a wood-panelled ceiling edged with tiles featuring Scottish place names from Teuchterland. There are two smaller rooms and a large conservatory opening out onto a pontoon floating on the Water of Leith. The varied food menu, available all day, features meals served in mugs. An excellent selection of malt whiskies is available. Children are allowed in the back rooms. Alcoholic drinks are served from 11am. ➳❀❶♿♣➡❤❄☏

Windsor

45 Elm Row, EH7 4AH (¾ mile N of centre)

☎ (0131) 556 4558

Caledonian Deuchars IPA; 3 changing beers (sourced nationally; often Fyne Ales, Orkney, Stewart) Ⓗ

This late-Victorian locals' bar retains a traditional look and fine ceiling cornices but is now brighter and more open plan. Comfortable green leather armchairs and bench seating complement the extensive wood panelling; a raised area at the back features a mirror and window with the pub logo. The three changing real ales come from a range of Scottish and north-east English breweries. Simple bar snacks are served. Children are not admitted. ❀Ꝗ♣➡❤❄☏

Edinburgh: South

Bennets Bar ★

8 Leven Street, EH3 9LG (¾ mile SE of centre)

☎ (0131) 229 5143

4 changing beers (sourced regionally; often Stewart) Ⓗ/ℙ

One of the city's top pub interiors in a Grade B-listed building, this is quintessential late-Victorian Edinburgh pub architecture – from the Jeffrey's Brewery etched door panels and window screens to the snug and a wonderful Bernard's mirror. The magnificent gantry houses a top-class range of malts and spirit barrels. A range of food is available all day in the bar and adjoining restaurant. Children are permitted until 8pm. Q➳❶➡❤❄☏Ⓤ

Cask & Barrel (Southside)

24-26 West Preston Street, EH8 9PZ (1 mile S of centre)

☎ (0131) 667 0856 ⊕ caskandbarrelsouthside.co.uk

Stewart Jack Back; Swannay Orkney Best; Tryst Drovers 80/-; 5 changing beers (sourced nationally; often Cromarty, Fyne Ales, Oakham) Ⓗ

A modern re-creation of a Scottish city or tenement bar. The single room, with windows front and back, is divided by a horseshoe bar with a dark-wood gantry adorned with decorative wooden casks. The walls support a fine range of old photos, advertisements and historic brewery and distillery mirrors. Sport is screened on multiple TVs with the sound usually low. This is a good place to try real ales from interesting breweries UK-wide. Children are not admitted. Winner of the CAMRA Edinburgh and SE Scotland Real Ale Quality Award in 2019. 🖨🛜♿

Cloisters Bar

26 Brougham Street, EH3 9JH (¾ mile SW of centre)
☎ (0131) 221 9997 ⊕ cloistersbar.com
10 changing beers (sourced nationally; often Black Isle, Stewart, Swannay) Ⓗ
Established in 1995 in the former All Saints Parsonage, many traditional features have been maintained in this warm and friendly bar. The real ales are generally from interesting breweries UK-wide. Frequent tap takeovers and Meet the Brewer events are held. The wide range of single malt whiskies, gins and rums does justice to the outstanding gantry. Freshly prepared meals may be served lunchtime and evenings (check with pub). Under-16s are not admitted. Q🕐🍴♣🖨🐱🛜♿

Dagda Bar

93-95 Buccleuch Street, EH8 9NG (¾ mile S of centre)
☎ (0131) 667 9773
Oakham Citra; 3 changing beers (sourced regionally; often Cromarty, Ferry, Stewarts) Ⓗ
Small ground-floor bar in an 18th-century tenement terrace, in the heart of a university area. A stone-flagged floor surrounds the large rectangular counter which takes up at least a third of the room. The colourful, mirrored gantry blends with the cornice, the joins blurred by an extensive collection of pumpclips. The bar is often busy, especially on Tuesday evening when a quiz is held. Children are not admitted. ♣🖨🐱🛜

John Leslie ★

45-47 Ratcliffe Terrace, EH9 1SU (1½ mile S of centre)
☎ (0131) 667 7205
Caledonian Deuchars IPA; Timothy Taylor Landlord; house beer (by Allendale); 3 changing beers (sourced nationally; often Alechemy, Kelburn, Windswept) Ⓗ
Located on the ground floor of a four-storey tenement, this superb pub is divided in two by a fine mahogany counter, gantry with clock and a mirrored snob screen with small 'ticket window' hatches. The bar has an alcove with banquettes while the lounge has three areas, a small snug by the door, an area around the fire and a quieter corner with more banquette seating. The elaborate late 19th-century decorative plaster work includes a lincrusta frieze. 🚶♣🖨🐱🛜♿

Spylaw ✓

27 Spylaw Street, Colinton, EH13 0JT (3½ miles SW of centre)
☎ (0131) 441 2783 ⊕ thespylaw.com
Timothy Taylor Landlord; 2 changing beers (sourced nationally; often Fyne Ales, Stewart) Ⓗ
Attractive, comfortable pub set in an historic village now absorbed by the city. The bar is located at the front and furnished with high stools/tables. To the rear are other areas, used mainly for dining, with booths and tables. A conservatory overlooks the garden and Colinton Dell. Freshly prepared food is served all day and the menu has children's options. The place makes an ideal stop when walking the Water of Leith path. 🚶😀🛏🕐♿♣🖨🐱🛜

Edinburgh: West

Athletic Arms (Diggers) ✓

1-3 Angle Park Terrace, EH11 2JX (1½ miles SW of centre)
☎ (0131) 337 3822

Fyne Ales Jarl Ⓐ; **Timothy Taylor Landlord** Ⓗ; **house beer (by Stewart)** Ⓐ; **3 changing beers (sourced nationally; often Bellfield, Loch Leven, Stewart)** Ⓗ
Dating from 1897, this legendary Edinburgh pub is known as Diggers due to its location between two graveyards. Banquette seating lines the walls, and the wooden floor features a compass drawing. Children over five are allowed in the two smaller back rooms if dining. There is more seating here, and the larger room has a dartboard. The pub gets busy when Hearts are playing at home. Outstanding pies are available. Autovacs are only used with the tall founts. 🚶♣🖨🐱🛜♿

Roseburn Bar ✓

1 Roseburn Terrace, EH12 5NG (1½ miles W of centre)
☎ (0131) 337 1067 ⊕ roseburnbar.co.uk
Fyne Ales Jarl; Stewart Pentland IPA; 2 changing beers (sourced nationally; often Cromarty, Tryst) Ⓗ
A traditional pub that is popular with locals, and close to Murrayfield for rugby and Tynecastle for football. It boasts high ceilings and a largely wooden interior, with interesting mirrors and period photos on the walls. There are numerous comfortable booths along the walls and two separate lounge areas. Three TVs show sporting events, though the volume is typically kept low. Live music plays on Friday and Saturday evenings. Children are not admitted. 🎵♿🖨🐱🛜

Winstons ✓

20 Kirk Loan, Corstorphine, EH12 7HD (3 miles W of centre, off St Johns Rd)
☎ (0131) 539 7077 ⊕ winstonslounge.co.uk
Stewart Pentland IPA Ⓟ; **3 changing beers (sourced regionally; often Harviestoun, Swannay)** Ⓗ
Comfortable lounge bar in Corstorphine, just over a mile from Murrayfield Stadium and a half mile from the zoo. A small, modern building, this warm and welcoming community pub is popular with old and young alike, with sports TV and monthly live music. The decor features golf and rugby along with historical photos of Corstorphine. Real ales are usually from a variety of Scottish breweries. The lunchtime food menu features wonderful home-made pies. Children are not admitted. 🎵🕐🖨🐱🛜

Gifford

Tweeddale Arms Hotel

High Street, EH41 4QU
☎ (01620) 810240 ⊕ tweeddalearmshotel.com
Hop Back Summer Lightning; 1 changing beer (sourced nationally; often Broughton, Stewart) Ⓗ
Clad in traditional black and white and sitting opposite the village green, this hotel can be identified by its coat of arms suspended on wooden posts. The cosy locals' bar, with a wood-burning stove, is where you will find the handpumps. The larger lounge bar is set up for dining, and there is also an elegant lounge area across the corridor. Food is served all day at weekends with a children's menu available. Wheelchair access is via the hotel entrance. 🚶🎵🛏🕐♿♣🖨(123)🐱🛜

Gullane

Bonnie Badger

Main Street, EH31 2AB
☎ (01620) 621111 ⊕ bonniebadger.com
3 changing beers (sourced regionally; often Harviestoun, Stewart) Ⓗ
Country hotel with a bar and the elegant Stables dining room. The rooms are open plan, tastefully decorated in a modern style yet retaining a cosy informality, with sporting photos on the walls. There is also a free pool

table in its own room. Food is served all day in the bar with several menus available at different times. Choices range from sandwiches to bar meals to award-winning gastro-quality meals. Families are welcome until 10pm. Q☺✿🍴◑🕭🛗♣🚗🐕☕🛜

Old Clubhouse

East Links Road, EH31 2AF (W end of village, off A198)
☎ (01620) 842008 ⊕ oldclubhouse.com
Timothy Taylor Landlord; 3 changing beers (sourced nationally) ℗
There's a colonial feel to this pub, with views over the golf links to the Lammermuir Hills. The half-panelled walls are adorned with historic memorabilia and stuffed animals. Caricature figures of the Marx Brothers and Laurel and Hardy look down from the gantry. Food features highly and is served all day. The extensive varied menu, including simple snacks and vegetarian choices, is supplemented with daily specials and children's options. Q☺✿🕭◑♣🚗🐕☕🛜

Haddington

Waterside Bistro

1-5 Waterside, EH41 4AT
☎ (01620) 825674 ⊕ thewatersidebistro.co.uk
3 changing beers (sourced nationally; often Orkney, Stewart, Winton) Ⓗ
Occupying a picture-postcard setting by the old Nungate Bridge, this bistro enjoys views across the River Tyne to historic St Mary's Collegiate Church. While the emphasis is on dining, drinkers are warmly welcomed. Food is served all day and there is a children's menu. The bar features a long light-oak counter fronted by bar stools and a real ale from Winton, who brew in the town, is served. A great spot for outdoor drinking by the river. Q☺✿🕭◑P🚗🐕☕🛜

Juniper Green

Kinleith Mill

604 Lanark Road, EH14 5EN
☎ (0131) 453 3214 ⊕ kinleithmill.com
3 changing beers (often Fyne Ales, Orkney, Stewart) Ⓗ
This well-maintained pub has a friendly atmosphere, welcoming locals and visitors alike. The large room is decorated with old village pictures and has an island bar separating the public bar and the lounge/dining areas. A full range of sports is shown on TVs. Dogs are allowed in some areas. The garden is in the car park area and has been fenced off, laid with artificial grass, surrounded by planters and has covered spaces.
☺✿🕭◑♣P🚗(44,45) 🐕☕🛜

Linlithgow

Four Marys ✔

65-67 High Street, EH49 7ED
☎ (01506) 842171 ⊕ fourmarys-linlithgow.co.uk
6 changing beers (sourced nationally; often Cromarty, Fyne Ales, Redcastle) Ⓗ
Close to Linlithgow Palace, birthplace of Mary Queen of Scots, the building dates back to around 1500 and is

> How easy can the barley-bree
> Cement the quarrel.
> It's aye the cheapest lawyer's fee
> To taste the barrel.
> **Robert Burns**

named after Mary's four ladies-in-waiting. Initially a dwelling house, the building has had several changes of use over the centuries – it was once a chemist's run by the Waldie family whose most famous member, David, helped establish the anaesthetic properties of chloroform in 1847. The pub serves good-quality food and at least six real ales from breweries across Scotland and the UK. A frequent local CAMRA Pub of the Year. Q✿◑🕭🛗♿🚗🐕🛜

Platform 3 ✔

1A High Street, EH49 7AB
☎ (01506) 847405 ⊕ platform3.co.uk
Stewart Pentland IPA; 2 changing beers (sourced regionally; often Cairngorm, Harviestoun, Tryst) Ⓗ
Small, friendly hostelry on the railway station approach, originally the public bar of the hotel next door and renovated in 1998 as a pub in its own right. Look out for the miniature goods train that travels from the station above the bar, with ducks waiting for a train that never comes. Two Scottish beers are served in addition to the regular ale. Dogs are welcomed with biscuits. A live departures board keeps travellers informed. Alcoholic drinks are served from 11am. 🚗🚌🐕☕🛜

Lothianbridge

Sun Inn

EH22 4TR (on A7 near Newtongrange)
☎ (0131) 663 2456 ⊕ thesuninnedinburgh.co.uk
2 changing beers (sourced regionally; often Cross Borders, Ferry, Stewart) Ⓗ
Award-winning gastro-pub overlooked by the impressive 23-span Waverley Line viaduct. At the front is the dining area with a tasteful mix of exposed stone and papered walls; to the rear is a more modern bar area for drinkers, and a coffee shop with glass doors opening out to the garden. Full meals are served all day on Sunday. The bar may close earlier if quiet. It is likely to open at 8am but alcoholic drinks are available from 11am.
☺✿🍴◑🕭🛗♿AP🚗(29,339) 🐕☕🛜

Musselburgh

Levenhall Arms

10 Ravensheugh Road, EH21 7PP (on B1348, 1 mile E of centre)
☎ (0131) 665 3220
Inveralmond Ossian Ⓐ; 1 changing beer (sourced regionally) Ⓗ/Ⓐ
A three-roomed hostelry dating from 1830 and close to the racecourse. Changing real ales are usually from smaller Scottish breweries, with two on at weekends. The lively, cheerfully decorated public bar is half timber-panelled and carpeted. Dominoes is popular here and there is a TV for sporting events. A smaller area leads off, with a dartboard and pictures of old local industries. The pleasant lounge, where families are welcome until 8pm, has comfortable seating. Q☺✿🕭♿♣P🚗🐕☕🛜

Volunteer Arms (Staggs)

81 North High Street, EH21 6JE (behind The Brunton)
☎ (0131) 665 9654
Loch Lomond Silkie Stout; Oakham JHB, Bishops Farewell; 4 changing beers (sourced nationally; often Fyne Ales, Nene Valley, Two by Two) Ⓗ
Superb pub run by the same family since 1858. Its bar and snug are traditional, with wooden floors, wood panelling, mirrors from defunct local breweries, and an attractive gantry topped with old casks. The more modern lounge opens at the weekend, and there is a partially covered garden to the rear. Real ales change regularly and are mostly pale and hoppy. Local CAMRA

Pub of the Year 2020, and winner of many previous awards. Likely to be closed until 4.30pm Monday to Thursday. ኄ❀&♣P🖨❀🕏ÖU

Newtongrange

Dean Tavern
80 Main Street, EH22 4NA
☎ (0131) 663 2419 ⊕ deantavern.co.uk
1 changing beer (sourced regionally; often Born, Cross Borders, Stewart) Ⓗ
Superb pub run by trustees on Gothenburg principles, with profits returned to the local community. The spacious bar was designed to help miners recover from their day in darkness, with roof lights in a high ceiling supported by arched iron beams. There is also the Lamp Room restaurant and a function room with a large mural depicting the town's mining past. Meals are available all day; children are permitted until 8pm if dining.
ኄ❀❶&▲⇌♣🖨❀🕏

North Berwick

Auld Hoose
19 Forth Street, EH39 4HX (N edge of centre)
☎ (01620) 892692 ⊕ auldhoosenorthberwick.co.uk
2 changing beers (sourced nationally; often Greene King, Theakston, Timothy Taylor) Ⓗ
Interesting high-ceilinged and friendly traditional Scottish drinking shop tastefully updated with bare floorboards around a mahogany bar, carpeted areas and a welcoming atmosphere enhanced by a real fire in winter. The gantry has four carved pillars and supports six old numbered whisky casks. The through lounge has varied seating, a pool table and pictures of sporting heroes. Built in 1896 and said to be the oldest licensed premises in the town, it is certainly the closest to the sea, and supports the RNLI. A stones throw from the Scottish Seabird Centre. ኄ▲⇌♣🖨❀🕏

Nether Abbey Hotel
20 Dirleton Avenue, EH39 4BQ (on A198, ¾ mile W of centre)
☎ (01620) 892802 ⊕ netherabbey.co.uk
4 changing beers (sourced nationally; often Fyne Ales, Stewart, Williams Bros) Ⓗ
Family-run hotel in a stone-built villa with a bright, contemporary, open-plan interior, situated on a busy main road. The Fly Half Bar is in a split-level glass extension; large folding doors open out onto the patio. Real ales can be served without sparklers on request. The award-winning restaurant is famed for its freshly cooked and locally sourced food, available seven days a week and served all day Friday to Sunday. Children are

welcome until 8pm (7pm in the bar). Alcoholic drinks are served from 11am. Accommodation is in 12 comfortable rooms. ኄ❀🛏❶&⇌P🖨❀🕏

Ship Inn
7-9 Quality Street, EH39 4HJ (E edge of centre)
☎ (01620) 890699 ⊕ theshipinnnorthberwick.com
Fyne Ales Jarl; 3 changing beers (sourced nationally; often Greene King, Orkney, Williams Bros) Ⓗ
Spacious, often lively, open-plan venue with a wide variety of seating and tables. The bar area has pine floorboards and a tastefully modernised bar and gantry. To the side and rear is a quieter carpeted area and there is maritime artwork throughout. It is popular for food, which is served all day until 8pm, with good children's, vegetarian, vegan and gluten-free choices. Sparklers are happily removed on request. Try the suntrap rear patio garden in the summer. ኄ❀❶🖨❀🕏

Penicuik

Navaar House Hotel
23 Bog Road, EH26 9BY (¼ mile W of centre)
☎ (01968) 672683 ⊕ navaarhouse.co.uk
Fyne Ales Jarl; 1 changing beer (sourced regionally; often Stewart) Ⓗ
A lively pub with a strong community spirit. The large bar is open plan with a log/coal stove, a pool table and TV screens. A restaurant serves locally sourced food lunchtimes, evenings and all day on Saturday and Sunday. Children are allowed in the restaurant only. There is a beer garden outside for warmer days. The bar opens at 3pm Monday to Friday, but real ale is served in the restaurant before then. ኄ❀🛏❶♣P🖨❀🕏

Whitecraig

Mercat Bar & Grill
10 Whitecraig Road, EH21 8PG
☎ 0800 124 4112 ⊕ mercatgrill.com
1 changing beer (sourced regionally; often Cross Borders, Stewart) Ⓗ
Pleasantly decorated and furnished dining pub that focuses on food but where drinkers are made welcome. Meals are served all day throughout the three linked areas, including the popular conservatory restaurant, although there is likely to be a reduced choice Monday to Wednesday. The menu offers a good range of dishes supplemented by daily specials, with smaller portions and children's dishes available. The Sunday roast rib of beef is a highlight. An electric car charging point is provided. May close early if quiet. ኄ❀❶&♣P🖨❀🕏

Return trays

Also known as an Autovac or beer economiser, a return tray is a device that collects beer spilled in the pouring process, recycles it by mixing it with fresh beer, and returns it to the glass.

It can be identified by a stainless steel drip tray below the nozzle on a handpump, with a pipe connected from the bottom of the tray to the draw line of the cask. They are commonly found in use in Yorkshire and parts of south-east Scotland and have been seen in north-east Scotland and north-west England.

A symbol will appear next to entries in the Guide where a return tray is in use on some or all of the beers (see inside cover key).

GREATER GLASGOW & CLYDE VALLEY

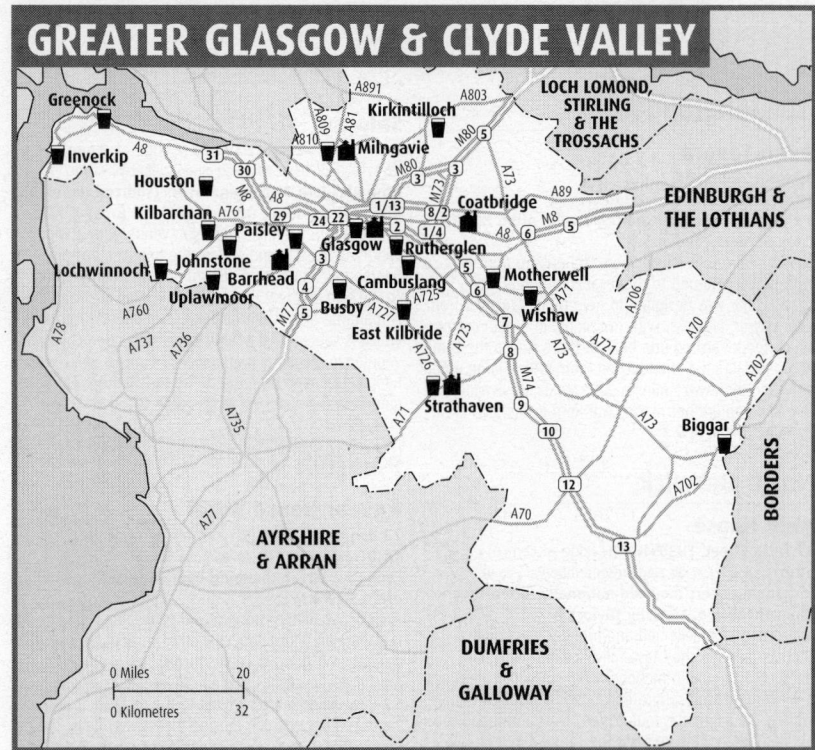

Authority areas covered: City of Glasgow UA, Dunbartonshire UAs, Inverclyde UA, Lanarkshire UAs, Renfrewshire UAs

Biggar

Crown Inn 🗽

109-111 High Street, ML12 6DL

☎ (01899) 220116 🌐 thecrownbiggar.co.uk

House beer (by Broughton); 5 changing beers (sourced nationally; often Broughton, Strathaven) Ⓗ
A pleasant and friendly inn in the centre of this market town, the Crown has hundreds of years of tradition behind it, officially dating from the mid-17th century. The bar area is directly accessed from the street and there is a small, quiet room, conservatory and beer garden to the rear. Six handpumps offer beers from a range of breweries, which can be served in flights of three third-pints if you want to try some different ones.
🛇🕏🅿🌂🌳(91,191) 🐾❀☆

Elphinstone Hotel ✓

145 High Street, ML12 6DL

☎ (01899) 220044 🌐 elphinstonehotel.co.uk

2 changing beers (sourced regionally; often Broughton, Fyne Ales) Ⓗ
An old coaching inn dating from the 18th century with a bright, modern public bar, a lounge bar, guest rooms and a large outdoor drinking area. There are four handpumps but in winter only two are in use to ensure that quality is maintained. The beers come in rotation from a selection of Scottish breweries. The bar has a pool table and dartboard and features live music on a Saturday. Accommodation is in 11 en-suite bedrooms.
🛇🕏🚪🅿🌂(91,191) 🐾☆

Busby

White Cart ✓

61 East Kilbride Road, G76 8HX

☎ (0141) 644 2711

Greene King IPA; 2 changing beers (sourced regionally; often Belhaven, Kelburn, Williams Bros) Ⓗ
A lovely and lively Chef & Brewer pub, located in the Busby conservation village, with a bright and spacious bar and restaurant area. It has been a public house since the 1860s and takes its name from the nearby River Cart. The emphasis here is on food, with meals available daily, but there are five handpumps serving three guest beers plus Greene King IPA. A large patio area at the front is popular in the summer and there is an area for families inside. An added bonus is the roaring fires in winter.
🛇🕏🍽️♿🌂🚆🅿🐾❀☆

Cambuslang

John Fairweather ✓

52-58 Main Street, G72 7EP

☎ (0141) 646 2411

Caledonian Deuchars IPA; Greene King Abbot; Sharp's Doom Bar; 3 changing beers (sourced nationally) Ⓗ
Impressive Wetherspoon conversion of the Savoy cinema and named after the man who designed it. Many original features have been retained and restored. The former ticket office leads to the bar, and the area upstairs where the screen used to be remains. The pub is watched over by old moviegoers sitting in the balcony. There is a small beer garden outside at the rear. Beers are available both from local and national breweries. 🛇🕏🍽️♿🌂🚆🅿🐾☆

East Kilbride

Hay Stook 🅛 ✅

26-36 Princes Avenue, G74 1JU (at Brouster Gate entrance to shopping centre)

☎ (01355) 244323

Caledonian Deuchars IPA; Greene King Abbot; Sharp's Doom Bar; 5 changing beers (sourced nationally; often Broughton, Strathaven) ⊞

This Wetherspoon pub opened in 2015, and is handy for shoppers and the nearby cinema complex. Bare walls and a wooden ceiling give it a rustic air. The interior is divided in two by the staircase up to the toilets, with the family area on the left and the bar to the right. There is a small beer garden beside the mall entrance. Up to six guest ales from local and national breweries are available. 🅑⊛⊙🖐♿⇌🍴�☗

Glasgow

Babbity Bowster

16-18 Blackfriars Street, Merchant City, G1 1PE

☎ (0141) 552 5055 ⊕ babbitybowster.com

Caledonian Deuchars IPA; Fyne Ales Jarl; 1 changing beer (sourced regionally) ⊞

A long established pub/hotel/restaurant that reopened in July 2020 after an extensive refurbishment. The furniture in the bar is simple and practical with plain tables and free-standing chairs, augmented by wall seating. Outside, there is more seating in the beer garden (a Glasgow city rarity). Three pumps serve Scottish beers plus a guest which is usually local. Fine meals are served in the restaurant upstairs – the quality is reflected in the daily specials available in the bar. Q⊛🏠⊙⇌(High St) 🏠🚆☗

Bon Accord 🅛

153 North Street, Charing Cross, G3 7DA

☎ (0141) 248 4427 ⊕ bonaccordpub.com

Caledonian Deuchars IPA, Edinburgh Castle 80/-; 8 changing beers (sourced nationally) ⊞

One of the pioneers of the real ale scene in Glasgow, the Bon serves more than 800 different real ales each year. The wall opposite the bar is adorned with an impressive array of award certificates, including some from CAMRA. A dining area at the rear also hosts quiz, poker and live music nights. The pub's owner is passionate about malt whisky and there are 400 varieties behind the bar to complement the wide choice of real ales. 🅑⊛⊙♿⇌🚆🍴🚆☗

Drum & Monkey ✅

91 St Vincent Street, G2 5TF

☎ (0141) 221 6636

St Austell Nicholson's Pale Ale; 5 changing beers (sourced nationally; often Inveralmond, Stewart) ⊞

This corner pub, housed in a former American-style bank, has an opulent marble and wood-panelled interior and ornate ceilings. Convenient both for main railway stations and numerous bus routes, it is usually busy with a varied clientele. Family groups are welcome until 8pm when dining. The large P-shaped central bar features six handpulls offering a wide variety of styles, from local and national favourites to contemporary microbrews. 🅑⊙♿⇌(Central) 🚆🚆⊛☗

Drygate 🅛

85 Drygate, Dennistoun, G4 0UT (off John Knox St)

☎ (0141) 212 8815 ⊕ drygate.com

Drygate Pale Duke, Seven Peaks ⊞

Situated on the historic Wellpark Brewery site, this brewpub offers numerous cask, keg and bottled beers, firmly positioned towards the craft beer market and

younger drinkers. Lively, with an industrial aesthetic, there are two bars over the ground and first floors, an outside terrace and a panoramic view of the brewery. Food is served throughout the day – the menu varies from modern British to street-inspired. Live music and comedy feature regularly in the upstairs beer hall. 🅑⊛⊙🖐♿⇌(High St) P🚆⊛☗

Esquire House ✅

1487 Great Western Road, Anniesland, G12 0AU

☎ (0141) 341 1130

Caledonian Deuchars IPA; Greene King Abbot; Williams Bros Joker IPA; 3 changing beers (sourced nationally; often Broughton, Loch Lomond) ⊞

A compact Wetherspoon, built in the mid 1990s in what was once a dry area of the city and replacing a function suite of the same name. There are six cask beers on offer, with guests usually from Scottish breweries such as Broughton and Loch Lomond. The pub caters mostly for a local clientele, with TV screens showing racing and football, and the community atmosphere is enhanced by the Monday night quiz. A Meet the Brewer event is held every six weeks. 🅑⊛⊙♿⇌🍴P🚆☗

Hengler's Circus

351-363 Sauchiehall Street, Charing Cross, G2 3HU

☎ (0141) 331 9810

Caledonian Deuchars IPA; Greene King Abbot; Sharp's Doom Bar; 7 changing beers (sourced nationally; often Broughton, Kelburn, Loch Lomond) ⊞

A Wetherspoon named after the indoor circus that used to be on the other side of Sauchiehall Street nearer Charing Cross. It is an L-shaped pub, with the bar down both sides of the L, and a family area to the right of the entrance. Popular during the week with students and office workers, it is also busy at weekends as it is handy for the King's Theatre and other attractions. Q🅑⊙♿⇌🚆🍴🚆☗

Horse Shoe ★ ✅

17-19 Drury Street, City Centre, G2 5AE

☎ (0141) 248 6368 ⊕ thehorseshoebarglasgow.co.uk

Caledonian Deuchars IPA ⊞**; Harviestoun Bitter & Twisted** ℗**; 2 changing beers (often Fuller's, Timothy Taylor)** ⊞

Close to Central station, and very busy in the evenings and at weekends, the downstairs bar has four handpumps, with Timothy Taylor Landlord and Fuller's London Pride often featuring as guest beers. Dating from 1870, this Victorian pub is recognised by CAMRA as having a nationally important historic interior, which includes Scotland's longest bar. The horseshoe theme is everywhere, from the shape of the long bar to the fireplaces, mirrors and clock. Above the bar there is a lounge/diner where children are welcome. 🅑⊙♿⇌(Central) 🚆🚆☗

SCOTLAND

Inn Deep
445 Great Western Road, Hillhead, G12 8HH
☎ (0141) 264 2777 ⊕ inndeep.com
3 changing beers (sourced nationally; often Williams Bros) Ⓟ
Below Great Western Road on the banks of the River Kelvin, Inn Deep is set in the arches of an old railway station. The middle arch houses the bar, which stocks three guest cask ales, and there is an extensive range of keg beers. The pub offers good food and hosts regular poetry nights and occasional music sessions. There is a small outdoor seating area in the adjacent arch.
☒❄❍Ⓟ(Kelvinbridge) ☷(20,6)✿🛜

Laurieston Bar ★
58 Bridge Street, Tradeston, G5 9HU
☎ (0141) 429 4528
Fyne Ales Jarl; 2 changing beers (sourced locally; often Fyne Ales, Jaw) Ⓗ
Unchanged over decades, the Laurieston is owned and run by two brothers, assisted by family members, and a warm welcome is assured. The horseshoe bar is surrounded by formica-top tables, with walls covered in vintage photographs, mirrors, memorabilia and the occasional painting. The lounge is roomier with a much smaller bar and some unusual artwork on the walls. Pies are served from a traditional counter-top display unit. Close to Bridge Street subway station and over the Clyde from Glasgow Central, the pub can be busy at weekends.
≷(Central) Ⓠ(Bridge St) ☷✿🛜

Pot Still
154 Hope Street, G2 2TH
☎ (0141) 333 0980 ⊕ thepotstill.co.uk
4 changing beers (sourced regionally; often Ayr, Broughton) Ⓗ
Near both main rail stations and major bus routes, this classic city centre bar is one of Scotland's leading whisky pubs with a collection of around 750 malts. Listening to the staff describe the virtues of various drams to appreciative visitors is an education. Four handpumps offer Scottish beers, some not often seen in Glasgow. Food of the pie-and-beans school is available during the day. The main bar area is small but there is a mezzanine level providing additional seating.
☒❍≷(Central) Ⓠ☷✿🛜

Sir John Moore ⊘
260-292 Argyle Street, G2 8QW
☎ (0141) 222 1780
Greene King Abbot; Sharp's Doom Bar; 8 changing beers (sourced nationally; often Stewart, Williams Bros) Ⓗ
A Wetherspoon pub located across the road from Glasgow Central Station's (lower level) Hope Street exit. With live departure screens inside, this is an ideal place to wait for a train. It is also handy for breakfast after a night on the sleeper. Converted from several shops into one very large room, it has several distinct areas marked with screens and a licensed pavement area. It takes its name from a Glasgow-born soldier whose statue can be found in George Square. ❄❍≷(Central)Ⓠ♠☷🛜

Sir John Stirling Maxwell ⊘
136-140 Kilmarnock Road, Shawlands, G41 3NN
☎ (0141) 636 9024
Caledonian Deuchars IPA; Greene King Abbot; Sharp's Doom Bar; 3 changing beers (sourced nationally; often Broughton, Kelburn) Ⓗ
A popular Wetherspoon named after a local benefactor and landowner. The pub is at the end of the Shawlands Arcade in a converted supermarket. Photographs of former local cinemas adorn the walls as at one time the

Embassy used to occupy this site. To the rear there is a raised TV-free family area. There is often a good selection of dark and light beers, both from traditional and newer breweries. ☒❍点≷☷🛜

Society Room ⊘
151 West George Street, G2 2JJ
☎ (0141) 229 7560
Caledonian Deuchars IPA; Greene King Abbot; 4 changing beers (sourced nationally) Ⓗ
Wetherspoon's only Lloyd's No.1 bar in Glasgow. It can be lively; however, the music doesn't start until 8pm on weekdays and Sundays, and the pub is popular with older people during the day. On Saturdays there is music from 5pm, with a DJ from 9pm. The building's low ceiling and lack of windows at the back give it a cavernous feel. The beer choice often features several high-strength beers. ❍点≷(Central)Ⓠ(Buchanan St)☷🛜

State Bar
148 Holland Street, Charing Cross, G2 4NG
☎ (0141) 332 2159
House beer (by Stewart); 6 changing beers (sourced nationally; often Oakham) Ⓗ
A regular local CAMRA Pub of the Year, this popular town-centre pub with a traditional island bar gets busy at lunchtimes and weekends. The changing beers are rarely seen in Glasgow, and include at least one from Oakham. Old pictures and show bills displayed around the walls reflect the pub's proximity to the King's Theatre. There is a blues session on Tuesday in the main bar and a comedy club downstairs on Saturday. ❍≷☷✿🛜↺

Tennent's ⊘
191 Byres Road, Hillhead, G12 8TN
☎ (0141) 339 7203 ⊕ thetennentsbarglasgow.co.uk
Caledonian Deuchars IPA; Draught Bass; Fuller's London Pride; Marston's Pedigree; Stewart 80/-; Timothy Taylor Landlord; 2 changing beers (sourced nationally; often Brains) Ⓗ
Large traditional pub at a busy junction in the centre of the West End in the shadow of Glasgow University. It was established in the 1880s by a member of the Tennent family, but not originally associated with the brewery. The open-plan room is dominated by the rectangular bar and by large TV screens mostly showing sporting events (the sound is turned up for big matches). A small lounge to one side provides extra seating. Food is served all day. ❍点☷✿🛜

Three Judges Ⓛ ⊘
141 Dumbarton Road, Partick, G11 6PR
☎ (0141) 337 3055 ⊕ threejudges.co.uk
Sharp's Doom Bar; 8 changing beers (sourced nationally) Ⓗ
Traditional corner tenement pub on a busy junction at the bottom of Byres Road. Many customers come from the local community to watch the racing or listen to the jazz on Sunday afternoon. But others also travel from afar to enjoy the wide range of beers, which has been a feature for nearly 30 years. A selection of guest ciders is also on offer, and a cider festival hosted annually. No food is available but it can be brought in. ≷Ⓠ♠☷✿🛜

Greenock

James Watt ⊘
80-92 Cathcart Street, PA15 1DD
☎ (01475) 722640
Greene King Abbot; Sharp's Doom Bar; 4 changing beers Ⓗ
Situated across the road from Greenock Central Station and 200 yards from the bus station, this large open-plan

Wetherspoon, in a former post office, is named after one of Greenock's famous sons who improved steam engine technology and has the SI unit of power named after him. The chain's standard value-for-money food is available all day and beer festivals are hosted at various times throughout the year. This pub is an oasis in a beer desert. ⑪&≉(Central)☂

Houston

Fox & Hounds 🄻
South Street, PA6 7EN
☎ (01505) 808604 ⊕ foxandhoundshouston.co.uk
Kelburn Goldihops; 4 changing beers (sourced nationally; often Kelburn, Fuller's, Fyne Ales) Ⓗ
Excellent traditional village pub established in 1779. The bar, lounge and restaurant are downstairs, a cocktail bar upstairs. It offers a range of beers on five handpumps alongside a selection of canned and bottled craft beers and a wide choice of spirits including 130 whiskies. Gastro-pub food made wholly on the premises is served throughout. An annual beer festival is held on the late May bank holiday weekend. There is a pool table upstairs and board games are played every Wednesday.
Q🌣❀⑪&♣P🚍❀☂

Inverkip

Inverkip Hotel
Main Street, PA16 0AS
☎ (01475) 521478 ⊕ inverkip.co.uk
Fyne Ales Jarl; 1 changing beer (sourced regionally; often Fallen, Fyne Ales) Ⓗ
Small, family-run hotel in the heart of a conservation village and just a short walk from the large Inverkip Marina, making it an ideal staging post for those just messing about on the river or passing through on the way to Largs and the Ayrshire coast. Food options range from snacks through to special-occasion dining. All-ticket Battle of the Brewer nights are popular.
❀✉⑪≉P🚍(578,580) ☂

Johnstone

Callum's 🄻
26 High Street, PA5 8AH
☎ (01505) 322925
5 changing beers Ⓗ
Popular town-centre pub offering a friendly welcome and a comfortable atmosphere. In an area short of real ale outlets, three permanent beers and four changing guests are on offer. A large TV screen shows sporting events. Food is served in the lounge, with themed events including Thursday curry night. Occasional live music is hosted at the weekend.
🌣⑪&≉(Strathclyde)🚍(36,38) ☂

Kilbarchan

Trust Inn
8 Low Barholm, PA10 2ET
☎ (01505) 702401 ⊕ thetrustinn.com
3 changing beers Ⓗ
Small, popular, single-roomed pub in the centre of a conservation village, with old village photographs adorning the walls. A superior bar meal menu and special promotions mean it can be busy at mealtimes. Children are welcome in the evening if dining. Regular live events including local bands and other entertainment are advertised via social media.
🌣⑪🚍(38) ☂

Kirkintilloch

Kirky Puffer ✅
1-11 Townhead, G66 1NG (by canal)
☎ (0141) 775 4140
Caledonian Deuchars IPA; Sharp's Doom Bar; 3 changing beers (sourced nationally; often Loch Lomond, Oakham, Williams Bros) Ⓗ
A Wetherspoon establishment with a modern interior and Mackintosh-style wood panelling. The pub has developed a strong reputation for the quality and range of its beers – the enthusiastic and knowledgeable manager endeavours to supplement the core and seasonal range of ales with those from a variety of leading breweries, reflecting the clientele's preference for pale, hoppy beers. The spacious, attractive building sits alongside the Forth and Clyde Canal and has an extensive beer garden. 🌣❀⑪&●🚍☂

Lochwinnoch

Brown Bull
32 Main Street, PA12 4AH
☎ (01505) 843250
Harviestoun Bitter & Twisted; 3 changing beers (sourced nationally; often Cromarty, Fyne Ales, Kelburn) Ⓗ
More than 200 years old, this family-run pub attracts locals and visitors throughout the year. A wide choice of national ales is offered, with an emphasis on regional breweries. The upstairs restaurant uses local produce and bar meals are also available. It hosts a quiz night on Tuesday and live music monthly. At the rear is a quirky outdoor seating area and garden with cooperage tools. Located close to Lochwinnoch RSPB nature reserve and Castle Semple loch and visitor centre.
Q🌣❀⑪●🚍(X34,X36) ❀

Milngavie

Jaw Brew Bar 🄻
26 Crossvegate, G62 6RA
☎ 07880 690995 ⊕ jawbrew.co.uk
3 changing beers (sourced locally; often Jaw) Ⓗ
This two-room micropub opened in December 2019 as Jaw Brew's brewery tap. The interior has a rustic feel with wooden tables and chairs. As well the three cask ales there are four keg beers on tap. Visitors can take home some of Jaw Brew's ales and also Bardowie Gin, from the brewer's family's own distillery. Conveniently situated close to the town's station car park. Q❀≉🚍❀

Motherwell

Brandon Works ✅
45-61 Merry Street, ML1 1JJ
☎ (01698) 210280
Caledonian Deuchars IPA; Greene King Abbot; Sharp's Doom Bar; 2 changing beers (often Kelburn, Loch Lomond, Strathaven) Ⓗ
This central Wetherspoon, handy for buses and trains, takes its name from the ironworks that sat behind the pub's site until the 1960s. A wide range of cask ales is available, listed on blackboards at each end of the bar. A quiz night is held monthly and there are occasional Meet the Brewer events. The pub has a display of prints illustrating Lanarkshire's traditional industries and influential historical figures including locally born Keir Hardie and Robert Owen. ⑪&≉🚍☂

Paisley

Bull Inn ★ ✅

7 New Street, PA1 1XU
☎ (0141) 849 0472
4 changing beers (sourced regionally; often Jaw, Kelburn, Loch Lomond) Ⓗ

Established in 1901 and identified by CAMRA as having a nationally important historic interior, this is the oldest inn in Paisley. The pub retains many original features including stained-glass windows, three small snugs and a spirit cask gantry, and boasts the only original set of spirit cocks left in Scotland. Live sport is shown on large screens in the main bar and the snugs. Four changing guest ales come from the likes of Kelburn, Jaw, Loch Lomond, Orkney, Stewart and Strathaven breweries. Local CAMRA Pub of the Year for the past two years.
🌐≉(Gilmour St) 🖥🐾🛜

Last Post 🅛 ✅

2 County Square, PA1 1BN
☎ (0141) 849 6911
Caledonian Deuchars IPA; Greene King Abbot; Sharp's Doom Bar; 6 changing beers Ⓗ

Large Wetherspoon pub converted from the town's main post office, originally built in 1893. Open plan in design on two levels, there is plenty of seating and good wheelchair access. The standard Wetherspoon food menu is served and six guest ales are usually available. Next to Gilmour Street railway station and close to the bus station, it is a handy place to enjoy a pint while you wait. ◖▶🌐≉(Gilmour St)🍴🖥(9,36)🛜

Northern Way

13-19 Causeyside Street, PA1 1UW
4 changing beers (sourced nationally) Ⓗ

This Northern Way-branded Amber Taverns pub has undergone a massive refurbishment from previous incarnations and is extremely well appointed throughout. It currently serves up to four different ales, primarily from the north of England, as well as a huge selection of premium gins. Live sporting events are shown on a number of large-screen TVs. Separate areas are available to book for events. Children are not permitted. 🌐≉(Gilmour St)🛜

Sandpiper

Before Security, Glasgow Airport, PA3 2SW
☎ (0141) 842 7858
Greene King Abbot; 4 changing beers Ⓗ

On the ground floor, in the public area of the airport, the Sandpiper is a Wetherspoon outlet and is ideal if you are looking for an ale before heading through security, waiting for family or friends arriving on an incoming flight, or if you are a plane spotter in need of refreshment. With six handpumps you are spoilt for choice and can relax watching one of the many TV screens showing 24-hour news and sporting events. Opening hours are slightly longer in the summer season.
Q🌐◖▶🌐🍴P🖥🛜

Wee Howff ✅

53 High Street, PA1 2AN
☎ (0141) 887 8299
2 changing beers (sourced nationally; often Kelburn) Ⓗ

The Wee Howff has appeared in more than 25 editions of The Good Beer Guide and is a little piece of heaven in an otherwise crowded area of cheap drinking establishments. A small, traditional pub with a loyal regular clientele, it offers up to three guest ales from all four corners of Britain from a quarterly rotating list. It has an open mic night on the first Monday of each month

and a pub quiz every Thursday. The jukebox caters for even the most eclectic of tastes.
🌐≉(Gilmour St) 🖥(9,36)🐾🛜

Rutherglen

Ruadh-Ghleann ✅

40-44 Main Street, G73 2HY
☎ (0141) 613 2370
Caledonian Deuchars IPA; Greene King Abbot; Sharp's Doom Bar; 4 changing beers (sourced nationally) Ⓗ

Busy Wetherspoon pub that takes its name from the Gaelic name of the town. It has a long, narrow bar decorated in a contemporary style, and a family area at the far end leading to the beer garden. There is also a window into the cellar. The beer garden is on two levels and affords a view of the Cathkin Braes. Six of the 12 handpumps are usually in use. Q🌐🌸◖▶🌐≉🖥🛜

Strathaven

Weavers 🅛 ✅

1-3 Green Street, ML10 6LT
4 changing beers (sourced nationally; often Strathaven) Ⓗ

A frequent local CAMRA Pub of the Year, this family-run bar is in the centre of the town with links to the 19th-century weaving industry. The single room has modern and comfortable furnishings and is decorated with an assortment of black and white pictures of film stars. Three handpumps offer ales from an ever-changing range and the fourth serves beers exclusively from the nearby Strathaven Brewery. A range of imported bottled beers is also available. 🌐🖥(254,256)🛜

Uplawmoor

Uplawmoor Hotel

66 Neilston Road, G78 4AF (off A736)
☎ (01505) 850565 ⊕ uplawmoor.co.uk

In a tranquil village setting just over 10 miles from Glasgow, the building dates back to the 18th century. It was originally a coaching inn used by travellers and customs officers chasing smugglers en route between Glasgow and the south-west coast of Scotland. Today the hotel continues to offer travellers the opportunity to relax and explore. The interior is rustic and cosy, with a public bar, pool room and lounge bar. The beer is always from the local Kelburn Brewery.
🌐🌸🛏◖▶🌐P🖥🖥(395,X44B) 🛜

Wishaw

Wishaw Malt ✅

62-66 Kirk Road, ML2 7BL
☎ (01698) 358806
Caledonian Deuchars IPA; Greene King Abbot; Sharp's Doom Bar; 3 changing beers Ⓗ

A town-centre bar converted from a furniture store at the beginning of the century, the Wishaw Malt has six handpumps, with guest beers from all over the UK supplementing the three regulars. Around the walls are information panels and photographs of old Wishaw. The pub takes its name from a 19th-century distillery and bonded warehouse. Ironically, a church to the rear once hosted the Wishaw Templar Lodge of Temperance.
🌐🌸◖▶≉🖥🛜

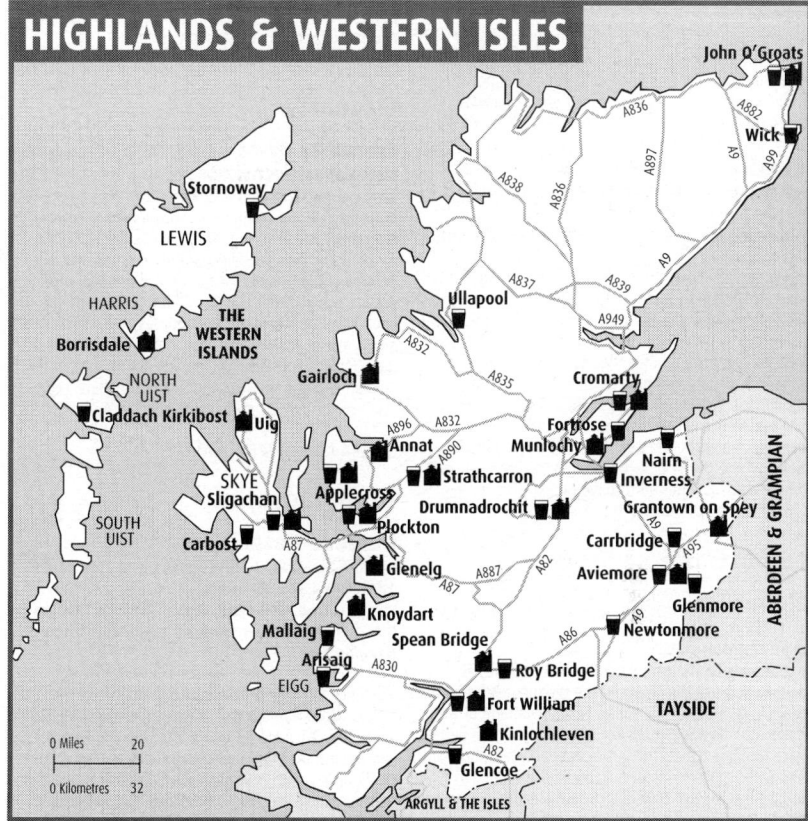

HIGHLANDS & WESTERN ISLES

Authority areas covered: Highland UA, Western Isles UA

Applecross

Applecross Inn
Shore Street, IV54 8LR NG70974444
☎ (01520) 744262 ⊕ applecrossinn.co.uk

This remote multi award-winning iconic inn is reached by a hair-raising road over one of the highest vehicular ascents in Britain or by a longer scenic coastal route. Renowned for its local seafood and venison, with a massive chalkboard menu, the pub is a must for foodies. Beers come from local microbrewery Applecross Ales. There are additional tables outside, with the Inn-Side-Out Airstream caravan offering light refreshments and takeaways. The pub is a popular stop-off on the North Coast 500. CAMRA branch Pub of the Year runner-up 2020. ㅂ愛❀dஇ◐৬AP🖰❀🐾⌘

Arisaig

Arisaig Hotel (Crofters Rest)
Main Road, PH39 4NH (on B8008 off A830)
NM65808650
☎ (01687) 450210 ⊕ arisaighotel.co.uk
2 changing beers (often Cromarty) Ⓗ
An old coaching inn built around 1720, this hotel is just off the main road to Mallaig and looks out over the turquoise waters of the bay towards Eigg, Rum and Skye. The Crofters Bar offers up to two Cromarty beers. Locally caught seafood dominates the lunch and dinner menus, with a menu for vegetarians. It stages music on Friday nights and Sunday afternoons, as well as two music

festivals. For train spotters, The Jacobite steam special chugs through the local station during the season. There are many scenic costal walks nearby.
Q㇏愛❀dஇ≠৬P🖰❀🐾⌘

Aviemore

Cairngorm Hotel Ⓛ
77 Grampian Road, PH22 1PE
☎ (01479) 810233 ⊕ cairngorm.com
Cairngorm Gold, Stag Ⓗ
Just over the road from the train station and bus stop, this is often the first watering hole for many after a long journey. The privately owned Cairngorm Hotel has a warm and familiar feel about it, with comfy seats in the lobby to the bar and seating under cover outside. Although not tied, Cairngorm beers feature on the two handpumps. Large-screen TVs show popular sporting events and there is Scottish entertainment for the many visitors most evenings. Food with a Scottish twist is available much of the day. ㅂ愛❀dஇ◐৬A≷P🖰⌘

Old Bridge Inn Ⓛ
23 Dalfaber Road, PH22 1PU
☎ (01479) 811137 ⊕ oldbridgeinn.co.uk
4 changing beers (sourced locally; often Cairngorm, Caledonian, Windswept) Ⓗ
Close to the gently flowing River Spey, this gem of a pub off the main drag is worth seeking out. The cosy, intimate inn, converted from a cottage in 1982, is an ideal place to relax after a busy day on the hills, or even just touring in the area. Four handpumps offer a mix of

local and regional beers. Booking is recommended for the restaurant, with a menu using produce with low food miles. Entertainment is hosted most nights. There is a bunkhouse adjacent and self-catering accommodation available. Handy for the Strathspey Steam Railway.
ॐ⊛≒◑&▲≉Ω❀♈

Winking Owl L ✅

123 Grampian Road, PH22 1RH (N end of village)
☎ (01479) 812368 ⊕ thewinkingowl.co
6 changing beers (sourced locally; often Cairngorm, Caledonian) Ⓗ
The Winky has been the brewery tap for the award-winning Cairngorm Brewery since 2014, with the addition of the Bothy Bar downstairs in 2018 massively increasing its popularity. Both bars offer four Cairngorm and two Caledonian beers. Hearty pub grub – including children's, vegetarian, gluten- and dairy-free – is served throughout. Live music plays in the Bothy. The rustic courtyard has a covered seating area made from upcycled materials and logs. Once a farmhouse, this is probably one of the oldest hostelries in Aviemore, and Robert Burns is reported to have breakfasted here in 1787. ॐ⊛◑&▲≉Ω❀♈

Carbost: Isle of Skye

Old Inn

IV47 8SR NG379318
☎ (01478) 640205 ⊕ theoldinnskye.co.uk
3 changing beers (often Cuillin, Isle of Skye) Ⓗ
On the shores of Loch Harport, the Old Inn nestles on the tideline. Outside, trestle tables take advantage of the views that Skye is famous for – there can be no better place to enjoy a pint. The pub is busy all year round with an eclectic mix of outdoor folk, and those touring Skye or visiting the Talisker Distillery close by. Seafood is top of the menu, most of it coming from the loch.
Q ॐ⊛≒◑👜Ω❀

Carrbridge

Cairn Hotel L

Main Road, PH23 3AS (just off A9 on B9153)
☎ (01479) 841212 ⊕ cairnhotel.co.uk
3 changing beers (sourced regionally; often Cairngorm, Cromarty, Orkney) Ⓗ
The Cairn Hotel is the hub of this small village, with the lure of a warming open fire and excellent gastro-pub style menus. The licensee selects the best cask ales from the Highlands and Islands for his three handpumps and deservedly the pub is popular with loyal locals and the many visitors to the area. There are 14 rooms for overnight stays – the 1717 Packhorse Bridge and Landmark Forest Adventure Park are in the village.
ॐ⊛≒◑♣Ω❀♈

Claddach Kirkibost: North Uist

Westford Inn

HS6 5EP (2½ miles NW of Clachan on A865)
NF7551066195
☎ (01876) 580653 ⊕ westfordinn.com
3 changing beers (sourced regionally; often Fyne Ales, Isle of Skye) Ⓗ
The owners took on the Westford Inn in 2015 and have turned around its fortunes. It is very much the hub of the community, with live music and an annual beer festival. A second Skye ale is on rotation in winter, with three ales in summer, as well as a range of bottled beers. Good-quality pub food is served and also available to take away. Probably one of the most remote bars in the

Guide, it is well worth making the effort to visit. Accommodation is in The Bothy, a former byre.
Q ॐ⊛≒◑▲♣Ω❀♈

Cromarty

Cromarty Arms L

Church Street, IV11 8XA
☎ (01381) 600230 ⊕ cromartyarms.com
Cromarty Happy Chappy; 1 changing beer (often Cromarty) Ⓗ
A family-run pub providing B&B accommodation and delicious home-made bar meals. A traditional music session is held on the second Friday of every month. The beers are from Cromarty Brewery less than three miles away. Just opposite is the National Trust for Scotland's Hugh Miller's Cottage and Cromarty Courthouse, or take a dolphin-spotting tour from the harbour where you can also see the oil rigs in for maintenance. A two-car ferry operates during the summer to Nigg.
Q ॐ⊛≒◑&♣Ω (26,26A) ❀♈

Drumnadrochit

Benleva Hotel L

Kilmore Road, IV63 6UH (signed off A82) NH513295
☎ (01456) 450080 ⊕ benleva.co.uk
Hanging Tree After Dark, Eighty Shillings, Hangmans IPA; 1 changing beer (sourced regionally; often Hanging Tree) Ⓗ
The 400-year-old sweet chestnut outside the Benleva was once a hanging tree, hence the name of the brewery in the bothy just outside. The bar in this 300-year-old former manse offers four Hanging Tree beers and a guest ale. The food menu features classic home-made dishes with a Scottish twist. Regular music and themed nights are held throughout the year and an annual beer festival in September.
ॐ⊛≒◑▲♣Ω❀♈

Fort William

Ben Nevis Bar

103 High Street, PH33 6DG
☎ (01397) 702295 ⊕ bennevisbarfortwilliam.com
Hanging Tree After Dark, Hangmans IPA; 1 changing beer (often Hanging Tree) Ⓗ
Built in 1806 and under new ownership since 2019, this pleasant two-roomed traditional locals' pub on the pedestrianised High Street is said to have a resident

REAL ALE BREWERIES

Applecross Applecross (NEW)
Ardgour Fort William (NEW)
Black Isle Munlochy
Cairngorm Aviemore
Cromarty Cromarty
Cuillin 🍺 Sligachan: Isle of Skye
Dun Glenelg
Glen Spean Spean Bridge
Hanging Tree 🍺 Drumnadrochit
Isle of Harris Borrisdale
Isle of Skye Uig: Isle of Skye
John O'Groats John O'Groats
Knoydart Knoydart
Old Inn 🍺 Gairloch (brewing suspended)
Plockton Plockton
River Leven Kinlochleven
Strathcarron Strathcarron
Two Thirsty Men Grantown on Spey
Wild Barn Annat (brewing suspended)

ghost in the loft. A decked area at the rear gives splendid views of Loch Linnhe. As well as the three ales, over 50 malt whiskies are stocked. A food menu of good honest pub favourites is available all day. Live music plays at weekends. ♿🏠🏮🛏♿≠♣🚌🐕🎵🛜

Ben Nevis Inn 🅛

Achintee Road, Claggan, PH33 6TE NN12477293
☎ (01397) 701227 ⊕ ben-nevis-inn.co.uk
3 changing beers (sourced locally; often Cairngorm, Isle of Skye, River Leven) 🅗

Traditional 200-year-old stone-built barn at the start of the Ben Nevis mountain path, popular with outdoor enthusiasts. The small bar counter has three handpumps offering beers from local breweries. The barn, with long beer hall-style tables and a beckoning stove, and decorated with mountaineering and skiing paraphernalia, is a warm, informal and friendly setting – an ideal venue for live music. A hearty food menu is available, changing daily. There is an adjacent bunkhouse. Check ahead for opening hours in winter (closed November). Q♿🏮🏠♿♣P

Grog & Gruel 🅛

66 High Street, PH33 6AE (in pedestrianised area)
☎ (01397) 705078 ⊕ grogandgruel.co.uk
6 changing beers (sourced regionally) 🅗

The Grog & Gruel alehouse is busy all day every day with a mix of locals and tourists. A regular in the Guide since 1997, the pub has up to six handpumps often dispensing local and sometimes regional beers, making it a draw for the real ale connoisseur. The bar menu has imaginative and interesting food at affordable prices all day. In the evening the restaurant upstairs opens, offering a wider selection for hungry hill walkers. Open mic features on most Friday evenings. A former winner of local CAMRA Pub of the Year. ♿🏮♣≠🔥🚌🐕🎵🛜

Fortrose

Anderson

Union Street, IV10 8TD (corner of High St)
☎ (01381) 620236 ⊕ theanderson.co.uk
2 changing beers (sourced nationally; often Cromarty, Inveralmond) 🅗

A regular in The Good Beer Guide since 2005, the Anderson offers well-chosen ales – mostly local or regional – drawn from the 200-year-old cellar. The whisky lounge has a single cider handpump and more than 250 single malts. The restaurant also has a reputation for excellence and is a popular destination for foodies. Regular music, quiz and special food nights feature throughout the year. Nine bedrooms are available, with local attractions including the golf course and dolphin watching at Chanonry Point. Closed before Christmas – phone ahead to check.
Q♿♿🏠🏮♿♣🔥P🚌(26,26A)🐕🛜

Glencoe

Clachaig Inn 🅛

PH49 4HX (3 miles SE of village, off A82) NN12705668
☎ (01855) 811252 ⊕ clachaig.com
10 changing beers (sourced regionally; often Cairngorm, Orkney, River Leven) 🅗

The Clachaig is a must for outdoor enthusiasts and beer lovers alike, set in a remote location among the spectacular hills and scenery of Glencoe. Having worked up a hunger on the hills, a huge choice of well-kept beers and hearty grub will replenish your energy. There are also more than 400 whiskies and 130 gins to distract you. On cooler days, wood-burning stoves keep the three

bars and snugs warm. Beer festivals are held during the year and music hosted most weekend evenings.
♿🏠🏮🛏♿♣P🐕🛜

Glenmore

Pine Marten Bar & Scran

PH22 1QU (on ski road by Loch Morlich) NH974098
☎ (01479) 861253 ⊕ aviemoreski.co.uk
Cairngorm Trade Winds, Black Gold, Wildcat 🅗

Although it looks unassuming from the outside, this 'wee snug of a bar' has a welcoming wood-burning stove and a bar topped with three handpumps. The minimalist building is designed to emulate mountain refuges in Austria, Switzerland and Bavaria, and ice axes and skis decorate the walls along with quirky artefacts from across Europe. The kitchen serves some great grub, and there is also a shop, ski hire, and accommodation including glamping pods and a tree house. Live music plays most Friday and Saturday nights.
♿🏠🏮♿♣P🐕🛜

Inverness

Black Isle Bar 🅛

68 Church Street, IV1 1EN
☎ (01463) 229920 ⊕ blackislebar.com
Black Isle Yellowhammer, Red Kite; 4 changing beers (sourced locally; often Black Isle) 🅟

Popular right from the start, this bar opened in 2016, offering up to three real ales and 23 craft font beers. Two big screens show the eclectic beer menu, mostly from Black Isle but including some guests, with prices for pints, halves and thirds. The open-plan bar area offers a mix of seating. Upstairs, the secret garden utilises upcycled pallet tables and stools under a cover of reclaimed corrugated iron. Organic ingredients from the brewery farm are used in an interesting food menu, with pizzas the speciality. Q🏮🏠♿≠P🚌🐕🛜

Castle Tavern 🅛

1 View Place, IV2 4SA (top of Castle St)
☎ (01463) 718178 ⊕ castletavern.pub
6 changing beers (sourced regionally; often Cromarty, Isle of Skye, Windswept) 🅗

Just a short walk from town, the Castle Tavern is popular with tourists visiting the castle opposite and with locals who know their beer. Six handpumps offer an interesting rolling selection of beers, mostly from Scottish independents, and a changing cider. There is plenty of seating inside but the covered canopy area outside is always busy, even in winter, with panoramic views along the River Ness. Bar meals are available all day; the restaurant upstairs opens in the evening.
♿🏠🏮♿♣🔥P🚌🐕🛜

Clachnaharry Inn

17-19 High Street, IV3 8RB (on A862 Beauly road)
☎ (01463) 239806 ⊕ clachnaharryinn.co.uk
Fyne Ales Jarl; Harviestoun Bitter & Twisted; Inveralmond Ossian; 2 changing beers (sourced nationally; often Cairngorm) 🅗

The Clach has featured in the Guide for more than 35 years and is where many may have enjoyed their first pint of real ale. The 17th-century coaching inn offers a warm welcome to all, with an open fire most days. Food is available in both the bar area and the quieter restaurant. Quiz and music nights feature regularly. Outside, the occasional train rumbles by or boat using the Caledonian Canal. Beyond are stunning views of the Beauly Firth and Ben Wyvis, often snowcapped.
Q♿🏠🏮♿♣P🚌(28,28A)🐕🛜

Corriegarth 🅛

5-7 Heathmount Road, IV2 3JU (in Crown area)

☎ (01463) 242730 🌐 sites.google.com/view/
the-corriegarth/inicio

Caledonian Deuchars IPA; Cromarty Happy Chappy; 2 changing beers (sourced nationally) 🅗

The Corrie is in the quiet Crown area of Inverness, just five minutes from the town centre. The imposing red sandstone building was once a hotel and did a stint as a club for Navy and RAF officers. Two guest ales from the Punch list are on the bar nearly all the time in this busy and popular local. In the summer, there is a large area to sit outside. Six boutique en-suite rooms make it a great place to stay. Q🖰🏠🍽◑🛋⬅️🅿️🚫🐾🎵

King's Highway ✔

72-74 Church Street, IV1 1EN

☎ (01463) 251830

Caledonian Deuchars IPA; Fuller's London Pride; Greene King Abbot; Sharp's Doom Bar; 6 changing beers (sourced nationally) 🅗

Situated centrally, this Wetherspoon pub has offered good-value fare since 2001 and is now in its 12th year in the Guide. Up to 10 handpumps mainly feature Scottish beers, many of them local to the area. A popular meeting point, it is handy for the town's bus and train stations. Even when busy, you can always find a quiet place to sit and enjoy a pint, and there is now a decked area outside. Accommodation is available. Alcoholic drinks are served from 11am. 🖰🏠🍽◑🛋⬅️🚶🅿️🚫🎵

MacGregor's

109-113 Academy Street, IV1 1LX (corner of Friars Lane)

☎ (01463) 719629 🌐 macgregorsbars.com

2 changing beers (often Cromarty, Spey Valley, Swannay) 🅗

Crowdfunding allowed Blazin' Fiddles musician Bruce MacGregor's pub to become an instant hit on opening in 2017, offering an insight into Scottish history, culture, food and drink. Two handpumps and a font gantry feature beers from local breweries, alongside an extensive menu of bottled beers, gins and whiskies. A simple but elegant Scottish-themed food menu is served all day. Wood-burning stoves warm both the main bar and side whisky room. There is a patio area outside. Bruce is often in the bar playing his fiddle on a Sunday afternoon. 🖰◑🛋⬅️🅿️🚫

Number 27 🅛

27 Castle Street, IV2 3DU (opp castle)

☎ (01463) 832824 🌐 number27inverness.uk

4 changing beers (sourced regionally; often Windswept) 🅗

Opposite the castle, the entrance to the pub is on the corner, leading you into a bar area with a mix of seating, then on to a raised area towards the rear for dining. Four handpumps normally offer ales from the Windswept Brewery, with beers from other local breweries making an occasional appearance, alongside an extensive selection of keg and bottled beers. Food menus cater for both a quick pub lunch and a more substantial offering in the evening, including an all-day children's menu. 🖰◑⬅️🅿️🚫🎵

John o' Groats

Seaview Hotel 🅛

County Road, KW1 4YR (A99/A863 jct) ND380727

☎ (01955) 611220 🌐 seaviewjohnogroats.co.uk

John o' Groats Swelkie; 1 changing beer (sourced locally; often John o' Groats) 🅗

The family-run Seaview Hotel must be the most northerly pub on the UK mainland and is also the tap for John o' Groats Brewery, with two handpulls on the bar. Meals are served throughout the day. Accommodation is available in the hotel itself, the annexe and cottage over the road, and in pods with hammocks. The pub is a popular stop-off for End to Enders and the many visitors with John o' Groats on their bucket list. The surrounding area, including Duncansby Head, offers great views and walking. 🖰🏠◑🛋🅿️🚫🐾🎵

Mallaig

Steam Inn

Davies Brae, PH41 4PU (off top of Station Rd)

☎ (01687) 462002 🌐 steaminnmallaig.co.uk

2 changing beers (often Isle of Skye) 🅗

In summer, hanging baskets adorn the striking frontage of this pub. The bar has a wood-burner at one end and an open fire at the other for cooler days. The beer garden at the rear comes into its own in fine weather, particularly when the pub fills up because the Skye ferry docks or the Hogwarts Express arrives – both just a short walk away. An extensive food menu features locally caught seafood, bar food and children's options. 🖰🏠◑🛋⬅️🅿️🚫🎵

Nairn

Bandstand 🅛 ✔

Crescent Road, IV12 4NB (E end of town towards beach)

☎ (01667) 452341 🌐 braevalhotel.co.uk

5 changing beers (sourced nationally; often Cairngorm, Cromarty, Orkney) 🅗

Overlooking the green, with its bandstand and the Moray Firth beyond, the bar has five handpumps offering a great selection of local and regional Scottish beers, including the occasional English ale. The annual free beer festival in May is said to be the biggest independent event in the UK, with around 150 ales and ciders from all over the UK, accompanied by themed food and live music over three days. The restaurant offers good-value quality food. Music features at the weekend. CAMRA branch Pub of the Year 2020.
Q🖰🏠🍽◑🛋⬅️⬆️🅿️🚫🎵

Newtonmore

Glen Hotel 🅛

Main Street, PH20 1DD (S of village)

☎ (01540) 673203 🌐 theglenhotel.co.uk

4 changing beers (often Cairngorm, Caledonian, Cromarty) 🅗

The Glen was a trailblazer in the Highlands when it started serving real ale, and has appeared in the Guide for 19 years. With four handpumps offering both local and regional beers, it is an oasis for CAMRA members in the area. Good honest pub grub is served in the bar, restaurant and at dining tables outside. A handy stop-off for visitors to the Cairngorms National Park, Highland Wildlife Park and Folk Museum. Accommodation is available in eight rooms. Alcohol is served from 11am (12.30pm Sun). 🖰🏠◑🛋⬅️⬆️🅿️🚫

Plockton

Plockton Hotel ✔

41 Harbour Street, IV52 8TN NG80293343

☎ (01599) 544274 🌐 plocktonhotel.co.uk

5 changing beers (often Cromarty, Fyne Ales, Swannay) 🅗

Plockton was the setting for TV's Hamish Macbeth, which is a draw for visitors to this pretty village, many of whom

arrive by train on the picturesque Kyle Line. The bar proudly offers four handpumps dispensing both local and regional beers, which can be enjoyed on the terrace with views of the sea. The food menu features locally sourced seafood, beef and venison. A real ale and gin festival is held in May. Closed throughout January.
Q🔥❀🛏🍴♿P🚌📶

Plockton Inn [L] ✔

Innes Street, IV52 8TW NG802333
☎ (01599) 544222 🌐 plocktoninn.co.uk
2 changing beers (sourced locally; often Plockton) [H]
Set in a picture-postcard Highland village, this popular inn has been owned and run by a local family for many years. A regularly changing selection of real ales includes locally brewed beers from Plockton Brewery. Locally caught fish and shellfish take pride of place on the menu – the seafood platter includes fish smoked on the premises. Every Tuesday (and Thursday in summer) live music plays in the public bar. There is outdoor seating in the garden behind and tables at the front.
Q🔥❀🛏🍴♿⛺♣P🐾

Roy Bridge

Stronlossit Inn [L]

Main Street, PH31 4AG (on A86) NN27228117
☎ (01397) 712253 🌐 stronlossit.co.uk
3 changing beers (sourced regionally; often Cairngorm, Isle of Skye, Orkney) [H]
The location of the Stronlossit makes it attractive to those keen on the outdoors and, with the railway station just over the road, you can abandon the car and arrive by train from Fort William or London. The train can also take you for a day trip to Corrour, to walk around Loch Ossian. Up to four handpumps spoil real ale fans, with beers from varying Scottish breweries including the local Glen Spean. Great food is served all day, and it has rooms for all budgets. Q🔥❀🛏🍴♿⛺🚉🍏P🚌📶

Sligachan: Isle of Skye

Sligachan Hotel (Seumas' Bar) [L]

IV47 8SW (at A87 jct with A863) NG485298
☎ (01478) 650204 🌐 sligachan.co.uk
Cuillin Eagle Ale, Old Bridge, Black Face; 1 changing beer [H]
Enjoying a splendid setting between the Black Cuillin and the sparkling waters of Loch Sligachan and home to the Cuillin Brewery, the Sligachan Hotel has served mountaineers, walkers and lovers of the wild Highland scenery for nearly 180 years, and has been in the same family for the last century. The hotel opens from March to the end of October, with the larger Seumas' Bar open May to September, serving up to four ales in season, usually from Cuillin but sometimes from elsewhere. The bar also stocks over 370 Scottish malts, 90 of them on optics. 🔥❀🛏🍴♿⛺P🚌🐾📶

Stornoway: Isle of Lewis

Crown Inn (Harbour Bar) ✔

Castle Street, HS1 2BD
☎ (01851) 703734 🌐 crownhotelstornoway.com
2 changing beers (sourced nationally; often Caledonian, Inveralmond, Isle of Skye) [H]
The Harbour Bar is the public bar on the ground floor here with an improved entrance. The Harbour View Restaurant on the first floor also has its own entrance; other than being the eating area, it also has bar stools which would challenge some mountaineers! Both the upstairs and downstairs bars have two handpumps and have the same beers on, which include choices from Scotland and England. However, a testament to their popularity is that they do run out very quickly. 🔥🛏🍴♣P🚌

Strathcarron

Strathcarron Hotel

IV54 8YR (on A890 at head of Loch Carron) NG941421
☎ (01520) 722227 🌐 strathcarronhotel.com
2 changing beers (often Strathcarron) [H]
The Victorian railway hotel bar offers up to two ales, mainly from the nearby Strathcarron Brewery. Take your beer outside to one of the trestle tables and you may catch sight of the excursion train that chugs the spectacular Kyle Line from Inverness to Kyle of Lochalsh. The hotel is a popular destination for motorcyclists, and cyclists and walkers are all equally welcome.
Q🔥❀🛏🍴♿🚉♣P🚌(164) 📶

Ullapool

Morefield Motel [L]

North Road, IV26 2TQ (signed off A835)
☎ (01854) 612000 🌐 morefieldmotel.co.uk
3 changing beers (sourced locally) [H]
Although principally a restaurant, there is room at the bar to enjoy a beer and everyone is welcome. The three handpumps offer a selection of Scottish ales, boosted to 20 in late October during the popular annual beer and cider festival, with music in the evenings. Locally landed seafood is a speciality in the lounge and conservatory restaurants. The motel rooms are an ideal base for exploring the spectacular and dramatic west coast of Scotland. Q❀🛏🍴♿⛺♣P🚌🐾📶

Wick

Alexander Bain ✔

Market Place, KW1 4LP (in pedestrianised area just off High St)
☎ (01955) 609920
Caledonian Deuchars IPA; 2 changing beers (sourced nationally) [H]
This most northerly Wetherspoon in the UK opened in 2003, taking over the old Post Office. It was due to be sold in 2019, but received a reprieve. The large single-room bar has many side areas and quiet corners, and there is decking outside. The bar sports six handpumps, although only three are in operation, two in winter. Offering the chain's usual reasonably priced drinks and meals, the pub is popular with locals. Music groups play regularly. Alcoholic drinks are served from 11am.
Q🔥❀🍴♿⛺🚉P🚌📶

Sick note

Me and some of the fellers decided to cook up a batch of home brew and the instructions on the yeast said 'Add one packet and wait three days' so we added three packets and waited one day. Well, we drank all that brew right up the very next day. Never been sicker in my life. **American home brewer during Prohibition**

SCOTLAND

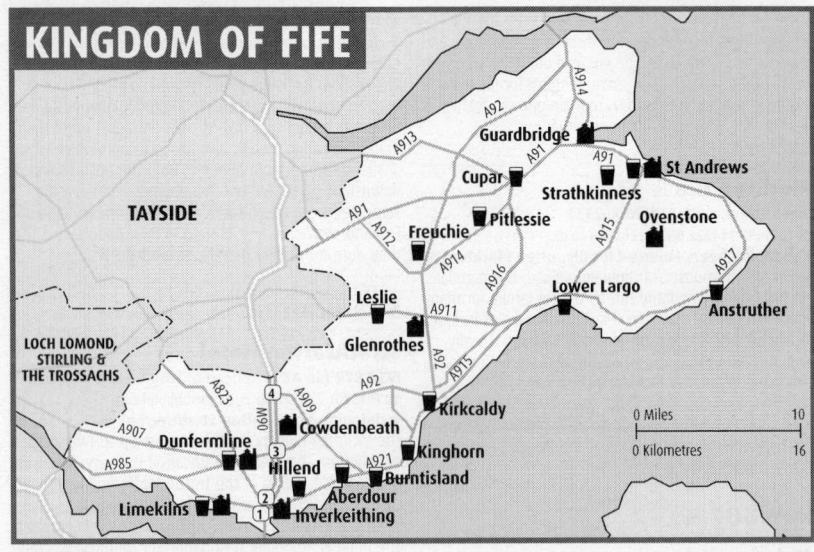

KINGDOM OF FIFE

Authority area covered: Fife UA

Aberdour

Foresters Arms
35 High Street, KY3 0SJ
☎ (01383) 861245 ⊕ theforestersarms.pub
3 changing beers (sourced nationally; often Adnams, Born, Robinsons) Ⓗ
This corner pub is only a few hundred yards from the railway station and Aberdour Castle. It sits in the middle of the village and is an ideal stop-off point for tourists and ramblers using the Fife coastal path. As you would expect from a pub right at the heart of the community, several weekly events are held, ranging from bingo to raffles to live music. You will also find a jukebox, pool table and live sporting events on a big screen.
🏵️♿🚲♣🚌(7) 🐾 📶

Anstruther

Boathouse ✅
28 Shore Street, KY10 3AQ
☎ (01333) 312105 ⊕ anstrutherboathouse.com
3 changing beers (sourced nationally; often Orkney, Timothy Taylor) Ⓗ
Situated in the picturesque East Neuk of Fife, this historic former coaching inn on the harbour-front is conveniently located for tourists, sailors and coastal path ramblers. These multi-purpose premises comprise a spacious bar, an adjoining bistro and an attractive beer garden at the rear. The bar hosts live music, TVs, sports and other entertainment. The Scottish Fisheries Museum is within walking distance. Accommodation is in three rooms accessed by a separate dedicated entrance adjacent to the bar and restaurant. 🛏️🏵️🍽️◖🅰♣🅿🚌(X60,95)🐾 📶

Dreel Tavern ✅
16 High Street, KY10 3DL
☎ (01333) 279238 ⊕ dreeltavern.co.uk
3 changing beers (sourced nationally; often Adnams, Redcastle, Stewart) Ⓗ
Anstruther was founded as a fishing village, but these days the harbour is mostly used by small yachts and leisure craft. One of the town's most historic buildings, the Dreel's history goes back to at least the early 18th century. A traditional pub, popular with locals, walkers

and visitors to the area, it has an open fire in winter adding to the cosy atmosphere. At the rear is a sunny beer garden overlooking the Dreel Burn, from which the pub takes its name. Q🛏️🏵️♿◖♣🚌(95,X60)🐾 📶

Burntisland

Sands Hotel Ⓛ
Kinghorn Road, KY3 9JX
☎ (01592) 872230 ⊕ burntislandsands.co.uk
2 changing beers (sourced regionally; often Beath) Ⓗ
A warm welcome awaits at this family-run hotel by the seafront in this picturesque coastal town. Burntisland is home to the second oldest Highland Games in the world, held at the end of July, traditionally the start of the Fife/Glasgow Fair fortnight. The hotel has a choice of restaurants and is renowned for its excellent high teas – book ahead to avoid disappointment. 🏵️🍽️◖🅿🚌

Cupar

Boudingait
43 Bonnygate, KY15 4BU
☎ (01334) 208310 ⊕ theboudingaitcupar.co.uk
2 changing beers (sourced nationally) Ⓗ
This family- and dog-friendly pub is at the centre of this old market town, and is known for its locally sourced food, served seven days a week. The bar can be busy at the weekend, especially when the local farmers' market comes to town. Weekly activities ranging from live music to quizzes are enjoyed by all. Q🛏️◖♿🚲🚌🐾 📶

REAL ALE BREWERIES

Beath Cowdenbeath
Brew Shed Limekilns
Coul Glenrothes
Eden Mill Guardbridge (brewing suspended)
Inner Bay Inverkeithing
Ovenstone 109 Ovenstone
SaltRock Dunfermline (NEW)
Seven Kings Dunfermline
St Andrews Brewing St Andrews

Dunfermline

Commercial Inn

13 Douglas Street, KY12 7EB

☎ 07500 119408

Caledonian Deuchars IPA; Inveralmond Ossian; Orkney Dark Island; Stewart 80/-; 2 changing beers (sourced nationally; often Harviestoun, Orkney) Ⓗ

Located at the heart of the town centre, close to the main retail area, the pub attracts an eclectic clientele and gets busy on match days. Formerly a hotel, this 19th-century listed building is full of character and retains the high ceilings and decorative cornices of that period. A spiral staircase leads down to the lower levels.

◑≋(Town)🖵❀🛜

East Port ✓

7 East Port, KY12 7JG

☎ (01383) 736678

4 changing beers (sourced nationally; often Born, Stewart, Timothy Taylor) Ⓗ

On the High Street, just a short distance from the main shopping area, this town-centre pub is worth a visit when out and about in Dunfermline. A sports bar with plasma screens showing sport from football to golf, it is also a great place to relax with a beer in one of the many cosy booths. The interior features wood panelling and a wooden bar and gantry. Soft background music usually plays. ❀&≋(Town)🖵🛜

Freuchie

Albert Tavern

2 High Street, KY15 7EX

☎ 07876 178863 ⊕ alberttavern.wixsite.com/albert

5 changing beers (sourced nationally; often Fuzzy Duck, Stewart) Ⓗ

This welcoming 18th-century coach house is the heart and soul of the village, and has the feel of an old English inn with its low-beamed ceiling and cosy atmosphere. The two-roomed interior includes a lounge with a TV and the bar with five handpumps. Ales come from throughout the UK, and three real ciders are also on the bar. The pub hosts a number of community events, from the famous pie night to the quarterly meeting of the malt whisky society. Q❀♣●🖵🛜

Hillend

Hillend Tavern ✓

37 Main Street, KY11 9ND

☎ (01383) 415391 ⊕ hillendtavern.co.uk

4 changing beers (sourced nationally; often Greene King, Stewart, Timothy Taylor) Ⓗ

Located near Dalgety Bay, this is a traditional village pub with cosy coal fires, a beer garden and real ales, all adding to the friendly and welcoming atmosphere. It has a traditional bar, a spacious recently refurbished room at the rear and a large covered area outside. The Tav, as it is known, is community-focused and hosts many village events. Live music nights and two quiz nights each month are well attended. ➷❀≋♣🖵(7,87)❀🛜

Kinghorn

Crown Tavern ✓

55-57 High Street, KY3 9UW

☎ (01592) 891363

2 changing beers (sourced nationally; often Elland, Sharp's) Ⓐ

Affectionately known as the Middle Bar by locals, this two-roomed venue is right at the centre of a pleasant coastal village, only a short walk from the train station. Very much a community pub, it is a sports bar at heart, with a large screen and a number of smaller screens showing sports. Two ales are served from traditional Scottish tall founts, as well as three real ciders. ≋♣●🖵(7)❀🛜

Kirkcaldy

Betty Nicols

297 High Street, KY1 1JL

☎ (01592) 591408

Fyne Ales Jarl; 1 changing beer (sourced regionally) Ⓗ

Betty Nicols has long been one of Kirkcaldy's most popular places to enjoy a drink in a relaxed and comfortable atmosphere. This traditional bar attracts a varied clientele due to its location on the High Street. Live music nights are popular, as is the quiz which is held twice a month on a Thursday night. The modern bistro serves lunchtime meals and afternoon teas (booking essential). ➷◑&≋🖵❀🛜

Harbour Bar

471-475 High Street, KY1 2SN

☎ (01592) 264270

6 changing beers (sourced nationally; often Fyne Ales, Mallinsons, Oakham) Ⓗ

On the edge of the town's old harbour, a short distance from the main shopping area, this 19th-century building was originally a ship chandler, and converted to a pub in 1924. This Grade C-listed building retains its jug bar at the entrance, and the main bar on the right retains its original mirrored back gantry with fluted pilasters, bar counter and half-height panelled walls, earning the bar a place in Scotland's True Heritage Pubs. Q●🖵(X60)❀

Leslie

Burns Tavern

184 High Street, KY6 3DB

☎ (01592) 741345

Timothy Taylor Landlord; 1 changing beer (sourced nationally; often Stewart) Ⓗ

Located in this former paper-making town, this traditional tavern has a public bar and a lounge. The main bar is divided into two sections – the lower level with the main bar and the higher area with a pool table. The Burns is the hub of the community, where you can sit back, relax and enjoy your pint of Landlord while watching sporting events on numerous TVs. Q❀🚃Å♣P🖵(39A)❀

Limekilns

Bruce Arms Ⓛ

2 Main Street, KY11 3HL

☎ (01383) 872259 ⊕ brucearmslimekilns.co.uk

2 changing beers (sourced nationally; often Inner Bay) Ⓗ

An old settlement dating back to the 14th century, Limekilns is a scenic and historic village on the Fife Coastal Path. The Bruce is a warm and welcoming public house, with stunning views across the Firth of Forth to admire while enjoying a bite to eat or a relaxed pint. A champion of LocAle, a beer or two from local brewery Inner Bay can usually be found on the bar. ➷❀◑♣P🖵❀🛜

Ship Inn Ⓛ

Halketts Hall, KY11 3HJ

☎ (01383) 872247

3 changing beers (sourced nationally; often Brewshed, Greene King) ⊞
A wee gem on the way out of Limekilns, which in its early days was a fishing village. The pub sits on the River Forth, with views of the three bridges spanning the water. The Ship Inn today is a family-run business and prides itself on a warm, relaxed atmosphere. Numerous artefacts relating to ships and shipping adorn the interior, including the engine order telegraph that takes pride of place on the bar. Q ☞ ❀ ◑ P 🖴 (6) ❀

Lower Largo

Railway Inn ⑃
1 Station Wynd, KY8 6BU
☎ (01333) 320239 ⊕ railwayinnlargo.co.uk
5 changing beers (sourced regionally; often Born, Coul, Stewart) ⊞
The Railway is a friendly and traditional village public house, established since 1749, located in a picturesque village. It rests in the shadow of the old railway viaduct, with views of Largo harbour. A little gem, the small two-roomed interior is warmed by a cosy real fire. A champion of LocAle, you can usually find a beer from a Fife brewery on one of the five handpulls.
Q ☞ ❀ 🖴 (95) ❀ 📶

Pitlessie

Pitlessie Inn & Pantry
Cupar Road, KY15 7SU
☎ (01337) 830595 ⊕ pitlessievillageinn.com
1 changing beer (sourced nationally) ⊞
A traditional old coaching inn, on the main road between Cupar and Glenrothes, decorated with pictures of the maltings that was once opposite. A family-run bar, restaurant and pantry, right at the heart of the community, it offers a relaxed dining experience and locally sourced food. Coffee and tea are served, and produce from the surrounding area. 🝖◑P🖴

St Andrews

Central Bar ✅
77 Market Street, KY16 9NU
☎ (01334) 478296 ⊕ centralbar-standrews.co.uk
6 changing beers (sourced nationally) ⊞
The pub is in the busy cobbled Market Square of this historic university town. It has a Victorian-style interior with an island bar, ornate ceiling and a fine collection of historic brewery mirrors. Customers are a mix of locals, tourists, students and golfers. A wide selection of real ales is available, mainly from Scottish breweries. Enjoy a drink and watch life go by in the small seating area at the front of the building. ☞ ❀ ◑ 🖴 ❀ 📶

Criterion ⑃ ✅
99 South Street, KY16 9QW
☎ (01334) 474543 ⊕ criterionstandrews.co.uk
5 changing beers (sourced nationally; often Caledonian, Coul, Stewart) ⊞
This small establishment dates from 1874, and is one of the few remaining family-run pubs in the area. On one of the main shopping streets, it is popular with locals, tourists, students and golfers. A locally sourced menu is served, with the famous Cri Pies available all day. In addition to the five cask ales, a large selection of whiskies and gins is stocked. ☞ ❀ ◑ 🖴 ❀ 📶

Whey Pat Tavern ✅
1 Bridge Street, KY16 9EX
☎ (01334) 477740
Greene King IPA; 4 changing beers (often Broughton, Inveralmond, Timothy Taylor) ⊞
The birthplace of the Kingdom of Fife Branch of CAMRA, this is a busy corner pub adjacent to the historic West Port and handy for the bus station. It is popular with the usual mix of locals, tourists, students and golfers found in the town. The building is on two levels, with a lively public bar at the front and a spacious lounge to the rear. ❀ ◑ & ♣ 🖴 ❀ 📶

Strathkinness

Tavern
4 High road, KY16 9RS
☎ (01334) 850085 ⊕ strathkinnesstavern.co.uk
2 changing beers (sourced nationally; often Cromarty, Stewart) ⊞
From its outdoor seating area The Tavern has wonderful views over the Eden Estuary, and north to the Grampian Mountains. Owned and run by the Wilkie family, it is renowned for its friendly hosts, excellent food and varying beer selection. Lunches and evening meals are served in the bar and restaurant, and traditional pub games played in the cosy lounge.
Q ☞ ❀ ◑ ▲ ♣ P 🖴 (64,64A) 📶

What is real ale?

Real ale is also known as cask-conditioned beer or simply cask beer. In the brewery, the beer is neither filtered nor pasteurised. It still contains sufficient yeast and sugar for it to continue to ferment and mature in the cask. Once it has reached the pub cellar, it has to be laid down for maturation to continue, and for yeast and protein to settle at the bottom of the cask. Some real ale also has extra hops added as the cask is filled, a process known as 'dry hopping' for increased flavour and aroma. Cask beer is best served at a cellar temperature of 11–12 degrees C, although some stronger ales can benefit from being served a little warmer. Each cask has two holes, in one of which a tap is inserted and is connected to tubes or 'lines' that enable the beer to be drawn to the bar. The other hole, on top of the cask, enables some carbon dioxide produced during secondary fermentation to escape. It is vital that some gas, which gives the beer its natural sparkle or condition, is kept within the cask: the escape of gas is controlled by inserting porous wooden pegs called spiles into the spile hole. Real ale is a living product and must be consumed within three or four days of a cask being tapped as oxidation develops.

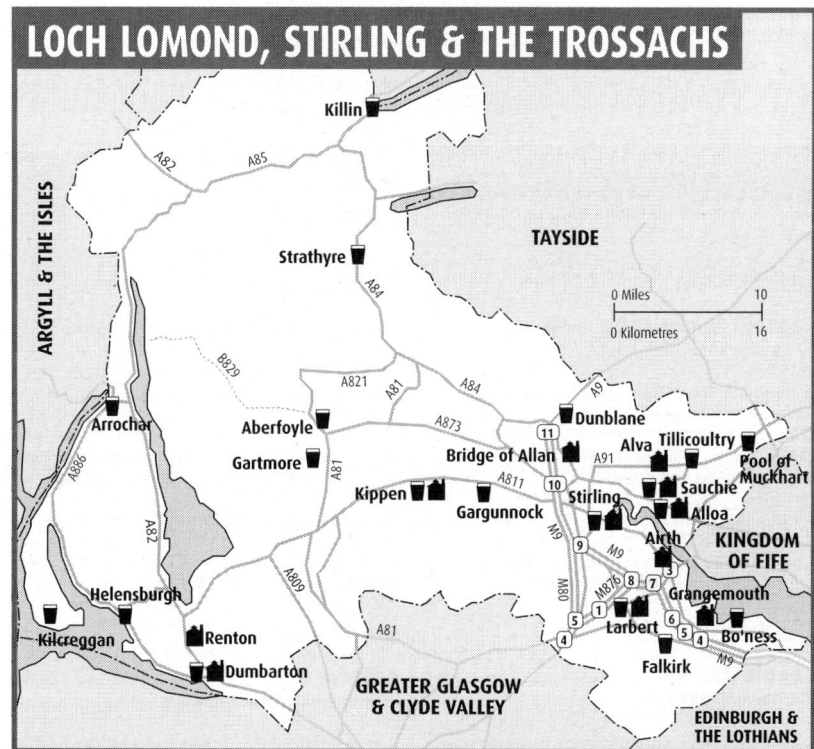

Aberfoyle

Forth Inn ✪

Main Street, FK8 3UQ

☎ (01877) 382372 ⊕ forthinn.com

Harviestoun Schiehallion; 3 changing beers (sourced regionally; often Belhaven, Cairngorm, Fallen) Ⓗ
This 100-year-old inn is by the River Forth within the Trossachs National Park. The cosy wood-panelled bar is decorated with historic photographs of the area and is a magnet for tourists and locals alike. The pub proudly serves only Scottish ales on up to four handpumps (just one in January and February), with third-pint taster glasses available. The restaurant offers wholesome food featuring locally sourced produce. There is a separate dining room and a baronial dining hall. Accommodation is in six en-suite bedrooms.
Q ➺ ✿ ⇔ ◑ & Å ♣ P ➡ (X10A) ❁

Alloa

Bobbing John ✪

46 Drysdale Street, FK10 1JL

☎ (01259) 222590

Caledonian Deuchars IPA; Greene King Abbot; Sharp's Doom Bar; 3 changing beers (sourced regionally; often Harviestoun, Hybrid, Williams Bros) Ⓗ
The pub is situated in a traditional three-storey sandstone building, purpose-built in 1895 for the Alloa Co-operative Society. It commemorates locally born John Erskine, who developed the town as a coal-mining centre, and was nicknamed Bobbing John. Much of the building's original stonework has been retained and a Victorian shopfront reintroduced. Alcoholic drinks are served from 11am. Q ➺ ✿ ◑ & ⇌ ♣ ➡ ☗

Arrochar

Village Inn ✪

Shore Road, G83 7AX (down A814 from A83 jct)

☎ (01301) 702279 ⊕ villageinnarrochar.co.uk

5 changing beers (sourced nationally; often Fallen, Fyne Ales, Loch Lomond) Ⓗ
A picturesque inn, built in 1827 as the local manse, offering views over Loch Long to the Arrochar Alps. The bar and restaurant are decorated in a traditional Scottish country style. Five handpumps offer ales from a variety of Scottish breweries. The large front lawn is a pleasant spot to enjoy a beer overlooking the loch. The pub is popular with locals, day trippers, hill walkers and weekending tourists staying at the inn.
➺ ✿ ⇔ ◑ & Å ♣ P ➡ (926,976) ❁ ☍

Bo'ness

Corbie Inn

84 Corbiehall, EH51 0AS

☎ (01506) 825307 ⊕ corbieinn.co.uk

6 changing beers (sourced regionally; often Hybrid, Strathbraan, Tryst) ⊞
Up to six ales are available, mainly from Scottish breweries plus a few from England. The inn has a large lounge area serving bar lunches and meals and, outside, a large covered beer garden with a pizza oven. Very much a community pub, the Corbie is involved with local charities and supports the Bo'ness Real Ale Society festival. Handy for the Bo'ness & Kinneil Railway, Bo'ness Motor Museum and the Hippodrome, Scotland's oldest purpose-built picture house. Q ☕ 🕸 ◑ ▮ 🚃 ░

Dumbarton

Captain James Lang ⍁ ✅
97-99 High Street, G82 1LF
☎ (01389) 742112
Greene King Abbot; 4 changing beers (sourced nationally; often Loch Lomond) ⊞
There are few pubs in the Glasgow area that boast a beer garden, but this well-designed Wetherspoon features a large outdoor area overlooking the River Leven. It was converted from a Woolworths store and has a light, open layout with a variety of seating options. It is named after the renowned captain of the paddle steamer Leven, which was built in the town. Frequent trains and buses serve the area. ☕ 🕸 ◑ & ⇌ (Central) 🚃 ░

Dunblane

Tappit Hen ✅
Kirk Street, FK15 0AL
☎ (01786) 825226 ⊕ thetappithen-dunblane.co.uk
Greene King IPA; 3 changing beers (sourced regionally; often Broughton, Inveralmond, Kelburn) ⊞
Taking its name from a type of Scottish pewter drinking vessel, this is a traditional one-room pub with a friendly atmosphere and knowledgeable staff. Refurbished in 2019 to an excellent standard, it is opposite one of Scotland's oldest cathedrals. The three guest beer pumps serve a regularly changing choice of ales. It holds charity and community events, and a real ale festival once or twice a year. The railway station and car parking are both close by. ☕ ⇌ 🚃 ░ ░

Falkirk

Wheatsheaf Inn ✅
16 Baxters Wynd, FK1 1PF
☎ (01324) 638282 ⊕ wheatsheaffalkirk.co.uk
Caledonian Deuchars IPA; 3 changing beers (sourced nationally; often Cromarty, Hybrid, Orkney) ⊞
Falkirk's oldest public house, dating from the late 18th century, can be found off the High Street via one of the vennels. Retaining much of its original character, the wood-panelled bar is furnished in traditional style with plenty of interesting features from the past. Guest beers come from microbreweries in Scotland and England, with two on offer midweek and three at the weekend. Outside, there is a small secluded beer garden at the rear. 🕸 ⇌ 🚃 ░ ░

Gargunnock

Gargunnock Inn
8 Main Street, FK8 3BW
☎ (01786) 860333 ⊕ gargunnockinn.co.uk
2 changing beers (sourced nationally) ⊞
This 18th-century building has been extensively modernised to create a roomy yet cosy pub/restaurant. The bar room has original features, comfortable seating

and two wood-burning stoves in winter. There are numerous separate dining areas. An extensive menu of quality food (notably chicken with haggis and Aberdeen Angus steaks) is served throughout. There is just one bar, with two handpumps serving at least one Scottish ale. The pub hosts an annual beer festival on the second Sunday in August. Popular local walks abound.
Q ☕ 🕸 ◑ & ♣ ▮ 🚃 (X10) ░ ░

Gartmore

Black Bull Hub & Pub
Main Street, FK8 3RW
☎ (01877) 382054 ⊕ blackbullgartmore.com
Harviestoun Schiehallion; Morland Old Speckled Hen ⊞
The Black Bull is now owned by the community. The family- and dog-friendly establishment is now a village pub, hotel and local hub. The fine old building, largely unspoilt and comprising a warren of small rooms, has a cosy bar with a real fire, two dining rooms and a games room. It is mainly staffed by enthusiastic and keen volunteers, supported by a chef and cellarman. Pleasantly furnished bedrooms are available. A free shuttle bus service to and from two local campsites and Aberfoyle and Buchlyvie is available on request.
Q ☕ 🕸 ◑ ◑ ▲ ♣ ▮ 🚃 (X10A) ░ ░

Helensburgh

Ashton
74 West Princes Street, G84 8UG
☎ (01436) 675900
Stewart Pentland IPA; 2 changing beers (sourced nationally) ⊞
A warm welcome awaits at this genuine local. The bar has been tastefully modernised and decorated with a nautical theme while retaining its original charm. There is a small room for playing darts. A changing selection of ales from Scottish microbreweries is complemented by quality English beers. Live music is a regular Saturday night feature. ⇌ (Central) ♣ 🚃 (1B,316) ░ ░

Henry Bell ✅
19-29 James Street, G84 8AS
☎ (01436) 863060
Greene King Abbot; changing beers (sourced nationally; often Loch Lomond) ⊞
Close to the recently revamped town centre and esplanade, this sympathetic Wetherspoon conversion of an old furniture showroom has now established itself as an important real ale outlet in the area, offering a wide range of ales from across Britain. It is a busy and popular venue both with locals and visitors. The walls are adorned with TVs in homage to Helensburgh-born John Logie Baird and the decor is in the style of Charles Rennie Mackintosh. Q ☕ 🕸 ◑ & ⇌ (Central) 🚃 (1B,316) ░

Kilcreggan

Creggans
Princes Terrace, Shore Road, G84 0JJ
☎ (01436) 842700
2 changing beers (sourced nationally; often Fyne Ales, Morland) ⊞
Ideally placed opposite the Gourock ferry pier, the front patio offers fine views of the Firth of Clyde. The single-room bar has a wooden floor and a mix of tables and chairs, with a pool table and sports TV. Live music is hosted from time to time. Two beers are generally available – one national brand, the other sourced locally.
🕸 ◑ & 🚃 (316) ░ ░

Killin

Courie Inn

Main Street, FK21 8UT
☎ (01567) 831000 ⊕ thecourieinn.com
1 changing beer (sourced locally; often Fallen, Strathbraan) ⑭

A cosy wee family-owned bar in a lovely village, just up the road from the picturesque Falls of Dochart. It is attached to a bistro-style café serving excellent locally sourced food, and is popular with regulars and tourists alike. Decorated in a contemporary style, it has a relaxed, comfortable atmosphere. One handpump offers ales mainly from Fallen Brewery. Accommodation is available. Winter opening times vary so phone ahead to check. ⚄⬤🚌

Kippen

Cross Keys

Main Street, FK8 3DN
☎ (01786) 870293 ⊕ kippencrosskeys.com
House beer (by Fallen); 2 changing beers (sourced locally; often Fallen) ⑭

Attractive old coaching inn with a rustic feel – one of the oldest of its kind in Stirlingshire. A locals' pub with a traditional feel, it has low ceilings, wood-panelled walls and a wooden floor. Log fires warm the bar in winter and the beer garden has great views in summer. It is popular with walkers, cyclists, golfers and anglers. Ideal as a stopover whether travelling north or south, it is near Loch Lomond & the Trossachs National Park, with Stirling close by. Q🕭⊛⬤⬤🅟🚌(X10)🐾🕈

Larbert

Station Hotel ✅

2 Foundry Loan, FK5 4AW
☎ (01324) 557186 ⊕ stationhotellarbert.com
5 changing beers (sourced nationally; often Black Iris, Mallinsons, Titanic) ⑭

A popular local next to the railway station and on regular bus routes. Three to five cask ales are usually on offer and efforts are made to provide a variety of local, regional and national ales. It has a cosy lounge area and a large enclosed beer garden. Large-screen TVs show sporting events. The pub is a supporter of CAMRA's Larbert Real Ale Festival in nearby Dobbie Hall in the spring. It prides itself on the help it gives to a number of community groups. ⊛⬤⬤🅟🚌

Pool of Muckhart

Inn at Muckhart

FK14 7JN
☎ (01259) 781324 ⊕ theinnatmuckhart.com
Devon Original (70/-), Pride ⑭

Single-storey former coaching inn in a picturesque rural village on the south-east edge of the Ochil Hills. It has a friendly atmosphere with low ceilings, exposed timbers and a welcoming open fire. There is a beer garden to the rear. The restaurant produces good food, attracting locals on winter weekends and tourists throughout the summer. Devon ales are brewed at the inn's sister pub, the Mansfield Arms in Sauchie. Q⊛⬤⬤🅟🚌🐾

Sauchie

Mansfield Arms

7 Main Street, FK10 3JR
☎ (01259) 722020 ⊕ devonales.com
Devon Original (70/-), Pride ⑭

A traditional two-bar pub and the oldest operating microbrewery in the county, it brews four Devon ales which are dispensed from two handpumps. Owned and run by the family, it is situated within an ex-mining community. The bar is popular with the locals who enjoy lively banter, while families come to enjoy the food served in the comfortable lounge. Both beer and meals are excellent value for money. The pub is on the Stirling via Alloa circular bus route. 🕭⬤🅟🚌🐾🕈

Stirling

Birds & Bees

Easter Cornton Road, FK9 5PB (off Causewayhead Rd)
☎ (01786) 473663 ⊕ thebirdsandthebees-stirling.com
3 changing beers (sourced regionally; often Fallen, Inveralmond, Williams Bros) ⑭

A welcoming converted rustic farmstead, located between the historic Wallace Monument and Stirling Castle, in a residential area on the northern outskirts. An award-winning gastropub, it serves locally sourced food. Three handpumps offer a variety of quality Scottish real ales. Outside, there are two large, well-maintained beer gardens, with a barbecue area in the courtyard. This popular pub attracts a good mix of regulars and tourists. ⊛⬤⬤🅟🚌🐾

Settle Inn

91 St Marys Wynd, FK8 1BU
3 changing beers (sourced nationally; often Castle Rock, Oakham, Titanic) ⑭

Warm, friendly and atmospheric inn frequented by a mix of locals, students and tourists. Situated on a hill descending from Stirling Castle, it was built in 1733 and is the oldest pub in the city. There is music on Monday, Wednesday, Friday and Saturday evenings, and a quiz on Sunday. The pub hosts an annual beer festival. 🕭🚄🐾🚌🐾🕈

Strathyre

White Stag

Main Street, FK18 8NA
☎ (01877) 384333 ⊕ thewhitestag.co.uk
3 changing beers (sourced nationally; often Fallen, Fyne Ales, Strathbraan) ⑭

Recently renovated, this cosy pub serves meals in its bar and bistro, all made with local produce. The beers are mainly Scottish, with a few from England. Dogs and children are welcome in the bar. Hill walking, fishing, golf and watersports opportunities are all close at hand, and Stirling, Callander and the Trossachs are within easy travelling distance. Accommodation is available on-site. Opening hours are reduced in winter – check before setting out. Q🕭⊛⬤⬤🅐🐾🅟🚌🐾🕈

Tillicoultry

Royal Arms

2 High Street, FK13 6AE
☎ (01259) 753037
3 changing beers (sourced nationally; often Morland, Stewart, Timothy Taylor) ⑭

This unpretentious, drinks-only pub continues to thrive under an enthusiastic owner. The bar caters mainly for local trade, with a dartboard, large sports TVs and a fruit machine. It is furnished with bar stools and comfortable seating, and warmed by a log-burner in the Victorian fireplace. A quieter side room with service via a small counter is ideal for families. Three handpumps are in use, dispensing changing beers. The pub is well served by regular bus routes to Stirling and Alloa. 🕭⊛🐾🚌🐾🕈

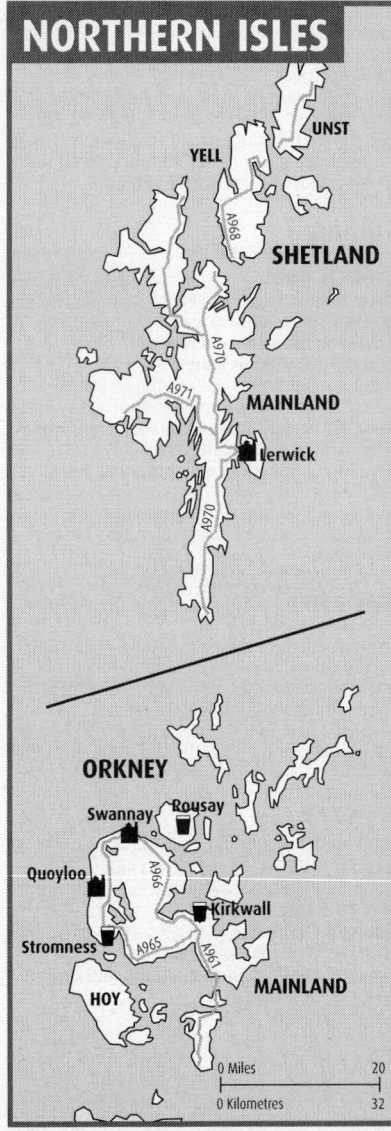

NORTHERN ISLES

Swannay Scapa Special Ⓗ

Overlooking Kirkwall harbour, the Ayre dates back to 1791 in parts and was at one time a temperance hotel. There are plenty of comfortable seats in the lounge to relax with a pint after a day exploring local visitor attractions. Meals are served lunchtimes and evenings featuring Orkney beef, fish and other local produce. A new conservatory is used for dining (booking advised for meals). Close to the bus station and ferries to the outer isles of Orkney. 🏠◑ᵱ&Å♣P🛏🛜

Helgi's Bar
14 Harbour Street, KW15 1LE (by harbour)
☎ (01856) 879293 ⊕ helgis.co.uk
Swannay Scapa Special; 2 changing beers (sourced locally; often Swannay) Ⓗ
Converted from a former shipping office, this small, smart bar has the look of a modern café with wood panelling and a floor of local stone. There is always one dark beer available. Special nights where food is matched with ales are a highlight. Regular music sessions and a weekly Thursday quiz night are also hosted. Set on the harbour front where seafood is landed daily, this is a handy place to fill in time before island hopping on the many ferries to outlying parts. A former local CAMRA Pub of the Year. No under-18s. ◑ᵱ&Å🛏🛜

Skippers Bar
Bridge Street, KW15 1LE (corner of Harbour Street)
☎ (01856) 872232 ⊕ kirkwallhotel.com
Swannay Scapa Special Ⓗ
A vibrant, busy bar, especially in the evenings, with a mainly youngish clientele. It is part of the Kirkwall Hotel, which overlooks the harbour. It's a smart, modern hotel, which also has a large lounge area, often hosting functions and wedding parties. Both the lounge and Skippers Bar serve real ale and you can move between the two via a connecting corridor. 🏠◑♣❀🛜

St Ola Hotel
Harbour Street, KW15 1LE
☎ (01856) 875090 ⊕ stolahotel.co.uk
Swannay Scapa Special; 1 changing beer (sourced locally; often Swannay) Ⓗ
Built overlooking the harbour on the site of the Inns of Sinclair dating back to the 14th century, the Ola is a short walk from all of Kirkwall's attractions. It has a traditional public bar complete with a roaring fire in winter and a larger lounge to the rear where food is served. Ales are available in both bars along with an extensive range of whiskies. A music session is held on the last Sunday afternoon of the month. A former joint local CAMRA Pub of the Year. 🏵🏠◑ᵱ&Å♣🛏❀🛜

Rousay: Orkney

Taversoe
Frotoft, KW17 2PT (2 miles W of ferry) HY405273
☎ (01856) 821325 ⊕ taversoehotel.co.uk
1 changing beer (often Swannay)
A little gem on the island of Rousay, run almost single-handedly by the owner. It offers an enticing selection of reasonably priced home-cooked food including Orkney beef and locally caught seafood. The stunning views of the sea over the Eynhallow Sound from the dining area is worth the trip in itself. There is a meet-and-greet from

Kirkwall: Orkney

Auld Motor Hoose
26 Junction Road, KW15 1AB
☎ (01856) 871422 ⊕ auldmotorhoose.co.uk
Swannay Scapa Special Ⓗ
A friendly motor-themed pub with a single bar room, featuring lots of motoring memorabilia and with car parts scattered throughout. The jukebox tends to blast out rock classics. There is regular live music, mainly at weekends, and the pub is one of the venues for the Orkney Rock Festival. Outside, the patio has a smoking area. It is the sister bar to the Torvhaug in Bridge Street and convenient for the bus station. Two-times local CAMRA Pub of the Year. 🏵&Å♣🛏(X1)❀🛜

Ayre Hotel
Ayre Road, KW15 1QX
☎ (01856) 873001 ⊕ ayrehotel.co.uk

REAL ALE BREWERIES
Lerwick ✦ Lerwick: Shetland
Orkney ✦ Quoyloo: Orkney
Swannay Orkney: Swannay

the Tingwall ferry, otherwise the inn is around a two-mile walk. Rousay, dubbed the Egypt of the North, has more than 160 archaeological sites. B&B accommodation is in four en-suite rooms. Q ☼ ❀ ✇ ◑ ⅃ ⅄ AP ☺ ☎

Stromness: Orkney

Ferry Inn

10 John Street, KW16 3AD (across from ferry terminal)
☎ (01856) 850280 ⊕ ferryinn.com

Swannay Scapa Special; 2 changing beers (sourced locally; often Orkney, Swannay) ⊞

An easy walk from the harbour front, the Ferry is handy for buses to Kirkwall and the mainland ferry from Scrabster. It is popular with locals and visitors, including divers who come to Orkney to explore the sunken German fleet at Scapa Flow. Attractions nearby include the Ring of Brodgar and Skara Brae village. Annual folk and blues festivals are held, with a marquee erected outside complete with an ale pump. A previous local CAMRA Pub of the Year winner. ❀✇◑▲♣P☒☺☎

Ferry Inn, Stromness: Orkney (Photo: Tom Bastin/Flickr CC BY 2.0)

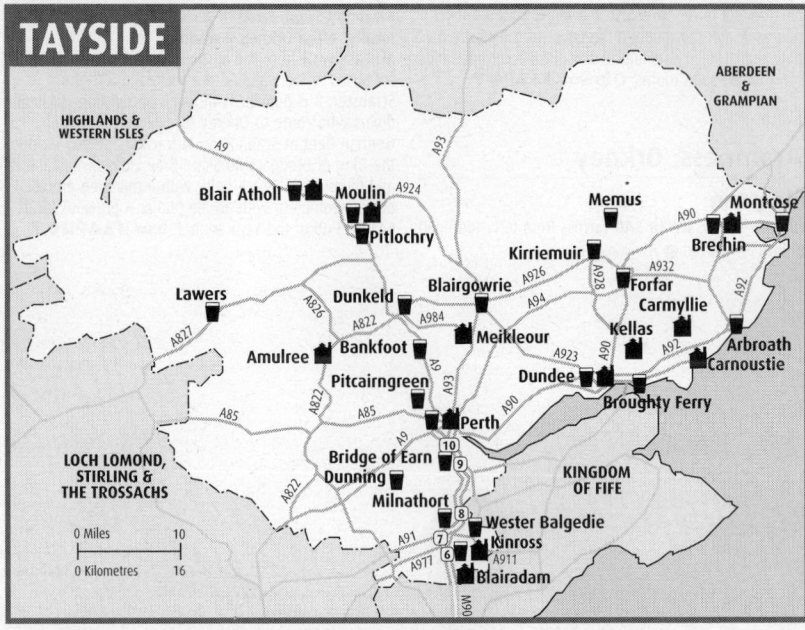

TAYSIDE

Authority areas covered: Angus UA, City of Dundee UA, Perth & Kinross UA

Arbroath

Corn Exchange ✔

14 Olympic Centre, Market Place, DD11 1HR
☎ (01241) 432430

Caledonian Deuchars IPA; Greene King Abbot; Sharp's Doom Bar; 3 changing beers (sourced nationally) Ⓗ

Located just off the High Street, this Wetherspoon is in what used to be a corn exchange in the 19th century. Although it is largely open plan there are a number of booths providing some privacy. A varied selection of real ales is always on offer, with alcoholic drinks served from 11am. Boat trips offering fishing or a visit to the 200-year-old Bell Rock lighthouse are available from the nearby harbour. ⭐😃🍽️&≢🅿️♿🎵

Bankfoot

Bankfoot Inn Ⓛ

Main Street, PH1 4AB
☎ (01738) 787243

2 changing beers (sourced regionally; often Cromarty, MòR Beers, Strathbraan) Ⓗ

Real ale and a commitment to local breweries are features of this pub. It comprises a public bar, small lounge and adjoining restaurant, all warmed by two real fires in winter. Good food is available, with fish & chips a highlight either to eat inside or take away. There is a large whisky selection. Outdoor seating at the front of the pub catches the sun on fine days. ⭐😃🍽️🅿️(23,27)♿🎵

Blair Atholl

Atholl Arms Hotel Ⓛ

PH18 5SG
☎ (01796) 481205 ⊕ athollarmshotel.co.uk

Moulin Light, Braveheart, Ale of Atholl, Old Remedial Ⓗ

The Atholl Arms has a grand and imposing façade in the Victorian Highland style. The characterful Highland Bothy Bar serves four ales produced by the local Moulin Brewery, as well as freshly cooked food served throughout the day. Blair Atholl and the surrounding area is a popular destination for walking, climbing and biking as well as sightseeing. Off season, Bothy Bar opening hours maybe reduced but all four ales can be brought through to the lounge bar. Q⭐😃🍽️🛏️◐≢🅿️🚆(M91,87)♿🎵

Blairgowrie

Ericht Alehouse

13 Wellmeadow, PH10 6ND
☎ (01250) 872469

6 changing beers (sourced nationally) Ⓗ

Classic town-centre pub with a friendly atmosphere, close to the River Ericht. There are two seating areas separated by a well-stocked bar offering a wide range of ever-changing ales and ciders, served in lined glasses, and an increasing number of Scottish gins, malts and rums. No food is available but customers are welcome to bring their own. A winner of local CAMRA Pub of the Year several times during the current landlord's 20-year tenure. Q🌳♣●🍴🎵♿🎵

REAL ALE BREWERIES

Blunt Chisel Blairadam
Cullach ✦ Perth
Dalrannoch Meikleour
Inveralmond Perth
Law Dundee
Loch Leven Kinross
MòR Kellas
Moulin 🍺 Moulin
Park Brew Brechin (brewing suspended)
Redcastle Carmyllie
Shed 35 Carnoustie (NEW)
Strathbraan Amulree
Wasted Degrees ✦ Blair Atholl

Fair o' Blair 🅛 ✅
25-29 Allan Street, PH10 6AB
☎ (01250) 871890
Caledonian Deuchars IPA; 4 changing beers (sourced regionally; often Inveralmond, Redcastle, Stewart) 🅗
Town-centre Wetherspoon run by a real ale enthusiast. It has a small beer garden to the rear on two levels, the lower of which is accessible by wheelchair. The pub is near the Wellmeadow, a grassy triangular plot that has been a venue for markets and outdoor entertainment since 1824. Alcoholic drinks are served from 11am.
ᕼ◑ᕼ♣♠♥🛜

Stormont Arms 🅛
101 Perth Street, PH10 6DT
☎ (01250) 873142
1 changing beer (sourced regionally; often Kelburn, Strathaven, Strathbraan) 🅗
Real ale is served from two handpulls in this traditional Scottish two-roomed pub, with Strathbraan ales featuring more than most. The friendly bar has wooden bench seating and a dartboard, and hosts a darts league during the week. A small seating area outside includes space for smokers. The pub may close early if quiet so check before travelling. It is a 10-minute walk from the town centre but many buses stop nearby. Q♣♠♥🛜

Brechin

Brechin Arms
44 St David Street, DD9 6EQ
☎ (01356) 625405
1 changing beer (sourced regionally; often Orkney, Stewart) 🅗
Small, cosy, family-run pub with a mixed clientele in the town's main street, where the interior features a lounge and quiet alcoves within easy access from the bar. The single handpump serves a regularly changing Scottish real ale. Sport and other events are screened. Brechin has historically been described as a city due to its impressive cathedral. ♠♣♥

Bridge of Earn

Cyprus Inn 🅛
Back Street, PH2 9AB
☎ (01738) 812313
1 changing beer (sourced locally; often MòR Beers, Strathbraan) 🅗
A friendly wee pub with a great community atmosphere. It has a small, cosy bar area with fixed bench seating and a low ceiling, a separate lounge/function room and a large beer garden. The inn itself dates back to around 1790 and is a category C listed building. Original rings on external walls for tying up horses are now used by cyclists. There is only one handpull but the next cask is always tapped ready for a quick changeover.
Qᕼ♦🚲🖥♥🛜

Broughty Ferry

Fisherman's Tavern
12-16 Fort Street, DD5 2AD
☎ (01382) 775941 🌐 fishermanstavern-broughtyferry.co.uk
Greene King IPA; 5 changing beers (sourced nationally; often Belhaven) 🅗
Licensed since 1857, this famous hostelry was originally three fishermen's cottages, later converted into a small hotel. The bar is to the right of the entrance, and a snug is to the left, leading to the dining room/lounge, warmed by a real fire. The lounge to the rear has wheelchair access from Bell's Lane. This Belhaven managed house serves ales from Scottish and English breweries. It hosts an annual beer festival in July.
ᕼ♠ᕼ♦♿⇌♥🛜

Royal Arch Bar ✅
285 Brook Street, DD5 2DS
☎ (01382) 779741 🌐 royal-arch.co.uk
3 changing beers (sourced nationally) 🅗
This popular locally owned pub in the centre of the Ferry has three TVs in the public bar for its many sports fans, and good-quality meals are served in the Art Deco lounge. Ales from all over Britain as well as from local breweries are served through three handpulls. The gantry in the public bar was rescued from the demolished Craigour Bar in Dens Road. ♠◑♦⇌🖥♥🛜

Ship Inn
121 Fisher Street, DD5 2BR
☎ (01382) 779176 🌐 theshipinn-broughtyferry.co.uk
Timothy Taylor Landlord; 2 changing beers 🅗
A traditional free house on the waterfront here, with views over the Tay towards Fife. Dating back to 1847, this cosy retreat is atmospheric and interesting, with nautical features. Three well-kept real ales are usually available. A range of tasty bar meals is on offer and there is a restaurant upstairs. Pavement seating outside is pleasant for fine weather. ♦◑⇌♥🛜

Dundee

Bank Bar ✅
7-9 Union Street, DD1 4BN
☎ (01382) 205037 🌐 thebankbardundee.com
Fyne Ales Jarl; house beer (by Marston's); 2 changing beers (sourced nationally) 🅗
A former bank with bare-board floors, wooden furnishings and a series of alcoves with tables, in the tradition of older Scottish city pubs. Two or three ales are usually available and food is served until the evening every day. Quality live music features on most Friday and Saturday nights. The rail station is close by. ◑⇌🖥♥🛜

Phoenix
103 Nethergate, DD1 4DH
☎ (01382) 200014
Caledonian Deuchars IPA; Timothy Taylor Landlord; 3 changing beers (sourced nationally) 🅗
One of Dundee's oldest pubs, this traditional inn has a great atmosphere. Subdued lighting, sturdy wooden tables and chairs, green leather benches and a rare Ballingall Brewery mirror give the place character. Five ales are on offer, along with excellent pub food at sensible prices. The location is handy for the Rep Theatre, Dundee Contemporary Arts and Bonar Hall. Warm and cosy, like pubs used to be. ◑⇌🖥(73)♥🛜

Speedwell Bar (Mennies) ★ ✅
165-167 Perth Road, DD2 1AS
☎ (01382) 667783 🌐 speedwell-bar.co.uk
3 changing beers (sourced nationally) 🅗
Built in 1903 for James Speed, this pub is known as Mennie's after the family who ran it for more than 50 years. The L-shaped bar is divided by a part-glazed screen and has a magnificent mahogany gantry and counter, dado-panelled walls and an anaglypta Jacobean-style ceiling. There are usually three ales to choose from, alongside a selection of Belgian bottled beers and around 150 malt whiskies. You can take in your own food. 🖥♥🛜

Dunkeld

Perth Arms 🄻

High Street, PH8 0AJ
☎ (01350) 727270
Strathbraan Due South, Head East Ⓗ
Cosy one-room establishment serving a mix of locals and tourists. This friendly inn has been in the same family for almost 50 years and is the area's oldest trading pub, dating back to 1795. Its two handpulls dispense ales mostly from local breweries. The beer garden at the back has an area for smokers. ❀🕮◖🖳🌸🎇

Dunning

Kirkstyle Inn ✅

Kirkstyle Square, PH2 0RR
☎ (01764) 684248 🌐 thekirkstyleinn.co.uk
House beer (by Marston's); 2 changing beers (sourced nationally) Ⓗ
A traditional village inn dating from 1760, overshadowed by the impressive Norman steeple of St Serf's Church, home to the ancient Dupplin Cross and other Pictish relics. One or two ales in the cosy public bar come from a variety of Scottish independents, as well as English and Welsh regional breweries. The pub also serves a house ale, Risky Kelt. There is a separate restaurant.
❀🕮◖🖳(17)🌸🎇

Forfar

Osnaburg Bar

23 Osnaburg Street, DD8 2AA
☎ (01307) 640339 🌐 theosnaburgbar.co.uk
Fyne Ales Jarl; 2 changing beers (often Fyne Ales, Greene King, Inveralmond) Ⓗ
A cosy low-ceilinged bar down a pend off the main street. One of the oldest licensed premises in Forfar dating from 1827, its name derives from the town's textile industry history. It is a Belhaven tenancy, with varying beers being served from three handpulls, usually Inveralmond or Fyne Ales, but occasionally other guest ales. ❀◖♣🖳🌸

Kinross

Loch Leven Brewery Tap Room 🄻

The Muirs, KY13 8AS
☎ (01577) 864881 🌐 lochleven.beer
Loch Leven Warrior Queen, Shining Knight, Outlaw King, King Slayer Ⓗ
This taproom attached to the brewery offers the full range of Loch Leven beers, three on handpull, plus three keg taps, with tables inside and outside. A growler dispenser enables both cask and craft beers to be purchased to take home, and bottled beers and brewery gifts/souvenirs are sold in the shop. The premises is conveniently situated next to the express bus stop to Perth and Edinburgh. Check the website for current opening times. 🕮♿🖳🌸🎇

Kirriemuir

Airlie Arms

St Malcolm's Wynd, DD8 4HB
☎ (01575) 218080 🌐 airliearms.net

> Beer: a high and mighty liquor.
> **Julius Caesar**

2 changing beers (often Burnside, MòR Beers, Redcastle) Ⓗ
After many years of closure, this large 18th-century establishment was substantially renovated and reopened in 2015 by the local Ewart family, with real ale making a welcome appearance. There are two handpulls on the bar offering a good selection of beers. Food is served in the bar every day, and the restaurant too at weekends. An ideal base for hill walking, sightseeing, fishing and golfing, with accommodation available.
❀🕮◖♣P🖳🌸🎇

Lawers

Ben Lawers Hotel 🄻

Loch Tay, PH15 2PA
☎ (01567) 820436 🌐 benlawershotel.co.uk
3 changing beers (often Strathbraan) Ⓗ
In the heart of one of Scotland's most beautiful and accessible unspoilt areas, this small hotel provides fantastic views over Loch Tay. It is popular with walkers, having the Ben Lawers mountain range, including numerous Munros, on its doorstep. Its handpulls serve Strathbraan ales, alongside Helles lager and a selection of bottled and canned Tempest beers. Good food and accommodation are offered. Closed in January, and on Tuesdays and Wednesdays in winter. ❀🕮◖P🌸🎇

Memus

Drovers Inn

DD8 3TY
☎ (01307) 860322 🌐 the-drovers.com
Timothy Taylor Landlord; 1 changing beer (often Harviestoun) Ⓗ
In a rural setting just north of Forfar and handily placed for the Angus Glens, the Drovers is a traditional Scottish inn with a contemporary look. An old range fire in the bar adds to the atmosphere, especially on a chilly day. Two ales are usually served, and excellent food using locally sourced seasonal produce is available daily. There is a large outdoor dining area under the trees, with an adjoining play area for children. Q❀🕮◖🌸

Milnathort

Village Inn

36 Wester Loan, KY13 9YH
☎ (01577) 863293
3 changing beers (sourced nationally) Ⓗ
Friendly local with a semi open-plan interior featuring classic brewery mirrors and local historical photographs. The comfortable lounge has low ceilings, exposed joists and stone walls, and the bar is warmed by a log fire. The pub has been family-owned since 1985 and usually serves three beers, mostly locally sourced. Milnathort links some great cycling routes through the Ochils, via Burleigh Castle, to the more leisurely Loch Leven Heritage Trail. 🕮♿♣🖳🌸🎇

Montrose

Market Arms

95 High Street, DD10 8QY
☎ (01674) 673384
2 changing beers (sourced regionally; often Inveralmond, MòR Beers) Ⓗ
Stylishly renovated a few years ago, this busy town-centre pub provides a comfortable retreat for its wide mix of customers. Two handpulls are sited on a long bar near the entrance in the main open area. Several TVs show live sport, and there is a snug at the front for those

wishing to enjoy a quiet pint. Beers are mostly from Scottish brewers. Convenient for visitors to the nearby Montrose Air Station Heritage Centre. ✿◐♿🅰🚶🕿🏠🐾🤶

Moulin

Moulin Inn 🅛

11-13 Kirkmichael Road, PH16 5EH
☎ (01796) 472196 ∰ moulininn.co.uk
Moulin Light, Braveheart, Ale of Atholl, Old Remedial 🅗

First opened in 1695, the inn is the oldest part of the Moulin Hotel, situated within the village square at an ancient crossroads just east of Pitlochry. Full of character and charm, it is traditionally furnished and has two log fires. A good choice of home-prepared local fare is available, along with four Moulin beers, brewed in the old coach house behind the hotel. There is an area outside for dining and drinking in good weather. An ideal base for outdoor pursuits, with several marked walks nearby. Q✿🕿🛏◐🅰🅿🏠🐾🤶

Perth

Cherrybank Inn 🅛

210 Glasgow Road, PH2 0NA
☎ (01738) 624349 ∰ cherrybankinn.co.uk
Harviestoun Bitter & Twisted; Inveralmond Ossian; 3 changing beers (sourced nationally) 🅗

This 250-year-old former drovers' inn is a popular watering hole and stopover for travellers. Five ales from Inveralmond and other Scottish independents are dispensed in the public bar or the larger L-shaped lounge. Good bar lunches and evening meals are served. There is a large, sunny elevated wooden deck to the rear. The inn has seven en-suite rooms, and golf can be arranged for residents. 🛏✿🕿◐🅰🅿🏠🐾🤶

Cullach Tap Room 🅛

50 Princes Street, PH2 8LJ
∰ cullachbrewing.co.uk
House beer (by Cullach); 6 changing beers (sourced locally; often Cullach) 🅟

Central Perth's first microbrewery and taproom, in a quiet side street, with a well-appointed and comfortable seating area. It serves Cullach beers, typically Tayside IPA, Red IPA and Cabin Porter, plus guests. Open Thursday to Sunday. Q🛏🕿🚶🤶🍴

Old Ship Inn ✔

31 High Street, PH1 5TJ
☎ 07956 924767 ∰ oldshipinnperth.co.uk
House beer (by Belhaven); 2 changing beers (often Belhaven, Fyne Ales, Harviestoun) 🅗

Said to be the oldest pub in Perth, having traded under the same name since 1665. This was the city's oasis for real ale in the 1980s, and now serves one regular beer and two changing ales. A large oil painting of a sailing

ship adds interest in the timber-lined bar, which is lightened by a frieze and a white-painted ceiling. The upstairs lounge was closed for 20 years before reopening a few years ago. ✿🖨(7)🐾🤶

Pitcairngreen

Pitcairngreen Inn 🅛

PH1 3LP
☎ (01738) 583022 ∰ pitcairngreeninn.co.uk
2 changing beers (sourced locally; often Strathbraan) 🅗

A fairly large establishment with several different areas including a snug warmed by an open log fire. The inn has a real enthusiasm for good beer, served on three handpulls. This is also the finest place in Tayside to enjoy real ciders and perries, presented professionally and with passion. The car park is just across the road. Food is served daily except Tuesday. Local CAMRA Cider Pub of the Year. Q✿◐🅿🖨(14,15)🐾🤶

Pitlochry

Old Mill Inn

Mill Lane, PH16 5BH
☎ (01796) 474020 ∰ theoldmillpitlochry.co.uk
4 changing beers (sourced regionally; often Strathbraan) 🅗

This place was built in the 19th century as a mill, and still has a mill wheel driven by the stream, which customers can sit beside when the weather allows for outdoor drinking. It is a well-run family-owned establishment in the town centre. The large bar serves a varied selection of guest ales, with usually three or four on, including some from local microbrewery Strathbraan. 🛏✿🕿◐♿🚶🅿🏠🐾🤶

Wester Balgedie

Balgedie Toll Tavern 🅛

KY13 9HE (at jct of A911 and B919)
☎ (01592) 840212
Harviestoun Bitter & Twisted; Loch Leven Warrior Queen; 1 changing beer (sourced locally; often Inveralmond) 🅗

Welcoming country tavern dating from 1534, originally situated at a road toll where travellers would break their journey and pay levies. Now much extended, there are seating areas on two levels. The oldest part of the building is now the Harness Bar, with low ceilings, oak beams, horse brasses and wooden settles. A fine selection of meals and bar snacks is available. Cask conditioned beers from local breweries are served from two handpulls in the lower bar area. 🛏✿◐♿🅿🖨(201) 🐾🤶

Cask beer

Real ale is often described as 'beer from a barrel' and pubs are said to have 'barrels behind the bar'. In fact, barrels are large containers, too big for most bars. The correct generic term for the containers for real ale is cask and casks come in the following sizes:

Pin – 4.5 gallons
Firkin (from old Dutch word meaning 'fourth') – 9 gallons
Kilderkin (from old Dutch word meaning 'small cask') – 18 gallons
Barrel – 36 gallons
Hogshead – 54 gallons

SHETLAND

NORTHERN
ISLES

HIGHLANDS
&
WESTERN ISLES

ABERDEEN
& GRAMPIAN

TAYSIDE

ARGYLL &
THE ISLES

LOCH LOMOND
STIRLING
& THE
TROSSACHS

FIFE

GREATER
GLASGOW &
CLYDE

EDINBURGH & LOTHIANS

AYRSHIRE
& ARRAN

BORDERS

NORTHERN
IRELAND

DUMFRIES &
GALLOWAY

NORTHUMBERLAND

TYNE &
WEAR

CUMBRIA

DURHAM

ISLE OF
MAN

NORTH
YORKSHIRE

LANCASHIRE

WEST
YORKS

EAST
YORKS

MERSEYSIDE

GREATER
MANCHESTER

SOUTH
YORKS

NW
WALES

NE
WALES

CHESHIRE

DERBYSHIRE

NOTTINGHAM-
SHIRE

LINCOLNSHIRE

SHROPSHIRE

STAFFORD-
SHIRE

LEICESTERSHIRE

NORFOLK

MID
WALES

WEST
MIDLANDS

WORCESTER-
SHIRE

WARWICK-
SHIRE

NORTHAMPTON-
SHIRE

CAMBRIDGE-
SHIRE

SUFFOLK

WEST
WALES

HEREFORD-
SHIRE

GWENT

GLOUCS &
BRISTOL

OXFORD-
SHIRE

BUCKINGHAM-
SHIRE

HERTFORD-
SHIRE

ESSEX

GLAMORGAN

GREATER
LONDON

WILTSHIRE

BERKSHIRE

KENT

CHANNEL
ISLANDS

SOMERSET

HAMPSHIRE

SURREY

WEST
SUSSEX

EAST
SUSSEX

DEVON

DORSET

CORNWALL

ISLE OF
WIGHT

Northern Ireland
Channel Islands
Isle of Man

NORTHERN IRELAND

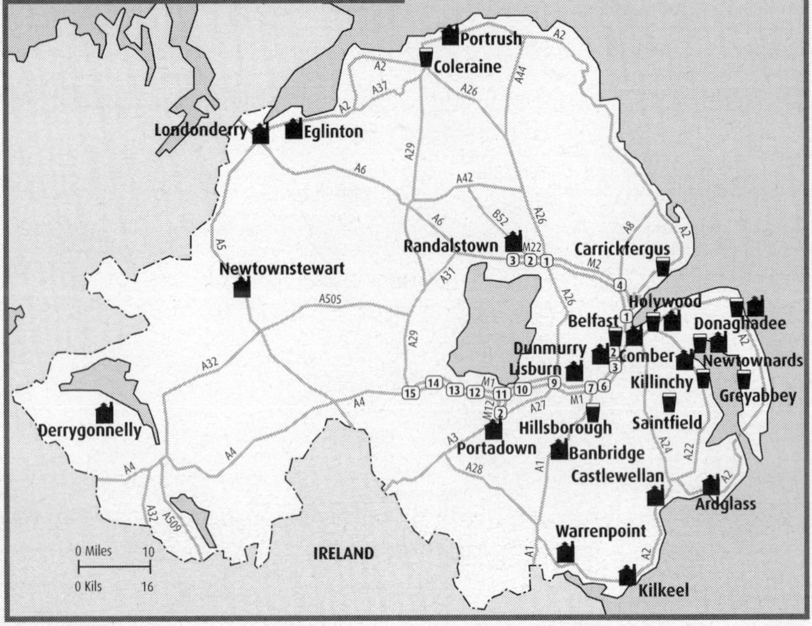

Belfast

Bridge House

37-43 Bedford Street, BT2 7EJ

☎ (028) 9072 7890

Greene King Abbot; Sharp's Doom Bar; changing beers (sourced nationally) [H]

Twice a CAMRA Northern Ireland Pub of the Year, this is a very busy bar near the city centre. It has a large L-shaped ground floor with a smaller more family-oriented bar upstairs, and a recently added beer garden at the rear. The main bar has eight handpumps serving a range of national brews, and the seating area includes a mixture of tables and booths. Open for food from 8am, with alcoholic drinks served from 11.30am (12.30pm Sun). Q👶✿◑♿⇌🚌📶

Crown ★

46 Great Victoria Street, BT2 7BA (opp Europa Hotel and Great Victoria St station)

☎ (028) 9024 3187

Mourne Mountains Mourne Gold; St Austell Nicholson's Pale Ale; 4 changing beers (sourced nationally) [H]

Alongside its historic architecture, the Crown Liquor Saloon has one of Belfast's most wide-ranging choices of real ales. There are six handpumps regularly serving Nicholson's Pale Ale and a mixture of local and national ales. Upstairs is the Crown Dining Rooms where there are three more handpumps. Bag-in-box cider is also occasionally available. Good food is served both upstairs and in the main bar. This former CAMRA Northern Ireland Pub of the Year is a must-see. Q◑♿⇌🚌

Errigle Inn

312-320 Ormeau Road, BT7 2GE

☎ (028) 9064 1410 🌐 errigle.com

5 changing beers (sourced locally; often Farmageddon, Knockout, Whitewater) [H]

The Errigle Inn is a beer enthusiast's haven. Some craft beers can be found in the main bar but the real treasures are in the quiet back bar, the Oak Lounge, where ales can be enjoyed in peace. Beers from local breweries including Hilden, Whitewater, Farmageddon, Knockout, Bullhouse, Beer Hut and Lacada are often available, as well as some national brands. On occasion there are tap takeovers, beers from the wood and handpulled cider. Q◑♿🚌📶

John Hewitt

51 Donegal Street, BT1 2FH (100yds from St Anne's Cathedral)

REAL ALE BREWERIES

Ards Newtownards
Baronscourt Newtownstewart
Beer Hut Kilkeel
Black Mountain 🍺 Lisburn
Boundary ◆ Belfast
Bullhouse Newtownards
Farmageddon Comber
Fermanagh Derrygonnelly
Hercules Belfast
Hilden Lisburn
Hillstown Randalstown
Knockout Belfast
Lacada Portrush
Lecale Ardglass
MashDown Banbridge
McCracken's Portadown
Modest Holywood
Mourne Mountains Warrenpoint
Norn Iron Dunmurry
Northbound Eglinton
Rough Brothers Londonderry
Twisted Kettle Donaghadee
Walled City 🍺 Londonderry
Whitewater Castlewellan

☎ (028) 9023 3768 ⊕ thejohnhewitt.com
Shepherd Neame Master Brew Ⓗ
Named after the renowned poet, this is a busy single-room bar with a large snug and a stage area. The pub has become a popular venue for live music, quizzes and art exhibitions. It is run by the Belfast Unemployed Resource Centre and profits fund the organisation's charitable work. One handpump dispenses a Shepherd Neame beer or a local brew from Hercules. Q☕◑₺⅃

McHughs

29-31 Queens Square, BT1 3FG (nr Albert Clock)
☎ (028) 9050 9999
Whitewater Maggie's Leap IPA Ⓗ
Housed in Belfast's oldest building, McHughs is a lively pub with several different drinking and eating areas. The main public bar has a handpump exclusively dispensing ales from Whitewater Brewery, mainly Maggie's Leap. Next to it is the restored old bar where wall paintings depict scenes from Belfast's history. Good food can be obtained from the restaurant upstairs. Sport is a big draw along with music. There are folk and traditional acts in the bar and in the basement. Patrons include dedicated regulars, tourists and visitors to nearby music venues. Q◑♠₺⇌⅃🎵

Northern Lights

451 Ormeau Road, BT7 3GQ
☎ (028) 9029 0291 ⊕ galwaybaybrewery.com/northernlights
1 changing beer (sourced regionally) Ⓗ
Galway Bay Brewery's first pub in Northern Ireland is very much a modern craft beer bar, with rows of taps and long tables. It serves around 10 of its own beers alongside others from a variety of craft producers. There is also an impressive selection of bottles and canned beer. One handpump dispenses cask ales from a number of Irish breweries. CAMRA Northern Ireland Pub of the Year 2020. Q◑₺♣⅃🐾🎵

Sunflower

65 Union Street, BT1 2JG
☎ (028) 9023 2474 ⊕ sunflowerbelfast.com
1 changing beer (sourced locally; often Hilden) Ⓗ
This is a corner pub with a traditional feel. One handpump offers a variety of beers from Hilden, alongside a broad selection of craft beers. Ireland's most famous beverage has been replaced with Double Stout from the local Hercules Brewery. Tap takeovers are hosted and there is music seven days a week. The large beer garden is a popular attraction, with pizza available Thursday, Friday and Saturday evenings. Q🍴⇌⅃🐾🎵

Carrickfergus

Central Bar

13-15 High Street, BT38 7AN (opp Castle)
☎ (028) 9335 7840
Greene King Abbot; Sharp's Doom Bar; 3 changing beers (sourced nationally) Ⓗ
Lively market-town community local with a loyal clientele. This Wetherspoon pub has a ground-floor public bar of robust character and a quieter family-friendly loggia-style sitting room on the first floor with exposed timber trusses, affording fine views from its many windows over Belfast Lough and the adjacent 12th-century castle. Handpumps on both levels serve two house beers and three guest ales, usually from mainland

> There can't be a good living where there is not good drinking. **Benjamin Franklin**

micros, and seasonal specials from various breweries. Alcoholic drinks are served from 11.30am (12.30pm Sun). Q☕🍴◑₺⇌⅃(563)

Coleraine

Fairley's Bar

62-64 Railway Road, BT52 1PF
☎ (028) 7032 0047
4 changing beers (sourced locally; often Lacada) ℗
A bar and off-licence near Coleraine's railway station. The ale is from Lacada Brewery in Portrush and dispensed from KeyKegs – the brewery has confirmed its beers are real ale. Drinks can also be purchased from the well-stocked off-licence and consumed in the bar with a corkage charge. The bar area opens up to a quieter area which leads to a lounge with a real fire. Closed Sunday. ₺⇌⅃🎵

Donaghadee

Moat Inn

102 Moat Street, BT21 0ED
☎ (028) 9188 3297 ⊕ themoatinn.com
Whitewater Belfast Ale; 1 changing beer (sourced locally; often Whitewater) Ⓗ
On the main road into Donaghadee, about 20 miles from Belfast, the Moat Inn is a long-established hostelry conveniently located for landmarks of the Ards Peninsula. It houses a public bar, a lounge, Henry's Bistro and a beer garden. The bar is compact though comfy and is populated with rugby-loving locals. There are two handpumps with beers from Whitewater Brewery. In addition, good food is served in the lounge and the bistro. Q☕🍴◑₺⅃(7)

Greyabbey

Wildfowler Inn

1 Main Street, BT22 2NE (6 miles S of Newtownards on A20)
☎ (028) 4278 8234 ⊕ wildfowlerinn.co.uk
Ards Scrabo Gold; 1 changing beer (sourced locally; often Ards) Ⓗ
A restaurant and a smaller public bar with a tiled and stone floor, exposed oak beams and stained-glass windows. There are two handpumps, one in the restaurant and one in the public bar. The ales are all from Ards Brewing Company less than two miles away. Phone ahead to find out which beers are on. Q☕🍴◑₺P⅃🐾

Hillsborough

Hillside

21 Main Street, BT26 6AE
☎ (028) 9268 9233 ⊕ hillsidehillsborough.co.uk
Hilden Twisted Hop; house beer (by Hilden) Ⓗ
A bar and restaurant dating from 1752, with two handpumps serving beers from Hilden Brewery. The interior has been opened up to make three drinking areas in addition to the restaurant at the back, although food is served throughout. The walls are decorated with pictures of hunting scenes and old Hillsborough. Live music acts play at the weekend and there is a summer beer festival in the cobblestone beer garden. Q☕🍴◑₺⅃(38,238) 🐾🎵

Holywood

Dirty Duck Ale House

3 Kinnegar Road, BT18 9JN
☎ (028) 9059 6666 ⊕ thedirtyduckalehouse.co.uk

House beer (by Hilden); 3 changing beers (sourced nationally; often Inveralmond, Sharp's, Shepherd Neame) Ⓗ
Located mere yards from Belfast Lough, the Dirty Duck has some of the best views of any pub in the province. Downstairs the cosy and traditional single-room bar has a corner celebrating local golfer Rory McIlroy, and upstairs is a restaurant with panoramic views. Outside there is another bar and a beer garden with new retractable roofing. There are three changing ales to complement the good food, and a regular beer festival. Two-times winner of CAMRA Northern Ireland Pub of the Year.
Q❀☰❀◑❀&≠🛜

Killinchy

Daft Eddy's Ⓛ

Sketrick Island, BT23 6QH (2 miles N of Killinchey at Whiterock Bay)
☎ (028) 9754 1615 ⊕ dafteddysni.co.uk
1 changing beer (sourced locally; often Farmageddon)
Another loughside pub, this time Strangford Lough. The lounge bar area, with a wood-burning stove, has a modern feel, while Little Eddy's coffee bar is a more recent addition. The handpump on the restaurant side often serves a beer from the nearby Farmageddon Brewery. The restaurant continues to offer quality local food, with oysters and lobster among the specialities. Food can also be enjoyed in the alfresco dining area.
Q❀☰❀◑&P❀🛜

Newtownards

Spirit Merchant

54-56 Regent Street, BT23 4LP (next to bus station)
☎ (028) 9182 4270
Greene King Abbot; Sharp's Doom Bar; 2 changing beers (sourced nationally) Ⓗ
This Wetherspoon is about 10 miles from Belfast, close to the bus station. It has a long bar and a large outside area. There is a mixture of seating, with booths on the right of the entrance and a raised area at the back. Regularly changing good quality ales are served from the five handpumps. As with the other pubs in the chain, it opens from 8am with alcoholic drinks served from 11.30am (12.30pm Sun). Q❀☰❀◑&▲🚆(7)🛜

Saintfield

White Horse

49-53 Main Street, BT24 7AB
☎ (028) 9751 1143 ⊕ whitehorsesaintfield.com
Whitewater Copperhead, Maggie's Leap IPA Ⓗ
Former coaching inn located about 11 miles from Belfast. A busy food-oriented establishment, the modern interior retains some of the old walls in the bar and restaurant area. It is the tap for Whitewater Brewery, with two of the brewery's ales on handpump, often Copperhead and Maggie's Leap. There is music at the weekend and a pizza parlour downstairs along with the beer garden. A former CAMRA Northern Ireland Pub of the Year.
Q❀☰❀◑&🚆(15,215)

Crown, Belfast (Photo: James Cridland/Flickr CC BY 2.0)

CHANNEL ISLANDS

GUERNSEY

Cobo
Kings Mills
Castel
St Martin
St Peter Port

Braye
ALDERNEY

Herm Island

Sark

JERSEY

St Ouen
St Lawrence
St Peter
St Brelade
St Helier
Trinity
St Saviour
St Martin

0 Miles 3
0 Kilometres 5

ALDERNEY
Braye

Divers Inn
Braye Street, GY9 3XT
☎ (01481) 822632 ⊕ brayebeach.com
2 changing beers (sourced nationally; often Butcombe) Ⓗ
Traditional pub with a great atmosphere, attached to the Braye Beach Hotel. It serves two real ales and has a good bar menu. The interior features wooden tables, chairs and a counter, and is warmed by real fires. Walking through the bar area reveals sea views and a superb outdoor seating space overlooking the beach. Themed and musical events attract locals and visitors alike, making this a must-visit location when on Alderney.
🛋️◑≈♣

GUERNSEY
Cobo

Rockmount Restaurant & Bar
Cobo Coast Road, GY5 7HB
☎ (01481) 252778 ⊕ therocky.gg
4 changing beers (often Randalls) Ⓗ
The pub comprises a large lounge bar and a taproom that shows sport on TV. The lounge has an emphasis on food, served lunchtimes and evenings, but there are comfy chairs near the fare for drinkers. Five handpumps offer a changing range of beers and you can also try a tasting paddle of different ales. Q🕸️🌟◑🚻♿🅿️🚃(41,42)♣️🎵🎶

Herm Island

Mermaid Tavern ✓
GY1 3HR
☎ (01481) 750050 ⊕ herm.com/mermaid
Liberation Herm Island Gold; house beer (by Liberation); 2 changing beers
A welcoming inn on the beautiful island of Herm, a short trip by ferry from Guernsey. The large courtyard is a popular spot in summer; an open fire adds to the charm in winter. The house beer is from Liberation, brewed specially for the island. The pub holds regular themed music and food events, and hosts real ale and cider festivals in June and September. 🌟◑♣♿♣🎵🎶

Kings Mills

Fleur du Jardin ✓
GY5 7JT
☎ (01481) 257996 ⊕ fleurdujardin.com
3 changing beers (sourced regionally; often Little Big Brew) Ⓗ
A building of unique charm with two bars – one traditional, small and cosy, attached to the restaurant, the other renovated in a more contemporary style to create a comfortable, relaxing area to enjoy a beer. A door leads to a large covered patio and out to the garden. Menus in both the bar and restaurant feature fresh local produce. The car park can be busy in summer. Q🕸️🌟🛋️◑♿🅿️🚃♣

St Martin

Les Douvres Hotel
La Fosse, GY4 6ER
☎ (01481) 238731 ⊕ lesdouvreshotel.co.uk
3 changing beers (often Little Big Brew) Ⓗ
Former 18th-century manor house, set in private gardens in St Martin near the south coast, two and a half miles from St Peter Port, with cliff walks and a tiny fishing harbour. A well-maintained, changing range of beers is offered on three handpumps, and real cider during the season. Excellent meals, including pizzas, are served in the bar and separate restaurant. Live music features on Friday night and occasional Wednesdays. 🌟🛋️◑♣🅿️🚃

St Peter Port

Cock & Bull
2 Lower Hauteville, GY1 1LL
☎ (01481) 722660 ⊕ cockandbullguernsey.com/home
5 changing beers (often Marston's, Randalls) Ⓗ
The pub is just up the hill from the town church. It serves a good mix of local and national ales, with Marston's beers a regular feature, plus real cider in summer. Seating is on three levels, with a pool table on the lower level. Live music features throughout the week, with blues, jazz or baroque on Monday, open mic on Tuesday and Irish folk on Thursday. A meat draw is held on Friday. Open on Sundays when rugby is on. ♣🚃🛜

Golden Lion
7 Market Street, GY1 1HF
☎ (01481) 726634 ⊕ thegoldenlion.gg
4 changing beers (sourced nationally) Ⓗ
Town-centre pub opposite the former market. The single room has the feel of a modern craft beer bar, with a long bar serving up to six real ales and four real ciders. (The beer range is reduced in winter.) Gluten-free ales are available in bottles. Live music is performed at weekends. The first-floor Lions Den is open in the evenings and available for private hire. ♣🚃🛜

Red Lion
Les Banques, GY1 2RX (on seafront to N of St Peter Port)
☎ (01481) 724042
4 changing beers (often Randalls) Ⓗ

REAL ALE BREWERIES
Bliss 🍺 St Helier: Jersey (NEW)
Isle of Sark Le Seigneurie: Sark
Liberation St Saviour: Jersey
Little Big St Peter Port: Guernsey (NEW)
Randalls Guernsey: St Peter Port
Stinky Bay St Lawrence: Jersey (NEW)

ISLANDS

Friendly pub on the outskirts of St Peter Port with two bar areas – a lounge overlooking Belle Greve Bay to the front and a public area at the rear. Gluten-free beer is available in bottles, and real cider is served in summer. Numerous TVs show sport. Meat draws are held on Friday and Saturday evenings. The pub is on several bus routes and on the cycle route between St Peter Port and St Sampson. ✤❀◑●🖨😺❦🖥

Ship & Crown ✔

North Esplanade, GY1 2NB
☎ (01481) 721368
3 changing beers Ⓗ
Traditional venue in the heart of the town with fantastic views of the harbour, neighbouring islands and Castle Cornet. It is decorated with photos of local shipwrecks, Guernsey and the pub under German occupation. Popular with regulars, yachtsmen and tourists alike, this is the perfect place to enjoy a pint and a good meal. All major sports events are shown in a friendly and lively atmosphere. Liberation and Butcombe beers are served, and real cider is also on handpump. ◑●🖨😺🖥

Slaughterhouse

Castle Pier, GY1 1AN
☎ (01481) 712123 🌐 slaughterhouse.gg
6 changing beers (often Randalls) Ⓗ
Busy harbourside bar and eatery offering fine views over Havelet Bay and the harbour from its mezzanine restaurant and large outdoor terrace. The Randalls-managed pub serves a changing range of up to six real ales, some from small breweries. Winner of a CAMRA design award in 2019 for its conversion from an abbatoir. ❀◑&

JERSEY
St Brelade

Old Smugglers Inn ✔

Le Mont du Ouaisne, Ouaisne, JE3 8AW
☎ (01534) 741510 🌐 oldsmugglersinn.com
Draught Bass; house beer (by Liberation); 2 changing beers (often Marston's, Ringwood, Skinner's) Ⓗ
Perched on the edge of Ouaisne Bay, the Smugglers has been the crown jewel of the Jersey real ale scene for many years. Steeped in history, dating back to when pirates came to enjoy an ale or two here, it is set within granite-built fishermen's cottages with foundations reputedly from the 13th century. Up to four ales are available including one from Skinner's, and mini beer festivals are regularly held. Renowned for its good food and fresh daily specials. Q✤✤◑●P❦

Trafalgar Inn ✔

Charing Cross, St Aubin, JE3 8AA
☎ (01534) 741334 🌐 trafalgarinn.com
5 changing beers (often Butcombe, Liberation, St Austell) Ⓗ
Traditional community pub with a nautical theme. There are two bars – the saloon bar at the front and a sports bar with pool, darts and sports TV behind. The handpumps are in the sports bar – beers are regularly rotated but usually include one from Liberation Brewery. See the website for what's in the cellar. Popular with local rugby fans, the Jersey Reds usually come here after Saturday home matches. &♣🖨❦

St Helier

Biere Atelier

Bath Street, JE2 4ST
☎ (01534) 874059 🌐 labastille.bar

Purity Pure Gold, Mad Goose, Pure UBU; 1 changing beer (sourced nationally) Ⓗ
Possibly Jersey's first micropub, this single-room bar has a few tables and stools around the walls. The small counter has real ales on handpump and a craft beer wall behind. Popular with office workers, it is fast becoming a destination bar for real beer lovers. On the corner of Bath Street and Hilgrove Street, it is interconnected with the nearby Bastille restaurant and bar, where the beers are also available. Food from the Bastille can also be enjoyed at tables outside on the pedestrian street. &

Lamplighter Ⓛ ✔

9 Mulcaster Street, JE2 3NJ
☎ (01534) 723119
8 changing beers (sourced nationally) Ⓗ
A traditional pub with a modern feel. The gas lamps that gave the pub its name remain, as does the original antique pewter bar top. An excellent range of up to eight real ales is available – the largest selection on the island – including one from Skinner's. All real ales are served direct from the cellar. A real cider is sometimes also on offer. A repeat winner of local CAMRA Pub of the Year. ●🖨😺🖥

Post Horn Ⓛ ✔

Hue Street, JE2 3RE
☎ (01534) 872853
Butcombe Original; Draught Bass; Liberation Ale, IPA; 1 changing beer (often Liberation) Ⓗ
Busy, friendly pub adjacent to the precinct and five minutes' walk from the Royal Square. Popular at lunchtimes with its own nucleus of regulars, it offers up to four draught ales. The large L-shaped public bar extends into the lounge area where there is an open fire and TV showing sport. A good selection of freshly cooked food is served. There is a large function room on the first floor, a drinking area outside and a public car park nearby. ❀◑😺🐾🖥

Prince of Wales Tavern

8 Hilgrove Street, JE2 4SL
☎ (01534) 737378
Courage Best Bitter; Fuller's London Pride; Ringwood Boondoggle; Sharp's Doom Bar; Wychwood Hobgoblin Gold; 5 changing beers (sourced nationally; often Shepherd Neame) Ⓗ
A traditional pub, next to the historic central market, offering a large selection of up to eight cask ales advertised on blackboards. The Victorian-style interior has a bright and sparkling bar-back which features a large selection of whiskies. No food is served but there are a number of eateries nearby. The beer garden at the rear is a pleasant spot for a relaxing drink. ❀●❦

St Martin

Royal

La Grande Route de Faldouet, JE3 6UG
☎ (01534) 856289
Courage Directors; Skinner's Lushingtons Ⓗ**; 1 changing beer (often Bombardier)** Ⓗ/Ⓖ
Originally a coaching inn, this large country-style hostelry is located at the centre of St Martin with sizeable public and lounge bars, a restaurant area, and a spacious alfresco area. The interior features traditional furnishings, cosy corners and a real fire in colder months. Owned by Randalls Brewery, it serves guest ales from the Marston's, Sharp's and Skinner's stables. Quality food is popular with locals and visitors alike, with a good menu available lunchtimes and evenings (no food Sun eve). ✤❀◑&🅰♣P🖨(3)❦

St Ouen

Farmers Inn ✓

La Grande Route de St Ouen, JE3 2HY

☎ (01534) 485311

Butcombe Original; Liberation Pale Ale, Herm Island Gold; 2 changing beers (often Liberation) ⊞

Situated in the hub of St Ouen, near the war memorial and parish hall, the rustic Farmers Inn is a typical country inn offering up to three ales as well as a locally-made cider when available (usually April to July). Traditional pub food is served in generous portions. Best described as a friendly community local, there is a good chance of hearing Jersey French (Jerriais) spoken at the bar. There is an outside seating area at the front. ⏰ ♪ ♣ ♦ P 🖵

Moulin de Lecq ✓

Le Mont De La Greve De Lecq, Greve de Lecq, JE3 2DT

☎ (01534) 482818 ⊕ moulindelecq.com

Shepherd Neame Spitfire; house beer (by Liberation); 2 changing beers (often Marston's, Skinner's) ⊞

A free house on the island offering a range of real ales, the Moulin is a converted 12th-century watermill situated in the valley above the beach at Greve de Lecq. The waterwheel is still in place and the turning mechanism can be seen behind the bar. A restaurant adjoins the mill. The children's play space and a barbecue area are used extensively in the summer. The 120-seat restaurant can be hired for functions. Pool can be played in the second-floor games room.
Q ⏰ ❀ ◑ ♿ ♣ ♦ P 🖵 🐾 ❧ 🤶

St Peter

Tipsy

La Route de Beaumont, JE3 7BQ

☎ (01534) 485556 ⊕ thetipsy.co.uk

6 changing beers (sourced nationally; often Castle Rock, Elland, Liberation) ⊞

The Tipsy, formerly The Tipsy Toad, was the site of the original Skinner's Brewery before it moved to Cornwall. The friendly pub has been refurbished to provide a main bar with comfortable seating. Six handpumps dispense a rotating selection of ales, including a house beer from Liberation, Tipsy Toad Ale, a 3.8% ABV bitter. The separate restaurant area offers an extensive menu. Outside is a patio with heating. There are plans to reopen the microbrewery. ⏰ ❀ ◑ ♿ P 🖵 (9) 🐾 ❧

Trinity

Trinity Arms ⌷ ✓

La Rue es Picots, JE3 5JX

☎ (01534) 864691

Liberation Ale; 1 changing beer (often Butcombe, Liberation) ⊞

Sporting the parish's ancient symbol of the Trinity, this place, built in 1976, is modern by Jersey country pub standards but has plenty of character. Owned by Liberation Group, it is central to and popular within village community life. It has recently undergone a full refurbishment and both bars have been merged into one, with a central island bar. Food is served at breakfast, lunchtime and evenings. There is seating outside, a children's play area and car parking. Not far from Jersey Zoo. ⏰ ❀ ◑ ♿ ♣ P 🖵 (4) 🐾 ❧

SARK
Sark

Bel Air

Harbour Hill, GY10 1SB

☎ (01481) 832052

2 changing beers (often Randalls) ⊞

Popular, family-friendly pub at the top of Harbour Hill but worth the walk or tractor ride. It serves two real ales and real cider, and offers food all day. There is a cosy fire for cold weather, and a large beer garden and courtyard where food and drink can be enjoyed on warm days. Barbecues and live music feature at the weekend in summer. ⏰ ❀ ◑ ♿ ♣ ♦ 🐾

Mermaid Tavern

Main Street, GY10 1SG

☎ (01481) 832022

Butcombe Original; 1 changing beer (sourced nationally) ⊞

A pub established before WWII, the Mermaid harks back to an earlier time and the decor has remained unchanged since the 1960s. A no-frills local with a warm welcome for island visitors, it is child-friendly and serves snacks such as pizza and sandwiches. Darts, pool and shove-ha'penny can be played, and there is a jukebox and a piano available for spontaneous singsongs or a dance. After exploring Sark, the seating area outside is a pleasant place to end the day. ⏰ ♣ ❧

Kitchen of an inn

In the evening we reached a village where I had determined to pass the night. As we drove into the great gateway of the inn, I saw on one side the light of a rousing kitchen fire beaming through a window. I entered, and admired for the hundredth time that picture of convenience, neatness, and broad honest enjoyment, the kitchen of an inn. It was of spacious dimension, hung around by copper and tin vessels, highly polished, and decorated here and there with a Christmas green. Hams, tongues, and flitches of bacon were suspended from the ceiling; a smoke-jack made its ceaseless clanking behind the fireplace, and a clock ticked in one corner. A well-scoured deal table extended along one side of the kitchen, with a cold round of beef, and other hearty viands upon it, over which two foaming tankards of ale seemed mounting guard. Travellers of inferior order were preparing to attack this stout repast, while others sat smoking or gossiping over their ale, on two high-backed oaken settles beside the fire.

Washington Irving, Travelling at Christmas, 1884

ISLANDS

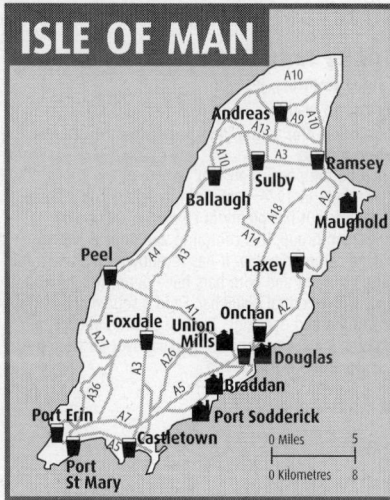

ISLE OF MAN

Okell's Manx Pale Ale, Bitter; 1 changing beer H
An imposing historic building in the ancient capital of Mann, dating back to 1833. Steeped in history, some a little dark, the George has a well-earned place on the Castletown ghost walk. It has recently been refurbished and offers accommodation of a high standard. The front rooms provide superb views of the castle just across the market square. Photos on the walls show scenes from around the island. ✿⌂◁▷≢≉♣🖵(1)🛜

Sidings L
Victoria Road, IM9 1EF (next to railway station)
☎ (01624) 823282
Bushy's Castletown Bitter, Bitter; Okell's Bitter; 8 changing beers (sourced nationally) H
Traditional beer-drinkers' pub with a main bar area, a games room with pool and sports TVs, and a dining area that is also used for live music and quizzes. It usually serves up to eight real ales and three local beers. The reasonably priced food has been improved in recent years, and it has pool and darts teams.
Q🌭✿◁▷&≢♣P🖵😺🛜

Union Hotel L
Arbory Street, IM9 1LH
☎ (01624) 825286
Okell's Bitter; 1 changing beer (sourced nationally) H
Rich in history and full of character, the Union has been an inn since 1853 and was a brewery before that. It is a friendly and informal locals' pub with a relaxed atmosphere, and can be busy at weekends. The building is constructed of Manx stone; a feature has been made of this in the main bar areas. There is also a snug, plus a bespoke sports room to the rear. Q≢♣🖵😺

Douglas

Albert Hotel
3 Chapel Row, IM1 2BJ
☎ (01624) 673632 ⊕ albertiom.com
Bushy's Castletown Bitter, Bitter; Okell's Bitter; 1 changing beer (sourced locally) H
The Albert is a traditional and well-maintained pub close to Douglas Harbour, and the one nearest to the sea terminal. It has an interior recognised by CAMRA as being of regional historic importance. A central bar area serves two rooms – the one to the right features pool, darts and sports TV; to the left is a quieter bar with photographs of Steam Packet boats adorning the walls. The cellar areas are thought to be some of the oldest structures in Douglas. Q≢♣🖵😺🛜

Old Market Inn L
Chapel Row, IM1 2BJ
☎ 07624 381076
2 changing beers (often Bushy's)
Under the same ownership for many years, the Market has the smallest bar on the island, serving two separate rooms. The landlord is a keen TT supporter and the inn's walls are adorned with photos of the races. Friendly and very popular with locals, the pub is also welcoming to visitors. It is close to both the bus station on Lord Street and the ferry terminal, so makes an ideal waiting room. ≢(Isle of Man) 🖵

Andreas

Grosvenor Country Inn L
Andreas Road, IM7 4HE
☎ (01624) 888007
Odin Manx Mild; Okell's Bitter; 1 changing beer (sourced nationally) H
The Isle of Man's most northerly pub, this free house is popular for both drinking and dining, and is a meeting place for many local groups. The informal public bar hosts pub games. Quiz nights and musical events are held. A large collection of old Shell advertising pictures is on display. The pub provides a takeaway food service.
🌭✿◁▷&♣P🖵😺🛜

Ballaugh

Raven L
The Main Road, IM7 5EG
☎ (01624) 896128
Okell's Bitter; house beer (by Okell's); 1 changing beer (sourced nationally) H
Village-centre pub next to Ballaugh Bridge on the TT course. There is a comfortable main bar area with dining spaces off to the right and left. To the rear is a separate darts, pool and TV room. Seating space outside is heavily used in summer especially during race periods, when motorbikes leap over the bridge. The house beer is Raven's Claw, an Okell's brew available only in this pub.
Q🌭✿◁▷&♠♣P🖵(5,6) 😺🛜

Castletown

Castle Arms L
The Quay, IM9 1LD
☎ (01624) 824673
Okell's Manx Pale Ale, Bitter, IPA; 1 changing beer H
Also known locally as the Glue Pot, this two-roomed bar is superbly located near the castle and harbour. It is featured on the Manx £5 note – the only pub in the British Isles to appear on a banknote. One room houses nautical memorabilia, the other celebrates the TT races. The patio overlooking the picturesque harbour is popular in summer. Q🌭✿♠≢♣(1,2)😺🛜

George Hotel L
The Parade, IM9 1LG
☎ (01624) 822533

REAL ALE BREWERIES
Bushy's Braddan
Kaneen's Union Mills (NEW)
Odin Maughold
Okell's Douglas
Radical Port Sodderick (NEW)

Prospect Hotel Ⓛ

Prospect Hill, IM1 1ET

☎ (01624) 616773

Okell's Manx Pale Ale, Bitter, IPA; 5 changing beers (often Okell's) Ⓗ

Opened in 1857 in the finance sector of the island's capital, this large single-room pub has different areas, some decorated with pictures of the law profession, reflecting its proximity to the law courts. There are eight handpumps in two banks of four on separate sides of the bar. Guest ales change regularly, and occasionally real cider and perry are available. Wednesday is quiz night. Weekday night closing times vary significantly.
◖≢♣🖨(3,11) ✿ 🛜

Rovers Return Ⓛ

11 Church Street, IM1 2AG (on pedestrian street behind town hall)

☎ (01624) 676459

Bushy's Bitter; 4 changing beers (often Bushy's) Ⓗ

Fascinating pub tucked away in a street behind Douglas Town Hall, featuring handpumps fashioned from fire hoses, a traditional coal fire, and a shrine to Blackburn Rovers in a back room. The almost warren-like series of rooms is frequented by a truly eclectic and loyal clientele. Bushy's regular and seasonal beers are always available, along with real cider. Famously large food portions are served at lunchtime. ✿◖≢♣●🖨✿🛜

Terminus Tavern Ⓛ

Strathallan Crescent, IM2 4NR

☎ (01624) 624312

Okell's Bitter; 3 changing beers (sourced nationally; often Okell's) Ⓗ

Found at the Manx Electric Railway station at the northern end of the prom, the Terminus has a large front bar with bay windows, a smaller rear bar and a side area for games. Decoration in the front bar illustrates interesting architectural features. Excellent food is served. Outside at the front is a large patio with views over Douglas Bay.
Q🛏◖🅳≢(Derby Castle) ♣P🖨(1,10) ✿ 🛜

Thirsty Pigeon Ⓛ

38/40 Victoria Street, IM1 2LW

☎ (01624) 675584 ⊕ thirstypigeon.com

4 changing beers (sourced locally) Ⓗ

One-room pub with welcoming staff, popular with frequenters of wine bars and traditional drinkers alike. The dark-wood interior has clean lines and unfussy decor, complemented by button-back seating and matching bar stools. Good use is made of the space to accommodate numerous customers without the place feeling crowded. Live music is performed regularly at weekends. ◖🛆≢🖨

Woodbourne Hotel Ⓛ

Alexander Drive, IM2 3QF (in Woodbourne area of Douglas)

☎ (01624) 676754

Okell's Manx Pale Ale, Bitter, IPA; 3 changing beers (sourced nationally) Ⓗ

Handsome red-brick Victorian local in a residential setting within walking distance of the town centre. This is a popular pub with a strong community spirit and a proud tradition of charity fundraising. Its three bars and games/music room underwent a tasteful makeover in 2019. The central bar displays original watercolours by a renowned local artist, detailing historical characters from when this was a male-only pub. Q🛆♣●🖨✿🛜

Foxdale

Baltic Inn Ⓛ

1 Glentramman Terrace, IM4 3EE

☎ (01624) 801305 ⊕ balticinn.pub

Okell's Manx Pale Ale, Bitter; 1 changing beer (sourced nationally) Ⓗ

The only pub in a former mining town, with one main room divided into separate seating areas. A roaring real fire in winter adds to the atmosphere. Up to three real ales are on handpump along with Okell's IPA and Maclir in bottles. There are some fascinating historical photos on the walls of Foxdale during the mining boom. This friendly village pub is the essential hub of the village. It once again offers accommodation, after a long gap.
Q🛏🛆✿🍴◖🛆♣🆗(4) ✿ 🛜

Laxey

Mines Tavern Ⓛ

Captains Hill, IM4 7AY

☎ (01624) 861484

Okell's Manx Pale Ale, Bitter; 1 changing beer (sourced locally) Ⓗ

Former mine captain's home in a picturesque setting alongside Laxey's historic tram station, with an unusual bar made from a 1902 tram car. A warming fire welcomes visitors in winter; in good weather the garden is popular. Trams run to Douglas, Ramsey and the summit of Snaefell, the island's mountain. The pub is close to the famous Laxey Wheel and features memorabilia from the local mines and railways. Opening times and food availability are seasonal.
🛏✿◖🛆≢♣🖨(3A,3) ✿

Queen's Hotel Ⓛ

New Road, IM4 7BP (600yds S of village centre)

☎ (01624) 861195

Bushy's Bitter; Odin Laksaa Pale; 3 changing beers (sourced locally) Ⓗ

A large, traditional open-plan pub that dates back to 1863 and was almost destroyed by fire in 1905. The walls feature many photographs of the TT motorbike races and the surrounding area. The pub hosts pool, darts and live music, and shows sport on TV. Its sheltered rear beer garden overlooks the Manx Electric Railway, which runs between Douglas and Ramsey – as do buses that stop outside. 🛏✿🍴🛆≢♣●P🖨(3,3A)✿🛜

Onchan

Manx Arms Ⓛ

Main Road, IM3 1BE

☎ (01624) 675484

Okell's Bitter; 2 changing beers (often Okell's) Ⓗ

Traditional village inn on the main road with separate public and lounge bars. An extensive range of real ales and ciders is served. Live music features most Saturday evenings and occasional karaoke nights are held. TV screens in the public bar show sporting events. The pub is on the frequent bus route from Douglas to Ramsey, and on the former Clypse motorcycle racing course – pictured in historical photographs on the walls. Q🛆♣●P🖨✿🛜

Peel

Royal Hotel Ⓛ

Atholl Street, IM5 1HG

☎ (01624) 842217

4 changing beers (sourced nationally; often Bushy's, Odin) Ⓗ

For those entering for the first time, the unusual layout of the Royal comes as a surprise. The bar is set deeply to the rear of the building at the end of a long, narrow corridor within the well-furnished drinking area. A pool table and dartboard are offset from the bar area. Outside is an excellent suntrap garden. ✿♣🖳(5,6)🛜

The Miller's T'Ale
33 Michael Street, IM5 1HD
☎ 07624 307356
5 changing beers (sourced nationally) Ⓗ
The island's first micropub opened in 2018 in a former shop premises, and was renamed in 2020 following a makeover. It serves varying styles of cask ales, mostly sourced from the UK, plus an extensive choice of real ciders. The pub is known for conversation and good company, and has no music or gaming machines. An excellent cheeseboard is provided on Sundays, with contributions invited. Q🕯🖳(5,6)🐾🛜

White House Hotel Ⓛ
2 Tynwald Road, IM5 1LA (200yds from bus station)
☎ (01624) 842252
Bushy's Bitter; Odin Manx Mild, Laksaa Pale, Asgard Bitter; Okell's Bitter; Timothy Taylor Landlord; 4 changing beers (sourced nationally) Ⓗ
Popular community venue featuring real fires, and a large room that hosts live music and TV sports events. A smaller snug with its own bar connects with the rest of the pub through a sliding door. A further room offers a pool table and darts. In addition to the extensive range of cask ales, it serves up to six real ciders and an excellent selection of gins and single malt whiskies. Isle of Man CAMRA Pub of the Year 2020. Q✿♣🕯P🖳(5,6)🐾🛜

Port Erin

Bay Hotel Ⓛ
Shore Road, IM9 6HL
☎ (01624) 832084
Bushy's Castletown Bitter, Bitter, Old Bushy Tail; house beer (by Bushy's); 2 changing beers (sourced locally) Ⓗ
Bushy's flagship pub is on one of the best beaches on the island. It has several traditional rooms including a public bar, a quiet room and a dining area. A good range of Bushy's brews is usually available. Beach concerts featuring local bands and a promenade patio help make the Bay a great venue. Q🕭✿🕦🕨よ≉♣♠🐾🛜

Station Hotel Ⓛ
Station Road, IM9 6AE
☎ (01624) 838991
Okell's Manx Pale Ale, Bitter, IPA; 1 changing beer (sourced nationally) Ⓗ
Opposite the steam train station and only 100 yards from the stunning bay, the Station is an ideal first or last pub to visit in Port Erin. Traditionally and informally furnished, it has a relaxed atmosphere and offers the town's largest Okell's beer selection. Drinkers and diners mingle comfortably in the spacious main bar area, also using the large function room at busier times. 🕭🕨よ≉P🖳🐾🛜

Port St Mary

Albert Hotel Ⓛ
Athol Street, IM9 5DS (opp harbour)
☎ (01624) 832118
Bushy's Bitter; Okell's Bitter; 2 changing beers (sourced nationally) Ⓗ
A hidden gem in the heart of this coastal village, the Albert boasts impressive views over the harbour. It has a

public bar with games area, a cosy lounge bar heated by a wood-burning stove, and a separate area with tables and seating. Light snacks are served. A pub quiz takes place on Sunday evening. Q✿よ♣🖳🛜

Ramsey

Mitre Ⓛ
16 Parliament Street, IM8 1AP
☎ (01624) 813045
Okell's Bitter; house beer (by Okell's); 2 changing beers (sourced locally) Ⓗ
A welcoming pub with a friendly clientele. It has been refurbished to good effect in recent years, offering a fine view of Ramsey's quayside and illuminated swing bridge. The first-floor Harbour Bar serves Okell's Jough. Food includes a Sunday lunchtime carvery (booking advised). The pub can be accessed from the main street or the quay. 🕨≉(Plaza)♣🖳(3,3A)🐾🛜

Swan Ⓛ
Parliament Square, IM8 2LN
☎ (01624) 814236
Okell's Manx Pale Ale, Bitter, IPA Ⓗ
Family-friendly pub on the TT race circuit, with a good reputation for food. Its interior has two main areas: to the left is a sports bar with pool table, to the right a dining room. One of two remaining Okell's pubs in Ramsey, it stocks a large range of the brewery's beers. Live music is hosted occasionally. The large garden is popular in summer, especially when motorcycle racing is taking place. Q🕭✿🕦🕨よ≉(Plaza)♣🖳🐾🛜

Trafalgar Hotel Ⓛ
West Quay, IM8 1DW
☎ (01624) 814601
Odin Manx Mild; 2 changing beers (sourced nationally; often Odin) Ⓗ
A long-standing real ale pub on the harbour, offering a warm welcome and a choice of excellent beers. Four ales are served, predominantly from Odin Brewery. Sport is shown on TVs downstairs; an upstairs room is open only during the day. Q🕭≉(Plaza)🖳🐾🛜

Sulby

Ginger Hall Ⓛ
Ballamanagh Road, IM7 2HB
☎ (01624) 897231
Okell's Bitter; 3 changing beers (sourced locally) Ⓗ
Welcoming pub that is a landmark on the TT course. Its interior features a real fire and an impressive beer engine that dispenses two local real ales plus regularly changing guests. Attractions include historic TT pictures, a large mirror behind the bar and a huge circuit map on the ceiling – do not spill your beer while admiring it. The pub has a separate Thai restaurant and offers en-suite accommodation. 🕭✿🕮🕨▲♣P🖳🐾🛜

Sulby Glen Hotel Ⓛ
Main Road, IM7 2HR
☎ (01624) 897240
Bushy's Bitter; Okell's Bitter; 2 changing beers (sourced locally) Ⓗ
Friendly and popular pub on the TT circuit's Sulby straight. Interesting photos of the area and the TT help attract race enthusiasts. A motorcycle engine set up on the main bar dispenses four keg beers. The excellent home-cooked food uses local ingredients. Features include a sports TV, pool table and warming open fire.
Q🕭✿🕮🕨よ▲♣P🖳(5,6)

The Breweries

BREWERIES OVERVIEW

The coronavirus pandemic continues to shape the brewing industry throughout 2021. Roger Protz takes a look at what's been happening over the past year.

The keynote events of 2021 were the remarkable falls from grace of two very different brewing operations: Brains in Wales and BrewDog in Scotland. Brains is a Welsh icon, family-owned since 1882. The imposing brewery chimney, embossed with the company name, on its old site soared over Cardiff and the Millennium Stadium.

BrewDog, in sharp contrast, is the pugnacious brewery near Aberdeen that has cast a dismissive eye over conventional beer making and raised millions with its Equity for Punks crowd-funding initiatives.

DRAGONS DOWN

The Welsh brewery Brains, famous for such beers as Dark, SA and Reverend James, has gone into free fall. In 2019 it closed the brewery close to the city's main train station and moved to a new site, the Dragon Brewery, in Cardiff Bay. The brewery cost £10 million and, with the decline in beer consumption compounded by the corona virus pandemic, the company racked up a mountain of debt.

It also made the serious mistake of moving outside its core business by opening a group of coffee shops called Coffee Number One. To reduce its debts, Brains sold the shops to Caffè Nero, and this was followed by the dramatic news in March 2021 that the company was handing over its entire 156-strong pub estate to Marston's.

The future of Brains Brewery is in doubt

Marston's will rent the pubs with an estimated annual income of £5.5 million for Brains. As a result of the merger of Marston's brewing interests with Carlsberg, this means the Danish group's lagers will appear in pubs that will be remain branded Brains.

With the banks still pulling the strings, the viability of the Dragon Brewery is in doubt. When asked, Brains will say only that the future of the brewery is under discussion. No ringing endorsement that Brains beers will remain in Wales – brands that support Welsh rugby, football and cricket and which would lose their lustre if production moved to England.

PUNKS WITH PURPOSE

There's no question of BrewDog closing its brewery. The company launched by James Watt and Martin Dickie in a garage in 2007 is now worth £2 billion, As well as the main brewery at Ellon near Aberdeen, where 220,000 hectolitres a year are produced, the company has a second brewery in Berlin and plans production sites in the United States and Australia. It has a chain of pubs in Britain with bars in Las Vegas, Tokyo, Shanghai and Brisbane.

The BrewDog story is one of spectacular success – but that success has been badly tainted by the departure from their core values by founders Watt and Dickie. In 2007 they offered something refreshingly different from what they called 'industrial lagers and stuffy ales'. Their main brand, Punk IPA, reached out to a young audience of bobble hats and beards who were happy to invest more than £80 million through the Equity for Punks crowd-funding scheme.

But a less than flattering image of BrewDog appeared in June 2021 when 250 former members of staff, calling themselves Punks with Purpose, published an open letter in which they accused Dickie and Watt of creating a 'rotten culture that damaged their mental health.' They said a policy of 'growth at all costs' compromised health and safety, and there was a 'toxic attitude' to junior members of staff. They also criticised the founders for pursuing 'vanity' public relations stunts.

The letter came in the wake of the news in 2017 that BrewDog had sold a quarter of its shares to two companies based in the tax haven of the Cayman Islands. One of the companies, TSG Consumer Partners, now controls 22.3 per cent of BrewDog's shares. The deal gives TSG priority over all other

BrewDog made the news in June 2021 when a group of former employees accused the company of toxic working practices

shareholders when important decisions are taken, such as BrewDog seeking a listing on the Stock Exchange, the bastion of the system the brewery was created to challenge. As many original shareholders are saying, BrewDog has lost its punk appeal.

GLOBAL GIANTS

The repercussions of ground-shaking developments at Greene King and Marston's, reported in last year's Guide, are still working their way through the system. Greene King, dating from 1799, is now owned by a Hong Kong property company, CK Asset Holdings. The group has no roots in brewing and the fears expressed in 2019 that the new owners would asset strip the brewery bore some fruit in 2021 when 66 'non-core' pubs were disposed of. But that still leaves an estate of more than 1,000 pubs and the beer portfolio remains intact.

Marston's shook the industry in 2020 when it merged to form the Carlsberg Marston's Brewing Company. While Marston's runs six breweries and Carlsberg has just one in Britain, the Danish group controls 60 per cent of the business and the chief executive previously ran Carlsberg Poland. As Carlsberg has no interest in cask beer, a question mark hangs over the future of some of the Marston's plants.

SQUEEZED MIDDLE

On a positive note, two new modern plants could be a showcase for the 'squeezed middle' of regional and family brewers caught between the grindstones of giant global producers with their deeply discounted products and small craft producers who enjoy the advantage of paying less duty on their beers.

Charles Wells in Bedford and Everards in Leicester have downsized to new breweries called Brewpoint and the Beer Hall that draw their inspiration from the American taproom model. Visitors can tour the breweries, drink the end products in adjacent bars and enjoy meals in restaurant areas, while beer is available for take home from brewery shops. The beers are also on sale in the companies' pubs.

A review of Small Brewers' Relief by the Treasury had not been completed when the Guide went to press. SBR means that brewers who produce up to 5,000 hectolitres a year enjoy duty relief as high as 50 per cent compared to bigger producers but there were rumours the Treasury could reduce these benefits. While such a move must be strenuously opposed, it's hoped that members of the 'squeezed middle' will also gain from the review.

YOUNG'S PUNCHED OUT

In July 2021 Young's in London shocked beer lovers by selling the bulk of its tenanted pubs. When the Wandsworth brewery was run by the Young family, such a move would have been seen as selling their birthright.

In the 1970s the family stood firm against the tide of keg beer inflicted on beer drinkers by national brewers and remained dedicated to cask ale. But when the chairman John Young died, the family sold the brewery, which closed in 2006 and became a pub company, its beers outsourced to first Charles Wells and then Marston's.

The sale of 56 of the 63 sites in the Ram Pub Company is disturbing as they have been bought by Punch Taverns with its record of closing perfectly viable pubs and selling them to property developers. And the price of £53 million seems cheap for pubs in London and the well-heeled Home Counties. It's a sad end to a brewery once run by a family proud of its history and heritage. It seems birthrights are cheap today.

Former editor of the *Good Beer Guide*, **Roger Protz** is considered one of the leading beer writers in the world, with a long career in journalism and publishing, and having won multiple awards. Roger has authored many books on beer and pubs, including *300 Beers to Try Before You Die*. Follow him on Twitter **@RogerProtzBeer** and **protzonbeer.co.uk**.

How to use the Breweries section

This section lists breweries operating in the United Kingdom, the Isle of Man and the Channel Islands. Breweries are listed in alphabetical order. They include independent companies (regional, family, micro-brewers and brewpubs), national brewers and global groups. If a brewery owns more than one site, these are cross-referenced. Within each brewery entry, regular beers are listed in increasing order of strength. Websites should be consulted when breweries produce occasional or seasonal beers that are available for less than six months of the year.

KEY TO BREWERY ENTRIES

BREWERY SYMBOLS

Brewpub: a pub that brews beer on the premises

Serve with tight sparkler: the brewery's beers can be acceptably served through a 'tight sparkler' attached to the nozzle of the beer pump, designed to give a thick collar of foam on the beer

Do not serve with tight sparkler: the brewery's beers should NOT be served through a tight sparkler. CAMRA is opposed to the growing tendency to serve southern-brewed beers with the aid of sparklers, which aerate the beer and tend to drive hop aroma and flavour into the head, altering the balance of the beer achieved in the brewery. When neither symbol is used it means the brewery in question has not stated a preference

Brewery tours available: check with individual breweries for details

Brewery shop: beer available to take away. Check opening hours in advance

LIVE Live beer: the brewery produces live, conditioned beer in bottles, cans or other small formats

Seasonal beers: the brewery produces seasonal beers in addition to its regular range

V Vegan: the brewery produces vegan beers (check with brewery for further details. Not all beers produced may be vegan)

GF Gluten free: the brewery produces gluten-free beers (check with brewery for further details. Not all beers may be gluten free)

Taproom: the brewery features an on-site taproom (always check ahead with brewery for up-to-date information about opening times and events)

BEER STYLES

The following styles are listed after each beer name in the brewery section. Please refer to pages 8-11 for more information.

BARLEY	Barley wine	**RED**	Red ale
BROWN	Brown ale	**MILD**	Mild; session or strong
IPA	IPA; British or New World	**PORTER**	Porter; session or strong
OLD	Old ale	**STOUT**	Stout; session or strong
BITTER	Bitter; session or premium	**SPECIALITY**	Speciality beer; differently produced or flavoured
BLOND	Blond ale; session or premium		
GOLD	Golden ale; session or premium	**STRONG**	Strong ale
PALE	Pale ale; session or premium		

ABBREVIATIONS

ABV Stands for Alcohol by Volume, which is a measure of the percentage of alcohol in finished beer

SIBA Indicates a member of the Society of Independent Brewers

IFBB Indicates a member of the Independent Family Brewers of Britain

NOTE: The Breweries section was correct at the time of going to press and every effort has been made to ensure that all regularly available cask-conditioned beers are included.

The Breweries

The breweries listed in this section include micro, small, family, regional, national and global companies. Please use the Beer index (p852) to help locate beers.

1086

Old Brewhouse, Cusworth Hall, Cusworth Lane, Doncaster, South Yorkshire, DN5 7TU
☎ (01302) 639880

Office: Doncaster Cutlure & Leisure Trust, The Dome, Doncaster Lakeside, Bawtry Road, Doncaster, DN4 7PD ⊕ 1086brewery.co.uk

🌐1086 was established in 2018, in the original brewhouse of Cusworth Hall, an 18th century, Grade I, country house in Cusworth, near Doncaster. The brewery shares space with its popular brewery tap, the Old Brewhouse. Beers are available in the taproom, and occasionally at the Leopard in Doncaster. ✦

1648

🍺 **Old Stables Brewery, Mill Lane, East Hoathly, East Sussex, BN8 6QB**
☎ (01825) 840830 ⊕ 1648brewing.co.uk

⊠ The 1648 brewery, set up in the old stable block at the King's Head pub in 2003, derives its name from the year of the deposition of King Charles I. One pub is owned and more than 40 outlets are supplied. ‼🍺✦LIVE

Hop Pocket (ABV 3.7%) GOLD
Triple Champion (ABV 4%) BITTER
Signature (ABV 4.4%) GOLD
Laughing Frog (ABV 5.2%) BITTER

3 Brewers of St Albans SIBA

The Potato Shed, Symonds Hyde Farm, Symonds Hyde Lane, Hatfield, Hertfordshire, AL10 9BB
☎ (01707) 271636 ☎ 07941 854615
⊕ 3brewers.co.uk

⊠ Launched in 2013, the 3 Brewers operates on a farm set in the picturesque Hertfordshire countryside. The brewery uses fresh water from its own borehole. Spent grains are donated to a local farmer. Beers are supplied to local pubs, restaurants and bars. The brewery has its own taproom, open every weekend, hosting events including an annual beer and music festival. ‼🍺✦

Dark Mild (ABV 3.6%) MILD
Golden English Ale (ABV 3.8%) GOLD
Copper (ABV 3.9%) BITTER
Classic English Ale (ABV 4%) BITTER
Blonde (ABV 4.2%) BLOND
Ruby English Ale (ABV 4.3%) BITTER
IPA (ABV 4.6%) PALE
Special English Ale (ABV 4.8%) BITTER

Contract brewed for B&T Brewery:
Plum Mild (ABV 3.8%) SPECIALITY
Shefford Bitter (ABV 3.8%) BITTER
Shefford Dark Mild (ABV 3.8%) MILD
Golden Fox (ABV 4.1%) GOLD
Black Dragon Mild (ABV 4.3%) MILD
Dunstable Giant (ABV 4.4%) BITTER
Dragon Slayer (ABV 4.5%) GOLD
Edwin Taylor's Extra Stout (ABV 4.5%) STOUT
Fruit Bat (ABV 4.5%) SPECIALITY
SPA (Shefford Pale Ale) (ABV 4.5%) PALE
SOD (ABV 5%) OLD
SOS (ABV 5%) OLD

3 Lamps (NEW)

🍺 **2 Castle Street, Swansea, SA1 3JE**
⊕ threelamps.co.uk

Brewing began in 2021 in a three-storey building which includes a taproom and roof terrace. Beers may be marketed as the Ugly Lovely Brewing Co. No real ale. ✦

3 Non Beards

🍺 **Rook & Gaskill, 12 Lawrence Street, York, YO10 3WP** ☎ 07980 994210 ⊕ 3nonbeards.co.uk

🌐Launched in 2019 as a partnership of three friends, this one-barrel plant is in the basement of the Rook and Gaskill pub. Advised by innovative local brewers, the beer range can be found in the pub and at beer festivals. Around 30 brews per year means an eclectic range of mainly one-offs and frequent single hop beers. ♦✦

360°

Unit 24b, Bluebell Business Estate, Sheffield Park, East Sussex, TN22 3HQ
☎ (01825) 722375 ⊕ 360degreebrewing.com

⊠ Under new management since 2020 but still brewing at Sheffield Park, adjacent to the famous Bluebell Railway. The brewery is committed to producing high quality cask conditioned ales and has increased its output of craft keg and cans. ‼🍺♦

Bluebell Best (ABV 4.2%) BITTER
West Coast Pale Ale (ABV 5%) PALE

3D Beer

See Epic Beers

3P's (NEW)

Burton Road, Woodville, Derbyshire, DE11 7JE
⊕ 3psbrewery.co.uk

Innovative nanobrewery with a 400-litre fermentation capacity, founded in 2020 by an enthusiastic homebrewer. Using only the freshest natural ingredients, all beers are vegetarian and vegan-friendly (apart from the milk stout). The brewery name is taken from Pits, Pots and Pipes, for which Woodville was once renowned. Beer is available in local outlets in Burton, Swadlincote and Derby. V

Fools Gold (ABV 4.3%) GOLD
Bob 'ole (ABV 4.5%) BITTER
Knocker Upper (ABV 4.8%) RED
Anthracite (ABV 5%) SPECIALITY
Big Butty (ABV 5%) BITTER
Bottom Knocker (ABV 5.3%) PORTER

4 Mice

🍺 **Coach & Horses, Main Street, Bolton-by-Bowland, Lancashire, BB7 4NW**
☎ (01200) 447331
⊕ coachandhorsesribblevalley.co.uk

🌐A four-barrel brewery in a gastro-pub, situated in the Trough of Bowland.

4Ts SIBA

Unit 20, Manor Industrial Estate, Lower Wash Lane, Latchford, Warrington, Cheshire, WA4 1PL
☎ (01925) 417820 ☎ 07917 730184
⊕ 4tsbrewery.co.uk

4Ts returned to Warrington in 2015 and in 2019 the brewing plant was replaced with a new 12-barrel brew kit. A core range of beers is regularly produced with many one-off specials. Occasional brews of Tipsy Angel beers are produced. Beers can be found in the Tavern, Warrington. A brewery tap room is anticipated. ‼♦

EPA (ABV 3.7%) PALE
SPA (ABV 3.8%) PALE
APA (ABV 4%) PALE
WA4 (ABV 4%) SPECIALITY
WSB (ABV 4.2%) BITTER
IPA (ABV 4.6%) PALE
Panzer Pils (ABV 4.8%) SPECIALITY
English Stout (ABV 5%) STOUT
Big Daddy DIPA (ABV 7.2%) IPA

Brewed under the Tipsy Angel Brewery name:
Angels Mild (ABV 3.8%) MILD
George Shaw Premium (ABV 4.3%) BITTER
Angels Folly (ABV 5.2%) OLD
Taipur (ABV 5.9%) GOLD

40FT SIBA

Bootyard, Abbott Street, Dalston, London, E8 3DP

The Printhouse, 18-20 Ashwin Street, Dalston, London, E8 3DL ⊕ 40ftbrewery.com

Six-barrel microbrewery 40FT began brewing in 2015 in two 20ft shipping containers. It has since expanded to a total of 150ft. Beers are produced for its taproom as well as pubs, bars, restaurants and off-licences. Output is nearly all keg and cans. ♦

71 Brewing

36-40 Bellfield Street, Dundee, DD1 5HZ
☎ (01382) 203133 ⊕ 71brewing.com

Brewing began in 2016, principally brewery-conditioned lagers. A taproom and bottle shop is open daily. ‼🍴♦V♦

8 Sail SIBA

Heckington Windmill, Hale Road, Heckington, Lincolnshire, NG34 9JW
☎ (01529) 469308 ☎ 07866 183479
⊕ 8sailbrewery.co.uk

8 Sail Brewery was established in 2010 and operates on a six-barrel brew plant. The brewery nestles in the shadow of Heckington Windmill, Britain's only eight-sailed windmill, from where the brewery takes its name. The Mill is now working and helps to mill malted grain for the brewery. The brewery shop stocks bottle-conditioned beers alongside local ciders. The front of the brewery has been converted into a Victorian-style bar, which has beer on handpump daily. The large outside area is weather dependent so hours may vary. 🍴♦LIVE♦

Ploughmans Lunch (ABV 3.8%) PALE
Windmill Bitter (ABV 3.8%) BITTER
Froglet (ABV 4%) PALE
Fenman (ABV 4.1%) BITTER
Pilgrim Pale Ale (ABV 4.2%) PALE
Rolling Stone (ABV 4.3%) PALE
Red Windmill (ABV 4.4%) SPECIALITY
King John's Jewels (ABV 4.5%) GOLD
Millstone (ABV 4.5%) BITTER

Windy Miller (ABV 4.6%) STOUT
Mayflower IPA (ABV 4.7%) PALE
Fen Slodger (ABV 4.8%) BITTER
Damson Porter (ABV 5%) SPECIALITY
Victorian Porter (ABV 5%) PORTER
Old Colony (ABV 5.3%) PALE
Black Widow (ABV 5.5%) MILD
John Barleycorn IPA (ABV 5.5%) PALE

81 Artisan

The Courtyard, Crowshall Farm, Chilgrove Road, West Dean, Chichester, West Sussex, PO18 9HP
✉ hello@81artisan.com

Brewing began in 2017 using a 10-barrel plant.

9 Lives

Unit 303, Ystradgynlais Workshops, Trawsffordd Road, Ystradgynlais, SA9 1BS ☎ 07743 559736
⊕ 9livesbrewing.co.uk

☺9 Lives Brewing was established in 2017 by Robert Scott, formerly the brewer at the now defunct Bryncelyn Brewery, using the same six-barrel plant. A number of beers are replications of former Bryncelyn beers, which have been renamed. ‼♦LIVE

Amber (ABV 4%) PALE
Pale amber with a hoppy aroma. A refreshing hoppy, fruity flavour with balancing bitterness; a similar lasting finish. A beer full of flavour for its gravity.
Dark (ABV 4%) MILD
Dark brown with an inviting aroma of malt, roast and fruit. A gentle bitterness mixes roast with malt, hops and fruit, giving a complex, satisfying and lasting finish.
Gold (ABV 4.5%) BITTER
An inviting aroma of hops, fruit and malt, and a golden colour. The tasty mix of hops, fruit, bitterness and background malt ends with a long, hoppy, bitter aftertaste. Full-bodied and drinkable.
Pale (ABV 4.7%) PALE

A-B InBev

Porter House Tun, 500 Capability Green, Luton, LU1 3LS
☎ (01582) 391166 ⊕ inbev.com
No real ale.

Abbey SIBA

Abbey Brewery, Camden Row, Bath, BA1 5LB
☎ (01225) 444437 ⊕ abbeyales.co.uk

Founded in 1997 Abbey Ales was the first brewery in Bath for more than 50 years. It supplies more than 80 regular outlets within a 20-mile radius and its beers are more widely available in the South West via wholesalers. Four pubs are operated in Bath. ♦

Bath Best (ABV 4%) BITTER
Bath Pale Ale (ABV 4.2%) PALE
Bellringer (ABV 4.2%) BITTER
A notably hoppy ale, light to medium-bodied, clean-tasting, refreshingly dry, with a balancing sweetness. Citrus, pale malt aroma and dry, bitter finish.

Abbeydale SIBA

Unit 8, Aizlewood Road, Sheffield, South Yorkshire, S8 0YX
☎ (0114) 281 2712 ⊕ abbeydalebrewery.co.uk

☺Established in 1996, Abbeydale, the second oldest, and one of the largest Sheffield breweries, produce more than 220 barrels a week. Investment and expansion enabled growth, including a substantial collection/mail-order offering. At least one new beer is produced weekly including some small batch, barrel-aged brews as part of the 'Funk Dungeon' project (highlighted in the annual 'Funk Festival.') One pub, the Rising Sun, Nether Green, is owned. ♦V

Daily Bread (ABV 3.8%) BITTER
Deception (ABV 4.1%) PALE
Heathen (ABV 4.1%) PALE
Moonshine (ABV 4.3%) PALE
Absolution (ABV 5.3%) PALE
Black Mass (ABV 6.6%) STOUT

Abernyte

South Latch Farm, Abernyte, Perthshire, PH14 9SU
☎ 07827 715915 ⊕ abernytebrewery.com

Established in 2016, the brewery overlooks the Carse of Gowrie. Brewing features a step mashing process in small batch, producing a range of unfiltered and naturally carbonated craft beers, packaged mainly in bottles.

Abyss SIBA

Unit 3, The Malthouse, Davey's Lane, Lewes, BN7 2BF
⊕ abyssbrewing.co.uk

⊠ Started 2017, the brewery relocated to the ex-Black Cat premises, Framfield later that year. It moved again in 2021 to part of the old Southdown Brewery malthouse, Lewes. Brew length is eight-barrels, although capacity has increased significantly recently. The beers (all vegan-friendly), are produced in rotation. Details are available from the website shop. It is hoped to offer a cask beer in the new brewery tap (open Fridays and Saturdays). V♦

Accidental

🗲 **The Old Stables, Bulk Street, Lancaster, LA1 1PU**
☎ 07930 592749

Second Site: Old Market Court, Morecambe, LA4 5HS
⊕ accidentalbrewery.com

Initially a brewpub located on the edge of Lancaster city centre in an 18th century converted stable block, which opened in 2018. A 140-litre brewplant is used. In 2021 it opened a second brewery in Morecambe. Occasional cask ale is produced.

Acid Brewing Cartel

78 Barrland Street, Glasgow, G41 1RA

A small brewery, which creates sour, wild and farmhouse ales, focussing on merging historical techniques and traditional yeasts in a modern context. LIVE V

Acorn SIBA

Unit 3, Aldham Industrial Estate, Mitchell Road, Wombwell, Barnsley, South Yorkshire, S73 8HA
☎ (01226) 270734 ⊕ acorn-brewery.co.uk

☺Acorn was set up in 2003 with a 10-barrel expanding to a 20-barrel plant when the brewery moved to larger premises. It currently has a 160-barrel a week capacity. All beers are produced using the Barnsley Bitter yeast strain, dating back to the 1850s. ‼🍺♦LIVE

Yorkshire Pride (ABV 3.7%) BITTER
Golden-coloured session beer, with pleasing fruit notes. A mouthwatering blend of malt and hops create a fruity taste which leads to a clean bitter finish.
Barnsley Bitter (ABV 3.8%) BITTER
Brown bitter, smooth, malty bitterness throughout with notes of chocolate and caramel. Fruity bitter finish.
Blonde (ABV 4%) PALE
A clean-tasting, golden-coloured, hoppy beer with a refreshing bitter and fruity aftertaste.
Barnsley Gold (ABV 4.3%) GOLD
Golden ale, fruit in the aroma with a hoppy and fruitiness flavour throughout. A well-hopped, clean, dry finish.
Old Moor Porter (ABV 4.4%) PORTER
A rich-tasting, moreish porter, smooth throughout with a hint of chocolate and a hint of liquorice.
Gorlovka Imperial Stout (ABV 6%) STOUT
This black stout is rich and smooth and full of chocolate and liquorice flavours with a fruity, creamy finish.

Ad Hop

18 Severs Street, Liverpool, L6 5HJ ☎ 07957 165501

Ad Hop started life in 2014 at the Clove Hitch pub, moving a couple of times before ending up in much larger premises in 2017 where a 5.5-barrel plant was added to its existing 2.5-barrel one. ♦LIVE V

Liverpool Pale (ABV 3.8%) PALE
Liver Bird (ABV 4.2%) PALE
Merseyful (ABV 4.2%) BITTER
Aotearoa Pale (ABV 4.4%) PALE
Paddy's Wigwam (ABV 4.6%) PALE
Robusta (ABV 5%) PORTER
Enigma (ABV 5.5%) IPA
Equinox (ABV 5.5%) IPA

Adnams SIBA

Sole Bay Brewery, East Green, Southwold, Suffolk, IP18 6JW
☎ (01502) 727200 ⊕ adnams.co.uk

⊠ Established in 1872 and still based in Southwold, Suffolk. More than 35 pubs are owned around East Anglia, with national distribution. Beers are from a 300-barrel plant within the confines of the present site. ‼🍺♦

Southwold Bitter (ABV 3.7%) BITTER
Aromas of toffee apple, caramel and sulphur. Taste is a complex mix of malt toffee and roast bitterness with hops. Malty bitter and apple flavours linger into the aftertaste.
Mosaic (ABV 4.1%) BITTER
Tropical fruit nose, intensely fruity flavour with complex hop characteristics, which linger in the aftertaste.
Ghost Ship (ABV 4.5%) PALE
Vibrant compote of orange and oily hoppiness underpinned by a biscuity sweetness. Great balance and easy-drinking.
Broadside (ABV 4.7%) PALE
Rich, malty aroma with blackberries and dried fruit. Rich and full flavours of malt and fruit, with roast and caramel notes and subtle hops. Well-balanced, long-lasting aftertaste.

Adur

Brick Barn, Charlton Court, Mouse Lane, Steyning, West Sussex, BN44 3DG
☎ (01903) 867614

Office: 2 Sullington Way, BN43 6PJ
⊕ adurvalleycoop.com

⊠ Adur Brewery, nestled in the heart of the South Downs, was launched in 2008 on a 5.5-barrel plant, marking the return of brewing to the Adur Valley after an interval of nearly 100 years. The brewery was sold to the Adur Valley Co-Operative in 2012, including the Adur

Brewery name and recipes. A large part of the output is sold as bottle-conditioned beer. ‼♦LIVE

Ropetackle Golden Ale (ABV 3.4%) GOLD
Hop Token: Amarillo (ABV 4%) BITTER
Hop Token: Summit (ABV 4%) BITTER
Velocity (ABV 4.4%) BITTER
Black William (ABV 5%) STOUT
Robbie's Red (ABV 5.2%) RED

Affinity

Grosvenor Arms, 17 Sidney Road, Brixton, London, SW9 0TP ☎ 07904 391807 ⊕ affinitybrewco.com

Established in 2016 in a container in Tottenham Hale and expanded in 2017 to the Bermondsey Beer Mile, 2020 saw the brewery start afresh in the basement of the Grosvenor Arms. Run as a separate business, cask, keg and canned beers are available in the pub as well as at its bottle shop in Crystal Palace. ⌀

Grosvenor Gold (ABV 3.8%) GOLD

Ainsty SIBA

Manor Farm, Intake Lane, Acaster Malbis, York, North Yorkshire, YO23 3UJ ☎ (01904) 703233 ☎ 07983 604989 ⊕ ainstyales.co.uk

☺Established in 2014 as a cuckoo brewery, its own 10-barrel brewery opened in 2016 in the ancient York & Ainsty Wapentake in York. Beers (cask, keg, can, bottle) can be found across York, across Yorkshire, and other areas of the UK, and on its online shop. ‼⊠♦⌀

Northern Lights (ABV 3.6%) GOLD
Angel (ABV 3.7%) PALE
Flummoxed Farmer (ABV 4%) BLOND
Bantam Best (ABV 4.2%) BITTER
Cool Citra (ABV 4.4%) PALE
Assassin (ABV 4.9%) STOUT

Aitcheson's

Windham Farm, Ferry Road, Wawne, East Yorkshire, HU7 5XY ☎ 07456 063670

Office: 2 Wheelhouse Court, Hull, East Yorkshire, HU6 5BF

☺Formerly the East Yorkshire Beer Company, Aitcheson's was established by Steve Aitcheson in 2020 after relocating from Beverley. Ingredients are sourced as locally as possible, grains malted in Bridlington and Castleford and UK hops used where possible. The beer range is named after historic Hull and East Yorkshire pubs. Brewing experience days can be booked. ♦V

Top House Mild (ABV 3.8%) MILD
King Billy Bitter (ABV 4.2%) BITTER
Earl de Grey IPA (ABV 4.5%) PALE
Full Measure Porter (ABV 4.5%) PORTER
Star of the West Pilsner (ABV 4.6%) SPECIALITY
Odd Fellows Irish Red (ABV 4.7%) RED

AJ's

Unit 11, Ashmore Industrial Estate, Longacre Street, Walsall, West Midlands, WS2 8QG ☎ 07841 459212 ✉ ajs-ales@hotmail.com

⊗ Set up by experienced brewer Andy Dukes and his wife Charlotte, AJ's Ales was established in 2015 and use a four-barrel plant with three fermenting vessels and a cool room. It brews three times a week and mainly supplies local Black Country pubs, and further afield through local wholesalers. ♦

Blackjack Mild (ABV 3.6%) MILD
Stuck on Blondes (ABV 3.9%) BLOND
Best Bitter (ABV 4%) BITTER
Dukey's Delight (ABV 4.1%) GOLD
SPA (ABV 4.2%) PALE
Gold (ABV 4.3%) GOLD
Stuck in the Mud (ABV 4.3%) STOUT
Ruby (ABV 4.4%) BITTER
IPA (ABV 4.6%) PALE
Stuck in the Doghouse (ABV 4.7%) GOLD

Alcazar

See Shipstone's

Aldwark Artisan

Lydgate Farm, Aldwark, Matlock, Derbyshire, DE4 4HW ☎ (01629) 540720 ☎ 07834 353807 ⊕ aabrewery.co.uk

⊗ Housed in an old milking shed on a rural working farm this 10-barrel brewery produced its first brew in 2017 using water from the farms own bore hole, filtered through the strong limestone hills of the peak district.

Aldwark Pale IPA (ABV 4.8%) PALE

Alechemy

Unit B, 1 Gregory Road, Kirkton Campus, Livingston, EH54 7DR ☎ (01506) 413634 ☎ 07748 156973 ⊕ alechemy.beer

Dr James Davies, a keen traditional brewer and chemist, started brewing in 2012. A 12-barrel plant is used. New beers are being produced regularly. Beers can be found in shops and pubs across the UK. Alechemy is now part of the Consolidated Craft Breweries group, which opened its first bar in 2019, the Froth & Flame in Edinburgh. Brewing may be undertaken for other breweries in the group. ♦LIVE

Charisma (ABV 3.7%) PALE
Ritual (ABV 4.1%) PALE
Well-balanced golden ale. A strong hop character, balanced by malt and fruit with a long and dry finish.
Photon (ABV 4.2%) PALE
Light pale ale with lots of American hops.
Five Sisters (ABV 4.3%) BITTER
Flavoursome tawny beer with excellent balance of malt, hops and fruit plus hints of roast and caramel. Lingering distinctive finish.
10 Storey Malt Bomb (ABV 4.5%) BITTER
Bad Day at the Office (ABV 4.5%) GOLD
Secret Citra (ABV 5.7%) IPA

Ales of Scilly

2b Porthmellon Industrial Estate, St Mary's, Isles of Scilly, TR21 0JY ☎ 07737 721599 ⊕ alesofscilly.co.uk

⊗ Opened in 2001, Ales of Scilly is the most south-westerly brewery in Britain. Several island pubs and restaurants are regularly supplied, plus the occasional mainland pub outlet and beer festival. Special one-off beers are produced in celebration of significant island events. ‼⊠♦

Challenger (ABV 4.2%) BITTER
Amber best bitter with faint malt and hop nose. A refreshing, light beer with apricot flavours throughout and gentle malty bitterness.

Alfred's

Unit 6, Winnall Farm Industrial Estate, Easton Lane, Winchester, Hampshire, SO23 0HA
☎ (01962) 859999 ⊕ alfredsbrewery.co.uk

Alfred's is a nine-barrel, state-of-the-art brewery located close to the centre of Winchester. Production of Saxon Bronze is complemented by returning favourites and experimental beers. ‼️☞♦

Saxon Bronze (ABV 3.8%) BITTER
Well-balanced, copper-coloured bitter, with minimal aroma. Malt dominates the taste with some hops in the finish

All Day

Salle Brewery Barns 14-16, Salle Moor Hall Farm, Wood Dalling Road, Salle, Norfolk, NR10 4SB
☎ (01603) 327656 ☎ 07825 604887
⊕ alldaybrewing.co.uk

⊗ Housed in a centuries old barn, the brewery has its own hop yard and an adjoining organic orchard. Many of the beers are barrel-aged, or sours, or involve fruit grown at the brewery. They are available in the taproom and kitchen, along with vegan food, pizza, real cider, and raw kombucha. Home of the Norfolk Hop Festival.
‼️☞♦LIVE⇗

All Hallows

▤ **Main Street, Goodmanham, East Yorkshire, YO43 3JA**
☎ (01430) 873849 ⊕ goodmanhamarms.co.uk

☺Abbie Logozzi, landlady of the Goodmanham Arms, started brewing in 2012 in outbuildings behind the pub. The ex-Goodmanham Brewery buildings were purchased and a five-barrel plant installed. The brewery name comes from the adjacent 12th century All Hallows Church. Local legendary characters are used in the naming of some of the beers. Brews are supplied to the pub and its sister pub, the Bay Horse, Burythorpe. ☞♦

Allanwater

▤ **Queens Lane, Bridge of Allan, FK9 4NY**
☎ (01786) 834555 ☎ 07831 224242
⊕ allanwaterbrewhouse.co.uk

☺Originally named Tinpot and then Wash House, the brewery was established in 2009 using a one-barrel plant designed to brew speciality beer. From 2018 all beers and branding are under the Allanwater Brewhouse name. The beer range varies depending on season and demand, which is increasing every year. ‼️☞LIVE

Allendale SIBA

Allen Mill, Allendale, Northumberland, NE47 9EA
☎ (01434) 618686 ⊕ allendalebrewery.com

☺Established in 2006, the brewery is a 20-barrel plant in a historic lead smelting mill in the heart of the North Pennines Area of Outstanding Natural Beauty. Many of the beers reflect the heritage and identity of the local area. ‼️☞♦

Wagtail Best Bitter (ABV 3.8%) BITTER
Amber bitter with spicy aromas and a long, bitter finish.
Golden Plover (ABV 4%) BLOND
Light, refreshing, easy-drinking blonde beer with a clean finish.
Pennine Pale (ABV 4%) PALE
Hop On (ABV 4.7%) GOLD
Adder Lager (ABV 5%) SPECIALITY

Anvil (ABV 5.5%) IPA
Wolf (ABV 5.5%) RED
Full-bodied red ale with bitterness in the taste giving way to a fruity finish.

AllGates

See Wigan Brewhouse

Almasty

Unit 11, Algernon Industrial Estate, New York Road, Shiremoor, NE27 0NB
☎ (0191) 253 1639

Benfield: Unit A2A, Benfield Business Park, Benfield, Newcastle upon Tyne, NE6 4NQ ⊕ almasty.co.uk

⊗ Opened in 2014, Almasty now has two sites, both brewing on 10-barrel kits, one running a mixed/natural fermentation and a barrel-aging programme and the other producing unfined, unfiltered beers with a continuously changing output, including heavily-hopped pale ales, IPAS and stouts. A taproom and shop located at Benfield Business Park is open weekends. Pumpclips are made from screen-printed, hand-sawn logs. Beers are supplied nationwide. ‼️☞♦V⇗

Alnwick SIBA

Unit E-F, Hawkhill Business Park, Lesbury, Northumberland, NE66 3PG
☎ (01665) 830617 ☎ 07788 433499
⊕ alnwickbrewery.co.uk

Brewing started in the 1860s in the centre of Alnwick, the capital of Northumberland. The brewery was acquired in 1978 by Scottish brewer Dryboroughs, who closed it in 1986, but relaunched in 2003 with the assistance of the Duchess of Northumberland. Beers are also brewed under the Holy Island name. More than 50 outlets are supplied in the north of England.

Alpha Delta

18 Riversdale Court, Newburn, Newcastle upon Tyne, NE15 8SG ⊕ alphadeltabrewing.com

Alpha Delta Brewing launched in 2019 in the Newburn district of Newcastle. Producing modern-style, high gravity beers in keg and can, the beers are unfined, unfiltered and unpasteurized. Collaborations with various breweries across Europe take place.

Alpha State

The Heath, Horsmonden, Kent, TN12 8JE
⊕ alphastatebeer.com

Alpha State was founded in 2012 by brewer Jonathan Queally, producing mainly bottled beer. In 2019 it launched a range of beer produced in collaboration with comedian Bob Mortimer. Beers are unfiltered and unpasteurised, supplied in bottles and KeyKeg

Alphabet SIBA

99 Northern Western Street, Manchester, M12 6JL
☎ (0161) 272 6532 ⊕ alphabetbrewing.co.uk

Founded in 2014, Alphabet Brewing Company is based in central Manchester in a railway arch with an on-site taproom. It focuses mainly on hop-forward, fruit-led session beers in keg and KeyKeg, which are unfiltered and unpasteurised. ‼️⇗

Altarnun

Unit 2, Southgate Technology Park, Pennygillam Industrial Estate, Launceston, PL15 7ED
☎ (01566) 86069 ⊕ penpontbrewery.co.uk

⊗ Formerly known as Penpont, Altarnun began brewing in 2008 and has steadily increased its range and production since then. The award-winning brewery currently uses a 25-barrel plant, with an eight-barrel plant for special brews. Beers are available in pubs across Cornwall. Beer is also brewed under the Firebrand Brewing label. ‼️🍴♦LIVE

St Nonna's (ABV 3.7%) BITTER
Tawny session bitter with floral nose and balanced malt and hop bitterness throughout with roast and sweet notes. Bitter finish.
Cornish Arvor (ABV 4%) BITTER
Golden bitter with good malt and pine/resin/earth hop presence. Complex mix of stone fruit and esters. Dry finish.
Creation Pale Ale (ABV 4.2%) PALE
Gold bitter with hop aroma. Quite hoppy taste with sweet peach, citrus zing and roast malt. Bitter, slightly dry finish.
Shipwreck Coast (ABV 4.4%) PALE
Gold bitter with sweet malt well-balanced by citrusy/ tropical fruits hop flavour. Dry finish.
Roughtor (ABV 4.7%) BITTER
Copper strong ale with malt and citrus hop aroma. Hop bitterness balanced by malt, plum and marmalade. Bitter, dry finish.
Beast of Bodmin (ABV 5%) BITTER
Tawny, strong ale. Burnt sugar, tobacco and leather with stone fruit flavour. Mellow toffee/caramel and earthy hop finish.
Stormer IPA (ABV 5.2%) PALE

Brewed under the Firebrand Brewery name:
Big Hop, Little Beer (ABV 3.6%) BITTER
Cross Pacific Pale Ale (ABV 4%) PALE
Graffiti IPA (ABV 5%) PALE

Alter Ego SIBA

Unit 11, Small Business Centre, Adams Close, Heanor, Derbyshire, DE75 7SW ☎ 07989 655828
✉ matt@alteregobrewing.co

Alter Ego is a 2.5-barrel brewery producing small batch beers. The brewery tap is the Tip Inn micropub, Loscoe.

Echo Chamber (ABV 3.8%) PALE
Mr Brown (ABV 4.2%) BITTER
Sidekick (ABV 4.5%) PALE
S'more Fire (ABV 5.2%) STOUT
Incognito (ABV 5.8%) IPA

Amazing

🍴 Ship Inn, 65 High Street, Sandgate, Kent, CT20 3AH
☎ (01303) 248525

⊗ Amazing was set up in 2016 using a four-barrel plant and is situated at the Ship Inn, Sandgate. The pub and local beer festivals are supplied. The brewery can be viewed from inside the pub. ‼️

Ambridge

Unit 2a, Priory Piece Business Park, Priory Farm Lane, Inkberrow, Worcestershire, WR7 4HT ☎ 07498 628238 ⊕ ambridgebrewery.co.uk

⊛ Ambridge commenced brewing in 2013, initially for the family pub, The Bulls Head in Inkberrow. Expansion was achieved by acquiring the Wyre Piddle Brewery. The range of beers has continued to change with seasonal and specials brewed. Some small run bottling and canning are also carried out at the brewery. ‼️♦LIVE

Sticky Dog (ABV 4%) GOLD
Best Bitter (ABV 4.3%) BITTER
Gold (ABV 4.3%) GOLD

Amity

🍺 15-16 Festoon Rooms Sunny Bank Mills, Farsley, Leeds, West Yorkshire, LS28 5UJ ⊕ amitybrew.co

Launching in 2020 with its online shop, Amity Brew Co was founded by Russ Clarke (ex-BrewDog, Buxton, North Brewing Co and Beer Hawk team member). Originally cuckoo brewing, its brewpub opened later the same year sporting a 10-hectolitre brew kit, producing modern interpretations of classic beer styles, as well as more experimental brews. No real ale. ‼️🍴♦

Ampersand SIBA

27-31 Sawmills Road, Diss, Norfolk, IP22 4GG
☎ (01379) 643944 ☎ 07791 086689
⊕ ampersandbrew.co

A small batch brewery established in 2017. Originally based on a family farm in South Norfolk, it relocated to Diss in 2021. 🍴♦

μIPA (ABV 2.9%) PALE
Bidon (ABV 3.9%) BITTER
The Cap Bitter (ABV 3.9%) BITTER
On the Wing (ABV 4.7%) PALE
Cocow (ABV 4.8%) SPECIALITY
Camphillisner (ABV 4.9%) SPECIALITY
Pulpit (ABV 5%) PALE

Amwell Springs SIBA

Westfield Farm House, Cholsey, Wallingford, Oxfordshire, OX10 9LS ☎ 07812 396619
⊕ asbco.co.uk

Brewing began in 2017 on a 70-litre plant using water from a spring in the farmhouse grounds. Capacity expanded in 2019 to six barrels. Beers are available in local pubs. LIVE

Chairman Dave (ABV 3.5%) BITTER
Stay Jammy (ABV 3.8%) BITTER
Rude Not To (ABV 4%) GOLD
Easy Geez (ABV 4.5%) GOLD
Mad Gaz (ABV 5.2%) PALE

Anarchy SIBA

Unit A1 Benfield Business Park, Newcastle upon Tyne, NE6 4NQ ⊕ anarchybrewco.com

A 20-barrel brewery, started in 2012 in Morpeth, and moved to Newcastle upon Tyne in 2018. Its focus is on session beers, plus an eclectic mix of one-offs and collaborations with a host of breweries from the UK and across the globe. ‼️LIVE V♦

Blonde Star (ABV 4.1%) BLOND
Citra Star (ABV 4.1%) BLOND
Skin Deep (ABV 4.2%) BITTER
Halfway Dead (ABV 4.7%) IPA
New Age Crisis (ABV 4.8%) IPA
Boot Boys (ABV 5%) OLD
X-Ray Eyes (ABV 5.1%) IPA
Hollow Heroes (ABV 5.3%) IPA
Hopped Up And Ready To Go (ABV 5.3%) IPA
Cult Leader (ABV 5.5%) IPA
Demon Fangs (ABV 5.6%) IPA

Cell Phone Zombies (ABV 5.9%) IPA
Hit the Juice (ABV 6%) IPA

Anchor House

c/o 3 Osmand Gardens, Plympton, Devon, PL7 1AA
☎ 07940 270918

A family-run brewery, established in 2019, to brew small-batch vegan-friendly, experimental beers using spare capacity at other local breweries. All ingredients are locally sourced where possible. A number of local charities are supported. **V**

Andwell SIBA

Andwell Lane, Andwell, Hampshire, RG27 9PA
☎ (01256) 761044 ⊕ andwells.com

⊠ Brewing commenced in 2008 on a 10-barrel plant. The brewery relocated and expanded in 2011 to an idyllic riverside location with a new bespoke 20-barrel plant. Beer is distributed within a 40-mile radius to Hampshire, Surrey, Wiltshire, Berkshire, Greater London and the Isle of Wight. More than 200 outlets are supplied. In 2020 Andwells new brewhouse shop, bar and café opened. **!! ☛ ♦ ◈**

Resolute Bitter (ABV 3.8%) BITTER
An easy-drinking bitter. The malty aroma, leads into a similarly malty flavour with some bitterness and a sweetish finish.
Gold Muddler (ABV 3.9%) BITTER
Light golden, standard bitter. Aroma of hops and malt; characteristics carried into flavour with solid bitterness and dry, biscuity finish.
King John (ABV 4.2%) BITTER
Malty bitter, low in hops with loads of caramel and toffee underlying sweetness, leading to some dryness in the finish.

Angel

▤ Angel, 7 Stoney Street, Nottingham, NG1 1LG
☎ (0115) 948 3343 ⊕ facebook.com/angelmicrobrewery

◉Situated inside one of Nottingham's oldest, haunted, and cave-filled pubs. The Angel Microbrewery uses a 2.5-barrel plant, nestled in the taproom of the 400-year-old pub. Beers are available at the Angel, and the Golden Fleece in Nottingham. **V◈**

Angel Ales SIBA

62A Furlong Lane, Halesowen, West Midlands, B63 2TA ☎ 07986 382919 ⊕ angelales.co.uk

Angel Ales began commercial brewing in 2011. The brewery building has been a chapel of rest, a coffin makers' workshop and a pattern makers' before becoming a brewhouse. Beers are produced using organic ingredients where possible. **!! ♦ LIVE V**

Ale (ABV 4.1%) PALE
Krakow (ABV 4.5%) SPECIALITY
Ginger Stout (ABV 4.8%) SPECIALITY

Angels & Demons

Great Cauldham Farm, Cauldham Lane, Capel-le-Ferne, Kent, CT18 7HQ
☎ (01303) 255666 ⊕ fantasticbeer.co.uk

Brewing began in 2016 using a 20-barrel plant. The brewery produces two ranges of beers, the McCanns range of traditional ales and the Angels & Demons range of more experimental brews.

49 Horses (ABV 2.8%) PALE
Bombay Social (ABV 3.8%) PALE
Racing Tiger (ABV 4.2%) SPECIALITY
Panama Jazz (ABV 4.8%) RED
I Spy Dragonfly (ABV 5%) GOLD
ADH Me (ABV 5.2%) PALE
Goldilocks is Dead (ABV 5.3%) GOLD
Black Taxi to the Moon (ABV 5.4%) SPECIALITY

Brewed under the McCanns brand name:
Harry Hop (ABV 3.7%) BITTER
Folkestone Best (ABV 4%) BITTER
Hockley Soul (ABV 4.2%) STOUT

Anglesey Brewhouse SIBA

Unit 12, Pen Yr Orsedd, Industrial Estate Road, Parc Bryn Cefni, Llangefni, LL77 7AW
☎ (01248) 345506 ☎ 07748 650368
⊕ angleseybrewhouse.co.uk

Microbrewery established in 2017 in the centre of Anglesey by a former homebrewer. The brewery relocated to larger premises in 2019 with a 10-barrel plant. Currently producing six bottle-conditioned beers sold direct from the brewery or in shops around North Wales. **LIVE**

Anglesey Brewing

Chwaen Ddu, Carmel, LL71 7DE
☎ (01248) 717734 ☎ 07943 697881
⊕ angleseybrewingcompany.co.uk

Brewing began in 2014 in Llanbadrig as Bragdy'r Bwthyn, producing bottle-conditioned beers. In 2017 the brewery relocated to Carmel under the Anglesey Brewing Co name and cask production began. Beers are mostly sold at events and outlets across Anglesey. Brewing is currently suspended. **LIVE**

Anglo Oregon

3 Traston Lane, Newport, NP19 4RR ☎ 07854 194966
⊕ aobc.co.uk

Set up in 2015 in Parkend (Forest Of Dean) the brewery moved to its current location in Nash, on the eastern outskirts of Newport, two years later. The name comes from the fact one of the founders is English and the other (in whose garage the brewery is located) is from Oregon. It has three fermenters and the brewing capacity is just 100 litres. Only bottle-conditioned ale is brewed (every few weeks, when necessary) in 330 ml bottles. In 2020 they acquired a license for off-sales from the brewery. **LIVE**

Animal

See XT

Anomaly

Glebe Gardens, Old Malden, KT3 5RU ☎ 07903 623993 ⊕ anomalybrewing.co.uk

Founded in 2017, beers started to appear at the end of 2018 brewed on a 100-litre home kit. Most production is available in bottles but cask is sometimes available for pubs and at beer festivals. Old Belgian, French and English styles are the regular range.

Another Beer (NEW)

c/o 21 Fetter Lane, York, YO1 9TA ☎ 07403 264242
⊕ anotherbeer.co.uk

Launched in 2019 by James Fawcett, Another Beer shares facilities with Ice Cream Factory Brewery (qv) in the historic Capaldi's building. Beers are available in York as well as having distribution across Yorkshire, Manchester and the Midlands.

Anspach & Hobday SIBA

Unit 11, Valley Point Industrial Estate, Beddington Farm Road, Beddington, CR0 4WP
☎ (020) 3302 9669 ⊕ anspachandhobday.com

⊠ Best known for its porter, Anspach & Hobday began brewing in 2014. In early 2020 a new brewery was commissioned in Croydon with its existing seven-barrel kit and a canning line. Its original railway arch site (on the Bermondsey Beer Mile) is now the home of its barrel-aged and sour beers. The brewery also has a bar in Camberwell called the Pigeon. ‼️ ⏢ LIVE V✦

The Ordinary Bitter (ABV 3.7%) BITTER
The Patersbier (ABV 4.1%) SPECIALITY
The London ESB (ABV 5.5%) BITTER
Seville marmalade aroma and flavour with zesty bitterness balanced by sweetness, spicy hops and roast. Hoppy, bitter and lingering finish.
The Smoked Brown (ABV 5.5%) SPECIALITY
Smoked nose with traces of coffee. Flavour has damsons, toffee, dark chocolate, an underlying smoked character and lasting dry roastiness.
The IPA (ABV 6%) IPA
Grapefruit, orange and lemon zesty American-style beer with spicy hops and sweet biscuit providing balance to the increasing bitterness.
The Porter (ABV 6.7%) PORTER
Black/brown beer with roasted notes throughout with caramel, dark fruit and hops in the flavour and finish which is slightly dry.
The Stout Porter (ABV 8.5%) STOUT

Anstey

46a Albion Street, Anstey, Leicestershire, LE7 7DE
☎ 07960 776843 ⊕ ansteyale.co.uk

Anstey Ale Brewery started as a one-barrel, part-time garage plant in 2015. It became full-time and upgraded some equipment, later moving to new premises and increased plant size to 2.5-barrels in 2017. On-site taproom, the Mash & Press, opened in 2019 in conjunction with Charnwood Ciders (Tuesday-Sunday). Regular one-off brews are released under the Anstey (cask) and Monstex (keg) brands. Beers are occasionally available at local freehouses. A new beer garden and plans for increased capacity are planned. ♦✦

Lakeside (ABV 3.9%) BITTER
Neddy's (ABV 3.9%) PALE
Brewsters Bitter (ABV 4%) BITTER
Packhorse Bridge (ABV 4%) BITTER
Fluthered (ABV 4.5%) SPECIALITY
Darkroom (ABV 4.7%) STOUT
Nook IPA (ABV 5%) PALE

Anthology

Unit 6, Armley Link, Armley Road, Leeds, West Yorkshire, LS12 2QN ⊕ anthologybrewing.co.uk

Established in 2018, Anthology is a small batch brewery based in Leeds with a 2.5-barrel kit. Liam brews an ever-evolving range of beers with a focus on bold flavours. Beers are available in outlets around the city with some distributed further afield. ✦

Antoine's

The Garden Shed, 25 Ashley Road, Westcott, Dorking, RH4 3QJ ☎ 07545 828589 ✉ antoine@1beer.co.uk

Having stopped due to other pressures, Antoine recommenced brewing in 2019 and produces occasional cask and KeyKeg beers. The brewer is hoping to expand to a larger kit.

Appleby

Unit 10, Castle Mills, Aynam Road, Kendal, Cumbria, LA9 7DE
☎ (01539) 726800 ☎ 07885 171210
⊕ bownessbaybrewing.co.uk

☺️Established by Fred Mills in 2015, the brewery outgrew its original premises in Appleby and moved to a former horse stable in a local village in 2016. It was taken over in 2018 and moved to shared premises at Bowness Bay Brewing, Kendal. The beers are available at selected pubs across Cumbria, but mainly in the Eden Valley area. ‼️

Senior Moment (ABV 3.9%) BITTER
Midlife Crisis (ABV 4.2%) PALE
Middle Aged Spread (ABV 5.2%) STOUT

Applecross (NEW)

Russel Yard, Kishorn, Applecross, IV54 8XF
⊕ applecrossbrewingcompany.co.uk

Applecross Brewing Co was established in 2016, produced in the remote wilderness of the Applecross Estate in the Highlands of Scotland.

Pale Ale (ABV 3.7%) PALE
Sanctuary (ABV 4%) RED
Inner Sound (ABV 4.7%) STOUT

Arbor SIBA

181 Easton Road, Easton, Bristol, BS5 0HQ
☎ (0117) 329 2711 ⊕ arborales.co.uk

⊠ Founded in 2007, Arbor has a brew length of 20 barrels with 12 fermenting vessels. Willing to experiment, more than 300 beers have been produced. The current range reflects modern tastes and leans towards hoppy pale ales and IPAs plus some interesting red and dark ales. ♦LIVE GF

Mosaic Gluten Free (ABV 4%) PALE
Shangri La (ABV 4.2%) BITTER
Yellow best bitter with hoppy aroma, light malt and tropical fruit on the palate and a clean, refreshing, bitter finish.
Blue Sky Drinking (ABV 4.4%) BITTER
Malty aroma and background flavour with hints of berry fruits and spice. Hop bitterness increases in the short, balanced finish.
C Bomb (ABV 4.7%) PALE
The Devil Made Me Brew It (ABV 5.5%) STOUT
A velvetty speciality beer in stout style. Floral and citrus hops in the aroma, coffee and slightly burnt toffee flavours – sweet but with a bitter finish.
Why Kick A Moo Cow (ABV 5.5%) BITTER
A strong amber ale with malt and hops on the nose, flavours of tropical fruit and a dry, bittersweet aftertaste.
Yakima Valley – American IPA (ABV 7%) STRONG
A strong, full-bodied IPA. Hoppy and very fruity. Sweetness which is well-balanced with bitterness, lasting into a soft bitter aftertaste.

Archers

See Evan Evans

Ardgour (NEW) SIBA

The Mance, Ardgour, Fort William, PH33 7AH
☎ 07785 763659 ⊕ ardgourales.scot

Opening in 2020, eight years after Fergus and Lizzy Stokes bought the crumbling Manse with a view to bringing great beer to Scotland's west coast, this new-build, five-barrel brewery is situated in the village of Ardgour on the edge of the remote Morvern and Ardnamurchan peninsulas. An on-site bakery is also in operation. **V**

Gobhar Odhar (ABV 4.3%) BITTER
Boc Ban (ABV 5.1%) PALE
Boc na Braiche (ABV 6.4%) PALE
Gobhar Reamhar (ABV 6.5%) STOUT

Ards

34B Carrowdore Road, Greyabbey, Newtownards, Co Down, BT22 2LX ☎ 07515 558406
✉ ardsbrewing@blackwood34.plus.com

Ards began brewing in 2011 using a 100-litre plant. A five-barrel plant is now in operation, allowing cask production in addition to the increasing range of bottle-conditioned and KeyKeg beers. Very much a local brewery with beers generally only supplied within a 15-mile radius. **LIVE**

Citra (ABV 4.8%) GOLD
Scrabo Gold (ABV 4.8%) GOLD
Hip Hop (ABV 5%) BITTER
Pig Island (ABV 5.2%) BITTER

Argyll

Unit 8a, Baliscate Industrial Estate, Tobermory, Isle of Mull, PA75 6QA
☎ (01688) 302821 ⊕ argyllbreweries.co.uk

Argyll Breweries was formed in 2010 following the merger of Oban Bay and Isle of Mull breweries, continuing to trade under those names.

Arkell's SIBA IFBB

Kingsdown, Swindon, Wiltshire, SN2 7RU
☎ (01793) 823026 ⊕ arkells.com

⊗ Arkell's Brewery was established in 1843 by John Arkell. The Arkell family still brew in the original Victorian brewhouse. The brewery owns nearly 100 pubs across Wiltshire, Gloucestershire, Oxfordshire, Berkshire and Hampshire. In 2018 a brewery shop and visitor centre was opened on-site to mark its 175th anniversary. Seasonal beers are brewed frequently, often linked to sporting and other national events. !! ▮◆

Wiltshire Gold (ABV 3.7%) GOLD
3B (ABV 4%) BITTER
A medium brown beer with a strong, sweetish malt/caramel flavour. The hops come through strongly in the aftertaste, which is lingering and dry.
Hoperation IPA (ABV 4.2%) PALE

Arran SIBA

Cladach, Brodick, Isle of Arran, KA27 8DE
☎ (01770) 302353 ⊕ arranbrewery.com

☺The brewery opened in Brodick in 2000 using a 20-barrel plant with water sourced from the nearby mountains and it has its own in-house bottling plant, shop and taproom. Its Arran View brewery site in Dreghorn has a 2.5-barrel plant for producing sour beers. Around 400 outlets around the UK are supplied direct, and via distributors. The brewery owns the rights to the former Devil's Dyke Brewery beers. !! ▮◆LIVE ◆

Guid Ale (ABV 3.8%) GOLD
Dark (ABV 4.3%) BROWN
A well-balanced malty beer with plenty of roast and hop in the taste and a dry, bitter finish.
Sunset (ABV 4.4%) GOLD
Blonde (ABV 5%) SPECIALITY
A hoppy beer with substantial fruit balance. The taste is balanced and the finish increasingly bitter. An aromatic strong bitter that drinks below its weight.
Brewery Dug (ABV 5.5%) IPA

Art Brew SIBA

Art Brew Barn, Brightwater Farm, Sutcombe, Holsworthy, Devon, EX22 7QE ☎ 07881 783626
✉ artbrewdevon@gmail.com

⊗ Brewing started in 2008 on a five-barrel plant near the Jurassic Coast in Dorset. In 2016, the brewery relocated to Devon, with a brewery tap, brewing 1,200 litres per week and distributing to more than 20 pubs and other outlets. Camping is available for 10 tents and four caravans/motorhomes all year round. Beer festivals are held at Easter and the first weekend in August. ▮◆LIVE V◆

Baby Anarchist (ABV 3.2%) BITTER
Pale (ABV 3.2%) PALE
Raspberry Pale (ABV 4.4%) SPECIALITY
Milk Stout (ABV 4.5%) SPECIALITY
Ab6 (ABV 4.6%) SPECIALITY
Black Cherry Chocolate Porter (ABV 4.8%) SPECIALITY
Ginger & Chilli IPA (ABV 6%) SPECIALITY
Love or Nothing (ABV 6%) BITTER
Orange IPA (ABV 6%) SPECIALITY

Artefact (NEW) SIBA

Bridge Farm, Bury Road, Ixworth, Suffolk, IP31 2HX
⊕ artefactbrewing.co.uk

Artefact Brewing is a nanobrewery established in 2020. The brainchild of husband-and-wife team Jack and Kat Lawson-Philips, it operates from a cleverly converted shipping container in the village of Ixworth. Committed to a classic range using local and seasonal hops, the brewery also experiments and collaborates to produce new and interesting beers.

Dark Mild (ABV 3.2%) MILD
Session Pale Ale (ABV 3.8%) PALE
English Pale Ale (ABV 4.8%) PALE
Ixworth Blonde (ABV 4.8%) GOLD
Amber Haze IPA (ABV 6.2%) IPA

Artisan

Building 1A, Aston Down Business Park, Minchinhampton, Stroud, Gloucestershire, GL6 8GA
☎ 07780 449102 ⊕ artisan-ales.co.uk

⊗ Artisan is located in a former fire station next to the gatehouse of a business park. It brews a range of beer styles, which are available for members of the public to purchase from the adjacent shop most Fridays, or through the new online shop. !! ▮◆LIVE

PA03 (ABV 3.6%) PALE
BB01 (ABV 3.7%) BITTER

PA02 (ABV 3.9%) PALE
BB02 (ABV 4.2%) BITTER
ST01 (ABV 4.6%) STOUT
PA04 (ABV 4.7%) PALE
PA01 (ABV 4.9%) PALE
DB01 (ABV 5.2%) BITTER

Arundel

Unit C7, Ford Airfield Industrial Estate, Ford, Arundel, West Sussex, BN18 0HY
☎ (01903) 733111 ⊕ arundelbrewery.co.uk

⊠ Founded in 1992, Arundel Brewery is the historic town's first brewery in 70 years. A brewery shop opened in 2014 by the quayside with a good selection of beers, both its own and from other breweries. It also brews for the Bison Crafthouse, Brighton. ‼️🍴◆

Black Stallion (ABV 3.7%) MILD
A dark mild with well-defined chocolate and roast character. The aftertaste is not powerful but the initial flavours remain in the clean finish.
Castle (ABV 3.8%) BITTER
A pale tawny beer with fruit and malt noticeable in the aroma. The flavour has a good balance of malt, fruit and hops, with a dry, hoppy finish.
Sussex Gold (ABV 4.2%) GOLD
A golden-coloured best bitter with a strong floral hop aroma. The ale is clean-tasting and bitter for its strength, with a tangy citrus flavour. The initial hop and fruit die to a dry and bitter finish.
Sussex IPA (ABV 4.5%) PALE
Stronghold (ABV 4.7%) BITTER
A smooth, full-flavoured, premium bitter. A good balance of malt, fruit and hops comes through in this rich, chestnut-coloured beer.
Wild Heaven (ABV 5.2%) PALE

Ascot SIBA

Unit 5, Compton Place Business Centre, Surrey Avenue, Camberley, Surrey, GU15 3DX
☎ (01276) 686696 ⊕ ascotbrewing.co.uk

⊠ Ascot started production in 2007 on a four-barrel plant in a small industrial unit. The brewery has successfully expanded over the years, and 2017 saw new owners. ‼️🍴◆LIVE

Starting Gate (ABV 3.8%) BITTER
A pale brown session bitter with malt flavours present throughout. Dry with a lasting sharp and bitter finish.
Gold Cup (ABV 4%) GOLD
A lemony aroma leads to a dry, bitter taste, with more citrus flavours. Hoppy finish with a hint of sweetness.
Final Furlong (ABV 4.2%) BITTER
A well-balanced, copper-coloured bitter, with biscuity malt sweetness to the fore. Some citrus fruitiness and clean hoppy aftertaste.
5/4 Favourite (ABV 4.6%) PALE
Grapefruit aroma, with Cascade hops providing a crisp bitterness in the taste, balanced with some biscuit in aroma and aftertaste.
Front Runner (ABV 4.8%) PALE
Anastasia's Stout (ABV 5%) STOUT
Burnt coffee aromas lead to a roast malt flavour in this black beer. Notably fruity throughout, with a bittersweet aftertaste.

Ashley Down

c/o 15 Wathen Road, St Andrews, Bristol, BS6 5BY
☎ (0117) 983 6567 ☎ 07563 751200
✉ ashleydownbrewery@gmail.com

⊠ Ashley Down began brewing in 2011 using a 5.5-barrel plant in the owner's garage. It suffered a major fire in 2017 and for a while brewed occasionally using spare capacity at another brewery. Brewing is to restart, in the owner's garage, during the currency of this Guide. ◆LIVE

Ashover SIBA

Unit 1, Derby Road Business Park, Clay Cross, Derbyshire, S45 9AG
☎ (01246) 251859

Ashover: 1 Butts Road, Ashover, S45 0EW
⊕ ashoverbrewery.com

⊠ Brewing began in 2007 on a 3.5-barrel plant in the garage of the cottage next to the Old Poets' Corner, Ashover. Since its acquisition of a 10-barrel brewery in the neighbouring village of Clay Cross in 2015, Ashover now brews at both sites. The brewery serves local freehouses across Derbyshire and further afield as well as the Old Poets' Corner. ‼️LIVE

Light Rale (ABV 3.7%) BITTER
Light in colour and taste, with initial sweet and malt flavours, leading to a bitter finish and aftertaste.
Font (ABV 3.8%) GOLD
Poets Tipple (ABV 4%) BITTER
Complex, tawny-coloured beer that drinks above its strength. Predominantly malty in flavour, with increasing bitterness towards the end.
Littlemoor Citra (ABV 4.1%) PALE
The Fabrick (ABV 4.4%) GOLD
Rainbows End (ABV 4.5%) GOLD
Slightly smooth, bitter golden beer with an initial sweetness. Grapefruit and lemon hop flavours come through strongly as the beer gets increasingly dry towards the finish, ending with a bitter, dry aftertaste.
Red Lion (ABV 4.6%) RED
Coffin Lane Stout (ABV 5%) STOUT
Excellent example of the style, with a chocolate and coffee flavour, balanced by a little sweetness. Finish is long and quite dry.
Butts Pale Ale (ABV 5.5%) GOLD
Pale and strong yet easy to drink golden bitter. Combination of bitter and sweet flavours mingle with an alcoholic kick, leading to a warming yet bitter finish and aftertaste.
Milk Stout (ABV 6%) STOUT

Ashton

Cheltenham, Gloucestershire ☎ 07796 445822
⊕ ashtonbrewery.co.uk

Nanobrewery established in Ashton Keynes, Wiltshire, in 2018. The brewery moved in 2020 to Cheltenham. A range of real ales are produced which are unfined cask and bottle-conditioned. There are plans for new beers in the near future. LIVE

Mosaic (ABV 4.4%) GOLD
Gold (ABV 4.5%) PALE
Shot In the Dark (ABV 4.6%) SPECIALITY

Atlantic

Treisaac Farm, Treisaac, Newquay, Cornwall, TR8 4DX
☎ (01637) 880326 ⊕ atlanticbrewery.com

⊠ Specialist microbrewery producing organic and vegan ales. All ales are unfiltered and finings-free. There are eleven core brews including four food-matched dining ales developed with Michelin recognised chef Nathan Outlaw. Casks are supplied locally and to London, with bottle-conditioned beers available nationally. ◆LIVE V

Soul Citra (ABV 4%) PALE
Azores (ABV 4.2%) GOLD
Unfined golden ale. Citrus and resinous hops dominate the aroma and taste with tropical fruits. Refreshing bitter and dry finish.
Earl Grey PA (ABV 4.5%) SPECIALITY
Cloudy amber organic speciality ale. Hop aroma leads to powerful citrus fruit flavours becoming intense. Fairly bitter and dry.
Elderflower Blonde (ABV 4.5%) SPECIALITY
Pale yellow, light, crisp floral beer with elderflower nose. Elderflower and gooseberry fruits with soft citrus and pine hops flavours.
Mandarina Cornovia (ABV 4.5%) SPECIALITY
Pale gold speciality beer with full mandarin citrus fruit flavour matched by firm biscuit malt and resin/earthy hop notes.
Masala Chai PA (ABV 4.5%) SPECIALITY
Sea Salt Stout (ABV 4.5%) SPECIALITY
Dark brown stout. Roast malt, chocolate and toffee aroma. Complex smoky malt with underlying resinous hops and sweet stone fruits.
Simcotica (ABV 4.5%) GOLD
Blue (ABV 4.8%) PORTER
Smooth, rich porter with heavy roast malt aroma and taste. Smoky liquorice, bitter coffee and chocolate flavours with sweet fruit.
Honey Ale (ABV 4.8%) SPECIALITY
Fistral Pilsner (ABV 5.2%) SPECIALITY
Full-flavoured, copper, wheat beer. Sweet, stone-fruit flavours blend with biscuit malt and citrus hops. Malt finish with hops and dryness.

Atlas

See Orkney

Atom SIBA

Unit 4 Food & Tech Park, Malmo Road, Sutton Fields Industrial Estate, Hull, East Yorkshire, HU7 0YF
☎ (01482) 820572 ⊕ atombeers.com

⊠ Atom Brewing Co was founded in 2014 by Allan Rice and Sarah Thackray. Most of its production goes into can and keg, but cask ales are produced in rotation or on demand, around a core range of four. Atom's ethos is science and education based so, working with local colleges to inspire the next generation of scientists, it runs regular brewing schools and classes. All beers are unfined and unfiltered (so naturally hazy). ‼♦V

Schrodingers Cat (ABV 3.5%) BITTER
Blonde Ale (ABV 4%) BLOND
Dark Matter (ABV 4.5%) SPECIALITY
Critical Temperature (ABV 5.5%) SPECIALITY

Atomic

⊟ c/o Alexandra Arms, 72-73 James Street, Rugby, Warwickshire, CV21 2SL
☎ (01788) 542170 ☎ 07876 195895
⊕ atomicbrewery.com

Founded in 2006, by Nick Pugh and Keith Abbis, Atomic is located in the Alexandra Arms' outbuildings. The six-barrel plant was initially leased by the pub landlord, who also brewed Alex Ales on it. The Victoria Inn was acquired in 2007. At the end of 2010 the Alexandra Arms was put up for sale, threatening the existence of Atomic, but after some bargaining it bought its second freehold property including the brewery. ‼♦

Attic

29B Mary Vale Road, Stirchley, Birmingham, B30 2DA
☎ 07470 643758 ⊕ atticbrewco.com

A natural progression from homebrewing, Attic Brewery Co was launched in 2018 by two friends. Its taproom is open Friday evening and all day Saturday. Beer is mostly available in the tap but they are expanding into the local free trade as conditions allow. ♦

Aurora

Unit 6, Gallows Industrial Park, off Furnace Road, Ilkeston, Derbyshire, DE7 5EP ☎ 07740 783631

Aurora was established in 2016. Joint owner Mark Derbyshire, formerly of Hardy & Hanson's, brews on a 10-barrel plant. Many local outlets, and a few further away, are supplied direct. The brewery swaps beers with other breweries throughout the UK, many of which can be found in its micropub, the Ilson Tap.

Austendyke

The Beeches, Austendyke Road, Weston Hills, Spalding, Lincolnshire, PE12 6BZ ☎ 07866 045778

Austendyke Ales began brewing in 2012 using a seven-barrel plant. The brewery is operated on a part-time basis by brewer Charlie Rawlings and business partner Nathan Marshall, who handles sales. The brewery owns and runs micropub the Prior's Oven, Spalding. Production is currently suspended.

Long Lane (ABV 4%) BITTER
Sheep Market (ABV 4%) GOLD
Bakestraw Bitter (ABV 4.1%) PALE
Bake House (ABV 4.5%) BITTER
Holbeach High Street (ABV 4.5%) BITTER
Hogsgate (ABV 5%) BITTER

Autumn SIBA

8 East Cliff Road, Spectrum Business Park, Seaham, County Durham, SR7 7PS ⊕ autumnbrewing.co.uk

Autumn produce keg and bottled gluten free beers. No real ale.

Avalanche

5 Goodwood Close, Burton Latimer, Northamptonshire, NN15 5WP
⊕ avalanchebrew.co.uk

Avalanche Brew Co is a nanobrewery formed by two home brewers, Matt and Rob, producing modern, hoppy beers. The custom-built, 200-litre brewhouse with fermentation capacity of around 400 litres, produces beers that are unfined and unfiltered. Primarily cask and keg but occasional small batches are available in bottle and can.

Avid SIBA

Red Moss Farm, Quernmore Brow, Quernmore, LA2 0QW ☎ 07976 275762 ⊕ avidbrewing.co.uk

Avid was established in 2015 by two experienced homebrewers. The 7.5-barrel microbrewery is based in picturesque Quernmore, near Lancaster. Water is used from a local borehole.

Golden Ale (ABV 3.9%) GOLD
American Pale (ABV 4%) PALE
New Zealand Pale (ABV 4%) PALE
Milk Stout (ABV 4.5%) STOUT
IPA (ABV 5%) PALE

TropicAle (ABV 5%) PALE
Irish Coffee Stout (ABV 6%) SPECIALITY

Axholme

See Docks

Aye Been SIBA

Gunsgreenhill Industrial Estate, Eyemouth, TD14 5SF
✉ hello@ayebeenbrewing.com

Aye Been is a four-barrel brewery established in Eyemouth in 2020. It moved to new premises in 2021.

Aye PA (ABV 3.8%) PALE

Ayr

🍴 5 Racecourse Road, Ayr, KA7 2DG ☎ 07834 922142
🌐 ayrbrewingcompany.com

☺Ayr began brewing in 2009 on a five-barrel plant and is located at the Glen Park Hotel. In addition to the hotel, about 50 other outlets are supplied throughout Scotland and England. 🍺♦LIVE

B&T SIBA

The Brewery, Shefford, Bedfordshire, SG17 5DZ
☎ (01462) 815080 🌐 banksandtaylor.com

⊗ Banks & Taylor, now just B&T, was founded in 1982. It has four tied houses, all selling B&T beers. Beers are currently brewed by 3 Brewers (qv). ‼♦

Bacchus

🍴 Bacchus Hotel, 17 High Street, Sutton-on-Sea, Lincolnshire, LN12 2EY
☎ (01507) 441204 🌐 bacchushotel.co.uk

Bacchus began brewing in 2010 and now has a two-barrel plant supplying the Bacchus Hotel. ‼LIVE

Backyard SIBA

Unit 8a, Gatehouse Trading Estate, Lichfield Road, Brownhills, Walsall, West Midlands, WS8 6JZ
☎ (01543) 360145 🌐 tbb.uk.com

☺Backyard began brewing in 2008 and expanded in 2012 to a 12-barrel plant brewing up to 50 barrels a week. Its award-winning ales are distributed to its two pubs, the Fountain, Walsall and the Saddlers Arms, Solihull. A half-barrel experimental plant is also in operation, and a tap house is open every Friday (1-8pm). ‼🍺♦♦

Bitter (ABV 3.8%) BLOND
The Hoard (ABV 3.9%) GOLD
Blonde (ABV 4.1%) BLOND
Americana (ABV 4.3%) PALE
Gold (ABV 4.5%) GOLD
IPA (ABV 5%) PALE
Antipodean (ABV 5.6%) IPA

BAD SIBA

Unit 3, North Hill Road, Dishforth, North Yorkshire, YO7 3DH
☎ (01423) 324005 🌐 wearebad.co

BAD Co commenced brewing in 2014, originally using a 13-barrel plant, since upgraded to cope with demand. A new and evolving Off Tempo range has been developed, focusing on experimental and radical brews. ♦V

Pale Aura (ABV 3.8%) GOLD

Yorkshire Bitter (ABV 3.8%) BITTER
Love Over Gold (ABV 4.1%) BLOND
Wild Gravity (ABV 5.2%) PALE
Dark Necessities (ABV 5.5%) STOUT
Boston Tea Party (ABV 5.8%) SPECIALITY
Milkshake IPA (ABV 5.8%) SPECIALITY
DIPA 3 (ABV 7.4%) IPA

Bad Bunny

26 Bullbridge Cottage, Ambergate, Derbyshire, DE56 2EW ☎ 07519 605362
🌐 badbunnybrewery.co.uk

Founded by husband-and-wife team Mike and Clare Chettle using a self-built 300-litre brewery in the back garden of their family home. Brewing commenced in 2019. LIVE

Bad Seed

7 Rye Close, York Way Industrial Estate, Malton, North Yorkshire, YO17 6YD
☎ (01653) 695783 🌐 badseedbrewery.com

☺Bad Seed produce an award-winning range of new wave and traditional beers in cask, keg and can. Established in 2013, the brewery is based in Malton, the 'food capital' of Yorkshire, and operates on a 12-barrel brew kit. Alongside the core range it makes regular specials, unique brews and collaborations with other cutting-edge breweries. All beers are unfined, unfiltered and vegan-friendly. ‼♦V

Kiwi (ABV 3.8%) PALE
Dalliance (ABV 4%) PALE
Session IPA (ABV 4%) PALE

Badger

See Hall & Woodhouse

Bakehouse

See Warwickshire

Bakers Dozen SIBA

Unit 5, Ketton Business Estate, Pit Lane, Ketton, PE9 3SZ
☎ (01780) 238180 🌐 bakersdozenbrewing.co.uk

☺Brewing takes place on a five-barrel plant installed in 2015 by the owners of the Jolly Brewer, Stamford, where the beers are always available. The beers favour hoppy styles with some occasional brews unfined. ♦

Jentacular (ABV 3.5%) GOLD
Magic Potion (ABV 3.8%) GOLD
Stamford Pale (ABV 4%) PALE
System of a Brown (ABV 4.1%) BROWN
Straight Outta Ketton (ABV 4.5%) PALE
Electric Landlady (ABV 5%) GOLD

Balcombe (NEW)

🍴 Half Moon, Haywards Heath Road, Balcombe, West Sussex, RH17 6PA
☎ (01444) 811582 ✉ mail@halfmoonbalcombe.com

Balcombe is a microbrewery established in 2021 by 13 beer enthusiasts.

Ballard's

See Greyhound

Bang The Elephant

Unit 14, Bailey Brook Industrial Estate, Amber Drive, Langley Mill, Derbyshire, NG16 4BE ☎ 07539 652055 ✉ bangtheelephantbrewing@hotmail.com

⊗ Bang The Elephant are a neo-victorian, steam punk-inspired, six-barrel brewery, creating small batch beers for the cask, keg and bottle market. **V**

Malty Coves (ABV 3.8%) BITTER
Gigglemug (ABV 4%) BITTER
Podsnappery (ABV 4%) GOLD
Half Rats (ABV 4.4%) PALE
Penny Dreadful (ABV 4.5%) STOUT
Sons of Liberty APA (ABV 5%) PALE
Kali Yuga (ABV 5.9%) PORTER
Odissi (ABV 6%) IPA

Bang-On

Unit 3, George Street, Bridgend Industrial Estate, Bridgend, CF31 3TS
☎ (01656) 760790 🌐 bangonbrewery.beer

Established in 2016, this five-barrel plant produces a variety of unique beers. An on-site taproom offers tours and brew day experiences. Limited edition beers are also available. A bespoke service is offered with personalised labels (minimum of six bottles). ᛁ🍴🍺🛠

Tidy (ABV 4%) BARLEY
Cariad (ABV 4.1%) BITTER
Bohemian Pilsner (ABV 4.2%) BARLEY
Fuster Cluck (ABV 9.5%) STRONG

Bank Top SIBA

The Pavilion, Ashworth Lane, Bolton, BL1 8RA
☎ (01204) 595800 🌐 banktopbrewery.com

☺Bank Top was established in 1995. Since 2002, the brewery has occupied a Grade II-listed tennis pavilion housing an 11-barrel plant. Bank Top Brewery Estates was formed in 2010 and now owns three pubs, Bank Top Brewery Tap, Bank Top Ale House and Olde England Forever. ᛁ🛠

Draymans Draught (ABV 3.6%) PALE
Bad to the Bone (ABV 4%) BITTER
Dark Mild (ABV 4%) MILD
Coffee roast aroma. Smooth mouthfeel, with roasted malt prominent throughout and some fruit. Moderate bitterness in aftertaste.
Flat Cap (ABV 4%) BITTER
Amber-coloured beer with a malty aroma. Balanced and lasting flavour of malt, fruit and bitter hops.
Pavilion Pale Ale (ABV 4.5%) PALE
A yellow beer with a citrus and hop aroma. Big fruity flavour with a peppery hoppiness; dry, bitter yet fruity finish.
Palomino Rising (ABV 5%) PALE
Port O Call (ABV 5%) SPECIALITY
Dark brown beer with a malty, fruity aroma. Malt, roast and dark fruits in the bittersweet taste and finish.

Banks's

Park Brewery, Wolverhampton, West Midlands, WV1 4NY
☎ (01902) 711811 🌐 bankssbeer.co.uk

Banks's was founded as maltsters in 1840, commencing brewing in 1874 and moving to the current Park Brewery in 1875. It became the principal brewery of Wolverhampton and Dudley Breweries (W&DB), founded in 1890. In 2007 the Marston's name was adopted following the takeover by W&DB in 1999. A joint venture

with Carlsberg in 2020 led to the company being renamed Carlsberg Marston's Brewing Company. Alongside the traditional Banks's beers it also produces Wainwrights, Lancaster Bomber and Bombardier, as well as contract brewing. Part of Carlsberg Marston's Brewing Co. ᛁ🍺

Mild (ABV 3.5%) MILD
An amber-coloured, well-balanced, refreshing session beer.
Amber Ale (ABV 3.8%) BITTER
A pale brown bitter with a pleasant balance of hops and malt. Hops continue from the taste through to a bittersweet aftertaste.
Sunbeam (ABV 4.2%) BLOND

Brewed for Marston's:
Wainwright (ABV 4.1%) GOLD
Lancaster Bomber (ABV 4.4%) BITTER

Brewed under the Bombardier brand name:
Bombardier (ABV 4.1%) BITTER
A heavy aroma of malt and raspberry jam. Traces of hops and bitterness are quickly submerged under a smooth, malty sweetness. A solid, rich finish.
Gold (ABV 4.1%) GOLD

Brewed under the Mansfield brand name:
Cask Ale (ABV 3.9%) BITTER

Barefaced

Unit 1, Holland Business Park, Blandford, Dorset, DT11 7TA ☎ 07435 157767
🌐 barefacedbrewing.co.uk

⊗ Barefaced Brewing was established in 2017 by two friends, Nick Horne and Tom Cooper, in one of their garden sheds in Wimborne. A move to Bournemouth was followed by a move to its new location in Blandford, which has allowed for expanded production and a taproom bar. ᛁ◆LIVE🛠

Speak Out (ABV 3.5%) PALE
So You've Travelled (ABV 4.4%) GOLD
What's Shakin? (ABV 4.7%) SPECIALITY
Heartbreak Stout (ABV 5.4%) STOUT
Flash IPA (ABV 5.9%) IPA

Barker's

14 Midway, South Crosland, Huddersfield, West Yorkshire, HD4 7DA ☎ 07876 540211
✉ jimrbarker1978@me.com

James Barker started as a homebrewer five years ago, producing beers for friends. With invaluable help and guidance from Summer Wine Brewery and Neil at Milltown, he made the leap from homebrewer to commercial production in 2019. He continues to use his handbuilt 60-litre brewplant, bottling a core range of seven beers.

Barn Owl

Buildings Farm, Faringdon Road, Gozzard's Ford, Oxfordshire, OX13 6QH ☎ 07724 551086

⊗ Located in a spacious barn on a farm just outside Abingdon, brewing began in 2016 using a four-barrel plant. Beers can be found in local free trade outlets.

Old Scruttock's Bitter (ABV 3.9%) BITTER
Golden Gozzard (ABV 4%) GOLD
Gozzard's Guzzler (ABV 4.4%) BITTER
Old Scruttock's Dirigible (ABV 5%) PORTER

Barnaby's

The Old Stable, Hole Farm, Staverton, Devon, TQ11 0LA
☎ (01803) 762730 ⏺ barnabysbrewhouse.com

Soil Association-certified organic brewery established in 2016. Occasional cask ale production. A planned doubling of the size of the premises will enable a four-fold increase in production. New beers have been added to the range. ♦V

Dark Dunkel (ABV 4.8%) SPECIALITY
Pilsner (ABV 4.8%) SPECIALITY
Red Helles (ABV 4.8%) SPECIALITY
English IPA (ABV 5.4%) PALE
Green Tomato Saison (ABV 6%) SPECIALITY

Barnard Castle SIBA

Quaker Yard, Rear of 24 Newgate, Barnard Castle, DL12 8NG ☎ 07591 236210
⏺ barnardcastlebrewing.com

Brewing commenced in 2017 on a 3.6-barrel plant situated in one of the many yards at Barnard Castle. The brewery has an on-site bottle shop and taproom, while a mobile bar enables it to take beers to events further afield. Beers are named after local themes. ♦

Low Force (ABV 2.8%) BITTER
Quaker Yard (ABV 3.5%) MILD
Deliberation (ABV 3.7%) BITTER
Bishops Blessing (ABV 3.8%) BLOND
Mechanical Swan (ABV 4.5%) GOLD
DLIPA (ABV 4.8%) GOLD
Peg Powler (ABV 5.6%) PORTER

Barnet

⬛ c/o Black Horse, 80 Wood Street, High Barnet, Hertfordshire, EN5 4BW
☎ (020) 8449 2230 ⏺ blackhorsebarnet.co.uk

⊗ Opened in 2013, it is a small 2.5-barrel plant behind the Black Horse. Beers are brewed on a rotating basis, using traditional recipes from long since closed breweries. Seasonal beers are brewed occasionally. The beers are mainly supplied to the Black Horse, but small quantities may be found in other local pubs and the Oak Taverns chain. ♦

Pryor Reid Dark Mild (ABV 3.5%) MILD
Mr Swifts (ABV 3.8%) BITTER
Glory (ABV 3.9%) BITTER
Palomino (ABV 4%) GOLD
Battle of Barnet (ABV 4.4%) BITTER
Malty, sweet, smooth bitter with a little toffee balanced by some bitterness. A little spicy hop throughout. Trace of pineapple.
Angelic Upstart (ABV 4.5%) BITTER
Fookes Bros (ABV 4.8%) BITTER
High Speed (ABV 5.1%) BITTER
Malt, caramel and fruity hoppy aroma. Balanced flavour of malt, hops, caramel, treacle and toffee. Hoppy and slightly resinous finish.

Barney's SIBA

Summerhall Brewery, 1 Summerhall, Edinburgh, EH9 1PL ☎ 07512 253660 ⏺ barneysbeer.com

The only microbrewery in Edinburgh's city centre, Barney's Beer was founded in 2010 and now brews on the site of the original 1800s Summerhall Brewery. Summerhall is Edinburgh's centre for the arts and science. ‼LIVE

Good Ordinary Pale Ale (ABV 3.8%) BITTER
Barney's Extra Pale (ABV 4%) PALE
Red Rye (ABV 4.5%) RED
Warming spicy notes from the rye malt create an interesting twist.
Volcano IPA (ABV 5%) PALE
Nice floral aroma to this moderately bitter IPA.

Barngates SIBA

Barngates, Ambleside, Cumbria, LA22 0NG
☎ (01539) 436575 ⏺ barngatesbrewery.co.uk

⊛Barngates was established in 1997 to supply only the Drunken Duck Inn. It became a limited company in 1999. Expansion over the years, plus a new purpose-built, 10-barrel plant in 2008, means it now supplies more than 150 outlets throughout Cumbria, Lancashire and Yorkshire. ‼

Pale (ABV 3.3%) PALE
A well-balanced, fruity, hoppy pale ale with plenty of flavour for its strength.
Cat Nap (ABV 3.6%) BITTER
Pale beer, unapologetically bitter, with a dry astringent finish.
Cracker (ABV 3.9%) BITTER
A full-bodied, hoppy beer with some balancing sweetness and fruit. There is plenty of taste in this brown beer. Cleverly constructed.
Brathay Gold (ABV 4%) PALE
Attractive sweet and rich aroma is followed by plenty of fruit and hops then a long, bitter finish.
Goodhew's Dry Stout (ABV 4.3%) STOUT
The inviting roast aroma leads to an easy-drinking, full-bodied, well-balanced roasty stout.
Tag Lag (ABV 4.4%) BITTER
This traditional bitter is full on: fruit, noble hops, malt balance, good body with a crisp clean finish.
Red Bull Terrier (ABV 4.8%) RED
An assertive, roasty, red beer with full mouthfeel. Initial sweetness and luscious fruit, give way to a lingering bitter finish.

Baronscourt

38 Baronscourt Road, Newtownstewart, County Tyrone, BT78 4EY ☎ 07734 267164
⏺ baronscourtbrewery.com

Beers are produced using locally-sourced ingredients, and it is one of the first craft beer producers with a zero carbon footprint.

Barsham SIBA

Estate Office, West Barsham, Fakenham, Norfolk, NR21 9NR
☎ (01328) 864459 ☎ 07760 551056
⏺ barshambrewery.co.uk

⊗ Barsham Brewery was purchased by the present brewers in 2017. Maris Otter is grown on-site and a private bore hole supplies water for the brewery. ▰LIVE V

Oaks (ABV 3.6%) BITTER
Norfolk Topper (ABV 3.8%) BITTER
A sweet cereal nose with a well-defined initial bitter taste. Malt and citrus notes subside under an increasingly dryness.
Pilgrims Ale (ABV 4%) BLOND
B.O.B (ABV 4.3%) BITTER
Stout Robin (ABV 4.6%) STOUT
A rich creamy caramel roastiness permeates aroma and taste. Vanilla jostles with Oxo for recognition in a soft, creamy melange.

Golden Close IPA (ABV 5%) PALE

Bartleby's

1d Campbell Street, Belper, Derbyshire, DE56 1AP
☎ (01273) 275012 ☎ 07518 485342
⊕ bartlebysbrewery.com

Originally established as a workers co-operative in Lancaster in 2012, Bartleby's began trading in 2014 in Brighton before relocating to Derbyshire in 2019. The vegan beers are delivered locally by veloelectric tricycle and that green ethos extends to their brewery operations. A taproom is planned. !!▛♦V

Barum SIBA

🖿 c/o Reform Inn, Pilton High Street, Pilton, Barnstaple, Devon, EX31 1PD
☎ (01271) 329994 ⊕ barumbrewery.co.uk

⊠ Barum Brewery was established in 1996 by Tim Webster and is housed in a conversion attached to the Reform Inn, which is now run by Tim. The Reform continues to act as the brewery tap as well as serving other locally sourced ales. Distribution is exclusively within Devon. !!♦LIVE

Basement Beer

32 Upper York Street, Stokes Croft, Bristol, BS2 8QN
☎ 07702 430808 ⊕ basementbeer.co.uk

⊠ Basement Beer moved into the former Croft Ales brewery in 2021, having originally started brewing in the basement (hence the name) of the Robin Hood pub in the St Michael's Hill area of Bristol.

Bason Bridge SIBA

Unit 1 & 2, 129 Church Road, Bason Bridge, Highbridge, Somerset, TA9 4RG
☎ (01278) 787210 ⊕ 7daycellar.co.uk

⊠ Brewery founded in Somerset in 2018. Initially, two beers were brewed, but after the successful launch, a third is now available. All beer is brewed on the 12-barrel plant.

Batemans SIBA IFBB

Salem Bridge Brewery, Mill Lane, Wainfleet, Lincolnshire, PE24 4JE
☎ (01754) 880317 ⊕ bateman.co.uk

☺Bateman's Brewery is one of Britain's few remaining independent family-owned and managed brewers. Established in 1874, it has been brewing award-winning beers for four generations. Justifiably proud of its heritage it is, nevertheless, forward-looking and progressive. All 62 tied and managed houses serve cask-conditioned beer. See website for seasonal and speciality beers. !!▛♦⏧

XB (ABV 3.7%) BITTER
A well-rounded, smooth malty beer with a blackcurrant fruity background. Hops flourish initially before giving way to a bittersweet dryness that enhances the mellow malty ending.
Gold (Also known as Yella Belly Gold) (ABV 3.9%) GOLD
Salem Porter (ABV 4.8%) PORTER
A black and complex mix of chocolate, liquorice and cough elixir.
XXXB (ABV 4.8%) BITTER

A brilliant blend of malt, hops and fruit on the nose with a bitter bite over the top of a faintly banana maltiness that stays the course. A russet-tan brown classic.

Bath

Hare Brewery, Southway Drive, Warmley, Bristol, BS30 5LW
☎ (0117) 947 4797 ⊕ bathales.com

⊠ Established in 1995, Bath Ales was taken over by St Austell in 2016. Since 2018 Bath Ales beers have been brewed in new high-tech brewery, with bottling and kegging lines at Hare Brewery. !!▛♦⏧

Prophecy (ABV 3.9%) BITTER
Straw-coloured, refreshing bitter with fruity aroma. Bittersweet taste blends subtle citrus fruits with pine notes. Crisp, dry, bitter finish.
Gem (ABV 4.1%) BITTER
Pale brown best bitter with sweet fruit and malt flavours and a hint of caramel. Little aroma but a balanced taste with a short bitter finish.

Bath Brewhouse

🖿 City Pub Company, 14 James Street West, Bath, BA1 2BX
☎ (01225) 805609

Office: City Pub Group Plc., Essel House, 2nd Floor, 29 Foley Street, London, W1W 7TH
⊕ thebathbrewhouse.com

⊠ Previously known as the James Street Brewery, Bath Brewhouse opened in 2013 and is owned by the City Pub Company, which owns several other pubs and brewpubs around the country. The compact brewery is on the ground floor, with the fermenting vessels and conditioning tanks on the first floor. The on-site brewer produces a wide range of beers. The company's other pub, the Cork, Bath, is also supplied. !!▛♦

Bathams IFBB

Delph Brewery, Delph Road, Brierley Hill, West Midlands, DY5 2TN
☎ (01384) 77229 ⊕ bathams.com

☺A classic Black Country small brewery established in 1877. Tim and Matthew Batham represent the fifth generation to run the company. The Vine, one of the Black Country's most famous pubs, is also the site of the brewery. The company has 12 tied houses and supplies around 30 other outlets. Batham's Best Bitter is delivered in 54-gallon hogsheads to meet demand. A sixth generation family member, Tim's daughter, Claire, has joined the on-site team as Business Development Manager. ♦

Mild Ale (ABV 3.5%) MILD
A fruity, dark brown mild with malty sweetness and a roast malt finish.
Best Bitter (ABV 4.3%) BITTER
A pale yellow, fruity, sweetish bitter, with a dry, hoppy finish. A good, light, refreshing beer.

Battersea

12-14 Arches Lane, Battersea Power Station, Nine Elms, London, SW11 8AB
☎ (020) 8161 2366 ⊕ batterseabrew.co.uk

Opening in 2018, the brewery consists of two railway arches, one for the brewery and one for the taproom. A changing range of beers is produced in cask and keg available at the taproom and in pubs run by the brewery owners, the Mosaic Pub Company. ♦

Session Pale (ABV 3.8%) PALE

Battle

The Calf House, Beech Farm, North Trade Road, Battle, East Sussex, TN33 0HN
☎ (01424) 772838 ⊕ battlebrewery.co.uk

Battle Brewery is an eight-barrel brewery located in the heart of 1066 country in the historic town of Battle, East Sussex. Established in 2017, local pubs, cafés and shops are supplied. A brewtap/micropub opened in 2021 at the top of Battle High Street selling beers direct from the cask plus its bottled range. The taproom at the brewery is open on Saturdays only (May-Sep). ♣V◈

Tostig (ABV 3.2%) GOLD
Fyrds Gold (ABV 3.8%) GOLD
Conquest (ABV 4%) BITTER
One Hop Wonder (ABV 4.3%) GOLD
Alan the Red (ABV 4.4%) RED
Black Arrow (ABV 4.5%) PORTER
Stigand (ABV 4.9%) STOUT
Abbey Pale (ABV 5%) PALE
Russian Imperial Stout (ABV 8.3%) STOUT
Senlac Imperial Stout (ABV 10.5%) STOUT

Battledown SIBA

Coxhorne Farm, London Road, Cheltenham, Gloucestershire, GL52 6UY ☎ 07734 834104
⊕ battledownbrewery.com

⊠ A family brewery since 2005, it brews a range of ales, lager and craft beers on its new 13-hectolitre plant, installed in 2020. The brewery is supplied by spring water from the Cotswold hills, which are located behind the brewery. ‼♣◆LIVE

Pale Ale (ABV 3.8%) PALE
Original (ABV 4.4%) BITTER
Four Kings (ABV 7.2%) STRONG

Bays SIBA

Aspen Way, Paignton, Devon, TQ4 7QR
☎ (01803) 555004 ⊕ baysbrewery.co.uk

Bays Brewery is a multiple award-winning, family-run business based in Torbay on the Devon coast. Its passion is to brew premium ales using the finest local ingredients whilst also supporting the community and protecting the environment. ‼♣◆

Topsail (ABV 4%) BITTER
A tawny session bitter with complex aroma. Malty, bitter taste leading to a long, dry and refreshing aftertaste.
Gold (ABV 4.3%) GOLD
Smooth, golden ale. Light aroma and taste of hops, malt and caramel. Lingering hoppy aftertaste.
Breakwater (ABV 4.5%) PALE
Trunk Ale (ABV 4.5%) BITTER
Devon Dumpling (ABV 5.1%) BITTER
Strong ale, easily drinkable. Light aromas of hops and fruit continue through taste and lingering aftertaste.

BB18 (NEW)

🯄 BB18 Brewing Tap, 31-33 Victoria Road, Earby, BB18 6UN ☎ 07908 591343
✉ bb18brewing@gmail.com

This brewpub opened 2020. A five-barrel plant is used.

Beach

See Milton

Beacon Brauhaus

Pilgrims Coffee Falkland House, Marygate, Holy Island, Berwick upon Tweed, TD15 2SJ
☎ (01289) 389109 ⊕ pilgrimscoffee.com

Nanobrewery situated on Holy Island, the first brewery to be based there in around 500 years. Local outlets are supplied. Brewing is currently suspended.

Beak

Unit 14, Cliffe Industrial Estate, Lewes, East Sussex, BN8 6JL ☎ 07985 708122 ⊕ beakbrewery.com

Originally a gypsy brewery, with recipes tested on a nano-kit, Beak now has its own 15-barrel brewery and taproom in Lewes. ◆

Bear Claw

Unit 3 Meantime Workshops, Spittal, Northumberland, TD15 1RG ☎ 07919 276715
⊕ bearclawbrewery.weebly.com

Bear Claw began brewing in 2012 using a two-barrel plant, producing a variety of mainly highly-hopped, cask-conditioned ales, and many bottle-conditioned beers, including continental styles. Beers are available in the Green Shop and Curfew pub in Berwick upon Tweed. LIVE

Beartown SIBA

Bromley House, Spindle Street, Congleton, Cheshire, CW12 1QN
☎ (01260) 299964 ⊕ beartownbrewery.co.uk

☺Beartown began brewing in 1994 and uses a 25-barrel plant. It supplies more than 250 outlets. It is now in partnership with Manning Brewers (qv), also of Congleton. ‼♣◆

Glacier (ABV 3.6%) BLOND
Best Bitter (ABV 3.7%) BITTER
Bluebeary (ABV 4%) SPECIALITY
Kodiak (ABV 4%) PALE
Hops and fruit dominate the taste of this crisp yellow bitter and these follow through to the dryish aftertaste. Biscuity malt also comes through on the aroma and taste.
Skinful (ABV 4.2%) BITTER
Biscuity malt dominates the flavour of this amber best bitter. There are hops and a hint of sulphur on the aroma. A balance of malt and bitterness follow through to the aftertaste.
Peach Melbear (ABV 4.4%) SPECIALITY
Kahuna (ABV 4.5%) SPECIALITY
Lit (ABV 4.5%) BLOND
Creme Bearlee (ABV 4.8%) SPECIALITY
Polar Eclipse (ABV 4.8%) STOUT
Classic black, dry and bitter stout, with roast flavours to the fore. Good hop on the nose follow through the taste into a long dry finish.
Quantock (ABV 5%) MILD

Beat SIBA

9 Old Forge Trading Estate, Dudley Road, Lye, West Midlands, DY9 8EL ☎ 07821 132297
⊕ beatbrewery.co.uk

⊠ Beat Ales has been remarketed as Beat Brewery. Originally brewing in North Curry, it moved to Lye in the Black Country in 2018. Beer names reflect the owners musical inspiration, taking in different genres. Its taproom is open Friday and Saturday afternoons. ♣◆LIVE V◈

Raver (ABV 3.8%) PALE

New Wave (ABV 4.5%) GOLD
Metal Head (ABV 4.8%) STOUT
Jungle Drum Machine (ABV 5%) PALE
Rocka (ABV 5.3%) GOLD
Funk (ABV 5.5%) IPA
Cosmic Pop (ABV 6%) IPA

Beath SIBA

54 Foulford Road, Cowdenbeath, KY4 9AS ☎ 07792 369678 ⊕ beathbrewing.com

☺Beath began brewing in 2016, originally with a 20-litre capacity upgraded to 100-litre within a few months. There are plans for a further expansion. The beer range varies from week to week. LIVE

Mad World (ABV 4%) PORTER
Are You With Me (ABV 4.5%) BITTER
Ella Ella Ella (ABV 4.5%) SPECIALITY
Funky Town (ABV 5%) BITTER

Beatnikz Republic

Unit 15, Red Bank Court, Green Quarter, Manchester, M4 4HF ☎ 07437 018918 ⊕ beatnikzrepublic.com

☺Beatnikz Republic brews out of a railway arch near Manchester Victoria Station. Beers are available unfiltered in keg, can and cask. Its brewery tap opened in Manchester's Northern Quarter in 2018. ☛♦V

2am Poet (ABV 3.8%) BITTER
Boardwalk (ABV 4%) GOLD
Light and hoppy beer, balanced with a sweet fruitiness and a fruity aroma. Dry finish.
Tropic Fiesta (ABV 4%) BITTER
Leather Soul (ABV 4.3%) BITTER
Midtown (ABV 4.9%) PORTER
Beach Bum (ABV 5%) GOLD
Dry and hoppy with pronounced bitterness.
Kentucky Riot (ABV 5%) STOUT

Beavertown

Units 17 & 18, Lockwood Industrial Park, Mill Mead Road, Tottenham Hale, London, N17 9QP ☎ (020) 8525 9884

Ponders End: Unit 7, Ponders End Industrial Estate, 102 East Dock Lees Lane, Ponders End, EN3 7SR

Tottenham Hotspurs Stadium: 748 High Road, Tottenham, London, N17 0AP ⊕ beavertownbrewery.co.uk

⊗ Beavertown, established in 2012, opened its Tottenham Hale site in 2018. After selling a stake to Heineken in 2018, further investment saw the opening of 'Beaverworld' in Ponders End in 2020 (a ten-fold production increase). Tottenham Hale is being used to expand the Tempus Project (barrel-ageing). An on-site brewery and bar opened in the newly-built Tottenham Hotspur's football ground in 2019 (access to ticket holders only). The Tottenham Hale taproom is open at weekends. No real ale. ☛♦🥾

Beccles

The Studios, London Road, Brampton, Suffolk, NR34 8DQ ☎ 07815 519576 ⊕ becclesbrewco.co.uk

⊗ The brewery was originally owned and run by two friends alongside existing jobs, but is now run by just one of the original owners with the assistance of family and friends. It has a production run three times a week, with a 700-litre capacity. Regular trial beers can be found in local pubs. Beers are also available in bottle and mini-keg. 🥾

Hodgkins Hop (ABV 3.6%) GOLD
Neil, Neil Orange Peel (ABV 4.2%) PALE
Paint the Town Red (ABV 4.5%) RED
Boney's Island (ABV 4.6%) STOUT
Nelson's Tree (ABV 4.8%) BITTER

Beckstones

Upper Beckstones Mill, The Green, Millom, Cumbria, LA18 5HL
☎ (01229) 314900 ☎ 07544 883802
✉ info@beckstonesbrewery.co.uk

⊗ On the site of an 18th century mill, with its own water supply, this five-barrel operation continues to win awards. Beer names have connections to the long-closed Millom Iron Works or local characters, and the brewer designs the distinctive pump clips. ♦

Leat (ABV 3.6%) MILD
Rich and fruity light mild with refreshing hops in the finish.
Barley Blonde (ABV 3.7%) BLOND
Full-flavoured, beautifully-balanced, emphatically fruity, hoppy beer.
Black Dog Freddy Mild (ABV 3.9%) MILD
A full-bodied, beautifully-balanced, ruby dark mild, replete with fruit and roast malt.
Border Stones (ABV 4.1%) BITTER
An old-fashioned style, tawny bitter with a sweet start, some bitter notes and plenty of aftertaste.
Iron Town (ABV 4.1%) BITTER
Creamy, sweet amber ale which fills the mouth with well-balanced fruit and hop.
Rev Rob (ABV 4.6%) PALE
Very well-balanced. Bitter, fills the mouth with sweet malt fruit and complementary hops leaving a pleasing finish.

Bedlam SIBA

St. Helena Fram, St Helena Lane, Plumpton Green, East Sussex, BN7 3DH
☎ (01273) 978015 ⊕ bedlambrewery.co.uk

Eco-friendly Bedlam Brewery operates from the heart of the South Downs on a farm with solar power. All spent grain is donated to cattle on the farm and hops are composted. More than 1,000 pubs and bars are supplied across London and the South of England. 🍴LIVE

Phoenix IPA (ABV 3.9%) PALE
Benchmark Sussex Best Bitter (ABV 4%) BITTER

Beech Avenue (NEW)

Lodge Farm, Borras Road, Holt, LL13 9TE ☎ 07917 841304 ⊕ beechavenuebrewery.co.uk

Brewing commenced using a 30-litre kitchen plant. In 2020 the brewery upscaled and relocated to eco-friendly converted farm buildlings. Speciality fruit or dry-hopped beers are available at various times in addition to a range of four cask-conditioned ales, all available as bag-in-box.

Beer Brothers SIBA

335 Ranglet Road, Walton Summit Centre, Bamber Bridge, Lancashire, PR5 8AR ☎ 07921 519129
⊕ beerbrothers.co.uk

Founded in 2015 as a nanobrewery, Beer Brothers has seen massive growth over the years and is currently a 10-barrel plant with nine fermenting vessels, with further plans to expand. The ever-growing brewery has its own taproom, which is open four days a week, along with an on-site shop. Beer can also be found in Booths and other local independent outlets. !! ▬ V ◆

Gold (ABV 3.8%) BLOND
True Brit (ABV 3.8%) BITTER
Session IPA (ABV 3.9%) PALE
Hop Chocolate (ABV 4.3%) SPECIALITY
Gunslinger (ABV 4.7%) PALE

Beer Engine SIBA

Newton St Cyres, Devon, EX5 5AX
☎ (01392) 851282 ⊕ thebeerengine.co.uk

⊗ The Beer Engine was established in 1983 and is the oldest working microbrewery in Devon. The brewery is visible in the downstairs bar in the pub through multiple viewing windows. Several outlets are supplied, as well as local beer festivals. !! ◆

Rail Ale (ABV 3.8%) BITTER
A straw-coloured beer with a fruity aroma and a sweet, fruity finish.
Piston Bitter (ABV 4.3%) BITTER
A mid-brown, sweet-tasting beer with a pleasant, bittersweet aftertaste.
Sleeper Heavy (ABV 5.4%) BITTER
A red-coloured beer with a fruity, sweet taste and a bitter finish.

Beer Hut

6 Riverside Park, Kilkeel, BT34 4NA
✉ andrew@beerhutbrewing.co.uk

Microbrewery situated near Kilkeel harbour. Established in a flat pack hut using a 100-litre kit, it has since upscaled twice and now operates using a 1,000-litre plant. Further expansion is planned. V

Citra Ella (ABV 4.5%) GOLD
Fluffy Bunny (ABV 5%) SPECIALITY
Wahey IPA (ABV 5.6%) IPA
There's Something in the Water (ABV 6%) IPA
Simcoe Simon (ABV 6.5%) IPA
Ahoy Captain (ABV 7.4%) IPA

Beer Ink

Plover Road Garage, Plover Road, Lindley, Huddersfield, West Yorkshire, HD3 3HS
☎ (01484) 643368 ☎ 07885 676711 ✉ sales@beer-ink.co.uk

The Beer Ink Brewery is based in Lindley and opened in 2015 using an eight-barrel plant. It specialises in barrel-aged beers. Regularly collaborates with other forward-looking breweries. On-site taproom and facilities were expanded and improved in 2020. ◆ ◈

Vellum (ABV 4%) PALE
Gutenberg (ABV 4.2%) SPECIALITY
Typo (ABV 4.4%) PALE
Lampblack (ABV 4.6%) STOUT
Scrawler (ABV 5%) IPA

Beer Me

▤ The Belgian Café, 11/23 Grand Parade, Eastbourne, East Sussex, BN21 3YN
☎ (01323) 729967 ⊕ beermebrewery.co.uk

⊗ Beer Me was launched in 2014 by the owners of the Belgian Café in Eastbourne, building on 10 years in the catering industry. It uses a 2.5-barrel plant and produces continental-style beers which are served direct from the brewery. !! ◆

Beer Nouveau

75 North Western Street, Ardwick, Manchester, M12 6DY ⊕ beernouveau.co.uk

☺ Beer Nouveau has been producing heritage and experimental beers since 2015. Barrel-aging and beers from the wood are a strong focus, and always feature at its weekend brewery tap. A passion for sustainability sees one-off brew runs using hops or fruit grown in Manchester, and the brewery tap caters from a 'waste food' social enterprise. The tap encompasses a beer garden in its urban orchard and frequently hosts special events, often posited as alternatives to the mainstream. !! ▬ ◆ LIVE V ◈

Peterloo Porter (ABV 4%) PORTER
Sunny Lowry (ABV 4.1%) BITTER

Beer Station (NEW)

▤ 3 Victoria Buildings, Victoria Road, Formby, Merseyside, L37 7DB
☎ (01704) 807450

☺ A small half-barrel plant set up in 2019 at the rear of the Beer Station micropub opposite Freshfield station. The beers are railway themed and generally only available in the Beer Station but are occasionally seen elsewhere.

Beer Studio

See Hydes

Beerblefish SIBA

Unit 2A-4, Uplands Business Park, Blackhorse Lane, Walthamstow, London, E17 5QJ ☎ 07594 383195 ⊕ beerblefish.co.uk

Starting at UBrew in Bermondsey in 2015, the Edmonton site began production in 2016. A move to Walthamstow occurred in 2021. Bottle-conditioned beers were the main output, but cask has appeared regularly in London pubs and CAMRA festivals since. A range of Victorian heritage beers was launched in 2018 comprising an IPA, an ESB and a porter. LIVE ◈

Hoppy Little Fish (ABV 3.5%) PALE
Hackney TNT (ABV 4%) RED
Edmonton Best Bitter (ABV 4.3%) BITTER
Pan Galactic Pale (ABV 4.6%) BLOND
Floral nose with hints of sweet biscuit. Malty, tropical fruit overlaid with a developing hoppy spiciness and some dry bitterness.
Blackbeerble Stout (ABV 5.2%) STOUT
1853 ESB (ABV 5.3%) BITTER
Floral hops, orange and Brett yeasty nose. Spicy hoppy flavour is balanced by sweet caramel, vanilla and a little fruit.
1820 Porter (ABV 6.6%) PORTER
Aged, dark brown porter. Malty with supporting fruit (blackcurrant) and bitterness in the taste. Malty, bitter, fruity finish.
1892 IPA (ABV 6.9%) IPA
Rich, with hints of Demerara sugar and blood orange complementing the hops. Flavours slowly fade in the warm, oaky finish

Beercraft Brighton

See Brewery at the Watchmakers

Beermats SIBA

New Yard, Winkburn, Nottinghamshire, NG22 8PQ
☎ (01636) 639004 ⊕ beermatsbeer.co.uk

⊛Beermats was founded in 2017 by three friends while drinking in a pub. The brewery is located on the Winkburn Estate in old dairy buildings. Beers are named around the theme of the humble beermat. ‼☗♦V

Charismatic (ABV 3.8%) BITTER
Pragmatic (ABV 3.8%) BITTER
Format (ABV 3.9%) PALE
Team Mates (ABV 3.9%) PALE
Soul Mate (ABV 4.2%) GOLD
Diplomat (ABV 4.6%) STOUT
Ultimate (ABV 4.9%) RED

Beerology

See Blue

BeerRiff

Pilot House Wharf, Swansea, SA1 1UN ☎ 07897 895511 ⊕ beerriffbrewing.com

⊠ The proprietors of Pilot Brewery, Mumbles, have set up this four-barrel brewery mainly producing beer in keg and can. All beers are unfined, unfiltered and of a wide variety or styles. The taphouse bar has great views over the Swansea Marina.

BEEspoke

▤ The Fox, 41 Briggate, Shipley, West Yorkshire, BD17 7BP
☎ (01274) 594826 ⊕ thefoxshipley.co.uk

⊛Brewing began in 2015 in the cellar of the Fox pub using a one-barrel plant. Beers are available in the pub and at local beer festivals. Shiny Cowbird Gin now also produced. ♦

Beeston SIBA

Fransham Road Farm, Beeston, Norfolk, PE32 2LZ
☎ (01328) 700844 ☎ 07768 742763
⊕ beestonbrewery.co.uk

⊠ The brewery was established in 2006 in an old farm building using a five-barrel plant. Brewing water comes from a dedicated borehole and raw ingredients are sourced locally whenever possible. ‼LIVE

The Squirrels Nuts (ABV 3.5%) MILD
Cherry, chocolate and vanilla aroma. A malt and cherry sweetness comes to the fore but quickly fades. Short finish.
Worth the Wait (ABV 4.2%) BITTER
Hoppy throughout with a growing dryness. Complex and grainy with fruit notes, malt and understated bitterness.
Stirling (ABV 4.5%) BITTER
The Dry Road (ABV 4.8%) BITTER
Village Life (ABV 4.8%) BITTER
Copper-coloured with a nutty character. Malty throughout, a bittersweet background gives depth. Strong toffee apple finish.
On the Huh (ABV 5%) BITTER
A fruity raisin aroma. A bittersweet maltiness jousts with caramel and roast. A dry hoppiness adds to a strong finale.
Old Stoatwobbler (ABV 6%) STOUT

Contract brewed for Brancaster:
Brancaster Best (ABV 3.8%) BITTER
Malthouse Bitter (ABV 4.2%) BITTER

Beeston Hop

Windmill Lane, Sneinton, Nottingham, NG2 4QB
✉ john@beestonhop.co.uk

⊠ A nanobrewery launched in 2015 producing mainly bottle-conditioned beers. Cask beers are occasionally produced for festivals using capacity at other breweries. The beers are unfined, unfiltered and unpasteurised. LIVE

Belgian Brewer, The

Unit 11, The Links Business Centre, Raynham Road, Bishop's Stortford, Hertfordshire, CM23 5NZ
☎ (01279) 507515 ⊕ thebelgianbrewer.co.uk

Situated just outside Bishop's Stortford town centre, The Belgian Brewer is a small brewery and taproom. Established in 2018, it produces Belgian-style beers brewed to traditional Belgian methods using family recipes. Currently producing under 5,000 litres per month, demand is increasing week by week, especially for its speciality fruit beers. ‼☗♦LIVE ✿

Belhaven

Brewery Lane, Dunbar, EH42 1PE
☎ (01368) 862734 ⊕ belhaven.co.uk

⊛Belhaven is Scotland's oldest working brewery, established 1719. Nestling between the rolling hills of East Lothian and a beautiful bay (the meaning of Belhaven), it brews beers using 100% Scottish malted barley, fresh water from a local source and its own Belhaven yeast. Part of Greene King PLC. ‼☗♦

80/- Ale (ABV 3.9%) BITTER
One of the last remaining original Scottish 80 Shillings. Malt is the predominant flavour characteristic, though it is balanced by fruit and a little hop. A complex ale, true to the 80/- style.

Belleville

Unit 36, Jaggard Way, Wandsworth Common, London, SW12 8SG
☎ (020) 8675 4768 ⊕ bellevillebrewing.co.uk

Belleville began brewing in 2012. It was formed by a group of parents who met in the playground at a local primary school. It specialises in American-style beers, a core range and quarterly seasonals, available in keg and can. The taproom is a few units along from the brewery. No real ale. ‼♦✿

Bellfield SIBA

46 Stanley Place, Edinburgh, EH7 5TB
☎ (0131) 656 9390 ⊕ bellfieldbrewery.com

⊛Bellfield was established in 2014 and was the UK's first certified gluten-free brewery. It is accredited by Coeliac UK and registered with the Vegan Society. A site with taproom and beer garden opened in 2019. ‼♦GFV✿

Lucky Spence Ale (ABV 3.5%) BITTER
Session Ale (ABV 3.8%) BLOND
Light citrus tones flavour this balanced bitter.
Lawless Village IPA (ABV 4.5%) PALE
Eighty Shilling (ABV 4.8%) BROWN
Jex-Blake Mosaic IPA (ABV 5.6%) IPA

Belvoir SIBA

Crown Park, Station Road, Old Dalby, Leicestershire, LE14 3NQ
☎ (01664) 823455 ⊕ belvoirbrewery.co.uk

Belvoir (pronounced 'beaver') Brewery was set up in 1995 by former Shipstone's and Theakstons brewer Colin Brown. Long-term expansion has seen the introduction of a 25-barrel plant that can produce 120 barrels a week. The visitors centre incorporates brewery memorabilia, a bar, restaurant and shop. Around 150 outlets are supplied direct. Contract brewing is undertaken for Steamin' Billy and Hoskins Bros. There are plans to relocate during the currency of this guide. !! ♦ LIVE

Dark Horse (ABV 3.4%) MILD
Whipling (ABV 3.6%) BITTER
Star Bitter (ABV 3.9%) BITTER
Reminiscent of the long-extinct Shipstone's Bitter, this mid-brown bitter lives up to its name as it is bitter in taste but not unpleasantly so.
Gordon Bennett (ABV 4.1%) BITTER
Beaver Bitter (ABV 4.3%) BITTER
A light brown bitter that starts malty in both aroma and taste, but soon develops a hoppy bitterness. Appreciably fruity.
Oatmeal Stout (ABV 4.3%) STOUT
Peacock's Glory (ABV 4.7%) GOLD
Old Dalby (ABV 5.1%) BITTER

Contract brewed for Hoskins Bros:
Hob Bitter (ABV 4%) BITTER
IPA (ABV 4%) BITTER

Contract brewed for Steamin' Billy:
Tipsy Fisherman (ABV 3.6%) BITTER
Bitter (ABV 4.3%) GOLD
1485 (ABV 5%) BITTER
Skydiver (ABV 5%) BITTER

Ben's (NEW)

Unit 17, Yarrow Business Centre, Yarrow Road, Chorley, Lancashire, PR6 0LP
☎ (01257) 367480 ⊕ bensbrewery.co.uk

Established in 2021, the brewery is situated in part of an office furniture suppliers showroom. The taproom is only open for special events. ♦

Chorley Brown Ale (ABV 4%) BROWN
The Light Brigade (ABV 4%) PALE
Blighty (ABV 4.5%) PALE
The Duke (ABV 4.5%) BITTER
Proper Grafter (ABV 5.7%) STOUT

Benchmark (NEW) SIBA

Benchmark Barn, Groombridge Lane, Eridge Green, East Sussex, TN3 9LA
✉ enquiries@benchmarkbrewery.co.uk

Benchmark Brewery is a family partnership built around a passion for beer. The name comes from the Ordnance Survey Bench Mark engraving found chiseled into the brickwork of the barn that houses the brewery. All beers are brewed using English malts and hops sourced from a local farm. LIVE

Bentley Brook

Unit 3, Lumsdale Mill, Lumsdale, Matlock, Derbyshire, DE4 5EX ☎ 07483 831640

Office: 1 Hilltop Terrace, The Cliff, Matlock, DE4 5FY
⊕ bentleybrook.co.uk

⊗ Formed in 2018, this 1.5-barrel brewery is located in the heart of Lumsdale Valley and named after the local brook. It offers unfined, small batch beers available to purchase in the local area and at the brewery. LIVE ♦

Beowulf

Forest of Merica, Chasewater Country Park, Pool Lane, Brownhills, Staffordshire, WS8 7NL
☎ (01543) 454067 ☎ 07714 291226
⊕ beowulfbrewery.co.uk

Beowulf Brewing Company started off small in Yardley in Birmingham before moving to its current site in the Chasewater County Park. Its award-winning ales appear throughout the Midlands. !! ♦ LIVE V

Beorma (ABV 3.9%) BITTER
A perfectly balanced session ale with a malty hint of fruit giving way to a lingering bitterness. Background spice excites the palate.
Chasewater Bitter (ABV 4.4%) BITTER
Golden bitter, hoppy throughout with citrus and hints of malt. Long mouthwatering, bitter finish.
Black & Blueberry (ABV 4.5%) SPECIALITY
Boomer (ABV 4.5%) BITTER
Pale brown with lots of caramel aroma. Bitter start with a sweet, malty background, which develops to a mouthwatering finish with dry lips.
Chase Buster (ABV 4.5%) BLOND
Dark Raven (ABV 4.5%) MILD
So dark with apple and bonfire in the aroma, so sweet and smooth, like liquid toffee apples with a sudden bitter finish.
Swordsman (ABV 4.5%) BITTER
Pale gold, light fruity aroma, tangy hoppy flavour. Faintly hoppy finish.
Folded Cross (ABV 4.6%) BITTER
Malt and caramel aromas and tastes with hints of fruity biscuits are nudged aside by the robust hops which give lingering bitter edges.
Hurricane (ABV 4.6%) BITTER
Wuffa (ABV 4.6%) GOLD
Chocolate Porter (ABV 4.7%) PORTER
Dragon Smoke Stout (ABV 4.7%) STOUT
Black with a light brown creamy head. Tobacco, chocolate, liquorice and mixed fruity hints on the aroma. Bitterness fights through the sweet and roast flavours and eventually dominates. Hints of a good port emerge.
Finn's Hall Porter (ABV 4.7%) PORTER
Dark chocolate aroma, after dinner mints, coffee and fresh tobacco. Good bitterness with woodland hints of autumn. Long late bitterness with lip drying moreishness.
Heroes Bitter (ABV 4.7%) BITTER
Gold colour, malt aroma, hoppy taste but sweetish finish.
Mercian Shine (ABV 5%) BITTER
Amber to pale gold with a good bitter and hoppy start and a hint of nutmeg. Plenty of caramel and hops with background malt leading to a good bitter finish with caramel and hops lingering in the aftertaste.
Clout (ABV 6%) BITTER
Nordic Noir (ABV 6%) MILD
Dark brown with full liquorice aroma. Rich liquorice tastes with subtle tastes of chocolate and cinnamon. Gently moreish.
IPA (ABV 7.2%) STRONG
Killer Stout (ABV 7.3%) STOUT

Bere

Homefield, Bere Alston, Devon, PL20 7JA
☎ (01822) 840382 ⊕ berebrewery.co.uk

Established in 2016 by growers Jeremy and Buffy on their Bere Penisula smallholding. Since 2019, the brewery is self-sufficient in hop growing. Bottle-conditioned beers are made using the hops, with a 1.3-barrel system and a 50-litre small batch kit. There are six regular beers, with seasonal and one-off brews. Beers are sold at the brewery Wednesday and Saturday. They're also available from Roots & Vines bottle shop, Tavistock, The Olde Plough Inn, Bere Ferrers, and Tavistock Farmers Market. ☕♦LIVE♦

Bespoke SIBA

Church Farm, Church Street, Littledean, Gloucestershire, GL14 3NL
☎ (01452) 929281 ☎ 07951 818668
⊕ bespokebrewery.co.uk

⊗ Brewing has moved to new premises at Littledean, with a new farm tap. Both cask-conditioned and keg beers are produced using a 12-barrel plant. Beers are available from the farm tap and brewery shop. Speciality-labelled bottles are offered for celebratory occasions. ‼☕♦♦

Saved by the Bell (ABV 3.8%) BITTER
Forest Gold (ABV 4%) GOLD
Beware the Bear (ABV 4.2%) BITTER
Going Off Half-Cocked (ABV 4.6%) PALE
Money for Old Rope (ABV 4.8%) STOUT
Over a Barrel (ABV 5%) OLD

Bestens

Unit 17 Church Lane Farm Estate, Church Lane, Lower Beeding, West Sussex, RH13 6LU
☎ (01403) 892556 ⊕ bestensbrewery.co.uk

The brewery opened in 2018 in Lower Beeding as a one-barrel plant, increasing to four-barrel capacity in 2020. A percentage of all beer sold is donated to a community fund, which supports local charities and initiatives. The brewery operates a mobile taproom in Haywards Heath, as well as hosting events at the brewery itself. No real ale. ☕

Bewdley SIBA

Unit 7, Bewdley Craft Centre, Lax Lane, Bewdley, Worcestershire, DY12 2DZ
☎ (01299) 405148 ⊕ bewdleybrewery.co.uk

⊗ Bewdley began brewing in 2008 on a six-barrel plant in an old school. This was upgraded to a 10-barrel plant in 2014. Beers are brewed with a railway theme for the nearby Severn Valley Railway. The brewery has an on-site tap and shop. Element gin is also produced. ☕♦LIVE♦

Worcestershire Way (ABV 3.6%) GOLD
Refreshing golden ale with a citrus, faintly orange peel aroma, leads to a balanced hop, malt and grapefruit taste and a lingering, hoppy finish.
Baldwin IPA (ABV 4.2%) GOLD
Jubilee (ABV 4.3%) BITTER
Pale colour, fruit and citrus aroma, sweet malt with underlying citrus taste.
Red Hill (ABV 4.4%) BITTER
Sir Keith Park (ABV 4.5%) BITTER
Pale amber colour, full fruity and balanced flavour followed by a long hoppy finish.
Worcestershire Sway (ABV 5%) BITTER
Complex amber-coloured bitter, sometimes badged as 2857. Fragrant malty aroma, well-balanced slightly sweet malt and hops taste with hints of toffee and marmalade, malt with citrus and meadow grass finish.
William Mucklow's Dark Mild (ABV 6%) MILD
Dark in colour, malty, sweetish fruity flavour with slight liquorice finish.

Bexley SIBA

Unit 18, Manford Industrial Estate, Manor Road, Erith, Kent, DA8 2AJ
☎ (01322) 337368 ⊕ bexleybrewery.co.uk

Bexley Brewery was founded in 2014. Brewers Cliff and Jane Murphy produce regular, seasonal and experimental brews as well as selling own-brand beer mustard. The Bird & Barrel in Barnehurst, opened in 2018, replaced the taproom as the main source of the beers locally. ‼☕♦

Bursted Session Bitter (ABV 3.8%) BITTER
Golden Acre (ABV 4%) GOLD
Smooth golden ale with citrus aroma. Flavour is of grapefruit, hops and a strong bitterness, continuing in the dry-fruity finish.
Bexley's Own Beer (ABV 4.2%) BITTER
Pale brown beer with a balance of fudge, floral hop, stone fruit and some bitterness growing in the dry finish.
Redhouse Premium (ABV 4.2%) BITTER
Copper best bitter with roast and sweet orange marmalade. Dry finish with a touch of chocolate in finish and aroma.
Anchor Bay IPA (ABV 4.8%) PALE
Spike Island Stout (ABV 5.3%) STOUT

Bianca Road

83-84 Enid Street, Bermondsey, London, SE16 3RA
☎ (020) 3221 1001 ⊕ biancaroad.com

After starting in 2016 in Peckham, the brewery moved to a bigger site in 2017, and again in 2019 to two arches along the Bermondsey Beer Mile which double up as the taproom. Output is mostly keg and cans. No real ale. ♦

Bicester

🗒 Angel, 102 Sheep Street, Bicester, Oxfordshire, OX26 6LP
☎ (01869) 360410 ⊕ theangelbicester.co.uk

Brewing commenced in 2017 in an outhouse behind the Angel, Bicester. Beers are supplied solely to the pub.

Bier Edinburgh (NEW)

🗒 Keller Taproom, 23-27 Broughton Street Lane, Edinburgh, EH39 5NG ⊕ kellertaproom.com

This in-house brewery operates from a space next to, and visible from, the Keller Taproom. There is also a distillery. The first unfiltered craft lager appeared in mid 2021. No real ale.

Big Bog SIBA

74 Venture Point West, Evans Road, Speke, Merseyside, L24 9PB
☎ (0151) 558 0290 ☎ 07867 792466
⊕ bigbog.co.uk

Big Bog started life in Waunfawr, Wales in 2011, sharing its site with the Snowdonia Parc brewpub. Due to growth and expansion in 2016, the brewery moved to its present location in Speke, Liverpool, into a custom-built plant with a 10-barrel brew length. The brewery has its own licenced bar and is open to the public on Fridays. ☕♦♦

Bog Standard Bitter (ABV 3.6%) BITTER
Mire (ABV 3.8%) BITTER
Pride of England (ABV 3.8%) BITTER
Blonde Bach (ABV 3.9%) BITTER
Hinkypunk (ABV 4.1%) GOLD
Full-flavoured golden ale, fruity (citrus) hoppy aromas, dry hoppy beer, slightly sweet with a little pepperiness and a satisfying bitter finish.

THE BREWERIES

Stog (ABV 4.1%) STOUT
Jack O Lantern (ABV 4.2%) BROWN
Welsh Pale Ale (ABV 4.2%) BITTER
Morast (ABV 4.3%) SPECIALITY
Billabong (ABV 4.4%) GOLD
Blueberry Hill Porter (ABV 4.5%) SPECIALITY
Swampy (ABV 4.7%) RED
Will O the Wisp (ABV 4.7%) GOLD
Peat Bog Porter (ABV 4.9%) SPECIALITY
Bayou (ABV 5%) PALE
Quagmire (ABV 6%) BROWN

Brewed under the Strawberry Fields Brewery brand:
Lucy (ABV 4.5%) GOLD
Marmalade Skies (ABV 4.5%) STOUT
An oatmeal stout with rich roasted malt and caramel aromas with orange notes. Raisin and orange flavours with dry hop bitterness. A light hop pine finish.

Big Clock

Grants, 1 Manchester Road, Accrington, Lancashire, BB5 2BQ
☎ (01254) 393938 ☎ 07766 163497
⊕ thebigclockbrewery.co.uk

Brewing commenced at the iconic Grants Pub and Brewhouse, just off Accrington town centre, in 2014. The specially commissioned brewery can be viewed from the bar area. A new, smaller brewery has been installed. This is to run along side the existing larger six-barrel plant, for production of smaller, speciality beers for a new canning line. Beer is supplied to around a dozen outlets across East Lancashire.

Big Fish

c/o 45 Glenury Crescent, Stonehaven, AB39 3LF
A gypsy brewery established in 2017.

Big Hand

Unit A1, Abbey Close, Redwither Business Park, Wrexham, LL13 9XG
☎ (01978) 660709 ☎ 07946 514238
⊕ bighandbrewing.co.uk

⊕Big Hand began brewing in 2013 and continues to operate via a 10-barrel plant on the outskirts of Wrexham. Its broad-ranging selection of beers have won several awards and are widely available throughout North Wales and West Cheshire as well as at the Big Hand Alehouse in Chester. ‼◆

Seren (ABV 3.7%) PALE
Pale, full-flavoured and hoppy with a fruity aroma and taste
Pila Pala (ABV 3.8%) PALE
Pendragon (ABV 3.9%) BITTER
Copper-coloured and well-balanced with a smooth rich taste, juicy mouthfeel and hints of spice in the finish.
Super Tidy (ABV 4%) PALE
A pale brown bitter beer with some citrus notes in the taste and peppery hops in the finish.
Bastion (ABV 4.2%) BITTER
A dry, malty best bitter, mahogany in colour with a full mouthfeel. Biscuity flavours and faint roast notes feature throughout.
Domino (ABV 4.4%) STOUT
A smooth and fruity stout, quite hoppy and roasty with hints of berries in the initial sweetness leading to a satisfying hoppy finish.
Appaloosa (ABV 4.5%) PALE

A full-bodied pale ale, some initial sweetness with strong New World hop flavours in the taste and spicy finish.
Havok (ABV 5%) PALE
A powerfully-hopped American IPA with strong and tangy citrus fruit bitterness throughout.

Big Lamp

Grange Road, Newburn, Newcastle upon Tyne, NE15 8NL
☎ (0191) 267 1689 ⊕ biglampbrewers.co.uk

⊕Big Lamp started in 1982 and relocated in 1997 to a 55-barrel plant in a former water pumping station. It is the oldest microbrewery in the North East of England. Around 160 outlets are supplied and two pubs are owned, one of which, the Keelman, is attached to the brewery. Beers are contract brewed for Stables Brewery. ‼◆LIVE

Sunny Daze (ABV 3.6%) GOLD
Golden, hoppy session bitter with a clean taste and finish.
Bitter (ABV 3.9%) BITTER
A clean-tasting bitter, full of hops and malt. A hint of fruit with a good, hoppy finish.
Lamplight Bitter (ABV 4.2%) BITTER
Summerhill Stout (ABV 4.4%) STOUT
A rich, tasty stout, dark in colour with a lasting rich roast character. Malty mouthfeel with a lingering finish.
Prince Bishop Ale (ABV 4.8%) GOLD
A refreshing, easy-drinking bitter. Golden in colour, full of fruit and hops. Strong bitterness with a spicy, dry finish.
Premium (ABV 5.2%) BITTER
Hoppy ale with a good bitter finish.
Keelman Brown (ABV 5.7%) OLD

Big River

Building 1a, Aston Down Business Park, Stroud, Gloucestershire, GL6 8GA ☎ 07939 273697
⊕ bigriverbrew.co

Formed in 2018, using spare capacity at the now closed Ciren Ales, in Cirencester. Three core beers are available, all of which are brewed with a gluten-reducing enzyme. The brewery relocated to Stroud in 2019. ◆LIVE GF

Pale Ale (ABV 3.6%) PALE
Session IPA (ABV 3.6%) GOLD
All About Cascade (ABV 4%) GOLD
Rolling Hills (ABV 4%) PALE
Saint Louis (ABV 4%) GOLD

Big Smoke SIBA

Unit D3, Sandown Industrial Estate, Esher, Surrey, KT10 8BL
☎ (01372) 469606 ☎ 07859 884190
⊕ bigsmokebrew.co.uk

⊗ Brewing began at the Antelope, Surbiton, in 2014. In 2019 Big Smoke moved to a new purpose-built 30-hectolitre brewery in Esher with an on-site taproom. ◆V◆

Solaris Session Pale Ale (ABV 3.8%) PALE
Unfined golden ale with bitter grapefruit flavour, some malt and a long dry bitter finish. Hoppy, fruity nose.
Dark Wave Porter (ABV 5%) PORTER
Creamy, black porter with a dry roasty bitter character balanced by a caramelised sweetness.
Electric Eye Pale Ale (ABV 5%) PALE
Underworld (ABV 5%) SPECIALITY

Sweet smooth stout with hints of chocolate and coffee in the aroma and taste coupled with toasted nuts and vanilla.

Big Stone SIBA

Ashen Clough, Maynestone Road, Chinley, Derbyshire, SK23 6AH ☎ 07867 652062
✉ bigstonebeer@gmail.com

This small operation started brewing on a 2.5-barrel kit in 2019. It is based in large out-buildings connected to a private house, on the outskirts of Chinley, in the heart of the Peak District. Beers are available in bottles from local outlets. Casks are supplied to a limited number of local pubs. An on-site spring provides all the water used in production. ♦LIVE V

Kinder Stout (ABV 4.2%) STOUT
Downfall (ABV 4.3%) PALE
Rough Rock (ABV 4.3%) BITTER
The Naze (ABV 4.5%) SPECIALITY
White Rakes (ABV 5%) BLOND

Billericay SIBA

Essex Beer Shop, 54c Chapel Street, Billericay, Essex, CM12 9LS
☎ (01277) 500121 ☎ 07788 373129 .
⊕ billericaybrewing.co.uk

Billericay Brewing opened at its present site in 2014, using a 4.5-barrel plant. A micropub and beershop are next door. ‼🍽♦LIVE

Billericay Zeppelin (ABV 3.8%) BITTER
Billericay Blonde (ABV 4%) GOLD
Billericay Dickie (ABV 4.2%) BITTER
Vanilla Woods (ABV 4.2%) SPECIALITY
Woody's Wag (ABV 4.2%) PORTER
Rhythm Stick (ABV 4.8%) BITTER
Sex & Drugs & Rock & Roll (ABV 5%) PALE
Chapel Street Porter (ABV 5.9%) PORTER
Chilli Porter (ABV 5.9%) SPECIALITY
Mayflower Gold (ABV 6.5%) IPA

Binghams SIBA

Unit 4a, Woodley Park Estate, Reading Road, Woodley, Berkshire, RG5 3AW
☎ (0118) 934 4376 ⊕ binghams.co.uk

Brewing originally started in Twyford in 2010, but after its sale in 2020, it has moved a few miles south-west to Woodley. There, a taproom has been added. However the equipment did not survive the move and any beers brewed will be under contract until a complete refit can be arranged. ♦

Bingley SIBA

Unit 2, Old Mill Yard, Shay Lane, Wilsden, West Yorkshire, BD15 0DR
☎ (01535) 274285 ⊕ bingleybrewery.co.uk

Bingley is a small, family-run brewery that opened in 2014 using a six-barrel plant. It is located in a rural setting in the village of Wilsden, part of Bingley Rural Ward. Beers are distributed coast to coast and as far south as Derby. ‼♦

Endeavour (ABV 3.7%) BLOND
Goldy Locks Blonde (ABV 4%) BLOND
Azacca (ABV 4.1%) GOLD
Aire Gold (ABV 4.2%) GOLD
Session IPA (ABV 4.2%) GOLD
Steady State (ABV 4.2%) BITTER
Centennial (ABV 4.4%) GOLD

Tri State (ABV 4.5%) PALE
1848 Stout (ABV 4.8%) STOUT
Jamestown APA (ABV 5.4%) PALE

Bini (NEW)

1b Railway Road, Ilkley, LS29 8HQ ⊕ binibrew.co

Nanobrewery located on the edge of Ilkley Moor producing hazy beers. Launched in 2020.

Biochemist (NEW)

19 Boundary Road, Red Lodge, IP28 8JQ ☎ 07821 540237 ⊕ biochemistbrewery.com

Established in 2020, Biochemist is a 100-litre nanobrewery producing unfiltered, unfined beer for sale at local markets and local delivery. Small batches of seasonal, dry ciders also produced. LIVE V

Birch Cottage

Birch Cottage, Wilne Road, Sawley, Derbyshire, NG10 3AP ☎ 07966 757407
✉ birchcottagebrewery@outlook.com

Birch Cottage is a nanobrewery established in 2018 brewing small batch beers. Its brewery tap, Sawley Junction, opened in 2018.

Birchover

⊟ Red Lion, Main Street, Birchover, Derbyshire, DE4 2BN
☎ (01629) 650363 ⊕ red-lion-birchover.co.uk

⊗ Brewing started at the Red Lion pub in the picturesque Peak District village of Birchover in 2016, and upgraded to a five-barrel plant by enthusiastic pub/brewery owner in 2017. Core range beers are named after local Stanton Moor landmarks and are to be found alongside seasonal specials on the pub bar. ♦LIVE

Birdhouse

Revell Road, Downham Market, Norfolk, PE38 9SE
☎ 07858 628183 ⊕ birdhousebrewery.co.uk

⊗ Birdhouse Brewery, a picobrewery, was established in 2019 by Paul Bird. It produces only 150 bottle-conditioned beers per batch, making it one of the smallest breweries in the country. It produces a range of eight beers. Available in shops, local markets and online. LIVE

Birmingham SIBA

Unit 17, Stirchley Trading Estate, Hazelwell Road, Birmingham, B30 2PF
☎ (0121) 724 0399 ☎ 07717 704929
⊕ birminghambrewingcompany.co.uk

Birmingham Brewing Co was established in 2016 and is based in a small unit on a trading estate in Stirchley. Beers are available in the trade in cask or keg, and also in cans direct from the brewery, or many local bottle shops. ‼♦

Pale Brummie (ABV 4%) PALE
Bitter Brummie (ABV 4.1%) BITTER

Bishop Nick SIBA

33 East Street, Braintree, Essex, CM7 3JJ
☎ (01376) 349605 ⊕ bishopnick.com

⊗ Bishop Nick was launched in 2011 by Nelion Ridley, a member of the family that started Ridley's brewery near

Chelmsford in 1842. In 2013 a new brewery was established in Braintree using a 20-barrel plant. ♯◆LIVE

Ridley's Rite (ABV 3.6%) BITTER
Heresy (ABV 4%) GOLD
1555 (ABV 4.3%) BITTER
Devout (ABV 4.5%) STOUT
Martyr (ABV 5%) PALE
Divine (ABV 5.1%) BITTER

Bishop's Crook

51 Woodcroft Close, Penwortham, Lancashire, PR1 9BX ☎ 07977 220742
⊕ bishopscrookbrewery.com

A small brewery based at the home of the owner. It started brewing commercially in 2013 and gradually built up a handful of regular outlets. Due to construction work the brewery was out of action for a lengthy period from 2017, and subsequently it was mothballed. Beer production was to re-commence in 2020, but is currently suspended.

Bitter End

See Tirril

Black Bear

⊜ c/o Bear Inn, 8-10 North Street, Wiveliscombe, Somerset, TA4 2JY
☎ (01984) 623537 ⊕ blackbearbrewery.co.uk

⊠ The brewery relocated from the Northbrook Arms, East Stratton, Hampshire in 2013. It produces four main beers and occasional seasonals. It tends to supply the other outlets owned by the brewer and pub owner, Jon Coward: Marlet Arms, Langford Budville; Lamb & Flag, Blagdon Hill, and Milverton Cricket Club. ◆✦

Black Cloak

⊜ 71 Abergele Rd, Colwyn Bay, LL29 7RU ☎ 07701 031121

Office: Glog Ddu, Llangernyw, Abergele, LL22 8PS

Black Cloak opened in 2018 in a former café using a one-barrel plant producing cask and keg beer. Beers are usually only available in the bar.

Black Country IFBB

⊜ Rear of Old Bulls Head, 1 Redhall Road, Lower Gornal, West Midlands, DY3 2NU
☎ (01384) 401820

Office: 69 Third Avenue, Pensnett Trading Estate, Kingswinford, DY6 7FD ⊕ blackcountryales.co.uk

☺A compact brewery located at the back of the Bull's Head in Lower Gornal, which recommenced brewing in 2004. In 2012 much of the old equipment was replaced with a new kit, which can brew up to 15 barrels at a time. Its sister company, Black Country Inns, now has 37 pubs in its portfolio. ◆

Bradley's Finest Golden (ABV 4.2%) GOLD
Pig on the Wall (ABV 4.3%) MILD
Fireside (ABV 5%) BITTER

Black Dog

See Hambleton

Black Falls

See Neath

Black Flag

Unit 1D, New Road, Perranporth, TR6 0DL
☎ (01872) 858004 ⊕ blackflagbrewery.com

⊠ Black Flag began brewing in 2013 and relocated to Perranporth in 2019. A new eight-barrel plant was installed in 2020 and the brewery began producing a wider range of beer styles, all unfined and unpasteurised, available in cans, bottles and kegs. A small amount of cask-conditioned beer is often available in the taproom during summer months. ◆LIVE ✦

Black Hole SIBA

Unit 3a, Old Hall Mill Business Park, Alfreton Road, Little Eaton, Derbyshire, DE21 5EJ
☎ (01283) 619943 ☎ 07812 812953
⊕ blackholebrewery.co.uk

⊠ Black Hole was established in 2007 with a 10-barrel plant in the former Ind Coope bottling stores in Burton-on-Trent, but moved to its current location in 2017. Fermenting capacity of 36 barrels enables the production of up to four brews per week, some of which are marketed under the Little Eaton and Mr Grundy's Brewery names. Around 400 outlets are supplied direct, and many more via wholesalers. Since 2014, the brewery has been owned by GHH Llp, which also owned the now closed Mr Grundy's Brewery. ‼◆

Bitter (ABV 3.8%) BITTER
Amber glow, with malt and spicy hop aroma. Fresh, lively, session beer, hopped to give a clean crisp finish of hoppy dryness and touch of astringency.
Cosmic (ABV 4.2%) BITTER
Almost golden with an initial malt aroma. The complex balance of malt and English hops give lingering tastes of nuts, fruit and dry hoppy bitterness.
Supernova (ABV 4.8%) GOLD
Pure gold. Like marmalade made from Seville oranges and grapefruit the aroma mimics the sweet start but gives into the hops which deliver a dry, lingering, bitter finish.
IPA (ABV 5.2%) PALE
Milky Way (ABV 6%) SPECIALITY
Honey and banana nose advises the sweet taste but not the sweet, dry spicy finish from this wheat beer.

Brewed for Small Beer, Lincoln:
Lincoln Imperial Ale (ABV 3.8%) GOLD

Brewed under the Little Eaton brand name:
Bates' Pale Ale (ABV 3.8%) PALE
Bagnall Bros Bitter (ABV 4.2%) BITTER
Delver's Drop IPA (ABV 4.8%) SPECIALITY
Old Mill Stout (ABV 5%) SPECIALITY

Brewed under the Mr Grundy's brand name:
Passchendale (ABV 3.9%) PALE
Big Willie (ABV 4.3%) GOLD
Sniper (ABV 4.6%) BITTER
Lord Kitchener (ABV 5.5%) IPA

Black Iris SIBA

Unit 1, Shipstone Street, New Basford, Nottingham, NG7 6GJ
☎ (0115) 979 1936 ⊠ blackirisbrewery@gmail.com

☺Black Iris began brewing in 2011 using a six-barrel plant behind the Flowerpot pub in Derby. It expanded to a brand new 10-barrel plant in 2014 and relocated to premises in Nottingham. Beers are distributed nationally through wholesalers and by direct order to the local free trade. Innovation and collaboration ensure that new beers are consistently being added to the range. A brewery taproom opened in 2021. 🍺✦

Snake Eyes (ABV 3.8%) PALE
Golden-coloured ale with intense hoppy aroma and taste, with a lingering bitter finish.
Bajan Breakfast (ABV 4%) BITTER
Endless Summer (ABV 4.5%) BITTER
Golden in colour with a tropical citrus fruit presence throughout, from aroma to aftertaste with a gentle bitter finish.

Black Isle

Old Allengrange, Munlochy, IV8 8NZ
☎ (01463) 811 871 ⊕ blackislebrewery.com

☺Black Isle Brewery was set up in 1998 in the heart of the Scottish Highlands. It expanded substantially in 2011 with a new brewhouse and bottling line. All beers are organic with Soil Association certification. ‼🍺✦

Yellowhammer (ABV 3.9%) GOLD
A refreshing, hoppy golden ale with light hop and peach flavour throughout. A short, bitter finish.
Red Kite (ABV 4.2%) BITTER
Tawny ale with light malt on the nose and some red fruit on the palate. Slight sweetness in the taste.
Heather Honey (ABV 4.6%) SPECIALITY
Sweet blonde style beer brewed with organic malt, hops and Highland heather honey.
Porter (ABV 4.6%) PORTER
A hint of liquorice and burnt chocolate on the nose and a creamy mix of malt and fruit in the taste.
Blonde (ABV 5%) BLOND

Black Lodge

Kings Dock Street, Baltic Triangle, Liverpool, L1 8JU
☎ 07565 299879 ⊕ blacklodgebrewing.co.uk

Small-batch brewery producing experimental and speciality beers in cask, keg, bottle and tin that can be sampled in its own taproom. Moved to new brewery 2019 with ex-Mad Hatter brewery kit. Frequently brews specials and collaboration beers. ✦✦

Black Market

🍺 **The Workman's, 43 High Street, Warsop, Nottinghamshire, NG20 0AE** ☎ 07824 363373

Beers first appeared from Black Market in 2016. The 2.5-barrel plant is situated in the basement of the brewery tap, the Workman's/Black Market Venue in Warsop. There are three regular beers brewed. Nearly all the brews are consumed on-site, though a few go to pubs and beer festivals in the locality.

Black Metal SIBA

Unit 3, 6b Dryden Road, Loanhead, EH20 9LZ
☎ (0131) 623 3411 ☎ 07711 295385
⊕ blackmetalbrewery.com

Black Metal Brewery was established in 2012 by two old friends – metalheads and inspired brewers. Equipment was shared with Top Out (qv) brewery but it has now moved next door to its own site. ✦LIVE

Will-o'-the-Wisp (ABV 6%) SPECIALITY
Blood Revenge (ABV 6.6%) SPECIALITY
Yggdrasil (ABV 6.6%) GOLD

Black Mountain

🍺 **Speckled Hen Pub & Restaurant, 47 Derriaghy Road, Lisburn, BT28 3SH**
☎ (028) 9061 1113 ⊕ speckledhenlisburn.com/black-mountain-brewery

Small brewery attached to the Speckled Hen pub, established in 2016. The beer is only available in the pub, with a new ale every week.

Black Sheep SIBA

Wellgarth, Masham, Ripon, North Yorkshire, HG4 4EN
☎ (01765) 689227 ⊕ blacksheepbrewery.co.uk

☺Established in 1992 by Paul Theakston, a member of Masham's famous brewing family, the brewery operation is now run by his two sons. It is situated in the former Wellgarth Maltings and uses the traditional Yorkshire Square fermenting system. The company supplies the free trade across Yorkshire and the North, with national supply through pubcos and wholesale channels. It acquired York Brewery in 2018 and six pubs/bars are owned in Yorkshire. ‼🍺✦

Best Bitter (ABV 3.8%) BITTER
A hoppy and fruity beer with strong bitter overtones, leading to a long, dry, bitter finish.
Twilighter Pale Ale (ABV 4%) BITTER
Special Ale (ABV 4.4%) BITTER
Riggwelter (ABV 5.9%) BITTER
A fruity bitter, with complex underlying tastes and hints of liquorice and pear drops leading to a long, dry, bitter finish.

Brewed for Ember Inns:
Pale Ale (ABV 4%) BITTER

Brewed under York Brewery name:
Guzzler (ABV 3.6%) BITTER
Refreshing golden ale with dominant hop and fruit flavours developing throughout.
Yorkshire Terrier (ABV 4.2%) BITTER
Refreshing and distinctive amber/gold brew where fruit and hops dominate the aroma and flavour. Hoppy bitterness remains assertive in the aftertaste.
Centurion's Ghost Ale (ABV 5.4%) BITTER
Dark ruby in colour, full-tasting with mellow roast malt character balanced by light bitterness and autumn fruit flavours that linger into the aftertaste.

Black Storm SIBA

Unit 14, Stella Gill Industrial Estate, Pelton Fell, Chester-le-Street, DH2 2RG ☎ 07725 762102
⊕ blackstormbrewery.com

Beers were originally contract brewed by Hadrian Border Brewery (qv) but the former Blackhill brewery was purchased in 2019 with brewing commencing shortly afterwards.

Blonde (ABV 4%) BLOND
Pilsner (ABV 4.1%) PALE
Gold (ABV 4.3%) GOLD
Porter (ABV 5.2%) PORTER
IPA (ABV 5.5%) IPA

Black Tor SIBA

Units 5-6, Gidley's Industrial Estate, Christow, Exeter, Devon, EX6 7QB
☎ (01647) 252120 ⊕ blacktorbrewery.com

⊠ This independent, family-run brewery is located on the eastern edge of the beautiful Dartmoor National Park and has been under the current family ownership since

639

2015. Several changes of ownership and brewery name have occurred since brewing began on-site in 1998, with the present Black Tor name established in 2013. ◆

Pride Of Dartmoor (ABV 4%) BITTER
Raven (ABV 4.2%) BITTER
Devonshire Pale Ale (ABV 4.5%) PALE

Black Wolf

Unit 7c, Bandeath Industrial Estate, Throsk, Stirling, FK7 7NP
☎ (01786) 437187 ⊕ blackwolfbrewery.com

☺Established in 2005, the brewery is located in a former torpedo factory on the shores of the River Forth. In 2014 the brewery changed its name from Traditional Scottish Ales to Black Wolf Brewery and rebranded its range of beers. All Black Wolf beers are brewed on demand all year round at Throsk. The brewery also bottles beers for other breweries. ◆

Blackedge SIBA

Moreton Mill, Hampson Street, Horwich, BL6 7JH
☎ (01204) 692976 ☎ 07795 654895
⊕ blackedgebrewery.co.uk

☺Blackedge Brewery brews at a 10-barrel plant visible through a viewing window on the ground floor beneath the Brewery Bar – one of its two outlets. Its CAMRA and SIBA award-winning beers are available throughout NW England and beyond. A strong core range is supplemented by seasonal brews in both cask and unfiltered keg formats. Most are also now freshly canned and bottled on-site. !! ▶ ◆LIVE ◈

Session (ABV 3.5%) GOLD
Refreshing citrus hops, with a full-bodied citrus hop aroma. Clean, dry finish with lingering bitter hops.
Zinc (ABV 3.5%) GOLD
Hop (ABV 3.8%) BITTER
Dark Mild (ABV 3.9%) MILD
Pleasant chocolate and malt aroma leads to a full-bodied beer with dark fruits, sustained malt presence and roasty finish.
NZP3 (ABV 3.9%) PALE
Black (ABV 4%) STOUT
Well-rounded and creamy dark beer with roast malt and balanced sweetness. Dry, bitter roast finish.
Cascade (ABV 4%) GOLD
Pike (ABV 4%) PALE
Smooth, copper-coloured beer with bitter hops and balanced sweetness, leading to a dry bitter finish.
West Coast (ABV 4.1%) GOLD
Citrus hop aroma and flavour. Sweet fruitiness balances lasting bitter hops.
American (ABV 4.2%) GOLD
Platinum (ABV 4.4%) BLOND
Blonde (ABV 4.5%) BLOND
Ginger (ABV 4.5%) SPECIALITY
Amber-coloured, with fresh ginger prominent in aroma and taste. Spiciness balanced against sweet malt. Dry bitter finish.
Dark Rum (ABV 4.6%) SPECIALITY
Rich roast aroma and strong dry roast flavour. Accompanying taste of dried fruit and drawn-out, sweet finish.
IPA (ABV 4.7%) GOLD
Intense bitter hops with a long, drying finish.
Black Port (ABV 4.9%) SPECIALITY
Black beer with malty, fruity aroma. Rich, with chocolate and dark fruits to taste with a slightly drier finish.
Kiwi (ABV 5%) PALE

Blackened Sun

3 Heathfield, Stacey Bushes, Milton Keynes, Buckinghamshire, MK12 6HP ☎ 07963 529859
⊕ blackenedsunbrewing.co.uk

⊠ Blackened Sun began brewing in 2017 and is mainly focused on brewing beers using Belgian yeast. The brewery continues to diversify and innovate with its core range. It is involved in other brewing projects including a mixed fermentation programme and a project brewing with local home brewers. ◆LIVE ◈

Blackjack SIBA

34-36 Irk Street, Manchester, M4 4JT
☎ (0161) 819 2767

Office: The Smithfield, 37 Swan Street, Manchester, M4 5JZ ⊕ blackjack-beers.com

☺One of the longest established of Manchester's new wave of brewers, Blackjack began in a railway arch in the Green Quarter in 2012. A new modern brew plant was installed in 2021, enabling the brewery to develop a new and improved range of traditional and modern vegan beers. Beers are widely available across the North of England and nationally as well as in its own Smithfield Tavern and three Jack In The Box food market bars. !!◆V◈

Session IPA (ABV 4.5%) PALE
Amarillo Porter (ABV 5%) PORTER

Blackpit

Blackpit Farm, Silverstone Road, Stowe, Buckinghamshire, MK18 5LJ
☎ (01280) 827244 ⊕ blackpitbrewery.co.uk

⊠ Three friends, Ben, Duncan and Oly, began brewing in 2017 in a converted stable yard on Blackpit Farm, one mile south of Silverstone. !!◆◈

Day Tripper (ABV 3.8%) PALE
Cloud Nine (ABV 3.9%) BLOND
Loosehead (ABV 4.2%) BITTER
Goshawk (ABV 4.4%) BITTER

Blimey!

Branksome House, 166 St Clements Hill, Norwich, NR3 1RS
☎ (01603) 449298 ☎ 07775 788299
✉ adriankbryan@googlemail.com

⊠ Brewing began in 2017.

Son of Pale Face (ABV 4%) GOLD
Eleven APA (ABV 4.5%) PALE
Solid orange citrus notes dominate aroma and taste. Full-bodied and robust with malt adding balance. Short, bittersweet finish.
TEN DDH APA Cryo (ABV 4.5%) PALE
The Pale Face (ABV 4.5%) GOLD
Thirteen (ABV 4.5%) GOLD
First Born IPA (ABV 5.2%) PALE

Blindmans SIBA

Talbot Farm, Leighton, Frome, Somerset, BA11 4PN
☎ (01749) 880038 ⊕ blindmansbrewery.co.uk

Established in 2002 in a converted milking parlour and purchased by its current owners in 2004, this five-barrel brewery has its own water spring. In addition to its core range of ales, which are available locally and nationally, the brewery produces bespoke branded beers for pubs and other customers. ◆

Buff Amber (ABV 3.6%) BITTER
Funny Farm (ABV 4%) PALE
Golden Spring (ABV 4%) GOLD
Mine Beer (ABV 4.2%) BITTER
Icarus (ABV 4.5%) BITTER

Bliss (NEW)

🏠 4 Wharf Street, St Helier, Jersey, JE2 3NR
🌐 blissbrewco.com

Bliss Brew Co was formed during 2019, the first new commercial brewery in Jersey for over a century. A partnership between a talented former homebrewer and a local craft beer bar, it focuses on craft beers mainly served from KeyKeg, tentative steps have been taken in cask. Some beers have been made available in can.

Block

🏠 Wenlock Arms, 26 Wenlock Road, Hoxton, London, N1 7TA
☎ (020) 7608 3406 🌐 wenlockarms.com

⊠ Block is based in the cellar of the award-winning Wenlock Arms. Launched at the end of 2016, the beer is available at the pub in cask and keg formats. Specials are available for local beer festivals.

Blonde Brothers

Great Bathampton Farm, Wylye, Wiltshire, BA12 0QD
☎ 07538 872379 🌐 blondebrothers.beer

Established in 2019 on an organic family farm, it uses home-grown barley and water drawn from its own chalk aquifer borehole.

Blue

Unit G21, The Avenues, Eleventh Avenue, North Team Valley Trading Estate, Gateshead, Tyne & Wear, NE11 0NJ
☎ (0191) 491 0221 🌐 bluebrewing.co.uk

Gypsy brewery using spare capacity at other breweries. Established in 2019 it acquired the rights to the Mordue brand. Beerology branded beers are produced for the eponymous bar in Newcastle.

Brewed under the Mordue Brewery brand name:
5 Bridges (ABV 3.6%) BITTER
Blonde (ABV 4%) BLOND
Howay in a Manger (ABV 4.3%) BITTER
Workie (ABV 4.5%) BITTER
Radgie (ABV 4.8%) BITTER
IPA (ABV 5.1%) IPA

Blue Anchor

🏠 50 Coinagehall Street, Helston, Cornwall, TR13 8EL
☎ (01326) 562821 🌐 spingoales.com

😊A family-run, 15th century thatched brewpub, the oldest continuously brewing in the country. Home of the famous Spingo ales, which are produced from the well water beneath the pub. All regular brews are also available bottle-conditioned. ‼◆LIVE

Flora Daze (ABV 4%) BITTER
Pale brown session bitter with light flowery aroma and balanced malt, fruit and hops in the mouth. Gentle, lingering finish.
Jubilee IPA (ABV 4.5%) PALE
Amber, premium bitter with malty, fruity hop nose and taste, balanced by fresh hop bitterness. Gentle bitter finish with sweet malt.

Ben's Stout (ABV 4.8%) STOUT
Creamy dark stout with coffee roast aroma. Roast malt with liquorice and cherry flavours. Bittersweet finish with apples and cloves.
Spingo Middle (ABV 5%) BITTER
Heavy, tawny ale with dominant malt and balancing peppery hop bitterness. Nuts, spices and dates flavours. Long, malty, earthy finish.
Spingo Special (ABV 6.6%) STRONG
Smooth, red, strong old ale. Red wine aroma. Kaleidoscope of powerful sweet stone fruits, malt and hop flavours. Vinous and earthy.

Blue Bee SIBA

Unit 29-30, Hoyland Road Industrial Estate, Sheffield, South Yorkshire, S3 8AB ☎ 07375 659349
🌐 bluebeebrewery.co.uk

Established in 2010, this independently-owned, 10-barrel brewery supplies throughout Yorkshire and the East Midlands, although it is often seen further afield. Blue Bee produce regular innovative specials and collaborate frequently with other like-minded breweries. A stout and an IPA are always available. Many beers have an emphasis on New World hops. ◆

Hillfoot Best Bitter (ABV 4%) BITTER
Reet Pale (ABV 4%) PALE
American 5 Hop (ABV 4.3%) PALE
Triple Hop (ABV 4.3%) PALE
Ginger Beer (ABV 4.5%) SPECIALITY
Tempest Stout (ABV 4.8%) STOUT

Blue Bell

🏠 Cranesgate South, Whaplode St Catherine, Lincolnshire, PE12 6SN
☎ (01406) 540300 ☎ 07788 136663
🌐 thebluebell.net

😊Founded in 1998 behind the Blue Bell Pub. The brewery is owned by the pub after previously operating as a separate business. Beers are only available at the pub and to private customers. ‼◆LIVE

Blue Monkey SIBA

10 Pentrich Road, Giltbrook Industrial Park, Giltbrook, Nottingham, Nottinghamshire, NG16 2UZ
☎ (0115) 938 5899 🌐 bluemonkeybrewery.com

😊Blue Monkey was established in 2008 as a 10-barrel plant but moved in 2010 to a bigger site to meet increasing demand. It now brews around 15,000 pints a week to supply more than 200 local outlets and selected national distributors. The brewery has four pubs called the Organ Grinder, in Nottingham, Arnold, Loughborough, and Newark. ‼🚬

Marmoset (ABV 3.6%) BITTER
BG Sips (ABV 4%) PALE
Pale golden, hoppy beer, brewed mainly with Brewers Gold hops. Very fruity and bitter.
Primate Best Bitter (ABV 4%) BITTER
Infinity (ABV 4.6%) PALE
Golden ale packed with Citra hops.
Chocolate Amaretto (ABV 4.9%) SPECIALITY
Chocolate Guerilla (ABV 4.9%) SPECIALITY
Chocolate Orange (ABV 4.9%) STOUT
Guerrilla (ABV 4.9%) STOUT
A creamy stout, full of roast malt flavour and a slightly sweet finish.
Ape Ale (ABV 5.4%) PALE
Intensely-hopped, strong golden ale with dry, bitter finish.

Infinity Plus 1 (ABV 5.6%) BITTER

Blue Square

See Truth Hurts

Blueball

The Old Bakery, 31-33 Ashridge Street, Runcorn, Cheshire, WA7 1HU
☎ (01928) 775628 🌐 societyltd.co.uk

☺Founded by Alex Haycraft in 2010, Blueball relocated to its current site in Runcorn in 2017. The brewery and on-site taproom (Society Tap Room), is situated in a former bakery and local Co-op building underneath railway arches, a short walk from the station. ◆

Indie Girl (ABV 3.8%) PALE
Gold Digger (ABV 4%) GOLD
Communion (ABV 4.1%) BITTER
Ruby O'Reilly (ABV 4.3%) BITTER
Penny Black (ABV 4.5%) STOUT
Spank (ABV 6%) BITTER

Blueprint

See Moncada

Bluestone SIBA

Tyriet, Cilgwyn, Pembrokeshire, SA42 0QW
☎ (01239) 820833 🌐 bluestonebrewing.co.uk

A family-run business established in 2013 on a working farm in the Preseli Hills, within the Pembrokeshire Coast National Park. The 10-barrel brewery is housed in a 300-year-old dairy, and has a visitor facility/office (check website for opening times). Outdoor music and other events are held in the summer. Spring water, filtering down through the Preseli Bluestones to the brewery, gives the beers a unique taste. Local outlets plus wholesalers around the UK are supplied. Green Key accredited for environmental sustainability. ‼️🍺◆LIVE

Bedrock Blonde (ABV 4%) BLOND
Stone Cold (ABV 4.2%) PALE
Hammerstone IPA (ABV 4.5%) PALE
Rocketeer (ABV 4.6%) BITTER
Preseli Pils (ABV 4.7%) SPECIALITY

Blunt Chisel

Phoenix Mill, Sawmill Road, Blairadam, KY4 0JG
🌐 thebluntchisel.co.uk

A nanobrewery set up in a former sawmill on the north bank of the Kelty Burn. A range of bottle-conditioned beers is on sale at the monthly Kinross Farmers' Market and at Leith Market. LIVE

Blythe SIBA

Blythe House Farm, Lichfield Road, Hamstall Ridware, Staffordshire, WS15 3QQ
☎ (01889) 504461 ☎ 07483 248723
🌐 blythebrewery.co.uk

⊗ Blythe began brewing in 2003 using a 2.5-barrel plant in a converted barn. Only organic ingredients are used wherever possible. Following a buyout by two brothers in 2017, the brewery increased its range of beers. 15 outlets are supplied direct with others supplied by wholesalers throughout the region. ‼️LIVE

Bagot's Bitter (ABV 3.8%) BITTER

Amber in colour with a fruit start and sweetness which develops to a smooth, bitter finish. A lightly-hopped, easy-drinking beer.
Ridware Pale (ABV 4.3%) BITTER
Bright and golden with a bitter floral hop aroma and citrus taste. Good and hop-sharp, bitter and refreshing. Long, lingering bite with ripples of citrus across the tongue.
Summer Breeze (ABV 4.3%) BITTER
Staffie (ABV 4.4%) BITTER
Hoppy and grassy aroma with hints of sweetness from this amber beer. A touch of malt at the start is soon overwhelmed by hops. A full hoppy, mouthwatering finish.
Palmers Poison (ABV 4.5%) BITTER
Refreshing darkish beer. Tawny but light headed. Coffee truffle aroma, pleasingly sweet to start but with a good hop mouthfeel.
Gold Rush (ABV 4.6%) BITTER
Dark Horse (ABV 4.7%) STOUT
Knobbled Horse (ABV 4.7%) SPECIALITY
Dark Ruby (ABV 5%) MILD
Johnsons (ABV 5.2%) PORTER
Black with a thick head. Refreshingly hoppy and full-bodied with lingering bitterness of chocolate, dates, coal smoke and liquorice.

BMAN (NEW)

50 Monument Business Park, Chalgrove, Oxfordshire, OX44 7RW 🌐 bmanbrewery.co.uk

Established in 2021, BMAN produces beer in cans. Outlets include specialist craft beer shops such as Big Scary Monsters Social Club, Oxford.

BOA (Brothers of Ale)

Unit 3, Anglo Buildings, Baldwin Road, Stourport-on-Severn, Worcestershire, DY13 9AX
☎ (01299) 488100 ☎ 07725 724934
🌐 brothersofale.co.uk

What started as a hobby soon became a passion and BOA Brewery was established in 2018 before opening its doors in 2019. It is situated in the heart of Stourport on Severn producing hop-forward, New World-style beers. ◆

Peace Out (ABV 3.6%) BITTER
Lock N Load (ABV 4.2%) BARLEY
The 7 (ABV 4.2%) BITTER
2 Step (ABV 4.4%) PALE
VVD Oatmeal Stout (ABV 4.7%) STOUT
Bone Idle (ABV 4.8%) GOLD

Boat Lane

Unit 3, Streamside Business Park, Boat Lane, Offenham, Evesham, Worcestershire, WR11 8RS
☎ (01386) 719558 🌐 boatlanebrewery.co.uk

A microbrewery established in 2017 by Ian Hazeldene in a small village near Evesham. An ever-changing range of beers are brewed, with up to eight available in the brewery bar at weekends. ◆

Boden

Unit 3, 95 Boden Street, Glasgow, G40 3QF ☎ 07511 022231 🌐 bodenbrewing.co.uk

Launched in 2019, Boden Brewing is a one-man operation based in the east end of Glasgow. Six core beers are available in bottle and keg.

Bog Brew

See Six Hills

Bohem

Unit 5, Littleline House, 41-43 West Road, Tottenham, London, N17 0RE
☎ (020) 8617 8350 ☎ 07455 502976
⊕ bohembrewery.com

Traditional Bohemian lagers brewed by Czech expats in North London. The brewery moved to larger premises in 2018. Beers are supplied to local outlets, including the taproom near Bowes Park station. A second outlet was added in 2020, Bohemia House, West Hampstead, replacing the former Czech club. No real ale. 🚬◆

Boilerhouse

See JW Lees (under L)

Bollington SIBA

Adlington Road, Bollington, Cheshire, SK10 5JT
☎ (01625) 575380 ⊕ bollingtonbrewing.co.uk

⊠ Bollington began brewing in 2008 with the Vale Inn, Bollington, as the brewery tap. The Park Tavern, Macclesfield, and the Cask Tavern, Poynton, are also owned. Around 40 outlets are supplied direct. ‼◆

Chinook & Grapefruit (ABV 3.6%) GOLD
Ginger Brew (ABV 3.6%) SPECIALITY
White Nancy (ABV 3.6%) BLOND
Long Hop (ABV 3.9%) GOLD
Bollington Best (ABV 4.2%) BITTER
Dinner Ale (ABV 4.3%) BITTER
Oat Mill Stout (ABV 5%) STOUT
Eastern Nights (ABV 5.6%) IPA

Bond Brews

Units 3 & 4, South Barns, Gardeners Green Farm, Heathlands Road, Wokingham, Berkshire, RG40 3AS
☎ (01344) 775450 ⊕ bondbrews.co.uk

⊠ An award-winning brewery, Bond Brews was established in 2015 using a six-barrel plant. Beers are delivered to pubs within a 30-mile radius. Brewery tours and experience days are available by arrangement with the brewer. An online shop opened in 2020. ‼🚬◆LIVE

Goldi-hops (ABV 3.9%) PALE
A golden-coloured, session pale ale with a fruit and hop aroma. Bramble and apple flavours lead to a lingering fruity, dry, bitter aftertaste.
Best of British (ABV 4%) BITTER
A tawny-coloured, session bitter with malt, hops and fruit aroma. Dried fruit, earthy and caramel flavours lead to a sweet, nutty aftertaste.
Bengal Tiger (ABV 4.3%) PALE
A golden-coloured, session pale ale with a hoppy, fruity aroma. Initial fruity flavour leads to an earthy bitterness and a long, dry, bitter finish.
Railway Porter (ABV 4.5%) PORTER
A brown-coloured, session porter with roast malt and fruit aroma. Bitter and hoppy flavour with an earthy, peppery, bitter chocolate aftertaste.

Bone Idle

28 The Green, Idle, Bradford, West Yorkshire, BD10 9PX ☎ 07525 751574

Established in 2018 in a converted barn situated in the heart of Idle village. The brewery offers the public the opportunity to try brewing. All beers produced are sold exclusively in the Idle Draper pub next door. A mezzanine floor has a mini cinema/ function room.

Bone Machine

20 Pier Street, Hull, East Yorkshire, HU1 1ZA
☎ (01482) 618000 ☎ 07931 313438
✉ beer@bonemachinebrewing.com

Originally established in Pocklington in 2017, Bone Machine transferred operations to Hull's Fruit Market in 2019, brewing on an eight-barrel plant. Finnish brothers Marko and Kimmo previously worked at Atom and Brass Castle Brewery before setting up on their own. Beers are mainly available in keg and can, with a small amount in cask. V◆

Back Bone (ABV 3.7%) BITTER
Cloud Piercer (ABV 4.7%) BITTER
Dream Machine (ABV 5.2%) BITTER

Boot

See Burton Bridge

Boot Town

c/o Copper Kettle Brewing, Bosworths Garden Centre, 110 Finedon Road, Burton Latimer, Northamptonshire, NN15 5QA
☎ (01536) 725212 ⊕ boottownbrewery.co.uk

A microbrewery established in 2017 and based on the old Copper Kettle Brewery site, producing an ever-changing range of beers.

Born SIBA

Lanton Mill, Jedburgh, TD8 6ST
☎ (01835) 830495 ☎ 07802 416494
⊕ bornintheborders.com

Scotland's original plough-to-pint brewery, it started brewing as Scottish Borders Brewery in 2011, using its own barley, before changing name to Born in the Borders Brewery, and then Born Brewery in 2020. Beyond its core range of ales, projects have included the 'Wild Harvest' initiative, which sources locally-foraged ingredients. The brewery has a visitor centre, offering brewery tours, a café/restaurant, gin distillery and shop. Several retail units elsewhere feature the beer, produce and food. ‼🚬◆⬦

Lager BLOND
Blonde (ABV 3.8%) GOLD
Well-balanced hop and malt flavour, with bitterness coming through.
Amber (ABV 4%) BITTER
An amber ale with a balance of malty sweetness and hop bitterness, fruity and easy to drink.
Holy Cow (ABV 4.2%) GOLD
Gold Dust (ABV 4.3%) PALE
Dark (ABV 4.5%) BITTER

Borough Arms

🍺 2 New Henry Street, Neath, SA11 2PH
☎ (01639) 644902 ⊕ boroughbreweryneath.com

◉The Borough Arms and Borough Brewery were bought by new owners in 2019. The brewery is at the rear of the pub and has been refurbished. Beers brewed are only available at the pub.

Boss SIBA

176 Neath Road, Landore, Swansea, SA1 2JT
☎ (01792) 450978 ☎ 07825 525735
⊕ bossbrewing.co.uk

⊠ The brewery opened in 2015 by Roy Allkin and Sarah John, using a 10-barrel plant. It relocated in 2017 to larger premises opposite the Liberty Stadium which now includes an on-site tap – the Brewery Bar. Expansion has resulted in the setting up of bottling, canning, kegging as well as casking facilities. 250 outlets are supplied, bottles and cans are distributed to national retailers. In a further trade expansion, exports to France and Germany commenced in 2017. !! ♦ LIVE ✦

Blonde (ABV 4%) BLOND
Saint or Sinner (ABV 4%) PALE
Blaze (ABV 4.5%) GOLD
Beetlejuice (ABV 4.8%) PALE
Bare (ABV 5%) SPECIALITY
Black (ABV 5%) STOUT

Bosun's SIBA

Unit 4, Prospect Business Centre, Prospect Street, Huddersfield, West Yorkshire, HD1 2NU
☎ (01484) 412300 ☎ 07513 112188
⊕ bosunsbrewery.co.uk

⊛ The first brew was produced in 2013 by a father and son who had both served in the armed forces. The brewery relocated from Horbury to Huddersfield in 2018. The regular beers are produced on a 10-barrel plant with some given military-themed names. !! ⌷ ♦

Tell No Tales (ABV 3.8%) BITTER
Blonde (ABV 3.9%) BLOND
Maiden Voyage (ABV 3.9%) BITTER
Down the Hatch (ABV 4%) BITTER
King Neptune (ABV 4.3%) BITTER
IPA (ABV 5.6%) IPA

Botley

Botley Mills, Mill Hill, Botley, Hampshire, SO30 2GB
☎ (01489) 784867 ☎ 07909 337212
⊕ botleybrewery.com

⊠ Botley Brewery was established in 2010 and uses a five-barrel plant. A small bar next door, appropriately named the Hidden Tap, serves three of its ales Thursday-Saturday. ⌷ ♦ LIVE

Hampshire Pale Ale (ABV 3.8%) PALE
Pommy Blonde (ABV 4.3%) BITTER
Amber bitter with malty, orange and grapefruit nose. Hops come through in taste leading to pronounced bitterness and dry finish.
Barista (ABV 4.6%) SPECIALITY
Coffee milk stout with enticing coffee and blackberry aroma. Rather thin, roast and toffee leading to slightly sour, sharp finish.
English IPA (ABV 5.1%) PALE
An earthy rich and piney English IPA. Decent hoppiness with lasting, pronounced dryness, but a well-rounded malt character throughout.
Stinger Porter (ABV 5.2%) PORTER

Bottle Brook

Church Street, Kilburn, Belper, Derbyshire, DE56 0LU
☎ (01332) 880051 ☎ 07971 189915

⊠ A sister brewery to Leadmill (qv), Bottle Brook was established in 2005 using a 2.5-barrel plant on a tower gravity system. New World hops are predominantly used.

The core range of beers is supplemented by one-off brews.

Columbus (ABV 4%) GOLD
Heanor Pale Ale (ABV 4.2%) PALE
Roadrunner (ABV 4.8%) GOLD
Mellow Yellow (ABV 5.7%) GOLD
Rapture (ABV 5.9%) GOLD
Sand in the Wind (ABV 6.1%) GOLD

Boudicca SIBA

c/o S&P Brewery, The Homestead, Brewery Lane, Horsford, NR10 3GL ☎ 07864 321733

Office: 34 Clabon Road, Norwich, NR3 4HF
⊕ boudiccabrewing.co.uk

⊠ Established in 2015, Boudicca Brewery was based on a North Norfolk estate until 2020. S&P (qv) are currently brewing its beers under contract until a new home is located. It is an award-winning, independent brewery exclusively producing vegan beers, supplied to free trade outlets across East Anglia, including cafés, delicatessens and off-licences. !! ♦ LIVE V

Boundary SIBA

Unit A5 310, Portview Trade Centre, Newtownards Road, Belfast, BT4 1HE ⊕ boundarybrewing.coop

Boundary is a cooperative brewery based in Belfast, established in 2014. A taproom is open to the public. ♦ ✦

APA (ABV 3.5%) PALE
Export Stout (ABV 7%) STOUT
IPA (ABV 7%) IPA

Boutilliers

The Hop Shed, Macknade Fine Foods, Selling Road, Faversham, Kent, ME13 8XF ☎ 07743 372434
⊕ boutilliers.com

Founded in 2016, Boutilliers is a small brewery specialising in left field brews. Its beers are mainly bottled or canned. Cask-conditioned beers are supplied to a few local pubs and are sometimes available at the brewery on open days. ⌷ ♦ LIVE

Bowland SIBA

Holmes Mill, Greenacre Street, Clitheroe, Lancashire, BB7 1EB
☎ (01200) 443592 ⊕ bowlandbrewery.com

⊛ Founded in 2003, this family-run business uses a 30-barrel plant, together with a nanobrewery for experimental brews. The site features a beer shop and beer hall with 42 handpumps featuring beers from Lancashire and beyond. !! ⌷ ♦ LIVE

Pheasant Plucker (ABV 3.7%) BITTER
Gold (ABV 3.8%) PALE
Well-balanced, pale, hoppy ale with delicate citrus hop notes and a long, dry, bitter finish.
Boxer Blonde (ABV 4%) BLOND
Bumble (ABV 4%) SPECIALITY
Hen Harrier (ABV 4%) PALE
Gentle aromas of malt, hops and fruit start this satisfying, fruity bitter which has a lasting, rich finish.
Buster IPA (ABV 4.5%) PALE

Bowler's (NEW) SIBA

84 Lincoln Road, Deeping, Cambridgeshire, PE6 9BB
☎ 07480 064147 ⊕ bowlers.beer

⊠ Established in 2019, Bowler's began brewing bottled ales in 2020. The name comes from the owner's surnames, Bowyer and Gowler. ♦LIVE V

Brown Derby (ABV 4.8%) BROWN
Trusty Steed (ABV 5.2%) IPA
Lonesome Pine (ABV 5.7%) PALE
The Ryddler (ABV 6.4%) IPA

Bowman SIBA

Wallops Wood, Sheardley Lane, Droxford, Hampshire, SO32 3QY
☎ **(01489) 878110** ⊕ **bowman-ales.com**

⊠ Brewing started in 2006 in converted farm buildings. The brewery supplies more than 100 outlets. A 40-barrel plant came on stream in 2013, which works alongside the original 20-barrel plant. Bowman also brew the Suthwyk Ales range of beers. ‼♦LIVE

Swift One (ABV 3.8%) BLOND
Easy-drinking bitter, well-balanced with sweet maltiness leading to a bittersweet finish and slightly dry hoppy aftertaste.
Meon Valley Bitter (ABV 3.9%) BITTER
Well-balanced traditional, copper-coloured bitter; sweet with initial maltiness in taste and aroma leading to a more bitter finish.
Yumi (ABV 3.9%) BITTER
Wallops Wood (ABV 4%) BITTER
No particular flavour dominates this well-crafted beer. Malt flavours throughout balanced by toffee notes, sweetness and slightly dry finish.

Contract Brewed for Suthwyk Ales:
Old Dick (ABV 3.8%) BITTER
Pleasant, clean-tasting, pale brown bitter. Easy-drinking and well-balanced. Brewed using ingredients grown on Bowman's farm.
Liberation (ABV 4.2%) BITTER
Skew Sunshine Ale (ABV 4.6%) GOLD
An amber-coloured beer, brewed using Bowman's homegrown ingredients. Initial hoppiness leads to a fruity taste and finish.
Palmerston's Folly (ABV 5%) SPECIALITY

Bowness Bay SIBA

Unit 10, Castle Mills, Aynam Road, Kendal, Cumbria, LA9 7DE
☎ **(01539) 726800** ☎ **07823 347763**
⊕ **bownessbaybrewing.co.uk**

☺Bowness Bay Brewing moved to Kendal in 2015 and increased capacity from five to 16 barrels. Now expanded to a 2,500-litre automated four vessel brewing system, capable of brewing up to six times a day. The original five-barrel plant is used for small experimental brews. In 2020 grant funding allowed further expansion into keg beers. The brewery now has its own on-site taphouse, the Barrel House, and in 2021 a new live performance venue, which serves as a second taphouse. ‼♦◆

Lakeland Blonde (ABV 3.7%) BLOND
Swift Best (ABV 3.8%) BITTER
A tawny bitter where caramel sweetness dominates, leading to a gentle, bitter finish.
Swan Blonde (ABV 4%) BLOND
Sweet, fruity, mild beer with gentle bittering hops.
Fellwalker (ABV 4.1%) PALE
Raven Red (ABV 4.2%) BITTER
Sweet, malty bitter with fruit and roast aromas, gentle hop bitterness and a dry finish.
Swan Gold (ABV 4.2%) PALE
Swan Black (ABV 4.6%) STOUT

Stout-like beer with a fruity, raisin-like middle, grainy mouthfeel and roast, bitter finish.
Tern IPA (ABV 5%) PALE
Well-balanced with some sweet malt and fruit to balance the lingering hoppy finish.

Bowtie

78 Church Road, Watford, Hertfordshire, WD17 4PU
⊕ **bowtiebrewers.co.uk**

A 0.25-barrel nanobrewery founded in 2018 in a specially designed brewshed. Commercial brewing began in 2019, offering three ranges of small batch beers; traditional, craft and speciality. Beers are mostly available in bottles but cask-conditioned beer is occasionally produced. LIVE

Box Steam SIBA

15, The Midlands, Holt, Wiltshire, BA14 6RU
☎ **(01225) 782700** ⊕ **boxsteambrewery.com**

⊠ Founded in 2004, the brewery boasts a Fulton steam-fired copper, hence the name. New ownership since 2006 meant expansion and increased capacity with the brewery moving to larger premises in Holt in 2011. Two pubs are owned and more than 100 outlets supplied. ‼🛒♦V◆

Golden Bolt (ABV 3.8%) GOLD
Soul Train (ABV 4%) PALE
Tunnel Vision (ABV 4.2%) BITTER
New Normal (ABV 4.3%) IPA
Piston Broke (ABV 4.5%) GOLD
Derail Ale (ABV 5.2%) PALE

Boxcar

Unit 1, Birkbeck Street, Bethnal Green, London, E2 6JY
⊕ **boxcarbrewery.co.uk**

After being located in Homerton for two years, Boxcar moved to Bethnal Green in 2019 opening a larger brewery and taproom. An ever-changing range of hoppy beers in keg and cans forms the majority of production, with cask available, usually the popular Dark Mild. ◆

Dark Mild (ABV 3.6%) MILD
Roasty fruity black mild with a trace of roasty bitterness that lingers in the finish, which is dry.

Br3wery

253 Beckenham Road, Beckenham, BR3 4RP
⊕ **br3wery.com**

Established in 2019 producing bottle-conditioned beers at the nanobrewery. Bigger batches of beer were later brewed at Birmingham Brewery. The bottle shop opened in January 2021 with the on-site brewery starting production in 2021 with an ever-changing range of styles. ◆

Brack'N'Brew

Brackenrigg Inn, Watermillock, Cumbria, CA11 0LP
☎ **(01768) 486206** ⊕ **brackenrigginn.co.uk**

Alfred's Golden Ale (ABV 3.2%) GOLD
Boathouse Blonde (ABV 3.8%) BITTER
Rambling Bookkeeper Bitter (ABV 4.1%) BITTER
The Steamer Stout (ABV 4.4%) SPECIALITY
Aira Force IPA (ABV 5.9%) IPA

Bradfield SIBA

Watt House Farm, High Bradfield, Sheffield, South Yorkshire, S6 6LG
☎ (0114) 285 1118 ⊕ bradfieldbrewery.co.uk

☺One of the largest breweries in Sheffield, this family-run business was established in 2005. Utilising pure Millstone Grit spring water, it is based on a working farm in the Peak District. Direct delivery covers both the Midlands and the North, and beer is supplied further afield. There is also a local home-delivery service. Three pubs are owned: the King & Miller, Deepcar; the Nag's Head, Loxley (brewery tap since 2009); and the Wharncliffe Arms, Wharncliffe Side. Monthly specials are available. �♦LIVE

Farmers Bitter (ABV 3.9%) BITTER
Farmers Blonde (ABV 4%) BLOND
Farmers Brown Cow (ABV 4.2%) BITTER
Farmers Steel Cow (ABV 4.5%) BITTER
Farmers Stout (ABV 4.5%) STOUT
Farmers Pale Ale (ABV 5%) PALE
Farmers Sixer (ABV 6%) GOLD

Braemar (NEW) SIBA

Airlie House, Chapel Brae, Braemar, AB35 5YT
☎ 07709 199914 ⊕ brewbraemar.uk

Small brewery founded in 2021 and located in one half of Hazelnut Patisserie. Bottled beers are also sometimes available.

Pale Ale (ABV 4.2%) PALE

Brains IFBB

Dragon Brewery, Pacific Road, Cardiff, CF24 5HJ
☎ (029) 2040 2060 ⊕ sabrain.com

☺Brains, still in family ownership, was established in 1882 at the Old Brewery in the City Centre, moving in 1999 to the former Hancock's brewery site (soon to be part of the Central Quay development area). The new Dragon Brewery, Cardiff Bay, relaunched in 2019. It is hoped the redundant Craft Brewery would become part of a Visitor Centre in Central Quay. The Covid pandemic has affected Brains and it has approached Marston's to take over the running of most of its pub estate but plan to continue brewing at the Dragon brewery site. ♦

Dark (ABV 3.5%) MILD
A tasty, classic dark brown mild, a mix of malt, roast, caramel with a background of hops. Bittersweet, mellow and with a lasting finish of malt and roast.
Bitter (ABV 3.7%) BITTER
Amber-coloured with a gentle aroma of malt and hops. Malt, hops and bitterness combine in an easy-drinking beer with a bitter finish.
Rev James Gold (ABV 4.1%) GOLD
SA (ABV 4.2%) BITTER
A mellow, full-bodied beer. Gentle malt and hop aroma leads to a malty, hop and fruit mix with a balancing bitterness.
SA Gold (ABV 4.2%) GOLD
A golden beer with a hoppy aroma. Well-balanced with a zesty hop, malt, fruit and balancing bitterness; a similar satisfying finish.
Rev James Rye (ABV 4.3%) BITTER
Rev James (ABV 4.5%) BITTER
A faint malt and fruit aroma with malt and fruit flavours in the taste, initially bittersweet. Bitterness balances the flavour and makes this an easy-drinking beer.

Contract brewed for Molson Coors:
M&B Brew XI (ABV 3.6%) BITTER

Hancocks HB (ABV 3.7%) BITTER
Worthington's Bitter (ABV 3.7%) BITTER

Brakspear

Eagle Maltings, The Crofts, Witney, Oxfordshire, OX28 4DP
☎ (01993) 890800 ⊕ brakspear-beers.co.uk

Brakspear beers have been brewed in Oxfordshire since 1779. They continue to be traditionally crafted at the Wychwood Brewery (qv) in the historic market town of Witney using the original Victorian square fermenters and the renowned double drop fermenting system. Part of Carlsberg Marston's Brewing Co. ‼🚆♦LIVE⚒

Gravity (ABV 3.4%) BITTER
Oxford Gold (ABV 4%) GOLD

Brampton SIBA

Units 4 & 5, Chatsworth Business Park, Chatsworth Road, Chesterfield, Derbyshire, S40 2AR
☎ (01246) 221680 ⊕ bramptonbrewery.co.uk

☺The original Brampton Brewery closed in 1955. In 2007 a new brewery was established, and brewing commenced on an eight-barrel plant. Three tied houses are situated close to the brewery. ‼🚆♦LIVE

Golden Bud (ABV 3.8%) GOLD
Crisp and refreshing golden bitter with a pleasant balance of citrus, sweetness and bitter flavours. Light and easy to drink.
1302 (ABV 4%) PALE
Griffin (ABV 4.1%) PALE
Best (ABV 4.2%) BITTER
Classic, drinkable bitter with a predominantly malty taste, balanced by caramel sweetness and a developing bitterness in the aftertaste.
Impy Dark (ABV 4.3%) OLD
Strong, roasted coffee aroma and a rich flavour of vine fruit and chocolate combine to make this a tasty mild ale.
Jerusalem (ABV 4.6%) BITTER
Tudor Rose (ABV 4.6%) PALE
Wasp Nest (ABV 5%) BITTER
Strong and complex with malt and hop flavours and a caramel sweetness.
Speciale (ABV 5.8%) IPA

Brancaster

See Beeston

Branscombe SIBA

Branscombe, Devon, EX12 3DP
☎ (01297) 680511 ⊕ branscombebrewery.co.uk

⊗ The brewery was set up in 1992 in cowsheds at the back of a National Trust-owned farm, overlooking the sea at Branscombe. The brewery owners converted the sheds, digging their own well. In 2008 a new 25-barrel plant was shoehorned in through the roof to increase capacity. ♦LIVE

Branoc (ABV 3.8%) BITTER
Amber session bitter. Hops and malt throughout with good bitterness in taste and aftertaste.
Golden Fiddle (ABV 4%) GOLD
Summa This (ABV 4.2%) BITTER
Summa That (ABV 5%) GOLD

Brass Castle SIBA

10A Yorkersgate, Malton, North Yorkshire, YO17 7AB
☎ (01653) 698683 ⊕ brasscastle.co.uk

☺The brewery is based in the centre of Malton with a 12-barrel plant, having begun life in 2011 on a one-barrel kit in the owner's garage. It has an on-site taproom with many beers available for on and off-sales. ‼️🍽♦V

Northern Blonde (ABV 3.9%) BLOND
Misfit (ABV 4.3%) GOLD
Bad Kitty (ABV 5.5%) SPECIALITY
Sunshine (ABV 5.7%) IPA
Disruptor (ABV 7.4%) IPA

Breakwater

St Martin's Yard, Lorne Road, Dover, Kent, CT16 2AA
☎ (01304) 410144 ☎ 07979 867045
✉ andrea@breakwater.brewery.co.uk

⊗ Breakwater is a brewery and taproom established in 2016, behind Buckland Corn Mill in former industrial premises, and on the site of the former Wellington Brewery. ♦LIVE

Dover Pale Ale (ABV 3.5%) PALE
Hellfire Corner (ABV 4.1%) GOLD
East Kent Gold (ABV 4.2%) GOLD
Red Ensign (ABV 4.2%) BITTER
Blue Ensign (ABV 4.3%) BITTER
Castle on the Hill (ABV 4.4%) RED
Cowjuice Milk Stout (ABV 4.4%) STOUT
American Pale Ale (ABV 5%) IPA
Mogul West Country IPA (ABV 5.6%) IPA

Brecon

See Cold Black Label

Brentwood SIBA

Calcott Hall Farm, Ongar Road, Pilgrims Hatch, Brentwood, Essex, CM15 9HS
☎ (01277) 200483 ⊕ brentwoodbrewing.co.uk

⊗ Since its launch in 2006 Brentwood has steadily increased its capacity and distribution, relocating to a new purpose-built brewery unit in 2013 with a visitor centre. Seasonal and special beers are also available including more unusual beer styles under the Elephant School brand name. ‼️🍽♦LIVE

IPA (ABV 3.7%) PALE
Marvellous Maple Mild (ABV 3.7%) SPECIALITY
Brentwood Legacy (ABV 4%) PALE
Best (ABV 4.2%) BITTER
Gold (ABV 4.3%) GOLD
Hope & Glory (ABV 4.5%) BITTER
Lumberjack (ABV 5.2%) BITTER
Chockwork Orange (ABV 6.5%) SPECIALITY

Brewed under the Elephant School brand name:
Mallophant (ABV 4.1%) STOUT
Cheru Kol (ABV 4.5%) SPECIALITY
Sombrero (ABV 4.5%) SPECIALITY

Brew Buddies

Unit 14, Highlands Farm Business Park, Highlands Hill, Swanley Village, Kent, BR8 7NA ☎ 07962 369717
⊕ brew-buddies.co.uk

⊗ Owned and run by husband and wife Simon and Rebecca, Brew Buddies Brewery brew for cask, keg, bottle and can. Beers range from traditional to modern, and are unfined and vegan-friendly. Beers are available in the brewery taproom as well as venues across London and the South of England. ‼️🍽V♦

Brew By Numbers

79 Enid Street, Bermondsey, London, SE16 3RA
☎ (020) 7237 9794 ⊕ bbno.co

Established in 2012, Brew By Numbers (BBNo) has produced over 400 different beers across 38 styles. It currently has three taprooms including two at the main site located in the centre of the famed Bermondsey Beer Mile. The eponymous numbering system was simplified a couple of years ago. There are plans for a move to north Greenwich with a pilot kit remaining in SE16.
🍽LIVE♦

Brew Foundation

c/o Wincle Brewery, Toll Barn, Wincle, Cheshire, SK11 0QE
☎ (0114) 282 3098 ☎ 07545 618894

Office: 18 Jarrow Road, Sheffield, S11 8YB
⊕ thebrewfoundation.co.uk

A father-and-son brewery, currently using spare capacity at Wincle Brewery (qv). Beer is distributed both east and west of the Pennines.

Pop (ABV 3.6%) PALE
Little Bitter That (ABV 3.8%) BITTER
Hops & Dreams (ABV 4%) PALE
Laughing Water (ABV 4.3%) BLOND
First Light (ABV 4.6%) PALE
Janet's Treat Porter (ABV 4.8%) SPECIALITY
Hop & Glory (ABV 4.9%) PALE
Bitter That (ABV 5%) BITTER

Brew Monster SIBA

Unit 1, Lon Y Twyn, Caerphilly, CF83 1NW ☎ 07772 869856 ⊕ brewmonster.co.uk

⊗ Brew Monster launched in 2017. The original core range of four ales has grown and are available in all formats. The first 'Tap' bar was opened in Cardiff city centre 2019, another has opened in Cardiff Bay, and more are planned. Brewing relocated from Cwmbran to Caerphilly, behind a new restaurant/taproom. Brewing was suspended during the relocation, but recommenced in 2021. The 'White Label' series introduces new one-off or seasonal beers. ♦♦

Leviathan IPA (ABV 4%) PALE
Phoenix (ABV 4.5%) BITTER
Daemon Red Ale (ABV 4.6%) PALE
Tiamat IPA (ABV 5%) PALE
Black Widow (ABV 5.4%) STOUT
Mephisto IPA (ABV 5.6%) IPA

Brew Shack

Dairy Building, Manor Farm, Sixpenny Handley, Dorset, SP5 5NU ☎ 07580 120258
⊕ thebrewshack.co.uk

⊗ Brewing began in 2015 on a 1.5-barrel plant in purpose-built premises, later upgraded to 10 barrels. The brewery is located on a working farm so there is no access for the general public. V

Bills Bitter (ABV 3.8%) BITTER
A traditional style bitter with fruity aroma, good malt balance and moderate hoppiness leading to hoppy dry finish. Vegan-friendly
Pale Ale (ABV 4.5%) BITTER
Intense hop citrus taste with some fruit coming through. Leads to a pleasant, slightly dry, stringent finish. Unfined
Eight Grain Porter (ABV 5%) PORTER
Light, drinkable, porter with prominent roast notes in the aroma and taste with roast notes adding astringency in the taste leading to a fruity aftertaste.

Brew Shed

Wellheads House, Sandilands, Limekilns, KY11 3JD
☎ 07484 727672 ⊕ brewshedbeers.wordpress.com

Brewing began in 2016 in a tiny brewery behind the owner's house, the first brewery in Limekilns since 1849. Brew Shed Beers revives a tradition of local breweries serving the neighbourhood. **LIVE**

Brew Studio

39 Meadowview Road, Sompting, West Sussex, BN15 0HU
☎ (07980) 978350

⊗ Brew Studio started off as a 0.5-barrel nanobrewery in 2017 and has since upgraded to a 2.5-barrel plant. Around 20 outlets are supplied direct.

Brew Toon

72a St Peter Street, Peterhead, AB42 1QB
☎ (01779) 560948 ⊕ brewtoon.co.uk

Established in 2017, beers are brewed in small batches. The brewery has an on-site café/bar.

Brew Yonder

See Yonder

Brew York SIBA

Unit 6, Enterprise Complex, Walmgate, York, YO1 9TT
☎ (01904) 848448

Osbaldwick: Handley Park, Outgang Lane, Osbaldwick, YO19 5UP ⊕ brewyork.co.uk

⊚Established in 2016, Brew York was born out of two friends' passion for beer and brewing. The original brewery is located within York's historic city walls, a 15-minute walk from the station. A unique taproom and beer hall (including kitchen) with riverside beer garden sits alongside the original 10-barrel brewery which now specialises in barrel-aged and mixed fermentation beers. A new state of the art twin 30-barrel brewery has been built to the east of the city for larger scale production. ‼ ☞♦V✦

Calmer Chameleon (ABV 3.7%) PALE
Haze of Thunder (ABV 4.2%) PALE
Tonkoko (ABV 4.3%) SPECIALITY

Brew61 (NEW) SIBA

Greenfields Farm, Upton Warren, Bromsgrove, B61 7EZ
☎ (01527) 879472 ⊕ brew61.co.uk

Tim Dunkley started brewing as a hobby, opening a small 'pub' for friends and family on the farm. As his brewing prowess grew the equipment he used grew, and he needed more space. A purpose-built brewery with newer larger equipment, enabled him to supply a growing demand locally. Bottles and kegged ales are sold direct from the farm. ☞

Greenfields Gold (ABV 3.8%) PALE
Grazing Girls (ABV 4.5%) GOLD
Hop On (ABV 4.5%) GOLD

BrewBoard SIBA

Unit B3, Button End Industrial Estate, Harston, Cambridgeshire, CB22 7GX ⊕ brewboard.co.uk

Founded in 2017. Now brewing with 150-hectolitre plant. No real ale. ‼☞✦

Brewdog

Balmacassie Industrial Estate, Ellon, AB41 8BX
☎ (01358) 724924

Tower Hill: Unit 3, Minster Building, 21 Great Tower Street, Tower Hill, London, EC3N 5AR ☎ (020) 7929 2545 ⊕ brewdog.com

Established in 2007 by James Watt and Martin Dickie. Most of the production goes into cans and keg. In 2016 a KeyKeg initiative began, described as 'real ale for modernists'. More than 50 bars now exist in the UK. Beer is now also served as 'cask', conditioned in a KeyKeg. ‼☞

Brewdog Dead Pony (ABV 3.8%) BITTER
5am Saint (ABV 5%) GOLD

Brewers Folly

Ashton Farm House, Stanbridge, Wimborne, Dorset, BH21 4JD ⊕ brewersfolly.co.uk

⊗ Dean and Rufus have been avid homebrewers for a very long time. They began brewing on a 1.4-barrel system bought from Brew Shack in 2017. They currently work full-time and brew part-time, but hope to go full-time and expand the range in the future. ‼♦V

Session Pale Ale (ABV 4.2%) PALE
10w-40 (ABV 5%) STOUT
V1 Simco IPA (ABV 5.5%) IPA
V2 Ekuanot IPA (ABV 5.5%) IPA
V3 Galaxy (ABV 5.5%) IPA

Brewery at the Watchmaker's Arms

⬚ 84 Goldstone Villas, Hove, East Sussex, BN3 3RU

Hove's first micropub has its own 100-litre microbrewery, producing under the Beercraft Brighton brand name. Beer is primarily for the Watchmakers but is available in other local pubs.

Brewery58

58 Wantage Road, Wallingford, Oxfordshire, OX10 0LY
☎ (01491) 838262 ☎ 07798 674724
⊕ brewery58.com

A nanobrewery that started when the owner was given a brewing kit as a retirement present. Commercial production began in 2018. Bottle-conditioned ales are available at a few local pubs and shops. **LIVE**

Brewhouse & Kitchen SIBA

⬚ Bedford: 115 High Street, Bedford, MK40 1NU
☎ (01234) 342931

Bournemouth: 154 Commercial Road, Bournemouth, BH2 5LU ☎ (01202) 055221

Bristol: 31-35 Cotham Hill, Bristol, BS6 6JY ☎ (0117) 973 3793

Cardiff: Sophia Close, Pontcanna, Cardiff, CF11 9HW
☎ (029) 2037 1599

Cheltenham: Unit 7, The Brewery, St. Margaret's Road, Cheltenham, GL50 4EQ ☎ (01242) 509946

Chester: Forest House, Love Street, Chester, CH1 1QY
☎ (01244) 404990

Dorchester: 17 Weymouth Avenue, Dorchester, DT1 1QY ☎ (01305) 265551

Gloucester Quays: Unit R1 St. Anne Walk, Gloucester Quay, Gloucester, GL1 5SH ☎ (01452) 222965

Highbury: 2a Corsica Street, Highbury, N5 1JJ ☎ (0207) 226 1026

Horsham: 38 East Street, Horsham, RH12 1HL ☎ (01403) 788140

Hoxton: 397-400 Geffrye Street, Hoxton, London, E2 8HZ ☎ (020) 3861 8920

Islington: 5 Torrens Street, Angel, London, EC1V 1NQ ☎ (0207) 837 9421

Lichfield: 1 Bird Street, Lichfield, WS13 6PW ☎ (01543) 224740

Milton Keynes: 7 Savoy Crescent, Milton Keynes, MK9 3PU ☎ (01908) 049032

Nottingham: Trent Bridge, Nottingham, NG2 2GS ☎ (0115) 986 7960

Poole: 3 Dear Hay Lane, Poole, BH15 1NZ ☎ (01202) 771246

Portsmouth: 26 Guildhall Walk, Portsmouth, PO1 2DD ☎ (023) 9289 1340

Southampton: 47 Highfield Lane, Southampton, SO17 1QD ☎ (023) 8055 5566

Southbourne:147 Parkwood Road, Southbourne, Bournemouth, BH5 2BW ☎ (01202) 055209

Southsea: 51 Southsea Terrace, Portsmouth, PO5 3AU ☎ (023) 9281 8979

Sutton Coldfield: 8 Birmingham Rd, Sutton Coldfield, B72 1QD ☎ (01217) 966838

Wilmslow: 6-12 Swan Street, SK9 1HE ☎ (01625) 441850 ⊕ brewhouseandkitchen.com

Brewing started in 2013 in Portsmouth, the first in the growing Brewhouse & Kitchen chain. There are now 22 brewpubs, each producing its own particular range of beers and with its brewery on open display in the bar area. Local freehouses and beer festivals can be supplied. Carry outs and brewery experience days are available at all venues.

Brewing Brothers

▤ Imperial, 119 Queens Road, Hastings, East Sussex, TN34 1RL ⊕ brewingbrothers.org

⊗ Brewing began in 2016 in the Imperial, Hastings. The brewery has a 2.5-barrel capacity with four fermenting vessels. A wide range of brother-themed beers have been brewed to date, including a core range of seasonal beers, and a collaboration with Half Man Half Burger. ♦V

Brewis

Unit 4 Coquet Enterprise Park, Amble, Northumberland, NE65 0PE
☎ (01665) 714818 ⊕ brewisbeer.co.uk

Brewis Beer Co is a family-run nanobrewery featuring a bottle shop and taproom. ▨♦

Building Bridges (ABV 4.5%) PALE
Helm (ABV 4.7%) PORTER
Just Like Heaven (ABV 5.7%) IPA
Turning Tides (ABV 5.8%) IPA
Ebb & Flow (ABV 6.5%) IPA

Brewlab

See Darwin

Brewpoint (NEW)

Cut Throat Lane, Bedford, MK41 7FY
☎ (01234) 244444 ⊕ brewpoint.co.uk

Brewpoint was launched in 2020 by Wells & Co, which has brewed in Bedford since 1876. The new Brewpoint complex also houses the company head office and features conference and meeting rooms, a brewery shop and a taproom/restaurant plus beer garden open to the public. Beers are also brewed for the Charles Wells and John Bull brands, but not all are cask conditioned. ▨♦♦

Origin Pale Ale (ABV 3.7%) BLOND
Legacy Golden Ale (ABV 4.1%) GOLD
DNA Amber Ale (ABV 4.3%) BITTER

Brewshed

Place Farm, Ingham, Suffolk, IP31 1NQ
☎ (01284) 848066 ⊕ brewshedbrewery.co.uk

⊗ Brewshed began brewing in 2011 using a five-barrel plant in buildings located behind the Beerhouse, one of its outlets. It's now located in the nearby village of Ingham, using a 12-barrel plant, resulting in greater capacity and a wider beer range. ♦

Pale (ABV 3.9%) PALE
Best Bitter (ABV 4.3%) BITTER
American Blonde (ABV 5.5%) BLOND

Brewsmith SIBA

Unit 11, Cuba Industrial Estate, Stubbins, Ramsbottom, Bury, BL0 0NE
☎ (01706) 829390 ⊕ brewsmithbeer.co.uk

Brewsmith is a 10-barrel microbrewery established in 2014 by the Smith family – James, Jennifer and Ted. It produces a range of cask and bottle-conditioned ales in traditional British beer styles. ‼♦LIVE

Mosaic (ABV 3.5%) PALE
Amarillo (ABV 3.8%) PALE
Bitter (ABV 3.9%) PALE
New Zealand Pale (ABV 4.2%) PALE
Pale (ABV 4.2%) PALE
APA (ABV 5%) PALE
Oatmeal Stout (ABV 5.2%) STOUT
IPA (ABV 6%) IPA

Brewsters SIBA

Unit 5, Burnside, Turnpike Close, Grantham, Lincolnshire, NG31 7XU
☎ (01476) 566000 ⊕ brewsters.co.uk

⊗ Brewster is the old English term for a female brewer and Sara Barton - who was named Brewer of the Year by the All Party Parliamentary Beer Group 2018 - is a modern example. Originally established in the Vale of Belvoir in 1998, moving to Grantham in 2006, Brewster's produces a range of traditional and innovative beers with two regularly-changing ranges. ‼▨♦

Hophead (ABV 3.6%) BITTER
Marquis (ABV 3.8%) BITTER
A well-balanced and refreshing session bitter with maltiness and a dry, hoppy finish.
Aromantica (ABV 4.2%) BITTER
Hop A Doodle Doo (ABV 4.3%) BITTER
Decadence (ABV 4.4%) GOLD
Aromatic Porter (ABV 4.5%) PORTER
Stilton Porter (ABV 4.9%) PORTER
Rutterkin (ABV 5%) BITTER

Briarbank SIBA

⌷ 70 Fore Street, Ipswich, Suffolk, IP4 1LB
☎ (01473) 284000 ⊕ briarbank.org

The Briarbank Brewing Company was established in 2013, and is situated on the site of the old Lloyds Bank on Fore Street, Ipswich. The brewery is a two-barrel plant, and the bar above offers a core range of beers – including some speciality ales. ‼◆V

Brick SIBA

Units 13-14, Deptford Trading Estate, Blackhorse Road, Deptford, SE8 5HY
☎ (020) 3903 9441 ⊕ brickbrewery.co.uk

Established by owner and former homebrewer Ian Stewart in 2013. Due to continued expansion, the brewing operation relocated from Peckham to larger premises in nearby Deptford in 2017. The original Peckham railway arch site is retained as an expanded taproom. Beside the Foundation beers, frequent one-off and collaboration brews are produced, including a range of sours. �🍴◆

Peckham Pale (ABV 4.5%) GOLD
Dark gold beer with hoppy, floral aroma. Malt, hops, bitterness, citrus and floral flavours. Long bitter, fruity, hoppy, dryish finish.
Blackhorse (ABV 4.9%) STOUT
Extra Special Bitter (ABV 5.2%) BITTER

Bricknell

Bricknell Avenue, Hull, East Yorkshire, HU5 4ET
☎ 07729 722953 ⊕ bricknellbrewery.co.uk

Bricknell's range comprises of 17 bottle-conditioned, vegan-friendly ales, two of which are seasonal. Some hops are grown on-site, some sourced locally. Everything is hands-on, from brewing, to hand-bottling and labelling, to delivery. Brewing takes place twice a week, and includes many ales from 19th-century recipes. The brewery sells to local pubs, bars and restaurants as well as directly to the public and to local beer festivals. ⍾LIVE V

Anchor Pale Ale (ABV 4.1%) PALE
Cascade Pale (ABV 4.8%) PALE
Bosphorous 1875 Ruby Ale (ABV 5.4%) MILD
Double Anchor IPA (ABV 5.6%) IPA
Lodona 1862 (ABV 5.8%) IPA
Zoroaster 1818 (ABV 5.8%) IPA
Chocolate Porter (ABV 6.4%) SPECIALITY

Bridbrewer (NEW)

⌷ 2A Chapel Street / 5 King Street, Bridlington, East Yorkshire, YO15 2DN
☎ (01262) 674300 ☎ 07727 107435
⊕ bridbrewerandtaproom.co.uk

After two years developing his recipes as a homebrewer, Stuart Fisher launched his unfined beers commercially in 2020 from his brewpub, located in central Bridlington. A 20-litre Braumeister kit is used and most beers are vegan-friendly. ◆LIVE V

Bridge (NEW)

Unit 6, Northend Road Industrial Estate, Northend Road, Stalybridge, SK15 3AZ ☎ 07948 617145
⊕ bridgebeers.co.uk/brewery

Production commenced in 2021 using a 2.5-barrel plant. Cask-conditioned and bottled ales are supplied to the local area. ⍾

Citra (ABV 4%) PALE

El Dorado (ABV 4%) PALE
4Bs (ABV 4.2%) BITTER
Mumbai (ABV 4.2%) GOLD
Dark Ruby Mild (ABV 4.5%) MILD
Dark Matter (ABV 4.7%) STOUT

Bridgehouse SIBA

Airedale Heifer, Bradford Road, Sandbeds, Keighley, West Yorkshire, BD20 9LY
☎ (01535) 601222

Office: Unit 1, Aireworth Mills, Aireworth Road, Keighley, BD21 4DH ⊕ bridgehousebrewery.co.uk

☺Bridgehouse began brewing in 2010 using a 10-barrel plant. The brewery purchased the recipes and branding of Old Bear Brewery in 2014 and moved into its premises in Keighley. In 2015 the brewery relocated again to its present address behind the Airedale Heifer pub in Sandbeds, which it also operates. A bespoke 15-barrel brewery is used and the site includes a visitor centre. ‼◆

Tequila Blonde (ABV 3.8%) SPECIALITY
Initially sweet with hints of lime, finishing with a slight tingling aftertaste.
Blonde (ABV 4%) GOLD
A strong fruity aroma with a sharp burst of grapefruit on the tongue and a touch of sweetness in the background. Bitter finish.
Aired Ale (ABV 4.1%) BITTER
Brown beer with malty aroma. Malt, hops and fruit in equal balance with lingering fruitiness in a long, bitter finish.
Porter (ABV 4.5%) PORTER
Black beer with red hints. Aromas of malt and liquorice lead to coffee, chocolate, and wine fruit flavours, which carry through to a bitter finish.
Landlady IPA (ABV 5.1%) PALE
Holy Cow (ABV 5.6%) BITTER
Strong ale with juicy malt and full hop flavour, citrus overtones. Light hop aroma and a bitter finish.
Cherry Choc (ABV 6%) SPECIALITY

Bridgetown SIBA

Albert Inn, Bridgetown Close, Totnes, Devon, TQ9 5AD
☎ (01803) 863214 ⊕ albertinntotnes.com/ bridgetown-brewery

⊗ Bridgetown started brewing in 2008 using a two-barrel plant in the outbuildings of the Albert Inn, Totnes. Beers are available in an increasing number of local outlets ‼◆LIVE

Albert Ale (ABV 3.8%) BITTER
Pale bitter, malt dominating throughout. Roast and caramel in aroma, taste and aftertaste with a little bitterness on the tongue.
Bridgetown Bitter (ABV 4.2%) BITTER
A tawny-coloured bitter with malt on the nose. The taste is malt and slightly fruity with a bitter, malty, dry finish.
Cheeky Blonde (ABV 4.5%) GOLD
Shark Island Stout (ABV 4.5%) STOUT
Smooth stout with strong malt and roast throughout. Touches of liquorice and chocolate lead to a bitter finish.
Westcountry IPA (ABV 4.7%) PALE

Bridgnorth

See Severn Valley

Briggs Signature

c/o Unit 1, Waterhouse Mill, 65-71 Lockwood Road, Huddersfield, West Yorkshire, HD1 3QU ☎ 07427 668004 ⊕ briggssignatureales.weebly.com

⊗ Briggs Signature Ales started brewing in 2014 using spare capacity at Mallinsons (qv). Nick Briggs, also a member of the Mallinsons brewing team, produces a number of modern, hop-forward beers. ⊨LIVE

Northern Soul (ABV 3.8%) BITTER
Rock & Roll (ABV 4%) BITTER
Hip Hop (ABV 4.2%) GOLD
Techno (ABV 4.2%) BITTER
Blues (ABV 4.6%) GOLD
Metal (ABV 5%) PORTER

BrightBeer

Office: 70 Seabourne Road, Bournemouth, Dorset, BH5 2HT ☎ 07413 007022 ⊕ brightbbeer.com

⊗ Rod Macdonald, original brewer at Exmoor Ales, started brewing at the Weighbridge, Swindon, in 2019 under the name BrightBeer Ltd. Global beer styles are designed and brewed on rotation as cask ales and naturally carbonated craft cellar beer. Brewing is currently suspended as Rod is searching for new premises. ‼◆

Brighton Bier

Unit 10, Bell Tower Industrial Estate, Roedean Road, Brighton, East Sussex, BN2 5RU ☎ 07967 681203 ⊕ brightonbier.com

Brighton Bier was established in 2012. It operates a 15-barrel brewery close to the centre of the city and also owns the Brighton Bierhaus pub, Brighton. Beers are available throughout the UK and exported to Europe and Asia.

Thirty Three (ABV 3.3%) GOLD
Brighton Bier (ABV 4%) GOLD
West Pier (ABV 4%) GOLD
Underdog (ABV 4.2%) BITTER
IPA (ABV 5%) PALE
No Name Stout (ABV 5%) STOUT
Grand Porter (ABV 5.2%) PORTER

Brightside SIBA

Unit 10, Dale Industrial Estate, Radcliffe, M26 1AD ☎ (0161) 725 9644 ⊕ brightsidebrewing.co.uk

⊗ Brightside is a 20-barrel, family-run brewery producing real ales, craft beers and lager. A broad range of styles is produced, from traditional ales, to hop-heavy craft styles, and beers brewed with unusual yeasts or flavours under its Wildside label. It has a brewery shop on site for collections, and an online shop for local and national deliveries. Brightside prides itself on working as sustainably as possible, by limiting energy expenditure, recycling and reusing waste. ⊨◆GF V

Odin Blonde (ABV 3.8%) PALE
Refreshing bitter hops, with bitterness carrying into finish. Peachy hop aroma with some malt.
Chuck American Brown Ale (ABV 4%) BROWN
B-Side Gold (ABV 4.2%) GOLD
Academy Ale IPA (ABV 4.5%) PALE
The Mancunian (ABV 4.5%) BITTER
Full-bodied, sweet fruity beer with moderate bitter hops.
Maverick IPA (ABV 4.8%) PALE

Brightwater

9 Beaconsfield Road, Claygate, Surrey, KT10 0PN ☎ (01372) 462334 ☎ 07802 316389 ⊕ brightbrew.co.uk

⊗ Established in 2013 at Claygate in Surrey, Brightwater is a five-barrel brewery producing traditional beers. The range is available at its brewery tap, Platform 3, outside Claygate Station, and other Surrey and South London pubs.

Little Nipper (ABV 3.3%) BITTER
A rather thin, hoppy bitter with a hint of a citrus taste, and a bitter, slightly dry finish.
Top Notch (ABV 3.6%) BITTER
Citrus notes dominant the aroma of this mid-brown bitter. It has a reasonably well-balanced taste with some bitterness in the finish.
Ernest (ABV 3.7%) PALE
TPL (ABV 3.7%) BITTER
Village Green (ABV 3.8%) GOLD
Daisy Gold (ABV 4%) BITTER
Golden-coloured ale with a moderate, tropical fruit hoppy character and some balancing malt leading to a bittersweet finish.
Wild Orchid (ABV 4%) SPECIALITY
All Citra (ABV 4.3%) GOLD
Lip Smacker (ABV 4.8%) BITTER
Coal Porter (ABV 4.9%) SPECIALITY

Brimstage SIBA

Home Farm, Brimstage, Merseyside, CH63 6HY ☎ (0151) 342 1181 ⊕ brimstagebrewery.com

Neil Young began brewing in 2006 using a 10-barrel plant in the heart of the Wirral countryside. Wirral's first brewery since the closure of the Birkenhead Brewery in the late 1960s. Since Neil passed away in 2018, his two sons now own the brewery. Outlets are supplied across the Wirral, Merseyside, Cheshire and North Wales. ‼◆

Sandpiper Light Ale (ABV 3.6%) GOLD
Trapper's Hat Bitter (ABV 3.8%) BITTER
A nicely-balanced beer, strong malt aromas, sweet hoppy malt flavours and a smooth bitter finish.
Rhode Island Red (ABV 4%) RED
Red, smooth and well-balanced malty beer with a good dry aftertaste. Some fruitiness in the taste.
Elder Pale (ABV 4.1%) SPECIALITY
Scarecrow Bitter (ABV 4.2%) BITTER
This best bitter has a good balance of flavours, some bitterness and sweetness along with a little fruit, these flavours develop in the finish with increased hops.
Oyster Catcher Stout (ABV 4.4%) STOUT
Shed Day Session IPA (ABV 4.4%) PALE
IPA (ABV 6%) PALE

Brinkburn Street SIBA

3 Hume Street, Byker, Newcastle Upon Tyne, NE6 1LN ☎ (0191) 338 9039 ⊕ brinkburnbrewery.co.uk

Brewing began in 2015, much influenced by West Coast US beer styles. Citrus flavours and highly-hopped bitterness is a feature of many of its beers. The brewery relocated to a new site in 2018, which also incorporates a brewery tap. ◆

Byker Brown Ale (ABV 4.8%) BROWN

Briscoe's

16 Ash Grove, Otley, West Yorkshire, LS21 3EL ☎ (01943) 466515 ✉ briscoe.brewery@talktalk.net

THE BREWERIES

⊚The brewery was launched in 1998 by microbiologist/chemist Dr Paul Briscoe, in the cellar of his house with a one-barrel brew length. He is currently producing one brew per week on his original plant, several beers are produced on an irregular basis. The beers are available in local Otley pubs.

Bristol Beer Factory SIBA

Unit A, The Old Brewery, Durnford Street, Ashton, Bristol, BS3 2AW
☎ (0117) 902 6317

Office: 291 North Street, Ashton, Bristol, BS3 1JP
⊕ bristolbeerfactory.co.uk

⊗ A fiercely independent brewery at the heart of the Bristol beer scene since 2004. Based on North Street, the cultural hub of south Bristol, in a 200-year-old red brick building with 180 years of brewing heritage (including Ashton Gate Brewing Co, which closed in 1933). More than 40 beers are produced annually. ‼️🍺♦LIVE

Notorious (ABV 3.8%) BITTER
Fruity hop aroma, flavours of pale malt overlaid with tropical fruit and hop bitterness before a lasting, dry, bitter finish.
Fortitude (ABV 4%) BITTER
Amber ale with light malt and hop nose, mildly fruity flavours balanced with hop bitterness and a short, dry finish.
Milk Stout (ABV 4.5%) STOUT
Very sweet, full-bodied black stout with lactose creaminess. Finishes with smoky, roast bitterness.
Independence (ABV 4.6%) BITTER
Initial hop aroma, well-balanced flavours blend the fruity citrus hops with a malty backbone leaving a clean, bittersweet aftertaste.

BritHop

c/o Parsonage Manorway, Belvedere, Kent, DA17 6NG ☎ 07883 223127 ⊕ brithopbeer.com

Started in 2018, and still brewing at Franklins, beers are available around South East London and further afield. A penchant for the Britpop music scene of the 90s comes through in the beer names and most beers are available on cask. V

Pit (ABV 3.8%) BITTER
Sandstorm (ABV 3.8%) GOLD
One to Another (ABV 4.1%) BITTER
Sweet Symphony (ABV 4.2%) RED
Shakermaker (ABV 4.4%) GOLD
Marblehead (ABV 5.5%) IPA

Britt

See Pig Iron

Brixton

Arches 547 & 548, Brixton Station Road, Brixton, London, SW9 8PF
☎ (020) 3609 8880

Loughborough Junction: Units 1 & 2, Dylan Road Estate,, Dylan Road, Milkwood Road, Loughborough Junction, SE24 0HL ⊕ brixtonbrewery.com

The brewery opened in 2013 in central Brixton with beer names and branding reflecting this. An investment by Heineken in 2017 enabled expansion into a nearby industrial unit. As of 2021 Brixton is now owned outright by Heineken. The original arch is used for seasonal and experimental brews. The adjacent arch houses the

taproom. The bulk of production is in KeyKeg, cans and bottles. ‼️🍺♦LIVE V♦

Reliance Pale Ale (ABV 4.2%) PALE
Tropical notes and a little malt are noticeable in this refreshing amber-coloured beer. A gentle bitterness grows on drinking.

Broadtown

29 Broad Town Road, Broad Town, Wiltshire, SN4 7RB
☎ 07889 078648 ⊕ broadtownbrewery.co.uk

Opened in 2019, Broadtown is brewing in the old coach house of the 19th century Hart brewery. 118 years on, the village has a brewery again. Broadtown have a range of five core ales and produce an ever-changing list of seasonal and one-off ales. In 2021 the Hop Chapel, a Trappist-themed taproom and beer garden, opened on site. The brewery is home to three alpacas and a lime green double-decker bus. LIVE ♦

Brockley SIBA

31 Harcourt Road, Brockley, London, SE4 2AJ
☎ (020) 8691 4380 ☎ 07814 584338

Hither Green: Unit 28, Chiltonian Industrial Estate, Manor Road,, Hither Green, London, SE12 0TX
⊕ brockleybrewery.co.uk

Established in 2013, the original SE4 brewery now focuses on core cask ales, single batch specials and Brewschool. In 2019, a new 20-barrel brewery was opened on the former site of the Chiltonian Biscuit factory in Hither Green. The brewery concentrates on brewing cask beer and supplying outlets across SE London with the whole range available at the taprooms at both sites. 🍺♦♦

Pale Ale (ABV 4.1%) BITTER
Hints of citrus and lychee notes with a sweetness and spicy hops in the flavour and the bitterish finish.
Porter (ABV 4.3%) PORTER
Coffee and sweet chocolate with hints of blackcurrant. Becomes hoppier and bitter late in the taste. Fairly dry finish.
Red Ale (ABV 4.8%) RED
Smoky aroma on this well-balanced sweet, fruity American-style red ale with growing spice overlaid with dry, roasted bitter character.

Broken Drum

Heron Hill, Upper Belvedere, Kent, DA17 5ER
⊕ thebrokendrum.co.uk

Homebrewer that started trial brewing for the Broken Drum micropub in Blackfen, going commercial in 2018. Brewed in small batches for the micropub and local beer festivals. All output is in cask.

Brolly

Lowfold Farm, Wisborough Green, West Sussex, RH14 0ES ⊕ brollybrewing.co.uk

Brolly was established in 2017 by keen homebrewer Brook Saunders. Beers are available in local pubs and at the brewery's on-site bar. V♦

Little Pearl (ABV 3.5%) STOUT
Madre (ABV 4%) PALE
Chub IPA (ABV 4.3%) PALE
Spanky McDanky (ABV 4.5%) PALE
C.O.W (ABV 4.8%) PALE
Natural Spring Water (ABV 5%) PALE

Brooks

17 Birkenhead Road, Hoylake, Merseyside, CH47 5AE
🌐 **brooks-brewhouse.co.uk**

Brewing starting in 2017 at this nanobrewery, which predominately produces bottle-conditioned beers. LIVE

Broughton SIBA

Main Street, Broughton, ML12 6HQ
☎ **(01899) 830345** 🌐 **broughtonales.co.uk**

☺Founded in 1979, Broughton Ales was one of the first microbreweries. Broughton has developed since then, and though more than 60% of production goes into bottle for sale in Britain and abroad, it retains a sizeable range of cask ales. All beers are suitable for vegetarians and Hopo Lager is certified gluten-free. ‼️🍴♦GF

Merlin's Pale Ale (ABV 3.6%) BITTER
Crisp, fruity and malty ale. A darker shade of pale.
Hopo Session IPA (ABV 3.8%) PALE
Dry-hopped pale ale with slightly tart, fruit taste and distinctive tang.
Clipper IPA (ABV 4.2%) PALE
Merlin's Ale (ABV 4.2%) GOLD
A well-hopped, fruity flavour is balanced by malt in the taste. The finish is bittersweet, light but dry.
Wee Jock (ABV 4.6%) BITTER
Pleasant 80/- style. Light fruit and a malty sweetness.
Stout Jock (ABV 4.8%) BITTER
Glasgow Cross IPA (ABV 5%) PALE
A fruity, refreshing IPA with a good body and a pleasant hoppy flavour. A long-lasting bitterness in the finish.
Hopo Proper IPA (ABV 5%) PALE
Old Jock (ABV 6.7%) STRONG
A bold Scotch ale, full-bodied, sweetish and fruity in the finish.

Brown Cow

Brown Cow Road, Barlow, Selby, North Yorkshire, YO8 8EH
☎ **(01757) 618947** 🌐 **browncowbrewery.co.uk**

☺Brewing since 1997, Brown Cow has won awards at many festivals. Keith and Sue Simpson operate a six-barrel plant. Handcrafted cask beers brewed using traditional methods are delivered to the local area direct from the brewery. ♦V

Sessions (ABV 3.6%) PALE
White Dragon (ABV 4%) BITTER
Mrs Simpson's Thriller in Vanilla Porter (ABV 5.1%) SPECIALITY

Broxbourne

See Fallen Angel

Bruha

Unit 4, Progress Way, Eye, Suffolk, IP23 7HU
☎ **(01379) 882230** 🌐 **bruhabrewing.co.uk**

Originally known as Station 119, the brewery changed name in 2020 to Bruha Brewing. Established in 2014, it graduated to the current brewery and taproom premises in Eye, Suffolk, in 2017 and in 2018 a 12-barrel brewhouse was installed. All the beers are unfiltered and have an emphasis on East Anglian malt. LIVE V♦

Session Pale (ABV 3.9%) PALE
Heritage Pale (ABV 4.2%) PALE

Brumaison SIBA

Unit 7, Crest Industrial Estate, Pattenden Lane, Marden, Kent, TN12 9QJ ☎ **07719 308544**
🌐 **brumaison.beer**

⊠ The name Brumaison came about from ideas to set up in a small village in France. However, Peter and Caroline decided to keep their 'Brewing Maison' in England after another brewery got there first. Trading since 2016 using a 10-barrel plant, Peter started brewing full time in 2017. V

BB Traditional Ale (ABV 3.6%) BITTER
Flaxen XPA (ABV 3.8%) BLOND
Roister (ABV 4%) PALE
GB Golden Blonde Ale (ABV 4.4%) BLOND
Bullion (ABV 4.5%) BLOND
Beulter (ABV 4.6%) BITTER
1770 (ABV 4.7%) PORTER

Brunning & Price

See Phoenix & St Austell

Brunswick SIBA

🏭 **1 Railway Terrace, Derby, DE1 2RU** ☎ **07534 401352** 🌐 **brunswickbrewingcompany.co.uk**

⊠ Derby's oldest brewery. It is a 10-barrel tower plant built as an extension to the Brunswick Inn in 1991. Bought by Everards in 2002, the brewery is now run separately, yet in conjunction with the pub. It supplies the Brunswick Inn, Dead Poets Inn, Everards, wholesalers, and the free trade within 100 miles. Brunswick also swaps with other breweries. Beers are also produced under the Engine Shed Project brand name. ‼️♦LIVE

White Feather (ABV 3.6%) PALE
Triple Hop (ABV 4%) BLOND
The Usual (ABV 4.2%) BITTER
Railway Porter (ABV 4.3%) PORTER
Rocket (ABV 4.7%) PALE
Black Sabbath (ABV 6%) OLD

Brewed under the Engine Shed Project brand name:
Ubiquitous (ABV 6%) IPA

Brythonic

See Forest, The

BRZN

Unit 2, Cobblers Thumb, 10 New England Road, Brighton, East Sussex, BN1 4ZR
✉ **buybrzn@gmail.com**

BRZN was founded as a cuckoo brewery in 2019 but in 2020 moved into its own premises in the Preston Circus region of Brighton. Its range is brewed in small batches, without isinglass finings and in keg and cask. Seasonals and specials are always available. ♦

Buckland

Higher Thornhill Head, Bideford, Devon, EX39 5NU
☎ **(01805) 601625** ☎ **07882 019255**
🌐 **thebucklandbrewers.co.uk**

Brewing began in 2016. The original plant was replaced in 2018 with a new purpose-built microbrewery. It specialises in Belgian-style, bottle-conditioned beers, which are now supplied to more than 40 local pubs, farm shops, restaurants and visitor attractions. ‼🍴♦LIVE

Bucklebury (NEW) SIBA

Broad Lane, Upper Bucklebury, Berkshire, RG7 6QJ
☎ 07834 044468 ✉ info@buckleburybrewers.co.uk

A small-scale brewery which started production in 2020 using two 150-litre fermenting vessels. All the beers are unfiltered and unpasteurised. Beer in pressurised kegs is supplied to the Cottage Inn in the village, and bottled beers are supplied to local shops within a 10-15 mile radius of the brewery. LIVE

Bucks Star

23 Twizel Close, Stonebridge, Milton Keynes, Buckinghamshire, MK13 0DX
☎ (01908) 590054 ⊕ bucksstar.beer

⊗ A solar-powered brewery opened in 2015 using a 10-barrel, purpose-built plant. Only organic malt is used and no sugars or syrups are added. The beers are unfiltered, vegan, and primarily available through Bucks Star's own zero-waste innovation (Growler Swap). This range of beers are conditioned inside reusable glass growlers, and are available at farmers' markets both locally, and at various London locations. The brewery tap opened in the opposite unit in 2020. ‼🍴LIVE V♦

Copernicus (ABV 3.8%) BITTER
No. 1 Pale Ale (ABV 4%) BITTER
Magiovinium (ABV 4.5%) STOUT

Bull of the Woods

Brook Farm, Kirby Cane, Bungay, Norfolk, NR35 2PJ
☎ (01508) 518080 ☎ 07833 702658
✉ info@botwbc.co.uk

⊗ After 10 years of planning, Bull of the Woods started brewing in 2017 using a four-barrel plant. ♦LIVE

Rock Steady (ABV 3.8%) BITTER
Traditional malt and hop signature, with the added complexity of walnut and quinine flowing through. Long, increasingly bitter finish.
Vapour Trail (ABV 4.3%) BITTER
Dry walnut airs intrude into a hoppy biscuit beginning. Balanced rolling mix of flavours with background pluminess.
Inca Gold (ABV 4.4%) GOLD
Twisted Wheel (ABV 4.5%) PALE
Shine A Light IPA (ABV 5.7%) IPA

Bulletproof

91 Mutley Plain, Plymouth, Devon, PL4 6JJ ☎ 07703 733570

Office: Highlands, 1 Queen's Road, Lipson, Plymouth, PL4 7PJ ⊕ bulletproofbrewing.co

⊗ Small-scale brewery established in an outbuilding in 2016. It uses a 50-litre pilot plant to refine recipes before upscaling, using spare capacity at larger breweries. All beers are unfiltered and unfined. ♦

Bullfinch

Arches 886 & 887, Rosendale Road, Herne Hill, London, SE24 9EH ☎ 07795 546630
⊕ thebullfinchbrewery.co.uk

Bullfinch began brewing in 2014, sharing with Anspach & Hobday in Bermondsey, but opened in Herne Hill in 2016, using a 2.5-barrel plant. Production is mainly keg, but cask and bottle-conditioned beers are available in the taproom, at its Bull & Finch bar, Gipsy Hill, and increasingly in local pubs. ‼🍴LIVE ♦

Swift (ABV 4%) BITTER
Dark Side of the Moon (ABV 4.5%) PORTER
Chocolate and vanilla on the nose, fading to a bitterness. Chocolate, roast, black cherries and liquorice flavours. Light, dry finish.

Bullhouse SIBA

10 Greengraves Road, Newtownards, BT23 5AG

Bullhouse was set up in 2016 by beer enthusiast and homebrewer William Mayne. It has since expanded from a 2.5-barrel plant to a custom built, 1,000-litre brewhouse, with a fermentation capacity of 25,000-litres per year.

Road Trip (ABV 4%) GOLD
Small Axe (ABV 4.3%) BARLEY
Frank the Tank (ABV 5%) SPECIALITY
The Dankness (ABV 5.5%) BARLEY
Merc Bro (ABV 6.5%) SPECIALITY

Bumbling

See Xtreme

Bun Dubh SIBA

🏠 Ceabhar, Sandaig, Isle of Tiree, PA77 6XG
☎ (01879) 220684 ☎ 07792 789733
✉ us@ceabhar.com

Duncan Castling began brewing on his picobrewery in 2016, then catering solely for his restaurant, Ceabhar. The brewery expanded into the adjoining former guesthouse during winter 2020 and summer 2021, with his live beer now available in the local hotels. With an enviropunk ethos, all production goes into reusable containers, no bottles or cans, and distribution, though wider, remains exclusive to the island. ♦

Bundobust (NEW)

Bundobust, 61-95 Oxford Street, Manchester, M1 6EJ
⊕ bundobust.com

Bundobust Brewery was established in 2020 but brews were not commercially available until 2021. Beer is exclusively for the Bundobust restaurant chain. No real ale.

Buntingford

Greys Brewhouse, Therfield Road, Royston, Hertfordshire, SG8 9NW
☎ (01763) 250749 ☎ 07851 743799
⊕ buntingfordbrewery.com

⊗ Brewing commenced on the current site in 2005 and has expanded to a capacity of around 60 barrels per week. Regular beers are brewed alongside seasonal/occasional brews, and various themed specials. An on-site well supplies water, and all liquid waste is treated in a reed bed. The brewery is located on a conservation farm, and there is a wide variety of bird life visible from the doors of the brewhouse, often including rare and endangered species. ♦

Twitchell (ABV 3.8%) BITTER
Single Hop varieties (ABV 4%) GOLD
Hurricane (ABV 4.3%) BITTER
Polar Star (ABV 4.4%) GOLD

Burley Street

⧉ Fox and Newt, 7-9 Burley Street, Leeds, West Yorkshire, LS3 1LD
☎ (0113) 245 4527 ⊕ burleystreetbrewhouse.co.uk

☺Burley Street Brewhouse is in the cellar of the Fox & Newt pub where the first brewery was installed by Whitbread in the 1980s. The freehold was purchased by the current owners, and brewing recommenced in 2010. Following a two-year break, started again in 2015. The Fox & Newt pub is the only regular outlet for the beers. Brewing is currenlty suspended and currently contract brewed by Nomadic.

Burning Sky SIBA

Place Barn, The Street, Firle, East Sussex, BN8 6LP
☎ (01273) 858080 ⊕ burningskybeer.com

⊠ Burning Sky started brewing in 2013 using a 15-barrel plant, based on the Firle Estate in the South Downs. It is owned and run by Mark Tranter (ex-Dark Star head brewer). The brewery has its own yeast strains suited to the beer styles. It specialises in pale ales and Belgian-inspired farmhouse beers and has an extensive barrel-aging programme. LIVE

Plateau (ABV 3.5%) GOLD
Aurora (ABV 5.6%) IPA

Burning Soul

Unit 1, 51 Mott Street, Hockley, Birmingham, B19 3HE
☎ (0121) 439 1490 ☎ 07793 026624
⊕ burningsoulbrewing.com

Established in 2016, the name Burning Soul reflects a passion for beer and brewing. A five-barrel, full mash brewery, with an on-site brewery tap less that one mile from Birmingham City centre, offering KeyKeg real ale on tap. The core range is always available along with various special brews and selected guests. Beers are occasionally released into the trade in cask form. ‼☲♦V

Low Clarity (ABV 3%) BITTER
Mosaic Session IPA (ABV 4.5%) PALE
OCT IPA (ABV 6.7%) IPA
Belgian IPA (ABV 6.8%) SPECIALITY
Coconut Porter (ABV 6.9%) SPECIALITY

Burnside SIBA

Laurencekirk Business Park, Laurencekirk, AB30 1EY
☎ (01561) 377316 ⊕ burnsidebrewery.co.uk

Burnside began brewing in 2010 using a 2.5-barrel plant, and by 2012 had expanded to a 10-barrel plant. Since then the focus has been to establish the brand and range of cask-conditioned ales locally and to develop a range of bottle-conditioned beers. Further expansion is planned. ‼☲LIVE

Black Katz (ABV 3.6%) BITTER
No 1 Pale Ale (ABV 3.6%) PALE
3-BULLZ (ABV 3.8%) BITTER
Mad Dogz (ABV 3.8%) GOLD
Golden X (ABV 4.1%) BITTER
Wild Rhino (ABV 4.5%) GOLD
Chieftains Export (ABV 4.6%) BITTER
India Pale Ale (ABV 4.8%) PALE
After Dark (ABV 5%) STOUT
M-PIRE (ABV 5.2%) BITTER
Stealth (ABV 6%) OLD

Burnt Mill

Burnt Mill Brewery, Badley, Ipswich, Suffolk, IP6 8RS
☎ 07791 961974 ⊕ burntmillbrewery.com

This farm brewery was created by Charles O'Reilly in 2016 and is set in a former grain shed. In 2017 Sophie de Ronde joined the brewing team as Head Brewer. All beers brewed to date have been unfiltered and are available in both KeyKeg and 440ml cans.

Burscough

See Hop Vine

Burton Bridge SIBA

24 Bridge Street, Burton upon Trent, Staffordshire, DE14 1SY
☎ (01283) 510573 ⊕ burtonbridgebrewery.co.uk

☺The brewery was established in 1982 by Bruce Wilkinson and Geoff Mumford and owns three pubs in the local area, including its award-winning brewery tap. More than 300 outlets are supplied direct. ‼☲♦LIVE

Golden Delicious (ABV 3.8%) BITTER
A Burton classic with sulphurous aroma and well-balanced hops and fruit. An apple fruitiness, a sharp and refreshing start leads to a lingering, mouth-watering bitter finish with a hint of astringency. Light, crisp and refreshing.

Sovereign Gold (ABV 4%) BITTER
Sweet caramel aroma with a grassy hop start with malt overtones. Fresh and fruity with a bitterness that emerges and continues to develop.

XL Bitter (ABV 4%) BITTER
Another Burton classic with sulphurous aroma. Golden with fruit and hops and a characteristic lingering aftertaste hinting at toffee apple sweetness.

XL Mild (ABV 4%) MILD
Black treacle initial taste after liquorice aroma. Sweet finish with a touch of bitterness.

Bridge Bitter (ABV 4.2%) BITTER
Gentle aroma of malt and fruit. Good, balanced start finishing with a robust hop mouthfeel.

Burton Porter (ABV 4.5%) PORTER
Chocolate aromas and sweet, smooth taste of smoky, roasted grain and coffee.

Damson Porter (ABV 4.5%) SPECIALITY
Faint roast, caramel and dark fruit nose. Cough mixture and Blackjacks beginning. Uncomplicated profile with a fractious mix of bitter fruitiness and yeasty maltiness.

Draught Burton Ale (ABV 4.8%) BITTER
Fruity, orange aroma leads to hoppy start, hop and fruit body then fruity aftertaste. Dry finish with fruity hints.

Bramble Stout/ Top Dog Stout (ABV 5%) SPECIALITY
Smoky aroma with a fruit hint from black liquid. Roast start with briar dry fruit emerging, then a sharp black fruit taste emerges to balance the burnt effect with a sweetish, dry, blackberry finish, with prolonged mouth-watering.

Stairway to Heaven (ABV 5%) BITTER
Golden bitter. A perfectly balanced beer. The fruity and hoppy start leads to a hoppy body with a mouth-watering finish.

Festival Ale (ABV 5.5%) BITTER
Caramel aroma with plenty of hop taste balanced by a full bodied malty sweetness.

Thomas Sykes (ABV 10%) BARLEY
Kid in a sweetshop aroma. Rich fruity spirited tastes – warming and dangerously drinkable.

Contract brewed for Boot Beer:
Clod Hopper (ABV 3.9%) GOLD

Patriot (ABV 3.9%) GOLD
Bitter (ABV 4.3%) BITTER
Solstice (ABV 4.4%) PALE
Tuffer's Old (ABV 4.6%) PORTER
ESB (ABV 4.8%) BITTER
Beast (ABV 6.7%) STRONG

Burton Road

Office: 65 Kingsfield Drive, Manchester, M20 6HX
✉ contact@burtonroadbrewing.co.uk

Manchester brewery producing cask, keg, cans and
bottles focusing on pales and IPA. Available in bars,
restaurants and shops in Manchester and Cheshire. Beers
are contract brewed at Mobberley (qv). A small 30-litre
brewplant is located within Withington Public Hall.

Burton Town

Unit 8, Falcon Close, Burton upon Trent, Staffordshire,
DE14 1SG
☎ (01283) 510839 ☎ 07428 968702 ⊕ burton.town

⊠ Open since 2015, Burton Town Brewery is run by
Steve Haynes and head brewer Andrew Hollick from
converted premises off Hawkins Lane. The brewery was
expanded in 2019 to a 12-barrel plant. An on-site
taproom is open to the public. ‼ ☰ LIVE V ✦

Albion (ABV 3.9%) BITTER
Born Slippy (ABV 4%) SPECIALITY
That Burton Beer (ABV 4%) BITTER
Kolsch (ABV 4.5%) SPECIALITY
Modwena (ABV 4.8%) STOUT
Thomcat (ABV 5.1%) PALE
Cascade IPA (ABV 5.6%) IPA
Black as your Hat (ABV 6.2%) BITTER

Burtonwood

Bold Lane, Burtonwood, Warrington, Cheshire,
WA5 4TH
☎ (01925) 220022 ⊕ thomashardybrewery.co.uk

Thomas Hardy's only brewery was acquired by Molson
Coors in 2015. Currently producing no real ale, and
operating solely as a contract brewer.

Burwell

17 The Paddocks, Burwell, Cambridgeshire, CB25 0HQ
☎ 07788 311908 ⊕ burwellbrewery.com

⊠ Richard Dolphin and Paul Belton established Burwell
Brewery in 2019 in a purpose-built timber brewery at the
bottom of Richard's garden. The plant, recently upgraded
to 2.5-barrels, together with three conditioning tanks,
produces beer for cask, bottle and bag-in-box. ‼ ✦ GF V

Beer Fuggled Best Bitter (ABV 4%) BITTER
Priory Wood Rauch (ABV 4%) BROWN
Judy's Hole Chocolate Porter (ABV 4.5%) PORTER
Margaret's Field American IPA (ABV 5%) PALE
Moulin D'Etienne Wit Bier (ABV 5%) SPECIALITY
Stefans' Muhle Wheat Bier (ABV 5%) SPECIALITY
Sunshine Pale Ale (ABV 5%) PALE
Double Beer Fuggled Special Bitter (ABV 5.5%)
BITTER

Bushy's SIBA

Mount Murray Brewery, Mount Murray, Braddan, Isle
of Man, IM4 1JE
☎ (01624) 661244 ⊕ bushys.com

☺ Launched in 1986 as a brewpub, Bushys relocated in
1990 when demand outgrew capacity. Bushys goes one

step further than the Manx Pure Beer Law preferring the
German Reinheitsgebot (Pure Beer Law). The brewery
hosts a successful festival during the TT period at Villa
Marina Gardens, Douglas. Beer is also brewed for the Old
Laxey Brewery, available at the Shore Hotel, Old Laxey.
‼ ✦

Castletown Bitter (ABV 3.5%) BITTER
Bitter (ABV 3.8%) BITTER
A traditional malty and hoppy beer with good balance.
The fruit lasts through to the bitter finish.
Mannannan's Cloak (ABV 4%) BITTER
Old Bushy Tail (ABV 4.5%) BITTER
Red (ABV 4.7%) RED

Buswells

◪ Lime Kilns Pub, Watling Street, Burbage,
Leicestershire, LE10 3ED
☎ (01455) 631158 ⊕ limekilnsinn.co.uk

Brewing started at the Lime Kilns pub, Burbage, in 2016
as a small batch brewery. It expanded to a two-barrel
plant in 2017, providing up to 14 ales for the pub and
other outlets, on demand. Bespoke brews are provided
for events including several local beer festivals. V

Butcombe SIBA

Cox's Green, Wrington, Somerset, BS40 5PA
☎ (01934) 863963 ⊕ butcombe.com

⊠ Originally established in 1978, Butcombe moved to a
purpose-built brewery with a 150-barrel plant in 2005.
The brewery was bought by the Jersey-based Liberation
Group for a reported £15m in 2015. Around 500 outlets
are supplied direct and similar numbers via wholesalers
and pub companies. Butcombe opened a new
distribution centre with a bottling line in Bridgewater in
2018. The brewery has an estate of around 20 managed
and 20 tenanted pubs ‼ ☰ ✦

Adam Henson's Rare Breed (ABV 3.8%) GOLD
Subtle aroma of unripe fruit with sulphurous hints. Malty
flavour is masked by dry bitterness which continues into
the finish.
Butcombe Original (ABV 4%) BITTER
A brown bitter with little aroma. Sweet and malty taste
with faint fruit notes. The hop gradually asserts itself
leaving a slightly bitter finish.
Butcombe Gold (ABV 4.4%) GOLD
Amber golden ale with light aroma of fruit and hops,
leading to well-balanced flavours of malt, pale fruit and
hops. Bitter aftertaste.

Butts

Northfield Farm, Wantage Road, Great Shefford,
Berkshire, RG17 7BY
☎ (01488) 648133 ⊕ buttsbrewery.com

⊠ The brewery was set up in a converted barn in 1994.
In 2002 the owners took the decision to become
dedicated to organic production; all the beers brewed
use organic malted barley and organic hops, and are
certified by the Soil Association. ☰ ✦ LIVE

Jester (ABV 3.5%) BITTER
A pale brown, session bitter with a hoppy aroma and a
hint of fruit. The taste balances malt, hops, fruit and
bitterness with a hoppy aftertaste.
Traditional (ABV 4%) BITTER
Pale brown, session bitter with citrus hop aroma and
flavours. A long, dry aftertaste is dominated by fruity
hops.
Barbus Barbus (ABV 4.6%) GOLD

Premium golden ale with fruity hop aroma and hint of malt. Hops dominate the taste and aftertaste followed by some fruitiness and bitterness.

Buxton

Units 4 A & B, Staden Business Park, Staden Lane, Buxton, Derbyshire, SK17 9RZ
☎ (01298) 24420 ⊕ buxtonbrewery.co.uk

Set up in 2009 as a five-barrel plant, Buxton now uses a 20-barrel plant. Its brewery tap is in Buxton and there is a tasting room at the brewery with views of the Derbyshire countryside. A wide range of small-batch beers is brewed throughout the year. ◆LIVE

Moor Top (ABV 3.6%) PALE
Low Tor (ABV 3.8%) RED
Buxton SPA (ABV 4.1%) PALE

Bwthyn

See Anglesey Brewing

By The Horns SIBA

Units 21-27, Summerstown, London, SW17 0BQ
☎ (020) 3417 7338

Surrey: Unit 11, The IO Centre, Salbrook Road Industrial Estate, Salbrook Road, Salfords, Redhill, Surrey, RH1 5GJ ⊕ bythehorns.co.uk

⊠ By The Horns began brewing in 2011 with a 5.5-barrel plant but had outgrown the site by 2020. A new facility in Salfords, Surrey opened in 2021 with small batch brewing continuing at Summerstown taproom. Cask is a big part of production, the rest produced in keg and cans. The taproom benefits from the nearby newly built AFC Wimbledon stadium. ➡◆

Stiff Upper Lip (ABV 3.8%) BITTER
Classic, amber-coloured bitter, well-balanced with hops throughout with hints of citrus and honey. Dry, bitter finish.
Hopadelic (ABV 4.3%) GOLD
Smooth, golden ale with grapefruit, gooseberry, citrus and lemon rind notes overlaid with hops. Building bitterness in the lingering finish.
Lambeth Walk (ABV 5.1%) PORTER
Black-ruby, full-bodied porter with black cherry, sultanas, coffee and a sweet treacle character. Developing, lingering, dark bitter, roast cocoa.

By The Mile

22 Detling Avenue, Broadstairs, Kent, CT10 1SL
☎ 07900 954680 ✉ jon@bythemilebrewery.co.uk

⊠ By the Mile began brewing in 2016 in domestic premises. Brewing is currently suspended.

Byatt's SIBA

Unit 7-8, Lythalls Lane Industrial Estate, Lythalls Lane, Coventry, CV6 6FL
☎ (024) 7663 7996 ⊕ byattsbrewery.co.uk

☺Byatt's was established in 2011, and expanded in 2016. An extensive beer list is brewed throughout the year together with an increasing range of seasonal beers. A brewhouse bar with six handpumps also serves ciders on draught or gravity. Tours and tasting sessions can be booked and private hire is available. Coventry Building Society Arena is nearby. ‼➡◆LIVE◆

XK Dark (ABV 3.5%) MILD
Coventry Bitter (ABV 3.8%) BITTER

Platinum Blonde (ABV 3.9%) BLOND
Phoenix Gold (ABV 4.2%) GOLD
All Day Foreign Extra Stout (ABV 4.9%) STOUT
Regal Blond (ABV 5.2%) GOLD

C'84

Rear of New Inn, Cropton, North Yorkshire, YO18 8HH
☎ (01751) 469632 ⊕ c84.co.uk

☺Established in 1984, the brewery was built behind the New Inn in 1994. In 2010 Cropton Brewery rebranded as Great Yorkshire and again in 2019 to C'84. Beers are available throughout Yorkshire and nationally through wholesalers. A pilot kit was installed in 2020 for short run special batch brews. ‼◆LIVE

Yorkshire Pale (ABV 3.8%) BITTER
Yorkshire Golden (ABV 4.2%) GOLD
Yorkshire Blackout (ABV 5%) PORTER

Cabin

44 Brooksfield, Bildeston, Suffolk, IP7 7EJ ☎ 07990 845855 ⊕ cabinbrewery.co.uk

Owner and brewer Chris Smith has been brewing since 2013, with Cabin Ales available commercially since 2015. Demand soon outgrew the original plant and a new two-barrel kit was designed and installed in 2018.

Autumn Leaf (ABV 3.8%) BITTER
Chesn't (ABV 3.9%) BROWN
Gold Rush (ABV 4%) PALE
Mark's Gold (ABV 4%) PALE
Red Nek (ABV 4.3%) RED
Mary Celeste (ABV 4.5%) PALE
INNspiration (ABV 5%) PALE

Cader SIBA

Unit 4, Parc Menter Marian Mawr Enterprise Park, Dolgellau, LL40 1UU
☎ (01341) 388080 ☎ 07546 272372
⊕ caderales.com

Cader Ales was founded in 2012 by a husband-and-wife team. In the following years, the business has expanded to the point where it is now using the five-barrel, purpose built plant to its optimum. The brewery is situated close to the centre of the picturesque market town of Dolgellau. Deliveries are made to the licensed trade in North and Mid-West Wales. Beers in cask/ bottle are available to the general public direct from the brewery. ‼

Cregennan (ABV 3.8%) GOLD
Gold (ABV 3.8%) GOLD
Machlyd Mawddach (ABV 3.9%) BITTER
Arran Fawddy (ABV 4%) GOLD
Idris Bitter (ABV 4.1%) BITTER
Talyllyn Pale Ale (ABV 4.4%) PALE
Red Bandit (ABV 5%) BITTER

Caffle

The Old School, Llawhaden, Narberth, SA67 8DS
☎ (01437) 541502

Office: Park View Ropewalk, Llawhaden, Fishguard, SA65 9BT ⊕ cafflebrewery.co.uk

⊠ Started in 2013, Caffle is a four-barrel brewery which produces small batch, crafted ales, mainly for the local market. Production consists of a range of core and seasonal cask and bottle-conditioned ales. An annual green hop ale is produced using Pembrokeshire-grown hops via the brewery's hop co-op. ‼➡LIVE

Skirp Gold (ABV 3.8%) BITTER
Quay Ale (ABV 4%) BITTER
Sholly Amber (ABV 4%) BITTER
Sprilly Maid (ABV 4%) BITTER
Kift Blonde (ABV 4.3%) BLOND
In The Grip (ABV 4.7%) BITTER
Skaddly Pluck (ABV 4.8%) PALE
Drop Squint (ABV 5.2%) GOLD

Cairngorm SIBA

Unit 12, Dalfaber Industrial Estate, Aviemore, PH22 1ST
☎ (01479) 812222 ⊕ cairngormbrewery.com

☺Cairngorm brews using a 20-barrel plant. Now with its own bottling line, it supplies the free trade as far south as the central belt and nationally via wholesalers. In 2016, in partnership with the Cobbs Group, it bought the brands of the Loch Ness Brewing Co and now brews selected beers under the Loch Ness brand name. ‼🍽◆

Nessies Monster Mash (ABV 4.1%) BITTER
A fine best bitter with plenty of bitterness and malt flavour and a fruity background. Lingering bitterness in the aftertaste with diminishing sweetness.
Stag (ABV 4.1%) BITTER
A good mix of roasted malt, red fruits and hops throughout. This tawny brew also has plenty of malt in the lingering bittersweet aftertaste.
Trade Winds (ABV 4.3%) SPECIALITY
Award-winning brew with a strong elderflower and citrus fruity hop nose following on through to the bittersweet finish.
Black Gold (ABV 4.4%) STOUT
Roast malt dominates throughout, slight smokiness in aroma leading to a liquorice and blackcurrant background taste, giving it a background sweetness. Very long, dry, bitter finish.
Cairngorm Gold/ Sheepshaggers Gold (ABV 4.5%) GOLD
Fruit and hops to the fore with a hint of caramel in this sweetish brew.
Highland IPA (ABV 5%) PALE
Refreshing, light-coloured, citrus, American and South Pacific-hopped IPA. Some background biscuit and caramel.
Wildcat (ABV 5.1%) BITTER
A full-bodied warming strong bitter. Malt predominates but there is an underlying hop character through to the well-balanced aftertaste. Drinks dangerously less than its 5.1%.

Caledonian

42 Slateford Road, Edinburgh, EH11 1PH
☎ (0131) 337 1286 ⊕ caledonianbeer.com

☺The brewery was founded by Lorimer and Clark in 1869 and was sold to Vaux of Sunderland in 1919. In 1987 the brewery was saved from closure by a management buy-out and became independent. It was purchased by S&N in 2004, and became part of Heineken in 2008. Guest beers, sometimes of an unusual style, are produced for occasions throughout the year, and there is a rolling programme of special beers covering each of the seasons. A pilot brewery 'Wee George' named after the founding father George Lorimer, was opened in 2015 to allow small scale brews of new recipes. ◆

Deuchars IPA (ABV 3.8%) GOLD
Golden session ale with hop aroma and dry, bitter finish. Balanced, with malt adding body and fruit a balancing sweetness.
Edinburgh Castle 80/- (ABV 4.1%) BITTER

A predominantly malty, brown beer with soft roast and caramel throughout. Fruit gives sweetness, typical of a Scottish 80/-.

Contract brewed for Heineken:
John Smith's Bitter (ABV 3.5%) BITTER

Calverley's SIBA

23a Hooper Street, Cambridge, CB1 2NZ
☎ (01223) 312370 ☎ 07769 537342
⊕ calverleys.com

☺This small, central Cambridge brewery was started in 2013 by brothers Sam and Tom Calverley. It is located in a converted stable yard close to the city centre. The brewery is open to the public for on and off-sales (Thursday-Saturday). A large proportion of the production is sold on the premises, and local pubs are also supplied. Most of the beers are keg (various styles), but the brewery remains committed to cask ale and its porter is usually available. ‼🍽✦

Porter (ABV 5.1%) PORTER

Calvors SIBA

Home Farm, Coddenham Green, Suffolk, IP6 9UN
☎ (01449) 711055 ⊕ calvorsbrewery.com

Calvors Brewery was established in 2008 and brews three craft lagers, as well as cask-conditioned beers. V

Lodestar Festival Ale (ABV 3.8%) GOLD
Smooth Hoperator (ABV 4%) PALE

Cambridge

🍴 1 King Street, Cambridge, CB1 1LH
☎ (01223) 858155 ⊕ thecambridgebrewhouse.com

⊗ Brewing began in 2013 at the on-site microbrewery in the Cambridge Brew House. ◆

Camden Town

Morson Road, Ponders End, Enfield, London, EN3 4TJ
☎ (020) 7485 1671

Kentish Town: 55-59 Wilkin Street Mews, Kentish Town, NW5 3NN ⊕ camdentownbrewery.com

⊗ Bought by A-B InBev in 2016. A modern, automated brewhouse situated in railway arches underneath Kentish Town West railway station with an on-site brewery tap. A second brewery in Ponders End opened in 2017, and is the main production site, with a large taproom open for special events. No real ale. ‼✦

Camel

Aberaeron, SA46 0BB ☎ 07539 466105
✉ alistair@cwrwcamel.com

Established in 2019, Cwrw Camel uses spare capacity at Bluestone Brewing Co (qv). V

Camerons

Lion Brewery, Stranton, Hartlepool, County Durham, TS24 7QS
☎ (01429) 852000 ⊕ cameronsbrewery.com

☺Camerons was founded in 1865, and is a family-owned business. Brewing is done by various members of the Camerons team from office staff to brewery staff. The brewery produces a range of cask ales in association with the RNLI, throughout the year. A number of limited-run ales are produced through its Tooth & Claw pilot brewery.

It also has a pub estate of more than 70 pubs, including the Head of Steam pubs. ‼️🍴♦

Sanctuary Pale Ale (ABV 3.8%) PALE
Strongarm (ABV 4%) BITTER
A well-rounded, ruby-red ale with a distinctive, tight creamy head; initially fruity, but with a good balance of malt, hops and moderate bitterness.
Old Sea Dog (ABV 4.3%) BROWN
Boathouse Premium Blonde Beer (ABV 4.4%) BLOND
Road Crew (ABV 4.5%) PALE

Brewed for Carlsberg Marston's Brewing Co:
Bitter (ABV 3.7%) BITTER
Gold (ABV 4.1%) GOLD

Campervan

Unit 4, Bonnington Business Centre, 112 Jane Street, Edinburgh, EH6 5HG
☎ (0131) 553 3373 ☎ 07786 566000
⊕ campervanbrewery.com

Campervan began brewing in 2016 in a private garage but also in a 1973 VW campervan (hence the name). The van is used as a mobile sales outlet at beer festivals and other outdoor events. It expanded to a new 10-barrel facility in Edinburgh in 2017. in 2020, Lost in Leith Bar and Fermentaria was opened which houses an on-site, barrel-ageing project. Some barrel-aged beers are bottle conditioned. LIVE ♦

Blonde Voyage (ABV 3.8%) GOLD
All Shook Up (ABV 4%) SPECIALITY
Mutiny on the Bounty (ABV 4.2%) SPECIALITY
Leith Juice (ABV 4.7%) SPECIALITY
Juicy IPA, full of orange flavour and a strong dose of citrus hops. Naturally hazy.
West Coast IPA (ABV 5%) PALE

Cannon Royall

See White Rabbit

Canopy

Arch 1127, Bath Factory Estate, 41 Norwood Road, Herne Hill, London, SE24 9AJ
☎ (020) 8671 9496 ☎ 07792 463386
⊕ canopybeer.com

⊠ Canopy started brewing in a railway arch in Herne Hill in late 2014, with the taproom following in 2015 (open Wednesday-Sunday). Mostly available in keg and cans, cask does get out into pubs around south London. The taproom is the best place to get the widest range, including the regular specials. ‼️♦LIVE ♦

Sunray Pale Ale (ABV 4.2%) GOLD
Floral, fruity, hoppy aroma. Flavour is citrusy with floral hops and sweet biscuit character. Bitterness and dryness builds on drinking. Smooth mouthfeel.
Snapper (ABV 4.8%) GOLD
Refreshing, smooth, yellow beer. Mango, lemon and green pine notes lead to a dry, bitterish aftertaste with hints of tobacco/smokiness.
Full Moon Porter (ABV 5%) PORTER
Strong malt aroma with raisins, figs, dark vintage marmalade and coffee. Roasted flavour with dark treacly, dark chocolate sweetness.

Canterbury Ales SIBA

Canterbrew Ltd, Unit 7 Stour Valley Business Park, Ashford Road, Chartham, Kent, CT4 7HF

☎ (01227) 732541 ☎ 07944 657978
⊕ canterbury-ales.co.uk

⊠ Brewing commenced in 2010. An eight-barrel plant is used. ‼️♦

The Wife of Bath's Ale (ABV 3.9%) GOLD
A golden beer with strong bitterness and grapefruit hop character, leading to a long, dry finish.
The Reeve's Ale (ABV 4.1%) BITTER
The Miller's Ale (ABV 4.5%) RED

Canterbury Brewers SIBA

📇 Foundry Brew Pub, 77 Stour Street, Canterbury, Kent, CT1 2NR
☎ (01227) 455899 ⊕ thefoundrycanterbury.co.uk

⊠ Canterbury Brewers started in the Foundry Brewpub in the heart of Canterbury in 2011. The eight-barrel plant is purpose-built. Popular events are held there including the Kent Green Hop Festival (late September/early October). A wide range of spirits are now distilled in the brewpub, and three ciders are produced. ‼️♦LIVE ♦

Caps Off

17 Chester Street, Bishop Auckland, County Durham, DL14 7LP ☎ 07900 551754 ⊕ capsoff.co.uk

Opened in 2020, supplying the Caps Off micropub in Bishop Auckland. The brewery brings a wide variety of ales, stouts, and other beer styles. A barrel-ageing and wild fermentation project is underway. A new kit installed late 2020 on-site, is shared with Hops & Dots brewery.

Pale (ABV 4.3%) PALE
IPA (ABV 5%) PALE
Brown Ale (ABV 7.4%) STRONG

Captain Cook

White Swan, 1 West End, Stokesley, North Yorkshire, TS9 5BL
☎ (01642) 714985 ⊕ whiteswanstokesley.co.uk

⊛Having celebrated its 20th anniversary in 2019, the Captain Cook Brewery is located behind the 18th century White Swan pub. The brewery, which supplies the pub, uses a four-barrel plant. ‼️♦

Navigator (ABV 4%) GOLD
Sunset (ABV 4%) GOLD
Slipway (ABV 4.2%) BLOND
Endeavour (ABV 4.3%) BROWN
Skippy (ABV 4.3%) GOLD
Black Porter (ABV 4.4%) PORTER
APA (ABV 4.7%) PALE
Schooner (ABV 4.7%) STOUT
IPA (ABV 5.1%) PALE

Cardigan (Teifi) (NEW)

5a Morgan Street, Cardigan, SA43 1DF
☎ (01239) 614974 ✉ sales@cardiganbrewery.com

Cardigan Brewery was established in 2021, offering a range of bottled beers. Marketed as Bragdy Teifi for Welsh sales. ♦

Carlisle SIBA

Unit 2, 12a Kingstown Broadway, Kingstown Industrial Estate, Carlisle, Cumbria, CA3 0HA
☎ (01228) 594959 ☎ 07979 728780

Office: Spinners Arms, Cummersdale, Carlisle, CA2 6BD ⊕ carlislerealale.com

⊕Carlisle Brewing Company is a family-run brewery established in 2013. Initially using a 2.5-barrel plant in a shed behind the owner's freehouse, by 2015 it had expanded to a 10-barrel plant in an industrial unit. Beer is available in the Spinners Arms and other local outlets. �♦

Cumbrian Bitter (ABV 3.7%) BLOND
Carlisle Bell (ABV 3.8%) PALE
Citadel (ABV 3.8%) BITTER
Spun Gold (ABV 4.2%) PALE
Flaxen (ABV 4.5%) BITTER
Magic Number (ABV 4.5%) BITTER

Carlsberg-Tetley

Jacobson House, 140 Bridge Street, Northampton, NN1 1PZ
☎ (01604) 668866 ● carlsberg.co.uk

International lager brewery, which while brewing no real ales is a major distributor of cask beer. The Tetley-owned real ales are mostly brewed by Camerons Brewery of Hartlepool. Some Tetley beers are brewed at Leeds Brewery. A joint venture with Carlsberg in 2020 led to the company being renamed Carlsberg Marston's Brewing Company.

Carnival

Unit 2 King Edward Industrial Estate, Gibraltar Row, Liverpool, L3 7HR ● carnivalbrewing.me

Brewery and taproom opened in 2019 by keen homebrewers Dominic Smith and Adrian Burke. Specialist styles are brewed. It supplies online, retail, a few outlets in Liverpool, as well as beer festivals. ♦✦

Castle SIBA

Unit 9A, 7 Restormel Industrial Estate, Liddicoat Road, Lostwithiel, Cornwall, PL22 0HG ☎ 07880 349032
● castlebrewery.co.uk

⊗ The brewery was established in 2007 using a one-barrel plant. It was re-equipped in 2016 with a new 200-litre plant. All brews are unfined. The brewery carries out its own bottling, and some for other breweries. ☛♦LIVE V

Golden Gauntlet (ABV 4%) GOLD
Light, golden bitter with gentle fruity nose. Heavy malt and bitter taste dominate the fruity hop, persisting into the finish.
Restormel Gold (ABV 4.1%) PALE
Cornish Best Bitter (ABV 4.2%) BITTER
Once A Knight (ABV 5%) BITTER

Castle Eden SIBA

8 East Cliff Road, Spectrum Business Park, Seaham, SR7 7PS
☎ (0191) 581 5711 ☎ 07768 044484 ● cebl.co.uk

Using the name of the former Castle Eden Brewery (having acquired the intellectual rights and recipes), a new 20-barrel commercial plant was installed in 2015 along with a bottling/kegging plant. Besides its own brand production, the brewery also contract bottles for several local and national breweries. ☛♦

Blond (ABV 3.9%) BLOND
Ale (ABV 4.2%) GOLD
Red (ABV 4.4%) BITTER
Black (ABV 4.6%) PORTER

Castle Rock SIBA

Queensbridge Road, Nottingham, NG2 1NB

☎ (0115) 985 1615 ● castlerockbrewery.co.uk

⊕Castle Rock, established in 1998, quickly developed a reputation for producing high quality, consistent cask beers, which continues to this day, with three from the core range winning awards at national level. Throughout the year, Castle Rock brew an eclectic range of special and one-off beers in cask, keg and can, from the traditional to the more experimental and modern styles. �♦LIVE

Black Gold (ABV 3.8%) MILD
A dark ruby mild. Full-bodied and fairly bitter.
Harvest Pale (ABV 3.8%) PALE
Pale yellow, hop-dominated golden ale with delicate malt flavours, slightly hoppy and quite citrus-tasting with grapefruit flavours.
Session (ABV 4%) GOLD
Preservation (ABV 4.4%) BITTER
This best bitter is smooth with a strong malty character, slightly sweet with hints of caramel. Good body with roast aftertaste.
Sherwood Reserve (ABV 4.5%) STOUT
This smooth, full-bodied dry stout is rich and bold with roasted malts, coffee and hints of liquorice. The aftertaste lingers nicely with a delicate bitterness.
Elsie Mo (ABV 4.7%) BITTER
Strong malt amber ale with a heady aftertaste. Hoppy and bitter.
Midnight Owl (ABV 5.5%) BITTER
Black IPA with roast malts, fruity hops and a slightly sweet finish.
Screech Owl (ABV 5.5%) BITTER
This strong bitter is quite light with average hop flavours and delicate malt flavours, balanced with a little sweetness. It has a thin to average body with slight citrus notes.

Castor SIBA

30 Peterborough Road, Castor, Cambridgeshire, PE5 7AX
☎ (01733) 380337 ● castorales.co.uk

This three-barrel brewery, established in 2009, is located in a specially converted outhouse in the garden of the founder brewer. Several local outlets feature the beers as well as many national beer festivals. �♦V

Roman Gold (ABV 3.7%) GOLD
Hopping Toad (ABV 4.1%) GOLD
Roman Mosaic (ABV 4.2%) GOLD
Old Scarlett (ABV 4.6%) BITTER

Cat Asylum SIBA

12 Besthorpe Road, Collingham, Nottinghamshire, NG23 7NP
☎ (01636) 892229 ☎ 07773 502653
✉ henry.bealby@lineone.net

Established in 2017, Cat Asylum is a microbrewery specialising in historic recipes from Britain and around the world.

Wee Moggy (ABV 3.8%) PALE
Columbus Pale (ABV 4.9%) PALE
Simcoe Pale Ale (ABV 5.1%) PALE
Bohemian Pilsner (ABV 5.3%) SPECIALITY
The Big Smoke Stout (ABV 5.8%) SPECIALITY
St Wulfrum's IPA (ABV 6%) IPA
Newark IPA (ABV 6.1%) IPA
Double Brown Stout (ABV 8%) SPECIALITY
No. 1 Barley Wine (ABV 9%) BARLEY

Cellar Head SIBA

The Barn, Pillory Corner, Flimwell, East Sussex, TN5 7QG ☎ 07391 557407 ⊕ cellarheadbrewing.com

⊗ Cellar Head Brewery is situated on the border between Sussex and Kent, in the village of Flimwell. It has a capacity of more than 70 barrels, with plans for a further 20. The brewers use predominately local hops and malts to produce a range of beers, varying in style and taste. The modern brewery building also houses a taproom, shop and canning and bottling plants, allowing for off-sales. Besides core ales, new and innovative brews are often available. ‼️🍴◆

Sub Three (ABV 2.7%) BITTER
Session Bitter (ABV 3.5%) BITTER
Amber Ale (ABV 4%) GOLD
Session Pale Ale (ABV 4.2%) PALE
Single Hop Pale (ABV 4.6%) SPECIALITY
India Pale Ale (ABV 5%) PALE

Celt Experience

See Evan Evans

Cerddin

🖪 c/o Cross Inn, Maesteg Road, Maesteg, Cwmfelin, CF34 9LB
☎ (01656) 732476 ☎ 07949 652237
⊕ cerddinbrewery.co.uk

Established in 2010 using a 2.5-barrel plant in a converted garage adjacent to the owner's pub, now enlarged to a four-barrel plant. Beer is usually only available in the pub. Seasonal beers brewed. ‼️◆LIVE

Cerne Abbas SIBA

Chescombe Barn, Barton Meadows Farm, Cerne Abbas, Dorset, DT2 7JS
☎ (01300) 341999 ☎ 07506 303407

Office: The Mill House, Mill Lane, Cerne Abbas, DT2 7LB ⊕ cerneabbasbrewery.com

⊗ Established in 2014 by Vic Irvine and Jodie Moore. Operating on a five-barrel plant, the beers are made as naturally as possible using chalk-filtered water from its own spring. All beers are brewed with organic, locally-sourced barley. Some non-conventional ingredients are used in seasonal brews. On the last Saturday in September, a community brew is produced using hops grown by people living in the village and surrounding area. ‼️🍴◆◆

Ale (ABV 3.8%) BITTER
Blonde (ABV 4.2%) BLOND
A refreshing golden ale. Hops to the fore in the New World style, fairly light on palate with spicy bitterness balanced with sweetness which fades to astringency leaving the feeling of wanting another taste.
Tiger Tom Ruby Mild (ABV 4.4%) MILD
Mellow, malty, ruby brown ale with hints of chocolate in the aroma and taste and aftertaste. Malt is balanced by a bitterness that leads to a dry, slightly bitter aftertaste.
Watercress Warrior (ABV 4.5%) SPECIALITY
Gurt Stout (ABV 6.2%) STOUT
Gurt Coconuts Rum Stout (ABV 7.2%) SPECIALITY
A strong sweet stout with very prominent coconut elements in aroma, taste and aftertaste.

Chadkirk (NEW)

Lancashire House, Green Lane, Romiley, SK6 3LJ
☎ 07966 125257 ⊕ chadkirkbrew.co.uk

Brewing commenced in 2020 at an industrial unit in Romiley. The brewery focuses on a core range of hop-forward beers using a rotating selection of American hops.

New Zealand Pale (ABV 4%) PALE
US Triple Hop (ABV 4%) PALE
Motueka (ABV 4.2%) PALE
Centennial (ABV 4.4%) PALE
Citra (ABV 4.7%) PALE
Stout (ABV 5%) STOUT
APA (ABV 5.2%) PALE

Chadlington SIBA

Blaythorne Farm, Chadlington, Oxfordshire, OX7 3NE
☎ (01608) 676823 ☎ 07931 482807
⊕ chadlingtonbrewery.com

Based in the Cotswolds, brewing was small to start with, producing small-batch brews, but the new brewhouse which opened in 2019 is capable of supplying a growing range of customers. The brewery utilises renewables and pure spring water and is family-owned, making visitors very welcome, hosting events and holding Brew-your-Own days. A taproom is planned.

Golden Ale (ABV 4%) GOLD
Oxford Blonde (ABV 4%) BLOND
Oxford Blue (ABV 4.2%) GOLD

Chain House

20 Brookdale, New Longton, Lancashire, PR4 4XL
☎ 07732 688121 ⊕ chainhousebrewingco.uk

Brewing began in 2017, with the beers growing in popularity and appearing occasionally in a handful of pubs in the Preston area. In particular there have been successful collaborations with other breweries such as Rivington and Farm Yard Ales. Plans are in place to relocate the brewery to the heart of Preston city centre to create a brewery tap.

Chalk Hill

🖪 Rosary Road, Norwich, NR1 4DA
☎ (01603) 477077 ⊕ thecoachthorperoad.co.uk

⊗ Chalk Hill began production in 1993 on a 15-barrel plant. It supplies local pubs and festivals. A small plant is used to brew experimental beers, which if popular become part of the regular range. ‼️◆

Chantry SIBA

Unit 1-2, Callum Court, Gateway Industrial Estate, Parkgate, Rotherham, South Yorkshire, S62 6NR
☎ (01709) 711866 ☎ 07815 727285
⊕ chantrybrewery.co.uk

☺Brewing returned to Rotherham with the opening of Chantry in 2012 using the latest brewing technology in a 20-barrel plant built by Sheffield-based Moeschle UK. As well as the brewery tap, Cutlers Arms, two other pubs are owned; New York Tavern, Rotherham, and Chantry Inn, Handsworth. Six of Chantry's eight core beers are award-winning. Delivery is UK-wide, with free local delivery. 'Click and collect' is available from the brewery. ‼️🍴◆

New York Pale (ABV 3.9%) PALE
Iron & Steel Bitter (ABV 4%) BITTER
Steelos (ABV 4.1%) BLOND
Full Moon (ABV 4.2%) PALE
Diamond Black Stout (ABV 4.5%) STOUT
Kaldo (ABV 5.5%) PALE
Mighty Millers (ABV 5.5%) BITTER

Special Reserve (ABV 6.3%) OLD

Chapeau

Unit 8, Redkiln Close, Horsham, West Sussex,
RH13 5QL
☎ (01403) 252459 ⊕ chapeaubrewing.com

⊗ Chapeau Brewing is a microbrewery based in
Horsham, West Sussex. The brewery and beer names
reflect the owner's interest in cycling. A brewery tap is
owned and the a beer club operated (see website for
details). ☛

Slip Stream (ABV 3.5%) BITTER
Rouleur (ABV 4%) BITTER
Summit (ABV 4%) GOLD
Open Road (ABV 4.5%) STOUT
Hard Yards (ABV 4.6%) BITTER
Attrition (ABV 5.5%) IPA
Breakaway (ABV 6%) PORTER

Chapel

Dinesfield, Chapel Lane, Criftins, Shropshire, SY12 9LZ
☎ (01691) 690412 ☎ 07928 682174
⊕ chapelbrewery.co.uk

☺Chapel began brewing in 2013 using a one-barrel
plant behind the owner's bungalow. In 2016 the brewery
expanded to larger premises. Occasional specials are
brewed for festivals.

Angels Share (ABV 4%) BITTER
Miracle (ABV 4.4%) GOLD

Chapel Street

⧉ Thatched House, Ball Street, Poulton-le-Fylde,
Lancashire, FY6 7BG
☎ (01253) 891063
⊕ thethatchedhousepoulton-le-fylde.co.uk

☺This four-barrel plant is situated in the coach house of
the award-winning Thatched House pub in Poulton-le-
Fylde and has been brewing since 2014. The beers are
only available in the pub.

Chapel-en-le-Frith SIBA

5 Market Place, Chapel-en-le-Frith, Derbyshire,
SK23 0EW ☎ 07951 524003
✉ timboothman@aol.com

☺Opened in 2016, this small brewery is located at the
rear of Chapel-en-le-Frith post office. The brewing kit
consists of a single 200-litre capacity integrated system
supplemented by a 20-litre trial kit. Bottles and five-litre
mini casks are available from the post office. Cask ales
are available from a limited number of local outlets. V

Siena (ABV 4.1%) GOLD
Savinjski (ABV 4.2%) BARLEY
Rye the Hell Not (ABV 4.3%) RED
Isambard (ABV 4.4%) PALE
Busted Monkey (ABV 4.6%) BROWN
Leningrad (ABV 5%) RED
Elysium Amber Ale (ABV 5.4%) BITTER
Acadian (ABV 5.6%) IPA
Hoppy as Funk (ABV 5.8%) IPA
Sinamarian Black IPA (ABV 6%) IPA
USA (ABV 8%) IPA

Chapter SIBA

Unit 2a, Sutton Quays Business Park, Clifton Road,
Sutton Weaver, Cheshire, WA7 3EH ☎ 07908 004742
⊕ chapterbrewing.co.uk

Award-winning Chapter Brewing was established in
2016, using a 10-barrel brew plant. It produces diverse
'fictional beers' inspired by literature, from pales to
sours, smoked porters to Belgian styles and beyond.
‼☛♦V◈

22. Servant of Sadness (ABV 3.2%) BLOND
24. The Hay is Waiting (ABV 3.6%) PALE
02. Bread and Circuses (ABV 3.8%) PALE
17. Taller Than a House (ABV 3.9%) BITTER
18. Unconsenting Soul (ABV 4.2%) GOLD
A fruity and hoppy bitter beer with plenty of impact on
the palate, and sweetness drying out in the finish.
28. Practicable and Useful (ABV 4.3%) BLOND
09. Temos Tanta (ABV 4.4%) SPECIALITY
21. Pemberley (ABV 4.4%) STOUT
27. Puck at the Helm (ABV 4.5%) GOLD
08. Parabola (ABV 4.7%) PALE
11. That Old Rope (ABV 5.4%) PALE
03. Dead Man's Fist (ABV 5.5%) PORTER
14. Her Musket (ABV 5.7%) STOUT
01. As Lazarus (ABV 7.2%) IPA

Charles Wells

See Eagle

Charnwood SIBA

22 Jubilee Drive, Loughborough, Leicestershire,
LE11 5XS
☎ (01509) 218666 ☎ 07872 651561
⊕ charnwoodbrewery.co.uk

☺Family-run, 10-barrel brewery established in 2014,
producing three core beers and three monthly specials
with a wide range of styles. All beers are widely
available locally, including at its two micropubs, the
Sorrel Fox, Mountsorrel, and the Hall Croft Tap, Shepshed.
The front of the brewery features a shop, selling brewery
merchandise, bottled beers, and local gins, as well as a
bar with three handpumps and large glass windows,
giving a good view into the brewery. ‼☛♦◈

Salvation (ABV 3.8%) GOLD
Vixen (ABV 4%) BITTER
APA (American Pale Ale) (ABV 4.8%) PALE

Chasing Everest

15 Ponteland Square, Blyth, NE24 4SH
⊕ chasingeverestbrew.com

Founded in 2018 by Zak Everest, focusing on small batch
brews. Many of the beers are dry-hopped, giving bold,
hoppy flavours.

Plus One (ABV 3%) PALE
Sideswiper (ABV 4%) BITTER
Joana In Five Acts (ABV 4.2%) BITTER
Square Hammer (ABV 6.8%) STOUT

Checkstone

⧉ First & Last Inn, 10 Church Street, Exmouth, Devon,
EX8 1PE
☎ (01395) 263275

Checkstone Brewery, named after the Checkstone reef
outside the Exe Estuary, is a one-barrel plant inside the
First & Last pub, Exmouth, established in 2016. Like the
brewery, the beers are named after various sea features
around Exmouth. ♦

Cheddar SIBA

Winchester Farm, Draycott Road, Cheddar, Somerset, BS27 3RP
☎ (01934) 744193 ⊕ cheddarales.co.uk

⊗ Established in 2006 in the heart of the Mendips, Cheddar Ales has expanded capacity to enable it to brew up to 100 barrels a week. Production is split approximately 75% cask-conditioned ale, 25% bottle-conditioned. Its bottling plant produces around 120,000 bottles annually and all bottled ales are gluten-free. Around 450 outlets are supplied including pubs, clubs and the off trade. A visitor centre and brewery tap opened in 2020. ‼ ▆ ♦ LIVE GF ✦

Bitter Bully (ABV 3.8%) BLOND
Light session bitter with flowery hops on the nose and a dry, bitter finish.

Gorge Best (ABV 4%) BITTER
Malty bitter with caramel and fruit notes followed by a short, bittersweet aftertaste.

Piney Sleight (ABV 4%) GOLD
Potholer (ABV 4.3%) GOLD
Refreshing flavours combine soft fruit sweetness with hop bitterness on a light malt background before a clean, balanced finish.

Hardrock (ABV 4.4%) GOLD
Fruity hop aroma, balanced flavours of tropical fruit and bitterness on a pale malt background before a clean, bitter ending.

Totty Pot (ABV 4.5%) PORTER
Roasted malts dominate this smooth, well-flavoured porter. Hints of coffee and rich fruits follow with a well-balanced bitterness.

Crown & Glory (ABV 4.6%) BITTER
Lightly-hopped aroma, background malt balanced with fruity hops in the crisp, bittersweet flavour before a dry and bitter finish.

Goat's Leap (ABV 5.5%) IPA
Light malt aroma with enticing toffee and red liquorice hints. Traditional hop flavours and fruity sweetness, clean, bitter finish.

Chelmsford

2 Brewery Fields, Church Street, Great Baddow, Chelmsford, Essex, CM2 7LE
☎ (01245) 476267 ☎ 07972 145611
⊕ chelmsfordbrewco.co.uk

Chelmsford Brew Co is a family-operated brewery established in 2017, and located in Great Baddow, near the former Baddow Brewery. The brewery has a tap room, an on-site shop (open six days per week), and an online shop that provides a free delivery service for its own, and guest, beers to Chelmsford and adjacent areas. ▆ ✦

Cheshire Brew Brothers

See Oaks

Cheshire Brewhouse

Unit 13, Daneside Business Park, River Dane Road, Congleton, Cheshire, CW12 1UN
☎ (01260) 274788 ⊕ cheshirebrewhouse.co.uk

☺ Cheshire Brewhouse was established in 2012 using a five-barrel plant, expanding in 2014 to a 10-barrel one. The brewery moved to a larger unit in 2018. ‼ ♦ V

Cheshire Gap (ABV 3.8%) PALE
Loral (ABV 4%) PALE
Mosaic (ABV 4%) PALE

Citra (ABV 4.2%) PALE
Engine Vein (ABV 4.2%) BITTER
Lindow (ABV 4.5%) STOUT
DBA (ABV 4.6%) BITTER
Bluesbreaker (ABV 4.8%) PALE
Govinda Chevallier Edition (ABV 6.8%) IPA
Gibraltar Porter (ABV 8.1%) PORTER

Chevin

Office: 1 Mount Pisgah, Otley, West Yorkshire, LS21 3DX ✉ chevinotley@gmail.com

Chevin is an Otley-based brewery specialising in small batch, hand-crafted, artisan beers, primarily available in bottles but also on tap in a few local outlets.

Cheviot

Ford & Etal Estate, Cornhill on Tweed, Slainsfield, Northumberland, TD12 4TP ☎ 07778 478943
⊕ cheviotbrewery.co.uk

Brewing commenced in 2018 on a 7.5-barrel plant acquired from Goose Eye Brewery in West Yorkshire. The beers are named after local landmarks.

Upland Ale (ABV 3.8%) BITTER
ETale (ABV 4%) BITTER
Harbour Wall (ABV 4.3%) PALE
Trig Point (ABV 4.5%) PALE
Holy Bounty (ABV 4.8%) STOUT
Menhir (ABV 5.1%) STOUT
Flodden Thirst (ABV 5.4%) PALE
The Schil (ABV 6%) BITTER

Chickenfoot

🛢 **Barley Mow Inn, The Dale, Bonsall, Derbyshire, DE4 2AY**
☎ (01629) 825685 ⊕ barleymowbonsall.co.uk

⊗ A purpose built 2.5-barrel plant housed in the car park of the Barley Mow Inn, in the picturesque rural village of Bonsall. The brewery supplies a range of hen-named ales for the pub, which is famed as the Home of the World Hen Racing Championship. ♦

Chiltern SIBA

Nash Lee Road, Terrick, Aylesbury, Buckinghamshire, HP17 0TQ
☎ (01296) 613647 ⊕ chilternbrewery.co.uk

⊗ Founded in 1980, Chiltern was one of the first microbreweries in the country. It is also the oldest independent brewery in Buckinghamshire and the Chiltern Hills, growing from a capacity of five to its present 10-barrel plant. A major expansion is planned. Now run by the second generation of the Jenkinson family, George and Tom, it supplies around 100 outlets including its own brewery tap, at the Farmers' Bar, at the historic King's Head in Aylesbury. ‼ ▆ ♦ LIVE ✦

Pale Ale (ABV 3.7%) PALE
An amber, refreshing beer with a slight fruit aroma, leading to a good malt/bitter balance in the mouth. The aftertaste is bitter and dry.

Black (ABV 3.9%) PORTER
Beechwood Bitter (ABV 4.3%) BITTER
This pale brown beer has a balanced butterscotch/toffee aroma, with a slight hop note. The taste balances bitterness and sweetness, leading to a long bitter finish.

Chin Chin

Unit 53F Lidgate Crescent, Langthwaite Grange Industrial Estate, South Kirkby, West Yorkshire, WF9 3NS ☎ 07896 253650
✉ david@chinchinbrewing.co.uk

☺ Chin Chin was established in 2016 by brothers David and Andrew Currie. Brewing began on a one-barrel plant based in a domestic garage, relocating to larger premises with a five-barrel plant in 2018. An expanding range of small batch brews is supplied across Yorkshire and to beer festivals nationwide. ‼

Chorlton

Office: 69 North Western Street, Ardwick, Manchester, M12 6DX ⊕ chorltonbrewingcompany.com

Brewing ceased at Ardwick in late 2019. The beers are now intended to be contract-brewed in Belgium. Main production concentrates on canned sour beers although bottle-conditioned Dark Matter has an annual release.
LIVE

Church Aston

Church Aston, Shropshire, TF10 9EJ ☎ 07806 671436
✉ beer@churchastonbrewery.co.uk

☺ A small indepedent brewery established in 2013. In addition to the regular beers, bespoke brews are available on request.

Lower Bar Bitter (ABV 3.8%) BITTER
Upper Bar Bitter (ABV 4.5%) BITTER

Church End SIBA

Ridge Lane, Nuneaton, Warwickshire, CV10 0RD
☎ (01827) 713080 ⊕ churchendbrewery.co.uk

⊗ The brewery started in 1994 in an old coffin shop in Shustoke. It moved to its present site in 2001 and has expanded over the years, it currently operates a 24-barrel purpose-built plant. Many one-off specials and old recipe beers are produced. Its award-winning beers are available throughout the Midlands. ‼ 🍺 ♦ LIVE

Brewers Truth (ABV 3.6%) GOLD
Cuthberts (ABV 3.8%) BITTER
A refreshing, hoppy beer, with hints of malt, fruit and caramel taste. Lingering, bitter aftertaste.
Goat's Milk (ABV 3.8%) BITTER
Gravediggers Ale (ABV 3.8%) MILD
What the Fox's Hat (ABV 4.2%) BITTER
A beer with a malty aroma, and a hoppy and malty taste with some caramel flavour.
Vicar's Ruin (ABV 4.4%) BITTER
A straw-coloured best bitter with an initially hoppy, bitter flavour, softening to a delicate malt finish.
Stout Coffin (ABV 4.6%) STOUT
Fallen Angel (ABV 5%) BITTER

Church Farm SIBA

Church Farm, Budbrooke, Warwickshire, CV35 8QL
☎ (01926) 411569 ⊕ churchfarmbrewery.co.uk

After the dairy herd departed the farm, milking equipment was converted and brewing began in 2012. In 2016 production moved to a modern purpose-built 20-barrel plant. Local ingredients are a key feature, some barley is grown on the farm and water is from an on-site well. It supplies around 150 outlets, mainly in Warwickshire and across the south Midlands. Look out for the mobile bar at food festivals, outdoor music and motorsport events. LIVE

Pale Ale (ABV 3.8%) PALE
Session IPA (ABV 3.8%) PALE
Ren's Pride (ABV 4%) BITTER
Brown's Porter (ABV 4.2%) PORTER
Harry's Heifer (ABV 4.2%) BITTER
IPA (ABV 5%) PALE

Church Hanbrewery

Unit F2, New Yatt Business Centre, North Leigh, Oxfordshire, OX29 6TJ
☎ (01993) 774986 ☎ 07907 272617

Office: Tithe Barn South, Church Hanborough, OX29 8AB ⊕ churchhanbrewery.com

⊗ Brewing commenced 2016 on a small scale in the owner's kitchen. A year later, a 250-litre plant was installed in a small industrial unit in New Yatt near Witney. It was upgraded to 500-litres in 2021. It is now producing mainly bottles and keg, plus some cask ale for local distribution. Additional storage space has also been acquired. One-off brews regularly appear in the brewery's nanobar in Oxford's indoor market. 🍺 LIVE ♦

Ale X IPA (ABV 4.5%) PALE
Rauk (ABV 5%) SPECIALITY
Red Beetter (ABV 5%) SPECIALITY
Bluenette (ABV 5.5%) PORTER
Mat Black (ABV 5.5%) PALE

City of Cambridge

See Wolf

Clanconnel

Unit 5, 2 New Line, Gibson's Hill, Co Armagh, BT66 8TA ☎ 07711 626770

Office: PO Box 316, BT65 9AZ
⊕ clanconnelbrewing.com

Beers are contract brewed by the Rye River Brewery in Co Kildare in the Republic of Ireland under the McGraths Craft Beer Brand. No real ale.

Clark's

Office: 136 Westgate, Wakefield, West Yorkshire, WF2 9SW
☎ (01924) 373328

Beers are contract brewed elsewhere. Often Castle Eden (qv).

Classic Blonde (ABV 3.9%) BLOND
English Pale Ale (ABV 4%) PALE
Merrie City Atlantic Hop (ABV 4%) BITTER
Merrie City Crystal Gold (ABV 4.2%) GOLD

Clarkshaws

Arch 497, Ridgway Road, Loughborough Junction, London, SW9 7EX ☎ 07989 402687
⊕ clarkshaws.co.uk

Clarkshaws, established 2013, is a small brewery focusing on using UK ingredients for its core beers and reducing beer miles. The beers are suitable for vegetarians and are accredited by the Vegetarian Society. All beers are unfined and may be hazy. A small taproom operates on the premises for most of the year, check before travelling. V ♦

Gorgon's Alive (ABV 4%) BITTER

Unfined, golden-coloured beer with spicy hops throughout. The flavour has hints of orange and peach with a dry bitterness.
Phoenix Rising (ABV 4%) BITTER
Tawny beer with a creamy toffee nose. Bananas, pineapple, hops and caramel flavours. Dryish, short, fruity biscuit finish.
Strange Brew No. 1 (ABV 4%) GOLD
Easy-drinking, yellow-coloured beer. Flavour is of peppery hops, tropical fruits and biscuit sweetness with a trace of bitterness.
Four Freedoms (ABV 4.3%) PALE
Coldharbour Hell Yeah Lager (ABV 5.3%) SPECIALITY
Hops and mango notes that are also present on the flavour with some butterscotch. Dryish palate.
Hellhound IPA (ABV 5.5%) IPA
Spiced and citrus notes in this unfined amber beer with a bitterness in the flavour and finish, which is dry.

Clavell & Hind SIBA

The Old Haulage Yard, Old Cirencester Road, Birdlip, Gloucester, Gloucestershire, GL4 8JL
☎ **(01452) 238050** ⊕ **clavellandhind.co.uk**

Clavell & Hind is a 20-barrel brewery based in the Cotswold countryside with an on-site taproom. ⬩

Coachman (ABV 3.8%) SPECIALITY
Wicked Lady (ABV 4%) BITTER
Blunderbuss (ABV 4.2%) GOLD
Rook Wood (ABV 4.4%) BITTER

Clay Brow

256 Carfield, Skelmersdale, WN8 9DW ☎ **07769 581500** ✉ **claybrownano@gmail.com**

Nanobrewery that started production in 2017.

Eclipse (ABV 5.4%) STOUT
Mr P's (ABV 5.7%) SPECIALITY
Mrs P's (ABV 6%) IPA

Clearwater

Unit 1, Little Court, Manteo Way, Gammaton Road, Bideford, Devon, EX39 4FG
☎ **(01237) 420492** ⊕ **clearwaterbrewery.co.uk**

⊠ Established in 1999, Clearwater is a 10-barrel brewery regularly supplying more than 250 outlets across the south west and nationally with its Devon's Own-labelled beers. Beers are also available at the brewery tap, the Champ, Appledore. ‼⬩LIVE

Real Smiler (ABV 3.7%) GOLD
Broad Reach (ABV 4%) BITTER
Fruity aroma leads to crisp and fruity yet bitter taste. The aftertaste continues a balanced sweet/fruit/bitterness, which is slightly dry.
Mariners (ABV 4.2%) GOLD
Proper Ansome (ABV 4.2%) BITTER
A dark brown bitter, malty-flavoured, slightly sweet. In the style of a winter warmer.
Riff IPA (ABV 4.2%) PALE

Clevedon

Unit 1, Tweed Road Trading Estate, Clevedon, Somerset, BS21 6RR ☎ **07907 583415** ✉ **cheers@clevedonbrewery.co.uk**

A small brewery founded in 2016. Ownership changed in 2019. It is regarded as a local brewery by owners and patrons alike. Following a complete rebranding, most of the beers, including seasonal ones, are now named with

a twist to the locality. It focuses on using British malts and hops for its core beers. ‼▰♦⬩

Gold (ABV 3.8%) GOLD
BS21 (ABV 4.1%) BITTER
Best (ABV 4.4%) BITTER
Percy's Porter (ABV 4.4%) PORTER
Roasted malt with coffee and chocolate balanced with blackberry and liquorice notes on the palate before a short, dry finish.
IPA (ABV 5%) PALE
Blonde (ABV 5.2%) BLOND

Cliff Quay

Unit 1 Meadow Works, Kenton Road, Debenham, Suffolk, IP14 6RT
☎ **(01728) 861213** ⊕ **cliffquay.co.uk**

⊠ Cliff Quay was established in 2008 by Jeremy Moss (parliamentary brewer of the year 2005) and John Bjornson (owner of Earl Soham Brewery) in part of the historic Tolly Cobbold brewery in Ipswich. In 2012 the brewery relocated to Debenham, a small, picturesque market town, due to redevelopment of the Cliff Quay brewery site. It now operates alongside Earl Soham brewery, with shared production, offices and distribution facilities. ‼▰♦

Bitter (ABV 3.4%) BITTER
Pleasantly drinkable, well-balanced, malty, sweet bitter with a hint of caramel, followed by a sweet/malty aftertaste. A good flavour for such a low gravity beer.
Anchor Bitter (ABV 4%) BITTER
Black Jack Porter (ABV 4.2%) SPECIALITY
Unusual dark porter with a strong aniseed aroma and rich liquorice and aniseed flavours, reminiscent of old-fashioned sweets. The aftertaste is long and increasingly sweet.
Tolly Roger (ABV 4.2%) BITTER
Well-balanced, highly drinkable, mid-gold summer beer with a bittersweet hoppiness, some biscuity flavours and hints of summer fruit.
Tumble Home (ABV 4.7%) BITTER
Aroma of marzipan and dried fruit. Flavour reminiscent of Amaretto, leading to a short, bitter, slightly spicy aftertaste.
Sea Dog (ABV 5.5%) GOLD
Dreadnought (ABV 6.5%) STRONG

Cloak & Dagger

Unit 6a, Garcia Trading Estate, Canterbury Road, Worthing, West Sussex, BN13 1AL ☎ **07378 300570** ⊕ **cloakanddaggerbrewing.com**

Cloak & Dagger was established by three friends from Brighton in 2017. Beers are available in can and keg. The brewery tap is Cloak Room, Kemptown. ▰

Clockwork

See Tryst

Clouded Minds

Unit 5B Brailes Industrial Estate, Winderton Road, Lower Brailes, Warwickshire, OX15 5JW
☎ **(01608) 685739** ☎ **07530 998149**
⊕ **cloudedminds.co.uk**

Brewing began in 2013 using spare capacity at various breweries around London and Derbyshire. In 2015 the brewery moved to its own site near Banbury using a 10-barrel plant. The London area is mainly supplied but also some outlets in Birmingham, Nottinghamshire,

Warwickshire and Oxfordshire. Wholesalers also distribute the beers more widely. LIVE

N29 (ABV 3.7%) PALE
N253 (ABV 3.9%) PALE
99 steps (ABV 4%) PALE
N18 (ABV 4%) PALE
Luppol (ABV 4.2%) GOLD
Clout Stout (ABV 4.5%) STOUT
Hazelnutter (ABV 5%) BROWN
Elisir (ABV 5.3%) BITTER
Black Pike (ABV 6.1%) IPA
Dolce Vita (ABV 6.2%) IPA
Double Clout Stout (ABV 6.6%) SPECIALITY

Cloudwater SIBA

Units 7-8, Piccadilly Trading Estate, Manchester, M1 2NP
☎ (0161) 661 5943 ⊕ cloudwaterbrew.co

Cloudwater specialises in producing modern takes on classic styles, with a leaning towards hazy, hop-forward beers. It also releases a series of wild, spontaneous and aged beers from its barrel project, with a strong focus on seasonality of both styles and ingredients. The brewery tap is adjacent. !!♦⚡

Clun SIBA

🍴 White Horse Inn, The Square, Clun, Shropshire, SY7 8JA
☎ (01588) 640021 ⊕ whi-clun.co.uk

☺Established in 2007 behind the White Horse Clun as a tiny brewery. A 2.5-barrel plant was installed in 2010, and brewing has increased steadily since then, with beers supplied to the trade across the West Midlands and the Welsh Marches. Seasonal specials are regularly brewed. Cask, bottle-conditioned, and bright beer are available for sale to the public. Ad-hoc brewery tours are available (enquire at the bar). ♦

Loophole (ABV 3.5%) BITTER
Pale Ale (ABV 4.1%) BITTER
Solar (ABV 4.3%) SPECIALITY
Citadel (ABV 5.9%) BITTER

Coach

🍴 37 Cowbridge Road, Bridgend, CF31 3DH
Office: 2 Oldfield Road, Bocam Park, Bridgend, CF35 5LJ

The Coach Brewing Co is based out of the award-winning free house the Coach. Launched in 2018, it is in the middle of the pub for all to see. Occasional seasonal additions are brewed. Beers are also available in keg

Coach House SIBA

Wharf Street, Howley, Warrington, Cheshire, WA1 2DQ
☎ (01925) 232800 ⊕ coachhousebrewery.co.uk

Established in 1991 by three former employees of Greenall Whitley Brewery, Coach House was bought by Martin Bailey in 2015. The 40-barrel plant produces up to 240-barrels per week. ♦

Coachman's Best Bitter (ABV 3.7%) BITTER
A well-hopped, malty bitter, moderately fruity with a hint of sweetness and a peppery nose.
Gunpowder Mild (ABV 3.8%) MILD
Aromas of roast malts and caramel attract you to a pleasant sweet and toasty tasting mild with a gentle finish.

Honeypot Bitter (ABV 3.8%) SPECIALITY
Farrier's Best Bitter (ABV 3.9%) BITTER
Cromwells Best Bitter (ABV 4%) BITTER
Blonde (ABV 4.1%) BLOND
Cheshire Gold (ABV 4.1%) PALE
Dick Turpin (ABV 4.2%) BITTER
Malty, hoppy, pale brown beer with some initial sweetish flavours leading to a short, bitter aftertaste. Sold under other names as a pub house beer.
ClIPAty Hop (ABV 4.3%) PALE
Hoppy, fruity, bitter beer with balancing sweetness and a dry finish.
Flintlock Pale Ale (ABV 4.4%) PALE
Innkeeper's Special Reserve (ABV 4.5%) BITTER
A darkish, full-flavoured bitter. Quite fruity, with a strong, bitter aftertaste.
Postlethwaite (ABV 4.6%) PALE
Blueberry Classic Bitter (ABV 5%) SPECIALITY
Posthorn Premium (ABV 5%) PALE
Blunderbus (ABV 5.3%) BITTER

Coastal SIBA

12-14 High Street, Crewe, CW2 7BN ☎ 07305 559243
⊕ coastalbrewery.co.uk

⊗ Originally established in 2006 at Redruth in Cornwall, the brewer and the complete brewery relocated to Crewe in 2020 and is now in the basement of the Craft Beer Oasis Pub & Bottleshop. 🚋♦LIVE

Cobbydale

🍴 Red Lion, 47 Kirkgate, Silsden, West Yorkshire, BD20 0AQ
☎ (01535) 930884 ☎ 07965 569885
⊕ cobbydalebrewery.co.uk

☺Brewing began in 2017 at the Red Lion, Silsden. Originally only brewing one beer, others are now brewed on an occasional basis.

Colchester SIBA

Viaduct Brewhouse, Unit 16, Wakes Hall Business Centre, Wakes Colne, Essex, CO6 2DY
☎ (01787) 829422 ⊕ colchesterbrewery.com

⊗ Set up in 2012 by three friends, Tom Knox, Roger Clark and Andy Bone, using the double drop process. Popular during the early 20th century this process requires additional brewing vessels in a two-tier system resulting in clean beer with pronounced flavours. !!🚋♦LIVE

AKA Pale (ABV 3.7%) PALE
Metropolis (ABV 3.9%) GOLD
Jack Spitty's Smuggler's Ale (ABV 4%) BITTER
Number One (ABV 4.1%) BITTER
Sweeney Todd (ABV 4.2%) BITTER
Brazilian Coffee & Vanilla Porter (ABV 4.6%) SPECIALITY
Cat's Whiskers (ABV 4.8%) STOUT
Old King Coel London Porter (ABV 5%) PORTER

Cold Bath

🍴 46 Kings Road, Harrogate, North Yorkshire, HG1 5JW
☎ (0330) 880 7009 ⊕ coldbathbrewing.com

Launched in 2018, Cold Bath's on-site brewery can be viewed on the mezzanine level above the bar. All beers are exclusively available in the pub.

Cold Black Label SIBA

Guardian House, 5 Squire Drive, Brynmenyn Industrial Estate, Bridgend, CF32 9TX
☎ (01656) 728081 ⊕ coldblacklabel.co.uk

Cold Black Label was initially founded in 2004, concentrating on its eponymous lager brand, and expanded into cask-conditioned beers 10 years later. In 2018, Cold Black Label and Brecon Brewing merged, with Buster Grant taking over all brewing, and 14 new beers were created. In 2019, Lithic Brewing joined the group, with these gluten-free beers mainly available in keg and can, with the occasional release of casks. ⌷

Glyder Fawr (ABV 4.2%) PALE
Singing Sword (ABV 4.2%) SPECIALITY
Harlech Castle (ABV 4.4%) BITTER
Uncle Phil's Ale (ABV 4.4%) SPECIALITY
Bwlch Passage (ABV 4.5%) SPECIALITY
Chirk Castle (ABV 4.6%) GOLD
Miners Ale (ABV 4.6%) STOUT
Sand Storm (ABV 4.6%) GOLD
Guardian (ABV 4.7%) GOLD
Crib Goch (ABV 5%) PALE
Nutty Ale (ABV 5%) BROWN
Pirate Bay (ABV 5%) PALE
Red Beast (ABV 6%) IPA
Miners Imperial Ale (ABV 7.5%) STOUT

Brewed under the Brecon Brewing name:
Three Beacons (ABV 3%) PALE
Welsh Beacons (ABV 3.7%) PALE
Dark Beacons (ABV 3.8%) BITTER
Copper Beacons (ABV 4.1%) BITTER
Gold Beacons (ABV 4.2%) GOLD
Red Beacons (ABV 5%) BITTER
Mind Bleach (ABV 10%) BARLEY

Cold Town SIBA

8-10 Dunedin Street, Edinburgh, EH7 4JB
☎ (0131) 221 9978

Second site: 4 Grassmarket, Edinburgh, EH1 2JU
⊕ coldtownbeer.com

A Signature Pubs venture that began brewing lager in 2018. A brewpub has been opened at Cold Town House, Grassmarket, Edinburgh. No real ale.

Coles Family

White Hart Thatched Inn and Brewery, Llanddarog, SA32 8NT
☎ (01267) 275395 ⊕ thebestpubinwales.co.uk

The brewery is based at the ancient White Hart Inn, built in 1371, which historically had an on-site brewery. Brewing started again in 1999 on a nine-gallon plant. A one-barrel plant was fitted in 2000. In 2012 the brewery was opened to the public. Cider is also produced. ♦

College

See Hilden

Collyfobble SIBA

Peacock, Hackney Lane, Barlow, Derbyshire, S18 7TD
☎ (01142) 890340 ⊕ collyfobblebrewery.com

Collyfobble began brewing in 2018. ‼ ⌀

Colne Valley (NEW)

62 Braiswick, Colchester, Essex, CO4 5AX ☎ 07876 237137 ✉ lewisbarber2707@icloud.com

Colne Valley Brewing is a local, organic craft beer brewery, established in 2020. **V**

Colomendy

See Dovecote

Colonsay

The Brewery, Scalasaig, Isle of Colonsay, PA61 7YT
☎ (01951) 200190 ⊕ colonsaybrewery.co.uk

Colonsay began brewing in 2007 on a five-barrel plant. Beer is mainly bottled or brewery-conditioned for the local trade. LIVE

Combe

Unit 4, Lundy View, Mullacott Cross Industrial Estate, Ilfracombe, Devon, EX34 8PY
☎ (01271) 267030 ☎ 07973 488409
⊕ combebrewingcompany.co.uk

Combe Brewing Co was established in early 2020, in a recently closed brewery, just before the Covid-19 lockdown was put in place. Despite this inauspicious start, it continued brewing, producing bottle-conditioned ales to meet its small but growing client base. The owners, Richard and Michelle, have previous experience in the trade. A five-barrel plant is used. Bottle label artwork is designed by a local artist, Karen French. ‼⌷ LIVE ⌀

Harbour (ABV 3.7%) BITTER
Beach Blonde (ABV 4.1%) BLOND
Ruby Sunset (ABV 4.7%) RED
Dark and Stormy (ABV 5%) PORTER

Concept

166 Town Street, Horsforth, LS18 4AQ
☎ (0113) 467 2001

Office: Unit 5, Clayton Wood Court, West Park, Leeds, LS16 6PW ⊕ conceptbrewing.co.uk

☺Established in 2019 at the Malt Brewhouse, Horsforth, using a four-barrel brewing kit on open display in the bar area. It supplies up to six types of cask ales to each of the six West Yorkshire-based pubs and bars in its pub group.

Concrete Cow

59 Alston Drive, Bradwell Abbey, Milton Keynes, Buckinghamshire, MK13 9HB
☎ (01908) 316794 ☎ 07889 665745
⊕ concretecowbrewery.co.uk

Concrete Cow opened in 2007 on a 5.5-barrel plant. The beers are named after aspects of local history. The brewery supplies pubs, farmers' markets, local shops and restaurants. English single malt whisky is also available, produced from the brewery's own malt at a local distillery. ‼⌷♦LIVE

Pail Ale (ABV 3.7%) BLOND
Fenny Popper (ABV 4%) GOLD
Cock 'n' Bull Story (ABV 4.1%) BITTER
Old Bloomer (ABV 4.7%) BITTER

Concrete Island

Pavilion Terrace, Wood Lane, Shepherd's Bush, W12 0HT ⊕ concreteislandbrewery.co.uk

Established as Small Beer Brewing in 2016 and rebranded as Concrete Island Brewery in 2020. Run from a private flat in West London and with a brewlength of just 25 litres, it is probably the smallest commercial brewery in the country. Unpasteurised, unfiltered beers are available in bottles.

Coniston

Coppermines Road, Coniston, Cumbria, LA21 8HL
☎ (01539) 441133 ⊕ conistonbrewery.com

⊚The 10-barrel plant (purchased from Marston Moor) commenced brewing in 1995. The brewery is situated behind the Black Bull Inn, Coniston, and currently brews 40 barrels a week. Some bottle-conditioned Coniston beers are brewed using Ridgeway Brewery. It supplies over 100 outlets with cask beers across the North West, and bottled beers are available in Asda, Sainsburys and Booths, as well as online. Bottled Gold is gluten-free.
‼☞LIVE

Oliver's Light Ale (ABV 3.4%) BLOND
A fruity, hoppy, straw-coloured mild with plenty of flavour for its strength.
Bluebird Bitter (ABV 3.6%) PALE
A yellow-gold, predominantly hoppy and fruity beer, well-balanced with some sweetness and a rising bitter finish.
Asrai (ABV 4%) BLOND
Crisp on the palate, a gently-hopped beer with a full-bodied finish.
Bluebird Premium XB (ABV 4.2%) PALE
Well-balanced, hoppy and fruity golden bitter. Bittersweet in the mouth with dryness building.
Old Man Ale (ABV 4.2%) RED
Delicious fruity, winey beer with a complex, well-balanced richness.
Special Oatmeal Stout (ABV 4.5%) STOUT
A well-balanced, easy-drinking stout, fruity with a balanced ratio of malt to hop bitterness. A good starting point for novice stout drinkers.
Coniston K7 (ABV 4.7%) PALE
Balanced, fruity hoppy bitter, plenty of body and a long hoppy, bitter finish.
Golden Bitter (ABV 4.8%) PALE
Thurstein Pilsner (ABV 4.8%) SPECIALITY
True to style; mild but unusually sweet, with a hoppy fruitiness.
Blacksmiths Ale (ABV 5%) BITTER
A tawny ale which holds both roastiness and fruitiness in a pleasing balance.
Infinity IPA (ABV 6%) IPA
High impact IPA. Fruity aromas persist in the powerful but well-balanced hoppiness and sweetness with nothing being lost in the finish.
No 9 Barley Wine (ABV 8.5%) BARLEY
Hops and alcohol dominate with appropriate sweetness and fruit on the tongue. A full-bodied and beautifully-balanced beer.

Connoisseur

(Rear of) Wolverhampton House, 121-125 Church Street, St Helens, Merseyside, WA10 1AJ ☎ 07921 838831 ⊕ connoisseurales.com

Launched in 2014 by a family team of award-winning licencees, the brewery was run by Mark Yates until his death in 2017. The torch then passed to son Kevin who reinvigorated the range with a selection of new recipes to complement existing brews. Brewing is currently suspended while new premises are sought.

Consall Forge

3 Railway Cottages, Consall Forge, Staffordshire, ST9 0AJ

A one-barrel brewery set in the heart of the Staffordshire Moorlands adjacent to the Churnet Valley Railway. The Black Lion at Consall Forge is a regular outlet.

Dark Ruby Mild (ABV 5.2%) MILD
Equilibrium (ABV 6%) STOUT

Consett SIBA

🍺 **Grey Horse Inn, 115 Sherburn Terrace, Consett, County Durham, DH8 6NE**
☎ (01207) 591540 ⊕ consettaleworks.co.uk

Established 2005 in the stables of a former coaching inn at the rear of the Grey Horse, Consett's oldest pub. The name, beers and branding commemorates the former steelworks in the town which closed in 1980. Beers are also available throughout the North East. ‼◆

Pale Ale (ABV 3.8%) PALE
Steel Town Bitter (ABV 3.8%) BITTER
Steel River (ABV 4%) GOLD
Steelworkers Blonde (ABV 4%) BLOND
White Hot (ABV 4%) PALE
Men of Steel (ABV 4.3%) BITTER
Stout (ABV 4.3%) STOUT
Porter (ABV 4.5%) PORTER
Sweet malts and caramel dominate throughout, with some fruit and a lasting finish.
Red Dust (ABV 4.5%) RED
Sweet, fruit and malty lead to a creamy, full-bodied, balanced red ale with caramel flavours and a lasting finish.

Consortium

🍺 **Consortium, 13D Cornmarket, Louth, Lincolnshire, LN11 9PY**
☎ (01507) 600754 ⊕ theconsortiumlouth.co.uk

⊚The Consortium Brewing Company was setup in 2016 to serve the Consortium micropub and tasting lounge and is situated in the Cornmarket of Louth, down a small passageway close to the Masons Arms. A large, diverse range of ale and gin styles is now brewed on the Fairfield Industrial Estate. The brewery has produced more than 100 different ales since production started and bottle them for sale on the market (Wed, Fri & Sat), within 20 metres of the pub. ‼◆⏂

Lincolnshire Traditional Bitter (ABV 3.8%) BITTER
Where's My Fiorucci (ABV 3.8%) BITTER
Aisey Dubitz (ABV 3.9%) BLOND
Farming County (ABV 4%) BITTER
Saturday's Blonde (ABV 4%) BITTER
Wet Pocket (ABV 4.1%) RED
Best Bitter (ABV 4.2%) BITTER
Pleasant Blonde (ABV 4.2%) BLOND
Executioner's Assistant (ABV 4.3%) BLOND
Obliging Blonde (ABV 4.3%) BLOND
Black Frog (ABV 4.4%) BITTER
Queens (ABV 4.4%) GOLD
Willy Wickam's Posthumous Ale (ABV 4.4%) BITTER
England's Finest Hour (ABV 4.5%) GOLD
Fat Cat Fuller (ABV 5%) SPECIALITY
Nicholas De Luda (ABV 5.4%) STOUT
Seek Medical Help (ABV 5.5%) IPA
Thanks Pa (ABV 6%) IPA

Constellation (NEW)

Unit 21, Orchard Business Centre, Sanderson Way, Tonbridge, Kent, TN9 1QF
☎ (01732) 756564 ⊕ constellationbrewery.co.uk

From a nascent idea in 2019 to a fully formed brewery in 2020 Constellation is a 30-barrel brewery in the heart of Tonbridge. Owner/brewer Rob Jenner has over 10 years brewing experience. In addition to cask, beers are available in can and keg. ✦

Indus (ABV 3.9%) PALE
Draco (ABV 4.2%) BITTER
Aquila (ABV 4.6%) GOLD

Conwy SIBA

Unit 2, Ty Mawr Enterprise Park, Tan y Graig Road, Llysfaen, LL29 8UE
☎ (01492) 514305 ⊕ conwybrewery.co.uk

☺Conwy started brewing in 2003, and was the first brewery in Conwy for at least 100 years. In 2013 it increased capacity and moved to bigger premises in Llysfaen with its own brewery tap. Around 100 outlets are supplied. Monthly seasonals are available as well as the West Coast range showcasing American style beers. Part owner of the Albion Ale House and the Bridge, Conwy. Since 2021 the brewery is owned by the Cadman Capital Group, which also operates 360 Degrees Brewery.
‼ ➍ ◆LIVE ✦

Clogwyn Gold (ABV 3.6%) PALE
A full-flavoured golden ale featuring strong citrus fruit flavours throughout. Hoppy bitterness dominates the full mouthfeel and lasting finish.
Welsh Pride (ABV 4%) BITTER
Beachcomber Blonde (ABV 4.2%) BLOND
A pale beer with a citrus taste, initially sweetish with delicate hoppiness in the lingering bitter finish.
Rampart (ABV 4.5%) BROWN
A dark, fruity beer with a sweetish initial taste. Fruit flavours accompanied by the underlying hoppiness continue into the bittersweet aftertaste.
San Francisco (ABV 5.5%) IPA

Cooper Hill

Highcliffe Industrial Estate, Bruntcliffe Lane, Morley, Leeds, LS27 9LR
☎ (0800) 783 2989 ⊕ cooperhillbrewery.co.uk

Commenced brewing in 2018 on equipment from the former Trinity Brewery, now relocated to Morley.

Copper Dragon

Snaygill Industrial Estate, Keighley Road, Skipton, North Yorkshire, BD23 2QR
☎ (01756) 243243 ⊕ copperdragon.co.uk

☺Copper Dragon are now brewing back in Skipton on a 15-barrel plant. As well as the core range of Copper Dragon beers, Recoil Craft beers are also brewed, with both brands also featuring special editions.

Best Bitter (ABV 3.8%) BITTER
Golden Pippin (ABV 3.9%) BITTER
Golden session beer, fruity and hoppy in aroma and taste. Citrus comes comes through in the aftertaste, which is increasingly bitter.
Black Gold (ABV 4%) BITTER
Silver Myst (ABV 4%) SPECIALITY
Scotts 1816 (ABV 4.1%) BITTER
Sidewinder (ABV 4.2%) PALE

Copper Fox (NEW)

c/o 3 Essie Road, Rhynie, Aberdeenshire, AB54 4GF
☎ 07484 386496 ⊕ copperfoxbrewery.co.uk

Copper Fox Brewery Ltd, founded in 2017, is an independently run, one-man, small batch microbrewery. Production is exclusively in 330ml bottles, with 10p credit on bottle returns. Beers can be found at farmer's markets in the region and in Westhill.

Copper Street

8 Copper Street, Brewery Square, Dorchester, DT1 1GH ☎ 07970 766622
✉ copperstreetbrewery@outlook.com

⊗ Anthony and Ann Buckton started this 2.5-barrel brewery in 2018, after moving from King Alfred Ales (now closed). It is situated in the new Brewery Square development, ex-Eldridge Pope, next to Dorchester South station. The brewery can be seen from the shop, which sells a good selection of bottled beers. Nine or ten ales are produced throughout the year. A taproom is open Thursday-Saturday. ➍ ◆ ✦

Scramasax (ABV 4.1%) PALE
871 (ABV 4.3%) BITTER
Egbert's Stone (ABV 4.3%) BITTER
Shield Wall (ABV 4.3%) BITTER
Aethel Sword (ABV 4.5%) BITTER
Saxon Gold (ABV 4.7%) GOLD
Dark Ages (ABV 5.5%) PORTER

Corinium

Unit 1a, The Old Kennels, Cirencester Park, Cirencester, Gloucestershire, GL7 1UR ☎ 07716 826467 ⊕ coriniumales.co.uk

⊗ Established in 2012, Corinium Ales brew classic and contemporary award-winning ales on a 2.5-barrel plant located in small, historic old kennels in Cirencester Park, just outside the town centre. An on-site taproom showcases the range, which is also available at a growing number of local outlets, events and pubs.
‼ ➍ ◆LIVE ✦

Firebird VI (ABV 4%) BITTER
Corinium Gold I (ABV 4.2%) GOLD
Plautus V (ABV 4.5%) PALE
Bodicacia IV (ABV 4.7%) PALE
Centurion II (ABV 4.7%) STOUT
Ale Caesar III (ABV 5%) PALE

Corless

c/o Station Road, Scorton, Lancashire, PR3 1AN
☎ 07983 563917

Brewing began in 2018 using spare capacity at other brewers, mostly Avid.

Cornish Crown SIBA

End Unit, Badger's Cross Farm, Badger's Cross, Penzance, Cornwall, TR20 8XE
☎ (01736) 449029 ☎ 07870 998986
⊕ cornishcrown.co.uk

⊗ This six-barrel brewery was launched in 2012 on a farm high above Mounts Bay by the brewer, and landlord, of the Crown Inn, Penzance, which acts as the brewery tap. Beer is available locally and as far as the Southampton Arms in London. ‼LIVE ✦

Golden (ABV 4%) PALE
Causeway (ABV 4.1%) BITTER

Tawny bitter with a malty caramel nose. Initially malty with resinous hop bitterness gradually emerging. Stone fruits. Long bitter finish.

One Hop One Grain (ABV 4.1%) PALE
Helter Skelter (ABV 4.2%) PALE
Fruity, hoppy golden beer. Biscuit malt, pine hops and a touch of caramel honey provide a refreshing bitterness.
Honeyfuggle (ABV 4.5%) SPECIALITY
Golden speciality honey beer. Light, subtle honey and caramel flavours evolving into a refreshing, sweet, yet bitter beer.
SPA (ABV 4.8%) PALE
Amber, strong ale. Well-hopped with citrus, peach and grassy notes. Hints of honey leading to dry, bitter finish.
Porter (ABV 5.2%) SPECIALITY
Dark vanilla porter. Roasted malt aromas. Molasses, treacle, liquorice flavours with raisin, fig/plum fruits and earthy hops. Roast, dry finish.
IPA (ABV 5.5%) IPA
Amber IPA with hop aroma. Powerful, earthy hop bitter and persistent malt flavours. Kaleidoscope of fruitiness. Long, bitter finish.
Red IPA (ABV 5.9%) SPECIALITY
Strong, tawny, speciality ale. Resinous hops, biscuit malt, with plums, raspberries and oranges and later smoky hints. Long fruity finish.

Corvedale SIBA

🍺 Sun Inn, Corfton, Craven Arms, Shropshire, SY7 9DF
☎ (01584) 861239

Brewing started in 1999 behind the pub. Landlord Norman Pearce is also the brewer and uses only British malt and hops, with water from a local borehole. Bottle-conditioned beers are suitable for vegetarians and vegans. He is, through various agencies, able to supply well over 20 pubs. !! ♦ LIVE V

Cotswold SIBA

College Farm, Stow Road, Lower Slaughter, Bourton-on-the-Water, Gloucestershire, GL54 2HN
☎ (01451) 824488 ☎ 07760 889100
⊕ cotswoldbrew.co

An independent producer of craft lager and speciality keg beers. The brewery was established in 2005 and expanded in 2010. More than 150 outlets are supplied, mainly in the Cotswolds and London. !! 🍺 ♦ LIVE V

Cotswold Lion SIBA

Hartley Farm, Hartley Lane, Leckhampton Hill, Cheltenham, Gloucestershire, GL53 9QN
☎ (01242) 870164 ⊕ cotswoldlionbrewery.co.uk

⊗ Previously located in a grain store on a farm in the Cotswolds, Cotswold Lion brewery relocated in 2021. It produces a core range of five beers using a 10-barrel plant. 🍺 LIVE

Shepherd's Delight (ABV 3.6%) BITTER
Hogget (ABV 3.8%) BITTER
Best in Show (ABV 4.2%) BITTER
Golden Fleece (ABV 4.4%) PALE
Drover's Return (ABV 5%) BITTER

Cotswold Spring

See Severn

Cottage Beer Project (NEW)

Brockhole Cottage, Morebath, Tiverton, Devon, EX16 9BZ ☎ 07422 731152
✉ dan@cottagebeerproject.co.uk

Nano-brewery opened in 2021, using new 200-litre kit, and operating part-time. Bottle-conditioned beers are sold online, at local businesses and at numerous events, primarily within Devon and Somerset. Core range is supported by seasonal and one-off beers, with occasional cask for festivals. LIVE

Cotton End

🍺 Pomfret Arms, 10 Cotton End, Northampton, NN4 8BS
☎ (01604) 765544

⊗ Established in 2015, Cotton End Brewery is located in the garden of the Pomfret Arms, Northampton. A one-barrel plant, it brews specialist beers on sale at the pub, as well as other local outlets.

Coul SIBA

22 Laggan Crescent, Glenrothes, KY7 6FY
⊕ coulbrewing.co.uk

Coul Brewing Company is a family-owned and operated craft beer microbrewery, founded in Glenrothes in 2017.

Milestone (ABV 4%) BITTER
Baby Badger (ABV 4.2%) PALE

Country Life SIBA

The Big Sheep, Abbotsham, Bideford, Devon, EX39 5AP
☎ (01237) 420808 ☎ 07971 267790
⊕ countrylifebrewery.co.uk

⊗ Country Life is based at the Big Sheep tourist attraction. The brewery offers a beer show and free samples in the shop during the peak season (April-October). A 15.5-barrel plant was installed in 2005, making Country Life the biggest brewery in North Devon. Regular, seasonal and bottle-conditioned beers are available at approximately 100 outlets, the brewery shop and online. !! 🍺 ♦ LIVE

Old Appledore (ABV 3.7%) BITTER
Reef Break (ABV 4%) BITTER
Shore Break (ABV 4.4%) GOLD
Black Boar/Board Break (ABV 4.5%) PORTER
Complex, well-balanced aromas. Unusual dry, bitter hop taste, leading to softer aftertaste with unexpected roasted malt and caramel.
Golden Pig (ABV 4.7%) BITTER
Country Bumpkin (ABV 6%) OLD

Courtyard SIBA

Gosfield Cottage, The Street, Gosfield, CO9 1TP
☎ (01787) 475993 ☎ 07710 230662
⊕ courtyardbrewery.co.uk

Courtyard Brewery uses a six-barrel plant designed to perfectly fit into a 19th century coach house in the north Essex village of Gosfield. It is run by two brewers passionate about producing ales traditionally, but with a 21st century twist. ♦

IPA (ABV 3.8%) PALE
Gold (ABV 4.1%) GOLD
Dark (ABV 5%) PORTER

Cove

See Driftwood Spars

CrackleRock

The Old Cooperage, High Street, Botley, Hampshire, SO30 2EA ☎ 07733 232806 ⊕ cracklerock.co.uk

⊗ Cracklerock began brewing in 2014 at the Old Cooperage in the centre of Botley. Its taproom moved to larger premises near the brewery in 2018. !! ☛ ♦

Crackerjack (ABV 3.8%) BITTER
Verified (ABV 4%) PALE
Fire Cracker (ABV 4.2%) BITTER
Gold Rush (ABV 4.5%) GOLD
Dark Destroyer (ABV 4.9%) PORTER
Crafty Shag (ABV 5%) BITTER
Crackatoa IPA (ABV 6.2%) IPA

Craddock's

⧈ **Duke William, 25 Coventry Street, Stourbridge, West Midlands, DY8 1EP**
☎ **(01384) 440202 ⊕ craddocksbrewery.com**

⊗ Craddock's brews exclusively for its pubs; the Duke William and Plough & Harrow in Stourbridge, the King Charles, Worcester, and the Talbot, Droitwich. In 2019 The Good Intent, was opened in Birmingham as a not-for-profit enterprise selling Craddock's and other beers, with profits donated to charity. Ten beers in the core range, availability varies. !! ♦ LIVE

Craft Brews

The Old Dairy, Pierrepont Home Farm, The Reeds, Farnham, Surrey, GU10 3BS ☎ 0777 498 2174 ⊕ craftbrews.uk

⊗ Set in the Surrey countryside, the microbrewery and taproom (formerly known as Frensham Brewery) are situated in a 17th century restored barn, on a working dairy farm. Beers are not generally sold to pubs, so can only be obtained from the taproom. ☛ ♦

i. PL (ABV 3.2%) BITTER
RPA (ABV 3.7%) PALE
USB (ABV 4.3%) BITTER
i.PA (ABV 5.3%) PALE
CAB (ABV 6.3%) PORTER
Dark chocolate and malt in the aroma. Bitterness builds on initial sweetness leading to dry, balanced by chocolate and vanilla.

Craftsman (NEW)

21 Isis Close, Abingdon, Oxfordshire, OX14 3TA
☎ **07743 041916 ✉ justinlevans@btinternet.com**

Craftsman is a 100-litre microbrewery in the owner's garage, which started commercial production in 2021. Beers are available in bottles only at present.

Crafty Beers

The Stables, Hall Farm, Stetchworth, Cambridgeshire, CB8 0TY
☎ **(01223) 813938 ⊕ craftybeers.co.uk**

⊗ Crafty Beers have been brewed since 2012. Beers are available at pubs in the Cambridge and Newmarket areas, and beyond. Bottled beers are available for local delivery. All core ales are vegan-friendly. LIVE V

Carpenter's Cask (ABV 3.8%) BITTER

A well-balanced, amber brew with biscuit malt character giving way to hops on the palate and long finish.
Incognito (ABV 4%) BITTER
Wilbraham (ABV 4.1%) BITTER
Sauvignon Blonde (ABV 4.4%) BLOND
APA (ABV 4.6%) PALE

Crafty Brewing SIBA

Thatched House Farm, Loxhill, Dunsfold, Surrey, GU8 4BW
☎ **(01483) 276300 ☎ 07702 305595**
⊕ **craftybrewing.co.uk**

⊗ Opened in 2014 behind the famous Dunsfold aerodrome, Crafty opened a new 30-barrel plant in 2019. It produces contemporary versions of traditional ale styles. The 'Crafty Cares' beers support various charities, including Surrey Search & Rescue. It supplies nearly 200 regional pubs, local shops and markets. Since 2020 the beers have also been available nationally to order online in mini kegs, bottles and cans. Regular open days are held (see website for details). ♦

Loxhill Biscuit (ABV 3.6%) BITTER
Golden bitter which belies its strength. Initial biscuity aroma and taste with a dry, bitter finish, from the Challenger hops.
Crafty One (ABV 3.9%) PALE
Golden-yellow beer with Chinook and Sorachi Ace hops. Tropical fruits aroma, leads to full, dry, fruity finish. Hints of coconut.
Blind Side (ABV 4%) BITTER
A traditional, light brown bitter. Predominantly malty throughout. Toffee and some roast character lead to a bittersweet finish.
Hop Tipple (ABV 4.2%) GOLD
Beautifully-balanced pale ale. Light and easy-drinking with resinous modern hops and a crisp finish coming from dry-hopping.

Crafty Cats (NEW)

St Nicholas Farm, Dunt Lane, St Nicholas Hurst, Berkshire, RG10 0TA ☎ 07507 808390
⊕ **craftycats.beer**

A new microbrewery producing small-batch craft beer in cans and the occasional keg, for distribution to local shops and a few specialist craft beer bars and beer festivals. Established in 2020 and run by two brothers on the family farm, the plant is the old four-barrel kit from Ascot Brewing Co.

Crafty Devil

Unit 3, The Stone Yard, Ninian Park Road, Cardiff, CF11 6HE
☎ **(029) 2240 4355 ☎ 07766 014550**
⊕ **craftydevilbrewing.co.uk**

⊗ Brewery has been in current location since 2017. It does not currently brew cask ale regularly, but produces bottled, canned and keg beer, which they supply to markets and a number of other outlets in the local area. It currently operates two microbars, one in Cardiff and one in Penarth. !! ☛

Crafty Dragon

8 Castell Morlais, Ponsticill, Merthyr Tydfil, CF48 2YB
☎ **(01685) 723544 ☎ 07967 274272**
✉ **butchersbunkhouse@gmail.com**

☺ Crafty Dragon began brewing in 2017 and is situated within the Brecon Beacons National Park. Its brewery tap is the Butchers Arms in Pontsticill.

Goldings Bitter (ABV 3.8%) BITTER
Session IPA (ABV 3.8%) PALE
Bramling (ABV 4%) GOLD
Pen Y Fan Chocolate & Rum Porter (ABV 4.5%) SPECIALITY
Chocolate & Rum Porter (ABV 5%) SPECIALITY
Cwrw Coch (ABV 5%) BITTER
Red IPA (ABV 5%) PALE

Crafty Little SIBA

Office: 109 Alfred Gelder Street, Hull, East Yorkshire, HU1 1EP
☎ (01482) 661393 ⊕ thecraftylittlebrewery.co.uk

☺This family-run business, based in East Yorkshire, was founded in 2017. It is currently utilising contract brewing while new premises are sought. V◆

Apex Predator (ABV 3.8%) GOLD
ChamAleon (ABV 4%) BITTER
Red Tale (ABV 4.5%) MILD
Silk Stout (ABV 4.5%) STOUT
Black Ryeno (ABV 4.6%) PORTER
Perky Porter (ABV 4.8%) PORTER
Wolf Bite APA (ABV 4.8%) PALE
Snake Charmer (ABV 5.5%) SPECIALITY

Brewed for Three Sisters
Session Ale (ABV 4%) BITTER

Crafty Monkey SIBA

Benknowle Farm, Elwick, Hartlepool, TS27 3HF
⊕ shop.craftymonkey.beer

Brewing commenced in 2018 using a five-barrel plant in converted farm buildings. Beers are available throughout County Durham, Teesside and North Yorkshire. The brewery has a pop up bar for events. LIVE

Telegraph Session (ABV 3.8%) PALE
Moneypenny EPA (ABV 4%) PALE
New Era (ABV 4.3%) BITTER
Ruby Ruby Ruby Ruby (ABV 4.5%) RED
Reward IPA (ABV 4.7%) PALE
Cemetery Gates (ABV 4.8%) PORTER
Black Celebration (ABV 5%) STOUT

Crafty Pint

⧈ c/o Half Moon, 130 Northgate, Darlington, DL1 1QS
☎ (01325) 469965 ☎ 07804 305175

Established in 2013 in the cellar of the Half Moon in Darlington. Originally a 10-gallon brew length, it was upgraded to a one-barrel plant in 2015. One-off beers are produced solely for the pub. ◆

Crankshaft SIBA

17E Boxer Place, Leyland, Lancashire, PR26 7QL
☎ 07827 289200 ⊕ crankshaftbrewery.co.uk

☺The brewery, a 2.5-barrel plant, launched in 2016, moved to new premises in 2017, and expanded into the next unit in 2018. Capacity has been doubled with the addition of two 1,000-litre fermenters. A core range of beers (cask, keg, bottle and can) are supplemented by a number of special occasional beers. A popular taproom is open on Fridays and Saturdays. ‼⨼◆✦

Comet (ABV 3.8%) PALE
Propshaft (ABV 3.8%) BITTER
Foggy Gold (ABV 4%) GOLD
Testbed v4 (ABV 4.1%) BLOND
Sherpa (ABV 4.2%) PALE

Cote de Reiver (ABV 4.4%) BLOND
1511 (ABV 4.7%) PALE
Tenterhook (ABV 5%) PALE
Leyland Tiger Cub (ABV 5.5%) GOLD
Leyland Badger (ABV 5.8%) STOUT

Crate

⧈ White Building, Unit 7, Queens Yard, Hackney Wick, London, E9 5EN
☎ (020) 8533 3331 ⊕ cratebrewery.com

Created as a brewpub and pizzeria in 2012, expansion later saw a move to the Brew Shed across the yard. Falling into administration in mid-2020, the Brew Shed was bought by Trumans and Crate retreated back to the brewpub. The range of seven beers is available on keg and in bottles and cans. Beers are temporarily being brewed at Purity whilst the brew kit in the bar is refurbished. No real ale.

Creative Juices

Woodoaks Farm, Denham Way, Maple Cross, Hertfordshire, WD3 9XQ
☎ (01923) 771779
⊕ creativejuicesbrewingcompany.com

A craft brewery, taproom and beer garden. It opened in 2019 in a renovated dairy building, on a farm in Hertfordshire. Beers are unfiltered and unpasteurised and are either kegged or canned. No real ale is produced.
GF◆

Creaton Grange

Old Wash House, Creaton Grange, Grooms Lane, Creaton, Northamptonshire, NN6 8NN ☎ 07943 595829 ⊕ creatongrangeales.co.uk

Microbrewery started in 2017 and based in a converted disused building on a family farm in rural Northamptonshire.

Four Sons (ABV 3.5%) MILD
Pheasant Tale (ABV 3.8%) GOLD
March Yard (ABV 4.2%) PALE

Cromarty SIBA

Davidston, Cromarty, IV11 8XD
☎ (01381) 600440 ⊕ cromartybrewing.co.uk

Family-owned, Cromarty began brewing in 2011 in a purpose-built brewhouse. Many awards have been garnered. Fermenting capacity was increased during 2014 and again in 2015, while developing a varied portfolio of regularly brewed ales, and around eight occasional brews. A bottling line was commissioned in 2017, a warehouse in 2018, and a canning line in 2019. The brewer is constantly trialling new recipes and collaboration brews. ‼⨼◆

Whiteout (ABV 3.8%) SPECIALITY
Happy Chappy (ABV 4.1%) GOLD
An excellent golden ale with plenty of hop character. Floral citric hop aroma with a good bitter taste which increases in aftertaste and balanced with malt.
Red Rocker (ABV 5%) SPECIALITY
Red-coloured, rye, hop monster with a malty background leading to a bitter finish.
Rogue Wave (ABV 5.7%) IPA
Easy-drinking, strong, peachy, hoppy bitter.
Ghost Town (ABV 5.8%) PORTER
Classic, dark-roasted, malty porter with blackcurrant and liquorice background.
AKA IPA (ABV 6.7%) IPA

Strong IPA with a smooth, citrus, hoppy taste.

Cronx SIBA

Unit 6, Vulcan Business Centre, Vulcan Way, New Addington, Surrey, CR0 9UG
☎ **(020) 3475 8848** ⊕ **thecronx.com**

Croydon-based microbrewery, opened in 2012, brewing a range of core and seasonal beers in cask, keg, bottles, cans and mini-kegs. The brewery picked up a SIBA Gold regional award in 2019 and a SIBA Silver national award in 2020 for its Entire Porter. The Cronx Bar was opened in 2016 at BOXPark Croydon. ◆LIVE

Standard (ABV 3.8%) BITTER
Easy-drinking, brown bitter with sweetish fudge and spicy hoppiness notes throughout. Malty bitter finish with a dryness that remains.
Kotchin (ABV 3.9%) SPECIALITY
Grapefruity beer with pleasant hoppy notes. A little sweetness is balanced by a crisp, bitter finish that grows on drinking.
Nektar (ABV 4.5%) PALE
Full-bodied, dark gold, pale ale. Peach with citrus, sweet biscuit and floral hops, gently fade in the lingering, bitter finish.
Pop Up! (ABV 5%) PALE
Smooth, amber APA with strong tropical and grapefruit throughout. Hoppy and bitter on the palate and dry finish.
Entire (ABV 5.2%) PORTER
Dark brown porter with chocolate roast in the aroma, flavour and finish. Fruit character is of caramelised raisins and plums.

Crooked

Units 12-15, The Garages, Leeds East Airport, Church Fenton, LS24 9SE ☎ **07890 526505**
⊕ **crookedbrewing.co.uk**

☺After teaching homebrewing, Steve, Andy, Hudson and Mark started brewing in 2017 on the old RAF airfield at Church Fenton. Beers are increasingly available in a number of city centre pubs and bars in York and Leeds and many brews are canned for wider distribution. The brewery tap, Crooked Tap, opened in 2019 at Acomb Green in York. ◆✦

Spokes (ABV 4%) BITTER
Standard Bitter (ABV 4.2%) BITTER
The Lash (ABV 4.4%) PALE
XX (ABV 4.6%) PALE
Rufus (ABV 4.8%) PORTER

Cropton

See C'84

Cross Bay

Unit 1, Newgate, White Lund Industrial Estate, Morecambe, Lancashire, LA3 3PT
☎ **(01524) 39481** ⊕ **crossbaybrewery.co.uk**

☺Cross Bay commenced brewing in 2011 on a 28-barrel brew plant. An on-site taproom opened in 2018. The beers are widely available across north-west England. ‼🍴◆✦

Halo (ABV 3.6%) BLOND
A crisp and hoppy, pale bitter.
Vesper (ABV 3.8%) PALE
RIPA (ABV 4%) RED
Omega (ABV 4.2%) PALE
Sunset (ABV 4.2%) BLOND

Sweet bitter with a rising bitter finish.
Zenith (ABV 5%) BLOND
Gentle bitterness and fruity sweetness with some dryness in the finish.
Guell (ABV 5.1%) BITTER

Cross Borders SIBA

28-1, Hardengreen Industrial Estate, Dalkeith, EH22 3NX
☎ **(0131) 629 3990** ⊕ **crossborders.beer**

⊗ Established in 2016 by childhood friends Jonathan Wilson and Gary Munckton. Cross Borders brews BRAW traditional Scottish ales without pretension. The brewery has an on-site tap open Fridays and Saturdays. ‼🍴✦

Hop Series Pale (ABV 3.8%) PALE
Notes of citrus on the nose with a balanced, bitter finish.
Wee Braw (ABV 4%) PALE
A fresh, fruity beer with lots of hops creating a great aroma and a lightly bitter aftertaste.
Heavy (ABV 4.1%) BITTER
A malt-forward 'heavy', fruity with a slight bitterness not found in a traditional 80/-.
Bill's Beer (ABV 4.2%) PALE
Session IPA, a pale, full-flavoured ale with zesty fruits and a clean finish.
Porter (ABV 4.2%) PORTER
Flavours of coffee and chocolate come through in the finish of this easily-drinkable porter.
Stout (ABV 5%) STOUT
Braw (ABV 5.2%) PALE
Enticing citrus and tropical notes in the aroma of this juicy, refreshing golden ale.
IPA (ABV 6%) IPA

Crossed Anchors

▤ c/o Grapevine, 2 Victoria Road, Exmouth, Devon, EX8 1DL
☎ **(01395) 222208** ☎ **07843 577608**
⊕ **crossedanchors.co.uk**

⊗ Crossed Anchors was established in 2015. In 2016 a six-barrel plant became operational in the old stables of the Grapevine in Exmouth town centre. Beers are available across Devon and the South-west, as well as in the Grapevine. ‼🍴◆

Crosspool Alemakers Society

c/o 442 Manchester Road, Sheffield, South Yorkshire, S10 5DR ✉ **crosspoolalemakers@gmail.com**

⊗ Crosspool Ale Makers Society began brewing in 2019, taking over premises from Hopscotch Craft brewery. Spare capacity is used at Little Mesters (qv) in Sheffield. A small range of core beers and some specials, usually named with a local theme, are produced. Some beer is supplied in cans to local outlets. ◆LIVE V

Sandygate (ABV 3.6%) BITTER
Crosspale (ABV 4%) PALE

Crouch Vale SIBA

23 Haltwhistle Road, South Woodham Ferrers, Essex, CM3 5ZA
☎ **(01245) 322744** ⊕ **crouchvale.co.uk**

⊗ Founded in 1981 by two CAMRA enthusiasts, Crouch Vale is well established as a major player in Essex brewing, having moved to larger premises in 2006. The company is also a major wholesaler of cask ale from other independent breweries, which it supplies to more than 100 outlets, as well as beer festivals throughout the region. A tap room (Tap Room 19) is on-site. One tied house, the Queen's Head in Chelmsford, is owned. !! ⬛ ♦ LIVE 🖗

Blackwater Mild (ABV 3.7%) MILD
A dark bitter rather than a true mild. Roasty and very bitter towards the end.
Essex Boys Best Bitter (ABV 3.8%) BITTER
Brewers Gold (ABV 4%) PALE
Pale gold with a striking citrus nose. Sweet fruit and bitter hops are well matched throughout.
Yakima Gold (ABV 4.2%) GOLD

Crown

🍺 Crown, Green End, Little Staughton, Bedfordshire, MK44 2BU
☎ (01234) 376260 ⊕ thecrownstaughton.com

Brewing began in 2017 in a building behind the Crown public house in Little Staughton. The brewery is owned and run by the landlord of the Crown with the beers only being produced for the pub and local events. ♦

Crown Brewhouse

🍺 The Square, Elford, Staffordshire, B79 9DB
☎ (01827) 383602 ✉ bluecatsup@hotmail.com

A one-barrel plant, established in 2017, housed in a former store room attached to the Crown pub. Beers are brewed almost exclusively for the pub, but can be found at local beer festivals and events.

Crumbs

See Goddards

CTZN (NEW)

477 Upper Richmond Road West, East Sheen, London, SW14 7PU
☎ (020) 8109 5316 ⊕ ctznbrew.com

Originally Kew brewery, after being bought and refurbished, it started to brew again in 2021 as CTZN Brew. The beers are available from its new bar in Twickenham, where an on-site brewery is also planned. No real ale.

Cuillin SIBA

🍺 Sligachan Hotel, Sligachan, Carbost, Isle of Skye, IV47 8SW ☎ 07795 250808 ⊕ cuillinbrewery.com

☺The five-barrel brewery opened in 2004 and is situated in central Skye at the foot of the Cuillin mountains. The water from the Cuillins provides a distinctive colour and taste to the ales. Beers are available on-site at the Sligachan Hotel and at several other pubs and hotels on the Isle of Skye. The brewery is open by appointment only in winter (November-March). !!♦

Cullach

50 Princes Street, Perth, PH2 8LJ ☎ 07929 325890 ⊕ cullachbrewing.co.uk

⊗ The brewery opened in 2019 in an industrial unit on the outskirts of Perth. It moved into a retail unit closer to the town centre allowing a welcoming tap room to be set up for direct on-site sales. All draught beers are real ale in KeyKeg. Some cans are also produced. 🛒 LIVE 🖗

Cullercoats SIBA

Westfield Court, 19 Maurice Road Industrial Estate, Wallsend, Tyne & Wear, NE28 6BY ☎ 07895 692881 ⊕ cullercoatsbrewery.co.uk

☺Established in 2011, brewing takes place twice a week. The brewery champions English hops. ♦

Shuggy Boat Blonde (ABV 3.8%) BLOND
Lovely Nelly (ABV 3.9%) BITTER
Polly Donkin Oatmeal Stout (ABV 4.2%) STOUT
Jack the Devil (ABV 4.5%) BITTER
Grace Darling Gold (ABV 5%) BITTER

Cumberland

See Great Corby

Cumbrian SIBA

Old Hall Brewery, Hawkshead, Cumbria, LA22 0QF
☎ (01539) 436436 ⊕ cumbrianales.com

☺First established in 2003, the brewery is located in an idyllic position in a renovated barn on the shores of Esthwaite Water. The success of Loweswater Gold has meant the brewery is thriving. !!♦

Esthwaite Bitter (ABV 3.8%) PALE
Robust, refreshing bitter with plenty of hops, lasting well into the finish.
Langdale (ABV 4%) GOLD
Fresh grapefruit aromas with hoppy, fruity flavours and crisp, long, hop finish, make for a well-balanced beer.
Grasmoor Dark Ale (ABV 4.3%) MILD
Dark fruity beer with complex character and roast nutty tones leading to a short, refreshing finish.
Loweswater Gold (ABV 4.3%) PALE
A dominant fruity body develops into a light, bitter finish. A beer that belies its strength.
American Invasion (ABV 5%) BLOND
Well-balanced, gold-coloured beer with big hop impact, and long, fruity finish.

Curious

Unit 1, Victoria Road, Ashford, TN23 7HQ
☎ (01580) 763033

Office: Level 2, Civic Centre, Tannery Lane, Ashford, Kent, TN23 1PL ⊕ curiousbrewery.com

⊗ Situated next to Ashford International Railway station, this multi-million pound investment by parent company Chapel Down opened in 2019. It is a modern, state-of-the-art brewery, with a shop, tasting room (ground floor), bar and 120-seater restaurant (upstairs) featuring the Curious Brew core range and special/seasonal brews. Products are widely available in keg, bottle and can, but were previously contract brewed. Fresh unpasteurised, filtered beer from the brewery is served from tanks above the bar. Tours and tastings offered. !! 🛒 🖗

Cwm Rhondda

Fforch Farm, Cemetry Road, Treorchy, CF42 6TF
☎ (01443) 777491 ⊕ cwmrhonddaales.co.uk

Cwm Rhondda Ales is a family-run brewery, situated on a farm in the Rhondda Valleys. Brewing commenced in 2015 on a 2.5-barrel plant, using the brewery's spring water, which gives a unique taste to the ales. Brewing was suspended in 2020. The proprietors have yet to decide the future of the brewery and have not ruled out the recommencement of brewing.

Cybi SIBA

4 Bryn Annex, Williams Street, Holyhead, LL65 1RN
☎ (01407) 769651 ⊕ bragdycybi.cymru

Nanobrewery established in 2020 using a 200-litre brew kit. It produces bottle-conditioned beers for local distribution on Anglesey. LIVE

Daleside SIBA

Camwal Road, Starbeck, Harrogate, North Yorkshire, HG1 4PT
☎ (01423) 880022 ⊕ dalesidebrewery.com

☺Daleside was established in the mid-1980s, and moved to its current site at Starbeck in 1992. Daleside Brewery beers are sold to local, regional and national customers and export markets include Denmark, Sweden and Australia. ➠♦

Bitter (ABV 3.7%) BITTER
Pale brown in colour, this well-balanced, hoppy beer is complemented by fruity bitterness and a hint of sweetness, leading to a long, bitter finish.
Blonde (ABV 3.9%) BLOND
A pale golden beer with a predominantly hoppy aroma and taste, leading to a refreshing hoppy, bitter but short finish.
Old Leg Over (ABV 4.1%) BITTER
Monkey Wrench (ABV 5.3%) OLD

Dalrannoch

Unit 16, The Old Dairy, Meikleour, Perth, PH2 6FB
☎ 07481 062862 ⊕ dalrannochbrewing.co.uk

Brewing began in 2016 using a five-barrel plant.

Dancing Duck SIBA

1 John Cooper Buildings, Payne Street, Derby, DE22 3AZ
☎ (01332) 205582 ☎ 07581 122122
⊕ dancingduckbrewery.com

⊗ Dancing Duck was established in 2010 by Rachel Mathews using a 10-barrel brew plant. Its name comes from the local greeting 'ay up me duck'. The Exeter Arms in Derby is the brewery tap. ‼➠♦

Ay Up (ABV 3.9%) PALE
Waitangi (ABV 4%) PALE
Ginger Ninja (ABV 4.1%) SPECIALITY
Nice Weather (ABV 4.1%) BITTER
Back, Sack & Quack (ABV 4.2%) MILD
22 (ABV 4.3%) BITTER
DCUK (ABV 4.3%) PALE
Dark Drake (ABV 4.5%) STOUT
Waddle It Be? (ABV 4.5%) PALE
Indian Porter (ABV 5%) PORTER
Quack Me Amadeus (ABV 5%) SPECIALITY
Abduction (ABV 5.5%) IPA
Imperial Drake (ABV 6.5%) STOUT

Dancing Man

Wool House, Town Quay, Southampton, Hampshire, SO14 2AR
☎ (023) 8083 6666 ⊕ dancingmanbrewery.co.uk

⊗ Dancing Man began brewing in 2011 in the Platform Tavern. In 2015 the brewery moved to the historic Wool House, the only surviving freestanding medieval building in Southampton, in order to expand and include an on-site bar and restaurant. One-off and rare brews are available throughout the year. ‼➠♦LIVE V✦

Bone Dry (ABV 3.4%) GOLD
Old Fashioned (ABV 3.9%) BITTER
Jesus Hairdo (ABV 4%) PALE
Vagrant (ABV 4.5%) PALE
Big Casino (ABV 5.7%) IPA

Dancing Men

⊟ Hill House Inn, The Hill, Happisburgh, Norfolk, NR12 0PW
☎ (01692) 650004 ☎ 07818 038768
⊕ hillhouseinn.co.uk

⊗ Brewing began in 2014 at the 16th century Hill House Inn on Happisburgh's fast-eroding clifftop. The microbrewery is named in honour of a Sherlock Holmes story by Sir Arthur Conan Doyle after he visited the pub in 1903. The five-barrel plant was acquired from Bees Brewery after its partial destruction during the tidal surge events in Walcott in 2013. New recipes have been crafted using exclusive hops and barley including locally-grown Norfolk varieties. ‼♦

Dark Horse SIBA

Coonlands Laithe, Hetton, Nr. Skipton, North Yorkshire, BD23 6LY
☎ (01756) 730555 ⊕ darkhorsebrewery.co.uk

☺Dark Horse began brewing in 2008. The brewery is based in an old hay barn within the Yorkshire Dales National Park. Around 50 outlets are supplied direct.

Craven Bitter (ABV 3.8%) BITTER
Well-balanced bitter with biscuity malt and fruit on the nose continuing into the taste. Bitterness increases in the finish.
Blonde Beauty (ABV 3.9%) GOLD
Hetton Pale Ale (ABV 4.2%) PALE
Earthy bitterness on the palate overlaying a malty base and a spicy citrus character.
Night Jar (ABV 4.2%) BITTER
A malty, fruity bitter in aroma and taste. Caramel and dark fruits lace the finish

Dark Revolution

Unit 3-5, Lancaster Road, Salisbury, Wiltshire, SP4 6FB
☎ (01722) 326993 ⊕ darkrevolution.co.uk

Dark Revolution started commercial brewing in 2015 using a one-barrel plant; the owner had been homebrewing for the previous decade. It upgraded to a 15-barrel brew plant in 2017, with more fermenting vessels added in 2019, retaining the smaller plant for trial brews and short runs. A canning line is now operational. An on-site taproom is open Fridays and Saturdays. Barrel-aging is a speciality. ➠♦LIVE V✦

Orbital (ABV 3.5%) BLOND
So.LA (ABV 4.5%) PALE
A cloudy, light, naturally-carbonated, West Coast-style, pale ale that surprises the nose and the palate with citrus hoppy freshness that fades to dry, citrus, floral finish.
Velveteen (ABV 4.8%) STOUT
A smooth, rich, black stout, served unfined. Noticeable malt and roast in the taste with balanced bitterness through to the finish.
Sonic (ABV 4.9%) PALE
A citrus, hop-forward, pale, unfined, premium ale with pronounced grapefruit taste from the American hops used.

Dark Star

22 Star Road, Partridge Green, West Sussex, RH13 8RA

☎ (01403) 713085 ⊕ darkstarbrewing.co.uk

⊠ The Dark Star Brewing Co is named after a Grateful Dead song and was established in the cellar of the Evening Star in Brighton back in 1994, moving to its current home in Partridge Green in 2010. Purchased by Fuller's in 2018 and subsequently sold to Asahi in 2019, the 45-barrel plant produces a wide range of beers.
‼ ➤ ♦ LIVE

The Art of Darkness (ABV 3.5%) BITTER
Hophead (ABV 3.8%) BLOND
A golden-coloured bitter with a fruity/hoppy aroma and a citrus/bitter taste and aftertaste. Flavours remain strong to the end.
Partridge Best Bitter (ABV 4%) BITTER
Espresso (ABV 4.2%) SPECIALITY
American Pale Ale (ABV 4.7%) PALE
Dark Star Original (ABV 5%) OLD
Festival (ABV 5%) BITTER
Revelation (ABV 5.7%) IPA

Dark Tribe

🍺 Dog and Gun, High Street, East Butterwick, Lincolnshire, DN17 3AJ
☎ (01724) 782324 ⊕ darktribe.co.uk

☺ Situated on the banks of the River Trent in the Dog & Gun pub, this 2.5-barrel brewing plant produces beers for the pub and local outlets. The award-winning brewery has been established since 1996. A range of one-off beers is produced throughout the year. ‼ ♦

Darkland

Unit 4C, Ladyship Business Park, Mill Lane, Halifax, West Yorkshire, HX3 6TA
☎ (01422) 320100 ⊕ darklandbrewery.co.uk

☺ Founded in 2018, Darkland is a microbrewery hidden away in a corner of an industrial estate. Regular and seasonal beers are named after ancient runes and are available at the brewery tap, Pallet Bar, Boothtown. Beers can be ordered online in can, bottle and bag-in-box. V

Bohemian Raspberry (ABV 3.8%) SPECIALITY
Reddish, amber-coloured, fruit ale. Subtle flavours of malt and raspberries develop in the mouth and become more intense in the aftertaste.
Othala (ABV 3.8%) BITTER
Isa (ABV 4%) BLOND
A pale ale with a hoppy citrus aroma. It is a smooth-tasting beer with a long, dry, bitter finish.
Wolfenbrau (ABV 4%) BITTER
A malty, traditional bitter with a subtle roast flavour. Sweet fruit quickly develops into a strong bitter aftertaste filling the mouth with depth of flavour.
Niflheim (ABV 4.2%) PALE
Drakkar (ABV 4.5%) PORTER
A dark and rich ale with complex, toasted, rich malt flavours. It has a robust and bitter farewell.
Cat's Eyes (ABV 4.8%) STOUT
A black, velvety, well-balanced oatmeal stout. Plenty of roast and nutty flavours develop on the palate. The long aftertaste retains complexity and is surprisingly refreshing.
Jera (ABV 5%) PALE
Refreshing well-balanced, hoppy, strong pale ale. Crisp and fruity with a developing bitter finish.

Dartford Wobbler

St Margaret's Farm, St Margaret's Road, South Darenth, Kent, DA4 9LB

☎ (01322) 866233 ⊕ dartfordwobbler.com

☺ John and Miriam Millis started with a 0.5-barrel plant at their home in Gravesend. Demand outstripped the facility and the brewery moved in 2003 to its current location – a former farm cold store – using a 10-barrel plant. It supplies around 40 outlets within a 50-mile radius. ♦ LIVE

Curiously Dark (ABV 3.6%) MILD
Guinea Guzzler (ABV 3.7%) MILD
Peddlars Best (ABV 4%) BITTER
Golden Wobbler (ABV 4.1%) GOLD
Dartford Wobbler (ABV 4.3%) BITTER
Thieves & Fakirs (ABV 4.3%) PORTER
Penny Red (ABV 4.4%) RED
Country Wobbler (ABV 4.8%) BITTER

Dartmoor SIBA

The Brewery, Station Road, Princetown, Devon, PL20 6QX
☎ (01822) 890789 ⊕ dartmoorbrewery.co.uk

⊠ Formerly named Princetown, Dartmoor Brewery was established in 1994. It is the highest brewery in England at 1,465 feet above sea level. In 2005 the brewery moved locally to a new, purpose-built building. In both 2012 and 2013 capacity was increased. In 2017 a further extension was built which now gives a brewing capacity of 540 barrels. The brewery is a traditional ale producer and all beer is brewed using English Malt. ‼ ➤ ♦

Best (ABV 3.7%) BITTER
IPA (ABV 4%) PALE
There is a flowery hop aroma and taste with a bitter aftertaste to this full-bodied, amber-coloured beer.
Dragon's Breath (ABV 4.4%) SPECIALITY
Sweet, winter warmer, best bitter. Full-bodied, sweet, fruity with treacle hints. Malt, roast and caramel from start to finish.
Legend (ABV 4.4%) BITTER
Complex beer full of aromas and flavours. Malt and caramel dominate balanced in an aftertaste of bitter hops. Well-rounded.
Jail Ale (ABV 4.8%) BITTER
Stronger session ale with complex notes dominated by malty sweet bitterness. Well-rounded caramel and fruit with a pleasant aftertaste.

Darwin SIBA

1 West Quay Court, Sunderland Enterprise Park, Sunderland, SR5 2TE
☎ (0191) 549 9450 ⊕ darwinbrewery.com

☺ Established in 1994, Darwin is based in purpose-built premises in Sunderland with a 3.5-barrel brew plant. A range of established Darwin beers are produced frequently, with core beers and seasonal offerings available around the North East. Some beers produced are based on analysis of historic recipes. Darwin Brewery supports students on brewing courses at sister company, Brewlab, who produce many unique specialist and international beers. ‼ ♦ LIVE

Expedition (ABV 3.8%) PALE
Evolution (ABV 4%) BITTER
Beagle Blonde (ABV 4.1%) BLOND
Rolling Hitch (ABV 5.2%) PALE
Galapagos (ABV 6%) STOUT

Davenports SIBA

Unit 5, Empire House, 11 New Street, Smethwick, West Midlands, B66 2AJ

☎ (0121) 565 5622
✉ info@davenportsbrewery.co.uk

☺Davenports brewery occupies part of a distribution warehouse in an industrial unit in Smethwick on the outskirts of Birmingham. The 7.5-barrel plant produces a selection of beers under the Davenports brand with some occasional beers from the former Highgate brewery of Walsall. ♦

Mild (ABV 3.5%) MILD
Gold (ABV 3.9%) PALE
Original Bitter (ABV 4.2%) BITTER
IPA (ABV 4.4%) PALE

Dawkins SIBA

Unit 2, Lawnwood Industrial Units, Lawnwood Road, Easton, Bristol, BS5 0EF
☎ (0117) 955 9503 ⊕ dawkinsgeorgesltd.selz.com

⊗ The established Dawkins Taverns group of independent Bristol pubs bought the Somerset-based Matthews Brewery in 2009. New premises in Easton, Bristol, opened in 2015 with a 20-barrel plant. The brewery distributes to its own five pubs and directly to another 80 outlets in the area. A sister company was set up in Edinburgh in 2017, reviving the long-defunct Steel Coulson brewing name for a bar in Leith. ‼ ▦ ♦ LIVE ✦

Bristol Blonde (ABV 3.8%) BLOND
Pale yellow-coloured, golden ale. Citrus aroma. Refreshing lemon taste with grassiness, which fades to astringent bitterness.
Bristol Best (ABV 4%) BITTER
Copper-coloured bitter with malty aroma and taste. Hints of apple. Astringent aftertaste.
Bristol Gold (ABV 4.4%) GOLD
Light hop aroma, pale malt with hops, spice and a hint of apple on the palate before a crisp bitter finish.
Easton IPA (ABV 4.4%) PALE
Hazy, golden yellow, unfined ale. Hop and ripe apple aroma. Slightly sour citrus on the palate. Dry and bitter aftertaste.
Foresters Black (ABV 4.8%) STOUT
Resolution IPA (ABV 5%) PALE
Naturally hazy, golden yellow with aromas of tropical fruit. Flavours of grapefruit and lemon continue into the bitter finish.

De Vossen (NEW)

Fox House, Bury Road, Stanningfield, Suffolk, IP29 4RU

Mike Grimmer, a former homebrewer, started brewing as a part-time business in 2020. He still brews at home with a maximum capacity of 100-litres per brew. The beers are Belgian-style, using continental hops and malt. All beer is bottled with some variation in ABV.

Dead End Brew Machine

Office: Flat 1-2, 10 Lawrence Street, Glasgow, G11 5HQ ⊕ deadendbrewmachine.com

Dead End Brew Machine produce small batch, artisinal beers specialising in brettanomyces and saccharomycetes blends, augmented with fruit and spices. Beers are available in bottle and can. ♦ LIVE

Dead Parrot

44 Garden Street, Sheffield, South Yorkshire, S1 4BJ

Established in 2018. An on-site taproom is planned.

Deeply Vale

Unit 25, Peel Industrial Estate, Chamberhall Street, Bury, BL9 0LU ☎ 07749 856043
⊕ deeplyvalebrewery.com

☺Deeply Vale is a family-run business established in 2012. The brewery's name immortalises the Deeply Vale area near Bury, famed for legendary 1970s music festivals. The range of traditional beers with a modern twist produced from the six-barrel plant are distributed largely across North West England and West Yorkshire. ♦

DV US (ABV 3.8%) GOLD
Equilibrium (ABV 3.8%) GOLD
Crisp and refreshing bitter with a pale malt flavour and clean bitter hops. Dry finish with lingering hops.
Hop (ABV 3.8%) BITTER
Citra Storm (ABV 4%) PALE
Optimum (ABV 4.2%) GOLD
DV8 (ABV 4.8%) STOUT
Supple, fruity sweetness accompanying luscious coffee roast. Clean, gentle malt finish, with lingering sweetness. Coffee and raisin aroma.
Freebird (ABV 5.2%) PALE

Deeside

The Steading, Lochton of Leys, Banchory, AB31 5QB
☎ (01330) 825598 ⊕ deesidebrewery.co.uk

First established in 2005, a change of ownership and location in 2012 led to substantial growth in the Scottish retail sector as well as export markets in Europe, USA, the Middle East and Asia, while maintaining its independent status. V

Macbeth (ABV 4.1%) BITTER

Delphic

26 The Martins, Thatcham, Berkshire, RG19 4FD
☎ 07595 386568 ⊕ delphicbrewing.com

Thatcham's first craft brewery, established in 2019 by head brewer Tom Broadbank. It is a 2.5-barrel plant brewing many seasonal beers destined for cask and keg. Bottles and cans are available too, with draught beer being kept local, and small pack beer available nationwide.

Level Crossing (ABV 4.2%) BITTER
World's End (ABV 4.6%) PALE

Denbigh

Crown Workshop, Crown Lane, Denbigh, LL16 3SY
☎ (01745) 817021 ☎ 07850 687701
⊕ bragdybinbych.co.uk

Brewing commenced in 2012 at the rear of the Hope & Anchor pub, relocating in 2015 to a dedicated brew house in the town. Output is cask and bottle in equal proportions. A tied micro pub, Y-Goron-Fach, is located next to the brewery. ♦ LIVE

Dent SIBA

Hollins, Cowgill, Dent, Cumbria, LA10 5TQ
☎ (01539) 625326 ⊕ dentbrewery.co.uk

☺Dent was set up in 1990 in a converted barn next to a former farmhouse in the Yorkshire Dales National Park. In 2005 the brewery was completely refurbished and capacity expanded. One pub is owned. More than 150 outlets are supplied direct. ‼ ▦ ♦

Golden Fleece (ABV 3.7%) BLOND
Light, hoppy and fruity, with a bitter aftertaste.

Aviator (ABV 4%) BITTER
This amber ale is characterised by citrus, caramel and hop flavours that evolve into a bitter finish.
Dales Way IPA (ABV 4%) PALE
Rambrau (ABV 4.5%) SPECIALITY
Ramsbottom Strong Ale (ABV 4.5%) BITTER
A well-balanced, malty best bitter.
Kamikaze (ABV 5%) PALE
Hops and fruit dominate this full-bodied, golden, strong bitter, with a dry bitterness growing in the aftertaste.
T'owd Tup (ABV 6%) STOUT
A rich, full-flavoured, strong stout with a coffee aroma. The dominant roast character is balanced by a warming sweetness and a raisiny, fruitcake taste that lingers on into the finish.

Derby SIBA

Masons Place Business Park, Nottingham Road, Derby, DE21 6AQ
☎ (01332) 365366 ☎ 07887 556788
⊕ derbybrewing.co.uk

A family-run microbrewery, established in 2004 in the old Masons paintworks varnish shed by Trevor Harris, founder and former brewer at the Brunswick Inn, Derby (qv). The business has grown over the years and four venues are now owned across Derbyshire and Staffordshire. More than 400 outlets are supplied including major retailers. In addition to the core range there are at least three new beers each month. !! ⬛ ♦

Hop Till You Drop (ABV 3.9%) GOLD
Triple Hop (ABV 4.1%) PALE
Business As Usual (ABV 4.4%) BITTER
Double Mash (ABV 4.6%) RED
Penny's Porter (ABV 4.6%) PORTER
Dashingly Dark (ABV 4.8%) STOUT
Mercia IPA (ABV 5%) PALE
Quintessential (ABV 5.8%) OLD

Derwent

Units 2a-2c, Station Road Industrial Estate, Silloth, Cumbria, CA7 4AG
☎ (01697) 331522 ⊕ derwentbrewery.co.uk

☺Derwent was set up in 1996 in Cockermouth and moved to Silloth in 1998. Owners Mark and Allie Johnston bought the brewery in 2013. ♦

Cote Light (ABV 3.6%) PALE
Carlisle State Bitter (ABV 3.7%) BITTER
Malty, biscuity, hoppy beer with a gold colour.
W&M Mild (ABV 3.7%) MILD
Parsons Pledge (ABV 4%) BITTER
Amber ale with a biscuity tang and a slightly fruity finish.
Blonde (ABV 4.2%) BLOND
Hudson Bay (ABV 4.3%) PALE
Reaper (ABV 4.3%) RED
Mutineer (ABV 4.4%) BITTER
W&M Pale Ale (ABV 4.4%) PALE
A sweet, fruity, hoppy beer with a bitter finish.
Tommy's Leg (ABV 4.5%) BITTER
Marshall Port Stout (ABV 5.2%) SPECIALITY

Deviant & Dandy SIBA

Arch 184, Nursery Road, Hackney, London, E9 6PB
⊕ deviantanddandy.com

Initially cuckoo-brewed at Enfield Brewery for the Off Broadway bar in London Fields, Deviant & Dandy started brewing at its current premises in 2018. Beer is available in bars and bottle shops and at the on-site taproom, open at the weekend. No real ale. ♦

Devil's Dyke

See Arran

Devil's Pleasure (NEW)

Higher Sigford Farm, Sigford, TQ12 6LD ☎ 07977 148006 ⊕ thedevilspleasure.com

New brewery founded on the edge of Dartmoor National Park, near Newton Abbot, in 2020. It specialises in brewing punchy bold craft beers which are unfiltered and naturally hazy.

Devilstone (NEW)

Unit 2d, Riverside Industrial Estate, Langley Park, DH7 9TT
☎ (0191) 375 9615 ⊕ devilstonebrewing.com

Brewing began in 2020 in an industrial unit in Langley Park situated on the outskirts of the historic city of Durham.

Devon

🍺 **Mansfield Arms, 7 Main Street, Sauchie, FK10 3JR**
☎ (01259) 722020 ⊕ devonales.com

☺Named after the nearby River Devon and the former Devon colliery, the brewery was established in 1992 and run by the Gibson family to supply their two pubs, the Mansfield Arms, and the Inn at Muckhart. Beer is also available to the free trade. !!

Devon Earth SIBA

Buckfastleigh, Devon ☎ 07927 397871

Office: 7 Fernham Terrace, Torquay Road, Paignton, TQ3 2AQ ✉ info@devonearthbrewery.co.uk

⊗ Devon Earth brewery is located on the banks of the River Dart on the edge of Dartmoor and is run on a part-time basis. The brewery is proud to support local charities and supplies local and national beer festivals and free houses. ♦

Devon Earth (ABV 4.2%) GOLD
Grounded (ABV 4.7%) BITTER
Lost in the Woods (ABV 5.2%) PORTER

Devon's Own

See Clearwater

DEYA SIBA

Unit 27, Lansdown Industrial Estate, Gloucester Road, Cheltenham, Gloucestershire, GL51 8PL
☎ (01242) 269189 ⊕ deyabrewing.com

DEYA Brewing Company was established in 2016. It brews innovative, hop-forward beers, all of which are unfiltered, unfined and unpasteurised, and available in keg and cans, with occasional casks. It has recently expanded into a new 25,000 sq ft premises with a bespoke 40-hectolitre four vessel brewhouse to significantly increase capacity. A new taproom has also been opened. ⬛ ♦

Dhillon's SIBA

14a Hales Industrial Estate, Rowleys Green Lane, Longford, West Midlands, CV6 6AL
☎ (024) 7666 7413 ⊕ dhillonsbrewery.com

Established in 2014 as Lion Heart and relaunched as Dhillon's in 2015 with a new range of beers. The main focus is on craft bottled and canned beers but cask ales are also brewed. The brewery tap is open Friday evenings and before rugby and football matches at the nearby Coventry Building Society Arena. **!! ♦ V ✦**

Bright Eyes GPA (ABV 3.8%) PALE
Fair Lady (ABV 4.5%) PALE
The Ambler Gambler (ABV 4.5%) GOLD
Red Rebel IPA (ABV 6.2%) IPA

Dig

43 River Street, Digbeth, Birmingham, B5 5SA
☎ **(0121) 773 2111 ⊕ digbrewco.com**

Dig Brew Company is a craft brewing project founded by Oliver Webb and Peter Towler of Mad O'Rourkes Pie Factory. The brewery and taproom is housed within a repurposed industrial unit in Digbeth, Birmingham. Beers available throughout the area. Most also available in cans and bottles for the take home trade.

Mad O'Rourkes Lump Hammer Bitter (ABV 3.6%) BITTER
9th July (ABV 4%) BITTER
Mad O'Rourke's Lump Hammer Gold (ABV 4.2%) GOLD
Space is the Place (ABV 4.5%) PALE
Mad O'Rourke's Sledge Hammer IPA (ABV 5.6%) BITTER

Digfield SIBA

Lilford Lodge Farm, Barnwell, Northamptonshire, PE8 5SA
☎ **(01832) 273954 ⊕ digfield-ales.co.uk**

⊠ Digfield Ales started brewing in 2005 and has continually expanded brewing capacity to keep up with demand. In 2012 they moved to a larger premises near Barnwell, where a reed bed was installed and the brewhouse was equiped with a new 15-barrel plant. More than 40 free houses are supplied. ♦

Fools Nook (ABV 3.8%) GOLD
The floral aroma, dominated by lavender and honey, belies the hoppy bitterness that comes through in the taste of this golden ale. A fruity balance lasts.
Chiffchaff (ABV 3.9%) GOLD
An amber-gold, pale ale with a distinct hoppy aroma.
Barnwell Bitter (ABV 4%) BITTER
A fruity aroma introduces a beer in which sharp bitterness is balanced by dry, biscuity malt.
Old Crow Porter (ABV 4.3%) PORTER
A rich, full-bodied porter with a balanced, roasted malt finish.
Shacklebush (ABV 4.5%) BITTER
This amber brew begins with a balance of malt and hop on the nose which develops on the palate, complemented by a mounting bitterness. Good, dry finish with lingering malt notes.
Mad Monk (ABV 4.8%) BITTER
Fruity beer with bitter, earthy hops in evidence.

Distortion

647 Portslade Road, Battersea, London, SW8 3DH
☎ **07557 307452 ⊕ distortionbrewing.co.uk**

Starting in the founder's garage in South London, the brewery was installed in a railway arch in 2020. The keg range is sold directly from serving tanks in the taproom. No real ale. ✦

Docks SIBA

The Church, King Edward Street, Grimsby, DN31 3JD

☎ **(01472) 289795 ⊕ docksbeers.com**

Brewing began in 2018 using a 15-barrel plant in a converted Edwardian Church in Grimsby. The brewery was originally named Axholme Brewing Co, with beers brewed under that name.

Brewed under the Axholme Brewing Co name:
Magnitude (ABV 3.9%) PALE
Hard Graft (ABV 4%) PALE
Cleethorpes Pale Ale (ABV 4.2%) SPECIALITY
Lightning Pale Ale (ABV 4.3%) PALE
Graveyard Shift (ABV 4.5%) STOUT
Never Say Die (ABV 6%) IPA
Special Reserve (ABV 7.2%) STRONG

Dog & Rabbit

▤ **Dog & Rabbit Micro Brew Pub, 36 Park View, Whitley Bay, Tyne & Wear, NE26 2TH** ☎ **07944 552716 ⊕ dogandrabbitbrewery.co.uk**

The Dog & Rabbit Brewery was established in 2015 and relocated to its current premises as a small one-barrel micro brewpub in 2016. **LIVE**

Dog Falls SIBA

Scaniport, IV2 6DL ⊕ dogfallsbrewing.com

Microbrewery founded by Bob Masson in 2019, Dog Falls brew modern interpretations of international beer styles. Beers are unfined and unfiltered, available mainly in can.

Dog's Grandad (NEW)

Arch 550, Brixton Station Road, Brixton, London, SW9 8PF ⊕ dogsgrandadbrewery.co.uk

Initially aiming to open in early 2020, the pandemic and paperwork delayed the project until later in the year. After occupying the railway arch before Christmas, the first brew was done in early 2021. No real ale. ✦

Dog's Window

8 Nant-Yr-Adar, Llangewydd Court, Bridgend, CF31 4TY ☎ **07929 292930**
⊕ **dogswindowbrewery.com**

Dog's Window is a small batch brewery which started production in 2018, producing a range of craft beers to its own recipes. It has a core range of eight beers with an ever-changing list of limited editions under the banner of the Experimental Series. The mainstay of production is bottled beers, with the occasional keg. The brewery can sell bottles direct to the public by appointment (see website). ⊨ ♦ **LIVE**

Dolphin

8 Corby Close, Woodley, Berkshire, RG5 4TL
⊕ **dolphinbrewery.co.uk**

A 130-litre brewery operating on a small scale from the garage of one of the brewers' parents, producing bottled beers and occasional KeyKeg. It specialises in niche styles; sours, gose, saison and porters.

Dominion

c/o Red Fox Brewery, Upp Hall Farm, Salmons Lane, Coggeshall, Essex, CO6 1RY

Office: Queen Street Brewhouse, Colchester, CO1 2PG
⊕ **dominionbrewerycompany.com**

⊠ Dominion Brewery was established in 2012 by Andy Skene. He was renting the premises and Pitfield brand names from the founder of Pitfield, Martin Kemp. In 2018

THE BREWERIES

Dominion Brewery moved and is now using spare capacity at Red Fox Brewery (qv). LIVE V

Pitfield Shoreditch Stout (ABV 4%) STOUT
Woodbine Racer (ABV 4.2%) GOLD
Woodbine Racer Turbo (ABV 6.2%) BITTER
Yukon Gold (ABV 9.7%) BARLEY
Mad Trappiste (ABV 10%) SPECIALITY

Contract brewed for Billericay Brewery:
A Mild With No Name (ABV 5.5%) MILD

Don Valley

The Old Airfield, Belton Road, Sandtoft, Lincolnshire, DN8 5SX
☎ (01709) 580254 ☎ 07951 212722
⊕ donvalleybrewery.co.uk

😊The brewery, established in 2016, changed ownership in 2018. It moved in 2019 to a new site in Sandtoft in Lincolnshire with new brewing equipment, doubling the capacity. A canning line was installed in 2020. ♦

Bit o' That (ABV 4%) BITTER
Atomic Blonde (ABV 4.3%) BLOND
Gongoozler (ABV 4.5%) STOUT
Go Your Own Way (ABV 5%) GOLD

Doncaster SIBA

7 Young Street, Doncaster, South Yorkshire, DN1 3EL
☎ (01302) 376436 ☎ 07921 970941
⊕ doncasterbrewery.co.uk

😊Established in 2012 and initially based at an industrial unit in Kirk Sandall, Doncaster, the brewery moved to new premises in 2014 using a 15-barrel plant, and opened a micropub taproom. The brewer frequently trials new recipes for beers. ♦LIVE ♦

Sand House (ABV 3.8%) BITTER
Cheswold (ABV 4.2%) BITTER

Donkeystone

Units A-D, Wellington Industrial Estate, Wellington Road, Greenfield, OL3 7AG
☎ (01457) 238710 ⊕ donkeystonebrewing.co.uk

😊Donkeystone started as a 10-barrel brewery in 2017 at the edge of the Peak District National Park featuring an on-site brewery tap and gin distillery. Brewer Thomas Phelan uses a custom-built stainless steel plant supplied by Oban Ales and recently expanded. It has a small kit for experimental brews and its own canning line. The brewery relocated to new premises in 2021. !! ♦♦

Ferris Muler (ABV 3.7%) PALE
Hoppinsesh (ABV 3.7%) PALE
Bad Ass Blonde (ABV 3.8%) GOLD
Floral hop aroma and a balanced, fruity hop flavour.
Modern Bitter (ABV 3.8%) BITTER
Cotton Clouds Craft Ale (ABV 4%) PALE
Neddy (ABV 4.9%) STOUT
Javanilla (ABV 5%) SPECIALITY
Kaihe (ABV 5%) BITTER
Madagaska (ABV 5%) SPECIALITY
Light-bodied stout. Moderate bitterness with vanilla flavour.

Donnington IFBB

Upper Swell, Stow-on-the-Wold, Gloucestershire, GL54 1EP
☎ (01451) 830603 ⊕ donnington-brewery.com

Thomas Arkell bought a 13th century watermill in 1827 and began brewing on-site in 1865. The waterwheel is still in use. Thomas's descendant Claude owned and ran the brewery until his death in 2007, supplying 20 outlets direct. It has now passed to Claude's cousin, James Arkell, also of Arkells Brewery, Swindon (qv). ⏴LIVE

BB (ABV 3.6%) BITTER
A pleasant, amber bitter with a slight hop aroma, a good balance of malt and hops in the mouth and a bitter aftertaste.
Donnington Gold (ABV 4%) GOLD
SBA (ABV 4.4%) BITTER
Malt dominates over bitterness in the subtle flavour of this premium bitter, which has a hint of fruit and a dry, malty finish.

Donzoko

Office: Brougham Terrace, Hartlepool, County Durham
☎ (TS24 8EY) 07463 863647 ⊕ donzoko.org

Donzoko Brewing Company, founded by Reece Hugill in 2017, takes its inspiration and influences from Germany and translates this beer tradition, combined with techniques from modern UK and US craft brewing, into its beers. It is a cuckoo brewery that has teamed up with Gipsy Hill (qv) to produce its flagship lager in London. Other beers are brewed at various breweries in the North East. No real ale.

Dopey Dick

Skeoge Industrial Estate, Derry, BT48 8SE
☎ (028) 7141 8920

Office: 4 Custom House St, Derry, BT48 6AA
⊕ dopeydick.co.uk

A microbrewery founded by the proprietors of the Grand Central Bar in Derry. Beers are contract brewed.

Dorking SIBA

Aldhurst Farm, Temple Lane, Capel, Surrey, RH5 5HJ
☎ (01306) 877988 ⊕ dorkingbrewery.com

⊠ Dorking started brewing in 2008 at premises in Dorking. In 2017 production moved to a new, larger site in Capel with a 30-barrel brew plant capable of producing 35,000 pints per week. Beers can be found in Surrey, West Sussex and South London. !!⏴♦♦

Surrey XPA (ABV 3.8%) BITTER
Washington Gold (ABV 3.8%) GOLD
Well-balanced golden ale with tangerine and peach aroma. Simcoe hops come through strongly throughout, with plenty of malt too.
Pilcrow Pale (ABV 4%) GOLD
Smokestack Lightnin' (ABV 4%) SPECIALITY
DB One (ABV 4.2%) BITTER
Hoppy best bitter with underlying orange fruit notes. Some balancing malt sweetness in the taste leads to a dry, bitter finish.
Black Noise (ABV 4.5%) PORTER
Rich, full-flavoured porter with blackberries dominating the aroma. Rounded bitterness with underlying hop character throughout with a biscuity finish.
Lunar White (ABV 4.6%) SPECIALITY
Red India (ABV 5%) RED
Buffalo Buffalo (ABV 5.1%) PALE
Dry pale ale with plenty of hops combined with a good malt presence. An immensely dry, long lasting, lip-smacking character.
Five Claw (ABV 5.1%) PALE

Dorset (DBC) SIBA

Unit 7, Hybris Business Park, Warmwell Rd, Crossways, Dorset, DT2 8BF
☎ (01305) 777515 ⊕ dbcales.com

⊠ Founded in 1996, Dorset Brewing Company started in Hope Square, Weymouth, which was once the home of the Devenish and Groves breweries. In 2010 it moved to purpose-built premises near Dorchester. Here spring water is used in its state-of-the-art brewing equipment. Beers are available in local pubs and selected outlets throughout the South West. !! ₮ ♦ ➔

Dorset Knob (ABV 3.9%) BITTER
Complex bitter ale with strong malt and fruit flavours despite its light gravity.
Jurassic (ABV 4.2%) BITTER
Clean-tasting, easy-drinking bitter. Well-balanced with lingering bitterness after moderate sweetness.
Origin (ABV 4.3%) GOLD
Durdle Door (ABV 5%) BITTER
A tawny hue and fruity aroma with a hint of pear drops and good malty undertone, joined by hops and a little roast malt in the taste. Lingering, bittersweet finish.

Double-Barrelled SIBA

Unit 20, Stadium Way, Tilehurst, Reading, Berkshire, RG30 6BX
☎ (0118) 942 8390 ⊕ doublebarrelled.co.uk

Brewing began in 2018 on a 15-barrel plant. The beer range is wide, including stouts, fruited sours, pale ales, IPAs and a lager. The majority of beers are only brewed once, with regular collaborations. A 120-litre pilot kit is used for test brews, with those beers only available at the taproom. The ever-popular taproom/shop opened in 2019. !! ₮ V ➔

Dove Street SIBA

82 St Helens Street, Ipswich, Suffolk, IP4 2LB
☎ (01473) 211270 ☎ 07880 707077
⊕ dovestreetbrewery.co.uk

⊠ Dove Street began brewing in 2011 using a 2.5-barrel plant in a garage opposite the Dove Street Inn. The pub, its sister pub and beer festivals are supplied. !!

Underwood Mild (ABV 3.2%) MILD
Gladstone Guzzler (ABV 3.6%) BLOND
Citra (ABV 3.9%) GOLD
Incredible Taste Fantastic Clarity (ABV 4%) GOLD
Dove Elder (ABV 4.1%) SPECIALITY
Apples & Pears (ABV 4.2%) PALE
Ed Porter (ABV 4.5%) PORTER
Thirsty Walker (ABV 4.6%) BITTER

Dovecote

Unit 2, Denbigh Enterprise Centre, Colomendy Industrial Estate, Denbigh, LL16 5TA
⊠ dovecote.brewery@gmail.com

⊠ Also known as Bragdy Colomendy, named after the industrial estate where it is located. Owner and head brewer Richard Green commenced brewing in 2017 on a five-barrel plant. All beers brewed are unfined and unfiltered. ₮ LIVE V

Dove Dark (ABV 3.6%) MILD
Dove Ale (ABV 4%) BITTER
Dove From Above (ABV 4.2%) PALE
Dove Down Under (ABV 4.8%) GOLD
Dove Pale (ABV 4.8%) GOLD

Dovedale

Damgate Farm, Stanshope, Derbyshire, DE6 2AD
☎ 07714 105035 ⊠ info@dovedalebrewing.co.uk

⊠ A small, independent craft brewery with a six-barrel (1,000-litre) capacity, specialising in small batch brewing, enabling it to produce a large range of different and limited edition beers. By concentrating on online sales locally and nationally, it has found new markets as well as consolidating its position as a premium local craft beer producer. Beer is available in cask, KeyKeg, bottle and minikeg. ♦ LIVE

Echo Beach (ABV 3.8%) PALE
Pale (ABV 3.8%) PALE
Stout (ABV 4.6%) STOUT
IPA (ABV 5.6%) IPA
Blonde (ABV 5.9%) BLOND

Dow Bridge

2-3 Rugby Road, Catthorpe, Leicestershire, LE17 6DA
☎ (01788) 869121 ☎ 07790 633525
⊕ dowbridgebrewery.co.uk

Dow Bridge commenced brewing in 2001 and takes its name from a local bridge where Watling Street spans the River Avon. The brewery uses English whole hops and malt with no adjuncts or additives. Seasonal and bottle-conditioned beers are also available. ₮ ♦ LIVE

Bonum Mild (ABV 3.5%) MILD
Complex, dark brown, full-flavoured mild, with strong malt and roast flavours to the fore and continuing into the aftertaste, leading to a long, satisfying finish.
Acris (ABV 3.8%) BITTER
Centurion (ABV 4%) BITTER
Legion (ABV 4.1%) GOLD
Ratae'd (ABV 4.3%) BITTER
Tawny-coloured, full-bodied beer with bitter hop flavours against a grainy background, leading to a long, bitter, dry aftertaste.
DB Dark (ABV 4.4%) MILD
Gladiator (ABV 4.5%) BITTER
Fosse Ale (ABV 4.8%) BITTER
Praetorian Porter (ABV 5%) PORTER
Onslaught (ABV 5.2%) BITTER

Downham Isle

19 Main Street, Littleport, Cambridgeshire, CB6 1PH
☎ (01353) 699695 ☎ 07732 927479
⊕ downhamislebrewery.co.uk

Downham Isle Brewery opened in 2016 in Little Downham in the north eastern Cambridgeshire fens. Brewing real and craft ales, the customer base spans the Isle of Ely, Cambridge and Dusseldorf! Artisan, small batch brewing methods are used. The brewery moved to premises in Littleport in 2021. !! ₮ ♦ LIVE V ➔

Duneham Ale (ABV 4%) BITTER
Goose Ely (ABV 4%) PALE
Nelson Blonde (ABV 4.8%) BLOND
Moturiki – Blowhole Pale Ale (ABV 5%) PALE

Downlands SIBA

Unit Z (2a), Mackley Industrial Estate, Small Dole, West Sussex, BN5 9XE
☎ (01273) 495596 ⊕ downlandsbrewery.com

⊠ A 10-barrel brewery set up in 2012 distributing beers across the south east of England. !! ♦

Root Thirteen (ABV 3.6%) GOLD
Best (ABV 4.1%) BITTER

Bramber (ABV 4.5%) BITTER
Devils Dyke Porter (ABV 5%) PORTER
Devils Dyke Salted Caramel (ABV 5%) SPECIALITY

Downton

Unit 11, Batten Road, Downton Industrial Estate,
Downton, Wiltshire, SP5 3HU
☎ (01725) 513313 ⊕ downtonbrewery.com

⊗ Downton was set up in 2003. The brewery has a 20-barrel brew length and produces around 1,500 barrels a year. Around 100 outlets are supplied direct. A range of regular beers is produced together with speciality and experimental beers. The brewery offers an off-site mobile bar service and has an online shop. A regular bar is open on Fridays and sales are available on-site.
🏃LIVE ⚘

New Forest Ale (ABV 3.8%) BITTER
An amber-coloured bitter with subtle aromas leading to good hopping on the palate. Some fruit and predominate hoppiness in the aftertaste.
Quadhop (ABV 3.9%) GOLD
Pale golden, session beer, initially hoppy on the palate with some fruit and a strong hoppiness in the aftertaste. Its all about the hops.
Elderquad (ABV 4%) SPECIALITY
Golden yellow bitter with a floral fruity aroma leading to a good, well-hopped taste with hints of elderflower. Dryish finish with good fruit and hop balance.
Honey Blonde (ABV 4.3%) SPECIALITY
Straw-coloured golden ale, easy-drinking with initial bitterness giving way to slight sweetness and a lingering, balanced aftertaste.
Nelson's Delight (ABV 4.5%) SPECIALITY
Downton Dream (ABV 4.8%) PALE
A premium pale ale with obvious East European influences. Hoppy on aroma and taste with a particularly dry finish and a hint of lemon citrus notes.
Moonstruck (ABV 5.5%) BITTER
A dark ruby-coloured premium bitter with malt and caramel in the aroma and taste which also carries notes of dried fruit and plum. A dry finish with some bitterness and lingering taste.
Chimera IPA (ABV 6.8%) IPA
Golden yellow, strong IPA with good balance of hops and fruit, slight sweetness and some malt notes, all through to the aftertaste.

Dowr Kammel

Deaconstowe, Lower Lank, St Breward, Cornwall,
PL30 4PW ☎ 07774 427635

Office: 9 Tregarne Terrace, St Austell, Cornwall,
PL25 4DD ✉ dowrkammel@btinternet.com

⊗ Brewing began in 2016. A small number of local free houses are supplied. LIVE

Blisland Gold (ABV 3.6%) BLOND
Light blond ale with strong citrus aroma. Dominant citrus and grassy hops with summer fruit sweetness. Long, bitter hop finish.
Demelza (ABV 4.2%) BITTER
Devil's Jump (ABV 4.6%) GOLD
Balanced, golden best bitter with malt and hops aroma. Assertive malt and bitterness in the mouth with smooth, zesty lemon hops.

Dragonfly

🍺 George & Dragon, 183 High Street, Acton, London,
W3 9DJ
☎ (020) 8992 3712 ⊕ georgeanddragonacton.co.uk

⊗ Dragonfly began brewing in 2014 with a Chinese-built, vertically-stacked brewing kit, installed in the back bar of the George & Dragon. After a short time in 2019 being run by Portobello, the kit is currently unused (brewing is currently suspended) but has been available for use by other breweries.

Draycott (Cambridgeshire)

Low Farm, 30 Mill Road, Buckden, Cambridgeshire,
PE19 5SS
☎ (01480) 812404 ☎ 07740 374710
⊕ draycottbrewery.co.uk

⊗ The brewery was set up by Jon and Jane Draycott in 2009, and is located in an old farm complex where they live. Focus is on bottle-conditioned beers which are available in a one-pint, traditionally-shaped bottle. Four regular beers are available, along with a cask beer brewed for the Grafham Trout pub, or to order. A seasonal ale made with local, wild hops is also produced. LIVE

Grafham Trout Bitter (ABV 3.8%) BITTER

Draycott (Derbyshire)

Ladywood Lodge Farm, Spondon Road, Dale Abbey,
Derbyshire, DE7 4PS ☎ 07834 728540
✉ draycottbrewingcompany@yahoo.co.uk

⊗ Microbrewery established in 2014, supplying local pubs and beer festivals. It relocated to new premises in 2015, which saw beer range and capacity increase. A tap house in Draycott village is also operated.

Top Of The Hops (ABV 3.8%) PALE
Lamb & Flag (ABV 4%) PORTER
Butcher's Bitter (ABV 4.2%) BITTER
California Steam Beer (ABV 4.2%) RED
Piano Man Blues (ABV 4.2%) RED
Lord Have Mercy (ABV 4.5%) SPECIALITY
Obsidian (ABV 4.5%) SPECIALITY
Tap House Tipple (ABV 4.5%) PALE
Minnesota North Star American Red Ale (ABV 4.7%) RED
Irish Red Ale (ABV 5%) RED

Drenchfoot (NEW)

Office: 65 Vicarage Road, Thetford, Norfolk, IP24 2LW
⊕ drenchfoot.co.uk

Drenchfoot is the result of a homebrew hobby gone wrong. Registered in 2019 it produces around 100 litres a week in a garden shed, supplying a growing number of pubs in and around Thetford. Pre-ordered polypins and bottles are available for sale direct to the public. ◆V

Dragon Slayer (ABV 3.6%) BITTER
Bigus Dickus (ABV 4.4%) PALE
Don't Panic (ABV 5%) IPA
To Pee or not to Pee (ABV 5.8%) IPA

Driftwood Spars SIBA

🍺 Driftwood Brewery, Trevaunance Cove, Cornwall,
TR5 0RY
☎ (01872) 552591 ⊕ driftwoodsparsbrewery.com

⊗ Established in 2000, production on the custom-built, five-barrel plant expanded with the installation of additional fermentation and conditioning capacity. Annual production now stands at 1,500 barrels. A small batch beer range named Cove is now produced.
‼️ 🏃 ◆ LIVE GF

Bawden Rocks (ABV 3.8%) BITTER

Refreshing, amber bitter. Grassy/honey aromas. Malt and citrus/resin hop taste with honey and stone fruits. Long, dry finish.

SPARS (ABV 3.8%) BITTER
Refreshing, copper session bitter with a balance of sweet malt and earthy hops, plum and orange flavours. Rising bitter finish.

Blue Hills Bitter (ABV 4%) BITTER
Pale brown, session bitter. Aroma of orange/marmalade. Peach, grapefruit and floral hop flavour. Long, bitter finish.

Bolster's Blood (ABV 5%) PORTER
Full-bodied, dark brown porter. Coal-smoke and peaty malt flavour with dark chocolate and dried fruits. Bitterness and burnt malt persist.

Lou's Brew (ABV 5%) GOLD
Golden beer laden with orange and grapefruit flavours, spice notes and some malt. Tropical fruit aromas and long-lasting tangy bitterness.

Alfie's Revenge (ABV 6.5%) STRONG
Rich, strong, red ale with dominant malt aroma and flavour. Kaleidoscope of dried and stone fruit, bittersweet flavours. Long, dry finish.

Drinkstone (NEW)

Foxhollies, Rattlesden Road, Drinkstone, Suffolk, IP30 9TL ☎ 07592 072140
✉ drinkstoneales@gmail.com

Drinkstone Ales is a 100-litre part-time nanobrewery owned by Colin Field and based in his converted garage. It commenced brewing in 2021, supplying local outlets and festivals. It concentrates on traditional cask ale using only English malt and hops.

Bitter (ABV 3.8%) BITTER
Road Apple Strong (ABV 5.2%)

Drone Valley SIBA

Unstone Industrial Complex, Main Road, Unstone, Dronfield, Derbyshire, S18 4AB ☎ 07794 277091
⊕ dronevalleybrewery.com

☺Community-owned, five-barrel brewery that began brewing commercially in 2016. All the brewing is carried out by volunteers under the supervision of qualified, experienced brewers. Profits go to local good causes. New owner members are always welcome. The brewery is open every Saturday and holds open days throughout the year. !! ▆ ♦ LIVE

Dronny Bottom Bitter (ABV 3.7%) BITTER
Gosforth Gold (ABV 4%) GOLD
Dronfield Best (ABV 4.3%) BITTER
Coal Aston Porter (ABV 4.5%) PORTER
Fanshaw Blonde (ABV 4.8%) PALE
Stubley Stout (ABV 5%) STOUT
Drone Valley IPA (ABV 5.2%) IPA
Candelriggs (ABV 5.8%) MILD
Carr Lane Black Label (ABV 6%) BITTER

Drop Bear SIBA

Gower House, Tir Y Farchnad, Gowerton, SA4 3GS

The brewery opened in 2019, specialising in low alcohol novelty bottled beers. Presently brewing is undertaken at Hambleton (qv), but some beers, especially for canning, may be produced at Boss (qv).

Drop Project (NEW) SIBA

Unit 8, Willow Business Centre, 17 Willow Lane, Mitcham, Surrey, CR4 4NX ⊕ drop-project.co.uk

Drop Project began brewing at Missing Link (qv) in Sussex with brewing commencing at the Mitcham site in 2021. Beers are mostly available in can but also keg. No real ale.

Drop The Anchor

9 East Close Farm, Lyndhurst Road, Hinton, Christchurch, Dorset, BH23 7EF ☎ 07806 789946
⊕ droptheanchorbrewery.co.uk

⊠ Neil Hodgkinson began brewing in 2017 using a 2.5-barrel plant situated in the loft area of the Christchurch Emporium. This has now relocated to Hinton. Beer is available in a number of local pubs, and a small bar and shop is situated in the brewery (open Friday-Sunday). All beers are unfined. ♦LIVE

Silent Stones (ABV 4.7%) PALE
Tucktonia (ABV 4.7%) PALE
Priest Hole Porter (ABV 4.9%) PORTER
Fusee Chain (ABV 5%) PALE

Druid

4 Dinorben Terrace, Penysarn, LL69 9YR ☎ 07766 608889 ✉ alan@druidbrewery.co.uk

A microbrewery, in the north of the Isle of Angelsey. It is fitted into an early 19th century cottage that was built to house miners working in the historic copper mines of the nearby Parys Mountain. It is also the home of the brewery owners. The beers and ciders are produced in a purpose-built brew room using the latest German and British fermenters. Bespoke beers can be supplied for special events. Brewing is currently suspended. !!LIVE

Drygate

▤ **85 Drygate, Glasgow, G4 0UT**
☎ **(0141) 212 8810** ⊕ drygate.com

Restaurant, bar and microbrewery, Drygate is a joint venture of Tennent's and Williams Bros, though operationally independent. The on-site brewery began production in 2014. A core range of keg and bottle beers is available. The brewery is also committed to cask ale, at least one ale is on at all times. !! ♦ LIVE ❧

Pale Duke (ABV 4%) BITTER
Reflex (ABV 4.2%) BITTER
Seven Peaks (ABV 5%) BITTER

Dukeries SIBA

▤ **18 Newcastle Avenue, Worksop, Nottinghamshire, S80 1ET**
☎ **(01909) 731171 ☎ 07500 119299**
⊕ dukeriesbrewery.co.uk

☺Founded in 2012, the brewery is located in the Dukeries tap premises using a five-barrel plant. Brewing capacity is restriced to three brews each week. ♦

Elsi Pale (ABV 3.6%) PALE
Blonde (ABV 3.8%) BLOND
Chapmans Map (ABV 3.9%) BITTER
A Ray of Sunshine (ABV 4.2%) GOLD
Castle Hill (ABV 4.2%) BITTER
De Lovetot (ABV 4.2%) PALE
Lime Tree Porter (ABV 4.4%) PORTER
Mining Stout (ABV 4.5%) STOUT
Bolt out of the Blue (ABV 5%) BITTER
Farmers Branch (ABV 5%) PALE
Gunsmoke (ABV 5.5%) BITTER
Bess of Hardwick (ABV 5.7%) IPA

Dun

Corrary Farm, Glen Beag, Glenelg, Kyle, IV40 8JX
☎ (01599) 522333 ∰ dunbrewing.co.uk

☺Established in 2018, this four-barrel brewery is named after the two neighbouring Iron Age brochs (forts) – Dun Telve and Dun Trodden. Using its own spring water, Soil Association-certified, 100% organic ingredients, and 100% renewable energy, the environmentally sustainable ales are unfiltered and naturally carbonated. Beers are only available locally at present. ⇟LIVE

Dunham Massey

100 Oldfield Lane, Dunham Massey, WA14 4PE
☎ (0161) 929 0663 ∰ dunhammasseybrewing.co.uk

☺Opened in 2007, Dunham Massey brews traditional North-Western ales using only English ingredients. Around 30 outlets are supplied direct, along with the brewery tap, Costello's Bar, Altrincham. A sister brewery, Lymm (qv), opened in 2013 with Costello's Bar in Stockton Heath tied to both breweries. ⇟◆LIVE

Castle Hill (ABV 3.5%) PALE
Walker's Bitter (ABV 3.5%) BITTER
Little Bollington Bitter (ABV 3.7%) BITTER
Straw-coloured, light ale with malt and citrus fruit taste and a dry, bitter finish.
Chocolate Cherry Mild (ABV 3.8%) SPECIALITY
Dunham Dark (ABV 3.8%) MILD
Dark brown beer with malty aroma. Fairly sweet, with malt, some roast, hop and fruit in the taste and finish.
Big Tree Bitter (ABV 3.9%) BITTER
Obelisk (ABV 3.9%) BLOND
Alty Ale (ABV 4%) BLOND
Dunham Milk Stout (ABV 4%) STOUT
Landlady (ABV 4%) BITTER
Dunham Stout (ABV 4.2%) STOUT
Dunham XPA (ABV 4.2%) BARLEY
Stamford Bitter (ABV 4.2%) BITTER
Deer Beer (ABV 4.5%) BITTER
Cheshire IPA (ABV 4.7%) PALE
Dunham Porter (ABV 5.2%) PORTER
East India Pale Ale (ABV 6%) IPA
Dunham Gold (ABV 7.2%) STRONG

Duration SIBA

Abbey Farm, West Acre, PE32 1TX
☎ (01553) 635000 ∰ durationbeer.com

Duration Brewing at Abbey Farm is situated at the historic West Acre Priory in Norfolk. This farmhouse brewery is located in the Nar Valley and surrounded by its Pilgrim Trail. All the beers are sold in cans, and there are plans to open a Taproom. ◆

Durham SIBA

Unit 6a, Bowburn North Industrial Estate, Bowburn, County Durham, DH6 5PF
☎ (0191) 377 1991 ∰ durhambrewery.com

☺Established in 1994, County Durham's oldest brewery has a portfolio of around 40 beers, some permanent, some on rotation, and with new beers appearing regularly. Beers are available throughout the North East. ‼⇟LIVE

Magus (ABV 3.8%) BLOND
Pale malt gives this brew its straw colour, but the hops define its character, with a fruity aroma, a clean bitter mouthfeel, and a lingering dry, citrus-like finish.
Citra Nova (ABV 3.9%) BITTER
Pale Ice (ABV 3.9%) BITTER

Apollo (ABV 4%) PALE
White Gold (ABV 4%) PALE
White Amarillo (ABV 4.1%) BITTER
Columbus IPA (ABV 4.2%) PALE
White Velvet (ABV 4.2%) BITTER
Evensong (ABV 5%) BITTER
Alabaster (ABV 7.2%) STOUT

Dwarfen

See Fownes

Dynamite Valley

Unit 6, Viaduct Works, Frog Hill, Ponsanooth, Cornwall, TR3 7JW
☎ (01872) 864532 ☎ 07775 570235
∰ dynamitevalley.com

⊠ Dynamite Valley was set up in 2015 following a successful crowdfunding campaign and is located close to a historic gunpowder site near Falmouth. Beers are influenced by European and US beer styles. The brewery has broadened its horizons by expanding into bottling. It also acquired the Rebel Brewery brand name and beers. ⇟V

Gold Rush (ABV 4%) BITTER
Smooth, gold bitter with light malt nose. Malt dominates throughout with bitterness, honey, lemon and apricot flavours. Long, malty, bitter finish.
Kennall Vale Pale (ABV 4.3%) PALE
TNT IPA (ABV 4.8%) PALE
Robust, amber, American IPA with malt and fruity hop aroma. Heavy hop bitter taste with sweet toffee apples and malt balance.
Black Charge (ABV 5%) STOUT
Black, oatmeal-style, sweet stout. Powerful flavours of roast coffee, dark chocolate, malt and molasses throughout. Smooth but short finish.

Brewed under the Rebel Brewery brand name:
Surf Bum IPA (ABV 3.5%) PALE
Golden beer with fruity hop nose. Dominant, grassy hop-bitterness with grapefruit, apples and apricots. Lingering hop bitterness and a little dryness.
Rebel Gold (ABV 3.8%) GOLD
Refreshing golden ale with light grassy hop and fruit nose. Sweet grapefruit and citrus marmalade throughout. Bitter and hoppy finish.
Bal Maiden (ABV 4%) BITTER
Tawny best bitter with malt aroma. Full malt and bitter ale with apple and lemon flavours. Lingering bitter finish. Dry throughout.
Penryn Pale Ale (ABV 4.3%) PALE
Pale brown best bitter with mainly hop aroma. Bitter taste, citrus fruit, and biscuit malt. Short, fresh, hop bitter finish.
Rebel Red (ABV 4.5%) PALE
Red best bitter with biscuit malt and toffee dominating the taste with bitter hop and light fruit. Light bitter finish.
80/- Scotch Ale (ABV 5%) PORTER
Dark brown porter with roast malt aroma. Smoky roast and biscuit malt balanced by sweet plum and bitterness. Long finish.

Eagle

Havelock Street, Bedford, MK40 4LU
☎ (01234) 272716 ∰ eaglebrewery.co.uk

☺Founded in 1876 and remained with the Wells Family until 2017, when the brewery and its brands were acquired by Marston's, and renamed Eagle Brewery. It has brewed Young's beers since 2007 after the closure of the Ram Brewery and the popular Bedfordshire Ale,

Eagle IPA, and forges strong links with the local area. Part of Carlsberg Marston's Brewing Co. ‼️🍴♦

IPA (ABV 3.6%) PALE
A refreshing, amber session ale with pronounced citrus hop aroma and palate, faint malt in the mouth, and a lasting dry, bitter finish.

Brewed under the Courage brand name:
Best Bitter (ABV 4%) BITTER
Directors (ABV 4.8%) BITTER

Brewed under the Young's brand name:
London Original (ABV 3.7%) BITTER
This light-drinking, amber bitter has citrus initially on the palate with sweet malt and a hint of hops that linger into a slightly dry, bitter finish.
London Special (ABV 4.5%) BITTER
Pale brown in colour, this rounded premium bitter has citrus throughout plus some slight creamy toffee, which balances the bitterness that grows in the aftertaste.

Eagles Crag

Unit 21, Robinwood Mill, Todmorden, West Yorkshire, OL14 8JA
☎ (01706) 810394 ⊕ eaglescragbrewery.com

☺Eagles Crag is named after, and overlooked by, a prominent landmark, famous in local folklore. Its eight-barrel plant is situated in a former textile mill. Commercial brewing began in 2017 and the two founders both have 35 years of brewing experience. Beers can be fined as vegan on request. The brewery supplies more than 120 outlets in Lancashire, Yorkshire and Manchester. 🍴♦V✿

The Eagle's Feather (ABV 3.8%) BITTER
Pale Eagle (ABV 4%) PALE
Easy-drinking, very well-balanced pale ale. Light citrus notes offset by a touch of sweetness giving a smooth, bitter finish.
Eye of the Eagle (ABV 4.3%) BITTER
An amber, traditional best bitter with malt and fruit to the fore, lingering dry finish.
Eagle of Kindness (ABV 4.4%) GOLD
Black Eagle (ABV 4.6%) STOUT
The Eagle has Landed (ABV 4.6%) BITTER
An amber best bitter with a good balance of fruit and malt. Moderate bitterness with a lingering malty finish.
Golden Eagle (ABV 4.7%) GOLD
A fruity, full-flavoured golden ale. Hoppy bitterness dominates the full mouthfeel and lasting finish.
Eagle of Darkness (ABV 5%) PORTER
Refreshing dark brown porter. A subtle blend of chocolate malt and raisin-like fruit develops into a mellow, sweet aftertaste.
Bald Eagle (ABV 6.9%) IPA

Ealing

Unit 2, The Ham, Brentford, TW8 8EX
☎ (020) 8568 9906 ☎ 07952 737499
⊕ ealingbrewing.com

⊗ Opening in 2019, Ealing brews a wide variety of ever-changing styles including European beers and lagers. The current beers are available at the taproom and the The Owl & The Pussycat, Northfields. Cask is popular but beers also appear in keg and bottle-conditioned. 🍴LIVE ♦

TW8 (ABV 5.8%) BITTER
Tawny beer with caramel malty nose. Caramel sweetness is over earthy herbal bitterness, and with a light fruity background.

Earl Soham SIBA

Meadow Works, Cross Green, Debenham, Suffolk, IP14 6RP
☎ (01728) 861213 ⊕ earlsohambrewery.co.uk

⊗ Earl Soham was set up behind the Victoria pub in 1984 and continued there until 2001 when the brewery relocated, moving again in 2013 to Debenham. Around 30 outlets are supplied and two pubs are owned. ‼️🍴♦LIVE

Gannet Mild (ABV 3.3%) MILD
A beautifully-balanced mild, sweet and fruity flavour with a lingering, coffee aftertaste.
Victoria Bitter (ABV 3.6%) BITTER
A light, fruity, amber session beer with a clean taste and a long, lingering hoppy aftertaste.
Elizabeth Ale (ABV 4%) BITTER
Sir Roger's Porter (ABV 4.2%) PORTER
Roast/coffee aroma and berry fruit introduce a full-bodied porter with roast/coffee flavours. Dry roast finish.
Albert Ale (ABV 4.4%) BITTER
Brandeston Gold (ABV 4.5%) GOLD
Popular beer brewed with local ingredients. Lovely sharp clean flavour, malty/hoppy and heavily laden with citrus fruit. Malty finish.

Earth Ale

Unit A007, The Chocolate Factory, 5 Clarendon Road, Wood Green, London, N22 6XJ ☎ 07508 553546
⊕ earthale.com

After brewing at various London breweries, Earth Ale settled down at the Chocolate Factory complex in 2019. Its taproom is a converted bus, the Earth Tap, in the nearby Blue House Yard. A wide range of beers is availabable in keg and bottles often including foraged wild herbs and spices adding to the eco-friendly ethos of the brewery. LIVE

East London

Unit 45, Fairways Business Centre, Lammas Road, Leyton, London, E10 7QB
☎ (020) 8539 0805 ⊕ eastlondonbrewing.com

⊗ East London Brewing Company is an award-winning, 25-barrel brewery established in 2011 by Stu and Claire. The brewery brews a core range of regular beers available for cask, keg, bottles and can. Regular specials are made, including an annual green-hopped beer each September, in collaboration with Walthamstow Beer (a collective of small-batch hop growers). ♦LIVE

Pale Ale (ABV 4%) BITTER
Amber bitter with spicy hops, bitter lemon, tropical fruits and biscuit in the dry aftertaste. Hoppy aroma.
Foundation Bitter (ABV 4.2%) BITTER
Well-balanced brown bitter with hoppy aroma and flavour overlaid with caramelised orange, fudge and tropical fruit. Short, bitter, marmalade finish.
Peacock English Pale Ale (ABV 4.2%) BITTER
Light-drinking, gold-coloured beer with a strong flavour of resinous hops, which are also on the bitter dryish finish.
Nightwatchman (ABV 4.5%) BROWN
Dark ruby-brown complex beer. Peach, caramelised fruit, toffee balanced by bitter, nutty and roasted malt flavours. Dry aftertaste.
Cowcatcher American Pale Ale (ABV 4.8%) PALE
Fruity hoppy rich golden ale with honey sweetness, mango and hints of passionfruit, lingering in the dry bitter finish.
Jamboree (ABV 4.8%) BLOND

Golden, strong, smooth bitter with hoppy, citrus and sweet biscuit aroma and flavour with peach. Dry, bitter, sweetish aftertaste.

Quadrant Oatmeal Stout (ABV 5.8%) STOUT
Smooth, rich oatmeal stout with liquorice, mocha and caramelised fruit. Roasted coffee aroma. A dry, slightly roasted bitter finish lingers.

East Side (NEW)

Unit 5b, Elms Industrial Estate, Church Road, Harold Wood, RM3 0HU
☎ **(020) 3355 1197** ☎ **07749 125264**
⊕ **theeastsidebrewery.co.uk**

The brewery was installed in early 2020, with opening delayed until 2021 due to Coronavirus. Beers are available in keg and bottle and can be found locally and in East London pubs. No real ale.

Eastcote

🏠 **Eastcote Arms, 6 Gayton Road, Eastcote, Northamptonshire, NN12 8NG**
☎ **(01327) 830086** ✉ **theeastcotearms@gmail.com**

Formerly Litchborough Artisan, Richard Bustin has taken ownership of the Eastcote Arms pub and installed a new eight-barrel brewery on the premises, brewing a range of beers to suit both traditional and modern tastes.

Eden River SIBA

Hawksdale House, Hartness Road, Penrith, Cumbria, CA11 9DB
☎ **(01768) 210565** ☎ **07729 677692**
⊕ **edenbrewery.com**

Originally named Eden Brewery, the name changed to Eden River in 2018. Set up in 2011, the brewery is run by Jason Hill, assisted by Linda and Chris. The five-barrel plant was located at historic Brougham Hall but moved in 2017 to premises on a Penrith industrial estate. ‼◆LIVE

Eden Best (ABV 3.8%) BITTER
A traditional bitter, with a hoppy beginning; a malty, bitter- sweet middle, and a gentle finish.
Eden Fuggle (ABV 3.8%) PALE
Initially sweet, a gently-hopped pale beer with a bitter finish.
Blonde Knight (ABV 4%) BLOND
Eden Dynamite (ABV 4%) BLOND
Eden Atomic Blonde (ABV 4.1%) BLOND
The initially inviting aroma of hops is followed by an intense hop flavour with some fruitiness.
Eden Gold (ABV 4.2%) BLOND
Gentle fruity and honey aromas to start, leading to a well-balanced sweet beer with a lasting hoppy finish.
Eden First Emperor (ABV 4.6%) PALE
Fascinatingly fruity beer with balanced malt and hops and a hint of butterscotch combining to a rich, bitter finish.

Eden St Andrews SIBA

Main Street, Guardbridge, KY16 0UU ☎ **07786 060013** ⊕ **edenbrewerystandrews.com**

☺The brewery was established in 2012 using a five-barrel plant in part of the former Guardbridge paper mills. In 2014 a new 20-barrel plant and distillery was installed. Brewing is currently suspended. ‼🍺LIVE

Edinburgh Beer Factory

Unit 15, 32 Bankhead Drive, Edinburgh, EH11 4EQ
☎ **(0131) 442 4562** ⊕ **edinburghbeerfactory.co.uk**

Family run brewery that began brewing in 2015. With packaging inspired by Leith born artist Eduardo Paolozzi the beers are available in bottle, keg and can. No real ale. ‼◆

Eight Arch SIBA

Unit 3a, Stone Lane Industrial Estate, Wimborne, Dorset, BH21 1HB
☎ **(01202) 889254** ☎ **07554 445647**
⊕ **8archbrewing.co.uk**

⊠ This award-winning brewery commenced in 2015 on a five-barrel plant on a small industrial estate on the outskirts of Wimborne. It has recently expanded into the unit next door with an on-site brewery bar. The ales are distributed to local pubs and clubs as well as nationally. ‼🍺◆LIVE V◆

Session (ABV 3.8%) PALE
Square Logic (ABV 4.2%) GOLD
Easy Life (ABV 5%) PALE
Corbel (ABV 5.5%) IPA
Strong golden ale with hops dominating, yet balanced with bitterness.

Electric Bear SIBA

Unit 12, Maltings Trading Estate, Locksbrook Road, Bath, BA1 3JL
☎ **(01225) 424088** ⊕ **electricbearbrewing.com**

Electric Bear began brewing in 2015 using a purpose-built, 18-barrel plant, expanding capacity in 2016, 2018, and 2020. Its brewery tap showcases a selection of the range, including exclusive one-offs. A wide range of beer is available in cans and kegs and all are unfiltered, unfined and unpasteurised. It also offers a single ever-changing cask-conditioned beer. ‼🍺◆LIVE◆

Electro (NEW)

Unit 19, Parc Teifi, Cardigan, SA43 1EW

Office: Glenydd Cwmin, St Dogmaels, SA43 3HF
✉ **contact@electrobrewing.com**

Artisan brewery established in 2021, producing a range of bottled beers with UK distribution.

Elements

Unit 2, Upton Downs Farm, Upton, Burford, Oxfordshire, OX18 4LY ☎ **07984 308670**
⊕ **elementsbrewery.co.uk**

Began brewing in 2018 on a six-barrel plant, producing small-batch, hop-forward beers initially in keg. A taproom opened in 2019. No real ale. 🍺◆

Elephant School

See Brentwood

Elgood's SIBA

North Brink Brewery, Wisbech, Cambridgeshire, PE13 1LW
☎ **(01945) 583160** ⊕ **elgoods-brewery.co.uk**

⊠ The North Brink brewery was established in 1795. Owned by the Elgood family since 1878, the fifth generation are now involved in running the business. Elgood's has approximately 30 tied pubs within a 50-mile radius of the brewery and a substantial free trade. Lambic style beers are produced using the brewery's old open cooling trays as fermenting vessels. Off-sales are available all year round from the shop in the brewery office when the visitor centre is closed. ‼☕♦V

Black Dog (ABV 3.6%) MILD
Black-red mild with liquorice and chocolate. Dry roasty finish.

Cambridge Bitter (ABV 3.8%) BITTER
Fruit and malt on the nose with increasing hops and balancing malt on the palate. Dry finish.

Blackberry Porter (ABV 4.5%) SPECIALITY
Plum Porter (ABV 4.5%) SPECIALITY

Elland SIBA

Units 3-5, Heathfield Industrial Estate, Heathfield Street, Elland, West Yorkshire, HX5 9AE
☎ **(01422) 377677** ⊕ **ellandbrewery.co.uk**

☺Orginally formed in 2002 as Eastwood & Sanders the company was renamed Elland in 2006 to reinforce its links with the town. The brewery has a capacity of 50 barrels (200 firkins) a week with further expansion and seasonal beers planned. The brewery tap, Elland Craft & Tap, opened in Elland in 2018. ‼♦LIVE

White Prussian (ABV 3.9%) SPECIALITY
A straw-coloured, lightly-flavoured, easy-drinking and refreshing, lager-style, speciality beer.

Blonde (ABV 4%) BLOND
Creamy yellow, hoppy ale with hints of citrus fruits. Pleasantly strong bitter aftertaste.

Beyond the Pale (ABV 4.2%) PALE
Gold-coloured, robust, creamy beer with ripe aromas of hops and fruit. Bitterness predominates in the mouth and leads to a dry, fruity and hoppy aftertaste.

Nettlethrasher (ABV 4.4%) BITTER
Smooth, amber-coloured beer. A rounded nose with some fragrant hops notes followed by a mellow nutty and fruity taste and a dry finish.

1872 Porter (ABV 6.5%) PORTER
Creamy, full-flavoured porter. Rich liquorice flavours with a hint of chocolate from roast malt. A soft but satisfying aftertaste of bittersweet roast and malt.

Elliswood

See New Buildings

Elmesthorpe

Church Farm, Station Road, Elmesthorpe, Leicestershire, LE9 7SG ☎ **07754 321283**

Elmesthorpe was established in 2017 by a beer enthusiast and pub landlord. The brewery has gone from strength to strength and now supplies many pubs and taprooms in Leicestershire, Nottinghamshire, Warwickshire, Derbyshire and Staffordshire.

CAPA (ABV 3.8%) PALE
Aylmers Ale (ABV 4.1%) BITTER
Barons Best Bitter (ABV 4.3%) BITTER
Lord Cullens Ruby (ABV 4.5%) BITTER

Elmtree SIBA

Unit 10, Oakwood Industrial Estate, Harling Road, Snetterton, NR16 2JU
☎ **(01953) 887065** ⊕ **elmtreebeers.co.uk**

⊗ Established in 2007, Elmtree brews on a six-barrel plant. More than 120 free trade outlets are supplied directly. The brewery specialises in high quality ales made with the best ingredients. Some of the strongest beers are only available in bottled-conditioned form. Bespoke beers for individual pubs are also brewed. ‼☕♦LIVE V

Burston's Cuckoo (ABV 3.8%) BLOND
Gentle malt airs. Biscuity sweet beginning with delicate lime hints. Full-bodied, short, sweet finish.

Bitter (ABV 4.2%) BITTER
Traditional malt and hop nose. Solid and well-balanced with a bittersweet, hoppy, maltiness throughout. Flowing, crisp, hoppy ending.

Norfolk's 80 Shilling Ale (ABV 4.5%) BITTER
Mixed fruit nose introduces a sweet fruity bitter with a bitter counterbalance. Short drying finish.

Dark Horse Stout (ABV 5%) STOUT
Solid coffee and malt aroma. A cornucopia of vanilla, dark chocolate, and roast with a sweet foundation. Long, strong finale.

Golden Pale Ale (ABV 5%) PALE
Sweet fruity aroma with hints of honey. Even-handed mix of lemon and crisp hoppiness with a defined bittering finale.

Nightlight Mild (ABV 5.7%) MILD
A heavy mix of liquorice, roast and malt infuses aroma and first taste. A sweet spiciness slowly develops.

Elusive SIBA

Units 3-5, Marino Way, Hogwood Lane Industrial Estate, Finchampstead, Berkshire, RG40 4RF ☎ **07917 541718** ⊕ **elusivebrewing.com**

Elusive is a five-barrel brewery, which was established in 2016. With a fermenting capacity of 32 barrels, it produces a diverse range of cask, KeyKeg and canned beers and continues to be involved in many brewery collaborations. A small canning line was added in 2020 and bottled beers have been discontinued. All canned beers are unfiltered and unpasteurised. The taproom sells beers from the Elusive range and other breweries, plus related merchandise. Level Up and Overdrive use different hop varieties in each rotation. ☕♦⌂

Calisto (ABV 4%) PALE
Mephisto (ABV 4%) PALE
Level Up (ABV 5%) RED
Morrisman (ABV 5%) SPECIALITY
Overdrive (ABV 5.5%) IPA
Oregon Trail (ABV 5.8%) IPA
Spellbinder (ABV 6%) SPECIALITY

Emperor's (NEW)

Newbold Farm, 2 Worthington Lane, Newbold Coleorton, Leicestershire, LE67 8PH
⊕ **emperorsbrewery.co.uk**

Former homebrewer now brewing imperial stouts and porters commercially.

Empire SIBA

The Old Boiler House, Unit 33, Upper Mills, Slaithwaite, Huddersfield, West Yorkshire, HD7 5HA
☎ **(01484) 847343** ☎ **07966 592276**
⊕ **empirebrewing.com**

☺Empire Brewing was set up 2006 in a mill on the bank of the scenic Huddersfield Narrow Canal, close to the centre of Slaithwaite. In 2011 the brewery upgraded from a five-barrel to a 12-barrel plant. Beers are supplied to local free houses and through independent specialist beer agencies and wholesalers. ‼♦LIVE

Golden Warrior (ABV 3.8%) GOLD
Strikes Back (ABV 4%) GOLD
Valour (ABV 4.2%) GOLD
Longbow (ABV 4.3%) GOLD
Imperium (ABV 5.1%) BITTER

Emsworth

Unit 45, Basepoint Business Centre, Havant, Hampshire, PO9 1HS ☎ 07840 876854
🌐 theemsworthbrewhouse.co.uk

Emsworth Brewhouse was launched in 2015 as a half-barrel plant, and upgraded to 1.5-barrels in 2016. It was sold in 2017 and is now in the capable hands of Jonathan Khoo, who has moved it to larger premises in Havant with a shop and taproom. The brewery has moved away from bottles and now sells all its beers in cans. All beers are unfined and vegan-friendly. ☒V✦

Mainsail (ABV 3.8%) GOLD
Starboard (ABV 4%) PALE
Flotilla (ABV 4.4%) BITTER
Wodehouse (ABV 4.8%) BITTER
Portside (ABV 5.2%) PORTER
SkIPA (ABV 5.4%) PALE

Enfield SIBA

Unit 17a, Eley Road, Edmonton, London, N18 3BB
☎ (020) 8807 1533 🌐 enfieldbrewery.co.uk

Brewing started in 2015 concentrating on bottled and keg beers with cask beers following in 2017. The beers use the brewery's well water and are sold under the Enefeld name, the Saxon spelling for Enfield. The range was expanded during 2019 with availability increasing around North London and beyond, the beers proving popular in local Wetherspoon pubs.

Brewed under the Enefield brand name:
EB (ABV 4%) BITTER
Light-bodied, amber, traditional bitter with caramel and slightly spicy hops aroma. Bready caramel taste with hoppy notes. Bitter finish.

Iron Brew (ABV 4.2%) RED
Ruby brown, rich, smooth, malty, sweet beer with a floral aroma, some fruit notes and lasting, bitter, hoppy finish.

Speculation (ABV 4.8%) BROWN
Raisins, citrus peel, hazelnuts flavours with a trace of caramel toffee. Finish is increasingly bitter, balanced by a smooth fruitiness.

London Pale Ale (ABV 5%) BITTER
Smooth beer with a sweet aroma. Digestive biscuit, apricot, citrus and bitterness on the palate buiilding in the spicy finish.

London Porter (ABV 5.5%) PORTER
Ovaltine and cocoa aroma. Chocolate flavour with damsons and a little apple. Dark chocolate with a little fruit that fades.

London IPA (ABV 6%) IPA
Smooth gold beer with spicy hops, a developing bitterness overlaid with sweet honey and tangerine in the lingering, dry aftertaste.

Engine Shed Project

See Brunswick

Ennerdale SIBA

Chapel Row, Rowrah, Cumbria, CA26 3XS
☎ (01946) 862977 ☎ 07918 626652
🌐 ennerdalebrewery.co.uk

⊕This family-owned brewery began brewing in 2010 as a 10-barrel brewery in a converted barn. In 2016 the brewery moved to larger premises with plans for expansion. It distributes throughout Cumbria and the North of England. The brewery tap is open daily. ‼☒✦

Blonde (ABV 3.8%) BLOND

A sweet, fruity, light-coloured beer with gentle bitterness.

Darkest (ABV 4.2%) BROWN
Complex brown beer with a velvety texture. Chocolate, coffee aromas and flavours combine with sweet fruitiness. The finish is of lasting dry roast malts.

Wild (ABV 4.2%) BITTER

Enville SIBA

Coxgreen, Hollies Lane, Enville, DY7 5LG
☎ (01384) 873728 🌐 envilleales.com

☒ Enville Brewery is sited on a picturesque Victorian, Grade II-listed farm complex, using natural well water, traditional steam brewing and a reed and willow-effluent plant. Enville Ale is infused with honey and is from a 19th century recipe for beekeeper's ale passed down from the former proprietor's great-great aunt. ☒✦

Simpkiss (ABV 4%) BITTER
Caramel smooth start, caramel body with sweet malt and hop bite. Fruity hop finish, easing finish and satisfying.

American Pale Ale (ABV 4.2%) PALE
White (ABV 4.2%) SPECIALITY
Yellow with a malt, hops and fruit aroma. Hoppy but sweet finish.

Ale (ABV 4.5%) SPECIALITY
Sweet malty aroma and taste, honey becomes apparent before bitterness finally dominates.

Old Porter (ABV 4.5%) PORTER
Black with a creamy head and sulphurous aroma. Sweet and fruity start with touches of spice. Good balance between sweet and bitter, but hops dominate the finish.

Ginger Beer (ABV 4.6%) SPECIALITY
Golden bright with gently gingered tangs. A drinkable beer with no acute flavours but a satisfying aftertaste of sweet hoppiness.

Epic

The Brewery, West Hewish, Somerset, BS24 6RR
☎ (01934) 384044 🌐 pitchforkales.com &
3D-beer.com

☒ Epic Beers was formed in 2017 on the site of the former RCH brewery, with several of the original staff. Epic trade under two distinct brands. Pitchfork beers are cask-conditioned and made with 100% British ingredients. Many specials add to the regular brews. 3D Beers produce monthly specials using international hops (mostly cask but some keg too). It opened its first pub in Weston-Super-Mare in 2019. In 2020 it set up its 'Beer Drive Thru' and national delivery service. Canned beers have just been introduced. ‼☒✦LIVE

Brewed Brewed under the 3D Beers brand name:
3D Sheridans (ABV 5%) STOUT

Brewed under the Pitchfork Brewery brand name:
Goldbine (ABV 3.8%) GOLD
PG Steam (ABV 3.9%) BITTER
Light malt and faint hop aroma. Pale fruit combines with dry bitterness in the flavour, before a lasting, dry aftertaste.

Pitchfork (ABV 4.3%) BITTER
Pale gold, some hops on the nose, flavours combine light malt with citric hop bitterness, lingering dry and bitter aftertaste.

Old Slug Porter (ABV 4.5%) PORTER
East Street Cream (ABV 5%) BITTER

Errant

Arch 19, Forth Goods Yard, Newcastle upon Tyne, NE1 3PG ☎ 07736 333303 🌐 errantbrewery.com

⊗ Nestled in the heart of Newcastle in an old victorian railway arch, Errant is a hidden gem in Newcastle's industrial playground. Founded in 2015, it brews an ever-changing range of cask, keg and canned beers.

Escape

Unit T, Dodd Lane Industrial Estate, Chorley Road, Westhoughton, BL5 3NA ☎ **07341 810387** ⊕ **escapebrewery.co.uk**

Small brewery launched in Bolton in 2019 brewing a range of regular beers and one occasional beer on a one-barrel plant. It relocated during 2021. ♦V

Avoid Detection (ABV 4.2%) PALE
The Shackles Are Off (ABV 4.2%) GOLD
Erik Weisz (ABV 4.4%) GOLD
Frank Morris (ABV 4.5%) GOLD
Tom, Dick & Harry (ABV 4.5%) PALE
Clocked Off (ABV 4.9%) PALE
Virgil Hilts (ABV 5%) GOLD

Essex Street

⧉ 46 Essex Street, Temple, London, WC2R 3JF ☎ **(020) 7936 2536** ⊕ **templebrewhouse.com**

☺Opened in 2014 within the Temple Brew House pub. Beers are neither filtered nor pasteurised. The City Pub Group also operates sister brewpubs in Bath, Bristol, Cambridge and Norwich. Also supplies some other City Pub Company pubs. ‼♦

Evan Evans SIBA

The New Brewery, 1 Rhosmaen Street, Llandeilo, Carmarthenshire, SA19 6LU ☎ **(01558) 824455** ⊕ **evanevansbrewery.com**

⊗ Evan Evans has been in operation since 2004. The range of beer brands produced includes: Evan-Evans, J Buckley, which focusses on hop flavour, Artisan, a US-style craft beer brand; Fire-Island, Celt Experience and Archers. The brewery also bottles its own brands as well as bottling product of other independent breweries. The brewery now markets its own traditional and berry flavour cider in standard and low alcohol lines as well as its own Liberty lager. ‼♦LIVE

WPA (Welsh Pale Ale) (ABV 4.1%) PALE
Cwrw (ABV 4.2%) BITTER
Brittania (ABV 4.6%) BITTER
Warrior (ABV 4.6%) BITTER
Organic Welsh Gold (ABV 5%) BITTER

Everards SIBA

Everards Meadows, Cooper Way, Leicester, Leicestershire, LE19 2AN ☎ **(0116) 201 4100** ⊕ **everards.co.uk**

Everards was established in 1849 by William Everard and remains an independent fifth generation family-owned company. It has a pub estate of more than 173 throughout the East Midlands. Its new state of the art brewery, comprising of offices, beer hall and shop and set in 70 acres of beautiful green meadows, opened fully in 2021. ‼♦

Beacon Hill (ABV 3.8%) BITTER
Light, refreshing, well-balanced, pale amber bitter in the Burton style.
Sunchaser (ABV 4%) GOLD
Tiger (ABV 4.%) BITTER
A mid-brown, well-balanced best bitter crafted for broad appeal, benefiting from a long, bittersweet finish.

Exale SIBA

Unit 2C, Uplands Business Park, Blackhorse Lane, Walthamstow, London, E17 5QJ ⊕ **exalebrewing.com**

Originally started as Hale Brewery in Tottenham in 2017. Expansion in 2019 saw a new brewery in Walthamstow and a new name. Most famous for Krankie, the Iron Brew Sour, the core range and collaborations are available in keg and cans. Cask ale was experimented with before the first lockdown. One of the destinations on the Blackhorse Beer Mile. ⎘♦

Exe Valley SIBA

Land Farm, Silverton, Exeter, Devon, EX5 4HF ☎ **(01392) 860406** ⊕ **exevalleybrewery.co.uk**

⊗ Exe Valley was established as Barron's Brewery in 1984. The brewery is located in a converted barn overlooking the Exe Valley and Dartmoor hills. Locally sourced malt and English hops are used, along with the brewery's own spring water. 2020 brought new owners, who are looking to expand availability of the brands. ♦LIVE

Bitter (ABV 3.7%) BITTER
Mid-brown bitter, pleasantly fruity, with underlying malt through the aroma, taste and finish.
Barron's Hopsit (ABV 4.1%) BITTER
Straw-coloured beer with strong hop aroma, hop and fruit flavour and a bitter hop finish.
Dob's Best Bitter (ABV 4.1%) BITTER
Delicate aroma, well-balanced taste with malt, hops and sweet fruit continuing into a bitter hoppy aftertaste.
Fryer's Thirst (ABV 4.3%) GOLD
Devon Glory (ABV 4.7%) BITTER
Mr Sheppard's Crook (ABV 4.7%) BITTER
Smooth, full-bodied, mid-brown beer with a malty-fruit nose and a sweetish palate leading to a bitter, dry finish.
Exeter Old Bitter (ABV 4.8%) BITTER
Mid-brown old ale with a rich fruity taste and slightly earthy aroma and bitter finish.
It's Phil's Ale (ABV 4.8%) PALE

Exeter SIBA

Unit 1, Cowley Bridge Road, Exeter, Devon, EX4 4NX ☎ **(01392) 259059** ⊕ **exeterbrewery.co.uk**

⊗ Exeter began brewing in 2003 and is the largest brewery in the city, supplying more than 600 outlets in Devon, Cornwall, Dorset and Somerset. It moved to its present site in 2012, having outgrown its previous location. ‼⎘♦⎘

Lighterman (ABV 3.5%) BITTER
Tomahawk (ABV 3.5%) BITTER
Slight biscuit/malty aroma, biscuit and a tinge of orange and a slight toffee bitter finish.
Avocet (ABV 3.9%) BITTER
A lager-coloured bitter, fruity and sweet from nose to aftertaste. Slight maltiness balances pineapple. Light session ale.
'fraid Not (ABV 4%) GOLD
Ferryman (ABV 4.2%) BITTER
Lovely-flavoured session bitter, a mix of sweet/bitterness.
County Best (ABV 4.6%) BITTER
Darkness (ABV 5.1%) STOUT
Full-bodied stout. Roasted malt dominates the aroma. Complex taste with roast chocolate. Hints of liquorice in a bitter finish.

Exile

See Exmoor

Exit 33

Unit 1, Petre Drive, Sheffield, South Yorkshire, S4 7PZ
☎ (0114) 270 9991 ✉ office@exit33.beer

⊛This eight-barrel brewery was founded in Sheffield in 2008 as Brew Company but rebranded in 2014. The brewer is also a joint partner at the Harlequin pub. Regular house beers are brewed for local pubs. Beers are available nationally. ♦

Thirst Aid (ABV 4%) GOLD
Mosaic (ABV 4.1%) PALE
Northern Best (ABV 4.2%) BITTER
Hop Monster (ABV 4.5%) GOLD
Oat Stout (ABV 5%) STOUT

Exmoor SIBA

Golden Hill Brewery, Old Brewery Road,
Wiveliscombe, Somerset, TA4 2PW
☎ (01984) 623798 ⊕ exmoorales.co.uk

Somerset's largest independent brewery was founded in 1980 in the old Hancock's brewery, which closed in 1959. In 2015 it moved to new, larger premises within 100 yards of the original site, doubling capacity. More than 250 outlets in the South West are supplied, plus others nationwide via wholesalers and pub chains. In 2017 it developed a sub-brand, Exile Ales, to represent a new, modern breed of beers. ♦

Ale (ABV 3.8%) BITTER
Mid-brown, medium-bodied, session bitter. Mixture of malt and hops in the aroma and taste lead to a hoppy, bitter aftertaste.
Fox (ABV 4.2%) BITTER
Gold (ABV 4.5%) BITTER
Golden best bitter with balance of malt and fruity hop on the nose and palate with sweetness following. Bitter finish.
Stag (ABV 5.2%) BITTER
A pale brown beer, with a malty taste and aroma, and a bitter finish.
Beast (ABV 6.6%) STRONG

Experimental

See Dog's Window

Eyam

Unit 4, Eyam Hall Craft Centre, Main Road, Eyam,
Hope Valley, Derbyshire, S32 5QW ☎ 07976 432682
⊕ eyamrealalecompany.com

Brewing began in 2017 using a 1.5-barrel plant producing keg and bottle-conditioned beers. Most output goes to its shop and events but 10 local outlets are also supplied. LIVE

Fable

Essex ✉ sam@fablebrewery.com

A cuckoo brewery specialising in vegan beers. V

Genesis Pale Ale (ABV 3.8%) PALE
Let's Get Lost in the Woods Together (ABV 4.5%)
SPECIALITY

Facer's

A8-9, Ashmount Enterprise Park, Aber Road, Flint,
CH6 5YL ☎ 07713 566370 ⊕ facers.co.uk

Set up in 2003 by the now retired Dave Facer, the brewery is now operated by long-time employee Toby Dunn, It is the oldest brewery in Flintshire. Sales average some 30 barrels per week to around 100 outlets in North Wales and north west England. ‼♦

Mountain Mild (ABV 3.3%) MILD
A fruity dark mild, not too sweet, with underlying roast malt flavours and a full mouthfeel for its low ABV.
Clwyd Gold (ABV 3.5%) BITTER
Clean-tasting, session bitter, mid-brown in colour with a full mouthfeel. The malty flavours are accompanied by increasing hoppiness in the bitter finish.
Flintshire Bitter (ABV 3.7%) BITTER
Well-balanced, session bitter with a full mouthfeel. Some fruitiness in aroma and taste with increasing hoppy bitterness in the dry finish.
Abbey Blonde (ABV 4%) BITTER
Abbey Original (ABV 4%) BITTER
A sweetish, golden beer with a good hop and fruit aroma, juicy taste and a dry, hoppy finish.
Abbey Red (ABV 4%) BITTER
A darker version of Abbey Original. Copper-coloured with a sweet, malty taste and a bittersweet aftertaste.
North Star Porter (ABV 4%) PORTER
Dark, smooth, porter-style beer with good roast notes and hints of coffee and chocolate. Some initial sweetness and caramel flavours followed by a hoppy, bitter aftertaste.
Sunny Bitter (ABV 4.2%) BITTER
An amber beer with a dry taste. The hop aroma continues into the taste where some faint fruit notes are also present. Lasting, dry finish.
DHB (Dave's Hoppy Beer) (ABV 4.3%) BITTER
A dry-hopped version of Splendid Ale with some sweet flavours also coming through in the mainly hoppy, bitter taste.
This Splendid Ale (ABV 4.3%) BITTER
Refreshing tangy best bitter, yellow in colour with a sharp hoppy, bitter taste. Good citrus fruit undertones with hints of grapefruit throughout.
Welsh Premium Lager (ABV 4.5%) BARLEY
Landslide (ABV 4.9%) BITTER
Full-flavoured, complex, premium bitter with tangy orange marmalade fruitiness in aroma and taste. Long-lasting hoppy flavours throughout.

Fairy Glen

5 The Corn Store, Heol Ty Gwyn, Maesteg, CF34 0BG
☎ 07968 847878

Office: 60 Oaklands Avenue, Bridgend, CF31 4ST
⊕ fgbltd.co.uk

Brewing began in 2018. No real ale.

Faithless

See RedWillow

Faking Bad

🖢 Prestoungrange Gothenburg, 227-229 High Street, Prestonpans, EH32 9BE

Faking Bad was established in 2018 by chemistry teachers and avid homebrewers Gareth Evans and Gordon Kidd. All beers are unfined and unfiltered and are available in the Prestoungrange Gothenburg.

Fallen

Kippen Station, Kippen, FK8 3JA ☎ 07507 862167
🌐 fallenbrewing.co.uk

Fallen began brewing in 2014 using a 10-barrel plant and now brews four times a week. The brewery has also installed a canning line. Electricity is from 100% renewable sources. All waste malt goes to local farmers for cattle feed, while waste hops are composted for the garden. Beers are supplied throughout central Scotland (and further afield) and its beer can always be found at the Cross Keys in Kippen. ◆LIVE

Local Motive (ABV 3.9%) BITTER
Odyssey (ABV 4.1%) BITTER
Grapevine (ABV 5.4%) PALE
Chew Chew (ABV 6%) SPECIALITY
Platform C (ABV 6.3%) IPA

Fallen Acorn SIBA

Unit 7, Clarence Wharf Industrial Estate, Mumby Road, Gosport, Hampshire, PO12 1AJ
☎ (023) 9307 9927 🌐 fallenacornbrewing.co

Fallen Acorn is a 20-barrel microbrewery in Gosport, Hampshire. Striving to deliver the highest quality beer from traditional styles and brewing techniques, to pushing modern boundaries and combining a range of brewing experience, with a passion for innovation. Offering a range of styles, it aims to brew something for all tastes, breaking the divide between traditional and craft. ‼🍺◆LIVE🍴

Pompey Royal (ABV 4.3%) BITTER
Well-balanced, malty, traditional bitter. Initial strong caramel flavours, with hints of chocolate leads towards a sweet and slightly bitter finish.
Hole Hearted (ABV 4.7%) GOLD
A golden ale with strong citrus hop aroma. This continues to dominate the flavour, leading to a long, bittersweet finish.
Expedition IPA (ABV 5.5%) IPA
British-style IPA. Well-hopped with a citrusy nose and balancing malt. Taste is similarly balanced, leading to a dry, bitter finish.

Fallen Angel

Unit 21c, Reeds Farm Estate, Roxwell Road, Writtle, Essex, CM1 3ST
☎ (01245) 767220 🌐 fallenangel-brewery.co.uk

Formerly known as the Broxbourne Brewery, the name changed to Fallen Angel in 2017. Brewing began in 2013 using a 12-barrel plant. A 15-barrel plant has been in operation since the brewery's move from Hertfordshire to Essex in 2015.

Ginger Beer (ABV 4%) SPECIALITY
Cowgirl Gold (ABV 4.2%) GOLD
Angry Ox Bitter (ABV 4.8%) BITTER
Fire in the Hole (ABV 4.9%) SPECIALITY
Black Death (ABV 5.2%) SPECIALITY

Falstaff

🍺 **24 Society Place, Normanton, Derby, DE23 6UH**
☎ (01332) 342902 ☎ 07947 242710
🌐 falstaffbrewery.co.uk

⊠ Attached to the Falstaff freehouse, the brewery dates from 1999 but was refurbished and reopened in 2003 under new management as a 3.5-barrel plant. Updated again in 2017, it now operates as a six-barrel plant producing a core range of six beers plus specials. More than 30 outlets are supplied. ◆

3 Faze (ABV 3.8%) GOLD
Fist Full of Hops (ABV 4.5%) GOLD
Phoenix (ABV 4.7%) BITTER
A smooth, tawny ale with fruit and hop, joined by plenty of malt in the mouth. A subtle sweetness produces a drinkable ale.
Smiling Assassin (ABV 5.2%) BITTER
Darkside (ABV 6%) MILD
Good, Bad & Drunk (ABV 6.2%) BITTER

Farm Yard

Gulf Lane, Cockerham, LA2 0ER
☎ (01253) 799988 ☎ 07717 081170
🌐 farmyardales.co.uk

☺This family-run brewery commenced brewing in 2017 and has now expanded to 12 barrels with a canning plant. It also provides contract brewing services. ‼🍺◆🍴

Holmes Stead (ABV 3.4%) BITTER
TVO 54 (ABV 3.7%) BLOND
Haybob (ABV 3.9%) GOLD
Sheaf (ABV 4.1%) PALE
Hoof (ABV 4.3%) SPECIALITY
Chaff (ABV 4.7%) PALE
Gulf IPA (ABV 5.8%) IPA

Farmageddon SIBA

25 Ballykeigle Road, Comber, BT23 5SD ☎ 07966 809481 🌐 farmageddonbrewing.com

Co-operative brewery, formed in 2014. All beers are unfiltered with no preservatives. ◆LIVE V

Gold (ABV 4.2%) PALE
Session (ABV 4.8%) BITTER
India Export Porter (ABV 5.2%) PORTER
IPA (ABV 5.5%) IPA
Mosaic IPA (ABV 6.3%) IPA

Farr Brew SIBA

Unit 7, The Courtyard, Samuels Farm, Coleman Green Lane, Wheathampstead, Hertfordshire, AL4 8ER
☎ 07967 998820 🌐 farrbrew.com

⊠ Farr Brew began brewing in 2014. The beers proved popular necessitating a move to a brand new 10-barrel brewery in 2016. Ecological and environmental concerns are at the forefront of everything Farr Brew creates. A micropub and bottle shop, the Reading Rooms, opened in Wheathampstead in 2018 and the brewery subsequently took over the Rising Sun, Slip End, the Red Cow, Harpenden, the Eight Bells, Old Hatfield, the Elephant & Castle, Amwell, and the Bull, Whitwell by the summer of 2021. ‼🍺◆🍴

Chief Jester (ABV 3.6%) PALE
Our Greatest Golden (ABV 4.1%) GOLD
Our Most Perfect Pale (ABV 4.2%) PALE
The Best Bitter (ABV 4.2%) BITTER
Black Listed IBA (ABV 4.5%) PALE
Our Most Potent Porter (ABV 5%) PORTER

Farriers Arms

🍺 **The Forstal, Mersham, Kent, TN25 6NU**
☎ (01233) 720444 🌐 thefarriersarms.com

Brewing commenced in 2010 in this brewpub owned by a consortium of villagers. ‼◆

Fat Belly

Unit 8F, Commercial Point, Mullacott Cross Industrial Estate, Ilfracombe, Devon, EX34 8PL
☎ (01598) 753496 ☎ 07946 133332
⊕ fatbellybrewery.co.uk

⊠ Established in Lynbridge in 2016 at the Cottage Inn, using a three-barrel plant located at the rear of the pub. It relocated to its current premises in 2018, installing a new 10-barrel plant. As well as the pub it also supplies a growing number of outlets in the Exmoor area. Further beers are planned. ♦LIVE V

FPA Pale Ale (ABV 3.8%) PALE
Guzzler (ABV 3.8%) BITTER
Ocean Gold (ABV 4.2%) GOLD
Carver Doone (ABV 4.5%) STOUT

Fat Cat

🖷 Fat Cat Brewery Tap, 98-100 Lawson Road, Norwich, NR3 4LF
☎ (01603) 788508 ☎ 07795 633368
⊕ fatcatbrewery.co.uk

⊠ Established in 2005 by the mini pub chain's founder, the brewery is based at the Fat Cat Brewery Tap in Norwich. Beers can be sampled in the other pubs in the Fat Cat chain. There are plans for the brewery to relocate as the pub has been sold. ‼♦LIVE

Norwich Bitter (ABV 3.8%) BITTER
Grapefruit on the nose. A strong, hoppy bitterness with underlying maltiness adds depth and complexity. Softly drying finale.
Hell Cat (ABV 4.1%) GOLD
A sulphurous hoppy nose. A distinctly astringent hop character with a biscuity background. A grainy mouthfeel with some grapefruit emerging.
Tom Cat (ABV 4.1%) GOLD
A crisp, citrus character with lemon, lime and orange in aroma and taste. Bitterness grows as cut grass hoppiness fades.
Milk Stout (ABV 4.6%) STOUT
Top Cat (ABV 4.7%) BITTER
A complex malt, caramel, and blackberry aroma leads into a similarly creamy beginning which continues to a richly satisfying finish.
Marmalade (ABV 5.5%) BITTER
Orange and malt pervades both aroma and taste. A full-bodied mix of balanced flavours. A bittersweet finish with hoppiness.
IPA (ABV 6.4%) IPA
Orange and lemon hoppiness floats over a solid bittersweet undercurrent. Good balance of flavours with a rich, creamy character.

Fat Pig

🖷 Fat Pig, 2 John Street, Exeter, Devon, EX1 1BL
☎ (01392) 437217 ⊕ fatpig-exeter.co.uk

⊠ Brewing commenced in 2013 using a 2.5-barrel plant to supply the Fat Pig pub. It is run as an experimental brewery, constantly playing with combinations of malts, hops and temperatures to improve the range of beers, and to push the boundaries. In 2018, the brewery briefly relocated to below St Thomas station in Exeter, alongside the distillery making gin and Exeter's first whisky. In 2019 it returned to the basement of the Fat Pig pub. ♦V

Fearless Nomad

🖷 Black Dog Beer House, 17 Albany Road, Brentford, TW8 0NF

☎ (020) 8568 5688 ⊕ blackdogbeerhouse.co.uk/fearless-nomad

The Fearless Nomad Brewery is owned by Pete Brew who previously helped to set up the Big Smoke Brewery. Beginning in 2020, it is a small one-barrel brew plant producing a variety of different beers served in the Black Dog Beer House. There are plans to increase brewing capacity, distribute to other venues and introduce a canned range.

Federation

🖷 48 Greenwood Street, Altrincham, WA14 1RZ
☎ (0161) 696 6870 ⊕ conclubuk.com

Located in the Con Club, a pub with restaurant that was formerly Altrincham Working Mens Conservative Club, this is a small 2.4-barrel plant that began brewing in 2017. Several new seasonal and speciality beers have been produced in addition to the core range.

Felday

🖷 Royal Oak, Village Green, Felday Glade, Holmbury St Mary, Surrey, RH5 6PF
☎ (01306) 730654 ⊕ feldaybrewery.co.uk

Brewing began in 2017 on a custom-made plant in a small, purpose-built, building next to the Royal Oak pub car park. Almost all of the beer is supplied to the pub although it may very occasionally be seen elsewhere. ♦

Felinfoel SIBA

Farmers Row, Felinfoel, Llanelli, SA14 8LB
☎ (01554) 773357 ⊕ felinfoel-brewery.com

Founded in the 1830s, the company is still family-owned and is now the oldest brewery in Wales. The present buildings are Grade II*-listed and were built in the 1870s. It supplies cask ale to half its 84 houses (though some use top pressure dispense), and to approximately 350 free trade outlets. ‼🍺♦

Felinfoel IPA (ABV 3.6%) PALE
Celtic Pride (ABV 3.9%) BITTER
Double Dragon (ABV 4.2%) BITTER
This pale brown beer has a malty, fruity aroma. The taste is also malt and fruit with a background hop presence throughout. A malty and fruity finish.
Stout (ABV 5%) STOUT

Fell

Unit 27 Moor Lane Business Park, Flookburgh, Cumbria, LA11 7NG
☎ (01539) 558980 ☎ 07967 503689
⊕ fellbrewery.co.uk

⊠ Fell Brewery was founded in 2012 by homebrewer Tim Bloomer and friend Andrew Carter, brewing beers inspired by their travels in the US and Belgium. Production capacity has now increased from 12 to 15 barrels. It has three retail outlets situated in Chorlton (near Manchester), Kendal and Penrith.

Ghyll (ABV 3.7%) GOLD
Inviting citrus aromas follow through nicely in this hoppy, bitter beer with fruit and sweetness present for balance.
Crag (ABV 3.8%) BITTER
Tinderbox IPA (ABV 6.3%) IPA

Fellows

2 Leopold Walk, Cottenham, Cambridge, Cambridgeshire, CB24 8XS
☎ (01954) 250262 ⊕ fellowsbrewery.co.uk

⊠ Fellows began production in 2010 though brewer Mark Burton had been developing recipes for a year or so before. Five regular beers are available with plans for a series of special ales. Beers are increasingly visible in the local free trade.

Cambridge Fellow (ABV 3.8%) GOLD
Gulping Fellow (ABV 4.2%) BITTER
Burton Snatch (ABV 4.8%) BLOND
Jolly Fellows (ABV 5%) BITTER
Clever Fellow (ABV 5.2%) BITTER

Fengate

23 Fengate, Marsham, Norfolk, NR10 5PT
☎ (01263) 479953 ☎ 07884 960697
✉ fengatebrewery@gmail.com

Fengate Brewery was established in 2019. Head brewer and owner Alistair brews a selection of traditional ales with a mix of new beer styles. Beers can be found in pubs and bottle shops in the surrounding area. ⌷

Nightjar Rye & Oat Stout (ABV 3.6%) STOUT
Sunstone Pale Ale (ABV 3.8%) PALE
Three Threads (ABV 4%) PORTER
John Barleycorn Bitter (ABV 4.4%) BITTER
California Common Ale (ABV 4.7%) SPECIALITY
Jamadhar (ABV 5.5%) IPA

Fermanagh

75 Main St, Derrygonnelly, BT93 6HW
☎ (028) 6864 1254

Now known as Fermanagh Beer Company but still using the Inishmacsaint brand, this small-scale brewery has been producing a range of bottle-conditioned beers since 2009. LIVE

Fernandes

⊟ 5 Avison Yard, Kirkgate, Wakefield, West Yorkshire, WF1 1UA
☎ (01924) 291709 ⊕ ossett-brewery.co.uk

☺Opened in 1997 and housed in a 19th century malthouse, Ossett Brewing Company purchased the brewery and tap in 2007, but independent brewing continues. Around 90 different beers are brewed each year. The tap sells Fernandes and Ossett beers as well as guest ales; the former are more widely available through Ossett's supply chain. ‼♦✦

Ferry Ales SIBA

Ferry Hill Farm, Ferry Road, Fiskerton, Lincolnshire, LN3 4HU ☎ 0800 999 3226 ⊕ ferryalesbrewery.co.uk

Ferry Ales Brewery (FAB) began brewing in 2016 using a five-barrel plant. It is situated just outside Fiskerton, Lincolnshire. Beers can be found in the Lincoln area and beyond. A range of between 12-15 beers are available in cask, keg, bottle and can. ⌷

Ferry Brewery SIBA

Bankhead Farm, Steading, Bankhead Road, South Queensferry, EH30 9TF
☎ (0131) 331 1851 ⊕ ferrybrewery.co.uk

The first brewery in South Queensferry since 1851, Ferry Brewery was established in 2016 by Mark Moran and has an on-site taproom and shop. Its beers combine traditional and historic beer recipes with a contemporary twist as well as modern-style beers. Brewery tasting tours are also available for group bookings. ‼⌷♦LIVE V✦

Ferry Fair (ABV 4%) PALE

Light and fruity with some bitterness. A complex, golden, session ale.
Smokey Jack (ABV 4%) RED
Smoked malt gives this beer the characteristic taste of a rauchbier. Sweetness in the initial taste followed by a smoky, bitter aftertaste.
40/- Fine (ABV 4.2%) BITTER
A light take on a traditional 80/- style. Malty with a balance of sweetness and bitterness.
Ferry Crossing (ABV 4.5%) BLOND
Refreshing, fruity golden ale with good malt balance. A fruity aroma and taste followed by increasing bitterness.
Ferry Witches Brew (ABV 4.5%) BITTER
Full-bodied, brown bitter with distinctive malt flavour and bittersweet finish.
Three Bridges (ABV 4.5%) PALE
Ferry Stout (ABV 4.9%) STOUT
Well-balanced stout with hints of chocolate and subtle roast coffee flavours.
Thomas Miller 1785 (ABV 5.5%) PORTER

Fierce

Unit 49, Howe Moss Avenue, Dyce, Aberdeen, AB21 0GP
☎ (01224) 035034 ⊕ fiercebeer.com

The multi-award-winning Fierce Beer was established by Dave Grant and David McHardy, brewing its first beer in 2016. It produces a range of hoppy, fruity, dark and speciality beers plus a limited range of spirits. Production is KeyKeg and bottles. Three bars are owned, in Aberdeen, Edinburgh and Manchester.

Fierce & Noble

25 Mina Road, St Werburgh's, Bristol, BS2 9TA
☎ (0117) 955 6666 ⊕ fierceandnoble.com

Founded in 2017 to supply beer to the Grounded community café chain in Bristol, beers can now be found across Bristol and the South West. A range of IPAs and occasional specials are brewed on an eight-barrel plant. The on-site tap room and brewery shop regularly hold events, and are open year round on Fridays, Saturdays and Sundays. ‼⌷✦

Session IPA (ABV 4.2%) PALE

FILO

The Old Town Brewery, Torfield Cottage, 8 Old London Road, Hastings, East Sussex, TN34 3HA
☎ (01424) 420212 ⊕ filobrewing.co.uk

⊠ Owners of the First In Last Out (FILO) set up their own brewery in the back of the pub in 1985, to become Hastings first brewpub. The current owners took over in 1988, and in 2011 relocated the brewery to the nearby Grade II-listed stable at Torfield Cottage. The brewery continues to supply ales to the FILO pub, together with many other pubs within Hastings, and throughout Sussex and Kent. ♦

Crofters (ABV 3.8%) BITTER
Churches Pale Ale (ABV 4.2%) PALE
Old Town Tom (ABV 4.5%) SPECIALITY
Gold (ABV 4.8%) GOLD

Fine Tuned SIBA

Unit 16, Wessex Park, Bancombe Trading Estate, Bancombe Road, Somerton, Somerset, TA11 6SB
☎ (01458) 897273 ☎ 07872 139945
⊕ finetunedbrewery.com

Established in Langport, Somerset in 2016, but relocated to its current site in 2017. ♦ LIVE

Pitch Perfect (ABV 3.8%) BITTER
Langport Bitter (ABV 4%) BITTER
Sunshine Reggae (ABV 4.2%) PALE
Free Style (ABV 4.5%) GOLD
Twist and Stout (ABV 4.5%) STOUT
Hop Culture (ABV 5%) GOLD

Finney's

51 Wrockwardine Road, Wellington, Shropshire, TF1 3DA
☎ (01952) 412224 ✉ finney@blueyonder.co.uk

A half-barrel capacity microbrewery operated by an experienced home brewer. It supplies local pubs in Wellington and Oakengates, as well as Shropshire beer festivals. The brewery produces a small range of hand-crafted ales, in a range of styles, using mostly traditional hop varieties upon request from the pubs in which they appear.

Firebird SIBA

Old Rudgwick Brickworks, Lynwick Street, Rudgwick, West Sussex, RH12 3UW
☎ (01403) 823180 ⊕ firebirdbrewing.co.uk

⊗ Firebird began brewing in 2013 and has grown rapidly with new beers, new vessels, an extended warehouse and an expanded team. There is a comfortable upstairs bar on-site. ‼ ⌷ ♦ LIVE V ♦

Two Horses (ABV 3.8%) PALE
Heritage XX (ABV 4%) BITTER
Parody (ABV 4.5%) GOLD
Festive 51 (ABV 4.8%) BITTER

Firebrand

See Altarnun

Firebrick SIBA

Units 10 & 11, Blaydon Business Centre, Cowen Road, Blaydon-on-Tyne, Tyne & Wear, NE21 5TW
☎ (0191) 4476543 ⊕ firebrickbrewery.com

Firebrick began brewing on a 2.5-barrel plant in 2013, expanding to a 15-barrel plant in 2014. Beers are mostly available in pubs within the Tyne & Wear area and a few outlets further afield. ♦

Blaydon Brick (ABV 3.8%) GOLD
Coalface (ABV 3.9%) MILD
Elder Statesman (ABV 3.9%) BITTER
Tyne 9 (ABV 3.9%) SPECIALITY
Pagan Queen (ABV 4%) BLOND
Little Belgium (ABV 4.2%) SPECIALITY
Trade Star (ABV 4.2%) GOLD
Stella Spark (ABV 4.4%) BITTER
Toon Broon (ABV 4.6%) BITTER
Cushie Butterfield (ABV 5%) STOUT
Wey-Aye PA (ABV 5.8%) IPA

Firehouse

13 Thames Street, Louth, Lincolnshire, LN11 7AD
☎ (01507) 608202 ☎ 07961 772905
⊕ firehouse-brewery.co.uk

☺ Owned by Jason Allen and Louise Darbon, Firehouse Brewery was founded in 2014 and started production in the village of Manby on part of the site of the former RAF station. In 2016 a 2.5-barrel plant was purchased from Fulstow Brewery and relocated to the Thames Street Brewery in Louth, where both brewery's beers are brewed. Beers are available in the free trade and from the bar located at the brewery, the Gas Lamp Lounge. ♦

Mainwarings Mild (ABV 3.6%) MILD
Marsh Mild (ABV 3.8%) MILD
FGB (ABV 3.9%) BITTER
NorthwayIPA (ABV 4.2%) PALE
Woodman Pale Ale (ABV 4.4%) BLOND
Pride of Fulstow (ABV 4.5%) PALE
Wobbly Weasel (ABV 4.9%) BITTER
Lincolnshire Country Bitter (ABV 5.1%) BITTER

FireRock

20-24 Outram Street, Sutton-in-Ashfield, Nottinghamshire, NG17 4FS ☎ 07875 331898
✉ firerock@mail.co.uk

☺ FireRock Brewing Co is an independent microbrewery and craft beer bar specialising in hop-forward craft beers.

Firs

⬚ Station Road, Codsall, Staffordshire, WV8 1BX
☎ (01902) 844674 ⊕ thefirscodsall.com

Beers are brewed on-site in the CAMRA award-winning Firs, and are exclusive to the club.

First & Last SIBA

⬚ Bird in Bush, Village Green, Elsdon, NE19 1AA
☎ (01830) 520804 ☎ 07757 286357
⊕ firstandlastbrewery.co.uk

First & Last was established in 2016 by Red Kelly, a founder member of Stu Brew (qv) in Newcastle upon Tyne. It was upgraded to a five-barrel plant in 2018, relocating from Rochester to the Bird in Bush, Elsdon. Other outlets in Northumberland and the Scottish Borders are supplied. ‼ ♦

First Ascents

See Top Out

First Chop

B2 Barton Hall Business Park, Hardy Street, Eccles, M30 7NB ☎ 07970 241398
⊕ firstchopbrewingarm.com

Brewing began at Outstanding Brewery (qv) in Bury in 2012 before transferring to Salford in 2013. The brewery relocated again to Eccles in 2017 with increased capacity. It specialises in producing gluten-free beers. GF

AVA (ABV 3.5%) BLOND
POD (ABV 4.2%) SPECIALITY
SYL (ABV 6.2%) IPA

Fish Key

⬚ c/o Woodlark Inn, Church Street, Lambley, NG4 4QB
☎ (0115) 931 2535 ☎ 07814 019250
⊕ woodlarkinn.co.uk/micro-brewery

⊗ The brewery was originally established in East Looe by Pete and Elaine Delaney in 2016, getting its name from its location on the old fish quay in Looe. It has now relocated and is firmly established in one of the cellars at the Woodlark Inn, Lambley. ♦

Fishponds

⬛ Star, 539 Fishponds Road, Fishponds, Bristol, BS16 3AF

Brewing began in 2018 at the family-run pub, the Star, where brothers Eimhin and Cillian look after the brewery while their father, Eimear, runs the attached pub.

Five Kingdoms SIBA

22 Main Street, Isle of Whithorn, DG8 8LF
☎ (01988) 500334 ⊕ fivekingdomsbrewery.com

☺Five Kingdoms was established in 2015 by Alastair Scoular, owner of the Steam Packet Inn, using a 2.5-barrel plant. It is situated in the harbourside village of Isle of Whithorn, the most southerly point of the Wigtownshire peninsular in Galloway and a tourist and sailing hotspot. The Brewery supplies numerous local and Scottish outlets, selected national beer festivals, and the Steam Packet Inn. Brewery tours and expansion are planned. ‼♦

Bright Idea (ABV 3.8%) BITTER
McGreggors Mild (ABV 3.8%) MILD
Bitter X Blonde (ABV 4%) GOLD
Rebus (ABV 4%) PALE
Wee McAsh Bitter (ABV 4.5%) BITTER
AufWiedersehen Blond (ABV 5.3%) GOLD
Captain Morrison IPA (ABV 6.5%) IPA
Dark Storm Stout (ABV 6.9%) STOUT

Five Points SIBA

61 Mare Street, London Fields, London, E8 4RG
☎ (020) 8533 7746 ⊕ fivepointsbrewing.co.uk

Five Points commenced brewing in 2013 on a 10-barrel plant in a railway arch under Hackney Downs Station. 2018 saw successful crowdfunding which helped buy the Pembury Tavern. In 2020, the brewery moved into the existing warehouse facility in Mare Street. Commitment to quality cask ale extends to a care scheme for stockists. LIVE ♦

Micro Pale (ABV 2.7%) PALE
XPA (ABV 4%) GOLD
Golden ale with strong citrus fruitiness, a developing bitterness and a sweet, biscuity flavour providing balance. Lingering dry, bitter finish.
Best (ABV 4.1%) BITTER
Full-flavoured, amber bitter with earthy hoppy aroma. Dry, roasty character overlaid with caramel and orange. Lingering, dry, bitter finish.
Pale (ABV 4.4%) PALE
Quaffable, strong, fruity, bitter golden ale. Citrus and tropical fruit fade in the aftertaste where the bitterness lingers.
Railway Porter (ABV 4.8%) PORTER
Full-bodied, dark brown porter. Dark chocolate throughout softened by a peppery, treacly sweetness and caramelised fruit. Finish mirrors the taste.

Five Towns

651 Leeds Road, Outwood, Wakefield, West Yorkshire, WF1 2LU
☎ (01924) 781887
✉ malcolmbastow@googlemail.com

☺Five Towns began production on a 2.5-barrel plant in 2008, supplying outlets mainly in Yorkshire, but as far afield as Berkshire and the North East. As well as the standard beers, a range of themed and speciality brews are also produced. ♦LIVE

Mi Usual (ABV 3.7%) PALE

Middle Un (ABV 4.6%) BITTER
Owt'll Do (ABV 4.6%) SPECIALITY
Nowt (ABV 6.7%) STOUT
One At T'End (ABV 6.7%) IPA
Summat Else (ABV 7.2%) IPA

Fixed Wheel

Unit 9, Long Lane Trading Estate, Long Lane, Blackheath, West Midlands, B62 9LD ☎ 07766 162794 ⊕ fixedwheelbrewery.co.uk

⊠ Set up in 2014 by cycling and brewing enthusiasts Scott Povey and Sharon Bryant, this full mash brewery is situated on a trading estate on the Blackheath/Halesowen border. It brews several times a week using an eight-barrel plant. Alongside the core range, there are regular single hop and other specials brewed. Its award-winning ales are available throughout the Midlands and further afield. A canning plant was purchased in 2021 to service the expanding market for small package beers. ‼🍽LIVE

Through and Off (ABV 3.8%) PALE
Wheelie Pale (ABV 4.1%) PALE
Chain Reaction Pale Ale (ABV 4.2%) PALE
Century Gold (ABV 4.8%) GOLD
Blackheath Stout (ABV 5%) STOUT
Mild Concussion (ABV 5.5%) MILD
Ruby in colour with a creamy head. Aroma is red fruit with a rich, balanced taste and satisfying finish.
No Brakes IPA (ABV 5.9%) IPA

Fizzy Moon

⬛ Fizzy Moon, 35 Regent Street, Leamington Spa, Warwickshire, CV32 5EE
☎ (01926) 888715 ⊕ fizzymoonbrewhouse.com

Fizzy Moon is a bar and microbrewery in the heart of Leamington, brewing a range of small batch beers, exclusively for consumption in the bar. All beers are unfined and so naturally hazy.

Flack Manor SIBA

8 Romsey Industrial Estate, Greatbridge Road, Romsey, Hampshire, SO51 0HR
☎ (01794) 518520 ⊕ flackmanor.co.uk

⊠ Flack Manor commenced brewing in 2010 using a 20-barrel plant purchased from Canada. The brewery employs the double drop method of fermentation. Beers are supplied to local outlets within 50 miles of Romsey and may also be found in Wetherspoon pubs. ‼🍽♦LIVE

Flack's Double Drop (ABV 3.7%) BITTER
A classic, amber, session bitter. Hops, malt and some bitterness in the taste, with more hop and some malt in the finish.
Romsey Gold (ABV 4%) GOLD
Catcher Pale Ale (ABV 4.4%) PALE

Flagship

c/o Ship & Mitre, 133 Dale Street, Liverpool, L2 2JH
☎ (0151) 236 0859

☺Launched in 2016, the Ship & Mitre Brewing Co rebranded as Flagship Beer in 2017, and primarily supplies the iconic city centre pub, the Ship & Mitre, with some sales locally and nationally. Beers are brewed using spare capacity at other breweries. ♦

Sublime (ABV 3.7%) GOLD
Lupa (ABV 3.8%) PALE
Silhouette (ABV 4.5%) STOUT

Vanilla and liquorice aromas with strong malt roast dominating the flavours. A good dry stout with a malt bitter finish.

Jar (ABV 4.7%) PORTER
Roast and prune aroma, dry through to finish with bitter roast flavours.

Century (ABV 5%) PALE
Appealing golden beer, very hoppy with light citrus flavours and a dry, hoppy finish.

Flash

**Moss Top Farm, Moss Top Lane, Flash, Quarnford, Staffordshire, SK17 0TA ☎ 07967 592345
⊕ flashbrewery.uk**

The brewery is located high in the Peak District and was founded by two friends who brew on a part-time basis. All natural ingredients are used including spring water and seaweed finings which make the beer suitable for vegans. Three bottle-conditioned beers are produced and are sold at Leek Market (only sales outlet). LIVE V

Flash House

**Unit 1a, Northumberland Street, North Shields, NE30 1DS ☎ 07481 901875
⊕ flashhousebrewing.co.uk**

Flash House was set up by Jack O'Keefe in 2016, after a life-long appreciation of ale, influenced by family associated with North East real ale pubs. It aims to bring the best beer styles the world has to offer to the North East, and continues to produce new guest ales. The brewery and taproom are situated a short walk from the revamped North Shields Fish Quay. !!

Kolsch (ABV 4.4%) BLOND
Tiny Dancer Pale Ale (ABV 5.4%) PALE

Flipside

**c/o Magpie Brewery, Unit 4 Ashling Court, Iremonger Road, Nottingham,, NG2 3JA
☎ (0115) 987 7500 ☎ 07958 752334**

Office: Old Volunteer, 35 Burton Road, Carlton, NG4 3DQ ⊕ flipsidebrewery.co.uk

⊗ Andrew and Maggie Dunkin established this six-barrel brewery in an industrial unit in Colwick in 2010, expanding to 12-barrels in 2013 in a larger adjacent unit. The brewery opened its own tap, the Old Volunteer, Carlton, in 2014. In 2016 it relocated again to share the plant at Caythorpe Brewery (qv). With the closure of that brewery it now shares with Magpie Brewery (qv). ♦LIVE V

Sterling Pale (ABV 3.9%) PALE
Golden ale with a citrus aroma and hoppy taste, leading to a bitter and peppery finish.
Dark Denomination (ABV 4%) MILD
BIt C01n (ABV 4.1%) GOLD
Copper Penny (ABV 4.2%) BITTER
Golden Sovereign (ABV 4.2%) GOLD
Franc in Stein (ABV 4.3%) GOLD
Golden ale with a floral hop aroma, leading to a hoppy and bitter finish.
Random Toss (ABV 4.4%) PALE
Kopek Stout (ABV 4.5%) STOUT
Full-bodied, dark stout with a coffee aroma and assertive roast flavours throughout and a balanced bitterness.
Flipping Best (ABV 4.6%) BITTER
Brown-coloured, malty, strong bitter with lasting malt, bitterness and subtle hop flavours.
Dusty Penny (ABV 5%) PORTER
Clippings IPA (ABV 6.5%) IPA
Russian Rouble (ABV 7.3%) STOUT

Strong, dark stout with balanced malt, roast and fruit flavours.

Flower Pots SIBA

**Brandy Mount, Cheriton, Hampshire, SO24 0QQ
☎ (01962) 771735 ⊕ theflowerpots.co.uk**

⊗ Flower Pots began production in 2006, now making it Hampshire's oldest independent brewery. The 10-barrel brewery, and neighbouring pub of the same name, are in a pretty Hampshire village. It brews six core beers, plus a monthly special. In 2019 the brewery and pub were taken over by three local partners, whilst the two sibling pubs (Wheatsheaf and Albion) were retained by the original owners. ♦

Perridge Pale (ABV 3.6%) GOLD
Very pale, easy-drinking, golden ale. Honey-scented with high hops, grapefruit and bitterness throughout. Crisp with some citrus notes.
Pots Bitter (ABV 3.8%) BITTER
Refreshing, easy-going bitter. Dry, earthy hop flavours balanced by robust maltiness. Bitter throughout with hoppy aroma, and a dry, bitter finish.
Buster's Best (ABV 4.2%) BITTER
Cheriton Porter (ABV 4.2%) PORTER
Dry porter packed with blackcurrant flavours. Distinctive roastiness and malty throughout, combining with pleasing bitterness leading to a bittersweet finish.
Goodens Gold (ABV 4.8%) GOLD
Complex, full-bodied golden ale, bursting with hops and citrus fruit and a snatch of sweetness, leading to long, dry finish.
IPA (ABV 6%) IPA
Rich, full-bodied IPA with uncompromising hoppiness and strong grapefruit character, a robust maltiness and rich, fruity finish.

Flowerhorn

The Bridge Studios, 454 Western Avenue, Cardiff, CF5 3BL ⊕ flowerhornbrewery.co.uk

Established in 2019 by two friends, Andrew and Arran. Brewing was initially on a gypsy basis, and beers were available in bottle and keg only. In 2020 the brewery moved to its own premises in Cardiff with a bespoke five-barrel plant. A taproom is open on Fridays and Saturdays. A canning line is planned. Beers are occasionally available cask-conditioned for beer festivals. ♦

Flying Gang (NEW)

Unit 3, Meadowfield Industrial Estate, Ponteland, Tyne & Wear, NE20 9SD ☎ 07789 958782

Brewing commenced in 2021 in an industrial unit in Ponteland, also incorporating a taproom which opens at weekends. The brewery is also involved in the running of the Left Luggage micropub in Monkseaton. ♦

Flying Monk SIBA

**Unit 1, Bradfield Farm, Hullavington, Wiltshire, SN14 6EU
☎ (01666) 838415 ⊕ newflyingmonkbrewery.com**

⊗ Following a change of ownership and a short closure, the Flying Monk Brewery recommenced brewing in 2020. Now owned by the farm business at which it is located, allowing reduced waste by using brewery by-product as cattle feed. The brewery is named after Elmer, an 11th century monk at nearby Malmesbury Abbey, who attempted flight from the tower using self-made wings. A stone-built barn next to the brewery is being converted to a reception area. 🍴♦

Elmers (ABV 3.8%) PALE
A refreshing session beer with floral and citrus aromas, followed by an encouraging bitter finish.
Hoptimistic (ABV 3.9%) PALE
Habit (ABV 4.2%) BITTER
An amber-coloured, traditional English best bitter with a contrast of sweet and bitter flavours from a Maris Otter mash and Kentish hops.
Mighty Monk (ABV 4.3%) BLOND

Folly (NEW)

18 Beech Close, Clayton le Dale, Lancashire, BB1 9JF
☎ 07709 306467 ⊕ follybrewery.com

☺Commercial home-based brewery set up in 2020 by a former Thwaites employee. A one-barrel plant is used. ♦

Impello (ABV 4%) SPECIALITY
Lux (ABV 4.5%) PALE
Vestigia (ABV 4.5%) SPECIALITY

Fonthill

▤ c/o George, 29 Mount Ephraim, Tunbridge Wells, Kent, TN4 8AA
☎ (01892) 539492
⊕ thegeorgepubtunbridgewells.co.uk

⊗ Fonthill is a small batch brewery located in the George pub. Beers are available in the pub as well as its two sister pubs in Tunbridge Wells.

Forest Road

Unit 1a, Elizabeth Industrial Estate, Juno Way, South Bermondsey, London, SE14 5RW
☎ (020) 7249 7033 ⊕ forestroad.co.uk

Home brewing began in Forest Road, London E8, in 2015, going commercial at the beginning of 2016 by brewing at Van Eecke in Belgium. More recently beers have been brewed at C'84. A brewery was acquired in 2019 and imported from San Francisco. It's taproom is in E8 at the foot of London Fields. No real ale. V

Forest, The

Hang Hill Works, Bream, GL15 6HT ☎ 07766 652837
⊕ theforestbrewery.co.uk

Originally named Brythonic Beer (a trading name which is still retained), The Forest nanobrewery began in a Bristol suburb in 2015. The brewery relocated several times within Gloucestershire, finally settling in the village of Bream, in The Forest of Dean, in 2020, at the historic Hang Hill Works. Beers can be found at the Dog House micropub and the Forest Deli, both Coleford – mainly available bottle-conditioned, but the occasional cask beer also makes an appearance. LIVE

Hang Hill Hazy (ABV 4%) PALE
Black Spell Porter (ABV 5.7%) SPECIALITY
FSB (Forest Strong Bitter) (ABV 5.8%) BITTER

Forge

Wilderland, Woolley Cross, Cornwall, EX23 9PW
☎ (01288) 331669 ☎ 07837 487800
⊕ forge-brewery.co.uk

⊗ This multi-award-winning brewery was set up near Bideford in Devon by Dave Lang, who commenced brewing in 2008 using a five-barrel plant. The brewery relocated to Cornwall in 2017. ♦LIVE

Discovery (ABV 3.8%) BITTER
Gold-coloured bitter bursting with hops from start to finish. Some subtle hints of fruit to the discerning palate too.
Blonde (ABV 4%) BLOND
Pale ale with light citrus aroma. Zesty citrus hop in the mouth balanced by a little malt. Bitter and dry.
Litehouse (ABV 4.3%) PALE
Pale ale with faint tropical fruit hop aroma. Light balance of sweet malt and hop bitterness fading into a short finish.
IPA (ABV 4.5%) PALE
Rev Hawker (ABV 4.6%) BITTER
Tamar Source (ABV 4.6%) BITTER
Premium bitter with malt and earthy hop aroma. Dominant crystal malt with bitterness and sweet stone fruit flavours. Bitterness rises.

Fosse Way SIBA

Unit 5a, Manor Farm, Hunningham Lane, Offchurch, Warwickshire, CV33 9AG ☎ 07956 179999
⊕ fossewaybrew.co.uk

⊗ Housed in a converted barn on Manor Farm near Offchurch is the five-barrel plant operated by Fosse Way Brewing Co. The core beer range includes a lager influenced by the owner's extensive experience in South Africa. There is a business relationship with Red Moon Brewery in Birmingham.

Aurora (ABV 3.6%) GOLD
Sentinel (ABV 4.5%) BITTER
Dark Side (ABV 4.8%) PORTER

Four Candles

▤ 1 Sowell Street, St Peter's, CT10 2AT ☎ 07947 062063 ⊕ thefourcandles.co.uk

⊗ Based in the cellar of the micropub of the same name, Four Candles uses a 2.5-barrel plant and produces up to 10 nine-gallon casks with each brew. Never brewing the same ale twice, the brewery supplies the micropub, which is named after the well known Two Ronnies sketch. ‼

Four Kings

Unit 15G, Newton Moor Industrial Estate, Lodge Street, Hyde, SK14 4LD ☎ 07951 699428
⊕ fourkingsbrewery.com

☺Four Kings has been brewing since 2016. It's a six-barrel brewery opened in Hyde by friends with a mutual love of beer. Its on-site bar is open most Friday evenings and Saturday afternoons and is also available for private functions. Beers can typically be found in pubs across Tameside and High Peak and at beer festivals in Greater Manchester and Yorkshire. ‼🍴♦LIVE V🥡

4Tune (ABV 4%) BITTER
4Ever (ABV 4.5%) PALE
4Most (ABV 5.5%) PORTER

Fourpure

22 Bermondsey Trading Estate, Rotherhithe New Road, South Bermondsey, London, SE16 3LL
☎ (020) 3744 2141 ⊕ fourpure.com

Fourpure began brewing in 2013. Beers are available in cans and kegs, unfiltered, unpasteurised and unfined. In 2018 the brewery was bought by Lion of Australia, part of Kirin of Japan. A substantial taproom opened along from the brewery in 2019, becoming a star of the Bermondsey Beer Mile. 🍴LIVE 🥡

Fowey

Unit 3F, 3-4 Restormel Industrial Estate, Liddicoat Road, Lostwithiel, Cornwall, PL22 0HG ☎ 07443 504644

Office: Pawton Mill, St Breock, Wadebridge, PL27 7LH ✉ info@foweybrewery.co.uk

Fowey began brewing in 2016, initially producing bottle-conditioned beers only. It relocated to a larger unit on the same industrial estate in 2017, allowing for a new eight-barrel plant. Cask-conditioned ales are occasionally available. ◆LIVE

Lostwithiel Amber (ABV 4.9%) BITTER

Fownes SIBA

Unit 2, Two Woods Estate, Talbots Lane, Brierley Hill, West Midlands, DY5 2YX ☎ 07790 766844

Office: 42 The Ridgeway, Sedgley, West Midlands, DY3 3UR ⊕ fownesbrewing.co.uk

⊕The brewery was established in 2012 by James and Tom Fownes in premises to the rear of the Jolly Crispin, Upper Gornal. A recent expansion saw the brewery moved to a new site in Brierley Hill. Frequent specials along a 'Dwarfen Ales' theme are brewed in addition to the core range. Fownes opened its first pub in Burton in 2020. ‼◆LIVE

Elephant Riders (ABV 4%) BITTER
Gunhild (ABV 4%) SPECIALITY
Bright with creamy, lingering head. Smooth mouthfeel. Pleasant earthy aroma with hints of blackcurrants and honey. Peardrops and caramel with some malt and blackcurrant flavour. Dry malty aftertaste.
Crispin's Ommer (ABV 4.1%) BITTER
Frost Hammer (ABV 4.6%) PALE
Blonde and bright with a clingy head. Pine resin, nutmeg, malt, lemon and floral aroma. Dry mouthfeel with coffee, sweet malt and grapefruit flavours. Grapefruit and hoppy aftertaste.
Firebeard's Old Favourite No. 5 Ruby Ale (ABV 5%) MILD
Creamy head, rich red colour. Malty, fresh earth, rhubarb and some coffee in the aroma. Smooth mouthfeel. Dark chocolate and plum dominate the flavour with hints of malt and coffee. A pleasant dryness in the aftertaste, with hints of coffee, plum and cocoa.
King Korvak's Saga (ABV 5.4%) PORTER
Peardrop and cocoa aroma with hints of coffee. Coffee, toasted malt, blackcurrant and slight cocoa taste, with rich malty tones in the aftertaste.

Fox

▌ 22 Station Road, Heacham, Norfolk, PE31 7EX
☎ (01485) 570345 ⊕ foxbrewery.co.uk

⊠ Based in an old cottage adjacent to the Fox & Hounds pub, Fox Brewery was established in 2002 and now supplies around 30 outlets as well as the pub. All the beers are brewed using malt from Crisps in Great Ryburgh. A hop garden next to the brewery, trialled during 2009, has been enlarged. ‼⬝◆LIVE

Heacham Gold (ABV 3.9%) GOLD
Red Knocker (ABV 3.9%) BITTER
Norfolk Strongarm (ABV 4%) BITTER
A well-balanced, malty brew with a hoppy, bitter background. Long finish with a growing sultana-like fruitiness.
Cerberus Stout (ABV 4.5%) STOUT
Nelson's Blood (ABV 4.7%) SPECIALITY
Grizzly Bear (ABV 4.8%) SPECIALITY

IPA (ABV 5.2%) PALE

Fox One (NEW)

11 Brecon Walk, Southville, Cwmbran, NP44 3QF
✉ accounts@foxonebrewing.co.uk

Brewing began in 2021, producing bottles and mini kegs.

Foxfield

▌ Prince of Wales, Foxfield, Cumbria, LA20 6BX
☎ (01229) 716238 ⊕ princeofwalesfoxfield.co.uk

⊕Foxfield is a 4.5-barrel plant in old stables attached to the Prince of Wales. Several other outlets are supplied. Tiger Tops in Wakefield is also owned. The beer range constantly changes. Brewing is currently suspended. ‼◆

Framework

The Old City Depot, 72-74 Friday Street, Leicester, LE1 3BW ⊕ frameworkbrewery.com

⊠ Framework is a six-barrel brewery in an historic Victorian red-brick City Centre building, that started brewing in 2016. Alongside its core range of ales it also offers changing seasonal beers, collaboration and one-off experimental brews. Both traditional and modern hop-forward beers are available. ‼◆V

Fosse (ABV 3.7%) BITTER
Jackpin Pale Ale (ABV 3.9%) PALE
Fox Paw (ABV 4%) BITTER
Friday St IPA (ABV 4.5%) PALE

Frank & Otis

See Hanlons

Frank's Head (NEW)

19 Dymoke Road, Methley, LS26 9FG ☎ 07949 846438 ⊕ franksheadbrewery.co.uk

Established in 2020 in Methley producing small batch, hop-forward beers for canned distribution.

Franklins SIBA

Highfields Farm, The Broyle, Ringmer, East Sussex, BN8 5AR ⊕ franklinsbrewery.co.uk

⊠ Owned by Steve Medniuk, Franklins moved to a new site in Ringmer in order to aid expansion. A 10-barrel brew plant is currently used. Beers are available throughout the South East, London and beyond. ‼V

English Garden (ABV 3.8%) GOLD
Lawless (ABV 3.8%) GOLD
Eclipse (ABV 4%) PORTER
What Mama Don't Know (ABV 4.1%) BITTER
Kaleidohop (ABV 5%) PALE

Freedom SIBA

1 Park Lodge House, Bagots Park, Abbots Bromley, Staffordshire, WS15 3ES
☎ (01283) 840721 ⊕ freedombrewery.com

Freedom specialises in producing hand-crafted English lagers, all brewed in accordance with the German Reinheitsgebot purity law. No real ale. ‼⬝

Freestyle

▌ Church Road, Shustoke, Warwickshire, B46 2LB
☎ (01675) 481205 ⊕ griffininnshustoke.co.uk

Griffin Inn started brewing in 2008 in the old coffin shop adjacent to the pub. In 2017 the brewery was updated to a modern, more efficient 2.5-barrel plant. At this time the name was changed to Freestyle though the business is still owned by the Pugh family who run the Griffin. Beers are available for the free trade as well as selling through the pub. ‼◆

Freetime

19 St Lukes Court, Clarke Way, Winch Wen, Swansea, SA1 7ER
☎ (01792) 713731 ☎ 07291 253227
⊕ hello@freetimebeer.co

Microbrewery operations began in 2016, brewing small batches of craft beer available in bottles, keg and cask, under the name West by Three. A broad variety of styles are produced using the finest ingredients and tasty Welsh water. Beers are always unfined, using instead a combination of time, temperature and, if appropriate, filtering, to achieve the specific clarity for the style.

Freewheelin'

Peebles Hydro, Innerleithen Road, Peebles, EH45 8LX
☎ 07802 175826 ⊕ freewheelinbrewery.co.uk

Freewheelin' began brewing in 2013 and is based in Peebles. It is located in a former joiners shed in the grounds of the Peebles Hydro Hotel. Local spring water is used in the brewing process. ‼◆

Blonde (ABV 3.8%) BLOND
IPA (ABV 4.2%) PALE
Ruby (ABV 4.4%) MILD
Stout (ABV 4.4%) BARLEY

Frensham

See Craft Brews

Fresh Standard (NEW)

Unit 1a, Aston Down Business Park, Stroud, Gloucestershire, GL6 8GA
☎ (01453) 802400

Office: 3 West Tynings, Nailsworth, GL6 0EH
⊕ thefreshstandard.co.uk

⊗ Founded at the end of 2020 by experienced brewer Richard Taylor, renting brewing space from Artisan Ales. Two core beers, alongside frequent, one-off, experimental brews are available. Beers may be purchased online from the website.

Solution (ABV 4.8%) PALE
Pothering (ABV 6.2%) IPA

Friday Beer

Unit 4, Link Business Centre, Link Way, Malvern, Worcestershire, WR14 1UQ
☎ (01684) 572648 ⊕ thefridaybeer.com

Founded in 2011, the Friday Beer Co primarily produces bottle-conditioned ales. The range of bottles now sells across the region and to a growing number of outlets, from Birmingham to London, and south of the M4 corridor (including local restaurants and venues). ‼ ⏵LIVE

Jubilee (ABV 3.1%) MILD
Summer Hill Blonde (ABV 4.3%) BLOND
Pinnacle (ABV 4.5%) BITTER
WR14 (ABV 4.7%) BITTER
Friday Gold (ABV 5.6%) GOLD

Friends Arms

▤ Old St Clears Road, Johnstown, Carmarthen, SA31 3HH
☎ (01267) 234073 ⊕ thefriendsarms.co.uk

⊗ Friends Arms Brewery opened in 2011 on the premises of the Friends Arms, a traditional local community pub, which acts as the brewery tap. Brewing has stalled for more than a year, and to date, there is no sign that brewing will resume soon.

Friendship Adventure (NEW) SIBA

Unit G1, Coldharbour Works, 245a Coldharbour Lane, Loughborough Junction, London, SW9 8RR
⊕ friendship-adventure.com

Friendship Adventure began cuckoo brewing at a range of breweries, most recently Signal (qv). Its new brewery at Loughborough Junction opened in 2021 with an on-site taproom selling its range of keg beers. Canned beers are also available. No real ale. ◆

Frisky Bear

Unit 1, Vantage Point, Howley Park Road East, Morley, Leeds, West Yorkshire, LS27 0SU ☎ 07590 540210 ⊕ friskybear.com

☺Established in 2016, Frisky Bear upgraded from a one-barrel to a six-barrel plant and relocated in 2019. The beers are available on a rotating brewing schedule. Regularly available in Oscar's Bar, Morley, but also around West Yorkshire. LIVE V◆

Grizzly Bear (ABV 4.5%) PALE

Frome SIBA

Unit L13, Marshall Way, Commerce Park, Frome, Somerset, BA11 2FB
☎ (01373) 467766 ⊕ fromebrewingcompany.com

⊗ Formerly Milk Street Brewery, the business changed its name in 2018. The brewery was established in 1999 behind the Griffin, Frome, before moving to an industrial unit on the edge of town in 2016, and increasing its capabilities to 60 barrels. Beer is supplied direct to local outlets and wholesalers are used to distribute further afield. ‼◆V

Funky Monkey (ABV 4%) BITTER
Ra (ABV 4.1%) GOLD
The Usual (ABV 4.4%) BITTER
Zig-Zag Stout (ABV 4.5%) STOUT
Gulp IPA (ABV 4.8%) BITTER
Beer (ABV 5%) BLOND
Galaxy Australian Pale Ale (ABV 5.2%) PALE

Front Row SIBA

Unit A3, The Old School, Outclough Road, Brindley Ford, Staffordshire, ST8 7QD ☎ 07861 718673
⊕ frontrowbrewing.co.uk

After starting operations in Congleton in 2012 on a 2.5-barrel plant, Front Row expanded to an eight-barrel plant in 2014. It moved to its current location at the end of 2018 to allow for further increase in capacity. There is a brewery tap in nearby Biddulph. ‼◆

Number 8 (ABV 3.7%) MILD
Crouch (ABV 3.8%) BITTER
LOHAG (Land of Hops and Glory) (ABV 3.8%) GOLD
Touch (ABV 4%) BITTER
Sin Bin (ABV 4.2%) GOLD
Try (ABV 4.2%) BITTER

Half-Time (ABV 4.5%) SPECIALITY
Pause (ABV 4.5%) STOUT
Red Roses (ABV 4.5%) STOUT
Pride (ABV 4.6%) BITTER
Blindside (ABV 4.7%) GOLD
Crafty Flanker (ABV 4.7%) GOLD
Rucked (ABV 5.2%) OLD
Converted (ABV 5.4%) PORTER
Oblensky (ABV 7.3%) PORTER

Froth Blowers

Unit P35, Hastingwood Industrial Park, Wood Lane,
Erdington, West Midlands, B24 9QR ☎ 07966 935906
⊕ frothblowersbrewing.com

⊗ Froth Blowers began brewing in 2013, the name
derived from the Ancient Order of Froth Blowers, an
organisation dedicated to 'Lubrication in Moderation'!
The brewery has the capacity to brew 20 barrels at a site
only metres away from its original one, with most of the
beers being consumed within 30 miles of the brewery.
The brewery has also started making its beers available
in five-litre minikegs. ♦

Piffle Snonker (ABV 3.8%) BLOND
Straw-coloured. Aroma is almost jammy with a little malt
and hop. Taste is well-balanced with a slightly hoppier
aftertaste.
Bar-King Mad (ABV 4.2%) BITTER
Wellingtonian (ABV 4.3%) PALE
John Bull's Best (ABV 4.4%) BITTER
Gollop With Zest (ABV 4.5%) GOLD
Hornswoggle (ABV 5%) BLOND

Fuddy Duck

Unit 12, Kirton Business Park, Willington Road,
Kirton, Lincolnshire, PE20 1NN ☎ 07881 818875
⊕ thefuddyduckbrewery.co.uk

Small brewery based in Kirton near Boston, where
brewing commenced in 2016.

Pale Ale (ABV 4%) PALE
American Red Ale (ABV 4.5%) RED
Blonde Ale (ABV 4.5%) SPECIALITY
Dark Porter (ABV 4.5%) PORTER
German Ale Altbier (ABV 4.5%) SPECIALITY
Biere De Garde (ABV 6.5%) SPECIALITY

Fuggle Bunny SIBA

Unit 1, Meadowbrook Park Industrial Estate, Station
Road, Holbrook, Sheffield, South Yorkshire, S20 3PJ
☎ (0114) 248 4541 ☎ 07813 763347
⊕ fugglebunny.co.uk

⊗ Fuggle Bunny was established in 2014 and is an
independent, family-run brewery. The plant, originally
obtained from Flipside Brewery, has since been
expanded. The core range is supplemented by occasional
seasonal and special brews. Beers are delivered direct
within a 40-mile radius of the brewery and are available
nationally through wholesalers. Its first pub opened in
Worksop in 2017. ‼♦

Chapter 5 Oh Crumbs (ABV 3.8%) BITTER
Chapter 9 La La Land (ABV 3.9%) PALE
Chapter 2 Cotton Tail (ABV 4%) GOLD
Chapter 6 Hazy Summer Daze (ABV 4.2%) GOLD
Chapter 8 Jammy Dodger (ABV 4.5%) BITTER
Chapter 1 New Beginnings (ABV 4.9%) BITTER
Chapter 3 Orchard Gold (ABV 5%) GOLD
Chapter 7 Russian Rare-Bit (ABV 5%) STOUT
Chapter 4 24 Carrot (ABV 6%) BITTER

Full Circle SIBA

Hoults Yard, Walker Road, Newcastle upon Tyne,
NE6 2HL
☎ (0191) 481 4114 ⊕ fullcirclebrew.co.uk

Brewing began in 2019 in Hoult's Yard in Byker, another
addition to the real ale scene in this area. It also
incorporates a taproom, plus the Pip Stop bottled beer
shop. ♦

Repeater (ABV 4.2%) PALE
Hoop (ABV 5.5%) IPA
Looper (ABV 6.4%) IPA

Full Mash

17 Lower Park Street, Stapleford, Nottinghamshire,
NG9 8EW
☎ (0115) 949 9262 ⊕ fullmash.co.uk

☺Brewing commenced in 2003 and has grown steadily
since, with a gradual expansion in outlets and capacity. ♦

Horse & Jockey (ABV 3.8%) GOLD
Easy-drinking golden ale with moderate hoppy aroma
and finish.
Whistlin' Dixie (ABV 3.9%) BITTER
Séance (ABV 4%) GOLD
Predominantly hoppy golden beer, with a refreshing
bitter finish.
Illuminati (ABV 4.2%) BITTER
Gently-hopped golden ale with initial hops and
bitterness giving way to a short, bitter finish.
Wheat Ear (ABV 4.2%) SPECIALITY
Warlord (ABV 4.4%) BITTER
Amber-coloured beer with an initial malt taste, leading
to a dry, bitter finish.
Apparition (ABV 4.5%) BITTER
A pale hoppy bitter brewed with Brewers Gold hops.
Northern Lights (ABV 4.7%) STOUT
Manhattan (ABV 5.2%) PALE
Bhisti (ABV 6.2%) IPA

Fuller's

Griffin Brewery, Chiswick Lane South, Chiswick,
London, W4 2QB
☎ (020) 8996 2000 ⊕ fullers.co.uk

⊗ The Griffin brewery has stood for more than 360 years
with the Fullers name coming from the partnership
formed in 1845. Gales of Horndean was bought in 2005
and closed a year later, the beers are now brewed at
Chiswick. Dark Star of Sussex was bought in 2018 and
brewing continues there. Fullers sold its brewing
interests to Asahi in 2019 but kept its pubs and hotels.
‼↝♦LIVE

Oliver's Island (ABV 3.8%) GOLD
Well-balanced golden ale with fruity aroma and flavour.
Gentle bitter hoppiness balances a sweet, malty
character flavour and short finish.
London Pride (ABV 4.1%) BITTER
Well-balanced, smooth bitter with orange citrus fruit,
malt and hops in aroma and flavour lingering into a
slightly bitter aftertaste.
Bengal Lancer (ABV 5%) PALE
Rich, creamy, well-balanced, pale brown IPA with a gold
hue. Hops with a dryish bitterness harmonise with the
fruit and malty sweetness that linger into the aftertaste.
ESB (ABV 5.5%) PALE
Bitter orange marmalade with hops, creamy toffee and
some raisins are all present in this multifaceted, strong
brown bitter. A satisfying long, bitter, dry finish balanced
by a malty sweetness.

Brewed under the Gale's brand name:
Seafarers Ale (ABV 3.6%) BITTER
A pale brown bitter, predominantly malty, with a refreshing balance of fruit and hops that lingers into the aftertaste where a dry bitterness unfolds.
HSB (ABV 4.8%) BITTER
Dates and dried fruit with some spicy hops in the nose adding to the caramelised orange and treacle in the flavour of this smooth, brown beer. Malty throughout with a bittersweet finish.

Fulstow

See Firehouse

Funk Dungeon

See Abbeydale

Funky Hop Donkey

See Silver

Furnace

9 Duke Street, Derby, DE1 3BX
☎ (01332) 385981

Six-barrel brewhouse in the beer garden of the Furnace Inn on Duke Street. Supply is mainly for the pub, but beers can be seen at beer festivals and specialist pubs across the UK. V

Reprazent! (ABV 4.2%) SPECIALITY
Fun Sponge (ABV 4.3%) PALE
My Milk Stout (ABV 4.9%) STOUT

Furnace Brook (NEW)

Trolliloes Lane, Hailsham, East Sussex, BN27 4QR
☎ (01435) 830 835 ⊕ furnacebrook.co.uk/beer

Small batch brewery producing hand crafted bottled beers with local hops and no finings or sulphites.

Futtle

Unit 2, The Bowhouse, St Monans, KY10 2FB
⊕ futtle.com

Organic farmhouse brewery producing European-style beers. A 1,000-litre, 'coolship' (a shallow, open fermentation vessel), has been installed in the rafters of the brewery.

Fuzzchat

Jolly Coopers, 84 Wheelers Lane, Epsom, Surrey, KT18 7SD
☎ (01372) 723222 ⊕ fuzzchatbrewery.co.uk

Fuzzchat is Epsom's first brewery in more than 90 years. Housed behind the Jolly Coopers, it used to be an old blacksmith's cottage, recently restored after being derelict for several years. A Fuzzchat is anyone born on Epsom Common. ‼◆

Fuzzy Duck SIBA

18 Wood Street, Poulton Industrial Estate, Poulton-le-Fylde, Lancashire, FY6 8JY ☎ 07904 343729
⊕ fuzzyduckbrewery.co.uk

Fuzzy Duck was established in 2006. It relocated to Poulton-le-Fylde later that year, expanding capacity to an eight-barrel plant. The brewery delivers over a wide area

of North-West England and Yorkshire. Most beers are available bottle-conditioned. ‼◆LIVE

Golden Cascade (ABV 3.8%) GOLD
Mucky Duck (ABV 4%) STOUT
Pheasant Plucker (ABV 4.2%) BITTER
Cunning Stunt (ABV 4.3%) BITTER
Ruby Duck (ABV 5.3%) OLD

Fyne SIBA

Achadunan, Cairndow, PA26 8BJ
☎ (01499) 600120 ⊕ fyneales.com

Fyne Ales has been brewing since 2001 and is situated at the head of Loch Fyne. In 2012 an on-site brewery tap was added. Expansion has allowed for the production of experimental brews. FyneFest runs annually, celebrating local fare and showcasing other breweries. ‼▰◆LIVE✦

Jarl (ABV 3.8%) GOLD
Maverick (ABV 4.2%) BITTER
Full-bodied, roasty, tawny best bitter. It is balanced, fruity and well-hopped.
Hurricane Jack (ABV 4.4%) GOLD
Vital Spark (ABV 4.4%) PORTER
Avalanche (ABV 4.5%) GOLD
This true golden ale starts with stunning citrus hops on the nose. Well-balanced with good body and fruit balancing a refreshing hoppy taste, it finishes with a long bittersweet aftertaste.
Highlander (ABV 4.8%) BITTER
Full-bodied, bittersweet ale with a good, dry hop finish. In the style of a Heavy although the malt is less pronounced and the sweetness ebbs away to leave a bitter, hoppy finish.
Sublime (ABV 6.8%) STOUT
Superior IPA (ABV 7.1%) IPA

Gadds

See Ramsgate

Gale's

See Fuller's

Gallus

Glasgow, G1 1GG ⊕ gallusbrewing.scot

Gallus is a Glasgow-based gypsy brewery established in 2016.

Gan Yam

3 Benson View Works, Shap Road Industrial Estate, Kendal, LA9 6NZ ⊕ ganyambrew.co.uk

Initially a commercial home-based brewery based in north London when founded in 2018, it relocated to Kendal in early 2021. An on-site taproom is planned. ▰◆

Pal (ABV 3.9%) PALE
Aye (ABV 6%) IPA
Tar (ABV 7%) PORTER

Garden City

22 The Wynd, Letchworth Garden City, Hertfordshire, SG6 3EN ☎ 07932 739558
⊕ gardencitybrewery.co.uk

A brewbar established in 2016 using a 2.5-barrel plant, serving a selection of its own ales plus guests on gravity.

Gasworks

First Street, Manchester, M15 4FN

Gasworks is a six-barrel brewpub from the team behind Dockyard, opened in 2016. It supplies Gasworks Tap, Dockyard, Salford Quays and Dockyard, Spinningfields.

Gates Burton

Reservoir Road, Burton upon Trent, Staffordshire, DE14 2BP
☎ (01283) 532567 ☎ 07957 930772
⊕ gatesburtonbrewery.co.uk

☺The Gates Burton Brewery was established in 2011 using a one-barrel plant. This has now expanded to a three-barrel plant, representing cottage brewing at its finest. All beer is available in cask in the free trade. !! ♦

Reservoir (ABV 4.6%) BITTER
Pale brown with a malty aroma and roast hint. Caramel and malt lead to a sweet hop, balanced taste. Hops arrive late on the palate to urge another mouthful.
Gates Burton Ale (GBA) (ABV 4.8%) BITTER
Damn (ABV 5%) BITTER
Reservoir Gold (ABV 7.5%) BARLEY

Geipel SIBA

Pant Glas, Llangwm, Corwen, LL21 0RN
☎ (01490) 420838 ⊕ geipel.co.uk

Geipel commenced brewing in 2013 producing unpasteurised and unfiltered beers. The brewery specialises in lagers, drawing inspiration from the classic styles of Germany and beyond. Available in keg, KeyKeg and bottle. LIVE

Gemstone

See Nelson

Gentlewood

Fir Tree Cottage, Tithe Barn, Gentleshaw, Staffordshire, WS15 4LR ☎ 07544 146900
✉ gentlewoodbrewery@hotmail.com

Gentlewood began in 2018 and is co-owned and run by Darren Williams and Ben Colthorpe, it is a Staffordshire-based brewery specialising in traditional cask ales using British hops and grain.

Heritage (ABV 4.2%) BITTER

George Samuel

Unit 3, Norland House Business Centre, Shildon, DL4 1HE ☎ 07840 892751

Named after the brewer's two sons, the brewery originally set up as a two-barrel plant in 2014 at the Duke of Wellington pub in Welbury near Northallerton before moving to Spennymoor and closing in late 2018. The brewery reopened as an eight-barrel plant in 2020 in Shildon, the 'Cradle of the Railways', in a unit which formerly housed the offices of Shildon Wagon Works. ♦

Locomotion No 1 (ABV 4%) PALE
Leaves on the Line (ABV 4.2%) GOLD
Travelling Light (ABV 4.5%) PALE
Harvey (ABV 5.2%) PORTER
Terminus (ABV 5.5%) IPA

George's SIBA

Common Road, Great Wakering, Essex, SS3 0AG

☎ (01702) 826755 ☎ 07771 871255
⊕ georgesbrewery.com

⊗ George's Brewery and Hop Monster Brewing Company (qv) are owned by the same brewer, using the same plant. George's concentrates on traditional styles and Hop Monster on the more unusual. !! ⟟ ♦LIVE

Wallasea Wench (ABV 3.6%) BITTER
Wakering Gold (ABV 3.8%) GOLD
8-Bit Bitter (ABV 4%) BITTER
Best (ABV 4%) BITTER
Cockleboats (ABV 4%) BITTER
Empire (ABV 4%) BITTER
Figaro (ABV 4%) PALE
Banshee Porter (ABV 4.4%) SPECIALITY
Broadsword (ABV 4.7%) BITTER
Excalibur (ABV 5.4%) GOLD
Excalibur Reserve (ABV 7.2%) STRONG

Brewed under the Hop Monster Brewery name:
Rakau (ABV 4.2%) GOLD
Snake Oil Stout (ABV 5%) STOUT

German Kraft

Mercato Metropolitano, 42 Newington Causeway, Borough, London, SE1 6DR

Mayfair: Mercato Metropolitano, 13a North Audley Street, Mayfair, London, W1K 6ZA

Dalston: Kraft Dalston, 130a Kingsland High Street, Dalston, London, E8 2LQ ⊕ germankraftbeer.com

Opening in 2017, to start with, beer was imported from its German brewery in Bavaria, Steinbach. In early 2018 the brewery officially opened and beers were replicated on-site. The core range and seasonals reflect traditional German styles including lagering for four weeks. Further breweries have opened in Mayfair and Dalston. No real ale. ♦

Gert Lush (NEW)

Hurn Farm Buildings, Ashmore Drove, Wells, Somerset, BA5 1NS ☎ 07476 662948
⊕ gertlushbeer.co.uk

Gert Lush is a new craft brewery established during the pandemic, situated near Wells on the Somerset Levels. All beers are brewed using organic malt, hops, carefully-cultured yeasts and spring water and are suitable for vegans. Most are also gluten-free. No real ale. GF V

Ghost

Unit D, Tong Business Centre, Otley Road, Baildon, West Yorkshire, BD17 7QD
☎ (0113) 418 2002 ☎ 01896 097882
⊕ ghostbrew.co.uk

Ghost Brew Co is the creation of Steve Crump and James Thompson.

Gibberish

15 Caryl Street, Liverpool, L8 5AA ☎ 07871 645864

Gibberish is a brewpub that opened in 2017 in Liverpool's Baltic Triangle. Brewing is currently suspended.

Gil's

12 Greenfield Avenue, Dinas Powis, CF64 4BW
☎ 07882 076321

Brewing began in 2018. Beer is available in kegs and bottles. No real ale.

Gilbert White's (NEW)

Gilbert White's House, High Street, Selborne, Hampshire, GU34 3JH
☎ (01420) 511275 ⊕ gilbertwhiteshouse.org.uk

One-barrel plant attached to the Gilbert White Museum. It produces bottle and cask-conditioned beer using a modern brewing kit in the original brewhouse established by renowned naturalist Gilbert White in 1765 and reopened late 2020 and staffed by volunteers. Bottled beer is sold through the museum shop; cask beer is often available in the nearby Selborne Arms. Other outlets are planned and the brewery's portable bar can be seen at local events. ⬛LIVE

New Bostal (ABV 4.3%) PALE
Capt Lawrence Oates (ABV 5.5%) IPA
Zig Zag Ale (ABV 6.7%) STRONG

Gilt & Flint (NEW)

Haye Farm, Haye Lane, Musbury, EX13 8ST ☎ 07904 035640 ⊕ giltandflint.com

This new brewery is based on the beautiful Haye Farm in an Area of Outstanding Natural Beauty in East Devon. Using age old traditional brewing techniques, it has created organic modern new world beers, ciders and soft drinks. All of the agricultural by-product goes to feed the free-range livestock on the farm.

Gipsy Hill SIBA

Unit 8, Hamilton Road Industrial Estate, 160 Hamilton Road, West Norwood, London, SE27 9SF
☎ (020) 8761 9061 ⊕ gipsyhillbrew.com

Gipsy Hill opened in 2014 at the same time and on the same site as London Beer Factory. It has since expanded into adjacent units and the taproom moved across the yard. A core range of six is supplemented by regular specials, all available in keg and cans. Cask had been dropped but was reinstated for 2021. ♦◆

Glamorgan SIBA

Unit B Llantrisant Business Park, Llantrisant, CF72 8LF
☎ (01443) 406080

Office: Unit J, Llantrisant Business Park, Llantrisant, CF72 8LF ⊕ glamorganbrewingco.com

⊛This family-owned and run brewery moved to its present site in 2013. Production capacity has increased significantly year-on-year and a new, bigger brewery is anticipated. A range of year-round and seasonal ales are produced, with additional special brews to mark notable events. The brewery shop is open daily and brewery tours are available for groups by prior arrangement. Direct deliveries are made throughout Wales and distributed further afield by selected wholesalers and breweries. ⬛♦

Cwrw Gorslas/Bluestone Bitter (ABV 4%) BITTER
Welsh Pale Ale (ABV 4.1%) PALE
Jemimas Pitchfork (ABV 4.4%) BITTER
Thunderbird (ABV 4.5%) BITTER

Glasgow Beer Works SIBA

Block 23, Unit 2, Queenslie Industrial Estate, Glasgow, G33 4JJ
☎ (0141) 258 1661

Office: Pavillion 1, Finnieston Business Park, Minerva Way, Glasgow, G3 8AU ⊕ glasgowbeerworks.com

Established in 2017 as Merchant City Brewing using a 12-barrel plant, Glasgow Beer Works moved and rebranded in 2020. In addition to the core range, small pilot batches and barrel-aged beers are produced. 25 outlets are supplied direct, plus specialist off-licences across central Scotland. A pop-up bar in Osborne Street, beneath the John Byrne mural of Billy Connolly opened in 2020.

Session Ale (ABV 3.9%) GOLD
Unit 1 Red Ale (ABV 4%) RED
American Pale Ale (ABV 4.7%) PALE
Vienna Lager (ABV 5%) SPECIALITY
IPA (ABV 5.8%) IPA

Glasshouse

Unit 6b, Waterside Business Park, Stirchley, B30 3DR
⊕ glasshousebeer.co.uk

Glasshouse opened in 2018 run by Josh Hughes and has since expanded to employ an experienced team. Brewing mainly keg and KeyKeg beers in a broad range of exciting new styles, with occasional casks sold to the local trade. It also cans a lot of the beers for local bottle shops and direct supply.

Glastonbury

Park Corner Farm, Glastonbury, Somerset, BA6 8JY
☎ (01458) 830750 ⊕ glastonburyales.com

Established in 2002 as Glastonbury Ales on a five-barrel plant, it changed ownership and moved to Somerton, increasing capacity to a 20-barrel plant. Cider is also produced. In 2019 it relocated to Glastonbury. ‼◆LIVE

Glen Affric

Unit 2 & 3, Lightbox, Knox Street, Birkenhead, Merseyside, CH41 5JG ☎ 07742 020275

Office: 53 Wood Street, Ashton-under-Lyne, OL6 7NB ⊕ glenaffricbrewery.com

⊠ Established in 2016, a small batch brewery producing only keg beers. Its extensive tank farm allows for a flexible brew length. The brewery contract brews for other breweries. ‼⬛◆

Glen Spean SIBA

Tirindrish Steading, Tirindrish, Spean Bridge, PH34 4EU ☎ 07487 953714
⊕ glenspeanbrewing.com

Based in a converted steading, brewing began in 2018.

Globe

▤ 144 High Street West, Glossop, Derbyshire, SK13 8HJ
☎ (01457) 852417 ⊕ globepub.co.uk

Globe was established in 2006 by Ron Brookes on a 2.5-barrel plant in an old stable behind the Globe pub. Grandson Toby now has a major role in the brewery under the watchful eye of Ron. The beers are mainly for the pub but special one-off brews are produced for beer festivals. ◆

Gloucester SIBA

Fox's Kiln, West Quay, The Docks, Gloucester, GL1 2LG
☎ (01452) 668043 ☎ 07503 152749
⊕ gloucesterbrewery.co.uk

⊠ Situated in the historic Gloucester Docks, brewing began in 2011 and has expanded into larger dockside premises to meet demand. Further expansion is planned.

The original site is now its bar, named Tank. The full range of beers is regularly available in Gloucestershire and beyond. Beers are brewed in cask, keg and cans, most are unfined. A range of gins and vodkas is also distilled on site. The brewery is committed to being carbon neutral by the end of 2022. !! ▰ ♦ LIVE V ✿

Session Pale (ABV 3.7%) PALE
Gold (ABV 3.9%) GOLD
Priory Pale (ABV 3.9%) PALE
Cascade (ABV 4.2%) BITTER
Session IPA (ABV 4.5%) PALE
Six Malt Porter (ABV 4.5%) PORTER
Dockside Dark (ABV 5.2%) PORTER
New England IPA (ABV 5.2%) PALE

Goacher's

Unit 8, Tovil Green Business Park, Burial Ground Lane, Tovil, Maidstone, Kent, ME15 6TA
☎ (01622) 682112 ⊕ goachers.com

A traditional brewery that uses only malt and Kentish hops for all its beers. Phil and Debbie Goacher have concentrated on brewing good wholesome beers without gimmicks. Two tied houses and around 30 free trade outlets in the mid-Kent area are supplied. Special is brewed for sale under house names. !! ♦

Real Mild Ale (ABV 3.4%) MILD
A rich, flavourful mild with moderate roast barley and a generous helping of chocolate malt.
Fine Light Ale (ABV 3.7%) BITTER
A pale, golden brown bitter with a strong, floral, hoppy aroma and aftertaste. A hoppy and moderately malty session beer.
Special/House Ale (ABV 3.8%) BITTER
Best Dark Ale (ABV 4.1%) BITTER
Dark in colour but light and quaffable in body, this ale features hints of caramel and chocolate malt throughout.
Crown Imperial Stout (ABV 4.5%) STOUT
A good, well-balanced, roasty stout, dark and bitter with just a hint of caramel and a lingering creamy head.
Gold Star Strong Ale (ABV 5.1%) BLOND
A strong pale ale brewed from 100% Maris Otter malt and East Kent Goldings hops.

Goddards SIBA

Barnsley Farm, Bullen Road, Ryde, Isle of Wight, PO33 1QF
☎ (01983) 611011 ⊕ goddardsbrewery.com

⊠ Anthony Goddard established, what is now the oldest, active brewery on the Isle of Wight, in 1993. Originally occupying an 18th century barn, a new brewery was built in 2008, quadrupling its capacity, which has since been further increased. Goddards' remain a locally-focused business distributing ales on the island and the easily accessible counties of southern England. Beers are also contract brewed for Crumbs Brewery, where breadcrumbs replace about a quarter of the malt usual in the brewing process. ♦

Ale of Wight (ABV 3.7%) BITTER
Starboard (ABV 4%) GOLD
Wight Squirrel (ABV 4.3%) BITTER
Fuggle-Dee-Dum (ABV 4.8%) BITTER
Brown-coloured strong ale with plenty of malt and hops.

Contract brewed for Yates':
Islander (ABV 4%) BITTER

Godstone SIBA

Flower Farm, Oxted Road, Godstone, Surrey, RH9 8BP
☎ 07791 570731

Office: 3 Willow Way, Godstone, RH9 8NQ
⊕ thegodstonebrewers.com

⊠ The Godstone Brewers was established in 2015 using a one-barrel plant but moved to larger premises on a farm in Godstone, using a 12-barrel plant. Beers are named with local themes. Local outlets are supplied. A taproom has been built. !! ▰ ♦ LIVE V ✿

Up Up and Away (ABV 2.7%) PALE
Trenchman's Hop (ABV 3.8%) BITTER
Redgate (ABV 4%) BITTER
Pondtail (ABV 4.1%) PALE
Junction 6 (ABV 4.2%) BLOND
Forever (ABV 4.3%) PALE
Rusty's Ale (ABV 4.4%) BITTER
Tunnel Vision (ABV 4.6%) SPECIALITY
Buzz (ABV 4.7%) SPECIALITY
Bitter Entropy (ABV 5.3%) BITTER
Polly's Potion (ABV 6.5%) PORTER

Goff's SIBA

9 Isbourne Way, Winchcombe, Cheltenham, Gloucestershire, GL54 5NS
☎ (01242) 603383 ⊕ goffsbrewery.com

⊠ Goff's is a family concern that has been brewing cask-conditioned ales since 1994. The ales are available regionally in more than 200 outlets and nationally through wholesalers. ▰ ♦

Lancer (ABV 3.8%) GOLD
Jouster (ABV 4%) BITTER
A drinkable, tawny-coloured ale, with a light hoppiness in the aroma. It has a good balance of malt and bitterness in the mouth, underscored by fruitiness, with a clean, hoppy aftertaste.
Tournament (ABV 4%) BITTER
Dark golden in colour, with a pleasant hop aroma. A clean, light and refreshing session bitter with a pleasant hop aftertaste.
Fallen Knight (ABV 4.4%) BITTER
Cheltenham Gold (ABV 4.5%) GOLD
White Knight (ABV 4.7%) BITTER
A well-hopped bitter with a light colour and full-bodied taste. Bitterness predominates in the mouth and leads to a dry, hoppy aftertaste.
Jester Brew 6 (ABV 5%) SPECIALITY

Golden Duck

Unit 2, Redhill Farm, Top Street, Appleby Magna, Leicestershire, DE12 7AH ☎ 07846 295179
⊕ goldenduckbrewery.com

Golden Duck began brewing in 2012 using a five-barrel plant. It is run by the father-and-son team of Andrew and Harry Lunn. Beers have a cricket-related theme and are always available in Mushroom Hall, Albert Village and Cellar Bar, Sir John Moore Hall, Appleby Magna (Friday evenings only). ♦ LIVE

Hayles' Ale (ABV 3.8%) BITTER
Golden Duck Extra Pale (ABV 4.2%) PALE
LFB (Lunns First Brew) (ABV 4.3%) GOLD
Lunnys No8 (ABV 4.8%) BITTER

Golden Triangle SIBA

Unit 9, Watton Road Industrial Estate, Norwich, NR9 4BG
☎ (01603) 757763 ☎ 07976 281132
⊕ goldentriangle.co.uk

⊠ Golden Triangle, named after an area of Norwich, has been brewing modern, hop-forward ales on a 10-barrel plant since 2011. The brewery continues to add new beers to its range. Beers are mainly found in pubs across Norwich. The Artichoke, Norwich, purchased by owner and brewer Kevin Tweedy in 2018, is the brewery tap (two beers permanently available). ◆

Table Bitter (ABV 3.3%) BITTER
Well-balanced bitterness with crisp hoppiness and a flowing malt background. An almond bitterness surfaces in a long, dry finish.
Mosaic City (ABV 3.8%) GOLD
Full-bodied, lemon citrus character throughout. Hops provide depth throughout. A subtle, malty bitterness quickly fades.
Simcoe City (ABV 3.8%) BITTER
Peach and lemon nose. A full-bodied and fruity, sweet malt beginning. A notable bitter edge to the finish.
Citropolis (ABV 3.9%) GOLD
Equinoxity (ABV 3.9%) PALE
Understated melange of hop, pineapple and lemon throughout. Gentle malt airs arrive in a short, sweet finish.

Goldmark SIBA

Unit 23, The Vinery, Arundel Road, Arundel, West Sussex, BN18 9PY
☎ (01903) 297838 ☎ 07900 555415
⊕ goldmarks.co.uk

⊠ Ex-biochemist and homebrewer Mark Lehmann began commercial brewing in 2013 using an 11-barrel plant. ‼LIVE

Ebony Mild (ABV 3.5%) MILD
Liquid Gold (ABV 4%) GOLD
Wurst Bitter (ABV 4%) SPECIALITY
Pheonix (ABV 4.1%) BITTER
Red IPA (ABV 4.3%) RED
American Hop Idol (ABV 4.4%) PALE
Warrior (ABV 4.6%) BROWN
Black Lion Porter (ABV 4.8%) PORTER
GSB (ABV 4.8%) BARLEY
Vertigo Craft Lager (ABV 4.8%) SPECIALITY
Pitch Shifter IPA (ABV 5%) PALE

Good Chemistry SIBA

Unit 2, William Street, St Philips, Bristol, BS2 0RG
☎ (0117) 903 9930 ⊕ goodchemistrybrewing.co.uk

⊠ Good Chemistry was established in 2015 in a warehouse in St Philips, Bristol by Bob Cary and Kelly Sidgwick, using a 10-barrel plant. As the name suggests, all brewery and beer logos have a scientific theme. Brewery open days are held. LIVE

Natural Selection (ABV 4%) PALE
Hops and pale malt aromas, initially sweet body is followed by hoppy bitterness which continues into the short, dry finish.
Kokomo Weekday (ABV 4.3%) PALE
Hazy, golden-coloured ale with hop and sweet fruit aroma which continues onto the palate before a short, bitter finish.

Good Stuff

▤ Abdication, 89 Mansfield Road, Daybrook, Arnold, Nottingham, Nottinghamshire, NG5 6BH
⊕ theabdication.co.uk

A nanobrewery located inside the Abdication micropub. Capacity is 0.5-barrels so occasional beers can only be found at the pub and local beer festivals.

Good Things

Rendlye Farm, Sandhill Lane, Eridge, TN3 9LP
☎ (020) 7780 7499 ⊕ goodthingsbrewing.co

Brewing began in 2018. Good things is a sustainable brewery, meaning that its aim is to be energy-efficient, with everything recycled and reused. Beer is available in kegs and cans in more than 100 outlets. No real ale.

Goodness

5a, Clarendon Yards, Coburg Road, Wood Green, London, N22 6TZ ⊕ thegoodnessbrew.co

⊠ A community-focused microbrewery, with taproom and event space, since 2019, having previously brewed at Sentinel and House. The range consists of six core and various one-offs. All are unfiltered and vegan beers which are variously available as cask, keg or can. Cask Wood Green Hopping is brewed annually with local hops from Harringey. V◆

Yes! Session IPA (ABV 4.5%) SPECIALITY
Gold, smooth rye beer. Impactful flavours of citrus, mango, perfumed hops and sweet biscuit. Finish starts bitter with a growing dryness.

Goodwood SIBA

The New Brewery, Stane Street, North Heath, West Sussex, RH20 1DJ ⊕ goodwood.com/estate/home-farm/goodwood-brewery

Beers are available in bottle and keg in restaurants and bars across the Goodwood estate. The beer is brewed by Hepworth (qv) using ingredients grown on the estate.

Goody SIBA

Bleangate Brewery, Braggs Lane, Herne, Kent, CT6 7NP
☎ (01227) 361555 ⊕ goodyales.co.uk

Goody Ales began brewing in 2012 using a 10-barrel plant. A wood-burning boiler is used to heat the water for the brews using wood from its copse, thereby minimising the use of non-renewable fuel. An on-site bar and shop, the Cathedral, is open (limited hours). ◆LIVE

Good Evening (ABV 3.4%) MILD
Genesis (ABV 3.5%) RED
Good Health (ABV 3.6%) BITTER
Good Life (ABV 3.9%) BLOND
Good Heavens (ABV 4.1%) BITTER
Good Sheppard (ABV 4.5%) BITTER
Goodness Gracious Me (ABV 4.8%) BITTER
Good Lord (ABV 5%) PORTER

Goose Eye SIBA

Unit 5, Castlefield Industrial Estate, Crossflatts, Bingley, West Yorkshire, BD16 2AF
☎ (01274) 512743 ⊕ goose-eye-brewery.co.uk

☺Goose Eye is a family-run brewery established in 1991, supplying numerous regular outlets, mainly in Yorkshire and Lancashire. The beers are available directly or through national wholesalers and pub chains. Goose Eye moved in 2017 to a custom-built brewery which has enabled them to increase production with a 20-barrel brew run. The new brewery bar is open every Friday and Saturday. ◆ ⚮

Springwell (ABV 3.6%) PALE
Blackmoor (ABV 3.9%) MILD
Goose Eye Bitter (ABV 3.9%) BITTER

Traditional, Yorkshire, brown, session bitter, well-balanced malt and hops with a pleasingly bitter finish.
Chinook Blonde (ABV 4.2%) BLOND
Assertive, grapefruit hoppiness in the aroma and tropical flavours
Golden Goose (ABV 4.5%) BLOND
Over and Stout (ABV 5.2%) STOUT
A full-bodied stout with roast and malt flavours mingling with hops, dark fruit and liquorice on the palate. Look also for tart fruit on the nose and a growing bitter finish.
Pommies Revenge (ABV 5.2%) BITTER
Golden, strong bitter combining grassy hops, a cocktail of fruit flavours, a peppery hint and a hoppy, bitter finish.

Goose Island

⬛ 222 Shoreditch High Street, Shoreditch, London, E1 6PJ
☎ (020) 3657 6555 ⊕ gooseislandshoreditch.com

The Chicago-based Goose Island brewery opened its London brewpub in 2018. The on-site kit brews a range of continually changing beers only available at the pub, including a bourbon barrel-aged version of a changing beer (the barrel can be seen behind the bar). One real ale from the range is usually available.

Gorgeous

⬛ Bull, 13 North Hill, Highgate, London, N6 4AB
☎ (020) 8341 0510 ☎ 07714 649988
⊕ gorgeousbrewery.com

⊗ Formerly the home of London Brewing, Gorgeous inherited the brewing kit on the purchase of the pub in 2017. At the beginning of 2018 a newly-built brewhouse at the rear of the pub came on stream. This extra capacity has seen a wider range of cask, keg and bottled beers, including collaborations, available in the pub and nationally. LIVE ◆

Greedyguts (ABV 3.5%) GOLD
Glowfly (ABV 4%) BITTER
Pale brown, easy-drinking bitter with apples and orange aroma. Hops, orange and caramel flavours with a lingering, peppery, bitter finish.
Geekhunter (ABV 4.2%) GOLD
Refreshing, dryish golden ale. Hint of honey sweetness and citrus in flavour and aroma with some hops. Spicy, bitterish finish.
Gunpowder (ABV 4.8%) BITTER
Amber, smooth beer with hoppy, tangy nose. Flavour is of orange and biscuit with notes of bitter, earthy hops.
Gravedigger (ABV 5%) SPECIALITY

Gorilla SIBA

Unit 3, Glasshouse Lane, Cliff Street, Mexborough, S64 9HU ☎ 07747 484368 ⊕ gorillabrewing.co.uk

Co-founders Jason White and Phil Paling launched Gorilla Brewing in 2020 next to the Sheffield and South Yorkshire Navigation canal. ◆

Silverback Blonde (ABV 3.8%) PALE
Monkey Magic (ABV 4.5%) SPECIALITY
Orang-A-Tang (ABV 4.5%) SPECIALITY
Kong (ABV 6%) IPA
Vanilla Gorilla (ABV 6%) SPECIALITY

Gower SIBA

Unit 25, Crofty Industrial Estate, Penclawdd, SA4 3RS
☎ (01792) 850681 ⊕ gowerbrewery.com

⊗ Established in 2011 on a five-barrel brew plant at the Greyhound Inn, Llanrhidian. Moved to a new 20-barrel

brewery in Crofty, Gower in 2015. Seasonal and speciality ales are brewed alongside established beers. ‼🍴◆

Brew 1 (ABV 3.8%) BITTER
Best Bitter (ABV 4.5%) BITTER
Gold (ABV 4.5%) GOLD
Rumour (ABV 5%) RED
Shipwreck (ABV 5.1%) PALE
Power (ABV 5.5%) BITTER

Grafham

30 Breach Road, Grafham, Cambridgeshire, PE28 0BA
☎ 07590 836241 ⊕ grafhambrewing.co

Grafham Brewing Co is a 1.8-barrel brewery that began commercial production in 2019.

Hodders Panama (ABV 4.8%) PALE

Grafton

Walters Yard, Unit 4 Claylands Industrial Estate, Worksop, Nottinghamshire, S81 7DW
☎ (01909) 307710 ☎ 07542 012610
Office: 8 Oak Close, Crabtree Park Estate, Worksop, S80 1BH ⊕ graftonfineales.co.uk

☺ Founded in 2007 as Grafton Brewing Company, behind the Packet Inn on Bescoby Street in Retford. Relocated to the present premises in Worksop in 2014, where the plant was increased in size from five to 15 barrels to meet demand. The brewery tap is its micro bar, the Malt House on Potter Street, Worksop ‼◆

Pasha Pasha (ABV 4%) GOLD
Raspberry Redemption (ABV 4%) SPECIALITY
Golden ale with a raspberry aroma and taste, leading to a sweet and slightly bitter finish.
Vanilla Heights (ABV 4%) SPECIALITY
Copper Jack (ABV 4.5%) BITTER
Garside Gold (ABV 4.5%) GOLD
Priorswell Pale (ABV 4.5%) PALE
Apricot Jungle (ABV 4.8%) SPECIALITY
Bananalicious (ABV 4.8%) SPECIALITY
Caramel Stout (ABV 4.8%) STOUT
Tango with a Mango (ABV 4.8%) SPECIALITY
Coco Loco (ABV 5%) SPECIALITY
Dark-coloured, smooth-drinking ale, infused with coconut, gentle bitterness.
Don Jon (ABV 5%) PALE

Grain SIBA

South Farm, Tunbeck Road, Alburgh, Norfolk, IP20 0BS
☎ (01986) 788884 ⊕ grainbrewery.co.uk

⊗ Grain Brewery was launched in 2006 by Geoff Wright and Phil Halls in a converted dairy in the Waveney Valley. It upgraded to an 18-barrel plant in 2012. Two pubs are owned: the Plough, Norwich, and the Spread Eagle, Ipswich. ‼🍴◆LIVE

Oak (ABV 3.8%) BITTER
Good balance of malt, toffee and bittersweet fruitiness. Caramel in initial taste fades as biscuit and bitterness dominate the aftertaste.
ThreeOneSix (ABV 3.9%) GOLD
Hop and grapefruit dominate throughout as an underlying bitterness slowly stifles a delicate malty echo. Crisp and well-defined.
Best Bitter (ABV 4.2%) BITTER
Brazil nut and malt introduce this well-balanced, complex bitter. Bittersweet caramel notes flourish before a gently tapering, malty finish.
Redwood (ABV 4.3%) BITTER

A fruity aroma introduces a smooth, full-flavoured bitter. A malty fruit base defined by bitter undertones. Lingering bitter finish.

Slate (ABV 6%) PORTER
Roast and dark fruits dominate throughout. Caramel and sweet malt add complexity and balance. Full-bodied with a short finish.

Lignum Vitae (ABV 6.5%) STRONG
Orange, toffee and banana on the nose and first taste. A smooth, digestive sweetness adds depth as bitterness slowly grows.

Grainstore SIBA

Station Approach, Oakham, Rutland, LE15 6RE
☎ (01572) 770065 ⊕ grainstorebrewery.com

☺Grainstore, the smallest county's largest brewery, has been in production since 1995, founded by Tony Davis and Mike Davies. After 45 years in the industry Tony decided to retire, handing the reins to his son, William. More than 200 outlets are supplied. ‼♦

Rutland Bitter (ABV 3.4%) BITTER
Rutland Panther (ABV 3.4%) MILD
This superb, reddish-black mild punches above its weight with malt and roast flavours combining to deliver a brew that can match the average stout for intensity of flavour.

Cooking (ABV 3.6%) BITTER
Tawny-coloured beer with malt and hops on the nose and a pleasant, grainy mouthfeel. Hops and fruit flavours combine to give a bitterness that continues into a long finish.

Red Kite (ABV 3.8%) BITTER
Rutland Osprey (ABV 4%) GOLD
Triple B (ABV 4.2%) BITTER
Initially hops dominate over malt in both the aroma and taste, but fruit is there, too. All three linger in varying degrees in the sweetish aftertaste of this brown brew.

GB Best (ABV 4.3%) BITTER
Ten Fifty (ABV 5%) BITTER
Pungent banana and malt notes on the nose. On the palate, rich malt and fruit is joined by subtle hop on a bittersweet base. Dry malt aftertaste with some fruit.

Rutland Beast (ABV 5.3%) OLD
Nip (ABV 7.3%) BARLEY

Brewed under the Stoney Ford brand name:
Sheepmarket Supernova (ABV 3.8%) GOLD
PE9 Paradise Pale (ABV 4%) PALE
All Saints Almighty (ABV 4.2%) BITTER

Grampus

🍴 Grampus Inn, Lee Bay, Devon, EX34 8LR
☎ (01271) 862906 ⊕ thegrampus-inn.co.uk

⊗ Grampus was established in 2014 at the back of the Grampus Inn by Bill Harvey, the pub owner and brewer. It is a small plant using traditional brewing methods, but combining unique and unusual ingredients. All beers are available in the local area. A small batch gin distillery was added in 2019. ♦LIVE

Grasmere

Lake View Country House, Lake View Drive, Grasmere, Cumbria, LA22 9TD
☎ (01539) 435572 ☎ 07840 059561
⊕ grasmerepub.com

Brewing began in 2017 in old farm buildings at Lake View Country House. Beers are available at its nearby taproom and restaurant, the Good Sport. Cider is also produced. 🍴

Helles Lager (ABV 3.8%) SPECIALITY

Pale Ale (ABV 4%) PALE
Bitter (ABV 4.1%) BITTER
IPA (ABV 5.5%) IPA

Grasshopper

Unit F2, Langley Bridge Industrial Estate, Linkmel Road, Langley Mill, Derbyshire, NG16 3RZ
☎ (01773) 530224 ⊕ grasshopperbrewery.co.uk

Grasshopper commenced brewing in 2017 using a purpose-built, 10-barrel plant. Beers started appearing in local pubs shortly after and have been well received. Its core range (five beers) can be found in pubs and at festivals throughout Nottinghamshire, Derbyshire, Leicestershire, Staffordshire and beyond.

Knee High (ABV 3.8%) PALE
Nymph (ABV 4.2%) RED
Cricket (ABV 4.5%) PALE
Devil's Horse (ABV 4.8%) STOUT
Kung Fu (ABV 5.8%) BITTER

Gravity Well

Arch 142, Tilbury Road, Leyton, London, E10 6RE
☎ 07833 226373 ⊕ gravitywellbrewing.co.uk

The brewery was installed during 2018 in a railway arch under the Gospel Oak to Barking Overground line. A bigger taproom opened in 2020 along the line by Leyton Midland station. The range of pale ales, sours and stouts (including double and imperial versions) is available in keg and cans with cask ale being considered. ⬦

Great British Breworks

34 Dove Way, Kirkby Mills industrial Estate, Kirkbymoorside, North Yorkshire, YO62 6QR
☎ (01751) 433111 ☎ 07876 827475

Office: c/o The Black Swan Hotel, 18 Birdgate, Pickering, YO18 7AL ⊕ blackswan-pickering.co.uk/breworks

☺Brewing started on a permanent basis in the yard of the Black Swan, Pickering, in 2016, on a 2.5-barrel plant. In 2020, the brewery expanded by taking over the 12-barrel brewing plant in Kirkbymoorside previously used by Turning Point brewery. Following the pandemic downturn in demand, the commencement of production at Kirkbymoorside was deferred until 2021. The Black Swan serves as the brewery tap. ♦

Great Scot (ABV 3.8%) BITTER
Lightheaded (ABV 4%) PALE
Istanbul (ABV 4.5%) BITTER
Coal Porter (ABV 4.6%) PORTER
Simcoe Pale (ABV 5.2%) PALE

Great Central

Unit B, Marlow Road Industrial Estate, Leicester, LE3 2BQ ☎ 07584 435332 ⊕ gcbrewery.co.uk

⊗ Brewing restarted in 2019 on a two-barrel plant primarily to supply the brewery tap, the Wheeltapper, Loughborough. Beers are named with a railway theme. ♦

Great Corby SIBA

The Green, Great Corby, Cumbria, CA4 8LR
☎ (01228) 560899 ⊕ greatcorbybrewhouse.com

☺Brewing commenced in the village in 2009. In late 2020 the brewery was purchased from US distilling and brewing giant, Alltech, by a local businessman. The office and cask-washing facilities are being transferred into the

THE BREWERIES

main brewery area, in the former honey factory. The original site, across the village green at The Forge, will see alternative use. Occasional new beers will continue to be produced throughout the year. !! ♦

Session Ale (ABV 3.8%) BITTER
A fruity session beer with sweetness leading to gentle bitterness in the aftertaste.
Blonde (ABV 4%) BLOND
Some fruit in the aroma and then a sweet fruity and lightly-bittered taste which continues for a short time.
Lakeland Summit (ABV 4%) GOLD
Signal Peak APA (ABV 4.4%) PALE
Stout (ABV 4.5%) STOUT
Fruity aroma, sweet, roast middle and dry finish.
Fox Brown Ale (ABV 4.6%) BROWN
A pleasing brown ale with a slight bitter finish.

Great Newsome SIBA

Great Newsome Farm, South Frodingham, Winestead, East Yorkshire, HU12 0NR
☎ (01964) 612201 ⊕ greatnewsomebrewery.co.uk

Nestled in the Holderness countryside, Great Newsome began brewing in 2007 in renovated farm buildings. A range of beers is now brewed using barley from the farm and brewing can be seen from a viewing area. Expansion into other farm buildings in 2018, and again in 2019, increased brewing capacity to 20-barrels. Beer is distributed throughout the UK and overseas. !! ☞ ♦

Sleck Dust (ABV 3.8%) BLOND
Pricky Back Otchan (ABV 4.2%) BITTER
Frothingham Best (ABV 4.3%) BITTER
Holderness Dark (ABV 4.3%) MILD
Jem's Stout (ABV 4.3%) STOUT
Liquorice Lads Stout (ABV 4.3%) SPECIALITY

Great North Eastern SIBA

Contract House (Unit E), Wellington Road, Dunston, Gateshead, NE11 9HS
☎ (0191) 447 4462 ⊕ gnebco.com

Brewing began in 2016 on a 10-barrel plant. In 2017 the brewery expanded into the adjacent premises and a tap and shop was opened, with an events space for live entertainment. Beers are supplied direct throughout the North-East, and nationally via wholesalers. ☞ ♦ ⚒

Claspers Citra Blonde (ABV 3.8%) BLOND
Styrian Blonde (ABV 3.8%) BLOND
Gold (ABV 4%) GOLD
Rivet Catcher (ABV 4%) GOLD
Taiheke Sun (ABV 4.2%) PALE
Delta APA (ABV 4.5%) PALE
Foxtrot Premium Ale (ABV 4.5%) BITTER
GNE Stout (ABV 4.6%) STOUT
Graphite (ABV 4.6%) IPA
Hopnicity (ABV 5%) PALE

Great Oakley SIBA

Ark Farm, High Street South, Tiffield, Northamptonshire, NN12 8AB
⊕ greatoakleybrewery.co.uk

Award-winning brewery established in 2005 in Great Oakley, relocating to Tiffield in 2012. It is run by Guy Jenkins who took over in 2017. More than 60 outlets are supplied, including brewery tap, the George, Tiffield. !! ♦ LIVE

Welland Valley Mild (ABV 3.6%) MILD
Egret (ABV 3.8%) GOLD

Wagtail (ABV 3.9%) GOLD
Wot's Occurring (ABV 3.9%) BITTER
Tiffield Thunderbolt (ABV 4.2%) PALE
Harpers (ABV 4.3%) BITTER
Gobble (ABV 4.5%) BLOND
Delapre Dark (ABV 4.6%) OLD
Abbey Stout (ABV 5%) STOUT
Tailshaker (ABV 5%) GOLD

Great Orme

See Snowdon Craft

Great Western SIBA

Stream Bakery, Bristol Road, Hambrook, Bristol, BS16 1RF
☎ (0117) 9572842 ⊕ gwbrewery.co.uk

Great Western is a 12-barrel brewery set up in 2008 by Kevin Stone in a former bakery. The property has been renovated resulting in a bespoke showpiece brewery retaining many of the building's original features. The brewery owns a single pub – the Rising Sun, Frampton Cotterell – and 500 outlets are supplied. The brewery may relocate and/or rebrand during the currency of this guide. !! ☞ ♦

HPA (ABV 4%) PALE
Hoppy, yellow bitter with zesty, citrus flavours and hints of tropical fruit, leading to a moreish, bittersweet finish.
Maiden Voyage (ABV 4%) BITTER
An amber bitter with a light aroma of malt and fruit which continues to the palate before leading to a strong, bitter finish.
Old Higby (ABV 4.8%) BITTER
Full-bodied, malty bitter with roast notes on the nose. Hints of fruit flavour give way to a bitter hop finish with some astringency throughout.
Moose River (ABV 5%) PALE
Light citrus aroma, delicate hop taste with long-lasting, bitter finish.

Great Yorkshire

See C'84

Green Dragon

🍺 **Green Dragon, 29 Broad Street, Bungay, Suffolk, NR35 1EF**
☎ (01986) 892681

The Green Dragon is Bungay's busiest pub and oldest existing brewery, established in 1991 by brothers Robert and William Pickard. In 1994 the plant was expanded and moved to a converted barn. The doubling of capacity allowed the production of a larger range of ales. !! ♦

Green Duck SIBA

Unit 13, Gainsborough Trading Estate, Rufford Road, Stourbridge, West Midlands, DY9 7ND
☎ (01384) 377666 ⊕ greenduckbrewery.co.uk

Green Duck began brewing in 2012 and relocated to its present site in Stourbridge in 2013. Experimental beers are brewed alongside a core range. The brewery has an on-site brewery tap, the Badelynge Bar, where the brewing equipment is visible through a glass partition. Demand for small package beers saw the brewery invest in a canning plant with Twisted Barrel Brewery in 2020. !! ♦ ⚒

Session IPA (ABV 4%) PALE

Pale gold with a tropical aroma derived from mosaic hops. Very refreshing with a dry pine and resin aftertaste.
Blonde (ABV 4.2%) SPECIALITY
Gold with a sharp fruity aroma. Lots of passionfruit in the taste. Aftertaste is balanced with fruit sweetness and hops.
American Pale (ABV 4.5%) PALE
Duck & Dive (ABV 5.9%) IPA
Amber with a fruity aroma. Citrussy hop and spicy orange peel sweetness in the taste with a long, bitter finish.

Green Jack SIBA

Argyle Place, Love Road, Lowestoft, Suffolk, NR32 2NZ
☎ (01502) 562863 ☎ 07902 219459
⊕ green-jack.com

⊗ After 10 years at Oulton Broad, Green Jack moved to the Triangle Tavern, Lowestoft in 2003 and then to a nearby 35-barrel plant in 2009. One pub is owned and more than 150 outlets supplied. ‼◆LIVE

Golden Best (ABV 3.8%) GOLD
Nightingale (ABV 4%) BITTER
LGM1 (ABV 4.2%) BITTER
Orange Wheat Beer (ABV 4.2%) SPECIALITY
Marmalade aroma with a hint of hops, leading to a well-balanced blend of sweetness, hops and citrus with a malt background. Mixed fruit flavours in the aftertaste.
Trawlerboys Best Bitter (ABV 4.6%) BITTER
Tawny beer with aroma of apple, sultana and malt plus hints of caramel and hops. Rich fig and plum base with malt and roast overtones. Strong finish with a sticky mouthfeel.
Lurcher Stout (ABV 4.8%) STOUT
Pleasant malt, roast and fruit aromas. Blackberry, raisin and port flavours. Long, dry, bitter, roast finish.
Red Herring (ABV 5%) SPECIALITY
Gone Fishing ESB (ABV 5.5%) BITTER
Mahseer IPA (ABV 5.8%) IPA
Ripper (ABV 8.5%) BARLEY
Baltic Trader (ABV 10.5%) STOUT
Worthog (ABV 11%) STRONG

Green Mill

⊟ Harewood Arms, 2 Market Street, Broadbottom, SK14 6AX ☎ 07967 656887 ⊕ greenmillbrewery.com

☺Green Mill started brewing in 2007 on a 2.5-barrel plant and moved in 2010 to the Cask & Feather in Rochdale. The brewery relocated again in 2013 to the Harewood Arms in Broadbottom. A number of occasional beers are brewed. Around 40 outlets are supplied. ◆

Greene King

Westgate Brewery, Westgate Street, Bury St Edmunds, Suffolk, IP33 1QT
☎ (01284) 763222

Office: Abbot House, Westgate Street, Bury St Edmunds, IP33 1QT ⊕ greeneking.co.uk

⊗ Greene King has been brewing in the market town of Bury St Edmunds since 1799. It brews its beers using water drawn from artisan chalk wells below its brewhouse, as well as local East Anglia malt. Beers are also brewed under the Tolly Cobbold brand name. ‼▀◆LIVE

IPA (ABV 3.6%) BITTER
Hop-infused, fruit cake aromas. Complex flavours of malt, caramel and hop with both sweetness and bitterness. A lingering, mellow aftertaste with blackberries.
London Glory (ABV 4%) BITTER

Yardbird (ABV 4%) PALE
St Edmunds (ABV 4.2%) GOLD
Abbot (ABV 5%) BITTER
Strong malt, toffee and caramel aromas. Rich, malty, caramel flavours with vine fruit and a little hop bite. Heavy, sweet finish with a subtle hint of bitterness in the aftertaste.

Brewed for Taylor Walker:
1730 (ABV 4%) BITTER

Brewed under the Hardys & Hansons brand name:
Bitter (ABV 3.9%) BITTER
Olde Trip (ABV 4.3%) BITTER

Brewed under the Morland brand name:
Original Bitter (ABV 4%) BITTER
Old Golden Hen (ABV 4.1%) GOLD
Old Speckled Hen (ABV 4.5%) BITTER
Smooth, malty and fruity, with a short finish.

Brewed under the Ruddles brand name:
Best Bitter (ABV 3.7%) BITTER
An amber/brown beer, strong on bitterness but with some initial sweetness, fruit and subtle, distinctive hop. Dryness lingers in the aftertaste.

Greenodd

⊟ Ship Inn, Main Street, Greenodd, Cumbria, LA12 7QZ
☎ (01229) 861553 ☎ 07782 655294
⊕ theshipinngreenodd.co.uk

☺Established in 2010 at the Ship Inn on a two-barrel plant. The majority of production goes to the Ship with the remainder going to the local free trade. Brewing is currently suspended. ‼◆

Greg's

⊟ Dambusters Inn, 23 High Street, Scampton, Lincolnshire, LN1 2SD
☎ (01522) 730123

☺Established in 2013, the microbrewery is situated on the premises of the Dambusters Inn. A number of house ales are produced by publican Greg Algar. ◆

Grey Friars

Featherstone Hall Farm, New Road, Featherstone, Staffordshire, WV10 7NW
☎ (01785) 840093 ☎ 07966 361443

Office: 17 Cranbrooks, Wheaton Aston, ST19 9PZ
⊕ greyfriarsbrewery.co.uk

Established in 2014 and using equipment originally from Upham Brewery in Hampshire, the three-barrel plant is installed in a barn, formerly used as a snooker room and which still contains the original wood panelling. Brewing is currently suspended.

Grey Trees SIBA

Unit 5-6, Gas Works Road, Aberaman, Aberdare, CF44 6RS
☎ (01685) 267077 ⊕ greytreesbrewing.com

National award-winning, small brewery from the Welsh heartlands, now in its eleventh year. Beer is available from its own National Tap in Aberdare, and from local free houses, sometimes further afield. Expansion is planned. ▀◆LIVE

Caradog (ABV 3.9%) BITTER
Black Road Stout (ABV 4%) STOUT
Diggers Gold (ABV 4%) GOLD
Drummer Boy (ABV 4.2%) BITTER

Mosaic Pale Ale (ABV 4.2%) PALE
Chinookan VPA (ABV 4.3%) PALE
Valley Porter (ABV 4.6%) PORTER
JPR Pale (ABV 4.7%) PALE
Afghan Pale (ABV 5.4%) PALE

Greyhound

Watershed, Smock Alley, West Chiltington, West
Sussex, RH20 2QX
☎ (01798) 815822 ☎ 07973 625510
⊕ greyhoundbrewery.co.uk

⊗ Established in 2015 by husband-and-wife team Nick
and Sarah Allen, Greyhound is a 7.5-barrel brewery. In
2017 the brewery took over production of Ballard's
Brewery beers, and continue to make its traditional ales
alongside the Greyhound range. All beer sold is now
unfined, unfiltered, gluten free and vegan-friendly. All
bottled beers are bottle-conditioned. !! ♦ LIVE GF V

Good Ordinary Bitter (ABV 3.8%) BITTER
Blonde Bird (ABV 3.9%) PALE
Amber Eyes (ABV 4.2%) BITTER
B-46 (ABV 4.6%) BITTER
Tree Frog (ABV 4.9%) PALE
White Bird (ABV 5.2%) SPECIALITY

Brewed under the Ballard's Brewery name:
Best Bitter (ABV 4.2%) BITTER
Nyewood Gold (ABV 5%) BITTER

Greywood

Sandford Avenue, Wood Green, London, N22 5EJ
⊕ greywoodbrewery.co.uk

☺ Commercial brewing began in 2020. It's one beer, the
Longest Road, is named after the nearby Green Lanes,
and was available at the Westbury in Wood Green.
Brewing is currently suspended.

Gribble

⬗ Gribble Inn, Oving, West Sussex, PO20 2BP
☎ (01243) 786893 ⊕ gribbleinn.co.uk

⊗ Established in 1980 using a five-barrel plant, the
Gribble Brewery is the longest-serving brewpub in the
Sussex area, independently owned and run by the
licensees since 2005. A number of local outlets are
supplied. ♦

Griffin

See Freestyle

Gritchie SIBA

Ashgrove Farm, Ashmore, Wiltshire, SP5 5AW
☎ (01747) 828996 ⊕ gritchiebrewingcompany.co.uk

⊗ Owned by film director Guy Ritchie, this 20-barrel
brewery, in converted farm buildings on the Ashcombe
Estate, started brewing in 2017, using its own borehole
water and estate-grown barley. Expansion to 40-barrel
capacity and a tap room are planned. Both cask and
KeyKeg beers are produced, with new
beers regularly developed. There are three five-barrel
fermenters for experimental beers. The beers are
distributed locally with plans to expand nationally. The
Lore of the Land, Fitzrovia, London, is the brewery tap. ♦

Moon Lore (ABV 3.6%) GOLD
Summer Lore (ABV 3.6%) GOLD
English Lore (ABV 4%) BITTER

A copper-coloured bitter with some hint of fruit in the
aroma. A sweet, slightly bitter taste which diminishes
quickly.

Grizzly Grains

342 Walkley Bank Road, Sheffield, South Yorkshire,
S6 5AR ☎ 07807 242545
✉ sambrewsbeers@gmail.com

Having purchased the equipment from Crosspool
Alemakers in 2019 Sam Bennett commenced brewing in
the Walkley area of Sheffield in 2020. ♦

Grounding Angels

6 Rear Battle Hill, Hexham, Northumberland,
NE46 1BB ☎ 07508 175512 ⊕ grounding-angels.com

Brewing started in 2018 by Jamie Robson, using his
family's experience of owning global drinks brand
Fentimans. Golden Promise malt is used as a base for all
of the beers, which are distributed nationwide.

GT

Unit 5, The Old Aerodrome, Chivenor Business Park,
Braunton, Devon, EX31 4AY
☎ (01271) 267420 ☎ 07909 515170 ⊕ gtales.co.uk

⊗ Established in 2013, GT Ales is housed in a characterful
World War II aircraft hanger at Chivenor near Braunton.
An on-site brewery shop has recently been added to the
five-barrel brewery. All six award-winning core ales are
available in cask, bottle and can. Limited edition small
batch brews are regularly produced. !! ☰ ♦ LIVE

Thirst of Many (ABV 4.2%) BITTER
North Coast IPA (ABV 4.3%) PALE
Blonde Ambition (ABV 4.5%) BLOND
Dark Horse (ABV 4.5%) BITTER
Atlantic Storm (ABV 4.7%) STOUT
Crimson Rye'd (ABV 4.8%) RED

Guisborough

14 South Buck Way, Guisborough, North Yorkshire,
TS14 7FJ ☎ 07703 002858
✉ info@guisboroughbrewery.co.uk

⊗ Established in 2020, using a five-barrel plant. The core
range consists of five beers using a variety of traditional
and more contemporary hops, together with the finest
malts. Events are held regularly and visitors, by
arrangement, are made most welcome. !!

Delight (ABV 3.7%) BITTER
Alchemy (ABV 3.8%) BITTER
Phoenix (ABV 4%) SPECIALITY
Elixir (ABV 4.7%) GOLD
Vypa (ABV 5.5%) IPA

Gun SIBA

Hawthbush Farm, Gun Hill, East Sussex, TN21 0JY
☎ (01323) 700200 ☎ 07900 683355
⊕ gunbrewery.co.uk

⊗ Gun Brewery is located on a 140-acre, organic, mixed
farm in the Sussex Weald. It generates much of its own
power from a 15-kW solar array and heating comes from
a wood-powered boiler. Spent grains keep the local
livestock happy and all the water used for brewing
comes from the brewery's spring. More than 30 outlets
are supplied. LIVE V

Scaramanga (ABV 3.9%) PALE
Parabellum (ABV 4.1%) STOUT

Chummy Bluster (ABV 4.4%) BITTER
Project Babylon (ABV 4.6%) PALE
Base Ejection (ABV 4.7%) RED
Spin Drift (ABV 5.7%) IPA
Zamzama (ABV 6.5%) IPA

Gun Dog

See Phipps

Gwaun Valley SIBA

Kilkiffeth Farm, Pontfaen, SA65 9TP ☎ 07854 767383
⊕ gwaunvalleybrewery.com

Gwaun Valley began brewing in 2009 on a four-barrel
plant in a converted granary. The brewery offers views of
the Preseli Hills and has a campsite, a holiday cottage
and pitches for five caravans. Folk music sessions are
held every Saturday evening. The owners retired early in
2019 and the business has been relaunched by a new
tenant brewer who has retained some of the core range
of beers, and added others. ‼ ⛟

Farmhouse Ale (ABV 4%) BITTER
Cwm Gwaun Porter (ABV 4.3%) PORTER
King of the Road (ABV 4.5%) BITTER
Pembrokeshire Best Bitter (ABV 4.5%) BITTER
Sir Benfro Bitter (ABV 4.5%) PALE
Blodwen (ABV 4.7%) BITTER
Cascade (ABV 4.7%) PALE
Cwrw Melyn (ABV 4.7%) BLOND
Cwrw Gwyn (ABV 5.3%) IPA

Gyle 59 SIBA

The Brewery, Sadborow Estate Yard, Thorncombe,
Dorset, TA20 4PW
☎ (01297) 678990 ☎ 07508 691178 ⊕ gyle59.co.uk

⊗ Gyle 59 is a 10-barrel brewery that began commercial
production in 2014. Bottling takes place on-site with
bottles being available by mail order. ‼ ⛟ ♦ LIVE V

Take It Easy (ABV 2.5%) BITTER
Freedom Hiker (ABV 3.7%) BITTER
Thoroughbred (ABV 3.7%) PALE
Cobb (ABV 3.9%) BITTER
Toujours (ABV 4%) SPECIALITY
C59's Special (ABV 4.2%) BITTER
Lyme Gold (ABV 4.2%) GOLD
Vienna Session Lager (ABV 4.2%) SPECIALITY
Capitalist Hippie – Skinny (ABV 4.3%) BITTER
Dorset Pearl (ABV 4.3%) PALE
Black Ven (ABV 5%) PORTER
Capitalist Hippie – Far Out (ABV 5%) PALE
Halcyon Daze (ABV 5%) SPECIALITY
IPA (ABV 5.3%) PALE
Nettle IPA (ABV 5.3%) SPECIALITY
Revenge (ABV 5.3%) PALE
Dorset GIPA (ABV 5.4%) SPECIALITY
Capitalist Hippie – Summer of Love (ABV 6.6%)
STRONG
Starstruck (ABV 6.6%) SPECIALITY
The Favourite (ABV 6.6%) PORTER
Double IPA (ABV 7.3%) IPA

Contract brewed for Lyme Regis Brewery:
Ammonite (ABV 3.7%) BITTER
Cobb (ABV 3.9%) BITTER
Lyme Gold (ABV 4.2%) GOLD
Dorset Pearl (ABV 4.3%) PALE
Town Mill Best (ABV 4.5%) BITTER
Black Ven (ABV 5%) PORTER
Revenge (ABV 5.3%) PALE

Hackney SIBA

Unit 10, Lockwood Way, Blackhorse Lane,
Walthamstow, London, E17 5RB
☎ (020) 3489 9595 ⊕ hackneybrewery.co.uk

⊗ Founded in 2011, Hackney was the oldest brewery in
the area. Expansion in 2021 saw a new brewery started
from scratch in Walthamstow close to the other
Blackhorse Lane breweries. The core range is available
on keg and in cans supplemented by regular specials. No
real ale at the moment. LIVE

Hackney Church

Arches 16 & 17, Bohemia Place, Hackney, London,
E8 1DU
☎ (020) 3795 8295 ⊕ hackneychurchbrew.co

Formerly known as St John at Hackney Brewery.
Comprising two railway arches, the brewery is in one,
the other being the taproom. Available only from the
taproom for quality control, beers come from kegs or the
tanks above the bar or in bottles or cans for take away.
All profits are used by the trust for worthy, church-based
projects at St John at Hackney. No real ale. ♦

Hadham SIBA

Unit 6c, Hadham Industrial Estate, Church End, Little
Hadham, Hertfordshire, SG11 2DY
☎ (01279) 771916 ☎ 07770 766376
⊕ hadhambrewery.co.uk

⊗ Hadham began brewing in 2015 with a 10-barrel
plant, using its own spring water found on-site. Outlets
are supplied within a 30-mile radius of the brewery.

Gold (ABV 3.7%) GOLD
Oddy (ABV 3.9%) BITTER
First (ABV 4%) BITTER

Hadrian Border SIBA

Unit 5, The Preserving Works, Newburn Industrial
Estate, Shelley Road, Newburn, NE15 9RT
☎ (0191) 264 9000 ⊕ hadrian-border-brewery.co.uk

Based in Newburn near Newcastle-upon-Tyne using a
40-barrel plant, the brewery can produce up to 200
barrels per week. Beer is delivered directly to the area
between Edinburgh, North Yorkshire, Carlisle and the East
Coast, and is also available nationally through
wholesalers. A three-barrel plant is used for
experimental craft brews. One pub is run – the Station
East, Gateshead. ‼ ♦ LIVE

Tyneside Blonde (ABV 3.9%) BLOND
Refreshing blonde ale with zesty notes and a clean, fruity
finish.
Farne Island Pale Ale (ABV 4%) PALE
A copper-coloured bitter with a refreshing malt/hop
balance.
Northern Pale (ABV 4.1%) PALE
Secret Kingdom (ABV 4.3%) BITTER
Grainger Ale (ABV 4.6%) PALE
Northern IPA (ABV 5.2%) PALE
Ouseburn Porter (ABV 5.2%) PORTER
Traditional, robust porter, made with chocolate and black
malt. Distinct, bitter coffee finish.

Hafod

Old Gas Works, Gas Lane, Mold, CH7 1UR
☎ (01352) 750765 ☎ 07901 386638

Office: Gorwel, Hafod Road, Pantglas, Gwernaffield,
Mold, CH7 5ES ⊕ welshbeer.com

⊚Hafod began brewing in 2011 on a small scale and relocated to the current premises in 2014 whilst retaining the original kit at the old site for low volumes. A number of one-off, special brews are produced on a regular basis. Also on a limited basis, speciality beers using ingredients from the local upland areas are made. ‼◆◈

Sunrise (ABV 3.8%) PALE
A pale and refreshing golden ale with citrus fruit bitterness evident throughout, and a mouthwatering, astringent finish.

Moel Famau Ale (ABV 4.1%) SPECIALITY
A speciality dark ale brewed using local heather giving a dry, roasty taste with underlying sweet malt flavours.

Landmark (ABV 4.6%) BITTER
Copper-coloured and malty with a juicy mouthfeel. Fruit and faint roast flavours also feature in the taste.

Moldbreaker (ABV 4.6%) SPECIALITY

Hairy Dog

Unit 38, More House Farm, Wivelsfield, Haywards Heath, West Sussex, RH17 7RE
⊕ **hairydogbrewery.beer**

Overlooking the South Downs National Park, the brewery's ethos is to use Sussex ingredients wherever possible and to pursue a policy of sustainability. An on-site taproom is open on Fridays. ◈

Hounded (ABV 4.1%) BITTER
Far Fetched (ABV 4.2%) PALE
Bloodhound (ABV 5.5%) RED

Hal's

22A, Woodmancote, Dursley, Gloucestershire, GL11 4AF ☎ 07765 890946

Hal's is a one-barrel microbrewery established in Dursley in 2016, occasionally producing a number of small-batch beers for the New Inn, Woodmancote, Dursley and beer festivals. Brewing is currently suspended. ◆

Half Moon

Forge House, Main Street, Ellerton, York, East Yorkshire, YO42 4PB
☎ **(01757) 288977 ☎ 07741 400508**
⊕ **halfmoonbrewery.co.uk**

Established in 2013 by Tony and Jackie Rogers, the brewery is situated in a former blacksmith's forge with a capacity of 5.5-barrels. Brewing takes place 2-3 times a week. ◆LIVE◈

Dark Masquerade (ABV 3.6%) MILD
Old Forge Bitter (ABV 3.8%) BITTER
F'Hops Sake (ABV 3.9%) BITTER

Halifax Steam

▤ **Conclave, Southedge Works, Brighouse Road, Hipperholme, West Yorkshire, HX3 8EF ☎ 07506 022504 ⊕ halifax-steam.co.uk**

⊚Brewing since 1999, the five-barrel plant supplies only the brewery tap, the Cock o' the North. It is now reputedly the oldest brewery in Calderdale. A range of permanent beers, and different rotating beers are brewed, including the only rice beers in the country. ◆

Hall & Woodhouse (Badger) IFBB

Bournemouth Road, Blandford St Mary, Blandford Forum, Dorset, DT11 9LS
☎ **(01258) 452141 ⊕ hall-woodhouse.co.uk**

⊠ Hall & Woodhouse has been brewing in the heart of the Dorset countryside since 1777. Owned and run by the seventh generation of the Woodhouse family, it brews with local spring water filtered through the Cretaceous chalk downs and drawn up 120ft from its wells. A leading, independent UK brewer, its well-known range of Badger ales is award-winning, and it has an estate (around 200 pubs) across southern England. Its ales are available exclusively in Hall & Woodhouse public houses. ‼▰◆◈

Badger Best Bitter (ABV 3.7%) BITTER
Well-balanced bitter with malt caramel sweetness and hop fruitiness.

Fursty Ferret (ABV 4.1%) BITTER
Easy-drinking best bitter with sweet bitterness that lingers into a dry after taste with a hint of orange.

Tanglefoot (ABV 4.7%) GOLD
Relatively sweet-tasting and deceptive, given its strength. Pale malt provides caramel overtones and bittersweet finish.

Halton Turner

Lakey Lane, Hall Green, Birmingham, West Midlands, B28 8QT ☎ 07821 447329 ⊕ haltonturnerbrew.co

Established in 2018, Halton Turner has a small plant in Hall Green, Birmingham. Brewing a wide range of beers in cask and KeyKeg, the beers are mainly found in the local area.

Hambleton SIBA

Melmerby Green Road, Melmerby, North Yorkshire, HG4 5NB
☎ **(01765) 640108 ⊕ hambletonbrewery.co.uk**

⊚Hambleton Ales was established in 1991 by Nick Stafford in a shed at the bottom of his in-laws' garden. It is now run by Nick's daughter and son-in-law. Since 2007 it has operated from purpose-built premises near Ripon. Capacity is 100 barrels a week. Recent development included a new storage facility. The core range (eight beers), is supplemented with monthly and seasonals. Village Brewer, Black Dog and Wharfe Brewery brands are contract brewed. A bottling line handles brands for other brewers. ‼▰◆

Session Pale (ABV 3.6%) PALE
Bootleggers Pale Ale (ABV 3.8%) PALE
Thoroughbred IPA (ABV 4%) BITTER
Pink Grapefruit (ABV 4.1%) SPECIALITY
Stallion Amber (ABV 4.2%) BITTER
A premium bitter, moderately hoppy throughout and richly-balanced in malt and fruit, developing a sound and robust bitterness, with earthy hops drying the aftertaste.

Stud Blonde (ABV 4.3%) GOLD
Black Forest (ABV 5%) SPECIALITY
Nightmare Porter (ABV 5%) STOUT
This impressively-flavoured beer satisfies all parts of the palate. Strong roast malts dominate, but hoppiness rears out of this complex blend.

Contract brewed for Black Dog Brewery:
Whitby Abbey Ale (ABV 3.8%) BITTER
Schooner (ABV 4.2%) PALE
Rhatas (ABV 4.6%) BITTER

Contract brewed for Village Brewer:
White Boar (ABV 3.8%) BITTER
Bull (ABV 4%) GOLD

Contract brewed for Wharfe Beers:
Verbeia (ABV 3.6%) BITTER
Tether Blond (ABV 3.8%) GOLD

Hammerton SIBA

Unit 8 & 9, Roman Way Industrial Estate, 149 Roman Way, Barnsbury, London, N7 8XH
☎ (020) 3302 5880 ⊕ hammertonbrewery.co.uk

Hammerton began brewing in London in 1868 but ceased brewing in the 1950s and was later demolished. In 2014, a member of the Hammerton family resurrected the name and opened a new brewery in Barnsbury. Expanded in 2019 after crowdfunding, the taproom is open more regularly, now complementing its nearby bar, the House of Hammerton. LIVE ◆

N1 (ABV 4.1%) PALE
Refreshing pale ale. Honey, caramelised citrus, floral hops, fading in the finish with a spicy hoppy bitterness. Malty, fruity aroma.
Life on Mars (ABV 4.6%) RED
Ruby ale with roast, toffee and fruit aroma. Peppery hops, nutty roasty flavour with dark bitter marmalade. Dry, lingering finish.
N7 (ABV 5.2%) PALE
Full-bodied pale ale. Sweet honey with marmalade, earthy hops and a hint of apricot. Spicy, sweet finish overlaid dry bitterness.
Pentonville Oyster Stout (ABV 5.3%) STOUT
Liquorice and dark fruit on the palate and aroma. Dry, roasty, malty finish and a touch of caramelised fruit.

Hand SIBA

33 Upper St James's Street, Kemptown, Brighton, East Sussex, BN2 1JN ☎ 07508 814541

Second Site: Unit 6a, Garcia Trading Estate, Canterbury Road, Worthing, BN13 1AL

☺Founded in 1989, the brewery is the smallest commercially operating tower brewery in the world. Originally operating under the Kemptown Brewery name before being used as a gypsy brewery by Brighton Bier for four years. Now operating as the Hand Brew Co since 2016. Around 10 other outlets are supplied. ‼

Kemptown (ABV 4%) PALE
Ye Olde Trout (ABV 4.5%) BITTER

Handley's

Willow Tree, Front Street, Barnby in the Willows, Newark, Nottinghamshire, NG24 2SA
⊕ willowtreebarnby.co.uk

☺Handley's began brewing in 2011 on a 0.5-barrel plant installed behind the Willow Tree pub. Beer is mostly sold in the pub, with at least two being on pump at all times, and can occasionally be found at local beer festivals.

Handsome

Bowstone Bridge Garage, Bowston, Cumbria, LA8 9HD
☎ (0344) 848 0888 ⊕ handsomebrew.co.uk

Originally Houston Brewery in Renfrewshire, it was re-established as Handsome in 2016 in the Lake District. It is situated on the River Kent in an old MOT garage, formerly the blacksmith's for James Cropper's paper mills.

Top Knot (ABV 3.7%) BLOND
Stranger (ABV 4.2%) BITTER
Bar Steward (ABV 4.8%) BITTER
Blacksmith (ABV 4.8%) STOUT

Contract brewed for Winster Valley Brewery:
Dark Horse (ABV 3.5%) MILD
Hurdler (ABV 3.5%) GOLD
Best Bitter (ABV 3.7%) BITTER
Lakes Blonde (ABV 3.7%) BLOND

An uncomplicated fruity, hoppy bitter.
Old School (ABV 3.9%) BITTER
Chaser (ABV 4.1%) RED

Handyman

461 Smithdown Road, Liverpool, L15 3JL
☎ (0151) 722 7422 ⊕ handymansupermarket.co.uk

Handyman Brewery is based within the Handyman Supermarket. For years this was a hardware store but has now been refurbished into the Handyman Pub, which opened in 2017. Its 400-litre brew kit is situated on a mezzanine floor above the bar. ◆

Hanging Bat

c/o Hanging Bat, 133 Lothian Road, Edinburgh, EH3 9AB
☎ (0131) 229 0759 ⊕ thehangingbat.com

☒ Brewing began in 2012 from within the Hanging Bat bar using a 50-litre brew kit from the United States.

Hanging Tree

Benleva Hotel, Kilmore Road, Drumnadrochit, IV63 6UH
☎ (01456) 450080

☺ Hanging Tree began brewing in 2017 using a two-barrel brew plant in an old bothy in the grounds of the Benleva Hotel. Named after the 400-year-old chestnut tree growing in the garden, which was used as the hanging tree for the local area. Beers are available in the pub and a few other local outlets.

Hanlons SIBA

Hill Farm, Half Moon Village, Newton St Cyres, Devon, EX5 5AE
☎ (01392) 851160 ⊕ hanlonsbrewery.com

☒ Hanlons, one of Devon's largest brewers since 2013, supply a range of award-winning ales nationwide. The purpose-built brewery also has a shop, bar and restaurant. In 2019, it bought Prescott Ales of Cheltenham. Bottled beers are contract brewed for Frank & Otis Brewing Ltd. ‼ ☕◆

Firefly (ABV 3.7%) BITTER
Malty and fruity, light bitter. Hints of orange in the taste.
Citra IPA (ABV 4%) PALE
An easy-drinking citrus/floral IPA.
Yellow Hammer (ABV 4.2%) PALE
Zesty fruit aroma, pineapples on taste with a nice sweetness counteracted by bitterness. Even though available all year, it has a summer ale style to it. Very refreshing.
Brewers Blend (ABV 4.5%) BITTER
Port Stout (ABV 4.8%) SPECIALITY
Strong, black, speciality ale. Mild coffee and chocolate with fruity port notes. Lots of body – like having a liquid meal.
Stormstay (ABV 5%) BITTER
Tawny and full-bodied. Caramel with hints of malt on the nose. Triumvirate of malt, caramel, hops develop into lingering bitterness.

Brewed under the Prescott Ales name:
Hill Climb (ABV 3.8%) PALE
Pit Stop (ABV 4%) PALE
Chequered Flag (ABV 4.2%) BITTER
Podium Finish (ABV 4.8%) STOUT
Grand Prix (ABV 5%) BITTER

Hapax

See Kingstone

Happy Valley

73 Oxford Road, Macclesfield, SK11 8JG
☎ (01625) 618360 ☎ 07768 107660
⊕ happyvalleybrewery.co.uk

⊗ Happy Valley was established in 2010 using a 2.5-barrel plant located in Bollington. In 2018 the brewery was sold and relocated to Macclesfield, and is based at the 73 & Pizza pub. ♦

Harbour

Trekillick Farm, Kirland, Bodmin, Cornwall, PL30 5BB
☎ (01208) 832131 ☎ 07870 305063
⊕ harbourbrewing.com

⊗ Harbour is an innovative brewery founded on the outskirts of Bodmin in 2011. Brewed using local spring water, the regular beers are established in an increasing number of outlets. A new 30-barrel plant was installed in 2016, and more conditioning tanks in 2017. The brewery produces cask and keg beers. Bottling and canning is done on-site (no RAIB). ♦

Light (ABV 3.7%) BLOND
Yellow beer with citrus hop aroma. Dominant, zesty, citrus hops with some pineapple and pear drops. Long, hoppy finish.

Daymer Extra Pale (ABV 3.8%) PALE
Pale ale with citrus aroma. Lemon and lime dominate with grainy malt and earthy hop. Bitterness remains, sweetness fades, becoming dry.

Amber (ABV 4%) BITTER
Pale brown bitter with a floral hop aroma and malt. Biscuit malt throughout with apple, peach and plum, balanced by hops.

Cornish Bitter (ABV 4%) BITTER
Amber session bitter with fruity aroma. Tropical and citrus fruit flavours with apple and biscuit malt notes. Bitter, dry finish.

New Zealand Gold (ABV 4.2%) GOLD
Golden ale with light hop nose. Strong, pine needle hop flavour. Bitter, sweet and dry throughout.

Ellensberg (ABV 4.3%) PALE
Amber ale with powerful tropical and citrus aroma. Strong, juicy mango and grapefruit flavour. Both sweet and bitter. Long finish.

Session IPA (ABV 4.3%) PALE

India Brown Ale (ABV 4.9%) BROWN
Smooth, copper hue. Heavy body and balanced sweet malt and bitter hop flavour, with plums, prunes and some butterscotch.

IPA (ABV 5%) GOLD
Amber, American India pale, with powerful, citrus hop aroma and taste. Marmalade, red grapefruit and orange flavours with assertive bitterness.

Panda Eyes (ABV 5%) SPECIALITY

Puffin Tears (ABV 5%) BITTER

Cascadia (ABV 5.2%) BITTER

Light no2 (ABV 5.2%) BITTER

Antipodean IPA (ABV 5.5%) IPA

Little Rock IPA (ABV 5.5%) IPA

Porter (ABV 5.5%) PORTER
Smooth, creamy, black porter with roast malt aroma. Malty, smoky and sweet, followed by a bitter tang. Sweet finish.

Hellstown West Coast IPA (ABV 5.8%) IPA

Harbour Pale (ABV 6%) IPA

New World IPA with powerful citrus hop aroma. Intense, citrus hop flavour with marmalade, orange and bitterness. Hoppy, slightly dry finish.

Harbwr Tenby

Sargeants Lane, St Julian Street, Tenby, SA70 7BU
☎ (01834) 845797 ⊕ harbwr.wales

Brewing commenced in 2015 on a five-barrel plant in an outbuilding of the Buccaneer Inn, Tenby. The beers are available in the pub, at the nearby Hope & Anchor, and further afield. Information boards explain the building's history and the brewing process. A mezzanine bar area is available for tastings, tapas and tours. ‼♦

M V Enterprise (ABV 4%) PALE
North Star (ABV 4.2%) BITTER
Caldey Lollipop (ABV 4.5%) PALE
RFA Sir Galahad (ABV 4.6%) BITTER

Harby

Bottle & Glass, 5 High Street, Harby, Nottinghamshire, NG23 7EB
☎ (01522) 703438
⊕ wigandmitre-lincoln.blogspot.co.uk

Harby Brewstore is a four-barrel malt extract brewery established in 2015 and located at the Bottle & Glass in Harby. Most output goes to the three pubs in the small Wig & Mitre pub group; the Wig & Mitre, Lincoln, Caunton Beck, Caunton and the Bottle & Glass itself.

Hardys & Hansons

See Greene King

Harrison's

Unit 1, 108 Carolgate, Retford, Nottinghamshire, DN22 6AS ☎ 07850 228383 ⊕ harrisonsbrewery.com

⊚A three-barrel brewery built completely from scratch by the brewer, Christopher Harrison-Hawkes. The first brew was in 2018. Shortly afterwards four beers were available at its own pub, the Brew Shed (which stands metres from the brewery). In 2019 the pub moved next door to larger premises (seven Harrison beers available) with an outside area next to the canal. 2019 saw the production of bottle-conditioned beers, and 2020 real ale in a can, produced on-site. ‼♦

Vacant Gesture (ABV 3.8%) BLOND
Best Bitter (ABV 4%) BITTER
Pale Ale (ABV 4%) PALE
Proof of Concept (ABV 4.3%) PALE
Stout (ABV 4.3%) STOUT
American Brown Ale (ABV 4.9%) BROWN
Plum Porter (ABV 5.6%) PORTER
Porter (ABV 5.6%) PORTER

Harrogate SIBA

Unit 7, Hookstone Centre, Hookstone Chase, Harrogate, North Yorkshire, HG2 7HW ☎ 07794 281225 ⊕ harrogatebrewery.co.uk

⊚Established in 2013, the brewery also uses the names Spa Town Ales, and It's Quicker By Ale on its logo and pumpclips. The brewery has a capacity of 10 barrels, and brews several times each week. 🍺♦

Harrogate Pale (ABV 4.2%) GOLD
Cold Bath Gold (ABV 4.4%) GOLD
Pinewoods Pale Ale (ABV 4.4%) PALE
Plum Porter (ABV 4.8%) SPECIALITY

Vanilla Porter (ABV 4.8%) SPECIALITY
Beeching Axe (ABV 5.2%) BITTER
Kursaal Stout (ABV 6.7%) STOUT

Hartlebury

**Station Park, Station Road, Hartlebury,
Worcestershire, DY11 7YJ**
☎ (01299) 253617 ☎ 07831 570117
✉ hartleburybrewingco@icloud.com

Hartlebury Brewing Co was established in 2019 by David
Higgs, the owner of the Tap House pub adjacent to
Hartlebury railway station. It supplies the Tap House and
local free trade.

Hooker (ABV 4%) PALE
Pale ale, malt and hops predominate on the nose,
background berry fruits, then notes of grapefruit, hops,
pear and melon in the taste. Finish is grapefruit fading
into bitterness and finally malt.
Off the Rails (ABV 4.2%) GOLD
Golden ale, fruity aroma with a hint of honey sweetness,
flavours of grapefruit, hint of nectarine and some toffee
leading to a spicy aftertaste of grapefruit and a long,
bitter finish.
Rambo Mango (ABV 4.3%) SPECIALITY
Yellow, speciality beer with mango, aromas of yeast,
biscuit and a hint of mango, fruity bitter taste of hops,
grapefruit, mango in the background, followed by a long,
hoppy, then bitter finish.
APA (ABV 4.5%) PALE
Smooth, yellow ale, malt and hops predominate on the
nose with some background berry fruits, grapefruit, hops
and pear, followed by grapefruit fading into bitterness
and malt in the aftertaste.

Hartshorns

**Unit 4, Tomlinsons Industrial Estate, Alfreton Road,
Derby, DE21 4ED** ☎ 07830 367125
⊕ hartshornsbrewery.com

⊠ Hartshorns began brewing in 2012 using a six-barrel
plant installed by brothers Darren and Lindsey Hartshorn.
The brewery owns two pubs, the Little Chester Ale
House, Derby and Belper House, Belper.

Barley Pop (ABV 3.8%) BITTER
Ignite (ABV 3.9%) GOLD
Porter (ABV 4.5%) PORTER
Fusion (ABV 4.6%) GOLD
Reaper (ABV 4.9%) GOLD
Shakademus (ABV 5.4%) GOLD
Psychotropic (ABV 5.8%) GOLD
Apocalypse (ABV 6.2%) GOLD

Harvey's IFBB

**Bridge Wharf Brewery, 6 Cliffe High Street, Lewes,
East Sussex, BN7 2AH**
☎ (01273) 480209 ⊕ harveys.org.uk

⊠ Established in 1790, this independent, family brewery
operates from the banks of the River Ouse in Lewes. A
major development in 1985 doubled the brewhouse
capacity to more than 38,000 barrels a year. There are
plans to re-establish small brew lengths of special beers,
including replicating old recipes. Harvey's supplies real
ale to all its 43 pubs and about 550 free trade outlets in
the South East. ‼⊫♦LIVE

Dark Mild (ABV 3%) MILD
A dark copper-brown colour. Roast malt dominates the
aroma and palate leading to a sweet, caramel finish.
IPA (ABV 3.5%) PALE
Sussex Wild Hop (ABV 3.7%) GOLD

Sussex Best Bitter (ABV 4%) BITTER
Full-bodied, brown bitter. A hoppy aroma leads to a good
malt and hop balance, and a dry aftertaste.
Old Ale (ABV 4.3%) OLD
Armada Ale (ABV 4.5%) BITTER
Hoppy, amber best bitter. Well-balanced fruit and hops
dominate throughout with a fruity palate.

Harviestoun SIBA

**Harviestoun Brewery, Alva Industrial Estate, Alva,
FK12 5DQ**
☎ (01259) 769100 ⊕ harviestoun.com

Harviestoun has grown from one-man brewing in a
bucket in the back of a shed, in 1983, to a 60-barrel,
multi award-winning brewery today. Now based in Alva,
Scotland. ‼⊫♦LIVE

Bitter & Twisted (ABV 3.8%) GOLD
Refreshingly hoppy beer with fruit throughout. A
bittersweet taste with a long, bitter finish. A golden
session beer.
Schiehallion (ABV 4.8%) SPECIALITY
A Scottish cask lager, brewed using a lager yeast and
Hersbrucker hops. A hoppy aroma, with fruit and malt,
leads to a malty, bitter taste with floral hoppiness and a
bitter finish.

Harwich Town

**c/o Unit 1, Upp Hall Farm, Salmons Lane, Coggeshall,
Essex, CO6 1RY** ☎ 07723 607917
⊕ harwichtown.co.uk

Founded in 2007 with a five-barrel plant in premises next
to Harwich Town railway station. In 2018 it moved out of
its original home and became a cuckoo brewery, using
spare capacity at Red Fox Brewery (qv). The owner/
brewer, a former customs officer, names the beers after
local characters and landmarks. Local pubs and beer
festivals are supplied, with reciprocal trading with other
breweries. It organises the Harwich Redoubt Beer
Festival in a Napoleonic fort in July each year. ♦LIVE

EPA Centenary (ABV 3.8%) PALE
Leading Lights (ABV 3.8%) BITTER
SS Brussels (ABV 3.8%) BITTER
Ganges (ABV 4%) BITTER
Bathside Battery Bitter (ABV 4.2%) GOLD
Phoenix (ABV 5%) GOLD

Hatherland (NEW)

**Hatherland Mill Farm, Lower Washfield, Devon,
EX16 9PG**
☎ (01398) 351165 ⊕ hatherland.co.uk

Owner and founder, Lawrence Bunning, decided to
combine his love for beer with reutilising unused space
on his family farm, setting up the brewery in the old
dairy shed in the yard of Hatherland Mill Farm. Water is
drawn from a bore hole. Passionate about the
environment, solar energy is utilised from panels on the
brewery roof and heat from the wood chip boiler.
Brewing waste is used to feed the farm's prize-winning
rare breed cattle.

Sand Martin (ABV 4.8%) PALE

Hattie Brown's

**c/o The Square & Compass, Worth Matravers, Dorset,
BH19 3LF**
☎ (01929) 439229

⊠ Hattie Brown's began brewing in 2014 at the Wessex
brewery. In 2015 it moved to its present location. It is

owned by the manager of the Square & Compass, Worth Matravers, and partner, Jean, the brewer.

HBA (ABV 3.8%) BITTER
Moonlite (ABV 3.8%) PALE
Mustang Sally (ABV 4.3%) BITTER
Kirrin Island (ABV 4.5%) PALE
Spangle (ABV 4.6%) BITTER
Crow Black (ABV 5.1%) PORTER
Dog on the Roof (ABV 6%) GOLD

Hawkshead

Beer Hall: Mill Yard, Staveley, Cumbria, LA8 9LR
☎ (01539) 822644 ⊕ hawksheadbrewery.co.uk

☺Established in 2002, it outgrew its original barn and moved to Staveley in 2006 to a purpose-built, 20-barrel brewery. Capacity has increased several times since. A micro packaging plant, Beer Hall, and the brewery tap were added. In 2018, production of the core range of beers was transferred to a brand new 240-barrel brewery in Flookburgh, with the Staveley plant continuing to produce small batch beers. Beers are also contract brewed for Sadler's Brewing Co. !! ➡ ♦LIVE ⚲

Iti (ABV 3.5%) GOLD
A beer packed with grapefruit aroma and taste. Beautifully balanced with a long lasting, hoppy bitter finish.
Windermere Pale (ABV 3.5%) BLOND
Crisp and fruity, yellow beer with hints of melon and grapefruit and a strong bitter aftertaste.
Bitter (ABV 3.7%) BITTER
Well-balanced, thirst-quenching beer with fruit and hops aroma, leading to a lasting, bitter finish.
Mosaic Pale (ABV 4%) PALE
Red (ABV 4.2%) RED
An impressive colour for this richly-flavoured beer; lots of fruitiness and good hop flavour with a lingering aftertaste.
Lakeland Gold (ABV 4.4%) PALE
Dry, refreshing beer with good body and bitterness staying to the end.
Dry Stone Stout (ABV 4.5%) STOUT
Black, dry, bitter stout with an astringent, roast finish.
Session IPA (ABV 4.7%) PALE
Prime Porter (ABV 4.9%) PORTER
Complex, dark brown beer with plenty of malt, fruit and roast taste. Satisfying full body with a clean finish.
Cumbrian Five Hop (ABV 5%) PALE
A robust, hoppy bitter with citrus hops and fruity middle.
Lakeland Lager (ABV 5%) SPECIALITY
NZPA (ABV 6%) IPA
A very hoppy bitter with a sweet, fruity taste and a resounding dry, bitter finish.

Contract brewed for Sadler's Brewing Co:
Peaky Blinder Pale Ale (ABV 4.3%) PALE
Worcester Sorcerer (ABV 4.3%) BITTER
Peaky Blinder Black IPA (ABV 4.4%) PALE
Black in colour with malt and fruit in the aroma. Smoky bitterness and toffee in the taste with powerful hops lingering.
Hop Bomb (ABV 4.6%) PALE
1861 White Beer (ABV 5.3%) SPECIALITY
Mud City Stout (ABV 6%) SPECIALITY
Dark brown. Soft fruity aroma, malty taste with caramel and raisins, lingering sweet aftertaste with a hint of bitterness.

Haworth Steam

▤ **Rose & Crown, 2 Westgate, Cleckheaton, West Yorkshire, BD19 5ET**

☎ (01535) 646059 ☎ 07974 483310
⊕ haworthsteambrewery.co.uk

☺Established in 2011, the five-barrel brewery is located at the Rose & Crown, Cleckheaton, this being the main outlet for the beers along with the Haworth Steam Bistro, Haworth. Beers are also sold under the Whitechapel brand name. ➡

Haywood Bad Ram SIBA

Callow Top Holiday Park, Buxton Road, Sandyacre, Ashbourne, Derbyshire, DE6 2AQ
☎ (01335) 344020 ☎ 07974 948427
⊕ badrambrewery.co.uk

⊠ Established in 2003, the brewery was based in a converted barn but a new brewery and bottling plant became operational in 2012. One pub is owned (on-site) and several other outlets are supplied. !! ➡LIVE

Thoroughbred Bad Ram (ABV 3.8%) PALE
Dr Samuel Johnson (ABV 4.5%) BITTER
Callow Top Imperial IPA (ABV 5.2%) PALE

Headcorn Hop

Shenley Road, Headcorn, Ashford, Kent, TN27 9HX
⊕ headcornhop.weebly.com

Headcorn Hop is a picobrewery producing small batch beers. Originally brewed in France, the owners now brew both in France and Kent.

Headstocks

See Rufford Abbey

Healey's

▤ **Wellington Inn, Main Street, Loppergarth, Cumbria, LA12 0JL**
☎ (01229) 582388

Healey's began brewing in the Wellington Inn in 2012 using a custom-made, 2.5-barrel, stainless steel plant. The brewery can be viewed through full-length windows in the pub. A range of different cask beer styles are brewed and are available at a variety of local pubs in the area including in the Wellington itself. Electrical power is provided by solar panels.

Golden (ABV 3.6%) BLOND
A fruity, moderately bitter, light ale.
Dark Mild (ABV 3.7%) MILD
Dark mild with a reddish hue. Roast flavours at outset mingle with fruit and sweetness in the middle. A drier finish completes the beer.
Blonde (ABV 4%) BLOND
Aromatic bitter, sweet and tasty from the start with increasing hops and a dry, bitter finish.
Give it Some (ABV 4%) PALE
Best (ABV 4.2%) BITTER

Heaney Farmhouse

c/o Boundary Brewing, Portview Trade Centre, Newtownards Road, Belfast, BT4 1HE
⊕ heaneyfarmhousebrewing.com

Founded in 2014. Bottled beers are currently brewed at Boundary (qv) in Belfast while its brewhouse project is underway at a farm in Bellaghy, Co Londonderry. No real ale.

Heart of Wales

▤ **Stables Yard, Zion Street, Llanwrtyd Wells, LD5 4RD**

☎ (01591) 610236 ⊕ heartofwalesbrewery.co.uk

☺The brewery was set up with a six-barrel plant in 2006 in old stables at the rear of the Neuadd Arms Hotel. Beers are brewed using water from the brewery's own borehole. Seasonal brews celebrate local events such as the World Bogsnorkelling Championships. Cambrian Heart Ale was commissioned by and is brewed for the Cambrian Mountains Initiative, inspired by the Prince of Wales, which aims to promote and support rural producers and communities in the region. ‼️🍺♦LIVE V

Heathen

Grape and Grain, 51 The Broadway, Haywards Heath, West Sussex, RH16 3AS
☎ (01444) 456217 ☎ 07825 429428
⊕ heathenbrewers.co.uk

Located in the basement of the Grape & Grain off-licence and delicatessen, brewing began in 2014 using a full mash, two-barrel plant. Local outlets and beer festivals are supplied. ‼️♦LIVE

ISA (ABV 3.9%) BITTER
Black Eye PA (ABV 4.9%) PALE
Stout (ABV 5%) STOUT
Pale (ABV 5.3%) PALE
West Coast (ABV 5.4%) PALE
Hoppler Effect (ABV 5.8%) IPA
Mocha (ABV 7%) SPECIALITY

Heathton

🍺 **Old Gate, Heathton, Shropshire, WV5 7EB**

This brewery is planned to be resurrected at the Old Gate pub, but its three beers are produced at present in three different breweries, and served only in the Old Gate.

Heavy Water

c/o Church Hanbrewery, Unit F2, New Yatt Business Centre, North Leigh, Oxfordshire, OX29 6TJ
☎ (01993) 868998

Office: Williams Stanley & Co, 43-45 Newcombe House, Notting Hill Gate, London, W11 3LQ
⊕ heavywaterbrewing.co.uk

Established in 2020, Heavy Water produces a wide range of craft beers in small batches. Canning replaced bottling in 2021, but all remain unfined, unfiltered and unpasteurised. Brewing currently takes place on the Church Hanbrewery (qv) kit and the beers are sold at select locations in the Oxford area and at the Cambridge Cheese Company. ♦

Heineken Royal Trafford

Royal Brewery, 201 Denmark Road, Manchester, M15 6LD

No real ale.

Heist

107 Neepsend Lane, Sheffield, South Yorkshire, S3 8AT ⊕ heistbrewco.com

Established by Dan Hunt and Adam France in 2017 as a craft bar and bottle shop, Heist began brewing operations in Clowne, Derbyshire in 2018. The development of the new brewery and taproom site in Neepsend, Sheffield, launched in 2021, showcases 30 beers on tap. ♦

Helmsley SIBA

18 Bridge Street, Helmsley, North Yorkshire, YO62 5DX
☎ (01439) 771014 ☎ 07525 434268
⊕ helmsleybrewingco.co.uk

☺Located within the North York Moors National Park, brewing began in 2014. The brewery has a viewing gallery, tasting room and brewery tap. Local pubs are supplied. LIVE ♦

Yorkshire Legend (ABV 3.8%) BITTER
Striding the Riding (ABV 4%) BITTER
Howardian Gold (ABV 4.2%) GOLD
Honey (ABV 4.5%) SPECIALITY
H!PA (ABV 5.5%) IPA

Hemlock

37 Main Street, Hemington, Derbyshire, DE74 2RB
☎ 07791 057994 ✉ hembrew@yahoo.com

Established in 2015 on the borders of Derby, Leicester and Nottingham, this two-barrel plant is located in the outbuildings of a 17th century thatched cottage. The brewery originally supplied beers in the immediate area but has now branched out with increasing sales in Derbyshire, Nottinghamshire, Leicestershire and Staffordshire. The brewery produces a growing number of pale ales plus seasonal beers. ‼️♦LIVE

There is a Light (ABV SEPA%)
Harvest Moon (ABV 4.1%) GOLD
Hoptimystic (ABV 4.3%) BITTER
Village Idiot (ABV 4.3%) BITTER
California Dreaming (ABV 4.5%) PALE
Call Me Blondie (ABV 4.5%) BITTER
Sparky's Dream (ABV 4.5%) BITTER
Six Pistols (ABV 6%) BITTER

Henry Smith

🍺 **Robin Hood, 4 Wakefield Road, Pontefract, West Yorkshire, WF8 4HN** ☎ 07547 573378

☺Set up behind the Robin Hood pub in Pontefract by Dean Smith in 2019 with the help of Revolutions Brewery (where Head Brewer, Paul Windmill, learned to brew). The plant is the former James & Kirkman kit with a few tweaks. One beer is brewed at Revolutions due to high demand. Small batch specials for Revolutions will be brewed in Pontefract.

Hepworth

Stane Street, North Heath, West Sussex, RH20 1DJ
☎ (01403) 269696 ⊕ hepworthbrewery.co.uk

⊗ Hepworth's was established in 2001. 274 outlets are supplied. Originally situated in Horsham, a new brewery site in North Heath opened in 2016. Its organic status is ratified by the Soil Association. ‼️🍺♦LIVE V

Traditional Sussex Bitter (ABV 3.5%) BITTER
A fine, clean-tasting, amber, session beer. A bitter beer with a pleasant fruity and hoppy aroma that leads to a crisp, tangy taste. A long, dry finish.
Dark Horse (ABV 3.8%) BITTER
Summer Ale (ABV 3.8%) BITTER
Pullman First Class Ale (ABV 4.2%) BITTER
A sweet, nutty maltiness and fruitiness are balanced by hops and bitterness in this easy-drinking, pale brown best bitter. A subtle bitter aftertaste.
Prospect Organic (ABV 4.5%) GOLD
Classic Old Ale (ABV 4.8%) OLD
Iron Horse (ABV 4.8%) BITTER

There's a fruity, toffee aroma to this light brown, full-bodied bitter. A citrus flavour balanced by caramel and malt leads to a clean, dry finish.

Hercules

Unit 5b, Harbour Court, Heron Road, Sydenham, Holywood, Belfast, BT3 9HB
☎ (028) 9036 4516 ✉ niall@herculesbrewery.com

The original Hercules Brewing Company, founded in the 19th century, was one of 13 breweries in Belfast at the time. The company has been re-established to produce small batch brews using old brewing traditions. Its output is all under the Yardsman brand name.

Brewed under the Yardsman brand name:
IPA (ABV 4.3%) PALE
Lager (ABV 4.8%) SPECIALITY
Belfast Pale Ale (ABV 5.6%) GOLD

Hereford

🖥 88 St Owen Street, Hereford, HR1 2QD
☎ (01432) 342125 ✉ jfkenyon@aol.com

😀Although there has been a small brewery on this site since 1992, Hereford began life as the Spinning Dog Brewery in 2000, changing its name in 2010. After a period as primarily a brewpub, in 2017 it began to expand its distribution to pubs in Herefordshire and Pembrokeshire. ‼◆LIVE

Herefordshire Owd Bull (ABV 3.9%) BITTER
Dark (ABV 4%) MILD
Herefordshire Light Ale (HLA) (ABV 4%) PALE
Celtic Gold (ABV 4.5%) GOLD
Mutley's Revenge (ABV 4.8%) BITTER
Mutts Nuts (ABV 5%) BITTER

Heritage SIBA

National Brewery Centre, Horninglow Street, Burton upon Trent, Staffordshire, DE14 1NG
☎ (01283) 777006
⊕ heritagebrewingcompany.co.uk

😀Heritage Brewing Company (formerly William Worthington's Brewery) was established in 2015 by Planning Solutions Ltd, operators of the National Brewery Centre (NBC). It purchased the 25-barrel brewery and nearby bottling plant from the previous owners, Molson Coors. The team has set out to utilise the resources, history and knowledge available at the NBC to breathe new life into heritage beers, including those produced 10-15 years ago by the former Museum Brewing Co. ‼🍺◆LIVE

Victoria Ale (ABV 3.8%) PALE
Charrington Oatmeal Stout (ABV 4%) SPECIALITY
Massey's Original Mild (ABV 4%) MILD
Offilers' Best Bitter (ABV 4%) BITTER
St. Modwen Golden Ale (ABV 4.2%) BLOND
Charrington IPA (ABV 4.5%) PALE
Masterpiece IPA (ABV 5.6%) IPA
Old-fashioned amber ale, strong with lots of bitterness.

Hermitage

Heathwaite, Slanting Hill, Hermitage, Berkshire, RG18 9QG
☎ (01635) 200907 ☎ 07980 019484
⊕ hermitagebrewery.co.uk

⊠ Established in 2013 by semi-retired, food science lecturer, Richard Marshall. After many years as a keen home brewer, the opportunity arose to go commercial on a very small scale. The 0.5-barrel brewery produces

bottle-conditioned, traditional beers and some casks. Volumes vary, but is about 200 bottles per week. A range of seven 'core' beers and four seasonal beers are sold to local shops and pubs, and festivals. LIVE

Tom Herrick's

The Stable House, Main Street, Carlton on Trent, Nottinghamshire, NG23 6NW ☎ 07877 542331
✉ tomherricksbrewery@hotmail.com

Tom Herrick installed his bespoke, 2.5-barrel, stainless steel brewery at the front of his premises during 2014, and began small scale commercial brewing the following year. The brewery is only operated on a part-time basis with output going to festivals and local pubs.

Bomber Command (ABV 4.2%) BITTER

Hesket Newmarket SIBA

Old Crown Barn, Back Green, Hesket Newmarket, Cumbria, CA7 8JG
☎ (01697) 478066 ⊕ hesketbrewery.co.uk

😀Founded in 1988, and bought by a co-operative in 1999 to preserve a community amenity. Cask beers are generally named after Cumbrian fells. Newer look beer styles have been introduced in recent years with traditional beers undergoing a rejuvenation. More than 10 cask ales are supplied across Cumbria with supply also available in bottles and cans. ‼◆

Haystacks (ABV 3.7%) BLOND
Light, easy-drinking, thirst-quenching blond beer; pleasant for its strength.
Skiddaw (ABV 3.7%) BITTER
Red Pike (ABV 3.8%) RED
Black Sail (ABV 4%) STOUT
A sweet stout with roast flavours.
Helvellyn Gold (ABV 4%) PALE
Complex, hoppy and fruity beer with malt presence and refreshing finish.
High Pike (ABV 4.2%) BITTER
A traditional style bitter; fruity with a dry finish.
Doris' 90th Birthday Ale (ABV 4.3%) BITTER
Scafell Blonde (ABV 4.4%) PALE
A hoppy, sweet, fruity, pale-coloured bitter.
Brim Fell IPA (ABV 4.5%) PALE
Catbells (ABV 5%) PALE
An ale with a nice balance of fruity sweetness and bitterness, almost syrupy but with an unexpectedly dry finish.
Smoked Porter (ABV 5.4%) SPECIALITY
Old Carrock Strong Ale (ABV 6%) OLD
Reddy brown strong ale, vine-fruity in flavour with slightly astringent finish.
West Coast Red (ABV 6.3%) RED
Double IPA (ABV 7.4%) IPA

Hetton Law

Hetton Law Farm, Lowick, Berwick upon Tweed, Northumberland, TD15 2UL
☎ (01289) 388558 ☎ 07889 457140
⊕ hettonlawbrewery.co.uk

Brewing began in 2015 using a 2.5-barrel plant. Run by retired dentists Judith and Nicholas Grasse, it uses local spring water and locally grown malt, which gives the beers a distinctive character. Due to the size of the brewery, availability on draught and in bottles is effectively limited to the local area on both sides of the border. ◆

Hetton Hermit (ABV 3.8%) BITTER
Hetton Howler (ABV 4.2%) SPECIALITY

Hetton Harlot (ABV 4.8%) BITTER
Hare Raiser (ABV 5.2%) GOLD

Hexhamshire SIBA

Dipton Mill Road, Hexham, Northumberland, NE46 1YA
☎ (01434) 606577 ⊕ hexhamshire.co.uk

Hexhamshire is Northumberland's oldest brewery and is run by the same family since it was founded in 1993. The Brooker family also run the brewery tap, the Dipton Mill. Outlets are supplied direct and via the SIBA Beerflex scheme.

Devil's Elbow (ABV 3.6%) BITTER
Amber brew full of hops and fruit, leading to a bitter finish.
Shire Bitter (ABV 3.8%) BITTER
A good balance of hops with fruity overtones, this amber beer makes an easy-drinking, session bitter.
Blackhall English Stout (ABV 4%) STOUT
Devil's Water (ABV 4.1%) BITTER
Copper-coloured best bitter, well-balanced with a slightly fruity, hoppy finish.
Whapweasel (ABV 4.8%) BITTER
An interesting, smooth, hoppy beer with a fruity flavour. Amber in colour, the bitter finish brings out the fruit and hops.
Old Humbug (ABV 5.5%) BITTER

Hidden Lane

Argyle Street, Finnieston, G3 8ND
☎ (0141) 258 2520 ⊕ hiddenlanebrewery.com

Organic brewery launched in Glasgow in 2019.

Hideaway (NEW)

57 Farm Lane, Worsley, M28 2PG ☎ 07887 732725
⊕ hideawaybrewing.co.uk

Nanobrewery who started brewing in 2020. Each production run is currently limited to 25 litres.

High House Farm SIBA

Matfen, Newcastle upon Tyne, NE20 0RG
☎ (01661) 886192/ 886769
⊕ highhousefarmbrewery.co.uk

The brewery was founded in 2003 by a Brewlab graduate on a working farm, with a visitor centre, brewery shop and function room. This has now expanded to include a restaurant and wedding venue. More than 350 regional outlets are supplied. ⏣🍴♦

Sundancer (ABV 3.6%) GOLD
Pullet Please (ABV 3.7%) GOLD
Auld Hemp (ABV 3.8%) BITTER
Tawny-coloured ale with hop, malt and fruit flavours and a good bitter finish.
Nel's Best (ABV 4.2%) BITTER
Golden hoppy ale full of flavour with a clean, bitter finish.
Matfen Magic (ABV 4.8%) BITTER
Well-hopped brown ale with a fruity aroma. Malt and chocolate overtones with a rich, bitter finish.

High Weald

Highgate Works, Forest Row, East Sussex, RH18 5AT
☎ 07836 291430

Office: 23 Hermitage Road, East Grinstead, RH19 2BP
⊕ highwealdbrewery.co.uk

⊠ Established in 2013, High Weald Brewery grew from its homebrew origins to a four-barrel plant, which moved to Hartfield in 2017. After about a year's temporary closure, High Weald moved to Forest Row in 2021 and now operates on a reduced scale using a two-barrel plant producing a small range of cask and bottle-conditioned beers. The brewery is again supplying local (and not so local) free houses and shops. LIVE

Chronicle (ABV 3.8%) BITTER
Greenstede (ABV 4%) GOLD
Dark Mild (ABV 4.1%) MILD
Charcoal Burner (ABV 4.3%) STOUT

Highgate

See Davenports

Higsons

See Love Lane

Hilden

Hilden House, Grand Street, Hilden, Lisburn, Co Antrim, BT27 4TY
☎ (028) 9266 0800 ⊕ hildenbrewery.co.uk

☺Established 1981, Hilden is Ireland's oldest independent brewery. Now in the second generation of family ownership, the beers are widely distributed across the UK. The beers are regularly available in Wetherspoon outlets in Northern Ireland. ⏣🍴♦

Nut Brown (ABV 3.8%) BITTER
Ale (ABV 4%) BITTER
An amber-coloured beer with an aroma of malt, hops and fruit. The balanced taste is slightly slanted towards hops, and hops are also prominent in the full, malty finish.
Barney's Brew (ABV 4.2%) SPECIALITY
Irish Stout (ABV 4.3%) STOUT
Scullion's Irish Ale (ABV 4.6%) BITTER
Twisted Hop (ABV 4.7%) BITTER
Halt (ABV 6.1%) RED

Brewed under the College Brewery brand name:
Headless Dog (ABV 4.3%) GOLD

Hildenborough (NEW)

8 Birch Close, Hildenborough, Tonbridge, Kent, TN11 9DU ☎ 07557 117078
⊕ hildenboroughbrewery.com

Hildenborough brewery is a small, family-run, home business with all beers brewed, bottled and labelled by hand. LIVE

Hill Island

Unit 7, Fowlers Yard, Back Silver Street, Durham, DH1 3RA ☎ 07740 932584
✉ hillisland73@gmail.com

☺Established in 2002, Hill Island is a literal translation of Dunholme, from which Durham is derived. It is part of Fowler's Yard Craft Workshops on the banks of the River Wear and can be reached by steps down from Silver Street. A pop-up bar operates at the brewery most Saturdays (see Facebook for updates) including weekends coinciding with Durham events such as the Durham Fire & Ice Festival, and the Durham Miner's Gala. ⏣🍴♦

Peninsula Pint (ABV 3.7%) BLOND
Bitter (ABV 3.9%) BITTER
Stout for the Count (ABV 4%) STOUT
Neptune's (ABV 4.2%) BITTER

Cathedral Ale (ABV 4.3%) BITTER
THAIPA (ABV 4.3%) SPECIALITY

Hillstown

128 Glebe Road, Randalstown, BT41 3DT
⊕ hillstownbrewery.com

Brewing began in 2014 in a converted barn on a farm in Randalstown producing bottle-conditioned beers. ◆LIVE

Hilltop

⊟ Sheffield Road, Conisbrough, South Yorkshire, DN12 2AY
☎ (01709) 868811 ☎ 07947 146746
⊕ thehilltophotel.co.uk

⊛Established in 2016, Hilltop Brewery is a 3.5-barrel plant situated in the outbuildings of the Hilltop Hotel in Conisbrough. Beers are available in the hotel and other local outlets. !!◆LIVE

Hinks

1 Dimon Villas, Hamstreet Road, Ruckinge, Kent, TN26 2NT ☎ 07518 569041

A nanobrewery established in 2018.

Hitchin (NEW)

The Outhouse, 16 Thatcher's End, Hitchin, Hertfordshire, SG4 0PD
✉ hitchinbrewery@gmail.com

Small brewery using a 100-litre brew kit. Established in 2018 it currently supplies three outlets with bottle-conditioned beers although cask and keg is planned. LIVE

Hive Mind

See Wye Valley Meadery

Hobsons SIBA

Newhouse Farm, Tenbury Road, Cleobury Mortimer, Shropshire, DY14 8RD
☎ (01299) 270837 ⊕ hobsons-brewery.co.uk

Established in 1993 in a former sawmill, Hobsons relocated to a farm site with more space in 1995. A second brewery, bottling plant and a warehouse have been added along with significant expansion to the first brewery. Beers are supplied within a 50-mile radius. The brewery utilises environmental sustainable technologies where possible. A visitor centre was added in 2014, which also now operates as a brewery tap. !!☞LIVE◆

Mild (ABV 3.2%) MILD
A classic mild. Complex layers of taste come from roasted malts that predominate and give lots of flavour.
Twisted Spire (ABV 3.6%) GOLD
Best (ABV 3.8%) BITTER
A pale brown to amber, medium-bodied beer with strong hop character throughout. It is consequently bitter, but with malt discernible in the taste.
Old Prickly (ABV 4.2%) PALE
Town Crier (ABV 4.5%) GOLD

Hogs Back SIBA

Manor Farm, The Street, Tongham, Surrey, GU10 1DE
☎ (01252) 783000 ⊕ hogsback.co.uk

⊠ This traditionally-styled brewery, established in 1992, boasts an extensive range of award-winning ales. The shop sells all its beers and related merchandise, plus more than 400 world beers and ciders. In 2014 it restored ancient Farnham White Bine hops on neighbouring farmland. A new on-site hop kiln has been added to dry its own hops. The brewery is planning on hosting events from its tap (live music, comedy nights and film showings). !!☞◆LIVE◆

HBB (ABV 3.7%) BITTER
Biscuity aroma with some hops and lemon notes. Well-balanced, plenty of hop in mouth with long-lasting, dry, bitter aftertaste.
Surrey Nirvana (ABV 4%) PALE
Refreshing session pale ale. Sweet, moderately full-bodied, leading to an initially sweet finish with hop bitterness becoming more evident.
TEA (ABV 4.2%) BITTER
A tawny-coloured best bitter with toffee and malt present in the nose. A well-rounded flavour with malt and a fruity sweetness.
Hop Garden Gold (ABV 4.4%) PALE
Full-bodied with an aroma of malt, hops and fruit. Hoppy bitterness grows in an increasingly dry aftertaste with a hint of sweetness.
Rip Snorter (ABV 5%) BITTER
Well-balanced sweet and malty bitter. Red brown in colour, with a moderate bitterness that grows into the aftertaste.

Hogs Head

⊟ 1 Stanley Street, Sowerby Bridge, West Yorkshire, HX6 2AH
☎ (01422) 836585 ⊕ hogsheadbrewhouse.co.uk

⊛The Hogs Head Brewery opened in a huge 18th-century former malthouse at the end of 2015. The sixteen-barrel brew house has increased from eight-barrels since 2018. The handsome copper and stainless steel brewing vats of the original brewery are on display at the back of the bar area with the newer brewing vessels being accommodated in the cellar. Almost all the production is sold on the premises with occasional casks being provided to beer festivals. ◆

Holcot Hop-Craft

Chequers Row, Main Street, Holcot, NN6 9SP
✉ roger@gunnett.co.uk

This small brewery started brewing in 2017, and is located in the tiny village of Holcot, Northamptonshire. It is a one-hectolitre brewery, brewing once a week producing 180 pints either in pins or firkins. The beer is usually on tap at the Queens Arms at Orlingbury and is available in other pubs, clubs and beer festivals within a 10 mile radius of the brewery.

Holden's SIBA IFBB

George Street, Woodsetton, Dudley, West Midlands, DY1 4LW
☎ (01902) 880051 ⊕ holdensbrewery.co.uk

⊛A family brewery spanning four generations, Holden's began life as a brewpub in 1915. Continued expansion means it now has 19 tied pubs in its estate. !!☞◆

Black Country Mild (ABV 3.7%) MILD
A good, red/brown mild; a refreshing, light blend of roast malt, hops and fruit, dominated by malt throughout.
Black Country Bitter (ABV 3.9%) BITTER
A medium-bodied, golden ale; a light, well-balanced bitter with a subtle, dry, hoppy finish.
Golden Glow (ABV 4.4%) GOLD
Special (ABV 5.1%) BITTER

A sweet, malty, full-bodied amber ale with hops to balance in the taste and in the good, bittersweet finish.

Hollow Stone

See Shipstone's

Hollow Tree

3 Glen Road, Whatstandwell, Derbyshire, DE4 5EH
☎ **07920 843754** ⊕ **hollowtreebrewing.co.uk**

☺Nanobrewery with five core beers. Brewing began in 2019. There are also limited and seasonal releases which use ingredients sourced and foraged from the local area. ♦LIVE

Holsworthy

Unit 5, Circuit Business Park, Clawton, Holsworthy, Devon, EX22 6RR
☎ **(01566) 783678** ☎ **07879 401073**
⊕ **holsworthyales.co.uk**

⊠ Holsworthy Ales is a 5.5-barrel microbrewery situated in the heart of Devon's Ruby Country. Brewing began commercially in 2011. Its intention is to make its beers taste as clean and natural as possible, so no chemicals or finings are added to the soft Devon water used in many of its ales. ‼☲♦LIVE V

Mine's A Mild (ABV 3.5%) MILD
Sunshine (ABV 4%) GOLD
Smooth golden ale. Hops overwhelm all else. Hints of fruit. Fresh and bitter hoppy aftertaste.
St George (ABV 4.1%) GOLD
Bang On (ABV 4.2%) BITTER
Muck 'n' Straw (ABV 4.4%) BITTER
Hops dominate with hints of malt in aroma and taste. Well-balanced with slight dryness in aftertaste.
Tamar Black (ABV 4.8%) STOUT
Dark stout with hints of liquorice and coffee. A complex mix full of malt, roast, fruit, hops and caramel.
Hop on The Run (ABV 5%) PALE
Proper Lager (ABV 5%) SPECIALITY
Old Market Monk (ABV 6.1%) SPECIALITY

Joseph Holt SIBA IFBB

The Brewery, Empire Street, Cheetham, Manchester, M3 1JD
☎ **(0161) 834 3285** ⊕ **joseph-holt.com**

☺Founded in 1849, Joseph Holt is one of the UK's, leading, independent, family breweries. Now in its sixth generation, the business operates 123 pubs across Manchester and the North West and supplies ales to many pubs and clubs nationally. ☲

Mild (ABV 3.2%) MILD
A dark brown/red beer with a fruity, malty nose. Roast, malt, fruit and hops in the taste, with strong bitterness for a mild, and a dry malt and hops finish.
IPA (ABV 3.8%) BITTER
Golden bitter with biscuity malt, hops and restrained lemony notes. Dry, bitter finish.
Bitter (ABV 4%) BITTER
Pale brown beer with malt and hops in the aroma. Bitter taste with balanced malty flavour. Increased bitter finish.
Two Hoots (ABV 4.2%) GOLD

Holy Island

See Alnwick

Hook Norton SIBA IFBB

Brewery Lane, Scotland End, Hook Norton, Oxfordshire, OX15 5NY
☎ **(01608) 737210** ⊕ **hooky.co.uk**

⊠ One of the finest examples of a Victorian tower brewery, and the oldest independent brewery in Oxfordshire, Hook Norton has been brewing since 1849. The current premises were built in 1900 and still house much of the original machinery, including a 25hp steam engine (occasionally in use). Shire horses make deliveries to local pubs. Family-owned, it combines its heritage with a modern approach. Various parts of the brewery are available for hire. Customers can spend a day brewing their own beer. ‼☲♦LIVE ♦

Hooky Mild (ABV 2.8%) MILD
A chestnut brown, easy-drinking mild. A complex malt and hop aroma give way to a well-balanced taste, leading to a long, hoppy finish that is unusual for a mild.
Hooky (ABV 3.5%) BITTER
A classic, golden, session bitter. Hoppy and fruity aroma followed by a malt and hops taste and a continuing hoppy finish.
Hooky Gold (ABV 4.1%) PALE
Old Hooky (ABV 4.6%) BITTER
A strong bitter, tawny in colour. A well-rounded fruity taste with a balanced, bitter finish.

Hop & Stagger

The Old Cow Shed, Astol Farm, Norton, Shropshire, TF11 9EW
☎ **(01952) 730737** ☎ **07487 898151**
⊕ **hopandstaggerbrewery.co.uk**

Hop & Stagger began brewing in 2011, having set up a 2.5-barrel plant at the White Lion Inn in Bridgnorth. In 2015 the brewery relocated to a farm between Bridgnorth and Telford, with all new brewing equipment, and an increase in capacity to six barrels. Currently it produces six permanent beers, with additional seasonal brews. ♦

Shropshire Pale Ale (ABV 3.8%) PALE
Golden Wander (ABV 4.1%) GOLD
Beckbury Bitter (ABV 4.2%) BITTER
Strategic Blonde (ABV 4.3%) PALE
Bridgnorth Porter (ABV 5%) PORTER
Triple Hop IPA (ABV 5%) PALE

Hop Back

Units 22-24, Batten Road Industrial Estate, Downton, Wiltshire, SP5 3HU
☎ **(01725) 510986** ⊕ **hopback.co.uk**

⊠ Founded in 1987, Hop Back owns 10 pubs and distributes nationally. The flagship beer, Summer Lightning, has won numerous CAMRA awards. ‼☲♦LIVE V

GFB (ABV 3.5%) BITTER
A light gold, refreshing, session bitter. The hoppy aroma leads to bitterness initially, lasting through to the finish with some fruit.
Citra (ABV 4%) BLOND
Pale yellow, almost straw-coloured with lemon and grapefruit on the aroma and taste, rapidly developing a balanced hoppy aftertaste.
Fuggle Stone (ABV 4%) BITTER
Fresh-tasting, slightly sweet, malty, session bitter with the sweetness and hops leading to a gentle, dry aftertaste.
Crop Circle (ABV 4.2%) GOLD

A pale yellow best bitter with a fragrant hop aroma, complex hop, fruit and citrus flavours with a balanced hoppy, bitter/sweet aftertaste.

Taiphoon (ABV 4.2%) SPECIALITY
A clean-tasting, light, fruity beer with hops and fruit on the aroma, complex hop character and lemongrass notes in the taste, slight sweetness balanced with some astringency in the aftertaste.

Entire Stout (ABV 4.5%) STOUT
A smooth, rich, ruby-black stout with strong roast and malt aromas and flavours, with a long, bittersweet, malty aftertaste.

Summer Lightning (ABV 5%) BLOND
Strong golden ale with a hoppy aroma and slightly astringent bitterness in the taste, balanced with some fruit sweetness, in the dry aftertaste.

Hop Fuzz SIBA

Unit 8, Riverside Industrial Estate, West Hythe, Kent, CT21 4NB ☎ 07858 562878 ⊕ hopfuzz.co.uk

Hop Fuzz was started by two friends in 2011. It is situated on an industrial estate next to the Royal Military Canal at West Hythe. The brewery delivers bottles, minikegs and cans within 20 miles. The Unit 1 microbar, on the same estate, has been community owned and run since 2019. ♦V

Martello (ABV 3.8%) RED
American (ABV 4.2%) GOLD
Bullion (ABV 5%) BLOND

Hop Kettle SIBA

☰ Swindon: Unit 4, Hawksworth Industrial Estate, Newcombe Drive, Swindon, Wiltshire, SN2 1DZ ☎ (01793) 490556

Cricklade: Red Lion, 74 High Street, Cricklade, Wiltshire, SN6 6DD ☎ (01793) 750776 ⊕ theredlioncricklade.co.uk

Brewing began in a barn behind the Red Lion Inn, Cricklade, in 2012, using a one-barrel plant. Due to demand a larger four-barrel plant followed, which supplies the pub and is also used for experimental brews. A new 10-barrel plant was installed in an old Royal Mail warehouse in Swindon in 2016. ♦⚲

Cricklade Ordinary Bitter (ABV 3.8%) BITTER
Chameleon (ABV 4%) BITTER
Lode Star (ABV 4.3%) PALE
North Wall (ABV 4.3%) BITTER
Rising Star (ABV 4.8%) GOLD
East Star (ABV 5%) BITTER
Red Star (ABV 5.2%) RED
Evening Star (ABV 5.5%) STOUT

Hop Monster

See George's

Hop Shed SIBA

Old Chicken Shed, Stocks Farm, Suckley, Worcestershire, WR6 5EQ ☎ (01886) 884110 ☎ 07484 688026 ⊕ hopshed.co.uk

Originally named Unity Brew House, brewing began in 2016, using a 10-barrel plant. It is the only brewery in the UK located on a commercial hop farm. Based in an old chicken shed, the beers are named after breeds of chicken. An on-site bar is open on Fridays and Saturdays.

Wybar (ABV 3.6%) BITTER

Sebright Golden Ale (ABV 3.8%) GOLD
Pekin (ABV 4%) PALE
Sultan (ABV 4.2%) GOLD
Frizzle British IPA (ABV 4.5%) GOLD

Hop Studio SIBA

Unit 3, Handley Park, Elvington Industrial Estate, York Road, Elvington, North Yorkshire, YO41 4AR ☎ (01904) 608029 ⊕ thehopstudio.com

⊛Founded in 2012, the Hop Studio brews on a 10-barrel plant in an industrial unit just outside York. Under new ownership from 2020, a new beer range was established during 2021. Outlets in Yorkshire are supplied direct and the rest of the UK via wholesalers. ‼☰♦LIVE⚲

Hometown Hero (ABV 3.9%) BITTER
New Horizons (ABV 4.3%) PALE
Tidal Wave (ABV 4.5%) PALE

Hop Vine

☰ Hop Vine, Liverpool Road North, Burscough, Lancashire, L40 4BY ☎ (01704) 893799 ☎ 07920 002783 ✉ mikejulie6465@gmail.com

⊛Hop Vine began brewing in 2017 using the four-barrel plant of the defunct Burscough Brewery. It is situated in old stable buildings in the courtyard to the rear of the Hop Vine. Beer is usually only supplied to the pub and the Legh Arms, Mere Brow. ☰♦

Hopdaemon SIBA

Unit 1, Parsonage Farm, Seed Road, Newnham, Kent, ME9 0NA ☎ (01795) 892078 ⊕ hopdaemon.com

Tonie Prins originally started brewing in Tyler Hill near Canterbury in 2000 and moved to a new site in Newnham in 2005. The brewery currently supplies more than 100 outlets. ‼♦LIVE

Golden Braid (ABV 3.7%) BITTER
A refreshing, golden, session bitter with a good blend of bittering and aroma hops underpinned by pale malt.
Incubus (ABV 4%) BITTER
A well-balanced, copper-hued best bitter. Pale malt and a hint of crystal malt are blended with bitter and slightly floral hops to give a lingering, hoppy finish.
Skrimshander IPA (ABV 4.5%) BITTER
Green Daemon (ABV 5%) SPECIALITY
Leviathan (ABV 6%) BITTER

Hophurst SIBA

Unit 8, Hindley Business Centre, Platt Lane, Hindley, WN2 3PA ☎ (01942) 522333 ⊕ hophurstbrewery.co.uk

⊛Hophurst Brewery was started in 2014 by Stuart Hurst. Stuart's passion for producing craft ales, combined with 20 years of supporting businesses and re-skilling unemployed people, created a unique social enterprise brewery. It employs people over the age of 50 and guides them through its training programme. Twisted Vine Ale House is its award-winning microbar in Ashton-in Makerfield town centre. ♦

2 Rounds of 6 Before Breakfast (ABV 3.5%) PALE
Mellors (ABV 3.8%) BLOND
Light and refreshing beer with fruity, bitter hops and a bitter finish.
Quench (ABV 3.8%) PALE
Full-bodied, session bitter with lasting hops and dry finish.

Campfire (ABV 3.9%) MILD
Light-bodied beer with bitter roasted malt.
Cosmati (ABV 4.2%) GOLD
Debonair (ABV 4.9%) STOUT
Porteresque (ABV 5.5%) PORTER
Complex dark beer, with roast and fruit in aroma. Strong roast flavour with a developing sweet fruitiness. Lasting roast finish.

Hopper House Brew Farm

Racecourse Road, Sedgefield, TS21 2HL ☎ 07947 874278 ⊕ hopperhousebrewfarm.co.uk

Brewing commenced in 2019 on a one-barrel plant situated in a working dairy farm on the outskirts of Sedgefield. There is a taproom in an old milking parlour. Currently it only has a licence for bank holidays and occasional weekends but aspires to get a full licence. ⚓

Hoppy Family

Harcourt Street, Kettering, Northamptonshire, NN16 0RS ☎ 07986 019579 ⊕ hfbrewery.com

Microbrewery established in 2017 brewing a range of bottled-conditioned beers using ingredients such as blueberries, raspberries and chillies. LIVE

Hops & Dots

17 Chester Street, Bishop Auckland, DL14 7LP ☎ 07400 558848 ⊕ hopsanddots.com

⊗ Established in 2019 in the Linthorpe suburb of Middlesbrough, the brewery moved in 2021, to share facilities with Caps Off in Bishop Auckland. Hops & Dots was founded by a teacher of the visually impaired, and a solicitor who believe that craft beer should always be accessible to all, which is why it promotes braille alongside its beers. Available in cask, keg and can. Shared on-site taproom is planned. ♦V

Do you want to buy a Speedboat? (ABV 3.9%) PALE
Fat Fingers (ABV 5.1%) SPECIALITY
Porterhouse 5 (ABV 5.5%) PORTER
Sim Specs (ABV 6.4%) IPA
Coffee Switch (ABV 6.8%) STOUT

Hopshackle

Unit F, Bentley Business Park, Blenheim Way, Northfields Industrial Estate, Market Deeping, Lincolnshire, PE6 8LD ☎ (01778) 348542 ⊕ hopshacklebrewery.co.uk

⊚ Hopshackle was established in 2006 using a five-barrel plant. A 10-barrel plant was installed in 2015. More than 40 outlets are supplied direct. ‼♦LIVE

Simmarillo (ABV 3.8%) GOLD
Zen (ABV 3.8%) BITTER
American Pale Ale (ABV 4.3%) PALE
Hopnosis (ABV 5.2%) GOLD

Hopstar SIBA

Unit 9, Rinus Business Park, Grimshaw Street, Darwen, BB3 2QX ☎ 07933 590159 ⊕ hopstarbrewery.co.uk

⊚ Hopstar first brewed in 2004 on a 2.5-barrel plant and expanded in 2010 to a new unit with a six-barrel plant. More than 100 outlets are supplied around Lancashire and the Greater Manchester area. The brewery tap is Number 39 in Darwen. ‼♦LIVE

Chilli (ABV 3.8%) SPECIALITY
Dizzy Danny Ale (ABV 3.8%) GOLD
Dark Knight (ABV 3.9%) MILD
Off T'Mill (ABV 3.9%) PALE
Smokey Joe's Black Beer (ABV 3.9%) STOUT
Darwen Spitfire (ABV 4%) BITTER
JC (ABV 4%) BITTER
Lancashire Gold (ABV 4%) BLOND
Lush (ABV 4%) BITTER
Saaz Blonde (ABV 4%) BLOND

Horbury

⬒ The Brewhouse, Cherry Tree Inn, 19 Church Street, Horbury, West Yorkshire, WF4 6LT ☎ 07970 299292

⊚ Following the closure of Bob's Brewing Co, Horbury Ales took over the plant in 2016 and transferred production to the rear of the brewery tap, Cherry Tree Inn. Beers are available locally, regionally and nationally.

Now Then (ABV 3.8%) PALE
5 Hops (ABV 4.1%) PALE
First Light (ABV 4.1%) PALE
Tiramisu (ABV 4.3%) PORTER

Horncastle

⬒ Old Nicks Tavern, 8 North Street, Horncastle, Lincolnshire, LN9 5DX ☎ (01507) 526862 ⊕ horncastleales.co.uk

Brewing began in 2014 using a 3.75-barrel plant. The brewery is situated in Old Nicks Tavern with beer available in the pub plus other Lincolnshire outlets. It has its own bottling plant and a beer in box scheme is also available for pre-ordering. ‼🍴

Hornes SIBA

19b Station Road, Bow Brickhill, Buckinghamshire, MK17 9JU ☎ (01908) 647724 ⊕ hornesbrewery.co.uk

A purpose-built, six-barrel brewery established in 2015. It produces a range of beers called Triple Goat after the three goats kept in a paddock at the brewery. A taproom and shop were added in 2018. 🍴♦⚓

Featherstone Amber Ale (ABV 3.6%) BITTER
Dark Fox (ABV 3.8%) BITTER
Ryestone (ABV 4%) RED

Brewed under the Triple Goat brand name:
Pale Ale (ABV 3.9%) PALE
Porter (ABV 4.6%) PORTER
IPA (ABV 5%) PALE

Horsetown

See Malton

Horsforth SIBA

Unit 1a, Station Road, Horsforth, Leeds, West Yorkshire, LS18 5NX ☎ 07854 078330 ⊕ horsforthbrewery.co.uk

Brewing began on a part-time basis on a one-barrel plant in 2017 in the owner's garage. In addition to the flagship beer an ever-changing range of specials is produced. The taproom is open on the first Saturday of the month. V⚓

My Horse Came Fourth (ABV 3.5%) SPECIALITY
Horsforth Pale (ABV 4.5%) PALE
Schwarz Rose (ABV 5%) SPECIALITY
Mosaic (ABV 5.1%) PALE
Weise Rose (ABV 5.4%) SPECIALITY

Aubretia (ABV 5.5%) IPA
Night Ryder (ABV 5.5%) RED
Rubis (ABV 6.2%) SPECIALITY

Horsham (NEW)

Unit 3, Blatchford Close, Horsham, West Sussex, RH13 5RG ✉ horshambrewingco@mail.com

Horsham Brewery Company Ltd began brewing in 2021.

HBC Best Bitter (ABV 4.2%) BITTER

Hoskins Brothers

See Belvoir

Howard Town SIBA

Hawkshead Mill, Hope Street, Glossop, Derbyshire, SK13 7SS
☎ (01457) 869800 ⊕ howardtownbrewery.co.uk

☺Established in 2005, this award-winning brewery moved to its current location in 2007. In 2019 it moved into the premises next door, increasing the capacity of the brewery from eight-barrels to 15-barrels. Six core beers are brewed for the free trade, along with seasonal beers. Its brewery tap is open from Thursday to Saturday. ‼🍺♦LIVE🌿

Mill Town Mild (ABV 3.5%) MILD
Longdendale Lights (ABV 3.9%) BLOND
Monk's Gold (ABV 4%) GOLD
Wren's Nest (ABV 4.2%) BITTER
Super Fortress (ABV 4.4%) BITTER
Dark Peak (ABV 6%) SPECIALITY

Howfen

66 Green Meadows, Westhoughton, BL5 2BN
⊕ howfenbrew.co

Howfen began brewing in 2018 and is situated in the owner's garage. After a year's hiatus it has resumed brewing. It is named after the dialect word for Westhoughton.

Howling Hops

≣ Unit 9a, Queen's Yard, White Post Lane, Hackney Wick, London, E9 5EN
☎ (020) 3583 8262 ⊕ howlinghops.co.uk

⊠ Brewing began in 2012 at the Cock Tavern in Hackney, later opening a new brewery and Tank Bar in 2015 at Hackney Wick. Beers are now widely available and cover many styles from a standard range to taproom specials; hoppy styles being the favourite. 🌿

Howzat

≣ Cricketers Arms, Peter Street, St Helens, Merseyside, WA10 2EB
☎ (01744) 758021

A brewery in the grounds of the Cricketer's Arms – a former CAMRA National Pub of the Year.

Sarah Hughes

≣ Beacon Hotel, 129 Bilston Street, Sedgley, West Midlands, DY3 1JE
☎ (01902) 883381 ⊕ sarahhughesbrewery.co.uk

⊠ Traditional, Black Country, Victorian tower brewery, taken over by Sarah Hughes in 1921. Brewing ceased in the 1950s, and recommenced in 1987. The original grist case and rare open-topped copper give a unique character to the brews. The Beacon Hotel is the brewery tap. Famous for its Dark Ruby, the beers can be found far and wide. ‼♦

Pale Amber (ABV 4%) BITTER
Sedgley Surprise (ABV 5%) BITTER
A bittersweet, medium-bodied, hoppy ale with some malt.
Dark Ruby Mild (ABV 6%) MILD
A dark ruby, strong ale with a good balance of fruit and hops, leading to a pleasant, lingering hops and malt finish.

Humber Doucy SIBA

St Edmunds Garage, Broad Road, Bacton, Stowmarket, Suffolk, IP14 4HP
☎ (01449) 780151 ⊕ humberdoucybrew.co

Humber Doucy started brewing in 2019. Located in Bacton, Suffolk, within the Jeffries of Bacton Subaru dealership, it is a son and father business. The family have a background in grain and malt with connections to Stowmarket-based maltsters Muntons.

King Slayer (ABV 3.6%) BITTER
Pale Ale (ABV 4.4%) PALE
American Porter (ABV 5%) PORTER

Humpty Dumpty SIBA

Church Road, Reedham, Norfolk, NR13 3TZ
☎ (01493) 701818 ☎ 07843 248865
⊕ humptydumptybrewery.co.uk

⊠ Established in 1998, this 11-barrel, award-winning brewery continues to grow and expand its range of beers, including a new Norfolk Broads Brewing series of occasional one-off brews. ‼🍺♦LIVE

Little Sharpie (ABV 3.8%) PALE
Fruity aroma with malt and hop. Bitter throughout with balanced malt and hop in the background. Crisp, slightly astringent finish.
Branch Line Bitter (ABV 3.9%) BITTER
Lemon & Ginger (ABV 4%) SPECIALITY
Swallowtail (ABV 4%) PALE
Full-bodied marmalade and biscuit aroma with matching beginning. Grainy texture is enhanced by solid bitter notes flowing onward.
Broadland Sunrise (ABV 4.2%) BITTER
Red Mill (ABV 4.3%) BITTER
Full-bodied, robust and fruity. Coffee, dark fruits and caramel vie for dominance against a malty bitter base. Powerful, rich ending.
Reedcutter (ABV 4.4%) GOLD
A sweet, malty beer; golden-hued with a gentle malt background. Smooth and full-bodied with a quick, gentle finish.
Cheltenham Flyer (ABV 4.6%) BITTER
A full-flavoured, golden, earthy bitter with a long, grainy finish. A strong hop bitterness dominates throughout. Little evidence of malt.
EAPA (East Anglian Pale Ale) (ABV 4.6%) PALE
Amber gold with an orange marmalade nose. A bittersweet caramel beginning slowly dries out as malty nuances fade away.
Railway Sleeper (ABV 5%) OLD
A rich, Christmas pudding aroma introduces this delightfully fruity brew. Malt, sultanas and raisins dominate a bittersweet backdrop. Full-bodied, smooth finish.

Hunters SIBA

Bulleigh Barton Farm, Ipplepen, Devon, TQ12 5UA

☎ (01803) 873509 ☎ 07540 657115
⊕ thehuntersbrewery.co.uk

⊗ Hunters began brewing in 2008. The award-winning brewery has a 60-barrel brew length and 4,000 gallon fermenting capacity. A bottling, labelling and packing plant means it can turn out 3,000 bottle-conditioned beers per hour; this, coupled with a dedicated conditioning room, is enabling Hunters to bottle for others as well as itself. ‼ ▀ ♦LIVE

Old Charlie (ABV 3.8%) BITTER
Crispy Pig (ABV 4%) SPECIALITY
Very different ale, a cross between a golden bitter and cider. Very strong apples aroma, and tastes of apples. A refreshing drink which would go well on a hot summers day.
Half Bore (ABV 4%) SPECIALITY
Light colour and body. Malt dominates from start to finish. Lots of flavour and slightly flowery.
Devon Dreamer (ABV 4.1%) BITTER
Amber best bitter with hop aroma and undertones of caramel. Hops in the taste and slight bitterness develops later.
Pheasant Plucker (ABV 4.3%) BITTER
Best bitter ale leans slightly towards an old ale style in looks and taste. Slight charcoal sweet taste.
Premium (ABV 4.8%) BITTER
A nice, traditional, strong best bitter. Slight winter fruits on taste with after tones of a bitter pine finish.
Royal Hunt (ABV 5.5%) BITTER
An easy-drinking strong ale. Malt dominates, with rich roast and caramel tones bursting through.
Black Jack (ABV 6%) SPECIALITY
A sweet strong stout, very drinkable with a woody caramel taste on the palate.
Full Bore (ABV 6.8%) SPECIALITY

Hurly Burly SIBA

**Unit 1, Block 4, Inveresk Industrial Estate, Musselburgh, EH21 7UL ☎ 07796 124124
⊕ hurlyburlybrewery.co.uk**

Small, family-run brewery. Originally based in the brewer's kitchen, the brewery moved to larger premises in 2019. LIVE

Hurns

See Tomos Watkin (under W)

Hurst SIBA

**Highfields Farm, Hurstpierpoint, West Sussex, BN6 9JT
☎ 07866 438953 ⊕ hurstbrewery.co.uk**

Hurst was founded in 2012, but reviving a name dating back to 1862.

Hush (NEW)

**4 St Michaels Close, Little Leigh, Cheshire, CW8 4SA
☎ 07973 797500 ⊕ hushbrewing.co**

⊕Hush Brewing Co was established in 2021, using a 1.5-barrel plant producing traditional and craft beers. The core beers are themed to the area and distributed locally to selected free trade outlets. Expansion is planned as is opening a bar in Northwich. ♦

My Green is Earl (ABV 3.7%) PALE
Northwich Pale Ale (ABV 4%) PALE
Weaver Las Vegas (ABV 4.3%) PALE

Husk SIBA

**Unit 58a, Railway Arches, North Woolwich Road, West Silvertown, London, E16 2AA
☎ (020) 7474 3827 ⊕ huskbrewing.com**

Brewing in West Silvertown, along from the Royal Docks, since 2015. The first brewery in the area, now has its taproom and newly-opened kitchen open every Friday and Saturday. Beers available in cask, keg and occasional RAIB with eye-catching clip and label designs. LIVE ♠

Pale Ale (ABV 5.1%) GOLD
Light, citrusy, hoppy, bready aroma. Slightly sweet, balanced with lemon peel, spiciness and grapefruit becoming more bitter. Crisp, bitter finish.

Hwgga (NEW) SIBA

6 Park Crescent, Llandrindod Wells, LD1 6AB ☎ 07739 312917 ⊕ hwggabrew.com

Set up in 2021, Hwgga produces a range of cask, keg and bottled beers. Each brew is devised, brewed, bottled and labelled on the premises. The range is inspired by and named after community icons, from landmarks to individuals and businesses, with labels featuring original artwork by a local artist.

Hybrid SIBA

**Unit 14C, Abbotsinch Industrial Estate, Abbotsinch Road, Grangemouth, FK3 9UX ☎ 07854 288685
⊕ hybridbrewing.com**

Hybrid began brewing in 2016 using a 10.5-barrel dual train brewplant, allowing for two different beers to be brewed at a time. Up to 40 outlets are supplied direct, mostly in the Forth Valley. Six core beers are brewed, with seasonal and special beers brewed throughout the year. The pandemic has driven Hybrid to not only produce bottle-conditioned beers but also an effective local delivery service for bottles and mini kegs alike. All beers are now vegan-friendly. LIVE V

Sesh (ABV 3.6%) BITTER
Groat (ABV 3.8%) GOLD
GTF (ABV 4%) PALE
Apex (ABV 4.1%) BITTER
Hindsight (ABV 4.4%) BITTER
Citra Storm (ABV 4.5%) BITTER
Lost Angel (ABV 4.6%) BLOND
Magic Porridge (ABV 4.7%) STOUT
Street Legal (ABV 4.7%) BITTER

Hydes SIBA IFBB

**The Beer Studio, 30 Kansas Avenue, Salford, M50 2GL
☎ (0161) 226 1317 ⊕ hydesbrewery.com**

⊕Hydes Brewery has been in the Manchester area since 1863. In 2012 it relocated to Salford's MediaCityUK area. The brewery produces more than forty beers per year, four of which are core brands brewed on a permanent basis. The Kansas Avenue range consists of 12 new beers every year, while the Provenance range offers 12 beers brewed using ingredients sourced from around the world. The Beer Studio range consists of six fruit-based beers. ♦

1863 (ABV 3.5%) BITTER
Lightly-hopped, pale brown session beer with some hops, malt and fruit in the taste and a short, dry finish.
Old Indie (ABV 3.5%) MILD
Dark brown/red in colour, with a fruit and malt nose. Taste includes biscuity malt and green fruits, with a satisfying aftertaste.
Original (ABV 3.8%) BITTER

Pale brown beer with a malty nose, malt and an earthy hoppiness in the taste, and a good bitterness through to the finish.

Lowry (ABV 4.7%) GOLD
Malt, hops and fruit compete for dominance in this strong beer. Fruit and bitter prominent in finish.

Iâl

Pant Du Road, Eryrys, CH7 4DD ☎ 07956 440402

Office: Bryntirion Cottage, Fford Rhiw Ial, Llanarmon Yn Ial, CH7 4QE ⊕ cwrwial.com

Cwrw Iâl Community Brewery is run as a social enterprise with profits used for local community projects. The 10-barrel plant brews a core range as well as regular specials. It mainly supplies outlets along the North Wales coast and the North West.

Pocket Rocket (ABV 4%) PALE
Yellow in colour with citrus fruit prominent in the aroma and sharp, hoppy taste.
Kia Kaha! (ABV 4.3%) PALE
A dry, bitter beer, gold in colour with a fruity aroma leading to a good hoppy taste and finish.
Limestone Cowboy (ABV 4.5%) BITTER
A copper-coloured best bitter, malty with faint roast notes and fruit flavours. Hops dominate in the dry, bitter finish.
Pothole Porter (ABV 5.1%) PORTER
A rich and fruity porter with a smooth mouthfeel and good roast notes in aroma and taste.

Ice Cream Factory (NEW)

21 Fetter Lane, York, YO1 9TA ☎ 07880 547393
⊕ theicecreamfactory.com

Nanobrewery located in the old Capaldi's ice cream factory, established in 2017.

Iceni

The Walled Garden, Elveden Courtyard, London Road, Elveden, Suffolk, IP24 3TQ
☎ (01842) 878922 ☎ 07949 488113

Office: 70 Risbygate Street, Bury St Edmunds, Suffolk, IP33 3AZ ✉ icenibrewe@aol.com

The Iceni Brewery is owned by Brendan Moore, who set it up in 1995. In 2020 a micropub, the Magic Hammer, opened, and planning permission was granted for a garden centre on the Elveden Estate. ◆LIVE

Fine Soft Day (ABV 4%) BITTER
Golden-hued with toffee notes throughout. A creamy, lightly-hopped backdrop softly sinks into a pleasant sweetness.

Idle

🍺 White Hart Inn, Main Street, West Stockwith, DN10 4EY
☎ (01427) 892672 ☎ 07949 137174
✉ theidlebrewery@btinternet.com

☺The brewery began production in 2007 and is situated in a converted stable at the back of the White Hart Inn, which Brian Cooper, the brewer, now owns. ‼◆

Ignition

44a Sydenham Road, Sydenham, London, SE26 5QF
☎ (020) 8852 4100 ⊕ ignition.beer

Ignition is a not-for-profit South London brewery, which employs and trains people with learning disabilities to

brew beer. Beers are available in KeyKeg and bottled-conditioned. An on-site taproom was opened in 2018, providing the staff with customer-facing experience. LIVE ✦

Ilkley SIBA

The New Brewery, 40 Ashlands Road, Ilkley, West Yorkshire, LS29 8JT
☎ (01943) 604604 ⊕ ilkleybrewery.co.uk

☺Ilkley Brewery was founded in 2009 and has expanded rapidly since. Ilkley beers can be found throughout the UK and are now exported into Europe, as far as Russia. The brewery is a frequent sponsor of local beer festivals and also holds regular on-site social events and brewery tours. ‼◆LIVE

Mary Jane (ABV 3.5%) PALE
Joshua Jane (ABV 3.7%) BITTER
Blonde (ABV 3.9%) GOLD
Pale (ABV 4.2%) PALE
Alpha Beta (ABV 4.5%) IPA
Stout Mary (ABV 4.5%) STOUT
Lotus IPA (ABV 5.5%) IPA

Imperial

🍺 Arcadia Hall, Cliff Street, Mexborough, S64 9HU
☎ (01709) 584000 ☎ 07428 422703
✉ impbrewery@gmail.com

☺Brewing began in 2010 using a six-barrel tower brewery system located in the basement of the Imperial Club, Mexborough. Beer is available in the club as well as local outlets. ‼◆LIVE

Inadequate

🍺 Holy Inadequate, 67 Etruria Old Road, Stoke-On-Trent, ST1 5PE
☎ (01782) 915170 ☎ 07771 358238
✉ paulcope.cope@gmail.com

☺This one-barrel plant commenced brewing behind the Holy Inadequate in 2018 and mainly supplies the pub with an ever-changing range of beers (up to four at any one time). Other local pubs are sometimes supplied, along with local beer festivals.

Incredible SIBA

214/224 Unit 1, Broomhill Road, Brislington, Bristol, BS4 5RG ☎ 07780 977073
⊕ incrediblebrewingcompany.com

⊠ This microbrewery specialises in producing small batches of beer using a 2.5-barrel plant. It was established in 2014 by head brewer Stephen Hall with the aim of promoting experimental beers and traditional recipes. ‼◆LIVE V

Milk Stout (ABV 4.4%) STOUT
Pale Ale (ABV 4.4%) PALE
Amber Ale (ABV 5.2%) BITTER
Black IPA (ABV 5.6%) IPA
Grapefruit IPA (ABV 5.6%) IPA
Indian Pale Ale (ABV 6.6%) IPA

Independent Lakeland

See Strands

Indian

119b Baltimore Trading Estate, Baltimore Road, Great Barr, B42 1DD

☎ (0121) 296 9000 ⊕ indianbrewery.com

This six-barrel brewery, established in 2005 as the Tunnel Brewery at the Lord Nelson Inn, relocated to the picturesque stable block at Red House Farm in 2011. In 2015 the owners of Tunnel Brewery went their separate ways, with Mike Walsh retaining the brewery and renaming it the Indian Brewery. Later that year the Indian Brewery was sold to new owners and relocated to the outskirts of Birmingham. ‼

Indian Summer (ABV 4%) GOLD
IPA (ABV 4.9%) PALE
Bombay Honey (ABV 5%) SPECIALITY
Peacock (ABV 5%) BITTER

Indigenous

Peacock Cottage, Main Street, Chaddleworth, Berkshire, RG20 7EH
☎ (01488) 505060 ⊕ indigenousbrewery.co.uk

⊗ An occasional and informal microbrewer for many years, Kevin Brady established Indigenous in 2014, increasing production using a 2.5-barrel plant. Availability is restricted to local pubs, shops and an increasing number of regional beer festivals. ‼🍺♦LIVE

Baldrick (ABV 3.4%) MILD
Forager's Gold (ABV 4%) GOLD
Summer Solstice (ABV 4.1%) PALE
Billy No Mates (ABV 4.2%) PALE
Frisky Mare (ABV 4.2%) GOLD
Silly Moo (ABV 4.2%) STOUT
Monocle (ABV 4.5%) STOUT
Nutcracker (ABV 4.5%) OLD
Old Cadger (ABV 4.5%) BITTER
Moonstruck (ABV 4.8%) PORTER
Dark brown session porter with malt, chocolate and coffee aromas. Full mouthfeel of hops, caramel and fruit with a bitter finish.
Nosey Parker (ABV 5.5%) MILD
Strong ruby mild with a malt and toffee note aroma. Malt dominates the taste with a balanced malt and hop aftertaste.
AMMO Belle (ABV 5.6%) IPA
Amber New World IPA with fruit, hops and malt on the nose followed by some bitterness in the taste. Malty aftertaste joined by a fruity hoppiness.
Double Warp (ABV 5.8%) STOUT
Dark brown, strong stout with malt aroma and coffee notes. Roasted, sweet, malt flavour finishes with a balanced aftertaste.

Industrial

See Silver

Inferno

17 Station Street, Tewkesbury, GL20 5NJ
☎ (01684) 294873 ☎ 07854 949731
✉ infernobrewery@yahoo.com

⊗ Inferno began in 2018, after many years of home brewing, using a 2.5-barrel kit which was installed in 2019. Four regular ales and a number of well-received seasonal ales are brewed. The beers are available in local Gloucestershire pubs, clubs and at beer festivals. ♦

Arsonist (ABV 4%) BARLEY
Tinder Box (ABV 4%) BARLEY
Golden Embers (ABV 4.2%) GOLD
Cinder Stout (ABV 4.8%) STOUT

Inishmacsaint

See Fermanagh

Inkspot

Rookery Barn, The Rookery, 40 Streatham Common South, Streatham Common, Streatham, SW16 3BX
☎ (020) 8679 7322 ☎ 07787 832292
⊕ theinkspotbrewery.com

Started in 2012 as Perfect Blend after a bar in Streatham, the brewery changed its name to Inkspot a few years later. Originally cuckoo brewing, brewing began at its own premises in the middle of Streatham Common in 2018. Its Art & Craft bottle shops are the best places to find the beers along with when the brewery taproom is open. No real ale. ♦

Inner Bay SIBA

Seacliffe Villa, Hill Street, Inverkeithing, KY11 1AB
⊕ innerbay.co.uk

Brewing began in 2016. Inner Bay is a family-run brewery using traditional ingredients and methods producing bottle-conditioned beers in small batches. LIVE

INNformal

🍺 **14 Charnham Street, Hungerford, Berkshire, RG17 0ES** ⊕ john-o-gaunt-hungerford.co.uk

⊗ The INNformal brewery was established in 2015 at the Five Bells pub in Wickham. In 2019 the brewery expanded to a four-barrel plant and moved to Hungerford. A selection of the beers can always be found at the John O'Gaunt in Hungerford. ‼♦

Innis & Gunn SIBA

See Inveralmond

Instant Karma

🍺 **4 John Street, Clay Cross, Derbyshire, S45 9NQ**
☎ (01246) 250366 ⊕ instantkarmabrewery.co.uk

Instant Karma began brewing in 2012 using a five-barrel plant with a brew length of 15 barrels per week. The brewery is part of the Rykneld Turnpyke brewpub.

Interbrew UK

Porter Tun House, Capability Green, Luton, Bedfordshire, LU1 3LS
☎ (01582) 391166

Interbrew (Magor): Magor Brewery, Magor, NP26 3DA

Interbrew (Samlesbury): Cuerdale Lane, Samlesbury, PR5 0XD

UK subsidiary of A-B InBev. No real ale.

Intrepid SIBA

Unit 12, Vincent Works, Stretfield Road, Bradwell, Derbyshire, S33 9HG ☎ 07936 174364
⊕ intrepidbrewing.co

Based in the Hope Valley in the Peak District, Intrepid commenced brewing in 2014 using an eight-barrel plant.

Inveralmond

22 Inveralmond Place, Perth, PH1 3TS
☎ (01738) 449448 ⊕ inveralmond-brewery.co.uk

⊙Established in 1997, Inveralmond was the first brewery in Perth for more than 30 years. In 2016, Inveralmond became part of the Innis & Gunn family, an independent Scottish craft brewer based in Edinburgh. I&G makes no real ale but the Inveralmond range continues. ‼☛♦

EPA (ABV 3.8%) PALE
Ossian (ABV 4.1%) GOLD
Well-balanced best bitter with a dry finish. This full-bodied amber ale is dominated by fruit and hop with a bittersweet character although excessive caramel can distract from this.
Lia Fail (ABV 4.7%) BITTER
The Gaelic name means Stone of Destiny. A dark, robust, full-bodied beer with a deep malty taste. Smooth texture and balanced finish.

Iron Pier SIBA

Units 6 & 7, May Industrial Estate, May Avenue, Northfleet, Gravesend, Kent, DA11 8RU
⊕ ironpier.beer

⊠ Iron Pier Brewery was established in 2017 using a 15-barrel plant. It takes its name from the oldest iron pier in existence residing on the River Thames at Gravesend. An on-site taproom offers the brewery's beers plus other local brews. ‼♦V⌀

Perry St Pale (ABV 3.7%) GOLD
Joined at the Hop Pale Ale (ABV 3.8%) GOLD
Bitter (ABV 4%) BITTER
Cast Iron Stout (ABV 4.7%) STOUT
Porter (ABV 5.3%) PORTER

Irving SIBA

Unit G1, Railway Triangle, Walton Road, Portsmouth, Hampshire, PO6 1TQ
☎ (023) 9238 9988 ☎ 07946 906234
⊕ irvingbrewers.co.uk

⊠ Established in 2007 by former Gale's brewer Malcolm Irving using a 15-barrel plant. Around 120 outlets are supplied in Hampshire, Sussex and Surrey with beers available further afield through beer swaps with other breweries. Speciality beers may be ordered for festivals. Off sales available Thursdays and Fridays. ‼☛♦

Frigate (ABV 3.8%) PALE
Satisfying session bitter. Hoppy, with a floral aroma and initial sweetness, leading to bitterness and a smooth, slightly dry finish.
Type 42 (ABV 4.2%) BITTER
Traditional brown bitter. Burnt toffee aroma leads to hedgerow fruitiness complementing crystal malt. Resinous hops grow into surprisingly dry finish.
Admiral Stout (ABV 4.3%) STOUT
Well-balanced oatmeal stout, with plenty of fruit and roast, together with a pleasant hint of coffee and a short bitter finish.
Invincible (ABV 4.6%) BITTER
Tawny-coloured, strong bitter. Sweet and fruity with underlying maltiness throughout and gradually increasing dryness, contrasting with the sweet finish.
Iron Duke (ABV 5.3%) PALE
Refreshing, well-balanced IPA. Marmalade nose, with a strong bitterness, and a robust sweetness throughout, which softens the lemon sherbet finish.

Irwell Works

Irwell Street, Ramsbottom, BL0 9YQ
☎ (01706) 825019 ⊕ irwellworksbrewery.co.uk

⊙Irwell Works have been brewing since 2010 in a building that once housed the Irwell Works steam, tin, copper and iron works. The brewery has a six-barrel plant, and brews nine regular beers, plus a range of seasonal beers. There is a very pleasant brewery tap on the first floor with most of the brewery's beers available. ‼♦⌀

Lightweights & Gentlemen (ABV 3.2%) GOLD
Light, refreshing, very pale ale with some fruitiness and a hoppy, bitter finish.
Breadcrumbs (ABV 3.6%) PALE
Tin Plate (ABV 3.6%) MILD
Copper Plate (ABV 3.8%) BITTER
Traditional northern bitter. Copper-coloured with satisfying blend of malt and hops and good bitterness.
Costa Del Salford (ABV 4.1%) GOLD
Steam Plate (ABV 4.3%) BITTER
Malty bitter beer with increasing bitter finish.
Iron Plate (ABV 4.4%) STOUT
Roast malt in the aroma is joined by hop and a toasty bitterness in the taste and finish.
Marshmallow Unicorn (ABV 4.4%) STOUT
Sweet stout with a balanced bitter roast and dry bitter finish.
Mad Dogs & Englishmen (ABV 5.5%) IPA
Full-bodied, bittersweet beer. Pronounced peppery and earthy hops. Hops develop to pine and citrus in aftertaste with prolonged bitterness.

Isaac Poad SIBA

Office: Hay House, Baxby Manor, Husthwaite, North Yorkshire, YO61 4PW
☎ (01423) 358114 ⊕ isaacpoadbrewing.co.uk

⊙Established in 2016 by a local grain merchant, which formerly supplied malting barley to local maltsters, the brewery continues despite the subsequent demise of the parent company. Pending construction of its own brew plant, production is actually carried out at another local brewery with the emphasis on using local Yorkshire malt and British hops. ♦

No. 86 Golden Ale (ABV 3.6%) GOLD
1863 Best Bitter (ABV 3.8%) BITTER
No.91 Craft Ale (ABV 3.9%) GOLD
All Four Yorkshire Red Ale (ABV 4.2%) RED
No.84 India Pale Ale (ABV 4.5%) PALE
Piccadilly Porter (ABV 4.8%) PORTER

Isca SIBA

Court Farm, Holcombe Village, Dawlish, Devon, EX7 0JT ☎ 07773 444501 ✉ iscaales@yahoo.co.uk

⊠ Established in a disused milking parlour in 2009, Isca has developed a large range of ales. Seasonal and special brews are often available at beer festivals, including outside of the region. ♦LIVE

Citra (ABV 3.8%) BITTER
Dawlish Summer (ABV 3.8%) GOLD
Golden Ale (ABV 3.8%) GOLD
Dawlish Bitter (ABV 4.2%) BITTER
Glorious Devon (ABV 4.4%) BITTER
Holcombe White (ABV 4.5%) SPECIALITY
ISCA Gold (ABV 4.5%) GOLD
Dawlish Pale (ABV 5%) PALE
Black IPA (ABV 6%) IPA
Devon Pale (ABV 6.8%) IPA

Isla Vale

17 Westbrook Gardens, Margate, Kent, CT9 5DJ

☎ (01843) 292451 ☎ 07980 174616
✉ info@islavalealesmiths.co.uk

⊠ Isla Vale was established in 2014 from a residential address in Westbrook (Margate) and supplies local micropubs. A one-barrel plant is used to brew its core range as well as a specially commissioned beer for the Wheel Alehouse, Birchington. Outlets are supplied locally. ♦

Golding Delicious (ABV 3.8%) BITTER
Hopping Mad (ABV 4%) BROWN
Two Halves (ABV 4%) BITTER
Ninkasi Pale Ale (ABV 4.5%) SPECIALITY
Big Red Beer (ABV 4.6%) RED
Cock-A-Snook (ABV 4.6%) BITTER
Natural Blonde (ABV 4.7%) BLOND
Befuggled (ABV 5.2%) BITTER
IPA (ABV 5.5%) IPA

Island SIBA

Dinglers Farm, Yarmouth Road, Newport, Isle of Wight, PO30 4LZ
☎ (01983) 821731 ⊕ islandbrewery.co.uk

⊠ Island Brewery is the realisation of Tom Minshull's ambition to brew real ales to complement the existing family-owned drinks distribution business. Brewing commenced in 2010 using a 12-barrel brewery. More than 100 outlets are supplied direct. ‼♦

Nipper Bitter (ABV 3.8%) GOLD
Wight Gold (ABV 4%) BITTER
Yachtsmans Ale (ABV 4.2%) BITTER
Wight Diamond (ABV 4.4%) SPECIALITY
Wight Knight (ABV 4.5%) BITTER
Vectis Venom (ABV 4.8%) BITTER
Earls RDA (ABV 5%) STOUT

Islay SIBA

The Brewery, Islay House Square, Bridgend, Isle of Islay, PA44 7NZ
☎ (01496) 810014 ⊕ islayales.com

☺The only brewery on an island famous for its malt whiskies, Islay Ales started brewing in 2004 and continues to use a four-barrel plant. Situated in converted farm buildings, including a visitor centre and shop. The brewery tap is the only outlet for the brewery's cask-conditioned beers. ‼🛒♦

Isle of Avalon

Little Whitley, Stagman Lane, Ashcott, Somerset, TA7 9BJ
☎ (01458) 210050 ☎ 07809 056855
⊕ avalonwholesaleandbrewing.co.uk

⊠ Brewing began in 2008. Isle of Avalon has a 100-litre plant, brewing very occasionally for one-off events and local supply. Wessex Brewing (qv) are occasionally contracted to brew for the parent company Avalon Wholesale on an 'on demand' basis.

Isle of Harris

Croft No. 6, Borrisdale, Outer Hebrides, HS5 3UE
☎ 07584 354144 ⊕ isleofharrisbrewery.com

Established in 2020, small batch, limited edition beers are produced in a tiny brewshed overlooking the Sound of Harris. Beers are bottled and labelled by hand. LIVE V

Isle of Mull

See Argyll

Isle of Purbeck SIBA

🏭 Manor Road, Studland, Dorset, BH19 3AU
☎ (01929) 450227 ⊕ isleofpurbeckbrewery.com

⊠ Founded in 2003, and situated in the grounds of the Bankes Arms Hotel, the brewery overlooks Studland Bay on the Dorset section of the Jurassic World Heritage Coast. This 10-barrel plant produces its core beers which are available locally as well as being available nationwide via exchange swaps with other microbreweries and at local beer festivals. ♦LIVE

Purbeck Best Bitter (ABV 3.6%) BITTER
A classic malty best bitter with rich malt aroma and taste and smooth, malty, bitter finish.
Force Four (ABV 4%) BITTER
Fossil Fuel (ABV 4.1%) BITTER
Amber bitter with complex aroma with a hint of pepper; rich malt dominates the taste, leading to a smooth, dry finish.
Solar Power (ABV 4.3%) GOLD
Tawny mid-range ale brewed using Continental hops. Well-balanced flavours combine to provide a strong bitter taste but short, dry finish.
Studland Bay Wrecked (ABV 4.5%) BITTER
Deep red ale with slightly sweet aroma reflecting a mixture of caramel, malt and hops that lead to a dry, malty finish.
Purbeck IPA (ABV 4.8%) BITTER
Mid-brown beer with hop/malt balance in the flavour and a long dry aftertaste.

Isle of Sark

Le Seigneurie, Sark, GY10 1SF ☎ 07781 439881
⊕ sarkbrewing@gmail.com

Nanobrewery established in 2016 using a 2.5-barrel plant, the first brewery to be established in Sark, Channel Islands.

Isle of Skye SIBA

The Pier, Uig, Isle of Skye, IV51 9XP
☎ (01470) 542477 ⊕ skyeale.com

☺The Isle of Skye Brewery was established in 1995. Originally a 10-barrel plant, it was upgraded to 20 barrels in 2004. ‼🛒♦

Skyelight (ABV 3.8%) GOLD
Tarasgeir (ABV 4%) SPECIALITY
YP (Young Pretender) (ABV 4%) BITTER
A refreshing, amber, hoppy, grapefruit bitter. Some sweetness in the taste but continuing into a lingering bitter finish.
Skye Red (ABV 4.2%) BITTER
A light, fruity nose with a hint of caramel leads to a hoppy, malty, fruity flavour and a dry, bittersweet finish.
Skye Gold (ABV 4.3%) SPECIALITY
Porridge oats are used to produce this delicious speciality beer. Nicely balanced. It has a refreshingly soft lemon, bitter flavour with an oaty background.
Skye Black (ABV 4.5%) OLD
Full-bodied with a malty richness. Malt holds sway but there are plenty of hops and fruit to be discovered in its varied character. A delicious Scottish old ale.
Skye IPA (ABV 4.5%) PALE
Blaven (ABV 5%) BITTER
A well-balanced, strong, amber bitter with kiwi fruit and caramel in the nose and a lingering sharp bitterness.

THE BREWERIES

Skye Blonde (ABV 5.5%) BLOND
Cuillin Beast (ABV 7%) BARLEY
A winter warmer; sweet and fruity, and much more drinkable than the strength would suggest. Plenty of caramel throughout with a variety of fruit on the nose.

It's Quicker by Ale

See Harrogate

Itchen Valley SIBA

Unit D, Prospect Commercial Park, Prospect Road, New Alresford, Hampshire, SO24 9QF
☎ (01962) 735111 ⊕ itchenvalleybrewery.com

⊗ Established in 1997, Itchen Valley moved to new premises in 2006 with a 20-barrel plant. More than 350 pubs are supplied, with wholesalers used for further distribution. ‼ ➠ ♦ LIVE

Pride of the Valley (ABV 3.8%) BITTER
Hampshire Rose (ABV 4.2%) GOLD
New Hampshire (ABV 4.3%) PALE
Pure Gold (ABV 4.8%) PALE
Aromatic hoppy, pale ale. Golden-coloured, with initial maltiness and grapefruit counter-balanced with some sweetness, leading to dry finish.

IVO SIBA

10 Church Street, Somersham, Cambridgeshire, PE28 3EG ☎ 07823 400369 ⊕ ivobrewery.co.uk

Established in 2020, IVO Brewery is run by two friends and neighbours, Charlie Abbott and Jason Jones both of whom had been successful homebrewers previously. Every beer is naturally fined and vegan-friendly. Despite being a small brewery, the core range is currently six beers ranging from a Kolsh style beer to a session porter. V

Light on the Chips (ABV 2.5%) PORTER
Car Park Cuddle (ABV 3.8%) PALE
No Man (ABV 4.5%) STOUT
She Keeps It Nice (ABV 4.5%) PALE
Evening Brown (ABV 5%) BROWN
Heavy on the Chips (ABV 6%) PORTER

Ivybridge

Unit 3, Glanvilles Mill, Ivybridge, PL21 9PS
☎ (01752) 894295 ☎ 07512 961085

Office: 41 Rue St Pierre, Ivybridge, PL21 0HZ
⊕ ivybridgebrewing.co.uk

Established in 2018, Ivybridge is a social enterprise brewery that provides training and employment for people with learning disabilities. It currently produces two bottle-conditioned beers. ➠ LIVE ♦

Izaac Walton

See under W

JackRabbit

Hops Farm, Hungerdown Lane, Lawford, Essex, CO11 2LX ☎ 07506 596597
⊕ jackrabbitbrewingco.uk

JackRabbit Brewing Co was founded in 2019 by three craft beer lovers. An eight-barrel plant is used to create unfiltered, unfined beers. ➠ V

Roasted (ABV 3.8%) STOUT
College Hop-Out (ABV 4%) PALE

Down the Rabbit Hole (ABV 4.7%) SPECIALITY

James Street

See Bath Brewhouse

Jaw SIBA

26 Crossveggate, Milngavie, G62 6RA ☎ 07880 690995 ⊕ jawbrew.co.uk

An independent, family-run, craft microbrewery from Glasgow. Committed to producing the absolute pinnacle of high quality beer. LIVE ♦

Fathom (ABV 4%) MILD
Drop (ABV 4.2%) BITTER
Surf (ABV 4.3%) PALE
Drift (ABV 4.6%) GOLD
Wave (ABV 4.7%) SPECIALITY

Jawbone (NEW)

Swan Island, Unit C, 1 Strawberry Vale, Twickenham, TW1 4RY ⊕ jawbonebrewing.com

Brewing commenced 2020 with the first brew available canned. The BrewDeck taproom sells the range of beers. Brewing capacity is 80-hectolitres. ♦

Jeffersons

Brew Shed, 84 Verdun Road, Barnes, London, SW13 9AX ☎ 07960 597311
⊕ jeffersonsbrewery.co.uk

Brewing began in 2017 at this family-run nanobrewery. Most output is in cans, which are sold online, at markets, and (along with kegs) in pubs and beer festivals. A core range, and 7-10 seasonal or special brews are produced, after experimenting with yeast strains. Not currently brewing cask beers.

Jennings

Castle Brewery, Cockermouth, Cumbria, CA13 9NE
☎ (01900) 820362 ⊕ jenningsbrewery.co.uk

⊛ Jennings Brewery was established as a family concern in 1828 in the village of Lorton. The company moved to its present location in 1874. Pure Lakeland water is still used for brewing, drawn from the brewery's own well. All beers were re-branded in 2019 with some beers becoming seasonal, and new beers added to the portfolio. Part of Carlsberg Marston's Brewing Co. ‼ ➠ ♦

Night Vision (ABV 3.5%) BITTER
A malty beer with a good mouthfeel that combines with roast flavour and a hoppy finish.
Atomic Theory (ABV 3.8%) PALE
Cumberland Ale (ABV 4%) BITTER
Fruit and caramel in the aroma gives way to a sweet middle, balanced by a gentle bitter finish.

Jesus College

Jesus College, Cambridge, CB5 8BL

In-house brewery for Jesus College at the University of Cambridge. Beers are produced for college use only and are not available to the general public.

John O'Groats

County Road, John O'Groats, KW1 4YR
☎ (01955) 611220 ☎ 07842 401571
⊕ johnogroatsbrewery.co.uk

⊕Brewing began in 2015 with a four-barrel plant. It is housed in the old John O'Groats Fire Station almost opposite its tap, the Seaview Hotel. A second three-barrel plant is installed in the Last House by the harbour, which is now a visitor centre complete with shop, bar and brewery tours. A bottling facility is being added next to the Fire Station plant. ‼▆

Swelkie (ABV 4%) BITTER
Slight honey taste in this citrus hoppy brew.
Duncansby (ABV 4.2%) BITTER
Deep Groat (ABV 4.8%) STOUT
Nearly black brew full of chocolate and coffee with some background roast.

John Smith's

See under S

Jolly Boys

Unit 16a, Redbrook Business Park, off Wilthorpe Road, Redbrook, South Yorkshire, S75 1JN ☎ 07808 085214 ⊕ jollyboysbrewery.co.uk

⊕Jolly Boys started brewing using spare capacity at a local brewery in 2016, prior to brewing on its own plant later the same year. The Jolly Tap, Wakefield, and the Jolly Tap on the Arcade, Barnsley, are owned. ‼♦V♦

Yorkshire Bitter (ABV 3.8%) BITTER
Blonde (ABV 4%) BLOND
Jolly Cascade Blonde (ABV 4%) BLOND
La Joll'a Blonde (ABV 4%) BLOND
Golden Best (ABV 4.5%) GOLD
Yorkshire Pale Ale (ABV 4.8%) PALE
Jolly Collier Porter (ABV 5%) PORTER
Jolly IPA (ABV 5.8%) IPA

Jolly Sailor SIBA

▤ Olympia Hotel Tap House, 77 Barlby Road, Selby, North Yorkshire, YO8 5AB
☎ (01757) 707564 ☎ 07923 635755
⊕ jollysailorbrewery.co.uk

⊕The Jolly Sailor Brewery is an independent family-run microbrewery established in 2013 in the grounds of the Olympia Hotel Tap House in Selby, on the nearby River Ouse and close to the 11th century abbey. Beers are brewed on a six-barrel plant and available at the brewery's Jolly Sailor Inn, Cawood, and extensively in the free trade. ‼▆♦♦

Selby Bitter (ABV 3.8%) BITTER
Selby Blonde (ABV 3.8%) BLOND
Selby Pale (ABV 3.9%) PALE
Selby Mild (ABV 4%) MILD
Milk Stout (ABV 4.5%) STOUT
Dark Nights Porter (ABV 5%) PORTER

Joseph Holt SIBA

See under H

Joule's

The Brewery, Great Hales Street, Market Drayton, Shropshire, TF9 1JP
☎ (01630) 654400 ⊕ joulesbrewery.co.uk

Re-established in 2010, following a break of 40 years. Joule's is situated in Market Drayton, and has access to pure mineral water drawn from the same aquifer as the original brewery. It runs a collection of 43 Brewery

Taphouses across its heartland, Shropshire, Staffordshire and Cheshire. ‼♦

Pure Blonde (ABV 3.8%) BLOND
Pale Ale (ABV 4.1%) PALE
Slumbering Monk (ABV 4.5%) BITTER

Junction

▤ 1 Baildon Road, Baildon, West Yorkshire, BD17 6AB
☎ (01274) 582009 ☎ 07539 923744
✉ andydoug48@gmail.com

Junction is a microbrewery established in 2012 in the cellar of the Junction pub in Baildon, brewing around 300 gallons a week. Beer is sold in the pub and other local outlets. LIVE

Kaneen's (NEW)

Kaneens Garage, Main Road, Union Mills, Isle of Man, IM4 4AE ☎ 07624 302245 ⊕ kaneensbrewery.com

Launched in 2021, head brewer Peter Kaneen converted a vehicle repair garage into Kaneen's Microbrewery. V

Kansas Avenue

See Hydes

Keep

▤ Village Inn, The Cross, Nailsworth, Gloucestershire, GL6 0HH
☎ (01453) 835715 ☎ 07877 569586
✉ paul@dropinpubs.com

After a break of 96 years, brewing returned to Nailsworth in 2004, at the Village Inn. The pub and brewery were sold in 2016 to Paul Sugden and Adam Pavey, who changed the brewery name from Nailsworth to Keep Brewing. Brewing takes place on a six-barrel kit below the bar, with new recipes trialled on a 40-litre pilot plant. ♦LIVE

Keith

Malcomburn, Mulben, Keith, AB55 6YB
☎ (01542) 488 006 ⊕ keithbrewery.co.uk

Formerly known as Brewmeister and established in 2012, the brewery was renamed Keith Brewery in 2015. It moved production to Malcolmburn, Mulben, sharing facilities with Spey Valley Brewery (qv). Keith Brewery is part of the Consolidated Craft Breweries Group. ‼▆♦LIVE

Herr Keith (ABV 4.5%) SPECIALITY
Cloudy, white/yellow wheat beer with hints of coriander.
Larger Keith (ABV 4.5%) SPECIALITY
Cask-conditioned lager using Scottish malts (Pils Wheat Acid) and Saaz and Magnum hops.
Pale Keith (ABV 5%) BITTER
Grapefruit hoppy bitter.
Stout Keith (ABV 5%) SPECIALITY
Sir Keith (ABV 10.1%) BARLEY

Kelburn SIBA

10 Muriel Lane, Barrhead, G78 1QB
☎ (0141) 881 2138 ⊕ kelburnbrewery.com

⊗ Kelburn is an award-winning family business established in 2002. ‼♦

Sunriser (ABV 3.4%) GOLD
Goldihops (ABV 3.8%) GOLD

Well-hopped, session ale with a fruity taste, and a bitter finish.

Pivo Estivo (ABV 3.9%) GOLD
Misty Law (ABV 4%) BITTER
Red Smiddy (ABV 4.1%) BITTER
This bittersweet ale predominantly features an intense citrus hop character that assaults the nose and continues into the flavour, balanced perfectly with fruity malt.
Regnitz (ABV 4.4%) BITTER
Dark Moor (ABV 4.5%) MILD
Jaguar (ABV 4.5%) GOLD
Cart Noir (ABV 4.8%) STOUT
Cart Blanche (ABV 5%) GOLD
A golden, full-bodied ale. The assault of fruit and hop camouflages the strength of this easy-drinking ale.

Kelchner SIBA

Unit D, The Sidings, Station Road, Ampthill, Bedfordshire, MK45 2QY ☎ 07508 305754
✉ kelchnerbrewery@gmail.com

Kelchner began brewing began in 2018. Beers tend to be themed on local features and/or Luton Town FC. The brewery is keen to support various local community organisations. !! ➤ LIVE

Local is Lekker (ABV 3.9%) GOLD
Ampthill Gold (ABV 4.1%) GOLD
Hat Trick (ABV 4.1%) GOLD
Masquerade (ABV 4.3%) RED
IPA (ABV 4.5%) PALE
After Dark (ABV 4.8%) PALE
Ammetelle (ABV 5%) STOUT

Kelham Island SIBA

23 Alma Street, Sheffield, South Yorkshire, S3 8SA
☎ (0114) 249 4804

Office: Prospect House, 17 Alma Street, Sheffield, S3 8RY ⊕ kelhambrewery.co.uk

☺ Opened in 1990 behind the Fat Cat pub, the brewery moved to new purpose-built premises in 1999. The old building is used as a visitor centre, and there is a separate brewery shop together with offices and a function room in nearby Prospect House. !! ➤ ♦ LIVE

Best Bitter (ABV 3.8%) BITTER
Pride of Sheffield (ABV 4%) BITTER
Easy Rider (ABV 4.3%) GOLD
A pale, straw-coloured beer with a sweetish flavour and delicate hints of citrus fruits. A beer with hints of flavour rather than full-bodied.
Riders on the Storm (ABV 4.5%) PALE
Pale Rider (ABV 5.2%) PALE
A full-bodied, straw pale ale, with a good fruity aroma and a strong fruit and hop taste. Its well-balanced sweetness and bitterness continue in the finish.

Keltek SIBA

Candela House, Cardrew Way, Redruth, Cornwall, TR15 1SS
☎ (01209) 313620 ⊕ keltekbrewery.co.uk

☺ Keltek (meaning Celtic in Cornish) began brewing award-winning ales in 1997, and was founded by Stuart Heath. It started as a 2.5-barrel plant in Stuart's disused stable block on the Roseland Peninsula. Several moves and expansions mean it is now based in Redruth, and can brew more than 250 barrels a week. In 2013 Keltek acquired four pubs in south-west Cornwall (the second brewery in Cornwall to own an estate of pubs). Two more pubs were acquired in 2016. ➤ ♦

Even Keel (ABV 3.4%) BITTER
Pale brown session bitter. Refreshing malt and hop taste with apple, plum and pear drops. Gentle dry and bitter finish.
Lance (ABV 4%) PALE
Gold bitter with light fruity aroma. Grassy citrus hops, apples, malt and hints of elderflower and butterscotch. Long bitter finish.
Magik (ABV 4%) BITTER
Pale brown bitter with smoky malt and zesty hop aroma. Sweet, woody malt with spicy and orange marmalade hop flavours.
Kober (ABV 4.2%) BITTER
Phoenix (ABV 4.5%) BITTER
Golden best bitter. Powerful fruity hops with high bitterness but backed with solid malt which lingers well on the finish.
Wayward Knight (ABV 4.5%) BITTER
Lowenek (ABV 4.8%) BLOND
Parbaydos (ABV 4.8%) GOLD
King (ABV 5.1%) BITTER
Copper-coloured, premium bitter with a mix of malt and hop aromas. Biscuit malt balanced by tropical and citrus hops.
Pilot Gig Porter (ABV 5.2%) PORTER
Reaper (ABV 6%) BITTER
Beheaded (ABV 7.5%) STRONG
Tawny, strong old ale with a balanced heavy body. Rich vine fruit accompanied by plum, raisin, apple and sherry flavours.

Kent SIBA

The Long Barn, Birling Place Farm, Stangate Road, Birling, Kent, ME19 5JN
☎ (01634) 780037 ⊕ kentbrewery.com

Kent Brewery was founded in 2010 by Toby Simmonds (ex-brewer from Dark Star) and Paul Herbert. Originally brewed at Larkins, a 10-barrel plant has been in operation at the Birling site since 2011. More than 300 outlets are supplied direct, mainly throughout Kent, Sussex and London. In addition to a constantly changing list of around three specials, a dozen regular beers are produced. House beers are also brewed for The Craft Beer Co pubs. ♦ LIVE

Session Pale (ABV 3.7%) PALE
Black Gold (ABV 4%) BITTER
Pale (ABV 4%) PORTER
Cobnut (ABV 4.1%) BITTER
KGB (Kent Golding Bitter) (ABV 4.1%) BITTER
Zingiber (ABV 4.1%) SPECIALITY
Quiet American (ABV 4.2%) GOLD
Single Hop (ABV 4.5%) GOLD
Prohibition (ABV 4.8%) PALE
The New Black (ABV 4.8%) PALE
Tropic Ale (ABV 4.9%) IPA
Brewers Reserve (ABV 5%) GOLD

Kentish Town

Ingestre Road, Kentish Town, London, NW5 1UF
⊕ kentishtownbrewery.com

Fleet Lager has been brewed at home in small batches with larger batches and other beers brewed at various London breweries. Brewing suspended in 2019 allowing the brewer to take a sabbatical in Australia, with brewing to start again on his return. No real ale.

Kernel SIBA

Arch 11, Dockley Road Industrial Estate, Dockley Road, Bermondsey, London, SE16 3SF
☎ (020) 7231 4516

Office: 1 Spa Business Park, Spa Road, Bermondsey, London, SE16 4QT ⊕ thekernelbrewery.com

The Kernel was established in 2009 by Evin O'Riordain and moved to larger premises in 2012 to keep up with demand. The brewery produces bottle-conditioned and keg beers, and has won many awards for its wide, ever-changing range. Bottles are available from the brewery as well as pubs and bottle shops around the country. A new taproom, a few arches along, opened in 2020. ⎚LIVE◆

Keswick SIBA

The Old Brewery, Brewery Lane, Keswick, Cumbria, CA12 5BY
☎ (01768) 780700 ⊕ keswickbrewery.co.uk

Keswick, owned by Sue Jefferson, began brewing in 2006 using a 10-barrel plant on the site of a brewery that closed in 1897. The brewery is set up to be environmentally-friendly using sheeps wool insulation in the vessels and reducing its environmental impact. Outlets include the Fox bar at the brewery, the Dog & Gun, Keswick, and many other pubs across Cumbria. ‼⎚◆◆

Black Star (ABV 3.5%) BITTER
Gold (ABV 3.6%) BITTER
Predominantly hoppy bitter with malts, sweetness and fruit, and a dry, bitter finish.
Bitter (ABV 3.7%) BITTER
Gentle bitter with hints of roasted malt and a sweetness which fades.
Thirst Rescue (ABV 3.8%) BITTER
Bitter beer with some fruitiness, full-bodied and a lasting bitter finish.
Park Your Thirst (ABV 3.9%) BITTER
Fox Dark (ABV 4%) BARLEY
Fox Pale (ABV 4%) BARLEY
Thirst Run (ABV 4.2%) PALE
A well-balanced golden beer that maintains its fruitiness from start to finish.
Waimia Pale (ABV 4.2%) PALE
Thirst Quencher (ABV 4.3%) BLOND
Light-bodied, fresh, hoppy beer with fruit in the middle and a balancing sweetness.
Pale Ale (ABV 4.4%) PALE
Special Bitter (ABV 4.8%) BITTER
Thirst Celebration (ABV 7%) STRONG

Kettlesmith SIBA

Unit 16, Treenwood Industrial Estate,, Bradford-On-Avon, Wiltshire, BA15 2AU
☎ (01225) 864839 ⊕ kettlesmithbrewing.com

⊠ Kettlesmith is an independent microbrewery established in 2016. It brews modern interpretations of a wide variety of beer styles, drawing inspiration from the brewer's background in America and England, as well as a love of Belgian beer. ‼⎚◆LIVE V

Outline (ABV 3.8%) BITTER
Faultline (ABV 4.1%) PALE
Streamline (ABV 4.2%) SPECIALITY
Plotline (ABV 4.4%) STOUT
Fogline (ABV 4.7%) SPECIALITY
Coastline (ABV 4.9%) SPECIALITY
Ridgeline (ABV 5%) RED
Timeline (ABV 5.4%) PALE
Skyline (ABV 5.6%) SPECIALITY

Kew

See CTZN

Keystone SIBA

Old Carpenters Workshop, Berwick St Leonard, Wiltshire, SP3 5SN
☎ (01747) 820426 ⊕ keystonebrewery.co.uk

⊠ Set up in 2006 with a 10-barrel plant, the brewer aims to be as sustainable and efficient as possible, brewing traditional southern English-style beers using local ingredients whenever possible. The beers are available in the brewery-run Benett Arms, Tisbury. Around 150 other outlets are also supplied. ‼⎚◆

Bedrock (ABV 3.6%) BITTER
Copper-coloured bitter, hops and malt in the aroma, followed by fruit and bitterness in the taste. Long, lingering aftertaste.
Large One (ABV 4.2%) BITTER
Copper-coloured, malty best bitter, fruit and bitterness to the fore initially, long fruit and bitter hop flavours to the finish.

Kibble (NEW)

🮲 Crystal Palace, 11 Towngate, Thurlstone, South Yorkshire, S36 9RH ☎ 07952 790245

☺Brewing began in 2021 in a former stable block in the car park of the Crystal Palace pub. The brewer used to be a miner, hence the brewery is named after the large bucket used in pit shafts.

Kickabo (NEW)

Unit 7B, Harvey Works, Lingard Street, Stoke On Trent, ST6 1ED ⊕ kickabobrewery.com

Small, three-barrel brewery set up in Burslem in the Potteries. Beers will feature styles from across the world.

Kiln

Chiddinglye Farm, West Hoathly, RH19 4QS ☎ 07800 556729

Office: 1st Floor, 30 Church Road, Burgess Hill, RH15 9AE ⊕ thekilnbrewery.co.uk

Kiln brewery was set up by two friends in 2014. Following a search for new premises, they have joined forces with Missing Link brewery. Although Kiln's website is focusing on keg and canned beer, they are continuing to produce cask beers, but are no longer sticking with a core range.

King Street SIBA

🮲 Riverside House, Welsh Back, Bristol, BS1 4RR
☎ (0117) 405 8948

Office: City Pub Group PLC, Essel House, 2nd Floor, 29 Foley Street, London, W1W 7TH
⊕ kingstreetbrewhouse.co.uk

⊠ The King Street Brew House is owned by The City Pub Group, which has several pubs and brewpubs around the country. The compact brewery is on the ground floor, with the fermenting vessels and conditioning tanks in the basement. The enthusiastic on-site brewer produces a wide range of beers, from regular favourites, available all year, to one off/seasonal specials. Guest beers are also available. The Group's other pub in Bristol, the Prince Street Social, is also supplied. ‼◆LIVE

King's Cliffe

Unit 10 Kingsmead, Station Road, King's Cliffe, Northamptonshire, PE8 6YH ☎ **07843 288088**
⊕ kcbales.co.uk

⊠ In 2014, exactly 100 years after the last brewery in King's Cliffe ceased brewing, village resident Jeremy O'Neill set up this venture. It currently produces five barrels a week. ‼◆

5C (ABV 3.8%) GOLD
A light bitter with balanced taste of malt and hops and a refreshing bitter finish.
No. 10 (ABV 4%) PALE
Amber beer with a clean malty taste and a long bitter finish.
66 Degrees (ABV 4.6%) BITTER
Amber beer with a floral aroma, a balanced taste of malt and hops, and a long bitter finish.

Kings Clipstone

Keepers Bothy, Kings Clipstone, Nottinghamshire, NG21 9BT
☎ **(01623) 823589** ☎ **07790 190020**
⊕ kingsclipstonebrewery.co.uk

Located close to the heart of Sherwood Forest, Kings Clipstone began brewing in 2012 using a five-barrel plant. The owners, David and Daryl Maguire, produce a range of core beers plus one-off brews and seasonals. Beers are available to freehouses, festivals and wholesale markets. ◆

Palace Pale (ABV 3.6%) GOLD
Hop On (ABV 3.8%) PALE
Amazing Gazing (ABV 4%) BITTER
Tabaknakas (ABV 4.1%) GOLD
Moonbeam (ABV 4.2%) BITTER
Sire (ABV 4.2%) BITTER
Royal Stag Stout (ABV 4.5%) STOUT
Queen Bee (ABV 5.1%) BITTER

Kings Head

⬛ **Kings Head, 132 High Street, Bildeston, Suffolk, IP7 7ED**
☎ **(01449) 741434** ⊕ bildestonkingshead.co.uk

⊠ Kings Head has been brewing since 1996 in an old cart lodge at the back of the pub. Under new ownership since 2008, the 2.5-barrel plant brews fortnightly. ‼◆

Kingstone

Tintern, NP16 7NX
☎ **(01291) 680111** ⊕ kingstonebrewery.co.uk

Kingstone Brewery is located in the Wye Valley close to Tintern Abbey. Brewing began on a four-barrel plant in 2005. Special brews are marketed under the 'Hapax Brewing Co' label. ☞LIVE

Tewdric's Tipple (ABV 3.8%) BITTER
Challenger (ABV 4%) BITTER
Gold (ABV 4%) GOLD
Llandogo Trow (ABV 4.2%) BITTER
Premium Stout (ABV 4.4%) STOUT
Classic (ABV 4.5%) BITTER
1503 (ABV 4.8%) BITTER
Abbey Ale (ABV 5.1%) BITTER
Humpty (ABV 5.8%) IPA

Kinver SIBA

Unit 1, Britch Farm, Rocky Wall, Kinver, Staffordshire, DY7 5NW ☎ **07715 842676** ⊕ kinverbrewery.co.uk

☺Established in 2004, Kinver brewery produces a wide range of different beer styles including one-off specials. The brewery relocated in 2012 to a new 10-barrel plant on the edge of Kinver due to increased demand. An ever-increasing number of pubs, mainly in the midlands, and beer festivals are supplied with the award-winning ales. ‼◆LIVE

Light Railway (ABV 3.8%) BLOND
Straw-coloured, session beer. A fruity and malty start quickly gives way to well-hopped bitterness and lingering, hoppy aftertaste.
Cavegirl Bitter (ABV 4%) BLOND
Edge (ABV 4.2%) BITTER
Amber with a malty aroma. Sweet fruity start with a hint of citrus marmalade in the spicy edged malt. Lasting hoppy finish that is satisfyingly bitter.
Noble (ABV 4.5%) GOLD
Fruity hop aroma. Very fruity start then the grassy hops give a sharp bitter finish with malt support.
Maybug (ABV 4.8%) BLOND
Half Centurion (ABV 5%) BITTER
A golden best bitter. Malty before the American Chinook hop takes command to give a balanced hoppy finish and provide the great aftertaste.
Black Ram Stout (ABV 5.2%) STOUT
Witchfinder General (ABV 5.5%) PORTER
Khyber (ABV 5.8%) BITTER
Golden strong bitter with a Centennial hop bite that overwhelms the fleeting malty sweetness and drives through to the long dry finish.

Kirkby Lonsdale SIBA

Royal Barn, New Road, Kirkby Lonsdale, Cumbria, LA6 2AB
☎ **(01524) 272221** ⊕ klbrewery.com

☺Kirkby Lonsdale is a family-run business established in 2009 on a six-barrel plant. In 2016 a further six-barrel plant was installed in its new brewery tap, the Royal Barn, Kirkby Lonsdale. ‼◆✦

Crafty Mild (ABV 3.6%) MILD
A typical mild with powerful malty aromas and some caramel, which follows through in the taste and finish.
Tiffin Gold (ABV 3.6%) BLOND
A full-flavoured, grapefruity, hoppy and bitter beer with a dry finish.
Stanley's Pale Ale (ABV 3.8%) PALE
Hops dominate this sweet and fruity, well-balanced beer.
Ruskins Bitter (ABV 3.9%) PALE
A tawny bitter with a distinctive aroma of fruit and malt. The clean, hoppy flavour is well-balanced with fruity sweetness leading to a sustained bittersweet finish.
Singletrack (ABV 4%) GOLD
Crisp citrus hops predominate in a well-balanced beer with a pleasant bitter finish.
Pennine Ambler (ABV 4.1%) BITTER
Radical Red (ABV 4.2%) RED
Malty beer with a caramel sweetness that is balanced by a bitter finish.
Monumental Blonde (ABV 4.5%) BLOND
Distinctly hoppy, a fruity, sweet, pale-coloured, full-bodied bitter.
Jubilee Stout (ABV 5.5%) STOUT
Rich, well-balanced stout with malt. A long aftertaste retains this complexity and is surprisingly refreshing.
Imperial Dragon (ABV 8.2%) IPA

Kirkstall SIBA

100 Kirkstall Road, Leeds, West Yorkshire, LS3 1HJ
☎ **(0113) 898 0280** ⊕ kirkstallbrewery.com

☺The brewery was established in 2011 a few yards from the original Kirkstall Brewery beside the Leeds-Liverpool canal. In 2017 it moved to a new state-of-the-art brewery incorporating a 60-barrel plant, malting unit and canning line. Nearby Kirkstall Abbey (which had its own brewhouse), and lost local industries are the inspiration for the beer names. The range can be sampled in the Kirkstall Bridge Inn, the brewery tap, as well as its other pubs, the Cardigan Arms, Burley, and the Black Horse, Otley. !!♦

Pale Ale (ABV 4%) PALE
Three Swords (ABV 4.5%) GOLD
Dissolution IPA (ABV 5%) PALE
Black Band Porter (ABV 5.5%) PORTER

Kissingate

Pole Barn, Church Lane Farm Estate, Church Lane, Lower Beeding, West Sussex, RH13 6LU
☎ **(01403) 891335**

Office: 2 Drury Close, Maidenbower, Crawley
⊕ **kissingate.co.uk**

⊗ Kissingate Brewery was founded in 2010 by husband-and-wife team Gary and Bunny Lucas. Current production capacity is eight barrels. The brewery building is a converted barn set in a wooded valley near the village of Mannings Heath. It has a taproom and minstrels gallery. The brewery is available to hire for private events.
!!☞♦LIVEV⌀

Ripple Raspberry Stout (ABV 4%) STOUT
Sussex (ABV 4%) BITTER
Black Cherry Mild (ABV 4.2%) SPECIALITY
Moon (ABV 4.5%) BITTER
Old Tale Porter (ABV 4.5%) PORTER
Chocolate & Vanilla Oatmeal Stout (ABV 4.8%) STOUT
Mandarina Red (ABV 4.8%) PALE
Chennai (ABV 5%) BITTER
Micro Lot Coffee Porter (ABV 5%) SPECIALITY
Pernickety Pale (ABV 5%) BITTER
Smelter's Stout (ABV 5.1%) STOUT
Powder Blue (ABV 5.5%) PORTER
Stout Extreme Jamaica (ABV 6%) STOUT
Six Crows (ABV 6.6%) STOUT
Blackeyed Susan (ABV 7%) STRONG
Murder of Crows (ABV 10%) STOUT

Knight Life

27 Feversham Avenue, Queenspark, Bournemouth, Dorset, BH8 9NH ☎ **07722 564444**
⊕ **knightlifebrewing.com**

Established in 2018 brewing on 20-litre Braumeister plant. Keg only beer and off-sales are available direct from the brewery (Monday – Saturday) with some availability in local pubs.

Knockout

Unit 10 Alanbrooke Park, Alexander Road, Belfast, BT6 9HB

Founded in 2009 by Joseph McMullan, Knockout produces a range of bottle-conditioned beers. Each brew is usually in small 900-litre batches. LIVE

Knoydart

St Agathas Chapel & Manse, Knoydart, PH41 4PL
☎ **(01687) 462372** ⊕ **knoydartbrewery.co.uk**

Knoydart is one of the most remote breweries on mainland Britain, there are no road links so access is by ferry boat or on foot over mountain passes. Beers are brewed in part of an old chapel using a 60-litre electric brewery and a five-barrel plant with four fermenters.

Koomor (NEW)

New Dartford Sports Bar, 13 Spital Street, Dartford, Kent, DA1 2DJ

A new brewery from Dartford, Koomor produce cask and bottled beers, currently only for the local area. The beers are all vegan and utilise whole hops from Kent, and may be cloudy. V

Trunk (ABV 3.8%) BITTER
Branch (ABV 4.2%) GOLD
Earth (ABV 4.8%) PORTER
Petal (ABV 4.8%) PALE

Krafty Braumeister SIBA

Unit 4a, Eastlands Industrial Estate, Leiston, Suffolk, IP16 4LL ☎ **07508 435893** ⊕ **kraftybraumeister.co.uk**

Krafty Braumeister was established in 2018 and produces historic German beer styles, matured naturally in bottles and kegs.

Krow

Penventon Terrace, Redruth, Cornwall, TR15 3AD
✉ **contact@krowbrewing.co.uk**

Microbrewery established in Redruth. The head brewer gained experience brewing with several breweries in Cornwall, having initially started out as a home brewer. It is currently making small batch brews, and developing a core range.

Kult (NEW)

See Plain

LabRat

33 Bernham Avenue, Stonehaven, AB39 2WD
☎ **07542 072774**

Commercial nanobrewer Peter Mackenzie started brewing in 2019, producing beers based on international styles.

Lacada SIBA

7a Victoria Street, Portrush, BT56 8DL
☎ **(028) 7082 5684** ⊕ **lacadabrewery.com**

Lacada is a co-operative brewery founded in 2015. It produces a wide variety of styles. It is situated on the scenic north coast of Northern Ireland, and each beer is named after a feature of the coast line (along with a picture of the feature on the cans and bottles). V

West Bay (ABV 4.6%)
Devil's Washtub (ABV 5.2%)
East the Beast (ABV 6%)

Lacons SIBA

The Courtyard, Main Cross Road, Great Yarmouth, Norfolk, NR30 3NZ
☎ **(01493) 850578** ⊕ **lacons.co.uk**

⊗ Lacons Brewery has a rich history dating back to 1760, but was closed by Whitbread in the 1960s. It relaunched in 2013 and the Falcon Brewery is now nestled in a courtyard in Great Yarmouth. Beers are available across East Anglia and use the original Lacons yeast. A range of heritage seasonal ales is also produced, based on the brewery's original recipes from the archives. ‼️ 🍺 ◆LIVE

Charter (ABV 3.7%) BITTER
Encore (ABV 3.8%) PALE
A solid hop backbone with strong citrus support. Sweetness subsides as a crisp dryness emerges in the long, strong finale.
Patriot (ABV 4%) GOLD
A powerful hop presence from the nose to the long, dry finish. Citrus notes and malt give balance and depth.
Legacy (ABV 4.4%) GOLD
Grapefruit and lemon nose and first taste where a crisp bitterness is also encountered. Some malt in a bitter finish.
Audit (ABV 8%) BARLEY
Honey, orange marmalade and maltiness define this full-bodied ale. Damson, toffee and a refreshing bitterness sharpens the palate.

Lacuna (NEW)

Unit 19, Kernick Industrial Estate, Penryn, Cornwall, TR10 9EP ⊕ lacunabrewing.com

Owners Tristan and Ben's ethos for Lacuna Brewing is simple and sustainable, being committed to reaching zero carbon brewing as soon as possible. Three canned beers are available. Its taproom is open every Saturday. No real ale. ◆

Lady Luck

☰ Little Angel, 18 Flowergate, Whitby, North Yorkshire, YO21 3BA
☎ (01947) 820475 ☎ 07920 282506

⊛Lady Luck is a 0.5-barrel brewery situated at the back of the Little Angel, Whitby. Brewing began in 2018 and takes place twice a week. Beers, some infused with spirits, are distributed across North Yorkshire as well as at beer festivals. ◆LIVE

Laine

☰ Brighton: North Laine Bar & Brewhouse, 27 Gloucester Place, Brighton, East Sussex, BN1 4AA
☎ (01273) 683666

Victoria Park: People's Park Tavern, 360 Victoria Park Road, South Hackney, London, E9 7BT ⊕ laine.co.uk

⊠ Laine launched its first brewery in 2012, in Brighton, using a five-barrel plant based within the North Laine pub. The brewing equipment and process can be viewed from the bar. In 2013 a sister brewery was opened in Acton, London (now closed). Since then two more Laine breweries have been established in London, in Hackney (2014) and Battersea (2015; now closed). The beer range varies in each establishment. ‼️ 🍺

Lakedown (NEW)

Lakedown Farm, Swife Lane, Burwash, East Sussex, TN21 8UX
☎ (01435) 685001 ⊕ lakedownbrewing.com

Lakedown Brewing Co was established in 2020 and is situated on a family farm surrounded by fishing lakes. Beers are available in can, bottle, keg and cask. ◆

Lakehouse

Lake House, Peachfield Road, Malvern, Worcestershire, WR14 3LE ☎ 07532 440634
⊕ lakehousebrewery.com

⊛Lakehouse was established in 2016 and is situated at the foot of the idyllic Malvern Hills, within the grounds of a country house and fishing lake, from which it takes its name. Beers can be found in pubs, bottle shops, restaurants, supermarkets and online retail outlets. ‼️LIVE

Amber Session Ale (ABV 3.9%) BITTER
Golden-coloured session beer, aroma of hops and citrus fruits, complex slightly citrus taste with grassy undertones, followed by a pleasant, hoppy finish.
Citrus Pale Ale (ABV 4%) PALE
Pale amber, aroma of hops with hints of apple and grapefruit, pronounced hoppy taste with lemon and orange peel followed by a lingering citrus then bitter, hoppy aftertaste.

Lakeland SIBA

Unit 3, Low Mill Business Park, Ulverston, Cumbria, LA12 9EE
☎ (01229) 581387 ⊕ lakelandbrewhouse.co.uk

⊛Lakeland Brewhouse was founded in 2020 following the takeover of Stringers by the local Lakeland Inns pub group. ◆LIVE

Gold (ABV 3.5%) GOLD
A hoppy aroma and a fruity, full-bodied taste of hops, finishes with a drying bitterness.
Plan B (ABV 3.7%) SPECIALITY
An easy-drinking, zingy, pale thirst-quencher.
Copper (ABV 3.9%) BITTER
Stout (ABV 4%) STOUT
A robust drying stout full of roast and hop bitterness.
Yellow Lorry (ABV 4%) GOLD
Bitter (ABV 4.2%) BITTER
Blonde (ABV 4.2%) BLOND
The North (ABV 4.9%) BITTER
Turbine Porter (ABV 5.1%) PORTER
IPA (ABV 5.5%) IPA

Lakes (NEW) SIBA

Mintsfeet Road South, Kendal, Cumbria, LA9 6ND
☎ (01539) 324005 ⊕ lakesbrewco.com

Brewery opened in 2021 by former employees of Hawkshead brewery. ◆

Pale Ale (ABV 3.5%) PALE

LAMB

Queens Arms, Litton, North Yorkshire, BD23 5QJ
☎ 07900 013245 ⊕ lambbrewing.com

⊛The LAMB Brewing Company brews on a 600-litre plant behind the Queen's Arms in Litton, in the heart of the Yorkshire Dales National Park. Independently owned, the beer is served in the pub, as well as a few other outlets in the local area. Cask, boxed and pouched beers are available.

X Mild (ABV 3.2%) MILD
X Mild (Dark) (ABV 3.2%) MILD
Bitter (ABV 3.7%) BITTER
Pale (ABV 3.9%) GOLD

Lancaster SIBA

Lancaster Leisure Park, Wyresdale Road, Lancaster, LA1 3LA
☎ (01524) 848537 ⊕ lancasterbrewery.co.uk

⊛Lancaster began brewing in 2005. The brewery moved to new premises in 2010 and installed a larger 60-barrel brewing plant. As well as the regular beers, seasonal beers are brewed under the T'ales from the Brewhouse name. ‼️➥♦

Amber (ABV 3.6%) BITTER
Amber-coloured. Malt flavours lead to an increasingly astringent, bitter finish.
Blonde (ABV 4%) BLOND
Well-balanced, pale bitter with fruity body and hops lasting well into the finish.
IPA (ABV 4.2%) PALE
Black (ABV 4.5%) STOUT
A satisfying and robust, roast bitter beer with hints of sweet fruitiness.
Red (ABV 4.8%) RED
A characterful beer with plenty of fruits, roast malt and hops, well-balanced with a lasting finish.

Langdale SIBA

Cross Houses Farm, Docker, Cumbria, LA8 0DE
☎ 07876 838051 ⊕ langdalebrewing.co.uk

☺Langdale Brewing was formed in 2018 by Steve Mitchell formerly of Eden Brewery, and Paul Fry of the Britannia Inn, Elterwater. The brewery USP is producing a range of cask ales using water harvested from a Langdale spring.

Bowfell Bitter (ABV 3.5%) BITTER
Elterwater Gold (ABV 3.8%) GOLD
Pikes Pale (ABV 3.9%) PALE
Bowfell Blonde (ABV 4.2%) BLOND
Bowfell Amber (ABV 4.3%) BITTER
Weiss Ghyll (ABV 4.5%) SPECIALITY

Langham SIBA

Old Granary, Langham Lane, Lodsworth, West Sussex, GU28 9BU
☎ (01798) 860861 ⊕ langhambrewery.co.uk

⊗ Langham Brewery was established in 2006 in an 18th century granary barn and is set in the heart of West Sussex with fine views of the rolling South Downs. It is owned by Lesley Foulkes and James Berrow who brew and run the business. The brewery is a 10-barrel, steam-heated plant and more than 200 outlets are supplied. ‼️➥♦V

Session Bitter (ABV 3.5%) BITTER
Saison (ABV 3.9%) SPECIALITY
Hip Hop (ABV 4%) BLOND
TRIPLE XXX (ABV 4.4%) MILD
Best (ABV 4.5%) BITTER
Arapaho (ABV 4.9%) PALE
Langham Special Draught/LSD (ABV 5.2%) BITTER

Langton SIBA

Grange Farm, Welham Road, Thorpe Langton, Leicestershire, LE16 7TU
☎ (0185) 854 0116 ☎ 07840 532826
⊕ langtonbrewery.co.uk

Established in 1999 in outbuildings behind the Bell Inn, East Langton, the brewery relocated in 2005 to a converted barn at Thorpe Langton, where a four-barrel plant was installed. Further expansion in 2010 and 2016 significantly increased capacity. ‼️♦LIVE

Rainbow Bridge (ABV 3.8%) GOLD
Caudle Bitter (ABV 3.9%) BITTER
Copper-coloured, session bitter that is close to pale ale in style. Flavours are relatively well-balanced throughout with hops slightly to the fore.
Union Wharf (ABV 4%) BITTER
Inclined Plane Bitter (ABV 4.2%) BLOND

Thomas Lift (ABV 4.4%) BITTER
Bullseye (ABV 4.8%) STOUT

Larkins SIBA

Larkins Farm, Hampkins Hill Road, Chiddingstone, Kent, TN8 7BB
☎ (01892) 870328

⊗ Larkins brewery was founded by the Dockerty family in Rusthall in Kent in 1986, on the site of the original Royal Tunbridge Wells Brewery. In 1988 the brewery relocated to Larkins Farm in Chiddingstone. All beers include hops grown on a four-acre site near Larkins Farm and are brewed with its own yeast strain (est. 1993). The brewery delivers direct to around 40-50 pubs and restaurants within a 20-mile radius. The brewery celebrated its 35th anniversary in 2021. ‼️♦

Traditional Ale (ABV 3.4%) BITTER
Pale (ABV 4.2%) PALE
Best (ABV 4.4%) BITTER
Full-bodied, slightly fruity and unusually bitter for its gravity.

Larrikin

🍴 Urchin, 15-17 Belfast Street, Hove, West Sussex, BN3 3YS
☎ (01273) 241881 ✉ hello@urchinpub.co.uk

Following two years of homebrewing research, commercial brewing began in 2018 in the Urchin, Hove, a shellfish and craft beer pub. Beer is only available in the pub, mainly in keg, with cask-conditioned beer available infrequently.

Laverstoke Park

Laverstoke Park, Overton, Basingstoke, Hampshire, RG25 3DR

A bottle-conditioned beer is contract brewed for Laverstoke Park by an unnamed brewery.

Law

Unit 17, Mid Wynd, Dundee, DD1 4JG ☎ 07893 538277 ⊕ lawbrewing.co

Law was established in 2016 and is named after Dundee's most distinctive landmark; the volcano-like slopes of the Law.

Lazy Bay

89 Julian Road, Lady Bay, Nottingham, NG2 5AL
☎ 07400 196036 ⊕ lazybaybrewery.co.uk

Lazy Bay was established in 2018 by ex-teacher and former home brewer Brett Phillips using a purpose-built, 2.5-barrel plant brewing a small core range while experimenting with one-off specials. All beers are unfined, and the higher gravity beers are brewed with Norwegian Kveik yeast. Beers are delivered direct to local pubs and beer festivals. V

Culture Vulture (ABV 4.2%) PALE
El Dorado (ABV 4.5%) PALE
Rebel for Life (ABV 6.5%) IPA
Sy Fy (ABV 7%) IPA
Chikara (ABV 7.5%) STOUT
Scene Deleted (ABV 10%) SPECIALITY

Lazy Turtle

Meadowbeck, Barnside Lane, Hepworth, Holmfirth, West Yorkshire, HD9 1TN

☎ (01484) 680589 ☎ 07590 532880
⊕ lazyturtlebrewing.com

Founded in 2018 by Dave Bore, a member of the Penistone Homebrew Collective, after he decided to move into commercial brewing. Production is mostly bottled but cask-conditioned beers are occasionally available.

Leadmill

Unit 3 Heanor Small Business Centre, Adams Close, Heanor, Derbyshire, DE75 7SW ☎ 07971 189915
✉ leadmill@fsmail.net

⊠ Set up in Selston in 1999, Leadmill moved to Denby in 2001 and again in 2010 to Heanor. A sister brewery to Bottle Brook (qv), the brewery tap is at the Old Oak, Horsley Woodhouse. ♦

Langley Best (ABV 3.6%) BITTER
Mash Tun Bitter (ABV 3.6%) BITTER
Old Oak Bitter (ABV 3.7%) BITTER
B52 (ABV 5.2%) BITTER
Slumdog (ABV 5.9%) GOLD

Leatherbritches

≣ Brewery Yard, Tap House, Annwell Lane, Smisby, Derbyshire, LE65 2TA ☎ 07976 279253
⊕ leatherbritches.co.uk

⊛The brewery, founded in 1993 in Fenny Bentley, has relocated and expanded over the years. It moved to its current address in 2011, where it effectively took over the existing Tap House Brewery (established 2010) but continued to brew the latter's beers. Since 2015, however, Tap House beers have become rebadged Leatherbritches products. ‼♦LIVE

Goldings (ABV 3.6%) BITTER
Bounder (ABV 3.8%) GOLD
Lemongrass & Ginger (ABV 3.8%) SPECIALITY
Ashbourne Ale (ABV 4%) PALE
Cad (ABV 4%) BITTER
Dr Johnson (ABV 4%) BITTER
Scoundrel (ABV 4.1%) PORTER
Mad Ruby (ABV 4.4%) BITTER
Raspberry Belter (ABV 4.4%) SPECIALITY
Ashbourne IPA (ABV 4.7%) PALE
Hairy Helmet (ABV 4.7%) GOLD
Spitting Feathers (ABV 4.8%) BITTER
Bespoke (ABV 5%) BITTER
Game Over (ABV 5%) BITTER

Lecale

5 High Street, Ardglass, County Down, BT30 7TU
☎ 07763 142100 ⊕ lecalebrewery.com

Based in the historic fishing village of Ardglass on the east coast of County Down, Lecale uses local malts and hops with water from the Mourne Mountains.

Ledbury SIBA

Gazerdine House, Hereford Road, Ledbury, Herefordshire, HR8 2PZ
☎ (01531) 671184 ☎ 07957 428070
⊕ ledburyrealales.co.uk

⊛Established in 2012, Ledbury Real Ales uses hops grown in Herefordshire and Worcestershire with other materials sourced locally, where possible. The beers are sold mainly within a 15-mile radius of the brewery. ‼♦

Bitter (ABV 3.8%) BITTER
Dark (ABV 3.9%) MILD

Gold (ABV 4%) GOLD
Ledbury Pale ale (ABV 4%) PALE

Leeds SIBA

1 Westland Road, Leeds, West Yorkshire, LS11 5SE
☎ (0113) 244 5866 ⊕ leedsbrewery.co.uk

⊛Production began in 2007 and Leeds Brewery is now one of the largest in the city. It uses a unique strain of yeast originally taken from a now defunct West Yorkshire brewery. Beer is supplied directly across the region and as far as Nottinghamshire, Lancashire and the North East. It formerly ran an estate of pubs, still trading, across Leeds and York. In 2020 the brewery invested in new, state-of-the-art brewing equipment following a move into new premises. ♦

Pale (ABV 3.8%) PALE
Yorkshire Gold (ABV 4%) GOLD
Best (ABV 4.3%) BITTER
Midnight Bell (ABV 4.8%) MILD

JW Lees IFBB

Greengate Brewery, Middleton Junction, Middleton Junction, M24 2AX
☎ (0161) 643 2487 ⊕ jwlees.co.uk

⊛Family-owned since its foundation by John Lees in 1828, the brewery has a tied estate of 150 pubs, mostly in north Manchester, Cheshire, Lancashire and North Wales. The vast majority serve cask beer. The current head brewer is a family member. An in-house microbrewery, Boilerhouse, came on stream in 2018. ‼♦

Dark (ABV 3.5%) MILD
Formerly GB Mild, this is a dark brown beer with a malt and caramel aroma. Creamy mouthfeel, with malt, caramel and fruit flavours and a malty finish.
Supernova (ABV 3.5%) MILD
Manchester Pale Ale (ABV 3.7%) PALE
Golden beer, moderately-hopped and with gentle bitterness.
Bitter (ABV 4%) BITTER
Smooth, copper-coloured beer with caramel malt in aroma and flavour. Dry, bittersweet aftertaste.
Dragon's Fire (ABV 4%) BITTER
Game On (ABV 4.2%) BITTER
Stout (ABV 4.2%) STOUT
Founder's (ABV 4.5%) BITTER
Moonraker (ABV 6.5%) STRONG
A reddish-brown beer with a strong, malty, fruity aroma. The flavour is rich and sweet, with roast malt, and the finish is fruity yet dry. Available only in a handful of outlets.

Brewed under the Boilerhouse brand name:
Craft Pale (ABV 4.2%) PALE

Left Bank

Ty Newydd Farm, Llangorse, LD3 7UA ☎ 07815 849523 ⊕ leftbankbrewery.co.uk

The present brewery location commenced operation in 2019 and occupies the premises of the former Lithic Brewery. The 400-litre (2.5-barrel) plant produces cask, bottled and canned beers.

Left Handed Giant

Unit 3, Wadehurst Industrial Park, St Philips Road, St Philips, Bristol, BS2 0JE ⊕ lefthandedgiant.com

Originally launched in 2015 as a cuckoo brewery using spare capacity at other local breweries, Left Handed Giant has operated since 2017 using its own 15-barrel plant to brew modern, progressive beers. A second 15-barrel plant was added in 2019 when the Left Handed Giant Brewpub in Bristol city centre was added, doubling its capacity. A small amount of the output goes into cask. !! ▅ ♦ LIVE ⬩

Legitimate Industries SIBA

10 Weaver Street, Leeds, West Yorkshire, LS4 2AU
⊕ legitimateworldwide.com

Founded in 2016, the 30-barrel plant mainly brews keg beer for the company's Red's True Barbecue restaurant chain. However, under new ownership a wider portfolio of non-permanent beers are being produced, with canned output substantially increasing too, aided by the installation of a 200-litre pilot kit. A limited amount of cask beer is sometimes available in the local free-trade.

Leigh on Sea SIBA

35 Progress Road, Leigh-on-Sea, Essex, SS9 5PR
☎ (01702) 817255 ⊕ leighonseabrewery.co.uk

⊠ Established in 2017 to produce vegan-friendly beer, which is unfiltered, unpasteurised and unfined (except for Renown). Initially brewing on a one-barrel kit, it rapidly progressed to a 10-barrel plant. Many of the names of the beers are based on Leigh's maritime heritage !! ▅ ♦ V ⬩

Legra Pale (ABV 3.8%) PALE
Boys of England (ABV 3.9%) BITTER
Brhubarb (ABV 3.9%) SPECIALITY
Renown (ABV 4%) STOUT
Six Little Ships (ABV 4.2%) BITTER
Two Tree Island Red (ABV 4.5%) RED
Crowstone (ABV 5.5%) BITTER
Cockle Row Spit (ABV 5.6%) BITTER
SS9 (ABV 9%) STOUT

Leighton Buzzard SIBA

Unit 31, Harmill Industrial Estate, Grovebury Road, Leighton Buzzard, Bedfordshire, LU7 4FF
☎ (01525) 839153 ☎ 07538 903753
⊕ leightonbuzzardbrewing.co.uk

The first brewery to operate in Leighton Buzzard for more than 100 years. Established in 2014, the brewery changed hands in 2019 and is now run by local CAMRA member Mark Debrick. !! ▅ ♦

Golden Buzzard (ABV 4.1%) GOLD
Bavarian Dragon (ABV 4.2%) GOLD
Best Buzzard (ABV 4.3%) BITTER
Vimy Bomber (ABV 4.3%) BITTER
Restoration Ale (ABV 4.6%) BITTER
Black Buzzard (ABV 5.8%) PORTER

Leila Cottage

▤ **Countryman, Chapel Road, Ingoldmells, Skegness, Lincolnshire, PE25 1ND**
☎ (01754) 872268
✉ countryman_inn@btconnect.com

Leila Cottage started brewing in 2007 and now uses a 2.5-barrel plant. The brewery is situated at the Countryman pub – Leila Cottage was the original name of the building before it became a licensed club and more recently a pub. The history of the Countryman and the brewery is on display in the pub. 2021 saw ongoing works to the building, with beers temporarily brewed at 8-Sail Brewery (qv). !! ▅ LIVE

Leith Hill

▤ **c/o Plough Inn, Coldharbour Lane, Coldharbour, Surrey, RH5 6HD**
☎ (01306) 711793 ⊕ ploughinn.com

⊠ Leith Hill was established in 1996 at the Plough Inn and was moved to converted storerooms at the rear in 2001, increasing capacity to 2.5 barrels in 2005. New owners took over in 2016. !! LIVE V

Lennox

25 Lime Road, Dumbarton, G82 2RP
☎ (01389) 298642 ☎ 07709 192168

Office: 62 Glencairn Road, Dumbarton, G82 4DW
⊕ lennoxbrewery.com

Established in 2018 and brewed on the banks of the River Leven, inspired by the rich local history of the area and the raw ingredients that the local countryside provides. All the beers use as many locally sourced ingredients as possible. Expansion took place in 2020.

Sons Pale Ale (ABV 4%) PALE
Golden Ale (ABV 4.6%) GOLD

Lenton Lane SIBA

Unit 5G, The Midway, Lenton Industrial Estate, Nottingham, NG7 2TS
☎ (0333) 003 5008 ⊕ lentonlane.co.uk

⊠ Lenton Lane began brewing in 2014 under the name Frontier, after taking over the brewing plant at the Flower Pot pub in Derby. Lenton Lane changed its name in 2016 and relocated to a purpose-built brewery in Nottingham using a 10-barrel plant. The brewery produces a range of single malt and single hop beers (SM&SH), available throughout the year. ▅ ♦ LIVE

Newbird (ABV 3.7%) PALE
Pale Moonlight (ABV 3.7%) PALE
Bluebird (ABV 3.8%) PALE
36 North (ABV 3.9%) BITTER
Atlas Stout (ABV 4.2%) STOUT
Gold Rush (ABV 4.2%) GOLD
Pioneer (ABV 4.3%) GOLD
Outpost (ABV 4.5%) BITTER
200 Not Out (ABV 6%) IPA

Lerwick SIBA

Staneyhill, North Road, Lerwick, Shetland, ZE1 0NA
☎ 07738 948336 ⊕ lerwickbrewery.co.uk

Lerwick Brewery was established in 2011 using a 12-barrel plant and sits at the very edge of the North Atlantic. Originally only brewing keg beer, a cask-conditioned range was launched in 2015. ▅ ♦ V ⬩

Skipper's Ticket (ABV 4%) BITTER
Azure (ABV 4.3%) GOLD
Refreshing, grapefruity/peachy, hoppy, golden bitter.
Lerwick IPA (ABV 5%) PALE
Grapefruity, hoppy bitter with a slight biscuit background.
Tushkar (ABV 5.5%) STOUT
Very good, dark brown, roasted, malty stout with chocolate, coffee and liquorice.

Leviathan

Unit 4, 17 Reddicap Trading Estate, Sutton Coldfield, West Midlands, B75 7BU ☎ 07983 256979
⊕ leviathanbrewing.co.uk

Leviathan was established in 2018 by keen homebrewer Chris Hodgetts. Initial production was of keg and canned beers, but cask ales are now becoming increasingly available for festivals and the new on-site taproom. ◆

Liberation

Tregar House, Longueville Road, St Saviour, Jersey, JE2 7WF
☎ (01534) 764089 ☎ 07911 744568
⊕ liberationgroup.com

⊠ The Liberation Brewery (owned by the Liberation Group, which also owns Butcombe Brewery) is located at Longueville, just outside St Helier. Its multi-award-winning flagship beer Liberation Ale can be found in many of the Group's predominantly freehold pubs (43 in Jersey, 26 in Guernsey, three in Alderney and 44 in the UK). Seasonal and one-off beers, often event driven, are produced throughout the year. ‼️🍽◆

Ale (ABV 4%) GOLD
Herm Island Gold (ABV 4.2%) GOLD
IPA (ABV 4.8%) PALE

Lincoln Green SIBA

Unit 5, Enterprise Park, Wigwam Lane, Hucknall, Nottingham, NG15 7SZ
☎ (0115) 963 4233 ☎ 07748 111457
⊕ lincolngreenbrewing.co.uk

☺Anthony Hughes established the Lincoln Green Brewing Company in 2012 using a 10-barrel plant. The brewery takes its name from the colour of dyed woollen cloth associated with the legend of Robin Hood. Beers are named with a respectful nod towards the Nottinghamshire legend. A range of craft beers is available in KeyKeg. Bottled beers are available online and in supermarkets, including limited edition, special bottle-aged, bottle-conditioned beers. 🍽◆LIVE GF

Marion (ABV 3.8%) PALE
Subtly-hopped golden ale with a citrus aroma and dry, bitter finish.
Archer (ABV 4%) PALE
Citrus golden ale with American hops and a moderately bitter finish.
Hood (ABV 4.2%) BITTER
Tawny-coloured ale with balanced hops and bitterness.
Fountain Dale (ABV 4.3%) GOLD
Tuck (ABV 4.7%) PORTER
Full-bodied and rich dark ale with roast and malt flavours throughout.
Longbow (ABV 5%) GOLD
Quarterstaff (ABV 5%) STOUT
Black in colour with roasty aromas and taste, leading to a dry coffee and bitter finish.
Buttermuch (ABV 5.5%) STOUT
Dark brown beer with a strong butterscotch caramel taste throughout, and a gentle bitter finish.
Sheriff (ABV 5.5%) IPA
Golden, full-bodied IPA, citrus hop taste and bitterness balanced throughout.

Lincolnshire Craft SIBA

Race Lane, Melton Ross, Lincolnshire, DN38 6AA
☎ (01652) 680001 ⊕ lincolnshirecraftbeers.com

Lincolnshire Craft Beers is the company formed by Mark Smith who bought the Tom Wood Brewery in 2017. It continues to brew the Tom Wood range of beers on the 60-barrel Melton Ross plant. ◆

Best Bitter (ABV 3.7%) BITTER
A good citrus, passion fruit hop dominates the nose and taste, with background malt. A lingering hoppy and bitter finish.

Lincoln Gold (ABV 4%) GOLD
Bomber County (ABV 4.8%) BITTER
An earthy, malt aroma but with a complex, underlying mix of coffee, hops, caramel and apple fruit. The beer starts bitter and intensifies to the end.

Linear

Bingham, Nottinghamshire, NG13 8EU ⊕ linear.beer

Linear is a small-scale, 50-litre brewery, which began production in 2016 and is located at the owner's home. It concentrates on a series of one-offs in a range of styles (sometimes in collaboration), supplied to three local outlets in cask and bottle. LIVE

Lines (NEW)

🏠 37a Bridge Street, Usk, NP15 1BQ
☎ (029) 2085 0706 ⊕ linesbrewco.com

Lines relocated to the centre of Usk in 2020, with a brewpub venue on the high street. The brewery, led by the former Celt Experience head brewer, occupies the ground floor through which you pass through to access the rustic upper taproom serving beer and pizza. ◆

Linfit

🏠 Sair Inn, 139 Lane Top, Linthwaite, Huddersfield, West Yorkshire, HD7 5SG
☎ (01484) 842370

☺A 19th century brewpub that started brewing again in 1982. The beer is only available at the Sair Inn.

Liquid Light

Unit 9, Robin Hood Industrial Estate, Alfred Street South, Nottingham, NG3 1GE ☎ 07530 737842
⊕ liquidlightbrewco.com

The beer range has been named with a strong heavy rock and psychedelic influence, referencing the likes of Frank Zappa and Black Sabbath. It has an emphasis on pale-coloured, hoppy beers and fruit beers. The brewery moved to its own premises in 2021 and opened a taproom. ◆◆

Lister's SIBA

The Old Dairy, Ford Lane, Ford, West Sussex, BN18 0DF
☎ (01903) 739117 ☎ 07775 853412
⊕ listersbrewery.com

Brewing began in 2012 using a 0.25-barrel kit. The brewery relocated in 2014 and expanded to a five-barrel plant. Lister's donates 5p from every pint and bottle of Best Bitter and Tail Wagger sold to the Battersea Dogs & Cats Home, and 5p of every pint of Pride of Sussex sold goes to the LGBT Foundation.

Best Bitter (ABV 3.9%) BITTER
Golden Ale (ABV 4.1%) GOLD
Limehouse Porter (ABV 4.1%) PORTER
American Pale Ale (ABV 4.2%) PALE
IPA (ABV 4.3%) PALE
Special (ABV 4.6%) BITTER

Litchborough Artisan

See Eastcote

Lithic

See Cold Black Label

Little Big Dog (NEW)

7 Oak Grove, Barrow-Upon-Humber, DN19 7SH
⊕ littlebigdogbeer.co.uk

Commercial home-based brewery, first brewed in 2020. Beers are available in cans.

Little Big (NEW)

23 St George's Esplanade, St Peter Port, Guernsey, GY1 2BG ⊕ littlebigbrewco.com

Little Big Brew Co was founded in 2020 during the global pandemic.

Little Black Dog

Carlton Brewery, Duddings Farm, Carlton, North Yorkshire, DN14 9LU ☎ 07495 026173
⊕ littleblackdogbeer.com

Established in 2015, Little Black Dog is a small batch, family-run brewery. All beer is unfined, unpasteurised and unfiltered. The brewery tap is the Doghouse, Selby.
🍺♦V

Yorkshire Bitter (ABV 3.8%) BITTER
Big Red American Amber (ABV 4.5%)
Oatmeal Stout (ABV 4.5%) STOUT

Little Creatures

🍺 **1 Lewis Cubitt Walk, Kings Cross, London, N1C 4DL**
☎ (020) 8161 4446 ⊕ littlecreatures.co.uk

This US-style brewpub opened in 2019 under Little Creatures of Freemantle, Australia but ultimately Lion of Kirin Group ownership. A couple of changing keg house beers are available from tanks behind the bar under the Regents Canal name along with imported Little Creatures beers. Close to the rejuvinated Coal Drops Yard development. No real ale.

Little Critters SIBA

80 Parkwood Road, Sheffield, South Yorkshire, S3 8AG
☎ (0114) 276 3171

Office: Horizon House, 2 Whiting Street, Sheffield, S8 9QR ⊕ littlecrittersbrewery.com

A small batch, family-owned microbrewery. It opened in 2016, and operates on a 10-barrel brewing plant. Pubs are supplied throughout Yorkshire, the East Midlands and nationally. Brewery improvements took place in 2020 and the core range expanded. It now also supplies beer in cans through a number of bottle shops. ♦LIVE

Little Hopper (ABV 3.6%) GOLD
Blonde Bear (ABV 4.2%) BLOND
Raspberry Blonde (ABV 4.5%) BLOND
Sleepy Badger (ABV 4.5%) SPECIALITY
White Wolf (ABV 5%) PALE
Coco Nutter (ABV 6%) STOUT
Nutty Ambassador (ABV 6%) STOUT
Sultanas of Swing (ABV 6%) SPECIALITY
C Monster (ABV 6.5%) IPA

Little Dewchurch

🍺 **Plough, Little Dewchurch, Hereford, HR2 6PW**
☎ (01432) 840542 ⊕ littledewchurchbrewery.co.uk

☺The Little Dewchurch Brewing Company was established in 2019. The brewery is located in a former store room at the Plough Inn in the village of Little Dewchurch. It is a three-barrel brewery, with five ales to its name. The brewery's ales are available on draft in the Plough Inn. Bottling is also done on the premises.

Little Earth Project

Mill Green, Edwardstone, Sudbury, Suffolk, CO10 5PX
☎ (01787) 211118 ⊕ littleearthproject.com

Mill Green Brewery started 2008, becoming Little Earth Project in 2016. Built on an old stable site, using local wood, reclaimed bricks, sheep wool and lime plaster. It has its own borehole, brewing liquor is heated using bio and solar power, and its 3,000-litre storage is heated by solar panels, and a wood boiler. It creates innovative beers and sours. Most use local ingredients, and age in old wine barrels. About half is KeyKeg, the rest is bottled, with some cask available.

Little Eaton

See Black Hole

Little Giant SIBA

Unit 3, Stoke View Business Park, Fishponds, Bristol, BS16 3AE
☎ (0117) 939 2589 ⊕ littlegiantbrewery.co.uk

⊗ Microbrewery established in the Fishponds area of Bristol in 2017. Its fully programmable, 600-litre brew plant was commissioned in 2018. Its parent company Reyam Ltd manufacture these microbreweries. Six core beers are produced, along with occasional one-off specials. ‼🍺LIVE

Golden Gosling (ABV 3.6%) GOLD
Citrus and pine aroma, bitterness on the palate with grapefruit and pineapple flavours cutting through the resinous, hoppiness. Bitter, hoppy ending.
Fi (ABV 4.1%) BITTER
Full-bodied with malty backbone, caramelised fruit and hints of toffee with balancing hop bitterness before a gentle, bittersweet finish.
Fo (ABV 4.1%) PALE
Hop aroma, light biscuit malt and background bitterness, overlaid with soft fruit and crisp, hop flavours. Dry, bitter aftertaste.
Fe (ABV 5%) BITTER
Malty nose, spiced fruit cake flavours with hints of caramel cutting across the bitterness and malt. Long-lasting, satisfying finish.
Fum (ABV 5%) STOUT
Roasted malt aroma, complex flavours combine rich chocolate and coffee with treacle and dark fruit before a sweet, roasty finish.
Golden Goose (ABV 5.5%) BITTER
Powerfully-hopped aroma with zesty and tropical fruit flavours balancing the resinous hop bitterness which continues through the prolonged ending.

Little Goat

70 New Road, Ynysmeurdy, Pontardawe, SA8 4PP
☎ 07590 520457 ⊕ littlegoatbrewery.co.uk

Opened in a garden outbuilding by two enthusiastic home brewers, the four-barrel microbrewery was built with equipment from Langton's Brewery in Leicestershire, and commenced trading in 2018. The first ale was sold in bottles only, cask ale was added in 2019.

Scapegoat (ABV 4.3%) BITTER
Golden Goat (ABV 4.4%) GOLD
Jumping Jack (ABV 4.9%) BITTER
Yankee Doodle Nanny (ABV 6.5%) SPECIALITY
Santas Little Helper (ABV 6.6%) STOUT
Duffel Goat (ABV 7.2%) STRONG

Little London

Unit 6B, Ash Park Business Centre, Ash Lane, Little London, Hampshire, RG26 5FL
☎ (01256) 533044 ☎ 07785 225468
⊕ littlelondonbrewery.com

⊗ Brewing began in 2015 using a six-barrel plant. Three fermentation vessels ensure a production capability of 60 firkins per week, with capacity for expansion.

Doreen's Dark (ABV 3.2%) MILD
Blacksmith's Gold (ABV 3.5%) GOLD
Red Boy (ABV 3.7%) BITTER
Hoppy Hilda (ABV 3.8%) GOLD
Luvly (ABV 3.9%) BITTER
Pryde (ABV 4.2%) BITTER
Ash Park Special (ABV 4.9%) BITTER

Little Mesters (NEW) SIBA

352 Meadowhead, Sheffield, South Yorkshire, S8 7UJ
☎ 07859 889547 ⊕ littlemestersbrewing.co.uk

Microbrewery and taproom established in 2020 producing beers in cask, keg and can. V♦

Little Monster

Office: Burton Warren, Burton Park Road, Petworth, West Sussex, GU28 0JS ⊕ littlemonsterbrew.com

Brewing began in 2018. Owner Brenden collaborates with other breweries to produce his beers.

Little Ox SIBA

Unit 6, Wroslyn Road Industrial Estate, Freeland, Oxfordshire, OX29 8HZ
☎ (01993) 881941 ☎ 07730 496525
Office: 25 Castle Road, Wootton, OX20 1EQ
⊕ littleoxbrewery.co.uk

⊗ An award-winning brewery, Little Ox began production in 2016 and merged with Oxbrew in 2019 with a new company name of Little Ox Brew Co. It uses a 17-hectolitre (10-barrel) plant. A one-off beer is brewed every month, which usually gets bottled, with some put into kegs and sold to pubs. A canning line was installed in 2021. More than 50 pubs, restaurants and off licences around Oxfordshire are supplied direct. ⬛♦GF V

Hufflepuff (ABV 3.8%) GOLD
Wipeout (ABV 4.2%) GOLD
Ox Blood (ABV 4.3%) RED
Yabba Dabba Doo (ABV 4.8%) BITTER
Dark & Seedy (ABV 5.5%) STOUT

Little Valley SIBA

Unit 3, Turkey Lodge Farm, New Road, Cragg Vale, Hebden Bridge, West Yorkshire, HX7 5TT
☎ (01422) 883888 ⊕ littlevalleybrewery.co.uk

⊕Little Valley began brewing in 2005 on a 10-barrel plant. All beers are organic and vegan, and Radical Roots is licensed by the Fairtrade Foundation. Around 300 outlets are supplied. ⬛♦LIVE V

Withens Pale (ABV 3.9%) PALE
Creamy, light gold-coloured, refreshing ale. Fruity hop aroma, flavoured with hints of lemon and grapefruit. Clean, bitter aftertaste

Radical Roots (ABV 4%) SPECIALITY
Full-bodied, speciality ale. Ginger predominates in the aroma and taste. It has a pleasantly powerful, fiery and spicy finish.

Cragg Bitter (ABV 4.2%) BITTER

Tawny best bitter with a creamy mouthfeel. Malt and fruit aromas move through to the palate which is followed by a bitter finish.

Dark Vale (ABV 4.5%) SPECIALITY
Dark brown, speciality beer. Dark roast and fruit blend successfully with flavours of vanilla to create a smooth, mellow porter.

Hebden's Wheat (ABV 4.5%) SPECIALITY
A pale yellow, creamy wheat beer with a good balance of bitterness and fruit, a hint of sweetness but with a lasting, dry finish.

Stoodley Stout (ABV 4.8%) STOUT
Very dark brown, creamy stout with a rich roast aroma and luscious fruity, chocolate, roast flavours. Well-balanced with a clean, bitter finish.

Tod's Blonde (ABV 5%) BLOND
Bright yellow, smooth golden beer with a citrus hop start and a dry finish. Fruity, with a hint of spice. Similar in style to a Belgian blonde beer.

Moor Ale (ABV 5.5%) SPECIALITY
Tawny in colour with a full-bodied taste. It has a strong malty nose and palate with hints of heather and peat-smoked malt. Well-balanced with a bitter finish.

Python IPA (ABV 6%) IPA
Amber-coloured, creamy beer with a complex, bitter fruit palate, subtly balanced by a malty sweetness, leading to a strongly lingering bitter aftertaste.

Littleover SIBA

Unit 9, Robinson Industrial Estate, Shaftesbury Street, Derby, DE23 8NL
☎ (01332) 987100 ⊕ littleoverbrewery.co.uk

Littleover was established in 2015 using a six-barrel plant.

Gold (ABV 3.8%) GOLD
8 O'Clock Bus (ABV 3.9%) GOLD
King George's (ABV 4%) BITTER
Epiphany (ABV 4.1%) PALE
The Panther (ABV 4.2%) STOUT
Dazzler (ABV 4.5%) PALE
Hollow Legs (ABV 5.2%) PALE

Live

Unit 2, Reeth Dales Centre, Silver Street, Reeth, Richmond, North Yorkshire, DL11 6BW
✉ livebrewco@gmail.com

⊕Four-barrel microbrewery run by the team behind the 2016 National Pub of the Year, the George & Dragon, Hudswell. It specialises in small-scale one-off brews utilising traditional techniques and locally foraged ingredients, mainly produced for cask with small bottle runs, all naturally conditioned. ‼LIVE

Liverpool Brewing SIBA

39 Brasenose Road, Liverpool, L20 8HL
☎ (0151) 933 9660
⊕ liverpoolbrewingcompany.com

⊕Liverpool Brewing Company Limited was established in 2018. A 20-hectolitre brew kit with a fermenting volume of 200 hectolitres is used with cold store capacity for up to 440 hectolitres. Beers are brewed for Team Toxic and delivered nationally. A number of its own venues are due to open, which will be a mixture of styles from traditional pub to craft bar. ‼⬛

Cascade (ABV 3.8%) GOLD
A medium-bodied, pale golden beer with honeyed flowery citrus hop aromas, dry, bitter citrus hops flavours with a dry, fruity bitter finish with some light pine.

Liverpool Pale Ale (ABV 4%) BLOND
Light, fruity hop aromas, sweet bitter flavours with a light malty finish.
24 Carat Gold (ABV 4.1%) GOLD
A medium-bodied straw beer with hoppy citrus fruity (clementine) aromas. Sweet, fruity, slightly honeyed flavours and dry hop bitterness. Dry, fruity hop finish.
Bier Head (ABV 4.1%) BITTER
Light amber beer with malt/roast and hop aromas with light apple notes, bitter hop and roasted malt flavours, with a light peppery hop finish.
Modern Bitter (ABV 4.2%) BITTER
Session IPA (ABV 4.3%) PALE
Liverpool Stout (ABV 4.7%) STOUT

Contract brewed for Team Toxic:
Temple (ABV 3.8%) BITTER
Black Custard (ABV 5%)
Campania (ABV 5%) STOUT
Oscillate Wildly (ABV 5.2%) SPECIALITY

Lizard

The Old Nuclear Bunker, Pednavounder, Coverack, Cornwall, TR12 6SE
☎ (01326) 281135 ⊕ lizardales.co.uk

⊗ Launched in 2004 in St Keverne, Lizard Ales is now based at former RAF Treleaver, a massive disused nuclear bunker in the countryside near Coverack on the Lizard Peninsula. Specialising in bottle-conditioned ales, it mainly supplies local shops and pubs. ‼LIVE

Llangollen

⧗ **Abbey Grange Hotel, Horseshoe Pass Road, Llantysilio, Llangollen, LL20 8DD**
☎ (01978) 861916 ⊕ llangollenbrewery.com

Brewing began in 2010 on a 2.5-barrel plant. The brewery was updated and upgraded in 2014 to a 10-barrel plant. ‼☞LIVE

Lleu SIBA

Unit A9, Penygroes Industrial Estate, Caernarfon, LL54 6DB ☎ 07840 910460 / 07724 902532
⊕ bragdylleu.cymru

☺Brewing began in 2014 using a 1.25-barrel plant and was upgraded to six barrels in 2016 to meet demand, with plans for further expansion during the currency of this Guide. The four beers are named after Welsh folklore characters of the Mabinogi. ‼☞

Blodeuwedd (ABV 3.6%) GOLD
Lleu (ABV 4%) BITTER
Gwydion (ABV 4.7%) BITTER
Bendigeidfran (ABV 5%) PALE

Llyn

1 Parc Eithyn Ffordd Dewi Sant, Nefyn, Gwynedd, LL53 6EG
☎ (01758) 721981 ☎ 07792 050134
⊕ cwrwllyn.cymru

☺Brewing began in 2011. In 2016 the brewing moved into a new, purpose-built, 15-barrel brewery that includes a brewery shop, taphouse, and a visitor's gallery for tours. ‼☞

Y Brawd Houdini (ABV 3.5%) PALE
Brenin Enlli (ABV 4%) BITTER
A fruity bitter, the initial malty taste leads to a hoppy, bitter aftertaste.
Cwrw Glyndwr (ABV 4%) GOLD

A full-bodied, well-balanced, amber beer, quite fruity with a good, hoppy finish.
Seithenyn (ABV 4.2%) GOLD
A fruity golden ale with a tangy, citrus taste and a dry, hoppy finish.
Porth Neigwl (ABV 4.5%) PALE

Loch Leven SIBA

The Muirs, Kinross, KY13 8AS
☎ (01577) 864881

Office: Loch Leven, Wymet House, 87 New Row, Dunfermline, KY12 7DZ ⊕ lochleven.beer

Based opposite the Green Hotel in Kinross, the brewery started production in 2017. Brewing plant and casks have been acquired from the former Loch Leven Brewery in Fife. ‼☞

Warrior Queen (ABV 3.8%) PALE
Shining Knight (ABV 4%) SPECIALITY
Outlaw King (ABV 5%) MILD
King Slayer (ABV 5.2%) OLD

Loch Lomond SIBA

Vale of Leven Industrial Estate, Unit 11, Block 2, Renton, G82 3PD
☎ (01389) 755698 ☎ 07891 920213
⊕ lochlomondbrewery.com

☺Established in 2011 by Fiona and Euan MacEachern, Loch Lomond was the first brewery to be established in the area. Having reached brewing capacity at its original site, it moved to a new purpose-built 35-hectolitre brewery, which also houses a canning line. ☞♦LIVE

West Highland Way (ABV 3.7%) BITTER
Bonnie & Blonde (ABV 4%) BITTER
Southern Summit (ABV 4%) BLOND
The Ale of Leven (ABV 4.5%) BITTER
Bonnie 'n' Clyde (ABV 4.6%) BITTER
Silkie Stout (ABV 5%) STOUT
Kessog Dark Ale (ABV 5.2%) BITTER
Bravehop Amber IPA (ABV 6%) IPA
Bravehop Dark IPA (ABV 6%) IPA

Loch Ness

See Cairngorm

Lock 81

Unit 21, Wenta Business Centre, Colne Way, Watford, WD24 7ND ⊕ lock81brewery.co.uk

Named after the Batchworth lock on the Grand Union Canal at Rickmansworth. Brewing takes place on a one-barrel plant, supplying bottled beer to local bottle shops and off-licences.

Loddon SIBA

Dunsden Green Farm, Church Lane, Dunsden, Oxfordshire, RG4 9QD
☎ (0118) 948 1111 ⊕ loddonbrewery.com

☺This family-run brewery was established in 2002 in a brick-and-flint barn (originally a grain store). The custom-built, 17-barrel plant typically produces 120 barrels per week and supplies more than 700 outlets far and wide. An on-site taproom opened in 2018. Citra Quad is unfined and unfiltered, so therefore vegan-friendly.
‼☞♦V✿

Hoppit (ABV 3.5%) BITTER

Pale session bitter with hops dominating the aroma. Malt and hops in the balanced taste followed by a bitter aftertaste.

Hullabaloo (ABV 4.2%) BITTER
Session bitter with fruit in the initial taste. This develops into a balance of hops and malt in the mouth followed by a bitter aftertaste.

Citra Quad (ABV 4.4%) GOLD
Ferryman's Gold (ABV 4.4%) GOLD
Premium golden ale with a strong hoppy character throughout, accompanied by fruit in the taste and aftertaste.

Hocus Pocus (ABV 4.6%) OLD
Ruby-coloured old ale with dark malt, fruit and caramel aroma, joined by sweetness in the taste. There is a malty, bitterness to the finish.

Dragonfly (ABV 5.2%) PALE

Logan Beck

The Barn at Beckfoot Farm, Duddon Bridge, Cumbria, LA20 6EU ☎ 07926 179749
✉ loganbeckbrewing@gmail.com

The brewery started in 2019. During the currency of this Guide, expansion from 0.75 to a 4.5-barrel plant (formerly Chadwicks) is expected. Cans should be available during 2022. All recipes use as many locally-sourced ingredients as possible (Proper Cumbrian features Cumbrian-grown hops). Beers currently only available within Cumbria.

(Off) Target (ABV 3.3%) BITTER
Prime (ABV 3.7%) BITTER
Proper Cumbrian (ABV 4.2%) RED

Lola Rose

⬚ Wanlockhead Inn, Wanlockhead, ML12 6UZ
☎ (01659) 74535 ☎ 07500 663405
⏾ lola-rose-brewery.co.uk

Lola Rose is based in the family-run Wanlockhead Inn, situated in the scenic Lowther Hills of the Scottish Lowlands. Local outlets only are supplied at present. LIVE

London Beer Factory SIBA

Units 4 & 6, Hamilton Road Industrial Estate, 160 Hamilton Road, West Norwood, London, SE27 9SF
☎ (020) 8670 7054 ⏾ thelondonbeerfactory.com

London Beer Factory started brewing in 2014 using a 20-barrel plant on the same estate and at the same time as Gipsy Hill. As well as a new bar in West Norwood, The Warehouse, it also runs the Barrel Project along the Bermondsey Beer Mile, showcasing its range, and providing an impressive display of barrels used for aging beer. ◆

London Beer Lab SIBA

Arch 283, Belinda Road, Loughborough Junction, Brixton, London, SW9 7DT
☎ (020) 8396 6517

Brixton (2): Arch 41, Railway Arches, Nursery Road, Brixton, London, SW9 8BP ⏾ londonbeerlab.com

Opened in Brixton in 2013 as a bottle shop and homebrew supplies outlet, also offering brewing workshops and tastings. Commercial brewing began in 2015 for larger batches with the shop focusing on small batch production and collaborations, available downstairs at the 14-line taproom. ₪ ◆

Session IPA (ABV 4.2%) GOLD
Tip Top Citra (ABV 5%) PALE

Amber beer with citrus nose and flavour with some biscuity sweetness. The pithy, bitter astringency builds in the bitter finish.

London Brewing SIBA

⬚ Bohemia, 762-764 High Road, North Finchley, London, N12 9QH
☎ (020) 8446 0294 ⏾ londonbrewing.com

⊠ London Brewing Co began brewing in 2011 at the Bull in Highgate, using a 2.5-barrel plant. In 2014 it acquired its second pub, the Bohemia in North Finchley, at which brewing began in 2015 on a new 6.5-barrel, publicly visible brewhouse, becoming its sole location when the Bull was sold in 2016. Beer is now widely available through pub chains and the free trade. ◆◆

London Lush (ABV 3.8%) BITTER
A pale, hoppy bitter with a good balance of hop and malt and a little fruit. The finish is dry but with some lingering hoppiness.

Beer Street (ABV 4%) BITTER
Well-balanced, coppery brown best bitter with the hoppy bitterness underpinned by the caramelised malt character. Fruit is present throughout.

100 Oysters Stout (ABV 4.6%) STOUT
Sweet, chocolaty treacle and soft dark fruit on this smooth stout. Finish is long, dry roast with a little bitterness.

London Fields

365-366 Warburton Street, London Fields, London, E8 3RR
☎ (020) 7254 7174 ⏾ londonfieldsbrewery.co.uk

After brewing was suspended in 2014, beers were brewed at Tom Woods. Taken over by Carlsberg UK in 2017, the company was relaunched in 2018. The London Fields site itself returned to brewing in 2019 along with a large taproom. Part of Carlsberg Marston's Brewing Co. ◆

London Road Brew House

⬚ 67-75 London Road, Southampton, Hampshire, SO15 2AB
☎ (023) 8098 9401 ☎ 07597 147321
⏾ londonroadbrewhouse.com

⊠ Brewing commenced in 2017 in the London Road Brew House using a six-barrel plant. Beer is brewed for the pub, the City Pub Co estate and the trade. ◆

Long Arm

⬚ Long Arm, 20-26 Worship Street, Shoreditch, London, EC2A 2DX
☎ (020) 3873 4065 ⏾ longarmpub.co.uk

Opened in 2017, this brewpub took over all Long Arm beers when brewing at the Ealing Park Tavern stopped. Beers are served on-site from tanks and in keg in other pubs in the ETM chain, the brewery's owners. No real ale. ◆

Long Man SIBA

Church Farm, Litlington, East Sussex, BN26 5RA
☎ (01323) 871850 ☎ 07943 858111
⏾ longmanbrewery.com

⊠ Long Man began brewing in 2012 using a 20-barrel stainless steel plant. Hops and grain are sourced locally alongside homegrown barley and locally-drawn water. A traditional strain of Sussex yeast is used. ‼ ₪ ◆

Long Blonde (ABV 3.8%) BLOND

Best Bitter (ABV 4%) BITTER
Copper Hop (ABV 4.2%) BITTER
Old Man (ABV 4.3%) OLD
Sussex Pride (ABV 4.5%) BITTER
American Pale Ale (ABV 4.8%) PALE

Longdog

Unit A1 Moniton Trading Estate, West Ham Lane, Basingstoke, Hampshire, RG22 6NQ
☎ (01256) 324286 ☎ 07579 801982
⊕ longdogbrewery.co.uk

⊗ Established in 2011, the Longdog Brewery is named after a type of Lurcher used for hare coursing – once a popular pastime in the North Hampshire downs. ‼🏭◆LIVE

Bunny Chaser (ABV 3.6%) BITTER
Golden Poacher (ABV 3.9%) BITTER
Golden-coloured bitter with fruity nose and plenty of hops, balanced by malty sweetness, building to a faint, astringent finish.
Red Runner (ABV 4.2%) BITTER
Lamplight Porter (ABV 5%) PORTER
Splendid porter, smoky and drier than many, with strong roast flavours giving way to blackberry taste and slightly vinous finish.

Longhill

Longhill Cottage, Whitstone, Holsworthy, Cornwall, EX22 6UG
☎ (01288) 341466

⊗ Longhill began brewing in 2011 using a 0.5-barrel plant, upgraded in 2012 to a four-barrel plant to meet demand. Paul and Sue brew one beer, available in the bar at the rear of the brewery.

Hurricane (ABV 4.8%) BITTER
Full-bodied, tawny, premium bitter with earthy malt aroma. Quite bitter, with fruit and resinous hop flavours. Refreshing and persistent bitterness.

Loomshed SIBA

Iomairt an Obain, Tarbert, HS3 3DS ☎ 07808 098860
⊕ loomshed.scot

Brewing commenced in 2019 on the outskirts of Tarbert. The brewery backs onto the Minch, with views of the Scottish mainland. An eco-friendly approach to brewing extends to the on-site taproom. No real ale. Brewing is currently suspended. ◆

Loose Cannon SIBA

Unit 6, Suffolk Way, Abingdon, Oxfordshire, OX14 5JX
☎ (01235) 531141 ⊕ lcbeers.co.uk

Brewing began in 2010 using a 15-barrel plant, reviving Abingdon's brewing history after the Morland Brewery closed in 2000. Beers can be found in an increasing number of local pubs and within 50 miles of the brewery. Popular brewery evenings take place on the first Tuesday of the month. ‼🏭◆◆

Gunners Gold (ABV 3.5%) GOLD
Abingdon Bridge (ABV 4.1%) BITTER
Detonator (ABV 4.4%) BITTER
Porter (ABV 5%) PORTER
India Pale Ale (ABV 5.4%) PALE

Lord Conrad's

Unit 21, Dry Drayton Industrial Estate, Scotland Road, Dry Drayton, Cambridge, Cambridgeshire, CB23 8AT
☎ 07736 739700 ⊕ lordconradsbrewery.co.uk

⊗ Lord Conrad's was established in 2007 and moved to Dry Drayton in 2011, using a 2.5-barrel plant. One permanent outlet is supplied, the Black Horse, Dry Drayton, along with other local free houses and beer festivals. The brewery adheres strongly to green principles, using low energy systems, recycled materials and local ingredients. ‼🏭

Zulu Dawn (ABV 3.5%) PALE
Hedgerow Hop (ABV 3.7%) BITTER
Her Majes Tea (ABV 3.8%) SPECIALITY
Lickety Split (ABV 3.8%) BROWN
Tangerine Dream (ABV 3.8%) SPECIALITY
Spiffing Wheeze (ABV 3.9%) PALE
Big Bad Wolf (ABV 4%) PALE
Conkerwood (ABV 4%) PORTER
Fools Gold (ABV 4%) PALE
Gubbins (ABV 4%) BITTER
Lobster Licker (ABV 4.2%) RED
Slap N'Tickle (ABV 4.3%) BLOND
Zulu (ABV 4.5%) BITTER
Horny Goat (ABV 4.8%) SPECIALITY
Pheasant's Rise (ABV 5%) BITTER
Stubble Burner (ABV 5%) BLOND

Lord Randalls

Holme View Farm, High Street, Laxton, Newark, Nottinghamshire, NG22 0NX ☎ 07712 078346
✉ randallig@aol.com

The five-barrel brewery equipment was purchased in 2018 from the defunct Market Harborough Brewery. Brewing commenced 2020. The proprietors are the Randall family and the head brewer is Dean Penny.

Honey Hole (ABV 3.8%)
Laxton Original (ABV 4%)
Farmers Grundy Stout (ABV 4.6%)

Lord's SIBA

Unit 15, Heath House Mill, Heath House Lane, Golcar, West Yorkshire, HD7 4JW ☎ 07976 974162
⊕ lordsbrewing.com

Established in 2015, Lord's Brewing Co is the brain child of three brothers-in-law, Ben, John and Tim. A picturesque 19th century mill houses the eight-barrel plant, large taproom and gift/bottle shop. ◆◆

Hodl Ultra Pale (ABV 3.8%) PALE
To the Moon (ABV 3.9%) PALE
Expedition Blonde (ABV 4%) BLOND
Ape Mafia American IPA (ABV 4.2%) IPA
Chosen Man (ABV 4.4%)
Malamute (ABV 4.5%)
Silver Spur (ABV 4.6%)
The Bandon Car Porter (ABV 4.8%) PORTER
Mount Helix West Coast Pale (ABV 5%) PALE

Lost + Found

12-13 Ship Street, Brighton, East Sussex, BN1 1AD
⊕ lostandfoundbrewery.com

Brewing began in 2016. No real ale.

Lost & Grounded SIBA

91 Whitby Road, Bristol, BS4 4AR
☎ (0117) 332 7690 ⊕ lostandgrounded.co.uk

Brewing began in 2016. The brewery has a focus on German and Belgian-style beers. No real ale.

Lost Industry

14a Nutwood Trading Estate, Sheffield, South Yorkshire, S6 1NJ
☎ (0114) 231 6393
✉ beer@lostindustrybrewing.com

Lost Industry is run by a family of beer enthusiasts and was established in 2015. A wide range of beer styles is brewed with no core range, although favourites may be repeated from time to time. A barrel-aging programme began in 2018. Spare brewing capacity is utilised by Steel City (qv).

Lost Pier

28 Fourth Avenue, Hove, BN3 2PJ ⊕ lostpier.com

Launched in 2017, the three founders transferred more than 50 years of joint experience in the wine industry to brewing. Cuckoo brewing at two local breweries, the beer is unpasteurised, unfiltered and vegan-friendly. The Assemblage series blends beer and wine. V

Loud Shirt SIBA

Unit 5, Bell Tower Industrial Estate, Roedean Road, Brighton, East Sussex, BN2 5RU
☎ (01273) 087077 ☎ 07979 087945
⊕ loudshirtbeer.co.uk

⊗ The brewery was set up by two old friends, Martyn and Mike, in 2016, using a 10-barrel plant. The current owner, Elias, took over in 2021. The taproom is open Thursday-Sunday. Look out for its psychedelic van around town and at festivals. Beers are available at selected Sussex pubs and bottle shops. ‼🍺🍴

Love Lane

🏠 62-64 Bridgewater Street, Liverpool, L1 0AY
☎ (0151) 317 8215 ⊕ lovelanebeer.com

Established in 2017 in the Baltic Triangle area of Liverpool, the 30-barrel plant can be seen from the Love Lane Bar and Kitchen pub. Craft beers are produced under this name, cask-conditioned beers are badged as Higsons.

Brewed under the Higsons Brewery name:
Pale (ABV 3.8%) PALE
Amber (ABV 4.1%) BITTER
Best Bitter (ABV 4.2%) BITTER

LoveBeer SIBA

95 High Street, Milton, Oxfordshire, OX14 4EJ
☎ 07889 455845 ⊕ lovebeerbrewery.com

Established in a garage in 2013, LoveBeer's original 0.5-barrel plant grew to six barrels in 2017. The brewery supplies local pubs including the Plum Pudding, Milton, as well as beer festivals and farm shops. 🍺LIVE

Doctor Roo (ABV 3.7%) BITTER
Molly's (ABV 4%) BITTER
OG (ABV 4.1%) PALE
Bonnie Hops (ABV 4.6%) PALE

Lovibonds

Friar Park Stables, Badgemore, Henley-on-Thames, Oxfordshire, RG9 4NR
☎ (01491) 576596 ⊕ lovibonds.com

Lovibonds was founded by Jeff Rosenmeier and has been brewing American-style craft beer since 2005. It is named after Joseph William Lovibond (inventor of the Tintometer to measure beer colour). Beers are unfiltered and unpasteurised. In 2017, a purpose-built brewery was established on the outskirts of Henley, with a steam-heated mash tun and copper. Beers are available at a number of local outlets.

Lowes Arms (NEW)

🏠 301 Hyde Road, Denton, M34 3FF
☎ (0161) 336 3064 ☎ 07931 986794
⊕ lowesarms.co.uk

☺Single-barrel brewery located in the cellar of the Lowes Arms, brewing a core range of four beers exclusively for the pub, based on traditional recipes with a modern twist. Traditional stillages are used, together with cellar craft management.

Lowland

8 Well Street, Lockerbie, DG11 2EY ☎ 07493 716521
⊕ lowlandbrewery.co.uk

⊗ Brewing began in 2018 using a five-barrel plant. Three regular beers are produced with plans to expand the range as the brewery develops. The brewery is located in converted premises in the town centre and supplies direct to pubs in Dumfries & Galloway, Scottish Borders and north Cumbria. ‼♦

Rabbie's Drouth (ABV 3.8%) PALE
Twa Dugs (ABV 4%) PALE
Dryfe Blonde (ABV 5%) BLOND

Lowlands (NEW)

Pityme Industrial Estate, St Minver, Cornwall, PL27 6NS

Office: 1a Eddystone Road, Wadebridge, PL27 7AL

Lowlands is a new microbrewery which commenced brewing in three converted shipping containers in 2021. ♦🍴

Loxley

🏠 539 Loxley Road, Sheffield, South Yorkshire, S6 6RR
☎ (0114) 233 4310 ⊕ loxleybrewery.co.uk

Established in 2018, Loxley use a five-barrel plant located in the cellar of the Wisewood Inn. Five regular beers complement occasional specials. Vegan bottle-conditioned beers are bottled on-site. The beers, brewed with water from a natural spring, are becoming increasingly locally available. In 2019, a second pub, the Raven, opened in nearby Walkley. Branded merchandise is available. More than 30 pubs are supplied. LIVE V

Fearn (ABV 3.8%) PALE
Halliday (ABV 3.9%) BITTER
Revill (ABV 4%) BLOND
Lomas (ABV 4.4%) PALE
Gunson (ABV 4.8%) PALE

Lucifer (NEW)

9, Ellencroft Road, Wotton-Under-Edge, Gloucestershire, GL12 7AX ☎ 07886 604690
⊕ luciferbrewhouse.co.uk

Lucifer Brewhouse was established in 2020 using a one-barrel plant. It produces a growing number of small batch beers for pubs in the local area. Most of the cask-conditioned beers are also available bottle conditioned. ♦LIVE

Mild Side (ABV 3.6%) MILD
Mocha Choc Stout (ABV 4.2%) STOUT
Fallen Angel Bitter (ABV 4.3%) BITTER
Wotton Hop Project (ABV 4.4%) GOLD
GL12 (ABV 4.7%) PALE

Lucky 7

Hay On Wye, HR3 5AW
☎ (01497) 822778 ☎ 07815 853353
⊕ lucky7beer.co.uk

A four-barrel brewery offering unfined beers suitable for
vegans. No real ale. V

Luddite SIBA

▤ Calder Vale Hotel, Millfield Road, Horbury Junction,
Wakefield, West Yorkshire, WF4 5EB
☎ (01924) 277658

Brewing began in 2019 at the Calder Vale pub in Horbury
Junction. The pub was shut for five years until being
reopened by a group of three former Horbury School
friends, Ian Sizer, Tim Murphy and Gary Portman. The six-
barrel plant brews, on average, once per week.

Ludlow SIBA

The Railway Shed, Station Drive, Ludlow, Shropshire,
SY8 2PQ
☎ (01584) 873291
⊕ theludlowbrewingcompany.co.uk

☺Established in 2006, the brewery occupies a converted
railway sidings shed. Beers are produced using a 20-
barrel plant and a recently installed pilot plant for one-off
beers. The premises also function as a brewery tap
(which now has regularly-changing beer from the pilot
plant), visitor centre and event's area. ‼🍺◆

Best (ABV 3.7%) BITTER
Blonde (ABV 4%) BLOND
Gold (ABV 4.2%) GOLD
Black Knight (ABV 4.5%) STOUT
Boiling Well (ABV 4.7%) BITTER
Stairway (ABV 5%) GOLD

Luna

See White Horse

Lydbrook Valley

▤ Forge Row, Lydbrook, Gloucestershire, GL17 9NP
☎ (01594) 860310 ✉ andy@theforgehammer.co.uk

Brewing commenced in 2018 in the Forge Hammer pub
in Lydbrook. Alison and Andrew Jopson use full mash to
produce beers for sale in the pub. V

Lyme Regis

Lyme Regis Brewery, Mill Lane, Lyme Regis, DT7 3PU
☎ (01297) 444354 ⊕ lymeregisbrewery.com/

⊗ Lyme Regis Brewery (formerly Town Mill Brewery)
began brewing in 2010 situated in a part of the Town Mill
that previously housed the Lyme Regis electricity
generator. Historically also used as a brewer's
malthouse, the building now houses its licenced taproom
with a one-barrel pilot kit. All cask beers are currently
brewed on contract by Gyle 59 Brewery to the original
Town Mill Brewery recipes. 🍺◆LIVE V

Rebel (ABV 4.2%) BITTER

Lymestone SIBA

The Brewery, Mount Road, Stone, Staffordshire,
ST15 8LL
☎ (01785) 817796 ☎ 07891 782652
⊕ lymestonebrewery.co.uk

☺Lymestone commenced brewing in 2008. Based in the
old Bents Brewery, it uses a 10-barrel plant. A family-run
business, daughter Sarah has joined the brew team as
one of the UK's youngest brewsters. The brewery
delivers in a 50-mile radius, works with national
wholesalers and owns three pubs. ‼🍺◆

Stone Cutter (ABV 3.7%) BITTER
Hoppy and grassy aroma, clean, sharp and refreshing. A
hint of caramel start, then intense bitterness emerges
with a good bitter aftertaste and touch of mouthwatering astringency.
Stone Faced (ABV 4%) BITTER
Foundation Stone (ABV 4.5%) BITTER
An IPA-style beer with pale and crystal malts. Faint
biscuit and chewy, juicy fruits burst on to the palate then
the spicy Boadicea and Pilot hops pepper the taste buds
to leave a dry, bitter finish.
Ein Stein (ABV 5%) GOLD
Stone the Crows (ABV 5.4%) STOUT
A rich dark beer from chocolate malts. Fruit, roasts and
hops abound to leave a deep, lingering bitterness from
the Styrian Goldings and Millennium hop mix.
Abdominal Stoneman (ABV 7%) STRONG

Lymm

18 Bridgewater Street, Lymm, Cheshire, WA13 0AB
☎ (0161) 929 0663 ⊕ lymmbrewing.co.uk

☺Lymm is a small, family-run brewery, launched in
2013. Located in an old post office, the brewing
equipment is downstairs, in what used to be the mess
rooms, with a brewery tap upstairs, in what was the
sorting office/post office counter. A sister brewery to
Dunham Massey (qv), a joint bar opened in 2013,
Costello's Bar, Stockton Heath. ◆

Dark (ABV 3.4%) MILD
Bitter (ABV 3.8%) BITTER
Bridgewater Blonde (ABV 4%) BLOND
Gold Leaf (ABV 4.5%) BITTER
Heritage Trail Ale (ABV 4.5%) BITTER
IPA (ABV 4.8%) PALE
Dam Strong Ale (ABV 7.2%) STRONG

Lynn (NEW)

5 Hayfield Road, North Wootton, Norfolk, PE30 3PR
☎ 07706 187894 ⊕ lynnbrewery.co.uk

Lynn Brewery is an independent, family-owned brewery
based in King's Lynn, making small batch, hand bottled
craft beer. It is passionately local; the grain used comes
from a local malting group and all beers are inspired by
and named after the people and places of Lynn. LIVE

Lytham

Old Bank, 30 Preston Street, Kirkham, Lancashire,
PR4 2AB ☎ 07738 275438 ⊕ lythambrewery.co.uk

☺Lytham is a well-established, family-run brewery that
began brewing in 2007. In 2021 it moved to Kirkham
where the brewery is situated in the Old Bank
restaurant. ◆🍺

Amber (ABV 3.6%) BITTER
Blonde (ABV 3.8%) BLOND
Smooth golden ale with a dry finish.
Gold (ABV 4.2%) GOLD

THE BREWERIES

Royal (ABV 4.4%) RED
Stout (ABV 4.6%) STOUT
IPA (ABV 5.6%) IPA

McColl's

Unit 4, Randolph Industrial Estate, Evenwood, Bishop Auckland, DL14 9SJ
☎ (01388) 417250 ⊕ mccollsbrewery.co.uk

Brewing commenced in 2017 using a 20-barrel plant. Outlets are supplied across the North-East and further afield. A brewery tap is open on the last Friday and Saturday of each month. ✦

Petite Blonde (ABV 4.1%) BLOND
Lady Marmalade (ABV 4.4%) BITTER
North South (ABV 4.6%) PORTER
Suma IPA (ABV 5%) PALE

McCracken's

Derryall Road, Portadown, BT62 1PL
⊕ mccrackensrealale.com

Currently Co Armagh's only real ale brewery, established in 2018. Producing a range of bottle-conditioned beers. LIVE

McGivern

⊟ c/o The Bridge End Inn, 5 Bridge Street, Ruabon, LL14 6DA
☎ (01978) 810881 ☎ 07891 676614
⊕ mcgivernales.co.uk

.☺The brewery was established in 2008 and was originally based at the brewer's home in Wrexham, but moved in 2011 to the award-winning Bridge End Inn, Ruabon using a 2.5-barrel plant. Production is continuing on an occasional basis. ✦

McMullen SIBA IFBB

26 Old Cross, Hertford, SG14 1RD
☎ (01992) 584911 ⊕ mcmullens.co.uk

☺McMullen, Hertfordshire's oldest, independent brewery, was founded in 1827. Its famous brew, AK, is traceable back to the 19th century. The 'Authentic Heritage' tag promotes its core beers. Additional seasonal ales are produced throughout the year, sometimes produced under the Rivertown Brewing name. A microbrewery supplements the main plant. Almost all 125 tied pubs, spread across South-East England, serve cask beer. ‼✦

AK Original Mild (ABV 3.7%) MILD
A pleasant mix of malt and hops leads to a distinctive, dry aftertaste.
Country Bitter (ABV 4.3%) BITTER
A full-bodied beer with a well-balanced mix of malt, hops and fruit throughout.
IPA (ABV 4.8%) PALE

Mabby

⊟ Mabby Brew Pub & Kitchen, Forest Road, Trefforest, CF37 1SY
☎ (01443) 402033

A microbrewery situated in the cellar of the Otley Arms supplying the pub and a few other outlets. The name is derived from a partnership between Matt Otley and his wife Gabby. The beers have no names and each recipe is referred to as a colour, with the colour being reflected on the pumpclip. V

Macintosh (NEW)

Stamford Brook Road, Stamford Brook, London, W6 0XH ⊕ macintoshales.com

Garage-based, 250-litre brewery, which went commercial in 2019, brewing once a week and gypsy brewing for larger batches. A single beer is available in cask, keg and bottle around North and East London.

Best Bitter (ABV 4.6%) BITTER

Mad Cat SIBA

Brogdale Farm, Brogdale Road, Faversham, Kent, ME13 8XZ
☎ (01795) 597743 ☎ 07960 263615
⊕ madcatbrewery.co.uk

⊠ Established in 2012 by Peter Meaney in a refurbished cold store using an eight-barrel plant. Beers are distributed to local pubs. Bottles and polypins are available from the brewery and Peter often attends local markets, festivals and events. ‼✦

Red Ale (ABV 3.9%) RED
Crispin Ale (ABV 4%) BLOND
Golden IPA (ABV 4.2%) PALE
Platinum Blonde (ABV 4.2%) BLOND
Emotional Blackmail (ABV 4.5%) SPECIALITY
Jet Black Stout (ABV 4.6%) STOUT

Mad Dog

Shed 4, Unit 9, Park Farm, Plough Road, Penperlllini, NP4 0AL ☎ 07864 923231

Office: Unit 6a, Cwmtillery Industrial Estate, Abertillery, NP13 1LZ ⊕ maddogbrew.co.uk

Brewing began in 2014. The brewery was taken over in 2020, re-employing the former director as head brewer. GF ✦

Third Eye Blind (ABV 3.8%) PALE
Now in a Minute (ABV 4.2%) RED
Marmalade IPA (ABV 4.5%) IPA
Stouty McStoutface (ABV 4.5%) STOUT

Mad Scientist

⊟ c/o The Quakerhouse, 2-3 Mechanics Yard, Darlington, DL3 7QF
☎ (01325) 245052

Brewing commenced in 2017 on a half-barrel plant situated in the cellar of the Quakerhouse.

Mad Squirrel SIBA

Unit 18, Boxted Farm, Berkhamsted Road, Potten End, Hertfordshire, HP1 2SG
☎ (01442) 256970 ⊕ madsquirrelbrew.co.uk

⊠ Situated on the outskirts of Hemel Hempstead, brewing began in 2004. Since 2017 it has used a custom brew kit from the US, using water from an on-site borehole at Potten End. The brewery maintains an innovative outlook, introducing many specialised craft beers while maintaining a range of more traditional cask ales and beers. Output is distributed to venues throughout London and the South-East, including to its own chain of Tap & Bottle shops. ‼✦LIVE ✦

Hopfest (ABV 3.8%) GOLD
Mister Squirrel (ABV 4%) BITTER
Resolution (ABV 4.2%) GOLD
De La Crème (ABV 4.5%) STOUT
London Porter (ABV 5%) PORTER
Big Sea (ABV 5.5%) IPA

Mad Yank SIBA

Alandale Drive, Northwood Hills, HA5 3UP
🌐 madyank.com

Brewing is done on a small, home plant, after plans to install a large plant elsewhere fell through, but it is still searching for the right location. Mostly bottled output, with keg from time to time, often available at the Beer Asylum in Pinner.

Made of Stone

🍺 **8 Woodford Road, Bramhall, Stockport, SK7 2JJ**

Nanobrewery situated at the back of the Mounting Stone micropub in Bramhall. Brewing began in 2018 on a one-barrel plant at the rear of the pub. The brewery specialises in twice monthly, one-off brews and collaborations with local brewers. Beers are usually supplied to the pub and the Chiverton Tap, Cheadle Hulme.

Madrigal

Unit 2, Hele Business Park, Witheridge Place, Hele Bay, Devon, EX34 9RA ☎ 07857 560677
🌐 madrigalbrewery.co.uk

⊗ Originally established in Combe Martin in 2014, the brewery relocated to larger premises in Lynmouth and has now relocated again to a new site in Hele Bay, Ilfracombe. A taproom opened in 2021. ‼♦LIVE V✦

In the Pine IPA (ABV 3.9%) PALE
Severed Hand (ABV 4%) PORTER
Fossil (ABV 4.1%) BITTER
Hanged Man (ABV 4.2%) SPECIALITY
Wheatear (ABV 4.3%) SPECIALITY
Garland (ABV 4.4%) SPECIALITY
Surfer Rosa (ABV 4.7%) RED
Monkey's Fist (ABV 4.8%) OLD
Smooth, dark Old Ale with strong fruit and roast from start to lingering, slightly sour finish. Heavy, sweet but satisfying.
Lost & Found (ABV 5%) BLOND
North Coast Voodoo (ABV 5.1%) PALE
Burning House (ABV 5.2%) SPECIALITY

Magic Dragon SIBA

Plassey Brewery, Eyton, LL13 0SP
☎ (01978) 781675 🌐 magicdragonbrewing.co.uk

Originally called Plassey, and later New Plassey. Another new owner, brewer and personnel took over in 2017. Some beer replicates the old Plassey range but others are new recipes.

Burning Dragon (ABV 3.6%) PALE
Border Bitter (ABV 3.8%) BITTER
A well-balanced, session bitter with a fruity aroma, smooth, malty taste, and a satisfying hoppy finish.
Eyton Gold (ABV 4%) GOLD
A full-flavoured golden ale with a dry, hoppy taste and a long-lasting bitter finish.
Green One (ABV 4.2%) IPA

Magic Rock

Units 1-4, Willow Lane, Huddersfield, West Yorkshire, HD1 5EB
☎ (01484) 649823 🌐 magicrockbrewing.com

Magic Rock began brewing in 2011. The brewery is located about half a mile walk from Huddersfield town centre on an industrial estate. The site also houses a taproom and distribution centre. In 2019 Magic Rock was bought by Lion of Australia, who in turn are owned by Kirin of Japan. ♦LIVE ✦

Hat Trick (ABV 3.7%) BITTER
Ringmaster (ABV 3.9%) GOLD
Inhaler (ABV 4.5%) GOLD
Common Grounds (ABV 5.4%) PORTER
High Wire (ABV 5.5%) IPA
Dark Arts (ABV 6%) STOUT

Magic Spells

24 Rigg Approach, Leyton, London, E10 7QN
☎ (020) 3475 1781 🌐 magicspellsbrewery.co.uk

Magic Spells, owned and operated by Hare Wines, is located in its warehouse. The small on-site kit is used for trial brews and events with the main output coming from Firebrand. Usually only available in bottles or cans.

Magpie SIBA

Unit 4, Ashling Court, Ashling Street, Nottingham, NG2 3JA ☎ 07419 991310 🌐 magpiebrewery.com

☺Launched in 2006 using a six-barrel plant, the brewery upgraded to 17.5-barrels in 2017. Only British hops and malt are used in the core range, with the Wanderlust range taking more worldly influences and ingredients. Its shop/tap opened 2019 at the brewery. 📦♦✦

Hoppily Ever After (ABV 3.8%) BLOND
Golden bitter, gently-hopped with biscuit malt flavours and a bitter finish.
Best (ABV 4.2%) BITTER
A malty traditional pale brown best bitter, with balancing hops giving a bitter finish.
Cherry Raven (ABV 4.4%) SPECIALITY
Raven Stout (ABV 4.4%) STOUT
Dark stout with roast coffee aroma and taste leading to a dry, bitter finish.
Thieving Rogue (ABV 4.5%) GOLD
A hoppy golden ale with a long-lasting, bitter finish.
Jay IPA (ABV 5.2%) PALE

Mains

Office: 45a Alderman Road, Glasgow, G13 3YG
✉ mainsbrewco@gmail.com

Mains is a small-batch brewery, producing farmhouse-inspired beers.

Makemake

🍺 **39 Osborne Road, Southsea, PO5 3LR**
☎ (023) 9273 5939 🌐 makemake.beer

Makemake Brewing, based in the Greenwich Brewpub in Southsea, have been producing modern craft beers since 2019.

Mallard

Unit A, Maythorne, Southwell, Nottinghamshire, NG25 0RS ☎ 07811 193930
✉ stevenhussey@tiscali.co.uk

☺Mallard is a 2.25-barrel brewery run by Steve Hussey and Alison Ryan. Beer is available for local outlets in and across the county. ‼♦LIVE

Duck 'n' Dive (ABV 3.7%) BITTER
A bitter, pale golden beer, with a dry finish. Brewed with First Gold hops.
Greet Ale (ABV 3.7%) BITTER
Golden Duck (ABV 3.9%) GOLD
Quacker Jack (ABV 4%) BITTER

Feather Light (ABV 4.1%) GOLD
A straw-coloured, lager-style beer with a hoppy taste and aroma.
Duckling (ABV 4.2%) BITTER
A dry-hopped, golden ale. Very bitter; hops dominate in the aroma and aftertaste.
Specduckular (ABV 4.2%) GOLD

Mallinsons

Unit 1, Waterhouse Mill, 65-71 Lockwood Road, Huddersfield, West Yorkshire, HD1 3QU
☎ (01484) 654301 ☎ 07850 446571
⊕ drinkmallinsons.co.uk

☺Mallinsons was originally set up in 2008 on a six-barrel plant by CAMRA members Tara Mallinson and Elaine Yendall. The company moved to new premises in 2012 with a 15-barrel plant and specialises in hop-forward and single hop beers. It has a permanent presence in numerous Huddersfield pubs. ‼♦LIVE

Wappy Nick (ABV 3.8%) BITTER

Malt SIBA

Collings Hanger Farm, 100 Wycombe Road, Prestwood, Buckinghamshire, HP16 0HW
☎ (01494) 865063 ⊕ maltthebrewery.co.uk

⊗ Family-owned brewery, founded in 2012, using a 10-barrel plant. Based on a dairy farm in the heart of the Chiltern Hills, it has sustainability built into its brewing with spent grains going to feed the pigs on the farm and spent hops being composted. The brewery tasting bar stocks bottled beers that are suitable for vegans, alongside local ciders. In-house deliveries are made to trade and direct customers in six surrounding counties. National distribution is through leading distributors and wholesalers. ‼▆♦⌁

Moderation (ABV 3.4%) GOLD
Missenden Pale (ABV 3.6%) PALE
Starry Nights (ABV 4%) BITTER
Summer Daze (ABV 4%) GOLD
Harvest Ale (ABV 4.1%) BITTER
Voyager (ABV 5%) PALE

Malt Coast

Branthill Farm, Wells-next-the-Sea, Norfolk, NR23 1SB ☎ 07881 378900 ⊕ maltcoast.com

Brewing began in 2016. It grows its own barley on the farm. ‼▆

Malton (NEW)

5 Navigation Wharf, Off Yorkersgate, Malton, North Yorkshire, YO17 7AA ☎ 07946 776613
⊕ maltonbrewery.com

Microbrewery on the banks of the Derwent, operating since 2018. Owner Howard Kinder had previously launched Horsetown Beers in 2016 with a donation to racing welfare made for each sale. LIVE

Malvern Hills

15 West Malvern Road, Malvern, Worcestershire, WR14 4ND
☎ (01684) 560165 ⊕ malvernhillsbrewery.co.uk

⊗ Still in its original (1998) home of an old quarrying dynamite store. Established presence in the Three Counties, Birmingham and the Black Country. Seasonals and specials are determined more by ad-hoc requests from publicans, as opposed to a planned timetable.

Notable exceptions are the green-hopped beers in September. Plans for a taphouse on-site are progressing. ‼♦

Beacon Gold (ABV 3.7%) GOLD
Feelgood (ABV 3.8%) BITTER
Bertie's Best (ABV 4.2%) BITTER
Malvern Spring (ABV 4.2%) BITTER
Priessnitz Plzen (ABV 4.3%) SPECIALITY
Straw-coloured, pilsner-style, cask lager having a mix of soft fruit and citrus. Well-balanced, light in colour, with a resinous aromatic finish.
Black Pear (ABV 4.4%) BITTER
Citrus hoppiness is the main constituent of this golden best bitter that has a long, dry aftertaste.

Mammoth (NEW)

Unit DG02-03 & 04, Hackney Bridge, East Bay Lane, Hackney Wick, London, E15 2SJ ☎ 07970 927272
⊕ mammothbeer.com

Mammoth began brewing in 2021 and is located in a canal-side Hackney Bridge development for local enterprises.

Manchester

66 North Western Street, Manchester, M12 6DX
☎ (0161) 273 6167
✉ manchesterbrewingcompany@gmail.com

Commencing production in 2016, this eight-barrel brewery is housed in a railway arch in the Ardwick district of Manchester. It supplies outlets in Greater Manchester, West Yorkshire and further afield. A range of core beers plus seasonals and one-off specials are produced.

Factory Pale Ale (ABV 4%) PALE
Some Might Say Session IPA (ABV 4.4%) PALE
Elephant Juice NE Pale (ABV 4.5%) PALE

Manchester Union

96d North Western Street, Manchester, M12 6JL
⊕ manchesterunionbrewery.com

Manchester Union is a Central European-style, lager brewery co-founded by former Six O'clock brewer Ian Johnson. It uses a decoction technique in the mash and German lager malts. The beers undergo several weeks conditioning in tanks. Beers are unfiltered and unpasteurised and available across Greater Manchester. There is an on-site tap room. ⌁

Manning SIBA

Spindle Street, Congleton, Cheshire, CW12 1QN
☎ (01260) 299964 ⊕ manningbrewers.co.uk

A family-owned and run brewery using only British hops, opened in 2015. It has now joined forces with the established Beartown Brewery (qv), also of Congleton.

Woah Man (ABV 3.8%) PALE
Man Up! (ABV 4%) BITTER
Cave-Man (ABV 4.2%) BITTER

Mantle

Unit 16 Pentood Industrial Estate, Cardigan, SA43 3AG
☎ (01239) 623898 ☎ 07552 609909
⊕ mantlebrewery.com

From start-up in 2013 on a 10-barrel plant, Mantle has become a major player in the West Wales area. Engineer Ian Kimber and his scientist wife Dominique, formerly home brewers, have built a sound reputation for consistent quality. Over 200 outlets are supplied direct with wider distribution via carefully selected wholesalers. **!! ☞ ♦**

Rock Steady (ABV 3.8%) GOLD
MOHO (ABV 4.3%) PALE
Cwrw Teifi (ABV 4.5%) BITTER
Dark Heart (ABV 5.2%) PORTER

Manual

c/o 36-40 Bellfield Street, Dundee, DD1 5HZ
⊕ manualbrewing.co.uk

Launched in 2018, Manual Brewing Co uses spare capacity at 71 Brewing in Dundee.

Many Hands

Dunkeswell Airfield, Dunkeswell, EX14 4LF
⊕ manyhandsbrew.com

Many Hands Brew Co began brewing in 2017, producing small batch bottled beers. Each bottle sold makes a contribution to charity.

Marble SIBA

Unit 7, Boston Court, Salford, M50 2GN
⊕ marblebeers.com

Originally founded at the Marble Arch pub in 1997, Marble Beers moved to a 15-barrel plant in Salford and opened an on-site taproom. Vegetarian beers are available in both its core and speciality ranges. It supplies its own Marble Arch and more than 70 other outlets. **!! ♦ V ◈**

Petite (ABV 2.8%) BITTER
Pint (ABV 3.9%) GOLD
Fresh hop aroma of grapefruit. Clean citrus hop flavour with pale malt base. Dry, bitter aftertaste and lasting hop.
Manchester Bitter (ABV 4.2%) BITTER
Biscuity aroma with floral hops. Balanced bitter hop and malt in taste. Full, fruity palate. Dry, bitter finish.
North South (ABV 4.2%) PALE
Prominent citrus aroma. Bitter citrus hop flavour balanced with moderate sweetness. Bitterness predominates after the initial taste, with drying mouthfeel.
Lagonda IPA (ABV 5%) GOLD
Golden beer with a fruity nose. Powerful citrus and bitter hops backed by pale malt, and a bitter aftertaste.
Uppe Hela Natten (ABV 5.1%) SPECIALITY
Dry stout with prominent roast character throughout and balancing sweetness. Contains coffee.
Cross Collar (ABV 5.2%) PALE
Alf (ABV 5.4%) PALE
Pale (ABV 5.4%) PALE
Bitter orange taste, lasting with dryness. Fruity aroma. Lingering dry bitter.
Stout (ABV 5.7%) STOUT
Rich aroma of coffee and chocolate. Complex, bittersweet, roasted flavour with fruit and caramel. Smooth mouthfeel, with a drying finish.
Earl Grey IPA (ABV 6.8%) SPECIALITY
Sweet citrus aroma. Full-bodied, creamy mouthfeel. Bold bergamot flavour balanced with sweetness and pronounced bitterness. Lasting hoppy taste.
Cubbio Damage (ABV 7.2%) IPA

Market Bosworth

Unit 10, Willow Farm Business Centre, Stoke Golding, Leicestershire, CV13 6EU
☎ (01455) 377855 ⊕ marketbosworthbrewery.co.uk

⊠ The brewery was set up by Jon Skinner in 2016 as a natural progression from his homebrew retail business. Rich Brine joined in partnership in 2017, and the kit was doubled in size to two barrels, to meet demand. Its two main outlets are the Gate Hangs Well, Carlton, and the Horse & Jockey, Congerstone.

Stout (ABV 4.2%) STOUT
Best Bitter (ABV 4.8%) BITTER
Porter (ABV 5%) PORTER
Pale Ale (ABV 5.2%) PALE

Marko Paulo

🏠 Owl & the Pussycat, 106 Northfield Avenue, Northfields, London, W13 9RT
☎ (020) 8810 0880 ⊕ markopaulo.co.uk

A 1.25-barrel brewpub opened in 2016 in a former bookshop by two ex-teachers. The beer travels about 20 feet from mash tun to glass. Cask-conditioned beers are complemented by a wide range of European-style keg beers. Beers from the Ealing Brewery sometimes replace the on-site output. **V**

Marlix (NEW)

Berger Close, Petts Wood, Kent, BR5 1HR
⊕ marlix.co.uk

Longtime friends Mark and Alex built a sizable garden shed to contain the brewery, after brewing beer together for the past 20 years, going commercial in 2020. Beers are available in cask, keg and bottles, with names based on the TV show The Young Ones. The range can be found in local micropubs and clubs.

TPP (The People's Poet) (ABV 3.5%) BITTER

Marlpool

🏠 5 Breach Road, Marlpool, Heanor, Derbyshire, DE75 7NJ
☎ (01773) 711285 ☎ 07963 511855
⊕ marlpoolbrewing.co.uk

Marlpool was founded in 2010 by brothers Andy and Chris McAuley. The two-barrel brewery is situated behind the Marlpool Ale House. The brewery yard doubles up as a beer garden and the majority of the beer is sold through the Ale House and served unfined. The remainder is sold to reputable outlets. **!! ♦ LIVE**

Marston's

Shobnall Road, Burton upon Trent, Staffordshire, DE14 2BW
☎ (01283) 531131 ⊕ marstons.co.uk

☺Brewing in Burton since 1834, the brewery houses the only working Burton Union fermenters, in rooms known as the Cathedral of Brewing. Developed in the 19th century, they are used to cleanse the new style of pale ale yeast. Only Pedigree is fermented in the unions, but the yeast is used in other Marston's beers. A nanobrewery within the visitors centre (DE14) is used for small batch brews. Contract brewing includes Draught Bass brewed for AB Inbev. A joint venture with Carlsberg in 2020 led to the company being renamed Carlsberg Marston's Brewing Company. **!! ☞ ♦ LIVE**

EPA (ABV 3.6%)
61 Deep (ABV 3.8%) GOLD
Light, golden to amber ale with intense tropical fruit and citrus aromas. Sweet tropical start with hints of spice. Hoppy bitterness overcomes the fruit and leaves a pleasant, mouthwatering feel.
Saddle Tank (ABV 3.8%) BITTER

Overwhelming, sulphurous aroma supports a scattering of hops and fruit with an easy-drinking sweetness. The taste develops from the sweet middle to a satisfyingly, hoppy finish.

Pedigree (ABV 4.5%) BITTER
Pale brown to amber with a sweet hoppy aroma and hint of sulphur. Malt with a dash of hop flavours give a satisfying, tasty finish.

Old Empire (ABV 5.7%) IPA
Sulphur dominates the gentle malt aroma. Malty and sweet to start but developing bitterness with fruit and a touch of sweetness. A balanced aftertaste of hops and fruit leads to a lingering bitterness.

Brewed for A-B InBev:
Draught Bass (ABV 4.4%) BITTER
Hints of caramel aroma and taste, lightly hopped for a short, bitter finish.

Martland Mill

Colmart House, Stephens Way, Warrington Road Industrial Estate, Wigan, WN3 6PH
☎ (01942) 665656 ☎ 07944 814040
⊕ martlandmillbrewery.co.uk

☺Originally established in 2014 then reopened in 2019 under new ownership. The six-barrel brewery sits on the outskirts of Wigan town centre and brews a core range of traditional beers on a weekly basis. ♦

Spinner's Gold (ABV 3.8%) GOLD
Lancashire Loom (ABV 4%) GOLD
D Day Dodger (ABV 4.1%) BITTER
Brown, with subtle malty aroma. Malt dominates throughout, with hop notes. Initial sweetness gives way to a bitter, dry finish.

Wobbly Weaver (ABV 4.3%) GOLD
Bomber's Blonde (ABV 4.4%) BLOND
Arctic Convoy (ABV 4.5%) STOUT

MashDown

58 Castlewellan Road, Banbridge, BT32 4JF ☎ 07866 580077 ⊕ mashdownbrewery.com

Formerly brewing took place in collaboration with other breweries, MashDown now has its own nanobrewery.

Mashionistas

45 Rochester Road, Coventry, CV5 6AF ☎ 07960 196204 ⊕ mashionistas.com

Mashionistas was formed in 2018 by Flo, Jon and Simon, who built a one-barrel plant in a garage, with several years of home brewing experience between them. All output is vegan-friendly. Brewing in their spare time, they produce only small batches which gives them the flexibility to experiment using a host of different ingredients. Since its inception, a wide variety of well-received KeyKeg beers have been produced. **V**

Masquerade

c/o 25 Mina Road, St Werburghs, Bristol, BS2 9TA
⊕ masqueradebrewing.co

Tom Hebden and Sam Hipwell of Masquerade Brewing met at university where they laid plans to produce full-on juicy beers, which they started doing in 2017 on a custom-built, one-barrel plant in temporary premises. In 2018 the brewery moved and is now co-located at the Fierce & Noble Brewery (qv) in St Werburgh's.

Matlock Wolds Farm SIBA

South Barn, Cavendish Road, Farm Lane, Matlock, Derbyshire, DE4 3GZ
☎ (01629) 697989 ☎ 07852 263263
⊕ woldsfarm.co.uk

⊠ Since starting in 2014 there has been several expansions up to a five-barrel plant by this family-run brewery, in the converted barn on the owner's 17th century farm. The full range of cask and RAIB ales are vegan/ vegetarian friendly. The Pump It Up micro pub in Belper was acquired in 2019. ♦ **LIVE V**

Simcoe (ABV 3.8%) GOLD
High Tor (ABV 4%) PALE
To the Bitter End (ABV 4.2%) BITTER
Riber Gold (ABV 4.3%) GOLD
100cc (ABV 4.9%) BITTER
Classic Porter (ABV 4.9%) PORTER

Mauldons SIBA

13 Church Field Road, Sudbury, Suffolk, CO10 2YA
☎ (01787) 311055 ⊕ mauldons.co.uk

Mauldons started brewing in Sudbury in 1795, was taken over by Greene King in the 1960s, and reopened by the Sims family in 2000. A new 30-barrel plant and brewery were built. After 19 years they retired and sold to local farming-based company, Heathpatch. It is planned that its barley and hops will be used in production. A new website was launched in 2020 (bottled and draught beer available online). Three pubs are owned, and over 200 outlets supplied. ‼ ⬛ ♦ **LIVE**

Pale Ale (ABV 3.6%) BITTER
Moletrap Bitter (ABV 3.8%) BITTER
Plum and toffee on the nose. A good balance of malt, hops and fruit, leading to an increasingly bitter aftertaste.

Silver Adder (ABV 4.2%) BITTER
Light, fruity aroma, dry hoppiness and citrus fruit with rich honey in the taste, and a long fruity sweet aftertaste. Refreshing and well-balanced.

225 (ABV 4.5%) PALE
Blackberry Porter (ABV 4.8%) SPECIALITY
Suffolk Pride (ABV 4.8%) BITTER
A full-bodied, copper-coloured beer. A bubblegum nose leads to a spicy taste, with mild astringency in the aftertaste.

Black Adder (ABV 5.3%) STOUT
Malty, roasty aroma leads to a well-balanced, full-bodied beer, malty with roast and dark soft fruit overtones.

Maule SIBA

Rothersthorpe Trading Estate, Northampton, NN4 8JH
⊕ maulebrewing.com

Brewing began in 2014 on a self-built plant. Production is mainly unfiltered keg and bottle-conditioned beers, but cask-conditioned ales are occasionally produced for festivals. The beers are available from various local stockists, including its tap in Northampton, as well as featuring on the London craft beer scene. **LIVE**

Maxim SIBA

1 Gadwall Road, Rainton Bridge South, Houghton le Spring, DH4 5NL
☎ (0191) 584 8844 ⊕ maximbrewery.co.uk

⊚Rising from the ashes of Sunderland brewer Vaux, Maxim was set up with a 20-barrel plant in Houghton-le-Spring in 2007. More than 100 outlets are supplied direct and two pubs are owned. ‼ ⬛ ♦

Lambtons (ABV 3.8%) GOLD
Samson (ABV 4%) BITTER
Ward's Best Bitter (ABV 4%) BITTER
Swedish Blonde (ABV 4.2%) BITTER
Double Maxim (ABV 4.7%) BROWN
A roasty, classic brown ale. Hops play their part giving a gentle bitterness to the dominant fruit, which reduces on drinking. A complex beer with an inviting smell of butterscotch.
Raspberry Porter (ABV 5%) SPECIALITY
Maximus (ABV 6%) OLD

Mayflower SIBA

2 Woodford Street, Hindley, WN2 4UR
☎ **(01942) 259071** ☎ **07703 816183**
✉ **enquiries@mayflowerbrewery.com**

☺Originally established in Standish in 2001, the brewery was mothballed before reopening in late 2018, using a five-barrel plant behind the old police station in Hindley, Wigan. As well as an expanding range of core ales, the brewery specialises in bespoke beers for occasions and events, both national and local, and for venues wishing to personalise or brand their bottled and cask ales.

Pie PA (ABV 3.9%) GOLD
Hoppy aromas dominate with hoppy bitter flavours, dry mouthfeel and a dry hop finish.
Douglas Valley (ABV 4%) GOLD
Best Bitter (ABV 4.1%) BITTER
Wigan Bier (ABV 4.2%) GOLD

Maypole

North Laithes Farm, Wellow Road, Eakring, Nottinghamshire, NG22 0AN ☎ **07971 277598**
⊕ **maypolebrewery.co.uk**

☺The brewery opened in 1995 in a converted 18th-century farm building. After changing hands in 2001 it was bought by the former head brewer, Rob Neil, in 2005. ♦

Monterey Hop (ABV 3.7%) BLOND
Celebration (ABV 4%) BITTER
Gate Hopper (ABV 4%) GOLD
Hop Fusion (ABV 4.2%) GOLD
Major Oak (ABV 4.4%) BITTER
Wellow Gold (ABV 4.6%) BLOND

Meantime

Lawrence Trading Estate, Blackwall Lane, East Greenwich, London, SE10 0AR
☎ **(020) 8293 1111**

Head Office: Norman House, 110-114 Norman Road, London, SE10 9EH ⊕ **meantimebrewing.com**

⊠ Founded in 2000, Meantime brews a wide range of continental-style beers. Two pubs are owned. In 2010 the brewery relocated to larger premises in Greenwich. Taken over by SABMiller in 2015 and now owned by Asahi UK. ‼🍺♦LIVE

Meanwood

1 Sandfield View, Leeds, West Yorkshire, LS6 4EU
⊕ **themeanwoodbrewery.com**

☺The Meanwood Brewery was started by brothers Baz and Graeme Phillips in 2017 and focuses on brewing keg and cask beer styles from around the world. In 2021, installation of an eight-barrel brewkit and canning line expanded production. The Terminus Tap Room & Bottle Shop opened in 2018. V⌀

Herald (ABV 3.9%) PALE
As Above, So Below (ABV 4.5%) PALE
Black Goddess (ABV 4.9%) PORTER
Arecibo Message (ABV 5.7%) PALE

Melbourn

All Saints Brewery, All Saints Street, Stamford, Lincolnshire, PE9 2PA
☎ **(01780) 752186**

A famous Stamford brewery that opened in 1825 and closed in 1974. It re-opened in 1994 and is owned by Samuel Smith of Tadcaster (qv). No real ale. ‼

Mellors (NEW)

Harringay, London, N8 0AJ ⊕ **mellorsbrewing.co.uk**

A homebrewer who went commercial during 2021, looking to expand to a 100-litre kit. Small scale cask conditioning is used and sold from bags-in-boxes at the Stroud Green Market once a month, usually the 3rd Sunday.

Melwood SIBA

The Kennels, Knowsley Park, Knowsley, Merseyside, L34 4AQ ☎ **07545 265283** ⊕ **melwoodbeer.co.uk**

☺Melwood began brewing in 2013 using a five-barrel plant in an old dairy. In 2016 the brewery moved to bigger premises in nearby old kennels on the Earl of Derby's Knowsley Estate. In 2019 it rebranded to add a small range of core beers, a series of modern beers, one-off specials and began experimenting with new styles and yeasts. ♦

Lovelight (ABV 3.8%) BLOND
Father Ted (ABV 4.2%) BITTER
High Time (ABV 4.3%) BITTER
Knowsley Blonde (ABV 4.3%) PALE
Moondance (ABV 4.3%) BITTER
Stanley Gold (ABV 4.3%) GOLD

Merakai (NEW)

Unit 12, Squires Farm, Palehouse Common, Framfield, East Sussex, TN22 5RB ⊕ **merakaibrewing.com**

Merakai Brewing was established in 2020. It produces cans and one-litre bottles.

Merchant City

See Glasgow Beer Works

Merlin

3 Spring Bank Farm, Congleton Road, Arclid, Cheshire, CW11 2UD
☎ **(01477) 500893** ☎ **07812 352590**
⊕ **merlinbrewing.co.uk**

☺Merlin started in 2010 using an eight-barrel plant in a farm unit just outside Sandbach. The family firm of three is gently expanding the brewery. The beers are normally supplied to outlets within a 30-mile radius. The brewery is environmentally-friendly, using power from solar panels and a wind turbine, and spent water soaks away naturally through reed beds on the farm. ‼♦LIVE

Merlin's Gold (ABV 3.8%) GOLD
Excalibur (ABV 3.9%) GOLD
Spellbound (ABV 4%) BITTER
Avalon (ABV 4.1%) PALE
The Wizard (ABV 4.2%) GOLD
Castle Black (ABV 4.4%) STOUT

Dark Magic (ABV 4.8%) MILD
Mythic IPA (ABV 5.5%) IPA
Dragonslayer (ABV 5.6%) OLD

Merrimen

See Litchborough Artisan

Mersea Island

Rewsalls Lane, East Mersea, Essex, CO5 8SX ☎ 07970 070399 ⊕ merseabrewery.co.uk

⊠ The brewery was established at Mersea Island Vineyard in 2005. It supplies several local pubs on a guest beer basis as well as beer festivals. It holds its own festival of Essex-produced ales over the four-day Easter weekend. The Cork 'n' Cap off sales and gift shop opened in 2020. ➡LIVE

Mersea Mud (ABV 3.8%) MILD
Yo Boy! (ABV 3.8%) BITTER
Gold (ABV 4.4%) GOLD
Skippers (ABV 4.8%) BITTER
Oyster Stout (ABV 5%) SPECIALITY

Metalhead SIBA

Unit 16e, Helmsman House, Norham Road North, North Shields, Tyne & Wear, NE29 8RZ ☎ 07923 253890 ⊕ metalhead-brewery.co.uk

☺Metalhead Brewery began life in 2019 following a career change and a love of real ale and music. Beers are available in its micropub, the Lounge, Blyth. Modest expansion of both brewery and range are planned. LIVE

Hammer Best Bitter (ABV 3.8%) BITTER
Old Knacker (ABV 3.8%) BITTER
Best Mate (ABV 4.2%) BITTER
Simpley Red (ABV 4.6%) BITTER
Axl Gold (ABV 4.8%) GOLD
Archer (ABV 5.1%) BITTER

Mighty Medicine

Unit 4, Daniel Street, Whitworth, Lancashire, OL12 8BX
☎ (01706) 558980 ⊕ mightymedicine.com

Established in 2016, this brewery is committed to using the finest ingredients to produce an eclectic range of beers. A tap room is attached to the brewery. ➡◆

Stunning Blonde (ABV 3.9%) BLOND
Greedy Boy (ABV 4%) BITTER
Madchester Cream (ABV 4.2%) PALE
Magic Malt (ABV 4.5%) RED

Mighty Oak

14b West Station Yard, Spital Road, Maldon, Essex, CM9 6TW
☎ (01621) 843713 ⊕ mightyoakbrewing.co.uk

⊠ Mighty Oak was formed in 1996 and has expanded considerably following a move to Maldon in 2001. Current capacity is 8,000 brewers barrels per year, following the acquisition of two adjacent buildings and an enlarged plant. Some 450 outlets are supplied. A popular free festive beer tasting day takes place each year in early December. The date is published in October on the company website. ‼➡◆LIVE

Oscar Wilde (ABV 3.7%) MILD
Roasty dark mild with suggestions of forest fruits and dark chocolate. A sweet taste yields to a more bitter finish.

Captain Bob (ABV 3.8%) BITTER
Maldon Gold (ABV 3.8%) GOLD
Pale golden ale with a sharp citrus note moderated by honey and biscuity malt.
Jake The Snake (ABV 4%) PALE
Old Man And The Sea (ABV 4.1%) STOUT
Gorgeous George (ABV 4.2%) BITTER
Kings (ABV 4.2%) GOLD
Cascade IPA (ABV 6.2%) GOLD

Mikkeller

▤ 37-39 Exmouth Market, Clerkenwell, London, EC1R 4QL
☎ (020) 3940 4991 ⊕ mikkellerbrewpublondon.com

Mikkeller of Denmark's second bar in London (sister pub to Mikkeller Shoreditch) in collaboration with Rick Astley. It opened during 2020. Regular new beers appear in the brewpub and in bottle, but a core range of favourites is emerging. Sometimes available at the Shoreditch bar. No real ale.

Mile Tree SIBA

29 Alfric Square, Woodston, Peterborough, Cambridgeshire, PE2 7JP ☎ 07858 930363 ⊕ miletreebrewery.co.uk

⊠ Mile Tree was established in 2012 at the Secret Garden Touring Park in Wisbech, and moved to Peterborough in 2018. Beer is brewed on a five-barrel plant. It serves the local area and beer festivals. ◆LIVE

Meadowgold (ABV 3.8%) GOLD
Mosaica (ABV 4.2%) GOLD
Larksong (ABV 4.5%) BITTER
Wildwood (ABV 4.9%) GOLD
Porter (ABV 5.2%) PORTER
Winter Ale (ABV 6%) OLD

Milestone SIBA

Great North Road, Cromwell, Newark, Nottinghamshire, NG23 6JE
☎ (01636) 822255 ⊕ milestonebrewery.co.uk

☺The brewery was established in 2005. Milestone currently brew on a 12-barrel plant and more than 150 outlets are supplied. ‼➡◆LIVE

Lion's Pride (ABV 3.8%)
Sherwood Pale Ale (ABV 3.9%) PALE
Classic Dark Mild (ABV 4%) MILD
Shine On (ABV 4%) BITTER
Azacca Gold (ABV 4.2%) BLOND
Loxley Ale (ABV 4.2%) GOLD
Black Pearl (ABV 4.3%) STOUT
Cromwell Best (ABV 4.4%) BITTER
Crusader (ABV 4.4%) BLOND
Rich Ruby (ABV 4.5%) RED
Olde English (ABV 4.9%) BITTER
Fletcher's Ale (ABV 5.2%)
Colonial Pale Ale (ABV 5.5%) PALE
Raspberry Wheat Beer (ABV 5.6%) SPECIALITY

Milk Street

See Frome

Mill Valley SIBA

The Brewhouse, 589 Halifax Road, Hightown, West Yorkshire, WF15 8HQ ☎ 07565 229560 ⊕ millvalleybrewery.co.uk

◎Launched in 2016 on a three-barrel plant in Cleckheaton, the brewery relocated to Liversedge in 2019, taking over the former Partners brewery site together with its 12-barrel plant. More than 40 outlets are supplied as well as numerous beer festivals. Two brewery taps are owned, one at both the old and new brewery sites, which hold regular events. ‼♦V✦

Luddite Ale (ABV 3.8%) GOLD
Panther Ale (ABV 4%) GOLD
Yorkshire Bitter (ABV 4%) BITTER
Mill Blonde (ABV 4.2%) BLOND
Yorkshire Rose (ABV 4.2%) PALE
Black Panther (ABV 4.6%) STOUT
XTRA Fudge Stout (ABV 4.6%) SPECIALITY

Millis

See Dartford Wobbler

Mills

Jumpers Lane Yard, Berkeley, Gloucestershire, GL13 9BW ☎ 07848 922558
✉ millsbrewing@gmail.com

Mills was established in Berkeley in 2016 by husband-and-wife team Genevieve and Jonny Mills. Wort is produced in multiple locations, which is then fermented in wooden vessels at its premises in Berkeley using 100% wild yeasts and bacteria from the local surroundings. The Lambic-style beers are mostly available bottle-conditioned. LIVE

Millstone SIBA

Unit 4, Vale Mill, Micklehurst Road, Mossley, Lancashire, OL5 9JL
☎ (01457) 835835 ⊕ millstonebrewery.co.uk

Established in 2003 by Nick Boughton and Jon Hunt, the brewery is located in an 18th century textile mill and uses an eight-barrel plant. More than 30 regular outlets are supplied. ♦

Tiger Rut (ABV 4%) PALE
Light, fruity beer with hop aroma and gentle bitterness.
Stout (ABV 4.5%) STOUT
True Grit (ABV 5%) GOLD

Milltown SIBA

The Brewery, The Old Railway Goods Yard, Scar Lane, Milnsbridge, West Yorkshire, HD3 4PE ☎ 07946 589645 ⊕ milltownbrewing.co.uk

◎Milltown began brewing in 2011 using a four-barrel plant. Two pubs are owned, the Dusty Miller at Longwood, which acts as the official brewery tap, and the Traveller's Rest, Meltham. ‼♦LIVE

Spud's (ABV 3.8%) BITTER
Weaver's Bitter (ABV 3.8%) BITTER
American Pale Ale (ABV 3.9%) PALE
Platinum Blonde (ABV 4%) BLOND
Tigers Tail (ABV 4.1%) GOLD
Black Jack Porter (ABV 4.5%) PORTER

Milton SIBA

Pegasus House, Pembroke Avenue, Waterbeach, Cambridgeshire, CB25 9PY
☎ (01223) 862067 ⊕ miltonbrewery.co.uk

⊠ The brewery has grown steadily since it was founded in 1999, moving to larger premises in the village of Waterbeach in 2012. It now operates three pubs in Cambridge through a sister company. In 2016 a separate brand, Beach Brewery, was created to market unpasteurised and unfiltered keg beers. ‼V

Minotaur (ABV 3.3%) MILD
A dark ruby mild with liquorice and raisin fruit throughout. Light, dry finish.
Dionysus (ABV 3.6%) BITTER
Yellow bitter with good balance of biscuity malt and citrus hop. Some malt and hops linger on long, dry aftertaste.
Justinian (ABV 3.9%) BITTER
Straw-coloured bitter with pink grapefruit hop character and light malt softness. Very dry finish.
Pegasus (ABV 4.1%) BITTER
Malty, amber, medium-bodied bitter with faint hops. Bittersweet aftertaste.
Sparta (ABV 4.3%) BITTER
A yellow/gold bitter with floral hops, kiwi fruit and balancing malt softness which fades to leave a long, dry finish.
Minerva (ABV 4.6%) GOLD
Nero (ABV 5%) STOUT
A complex black beer comprising a blend of milk chocolate, raisins and liquorice. Roast malt and fruit completes the experience.
Cyclops (ABV 5.3%) BITTER
Marcus Aurelius (ABV 7.5%) STOUT
A powerful black brew brimming with raisins and liquorice. Big, balanced finish.

Missing Link

The Old Dairy, Chiddinglye Farm, West Hoathly, West Sussex, RH19 4QS ☎ 07515 336785
⊕ missinglinkbrewing.com

Missing Link was established in 2017 by Jeremy Cook. A state of the art brewery, it welcomes other users, branding itself as a collective of like-minded breweries. Contract brewing and canning are also carried out. No real ale. ▰V✦

Mission: Creep

See Team Toxic

Mitchell's Hop House

354 Meadowhead, Sheffield, South Yorkshire, S8 7UJ
☎ (0114) 274 5587 ⊕ mitchellswine.co.uk

Brewing began in 2016 in a converted space at the back of Mitchell's Wine Merchants. Beers are available from the brewery shop and a growing number of local pubs and beer retailers. All production is now bottled.

Mithril

Aldbrough St John, North Yorkshire, DL11 7TL
☎ (01325) 374817 ☎ 07889 167128
✉ mithril58@btinternet.com

◎Mithril started brewing in 2010 in old stables opposite the brewer's house on a 2.5-barrel plant. Owner/brewer Pete Fenwick, a well-known craft brewer, brews twice a week to supply the local areas of Darlington, Richmond and Teesdale. A new beer is brewed every week. ♦

Dere Street (ABV 3.8%) BITTER
Flower Power (ABV 3.9%) SPECIALITY
A66 (ABV 4%) GOLD

Mobberley SIBA

Unit 2, Woodend Lane, Mobberley, Cheshire, WA16 7LZ

☎ (01565) 873601 ☎ 07879 771209
🌐 mobberleybrewhouse.co.uk

⊠ Mobberley began brewing in 2011. Beers are contract brewed for Burton Road Brewing Company. ♦

HedgeHopper (ABV 3.8%) BLOND
RoadRunner (ABV 3.8%) PALE
Mandalay (ABV 4%) SPECIALITY
Maori (ABV 4%) BITTER
WhirlyBird (ABV 4%) PALE
Red Vienna (ABV 4.2%) RED
Legacy (ABV 4.4%) PALE
1924 (ABV 4.5%) PALE
Solstice (ABV 4.5%) PORTER
Elysium (ABV 4.7%) PALE
Origin (ABV 4.7%) PALE

Modern Day Monks (MDM)

Opus @ Pyramid, Palmyra Square South, Warrington, Cheshire, WA1 1BL ☎ 07837 460923
🌐 mdmbrewery.co.uk

Inspired by the beer they drank travelling the world, Jon and Jim are 'modern day monks' (MDM) creating beers using malt, yeast and hops from around the world.

Modest

10a My Lady's Mile, Holywood, BT18 9EG

Small, independent brewery, notably the first in Northern Ireland to produce beer using the Sabro hop.

Moles

See Wickwar

Molson Coors

Molson Coors (Burton): 137 High Street, Burton upon Trent, Staffordshire, DE14 1JZ
☎ (01283) 511000

Molson Coors (Tadcaster): Tower Brewery, Wetherby Road, Tadcaster, LS24 9JR
🌐 molsoncoorsbrewers.com

Molson Coors is the result of a merger between Molson of Canada and Coors of Colorado, US. Coors established itself in Europe in 2002 by buying part of the former Bass brewing empire, when Interbrew (now A-B InBev) was instructed by the British government to divest itself of some of its interests in Bass. Coors owns several cask ale brands. It brews 110,000 barrels of cask beer a year (under licensing arrangements with other brewers) and also provides a further 50,000 barrels of cask beer for other breweries. In 2011 Molson Coors bought Sharp's brewery in Cornwall (qv) in a bid to increase its stake in the cask beer sector. No cask ale is produced in Burton or Tadcaster.

Mona

Unit 6, Gaerwen Industrial Estate, Gaerwen, Anglesey, LL60 6HR ☎ 07988 698260

Seven enthusiastic locals got together and set up Mona Brewery, which was launched in 2019. The present offering is one cask beer and a range of four keg beers.

Pabo (ABV 3.8%) BITTER
A full-bodied, smooth-tasting, session bitter. Underlying sweet malt flavours complement the big hoppy taste and bitter finish.

Moncada

37 Humber Road, Dollis Hill, London, NW2 6EN
☎ (020) 8438 6666 ☎ 07732 895349
🌐 moncadabrewery.co.uk

⊠ Established in 2011, Moncada was originally based in Kensal Town, but moved in 2018 to more spacious premises including a taproom and a larger brew plant. The range of beers in cask is duplicated in bottles and regular specials in the Blueprint series. ‼🚛♦V◈

Notting Hill Best Bitter (ABV 3.8%) BITTER
A fruity, biscuity, sweet beer with a gentle, lingering bitterness and spicy hops. Aroma is of biscuit and fruit.
Notting Hill Blonde (ABV 4.2%) BLOND
Fruity, earthy hoppy nose. Sweet biscuit flavour with citrus notes of tangerine, tart lemon and some tropical fruit. Lingering bitterness.
Notting Hill Pale (ABV 4.5%) GOLD
Grapefruit and mandarin dominate the bitterish flavour with some biscuit sweetness. Fruitiness slowly fades in the peppery, dry bitterness.
Notting Hill APA (ABV 4.7%) PALE
Sweet fudge and grapefruit overlaid with a developing bitterness that lingers in the spicy finish. Aromas of grapefruit and malt.
Notting Hill Oatmeal Stout (ABV 5%) STOUT
Creamy stout with strong, roasty, dark chocolate nose and flavour. A dark plum fruitiness and some malty, sweetness provides balance.
Notting Hill Ruby Rye (ABV 5.2%) SPECIALITY
Red-brown, smooth beer. Roast, chocolate fudge and caramel complemented by some hoppy fruitiness and tangy damsons. Dry, roasty, sweet finish.

Mondo SIBA

86-92 Stewarts Road, South Lambeth, London, SW8 4UG
☎ (020) 7720 0782 🌐 mondobrewingcompany.com

⊠ Mondo began brewing in 2015. An on-site taproom (open Wednesday-Sunday) showcases its wide range of beer styles. A cask collaboration in 2019 renewed enthusiasm for real ale and another cask collaboration appeared in the M&B chain in 2020, otherwise output is keg and cans. ‼♦◈

Monty's

Unit 1, Castle Works, Hendomen, SY15 6HA
☎ (01686) 668933 🌐 montysbrewery.co.uk

Montgomeryshire's longest operating brewery began in 2009. The brewery owns the Cottage Inn in Montgomery which acts as it's visitor centre, and houses a 250-litre plant producing occasional small runs of experimental beers. ♦LIVE

Old Jailhouse (ABV 3.9%) BITTER
Best Offa (ABV 4%) GOLD
MPA (ABV 4%) PALE
Sunshine (ABV 4.2%) GOLD
Masquerade (ABV 4.6%) GOLD
Mischief (ABV 5%) GOLD

Moody Fox

Hilcote Country Club, Hilcote Lane, Hilcote, Derbyshire, DE55 5HR ☎ 07702 253235
✉ moodyfoxbrewery@gmail.com

Established in 2016, Moody Fox is a microbrewery specialising in traditional ales using the finest hops and barley from around the world. One micropub is owned, the Garrison, Mansfield.

Cub (ABV 3.8%) BITTER
Pale Tale (ABV 5.4%) PALE

Moody Goose

▤ King William IV, 114 London Road, Braintree, Essex, CM77 7PU
☎ (01376) 567755 ☎ 07595 911046
⊕ moodygoosebrewery.co.uk

A three-barrel brewery, brewing approximately 15 times a year. The beers are currently only available in the King William IV, where the brewery is located, and select beer festivals.

moogBREW

Meads End, Ye Meads, Taplow, Berkshire, SL6 0DH
☎ 07941 241954 ⊕ moogbrew.co.uk

⊠ The brewery was set up in 2016 and moved to new premises in 2019. The majority of the production is keg, with bottle-conditioned beer and a small amount of cask also available. The focus of this tiny brewery is serving the local community and distribution is targeted to within a 10-mile radius. ‼ ▰ ◆LIVE ✦

Moon Gazer

Moon Gazer Barn, Harvest Lane, Hindringham, Fakenham, Norfolk, NR21 0PW
☎ (01328) 878495 ⊕ moongazerale.co.uk

⊠ Brewing began in 2012 using a 10-barrel plant. The brewery is owned and run by Rachel and David Holliday. Chalk-filtered water is used from the brewery's own well. ‼◆

Jumper (ABV 3.9%) BITTER
Gentle hop character with supporting sweet malt and bitterness. Caramel swirls in and out as a dry edge develops.

Jigfoot (ABV 4%) GOLD
Orange peel and honey nose. Marmalade intro bolstered by well defined bitterness. Initial sweetness fades into a sharp, astringent bitterness.

Nibbler (ABV 4%) MILD
Roasty, dark fruit nose flows through into the first taste. Increasing malt and caramel. Smooth, grainy mouthfeel. Short, bitter finish.

Bouchart (ABV 4.9%) MILD
Savoury, smoky bacon character throughout. Bittersweet dark chocolate nuances give depth. A smooth and creamy finish with hints of blackcurrant.

White Face (ABV 5%) PALE
Full-bodied with a rich tropical fruit aroma. Oranges the taste, mixing well with a piquant hoppy bitterness.

Moonface

13 Moira Street, Loughborough, LE11 1AU
☎ (01509) 700171 ⊕ moonfacebrewery.co.uk

⊠ Moonface Brewery has been running since 2018, brewing in six-firkin batches. Two beer types are on the bar in the tap at any time. ✦

X No.1 (ABV 3.6%) MILD
Mr B's Anniversary Pale (ABV 4%) PALE
Best Bitter (ABV 4.2%) BITTER
Mid Atlantic Pale (ABV 4.7%) PALE
London Porter (ABV 5.6%) PORTER
XSB (ABV 5.6%) BITTER
Burton Ale (ABV 6%) BITTER

Moonshine

Hill Farm, Shelford Road, Fulbourn, Cambridge, Cambridgeshire, CB21 5EQ ☎ 07906 066794

Office: 28 Radegund Road, Cambridge, CB1 3RS
⊕ moonshinebrewery.co.uk

⊠ Established in 2004, the brewery produces up to 20 barrels a week. Locally-produced ingredients are used, including water from the brewery's own well, and barley grown on the farm where the brewery is based. CAMRA beer festivals are supplied throughout the country, with 30 local outlets supplied direct. ◆LIVE

Trumpington Tipple (ABV 3.6%) BITTER
Cambridge Pale Ale (ABV 3.8%) PALE
Shelford Crier (ABV 3.8%) BITTER
Harvest Moon Mild (ABV 3.9%) MILD
Heavenly Matter (ABV 4.1%) GOLD
Cambridge Best Bitter (ABV 4.2%) BITTER
Nightwatch Porter (ABV 4.5%) PORTER
Black Hole Stout (ABV 5%) STOUT
Chocolate Orange Stout (ABV 6.7%) SPECIALITY

Moonwake (NEW)

6a Tower Street, Leith, Edinburgh, EH6 7BY
☎ (0131) 553 6995 ⊕ moonwakebeer.com

Brewing commenced in 2021 from a site close to the Water of Leith with a range of four keg beers. An accessible mezzanine level taproom is planned. No real ale.

Moor

Days Road, Bristol, BS2 0QS
☎ (0117) 941 4460 ⊕ moorbeer.co.uk

⊠ Starting in 1996, Moor is an established part of the Bristol beer scene. It exports throughout the UK and around the world. Proprietor Justin Hawke was named Guild of British Beer Writers Brewer of the Year 2017. It features a brewery tap and a shop, and there's a Moor London Vaults in Bermondsey (tap room, and facility for ageing beer). Beers are unfined, naturally hazy and vegan-friendly. It's canned beers were the first in the UK to be recognised as real ale by CAMRA. ‼ ▰ ◆LIVE V✦

All-Dayer (ABV 3.5%) PALE
Nano Cask (ABV 3.8%) BITTER
Revival (ABV 3.8%) PALE
Cloudy, orange colour with some peachy aroma, flavours of slightly resinous hops and a gentle bitterness in the short finish.

Lager (ABV 4%) SPECIALITY
Resonance (ABV 4.1%) PALE
Illumination (ABV 4.3%) BITTER
Amoor (ABV 4.5%) PORTER
Roasted malt and coffee aroma, taste adds chocolate and vanilla impressions before a smooth and almost spicy finish.

Claudia (ABV 4.5%) SPECIALITY
Distortion (ABV 4.7%) PALE
Stout (ABV 5%) STOUT
A classic black stout. Smoky, roast malts and dark fruit aroma with hint of vanilla. Prunes and liquorice notes follow into the taste. Pleasant dark chocolate aftertaste.

Pils (ABV 5.2%) SPECIALITY
PMA (ABV 5.3%) PALE
Aroma and flavours are both well-balanced with biscuity malt, hops and tropical fruit before a short, bittersweet ending.

B-Moor (ABV 6%) PORTER
Aromas of roasted malt and fruit, bitter chocolate and rich dark fruit on the palate with a dry, bitter aftertaste.

Hoppiness (ABV 6.5%) IPA
Hop-forward nose with hints of honey. Full-bodied, with
tropical fruit flavours and bitterness which increases into
the finish.
Old Freddy Walker (ABV 7.3%) STRONG
Roasted malt and dark fruit aromas, flavours balance
roasted malt with liquorice treacle and blackberry before
a slightly dry finish.

Moorhouse's SIBA

**The Brewery, Moorhouse Street, Burnley, Lancashire,
BB11 5EN**
☎ (01282) 422864 ⊕ moorhouses.co.uk

Established in 1865 as a soft drinks manufacturer, the
brewery started producing cask-conditioned ale in 1978.
A new brewhouse and visitor centre opened in 2012.
Three pubs are owned. ‼◆

Black Cat (ABV 3.4%) MILD
A dark, mild-style beer with delicate chocolate and
coffee roast flavours and a crisp, bitter finish.
Premier Bitter (ABV 3.7%) BITTER
A clean and satisfying bitter aftertaste rounds off this
well-balanced hoppy, amber session bitter.
White Witch (ABV 4%) GOLD
Delicate citrus aroma. Sweet, fruity taste balanced with
gentle bitterness. Increased bitterness in crisp citrus
finish.
Pride of Pendle (ABV 4.1%) BITTER
Well-balanced, amber best bitter with a fresh, initial
hoppiness and a mellow, malt-driven body.
Scaredy Cat (ABV 4.3%) GOLD
Blond Witch (ABV 4.5%) GOLD
Pronounced sweet taste with gentle pithy bitterness and
touch of citrus fruit. Dry finish. Slight fruity hop aroma.
Pendle Witches Brew (ABV 5.1%) BITTER
Well-balanced, full-bodied, malty beer with a long,
complex finish.

Moot

🍺 c/o Red Lion Inn, Matlock Green, Matlock,
Derbyshire, DE4 3BT
☎ (01629) 584888 ⊕ theredlionmatlock.co.uk

☺Established in 2018, Moot Ales brewery has its beers
available in the Red Lion pub and other local outlets. It
currently has three core brews; a blonde, a best bitter
and an IPA, with plans for more. **LIVE**

MòR SIBA

Old Mill, Kellas, DD5 3PD ☎ 07402 900755
⊕ morbeers.co.uk

Established in 2012 and now trading as MòR
Beers. Dominic Hughes, an experienced brewer, moved
to Scotland from London to take ownership of the
brewery in 2018. Dominic is brewing the same core
range although with slight changes to the recipes and
branding. ‼◆**LIVE**

MòR Tea Vicar? (ABV 3.8%) BITTER
MòR Ish! (ABV 4.2%) BITTER
MòR Please! (ABV 4.5%) GOLD

Mordue

See Blue

Morgan Brewmasters (NEW)

🍺 Spirit Vaults, 53 Church Street, Melbourne,
Derbyshire, DE73 8EJ ☎ 07946 851828
✉ matt@thespiritvaults.pub

Fully refurbished in 2020, this brewery is incorporated
into the Spirit Vaults, Melbourne (formerly the Bluebell
Inn, brewery tap for Shardlow Brewery), and can be
viewed from within the pub. It brews to new recipes plus
the most popular Shardlow beers, updated with a
modern twist. ‼◆

Morland

See Greene King

Morton

**Unit 10, Essington Light Industrial Estate, Essington,
Wolverhampton, Staffordshire, WV11 2BH** ☎ 07988
069647

Office: 96 Brewood Road, Coven, WV9 5EF
⊕ mortonbrewery.co.uk

☺This family-run brewery was established in 2006 on a
three-barrel, purpose-built plant. Beers are supplied
locally, further afield by reciprocal arrangements, to
various beer festivals and a selection is always available
at the brewery's own award-winning micropub, Hail to
the Ale. ‼◆

Essington Bitter (ABV 3.8%) BITTER
Merry Mount (ABV 3.8%) BITTER
Essington Blonde (ABV 4%) PALE
Essington Ale (ABV 4.2%) PALE
Jelly Roll (ABV 4.2%) GOLD
Essington Gold (ABV 4.4%) GOLD
Essington Supreme (ABV 4.6%) BITTER
Scottish Maiden (ABV 4.6%) BITTER
Essington IPA (ABV 4.8%) PALE
Yellow with lots of hop and fruit aromas. A good
mouthful of bitterness with hops and fruit jostling for
taste. Great, lingering bitter finish.

Morton Collins

🍺 Star, Standbridge Lane, Sandal, Wakefield, West
Yorkshire, WF2 7DY
☎ (01226) 728746 ☎ 07812 111960

Office: 49 Willow Garth, Durkar, Wakefield, WF4 3BX
✉ ged.morton@aol.com

☺Set up in 2016 by Ged Morton and Sam Collins using a
100-litre plant in Ged's garage. The brewery produces to
demand but can brew every day if required. It took over
the lease of the Star, Sandal, in 2016. Several of the
beers are named after the nearby Nature Reserve at
Wintersett. The brewery kit was upgraded to 200 litres
per brew in 2017.

Morwell

Morwellham Quay, Morwellham, Devon, PL19 8JL
☎ (01822) 832766 ⊕ morwellham.org

Established in 2017 at Victorian tourist attraction,
Morwellham Quay, near Tavistock, by brewer George
Lister. Using a 100-litre plant, three bottle-conditioned
beers are brewed, which are available in the on-site
shop and café, the Ship Inn, and a growing number of
local outlets. 🍺**LIVE**

Motley Hog (NEW)

🍺 The Tap House, 1 Millpond Street, Ross on Wye,
HR9 2AP ☎ 07510 156708
✉ motleyhogbrewery@gmail.com

Gaining HMRC registration early in 2021, Motley Hog is a
300-litre brewery based at The Tap House, Ross on Wye.
The aim is to bring small scale, commercial brewing back

to the town for the first time since 1956, with two core ales, and various specials during the year.

Motte & Bailey

🍺 Blue Bell Inn, 10 High Street, Annan, DG12 6AG

⊗ Brewing began in 2018 in the cellar of the Blue Bell Inn, Annan, using equipment from Andrews Ales. Brewing capacity is one barrel. The range varies and is only available at the pub. ☕♦

Moulin

🍺 2 Baledmund Road, Moulin, Pitlochry, PH16 5EL
☎ (01796) 472196

Office: Moulin Hotel, 11-13 Kirkmicheal Road, Moulin, Pitlochry, PH16 5EH ⊕ moulinhotel.co.uk

☺The brewery opened in 1995 to celebrate the Moulin Hotel's 300th anniversary. Two pubs are owned and four outlets are supplied. ‼LIVE

Mount St Bernard SIBA

Oaks Road, Coalville, Leicestershire, LE67 5UL
☎ (01530) 832298 ⊕ mountsaintbernard.org/tynt-meadow

This Cistercian Abbey has been brewing its Trappist beer since 2017, which is the first such beer as there are no historical records of any other previous brewing. It is available only as a 6.7% bottle-conditioned brew. The beer is widely available in Great Britain (website for details). ‼☕LIVE

Mountain Hare

🍺 Mountain Hare Inn, Brynna Road, Brynnau Gwynion, CF35 6PG
☎ (01656) 860453 ⊕ mountainhare.co.uk

☺Paul Jones, licensee of the Mountain Hare, finally realised his ambition of installing a brewery in his family-owned pub. A 1.5-barrel, custom-built brewing plant was installed in the pub, and the beer first went on sale in 2013. Paul plans to increase to a six-barrel plant to keep up with demand. Finings are no longer used so the beers have a slight natural haze and are suitable for vegans. Beer is only available in the pub. V

Mourne Mountains SIBA

Milltown East Industrial Estate, Upper Dromore Road, Warrenpoint, BT34 3PN
☎ (028) 4175 2299
⊕ mournemountainsbrewery.com

Brewing since 2015 with an extensive and varying range of seasonal, special and one-off brews produced throughout the year – some may appear in cask format. Isinglass finings are used in all cask products, except stouts, and so they are not suitable for vegans. Keg, can and bottled beers (not bottle-conditioned) are suitable for vegans. ♦V

Mourne Gold (ABV 4%) GOLD

Mouselow Farm

3 Mouselow Farm, Dinting, Glossop, Derbyshire, SK13 7QQ ☎ 07920 048252
✉ glossopowl@btinternet.com

Mouselow Farm began brewing in 2013 using a 2.5-barrel plant housed in a converted barn. Brewing is on a part-time basis. In recent times the products brewed have evolved, with more emphasis now on brewing

darker and traditional beers, rather than extremely hoppy beers. Local free houses, clubs and beer festivals are supplied. ♦

Mouse-low Mild (ABV 3.4%) MILD
Orpingtons Buff (ABV 3.9%) GOLD

Mr Bees

Unit D, Searsons Farm, Cordys Lane, Trimley, Suffolk, IP11 0UD ☎ 07503 773630 ⊕ mrbeesbrewery.co.uk

Mr Bees is based on the beautiful Suffolk Coast. All beers contain honey direct from the brewery's own beehives. All malted barley used comes from Suffolk and only English hops are used. Around 30 local outlets are supplied.

Best Bee-R (ABV 4%) BITTER
Beelightful (ABV 4.3%) BITTER
Black Bee (ABV 4.5%) STOUT

Mr Grundy's

See Black Hole

Mr Majolica

Units 7a & 15, Thurrock Enterprise Centre, Maidstone Road, Grays, Essex, RM17 6NF ☎ 07834 539761
⊕ mrmajolica.co.uk

⊗ A family-run microbrewery situated in Grays town centre, Mr Majolica began brewing in 2014 on a 2.5-barrel plant. Brewing is currently suspended.

Mr Winter's

8 Keelan Close, Norwich, NR6 6QZ
☎ (01603) 787820 ⊕ mrwintersbeers.co.uk

⊗ Winter's was established in 2001 by David Winter, who had previous award-winning success as a brewer for both Woodforde's and Chalk Hill breweries. Winter's ales has won many awards, with David now passing his brewing knowledge to his son, Mark, an award-winning brewer in his own right. The brewery rebranded as Mr Winter's in 2020; operating at 5-15 barrels. Some existing beers have been discontinued or renamed, and new brews commenced. ♦LIVE

Fusioneer (ABV 3.6%) MILD
Roast and dried fruit in both aroma and taste. Caramel, hazelnut and arrowroot add to a complex mix of flavours.
Twin Parallel (ABV 3.8%) PALE
Evolution APA (ABV 4%) PALE
Clementine on the nose is followed by lemon and grapefruit in the body. Hoppy bitterness develops in a full-bodied finish.
Quantum Gold (ABV 4.1%) GOLD
Just a hint of hops in the aroma. The initial taste combines a dry bitterness with a fruity, apple buttress. The finish slowly subsides into a long, dry bitterness.
Tranquility (ABV 4.2%) BITTER
Sulphurous hoppy nose. Balanced hoppiness throughout with cereal and bitter orange providing contrast. Short ending with a bitter signature.
Rorschach (ABV 4.5%) STOUT
A dark brown stout that has a smooth mouthfeel with a grainy edge. Roast dominates throughout but is balanced by a mix of malt, a bittersweet fruitiness and an increasingly nutty finish.
Vanilla Latte (ABV 4.6%) STOUT
Full on mix of coffee, vanilla and lactose with a smooth malty base. Continues to a long coffee creme ending.
Twisted Ladder (ABV 5%) PALE
Citrus Kiss IPA (ABV 6%) IPA

Strong citrus base with hop and malt in the background. Lemon and grapefruit continue as a bittersweet background provides depth.

Muckle SIBA

3 Bellister Close, Park Village, Haltwhistle, Northumberland, NE49 0HA ☎ 07711 980086 ⊕ mucklebrewing.co.uk

Established in 2016, Muckle Brewing is a tiny brewery in rural Northumberland, close to Hadrian's Wall. Beers are influenced by the local landscape.

Whin Sill Blonde (ABV 3.5%) BITTER
Tickle (ABV 4%) GOLD
Chuckle (ABV 4.2%) GOLD
Muckle Moss Stout (ABV 4.3%) STOUT
Buster (ABV 4.5%) BITTER
Kings Crag (ABV 5.4%)

Muirhouse

Unit 1, Enterprise Court, Manners Avenue, Manners Industrial Estate, Ilkeston, Derbyshire, DE7 8EW ☎ 07916 590525 ⊕ muirhousebrewery.co.uk

Muirhouse was established in 2009 in a domestic garage in Long Eaton. It expanded in 2011 to its present location in Ilkeston and the plant was upgraded in 2016 to 7.5 barrels. ‼◆

Shopping for Hops (ABV 3.9%) PALE
Summit Hoppy (ABV 4%) PALE
Blueberry Porter (ABV 4.1%) PORTER
Magnum Mild (ABV 4.5%) MILD
Pirate's Gold (ABV 4.5%) GOLD
Hat Trick IPA (ABV 5.2%) PALE

Mumbles SIBA

Unit 14, Worcester Court, Swansea Enterprise Park, Swansea, SA7 9FD ☎ (01792) 792612 ☎ 07757 109938 ⊕ mumblesbrewery.co.uk

⊗ Mumbles Brewery was established in 2011 and began brewing in 2013. In 2015, the brewery moved to a new permanent location, with a 10-barrel plant. Director/ brewer Rob Turner supplies numerous pubs in South Wales and the Bristol area. ⬛◆V

Hop Kick (ABV 4%) PALE
Mile (ABV 4%) PALE
Malt Bitter (ABV 4.1%) BITTER
Murmelt (ABV 4.2%) SPECIALITY
Gold (ABV 4.3%) PALE
Beyond The Pale (ABV 4.4%) SPECIALITY
Oystermouth Stout (ABV 4.4%) STOUT
Lifesaver Strong Bitter (ABV 4.9%) BITTER
India Pale Ale (ABV 5.3%) PALE
Albina New World Pale (ABV 5.7%) IPA
Chocolate Vanilla Porter (ABV 6.2%) PORTER

Munson's

⬛ Chequers, The Green Gazeley, Newmarket, Suffolk, CB8 8RF
☎ (01638) 551511 ⊕ munsons.co.uk

Microbrewery at the Chequers in Gazeley, specialising in small-batch hoppy IPAs and Belgian-style beers.

Musket SIBA

Unit 7, Loddington Farm, Loddington Lane, Linton, Kent, ME17 4AG

☎ (01622) 749931 ☎ 07967 127278
⊕ musketbrewery.co.uk

Launched in 2013 with a five-barrel plant, this family-owned brewery is based at Loddington Farm, Linton, in the heart of the Kent countryside. Expanding to a 15-barrel plant with on-site brewery tap, Musket Brewery now supplies more than 300 pubs, micropubs and clubs throughout Kent and Medway. ◆◆

Trigger (ABV 3.6%) BLOND
Fife & Drum (ABV 3.8%) BLOND
Matchlock (ABV 3.8%) MILD
Ball Puller (ABV 4%) BITTER
Flintlock (ABV 4.2%) BITTER
Muzzleloader (ABV 4.5%) SPECIALITY

Muswell Hillbilly

24-26 Avenue Mews, Muswell Hill, London, N10 3NP ☎ 07919 567164 ⊕ muswellhillbillybrewers.co.uk

⊗ Originally homebrewers, premises were acquired in Muswell Hill in 2017. Beers are brewed in small batches using N10 grown hops and named after the local area. Following the successful launch of the taproom in 2018 the brewery moved into a nearby unit in 2020, using the 500-litre brew kit formerly used by Hale, now Exale. ‼⬛V◆

Tetherdown Wheat Saison (ABV 5.1%) SPECIALITY
IPA (ABV 5.5%) IPA

Mutineers

London Lane, Bromley, Kent, BR1 4HE ⊕ mutineers.beer

Established in 2018, Mutineers brews in small batches using a 100-litre brew kit. Beers can be found locally and at beer festivals in cask and bottles.

Filibuster (ABV 3.4%) BITTER
Redacted (ABV 3.8%) BROWN
You Don't Know Jack (ABV 3.9%) PALE

Myrddins

Church Street, Barmouth, LL42 1EH ☎ (01341) 388060 ✉ myrddins@talktalk.net

Established in 2016 within a café bar in the centre of Barmouth, the brewery relocated a short distance away in 2018.

Nailmaker

Unit 9, Darton Business Park, Barnsley Road, Darton, South Yorkshire, S75 5NH ☎ (01226) 380893 ☎ 07973 824790 ⊕ nailmakerbrewing.co

⊙Nailmaker Brewery is located in an old carpet mill by the river Dearne, using an eight-barrel plant. Nailmaking was one of the largest occupations in the local area in the early 19th century. The extensive list of draught cask ales are supplemented by bottles, cans, pouches and beer in a box. In addition to the on-site tap, the brewery has a taphouse in nearby Darton (Anvil Arms) and two further taphouses in nearby Mapplewell (Talbot Inn and Wentworth Arms). New in 2021 will be brewery (and distillery) tours and other events in the visitor centre. ‼⬛◆◆

Yorkshire Bitter (ABV 3.6%) BITTER
Wapentake (ABV 3.8%) GOLD
Auckland (ABV 4%) BITTER
Cascade (ABV 4%) PALE
Chinook (ABV 4%) PALE

Jester Pale Ale (ABV 4%) PALE
Mango Magic Pale Ale (ABV 4%) PALE
Mosaic (ABV 4%) PALE
Paleton Pale Ale (ABV 4%) PALE
Citra Grapefruit Pale Ale (ABV 4.1%) PALE
Citra Pale Ale (ABV 4.1%) PALE
Anvil Porter (ABV 4.4%) PORTER
Plum Porter (ABV 4.4%) PORTER
Wentworth (ABV 4.8%) BITTER
Clout Stout (ABV 5%) STOUT
Chocolate Safari Stout (ABV 5.5%) STOUT
Triple Chocolate Stout (ABV 5.5%) STOUT
Eisenbrau Wheat Beer (ABV 5.8%) SPECIALITY
Imperial Cognac Barrel-Aged Stout (ABV 8.8%) STOUT
Imperial Stout (ABV 8.8%) STOUT

Nant (NEW)

Y Felin Pentrefoelas, Betws-y-Coed, LL24 0HU

Cwrw Nant began brewing in 2021 at a 16th century mill that was last operational in 1984. The brew plant was acquired from the former Bragdy'r Nant.

NauticAles

Sowell Street, St Peters, Broadstairs, Kent, CT10 2AT ☎ 07552 600919

Office: 347 Margate Road, Ramsgate, CT12 6SG ✉ nauticales@outlook.com

⊗ Beers are only available at the brewery's micropub in Ramsgate, and at local beer festivals.

Maiden Voyage (ABV 4.4%) BITTER

Navigation SIBA

🏠 **Trent Navigation Inn, 17 Meadow Lane, Nottingham, NG2 3HS** ☎ (0115) 986 9877 ⊕ navigationbrewery.com

☺ Located in Nottingham, just a stone's throw from the iconic Trent bridge, the brewery combines historic Victorian premises, cutting edge technology and a team of brewing experts. ‼🍺

Patriot (ABV 3.8%) BITTER
Tawny-coloured, malty bitter.
New Dawn Pale (ABV 3.9%) PALE
Golden-coloured ale with initial fruit and hops, and a bitter finish.
Eclipse (ABV 4.1%) STOUT
Dark roast stout aroma and aftertaste with bitterness and some sweetness.
Rebel (ABV 4.2%) GOLD
Saviour (ABV 5.5%) PALE
Golden in colour with assertive hop aroma and citrus fruit taste throughout with a balanced bitterness.

Naylor's SIBA

Midland Mills, Station Road, Cross Hills, North Yorkshire, BD20 7DT ☎ (01535) 637451 ⊕ naylorsbrewery.com

☺ The Naylor brothers started brewing 2005 at the Old White Bear, Cross Hills. The brewery relocated to Midland Mills in 2006, and moved to a larger unit on the same site in 2012. 100 outlets are supplied regularly and about 1,200 on an occasional basis. The on-site bar is open on Friday, Saturday, and Sunday afternoons to early evenings. Increased capacity for customers was created in 2019. Also operated is the Brewhouse in Yeadon. Brewing is currently suspended. ‼🍺♦⬧

Neath

Endeavour Close, Port Talbot, SA12 7PT ☎ 07772 468436 ⊕ neathales.co.uk

Established in 2009, the brewery produces a range of single hop beers. Special beers and one-off monthly brews are also available with some beers being released under the Black Falls brand name. ♦LIVE

Welsh Amber Ale (ABV 4.5%) BITTER
Dewi Sant (ABV 4.8%) PALE

Neatishead

See Pells & Co

Neckstamper SIBA

Unit 3, Cromwell Industrial Estate, Staffa Road, Leyton, London, E10 7QZ
☎ (020) 7018 1760 ☎ 07968 150075
⊕ neckstamper.com

Neckstamper began brewing in 2016 using a 10-barrel plant. No real ale. Beers are available in keg and cans at the taproom, and locally. ⬧

Neepsend

Unit 13, 92 Burton Road, Sheffield, South Yorkshire, S3 8DA
☎ (0114) 276 3406 ⊕ neepsendbrewco.com

☺ Established in 2015 by James Birkett and Gavin Martin, after taking over Little Ale Cart Brewery, and moving to new premises in Sheffield's Valley of Beer. A 10-barrel plant is used, supplying beers locally, including to the company's own pubs, Sheaf View, the Blake Hotel and the Wellington. Despite only having one core beer, the brewery produces an ever-changing range of hop-forward seasonal ales. There is an on-site taproom that opens occasionally. ♦⬧

Blonde (ABV 4%) BITTER

Nelson SIBA

Unit 2, Building 64, The Historic Dockyard, Chatham, Kent, ME4 4TE
☎ (01634) 832828 ⊕ nelsonbrewery.co.uk

☺ Nelson have been housed in the Historic Dockyard at Chatham since 1995. With over 330 outlets supplied it has recently teamed with a national courier to enable its ales to be sent further afield. Also the home to the Gemstone Ales range, it's beers are supplied to it's own pub The Fisherman's Arms, Maidstone, as well as in the free trade. All ales can be supplied in RAIB, cans, kegs and polypins as well as cask. ‼🍺♦LIVE⬧

Sirrius Session Pale (ABV 3.7%) BLOND
Admiral IPA (ABV 4%) BITTER
Midshipman Dark Mild (ABV 4%) MILD
Trafalgar Bitter (ABV 4.1%) BITTER
Buccaneer Pale Ale (ABV 4.2%) PALE
Powder Monkey (ABV 4.3%) BITTER
Friggin' in the Riggin' (ABV 4.5%) BITTER
Pursers Pussy Porter (ABV 4.8%) PORTER
Nelsons Blood (ABV 6%) BITTER

Nene Valley (NVB)

Oundle Wharf, Station Road, Oundle, Northamptonshire, PE8 4DE
☎ (01832) 272776 ⊕ nenevalleybrewery.com

⊗ Nene Valley Brewery (NVB) was established in 2011. A bespoke 15-barrel plant was installed in former Water Board premises in 2012. Further expansion in 2016 has doubled the floorspace. A brewery tap, Tap & Kitchen, opened on the same site in 2014. ‼️🍺◆LIVE V

Simple Pleasures (ABV 3.6%) GOLD
A light, clean and refreshing beer with a pleasing citrus hop aroma and flavour.
Blonde Session Ale (ABV 3.8%) GOLD
Manhattan Project (ABV 4%) BITTER
Bitter (ABV 4.1%) BITTER
Floral hop and malt aroma introduces a full, clean, biscuit malt taste, balanced by bitterness and some fruit, ending with a long malt and bitter finish.
Release the Chimps (ABV 4.4%) PALE
Egyptian Cream (ABV 4.5%) STOUT
Big Bang Theory (ABV 5.3%) PALE
Well-balanced pale ale with a huge hop aroma giving way to malty sweetness and a gentle bitter finish.
Bible Black (ABV 6.5%) PORTER
An inviting aroma of malt and fruit leads to a rich-tasting beer. Blackberry dominates but is balanced by malt, hops and some bitterness. The lingering finish is bittersweet, with fruit assertive.

Neolithic

Bradwell on Sea, Essex ⊕ neolithicbrew.co.uk

Nanobrewery established in 2019 using a one-barrel plant producing mainly bottled beers.

Neon Raptor

Unit 14, Avenue A, Sneinton Market, Nottingham, NG1 1DT ☎ 07367 358661
⊕ neonraptorbrewingco.com

Established in 2016 Neon Raptor is a small independent brewery that utilised spare capacity at neighbouring breweries. Production commenced in 2018 in a brand new 10-barrel plant in the Sneinton Market area of Nottingham, which also has a licensed taproom. All beers are unfiltered, unfined and unpasteurised. ◆

Neptune SIBA

Unit 1, Sefton Lane Industrial Estate, Maghull, Merseyside, L31 8BX
☎ (0151) 222 3908 ⊕ neptunebrewery.com

☺Neptune began brewing in 2015 using a six-barrel plant. Beers are unfined and unfiltered. In keeping with the brewery name the majority of beers are named on a water theme deriving from fish, the sea and mythological creatures. The brewery tap sits alongside the brewery and only opens Friday evening and Saturday. V◆

Ezili (ABV 4%) PALE
Mosaic (ABV 4.5%) PALE
Wooden Ships (ABV 4.7%) PALE
Abyss (ABV 5%) STOUT
Rich, roasted fruity aroma, sweet fruity oatmeal stout, with dry roast finish.

Nessie

Westoaks, Fort William Road, Fort Augustus, PH32 4BH

Set up in 2017 Nessie Brew is a nanobrewery that markets a range of bottled beers to the tourist trade around Fort Augustus.

Nethergate SIBA

The Brewery, Rodbridge Corner, Suffolk, CO10 9HJ
☎ (01787) 377087 ⊕ nethergate.co.uk

⊗ Nethergate was formed in 1986 by Dick Burge and Ian Hornsey in Clare, Suffolk, and was one of the original UK microbreweries. Dick Burge remains the Chairman but it is now owned by a group of beer lovers. The brewery moved to its current site at Rodbridge Corner, Long Melford, in 2017. It produces both traditional recipes and more modern beers and has recently added craft lager and low alcohol beer to its range. The establishment of a borehole means that all the water comes directly from the chalk bed. In 2021 a still was added and local craft gins are now produced. ‼️🍺◆V◆

Melford Mild (ABV 3.7%) MILD
Venture (ABV 3.7%) GOLD
Umbel Ale (ABV 3.8%) SPECIALITY
Pleasant, easy-drinking bitter, infused with coriander, which dominates.
Suffolk County Best Bitter (ABV 4%) BITTER
Dark bitter with roast grain tones off-setting biscuity malt and powerful hoppy, bitter notes.
Stour Valley Gold (ABV 4.2%) GOLD
Old Growler (ABV 5%) PORTER
Well-balanced porter in which roast grain is complemented by fruit.
Umbel Magna (ABV 5%) SPECIALITY
Old Growler flavoured with coriander. The spice is less dominant than in Umbel Ale, with some of the weight and body of the beer coming through.

New Bristol

20a Wilson Street, Bristol, BS2 9HH ☎ 07837 976871
⊕ newbristolbrewery.co.uk

⊗ Having started out in 2013 with his brother Tom, Noel James now brews on a 15-barrel plant with wife Maria and assistants. The premises house the Brewery Tap, and the Bristol Brewery School. Year-round beers are supplemented by regularly released brew series based on common, but varying themes. All beers are unfined and unfiltered with some oak barrel-aged. ‼️🍺◆LIVE V◆

Cinder Toffee Stout (ABV 4%) SPECIALITY
Caramelised honey and roasted malt aromas, sweet flavours of honeycomb and chocolate, some hop bitterness in the slightly dry finish.
Wonderland IPA (ABV 4.1%) PALE
Tropical fruit aroma and juicy fruit hop burst of pineapple and mango flavours with some bitterness in the short finish.
Joy of Sesh (ABV 4.2%) BITTER
Powerfully-hopped, naturally-hazy, unfined beer with citrus and tropical fruits on the palate and a long bitter finish.
Super Deluxe Stout (ABV 7%) SPECIALITY
Banana and vanilla aromas. The taste and mouthfeel is like vanilla ice cream, but this sweetness contrasts with an assertive bitterness.

New Buildings SIBA

Unit 3, Southways Industrial Estate, Coventry Road, Hinckley, Leicestershire, LE10 0NJ ☎ 07795 954392

Office: 24 Leicester Road, Hinckley, Leicestershire, LE10 1LS ⊕ newbuildingsbrewery.com

☺New Buildings Brewery (formerly Elliswood) brews a range of six core beers using a 5.5-barrel plant. Beers are available through swaps, particularly in Nottinghamshire and Derbyshire, and sometimes at local pubs.

Lighthouse Pale Ale (ABV 3.9%) PALE
Windmill Best Bitter (ABV 4.1%) BITTER
Farmhouse (ABV 4.2%) GOLD
Courthouse Porter (ABV 4.5%) PORTER
Cruck House (ABV 4.5%) RED
Manor House (ABV 4.5%) RED

New Devon

Froginwell Vineyard and Cider Barn, Woodbury Salterton, Exeter, EX5 1EP
☎ **(01395) 239900** ☎ **07976 981334**
⊕ **newdevonbrewing.co.uk**

A collective of brewers and cider makers who have been inspired by the craft beer movement. Initially producing one beer, New Devon Ale, but others will make an appearance during the year. ♦

New Devon Ale (ABV 4.5%) PALE

New Flying Monk

See Flying Monk

New Invention (NEW)

Unit 2, Pinfold Industrial Estate, Walsall, WS3 3JS
⊕ **newinventionbrewery.co.uk**

Opened in 2020, the brewery produces a wide range of beer styles, mainly in keg and can for its own taproom, and distribution into the local free trade. ♦

New Lion SIBA

Unit 6E, Webbers Way, Shinners Bridge, Dartington, Devon, TQ9 6JY
☎ **(01803) 226277** ⊕ **newlionbrewery.co.uk**

⊠ Community-owned brewery, established in 2013 and named after the Lion Brewery (renowned for Totnes Stout but closed in the 1920s). It is a modern, five-barrel brewhouse, producing a range of core ales, seasonals and dozens of one-off white label beers annually, many in collaboration with local producers and businesses. It runs a popular membership scheme and taproom/bottle shop, which also acts as a live venue. ☛♦LIVE V♦

Pandit IPA (ABV 4.9%) PALE
In the style of an American IPA. Slightly sweet with a fruity hop taste.

New River SIBA

Unit 47, Hoddesdon Industrial Centre, Pindar Road, Hoddesdon, Hertfordshire, EN11 0FF
☎ **(01992) 446200** ⊕ **newriverbrewery.co.uk**

⊠ New River commenced brewing in 2015 on a new 10-barrel plant. ♦

London Tap (ABV 3.8%) PALE
Twin Spring (ABV 4%) GOLD
Riverbed Red (ABV 4.2%) BITTER
Blind Poet (ABV 4.5%) PORTER
Five Inch Drop (ABV 4.6%) PALE
Isle Of Rye Pale Ale (ABV 5.2%) PALE

New Wharf SIBA

Hyde Farm, Marlow Road, Maidenhead, Berkshire, SL6 6PQ
☎ **(01628) 634535** ⊕ **newwharfbrewing.co.uk**

A 20-barrel brewery which was set up in 2017. After a pause in 2019/20, it restarted brewing in 2021 with an updated range, and a licence to sell on-site.

Newark

77 William Street, Newark, Nottinghamshire, NG24 1QU ☎ **07804 609917** ⊕ **newarkbrewery.co.uk**

Established in 2012 on the site of a former maltings, Newark Brewery uses an eight-barrel plant.

Best (ABV 3.8%) BITTER
NPA (Newark Pale Ale) (ABV 3.8%) PALE
BLH4 (ABV 4%) PALE
Norwegian Blue (ABV 4%) GOLD
Pure Gold (ABV 4.5%) GOLD
Summer Gold (ABV 4.5%) GOLD
Winter Gold (ABV 4.5%) BITTER
Phoenix (ABV 4.8%) BITTER
5.5 (ABV 5.5%) BITTER

Newbarns

13 Jane Street, Leith, EH6 5HE
⊕ **newbarnsbrewery.com**

The four founders moved north from London having worked at kernel and Siren breweries in the past decade, and opened Newbarns in 2020. No real ale. ☛

Newbridge

Unit 3 Tudor House, Moseley Road, Bilston, West Midlands, WV14 6JD ☎ **07970 456052**
⊕ **newbridgebrewery.co.uk**

First established in 2014, the five-barrel plant incorporates six original Grundy cellar tanks. Occasional specials are brewed to complement the regular beers. Bottle-conditioned beers are produced. LIVE

Little Fox (ABV 4.2%) BITTER
Solaris (ABV 4.5%) BITTER
Indian Empire (ABV 5.1%) BITTER

Newby Wyke SIBA

Unit 24, Limesquare Business Park, Alma Park Road, Grantham, Lincolnshire, NG31 9SN
☎ **(01476) 565682** ⊕ **newbywyke.co.uk**

⊠ The brewery is named after a Hull trawler skippered by brewer Rob March's grandfather. It started life in 1998 as a 2.5-barrel plant in a converted garage then moved to premises behind the Willoughby Arms, Little Bytham. In 2009 it moved back to Grantham. ‼♦

Banquo (ABV 3.8%) BLOND
Summer Session Bitter (ABV 3.8%) BITTER
Orsino (ABV 4%) BLOND
Comet (ABV 4.1%) BITTER
Kingston Topaz (ABV 4.2%) GOLD
Black Beerd (ABV 4.3%) STOUT
Bear Island (ABV 4.6%) BLOND
White Squall (ABV 4.8%) BLOND
Blonde-hued with a hoppy aroma. Generous amounts of hop are well-supported by a solid malty undercurrent. An increasingly bittersweet tang makes itself known towards the finish.
White Sea (ABV 5.2%) BITTER
Chesapeake (ABV 5.5%) BITTER

Newcastle

Arch 2, Stepney Bank, Ouseburn, Newcastle upon Tyne, NE1 2NP ☎ **07446 011941**
⊕ **newcastlebrewingltd.co.uk**

⊠ Mike and Leo Bell initially founded the brewery in the Quayside Development Centre in Ouseburn before moving to new premises under Byker Bridge. ‼☛LIVE

Newquay Steam (NEW)

59, Fore Street, Newquay, TR7 1HA

Newquay Steam Brewery commenced in 2020. Three beers, one cider, a rum and gin are currently produced under the name.

Newtown

25 Victoria Street, Gosport, Hampshire, PO12 4TX
☎ **(023) 9250 4294 ⊕ newtownbrewery.co.uk**

Brewing commenced in 2016 in this nanobrewery with just a half-barrel plant. Award-winning, full mash beers are produced on demand for local pubs and beer festivals.

Newtown Park (NEW)

Unit 9, Wadehurst Industrial Park, Bristol, BS2 0JE
⊕ **newtownparkbrewing.co**

Established by a small group of friends in 2020, it produces a range of beers that reflect a diversity of taste and flavours with five canned beers being available at any one time. 🍴◆

Nightjar

2 Richmond House, Caldene Business Park, Mytholmroyd, West Yorkshire, HX7 5QL ☎ 07412 008221 ⊕ nightjarbrew.co.uk

☺Nightjar Brew Co was initially established in 2011 and rebranded in 2018. The 10-barrel brewery is located in an industrial building in Mytholmroyd supplying over 100 free trade outlets across Northern England. The brewery produces more than 20 new beers annually, many of which are canned. Nightjar beers are always available in the two brewery taps; Nightjar, Hebden Bridge and The Exchange Craft Beer House, Bradford. ◆V

School Night (ABV 3.7%) PALE
Done N Dusted (ABV 3.8%) PALE
At One With Citra (ABV 3.9%) PALE
Chosen (ABV 3.9%) BITTER
Come As You Are (ABV 4%) PALE
Release the Pressure (ABV 4.1%) GOLD
Lost In Ikea (ABV 4.2%) PALE
Cosmonaut (ABV 4.4%) STOUT
Dark creamy stout with roasted malt dominating the aroma and taste.A liquorice flavour develops in the dry and bitter aftertaste.
Zed's Dead (ABV 4.5%) PALE
Moloko Mocha Porter (ABV 4.8%) SPECIALITY
A rich, smooth, well-balanced mocha porter with a light coffee and chocolate aroma. Richly roasted and chocolate flavours develop on the palate but are not overpowering. Lingering mocha finish with no hoppy bitterness.
Bollywood IPA (ABV 5%) PALE
Tune In, Hop Out (ABV 5%) PALE
Not All Heroes Wear Capes (ABV 5.5%) IPA
You Had Me At Hazy (ABV 5.9%) IPA
Don't Over Think Your Socks (ABV 6.2%) IPA
Supernova (ABV 6.9%) SPECIALITY
Emotional Support Hamster (ABV 7%) IPA

Nine Standards

See Settle

Nirvana SIBA

Unit T6, Leyton Industrial Village, Argall Avenue, Leyton, London, E10 7QP

☎ **(020) 3417 5580 ⊕ nirvanabrewery.com**

Established in 2017, Nirvana produces a range of bottled, low alcohol beers 0.5% or less, and some low alcohol beers over 0.5%. Sometimes available in keg. The range of modern styles includes a London porter as a nod to tradition. No real ale.

No Frills Joe

50 Wakefield Road, Greenhithe, Kent, DA9 9JE
☎ **07516 725577**

⊗ Unpasteurised, unfiltered, and unfined vegan beers are produced on a small five-barrel plant, and may be cloudy. The range is available in a small on-site taproom (check social media), and pubs nationwide. Up to eight different beers are available in cans. LIVE V◆

Candy Soup (ABV 4.5%) GOLD
Dreamland IPA (ABV 4.5%) GOLD
Lockdown Joe (ABV 4.8%) GOLD
Joe Solo Pale Ale (ABV 5.5%) GOLD

Nomadic SIBA

Unit 11 Sheepscar House, 15 Sheepscar Street, Sheepscar, Leeds, West Yorkshire, LS7 1AD ☎ 07868 345228 ⊕ nomadicbeers.co.uk

Established in 2017, beers were originally produced using spare capacity at other breweries. Following an expansion in 2018, Nomadic Beers found a new home in Sheepscar installing an eight-barrel kit. All beers produced are vegan-friendly and are distributed across the Yorkshire region. ‼🍴V◆

Pale (ABV 3.8%) PALE
Strider (ABV 4.4%) BITTER
Bandit (ABV 4.8%) PALE

Nook SIBA

🍴 **Riverside, 7b Victoria Square, Holmfirth, West Yorkshire, HD9 2DN**
☎ **(01484) 682373 ⊕ thenookbrewhouse.co.uk**

☺The Nook Brewhouse is built on the foundations of a previous brewhouse dating back to 1754, next to the River Ribble. Three brewery taps are supplied, two being restaurants with dishes matched to the beer, plus an on-site pub that rotates the 22 different ales. ‼◆LIVE

Norfolk Broads

See Humpty Dumpty

Norn Iron

Unit 30, The Cutts, Dunmurry, Belfast, BT17 9HN
✉ **nornironbrewcoltd@outlook.com**

Brewing began in 2018.

North SIBA

Springwell, Buslingthorpe Lane, Leeds, West Yorkshire, LS7 2DF
☎ **(0113) 345 3290**

Office: Regents Court. 39A Harrogate Road, Leeds, LS7 3PD ⊕ northbrewing.com

☺Having opened in 2015, the brewery initially supplied the North Bar group of bars in and around Leeds. Expansion to 15-barrels on the original site quickly followed as the number of other outlets supplied increased. Due to substantially increased canned production, including national availability in supermarkets, further expansion was required, with the current premises opening in 2021. ‼◆�

Session Pale (Action Against Hunger) (ABV 3.8%) BITTER

North Cotswold SIBA

Unit 3, Ditchford Farm, Stretton-on-Fosse, Warwickshire, GL56 9RD
☎ (01608) 663947 ⊕ northcotswoldbrewery.co.uk

⊛North Cotswold started in 1999 as a 2.5-barrel plant, which has since been upgraded to 10-barrel capacity. Beers are also produced under the Shakespeare brand name, available in cask and bottles. ⬛◆LIVE

Windrush Ale (ABV 3.6%) BITTER
Fosseway Flanker (ABV 3.8%) GOLD
Jumping Jack Flash (ABV 3.8%) GOLD
Moreton Mild (ABV 3.8%) MILD
Cotswold Best (ABV 4%) BITTER
Green Man IPA (ABV 4%) PALE
Shagweaver (ABV 4.5%) BITTER
Hung, Drawn 'n' Portered (ABV 5%) PORTER

Brewed under the Shakespeare's Brewery brand name:
Bard's Best (ABV 4.2%) GOLD
Falstaff's Folly (ABV 4.2%) BITTER

North Pier (NEW)

Unit 3a, Tow Law Industrial Estate, Tow Law, DL13 4BB ⊕ northpierbrew.co.uk

Brewing commenced in 2020.

Rokerite (ABV 4%) PALE
Pale (ABV 4.2%) PALE
Cold Brew (ABV 4.7%) PORTER
Bounty Hunter (ABV 4.8%) STOUT

North Riding (Brewery)

Unit 6, Barker's Lane, Snainton, North Yorkshire, YO13 9BD
☎ (01723) 864845 ⊕ northridingbrewery.com

⊛Having outgrown the brewpub in Scarborough, Stuart Neilson established a 10-barrel brewery in East Ayton on the outskirts of Scarborough in 2015. In early 2019 operations moved to a much larger premises in Snainton, enabling further expansion of brewing capacity. Concentrating on hop-forward beers, distribution is throughout the North of England and the Midlands. ◆LIVE

Mosaic Pale Ale (ABV 4.3%) PALE
Citra Pale Ale (ABV 4.5%) PALE

North Riding (Brewpub)

⬛ North Marine Road, Scarborough, North Yorkshire, YO12 7HU
☎ (01723) 370004 ⊕ northridingbrewpub.com

⊛Brewing commenced in 2011 using a two-barrel plant situated in the cellar of the pub, which is now brewing to capacity with three fermenting vessels. ◆

North Sea (NEW)

15 Primrose Court, Rosyth, KY11 2TE
✉ info@northseabrewery.co.uk

A microbrewery based in Rosyth, supplying craft beer locally to Fife, Scotland.

North Yorkshire SIBA

Unit 7, South Gare Court, Tod Point Road, Warrenby, North Yorkshire, TS10 5BN
☎ (01642) 497298 ⊕ nybrewery.co.uk

Founded in Middlesbrough in 1989 the brewery moved to Pinchinthorpe Hall, Guisborough in 1998. In 2017, following the purchase of the brewery, the new owner moved the entire operation to new premises on an industrial estate in Warrenby near Redcar, North Yorkshire. ◆LIVE

Temptation (ABV 3.8%) BITTER
Yorkshire Coble (ABV 3.8%) BITTER
Beckwatter (ABV 4%) BITTER
Yorkshire Porter (ABV 4.4%) PORTER
NYPA (ABV 4.6%) PALE
XPA (ABV 4.6%) PALE
Flying Herbert (ABV 4.7%) BITTER
White Stout (ABV 6.2%) STOUT

Northbound

Campsie Industrial Estate, McLean Road, Eglinton, BT47 3XX ☎ 07512 198686
⊕ northboundbrewery.com

Established in 2015, Northbound produce a range of bottle-conditioned beers named after their measurement of bitterness (IBUs). ◆LIVE

Northdown SIBA

Unit J1C/A, Channel Road, Westwood Industrial Estate, Margate, Kent, CT9 4JS ☎ 07791 441219
⊕ northdownbrewery.co.uk

⊠ Northdown began brewing in 2018 using a seven-barrel plant. It is run by Jonny and Katie Spanjar and takes its name from their original intention to run out of the Northdown area of Margate. The origins of a Northdown brewery date back to the 1600s. ‼⬛◆LIVE�

Merry Margate (ABV 3.8%) BLOND
Pale Ale Mary (ABV 4%) BITTER
Reginald Perrin (ABV 4%) BLOND
Papworth Victory Best Bitter (ABV 4.2%) PALE
Tidal Pool (ABV 4.6%) PALE
HE-BRU IPA (ABV 4.8%) GOLD
Muggy Porter (ABV 5%) PORTER
Magic Dragon (ABV 5.5%) BITTER
Tidal Moon (ABV 5.8%) STOUT
Hancock Shaker (ABV 6%) IPA

Northern Alchemy

The Old Coal Yard, Elizabeth Street, Byker, Newcastle upon Tyne, NE6 1JS ☎ 07834 386333
⊕ wearenorthernalchemy.com

Brewing began in 2014. The brewery was situated in a converted shipping container, known as the Lab, just behind the Cumberland Arms. In 2017 it moved to larger premises in a former coal depot. All beers are unfined and unfiltered. Beers are always available in the Cumberland Arms, and the brewery opens a tap on the last full weekend of the month. ◆V�

U.S Session Pale (ABV 4.1%) IPA

Northern Monk SIBA

Address 1: The Old Flax Store, Marshalls Mill, Holbeck, Leeds, West Yorkshire, LS11 9YJ
☎ (0113) 243 6430

Address 2: Unit 7 Sydenham Road, Leeds, LS11 9RU
⊕ northernmonkbrewco.com

☺After using spare capacity at other breweries in 2013, a 10-barrel plant was established in 2014 in a Grade II-listed mill. In 2017 a much larger second site with canning line was opened. 2019 saw further expansion into the adjacent former Leeds Brewery site, with a new 50-hectolitre brewkit installed in 2021. The mill hosts a taproom and events space. Most production is keg but cask-conditioned beer is available. ‼◆

Eternal (ABV 4.1%) PALE

Northern Monkey SIBA

68 Chorley Street, Bolton, BL1 4AL ☎ 07737 125629
⊕ northernmonkeybrew.co.uk

Established in 2016 and relocated in 2021, Northern Monkey Brew Co is a six-barrel brewery with an on-site tap bar. The original brewpub remains a town centre outlet. It brews a variety of ales, maintaining a traditional edge but with a modern twist. The ales rotate regularly so no core range is available. ◆◆

Northern Whisper

Hill End Mill, Hill End Lane, Cloughfold, Lancashire, BB4 7RN
☎ (01706) 230082
⊕ northernwhisperbrewingco.co.uk

First brewing in 2017, the brewery has expanded to own three pubs and a taproom. ◆

Blighty (ABV 3.8%) BITTER
Soft Mick (ABV 3.8%) PALE
Oppenchops (ABV 4%) GOLD
Yammerhouse (ABV 4.5%) PALE
Beltie (ABV 4.8%) STOUT
Chinwag (ABV 5.6%) IPA

Norton

Norton Priory, Tudor Road, Manor Park, Runcorn, Cheshire, WA7 1SX
☎ (01928) 716971 ☎ 07767 354674
⊕ nortonbrewing.com

Situated within the grounds of Norton Priory, the brewery was created as a social enterprise by Halton Borough Council to provide employment opportunities for people with learning disabilities, autism and other disabilities. It opened in 2011 with a 2.5-barrel plant. Beers in bottles, mini-kegs and casks are for collection from the brewery only. ☛

Noss Beer Works SIBA

Unit 6, Ash Court, Pennant Way, Lee Mill, Devon, PL21 9GE ☎ 07977 479634 ⊕ nossbeerworks.co.uk

⊗ Noss Beer Works was formed in 2012 using a six-barrel plant. The beers are made from only the finest locally-sourced hops and malts. Noss Beer Works now have an off-sales facility. ‼☛LIVE

Black Rock (ABV 4%) PALE
Church Ledge (ABV 4%) BITTER
Bitter dominated by hops and fruit throughout. Hoppy and citrusy, slight caramel balances bitter dryness. Slight kick at the end.
Mew Stone (ABV 4.3%) BITTER
Ebb Rock (ABV 4.9%) BITTER

Nottingham SIBA

Plough Inn, 17 St Peter's Street, Radford, Nottingham, NG7 3EN

☎ (0115) 942 2649 ☎ 07815 073447
⊕ nottinghambrewery.co.uk

The former owners of the Bramcote and Castle Rock Breweries re-established the Nottingham Brewery in 2000 in a purpose-built brewhouse behind the Plough Inn. Philip Darby and Niven Balfour set out to revive the brands of the original Nottingham Brewery, closed by Whitbread in the 1950s. Within the LocAle ethos, beers are supplied widely to the local trade including the brewery tap house, the Plough Inn, and its other tied house the Frame Breakers, Ruddington. ‼◆

Rock Ale Bitter Beer (ABV 3.8%) BITTER
A pale and bitter, thirst-quenching hoppy beer with a dry finish.
Rock Ale Mild Beer (ABV 3.8%) MILD
A reddish-black malty mild with some refreshing bitterness in the finish.
Trent Bridge Inn Ale (ABV 3.8%) BITTER
Legend (ABV 4%) BITTER
A fruity and malty pale brown bitter with a touch of sweetness and bitterness.
Extra Pale Ale (ABV 4.2%) PALE
A hoppy and fruity golden ale with a hint of sweetness and a long-lasting bitter finish.
Cock & Hoop (ABV 4.3%) BITTER
Dreadnought (ABV 4.5%) BITTER
Well-balanced best bitter. Blend of malt and hops give a rounded fruity finish.
Bullion (ABV 4.7%) GOLD
A refreshing premium golden ale. Brewed with a single malt variety, it is triple-hopped and exceptionally bitter.
Supreme (ABV 5.2%) BITTER
A strong amber fruity ale. A touch of malt in the taste is followed by a sweet and slightly hoppy finish.

O'Connor

12 Lime Road, Faughanvale, Greysteel, BT47 3EH
☎ 07748 004065 ⊕ oconnorbrewing.com

Brewing began in 2013. No real ale.

Oakham SIBA

2 Maxwell Road, Woodston, Peterborough, Cambridgeshire, PE2 7JB
☎ (01733) 370500 ⊕ oakhamales.com

⊠ The brewery was established in 1993 in Oakham, Rutland, and moved to Peterborough in 1998. The brewery's main production site is a 75-barrel plant. Around 350 outlets are supplied and four pubs are owned. ‼☛◆LIVE

JHB (ABV 3.8%) GOLD
Straw-coloured golden ale dominated by citrus hop character throughout. Long, dry finish.
Inferno (ABV 4%) GOLD
The citrus hop character of this straw-coloured brew begins on the nose and builds in intensity on the palate. Clean, dry, citrus finish.
Citra (ABV 4.2%) GOLD
Uncompromising grapefruit and tropical fruit with a long, deepening, dry finish, and an underlying, softening balance of sweet, biscuity malt.
Bishops Farewell (ABV 4.6%) GOLD
Powerfully citrusy, the hops and fruit on the aroma of this golden/yellow beer become bittersweet on the palate. Zesty, citrus aftertaste.
Green Devil (ABV 6%) GOLD

Oaks SIBA

Unit 6, Stanney Mill Industrial Estate, Dutton Green, Ellesmere Port, Cheshire, CH2 4SA ☎ 07526 437098 ⊕ oaksbrewing.co.uk

Founded as Cheshire Brew Brothers in 2013 and taken into new ownership in 2017. The beers can be found in free and tied trade across North-West England and West Yorkshire. An ever-changing range of beers is produced to satisfy customer demand.

Chester Gold (ABV 3.5%) GOLD
A fruity, hoppy bitter with a pleasant, sweet finish.

Oakwood

c/o Northfield Crescent, Wells-next-the-Sea, Norfolk, NR23 1LP ☎ 07512 111211 ⊕ oakwoodbrewery.com

Oakwood was established in 2015. After producing beers on a small scale from home, the brewer decided to turn his hobby into a full-time job. Barley is locally-grown by Teddy Maufe at Branthill Farm on the Holkham Estate in Norfolk. Beer is contract brewed elsewhere. LIVE

Oban Bay

See Argyll

Oddly

St John's Avenue, Friern Barnet, London, N11 3BX ✉ hello@oddlybeer.com

⊗ Originally founded on an island in the Thames at Hampton, it moved to be one of the three breweries in the Tottenham Brewery location during 2019 until later in the year. Since then it has been brewing at home and using spare capacity at other breweries such as Muswell Hillbilly. ♦ V

Rhia (ABV 4%) GOLD
Fezzik (ABV 7%) PORTER

Odin SIBA

Glen Mona Loop Road, Maughold, Isle of Man, IM7 1HJ ☎ 07624 266664

Established in 2019 using the 2.5-barrel brewery from Betteridge's of Hampshire. Founder and brewer Rob Storey brews six core beers in cask. LIVE

Manx Mild (ABV 3.4%) MILD
Rhumsaa Bitter (ABV 3.7%) BITTER
Laksaa Pale (ABV 3.8%) PALE
Asgard Bitter (ABV 4.2%) BITTER
Black Claw (ABV 4.5%) STOUT
Oyster Stout (ABV 4.8%) STOUT

Odyssey

Brockhampton Brewery, Oast House Barn, Bromyard, Herefordshire, WR6 5SH ☎ (01885) 483496 ☎ 07918 553152 ⊕ odysseybrewco.com

⊗ This six-barrel brewery was established in 2014 by Alison and Mitchell Evans, who previously owned the Beer in Hand, Hereford. The original building, a restored barn on a National Trust estate, has been retained. A wide range of beers is brewed, predominantly served in keg and can and occasionally bottled for special release.

Off Tempo

See BAD

Offa's Dyke

🏠 Chapel Lane, Trefonen, Shropshire, SY10 9DX ☎ (01691) 656889 ⊕ offasdykebrewery.com

☺Established in 2007, the brewery and adjoining Barley Mow pub straddle the old England/Wales border, Offa's Dyke. The Olde Vaults in Oswestry serves as an alternative brewery tap. ‼

Ogwen

5 Rhes Ogwen, Stryd Fawr, Bethesda, LL57 3AY ☎ (01248) 605715 ☎ 07545 684752 ⊕ cwrwogwen.cymru

The first brewery in the Ogwen valley for over a century. A local community venture, established in 2016 by a group of shareholders who perform all brewing operations. ‼ 🍺 LIVE

Cwrw Caradog (ABV 3.9%) PALE
Ryc (ABV 4%) BITTER
Tryfan (ABV 4.2%) BITTER
Chwalfa (ABV 4.5%) PALE

Okell's

Kewaigue, Douglas, Isle of Man, IM2 1QG ☎ (01624) 699400 ⊕ okells.co.uk

☺Founded in 1874 by Dr Okell, this is the main brewery on the island and moved in 1994 to a new, purpose-built plant at Kewaigue. All the beers are produced under the Manx Brewers' Act. ‼♦

Okells MPA – Manx Pale Ale (ABV 3.6%) PALE
A golden, fruity, session beer with background sweetness and a rising hoppy finish.
Bitter (ABV 3.7%) BITTER
Traditional bitter, malty and fruity aromas at the start, hops and caramel in the middle with the bitterness falling slightly at the end leaving the malts to enhance the finish.
Dr Okell's IPA (ABV 4.5%) BLOND
A clean, fruity, sweetish bitter with an alcoholic bite.

Old Boot (NEW)

Waterside Mill, Burnley Road, Bacup, OL13 8AW ☎ 07545 275278 ✉ stepill64@gmail.com

Old Boot started brewing during 2020. Although not based there, much of the output is sold through the Old Boot Café Bar in Bacup.

Old Cannon

🏠 86 Cannon Street, Bury St Edmunds, Suffolk, IP33 1JR
☎ (01284) 768769 ⊕ oldcannonbrewery.co.uk

⊗ The St Edmunds Head pub opened in 1845 with its own brewery. Brewing ceased in 1917, and George King closed the pub in 1995. It re-opened in 1999 as the Old Cannon Brewery complete with a unique state-of-the-art brewery housed in the bar area. The brewery supplies other pubs of shared ownership. ‼♦

Old Chimneys

c/o Old Chimneys, The Street, Market Weston, Suffolk, IP22 2NZ
☎ (01359) 221411 ⊕ oldchimneysbrewery.com

Old Chimneys was established in 1995, moving to a converted farm building in 2001. In 2019 Alan Thomson ceased brewing at Market Weston to concentrate on collaborative brewing projects with other breweries. !! ♦ LIVE

Old Dairy SIBA

Tenterden Station Estate, Station Road, Tenterden, Kent, TN30 6HE
☎ (01580) 763867 ⊕ olddairybrewery.com

⊠ Old Dairy was founded in 2009. It relocated from Rolvenden in 2014 to larger premises near the Kent & East Sussex Railway in Tenterden in order to increase capacity. A taproom and beer garden along with the brewery shop are open seven days a week. !! ☕ ♦ LIVE ✦

Red Top (ABV 3.8%) BITTER
A sweetish, copper-coloured bitter with hints of caramel and a subtle hop character.
Uber Brew (ABV 3.8%) PALE
Copper Top (ABV 4.1%) BITTER
Blue Top (ABV 4.8%) PALE
Rich and full-bodied, this pale brown ale has a long, bittersweet finish and a hint of aroma hop.

Old Farmhouse (NEW) SIBA

Upper Harglodd, St Davids, SA62 6BX
☎ (01437) 729248

Brewing commenced in 2021 in a renovated farmhouse. The brewery uses home-grown grain and its own well water in the brewing process.

Old Felixstowe (NEW)

30 Falkenham Road, Kirton, Suffolk, IP10 0NW
☎ 07889 238784 ⊕ tofbc.co.uk

⊠ Brewing began in 2018 in an outhouse in Old Felixstowe. The brewery was upgraded in 2020 to a four-barrel plant. Four core beers are produced, with more to follow. Beer is mostly available bottle-conditioned but cask beers are provided to a handful of local pubs. LIVE V

Old Fountain

⊟ Old Fountain, 3 Baldwin Street, Old Street, London, EC1V 9NU
☎ (020) 7253 2970 ⊕ oldfountain.co.uk

Brewing on-site since 2016 has been sporadic and is currently suspended awaiting appointment of a new brewer. Its keg Fountain Pils is brewed by Bavo Brewery in Belgium.

Old Friends

⊟ Old Friends Inn, 49 Soutergate, Ulverston, Cumbria, LA12 7ES
☎ (01229) 208195 ☎ 07563 521575
⊕ oldfriendsulverston.co.uk

☺Brewing began in 2019 in a room to the rear of the Old Friends pub in Ulverston. Beers are currently only available at the pub.

Old Inn

⊟ Old Inn & Brewpub, Flowerdale Glen, Gairloch, IV21 2BD
☎ (01445) 712006 ⊕ theoldinn.net

Brewing began in 2010 using a 150-litre plant. Brewing is currently suspended. ♦

Old Kent Road

Gordon Road, Peckham, London, SE15 3RB
✉ beer@oldkentrdbrewery.co.uk

An early user of the UBrew facility from 2016, and taking advantage of the larger commerical kit later on but ultimately a casualty of the closure in 2019. Brewing now continues irregularly on a smaller home kit and at other breweries.

Old Laxey

See Bushy's

Old Luxters

Old Luxters Vineyard, Dudley Lane, Hambleden, Buckinghamshire, RG9 6JW
☎ (01491) 638330 ⊕ chilternvalley.co.uk

Situated in a 17th century barn beside the Chiltern Valley Vineyard, Old Luxters is a traditional brewery established in 1990 and awarded a Royal Warrant of Appointment in 2007. The core range is bottle-conditioned beers. !! ☕ ♦ LIVE

Old Mill SIBA

Mill Street, Snaith, East Yorkshire, DN14 9HU
☎ (01405) 861813 ⊕ oldmillbrewery.co.uk

☺Opened in 1983 in a 200-year-old former malt kiln and corn mill, the brew-length is 60 barrels. The brewery is building a tied estate, now standing at 16 houses. Beers can be found nationwide through wholesalers and around 80 free trade outlets are supplied direct. The RT Brew Co range is produced for HB Clark (qv). !! ♦

Bullion IPA (ABV 3.7%) GOLD
Jack's Batch 34 (ABV 3.8%) BITTER
Traditional Bitter (ABV 3.8%) BITTER
A malty nose is carried through to the initial flavour. Bitterness runs throughout.
Blonde Bombshell (ABV 4%) BLOND
La Bolsa Coffee Porter (ABV 4.5%) SPECIALITY

Old Pie Factory

4 Montague Road, Warwick, CV34 5LW ☎ 07816 413026 ⊕ oldpiefactorybrewery.co.uk

☺Brewing began in 2011 using a 5.5-barrel plant and is a joint venture between Underwood Wines, Stratford upon Avon, and the Case is Altered, Five Ways.

Old Pie Bitter (ABV 3.9%) BITTER
Pie In The Sky (ABV 4.1%) PALE
Humble Pie (ABV 4.2%) BITTER
I.Pie.A. (ABV 4.5%) PALE
American Pie (ABV 5.5%) IPA

Old Sawley SIBA

⊟ White Lion, 352a Tamworth Road, Sawley, Derbyshire, NG10 3AT ☎ 07722 311209
⊕ oldsawley.com

⊠ A 10-barrel microbrewery installed at the rear of the White Lion in Sawley. The pub stocks the full range of beers and the brewery also supplies Midland beer festivals, local pubs and pubs across the East Midlands. !! ♦

Jobber (ABV 4.2%) BITTER
Little Jack (ABV 4.3%) PALE
Plummeth the Hour (ABV 4.5%) SPECIALITY
Tollbridge Porter (ABV 4.5%) PORTER

Old School SIBA

Holly Bank Barn, Crag Road, Warton, Lancashire, LA5 9PL

☎ (01524) 740888 ⊕ oldschoolbrewery.co.uk

😊A 12-barrel brewery, founded in 2012, located in a renovated 400-year-old former school outbuilding overlooking the picturesque village of Warton. Beer is mainly sold to free houses within a 40-mile radius. ‼♦◆

Junior (ABV 3.6%) PALE
Hopscotch (ABV 3.7%) GOLD
Initially hoppy, astringency builds in this satisfying beer, ending with a bitter finish.
Textbook (ABV 3.9%) BLOND
Pale beer with malt and hops in the taste, creamy texture and a dry, bitter finish.
Detention (ABV 4.1%) PALE
Light, amber, hoppy, bitter with lingering aftertaste.
Headmaster (ABV 4.5%) BITTER

Old Spot

Manor Farm, Station Road, Cullingworth, Bradford, West Yorkshire, BD13 5HN
☎ (01535) 691144 ⊕ oldspotbrewery.co.uk

😊Old Spot, named after the owner's sheepdog, started brewing in 2005. The beers are available in several outlets in West Yorkshire. The acting brewery tap is the George, Cullingworth. ‼♦

Light But Dark (ABV 4%) BITTER
OSB (ABV 4%) GOLD
Spot Light (ABV 4.2%) GOLD
This smooth-drinking, golden ale has a slightly fruity, hoppy aroma leading to a well-balanced fruit, hop flavour with hints of pineapple and a long bittersweet finish.
Spot O'Bother (ABV 5.5%) PORTER

Old Street

Hackney Wick: Unit 1, Queens Yard, White Post Lane, London, E9 5EN ☎ 07951 179085

Bethnal Green: Arch 11, Gales Gardens, Bethnal Green Road, London, E2 0EJ ⊕ oldstreet.beer

Brewing began in 2013 at the Queen's Head pub in King's Cross. In 2018, the brewery moved to a railway arch by Bethnal Green underground station, with an on-site taproom. A second brewing site was installed in Queens Yard, Hackney Wick in 2020. There are taprooms at both sites with the addition of a shop at Bethnal Green. ╦◆

Old Tree

Old Tree, Yachtwerks, 28-29 Richmond Place, Brighton, East Sussex, BN2 9NA ☎ 07413 064346 ⊕ oldtree.house

A co-operative based in Brighton producing a unique range of small-batch, probiotic and celebration drinks. It supplies its own zero-waste Silo restaurant. Brewing and gardening are combined, and a production process is used that contributes to land regeneration. LIVE

Old Vicarage

Old Vicarage, Walton, Cumbria, CA8 2DH
☎ (01697) 543002 ⊕ oldvicaragebrewery.co.uk

A microbrewery, bar and B&B accommodation in North Cumbria. Brewing experience days are offered.

Olde England

See Potbelly

Olde Potting Shed

See TOPS

Olde Swan

🏠 Old Swan, 89 Halesowen Road, Netherton, West Midlands, DY2 9PY
☎ (01384) 253075

😊A famous brewpub best known as Ma Pardoe's after the matriarch who ruled it for years. The pub has been licensed since 1835 and the present brewery and pub were built in 1863. Brewing continued until 1988 and restarted in 2001. More than 30 outlets are supplied. ‼♦

Original (ABV 3.5%) MILD
Straw-coloured, light mild, smooth but tangy, and sweetly refreshing with a faint hoppiness.
Dark Swan (ABV 4.2%) MILD
Smooth, sweet dark mild with late roast malt in the finish.
Entire (ABV 4.4%) BITTER
Faintly hoppy, amber premium bitter with sweetness persistent throughout.
NPA (Netherton Pale Ale) (ABV 4.8%) PALE
Bumble Hole Bitter (ABV 5.2%) BITTER
Sweet, smooth amber ale with hints of astringency in the finish.

Oldershaw

See Zest

On the Edge

Sheffield, South Yorkshire ☎ 07854 983197 ⊕ ontheedgebrew.com

On the Edge started brewing commercially in 2012 using a 0.5-barrel plant in the brewer's home. Brewing takes place once a week. Three local pubs are supplied as well as beer festivals. There is no regular beer list as new brews are constantly being tried.

One Mile End SIBA

Unit 2, Compass West Estate, 33 West Road, Tottenham, London, N17 0XL
☎ (020) 7998 0610

Whitechapel: The White Hart, 1-3 Mile End Road, Whitechapel, E1 4TP ⊕ onemileend.com

⊠ One Mile End took over the former premises of the Redemption Brewery using a 12.5-barrel plant, brewing up to four times a week. A three-barrel plant is also occasionally in operation at the White Hart in Whitechapel, its original home. Beer is available in cask, keg and cans. ‼╦◆

Salvation! (ABV 4.4%) GOLD
Citrus and tropical fruits are balanced by digestive biscuits in this easy-drinking golden ale. A spicy, hoppy, bitterness develops.
Juicy 4pm (ABV 4.9%) BLOND
Smooth, yellow beer with strong citrus and mango flavours and a little biscuit becoming more hoppy and bitter on drinking.
Snakecharmer (ABV 5.7%) IPA

One More Than Two (NEW) SIBA

Unit J, Portberry Street, South Shields, Tyne & Wear, NE33 1QX ☎ 07927 051236
⊕ 1morethan2brew.co.uk

Brewing commenced in 2020. The brewery gets its name from Two (the brewers) with One More being the community. Based in an industrial unit, the taproom is open from Thursday to Sunday, selling their own cask ales plus a selection of keg beers from other local microbreweries. Local food outlets are usually in attendance at weekends. ➥◆

Gold Parachute (ABV 3.8%) GOLD
Rollin Pale Ale (ABV 3.8%) PALE
IPA Wolf (ABV 4.6%) IPA
IPA Granny (ABV 4.7%) IPA
Ruby Riding Hood (ABV 4.7%) BITTER
Lighthouse Red IPA (ABV 5%) IPA

Only With Love (NEW)

Little Goldsmiths Farm, Beechy Road, Uckfield, East Sussex, TN22 5JG
☎ (01825) 608410 ☎ 07786 830368
⊕ onlywithlove.co

Only with Love was founded in 2020 by Steve Keegan and Roger Warner. It produces kombucha and beer in the heart of Sussex with all products sustainably created, packaged and delivered.

Opa Hay's

Glencot, Wood Lane, Aldeby, Norfolk, NR34 0DA
☎ (01502) 679144 ☎ 07916 282729
⊕ engelfineales.com

Opa Hay's began brewing in 2008. It is a small, family-run brewery, taking its name from the brewer's great grandfather. Only traditional brewing methods are used, with ingredients that are, where possible, sourced locally. ◆LIVE

Engels Fruity Little Number (ABV 3.6%) BITTER
Powerful citrus/grapefruit aroma with malt and hops. Smoky sweetish flavours with fruit notes, and a fruity, hoppy aftertaste.
Engel's Best Bitter (ABV 4%) BITTER
Hop Hop Hooray (ABV 4.3%) SPECIALITY
Matilda's Revenge (ABV 4.3%) GOLD
Samuel Engels Meister Pils (SEMP) (ABV 4.8%) SPECIALITY
Liquid Bread (ABV 5.2%) SPECIALITY
Bavarian Breakfast Beer (ABV 5.4%) SPECIALITY

Ora

Unit 16a, Rosebery Industrial Estate, Rosebery Avenue, Tottenham, London, N17 9SR ☎ 07703 563559 ⊕ orabeer.com

Originally split between Italy and cuckoo brewing at Ubrew, Ora took over Brewheadz in Tottenham in 2019. A variety of hop-forward beers are brewed complemented with styles incorporating classic Italian ingredients such as lemons, balsamic vinegar and vanilla. No real ale. ◆

Orbit SIBA

Arches 225 & 228, Fielding Street, Walworth, London, SE17 3HD
☎ (020) 7703 9092 ⊕ orbitbeers.com

Established in 2014 in a railway arch in Walworth, Orbit produce keg and bottled beers, focusing on traditional styles, especially continental European styles. The core range is supplemented by White Label specials. The design work and beer names relate to the founder's love of vinyl. LIVE ◆

Origami

75 North Western Street, Manchester, M12 6DY
Office: 83 Ducie Street, Manchester, M1 2JQ
⊕ origamibrewingcompany.com

Brewing began in 2016 at Beer Nouveau's Manchester site where Origami has its own brew plant. Most output is bottled, but cask beer is frequently available at the Beer Nouveau beer tap as well as Manchester beer festivals. Unfined, all beer is vegan. **V**

Fortune Teller (ABV 4%) PALE
1000 cranes (ABV 5%) BROWN
Valley Fold (ABV 5.3%) SPECIALITY
Rabbit Ear (ABV 5.5%) STOUT
Arctic Fox (ABV 7%) IPA

Orkney SIBA

Orkney Brewery, Quoyloo, Orkney, KW16 3LT
☎ (01667) 404555 ☎ 07721 013227
Office: Sinclair Breweries Ltd, Cawdor, IV12 5XP
⊕ orkneybrewery.co.uk

⊚Orkney was established in 1988 in an old village school building. Having incorporated sister brewery Atlas (qv), it moved next door in 2010 to enable an increase in capacity and the completion of an award-winning visitor centre in 2012. !! ➥◆◆

Raven (ABV 3.8%) BITTER
A well-balanced quaffable bitter. Malty fruitiness and bitter hops last through to the long, dry aftertaste.
Dragonhead (ABV 4%) STOUT
A strong, dark roasted malt aroma flows into the taste. The roast malt continues to dominate the aftertaste, and blends with chocolate to develop a strong, dry finish.
Northern Light (ABV 4%) GOLD
A well-balanced golden ale with a real smack of fruit and hops in the taste and an increasing bitter aftertaste.
Red MacGregor (ABV 4%) BITTER
This tawny red ale has a well-balanced mix of red fruit, malt and hops. Slight sweetness throughout.
Corncrake (ABV 4.1%) GOLD
A straw-coloured beer with soft citrus fruits and a floral aroma.
Puffin Ale (ABV 4.5%) BITTER
Dark Island (ABV 4.6%) MILD
A sweetish roast chocolate malt taste leads to a long-lasting roasted, slightly bitter, dry finish.
Skull Splitter (ABV 8.5%) BARLEY
An intense velvet malt nose with hints of apple, prune and plum. The hoppy taste is balanced by satiny smooth malt with sweet fruity spicy edges, leading to a long, dry finish with a hint of nut.

Brewed under the Atlas Brewery name:
Latitude (ABV 3.6%) SPECIALITY
This straw-coloured lager has a light citrus taste with a smack of hops and grapefruit in the light, bitter finish.
Three Sisters (ABV 4.2%) BROWN
Malt, summer fruits and caramel in the nose and blackcurrant in the taste, followed by a short, hoppy, bitter finish.
Wayfarer (ABV 4.4%) SPECIALITY
Full of citrus fruits and hops with a bitter finish.
Golden Amber (ABV 4.5%) SPECIALITY
Refreshing hops, honey, marmalade and grapefruit to the fore with a dry, hoppy finish.
Blizzard (ABV 4.7%) SPECIALITY
Light on malts and hops with ginger and spices coming through.
Nimbus (ABV 5%) BITTER
A full-bodied golden beer using some wheat malt and three types of hops. Sweet and fruity at the front, it

becomes slightly astringent with lasting fruit and a pleasant, dry finish.

Oscars

Unit 1, Riverside Works, Brunswick Street, Nelson, Lancashire, BB9 0HZ
☎ (01282) 616192 ⊕ oscarsbrewery.co.uk

Originally based in Preston, the brewery was taken over in 2017 by the Lancashire Beer Co, a pub supplies wholesaler in Nelson. In 2018 the brewery name was changed to Oscars and a new range of beers introduced. Production moved to purpose-built premises in Nelson at the parent company in 2019.

Top Dog (ABV 3.8%) PALE
Dog Father (ABV 3.9%) BITTER
Notorious D.O.G. (ABV 3.9%) PALE
Gun Dog (ABV 4%) BLOND
Space Dog (ABV 4.2%) PALE

Ossett SIBA

Kings Yard, Low Mill Road, Ossett, West Yorkshire, WF5 8ND
☎ (01924) 261333 ⊕ ossett-brewery.co.uk

☺Opened in 1997 by David James and housed in a 19th-century malthouse. Ossett Brewery was sold in 2007 and again in 2021, latterly to Liz Crosby, a former employee, with brewing under the supervision of Howard, Liz's husband. ‼️🍴◆◆

Butterley (ABV 3.8%) BITTER
Yorkshire Blonde (ABV 3.9%) BLOND
White Rat (ABV 4%) PALE
Silver King (ABV 4.3%) PALE
Voodoo (ABV 5%) SPECIALITY
Excelsius (ABV 5.2%) PALE

Ostlers

🍺 **White Horse, 2 York Street, Harborne, West Midlands, B17 0HG**
☎ (0121) 427 8004 ⊕ whitehorseharborne.com

Started up at the rear of the White Horse pub in Harborne, the brewery was in occasional production for a few years. It now has a 4.5-barrel plant, brewing a small range of core beers alongside frequent specials and seasonal beers, many available in KeyKeg as well as cask.

Other Monkey

C/O Three Wise Monkeys, 60 High Street, Colchester, Essex, CO1 1DN
☎ (01206) 543014 ⊕ othermonkeybrewing.com

⊠ Other Monkey is located in the basement of the Three Wise Monkeys pub. The brewery and pub are separately owned but beer is only brewed for the Three Wise Monkeys and two other outlets in Colchester. V

Pale Ale (ABV 4.4%) PALE

Otter SIBA

Mathayes, Luppitt, Honiton, Devon, EX14 4SA
☎ (01404) 891285 ⊕ otterbrewery.com

⊠ A family-run brewery set high up in the Blackdown Hills. Environmental responsibility lies at the heart of its ethos. Otter's eco cellar has been built underground and is naturally chilled. The beers are made from the brewery's own spring water and locally-sourced ingredients. ◆◆

Bitter (ABV 3.6%) BITTER
Well-balanced, amber session bitter with a fruity nose and bitter taste and aftertaste.

Amber (ABV 4%) BITTER
Light, refreshing and mellow with hints of citrus hoppiness. Creamy and delicate with hops and fruit.

Bright (ABV 4.3%) GOLD
A light and refreshing golden Ale with delicate malt, and fruit leading through hops to a lingering, bitter aftertaste.

Ale (ABV 4.5%) BITTER
Malt dominates from nose to throat. Sweet fruit, toffee and caramel with a dry aftertaste, full of flavour.

Head (ABV 5.8%) BITTER
Smooth strong ale. Caramel malt throughout. Full-bodied with rich malty fruitiness and a chocolate hint, leaving a bitter aftertaste.

Out of Town

84 Telford Road, Lenziemill Industrial Estate, Cumbernauld, G67 2NJ ⊕ outoftown.co

Originally set up in 2016 by three homebrewers, the brewery was sold and is now part of Consolidated Craft Breweries. Beers may be brewed by Alechemy (qv).

Out There

Unit 4, Foundry Lane Industrial Estate, Newcastle-upon-Tyne, NE6 1LH ☎ 07946 579534
⊕ outtherebrewing.com

Out There was established in 2012 by Steve Pickthall. Branding and beer names are themed around the 1950s space race.

Space is the Place (ABV 3.5%) BITTER
Laika (ABV 4.8%) SPECIALITY
Celestial Love (ABV 5.1%) BITTER

Outgang

🍺 **Kinsley Hotel, Wakefield Road, Kinsley, West Yorkshire, WF9 5EH ☎ 07747 694611**
✉ thepub@sky.com

☺Originally established in 2011, brewing resumed in 2017 after a period of inoperation. Local outlets are supplied as are outlets further afield due to increased production. ◆

Outhouse Brewery (NEW)

4 Southgate House, Alexandra Court, Denmark Street, Wokingham, Berkshire, RG40 2SL ☎ 07585 020917
⊕ theouthousebrewery.com

A new nanobrewery, established in 2021, using a 300-litre (1.8-barrel) plant, which can be seen by customers directly from the onsite taproom. This is the first brewery in Wokingham town centre since the Wellington Brewery (Headington's) closed in 1928. Beers are supplied mostly in 30-litre Euro Kegs (Sankey) and also in bottles. All beers are unfiltered and unpasteurised and can be purchased from the taproom, online and from local shops. ☰LIVE ◆

Outhouse Brewing

c/o Unit 16a, Redbrook Business Park, off Wilthorpe Road, Redbrook, Barnsley, South Yorkshire, S75 1JN
☎ 07572 164446

Office: Henry Morgan House, Industry Road, Carlton, Barnsley, S71 3PQ ⊕ outhousebrewing.co.uk

THE BREWERIES

☺After a 13 year teaching career Andy Jones established Outhouse Brewing in 2018 using spare capacity at Jolly Boys (qv). V

Outhouse Přístavba (ABV 3.7%) GOLD
Garden Shed (ABV 4%) BARLEY
Bikeshed (ABV 4.5%) GOLD

Outlaw

See Rooster's

Outpost

See Three Hills

Outstanding SIBA

Units 1 & 2 Foundry, Ordsall Lane, Ordsall, Salford, Manchester, M5 3AN
☎ (0161) 873 8090 ⊕ outstandingbeers.com

Established in 2008, the brewery operates a dual system, brewing on a 15-barrel plant and using a 2.5-barrel plant for special and experimental brews. Originally based in Bury, it moved to Ordsall in 2017. Selected free trade accounts are supplied nationally. ◆

3.9 (ABV 3.9%) PALE
UltraPale (ABV 4.1%) PALE
Straw in colour, with a light citrus aroma. Lemony fruit with hop bitterness to taste and a bitter, astringent finish.
Red (ABV 4.4%) BITTER
Blond (ABV 4.5%) BLOND
IPA (ABV 5.5%) GOLD
Stout (ABV 5.5%) STOUT
Imperial IPA (ABV 7.4%) IPA

Ovenstone 109 SIBA

Ovenstone Works, Ovenstone, Anstruther, KY10 2RR
☎ (01333) 311394 ⊕ ovenstone109.com

Established in 2018, Ovenstone 109 is a microbrewery in the East Neuk of Fife. The brewer aims to use renewable and sustainable technology in the brewing process.

Fifie (ABV 4%) BLOND
St Ayles Ale (ABV 4.1%) GOLD
Terra Nova (ABV 4.3%) GOLD

Overtone

Unit 19, New Albion Industrial Estate, Halley Street, Yoker, Glasgow, G13 4DJ ⊕ overtonebrewing.com

Established in 2018. No real ale.

Oxford SIBA

Coopers Yard, Manor Farm Road, Horspath, Oxfordshire, OX33 1SD
☎ (01865) 604620 ☎ 07710 883273
⊕ oxfordbrewery.co.uk

⊠ A family-owned and run brewery, it began brewing in 2009 and supplies outlets in the Oxford area. Recently changed its name from Shotover Brewery to Oxford Brewery. ‼▐◆V✿

Prospect (ABV 3.7%) BITTER
Trinity (ABV 4.2%) GOLD
Vivid Dreams (ABV 4.2%) GOLD
Let the Dragon See the Wolf (ABV 4.5%) BITTER
Scholar (ABV 4.5%) BITTER
Matilda's Tears (ABV 5%) PALE

Oxhey Village

14 Maxwell Rise, Watford, WD19 4DX ☎ 07470 422842 ⊠ shaun@ruthandshaun.co.uk

Oxhey Village Brewery is a nanobrewery set up by five drinking companions, which began commercial brewing in 2019. Currently brewing about once a week, it mainly produces mini-kegs for local clubs but cask beers are available on request for local pubs and beer festivals.

Padstow SIBA

The Brewery, Unit 4a, Trecerus Industrial Estate, Padstow, Cornwall, PL28 8RW
☎ (01841) 532169 ☎ 07834 924312
⊕ padstowbrewing.co.uk

⊠ Owners Des and Caron Archer established the brewery in 2013, using a 0.5-barrel plant, which has since been upgraded to 10 barrels. Besides the integral brewery shop, two licenced town-centre tasting rooms have been established. ‼▐◆LIVE

Pale Ale (ABV 3.6%) PALE
Golden beer with assertive hop aroma. Citrus hops dominate the taste with bitterness and dryness. Hoppy, refreshing and crisp finish.
Local (ABV 4%) BITTER
Windjammer (ABV 4.3%) BROWN
Tawny bitter. Light malty and citrus hop aromas leading to a combination of biscuit malt, pine and resin hops. Lasting bitterness.
IPA (ABV 4.8%) PALE
Refreshing IPA. Fully-hopped on nose and taste with orange bitterness. Sweet finish with citrus hops and faintly dry.
May Day (ABV 5%) PALE
Amber ale with citrus hop aroma. Trace of malt sweetness overwhelmed by strong lemon and stone fruit flavours. Quite bitter.

Palmers SIBA IFBB

Old Brewery, West Bay Road, Bridport, Dorset, DT6 4JA
☎ (01308) 422396 ⊕ palmersbrewery.com

⊠ Palmers is one of Britain's only thatched breweries and dates from 1794. It is situated in Bridport, the heart of the Jurassic Coast in south-west Dorset. The company continues to make substantial investment in its 54 tenanted pubs, all serving cask ale. An additional 400 outlets are supplied within the free trade. ‼▐

Copper Ale (ABV 3.7%) BITTER
Beautifully-balanced, copper-coloured, light bitter with a hoppy aroma.
IPA (ABV 4.2%) PALE
Hop aroma and bitterness stay in the background in this predominantly malty best bitter, with some fruit on the aroma.
Dorset Gold (ABV 4.5%) GOLD
More complex than many golden ales thanks to a pleasant banana and mango fruitiness on the aroma that carries on into the taste and aftertaste.
200 (ABV 5%) BITTER
This is a big beer with a touch of caramel sweetness adding to a complex hoppy, fruit taste that lasts from the aroma well into the aftertaste.
Tally Ho! (ABV 5.5%) OLD
A complex, dark old ale. Roast malts and treacle toffee on the palate lead in to a long, lingering finish with more than a hint of coffee.

Panther

Unit 1, Collers Way, Reepham, Norfolk, NR10 4SW
☎ 07766 558215 ⊕ pantherbrewery.co.uk

⊠ Panther began brewing in 2010 on an industrial estate near the old railway station, formerly the home of Reepham Brewery. ‼☷◆LIVE

Mild Panther (ABV 3.3%) MILD
Smooth, sweet base with contrasting, dry cobnut notes and a gentle roastiness. Short, clean finish with biscuit airs.

Ginger Panther (ABV 3.7%) SPECIALITY
Refreshingly clean, ginger wheat beer with a distinct fiery kick. It contains all the ingredients of a Thai curry.

Golden Panther (ABV 3.7%) GOLD
Refreshing orange and malt notes flow through this well-balanced, easy-drinking bitter. Hops and a soft bitterness add depth.

Honey Panther (ABV 4%) SPECIALITY
A gentle flowing brew with honey and malt throughout. Amber-coloured with a tapering bittersweet finale.

Red Panther (ABV 4.1%) RED
A distinctly malty nose with a nutty, bittersweet beginning. Rye, plum and caramel appear before a full-bodied hoppiness emerges.

American Pale Ale (ABV 4.4%) BLOND
Zesty lemon and hop character with a gentle sweet counterpoint. Light grapefruit notes bolster a short, crisp finish.

Black Panther (ABV 4.5%) PORTER
Vanilla rum and raisin throughout. Strong supporting mix of caramel, malt and robust roastiness. Mellow and complex finish slowly sweetens.

Beast of the East (ABV 5.5%) IPA
A hoppy resinous bouquet with hints of sweetness. Earthy, peppery beginning with a hoppy backdrop. Long, drying, bitter citrus finish.

Papworth SIBA

24 Earith Business Park, Meadow Drove, Earith, Cambridgeshire, PE28 3QF
☎ (01487) 842442 ☎ 07835 845797
⊕ papworthbrewery.com

Brewing began in 2014 in Papworth Everard. The brewery moved to new premises in Earith in 2017 and acquired an 11-barrel plant, significantly increasing its production. The brewery site is licensed for on and off-sales, with a new brewery tap and bottle shop opened in late 2020. ‼☷◆

Mild Thing (ABV 3.5%) MILD
Tooty Frooty (ABV 3.5%) GOLD
Mad Jack (ABV 3.8%) BITTER
The Whitfield Citrabolt (ABV 3.8%) GOLD
Whispering Grass (ABV 3.8%) BITTER
Crystal Ship (ABV 4.2%) BITTER
Half Nelson (ABV 4.2%) PALE
Red Kite (ABV 4.7%) BITTER
Off the Lip (ABV 5%) PALE
Robin Goodfellow (ABV 5.4%) PORTER
Pass the Porter (ABV 5.5%) PORTER
Koura (ABV 5.7%) SPECIALITY

Paradigm

4d Green End Farm, 93a Church Lane, Sarratt, Hertfordshire, WD3 6HH
☎ (01923) 291215 ⊕ paradigmbrewery.com

⊠ Founded by two friends, Neil Hodges and Rob Atkinson, Paradigm went into production in 2015. Its five-barrel plant is located in an industrial unit on a farm.

One-off beers are also brewed. The brewery and beer names are based on corporate jargon and buzzwords. ‼◆LIVE

fake news (ABV 3.8%) PALE
fyi (ABV 3.8%) BITTER
touchpoint (ABV 3.9%) PALE
juxtaposition (ABV 4%) BITTER
heads up (ABV 4.1%) BITTER
stir crazy (ABV 4.2%) GOLD
win-win (ABV 4.2%) BITTER
zeitgeist (ABV 4.5%) BITTER
black friday (ABV 6%) MILD

Parakeet City (NEW)

Meadvale Road, Pitshanger, London, W5 1NT
⊕ parakeetcitybrewing.com

Brewing began in 2020, based in Pitshanger, north of central Ealing. One canned beer is produced. No real ale.

Parish

6 Main Street, Burrough on the Hill, Leicestershire, LE14 2JQ
☎ (01664) 454801 ☎ 07715 369410
✉ bazbrewery@gmail.com

Parish began brewing in 1983 and now operates on a 20-barrel plant, with capacity to brew a further 12 barrels. The brewery is located in a 400-year-old building next to the Stag & Hounds, where its flagship beer, PSB, is permanently available. Other local outlets are also supplied and one-off brews are produced for beer festivals both locally and across surrounding counties. ‼LIVE

PSB (ABV 3.9%) BITTER
A refreshing pale session ale. Distinctive floral aroma with mild hints of pine. Sharp hop bitterness balanced with crisp malt flavours in the taste giving way to a lovely lingering floral finish.

Park Brew

Unit 10, Brechin Business Centre, Brechin, DD9 6DY
☎ 07905 998740 ✉ info@parkbrew.com

Established in 2016 by John Leatherbarrow and Andrew Donald. Brewing is currently suspended.

Park Brewery SIBA

Unit 7, Hampden Road, Norbiton, Surrey, KT1 3HG
☎ (020) 8541 1887

Office: 38 St Georges Road, Kingston upon Thames, KT2 6DN ⊕ theparkbrewery.com

⊠ Park was founded in 2014 in a former greengrocer's premises, using a one-barrel plant, increasing in 2015 to four barrels. After a year cuckoo brewing at Reunion, brewing at its new site commenced in 2018. With a strong emphasis on cask production, beers are named after locations in Richmond Park. ‼◆LIVE◆

Killcat Pale (ABV 3.7%) BITTER
Unfined, golden bitter with grapefruit throughout. Subtle malt and strong hoppy bitter notes in the flavour and short, dry finish.

Amelia (ABV 4.2%) PALE
Gallows Gold (ABV 4.2%) GOLD
Tropical fruit, orange and hop notes dominate. Malt is restrained with a gentle biscuit presence and growing bitterness. Well-balanced.

Spankers IPA (ABV 6%) IPA

An amber-coloured, hoppy, citrus, dry golden ale with a similar finish and a touch of dry bitterness.

Parker

Unit 3 Gravel Lane, Banks, Lancashire, PR9 8BY
☎ (01704) 620718 ☎ 07949 797889
⊕ theparkerbrewery.co.uk

😊 Parker was established in 2014 using a 25-litre plant, but quickly expanded to a five-barrel plant. In 2018 the brewery opened its own micropub, the Beer Den, Southport. ‼ LIVE

Centurion Pale Ale (ABV 3.9%) PALE
Barbarian Bitter (ABV 4.1%) BITTER
Saxon Red Ale (ABV 4.5%) RED
Viking Blonde (ABV 4.7%) BLOND
Dark Spartan Stout (ABV 5%) STOUT
Well-balanced stout with a burnt smoky roast aroma, roast strong on tasting with a little sweetness, ending with mellow flavours and some bitterness to finish

Parkway

Unit 11, Wessex Park, Somerton Business Park, Somerton, TA11 6SB
☎ (01458) 897240 ⊕ parkwaybrewing.co.uk

Parkway began its journey into brewing in 2018, having purchased the former Glastonbury Ales plant and equipment. Although located in the small market town of Somerton, Parkway is named after a road in North London's Camden Town. The brewery also contract brew under license. LIVE

Giggle & Titter (ABV 3.8%) BITTER
Cheeky Monkey (ABV 4%) BLOND
Norwegian Blue (ABV 4.2%) BITTER

Contract brewed for Glastonbury Brewery:
Mystery Tor (ABV 3.8%) BITTER
Golden, full-bodied bitter with floral hop and fruit on the nose and palate, sweetness giving way to bitter hop finish.
Lady of the Lake (ABV 4.2%) BITTER
Full-bodied, amber best bitter with hops balanced by fruity malt flavour and a hint of vanilla. Clean, bitter hop aftertaste.
Love Monkey (ABV 4.2%) GOLD
Black As Yer 'At (ABV 4.3%) STOUT
Hedge Monkey (ABV 4.6%) BITTER
Golden Chalice (ABV 4.8%) GOLD
Thriller Cappuccino Porter (ABV 5%) SPECIALITY

Partizan

34 Raymouth Road, Bermondsey, London, SE16 2DB
☎ (020) 8127 5053 ⊕ partizanbrewing.co.uk

Started in 2012, using an ex-Kernel kit in an early taproom on the Bermondsey Beer Mile. Expanded in 2017 by moving to an arch around the corner. The extensive range (available in keg, bottles and some cans), includes hop-forward pales and IPAs, stouts and experimental saisons. No real ale. ➤◆⚘

Pastore Brewing & Blending

Unit 2, Convent Drive, Waterbeach, CB25 9QT
⊕ pastorebrewing.com

⊗ Founded in 2019, Pastore Brewing & Blending specialise in mixed-fermentation sour and wild ales. Pastore (Pas-tor-ray) is Italian for shepherd, in honour of the brewer's Italian family. It ties rustic, wild brewing with a modern, semi-urban setting, making new-age fresh, fruited weisses, as well as barrel-aged old saisons.

Seasonals information can be found online. All beers are vegan. ➤◆LIVE V⚘

Patten

🍺 **The Patten Arms, Park Lane, Winmarleigh, PR3 0JU**
☎ (01524) 791484
✉ thepattenarmswinmarleigh@gmail.com

Brewing started in 2019 using a small plant in the cellar of the Patten Arms.

Peak SIBA

Barn Brewery, Chatsworth, Bakewell, Derbyshire, DE45 1EX
☎ (01246) 583737 ⊕ peakales.co.uk

😊 Peak Ales opened 2005 in a former derelict farm building on the Chatsworth estate, aided by a DEFRA Rural Enterprise Scheme grant and support from trustees of Chatsworth Settlement. Main production moved to a new facility at Ashford in the Water in 2014 to increase capacity. A shop and visitor centre opened in 2017 at the original site on the Chatsworth Estate, where a pilot brewery for experimental and occasional brews is now operational, with its own gin distillery. ‼ ➤◆

Swift Nick (ABV 3.8%) BITTER
Easy-drinking, copper-coloured bitter with balanced malt and hops and a gentle, hoppy, bitter finish.
Summer Sovereign (ABV 4%) BLOND
Bakewell Best Bitter (ABV 4.2%) BITTER
Full-bodied, tawny bitter with a hoppy bitterness against a malty background, leading to a hoppy dry aftertaste.
Paxton (ABV 4.4%) RED
Chatsworth Gold (ABV 4.6%) SPECIALITY
Speciality beer made with honey, which gives a pleasant sweetness leading to a hop and malt finish.
Black Stag (ABV 4.8%) STOUT
DPA (Derbyshire Pale Ale) (ABV 5%) PALE
IPA (ABV 6%) IPA

Peakstones Rock SIBA

Peakstones Farm, Cheadle Road, Alton, Staffordshire, ST10 4DH ☎ 07891 350908 ⊕ peakstonesrock.co.uk

⊗ Peakstones Rock are a family-run brewery established in 2005 with a five-barrel plant located on a farm in the Peak District National Park. The brewery was expanded to 10-barrel capacity in 2009. It supplies an expanding free trade market in the North Midlands and surrounding areas. ‼◆LIVE

Nemesis (ABV 3.8%) BITTER
Biscuity aroma with some hop background. Sweet start, sweetish body then hops emerge to give a fruity middle. Bitterness develops slowly to a tongue-tingling finish.
Pugin's Gold (ABV 4%) GOLD
Chained Oak (ABV 4.2%) BITTER
Alton Abbey (ABV 4.5%) BITTER
Black Hole (ABV 4.8%) OLD
Grassy aroma with malt background. Hops hit the mouth and intensify. Bitterness lingers with some mouth-watering astringency
Oblivion (ABV 5.5%) BITTER

Peerless SIBA

The Brewery, 8 Pool Street, Birkenhead, Merseyside, CH41 3NL
☎ (0151) 647 7688 ⊕ peerlessbrewing.co.uk

Peerless began brewing in 2009 and is under the directorship of Steve Briscoe. Beers are sold through festivals, local pubs and the free trade. ‼◆⚘

Pale (ABV 3.8%) PALE
Triple Blond (ABV 4%) BLOND
Skyline (ABV 4.2%) BITTER
Langton Spin (ABV 4.4%) GOLD
Oatmeal Stout (ABV 5%) STOUT
Knee-Buckler IPA (ABV 5.2%) PALE
Full Whack (ABV 6%) IPA

Pells & Co

🍺 White Horse Inn, The Street, Neatishead, Norfolk, NR12 8AD
☎ (01692) 630828
⊕ thewhitehorseinnneatishead.com

⊗ Formerly known as Neatishead Brewery, production began in 2015 at the White Horse Inn. The brew kit can be viewed through glass from the restaurant. Beer is only available in the White Horse and the owner's other pub, the Lion, Thurne. A range of semi-regular beers is brewed with at least one ever-changing ale. The range is currently being contract brewed by an unknown brewery.

Penlon

Panteg Farm, New Quay, SA45 9TL
☎ (01545) 561492 ⊕ penlonbrewery.co.uk

Established in 2004, Penlon is a six-barrel, farm-based brewery. In 2017 it opened the Granary taproom and pizza bar with stunning views across the Cardigan coastline. The brewery expanded in 2020. !! ☛ LIVE V

Tipsy Tup (ABV 3.8%) PALE
Cardi Bay (ABV 4%) BITTER
Heather Honey Ale (ABV 4.2%) SPECIALITY
Hidden Howler (ABV 4.3%) PALE
Ramnesia (ABV 6.2%) BITTER

Pennine SIBA

Well Hall Farm, Well, Bedale, North Yorkshire, DL8 2PX
☎ (01677) 470111 ⊕ pennine-brewing.co.uk

☺ Located in the village of Well near Masham, the brewery has been in production on this site since 2013 using an 18-barrel plant complete with lauter tun. Beer is supplied to pubs throughout the North of England as well as to beer festivals and local outdoor events. !! ♦

Amber Necker (ABV 3.9%) BITTER
Hair of the Dog (ABV 3.9%) BITTER
Heartland (ABV 3.9%) BITTER
Natural Gold (ABV 4.2%) GOLD
IPA (ABV 4.4%) PALE

Penton Park

Penton Park, Penton Mewsey, Andover, Hampshire, SP11 0RD
☎ (01264) 772400 ☎ 07764 691771
⊕ pentonparkbrewery.com

⊗ Started from homebrew equipment, this brewery has now expanded to five barrels and is located in the historic early Georgian kitchen of Penton Park. The room is nearly 300 years old, and the brewery draws water from a nearby well. Brewing is currently suspended. !! ♦

Pentrich SIBA

Unit B, Asher Lane Business Park, Asher Lane, Pentrich, Derbyshire, DE5 3RB
☎ (01773) 741700
✉ pentrichbrewingco@gmail.com

Two former home brewers began producing beer in their garage in Pentrich, before moving to share the plant of the Landlocked Brewing Co at the Beehive Inn, Ripley in 2014. In 2016 Pentrich moved into its own premises using second-hand equipment. In 2019 it purchased a made-to-order 16-barrel plant. Only one regular beer is produced now, preferring to concentrate on special beers.
♦

Brandrith Bitter (ABV 3.8%)

Penzance

🍺 Star Inn, Crowlas, Cornwall, TR20 8DX
☎ (01736) 740375 ☎ 07763 956333
⊕ penzancebrewingcompany.co.uk

⊗ Owner Peter Elvin began brewing in 2008 on a self-built, five-barrel plant in the old stable block of the Star Inn. The fermentation capacity has since been expanded, increasing the volume and range of beer produced. Production is now at full capacity of 1,400 barrels a year. Besides the pub, selected outlets and beer festivals are supplied. !! ♦

Mild (ABV 3.6%) MILD
Creamy, dark brown mild, chocolate and roast aroma. Coffee and chocolate dominate the taste with fruit notes, bittersweet, balanced finish.
Crowlas Bitter (ABV 3.8%) BITTER
Refreshing, copper session bitter with light malt aroma. Light biscuit maltiness and hops. Lingering finish of malty bitterness with dryness.
Potion No. 9 (ABV 4%) PALE
Refreshing pale ale. Grapefruit and tropical fruit flavours dominate with some pine resin notes, biscuit malt and flashes of bubblegum esters.
Crows-an-Wra (ABV 4.3%) BLOND
Straw blonde ale with grassy, hoppy aroma. Bitter hops dominate throughout, balanced by grapefruit and some malt. Long, clean finish.
Brisons Bitter (ABV 4.5%) BITTER
Brown best bitter, pleasant malt and hop balance. Biscuit malt accompanies bitter orange fruit with a lasting bitter, dry finish.
Trink (ABV 5.2%) BLOND
Blonde ale with grapefruit nose. Punchy pine-resin hop flavours with grapefruit, marmalade and peaches. Bittersweet and hoppy finish.
IPA (ABV 6%) IPA
Smooth, golden, genuine IPA with hoppy aroma. Powerful hop bitterness with light malt and tropical fruits, finishing bitter and dry.
Scilly Stout (ABV 7%) STOUT
Black, full-bodied, creamy stout with chocolate aroma. Chocolate roast malt with liquorice and plums. Long finish with strong roast malt.

People's Captain (NEW)

39 Sackville Road, Hove, East Sussex, BN3 3WD
⊕ peoplescaptain.co.uk

People's Captain was an idea conceived by Greg Bateman, a professional Rugby player. Along with friends Stewart Beale and Jason Reeves the company was established to brew craft beer while also contributing to positive mental health. Every beer sold raises money via the People's Captain Foundation.

People's

Mill House, Mill Lane, Thorpe-Next-Haddiscoe, Norwich, Norfolk, NR14 6PA
☎ (01508) 548706 ✉ peoplesbrewery@mail.com

⊠ A one-barrel brewery associated with the community-owned Queen's Head pub in Thurlton, which takes most of its draught output. Beers are also available at the Thurlton Community shop.

Northdown Bitter (ABV 3.8%) BITTER
Raveningham Bitter (ABV 3.9%) BITTER
Thurlton Gold (ABV 4.2%) PALE
Norfolk Cascade (ABV 4.5%) GOLD
Northern Brewers (ABV 4.6%) BITTER

Peregrine (NEW)

B9 Riverside Industrial Estate, Hermitage Street, Rishton, BB1 4NF ☎ 07757 404231
⊕ peregrinebrewingltd.com

Started brewing in late 2020 using a 1.5-barrel plant. ♦

What What? (ABV 3.6%) BITTER
Flight of the Falcon (ABV 3.7%) GOLD
Próst! (ABV 4%) PALE

Perivale

Horsenden Farm, Horsenden Lane North, Perivale, UB6 7PQ ☎ 07850 176177 ⊕ perivale.beer

Established in 2019, the brewery is based at a farm looked after by the Friends of Horsenden Hill. As well as other events, monthly tap room openings are hosted, selling beers using hops grown on the farm, and other local foraged ingredients. No real ale. ♦

Phantom

Unit 3, Meadow Road, Reading, Berkshire, RG1 8LB

A 12-barrel brewery, situated on the outskirts of Reading town centre, which began brewing in 2020. It produces a good range of differing beer styles including hop-heavy pale ales, fruit sours and stouts. Currently only KeyKeg beers are produced. ♦

Pheasantry SIBA

High Brecks Farm, Lincoln Road, East Markham, Nottinghamshire, NG22 0SN
☎ (01777) 872728 ☎ 07948 976749
⊕ pheasantrybrewery.co.uk

⊕Pheasantry began brewing in 2012 using a new 10-barrel plant from Canada. Situated in a listed barn on a farm, the brewery incorporates a wedding and events venue, with the brewery visible through glass partitions. It supplies more than 200 pubs and retail outlets in Nottinghamshire, Lincolnshire, Derbyshire and South Yorkshire. A bottling line was installed in 2018. !! ▰

Best Bitter (ABV 3.8%) BITTER
Pale Ale (ABV 4%) PALE
Black Pheasant (ABV 4.2%) PORTER
Lincoln Tank Ale (ABV 4.2%) BITTER
Ringneck Amber Ale (ABV 4.2%) BITTER
Amber-coloured best bitter, initial malt and caramel leading to a brief bitter, dry finish.
Excitra (ABV 4.5%) GOLD
Dancing Dragonfly (ABV 5%) BLOND

Philsters

Unit 16, Camp Industrial Estate, Rycote Lane, Milton Common, Oxfordshire, OX9 2NP ☎ 07747 827489

Office: Beehive Cottage, Little Haseley, Oxfordshire, OX44 7LH ⊕ philsters.co.uk

Named after the owner/brewer's nickname, this small brewery, established in 2015 at the brewer's home,

expanded with a 4.5-barrel plant into new premises in 2019. It supplies a number of local pubs. ♦V

Boosh (ABV 4%) BITTER
Milton Gold (ABV 4.1%) GOLD
Oxford Red (ABV 4.2%) RED
7th Phase (ABV 5%) PALE
Rising (ABV 5%) GOLD
Under the Wire (ABV 5%) PALE
Darkside (ABV 5.1%) SPECIALITY

Phipps SIBA

Albion Brewery, 54 Kingswell Street, Northampton, NN1 1PR
☎ (01604) 946606 ☎ 07717 078402
⊕ phipps-nbc.co.uk

Originally founded in Towcester in 1801, Phipps had been brewing in Northampton since 1817 until it was taken over by Watney Mann, and closed in 1974. Company name and recipes were acquired, and in 2008 the first beer reappeared. The Albion Brewery site, once owned by Phipps, was acquired and a new 15-barrel brewing plant was installed in 2014 to enable Phipps beers to be once again brewed in the town. Beer is also brewed under the Gun Dog Ales name. !! ♦LIVE

Thrupenny Bitter (ABV 3.6%) BITTER
Diamond Ale (ABV 3.7%) BITTER
Rich honey sweetish aroma, a full bitter flavour with citrus notes and a bitter aftertaste with hints of grapefruit.
Red Star (ABV 3.8%) BITTER
Honey malt aroma, a flavour of rye, some sweetness and hints of dark cherry and a dry bitter aftertaste.
Steam Roller (ABV 3.8%) BITTER
Biscuity aroma with some sweetness followed by earthy, spiced bitterness with hints of plum which continue in the dry aftertaste.
Midsummer Meadow (ABV 3.9%) BITTER
Cobbler's Ale (ABV 4%) BITTER
India Pale Ale (ABV 4.3%) BITTER
Ratliffe's Celebrated Stout (ABV 4.3%) STOUT
Becket's Ale (ABV 4.5%) BITTER
Bison Brown (ABV 4.6%) MILD
Black Star (ABV 4.8%) BITTER
Roasted malt aromas with liquorice notes followed by a bitter coffee chocolate flavour and a dry, bitter coffee aftertaste.
Last Orders (ABV 4.8%) BITTER
Kinky Boots (ABV 4.9%)
Gold Star (ABV 5.2%) PALE

Brewed under the Gun Dog Ales brand name:
Jack's Spaniels (ABV 3.8%) BITTER
Scrum Dog (ABV 4%) BITTER
Booze Hound (ABV 4.2%) BITTER
Lord Barker (ABV 4.2%) STOUT
Bad to the Bone (ABV 4.5%) BITTER
A light brown bitter with a fruity nose, biscuit malt flavour and a bitter finish.
Yankee Poodle (ABV 4.7%) PALE
A golden-coloured beer with a citrus hop aroma, citrus bitter flavour, and a bitter finish.

Phoenix SIBA

Green Lane, Heywood, OL10 2EP
☎ (01706) 627009 ⊠ tony@phoenixbrewery.co.uk

⊕Established in Ellesmere Port in 1982, Oak Brewery moved to the old Phoenix Brewery in Heywood and adopted the name in 1991. It now supplies more than 400 outlets plus wholesalers. Restoration of the old brewery, built in 1897, is ongoing. ♦

Hopsack (ABV 3.8%) GOLD
Navvy (ABV 3.8%) BITTER
Amber beer with a citrus fruit and malt nose. Good balance of citrus fruit, malt and hops with bitterness coming through in the aftertaste.
Monkeytown Mild (ABV 3.9%) MILD
Light roast aroma. Mild creamy roast flavour with sweet malt and some astringency. Lasting, dry, bitter finish.
Arizona (ABV 4.1%) GOLD
Yellow in colour with a fruity and hoppy aroma. A refreshing beer with citrus, hops and good bitterness, and a shortish dry aftertaste.
Spotland Gold (ABV 4.1%) GOLD
Pale Moonlight (ABV 4.2%) PALE
Black Bee (ABV 4.5%) SPECIALITY
White Monk (ABV 4.5%) PALE
Yellow beer with a citrus fruit aroma, plenty of fruit, hops and bitterness in the taste, and a hoppy, bitter finish.
Thirsty Moon (ABV 4.6%) BITTER
Tawny beer with a fresh citrus aroma. Hoppy, fruity and malty with a dry, hoppy finish.
West Coast IPA (ABV 4.6%) PALE
Golden in colour with a hoppy, fruity nose. Strong hoppy and fruity taste and aftertaste with good bitterness throughout.
Double Gold (ABV 5%) GOLD
Wobbly Bob (ABV 6%) BITTER
A red/brown beer with malty, fruity aroma and creamy mouthfeel. Strongly malty and fruity in flavour, with hops and a hint of herbs. Both sweetness and bitterness are evident throughout.

Brewed for Brunning & Price Pub Co:
Original (ABV 3.8%) BITTER

Pictish

Unit 9, Canalside Industrial Estate, Woodbine Street East, Rochdale, OL16 5LB
☎ (01706) 522227 ⊕ pictish-brewing.co.uk

☺The brewery was established in 2000 and supplies free trade outlets in the North-West and West Yorkshire. Famed for the consistency and clarity of its brews and its ever-changing single hop series of beers. ◆

Brewers Gold (ABV 3.8%) BITTER
Yellow in colour, with a hoppy, fruity nose. Soft maltiness and a strong hop/citrus flavour lead to a dry, bitter finish.
Talisman IPA (ABV 4.2%) PALE
Strong hoppy aroma; hops and fruit in the taste. Some initial sweetness, but with hoppy bitterness throughout.
Alchemists Ale (ABV 4.3%) BITTER
Bitter beer with malt aroma.

Piddle

Unit 24, Enterprise Park, Piddlehinton, Dorchester, Dorset, DT2 7UA
☎ (01305) 849336 ☎ 07730 436343
⊕ piddlebrewery.co.uk

⊗ Established in 2007, with new owners in 2014. The brewery produces a broad range of beers from its location in the Piddle Valley in Dorset. Some beer names reflect this unusual name. Beers are available in pubs and retail outlets across Dorset and beyond. ◆

Dorset Rogue (ABV 3.9%) BITTER
Piddle (ABV 4.1%) BITTER
Cocky (ABV 4.3%) PALE
Bent Copper (ABV 4.8%) BITTER
Slasher (ABV 5.1%) BLOND

Pied Bull

⊟ Pied Bull Hotel, 57 Northgate Street, Chester, CH1 2HQ
☎ (01244) 325829 ⊕ piedbull.co.uk

☺Pied Bull began brewing in 2011 using a one-barrel plant. Beer is mainly for in-house consumption, but local beer festivals are supplied and occasional brewery swaps occur. ◆

Pig & Porter

9 Chapman Way, Tunbridge Wells, Kent, TN2 3EF
☎ (01892) 615071 ⊕ pigandporter.co.uk

⊗ Originally brewing at several microbreweries in Sussex and Kent, brewing has taken place on its own plant in Tunbridge Wells since 2013, using a 10-barrel plant. ◆V

Blackbird (ABV 4%) STOUT
Skylarking (ABV 4%) PALE
Slave to the Money (ABV 4.1%) BITTER
Stone Free (ABV 4.3%) PALE
All These Vibes (ABV 5.3%) PALE

Pig Beer

Hop House, Setley Ridge, Brockenhurst, SO42 7UF
☎ (01590) 607237 ☎ 07747 462139 ⊕ pigbeer.com

Pig Beer is an 18-barrel brewery operated by two brothers and their cousin. Currently producing bottled beers only, but expected to produce KeyKeg beers for local outlets if there is a demand.

Pig Iron

Brittania Inn, Rowley Village, Rowley Regis, B65 9AT
☎ 07816 018777 ⊕ pigironbrewingco.co.uk

☺Set up in 2015, this three-barrel plant has relocated and is now sited to the rear of the Britannia pub in Rowley Village. The brewer, from a former baking family, acquired the kit from Brewmeister in Northern Scotland. The brewery supplies free trade outlets within 15 miles of the brewery and the brewers home, as well as Weavers Real Ale House, Kidderminster. ◆

Blonde (ABV 3.8%) PALE
EPA (ABV 4.2%) PALE
IPA (ABV 4.2%) PALE
Unbeweavable (ABV 4.2%) BITTER
APA (ABV 4.5%) PALE

Brewed under the Britt Brewery brand name:
Brew Britannia (ABV 4.2%) BITTER
Pop (ABV 4.9%) BITTER

Pig Pub

⊟ Pig In Muck, Manor Road, Claybrooke Magna, Leicestershire, LE17 5AY
☎ (01455) 202859 ⊕ piginmuck.com/brewery

Brewing began in 2013 using a two-barrel plant, upgraded to a five-barrel plant built by head brewer Kev Featherstone. ➹◆LIVE ⚒

Piglove

Unit 6, Cross Green Lane, Leeds, West Yorkshire, LS9 8LJ ☎ 07718 630467 ⊕ piglovebrewing.com

Piglove is a small craft brewery based in Leeds. Inspired by the heritage of craft brewing in the UK and influenced by its co-founders' Venezuelan roots, its beers are bold, fragrant, unusual and exotic. Beers are organic and vegetarian. ✦

OMNIA (ABV 4.5%) IPA
Phantasticum Hop Healer (ABV 6.5%) SPECIALITY

Pilgrim SIBA

11 West Street, Reigate, Surrey, RH2 9BL
☎ (01737) 222651 ☎ 07973 297410 ⊕ pilgrim.co.uk

⊠ Pilgrim was the first microbrewery in Surrey, set up in 1982 in Woldingham before moving to its current premises in Reigate in 1984. New owners from 2017 are developing new ales to complement the current selection, and have enlarged to a 12-barrel brew length and opened a taproom. Beers are available in many local outlets. ‼🍴♦✦

Surrey (ABV 3.7%) BITTER
Pineapple, grapefruit and spicy aromas. Biscuity maltiness with a hint of vanilla balanced by a hoppy bitterness and refreshing, bittersweet finish.
Session IPA (ABV 3.9%) PALE
Progress (ABV 4%) BITTER
Well-rounded, tawny-coloured bitter. Predominantly sweet and malty with an underlying fruitiness and hint of toffee, balanced with a subdued bitterness.
Quest (ABV 4.3%) GOLD
Pioneer APA (ABV 4.5%) PALE
Saracen (ABV 4.5%) STOUT

Pillars SIBA

Unit 2, Ravenswood Industrial Estate, Shernhall Street, Walthamstow, London, E17 9HQ
☎ (020) 8521 5552 ⊕ pillarsbrewery.com

Brewing began in 2016 as an exclusively keg lager brewery. The range has been expanded over the years but still sticks to its lager roots. 2021 saw the introduction of 330ml bottles. As well as the taproom, it runs the Untraditional Pub in the Crate development in Walthamstow. ✦

Pilot Beer

4B Stewartfield, Edinburgh, EH6 5RQ
☎ (0131) 561 4267 ⊕ pilotbeer.co.uk

Pilot began brewing in 2013 in an industrial unit in Leith using a five-barrel plant. A move to larger premises allowed for expansion. Beers are unfined and unfiltered. Almost all output is keg or can but cask-conditioned ale is occasionally available. LIVE

Pilot Brewery

🛢 **726 Mumbles Road, Mumbles, Swansea, SA3 4EL**
☎ 07897 895511 ⊕ thepilotbrewery.co.uk

⊙The Pilot Brewery began production on its 2.5-barrel plant in 2013. It is located at the rear of the Pilot Inn on the Mumbles sea front. The output is mainly for the pub but can also be supplied to festivals and other select outlets. The proprietors have also set up BeerRiff brewery (qv). V

Pin-Up

Unit 3 Block 3, Chalex Industrial Estate, Manor Hall Road, Southwick, West Sussex, BN42 4NH
☎ (01273) 411127 ☎ 07888 836892
⊕ pinupbrewingco.com

⊠ Pin-Up began brewing in 2011, initially having its beers contract brewed at an Essex brewery. In 2014 it obtained its own plant and began brewing in Southwick,

and expanded from a five-barrel to a 10-barrel plant in 2015. Its first pub, the United Brethren, Chelmsford, opened in 2016. ♦LIVE

Honey Brown (ABV 4%) BITTER
Session IPA (ABV 4.1%) PALE
Summer Pale (ABV 4.1%) PALE
Red Head (ABV 4.2%) RED
Milk Stout (ABV 4.5%) STOUT

Pinnora SIBA

Unit 2, rear of Jubilee Parade, Marsh Road, Pinner, HA5 1BB
☎ (0845) 744 2337 ⊕ pinnorabrewing.com

Family-run, craft brewery based in North West London. Refurbishment took place in 2021. The short four-hectolitre brew length means brewing focuses on seasonal beers and an evolving series of craft beers from their brew lab. This includes the official beer of the Chelsea Pensioners, released on Remembrance Sunday 2021. LIVE

Pipeline (NEW)

Town Meadow, St. Agnes, TR5 0UH ☎ 07973 178877
⊕ pipelinebrewing.co.uk

Pipeline Brewing Co crafts small batches of vibrant, hoppy, juicy beers on the North Cornwall coast. Using fresh ingredients and Cornish water, they create craft beers that showcase the best of New World hops. No real ale.

Pipes

183A Kings Road, Cardiff, CF11 9DF ☎ 07776 382244
⊕ pipesbeer.co.uk

Pipes Beer create examples of some of the unique and least known beer styles from around the globe, with no preservatives or additives used in production. The main output is bottled and keg beers although the occasional cask beer is produced. 🍴♦

Pit Top

See Wrytree

Pitchfork

See Epic Beers

Pitfield

See Dominion

Plain

17c Deverill Trading Estate, Sutton Veny, Wiltshire, BA12 7BZ
☎ (01985) 841481 ⊕ plainales.co.uk

⊠ Plain Ales started production in 2008 on a 2.5-barrel plant in a garage, and expanded to a 10-barrel plant in 2010 to keep up with demand for its award-winning ales. 2018 saw the introduction of its Kult Brewing Co brand to brew edgier beers. ‼♦✦

Sheep Dip (ABV 3.8%) BITTER
Innocence (ABV 4%) GOLD
Inspiration (ABV 4%) BITTER
Intrigue (ABV 4.2%) BITTER
Independence (ABV 4.5%) PALE
Incognito (ABV 4.8%) STOUT
India Plain Ale (ABV 5.2%) PALE

Plan B

Audley Avenue Enterprise Park, Audley Avenue, Newport, TF10 7DW
☎ (01952) 810091 ⊕ newbrew.co.uk

☺Plan B is a family-run brewery set up in 2016 using a 10-barrel plant. Cask-conditioned ale is available within a 30-mile radius of the brewery. It has its own bottling plant and all beers are available from the shop or online. ‼ ➡LIVE

New Alchemy (ABV 3.9%) BITTER
New Session IPA (ABV 4%) PALE
Boscobel Bitter (ABV 4.3%) BITTER
Newport Pale Ale (ABV 4.4%) PALE
Steam Stout (ABV 4.5%) STOUT

Platform 5 SIBA

2 Magdalene Mews, Torquay, Devon, TQ1 4AF
☎ 07779 000081 ⊕ platform5brewing.co.uk

⊗ This family-run brewery was established in 2013 using a six-barrel plant. The Railway Inn is supplied along with Molloys in Teignmouth and Torquay.

The Coaster (ABV 4%) BITTER
The Antelope (ABV 4.3%) PALE
APA (ABV 4.6%) PALE
The Whistleblower (ABV 4.6%) BITTER
Complex nose with roast and caramel leading to fruit and sweet hops with bitterness on the tongue. Dry aftertaste.
Western Gold (ABV 4.8%) PALE
Blitzen (ABV 5%) BITTER
IPA (ABV 5%) PALE
The Black Crow (ABV 5.2%) STOUT
Very smooth, satisfying oatmeal stout.

Play Brew SIBA

8 Cannon Park Way, Middlesbrough, North Yorkshire, TS1 5JU
☎ (01642) 244769 ⊕ playbrewco.com

Launched in 2019 by Phil Layton, Play Brew is a brewery, taproom and event space. The 20-hectolitre plant produces unfiltered beers available in keg, cans and occasionally in cask, distributed throughout the north. ♦ ✦

Plockton

5 Bank Street, Plockton, IV52 8TP
☎ (01599) 544276 ☎ 07823 322043
⊕ theplocktonbrewery.com

The brewery started trading in 2007 and expanded to a 2.5-barrel plant in 2009. Bottle-conditioned beers are available and are suitable for vegetarians. ‼♦LIVE

Yarrowale (ABV 4.2%)
Plockton Bay (ABV 4.6%) BITTER
A well-balanced, tawny-coloured, premium bitter with plenty of hops and malt which give a bittersweet, fruity flavour.
Starboard! (ABV 5.1%) GOLD
A fine, fruity golden ale with a light citrus bitterness. Hop and spicy fruit feature in the nose with a smack of grapefruit in the taste. The bitterness holds well into the aftertaste.
Ring Tong (ABV 5.6%) IPA

Poachers

439 Newark Road, North Hykeham, Lincolnshire, LN6 9SP

☎ (01522) 807404 ☎ 07954 131972
⊕ poachersbrewery.co.uk

☺The brewery was founded in 2001 in buildings on the former RAF Swinderby site. In 2006 the plant was relocated to outbuildings at the rear of the brewer's home. Regular outlets in Lincolnshire and surrounding counties are supplied direct; outlets further afield, via beer swaps with other breweries. An on-site bar is open to public on a Friday evening and for groups at other times by prior arrangement. ‼♦✦

Trembling Rabbit Mild (ABV 3.4%) MILD
Shy Talk Bitter (ABV 3.7%) BITTER
Rock Ape (ABV 3.8%) BITTER
Poachers Pride (ABV 4%) BITTER
Tedi Boy (ABV 4%) PALE
Bog Trotter (ABV 4.2%) BITTER
Lincoln Best (ABV 4.2%) BITTER
Billy Boy (ABV 4.4%) BITTER
Imp Ale (ABV 4.4%) BITTER
Black Crow Stout (ABV 4.5%) STOUT
Hykeham Gold (ABV 4.5%) SPECIALITY
Monkey Hanger (ABV 4.5%) BITTER
Jock's Trap (ABV 5%) BITTER
Trout Tickler (ABV 5.5%) BITTER

Point Break (NEW)

Trevelmond, Liskeard, Cornwall, PL14 4LZ
⊕ pointbreakbrewery.com

Established near Liskeard, Cornwall, in mid-2020 during the pandemic. Four bottled beers are brewed in small batches on its 65-litre plant. All bottle labels use uncoated paper and are plastic-free. The brewery supports Surfers Against Sewage. LIVE

Polarity

5 Abbotts Close, Worthing, West Sussex, BN11 1JB
☎ 07872 105300 ⊕ polaritybrewing.co.uk

A small brewery established in 2016 by two homebrewing enthusiasts, focusing on small batch, cask-conditioned beers. They now work full time as brewer's for other established breweries and come together at weekends to brew Polarity beers.

Rosetta's Comet (ABV 5.4%) PALE

Polly's

Holland Farm, Blackbrook, Mold, CH7 6LU
☎ (01244) 940621 ⊕ pollysbrew.co

Polly's Brew Co was established in 2016 (originally as Black Brook inside the stable of an old horse called Polly), and has continuously expanded to what is currently a 23-hectolitre plant. It concentrates on KeyKeg and canned beer, widely distributed throughout the UK and further afield. The beer range changes constantly.

Pomona Island

Unit 33, Waybridge Enterprise Centre, Daniel Adamson Road, Salford, M50 1DS
☎ (0161) 637 2140 ☎ 07972 445474
⊕ pomonaislandbrew.co.uk

Brewery set up in 2017, close to Salford's Media City. Part owned by the people behind the Gas Lamp in Manchester city centre. Head brewer James Dyer is formerly of Tempest Brew Co (qv). Its brewery tap opened in 2019 at 41 Waybridge Enterprise Centre, available to hire for private functions. ➡V

Pale (ABV 3.8%) PALE

Pungent fruity hop aroma. Sweet fruity taste with some bitterness. Gentle and balanced. Lasting, delicate, bitter finish.
Stout (ABV 4.5%) STOUT
APA (ABV 5.3%) PALE
Hoppy beer with fruit and moderate bitterness, leading to a rising bitter finish. Brewed with variable hops.

Pope's Yard

Cutter Room, Frogmore Mill, Apsley, Hertfordshire, HP3 9RY
☎ (01442) 767790 ⊕ popesyard.co.uk

Pope's Yard began commercial brewing in 2012 using a one-barrel plant. Relocation in 2015 also meant expansion to a five-barrel plant with a one-barrel pilot plant. In 2018 the brewery relocated to Apsley, Hemel Hempstead. LIVE V

Lacerta US (ABV 3.9%) PALE
Luminaire (ABV 3.9%) PALE
Quartermaster (ABV 4.4%) BITTER
Club Hammer Stout (ABV 5.5%) STOUT

Poppyland

46 West Street, Cromer, Norfolk, NR27 9DS
☎ (01263) 515214 ☎ 07802 160558
⊕ poppylandbrewery.com

Established in 2012, the 2.5-barrel brewery specialises in unusual brews. Beers are on sale at the brewery and at numerous specialist beer shops across East Anglia. Cask ales are available in some Norfolk and Norwich pubs. The brewery has recently collaborated with beer writer Martyn Cornell (owner Dave's brother), bringing a special twist to the formulation of recipes. ➠ LIVE V

East Coast IPA (ABV 5.4%) PALE
Sweet Chestnut Ale (ABV 6.7%) SPECIALITY

Portishead

🍺 Unit 3, The Precinct, Portishead, BS20 6AH
☎ (07526) 636167 ⊕ theportbar.uk

Brewing started in 2018 with just two beers being sold through local outlets. The following year the brewery moved into its permanent home, The Port, in Portishead town centre. Production increased and nine keg beers are brewed on the premises, (ranging from lagers to stouts). In 2020 it expanded into the adjacent unit. Customers can view the brewing equipment through a glass wall. The popular brewpub sells guest beers, coffee and food are also available. No real ale. ♦

Portobello SIBA

Unit 6, Mitre Bridge Industrial Estate, Mitre Way, North Kensington, London, W10 6AU
☎ (020) 8969 2269 ⊕ portobellobrewing.com

⊗ Established in 2012, and expanded to 50 hectolitres in 2014. The range of beers is available in cask with a similar range in keg, all widely available around London. The Market Porter is an award-winning version of a London porter. The management of some pubs has recently been taken on, including 13 from the Antic Pub Collective. ♦

Westway Pale Ale (ABV 3.8%) PALE
Refreshing, pale yellow beer with orange and apricot. Sweet biscuit, soft citrus and hoppy aroma. Spicy, bitter, lingering, dry aftertaste.
VPA (ABV 4%) PALE

Refreshing, yellow best bitter with citrus fruit throughout and a little peppery hop and biscuit notes. Bitterness builds on drinking.
Star (ABV 4.3%) BITTER
Fruity best bitter with caramel sweetness alongside marmalade and earthy hops. Growing spicy hoppyness and a lingering, dry, bitterish finish.
Market Porter (ABV 4.6%) SPECIALITY
A rye black porter with roasty chocolate flavour with a trace of caramelised, tart, red fruits and little dark toffee. Finish is of dark, dry, bitter roast.
APA (ABV 5%) PALE
Full-bodied, straw-coloured strong ale. The honey sweetness and soft citrus fruit balanced by bitter hops. Dry aftertaste.
Stiff Lip IPA (ABV 5%) PALE

Posh Boys

Riverside House, 8 Lower Southend Road, Wickford, SS11 8BB ☎ 07474 594379 ⊕ poshboysbrewery.com

⊗ Posh Boys is a small independent craft brewery in Essex, set up by two friends. Operating on a part-time basis producing beers in smaller quantities. Beers are available in the taproom, local pubs and occasionally at festivals. ➤

The Blind Butler (ABV 4%) BITTER
The Blonde Maid (ABV 4%) BLOND
Room No. 6 (ABV 4.1%) BLOND
The Bowlers Hat (ABV 4.5%) BITTER
The Coachman (ABV 4.5%) BITTER
The Night Porter (ABV 4.5%) PORTER

Potbelly SIBA

Sydney Street Entrance, Kettering, Northamptonshire, NN16 0JA
☎ (01536) 410818 ☎ 07834 867825
⊕ potbelly-brewery.co.uk

Potbelly started brewing in 2005 on a 10-barrel plant and supplies around 200 outlets. Beers are brewed under the Olde England Ales brand name. ‼ ➤ ♦ LIVE V

Piggoin Proud (ABV 3.7%) BITTER
Potbelly Best (ABV 3.8%) BITTER
Lager Brau (ABV 3.9%) SPECIALITY
A Piggin' IPA (ABV 4%) PALE
Hop-trotter (ABV 4.1%) GOLD
Piggin' Saint (ABV 4.2%) PALE
Beijing Black (ABV 4.4%) MILD
Pigs Do Fly (ABV 4.4%) GOLD
Hedonism (ABV 4.5%) BITTER
Black Sun (ABV 5%) BITTER
Crazy Daze (ABV 5.5%) BITTER

Potton

Unit 3, 8 Market Square, Potton, Bedfordshire, SG19 2NP ☎ 07789 680049
⊕ pottonbrewingcompany.com

⊗ Potton Brewing Company was founded in 2017 by the current owner in order to return brewing to the community after the previous local brewery shut down a few years before. The brewery uses a former Oban Ales 2.5-barrel plant, brewing 1-2 times a week. The brewery has a strong social ethic and gives 1p from every pint sold to charity. All bottled beers are unfined and suitable for vegans. ➤ V

Holly Pup (ABV 3.8%) MILD
Transmitter (ABV 4%) GOLD
Village Recycler (ABV 4.3%) BITTER
Crow (ABV 4.5%) STOUT

Sunny Days (ABV 4.8%) PALE

Powder Monkey (NEW) SIBA

Priddy's Hard, Gosport, Hampshire, PO12 4GB
☎ (023) 9252 2126 ⊕ powdermonkeybrewing.com

Powder Monkey is a 25-hectolitre brewery situated in a unique 1878 former gunpowder magazine.

Powderkeg SIBA

10 Hogsbrook Units, Woodbury Salterton, Devon, EX5 1PY
☎ (01395) 488181 ⊕ powderkegbeer.co.uk

⊗ Powderkeg was established in 2015 brewing small batches of beer. It combines international beer styles with new ingredients sourced from around the world. V

Idler (ABV 3.9%) BITTER
A classic session bitter, crisp, refreshing, malty ale, fruity (lemon) hop taste.
Speak Easy Transatlantic Pale Ale (ABV 4.3%) BITTER

Poynton

🍺 Royal British Legion Club, St George's Road West, Poynton, Cheshire, SK12 1JY ☎ 07722 050733

⊕ The Poynton Brewery was established in 2015 by Colin Bavens and Andy King, located at the Poynton Legion Club. Around 20 pubs, clubs and bars are supplied in the Stockport, Altrincham, East Cheshire and Macclesfield areas. Dre Scuglia joined in 2019 to replace Andy King, who retired. ♦

Prescott

See Hanlons

Pressure Drop SIBA

Unit 6, Lockwood Industrial Park, Mill Mead Road, Tottenham Hale, London, N17 9QP
☎ (020) 8801 0616 ⊕ pressuredropbrewing.co.uk

Run by three partners who were homebrewers but began commercial brewing in 2013, using a five-barrel plant and a small pilot kit. Moving to Tottenham in 2017, the original location is now a bar called the Experiment, operated with Verdant. Beers are mostly sold in KeyKeg and cans, cask versions are produced occasionally for beer festivals. LIVE ♦

Pretty Decent SIBA

Arch 338, Sheridan Road, Forest Gate, London, E7 9EF
☎ (020) 8638 6603 ⊕ prettydecentbeer.co

Brewing began in 2017 in a railway arch in Forest Gate. Production is mostly keg and cans in a range of mostly American styles, which was revamped and simplified in 2020. On demand cask beer is available for local pubs and festivals. A portion of profits is donated to charities such as Pump Aid, a water project in Africa. 🝙 ♦ LIVE ♦

Priest Town

139 Ribbleton Avenue, Preston, Lancashire, PR2 6YS
⊕ priesttownbrewing.com

Priest Town is a craft microbrewery in Preston, operational since 2017. Originally using a 2.5-barrel plant, it has recently acquired a larger kit and plans to increase production. It has a range of eight bottled beers which are sold at its bottle shop on Preston Market. LIVE

Printworks

🍺 Windsor Castle Inn, 7 Stourbridge, Lye, Stourbridge, DY9 7BS
☎ (01384) 897809 ⊕ printworksbrewery.co.uk

⊕ Printworks started full production in 2019 with Emily Sadler at the helm. Based at the Windsor Castle pub, Lye, which is the main outlet for the beers; mostly named after typefaces to reflect a family printing heritage. Core beers and various specials are produced. Equipment is visible through a window in seating area. ‼ ♦ ◈

Prior's Well SIBA

Unit 8, Block 22, Farm Way, Old Mill Lane Industrial Estate, Mansfield Woodhouse, Nottinghamshire, NG19 9BQ
☎ (01623) 632393 ☎ 07970 885204
⊕ priorswellbrewery.co.uk

Originally established in a National Trust building on the Clumber Park Estate, but brewing ceased there in 2014. The brewery was subsequently sold and the five-barrel plant modernised and relocated to a new site in Mansfield Woodhouse in 2016 with an on-site bar. ‼ ◈

Citra (ABV 3.9%) GOLD
Incensed (ABV 4%) BITTER
Silver Chalice (ABV 4.2%) GOLD
Blade (ABV 4.7%) BITTER
Priory Gold (ABV 4.7%) GOLD
Prior's Pale (ABV 4.8%) PALE
Resurrected (ABV 4.8%) BITTER
Wolfcatcher (ABV 4.8%) PALE
Dirty Habit (ABV 5.8%) IPA

Problem Child

🍺 Wayfarer Inn, Alder Lane, Parbold, Lancashire, WN8 7NL
☎ (01257) 464600 ☎ 07588 736926
⊕ problemchildbrewing.co.uk

Problem Child began brewing in 2013 using a five-barrel plant at the Wayfarer Inn, Parbold, where two beers from the range are always available. ‼

Prospect SIBA

Unit 10a, Great George Street, off Wallgate, Wigan, WN3 4DL
☎ (01257) 421329 ⊕ prospectbrewery.com

⊕ Prospect was founded as a five-barrel plant in 2007, expanded due to unprecedented demand to a 12-barrel plant in nearby commercial premises several years later and then relocated to its current town centre premises in 2017. In 2019 the brewery was sold to the current owners, a husband-and-wife partnership, though the majority of production staff and core beer range were retained. The owners have close links to a local drinks distribution business and now offer a range of other alcoholic products to complement the ales. ‼ 🝙 ♦

Whatever! (ABV 3.8%) PALE
Yellow beer with a light malt/hop aroma. Some malt in taste, but hop and bitterness dominate. Dry, bitter finish.
Nutty Slack (ABV 3.9%) MILD
Dark brown mild ale with malt and fruit in the aroma. Creamy and chocolatey on the palate, with both malt and fruit in evidence. Malty and moderately bitter finish.
Pioneer (ABV 4%) BITTER
Whatever Next! (ABV 4%) GOLD

Provenance

See Hydes

Pumphouse

Unit 10d, Twydale Business Park, Driffield, East Yorkshire, YO25 6JX ☎ 07811 180195
✉ david@pumphousebrewing.co.uk

Launched in 2019, Pumphouse Brewing are a craft brewery producing small batch, one-off beers available in keg and bottle. The constantly-changing range is unfined and unfiltered. ✦

Pumphouse Community

Green Man Barn, Church Lane, Toppesfield, Essex, CO9 4DR ☎ 07786 861009
⊕ pumphousebrewery.co.uk

⊗ Pumphouse is a community-owned brewery. Established in 2015 it uses a two-barrel plant and specialises in session beers with occasional one-off, experimental brews. Pubs, clubs, special events and festivals are supplied within a 10-mile radius as well as its Green Man tap outlet. ‼ ▆ ◆ LIVE

Toppesfied Tap (ABV 3.6%) BITTER
Allied Amber (ABV 3.8%) BITTER
St Margaret's Ale (ABV 3.8%) PALE
Pumphouse Gold (ABV 4.2%) GOLD
Paula's Pride (ABV 4.5%) BITTER

Purity SIBA

The Brewery, Upper Spernal Farm, Spernal Lane, Great Alne, Warwickshire, B49 6JF ☎ (01789) 488007 ⊕ puritybrewing.com

☺ Brewing began in 2005 in a purpose-designed plant housed in converted barns. The brewery prides itself on its eco-friendly credentials. It supplies its award-winning beers into the free trade within a 70-mile radius (plus London postcodes), delivering to more than 500 outlets. ‼ ▆ ◆

Bunny Hop (ABV 3.5%) PALE
Pure Gold (ABV 3.8%) GOLD
Mad Goose (ABV 4.2%) BITTER
Pure UBU (ABV 4.5%) BITTER

Purple Moose SIBA

Madoc Street, Porthmadog, LL49 9DB ☎ (01766) 515571 ⊕ purplemoose.co.uk

A 40-barrel plant housed in a former iron works in the coastal town of Porthmadog. It owns the 'Australia' pub on Porthmadog High Street as well as two shops, one in Porthmadog and the other Betws-y-Coed. The names of the beers reflect local history and geography. ‼ ▆ ◆

Cwrw Eryri/Snowdonia Ale (ABV 3.6%) GOLD
Golden, refreshing bitter with citrus fruit hoppiness in aroma and taste. The full mouthfeel leads to a long-lasting, dry, bitter finish.
Cwrw Madog/Madog's Ale (ABV 3.7%) BITTER
Full-bodied session bitter. Malty nose and an initial nutty flavour but bitterness dominates. Well-balanced and refreshing with a dry roastiness on the taste and a good, dry finish.
Cwrw Ysgawen/Elderflower Ale (ABV 4%) SPECIALITY
A pale and refreshing elderflower beer with a good citrus fruit aroma, bittersweet taste, and a zesty, hoppy, mouthwatering finish.

Cwrw Glaslyn/Glaslyn Ale (ABV 4.2%) BITTER
Refreshing light and malty, amber-coloured ale. Plenty of hop in the aroma and taste. Good, smooth mouthfeel leading to a slightly chewy finish. •
Whakahati (ABV 4.3%) BITTER
Ochr Dywyll y Mws/Dark Side of the Moose (ABV 4.6%) OLD
A dark, complex beer quite hoppy and bitter with roast undertones. Malt and fruit flavours also feature in the smooth taste and dry finish.

Q Brew

58 Lower North Road, Carnforth, Lancashire, LA5 9LJ ☎ (01524) 903105 ⊕ qbrew.co.uk

Q Brew started brewing in 2019 and is Carnforth's first microbrewery.

Q Brewery

16 The Ringway, Queniborough, Leicestershire, LE7 3DL ☎ 07762 300240 ⊕ qbrewery.co.uk

A microbrewery situated in a converted building behind the house of head brewer Tim Lowe. It was established in 2014 and uses a 0.5-barrel brew kit. Beers can also be brewed on demand.

Ridgemere Bitter (ABV 3.8%) BITTER
Q Hop (ABV 4.2%) GOLD
Invincibull Stout (ABV 4.4%) STOUT
Q IPA (ABV 5%) PALE
1630 (ABV 5.5%) BITTER

Quantock SIBA

Westridge Way, Broadgauge Business Park, Bishops Lydeard, Somerset, TA4 3RU ☎ (01823) 433812 ⊕ quantockbrewery.co.uk

⊗ Quantock is a family-run brewery that started trading in 2008 on an eight-barrel plant. It has since been expanded. The brewery supplies beer to outlets throughout the South West, and further afield via wholesalers. The brewery taproom and shop are open six days and three evenings a week. An annual beer festival is held over the last weekend in July. ▆ ◆ ✦

QPA (ABV 4%) PALE
Wills Neck (ABV 4.3%) GOLD
Stout (ABV 4.5%) STOUT
Plastered Pheasant (ABV 4.8%) PORTER
Titanium (ABV 5.1%) PALE

Quartz SIBA

Archers, Alrewas Road, Kings Bromley, Staffordshire, DE13 7HW ☎ (01543) 473965 ⊕ quartzbrewing.co.uk

☺ Quartz was established in 2005 by Scott and Julia Barnett. Around 50 outlets are supplied direct. ‼ ▆ ◆

Blonde (ABV 3.8%) BLOND
Little aroma, gentle hop and background malt. Sweet with unsophisticated sweet shop tastes.
Crystal (ABV 4.2%) BITTER
Sweet aroma with some fruit and yeasty Marmite hints. Hoppiness begins but dwindles to a bittersweet finish.
Extra Blonde (ABV 4.4%) BITTER
Sweet, malty aroma with a touch of fruit. Sweet start, smooth with a hint of hops in the sugary finish.
Heart (ABV 4.6%) BITTER
Pale brown with some aroma of fruit and malt. Gentle tastes of fruit and hops eventually appear to leave a bitter finish.
Cracker (ABV 5%) BITTER

Queen Inn

28 Kingsgate Road, Winchester, Hampshire, SO23 9PG
☎ (01962) 853898 ⊕ thequeeninnwinchester.co.uk

The 2.5-barrel brewery was installed in 2013 during a pub refurbishment. Currently brewing takes place about once or twice a month, and is almost always just for the pub.

Quiet

Woodend Barn, Burn O Bennie, Banchory, AB31 5QA
☎ (01330) 826530 ⊕ buchananfood.com

Quiet Brewery produces bottle-conditioned beers, supplied to Buchanan's Bistro, Banchory. ◆LIVE

Quirky

Unit 3, Ash Lane, Garforth, Leeds, West Yorkshire, LS25 2HG
☎ (0113) 286 2072 ⊕ quirkyales.com

☺Established in 2015, Quirky Ales brews two or three times a week on its 2.5-barrel plant. Simon Mustill and Richard Scott acquired the brewery in 2019. Its on-site taproom is open every weekend from Thursday evening. Bottled beers are available in the taproom, at delicatessens, and farm shops. ☛◆

Porter (ABV 3.5%) PORTER
Blonde Ale (ABV 3.8%) BLOND
Two Islands (ABV 3.8%) GOLD
Bitter (ABV 4%) BITTER
Ruby (ABV 4%) BITTER
1 Hop Wonder (ABV 4.1%) GOLD
ITA (ABV 4.8%) BITTER
Hip Hop (ABV 5.5%) IPA

Radical (NEW)

Lough Ned, Oak Hill, Port Sodderick, IM4 1AN
☎ 07624 493304 ⊕ radicalbrewing.im

Brewing began early 2021.

Ironic Rye (ABV 3.8%) PALE
Amarillo Dreamin (ABV 4.2%) PALE

Radnorshire

Timberworks, Brookside Farm, Mutton Dingle, New Radnor, LD8 2SU
☎ (01544) 350456 ☎ 07789 909748
✉ info@radnorhillsholidaycottages.com

☺Set up in 2012 in a barn on the grounds of a farm offering holiday cottage accommodation, Radnorshire uses its own spring water. Drinkers staying at the cottages are supplied, as well as a few local pubs. Brewing is currently suspended. ‼☛

Ralph's Ruin

c/o Royal Oak, Lower Bristol Road, Bath, BA2 3BW
☎ (01225) 481409 ⊕ ralphsruin.co.uk

Brewing commenced in 2017 using a two-barrel plant in the old kitchen of the Royal Oak. Beer is only available in the pub.

Ramsbury SIBA

Stockclose Farm, Aldbourne, Wiltshire, SN8 2NN
☎ (01672) 541407 ⊕ ramsburybrewery.co.uk

☒ The Ramsbury Brewing & Distilling Company started brewing in 2004 using a 10-barrel plant, situated high on the Marlborough Downs in Wiltshire. The brewery uses home-grown barley from the Ramsbury Estate. Expansion in 2014 saw an upgrade to a 30-barrel plant with a visitor centre and a well to provide the water. A distillery that uses grains grown on the estate became operational in 2015. ‼☛◆

Farmer's Best (ABV 3.6%) BITTER
Same Again (ABV 3.8%) BITTER
Deerstalker (ABV 4%) BITTER
Ramsbury Pale Ale (RPA) (ABV 4%) PALE
Flint Knapper (ABV 4.2%) BITTER
Gold (ABV 4.5%) GOLD
Red Ram (ABV 4.5%) SPECIALITY
Chalk Stream (ABV 5%) PALE
Belapur IPA (ABV 5.5%) IPA

Ramsgate (Gadds') SIBA

1 Hornet Close, Pyson's Road Industrial Estate, Broadstairs, Kent, CT10 2YD
☎ (01843) 868453 ⊕ ramsgatebrewery.co.uk

Ramsgate was established in 2002 at the back of a Ramsgate seafront pub. In 2006 the brewery moved to its current location, allowing for increased capacity and bottling. A 25-hectolitre brew plant is used. ‼☛◆

Gadds' Hoppy Pale (ABV 3.6%) BLOND
Gadds' No. 7 Bitter Ale (ABV 3.8%) BITTER
Gadds' Seasider (ABV 4.3%) BITTER
Gadds' No. 5 Best Bitter Ale (ABV 4.4%) BITTER
Gadds' SheSells SeaShells (ABV 4.7%) GOLD
Gadds' No. 3 Kent Pale Ale (ABV 5%) BLOND
Gadds' Faithful Dogbolter Porter (ABV 5.6%) PORTER
Gadds' Black Pearl (ABV 6.2%) STOUT

Randalls

La Piette Brewery, St Georges Esplanade, St Peter Port, Guernsey, GY1 3JG
☎ (01481) 720134 ⊕ randalls.gg

Randalls has been brewing in Guernsey since 1868. The company was bought out in 2006 and moved into a modern, purpose-built brewery in 2008. 19 pubs are owned and a further 70 outlets are supplied. ‼◆

Rat

Rat & Ratchet, 40 Chapel Hill, Huddersfield, West Yorkshire, HD1 3EB
☎ (01484) 542400 ✉ ratandratchet@ossett-brewery.co.uk

☺The Rat & Ratchet was originally established as a brewpub in 1994. Brewing ceased and it was purchased by Ossett Brewery (qv) in 2004. Brewing restarted in 2011 with a capacity of 30 barrels per week. A wide range of occasional brews with rat-themed names supplement the regular beers. ◆

Rat Attack (ABV 3.8%) BITTER
White Rat (ABV 4%) PALE
Black Rat (ABV 4.5%) PORTER
King Rat (ABV 5%) BITTER
Rat Against the Machine (ABV 7%) IPA

Raven Hill

Raven Hill Farm, Driffield, East Yorkshire, YO25 4EG
☎ 07979 674573 ⊕ ravenhillbrewery.com

Raven Hill Brewery started trading in 2018. Based on a Yorkshire farm near Kilham, it brews four regular beers of varied styles and produces regular seasonal beers in small batch quantities.

Summit (ABV 3.6%) PALE
Chalk Stream (ABV 4%) GOLD
Brook (ABV 4.3%) GOLD
Ridge Way (ABV 5.5%) STOUT
Elevation (ABV 6.2%) BARLEY

RBA

8 Oswestry Close, Oakwood, Derby, DE21 2RT
☎ 07943 367765 ✉ rbabrewery@gmail.com

In 2015 two friends, Richard Burton and Colin Fryer, began homebrewing in a shed in a back garden. Five years later they decided to sell commercially, and production increased accordingly. The 0.25-barrel plant brews three times a week with occasional brews being bottled.

Reaction

47 Erw Goch, Ruthin, LL15 1RS
✉ reactionbrewery@gmail.com

Brewing returned to Ruthin after many years when keen home brewer and CAMRA member Clwyd Roberts made his cask and key keg beers available commercially in 2019. One-off beers are produced on a monthly basis with most of the output going to Mold Alehouse which acts as the brewery tap.

Reality

127 High Road, Chilwell, Beeston, Nottingham, NG9 4AT ☎ 07801 539523
✉ alandenismonaghan@hotmail.com

⊗ Since starting in 2010, the brewery has built up a loyal following of pubs locally, while supplying beer festivals across the country, functions and individual customers. ♦

Virtuale Reality (ABV 3.8%) PALE
No Escape (ABV 4.2%) PALE
Bitter Reality (ABV 4.3%) BITTER
Stark Reality (ABV 4.5%) SPECIALITY
Reality Czech (ABV 4.6%) SPECIALITY

Rebel

See Dynamite Valley

Rebellion SIBA

Rebellion Brewery, Bencombe Farm, Marlow Bottom, Buckinghamshire, SL7 3LT
☎ (01628) 476594 ⊕ rebellionbeer.co.uk

⊗ Established in 1993, Rebellion has grown steadily with one site move and several expansion projects. It currently brews approximately 100,000 pints per week, supplying more than 600 local pubs and clubs within a 30-mile radius of Marlow. A taproom opened in 2021. Its ever-popular membership club now has over 4,500 active members. ‼▤♦◈

IPA (ABV 3.7%) BITTER
Copper-coloured bitter, sweet and malty, with resinous and red apple flavours. Caramel and fruit decline to leave a dry, bitter and malty finish.
Smuggler (ABV 4.2%) BITTER
A red-brown beer, well-bodied and bitter with an uncompromisingly dry, bitter finish.
Touchdown (ABV 4.3%) PALE
Roasted Nuts (ABV 4.6%) BITTER

Reckless Dweeb (NEW)

Forest Link, Bilsthorpe, Nottinghamshire, NG22 8PR
☎ 07969 779763 ⊕ recklessdweeb.com

Established in 2020, Reckless Dweeb Brew Co is a nanobrewery in a quiet village in the heart of Nottinghamshire.

Cabal on Mars (ABV 3.9%) SPECIALITY
Son of my Brother (ABV 5.1%) IPA
The Worst Thing About Prison is the Dementors! (ABV 5.1%) PALE
Did You See That Ludicrous Display Last Night? (ABV 8.2%) IPA
This is the One Boyz (ABV 10.8%) STOUT

Recoil

See Copper Dragon

Rectory

Streat Hill Farm, Streat Hill, Streat, Hassocks, East Sussex, BN6 8RP
☎ (01273) 890570 ✉ rectoryales@hotmail.com

⊗ Rectory was founded in 1995 by the Rev Godfrey Broster to generate funds for the maintenance of his three parish churches. 107 parishioners are shareholders. ‼♦

Rector's Pleasure (ABV 3.7%) BITTER
Rector's Light Relief (ABV 4.5%) GOLD
The Rector's Revenge (ABV 5%) BITTER

Red Cat SIBA

Unit 10, Sun Valley Business Park, Winnall Close, Winchester, Hampshire, SO23 0LB
☎ (01962) 863423 ⊕ redcatbrewing.co.uk

Red Cat Brewing Company was established in 2014 using an 11-barrel plant. It supplies Hampshire and bordering counties. A small bar and shop in the brewery sells a range of products. ‼▤

Art of T (ABV 3.6%) SPECIALITY
Easy-drinking, speciality pale ale with a slight fruit aroma. Refreshing, dry astringency and bitterness in the taste and lingering aftertaste.
Prowler Pale (ABV 3.6%) PALE
Pale yellow, session bitter with dominant hop flavours and some fruit in the taste and aftertaste.
Scratch (ABV 4%) BITTER
Session, pale golden bitter, low aroma but well-balanced hop, malt and fruit flavours in the taste and aftertaste.
Mr M's Porter (ABV 4.5%) PORTER
A rich, fruity porter, complex flavours with good roast aroma and taste, well-balanced with fruit flavours throughout.
Mosaic Pale (ABV 4.9%) PALE
American pale ale-style beer with rich floral aroma leading to balanced fruit and hop flavours fading to a hop, fruit and bitter finish.

Red Fox SIBA

The Chicken Sheds, Upp Hall Farm, Salmons Lane, Coggeshall, Essex, CO6 1RY
☎ (01376) 563123 ⊕ redfoxbrewery.co.uk

Red Fox began brewing in 2008 and has continued to expand in line with increasing demand. Brewery experience days are available and contract brewing services are offered. ‼▤♦LIVE

Mild (ABV 3.6%) MILD

IPA (ABV 3.7%) BITTER
Bitter (ABV 3.8%) BITTER
Hunter's Gold (ABV 3.9%) GOLD
Best Bitter (ABV 4%) BITTER
Coggeshall Gold (ABV 4%) GOLD
Surrex Gold (ABV 4.1%) GOLD
Black Fox Porter (ABV 4.8%) PORTER
Wily Ol' Fox (ABV 5.2%) PALE
Ruby Red Mild (ABV 6.9%) STRONG

Red Rock SIBA

Higher Humber Farm, Bishopsteignton, Devon, TQ14 9TD
☎ (01626) 879738 ⊕ redrockbrewery.co.uk

⊗ Red Rock first started brewing in 2006 using a four-barrel plant and upgraded in 2011 to a 7.5-barrel one. It is based in a converted barn on a working farm using locally-sourced malt, fresh hops and the farm's own spring water. It has a bar and can accommodate private functions. ‼ ☲ ♦ LIVE ✦

Lighthouse IPA (ABV 3.9%) PALE
Red Rock (ABV 4.2%) BITTER
Break Water (ABV 4.6%) BITTER

Red Rose

The Old Brewery, Back Square Street, Ramsbottom, BL0 9FZ
☎ (01706) 827582

Office: 2 Hameldon View, Great Harwood, BB6 7BL
⊕ redrosebrewery.co.uk

Brewing began in 2020.

Red Shoot

▤ Toms Lane, Linwood, Ringwood, Hampshire, BH24 3QT
☎ (01425) 475792 ⊕ redshoot.co.uk

⊗ The 2.5-barrel brewery was commissioned in 1998 and can be viewed from inside the pub. Production is slightly seasonal, about 2-3 brews a week. Surplus output is sold to a selection of other Wadworth pubs.

Redcastle SIBA

Drummygar Mains, Carmyllie, Arbroath, DD11 2RA
☎ (01241) 860516 ☎ 07967 226357
⊕ redcastlebrewery.co.uk

⊗ Established by local farmer and Clydesdale horse breeder John Anderson, Redcastle started brewing in rural Angus in 2016 in a purpose-built brewery on the family farm. The brewery takes its name from the nearby, ruined red castle at Lunan Bay. The beers are named accordingly with a historic theme. In addition to the 10-barrel plant, the brewery also includes a bottling line. **V**

Headstock (ABV 3.8%) PALE
Crusader (ABV 4%) BITTER
Red Lady (ABV 4%) MILD
Nobleman (ABV 4.2%) GOLD
Norseman (ABV 4.2%) BARLEY
Cannonball (ABV 4.5%) PALE
Tower IPA (ABV 4.8%) PALE
Courthill (ABV 5%) PALE
Dark Knight (ABV 5.6%) STOUT
Laird (ABV 5.6%) SPECIALITY
Monster Hop (ABV 6%) BITTER

Redchurch

15-16 Mead Park Industrial Estate, Harlow, Essex, CM20 2SE
☎ (01279) 626895 ☎ 07836 762173
⊕ redchurch.beer

⊗ Established in 2011 using an eight-barrel plant in railway arches at Bethnal Green. In 2016 most of the production moved to Harlow, leaving only the tap room on-site. It was purchased by new management in 2019, who closed that tap room. The current range (ten core beers, seasonals, and the Urban Farmhouse range of sours) are available only in keg and bottles. Beers can be collected from the brewery offices (during working hours), and there's a small tap room at the brewery. ☲ ♦ ✦

Redemption SIBA

Unit 16, Compass West Industrial Estate, 33 West Road, Tottenham, London, N17 0XL
☎ (020) 8885 5227 ⊕ redemptionbrewing.co.uk

⊗ Redemption began brewing in 2010 on a 12-barrel plant. In 2016 it moved into a larger unit with a 30-barrel plant. Most of the beer is supplied in cask to pubs in north and central London and to beer festivals. Successful crowdfunding in 2018 led to an expansion into keg, cans and bottles. ‼ ☲ ♦ LIVE ✦

Trinity (ABV 3%) GOLD
Refreshing golden ale with strong, hoppy, citrus character. Biscuit provides balance to the building, pithy, citrus and dry, hoppy bitterness.
Pale Ale (ABV 3.8%) PALE
Well-balanced, amber bitter with peppery hops and citrus throughout. Sweet toffee and fruit fades in the slightly dry, bitter finish.
Rock the Kazbek (ABV 4%) BLOND
Easy-drinking, blonde beer with citrus, earthy hops and a faint note of honey. A gentle, dry, bitter lingering aftertaste.
Hopspur (ABV 4.5%) BITTER
Dark amber, well-balanced, premium bitter with caramelised citrus and hazelnuts on the nose and palate with a spicy hoppiness
Urban Dusk (ABV 4.6%) BITTER
Full-bodied, brown best bitter. Chocolate and fudge in the aroma and flavour overlaid with citrus. Lingering, dry, bitter finish.
Fellowship Porter (ABV 5.1%) PORTER
Sweetish smooth porter. Treacle and caramelised fruit balances the dry, dark roast chocolate notes in the flavour. Faint spicy finish.
Big Chief (ABV 5.5%) IPA
New World IPA with sweet biscuit and hops throughout. Grapefruit and lemon on the palate. A growing, bitter, dry finish.

Redscar SIBA

▤ c/o The Cleveland Hotel, 9-11 High Street West, Redcar, North Yorkshire, TS10 1SQ
☎ (01642) 513727 ☎ 07828 855146
⊕ redscar-brewery.co.uk

☺Redscar first brewed in 2008. In 2014 it increased its capacity to a five-barrel plant. The brewery supplies the hotel, local pubs and beer festivals. ‼ ♦

Redwell

Under the Arches, Bracondale, Trowse Millgate, Norwich, NR1 2EF
☎ (01603) 624072 ⊕ redwellbrewing.com

⊗ Redwell was started in 2013 by a group of beer lovers, tracing their beery influences from around the world. It is now under new ownership and has appointed Belinda Jennings as its head brewer. ‼

RedWillow SIBA

The Lodge, Sutton Garrison, Byrons Lane, Macclesfield, Cheshire, SK11 7JW
☎ (01625) 502315 ⊕ redwillowbrewery.com

☺Established in 2010 by homebrewer Toby McKenzie and his wife Caroline. In 2015 brewing moved to a larger, purpose-built unit on the same site. The award-winning beers are distributed nationwide and are available from the brewery's own RedWillow bars in Macclesfield and Buxton. Experimental brews are branded under the Faithless label. ♦

Effortless (ABV 3.7%) BLOND
Headless (ABV 3.9%) GOLD
Nicely-balanced with some malty sweetness. Fruit and hops show in the drinking, with hop bitterness lasting to the end.
Feckless (ABV 4.1%) BITTER
Well-balanced best bitter, malt and hop in the taste with some fruit and roast flavours.
Weightless (ABV 4.2%) PALE
Well-rounded, pale ale with a promise of fruit and hop at the start, a full-bodied, bittersweet, fruity middle and lasting finish.
Wreckless (ABV 4.8%) PALE
Sleepless (ABV 5.4%) RED
Breakfast Stout (ABV 5.6%) STOUT
A dark beer with strong aromas of chocolate, coffee and hazelnut alongside expected malt and roast. Composed to give a long, smooth mouthfeel.
Smokeless (ABV 5.7%) SPECIALITY
Shameless (ABV 5.9%) IPA
Fruit and hops throughout with full-bodied sweetness and a long finish.
Ageless (ABV 7.2%) IPA
Restless (ABV 8.5%) SPECIALITY

Reedley Hallows SIBA

Unit B3, Farrington Close, Farrington Road Industrial Estate, Burnley, Lancashire, BB11 5SH ☎ 07749 414513 ⊕ reedleyhallow.co.uk

☺Brewing started on this four-barrel plant in 2012. Having moved to larger premises, the brewery now has nine fermenters to cope with demand. ‼

Old Laund Bitter (ABV 3.6%) BITTER
Beer O'Clock (ABV 3.8%) GOLD
Filly Close Blonde (ABV 3.9%) BLOND
Pendleside (ABV 4%) GOLD
Gentle malt and hops in the aroma, lead to a fruity and peppery bitterness which continues to a dry finish.
Monkholme Premium (ABV 4.2%) BLOND
New Laund Dark (ABV 4.4%) STOUT
Griffin IPA (ABV 4.5%) PALE
Fruity, hoppy bitter with sweet, fruity flavours and a light bitter finish.
New Zealand Pale (ABV 4.5%) PALE
Nook of Pendle (ABV 5%) BITTER

Regents Canal

See Little Creatures

Reids Gold

61 Provost Barclay Drive, Stonehaven, AB39 2GE
⊕ reidsgold.com

Reids Gold was established in 2018. It is a small-batch microbrewery with an average weekly production of five barrels. No real ale.

Remedy Oak (NEW) SIBA

Horton Road, Woodlands, Dorset, BH21 8ND
☎ (01202) 812070 ⊕ remedyoakbrewery.co.uk

The Remedy Oak Brewing Co was established in 2020. It is based in a redeveloped barn in the grounds of the Remedy Oak Golf Club. An on-site taproom opened in 2021. ◆

Republic of Liverpool

See Stamps

Revolutions SIBA

Unit B7, Whitwood Enterprise Park, Speedwell Road, Whitwood, West Yorkshire, WF10 5PX
☎ (01977) 552649 ☎ 07503 007470
⊕ revolutionsbrewing.co.uk

Revolutions began brewing in 2010. All beers are musically inspired. The Rewind 33 series of bi-monthly specials references music from 33 years ago. ‼♦V

Candidate US Session Pale (ABV 3.9%) PALE
Clash Porter (ABV 4.5%) PORTER
Switch (ABV 4.5%) GOLD
Swoon Chocolate Fudge Milk Stout (ABV 4.5%) STOUT
Marquee US IPA (ABV 5.4%) PALE
Manifesto Stout (ABV 6%) STOUT

Rhymney SIBA

Gilchrist Thomas Industrial Estate, Blaenavon, NP4 9RL
☎ (01495) 790456 ☎ 07831 350635
⊕ rhymneybreweryltd.com

☺Rhymney is now in its sixteenth year. The full range of beers are available in the 11 tied houses and are widely available in free houses throughout South Wales. Unashamedly traditional in its range of beers, the brewery continues to win a range of CAMRA awards. It is situated in the heart of a Unesco World Heritage Site, close to the National Mining Museum and the Blaenavon Iron Works. ‼▬♦LIVE

Hobby Horse (ABV 3.8%) BITTER
Dark (ABV 4%) MILD
Bevans Bitter (ABV 4.2%) BITTER
Golden Ale (ABV 4.2%) GOLD
General Picton (ABV 4.3%) BITTER
Bitter (ABV 4.5%) BITTER
King's Ale (ABV 4.7%) BITTER
Export (ABV 5%) BITTER

Richmond SIBA

Station Brewery, Station Yard, Richmond, North Yorkshire, DL10 4LD
☎ (01748) 828266 ⊕ richmondbrewing.co.uk

☺Richmond opened in 2008 in the renovated Victorian station complex beside the River Swale. Producion is split 50/50 between cask-conditioned and bottled beers. The former are available in the local area at the Hildyard Arms, Colburn, and the Castle Tavern, Richmond, as well as direct from the brewery. ‼▬♦LIVE

SwAle (ABV 3.7%) MILD
Gundog Bitter (ABV 3.8%) BITTER

Station Ale (ABV 4%) BITTER
Greyfriars Stout (ABV 4.2%) STOUT
Dale Strider (ABV 4.5%) GOLD
Stump Cross Ale (ABV 4.7%) OLD
Richmond Pale Ale (ABV 5%) PALE

Ride SIBA

Unit 1, Bridge Court, 12 Cook Street, Glasgow, G5 8JN
☎ 07463 667097 ✉ info@ridebrewingco.uk

Ride Brew Co is a social enterprise brewery established in 2017.

Charon (ABV 4.5%) PORTER

Ridgeside SIBA

Unit 24, Penraevon 2 Industrial Estate, Meanwood, Leeds, West Yorkshire, LS7 2AW ☎ 07595 380568 ⊕ ridgesidebrewery.co.uk

☺Ridgeside began brewing in 2010 using a four-barrel plant. Regular outlets are supplied around Leeds and beers can be found across West and North Yorkshire. Cask beers are unfiltered and unfined. ♦V♦

Plato (ABV 4%) PALE
Objects in Space (ABV 4.8%) PALE
Equator (ABV 5.6%) IPA
Milky Joe (ABV 5.6%) SPECIALITY

Ridgeway

Stane Street, North Heath, Pulborough, West Sussex, RH20 1DJ
☎ (01491) 873474

Office: Ridgeway Brewing Ltd, South Stoke, RG8 0JW
⊕ ridgewaybrewery.co.uk

Set up by ex-Brakspear head brewer Peter Scholey, Ridgeway specialises in bottle-conditioned beers, although cask beers are occasionally available at beer festivals and locally. A new brewery has been operational since 2016, located within Hepworth Brewery's new premises near Pulborough, sharing some facilities. LIVE

Rigg & Furrow

Acklington Park Farm, Acklington, Northumberland, NE65 9AA ⊕ riggandfurrow.com

Brewing commenced in 2017 in a former milking parlour. It is a family-run business celebrating the best of home-grown Northumbrian and British produce creating exciting and innovative beers. A brewery tap is open on selected dates (see website for details). ♦

Run Hop Run (ABV 4.2%) GOLD
Trickster (ABV 4.3%) BITTER
Land Bier (ABV 4.8%) PORTER
Farmhouse IPA (ABV 5.6%) IPA

Ringwood

Christchurch Road, Ringwood, Hampshire, BH24 3AP
☎ (01425) 471177 ⊕ ringwoodbrewery.co.uk

⊗ Ringwood was bought in 2007 by Marston's. Production has been increased to 50,000 barrels a year. Some 750 outlets are supplied. Ringwood beers are now available in Marston's pubs all over the country. Part of Carlsberg Marston's Brewing Co. ‼🍺♦

Razorback (ABV 3.8%) BITTER
Copper-coloured, session bitter dominated by malt with some toffee and berry fruit character, leading to a short, bittersweet finish.

Boondoggle (ABV 4.2%) BITTER
Golden-coloured, light, easy-drinking, session bitter. Quite malty with some peach and apricot on the nose, and sweet tropical fruit palate.
Fortyniner (ABV 4.9%) BITTER
Caramel, biscuity aroma, with hints of damson, lead to a sweet taste, balanced with some malt, fruit and hop flavours.
Old Thumper (ABV 5.1%) BITTER
Powerful, sweet, copper-coloured bitter. A fruity aroma preludes a sweet, malty taste with fruit and caramel and a bittersweet aftertaste.

Rising Sun

🍴 Rising Sun, 235 Stockport Road, Mossley, OL5 0RQ
☎ (01457) 238236 ⊕ risingsunmossley.co.uk

☺Brewing since 2016 using a two-barrel plant at the side of the Rising Sun. The beers are only available for sale in the pub. In addition to the regular beer, many others of differing styles and strengths are available throughout the year.

Rival

60 Theobald Road, Cardiff, CF5 1LQ ☎ 07889 596306
✉ info@rivalbrewing.co.uk

⊗ Commenced late 2017 with a one-barrel kit in a residential garage. Presently produces kegged beers and occasional bottles.

River Leven

Lab Road, Kinlochleven, PH50 4SG
☎ (01855) 831519 ☎ 07901 873273
⊕ riverlevenales.co.uk

Established in 2011, River Leven Ales is situated among stunning scenery on the West Highland Way in Kinlochleven. Beers are produced using the pure Kinlochleven water with no added sugars or unmalted grain.

Blonde (ABV 4%) GOLD
Traditional IPA (ABV 4%) PALE

Riverhead

🍴 2 Peel Street, Marsden, Huddersfield, West Yorkshire, HD7 6BR
☎ (01484) 841270 (pub) ⊕ ossett-brewery.co.uk

☺Riverhead is a brewpub that opened in 1995. Ossett Brewing (qv) purchased the site in 2006 but runs it as a separate brewery. It has since opened the Dining Room on the first floor, which uses Riverhead beers in its dishes. Many different beers are produced on a rotating basis. ‼♦

Riverside

Unit 6, Beeding Court Business Park, Shoreham Road, Upper Beeding, West Sussex, BN44 3TN
☎ (01903) 898030 ⊕ riversidebreweryltd.co.uk

Riverside began brewing in 2015 using a five-barrel plant. Beers are available locally. LIVE

Rambling Monarch (ABV 3.6%) BITTER
Steyning Stinker (ABV 4%) PALE
Beeding Best Bitter (ABV 4.2%) BITTER
Sneaky Steamer (ABV 5.1%) GOLD
Tubbers' Tipple (ABV 5.6%) BITTER

Rivertown

See McMullen

Riviera

4 Yonder Meadow, Stoke Gabriel, Devon, TQ9 6QE
☎ 07857 850110 ⊕ rivierabrewing.co.uk

⊛Riviera started brewing commercially in 2015 using a one-barrel plant. European and New World hops are used in addition to various British varieties. ♦

RBC Best (ABV 3.8%) BITTER
RPA (Riviera Pale Ale) (ABV 3.9%) PALE
Devonian (ABV 4.1%) BITTER
Gold (ABV 4.2%) GOLD

Rivington

Home Farm, Horrobin Lane, Rivington, Lancashire, PR6 9HE
☎ (01257) 480403 ⊕ rivingtonbrewing.co.uk

⊛Established in 2015 using a three-barrel plant, the brewery moved to its current address in 2020. A 12-barrel plant is now used. A number of local outlets are supplied direct from the brewery. Approximately 20 per cent of production is supplied in cask form, but all beers are unpasteurised, unfiltered and unfined. Experimental brews and collaborations are regularly available. ♦LIVE⦿

Roa Island

▤ Belfast Pier, Roa Island, Cumbria, LA13 0PN
☎ (01229) 825291

⊛Brewing commenced in 2017 in a small room at the back of the Roa Island Boat Club. Beers are brewed once a week in 50-litre quantities and are only available on-site. Following the installtion of solar panels, the beers now have a 'daylight' theme.

Roam SIBA

New Victoria House, Weston Park Road, Plymouth, Devon, PL3 4NU
☎ (01752) 396052 ☎ 07971 411727
⊕ roambrewco.uk

⊠ Roam produce small batch beers using a combination of traditional and modern brewing techniques and local ingredients. A six-barrel plant is used. Roam now produce traditional cask, keg and bottle-conditioned beers. The brewery relocated to the Peverell area of the city in 2019. ‼☲♦LIVE⦿

Tavy Gold (ABV 4%) BITTER
Hometown Pale (ABV 4.1%) PALE
A nice, fruity, hopped, American-style, pale ale. Fruit aroma, tastes of grapefruit and mango with lasting finish on the palate.
Tavy Best Bitter (ABV 4.3%) BITTER
Malt dominates the nose and taste with caramel, roast and hops overpowering a subtle hint of fruit. A complex aftertaste.
Sound Bitter (ABV 4.5%) BITTER
A good, drinkable best bitter, full-flavoured on body content.
Tavy IPA (ABV 4.8%) PALE
Gold ale dominated by hops and fruit from start to finish. Slight fruit/straw aroma. Citrus/hoppy dry taste. Dry/bitter finish.
Tavy Porter (ABV 5.2%) PORTER
Full-bodied porter. Malt, liquorice and chocolate nose. Slightly bitter fruity taste. Roasted coffee and touch of vanilla in the aftertaste.

Double Take (ABV 7.1%) STRONG
An American brown ale with lots of body, swimming in fruity hops. Sweet on taste, complex mix of malty/roast flavours. A beer to savour.

Robinsons SIBA IFBB

Unicorn Brewery, Lower Hillgate, Stockport, SK1 1JJ
☎ (0161) 612 4061 ⊕ robinsonsbrewery.com

⊛The sixth generation of the Robinson family now run the brewery, founded in 1838. Following a significant reduction in the tied estate in recent years, there is now gradual expansion. A wide portfolio of beers encompasses a core range, bi-monthly seasonals, occasional 'White Label' brews and one-off additions to the 'Trooper' range brewed with Iron Maiden's Bruce Dickinson. ‼☲♦

Wizard (ABV 3.7%) BITTER
Dizzy Blonde (ABV 3.8%) BLOND
A light-bodied beer, yellow in colour. It has malt and hops in the taste and a dry, bitter finish.
Cumbria Way (ABV 4.1%) BITTER
Pale brown with a malty aroma, this beer has a balance of malt, some hops and a little fruit, with sweetness and bitterness throughout.
Cwrw'r Ddraig Aur (ABV 4.1%) GOLD
Unicorn (ABV 4.2%) BITTER
Amber beer with a fruity aroma. Malt, hops and fruit in the taste with a bitter, malty finish.
Cascade IPA (ABV 4.8%) PALE
Pale brown beer with malt and fruit on the nose. Full, hoppy taste with malt and fruit, leading to a hoppy, bitter finish.
Trooper (ABV 4.8%) BITTER
Well-balanced, amber beer with malt and hops in aroma and taste.
Old Tom (ABV 8.5%) STRONG
A full-bodied, dark beer with malt, fruit and chocolate on the aroma. A complex range of flavours includes dark chocolate, full maltiness, port and fruits and lead to a long, bittersweet aftertaste.

Rock & Roll

19 Hall Street, Jewellery Quarter, Birmingham, B18 6BS ☎ 07922 554181
✉ rnrbrewhouse@outlook.com

⊠ The Rock & Roll brewery started as Birmingham's only rooftop pub brewery, set up by experienced brewer Mark Shepherd. In 2014 Brewster Lynn Crossland joined and now does all of the brewing. In 2016 the brewery moved and expanded to a six-barrel plant. In 2020 it moved to its current location in the Jewellery Quarter. Specials and experimental beers are regularly available. A brewhouse bar is open at weekends. All beers are suitable for vegans. ‼♦V

Brew Springsteen (ABV 4.2%) PALE
Thirst Aid Kit (ABV 4.2%) PALE
Mash City Rocker (ABV 4.5%) PALE
Voodoo Mild (ABV 5%) MILD

Rock Mill

1b Rock Mill Lane, New Mills, Derbyshire, SK22 3BN
☎ 07971 747050

Office: 81-83 Bridge Street, New Mills, SK22 4DN
✉ rbpine@Hotmail.co.uk

⊠ Rock Mill is a microbrewery established by Ray Barton, a former homebrewer, in 2016. ☲♦V

School Night (ABV 3.2%) BITTER

Mermaids Pool (ABV 3.5%) GOLD
Strange Ways (ABV 3.8%) BITTER
Back to the Future (ABV 4%) BITTER
Orangeytang (ABV 4.3%) SPECIALITY
Pitsburger (ABV 4.3%) SPECIALITY
Green Ant Racing Fuel (ABV 5.2%) BITTER

Rock Solid

Office: Thornebank, Blackpool, FY3 8QE ☎ 07963
860080 ✉ rocksolidbrewingcompany@gmail.com

⊕This brewery, based at the owner's home, started
brewing in 2017 using a one-barrel plant. ♦

Blonde (ABV 3.9%) BLOND
Pale, dry, bitter with modest hops and a dry, hoppy
finish.
Amarillo Gold (ABV 4%) GOLD
American Pale (ABV 4.5%) PALE

Rock the Boat SIBA

6 Little Crosby Village, Little Crosby, Crosby,
Merseyside, L23 4TS
☎ (0151) 924 7936 ☎ 07727 959356
⊕ rocktheboatbrewery.co.uk

Rock the Boat began brewing in 2015 in a converted
16th century wheelwright's workshop in the village.
Beer names relate to a local theme, often reflecting the
brewer's musical tastes and local landmarks. Specials are
often brewed for Market Town Taverns pubs in Liverpool.
A green hop beer is produced each year. LIVE

Liverpool Light (ABV 3.4%) BLOND
Light, hoppy aromas on this refreshing, straw bitter with
a delicate hop flavour and a dry, bitter finish.
(Sittin' on) The Dock (ABV 3.5%) BITTER
Rich chocolate malt aromas, with caramel roast flavours
and light sweetness with a mellow, caramel, roast finish.
Bootle Bull (ABV 3.8%) BITTER
Yellow Submarine Special (ABV 3.9%) GOLD
Waterloo Sunset (ABV 4.2%) BITTER
Smooth, medium-bodied, copper beer. Rich, malt, fruity
(orange) aromas, sweet malt and caramel flavours, fruity
with light hop bitterness, and a fruit and malt finish.
Fab Four Liverpool IPA (ABV 4.4%) BLOND
A medium-bodied, straw beer with fruity hop aromas,
sweet fruity flavours and dry hop bitterness, finishing
with light hop bitterness.

Rocket

The Orchard, Garden Farm, The Town, Great
Staughton, Cambridgeshire, PE19 5BE
☎ (01733) 390828 ☎ 07747 617527
✉ mikeblakesley@virginmedia.com

Originally using spare capacity at King's Cliffe Brewery
(qv), Rocket Ales relocated to its own site in 2017.

Atlas IPA (ABV 5.8%) IPA

Rockin' Robin

c/o Old Dairy Brewery, Tenterden Station Estate,
Station Road, Tenterden, Kent, TN30 6HE ☎ 07787
416110

Office: 6 Pickering Street, Loose, ME15 9RS
✉ sales@rockinrobinbrewery.co.uk

Brewing began in 2011 using a one-barrel plant in a
garden shed in Loose. It moved to Boughton Monchelsea
in 2014 and in 2019 began cuckoo brewing at Old Dairy
(qv).

Reliant Robin (ABV 3.7%) BITTER

Reckless Robin (ABV 4.5%) BITTER

Rockingham SIBA

Blatherwycke, Northamptonshire, PE8 6YN
☎ (01832) 280722

Office: 25 Wansford Road, Elton, PE8 6RZ
⊕ rockinghamales.co.uk

⊠ Rockingham is a small brewery established in 1997
that operates from a converted farm building near
Blatherwycke, Northamptonshire, with a two-barrel
plant producing a prolific range of beers. It supplies half a
dozen local outlets. ♦

Forest Gold (ABV 3.9%) BLOND
Hop Devil (ABV 3.9%) GOLD
White Rabbit (ABV 4%) GOLD
Saxon Cross (ABV 4.1%) BITTER
Fruits of the Forest (ABV 4.3%) SPECIALITY
Dark Forest (ABV 5%) BITTER

Roebuck SIBA

Roebuck, Tobys Hill, Draycott-in-the-Clay,
Staffordshire, DE6 5BT
☎ (01283) 703411 ☎ 07757 503851
⊕ roebuckdraycott.co.uk

⊕Brewing began in 2017 using a six-barrel plant, in a
purpose-built, English oak-framed, new building behind
the Roebuck Inn (on A515 and 402 bus route). Master
Brewer Steve Topliss was Carlsberg Tetley's last head
brewer in Burton. Enquiries welcomed for brewery visits
and tasting tutorials, with good food at the family-owned
pub adjacent. Near the A50 junctions for Ashbourne,
Lichfield (the National Football Centre near Burton)
National Trust's Sudbury Hall, and the Traction Engine
Club's Steam Centre. ‼

Roebuck Blonde (ABV 3.7%) BLOND
Hopzester (ABV 4.2%) BITTER
Roebuck Bitter (ABV 4.5%) BITTER
Porter (ABV 4.6%) PORTER
Roebuck IPA (ABV 5.2%) PALE

Roman Way

Building 79, The Old Depot, Bridge Street, Weedon
Bec, Northamptonshire, NN7 4PS ☎ 07950 234991
⊕ romanwaybrewery.co.uk

Roman Way Brewery was established in 2019. Its shop
and taproom is usually open to the public on Fridays and
Saturdays. ☕♦

Barbarian Best (ABV 3.8%) BITTER
Carpe Diem (ABV 3.9%) PALE
Tribune (ABV 3.9%) PALE
Senate Gold (ABV 4.1%) GOLD
Claudius (ABV 4.7%) GOLD
Boudicca (ABV 5.5%) IPA
Pantheon (ABV 6%) STRONG

Romney Marsh

Unit 7, Jacks Park, Cinque Ports Road, New Romney,
Kent, TN28 8AN
☎ (01797) 362333 ⊕ romneymarshbrewery.com

⊠ Romney Marsh Brewery launched in 2015. The team
consists of husband and wife, Matt Calais and Cathy
Koester, plus Matt's dad, Brian Calais. The barley, wheat
and oats used for the beers are sourced in Britain, and
hops are worldwide. Beer is supplied to outlets
throughout Kent and East Sussex, plus cases of bottled

THE BREWERIES

beers can also be ordered online for nationwide delivery. ❦ 🍺 LIVE

Bitter (ABV 4%) BITTER
Amber Ale (ABV 4.4%) PALE
APA (ABV 5%) PALE

Rooster's SIBA

Unit H5, Fifth Avenue, Hornbeam Park, Harrogate, North Yorkshire, HG2 8QT
☎ (01423) 865959 ⊕ roosters.co.uk

☺Rooster's Brewing is an independent, family-owned brewery and taproom, based in Harrogate. Weekly production capacity stands at 200 barrels, which includes one-off experimental beers brewed as part of the brewery's Outlaw Project. 🍺♦V✦

Buckeye (ABV 3.5%) GOLD
Highway 51 (ABV 3.7%) PALE
Capability Brown (ABV 4%) BITTER
YPA (Yorkshire Pale Ale) (ABV 4.1%) PALE
London Thunder (ABV 4.2%) PORTER
Yankee (ABV 4.3%) PALE
A straw-coloured beer with a delicate, fruity aroma leading to a well-balanced taste of malt and hops with a slight evidence of sweetness, followed by a refreshing, fruity/bitter finish.
TwentyFourSeven (ABV 4.7%) PALE
Baby-Faced Assassin (ABV 6.1%) IPA

Rossendale

🍺 Griffin Inn, 84 Hud Rake, Haslingden, Lancashire, BB4 5AF
☎ (01706) 214021 ⊕ rossendalebrewery.co.uk

☺The brewery acquired the brew plant previously used by Porter Brewing Co in 2007 and is based in the cellar of the Griffin Inn in Haslingden. The Sportsman in Hyde and many other local outlets are also supplied. 🍺

Rother Valley

Gate Court Farm, Station Road, Northiam, East Sussex, TN31 6QT
☎ (01797) 252922 ☎ 07798 877551
⊕ rothervalleybrewery.co.uk

☒ Rother Valley Brewey was established in Northiam in 1993, overlooking the Rother Levels and the Kent & East Sussex Railway. Brewing on a 10-barrel plant, around 100 outlets are supplied direct. Established and new hop varieties are sourced locally. ♦

Black Ops (ABV 3.8%) STOUT
Smild (ABV 3.8%) MILD
Valley Bitter (ABV 3.8%) BITTER
Level Best (ABV 4%) BITTER
Full-bodied, tawny, session bitter with a malt and fruit aroma, malty taste and a dry, hoppy finish.
Copper Ale (ABV 4.1%) BITTER
Hoppers Ale (ABV 4.4%) BITTER
Boadicea (ABV 4.5%) BLOND
Blues (ABV 5%) OLD
NIPA (ABV 5%) IPA
Exit (ABV 5.7%) IPA

Rothes

77 New Street, Rothes, AB38 7BJ ☎ 07336 233634
✉ therothesbrewery@sky.com

☒ Situated in the heart of the Spey Valley, production began in 2014. Beers are available in bottle, cask and KeyKeg. LIVE

Rough Brothers (NEW)

Unit 2d, Altnagelvin Industrial Estate, Trench Road, Londonderry, BT47 2ED ☎ 07946 638513

Brewery started with assistance from the Go For It business programme.

Roughacre

Clare Hall Barns, Clare, Cambridgeshire, CO10 8PJ
☎ (01799) 585956 ⊕ roughacre.com

☒ Established in 2018, Roughacre is a microbrewery based in the beautiful historic market town of Clare in West Suffolk. Its passion is for high quality, fine ales of character which range from classic amber ales and golden IPA, to Belgian-style abbey ale, and dark coffee porter... and quite a bit in-between. 🍺LIVE V✦

The Saintly One (ABV 1.5%) BITTER
Zestival (ABV 3.6%) PALE
Cavendish Red (ABV 3.8%) MILD
Alliance TPA (ABV 4.2%) PALE
Ashdon Amber (ABV 4.4%) BITTER
Nighthawker (ABV 4.6%) SPECIALITY
Three Counties (ABV 4.6%) BITTER
All Saints (ABV 4.8%) BITTER
La Belle Saison (ABV 4.8%) SPECIALITY
Camps Comfort (ABV 5%) SPECIALITY
Abbey Gold (ABV 5.2%) SPECIALITY
Mosquito IPA (ABV 5.2%) PALE
Hurricane ESB (ABV 5.4%) SPECIALITY
Saffron Sun (ABV 5.4%) SPECIALITY
Vulcan DIPA (ABV 7.4%) IPA

Round Corner

Melton Mowbray Market, Scalford Road (Gate 2), Melton Mowbray, Leicestershire, LE13 1JY
☎ (01664) 569855

Round Corner Brewing was launched in 2018. The state-of-the-art, 20-hectolitre brewery, and its taproom, can be found in the old sheep shed, at the heart of Melton Mowbray Market. A variety of cask-conditioned ales were introduced in 2019 to complement the keg range. A barrel-aged programme continues, most recently using Irish Whiskey barrels. Following the installation of a canning line in 2020 the brewery has instigated more direct sales via an online shop. ✦

Topside Golden Ale (ABV 3.8%) GOLD

Rowton SIBA

Stone House, Rowton, Telford, Shropshire, TF6 6QX
☎ 07854 885870 ⊕ rowtonbrewery.com

Rowton Brewery is family-run, and was established in 2008 in a converted Victorian cowshed, on a farm. The brewing operation is split over two locations. The original brewery is still in the village of Rowton and uses water from a borehole on the farm. A second brewery has been installed at the Pheasant Pub, Wellington. Combined brew length over the two plants is 10 barrels. ♦

Moonstruck Mild (ABV 3.3%) MILD
Star Light (ABV 3.6%) BITTER
Pure Gold (ABV 3.8%) GOLD
Bitter (ABV 3.9%) BITTER
Meteorite (ABV 4.2%) BITTER
Portly Stout (ABV 4.5%) SPECIALITY
Area 51 (ABV 5.1%) BITTER

RT Brew

See Old Mill

Ruddles

See Greene King

Rudgate SIBA

2 Centre Park, Marston Moor Business Park, Tockwith, York, North Yorkshire, YO26 7QF
☎ (01423) 358382 ⊕ rudgatebrewery.co.uk

☺Rudgate Brewery was established in 1992. It is situated in the heart of Yorkshire, in the Vale of York, on the old RAF Marston Moor airfield. The old Roman road of Rudgate runs through the airfield and led the Vikings into Jorvik (York), which is what inspires many of the beer names. ◆

Jorvik Blonde (ABV 3.8%) BLOND
Viking (ABV 3.8%) BITTER
An initially warming and malty, full-bodied beer, with hops and fruit lingering into the aftertaste.
Battleaxe (ABV 4.2%) BITTER
A well-hopped bitter with slightly sweet initial taste and light bitterness. Complex fruit character gives a memorable aftertaste.
Ruby Mild (ABV 4.4%) MILD
Nutty, rich ruby ale, stronger than usual for a mild.
Valkyrie APA (ABV 5%) PALE
York Chocolate Stout (ABV 5%) STOUT

Rufford Abbey

Meden Road, Boughton, Nottinghamshire, NG22 9ZD

Originally known as Headstocks, the brewery was established in 2017 to produce Prussia Lager in collaboration with a partner brewery in Kaliningrad on the Lithuania/Poland border. In 2018 cask-conditioned beer was added to the range.

Rufford Poacher (ABV 3.8%) BITTER
White Monk (ABV 4.2%) PALE
Warrior (ABV 5.2%) BITTER

Brewed under the Headstocks Brewery name:
Brakeman Best Bitter (ABV 4%) BITTER
Canary Pale Ale (ABV 4%) PALE
Early Rider (ABV 5%) BITTER

Runaway

Unit 4, Millgate, Dantzic Street, Manchester, M4 4JW
☎ (0161) 832 2628 ☎ 07505 237078
⊕ therunawaybrewery.com

Runaway is located in a railway arch outside Manchester Victoria station. It began brewing in 2014 producing KeyKeg and bottle-conditioned beers. All core range beers are unfiltered and unpasteurised, with many available locally. ‼◆LIVE

Running Man

26 Greenway, Davis Estate, Chatham, Kent, ME5 9UX

Running Man began brewing in 2018.

Rusty Garage (NEW)

Unit 115 Rivermead Business Centre, Westlea, Swindon, SN5 7EX ☎ 07889 928241
⊕ rustygaragecraftbrewery.com

Microbrewery established in Swindon in 2020, producing a range of small batch beers available in canned and bottle formats, all named after a motoring theme.

Ryedale

Roseberry, Moor Lane, Sinnington, North Yorkshire, YO62 6SE ☎ 07850 510859 ⊕ ryedalebrewing.co.uk

☺Ryedale began brewing in 2013 using a four-barrel plant. In 2016 it relocated to Cross Hills and again in 2019 to Sinnington. Brews only on an occasional basis.

S&P

Homestead, Brewery Lane, Horsford, Norfolk, NR10 3AN ☎ 07884 455425/ 07552 300768
⊕ spbrewery.co.uk

⊗ Production commenced in 2013 using a 10-barrel plant constructed upon land once owned by prominent Norfolk brewers Steward & Patteson (1800-1965), hence the name. Locally-produced malts are used, as is water from the brewery's own borehole. ‼V

Topaz Blonde (ABV 3.7%) BLOND
Blackberry Porter (ABV 4%) SPECIALITY
First Light (ABV 4.1%) GOLD
Dennis (ABV 4.2%) BITTER
Fruit and malt, with some caramel, dominate aroma and taste. Full-bodied throughout with an increasingly bitter tail.
Darkest Hour (ABV 4.4%) STOUT
Deep dark roast notes dominate this singularly dry stout. Sweet biscuit notes fade in an increasingly bitter chocolate finish.
Beano (ABV 4.5%) STOUT
NASHA IPA (ABV 5%) PALE
Strong banana and grapefruit character throughout. A good balance of malt and hop with a bittersweet background. Rich and filling.

Contract brewed for Boudicca Brewery:
Queen of Hops (ABV 3.7%) PALE
A definitive grapefruit hoppiness dominates throughout. A backdrop of ginger and gentle grassiness appears before a growing dryness gains ascendancy.
Three Tails (ABV 3.9%) BITTER
A bitter backbone dominates throughout. Malt, grapefruit and pepper in the first taste fades as a dry bitterness slowly grows.
Golden Torc (ABV 4.3%) GOLD
Malty bouquet with a hint of grassy hop. Biscuity beginning with a growing zesty citrus background appears. Clean grapefruit finish.
The Red Queen (ABV 4.5%) RED
Malt, dark fruits and caramel in nose and taste. Sweetness counters a growing hoppiness. Rye adds contrast and depth.
Spiral Stout (ABV 4.6%) STOUT
Burnt toast on the nose and black malt in the taste defines this traditional black and dry stout. Strong finish.
Prasto's Porter (ABV 5.2%) PORTER

S43 SIBA

Durham Road, Coxhoe, DH6 4HX
☎ (0191) 377 3039 ⊕ sonnet43.com

☺S43 started brewing in 2012. It owns four outlets. All but one is leased out as a free house. The death at a young age of its founder Mark Hird has precipitated a change in the core range of beers. The brewery will continue to produce specials but now two a month. It has an extensive free trade throughout the land. ◆LIVE

The Mark (ABV 3.9%) BLOND
The Doctor (ABV 4%) BITTER
The Raven (ABV 4.3%) STOUT
The Phoenix (ABV 4.5%) PALE

St Andrews Brewhouse

⬛ City Pub Co, 41 Saint Andrews Street, Norwich, NR2 4TP
☎ (01603) 305995 ☎ 07976 652410
⊕ standrewsbrewhouse.com

⊗ A city centre brewpub opened in 2015 in the premises formerly occupied by Delaney's Irish Bar. ‼◆

St Andrews Brewing

Unit 7, Bassaguard Business Park, St Andrews, KY16 8AL
☎ (01334) 208586
⊕ standrewsbrewingcompany.com

Established in 2012, the brewery is a four-barrel plant producing bottle-conditioned, cask and eco keg beers. In addition to its own three outlets (two in St Andrews, and one in Dundee), beers are supplied to a number of supermarket chains, local retailers and outlets. ‼LIVE

Oatmeal Stout (ABV 4.5%) STOUT
Mocha Porter (ABV 6%) SPECIALITY
Notorious BIPA (ABV 6%) SPECIALITY
Yippie IPA (ABV 6%) IPA

St Annes

St Annes Church, Shorthill, Lea Cross, Shrewsbury, Shropshire, SY5 8JE
☎ (01743) 860296 ☎ 07530 556951

Office: 38 Hafren Road, Shrewsbury, SY3 8NQ
⊕ shropshirebeers.co.uk

⊗ Brewing began in 2017, this independent brewery is in the quirky location of a restored and occasionally functioning church. Recipes are Scandinavian-influenced but traditional British real ales. A broad range of beers styles is produced. ‼◆

Three Erics (ABV 3.7%) BITTER
Golden Dart (ABV 3.8%) GOLD
Lea Cross Dark (ABV 3.9%) MILD
Tumbledown Dick (ABV 4.2%) BITTER
Round The Wrekin (ABV 4.7%) BITTER
Iron And Fire (ABV 7.5%) STOUT

St Austell IFBB

63 Trevarthian Road, St Austell, Cornwall, PL25 4BY
☎ 0345 241 1122 ⊕ staustellbrewery.co.uk

☺Founded in 1851, St Austell brewery remains fully independent and family-owned. Cask ale is available in all its pubs, and is widely available nationally. A ten-barrel, small-batch plant is used to brew monthly specials, including beers for its annual Celtic beer festival in November. Its beers are available in 40 selected outlets, and at Hicks Bar at the Brewery. In 2016 it purchased Bath Ales (qv). ‼➥◆LIVE⚭

Cornish Best Bitter (ABV 3.5%) BITTER
Light, refreshing bitter with malt aroma. Gentle biscuit malt and hops flavour with fruity bitterness. Malty, bitter, faintly dry finish.
Trelawny (ABV 3.8%) BITTER
Light, tawny bitter with aroma of malt and hops. Resinous hop-bitterness develops into toffee-malt sweetness. Crisp malty, fruity finish.
Nicholson's Pale Ale (ABV 4%) PALE
Copper bitter. Hops dominate the taste with citrus and tropical fruits and malt. Dry bitterness rises in the finish.
Tribute (ABV 4.2%) BITTER

Amber bitter with malt and fruity hop aroma. Dominant hop bitterness balanced by sweet malt, ending refreshingly bitter and fruity.
Proper Job (ABV 4.5%) GOLD
Smooth, premium golden ale with citrus hop aroma. Copious citrus fruits with bitterness, dryness and crisp hop bitter and grapefruit finish.
Hicks (ABV 5%) BITTER
Tawny, premium bitter with malt nose. Powerful malt and vine fruit flavour with balancing bitterness. Long, malty and floral finish.

St Botolphs

8 Gladwin Road, Colchester, Essex, CO2 7HS
☎ (01206) 511835 ⊕ stbotolphsbrewery.co.uk

Brewing began in 2014. Its Belgian-style bottled beers can be found in pubs, farm shops, specialist beer shops, markets and food festivals in Essex and Suffolk.

St Ives SIBA

Trewidden Road, St Ives, Cornwall, TR26 2BX
☎ (01736) 793467 ☎ 07702 311595
⊕ stives-brewery.co.uk

⊗ The two-storey brewhouse, with 10-barrel plant, integral visitor centre, gift shop and 60-seater café, was built in 2015. Owner Marco Amura started brewing commercially in 2016, with production steadily increasing since then. Bottled beers are the highest seller, due to strong demand from local restaurants and cafés. The brewery's café, which enjoys a panoramic view of St Ives Bay, is a popular venue. ‼➥◆LIVE

Hella Pale (ABV 4.2%) PALE
Porth Pilsner (ABV 4.4%) SPECIALITY
Meor IPA (ABV 4.8%) PALE
Slipway IPA (ABV 5%) PALE
Alba IPA (ABV 5.2%) PALE
Black Road East NEIPA (ABV 5.8%) IPA

St John at Hackney

See Hackney Church

St Judes

⬛ 2 Cardigan Street, Ipswich, Suffolk, IP1 3PF
☎ (01473) 413334 ☎ 07879 360879
⊕ stjudestavern.com

⊗ The 10-barrel brewery produces beer for the St Judes Brewery Tavern in Ipswich. It can also be found at some local festivals. ◆

St Mars of the Desert

90 Stevenson Road, Attercliffe, Sheffield, South Yorkshire, S9 3XG ☎ 07365 222101
⊕ beerofsmod.co.uk

St Mars of the Desert is a family-run brewery in the industrial area of Attercliffe, Sheffield. Recognised as one of the 'top ten new breweries in the world' by Rate Beer in 2020, Dann and Martha brew a range from IPA's through to Belgian inspired beers, to wood-fermented sour beers and malty, dark offerings. The taproom is open most weekends for drinks and cans to take away. The brewery supplies cans to many independent retailers nationwide. ➥◆

St Mary's

St Mary the Virgin, Elsworthy Road, Primrose Hill, London, NW3 3DJ

☎ (020) 7722 3238 ⊕ stmarysbrewery.co.uk

Based in the church crypt, this nanobrewery produces small-batch bottled beers sold in aid of the church's youth projects. Larger batches are produced elsewhere, the bottle label will display the origin. The first pint was blessed by the Bishop of Edmonton and the names have an ecclesiastical bias. LIVE

St Peter's SIBA

St Peter's Hall, St Peter South Elmham, Suffolk, NR35 1NQ
☎ (01986) 782322 ⊕ stpetersbrewery.co.uk

⊠ The brewery, built in 1996, is housed in traditional former agricultural buildings adjacent to moated, medieval St Peters Hall, dating from 1280. Brewing makes use of the water from an on-site bore hole combined with locally malted barley. Beer is distributed nationally across the UK and exported to more than 40 countries worldwide. ‼♥♦⬥

Best Bitter (ABV 3.7%) BITTER
A complex but well-balanced hoppy brew. A gentle hop nose introduces a singular hoppiness with supporting malt notes and underlying bitterness. Other flavours fade to leave a long, dry, hoppy finish.
Golden Ale (ABV 4%) GOLD
Amber-coloured, full-bodied, robust ale. A strong hop bouquet leads to a mix of malt and hops combined with a dry, fruity hoppiness. The malt quickly subsides, leaving creamy bitterness.
Organic Best (ABV 4.1%) BITTER
A very dry and bitter beer with a growing astringency. Pale brown in colour, it has a gentle hop aroma which makes the definitive bitterness surprising. One for the committed.
Ruby Red (ABV 4.3%) BITTER
Plum Porter (ABV 4.6%) SPECIALITY
Citrus (ABV 4.7%) PALE
Fudge as well as grapefruit on the nose. A refreshing fruit flavour, with hints of grapefruit peel in the aftertaste.
IPA (ABV 5.5%) IPA
Cream Stout (ABV 6.5%) STOUT

Sabrina

See Worcester

Saddleworth

⬛ Church Inn, Church Lane, Uppermill, Oldham, OL3 6LW
☎ (01457) 820902 ⊕ churchinnsaddleworth.co.uk

☺Set in an idyllic location near St Chad's Church, Saddleworth started brewing in 1997 in a 120-year-old brewhouse at the Church Inn. Brewery and inn are set above a valley overlooking Saddleworth Moor. Brewing capacity was significantly expanded in 2011 with a new 13-barrel plant. Most of the production is taken by the adjacent inn. ♦

Sadler's

See Hawkshead

Saints Row

Unit 1, Cleveland Industrial Estate, Darlington, DL1 2PB
☎ (01325) 464138 ☎ 07922 617622

Office: 18 Maude Street, Darlington, DL3 7PW
⊕ saintsrowbrewing.com

Formerly known as Hells Kettle, Saints Row commenced brewing in 2017 using equipment at Three Brothers Brewing (qv). In 2019 the brewery moved to its own premises in Darlington. A taproom is open at weekends. ⬥

Salcombe SIBA

Estuary View, Ledstone, Devon, TQ7 4BL
☎ (01548) 854888 ⊕ salcombebrewery.com

⊠ Salcombe Brewery was purpose built on the site of a decommisioned water reservoir, which utilises the natural ambient temperature of the underground facility for storing ales at perfect conditioning temperature. The brewery has close ties with both the RNLI and the Seahorse Trust. ‼♥♦⬥

Devon Amber (ABV 3.8%) BITTER
Gold (ABV 4.2%) GOLD
Shingle Bay (ABV 4.2%) BITTER
Seahorse (ABV 4.4%) BITTER
Toffee malt is evident throughout this complex, yet subtle mix of everything you would expect from a best bitter.
Lifesaver (ABV 4.8%) BITTER
A refreshing ale, deep copper in colour, with a smack of citrus and orange peel and luscious malty flavour. A dry citrus finish with a taste of liquorice.
Island Street Porter (ABV 5.9%) PORTER
Creamy head, aroma of chocolate/coffee and cherries giving a black forest gateau taste. Flavours linger on tongue during aftertaste.

Salopian SIBA

The Old Station Yard, Station Road, Hadnall, Shropshire, SY4 3DD
☎ (01743) 248414 ⊕ salopianbrewery.co.uk

☺The brewery was established in 1995 in an old dairy on the outskirts of Shrewsbury but moved in 2014 to its new location in an industrial unit in the village of Hadnall, where it now produces more than 150 barrels a week of its multi award-winning ales, for distribution throughout the midlands, and further afield. It has recently invested in a canning plant. ‼♥♦LIVE

Shropshire Gold (ABV 3.8%) GOLD
Oracle (ABV 4%) GOLD
Citrus aromas lead to an impressive dry, and increasing citrusy taste.
Darwins Origin (ABV 4.3%) BITTER
Pale brown in which hops and fruit are dominant. Hops top the aftertaste with a pleasing lingering bitterness. Well-balanced with a moreish demand.
Hop Twister (ABV 4.5%) GOLD
Lemon Dream (ABV 4.5%) SPECIALITY
Golden Thread (ABV 5%) GOLD
Kashmir (ABV 5.5%) BITTER
Automaton (ABV 7%) STRONG
Gold with pine forest aromas and peaches! Syrup with a kick. Dry hints and exotic astringency as hops give a dry finish but sweet balance.

Salt

199 Bingley Road, Shipley, West Yorkshire, BD18 4DH
☎ (01274) 533848 ⊕ saltbeerfactory.co.uk

Housed in a Grade II-listed Edwardian tramshed, Salt is a state-of-the-art, 200-hectolitre brew plant and one of the Ossett group of independently-run breweries. The site includes a taproom and live music space. Two bars, branded as Craft Asylum, are operated. ‼♦V⬥

Jute (ABV 4.2%) BITTER

Alpaca (ABV 6.6%) STRONG

Salt Steel SIBA

Office: 24 St Cuthberts Way, Darlington, DL1 1GB
⊕ saltsteelbrewing.com

Established in 2020 and forged from the industrial landscapes of Teeside and Cheshire, Salt Steel Brewing have been collaborating with other brewers in the North East.

Saltaire SIBA

Unit 7, County Works, Dockfield Road, Shipley, West Yorkshire, BD17 7AR
☎ (01274) 594959 ⊕ saltairebrewery.com

⊚Saltaire Brewery opened in a converted gasworks by the River Aire in 2006 and quickly established a presence through aggressive marketing of quality cask ales. Saltaire upgraded to a 40-barrel plant and added a modern bottling and packaging plant in 2018. There is an emphasis on quality control to ensure a consistent product, whilst maintaining a steadfast commitment to an expanding range of cask ales alongside KeyKeg ales. Supplies pubs and retail outlets across the UK and Europe. ‼ 🍺 ♦ ✦

South Island (ABV 3.5%) PALE
Titus (ABV 3.9%) BITTER
Blonde (ABV 4%) BITTER
Thirst-quenching and quaffable, this straw-coloured beer is slightly sweet and well-rounded with fruit, malt and hops in the taste and a fruity, hoppy finish.
Citra (ABV 4.2%) PALE
Best (ABV 4.4%) BITTER
Amarillo (ABV 4.5%) PALE
Cascade (ABV 4.8%) PALE
Triple Choc (ABV 4.8%) SPECIALITY
A creamy, dark brown, roast, chocolate stout with a dry bitter finish and a rich chocolate aroma.
Unity (ABV 6%) IPA

SaltRock SIBA

Lochend Farm, Dunfermline, KY12 0RY
⊕ saltrockbrewing.co.uk

SaltRock Brewing began brewing in 2021. Born of a desire to re-awaken a celebration of malt over the hop, it produces malt-forward beers. LIVE

Sambrook's SIBA

1 Bellwether Lane, The Ram Quarter, Wandsworth, London, SW18 1UR
☎ (020) 7228 0598 ⊕ sambrooksbrewery.co.uk

⊗ Sambrook's was founded in 2008 and supplies its award-winning ales throughout London. The range of beers is traditional in style and available in all formats but cask is the key focus. A move in 2021 saw a new brewery built in the redeveloped Youngs Brewery complex in central Wandsworth, including the private Ram Brewery. This ensures centuries of continuous brewing on the site has been maintained. ‼ 🍺 ♦ LIVE ✦

Wandle (ABV 3.8%) BITTER
Touch of dryness balances the rounded, sweetish malt flavour of this fruity, quaffable pale brown bitter. Gentle dry, bitter aftertaste
American Red (ABV 4.2%) BITTER
Fruity red beer with some chocolate notes in the palate. A developing dark chocolate on the spicy hoppy, dry finish.
Pumphouse Pale (ABV 4.2%) PALE

Refreshing golden beer. Citrus aroma becoming more pronounced on the palate with spicy hops, digestives and hints of vanilla.
APA (ABV 4.5%) PALE
A light-coloured, refreshing, smooth beer with hints of malt and fruit in the flavour.
Junction (ABV 4.5%) BITTER
Smooth, full-bodied premium bitter with sweet, caramelised orange, toffee, sultanas and spicy hops. A developing gentle, growing bitter, dryish finish.
Powerhouse Porter (ABV 4.9%) PORTER
Dark brown porter with a pleasant, roasted malt nose. Coffee, sweet milk chocolate, currants, spice with an underlying roasty bitterness.

Sandbanks SIBA

Unit 6, 4-6 Abingdon Road, Nuffield Industrial Estate, Poole, Dorset, BH17 0UG
☎ (01202) 671950 ⊕ sandbanksbrewery.net

⊗ Opened in 2018 on the site of the old Bournemouth Brewery with a new five-barrel plant. The beer is becoming increasingly availably in the local free trade with one-off and special beers from the one-barrel plant available in the taproom. 🍺 ♦ ✦

Sandbanks Bitter (ABV 3.9%) BITTER
Session bitter with lingering aftertaste.
Golden Years (ABV 4.3%) GOLD
Back in Black (ABV 5%) STOUT
Wayward Son IPA (ABV 5%) PALE

Sandstone

Unit 5, Wrexham Enterprise Park, Preston Road, off Ash Road, North Wrexham Industrial Estate, Wrexham, LL13 9JT
☎ (01978) 664805 ☎ 07851 001118
⊕ sandstonebrewery.co.uk

⊚Sandstone Brewery was established as a four-barrel plant in 2008. The brewery was taken over by the current owners in 2013. The beers are available at around 50 outlets in North-West England and North Wales. ‼ 🍺 ♦

Edge (ABV 3.8%) BITTER
A satisfying session ale, this pale, dry, bitter beer has a full mouthfeel and a lingering, hoppy finish that belies its modest strength.
American Proper Gander (ABV 4.1%) PALE
Quadrohopper (ABV 4.4%) BLOND
Dragon's Blood (ABV 4.5%) BITTER

Sarah Hughes

See under H

Saviour

🏠 White Hart Inn, Hamstead Marshall, Berkshire, RG20 0HW
☎ (01488) 657545 ✉ info@saviourwhitehart.co.uk

Brewing began in 2019 on a four-barrel plant in an outbuilding in the grounds of the White Hart. Beers are only available from the pub.

Scarborough SIBA

Unit 21b, Stadium Works, Barry's Lane, Scarborough, North Yorkshire, YO12 4HA
☎ (01723) 367506 ⊕ scarboroughbrewery.co.uk

⊚Scarborough is a family-run brewery established in 2010, now using a 10-barrel plant. Beers can be found in the family-owned Valley Bar and Rivelyn Hotel as well as being the sole suppliers to Merchant Bar in Scarborough. ◆

Trident (ABV 3.8%) PALE
Citra (ABV 4.2%) GOLD
Sealord (ABV 4.3%) GOLD
Stout (ABV 4.6%) STOUT
Hello Darkness (ABV 5%) PORTER

Scruffy Dog

▤ 94 Station Road, Sutton-In-Ashfield, Nottinghamshire, NG17 5HF
☎ (01623) 550826 ⊕ thescruffydog.co.uk

Microbrewery at the Scruffy Dog pub in Sutton-in-Ashfield.

Seagate

Seagate, Lamlash, Isle of Arran, KA27 8JN
☎ (01770) 600110 ⊕ seagatebrewery.co.uk

☺In 2020 Stephen Sparshott progressed from homebrewing in his kitchen into commercial brewing in a purpose-built shed on the shores of Lamlash Bay. Concentrating on Belgian and Scottish ales, nine core beers are brewed on his 30-litre and 50-litre kits, with a further two ales produced on a separate installation at Arran Botanical Drinks, Cladach, Brodick. ‼◆LIVE V

Rise Above 80/- (ABV 4.2%) BROWN
SAORSA Blonde Ale (ABV 5.2%) BLOND

Serious SIBA

Unit C5, Fieldhouse Industrial Estate, Fieldhouse Road, Rochdale, OL12 0AA ☎ 07840 301797
⊕ seriousbrewing.co.uk

Established in 2015 and run by husband and wife team Ken and Jenny Lynch. The beers are brewed using a six-barrel plant. The focus is on producing high quality beers drawing influences from traditional British ales, US craft beers and artisanal Belgian beers. Many outlets are supplied direct and the beers are available nationwide via wholesalers. A taproom opened at the brewery in 2019. ◆LIVE V✦

Prime (ABV 4.2%) PALE
Evergreen (ABV 4.5%) BITTER
Hoppy aroma. Taste of fruit and bitter hops, with lasting bitterness. Crisp and bitter throughout. Background of sweet malt.
Moonlight (ABV 4.5%) STOUT
Redsmith (ABV 4.5%) BITTER
Goldrush (ABV 5.6%) SPECIALITY

Settle SIBA

Unit 2b, The Sidings, Settle, North Yorkshire, BD24 9RP
☎ (01729) 824936 ⊕ settlebrewery.co.uk

☺Settle Brewery is located in an industrial unit adjacent to Settle railway station. Brewing started in 2013 using a 12-barrel plant. It supplies more than 40 outlets across Cumbria, the Yorkshire Dales, West Yorkshire and North Lancashire. The beers are also available through wholesalers. ‼◆

Blonde (ABV 3.6%) BLOND
Jericho Blonde (ABV 3.6%) BLOND
Mainline (ABV 3.8%) BITTER
Creamy, traditional Yorkshire Bitter. Good balance of rich malt and bittering hops, giving a pronounced raspberry fruitiness and hints of nuts in both aroma and taste.
Ribblehead Bitter (ABV 3.8%) BITTER

Nine Standards Golden Ale (ABV 4.1%) GOLD
Nine Standards Pale Ale (ABV 4.3%) PALE
Epic IPA (ABV 4.4%) PALE
Ernie's Milk Stout (ABV 4.5%) STOUT
Nine Standards Porter (ABV 4.7%) PORTER
Roasty porter with coffee and dark fruits. Hints of liquorice and plums in the aroma. The finish is bitter and roasty.

Seven Bro7hers SIBA

Unit 63, Waybridge Enterprise Centre, Daniel Adamson Road, Salford, M50 1DS
☎ (0161) 228 2404 ⊕ sevenbro7hers.com

Brewing began in 2014 using a 10-barrel plant. A new brewhouse and fermentation tanks doubled brewing capacity in 2017, and allowed for the brewing of speciality and one-off beers, plus a brewery tap. The Seven Bro7hers Beerhouse in Ancoats opened in 2016, and a new Beerhouse opened in 2019 in the Middlewood Locks area near Salford Central station. Further outlets are planned in Leeds, Liverpool and at Manchester Airport. ‼🏭

Session (ABV 3.8%) PALE
Fruity hop taste of tropical fruit, well-balanced with bitter and pale malt. Citrus hop aroma. Refreshing bitter finish.

Seven Kings SIBA

Lyneburn Industrial Estate, Halbeath Place, Dunfermline, KY11 4JT
Office: Wymet House, 87 New Row, Dunfermline, KY12 7DZ

Brewing began in 2019.

Seven Stars (NEW)

▤ Seven Stars, 73 The Terrace, Penryn, Cornwall, TR10 8EL
☎ (01326) 531398 ✉ info@sevenstarspenryn.co.uk

Brewing began in 2020 using a 2.5-barrel plant. The brewery is located in an outbuilding of the Seven Stars pub, adjacent to the beer garden. ◆

Severn SIBA

The Brewery, Tortworth Business Park, Tortworth, Gloucestershire, GL12 8HQ
☎ (01454) 269421 ⊕ s7n.co.uk

⊗ The brewery is owned by Foxstead Ltd, a drinks distribution company. All beers are brewed using a 30-barrel plant, with a five-barrel plant for experimental brews and small batches. ‼🏭◆GF

Copper Ale (ABV 3.8%) BITTER
Double Hopped Pale Ale (ABV 4.2%) PALE
Amarillo Citra APA (ABV 4.3%) PALE
Ruby Porter (ABV 4.8%) PORTER
Chocolate Stout (ABV 5%) STOUT
Extra Special (ABV 5.2%) BITTER
English IPA (ABV 5.5%) IPA

Brewed under the Cotswold Spring brand name:
Mystic (ABV 4.3%) BITTER
Waii-iti (ABV 4.3%) BITTER

Severn Valley

The Stables, Hollow Ash Lane, Bridgnorth, Shropshire, WV15 6ET ☎ 07402 636482 ⊕ severnvalleyales.co.uk

The trading name of Bridgnorth Brewery Ltd, Severn Valley Ales started brewing in 2019 producing a range of beers in different packaging formats. The main outlet is Bridgnorth Rugby club, but beers can be found in other pubs in Bridgnorth.

SVA (ABV 4%) BITTER
Cartway Gold (ABV 4.2%) GOLD
Old Mo (ABV 4.8%) BITTER

Shadow

44 Whiteley Croft Rise, Otley, West Yorkshire, LS21 3NR ☎ 07792 690536 ⊕ shadowbrewing.co.uk

Established in 2019 by Ian Shutt, one of the founders of the Chevin brewing collective, Shadow consists of a one-barrel plant in Ian's garage.

Shakespeare

See North Cotswold

Shalford SIBA

PO Box 10411, Braintree, Essex, CM7 5WP
☎ (01371) 850925 ☎ 07749 658512
⊕ shalfordbrewery.co.uk

Shalford began brewing in 2007 on a five-barrel plant at Hyde Farm in the Pant Valley in Essex. More than 50 outlets are supplied direct. ◆LIVE

1319 Mild (ABV 3.7%) MILD
Barnfield Pale Ale (ABV 3.8%) PALE
Pale-coloured but full-flavoured, this is a traditional pale ale. Malt persists throughout, with bitterness becoming more dominant towards the end.
Braintree Market Ale (ABV 4%) BITTER
Levelly Gold (ABV 4%) GOLD
Stoneley Bitter (ABV 4.2%) BITTER
Dark amber, session beer whose vivid hop character is supported by a juicy, malty body. A dry finish makes this beer very drinkable.
Hyde Bitter (ABV 4.7%) BITTER
Stronger version of Barnfield, with a similar but more assertive character.
Levelly Black (ABV 4.8%) STOUT
Rotten End (ABV 6.5%) STRONG

Sharp's

Pityme Business Centre, Rock, Cornwall, PL27 6NU
☎ (01208) 862121 ⊕ sharpsbrewery.co.uk

⊗ Sharp's was founded in 1994 and within 15 years had grown from producing 1,500 barrels a year, to 60,000. It was bought by Molson Coors in 2011. Heavy investment has brought the capacity up to 200,000 barrels a year. The company owns no pubs and delivers beer to more than 1,200 outlets across South England via temperature-controlled depots in Bristol and London. Molson Coors has stressed that it will maintain production in Cornwall. Part of Molson Coors PLC. ▰◆LIVE

Cornish Coaster (ABV 3.6%) BITTER
Pale brown bitter with malt and tropical fruit nose. Apples, citrus and hedgerow fruits with biscuit malt and caramel notes.
Doom Bar (ABV 4%) BITTER
Amber bitter with predominantly sweet taste, balanced biscuit malt and grassy hops. Plums and raisins. Malt and lingering, bitter finish.
Atlantic (ABV 4.2%) BITTER
Amber bitter with citrus hops and caramel aroma. Malt, elderflower and caramel sweetness balanced by grapefruit hops with resin notes.
Original (ABV 4.4%) BITTER

Mid-brown best bitter with pleasant hop and malt aroma. Prune and berry fruits on the palate with smoky malt.
Sea Fury (ABV 5%) BITTER
Smooth, auburn, premium bitter with malt and caramel aromas. Dominant sweet malt with berry, stone and dried fruits with spice hints.

Shaws of Grange

12 Station Yard, Grange-over-Sands, LA11 6DW
☎ (01229) 837955 ☎ 07951 009607
⊕ shawsofgrange.co.uk

This 0.5-barrel brewery began producing beers for sale in 2019. A range of four beers has been developed for sale in cask and by hand bottling. It relocated to new premises in late 2020.

Bay Walker (ABV 4.2%) BITTER
Clock Tower Blonde (ABV 4.2%) BLOND
Hampsfell (ABV 4.2%) GOLD
Old Pool (ABV 4.2%) SPECIALITY

Shed 35 (NEW)

Chapman Drive, Carnoustie, DD7 6DX ☎ 07530 430579 ⊕ shed35brewery.co.uk

Set up by friends Gary Mellon and John Wilson, Shed 35 commenced brewing in 2016. Although mainly producing bottle-conditioned beers for sale locally at farmers' markets and other outlets in Angus and the surrounding area, the brewery occasionally produces cask-conditioned beer. LIVE

Shed Ales

Broadfields, Pewsey, Wiltshire, SN9 5DT
☎ (01672) 564533 ☎ 07769 812643
⊕ shedales.com

Shed Ales was launched in 2012 operating from a one-barrel plant in a converted garden shed. The brewery currently produces three core ales and several bespoke beers, available at selected local outlets including the brewery-owned Shed Alehouse, a micropub in Pewsey. ◆

Dig It (ABV 3.7%) BITTER
Shed Some Light (ABV 3.8%) BLOND
Dibber (ABV 4.2%) BITTER

Sheffield SIBA

Unit 111, JC Albyn Complex, Burton Road, Sheffield, South Yorkshire, S3 8BT
☎ (0114) 272 7256 ⊕ sheffieldbrewery.com

☺Established in 2006, Sheffield Brewery Company is situated in a former Victorian factory, originally known for making Blanco polish. The 10-barrel plant operates on a gravity-fed tower based system. The brewery has its own on-site taproom. ‼▰✦

Crucible Best (ABV 3.8%) BITTER
Five Rivers (ABV 3.8%) PALE
Blanco Blonde (ABV 4.2%) SPECIALITY
Porter (ABV 4.4%) PORTER

Shepherd Neame IFBB

17 Court Street, Faversham, Kent, ME13 7AX
☎ (01795) 532206 ⊕ shepherdneame.co.uk

⊗ Shepherd Neame traces its history back to at least 1698 making it the oldest continuous brewer in the country. The company has 300 tied houses in the South-

East, nearly all selling cask ale. More than 2,000 other outlets are also supplied. The cask beers are made with mostly Kentish hops, and water from the brewery's own artesian well. The Cask Club offers a new and different cask ale every month. ‼🍺♦LIVE

Master Brew (ABV 3.7%) BITTER
A distinctive bitter, mid-brown in colour, with a hoppy aroma. Well-balanced, with a nicely aggressive bitter taste from its hops, it leaves a hoppy/bitter finish, tinged with sweetness.
Whitstable Bay Pale Ale (ABV 3.9%) BLOND
Spitfire Gold (ABV 4.1%) GOLD
Spitfire (ABV 4.2%) BITTER
Malty, caramel with bitter hops and caramelised fruit and citrus flavours. Spiciness builds and remains in the hoppy, dry finish.
Bishops Finger (ABV 5%) BITTER

Sherfield Village SIBA

Goddards Farm, Goddards Lane, Sherfield on Loddon, Hampshire, RG27 0EL ☎ 07906 060429
⊕ sherfieldvillagebrewery.co.uk

Production started in 2011 in a converted barn on a working dairy farm. Using a five-barrel plant, the brewery supplies local pubs and regional festivals. Extensive use is made of New World hops, particularly those from New Zealand. All beers are unfined. ♦LIVE

Southern Gold (ABV 4%) GOLD
Green Bullet (ABV 4.3%) GOLD
A strong lemony nose, with hops dominating the taste building to a strong aftertaste with a big astringent hit at the end.
Single Hop (ABV 4.3%) GOLD
Pioneer Stout (ABV 5%) STOUT

Shilling

🍺 92 West George Street, Glasgow, G2 1PJ
☎ (0141) 353 1654 ⊕ shillingbrewingcompany.co.uk
Brewing began in 2016.

ShinDigger

See Tractor Shed

Shiny SIBA

Unit 10, Old Hall Mill Business Centre, Little Eaton, Derby, Derbyshire, DE21 5EJ
☎ (01332) 902809

Brewing commenced in 2012 using a six-barrel plant sited in the beer garden of the Furnace Inn, Derby. After initially brewing solely for the pub, 2014 saw an increase in scale and output, with beers distributed across most of the country. A second 12-barrel brew plant was built in 2015 to increase capacity and host a visitor centre, taproom and shop. 🍺♦LIVE V♦

New World (ABV 3.7%) BITTER
Happy People (ABV 4.1%) PALE
Wrench (ABV 4.4%) STOUT
4 Wood (ABV 4.5%) BITTER
Affinity (ABV 4.6%) GOLD
Disco Balls (ABV 5.3%) PALE

Ship Inn

🍺 Ship Inn, Newton Square, Low Newton-by-the-Sea, Northumberland, NE66 3EL
☎ (01665) 576262 ⊕ shipinnnewton.co.uk

☺Brewing commenced in 2008 on a 2.5-barrel plant. The brewery now produces 7.5 barrels per week. All regular beers are brewed in constant rotation but are only available on the premises. A special beer is brewed for every 100 brews. ♦LIVE

Shipstone's SIBA

Little Star Brewery, Fox & Crown, 33 Church Street, Old Basford, Nottingham, NG6 0GA
☎ (0115) 837 4200 ⊕ shipstones.com

☺Established 1996 as Fiddlers Ales, becoming Alcazar Brewery on change of ownership in 1999. A full-mash, 10-barrel brewery, it is located behind the Fox & Crown. It changed hands in 2016, the name changed again, and a new portfolio of beers was established, but was short-lived. It soon reverted back to Alcazar. In late 2016 Shipstone's took over brewing, producing its range of beers that had previously been contract brewed at Belvoir Brewery (qv). Beers are also brewed under Hollow Stone Brewing Co. ‼♦

Original (ABV 3.8%) BITTER
Pale brown, malty, traditional bitter. Well-balanced in both hops and bitterness without either becoming overpowering.
Nut Brown (ABV 4%) BITTER
Gold Star (ABV 4.2%) GOLD
Golden in colour with a delicate citrus hop and slight dry, bitter finish.
IPA (ABV 5.5%) IPA

Brewed under the Hollow Stone Brewing Co name:
Oligo Nunk (ABV 4%) GOLD
Pale Ale (ABV 4.2%) PALE
Waitomo (ABV 4.5%) PALE
Aruru (ABV 4.7%) BITTER

Short Stack

🍺 Cock, 315 Mare Street, Hackney, London, E8 1EJ

Brewing began in 2018 on kit previously used by Howling Hops and Maregade. Its name reflects the limited headroom in the cellar where it is situated. Brewing is only sporadic and currently suspended due to the confined space.

Shortts SIBA

Shortts Farm, Thorndon, Eye, Suffolk, IP23 7LS
☎ 07900 268100 ⊕ shorttsfarmbrewery.com

An award-winning brewery established in 2012 by Matt Hammond on what has been the family farm for over a century. Ales are produced using carefully selected ingredients to create both traditional and more complex contemporary flavours. The beer names are based around a musical theme and can be found throughout East Anglia. LIVE V

The Cure (ABV 3.6%) BITTER
Strummer (ABV 3.8%) BITTER
Two Tone (ABV 3.8%) MILD
Blondie (ABV 4%) PALE
Rockabilly (ABV 4.3%) PALE
Skiffle (ABV 4.5%) BITTER
Black Volt (ABV 4.8%) STOUT
Indie (ABV 4.8%) PALE
Darkside (ABV 5%) PORTER

Shotover

See Oxford

Shottle Farm

c/o School House Farm, Lodge Lane, Shottle,
DE56 2DS
☎ (01773) 550056 ☎ 07877 723075
⊕ shottlefarmbrewery.co.uk

Located in the hills above Belper, the Grade II-listed farm
is part of the Chatsworth Estate. Established in 2011 with
a 10-barrel plant, beers are now contract brewed
elsewhere. Shottle Farm has an on-site bar (limited
opening hours), the Bull Shed, which is the only outlet
for its beers. ◆ LIVE ✦

Shottlecock (ABV 3.6%) BITTER
Black Peggy (ABV 3.9%) MILD
Shottle Pale Ale (ABV 4%) PALE
BOB (Best of Both) (ABV 4.1%) SPECIALITY
Eight Shilling (ABV 4.1%) BITTER
Shottle Gold (ABV 4.3%) GOLD
Dilks (ABV 5%) BITTER

Shugborough

Shugborough Estate, Milford, Staffordshire, ST17 0XB
☎ (01782) 823447 ⊕ shugborough.org.uk

Brewing in the original brewhouse at Shugborough,
home of the Earls of Lichfield, restarted in 1990, but a
lack of expertise led to the brewery being a static
museum piece until Titanic Brewery of Stoke-on-Trent
(qv) began helping in 1996. Brewing is currently
suspended. ‼

Signal SIBA

8 Stirling Way, Beddington Farm Road, Beddington,
Croydon, CR0 4XN
☎ (020) 8684 6111 ⊕ signalbeerco.com

Starting in 2016, Signal's lager was the staple product in
keg and cans. 2018 saw a change and a range of cask ale
is now produced along with an increased variety of keg.
Available at the taproom, its bar at the O2 Arena in North
Greenwich, and around South London. ‼ ✦

Absolutely Fuggled (ABV 4%) BITTER
Yellow-coloured, easy-drinking bitter with earthy hops
and orangey fruit on the sweetish nose and biscuit
flavour becoming bitter.
Sticky Hoppy Pudding (ABV 4.3%) SPECIALITY
Pale brown beer with a smooth mouthfeel. Distinct
caramel and biscuit aroma and flavour with a little hop
and fruit.

Signature SIBA

Unit 15, Uplands Business Park, Blackhorse Lane,
Walthamstow, London, E17 5QJ
☎ (020) 7684 4664 ⊕ signaturebrew.co.uk

Signature Brew has been brewing beer inspired by music
since 2011. Originally using spare capacity at a number of
breweries, a successful crowdfunding initiative resulted
in it owning its own brewery in Leyton, and later
expanding into larger premises in Walthamstow by 2019.
Special seasonal beers are brewed in collaboration with
music artists. ◆ LIVE ✦

Roadie All-Night (ABV 4.3%) GOLD
Well-balanced, yellow beer with hoppy and citrus and
tropical flavours. Flavour is juicy and refreshing with
tropical fruit character dominating.
Backstage (ABV 5.6%) IPA
Amber, unfined IPA with fruity hops and a bitterness,
overlaid with some banana and biscuity malty notes.
Lingering, dry finish.
Nightliner (ABV 5.7%) SPECIALITY

Silhill

Oak Farm, Hampton Lane, Catherine-de-Barnes,
Solihull, West Midlands, B92 0JB
☎ (0845) 519 5101 ☎ 07977 444564

Office: PO Box 15739, Solihull, B93 3FW
⊕ silhillbrewery.co.uk

⊠ Established in 2010, Silhill is a small, independent
brewery based in premises just outside Solihull town
centre using a 10-barrel plant. Bottling operations
commenced in 2015. Beers are available in Solihull,
Birmingham and Stratford-upon-Avon. ‼ LIVE

Gold Star (ABV 3.9%) SPECIALITY
Blonde Star (ABV 4.1%) BLOND
Hop Star (ABV 4.2%) PALE
Pure Star (ABV 4.3%) BITTER
Super Star (ABV 5.1%) GOLD

Silver

Units 3 & 4, Silver House, Adelphi Way, Staveley,
Chesterfield, Derbyshire, S43 3LJ
☎ (01246) 470074 ☎ 07496 757619
⊕ silverbrewhouse.com

⊠ Silver Brewhouse is a 12-barrel brewery producing
hop-forward and traditional ales. It also brews under the
brand names Industrial Ales and Funky Hop Donkey.
◆ LIVE V

West Coast Pale Ale (ABV 3.7%) PALE
Baby Ghost (ABV 3.9%) GOLD
Independance American IPA (ABV 4.1%) PALE
Grey Ghost IPA (ABV 5.9%) IPA

Brewed under the Industrial Ales brand name:
Brickworks Bitter (ABV 4%) BITTER
Stephensons Pale (ABV 4%) PALE
Arkwrights Pale (ABV 4.1%) PALE
Coal Face Stout (ABV 4.5%) STOUT

Silver Rocket (NEW)

6 Meadows, Hassocks, West Sussex, BN6 8EH
☎ 07950 099424 ⊕ silverrocketbrewing.co.uk

Silver Rocket Brewing is a microbrewery in Hassocks, run
by two friends who love craft beer and Sonic Youth.
Beers are available in can, keg and occasionally cask.

Silverstone SIBA

Kingshill Farm, Syresham, Northamptonshire,
NN13 5TH ☎ 07835 279400
⊕ silverstonebrewery.co.uk

Established in 2008 Silverstone Brewery is a traditional
tower brewery located near the celebrated motor racing
circuit. The brewery has won multiple awards for it's
beers which are supplied in bottles, cask and KeyKeg.
‼ ◆

Ignition (ABV 3.4%) BLOND
Pitstop (ABV 3.9%) BITTER
Polestar (ABV 4.1%) STOUT
Chequered Flag (ABV 4.3%) BITTER
Octane (ABV 4.8%) BITTER
Classic IPA (ABV 5.6%) SPECIALITY

Simple Things Fermentations SIBA

The Bakehouse, 6 Hazel Avenue Lane, Glasgow,
G44 3LJ
☎ (0141) 237 2202
⊕ simplethingsfermentations.com

Opened in 2019 by Phil Sisson, ex-Heriot-Watt and Harviestoun, the brewery has a 600-litre capacity. Beer is produced in bottle and keg, with one core cask-conditioned ale available. Other cask ales available on a seasonal/occasional basis. !!LIVE

Golden Ale (ABV 3.8%) GOLD

Simpsons

White Swan, Eardisland, Herefordshire, HR6 9BD
☎ (01544) 388635 ⊕ thewhiteswaneardisland.com

Tim Simpson acquired the White Swan in 2011 and set up the brewery at the rear of the pub in 2013. All beers are brewed for consumption in the White Swan. ♦

Siren SIBA

Unit 1, Hogwood Lane Industrial Estate, Weller Drive, Finchampstead, Berkshire, RG40 4QZ
☎ (0118) 973 0929

Office: Siren Tap Yard, Unit 18, Marino Way, Finchampstead, RG40 4RF ⊕ sirencraftbrew.com

⊗ Established in 2013, this is a state-of-the-art, 40-barrel craft brewery, which produces 70-100 unique beers every year. Beers are produced in cask, keg, bottled and canned, and distributed throughout the UK and Europe. 2021 saw the third birthday of the Siren Tap Yard at the brewery in Finchampstead. Siren has expansion plans funded by a successful crowdfunding project, including increasing brewing capacity, making further use of new brewing technologies and rolling out the Tap Yard concept to city centre locations. !!■♦GFV✔

Yu Lu (ABV 3.6%) SPECIALITY
Lumina (ABV 4.2%) PALE
Soundwave IPA (ABV 5.6%) IPA
Broken Dream Breakfast Stout (ABV 6.5%) SPECIALITY

six°north

Reekie House, Aberdeen Road, Laurencekirk, AB30 1AG
☎ (01561) 377047 ☎ 07840 678243
⊕ sixdnorth.co.uk

⊗ Established in 2013, the brewery brews beers in the Belgian tradition, using a purpose-built, 470-hectolitre plant. Depending on beer style, the beers are supplied as cask or keg. !!♦LIVE

Chopper Stout (ABV 4.1%) STOUT
Roasted coffee, malted, with background liquorice.

Six Hills SIBA

Rear of 31 High Street, Old Town, Stevenage, Hertfordshire, SG1 3AU ☎ 07973 673040
⊕ sixhillsbrewing.com

⊗ Previously known as Bog Brew, Six Hills brewing was established in 2017 when home brewer Paul Clinton began brewing commercially. Beers are available at local beer festivals, free houses around Hertfordshire and Bedfordshire, via the online shop and in the brewery tap, the Broken Seal, located next door to the brewery. Over the past year it has expanded from a two-barrel plant to 1,500 litres per month capacity, with plans for further expansion. There are several regular beers as well as seasonal specials dispensed from cask, tank, can and KeyKeg. !!■♦✔

Slingshot to Mars (ABV 3.8%) SPECIALITY
Running With the Big Dog (ABV 4.8%) PALE

Moving the Goalposts (ABV 5%) SPECIALITY
Hanging Around (ABV 5.5%) IPA
Making a Play (ABV 6.2%) SPECIALITY
John Drives a Superbus (ABV 6.5%) IPA

Six Towns

Wheatsheaf, 234 High Street, Tunstall, Staffordshire, ST6 5TT
☎ (01782) 922628 ⊕ sixtownsbrewery.com

Previously known as Sunset Taverns, Six Towns is a small independent brewery at the rear of the Wheatsheaf pub in the Potteries. Brewing is currently suspended.

Sixpenny SIBA

The Old Dairy, Holwell Farm, Cranborne, Dorset, BH21 5QP
☎ (01725) 762006 ⊕ sixpennybrewery.co.uk

⊗ Founded in 2007, Sixpenny moved into its present home of renovated Victorian farm buildings near Cranborne, in 2016. This allowed for the expansion of the brewery bar and shop (Sixpenny Tap), in converted stables next door. Sixpenny has been brewing to its 20-barrel plant capacity for some while now to meet demand. Plans are afoot to increase the amount of bottled beer available all year round. !!■♦✔

6d Best Bitter (ABV 3.8%) BITTER
6d Gold (ABV 4%) GOLD
6d IPA (ABV 5.2%) PALE

Skinner's SIBA

Riverside, Newham Road, Truro, Cornwall, TR1 2DP
☎ (01872) 271885 ⊕ skinnersbrewery.com

⊗ Award-winning brewery established in 1997. The brewery moved to bigger premises in 2003, and opened a shop and visitor centre. The 25-barrel plant produces more than 26,000 hectolitres per year. Single batch brews are produced throughout the year, but with limited availability. !!■♦✔

Sennen (ABV 3.8%) PALE
Gold pale ale with citrus peel and toffee aroma. Fresh fruit, malt and grassy citrus hops. Persistent, pleasant bitter flavour.

Betty Stogs (ABV 4%) BITTER
Deep amber bitter. Resinous hops balanced by sweet malt and fruit flavours. Sweet malt fades into the long, bitter finish.

Chapel Rock (ABV 4%) GOLD
Hops 'n' Honey (ABV 4%) SPECIALITY
A gold, speciality beer containing honey. Balance of light citrus, grassy hops, apple and sweet malt. Pleasant, long dry finish.

Lushingtons (ABV 4.2%) PALE
Refreshing, smooth blond ale. Lemon and marmalade citrus hop and malt flavours. Bittersweet, with stone fruits. Long, clean, dry finish.

Cornish Knocker (ABV 4.5%) PALE
Smooth, golden pale ale. Blend of citrus, floral, piney and earthy hops with biscuit malt with hints of toffee and honey.

Pennycomequick (ABV 4.5%) STOUT
Creamy, dark brown, sweet stout with roast grain aroma. Heavy roast coffee, malt, fig and cherry flavours. Roast, dry finish.

Porthleven (ABV 4.8%) PALE
Robust pale ale with citrus nose. Assertive citrus bitterness with sweet, fruity flavours and light malt. Bitter, dry citrus finish.

Seven Hop (ABV 5%) GOLD

Smooth golden ale. Strong hop aroma and heavy punch of grapefruit citrus hops throughout. Marmalade and stone fruits. Bitter, dry finish.

Slater's SIBA IFBB

St Albans Road, Common Road Industrial Estate, Stafford, ST16 3DR
☎ (01785) 257976 ⊕ slatersales.co.uk

⊛The brewery was opened in 1995 at the George in Eccleshall and in 2006 moved to new, larger premises. It has won numerous awards from CAMRA and SIBA. The brewery supplies an ever increasing number of outlets throughout the midlands and further afield. ‼🍽

Ultra (ABV 3.7%) BITTER
Rye IPA (ABV 3.8%) SPECIALITY
1 Hop (ABV 4%) GOLD
Yellow-hued with a fruit and hop nose. Big malty start leads to citrus hints with mouthwatering edges. Dry finish with tangs of lingering lemon bitterness.
Premium (ABV 4.4%) BITTER
Pale brown bitter with malt and caramel aroma. Malt and caramel taste supported by hops and some fruit provide a warming descent and satisfyingly bitter mouthfeel.
Smoked Porter (ABV 4.8%) SPECIALITY
Nose full of smoke, bonfire tastes with bacon. Hops break out to a bitter finish; a real treat.
Western (ABV 4.9%) PALE
Haka (ABV 5.2%) PALE
Exotic aromas of tropical fruits lead to a sweet fruity start with background bitterness. This erupts into a mouthy bitterness with a long finish.
Neon Kiss (ABV 6%) IPA
Strong golden ale with fruit and bitterness. Refreshing and dangerously strong.

Slaughterhouse SIBA

Bridge Street, Warwick, CV34 5PD
☎ (01926) 490986 ☎ 07951 842690
⊕ slaughterhousebrewery.com

⊛Production began in 2003 on a four-barrel plant in a former slaughterhouse. Around 30 outlets are supplied, mostly within five miles of the brewery. The brewery premises are licensed for off-sales direct to the public. In 2010 Slaughterhouse opened its first pub, the Wild Boar in Warwick, adding a two-barrel brew plant that brews specials for the pub. ‼

Saddleback Best Bitter (ABV 3.8%) BITTER
Extra Stout Snout (ABV 4.4%) STOUT
Boar D'eau (ABV 4.5%) GOLD
Wild Boar (ABV 5.2%) BITTER

SLOPEmeisteR

Oak House, Airth Castle Estate, Airth, FK2 8JF
☎ 07895 734867 ⊕ slopemeister.com

SLOPEmeisteR started brewing in 2018, initially at Hybrid Brewery in Grangemouth, then setting up a nanobrewery in a garage in Airth. Keg beer is supplied to Falkirk Rugby Club with cask-conditioned beer supplied to festivals. Recently purchased brewing equipment from the now closed Kinneil Brewery.

SlyBeast SIBA

🍺 Ram Inn, 68 Wandsworth High Street, Wandsworth, London, SW18 4LB
☎ (020) 7164 6691 ⊕ slybeastbrewing.com

The Ram Inn reopened in 2019, after being closed following the demise of the original adjacent Youngs

Brewery in 2006. Its in-house brewery can be seen in one corner of the pub. SlyBeast beers are available in the pub (cask and keg), and further afield.

Beam Engine Bitter (ABV 3.7%) BLOND
Ram Street Special (ABV 4.4%) BITTER

Small Beer

70-72 Verney Road, South Bermondsey, London, SE16 3DH
☎ (020) 7096 2353 ⊕ theoriginalsmallbeer.com

Small Beer Brewery was set up in 2017 as the world's first to specialise exclusively in the production of low strength beers (0.5-2.7% ABV). The core range of four beers is widely available on keg and in 350ml stubby bottles. No real ale.

Small Beer (Lincoln)

See Black Hole

Small Paul's

27 Briar Close, Gillingham, Dorset, SP8 4SS
☎ (01747) 823574 ✉ smallbrewer@btinternet.com

⊠ Launched in 2006, this half-barrel brewery is located in the owner's garage. There are usually two brews a month. A small number of local pubs, clubs and beer festivals are supplied direct and beers can be designed and brewed to order. ♦

Small World SIBA

Unit 10, Barncliffe Business Park, Near Bank, Shelley, West Yorkshire, HD8 8LU
☎ (01484) 602805 ⊕ smallworldbeers.com

⊛The brewery is situated in the former Barncliffe Mill near the picturesque village of Shelley. The beers are brewed on a 20-barrel Moeschle plant using spring water from an on-site bore hole. SALSA + Beer approved. ‼♦

Barncliffe Bitter (ABV 3.7%) BITTER
Long Moor Pale (ABV 3.9%) PALE
It's Never One (ABV 4%) GOLD
Port Nelson (ABV 4%) PALE
Spike's Gold (ABV 4.4%) GOLD
Thunderbridge Stout (ABV 5.2%) STOUT
Twin Falls (ABV 5.2%) PALE

Samuel Smith

The Old Brewery, High Street, Tadcaster, North Yorkshire, LS24 9SB
☎ (01937) 832225 ⊕ samuelsmithsbrewery.co.uk

⊛Fiercely independent, family-owned company. Tradition, quality and value are important, resulting in brewing without any artificial additives. The majority of products are vegan-friendly, with the exception of Old Brewery Bitter and Yorkshire Stingo. All real ale is supplied in traditional wooden casks. ☛LIVE V

Old Brewery Bitter (ABV 4%) BITTER

John Smith's

The Brewery, Tadcaster, North Yorkshire, LS24 9SA
☎ (01937) 832091 ⊕ heineken.com

The brewery was built in 1879 by a relative of Samuel Smith (qv). John Smith's became part of the Courage group in 1970 before being taken over by S&N and now Heineken UK. John Smith's cask Magnet has been discontinued. John Smith's Bitter in cask form is brewed by Caledonian Brewery (qv) in Edinburgh. No real ale.

Snaggletooth

c/o Rear of 11 Pole Lane, Darwen, Lancashire, BB3 3LD ☎ 07810 365701 ⊕ snaggletoothbrewing.com

Snaggletooth was established in 2012 by three beer geeks with a passion for crafting ales. A 2.5-barrel plant is used at the Hopstar Brewery (qv) in Darwen, Lancashire. Beers are available throughout East Lancashire and Manchester. ♦

Allotropic (ABV 3.8%) PALE
BeEr (ABV 3.9%) PALE
I Ain't Afraid of Noh Ghost (ABV 3.9%) GOLD
Three Amigos (ABV 3.9%) GOLD
Déjà Brewed (ABV 4%) PALE
Rolling Maul (ABV 4.1%) PALE
'Cos I'm a Lobster (ABV 4.2%) RED
Avonaco (ABV 4.3%) PALE

Snowdon Craft

Quinton Hazell Enterprise Parc, 55 Glan-y-Wern Road, Mochdre, LL28 5BS
☎ (01492) 545143 ⊕ snowdoncraftbeer.co.uk

☺Snowdon Craft, formerly Great Orme Brewery, is now located in Mochdre near Llandudno and uses an 18-barrel plant. It supplies the local area and the pub, the Albion, Conwy, which it part owns. !!♦

IPA (ABV 4%) IPA
Bitter (ABV 4.5%) BITTER
Summit Blond IPA (ABV 5.2%) PALE
Porter (ABV 5.7%) PORTER

Snowdonia Parc

⊟ Snowdonia Parc Brewpub & Campsite, Waunfawr, Caernarfon, LL55 4AQ
☎ (01286) 650409 ⊕ snowdonia-park.co.uk

Snowdonia Parc started brewing in 1998 in a two-barrel brewhouse. The brewing is now carried out by the owner, Carmen Pierce. The beer is brewed solely for the Snowdonia Parc pub and campsite.

Snowhill

Snowhill Cottage, Snow Hill Lane, Scorton, Lancashire, PR3 1BA
☎ (01524) 791352

☺Snowhill was established in 2015 by Nigel Stokes following several years of small scale brewing. A one-man operation, Nigel brews 3-4 times per month on a 1.5-barrel plant, to supply pubs in North-West Lancashire and South Cumbria. An environmentally-friendly set-up sees the spent grain feeding local cattle and waste water treated through a small reed bed. ♦

Pale (ABV 3.7%) GOLD
Copy Cat (ABV 3.8%) BITTER
Target (ABV 3.8%) BLOND
Blonded (ABV 3.9%) BLOND
Gold (ABV 3.9%) GOLD
Best Bitter (ABV 4.2%) PALE
Black Magic IPA (ABV 4.2%) PALE
Porter (ABV 4.8%) PORTER
Winter Porter (ABV 4.8%) PORTER

Sociable SIBA

6-8 Britannia Road, Worcester, WR1 3BQ ☎ 07957 583984 ⊕ thesociablebeercompany.com

☺A small craft brewery just outside Worcester city centre, established in 2017. An on-site taproom is open on Fridays. A small range of core beers is brewed, mainly for sale in the local area. ✦

Shindig (ABV 3.6%) BITTER
Bash (ABV 4%) BITTER
Wingding (ABV 4.2%) GOLD

Solvay Society

Arch 223, Dyers Hall Railway Arches, Leytonstone, London, E11 4AF ☎ 07999 554667
⊕ solvaysociety.com

Solvay Society started in Walthamstow in 2014, transferring to Islington in 2015 before taking on the former Ha'penny Brewery kit in Aldborough Hatch in 2016. After crowdfunding it moved next to its taproom in Leytonstone in 2021. Beers, modern Belgian in style, are available in keg, bottles and cans. No real ale. ✦

Son of Sid

⊟ Chequers, 71 Main Road, Little Gransden, Cambridgeshire, SG19 3DW
☎ (01767) 677348 ⊕ sonofsid.co.uk

⊠ Son of Sid was established in 2007. The three-barrel plant is situated in a room at the back of the pub and can be viewed from a window in the lounge bar. It is named after the father of the current landlord, who ran the pub for 42 years. His son has carried the business on as a family-run enterprise. Beer is sold in the pub and at local beer festivals. !! ⋤LIVE

Sonnet 43

See S43

Soul

Correspondence: 18 Broomfield Road, Heaton Moor, Stockport, SK4 4ND ☎ 07718 155191
✉ bill@soulbrewing.co.uk

⊠ Brewing commenced in 2017 using spare capacity at Manchester Brewing (qv). Beers are supplied to outlets in Greater Manchester and are inspired by Northern Soul music. A move to its own premises is planned. !!♦V

All Nighter (ABV 3.8%) PALE
Magic Touch (ABV 4.7%) GOLD
Powerfully-hopped beer with sweet, fruity flavour and bitter throughout.
The Snake (ABV 5.8%) IPA
Double-O Soul (ABV 5.9%) IPA

South Causey

South Causey Inn, Beamish Burn Road, Stanley, DH9 0LS
☎ (01207) 235555 ⊕ southcausey.co.uk

Brewer John Taylor recently moved equipment from the Stables brewery at Beamish Hall Hotel. A selection of beers are only available in the bar and restaurant at South Causey Inn. Bottled beers are available for sale to the public on-site. Bespoke beers can be brewed & personalised for special events held at the establishment. A small still has also been set up at the moment to produce gin but in future different types of spirits may be produced. Brewing is currently suspended.

South Hams SIBA

Stokeley Barton, Stokenham, Kingsbridge, Devon, TQ7 2SE
☎ (01548) 581151 ⊕ southhamsbrewery.co.uk

⊠ South Hams has been brewing ales for more than 13 years in Start Bay, Devon. A family-run brewery, it supplies more than 350 outlets in Plymouth and South Devon with wholesalers distributing further afield. It is owned and managed by Sam, Mark and Brenda Brooking. ‼️🍽️♦LIVE

Devon Pride (ABV 3.8%) BITTER
Stumble Bee (ABV 4.2%) SPECIALITY
Wild Blonde (ABV 4.4%) BLOND
Subtle notes of malt, roast and caramel, dominated by fruity hops. These persist to a refreshing hint of lemon.
Hopnosis (ABV 4.5%) GOLD
Eddystone (ABV 4.8%) BITTER
Strong, amber, summery ale. Hoppy, caramel, slightly citrus nose. Dryer taste with light fruit and hops. Dry yet fruity finish.
Pandemonium (ABV 5%) BITTER
A fruit/bready malty aroma. Tastes of toffee, caramel and blackcurrant. A slight old ale style to this strong beer.
Sherman (ABV 6.4%) IPA
A strong American pale ale, a thick-flavoured beer, very fruity and sweet on aroma/taste and aftertaste.

South Lakes

Unit 30, Ulverston Auction Mart, North Lonsdale Road, Ulverston, Cumbria, LA12 0AU ☎ 07795 363523
✉ aaronpos1@hotmail.com

South Lakes began brewing on a 1.5-barrel plant in 2016, in a part of the Auction Mart in Ulverston.

4 Cs Extra Pale (ABV 3.8%) PALE
Lucky Dip (ABV 3.8%) GOLD
Amacoe (ABV 4%) GOLD
Pronounced hoppiness in both the aroma and taste combines with a balancing sweetness and a lasting, bitter finish.
Poison Dwarf (ABV 4.1%) PALE
Hoppy and fruity aromas are followed by a full-bodied and lasting bitter finish.
Rakau (ABV 4.4%) PALE
A bitter beer with lots of hops, backed by fruit sweetness and some malt in the background. A well-constructed, ambitious bitter with full mouthfeel and lasting bitter finish.
American Pale Ale (ABV 4.8%) BLOND
Ripe (ABV 5.5%) BITTER

Southbourne SIBA

41-43 Poole Hill, Bournemouth, Dorset, BH2 5PW
☎ (01202) 421190 ☎ 07845 795464
⊕ southbourneales.co.uk

⊠ Jennifer Tingay, former technologist and brewer for Ringwood, began brewing in 2013 using spare capacity at Town Mill brewery. The brand quickly became established and a successful crowdfunding campaign allowed her to purchase the lease of a former car showroom on Bournemouth's West Cliff. The tap opened in 2017 and the brewery started production in 2018 using an 80-barrel plant. ‼️🍽️♦

Paddlers (ABV 3.6%) BITTER
Easy-drinking bitter with subtle malt flavour and hints of hop bitterness in the aftertaste.
Sunbather (ABV 4%) BITTER
Dry red ale with some caramel sweetness and a lingering nutty aftertaste.

Headlander (ABV 4.2%) BITTER
Traditional best bitter with intense malt aroma and sweet flavour. Complex and moreish with hop bitterness in aftertaste.
Beachcomber (ABV 5.7%) BROWN
Complex and full-flavoured with sweet aroma. Initial notes of sherry with pepper and bitter aftertaste breaking through.

Southbrew

Broyle Mill Farm, Ringmer, East Sussex, BN8 5AR
⊕ southbrewcompany.co.uk

Nanobrewery formed by three friends, influenced by both traditional and modern beer styles. No real ale.

Southey

21 Southey Street, Penge, London, SE20 7JD
⊕ southeybrewing.co.uk

⊠ Southey took over the old Late Knights brewery in 2017 in an old warehouse that has been an abattoir and a candle factory. The unfined beers are available in the three Beer Dispensary bars and the on-site taproom which is open Thursday-Sunday. ♦🍴

Pale (ABV 3.8%) BITTER
A fairly bitter, hoppy citrus beer balanced with some sweetness. A subtle aroma of citrus fruit and spices. Dry taste and aftertaste.
Session IPA (ABV 4.2%) GOLD
Best Bitter (ABV 4.5%) BITTER
Oatmeal Stout (ABV 5.5%) STOUT

Southport SIBA

Unit 3, Enterprise Business Park, Russell Road, Southport, Merseyside, PR9 7RF ☎ 07748 387652
⊕ southportbrewery.co.uk

☺Southport Brewery was established in 2004 on a five-barrel plant. Outlets are supplied in Southport, North-West England and nationally. ♦

IPA (ABV 3.6%) PALE
Sandgrounder Bitter (ABV 3.8%) PALE
Dark Night (ABV 3.9%) MILD
Full-bodied mild with fruity malt aromas dominating, lasting roast bitterness and hop, lots of flavour for the strength.
Golden Sands (ABV 4%) GOLD

Southsea

Southsea Castle, Clarence Esplanade, Southsea, Portsmouth, Hampshire, PO5 3PA ☎ 07939 063970
⊕ southseabrewing.co.uk

⊠ Launched in 2016, Southsea Brewing is located in an old ammunition storage room within the walls of a coastal defence fort built by Henry VIII in 1544. All beers are unfined, unfiltered and unpasteurised, and bottled on-site. ‼️🍽️LIVE

Low Tide (ABV 3.8%) PALE
Casemate IPA (ABV 5.4%) PALE

Southwark SIBA

46 Druid Street, Bermondsey, London, SE1 2EZ
☎ (020) 3302 4190 ⊕ southwarkbrewing.co.uk

⊠ Southwark opened in 2014 as the first cask venue on the emerging Bermondsey Beer Mile. The range of beers is very traditional, including a 5% beer with an ever changing hop, and is complemented by a small keg range. ⚑◆LIVE❧

Bankside Blonde (ABV 3.8%) BLOND
Refreshing golden ale with grapefruit aroma and bittersweet grapefruit flavour fading in the dry, lingering finish with some peppery hops.

Routemaster Red (ABV 3.8%) RED
Creamy, red ale with malty, fruity aroma. The dry, slightly hoppy, bitter flavour has caramel, peach and red berry notes.

London Pale Ale (ABV 4%) PALE
Easy-drinking, gold-coloured beer with sweet orange, caramelised biscuit on the palate and aroma. Dry, fruity and spicy bitter aftertaste.

Potters' Fields Porter (ABV 4%) PORTER
Raisins, prunes caramel, cocoa and bitter chocolate in the flavour fading in the dry roast bitter aftertaste. Roasty, caramel nose.

Mayflower (ABV 4.2%) GOLD
Bermondsey Best (ABV 4.4%) BITTER
Balanced best bitter. Nutty and caramelised fruit with a pithy, citrus character completed by a toffee sweetness. Spicy, dry finish.

Harvard (ABV 5.5%) IPA
Rich, smooth pale brown strong bitter with honey sweetness throughout. Hops, sweet orange and grapefruit marmalade becoming bitter and dry.

Spa Town

See Harrogate

Spartan

Arch 8, Almond Road, South Bermondsey, London, SE16 3LR ⊕ spartanbrewery.com

Spartan began brewing at UBrew in 2017, before moving in 2018 to premises on the Bermondsey Beer Mile vacated by Partizan Brewery. Beer is available in its on-site taproom and an increasing number of other outlets. Cask is a big part of the output having been introduced in 2019. ⚑V❧

Fog of War (ABV 2.8%) GOLD
Unfined, refreshing golden beer with a hoppy citrus aroma. Flavour is dry, hoppy bitter with orange notes. Dry, bitter finish.

Son of Zeus (ABV 3.6%) MILD
River Styx (ABV 3.7%) PORTER
Hoplite (ABV 3.8%) BLOND
Elysian Fields (ABV 4.1%) BITTER
Amber bitter with hoppy malty aroma. The digestive biscuit is balanced by bitter hops with caramel and stewed apple notes.

Swords & Sandals (ABV 4.6%) GOLD
Golden ale with powerful citrus flavours combining with pithy and piney notes overlaid with a hoppy bitterness, by sweet biscuit.

Phalanx (ABV 5%) MILD
Pole March (ABV 5.5%) IPA

Sperrin

⬛ **Lord Nelson Inn, Birmingham Road, Ansley, Warwickshire, CV10 9PQ**
☎ **(024) 7639 2305** ☎ **07917 772208**
⊕ sperrinbrewery.co.uk

Sperrin began brewing in 2012 on a six-barrel plant at the side of the Lord Nelson Inn. The pub always has five of its beers available and two or three at its sister pub, the Blue Boar, Mancetter. Around 25 other outlets are supplied direct. ‼◆LIVE

Spey Valley

Malcolmburn, Mulben, Keith, AB55 6YH
☎ **(01542) 488006** ☎ **07780 655199**
⊕ speyvalleybrewery.co.uk

⊠ Founded in 2007, Spey Valley Brewery merged with Keith Brewery in 2018 and is part of the Consolidated Craft Breweries Group, along with Alechemy Brewing (qv). It brews on a 20-barrel plant on a purpose-built site at Mulben. ‼⚑◆

Sunshine on Keith (ABV 3.5%) BITTER
Golden, malt with a light citrus bitter hop.

David's Not So Bitter (ABV 4.4%) BITTER
Light brown with a good mix of malts, hops and red fruits.

Stillman's IPA (ABV 4.6%) SPECIALITY
Amber, hoppy bitter with a whisky background.

1814 (ABV 5%) SPECIALITY
Spey's Hopper (ABV 5%) SPECIALITY
Spey Stout (ABV 5.4%) STOUT
A good, thick, dark, malty stout with a smoky blackcurrant background.

Spitting Feathers SIBA

Common Farm, Waverton, Cheshire, CH3 7QT
☎ **(01244) 332052** ☎ **07974 348325**
⊕ spittingfeathers.co.uk

⊛Spitting Feathers was established in 2005. The brewery is located in a sandstone building set around a cobbled yard. Around 200 local outlets are supplied. Monthly Brewbarn sessions throughout the year include a brewery tour but tickets must be purchased in advance. From 2021 all beers will be vegan-friendly and gluten free. ‼◆GF V

Session Beer (ABV 3.6%) PALE
Thirstquencher (ABV 3.9%) BLOND
Powerful hop aroma leads into the taste. Bitterness and a fruity, citrus hop flavour fight for attention. A sharp, clean golden beer with a long, dry, bitter aftertaste.

Brainstorm (ABV 4%) GOLD
Special Ale (ABV 4.2%) BROWN
Complex, tawny-coloured beer with a sharp, grainy mouthfeel. Malty with good hop coming through in the aroma and taste. Hints of nuttiness and a touch of acidity. Dry, astringent finish.

Old Wavertonian (ABV 4.4%) STOUT
Creamy and smooth stout. Full-flavoured with coffee notes in aroma and taste. Roast and nut flavours throughout, leading to a hoppy, bitter finish.

Rush Hour (ABV 4.5%) PALE
Empire IPA (ABV 5.2%) PALE

Spotlight

The Goddards, Goole Road, West Cowick, East Yorkshire, DN14 9DJ ☎ **07713 477069**
⊕ spotlightbrewing.co.uk

⊛Spotlight is a social enterprise that is passionate about good beer. All beers are brewed, packaged and delivered by people with learning disabilities. The beer names reference medical conditions. ‼⚑◆

One More (ABV 3.9%) BITTER
Bollingham Bitter (ABV 4.4%) BITTER
Spectrum (ABV 4.5%) GOLD
Undiagnosed (ABV 5%) GOLD
Fragile X (ABV 5.8%) PORTER

Springhead SIBA

Robin Hood Site, Main Street, Laneham,
Nottinghamshire, DN22 0NA
☎ (01777) 229020 ☎ 07721 892831
⊕ springhead.co.uk

☺Springhead Fine Ales opened in 1990, expanding and moving to bigger premises three years later to meet increased demand. In 2011 the brewery relocated to its current address. In 2018 the brewery was taken over and now trades as Springhead Ales with new owners. ‼ ⬛ ♦ V

Outlawed (ABV 3.8%) PALE
Drop of the Black Stuff (ABV 4%) PORTER
Left Lion (ABV 4%) BITTER
Blind Tiger (ABV 4.5%) GOLD
Leveller (ABV 4.8%) BITTER
Roaring Meg (ABV 5.5%) IPA

Squawk

Unit 4, Tonge Street, Ardwick, Manchester, M12 6LY
☎ 07590 387559 ✉ sales@squawkbrewingco.com

Squawk initially cuckoo-brewed in Huddersfield in 2013, with the first beers from the current Manchester railway-arch site appearing in 2014. In 2019, the brewery expanded to a 32-barrel capacity with additional fermenters and conditioning tanks. A barrel-ageing programme and a canning line were also introduced. All beers are widely available in the North of England as well as being distributed nationally. An on-line shop was added in early 2021. LIVE V

Pavo (ABV 3.8%) GOLD
Light, hoppy beer with balanced, fruity aroma and taste. Dry, bitter finish.
Crex (ABV 4.5%) PALE
Fruity and hoppy aroma. Sweet fruit balanced with bitter hops in the flavour, rising to a lasting dry bitter finish.
Aquila (ABV 6.2%) IPA
Corvus (ABV 7.4%) STOUT
Roast malt aroma and strong, lasting dark chocolate taste with touch of fruit.

Stables

See Big Lamp

Staffordshire

12 Churnet Court, Cheddleton, Staffordshire, ST13 7EF
☎ (01538) 361919 ☎ 07971 808370
⊕ staffordshirebrewery.co.uk

Brewing started in 2002. The brewery was renamed from Leek Brewery in 2013 at which time cask production ceased, being replaced by filtered, pasteurised bottled beers only. A small pilot plant is sometimes used to contract brew for Wicked Hathern (qv) when time permits. ‼

Contract brewed for Wicked Hathern Brewery:
Albion Special (ABV 4%) BITTER
Hawthorn Gold (ABV 4.6%) GOLD

Stag (Cheshire)

▤ Stag at Walton, Chester Road, Walton, Warrington,
Cheshire, WA4 6EG
☎ (01925) 261680 ⊕ thestagatwalton.co.uk

Nanobrewery based at the Stag at Walton, near Warrington. Beers are available in the pub and occasionally at local beer festivals.

Stag (Kent)

Little Engeham Farm, Woodchurch, Kent, TN26 3QY
☎ 07539 974068 ⊕ stagbrewery.co.uk

Stag began brewing in 2016.

Jane Doe (ABV 4%) BITTER
Screaming Sika (ABV 5%) GOLD

Staggeringly Good SIBA

Unit 10, St Georges Industrial Estate, Rodney Road,
Southsea, Hampshire, PO4 8SS
☎ (023) 9229 7033 ⊕ staggeringlygood.com

⊠ Brewing began in 2014, originally using spare capacity at other breweries. In 2015 a 10-barrel plant at its own premises came on stream. All beers are real ale but only available in KeyKeg or can, unfined and vegan-friendly. There is an on-site shop and taproom. In 2019 the brewery acquired a large unit to allow for more brewing kit and to expand the taproom. ‼ ⬛ ♦ LIVE V ♠

Stamps

St Mary's Complex, Waverley Street, Bootle,
Liverpool, L20 4AP ☎ 07913 025319
⊕ stampsbrewery.co.uk

☺Brewing began in 2012, producing beers named after famous world postage stamps. The brewery moved to its new site in 2017 on a temporary basis. There are plans to build a new brewery and pub as part of a local regeneration project alongside the Leeds-Liverpool canal in Bootle. The beers can be found regularly in Stamps Bar, Crosby, and the Lock & Quay, Irlam Road, Bootle. Beers are also brewed under the Republic of Liverpool brand name, and Stamps beers are sometimes rebadged as a cuckoo for Flagship. ‼ ⬛

Blond Moment (ABV 3.6%) GOLD
Ahtanum (ABV 3.9%) GOLD
First Class (ABV 3.9%) PALE
Mail Train (ABV 4.2%) BITTER
Inverted Jenny (ABV 4.6%) BITTER
Rum Porter (ABV 4.6%) PALE
Penny Black (ABV 5.5%) PORTER

Stancill SIBA

Unit 2, Oakham Drive, off Rutland Road, Sheffield,
South Yorkshire, S3 9QX
☎ (0114) 275 2788 ☎ 07809 427716

☺Stancill began brewing in 2014 and is named after the first head brewer and co-owner. It is situated on the doorstep of the late Stones' Cannon Brewery, taking advantage of the soft Yorkshire water. ‼

Barnsley Bitter (ABV 3.8%) BITTER
Blonde (ABV 3.9%) BLOND
India (ABV 4%) BITTER
No.7 (ABV 4.3%) BITTER
Stainless (ABV 4.3%) BITTER
Porter (ABV 4.4%) PORTER
Black Gold (ABV 5%) STOUT

Stannary

Unit 6, Pixon Trading Centre, Tavistock, Devon,
PL19 8DH
☎ (01822) 258130 ⊕ stannarybrewing.co.uk

Stannary began operating in 2016 using a 2.5-barrel plant, moving to larger premises with a six-barrel plant in 2018. The brewery tap is open on a Friday and

Saturday, showcasing its many unfined and unfiltered craft beers. 🍺♦◆

Stanway

Stanway House, Stanway, Cheltenham, Gloucestershire, GL54 5PQ
☎ (01386) 584320 ⊕ stanwaybrewery.co.uk

☺Stanway is a small brewery, founded in 1993 with a five-barrel plant, that confines its sales to the Cotswolds area (15 to 20 outlets). The brewery uses wood-fired coppers for all its production. Brewing is currently suspended. ♦

Star Wing SIBA

Unit 6, Hall Farm, Church Road, Redgrave, Suffolk, IP22 1RJ
☎ (01379) 890586 ⊕ starwingbrewery.com

Brewing began in 2017 after converting an old sawmill into a brewery. Half an acre of hops have been planted with plans to grow more. Part of the sawmill has been converted into a taproom, which opened in 2019. Around 75 outlets are supplied direct. 🍺◆

Dawn on the Border (ABV 3.6%) PALE
Electric Trail (ABV 3.7%) PALE
Gospel Oak (ABV 3.8%) BITTER
Spire Light (ABV 4.2%) GOLD
Into the Woods (ABV 4.5%) PALE
Red at Night (ABV 4.5%) RED
Pesky Pilgrim (ABV 4.7%) BITTER
Four Acre Arcadia (ABV 5%) PALE
Stain Glass Blue (ABV 5.4%) PORTER

Stardust SIBA

Unit 5, Howe Lane Farm Estate, Howe Lane, White Waltham, Berkshire, SL6 3JP
☎ (01628) 947325 ⊕ stardustbrewery.co.uk

⊗ An independent, family-owned and run brewery, Stardust was established in 2016. Located in a unit on a small farm estate, brewing takes place on a six-barrel plant. There is a brewery shop and taproom on-site. ‼🍺♦LIVE◆

Easy Pale Citra (ABV 3.8%) PALE
English Bitter (ABV 4%) BITTER
Optic (ABV 4.2%) GOLD
PK3 (ABV 5.6%) IPA

State of Kind (NEW)

Unit 4, Hemfield Court, Wigan, WN2 2ER ☎ 07765 808889 ⊕ stateofkindbrew.co

Launched in 2021, initially as a gypsy brewery. A brewery and taproom is planned.

Stealth

34 Old Broughton Road, Melksham, Wiltshire, SN12 8BX
☎ (01225) 707111 ☎ 07917 272482
⊕ stealthbrew.co

Brewing on present site since 2015 and under current name since 2018. Most beers are unfined and the range changes frequently. Some of the production is canned and an associated company operates two micropubs in Melksham and Devizes ‼♦V

Covert (ABV 3.9%) PALE
Doublecrosser (ABV 4%) PALE
Tiptoe (ABV 4.2%) BITTER

Camouflage Black IPA (ABV 4.7%) PALE
Hibernation (ABV 5%) GOLD
Huggermuggery Coffee Porter (ABV 5.9%) SPECIALITY
Surreptitious (ABV 7.3%) IPA

Steam Machine SIBA

Unit 14, The IES Centre, Horndale Avenue, Newton Aycliffe, DL5 6DS ☎ 07415 759945
⊕ steammachinebrew.com

Founded by a husband and wife team with a homebrewing background of more than 10 years. Since opening in 2015 production has expanded. Beers are available mainly in keg but KeyKegs are occasionally supplied to beer festivals.

Steam Town SIBA

🍴 **1 Bishopstoke Road, Eastleigh, Hampshire, SO50 6AD**
☎ (023) 8235 9130 ⊕ steamtownbrewco.co.uk

⊗ Steam Town is a five-barrel microbrewery with its own craft beer bar and restaurant, established in 2017. Many other local pubs, clubs and micropubs also sell Steam Town's ales, as well as beer festivals and outlets further afield by arrangement. ‼🍺♦LIVE

Steamin' Billy

See Belvoir

Steel Brew

Melville Building, Royal William Yard, Plymouth, Devon, PL1 3RP ☎ 07976 503844

Office: 22 Aquarius Drive, Sherford, PL9 8FH
⊕ steelbrew.co

Brewing began in a garage in 2018, producing a range of craft beers on a six-barrel plant. The brewery relocated to the Grade 1*-listed Melville Building in 2020. Four core beers and numerous one-off specials are brewed, available in its on-site taproom. Its bottled beers are now also sold in the Plymouth Gin Distillery on the Barbican. ‼🍺◆

Steel City

c/o Lost Industry Brewing, 14a Nutwood Trading Estate, Sheffield, South Yorkshire, S6 1NJ
⊕ steelcitybrewing.beer

⊗ Steel City was established in 2009 and operates as a cuckoo brewery, brewing on an occasional basis and when inspired. Brewing currently takes place at Lost Industry Brewing (qv). Much of the Steel City output is collaborations with other like-minded brewers, having a little fun producing interesting and experimental beers. ♦V

Steelfish (NEW)

c/o 75 North Western Street, Manchester, M12 6DY
✉ steelfishbrewing@gmail.com

Steelfish started brewing in 2020 as a cuckoo brewer based at Beer Nouveau (qv).

Stenroth

Kenmure Avenue, Edinburgh, EH8 7HD
⊕ stenrothbrewing.co.uk

Founded by partners Kat Drinnan and Jimmy Mehtala in 2019, this home-based, 60-litre nanobrewery produces four core beers.

Stewart SIBA

26a Dryden Road, Bilston Glen Industrial Estate, Loanhead, EH20 9LZ
☎ (0131) 440 2442 ⊕ stewartbrewing.co.uk

⊛Established in 2004 by Steve and Jo Stewart, the brewery moved to a larger, custom-built brewery in 2013. It produces a wide portfolio of beers including collaborations such as the Natural Selection Brewing partnership with the brewing school at Heriot Watt. The on-site Craft Beer Kitchen is a small 80-litre plant providing a brew-it-yourself facility. In 2021 expansion of the brewery commenced with a second building due to be completed giving more brewing and warehousing space. ‼️🍺♦LIVE✦

Jack Back (ABV 3.7%) PALE
A pale hoppy beer with strong citrus and tropical fruit aromas. The taste is light, crisp and refreshing.
Pentland IPA (ABV 3.9%) PALE
A delicately-hopped, deep golden-coloured session ale. The dry bitter taste is well-balanced by sweetness from the malt, and fruit flavours.
80/- (ABV 4.4%) MILD
Superb, traditional, Scottish heavy. The complex profile is dominated by malt with fruit flavours giving the sweetish character typical of this beer style. Hops provide a gentle balancing bitterness that intensifies in the dry finish.
Radical Road Reverse (ABV 4.6%) PALE
Well-hopped, gold/amber ale with hints of biscuit and oodles of tropical fruit (mango) flavour continuing into the aftertaste.
Edinburgh Gold (ABV 4.8%) GOLD
A full-bodied but easy-drinking, Continental-style golden ale. Bitterness from the hop character is strong in the finish and complemented in the taste by a little sweetness from malt, and fruit flavours.

Sticklegs

Primrose Farm, Hall Road, Great Bromley, Essex, CO7 7TR ☎ 07971 138038
✉ waterhouse.philip@btinternet.com

⊠ Sticklegs was established in 2008 at the Cross Inn, Great Bromley. The brewery expanded and relocated to Elmstead Market, where it continued to grow. In 2016 it moved to Primrose Farm. The brewery is owned and run by Phil Reeve and his wife Linda, the brewster. Brewing is currently suspended.

Stinky Bay (NEW)

St Lawrence, Jersey ☎ 07797 781703
⊕ stinkybay.com

Named after a rugged bay on the North-Western top of Jersey, Stinky Bay Brewing Co was established in 2017. 1% of its turnover is given back to the community to fund a variety of good causes.

Stockport

Unit 16, The Gate Centre, Bredbury Parkway, Stockport, SK6 2SN
☎ (0161) 637 0306 ☎ 07961 056198
⊕ stockportbrewingcompany.com

⊛A former cuckoo brewery, Stockport Brewing installed its own eight-barrel plant initially under the iconic Stockport Viaduct in 2014. It then moved to a larger,

modern facility in the Bredbury Industrial Estate north of Stockport. The beers are widely available throughout the UK through a trading agreement with other breweries. ‼️♦

Stockport Pale (ABV 3.9%) MILD
Cascade (ABV 4%) BITTER
Centaurus (ABV 4%) GOLD
South Island Pale (ABV 4.1%) PALE
Crown Best Bitter (ABV 4.2%) BITTER
Ginger Tinge (ABV 4.2%) BITTER
Jester (ABV 4.2%) GOLD
Stock Porter (ABV 4.8%) PORTER
Malty flavour and aroma with some treacle toffee. Coffee and chocolate roast notes and hint of dark fruit.

Stocks

See Welbeck Abbey

Stod Fold

Stod Fold Farm, Hays Lane, Halifax, West Yorkshire, HX2 8UL ☎ 07745 967740 / 07568 487182
⊕ stodfoldbrewing.com

⊛The 10-barrel Stod Fold Brewery is located on the edge of the moors in a renovated farm building. It supplies around 300 free trade outlets each year, mainly in Yorkshire, but occasionally distributes out of the region via nationwide brewing partners on the swaps scheme. Beers can always be sampled at the Stod Fold Brewery Tap at Dean Clough Mills, Halifax. ♦V

Gold (ABV 3.8%) GOLD
A refreshing, golden and fruity session ale with a smooth, hoppy aftertaste.
West APA (ABV 4%) PALE
A golden-coloured session bitter with a fruity and hoppy aroma. Light and refreshing citrus flavours develop in the mouth leading to a dry, crisp finale.
Blonde+ (ABV 4.3%) BLOND
Smooth-tasting fruity beer with a lingering, dry finish.
Dark Porter (ABV 4.8%) PORTER
Easy-drinking, well-balanced, dark brown porter. Smooth and mellow with roast to the fore.

Stonehenge SIBA

The Old Mill, Mill Road, Netheravon, Salisbury, Wiltshire, SP4 9QB
☎ (01980) 670631 ⊕ stonehengeales.co.uk

⊠ The brewery was founded in 1984 in what was originally a water-driven mill built in 1914. In 1993 the company was bought by Danish master brewer Stig Andersen and his wife Anna Marie, and now supplies more than 300 outlets. From 2013 a new borehole, accessing the Salisbury Plain aquifer, has been supplying the brewery's water. It is of such pristine quality that the brewery now bottle and sell it under the Stonehenge name. ‼️♦

Spire Ale (ABV 3.8%) BITTER
A pale golden-coloured session bitter with an initial bitterness giving way to a well-rounded, bitter aftertaste with discernible fruit balance.
Pigswill (ABV 4%) BITTER
A tawny-coloured session bitter with an initial pleasant hop aroma and slight bitterness to the initial taste moving to a well rounded bitter finish with slight malt and fruit in the finish.
Heel Stone (ABV 4.3%) BITTER
A copper-coloured best bitter with some malt and fruit in the aroma continuing into the initial taste along with pleasant hoppiness. Medium-bodied with plenty of

flavour in the aftertaste with noticeable malt, fruit and hops.

Great Bustard (ABV 4.8%) BITTER
A copper-brown-coloured, strong bitter. Complex malt and fruit flavours at first with a long fruit and bitter aftertaste.

Danish Dynamite (ABV 5%) GOLD
Golden ale with good hop and fruit aromas. Complex flavours in the initial taste with a beautifully-balanced, full-bodied aftertaste with hops and fruit to the fore.

Stonehouse SIBA

Stonehouse, Weston, Oswestry, Shropshire, SY10 9ES
☎ (01691) 676457 ⊕ stonehousebrewery.co.uk

Stonehouse is a family-run brewery, distillery and cider maker. Established in 2007, it operates a 22-barrel plant. It is next to the Cambrian Heritage Railways line and includes a shop, bar and restaurant. Direct delivery is within 30 miles of the brewery. ‼☛

Sunlander (ABV 3.7%) PALE
Station Bitter (ABV 3.9%) BITTER
Cambrian Gold (ABV 4.2%) GOLD
Kelly Point (ABV 4.4%) PALE
Off the Rails (ABV 4.8%) BITTER

Stoney Ford

See Grainstore

Storm SIBA

2 Waterside, Macclesfield, Cheshire, SK11 7HJ
☎ (01625) 431234 ⊕ stormbrewing.co.uk

☺Storm Brewing was founded in 1998. In 2001 it moved to its current location, an old riverside pub building, which until 1937 was called the Mechanics Arms. More than 60 outlets are supplied. ◆LIVE

Beauforts Ale (ABV 3.8%) BITTER
Desert Storm (ABV 3.9%) BITTER
Bosley Cloud (ABV 4.1%) BITTER
Dry, golden bitter with peppery hop notes throughout. Some initial sweetness and a mainly bitter aftertaste. Soft, well-balanced and quaffable.
Ale Force (ABV 4.2%) BITTER
Amber, smooth-tasting, complex beer that balances malt, hop and fruit on the taste, leading to a roasty, slightly sweet aftertaste.
Dexter (ABV 4.2%) GOLD
Downpour (ABV 4.3%) PALE
PGA (ABV 4.4%) SPECIALITY
Light, crisp, lager-style beer with a balance of malt, hops and fruit. Moderately bitter and slight dry aftertaste.
Hurricane Hubert (ABV 4.5%) BITTER
Silk of Amnesia (ABV 4.7%) BITTER
Smooth, premium, easy-drinking bitter. Fruit and hops dominate throughout. Not too sweet, with a good, lasting finish.
Isobar IPA (ABV 4.8%) PALE
Red Mist (ABV 4.8%) PORTER

Stow Fen

Fenview, Flixton Road, Bungay, Suffolk, NR35 1PD
☎ 07775 279181 ✉ stowfenbrewingco@gmail.com

⊗ Stow Fen Brewing Co Ltd was established in 2020 by Paul Holland and Philip Gilham, the head brewer. Malts are from Branthill Farms in Wells-next-the-Sea, and all hops are from the UK. At present beers are all sold directly from the brewery.

Gold (ABV 4.2%) GOLD

Angels Way Amber (ABV 4.4%) BITTER
Stock Bridge Best (ABV 4.6%) BITTER
Twisted Oak IPA (ABV 5%) IPA
Wolds ESB (ABV 5.8%) BITTER
Mouldings Porter (ABV 6.5%) PORTER

Stowey

Old Cider House, 25 Castle Street, Nether Stowey, Somerset, TA5 1LN
☎ (01278) 732228 ⊕ stoweybrewery.co.uk

Somerset's smallest brewery was established in 2006, primarily to supply the owners' guesthouse and to provide beer to participants at events run from the accommodation. The small quantities of beer produced are also supplied to the George, Nether Stowey. ‼◆

Strands

🏠 **Strands Inn, Nether Wasdale, Cumbria, CA20 1ET**
☎ (01946) 726237 ⊕ strandshotel.com

☺Strands Brewery is a ten-barrel plant with a 5,000-litre fermentation capacity. Six of the beers are available on the bar of the Strands Inn at all times or in the Screes, across the road. ‼◆LIVE

Pied Piper (ABV 2.7%) MILD
Lots of traditional mild characteristics: malty, caramel, roast, sweet and fruity.
Green Bullet (ABV 3.5%) SPECIALITY
High impact hop, so bitterness dominates this low strength, golden-coloured ale. Loads of finish, great for those who love hops.
Responsibly (ABV 3.7%) BITTER
Brown Bitter (ABV 3.8%) BITTER
A complex-tasting brown beer with a lingering, bitter aftertaste.
Errmmm... (ABV 3.8%) BITTER
A complex, traditional bitter.
Best Bitter (ABV 4.3%) BITTER
Red Screes (ABV 4.5%) RED
An interesting, rich-tasting, smooth, strong bitter; full-flavoured with plenty of roast and malt tastes.
T'errmmm-inator (ABV 4.9%) PORTER
A smooth, dark brown, roast-led beer. Full-bodied and well-balanced.
Traditional IPA (ABV 6%) IPA

Contract brewed for Independent Lakeland Breweries:
Gold Wing (ABV 4%) BITTER
A full-bodied, hoppy, bitter beer with a malty start.
Dark Knight (ABV 5%) PORTER

Strathaven SIBA

Craigmill Brewery, Sandford Road, Strathaven, ML10 6PB
☎ (01357) 520419 ⊕ strathavenales.com

☺Strathaven Ales is a 10-barrel brewery on the River Avon close to Strathaven and was converted from the remains of a 16th century mill. The range is distributed throughout Scotland and the North of England. ‼☛◆

Craigmill Mild (ABV 3.5%) MILD
Clydesdale (ABV 3.8%) PALE
Duchess Anne (ABV 3.9%) SPECIALITY
Avondale (ABV 4%) GOLD
Line Out (ABV 4%) BITTER
Old Mortality (ABV 4.2%) BITTER
Claverhouse (ABV 4.5%) RED
Teuchter (ABV 5.6%) BITTER
500 (ABV 7%) STRONG
Usquebae Ale (ABV 7%) SPECIALITY

Strathbraan SIBA

Deanshaugh, Amulree, Dunkeld, PH8 0EB
☎ (01350) 725264 ☎ 07747 857908
✉ strathbraan.bry@btinternet.com

Strathbraan began brewing in 2012 using a 10-barrel plant. LIVE

Due South (ABV 3.8%) BITTER
Head East (ABV 4.2%) BITTER

Strathcarron

Arinackaig, Strathcarron, IV54 8YN
☎ (01599) 577236 ⊕ strathcarronbrewery.com

⊠ Brewing since 2016 with a 2.5-barrel plant using its own on-site water supply. All beer is cask and bottle-conditioned, and is usually available on draught at four or five local pubs, and in bottles at a number of local shops and restaurants (see website). Bottles also available from the website. Labels are available in Gaelic or English. LIVE

Golden Cow (ABV 3.8%) GOLD
Black Cow (ABV 4.2%) STOUT
Red Cow (ABV 4.2%) BITTER
Highland Cow (ABV 5.4%) BITTER

Stratton Lane

Middle Barn, Burcot Farm, East Stratton, Winchester, Hampshire, SO21 3DZ ☎ 07990 528790
⊕ strattonlane.com

Having previously run their own businesses, Barnaby and Bernadette Wheller changed direction and opened their own brewery and taproom in 2019, taking over the old MASH brewhouse with its 10-barrel plant. ‼ ✦

First Gold (ABV 3.6%) BITTER
Tawny (ABV 3.6%) BITTER

Strawberry Fields

See Big Bog

Stringers

See Lakeland

Stripey Cat

🍺 Tiger Inn, 14-16 Barrack Street, Bridport, DT6 3LY
☎ (01308) 427543 ⊕ tigerinnbridport.co.uk/the-stripey-cat-craft-brewery

Brewing began in 2017 at the Tiger Inn producing ales exclusively for the pub.

Stroud SIBA

Kingfisher Business Park, London Road, Thrupp, Gloucestershire, GL5 2BY
☎ (01453) 887122 ⊕ stroudbrewery.co.uk

⊠ Established in 2006, Stroud Brewery supports the local economy and its ales are available in 40-50 pubs, independent retailers and its brewery shop. All beers have full organic status. ‼ 🍺 ✦ ✦

Tom Long (ABV 3.8%) BITTER
OPA (Organic Pale Ale) (ABV 4%) PALE
Big Cat (ABV 4.5%) STOUT
Budding (ABV 4.5%) PALE

Stu Brew

Newcastle University, Merz Court, Newcastle upon Tyne, NE1 7RU ⊕ stubrew.com

Stu Brew is Europe's first student-run microbrewery, based at Newcastle University. The brewery was set up as part of a research project aimed at reducing waste and costs in all parts of brewing. The university and local pubs are supplied. V

Lab Session (ABV 4.3%) PALE
Exam Room Tears (ABV 5%) SPECIALITY
Extended Overdraft (ABV 5.2%) PALE
Into the Black (ABV 5.6%) IPA

Stubborn Mule

Unit 2, Radium House, Bridgewater Road, Altrincham, WA14 1LZ ☎ 07730 515251
⊕ stubbornmulebrewery.com

Brewing began in 2015. Ed Bright, the owner/brewer continues to add new beers to the portfolio and is always searching for interesting ideas to brew. ‼ ✦ LIVE V

Mandarin Candidate (ABV 3.4%) SPECIALITY
Li'l Napoleom (ABV 3.9%) GOLD
Absolute Banker (ABV 4.7%) BITTER
Donkey Punch (ABV 5.5%) SPECIALITY
Pre-Prohibition Cream Ale (ABV 5.5%) GOLD
Single Hop IPA (ABV 5.7%) IPA
Chocolate Stout (ABV 5.8%) STOUT
WA15 Magnum IPA (ABV 7.2%) IPA

Stumptail

North Street, Great Dunham, Kings Lynn, Norfolk, PE32 2LR
☎ (01328) 701042 ✉ stumptail@btinternet.com

⊠ Stumptail began commercial homebrewing in 2011 using a 100-litre plant. Bottle-conditioned beers are produced with cask-conditioned versions brewed to order, all to bespoke recipes. Most parts of Norfolk can be supplied. LIVE

Sulwath SIBA

The Brewery, 209 King Street, Castle Douglas, DG7 1DT
☎ (01556) 504525 ⊕ sulwathbrewers.co.uk

☺Sulwath started brewing in 1995. Its award-winning beers are supplied to around 100 outlets and four wholesalers as far away as Devon and Aberdeen. The brewery has a popular, fully-licensed tap. ‼ 🍺 ✦ LIVE ✦

Cuil Hill (ABV 3.6%) BLOND
Distinctively fruity, session ale with malt and hop undertones. The taste is bittersweet with a long-lasting, dry finish.
Tri-ball (ABV 3.9%) GOLD
The Grace (ABV 4.3%) MILD
Black Galloway (ABV 4.4%) PORTER
Criffel (ABV 4.6%) BITTER
Full-bodied beer with a distinctive bitterness. Fruit is to the fore of the taste with hops becoming increasingly dominant in the taste and finish.
Galloway Gold (ABV 5%) GOLD
A cask-conditioned lager that will be too sweet for many despite being heavily-hopped.
Knockendoch (ABV 5%) BITTER
Dark, copper-coloured, reflecting a roast malt content, with bitterness from Challenger hops.
Solway Mist (ABV 5.5%) SPECIALITY

Summerskills SIBA

15 Pomphlett Farm Industrial Estate, Broxton Drive, Billacombe, Plymouth, Devon, PL9 7BG
☎ (01752) 481283 ⊕ summerskills.co.uk

⊠ Established in a vineyard in 1983 at Bigbury-on-Sea, Summerskills moved to its present site in 1985. It is the oldest brewery in Plymouth. Wholesalers and pub companies provide national distribution and the beers regularly appear in a selection of local outlets. In recent times the number of beers has increased and the brewer has won many awards. Locally-sourced ingredients are used wherever possible. ◆ LIVE

Start Point (ABV 3.7%) GOLD
Westward Ho! (ABV 4.1%) BITTER
Malt dominates a light nose. Gentle bitterness introduces its malty-fruit friends. Malt and bitterness remain, with bitterness dominating the conversation.
Tamar (ABV 4.3%) BITTER
Bitter hop taste and finish. A mid-strength best bitter.
Stout (ABV 4.4%) STOUT
Strong coffee aroma, slight sweetness on the taste with coffee/chocolates on tongue. Bitter finish.
Devon Dew (ABV 4.5%) GOLD
Pine aroma with a slight grapefruit taste. A refreshing golden ale.
Devon Frost (ABV 4.5%) GOLD
A slight nutty roast on the nose and also on taste with grapefruit flavours on the tongue.
Menacing Dennis (ABV 4.5%) BITTER
Bolt Head (ABV 4.7%) BITTER
Fruit-hop nose has roast-malt hints. Bitter flavours with sweet malt, roast and hoppiness. Lingering bitter finish with background malt and fruit.
Whistle Belly Vengeance (ABV 4.7%) RED
Full-flavoured strong red ale. Roast and malt aroma with roasted chestnut taste. Sweetness and bitterness mingle in the aftertaste.
Dragon Pioneer (ABV 4.8%) PALE
Ninja (ABV 5%) BITTER
Plymouth Porter (ABV 5%) PORTER
Strong, sweet, chocolate aroma, tastes of chocolate and toffee. Aftertaste dies off quickly, a nice, drinkable, sweet Porter.
First Light (ABV 5.5%) GOLD
Strong golden ale. Fruity, hoppy aroma. Sweet grapefruit and hops on the palate. Aftertaste continues with fruit and hops.
Indiana's Bones / South Star (ABV 5.6%) OLD
Old ale with good body. Rich, malty roasts aroma bursting with strong sweet flavours on the tongue. Slightly dryer finish.

Sunbeam

52 Fernbank Road, Leeds, West Yorkshire, LS13 1BU
☎ 07772 002437 ⊕ sunbeamales.co.uk

☺Sunbeam Ales was established in a house in Leeds in 2009, with commercial brewing beginning in 2011. Since moving, capacity has increased to a two-barrel plant based in a garage. The core range of ales (available in West and North Yorkshire at present) is brewed on rotation up to twice weekly, with occasional brews every six weeks or so. ◆

Bottoms Up (ABV 3.7%) PALE
Polka Hop (ABV 3.8%) PALE
Sun Beamer (ABV 3.8%) PALE
Bright Day (ABV 4.2%) PALE
Rain Stops Play (ABV 4.5%) BITTER

Sunset Taverns

See Six Towns

Surrey Hills SIBA

Denbies Wine Estate, London Road, Dorking, Surrey, RH5 6AA
☎ (01306) 883603 ⊕ surreyhills.co.uk

⊠ Surrey Hills began brewing in 2005 near Shere, moving to Dorking in 2011. Nearly 95% of production is sold within 15 miles of the brewery. The beers have won several local and national awards. ‼ ▣ ◆ ✦

Ranmore (ABV 3.8%) GOLD
Glorious light, flavoursome, session beer. An earthy hoppy nose leads into a grapefruit and hoppy taste and a clean, bitter finish.
Shere Drop (ABV 4.2%) PALE
Champion Beer of Britain 2019. Hoppy with some balancing malt. Pleasant citrus aroma, noticeable fruitiness in taste, with some sweetness.
Gilt Complex (ABV 4.6%) GOLD
Initial citrus fruitiness quickly gives way to a piercing hit of bitter hops, fading slowly in a big dry finish.
Gilt Trip (ABV 4.6%) GOLD
Greensand IPA (ABV 4.6%) PALE
A strong-flavoured and easily-drinkable IPA, with intense grapefruit and hops in the aroma and taste and soft citrusy finish.
Collusion (ABV 5.2%) GOLD
Golden Ale with changing hop mix. Has pale malt backbone, with citrus and tropical flavours combined with characteristics of marmalade.

Suspect (NEW)

34 Jane Street, Leith, Edinburgh, EH6 5HD ☎ 07468 436652 ⊕ suspectbrewing.co.uk

A new gluten-free brewery set up in the former Liquid Brewing premises. No real ale. GF

Sussex Small Batch

c/o 23 The Vinery, Poling, West Sussex, BN18 9PY
Office: 48 Henty Road, Worthing, BN14 7HE
✉ ssbbrewery@outlook.com

Jim Brown started the Sussex Small Batch Brewery in 2018, focusing on producing quality stouts with a difference. Brewing takes place using spare capacity at Goldmark Brewery (qv). Award-winning cask stout is available from time to time in a few select pubs in Worthing, West Sussex, but most production is canned and available throughout the UK via Eebria. V

Suthwyk

See Bowman

Swamp Bog

Church Lane, Enborne, Berkshire, RG20 0HB
⊕ swampbogbrewery.com

⊠ Under the same ownership and sharing the same kit as Two Cocks brewery (qv) this microbrewery, based on the edge of Hampshire/Berkshire, specialises in long-lost craft beer recipes from a time before brewing giants existed. The passion is for taste, not profit; low volume rather than mass production.

Bottom Biter (ABV 3.6%) BITTER
Edge Hopper (ABV 4.2%) GOLD

Pixie Pee (ABV 5%) PALE
The Ferryman's Brew (ABV 5%) SPECIALITY

Swan SIBA

Unit 17, Brunel Road, Enterprise Park, Leominster,
Herefordshire, HR6 0LX
☎ (01568) 617709 ☎ 07377 728822
⊕ swanbrewery.co.uk

Swan Brewery was established in 2016 by Jimmy Swan
and partner Gill Bullock using a 10-barrel plant in
Leominster. A 1.3-barrel plant is used to brew bespoke
beers for local pubs. ‼☲♦

Swan Blonde (ABV 3.7%) BITTER
Ruffled Feathers (ABV 3.8%) BITTER
Gold (ABV 4%) GOLD

Swan on the Green

☱ Swan on the Green, West Peckham, Maidstone,
Kent, ME18 5JW
☎ (01622) 812271 ⊕ swan-on-the-green.co.uk

⊗ The brewery was established in 2000 in an old coal
shed behind the Swan on the Green pub using a two-
barrel plant. ‼♦

Swannay SIBA

Swannay by Evie, Orkney, KW17 2NP
☎ (01856) 721700 ⊕ swannaybrewery.com

☺Brewing began in 2006 at the redundant Swannay
dairy on Orkney mainland's exposed North-Western tip.
Two brewing plants are utilised, a five and a twenty
barrel. Founder Rob is assisted by son Lewis plus a further
small team of passionate beer lovers. ‼☲♦

Orkney Best (ABV 3.6%) GOLD
A refreshing, light-bodied, low gravity, golden beer
bursting with hop, peach and sweet malt flavours. The
long, hoppy finish leaves a dry bitterness.
Island Hopping (ABV 3.9%) GOLD
Passionfruit hoppiness with some caramel with a lasting
bitter aftertaste.
Dark Munro (ABV 4%) MILD
The nose presents an intense roast hit which is followed
by plums and blackcurrant in the mouth. The strong roast
malt continues into the aftertaste.
Scapa Special (ABV 4.2%) BITTER
A good copy of a typical Lancashire bitter, full of
bitterness and background hops, leaving your mouth
tingling in the lingering aftertaste.
Sneaky Wee Orkney Stout (ABV 4.2%) STOUT
Bags of malt and roast with a mixed fruit berry
background. Dry, bitter finish.
Pale Ale (ABV 4.7%) PALE
Orkney IPA (ABV 4.8%) PALE
A traditional bitter, with light hop and fruit flavour
throughout.
Duke IPA (ABV 5.2%) PALE
Good, refreshing, citrus-fruited IPA with background
malt.
Orkney Blast (ABV 6%) BITTER
Plenty of alcohol in this warming, strong bitter/barley
wine. A mushroom and woody aroma blossoms into a
well-balanced smack of malt and hop in the taste.

Swansea SIBA

☱ Joiners Arms, 50 Bishopston Road, Bishopston,
Swansea, SA3 3EJ
☎ (01792) 232658

☺Opened in 1996, Swansea was the first commercial
brewery in the area for almost 30 years. Beers are
regularly available at the Joiners and also the Railway
Inn, Killay. ‼♦

T'ales from the Brewhouse

See Lancaster

Taddington

Blackwell Hall, Blackwell, Buxton, Derbyshire,
SK17 9TQ
☎ (01298) 85734

Taddington started brewing in 2007, and brews one
Czech-style unpasteurised lager in two different
strengths. No real ale

Tally Ho!

☱ 14, Market Street, Hatherleigh, Devon, EX20 3JN
☎ 07779 339089 ⊕ tallyhobrewery.co.uk

⊗ Having stood idle at the rear of the Tally Ho! pub for
14 years, the brewery was resurrected by four brewing
enthusiasts in 2015. The current owner and brewer took
over in 2018. As well as the pub, several local free
houses and other establishments are supplied. ♦

Tamworth

29 Market Street, Tamworth, Staffordshire, B79 7LR
☎ (01827) 319872 ☎ 07712 893353
⊕ tamworthbrewing.co.uk

Owner/brewer George Greenaway brought brewing
back to Tamworth town centre after a gap of 70 years.
Brewing started in 2017 in a former shop, which dates
back to Tudor times and also serves as a taproom. In
2020 brewing moved into the adjacent building, which
records indicate was a brewhouse in the 1750s. The
move allowed production on its five-barrel plant to
double, and included the provision of an off-licence.
Around 25 outlets are supplied. ‼☲♦♪

Hopmaster (ABV 4.2%) GOLD
Big Game (ABV 4.5%) BITTER
Amber-hued with a malty aroma. Generous malt taste
with spicy sides. Hints of pepper and lemon lurk under
the hop bitterness which emerges with a mouth-
watering bite.
Ethelfleda (ABV 4.5%) BITTER
Full malt aroma from this golden beer. Sweet and grassy
mix to start, developing to a bitter finish.
Hoppy Poppy (ABV 4.6%) GOLD
Our Aethel (ABV 4.8%) STOUT
Whopper (ABV 6.5%) IPA

Tankleys

Correspondence: Beech Avenue, Sidcup, Kent,
DA15 8NH ☎ 07901 333273 ⊕ tankleysbrewery.com

Tankleys is a cuckoo brewery based in South-East London
using spare capacity at Beerblefish brewery although
some small batches are made at home for local
micropubs. Its Australian brewer has been brewing for
almost 20 years and produces small batch brews,
available occasionally around the local area.

Golden Ale (ABV 4.5%) BITTER

Tanners

☱ The Old Stables, White Hart Inn, The Square,
Wiveliscombe, Somerset, TA4 2JP

☎ (01984) 623344

Office: 118 High Street, Staple Hill, Bristol, BS16 5HH
⊕ tanners-ales.co.uk

Tanners were established in late 2015 in the old stables at the rear of the White Hart Inn, Wiveliscombe.

Tap & Vent (NEW)

🏠 26 Poulton Street, Kirkham, Lancashire, PR4 2AB

😊 Brewing began in 2021. The brewpub is in the same ownership as Lytham Brewery (qv). ♦

TAP

Marsden Estate, Rendcomb, Cirencester, Gloucestershire, GL7 7EX
☎ (07931) 623001 ☎ 07931 920988
⊕ tapbrewery.co.uk

⊗ TAP is a microbrewery established near Cirencester in 2015. It prides itself on sourcing materials and services locally, with malt from Warminster, hops from Worcester and the beer labels produced in Cirencester. Twelve local pubs are regularly supplied. ‼♦LIVE

Old Dairy Mild (ABV 3.2%) MILD
Old Dairy Gold (ABV 3.9%) GOLD
Old Dairy Bronze (ABV 4.2%) BITTER

Tap East SIBA

🏠 7 International Square, The Great Eastern Market, Westfield Stratford City, Montfichet Road, Stratford, London, E20 1EE
☎ (020) 8555 4467 ⊕ tapeast.co.uk

⊗ Tap East is located in Westfield Stratford City Shopping Centre, opposite the main entrance to Stratford International Station. Brewing began in 2011 using a 2.5-barrel plant. One-off and collaborative beers with other breweries are also produced. Beers are available on-site or at Utobeer cage in Borough Market. 🍴♦V

Tap It SIBA

Unit 6, Muira Industrial Estate, William Street, Southampton, Hampshire, SO14 5QH ☎ 07484 649425 ⊕ tapitbrew.co.uk

The first brew by enthusiastic homebrewer Rob Colmer was in 2018. Tap It is an eight-barrel plant producing eight regular beers mainly in KeyKeg and bottles. Occasional cask-conditioned beers are available. There is an on-site brewery tap and a bar in Southampton is planned. ‼🍴◆

Tap Social Movement SIBA

27 Curtis Industrial Estate, North Hinksey Lane, Botley, Oxford, OX2 0LX
☎ (01865) 236330 ⊕ tapsocialmovement.com

The three founders have a background in the criminal justice system and established the brewery in 2016 to provide training and work opportunities for people serving prison sentences. Small volumes of cask beer are produced for the White House, Oxford, Lock 29, Banbury and for collaboration brews and beer festivals and is brewed on the original, refurbished 1,000-litre kit at a small industrial site in Botley. The majority of its output, which is for kegging and canning, is brewed nearby on the 4,000-litre plant at the former LAM brewery site in Kennington, south of Oxford. 🍴◆

Tapestry SIBA

Unit B, Totterdown Bridge Industrial Estate, Albert Road, St Philips, Bristol, BS2 0XH ☎ 07787 453222
⊕ tapestrybrewery.co.uk

Previously known as Cocksure, this 10-barrel brewery was established in 2017, and moved from the Severn Vale to Bristol in 2018. Occasional specials and collaboration brews with other breweries complement the core range, most of which have been renamed. ‼🍴♦LIVE V◆

Raconteur Amber Session (ABV 3.9%) BITTER
Slight citrus aroma, background sweet biscuit flavours overlaid with pine and citrus hoppiness which fade during the short finish.
Propeller Pale Ale (ABV 4.2%) PALE
African Hibiscus + Honey Golden Ale (ABV 4.8%) SPECIALITY
Initial hit of hoppy bitterness then the tart flavour of hibiscus combines with honey sweetness which lingers on the palate.
Swingball Session IPA (ABV 4.8%) PALE
Fruity hops on the nose combining on the palate with light malt and tropical fruit hints, lingering dry, bitter ending.
African Mango + Orange Pale Ale (ABV 5%) SPECIALITY
Definitely not a traditionalist's beer. The aroma, flavours and aftertaste are loaded with mango with an additional citrus orange punch.
Night Ride Cold Brew Stout (ABV 5%) SPECIALITY
Roasted malt and coffee aroma and flavours to match with hints of dark fruit before a slightly dry finish.
Topline IPA (ABV 6.5%) IPA

Tapped

🏠 Sheffield: Sheffield Tap, Platform 1b, Sheffield Station, Sheaf Street, Sheffield, South Yorkshire, S1 2BP
☎ (0114) 273 7558

Leeds: 51 Boar Street, Leeds, LS1 5EL
⊕ tappedbrewco.com

Brewing began in 2013 after the old Edwardian dining rooms were converted into an on-site brewery with a viewing gallery at the Sheffield Tap pub. The beer is supplied via the company's specialist beer wholesale business, Pivovar. A further on-site brewery opened at the Leeds Tap in 2014.

Tapstone

11 Bartlett Park, Millfield, Chard, Somerset, TA20 2BB
☎ (01460) 929156 ⊕ tapstone.co.uk

⊗ Founded in 2015, the brewery was custom built around a brewing process that preserves delicate hop oils – making beers with a saturated hop flavour. It is growing its own hops two miles from the brewery. There is a small, on-site taproom. All beers are unfined and hazy. ‼🍴◆

Zen Garden (ABV 3.6%) GOLD
Sea Monster (ABV 4.2%) PALE
Soma (ABV 4.6%) GOLD
Hop Wire (ABV 4.8%) GOLD
Kush Kingdom (ABV 5%) GOLD

Tarn 51

🏠 Robin Hood, 10 Church Road, Altofts, Normanton, West Yorkshire, WF6 2NJ
☎ (01924) 892911 ✉ realale@tarn51brewing.co.uk

Tarn 51 uses a three-barrel plant situated at the Robin Hood in Altofts. Expansion is planned. Five other outlets are supplied.

Tarn Hows

Low Bield, Knipe Fold, Outgate, Cumbria, LA22 0PU
☎ 07935 789581 ⊕ tarnhowsbrewery.com

This two-barrel microbrewery near Hawkshead in the Lake District National Park was named after a nearby beauty spot. It opened in 2015 and specialises in stouts and hoppy pale ales. Oak casks may be used for barrel-aging and occasional seasonal beers. Regular beers are suitable for vegans (except for Guji which is vegetarian). V

Beertrix Porter (ABV 4%) PORTER
A well-balanced, fruity beer with some liquorice aromas and a lasting finish of bitterness and roast.
Pale (ABV 4.6%) PALE
Blueberry and Vanilla Oatmeal Stout (ABV 5%) SPECIALITY
Easy-drinking dark beer with fruity aromas and sweet fruity taste. The finish lasts well with roast malt flavours coming through.
Guji Coffee Stout (ABV 5.4%) SPECIALITY

Tartan Shark (NEW)

5 Bangholm Park, Edinburgh, EH5 3BA ☎ 07746 432512 ⊕ tartanshark.co.uk

This self-styled 'smallest brewery in Edinburgh' began production in early 2020, brewing bottle-conditioned, can-conditioned and keg beers (often delivered by pushbike). LIVE

Tartarus (NEW)

Horsforth, LS18 4NR ✉ tartarus.brewing@gmail.com

Nanobrewery based in Horsforth, Leeds launched commercially in 2020. Producing small batch craft bottled beers on a 100-litre kit.

Tatton SIBA

Unit 7, Longridge Trading Estate, Knutsford, Cheshire, WA16 8PR
☎ (01565) 750747 ☎ 07738 150898
⊕ tattonbrewery.co.uk

⊛Tatton is a family-owned business based in the heart of Cheshire. Brewing commenced in 2010 using a steam-fired, custom-built, 15-barrel brewhouse. It supplies pubs throughout Cheshire and the North-West. ‼▆♦✦

Session (ABV 3.7%) BITTER
XPA (ABV 3.7%) PALE
Blonde (ABV 4%) PALE
Best (ABV 4.2%) BITTER
Black (ABV 4.5%) PORTER
Every Day IPA (ABV 4.5%) GOLD
Gold (ABV 4.5%) BITTER

Tavernale

▤ Bridge Tavern, 7 Akenside Hill, Newcastle upon Tyne, NE1 3UF
☎ (0191) 232 1122 ⊕ thebridgetavern.com

A two-barrel plant supplying beers to the Bridge Tavern only. All beers brewed are one-offs. ♦

Taw Valley

Westacott Farm, Westacott Lane, North Tawton, Devon, EX20 2BS ☎ 07900 002299
⊕ tawvalleybrewery.com

Established in 2017 in a Grade-II listed, 17th century thatched barn. Beer is delivered in the brewery dray, a VW camper van. ♦LIVE V

Black Ops (ABV 3.9%) BITTER
Tawton Session Ale (ABV 4%) PALE
Devon Jester (ABV 4.2%) PALE
Franken's Curse (ABV 4.3%) BITTER
Kennard's Steam (ABV 4.3%) BITTER
Copper Best (ABV 4.4%) BITTER
Taw Head IPA (ABV 4.8%) PALE

Timothy Taylor SIBA IFBB

Knowle Spring Brewery, Keighley, West Yorkshire, BD21 1AW
☎ (01535) 603139 ⊕ timothy-taylor.co.uk

⊛An independent, family-owned company established in 1858. It has occupied the Knowle Spring site since 1863. Pennine spring water is used to brew its award-winning ales on both the established main plant and a 10-barrel plant introduced in 2017 to develop new beers, including occasional specials. 19 pubs are operated.

Dark Mild (ABV 3.5%) MILD
Malt and caramel dominate throughout in this sweetish beer with background hop and fruit notes.
Golden Best (ABV 3.5%) MILD
Refreshing, amber-coloured, traditional Pennine mild. A delicate fruit hoppy aroma leads to a fruity taste with underlying hops and malt. Fruity finish.
Boltmaker (ABV 4%) BITTER
Tawny bitter combining, hops fruit and biscuity malt. Lingering, increasingly bitter aftertaste. Formerly (sometimes still) sold as best bitter.
Knowle Spring (ABV 4.2%) BLOND
Tropical fruitiness on the nose leads to a bittersweetness that carries through into the finish.
Landlord (ABV 4.3%) BITTER
A moreish bitter combining citrus peel aromas, malt and grassy hops with marmalade sweetness and a long, bitter finish.
Landlord Dark (ABV 4.3%) OLD
A black beer with red highlights topped by a coffee-coloured head. Burnt caramel on the nose, Dark fruits with caramel in the taste leading to a light, bitter finish.

Taylor Walker

See Greene King

Team Toxic

c/o Liverpool Brewing Co, Unit 39, Brasenose Road, Bootle, Liverpool, L20 8HL ☎ 07976 714585
✉ Gazza@theteamtoxic.co.uk

Team Toxic, led by Gazza Prescott and Sue Hayward, are a craft-forward commissioner of beers, producing a range of eccentric one-off brews as well as some core brands, some also appear under the name Mission Creep. All beers are brewed at Liverpool Brewing Company with some made in collaboration with other breweries. Gazza likes bitter, hoppy pale ales and experimenting with beer styles and ingredients, and is hoping to create more madness going forward.

Teignmouth SIBA

Warehouse 1, Old Quay Street, Teignmouth, TQ14 8ES

☎ (01626) 770846 ⊕ teignmouthbrewery.co.uk

The brewery opened in 2019 and is run by the brewer, John Norish and his wife Joanna. Currently a six-barrel brew length, brewing three regular beers (also available bottle-conditioned and in polykegs with local home delivery). Seasonal beers are also brewed on an individual basis. LIVE

Templer (ABV 4%) BITTER
Portside (ABV 4.3%) BITTER
Deckhand (ABV 4.5%) GOLD

Teignworthy

The Maltings, Teign Road, Newton Abbot, Devon, TQ12 4AA
☎ (01626) 332066 ⊕ teignworthybrewery.com

⊗ Teignworthy Brewery opened in 1994 within the historic Tucker's Maltings building. The 20-barrel plant produces 50 barrels a week and supplies around 300 outlets in Devon and Somerset. It diversified in 2017 with the addition of the Black Dog gin distillery. ‼ ⇟◆LIVE

Neap Tide (ABV 3.8%) PALE
Reel Ale (ABV 4%) BITTER
Subtle aromas. The taste is also gentle with malt and fruit dominating the hops. The aftertaste is dry.
Gun Dog (ABV 4.3%) BITTER
Easy-drinking, session best bitter. Fruity throughout. Dry aftertaste lingers; sweetness and fruit over malt and caramel, progressing into hoppiness.
Spring Tide (ABV 4.3%) BITTER
An excellent, full and well-rounded, mid-brown beer with a dry, bitter taste and aftertaste.
Old Moggie (ABV 4.4%) BITTER
Best bitter. Hoppy and bitter with fruity undertones. Complex aftertaste with a balance of malt, hops and fruit.
Beachcomber (ABV 4.5%) GOLD
A pale brown beer with a light, refreshing fruit and hop nose, grapefruit taste and a dry, hoppy finish.

Teme Valley SIBA

⊟ Talbot, Bromyard Road, Knightwick, Worcestershire, WR6 5PH
☎ (01886) 821235 ☎ 07792 394151
⊕ temevalleybrewery.co.uk

☺Teme Valley was established in 1997 to brew beer for the Talbot, Knightwick. Only hops grown in Herefordshire and Worcestershire are used in brewing. Beers are supplied throughout the West Midlands and Marches. ‼◆LIVE ✦

Tempest SIBA

Block 11, Units 1 & 2 Tweedbank Industrial Estate, Tweedbank, TD1 3RS
☎ (01896) 759500 ⊕ tempestbrewingco.com

Now well established in its premises at Tweedbank, Gavin Meiklejohn's brewery continues to evolve with specialised brews, many using lesser known hop varieties. Cask beers were restricted during Covid (with Armadillo the only ever-present), but many other beers were available in KeyKeg while the brewery remained open throughout, and expanded its bottle and can portfolio. Within the brewery is the shop where regular tap sessions and beer festivals are held. ‼⇟◆LIVE ✦

Armadillo (ABV 3.8%) GOLD
Modern Helles (ABV 4.1%) PALE
Elemental Porter (ABV 5.1%) PORTER

Tenby SIBA

Unit 15, The Salterns, Tenby, SA70 8EQ
☎ (01834) 218090 ☎ 07410 169447
⊕ tenbybrewingco.com

Formerly known as Preseli, Tenby Brewing Co uses a six-barrel plant. Beer is supplied to outlets in Pembrokeshire, neighbouring counties and further afield. Spent grain is fed to animals at a local eco farm and through energy savings the brewery is moving towards becoming carbon neutral. LIVE V

Son of a Beach (ABV 4.2%) GOLD
Hang Ten (ABV 4.3%) BITTER
Barefoot (ABV 4.7%) BLOND
Black Flag Porter (ABV 5.6%) PORTER

Tenby Harbour

See Harbwr Tenby

Thame

⊟ East Street, Thame, Oxfordshire, OX9 3JS
☎ (01844) 218202
✉ thamebrewery@btinternet.com

⊗ This one-barrel brewery was set up in 2009 by Peter Lambert and Oak Taverns in the old stables at the Cross Keys. Beer is produced from time to time for that pub.

Thames Side SIBA

Bridge Street, Staines-upon-Thames, Surrey, TW18 4TG
☎ (01784) 461112 ☎ 07703 518956
⊕ thamessidebrewery.co.uk

⊗ Founded in 2015 by CAMRA member Andy Hayward using a four-barrel plant. It moved to current brewery and taproom on the banks of the River Thames, in 2019. In 2020 a one-barrel pilot brew kit for experimental and developmental brews was added. A full range of beers are named after birds found on or near the nearby river, while specials follow a musical theme. ‼⇟◆✦

Harrier (ABV 3.4%) BITTER
Heron Ale (ABV 3.7%) BITTER
Malty traditional English bitter, with a tangerine fruit flavour. Balanced with impressive dry finish and loads of flavour for strength.
White Swan (ABV 4.2%) PALE
New World pale ale. Grapefruit pith and grassy hops almost overpowering biscuit maltiness. Some sweetness in finish with crisp biscuitiness.
Egyptian Goose (ABV 4.8%) PALE
English IPA with initial floral aroma leading to an earthy mango fruitiness as sweetness builds and a balanced bitter finish.
Wryneck Rye (ABV 5.6%) IPA
Spicy rye IPA, with lychees and increasing lemony taste balanced by rye and New World hops. Short, dry bitter finish.

Theakston

The Brewery, Masham, North Yorkshire, HG4 4YD
☎ (01765) 680000 ⊕ theakstons.co.uk

☺An independent, family business, established in 1827 by Robert Theakston. From 1984, for 19 years the brewery was in non-family hands. Following a successful buy back in 2003, the company returned to family control, managed by Simon Theakston and his three brothers (great-great grandsons of the founder). Significant capital investment in the Masham brewery since then, has provided additional capacity and flexibility to meet growing demand and variety of beers brewed. ‼♦♣

Best Bitter (ABV 3.8%) BITTER
Black Bull Bitter (ABV 3.9%) BITTER
A distinctively hoppy aroma leads to a bitter, hoppy taste with some fruitiness and a short, bitter finish.
Lightfoot (ABV 4.1%) PALE
XB (ABV 4.5%) BITTER
Old Peculier (ABV 5.6%) OLD
A full-bodied, dark brown, strong ale. Slightly malty but with hints of roast coffee and liquorice. A smooth caramel overlay and a complex fruitiness leads to a bitter chocolate finish.

Thirst Class

Unit 16, Station Road Industrial Estate, Reddish, Stockport, FY2 9EW
☎ (0161) 431 3998 ⊕ thirstclassale.co.uk

☺Thirst Class opened in 2014 in the centre of Stockport using a purpose-built, two-barrel plant. In 2016 the brewery relocated to larger premises and installed a 10-barrel plant. A collaboration brew is produced each month. ♦LIVE V

Don't Panic (ABV 3.5%) PALE
Kiss My Ace (ABV 4%) SPECIALITY
Hoppy Go Lucky (ABV 4.1%) PALE
High Five (ABV 4.2%) PALE
Mosaic Pale Ale (ABV 4.7%) PALE
Stocky Oatmeal Stout (ABV 4.7%) STOUT
Any Porter in a Storm (ABV 4.8%) PORTER
Dark roast in aroma and flavour with balanced sweetness and fruit. Dry throughout and lingering sweetness.
Green Bullet Pale Ale (ABV 4.8%) PALE
Strong hop aroma. Bitter hop flavour with prominent pale malt and balanced with sweet fruitiness. Dry, bitter finish.
American Brown Ale (ABV 5.6%) BROWN
Full-bodied and smooth brown ale with prominant chocolate roast, fruit notes and gentle hops. Long-lasting flavour.
Hopfordian IPA (ABV 6%) IPA
Hoppy Couple IPA (ABV 6.2%) IPA
Elephant Hawk IPA (ABV 6.5%) IPA

Thorley & Sons

30 East Street, Ilkeston, Derbyshire, DE7 5JB ☎ 07899 067723 ✉ dylan.thorley1@yahoo.co.uk

Thorley & Sons began brewing commercially in 2016 on a 1.5-barrel plant located in an old coach house at the rear of brewer Dylan Thorley's house.

Pale & Interesting (ABV 4.5%) PALE

Thornbridge SIBA

Riverside Business Park, Buxton Road, Bakewell, Derbyshire, DE45 1GS
☎ (01629) 815999 ⊕ thornbridgebrewery.co.uk

☺The first Thornbridge craft beers were produced in 2005 using a 10-barrel brewery, housed in the grounds of Thornbridge Hall. The beers have gained considerable success with over 300 consumer and industry awards won. A 30-barrel brewery opened in Bakewell in 2009. The original site continues to develop new, seasonal and speciality beers. 200 outlets are supplied direct. 12 pubs are managed and owned. ‼🍴♦LIVE

Wild Swan (ABV 3.5%) BITTER

Extremely pale yet flavoursome and refreshing beer. Plenty of lemony, citrus hop flavour, becoming increasingly dry and bitter in the finish and aftertaste.
Brother Rabbit (ABV 4%) BITTER
Lord Marples (ABV 4%) BITTER
Smooth, traditional, easy-drinking bitter. Caramel, malt and coffee flavours fall away to leave a long, bitter finish.
Ashford (ABV 4.2%) BITTER
Kipling (ABV 5.2%) GOLD
Golden pale bitter with aromas of grapefruit and passion fruit. Intense fruit flavours continue throughout, leading to a long bitter aftertaste.
Jaipur IPA (ABV 5.9%) IPA
Flavoursome IPA packed with citrus hoppiness that is nicely counter-balanced by malt and underlying sweetness and robust fruit flavours.
Saint Petersburg Imperial Russian Stout (ABV 7.4%) STOUT
Good example of an imperial stout. Smooth and easy to drink with raisins, bitter chocolate and hops throughout, leading to a lingering coffee and chocolate aftertaste.

Thornsett (NEW)

Thornsett Fields Farm, Briargrove Road, Birch Vale, Derbyshire, SK22 1AX ☎ 07803 477812
⊕ thornsettbrewery.co.uk

Thornsett is a small, family-owned brewery and hopyard tucked away on a farm in a village in the heart of the High Peak.

Three Acre SIBA

Dairy Yard, Little Goldsmiths Farm, Beechy Road, Blackboys, East Sussex, TN22 5JG
☎ (01825) 891144 ⊕ threeacrebrewery.co.uk

⊗ Three Acre Brewery was established in 2019 by three lifelong friends, shortly after finishing university. Based in the heart of rural Sussex, it takes the local rich brewing history and combines it with modern ingredients and techniques on its five-barrel plant, which is undergoing expansion. Home delivery of bottles, minicasks and boxes is available, alongside the supply of cask beer to selected pubs.

West Coast Pale (ABV 3.9%) PALE
English Best Bitter (ABV 4%) BITTER

Three B's

🏠 Black Bull, Brokenstone Road, Blackburn, Lancashire, BB3 0LL
☎ (01254) 581381 ⊕ threebsbrewery.co.uk

Robert Bell acquired the Black Bull in 2011 and the brewpub now supplies 50 outlets. ‼♦LIVE

Stoker's Slake (ABV 3.6%) MILD
Lightly-roasted coffee flavours are in the aroma and the initial taste. A well-rounded, dark brown mild with dried fruit flavours in the long finish.
Bees Knees (ABV 3.7%) PALE
Honey Bee (ABV 3.7%) SPECIALITY
Bobbin's Bitter (ABV 3.8%) BITTER
Bee Blonde (ABV 4%) GOLD
Black Bull (ABV 4%) BITTER
Ju-bee-lation (ABV 4.1%) PALE
Black Bull Lager (ABV 4.5%) SPECIALITY
Doff Cocker (ABV 4.5%) BLOND
Knocker Up (ABV 4.8%) PORTER
A smooth, rich, creamy porter. The roast flavour is foremost without dominating and is balanced by fruit and hop notes.
Old Bee (ABV 5.8%) OLD

Three Blind Mice

Unit W10, Black Bank Business Park, Black Bank Road, Little Downham, Cambridgeshire, CB6 2UA
☎ (01353) 864438 ☎ 07912 875825
✉ mice@threeblindmicebrewery.com

Award-winning, seven-barrel brewery, established in 2014. The name comes from the three owners/brewers, who reckoned they didn't have a clue what they were doing when they first started brewing. Beer is supplied regularly to the Drayman's Son micropub, Ely, plus other outlets in Ely, Cambridgeshire and further afield. Beers are also canned and the brewery has been experimenting with different lagered beers. ◆

Lonely Snake (ABV 3.5%) GOLD
Half Wit (ABV 4.2%) SPECIALITY
Old Brown Mouse (ABV 4.2%) BITTER
Juice Rocket (ABV 4.5%) PALE
Milk Worm (ABV 5.3%) PORTER
Fags & Coffee (ABV 8.1%) SPECIALITY

Three Brothers SIBA

Unit 4, Clayton Court, Bowesfield Crescent, Stockton-on-Tees, TS18 3QX
☎ (01642) 678084 ⊕ threebrothersbrewing.co.uk

The brewery is the vision of Kit Dodd, who after brewing for five years with another local brewery established it in 2016 together with his brother Dave and brother-in-law Chris. ‼ 🍺 ◆ LIVE V

The Bitter Ex (ABV 3.7%) BITTER
Trilogy (ABV 3.9%) PALE
DDH Pale (ABV 4%) PALE
ThaIPA (ABV 4.1%) SPECIALITY
Mangold (ABV 4.5%) GOLD
Ruby Revolution (ABV 4.5%) RED
Session IPA (ABV 4.5%) PALE
S'more Porter (ABV 4.8%) PORTER
Feel the Rhythm (ABV 5.3%) PALE
North East IPA (ABV 5.3%) PALE

Three Castles SIBA

Unit 12, Salisbury Road Business Park, Pewsey, Wiltshire, SN9 5PZ
☎ (01672) 564433 ☎ 07725 148671
⊕ threecastlesbrewery.co.uk

Three Castles is an independent, family-run brewery established in 2006. It delivers direct to around 80 pubs and independent retailers. Wholesalers and beer festivals are also supplied. ‼ 🍺 ◆ LIVE

Chain Mail Pale (ABV 3.8%) PALE
Barbury Castle (ABV 3.9%) PALE
Armour Plated (ABV 4%) BITTER
Saxon Archer (ABV 4%) BITTER
Heritage (ABV 4.2%) BITTER
Uffington Castle (ABV 4.2%) BITTER
Vale Ale (ABV 4.3%) GOLD
Corn Dolly (ABV 4.7%) GOLD

Three Daggers SIBA

47 Westbury Road, Edington, Westbury, Wiltshire, BA13 4PG
☎ (01380) 830940 ⊕ threedaggersbrewery.com

⊠ Three Daggers Brewery was established in 2013 using a 2.5-barrel brew plant in a farm shop next to a popular roadside pub. Malt is sourced locally from Warminster Maltings and hops from Charles Faram in Herefordshire. Hops are grown on-site for use in seasonal beers. ‼ ◆ LIVE

Daggers Blonde (ABV 3.6%) BLOND
Daggers Ale (ABV 4.1%) BITTER
Daggers Edge (ABV 4.7%) BITTER

Three Engineers SIBA

The Cow Byers, Winterbourne Medieval Barn, Church Lane, Winterbourne, BS36 1SD
⊕ threeengineersbrewery.co.uk

Nanobrewery established near Bristol in 2017. Seven cask beers are brewed and supplied to a number of local pubs and micropubs. Bottled beers are also available. After an extended period of cuckoo brewing at other Bristol breweries, Three Engineers moved back to its renovated and enlarged premises at Winterbourne Medieval Barn in 2020. A taproom and shop opened in 2021. 🍺 ◆

Beluga Wheat Beer (ABV 3.9%) SPECIALITY
Corsair American Pale Ale (ABV 4.1%) PALE
Gladiator (ABV 4.4%) BITTER
Sweetish malt aroma is overlaid on the palate with ripe fruit and hop bitterness, which continue into the long finish.
Vulcan (ABV 5%) PALE
Mosquito (ABV 5.1%) PORTER
Dark roasted malt on the nose, flavours of bitter dark chocolate with liquorice and blueberry hints, short and dry ending.
Red Wing (ABV 5.1%) RED
Fruity red ale with a rye tartness balancing the nutty malt background and plum sweetness, which lingers in the aftertaste.
Mustang (ABV 5.4%) PALE

Three Fiends

Brookfield Farm, 148 Mill Moor Road, Meltham, Holmfirth, West Yorkshire, HD9 5LN ☎ 07810 370430
⊕ threefiends.co.uk

The brewery was set up by three friends in 2015 and is based in one of the outbuildings at Brookfield Farm. The original two-barrel kit was upgraded to an eight-barrel plant in 2019. Beers are available around Huddersfield and at CAMRA beer festivals.

Bitter Not Twisted (ABV 3.8%) BITTER
Stelfox (ABV 4%) IPA
Two Face (ABV 4%) BITTER
Bad Uncle Barry (ABV 4.2%) PALE
Boomer (ABV 4.3%) BITTER
Bandito (ABV 4.5%) PALE
Mok Titi (ABV 4.6%) PALE
Fudge Unit (ABV 4.8%) STOUT
Super Sharp Shooter (ABV 5.2%) IPA
Dark Side (ABV 5.3%) PALE
Little Devil (ABV 5.3%) PALE
Mr Badman (ABV 5.3%) SPECIALITY
Punch Drunk (ABV 5.5%) PALE
Voodoo (ABV 6%) SPECIALITY
Panic Attack Espresso Stout (ABV 6.8%) SPECIALITY
Bukowski (ABV 7%) IPA
Stelfoxed (ABV 7.5%) IPA

Three Hills

4 Thrapston Road, Woodford, Northamptonshire, NN14 4HY ☎ 07400 706884

Outpost: Arch 7, Almond Road, Bermondsey, London, SE16 3LR ⊕ threehillsbrewing.com

Named after the ancient communal tombs that stand on the outskirts of the village of Woodford, Three Hills is a small batch brewery established in 2016. Initially producing only in bottle, can and KeyKeg, it, now produces a monthly series of varying styles of cask-conditioned ales called the Woodford Experiment. Three Hills purchased the Affinity brewery in 2020. Beers are produced under the Outpost name but existing beers may be brewed at either site, with all canning done at Woodford. ✦

Three Kings SIBA

14 Prospect Terrace, North Shields, NE30 1DX
☎ 07580 004565 ∰ threekingsbrewery.co.uk

Three Kings started in 2012 using a 2.5-barrel plant, and have steadily upgraded it to its current 25-barrel capacity. Two house beers are brewed for local pubs. As well as the regular beers it typically brews two one-off beers each month. ◆

Shieldsman (ABV 3.8%) BITTER
Billy Mill Ale (ABV 4%) BITTER
Dark Side of the Toon (ABV 4.1%) STOUT
Ring of Fire (ABV 4.5%) PALE
Silver Darling (ABV 5.6%) IPA

Three Legs

Unit 1, Burnt House Farm, Udimore Road, Broad Oak, East Sussex, TN31 6BX ☎ 07939 997622
∰ thethreelegs.co.uk

⊠ The Three Legs was started in 2014 by two friends who met studying winemaking and viticulture at university. It has grown from a nanobrewery to a 10-barrel plant in a converted farm barn. Regulars and beer-minded visitors find a warm welcome at the thriving brewery tap. Beers can be found in most free-houses and bottle shops across the south east. Beers are ever changing. Majority are modern, hop-forward, unfined, and with bags of flavour. ‼ ⏻ LIVE ✦

Three Peaks

Unit 6, Holt Court, Pendle Street, Nelson, Lancashire, BB9 7EB ☎ 07790 539867

Office: Lloyds Farm, Harden Road, Kelbrook, BB18 6TS
∰ threepeaksbrewery.co.uk

⊠ Named after the three Yorkshire Dales mountains and established in 2006, new owners Chris and Jennifer Holt have moved the five-barrel plant to new modern premises while retaining the services of previous owner/brewer, Colin Ashwell. Same philosophy remains; producing quality ales using premium ingredients to celebrate the great outdoors. Beers are currently supplied to outlets in the Dales, West Yorkshire and East Lancashire. ◆

Fell Walker (ABV 3.6%) BLOND
Pen-y-Ghent Bitter (ABV 3.8%) BITTER
The malty character of this mid-brown session bitter is balanced by fruit in the aroma and taste. The finish is malty and hoppy.
Ingleborough Gold (ABV 4%) GOLD
Whernside Pale Ale (ABV 4.2%) PALE
Blea Moor Porter (ABV 4.5%) PORTER
Dark brown porter has a predominantly roast malt character, with a background of dark fruit and a woody note
Scar Top Stout (ABV 5%) STOUT

Three Sisters

See Crafty Little

Three Sods SIBA

Arch 399, Mentmore Terrace, London Fields, London, E8 3PH ☎ 07554 457868 ∰ threesodsbrewery.com

⊠ Three Sods originally started in cramped conditions in the basement of the Bethnal Green Working Men's Club. It moved to a railway arch in London Fields in 2020, using the ex-Wild Card six-barrel brew plant. Its range of traditional English-style beer is augmented by seasonal specials. ✦

Vapour Trail Session Pale (ABV 3.8%) BLOND
BoHo Bitter (ABV 4.1%) BITTER
Amber-coloured best bitter. Bready, malty aroma and taste. Sweet taste and aftertaste, with just a hint of hops.
Session IPA (ABV 4.4%) GOLD
Citrus zesty nose and flavour where the biscuit sweetness cuts through the bitter hop. Finish is long, bitter and pithy.
Mon Cheri IPA (ABV 4.5%) PALE
Trade Union Pale Ale (ABV 4.5%) BITTER
Traditional, smooth, amber best bitter. Malt and fruit are balanced by plenty of bitter hops with a very dry finish.
Dark Magus Milk Stout (ABV 4.7%) STOUT
Rooi Kabouter Red Ale (ABV 4.9%) RED
Leap Year (ABV 5%) GOLD
Maelstrom IPA (ABV 5.3%) PALE

Three Tuns SIBA

🍺 **Salop Street, Bishop's Castle, Shropshire, SY9 5BN**
☎ (01588) 638392 ☎ 07973 301099

Office: 16 Market Square, Bishops Castle, SY9 5BW
∰ threetunsbrewery.co.uk

Brewing on this site started in the 16th century and was licensed in 1642. A small-scale tower brewery from the late 19th century survives. Three Tuns was one of only four pub breweries still running in the 1970s. ‼ ⏻ ◆ LIVE

Thurstons

The Courtyard, 102c High Street, Horsell, Surrey, GU21 4ST
☎ (01483) 729555 ☎ 07789 936784
∰ thurstonsbrewery.co.uk

⊠ Originally based in the Crown, Horsell, Thurstons moved next door in 2014 when the brewery upgraded to a 4.5-barrel plant. The brewery supplies pubs across Surrey. ◆LIVE

Horsell Best (ABV 3.8%) BITTER
Traditional, well-balanced bitter, initially malty with strong caramel and redcurrant flavours throughout and balancing bitterness, becoming drier in finish.
Horsell Gold (ABV 3.8%) PALE
Light fruit and slightly nutty aroma, lead to some bitterness and malt, which soon fades into a light bitter finish.
Milk Stout (ABV 4.5%) STOUT
Smooth, sweet stout, with chocolatey and sweet malt flavour. Pleasant sharpness as lactose comes through leading to slightly dry finish.
Un-American Pale Ale (ABV 4.6%) PALE
Well-hopped, American-style pale using English grown hops. Grapefruit and pineapple grow into full-bodied sweetness and lingering bitterness.

Thwaites IFBB

Myerscough Road, Mellor Brook, Lancashire, BB2 7LB
☎ (01254) 686868 ∰ thwaites.co.uk

☺Founded in 1807, Thwaites brewed in Blackburn until 2018 when it moved to a rural site five miles away in the

Ribble Valley. A 20-barrel plant brews exclusively for around 240 pubs, 11 managed Inns of Character, eight hotels and two lodges. All outlets can sell the regularly-brewed cask beers plus members of the 1807 Cask Club can sell the seasonal ales. Marston's, owner of the Wainwright and Lancaster Bomber brands, continues to sell these beers into Thwaites's outlets. ♦

Mild (ABV 3.3%) MILD
Refreshing dark mild with gentle fruit and roast in the nose, a sweet centre and a dry, clean finish.
Original (ABV 3.6%) BITTER
TBC (Thwaites Best Cask) (ABV 3.8%) BITTER
IPA (ABV 4%) PALE
Gold (ABV 4.1%) GOLD
Amber (ABV 4.4%) BITTER

Tigertops

22 Oakes Street, Flanshaw, Wakefield, West Yorkshire, WF2 9LN
☎ (01229) 716238 ☎ 07951 812986
✉ tigertopsbrewery@hotmail.com

⊛Tigertops was established in 1995 by Stuart Johnson and his wife Lynda who, as well as owning the brewery, ran the Foxfield brewpub in Cumbria (qv). Recently retired, the brewery is run on their behalf by Barry Smith, supplying five regular outlets. ♦

Cass 2CV (ABV 4.6%) BITTER

Tiley's

⊟ Salutation Inn, Ham, Gloucestershire, GL13 9QH
☎ (01453) 810284 ⊕ sallyatham.com

⊠ This 2.5-barrel microbrewery was established in an outbuilding of the award-winning Salutation Inn in 2015. It concentrates on producing small batches of award-winning beer, predominantly in cask, some in KeyKeg. Most of the brewery's output is sold on-site at the Salutation Inn, and the Butcher's Hook, Thornbury. The rest goes to selected local pubs.

Tilford

⊟ Duke of Cambridge, Tilford Road, Farnham, Surrey, GU10 2DD ☎ 07710 500967
✉ mark@tilfordbrewery.beer

⊠ Tilford Brewery was started in 2017 using a 2.5-barrel plant in an old coaching house on the site of the Duke of Cambridge pub. A shop, tasting room and mini maltings are planned for the upstairs of the building. Beer is supplied to pubs in Surrey and Hampshire. ‼ ⬟

Red Mist (ABV 3.7%) BITTER
Rushmoor Ripper (ABV 4.4%) BITTER
Wit (ABV 4.5%) SPECIALITY
Belgian wheat beer brewed in an English style, with a good balance of hop and fruit flavours.

Tillingbourne SIBA

Old Scotland Farm, Staple Lane, Shere, Surrey, GU5 9TE
☎ (01483) 222228 ⊕ tillybeer.co.uk

⊠ Tillingbourne was established in 2011 on a farm site previously used by Surrey Hills Brewery using its old 17-barrel plant. Around 25 local outlets are supplied. ‼⬟♦

The Source (ABV 3.3%) GOLD
Light and crisp golden ale with strong grapefruit flavours. Packed full of Citra hops and drinking well above its strength.
Black Troll (ABV 3.7%) PALE

A black IPA in which initial roast notes are eventually overpowered by citrus hop through to the finish.
Dormouse (ABV 3.8%) BITTER
Predominately sweet and malty, with strong toffee notes and a short fruity finish.
AONB (ABV 4%) GOLD
Golden ale in which Cascade hops dominates throughout. Some balancing malt in the aroma and taste.
Falls Gold (ABV 4.2%) GOLD
Whilst hops dominate, balancing malt is evident throughout. Hints of grapefruit in aroma and taste lead to a dry finish.
Whakahari (ABV 4.6%) PALE
Hop Troll (ABV 4.8%) PALE
Big hop flavours together with peach and apricot. Sweet, fruity taste leads to a floral bitter finish.
Summit (ABV 6%) IPA

Time & Tide

Statenborough Farm, Felderland Lane, Deal, Kent, CT14 0BX ☎ 07739 868256
⊕ timeandtidebrewing.co.uk

This award-winning brewery began brewing in 2013. It produces a number of cask beers using hops from the Deal Community Hop Farm. To date over 13 varieties of beer have been produced. In addition to these, KeyKeg and canned beers are produced, some of which are barrel-aged, ranging through IPAs, stouts, sours, lagers and mild. ⬟♦LIVE

Bitter (ABV 4%) BITTER
Green Hop (ABV 4.8%) BLOND
ESB (ABV 5.8%) BITTER

Tin Head

Unit 22f, Bradley Fold Trading Estate, Bradley Fold Road, Radcliffe, Bury, BL2 6RT ☎ 07980 262766
⊕ tinheadbrewery.co.uk

⊛Established in 2017, originally for canning Tank Beer, it now operates as a brewery run by father and son who are passionate about their beers. The dog-friendly taproom has recently been extended. The rear section offers performances from solo artists. Occasionally a guest beer is on offer. Generally eight craft keg beers are on tap, together with local gins distilled locally at Rivington. ‼⬟

Tindall

Toad Lane, Seething, Norwich, Norfolk, NR35 2EQ
☎ 07703 379116 ✉ info@tindallales.com

⊠ Tindall Ales began brewing in 1998. It was originally based in Ditchingham but moved to its current location in 2001. Mike is passionate about brewing a new generation of cask beer using the finest local ingredients, whenever possible, and live yeast. ‼⬟♦V

Best Bitter (ABV 3.7%) BITTER
Mild (ABV 3.7%) MILD
Soft malty, dark fruit bouquet. Balanced, with fig roll, roast and a crisp, bitterness leading to a strong savoury finish.
Liberator (ABV 3.8%) BITTER
Alltime (ABV 4%) BITTER
Seething Pint (ABV 4.3%) BITTER

Tintagel SIBA

Condolden Farm, Tintagel, Cornwall, PL34 0HJ
☎ (01840) 213371 ⊕ tintagelbrewery.co.uk

⊠ Established in 2009 in a redundant milking parlour on the highest farm in Cornwall, using a 7.5-barrel plant. A new purpose-built brewery, shop, restaurant and visitor centre opened in 2017. Around 80 outlets are supplied direct. ‼️🍺♦

Castle Gold (ABV 3.8%) PALE
Refreshing pale ale with faint malt aroma. Citrus hop, tropical fruits, sweet malt and distinctly bitter flavours. Hop bitter finish.

Cornwall's Pride (ABV 4%) BROWN
Pale brown bitter with malt aroma. Sweet, grainy malt with toffee and summer fruits. Late dried fruit and coffee hints.

Sir Lancelot (ABV 4.2%) BITTER

Arthur's Ale (ABV 4.4%) BITTER
Pale brown complex beer with balance of sweet toffee, malt and earthy hops. Hints of figs, vine fruits and liquorice.

Pendragon (ABV 4.5%) PALE
Golden beer with citrus hop nose. Refreshing, strong orange citrus and pine hop bitterness. Hints of toffee, honey and malt.

Poldark Ale (ABV 4.5%) MILD
Brown strong mild with malt aroma. Assertive malty flavour with stone fruits, dates, sweet caramel, smokiness and a citrus edge.

Harbour Special (ABV 4.8%) OLD
Tawny old ale with ripe fruity, malty aroma. Rich nutty malt, stone fruits and esters taste, finishing bitter and malty.

Merlins Muddle (ABV 5.2%) BITTER
Auburn, creamy, premium bitter. Spicy hop bitterness balanced by smoky malt flavours and a complex mixture of fruits. Bitter finish.

Caliburn (ABV 5.8%) OLD
Dark old ale. Smoky, roast malt and Christmas pudding fruits with rich and complex flavours including treacle and earthy hops.

Tinworks SIBA

Unit 20, 1 Trostre Industrial Park, Llanelli, SA14 9UU
☎ 07595 841958 ⊕ tinworksbrewery.co.uk

Brewery commenced operations on a rural farm but relocated and upgraded to a 10-barrel kit in 2019. 🍺

Old Castle Pale (ABV 4.6%) PALE
Mashfield Red (ABV 4.7%) BITTER
Ashburnham Porter (ABV 5%) PORTER
Dafen IPA (ABV 6.3%) IPA

Tiny Rebel

Wern Industrial Estate, Rogerstone, Newport, NP10 9FQ
☎ (01633) 547378 ⊕ tinyrebel.co.uk

⊛Established in 2012, Tiny Rebel moved to new, bespoke premises in 2017 having outgrown its previous site. Originally using a 12-barrel plant, the brewery now operates a dual-stream, 30-barrel plant, and consists of 23 fermentation tanks, and four conditioning tanks. It supplies its three tied pubs as well as numerous outlets across the UK. Beers are supplied in cask, keg, bottle and can, all packaging takes place in-house. ‼️🍺♦

Cwtch (ABV 4.6%) RED

Tiny Vessel

Unit 505, Platts Eyot, Hampton, TW12 2HF ☎ 07888 730210 ⊕ tinyvessel.co.uk

⊠ Tiny Vessel is a 1.5-barrel brewery established in 2016 on Platts Eyot, an island on the River Thames near Hampton. All beers are unfiltered and unfined, mostly available bottled or in keg, although at least one beer is usually available on cask in the Northumberland Arms, Brentford. LIVE

Dark Matter (ABV 4.5%) PORTER
Black porter, malty with chocolate and coffee notes. Malty finish with supporting hops and bitterness. Roasted, dry, bitter finish.

Tipples

Unit 3, The Mill, Wood Green, Salhouse, Norfolk, NR13 6NY
☎ (01603) 721310 ⊕ tipplesbrewery.com

⊠ Tipples was established in 2004 on a six-barrel brew plant. In addition to a full range of cask ales, an extensive range of bottled beers is produced, which can be found in some farmers markets and supermarkets in Norfolk. ♦LIVE

Bowline (ABV 3.8%) BITTER

Ginger (ABV 3.8%) SPECIALITY
A spicy aroma introduces this yellow-gold brew. Ginger dominates with supporting malty bitterness. Quick ginger nut finish.

Hanged Monk (ABV 3.8%) MILD
Strong roast and malt notes dominate the aroma and taste. A grainy mouthfeel with caramel and a growing vinous finish.

Longshore (ABV 3.8%) BITTER
A soft, peachy aroma and creamy mouthfeel. The initial fruity apricot flavour quickly subsides to a long, dry bitterness.

Sundown (ABV 3.9%) BITTER
Berries and malt introduce this smooth, creamy bitter. Bitterness gives depth to the fruity malt core as it slowly sweetens.

Aurous (ABV 4%) GOLD

Lady Evelyn (ABV 4.1%) BITTER
A crisp, hoppy aroma. Bitterness and hop throughout. Some malt and sweetness take the edge off a smoky finish.

Sea Lantern (ABV 4.1%) BITTER

Redhead (ABV 4.2%) BITTER
Malt and hops in both nose and palate. Toffee in the initial taste gives way to an increasing bitterness.

Lazy Summer (ABV 4.3%) SPECIALITY
Winter Moon (ABV 4.3%) BITTER
Malten Copper (ABV 4.4%) BITTER

Topper (ABV 4.5%) STOUT
Coffee and dark chocolate to the fore throughout. Just enough malt sweetness and bitterness to provide balance. Strong, big-hearted fiinish.

Brewers Progress (ABV 4.6%) BITTER
Solid and malty with strong caramel and vanilla support. Smooth and creamy with depth added by a bitter blackcurrant fruitiness.

Moonrocket (ABV 5%) BITTER
A complex golden brew. Malt, hop bitterness and a fruity sweetness swirl around in an ever-changing kaleidoscope of flavours.

Jack's Revenge (ABV 5.8%) BITTER
An explosion of malt, chocolate, roast and plum pudding. Full-bodied with a deep red hue and a strong solid finish.

Indian Hill (ABV 6.5%) STRONG
Black Moth (ABV 7.8%) STOUT

Tipsy Angel

See 4Ts

Tír Dhá Ghlas

🍽 Cullins Yard, 11 Cambridge Road, Dover, Kent, CT17 9BY
☎ (01304) 211666 ⊕ cullinsyard.co.uk

⊗ Brewing began in 2012 using a two-barrel plant. Beers are only available in the bar/restaurant and occasionally at the nearby Royal Cinque Ports Yacht Club.

Tirril SIBA

Red House, Long Marton, Cumbria, CA16 6BN
☎ (01768) 361846 ⊕ tirrilbrewery.uk

☺Established in 1999, Tirril Brewery has twice outgrown its premises. It delivers to more than 170 outlets, 100 of which regularly stock the beer. One pub is owned. Contract brewing is also carried out for Bitter End Brewery. ‼◆

Original Bitter (ABV 3.8%) BITTER
Ullswater Blonde (ABV 3.8%) BLOND
Grasmere Gold (ABV 3.9%) PALE
Kirkstone Gold (ABV 3.9%) GOLD
Old Faithful (ABV 4%) BITTER
Initially bitter, gold-coloured ale with an astringent finish.
1823 (ABV 4.1%) BITTER
Academy Ale (ABV 4.2%) BITTER
Borrowdale Bitter (ABV 4.2%) BITTER
Windermere IPA (ABV 4.3%) PALE
Red Barn Ale (ABV 4.4%) RED

Titanic SIBA

Callender Place, Burslem, Stoke-on-Trent, Staffordshire, ST6 1JL
☎ (01782) 823447 ⊕ titanicbrewery.co.uk

☺One of the earliest microbreweries, founded in 1985. Now owned by two local beer loving brothers, it has grown from a small, seven-barrel brewery, to producing over four million pints per year of its award-winning ales. With an expanding fleet of tied pubs and café bars, it also supply free trade customers in the Midlands, North West and further afield. Captain Smith, captain of the Titanic was born in Stoke on Trent, hence the name. ‼LIVE

Mild (ABV 3.5%) MILD
Fresh, fruity hop aroma leads to a caramel start then a rush of bitter hoppiness ending with a lingering, dry finish.
Steerage (ABV 3.8%) BITTER
Pale yellow bitter. Flavours start with hops and fruit but become zesty and refreshing in this light session beer with a long, dry finish.
Lifeboat (ABV 4%) BITTER
Dark brown with fruit, malt and caramel aromas. Sweet start, malty and caramel middle with hoppiness developing into a fruity and dry, lingering finish.
Anchor Bitter (ABV 4.1%) BITTER
Amber beer with a spicy hint to the fruity start that says go to the rush of hops for the dry, bitter finish.
Iceberg (ABV 4.1%) SPECIALITY
Yellow gold, sparkling, wheat beer with a flowery start leading to a great hop crescendo.
Cherry Dark (ABV 4.4%) SPECIALITY
Cappuccino Stout (ABV 4.5%) SPECIALITY
Black with a vanilla and strong coffee nose leading to a sweet taste again with strong coffee. Aftertaste is sweet.
Chocolate and Vanilla Stout (ABV 4.5%) SPECIALITY
Chocoholic paradise with real coffee and vanilla support. Cocoa, sherry and almonds lend depth to this creamy, drinkable 'Heaven in a glass' stout.
Stout (ABV 4.5%) STOUT

Roasty, toasty with tobacco, autumn bonfires, chocolate and hints of liquorice; perfectly balanced with a bitter, dry finish reminiscent of real coffee.
White Star (ABV 4.5%) BITTER
Hints of cinnamon apple pie are found before the hops take over to give a bitter edge to this well-balanced, refreshing, fruity beer.
Plum Porter (ABV 4.9%) SPECIALITY
Dark brown with a powerful fruity aroma. A sweet plum fruitiness gives way to a gentle bitter finish.
Captain Smith's Strong Ale (ABV 5.2%) BITTER
Red brown and full-bodied, lots of malt and roast with a hint of honey but a strong, bittersweet finish.

Titsey SIBA

Botley Hill Farmhouse, Limpsfield Road, Titsey, Surrey, CR6 9QH ☎ 07850 914189
⊕ titseybrewingco.com

⊗ A microbrewery established in 2017 on the Titsey Estate. It recently moved to larger premesis in a former nuclear bunker, still on the Titsey Estate, with a five-barrel plant, purchased through crowdfunding. It supplies two associated pubs, the Botley Hill Farmhouse and the White Bear at Fickleshole, and increasingly to other local outlets. Ales are named after historic owners of the Titsey Estate.

Gresham Hopper (ABV 3.7%) GOLD
Leveson Buck (ABV 3.7%) PALE
Gower Wolf (ABV 4%) BITTER

To The Moon

3 Woodcote Avenue, Bramhall, Stockport, SK7 3ND
☎ 07795 965053 ⊕ tothemoonbrewery.com

A nanobrewery capable of producing 6,000 litres per year, but currently operated part time by owner brewer. Concentrating on IPA or pale ale – all distributed in KeyKeg, mainly to microbars and the more adventurous pubs. Specialities produced for development with no guarantee they will be repeated.

Toll End

🍽 c/o Waggon and Horses, 131 Toll End Road, Tipton, West Midlands, DY4 0ET
☎ (0121) 502 6453 ☎ 07903 725574

The four-barrel brewery opened in 2004. With the exception of Phoebe's Ale, named after the brewer's daughter, all brews commemorate local landmarks, events and people. Nearly all of the brewery's output is sold in the Waggon & Horses. ‼LIVE

Tollgate SIBA

Unit 1, Southwood House Farm, Staunton Lane, Calke, Derbyshire, LE65 1RG
☎ (01283) 229194 ⊕ tollgatebrewery.co.uk

⊗ This six-barrel brewery was founded in 2005 on the site of the old Brunt & Bucknall Brewery in nearby Woodville, but relocated to new premises on the National Trust's Calke Park estate in 2012. Around 180 outlets are supplied direct, mainly in the north Midlands. The brewery operates three micropubs: Queens Road Tap, Leicester, Tap at No.76, Ashby-de-la-Zouch, and Town Street Tap, Duffield, plus a public bar on the premises, The Milking Parlour. ‼🍽◆LIVE V✦

Hackney Blonde (ABV 3.9%) SPECIALITY
Melbourne Bitter (ABV 4%) GOLD
California Steam (ABV 4.2%) SPECIALITY
Red Storm (ABV 4.2%) RED

THE BREWERIES

Duffield Amber (ABV 4.4%) BITTER
Ashby Pale (ABV 4.5%) PALE
Old Rasputin (ABV 4.5%) STOUT
Billy's Best Bitter (ABV 4.6%) BITTER
High Street Bitter (ABV 4.7%) BITTER
Spark IPA (ABV 5.6%) IPA

Tolly Cobbold

See Greene King

Tom Herrick's

See under H

Tom's Tap

4-6 Thomas Street, Crewe, Cheshire, CW1 2BD
☎ 07931 573425
⊕ tomstapandbrewhouse.wordpress.com

Tom's Tap & Brewhouse consists of three units; brewery equipment in the first, live music and special events in the middle (including meet the brewer events), and a taproom in the third (open to the public Thu-Sat). Beer is also distributed to four other outlets and local beer festivals. ‼ ◆

Tombstone

≋ 6 George Street, Great Yarmouth, Norfolk, NR30 4HU ☎ 07584 504444
⊕ tombstonebrewery.co.uk

⊠ Established in 2013, the brewery is run by former homebrewer Paul Hodgson. The original brewery backed onto the town cemetery, inspiring the name, but it has now relocated to the rear of its brewery tap, the Tombstone Saloon. Around 30 outlets are supplied around Norwich. ☞◆

Ale (ABV 3.7%) GOLD
Banana toffee aroma. Piquant, bitter, hoppy beginning softened by a biscuity maltiness. Dry, bitter finish.
Amarillo (ABV 3.8%) BITTER
Arizona (ABV 3.9%) BITTER
Malt and lemon nose. Initial lemongrass and sweet biscuit beginning quickly fades. Sweet, watery finish enhanced by malt.
Texas Jack (ABV 4%) BITTER
Toffee apple and vanilla aroma. Caramel leads the smooth, complex mix of flavours. A bittersweet fruitiness continues to the end.
Regulators (ABV 4.1%) GOLD
Gunslinger (ABV 4.3%) BITTER
Lone Rider (ABV 4.3%) OLD
Stagecoach (ABV 4.4%) OLD
A rich caramel and treacle aroma. Malt, roast and caramel dominate a hoppy, bittersweeet foundation. Short, increasingly dry finish.
Cherokee (ABV 4.5%) BITTER
Malty nose with plum and cherry. Initial mix of biscuit and roasty bitterness gently changes to a slightly spicy maltiness.
Santa Fe (ABV 5%) BITTER
Big Nose Kate (ABV 5.2%) BITTER
6 Shooter (ABV 6.6%) IPA
Stage Coach Reserve (ABV 8.5%) STRONG

Brewed for Brunning & Price Pub Co:
Blackfoot (ABV 4.8%) PORTER

Tomos a Lilford SIBA

Unit 11b, Vale Business Park, Llandow, Cowbridge, CF71 7PF

☎ (01446) 677757 ☎ 07747 858514

Office: 117 Boverton Road, Llantwit Major, CF61 1YA
✉ tomos.lilford@gmail.com

⊠ Tomos a Lilford was launched in 2013 by homebrewers Rolant Tomos, and brothers Rob and James Lilford. The brewery supplies pubs and clubs across the Vale of Glamorgan and further afield. All point of sale material is bilingual. ☞◆

Cob (ABV 4%) BITTER
Annwyl (ABV 5%) GOLD
Gaucho (ABV 5%) BITTER
O.P.A (ABV 5%) PALE
Rosemary Ale (ABV 5%) SPECIALITY
Hay (ABV 5.2%) PALE

Tonbridge SIBA

Unit 19, Branbridges Industrial Estate, East Peckham, Kent, TN12 5HF
☎ (01622) 871239 ⊕ tonbridgebrewery.co.uk

⊠ Tonbridge Brewery was launched in 2010 using a four-barrel plant, expanding to a 12-barrel one in 2013. It supplies pubs, clubs and restaurants throughout Kent, East Sussex and South-East London with a wide range of traditional and contemporary beers. While cask-conditioned beer remains its core focus, the brewery recently began bottling and canning, which has expanded its keg range. Tonbridge continue to use the live yeast which originated from the Barclay Perkins Brewery of Southwark. While the range has expanded to include beers hopped from Europe, North America and New Zealand, the majority of hops are still sourced in Kent. ◆

Golden Rule (ABV 3.5%) GOLD
Traditional Ale (ABV 3.6%) BITTER
Coppernob (ABV 3.8%) BITTER
Countryman (ABV 4%) BITTER
Rustic (ABV 4%) MILD
Blonde Ambition (ABV 4.2%) BLOND
Old Chestnut (ABV 4.4%) BITTER
American Pale (ABV 5%) PALE
Velvet Raven (ABV 5.2%) STOUT

Toolmakers SIBA

6-8 Botsford Street, Sheffield, South Yorkshire, S3 9PF
☎ 07956 235332 ⊕ toolmakersbrewery.com

Toolmakers is a family-run brewery established in 2013 in an old tool-making factory. The regular brews are supplemented by a varying range of different styles and strengths. Beers are based on a five-barrel plant. The function room at the brewery also doubles as the brewery taproom. The adjoining Forest pub is owned. ‼ ◆

Lynch Pin (ABV 4%) BITTER
Flange Noir (ABV 5.2%) STOUT

Tooth & Claw

See Camerons

Top-Notch

Haywards Heath, West Sussex, RH16 1UQ ☎ 07963 829368 ⊕ topnotchbrewing.co.uk

This 0.5-barrel brewery is situated in a converted residential outbuilding in Haywards Heath. LIVE

Hop Festival (ABV 3.9%) GOLD
Royal Fanfare (ABV 4.6%) BITTER

Top Out SIBA

Unit 3, 6b Dryden Road, Loanhead, EH20 9LZ
☎ (0131) 440 0270 ☎ 07742 234970
⊕ topoutbrewery.com

Brewing began in 2013 using a six-barrel plant. Branding has a topographical theme. A core range of eight beers is available, plus a changing 'First Ascents' range with an adventurous new style each time. ♦ LIVE V

Copperheid (ABV 3.4%) SPECIALITY
Refreshing, lightly-gingery beer.
Pale Ale (ABV 3.6%) PALE
Single hop pale ale. Same recipe but different hop each time.
Staple (ABV 4%) BITTER
Gold-coloured bitter. Intense hops but with malt coming through. Aroma has a hint of fruit. A lasting, dry finish.
Altbier (ABV 4.5%) BITTER
Based on a traditional German-style ale. Malty and fruity but with a certain amount of hop bitterness.
Schmankerl (ABV 4.9%) SPECIALITY
Simon Says-on (ABV 5.1%) SPECIALITY
Smoked Porter (ABV 5.6%) SPECIALITY
The Cone (ABV 6.8%) GOLD

Top Rope SIBA

Unit 6, Lipton Close, Liverpool, L20 8PU ☎ 07581 483075 ⊕ topropebrewing.com

Top Rope commenced brewing on a small scale on Merseyside in 2016 and expanded in 2018 moving to an industrial estate in North East Wales. Further expansion led to a return to Liverpool in early 2021. Output is keg, can and some cask with the beers often named on a wrestling theme. ‼

TOPS (The Olde Potting Shed)

Collingdon Buildings, Collingdon Road, High Spen, NE39 2EQ

TOPS began brewing in 2013 using a five-barrel plant with a small test kit for experimental beers. Pubs are supplied direct within a 30-mile radius of the brewery.

Blondie (ABV 3.8%) BLOND

Topsham

The Warehouse, Haven Road, Exeter, Devon, EX2 8GR

The brewery was established in 2018 and moved to its current location at the popular Exeter Quay in 2019, using a 3.5-barrel plant. The taproom, with an outside drinking area, is next to the brewery. There are frequent one-off brews normally available as keg, with some appearing as cask along with the regular and seasonal beers at the brewery tap. The regular beers are also available in the local free trade. ♦ 🎁

Ten (ABV 3.8%) BITTER
Ask Your Dad (ABV 4.3%)
Goat Walk (ABV 4.6%) PALE

Torrside

New Mills Marina, Hibbert Street, New Mills, Derbyshire, SK22 3JJ
☎ (01663) 745219 ☎ 07539 149175
⊕ torrside.co.uk

☺Established by three friends in 2015, Torrside brews a wide range of beers on a 10-barrel plant, under the tagline Hops, Smoke, Monsters. A changing line-up of largely hop-driven, smoked and strong beers are sold to pubs, bars and bottle shops within a 50-mile radius. All beers are unfined. Brewery tap events usually take place one weekend each month (April-September) and there's a smoked beer festival in early November. ‼ 🍴 LIVE V 🎁

Candlewick (ABV 4%) STOUT
Euro-Hop (ABV 4.5%) GOLD
West of the Sun (ABV 4.5%) GOLD
I am Curious Lemon (ABV 4.8%) SPECIALITY
Franconia (ABV 5.2%) SPECIALITY
I'm Spartacus (ABV 6.8%) IPA

Totally Brewed

Units 8 & 9, Meadow Lane Fruit & Veg Market, Clarke Road, Nottingham, NG2 3JJ ☎ 07702 800639
⊕ totallybrewed.com

⊠ Totally Brewed began brewing in 2014 using a seven-barrel plant previously used at White Dog Brewery. A diverse range of hop-forward beers are produced. ♦

Guardian of the Forest (ABV 3.8%) PALE
Slap in the Face (ABV 4%) BLOND
Golden-coloured ale with citrus fruit hop aroma and taste with a dry, bitter finish.
Crazy Like a Fox (ABV 4.5%) BITTER
Copper-coloured, malty best bitter with a caramel aroma and a gentle bitter finish.
Papa Jangle's Voodoo Stout (ABV 4.5%) SPECIALITY
Full-bodied dark stout oozing complex malt tastes throughout.
Punch in the Face (ABV 4.8%) PALE
Golden-coloured ale, assertive hop aroma leading to grapefruit and malt taste with a hoppy bitter finish.
Four Hopmen of the Apocalypse (ABV 5.2%) PALE
Immense big-hopped, fruity golden ale, moderate bitterness with a lasting hoppy finish.
Captain Hopbeard (ABV 5.5%) IPA
Amber-coloured ale with citrus hops aplenty with a strong bitter finish.

Totnes

🍴 59a High Street, Totnes, Devon, TQ9 5PB
☎ (01803) 849290 ☎ 07974 828971
⊕ thetotnesbrewingco.co.uk

⊠ Brewing began in 2014 at a family-run pub at the foot of Totnes Castle. The brewery is situated immediately behind the bar. An increase in the portfolio of the brewery has also meant a greater emphasis on keg and KeyKeg output. Beers are available almost exclusively at the pub. All ales are unfined and unfiltered. ♦

Towcester Mill SIBA

The Mill, Chantry Lane, Towcester, Northamptonshire, NN12 6AD
☎ (01327) 437060 ⊕ towcestermillbrewery.co.uk

⊠ A five-barrel brewery situated at the Grade-II listed Old Mill in Towcester. There is a brewery tap and beer garden on-site together with off-sale facilities. ‼ 🍴 ♦ 🎁

Old Mill Bitter (ABV 3.6%) BITTER
Crooked Hooker (ABV 3.8%) BITTER
Golden/amber colour with a honeyed fruit aroma, a slighlty earthy taste with some fruit and a bitter finish.
Mill Race (ABV 3.9%) BLOND
Slightly citrus aroma followed by a dry citrus taste with hints of grapefruit with a long bitter aftertaste.
Bell Ringer (ABV 4.4%) GOLD
Black Fire (ABV 5.2%) STOUT
Roman Road (ABV 5.2%) PALE
Tropical fruit aroma followed by a good balance of malt and hops with pineapple notes and a long bitter aftertaste.

Tower

Old Water Tower, Walsitch Maltings, Glensyl Way, Burton upon Trent, Staffordshire, DE14 1PZ
☎ (01283) 562888 ☎ 07771 926323
⊕ towerbrewery.co.uk

☺Tower was established in 2001 by John Mills, previously a brewer at Burton Bridge, in a converted derelict water tower, originally built for Thomas Salt'' Brewery in the 1870s. The conversion was given a Burton Civic Society award for the restoration of an industrial building. The premises incorporate a public bar (open Friday evenings only). Tower has around 20 regular outlets. ‼️☕♦️⚡

Salt's Burton Ale (ABV 3.5%) BITTER
Bitter (ABV 4.2%) BITTER
Gold-coloured with a malty, caramel and hoppy aroma. A full hop and fruit taste with the fruit lingering. A bitter and astringent finish.
Gone for a Burton (ABV 4.6%) BITTER
Imperial IPA (ABV 5%) PALE

Townes

🯄 **Speedwell Inn, Lowgates, Staveley, Chesterfield, Derbyshire, S43 3TT**
☎ (01246) 472252

Townes Brewery was started by Alan Wood in 1994 at an old ice cream factory and moved to its present site, the Speedwell Inn at Staveley, in 1997. The brewery and pub were taken over by Lawrie and Nicoleta Evans on Alan's retirement in 2013 who continue to use Alan's recipes at the five-barrel brewery. Townes beers are rarely found outside the pub, other than occasional swaps and at beer festivals.

Townhouse

Units 1-4, Townhouse Studios, Townhouse Farm, Alsager Road, Audley, Staffordshire, ST7 8JQ ☎ 07976 209437 ✉️ j.nixon2@btinternet.com

Townhouse was set up in 2002 with a 2.5-barrel plant. In 2004 the brewery scaled up to five barrels and in 2006 two further fermenting vessels were added. The bulk of its production can be found in the Potteries. ♦️

Enigma (ABV 3.5%) GOLD
Styrian Pale (ABV 3.5%) PALE
Rye Pale Ale (ABV 3.6%) SPECIALITY
Flowerdew (ABV 4%) BITTER
Golden with a wonderful floral aroma. Fabulous flavour of flowery hops delivering a crisp, hoppy bite and presenting a lingering taste of flowery citrus waves.
Meridian Mild (ABV 4%) MILD
Barney's Stout (ABV 4.5%) STOUT
Roast chocolate and toffee nose atop this black stout. Sweet start becoming bitter at the end, with velvety roast throughout.
Armstrong Ale (ABV 4.8%) BITTER
Gladstone Strong Ale (ABV 5%) BITTER

TQ

Unit 6 Kingswood Court, Long Meadow, South Brent, Devon, TQ10 9YS
☎ (01803) 364925 ⊕ tqbeerworks.com

TQ is a small, family-run brewery dedicated to bringing modern craft beer to Torbay and the surrounding area. A core range of five bottle-conditioned beers are available, plus a rolling programme of seasonal one-off brews. All beers are unfined, unfiltered and are vegan-friendly.
LIVE V

Track

5 Sheffield Street, Manchester, M1 2ND
☎ (0161) 273 4832 ☎ 07725 692096
⊕ trackbrewing.co

Track Brewing Co was established in 2014 and is based in a railway arch underneath Manchester's Piccadilly Railway Station. Since its inception the brewery has expanded considerably in size and now produces a wide variety of beer styles. A taproom opened in nearby Crusader Mill in 2018. ‼️V

Sonoma (ABV 3.8%) GOLD
Prominent fruit hop aroma. Balanced sweet fruity taste. Moderate bitterness at first with punchy citrus hop after. Unfined.

Tractor Shed SIBA

Tractor Shed, Calva Brow, Workington, Cumbria, CA14 1DB
☎ (01900) 68860 ⊕ tractor-shed.co.uk

☺Renamed from Mitchell Krause in 2014 and having previously had its beers brewed under contract, brewing started in an old tractor shed on the family farm in 2013. After initially focusing on bottled and kegged continental-style beers, the first cask-conditioned beer was produced in 2014. The brewery contract brews various beers for Shindigger (qv), mostly for bottle and keg. ‼️LIVE

Mowdy Pale Ale (ABV 3.9%) BITTER
An interesting, well-balanced beer with persistent fruitiness, sweet and hoppy centre giving way nicely to the hop in the finish.
Clocker Stout (ABV 4%) STOUT
Smooth, roasty stout, sweet middle. Short finish.

Trailhead (NEW)

Goldenlands Farm, Punchbowl Lane, Dorking, Surrey, RH5 4DX ⊕ trailheadbrew.com

Established in 2021 in farm buildings just south of Dorking. Beers are mostly available in keg, but may occasionally appear in cask. The taproom is open daily. ⚡

Traquair House SIBA

Traquair House, Innerleithen, EH44 6PW
☎ (01896) 830323 ⊕ traquair.co.uk/traquair-house-brewery

The 18th century brewhouse is based in one of the wings of the 1,000-year-old Traquair House, Scotland's oldest inhabited house. All the beers are oak-fermented and 60% of production is exported. ‼️☕♦️

Bear Ale (ABV 5%) BITTER
Malty aroma and a complex taste of malts, citrus fruit, sweetness and bitterness, all lasting into the aftertaste.

Treboom SIBA

Millstone Yard, Main Street, Shipton-by-Beningbrough, North Yorkshire, YO30 1AA
☎ (01904) 471569 ☎ 07761 608662
⊕ treboom.co.uk

Established in 2011 by scientist John Lewis and artist Jane Blackman, this 10-barrel brewery produces a range of core beers alongside monthly seasonal specials using water from its own borehole, whole hops and locally-malted barley. Green hops grown at the brewery are used in the autumn. The multi award-winning mix of contemporary and traditional beers are distributed throughout Yorkshire and via the online shop. ☕♦️LIVE

Tambourine Man (ABV 3.9%) GOLD
Yorkshire Sparkle (ABV 4%) PALE
Kettle Drum (ABV 4.3%) BITTER
Orions Belt (ABV 4.5%) STOUT
Hop Britannia (ABV 5%) PALE
Myricale (ABV 5%) SPECIALITY
Baron Saturday (ABV 5.2%) PORTER

Treen's

Unit 3, Viaduct Works, Frog Hill, Ponsanooth, Cornwall, TR3 7JW ☎ 07552 218788

Office: 18 St Michael's Road, Ponsanooth, TR3 7EA
⊕ treensbrewery.co.uk

⊗ This family-run brewery was founded in 2016, initially using spare capacity at another local brewery. It now has its own premises using a 12-barrel plant. Bottling was introduced in 2018. An additional 12-barrel fermentation vessel was acquired in 2021 to cope with increased demand. ♦

Essential (ABV 3.8%) PALE
Robustly bitter, golden pale ale with grassy, peppery hops and biscuit malt flavours. Citrus and stone fruit notes. Long, bitter finish.
Classic (ABV 4.3%) BITTER
Tawny bitter with malt aroma. Robust, malt balanced by spicy hop bitterness. Coffee, molasses with light summer and stone fruits.
Sunbeam (ABV 4.8%) PALE
Smooth, gold beer. Refreshing citrus, spicy hop and malt flavours with hints of fruits and caramel. Pronounced bitterness. Long, bitter finish.
Resolve (ABV 5.2%) STOUT
Dark brown, strong, sweet stout with dark chocolate aroma. Dominant smoky coffee, bitter chocolate, molasses flavours with malt and stone fruit.

Tremethick

Grampound, Cornwall, TR2 4QY ☎ 07726 427775
⊕ tremethick.co.uk

⊗ Tremethick began brewing in 2015, and are now well established as a small, village brewery with strong community support. Since a part-time brewer was recruited in 2018, other beers are increasingly being trialled. Brewery open evenings are popular with locals. ‼LIVE

Bitter (ABV 3.8%) BITTER
Amber bitter with bready malt and citrus hop aroma. Assertive malt is balanced by citrus hops with candied peel fruit.
Pale Ale (ABV 4.3%) PALE
Gold pale ale with light aroma. Dominant bitter grapefruit and grassy hops, underlying malt and fruit. Long, bitter, citrus finish.
Dark Ale (ABV 4.6%) MILD
Complex, dark brown ale. Nutty malt with kaleidoscope of fruit flavours. Quite sweet with hints of coffee-roast. Faintly bitter and hoppy.
Red IPA (ABV 4.6%) BITTER
Auburn bitter with light grapefruit and malt aroma. Grapefruit citrus flavour subordinated by bitterness and faint malt. Long bitter, dry finish.

Tring SIBA

Dunsley Farm, London Road, Tring, Hertfordshire, HP23 6HA
☎ (01442) 890721 ⊕ tringbrewery.co.uk

Founded in 1992, Tring Brewery moved to its present site in 2010. It brews more than 130 barrels a week, producing an extensive core range of beers augmented by monthly and seasonal specials, most taking their names from local myths and legends. ‼ ≢♦LIVE

Side Pocket for a Toad (ABV 3.6%) BITTER
Brock Bitter (ABV 3.7%) BITTER
Mansion Mild (ABV 3.7%) MILD
Citra Session (ABV 3.9%) PALE
Drop Bar Pale Ale (ABV 4%) PALE
Ridgeway (ABV 4%) BITTER
Moongazing (ABV 4.2%) BITTER
Pale Four (ABV 4.6%) GOLD
Tea Kettle Stout (ABV 4.7%) STOUT
Colley's Dog (ABV 5.2%) BITTER
Death or Glory (ABV 7.2%) BARLEY

Trinity (NEW)

Unit 4, The Shires, Essington Close, Lichfield, Staffordshire, WS14 9AZ ☎ 07886 809835
⊕ trinitybrewco.com

Set up in 2021, the name refers both to the three spires of Lichfield's cathedral and the three owners. An eight-barrel brew kit is used, along with a pilot plant for trial brews. A wide range of styles is produced, mainly for can and keg, but cask output is growing. Barrel-aged beers are planned. There is an on-site taproom, generally open at weekends. ✦

Triple fff SIBA

Magpie Works, Station Approach, Four Marks, Alton, Hampshire, GU34 5HN
☎ (01420) 561422 ⊕ triplefff.com

⊗ Established in 1997 close to a stop on the Watercress Line, the brewery and all the beers (except Alton's Pride) are named following a musical theme. The fff refers to fortissimo, meaning louder or stronger. Brewing on a 50-barrel plant since 2006, multiple CAMRA awards have been won. Two pubs are owned: the Railway Arms, Alton, and the Artillery Arms, Southsea. ‼ ≢♦LIVE

Alton's Pride (ABV 3.8%) BITTER
Full-bodied, brown session bitter. Initial maltiness fades as citrus notes and hoppiness take over, leading to lasting, hoppy, bitter finish.
Pressed Rat & Warthog (ABV 3.8%) MILD
Toffee aroma, hints of blackcurrant and chocolate lead to well-balanced flavour with roast, fruit and malt vying with hoppy bitterness.
Moondance (ABV 4.2%) PALE
An aromatic citrus hop nose, balanced by bitterness and sweetness in the mouth. Bitterness increases in finish as fruit declines.

Triple Goat

See Hornes

Triple Point SIBA

178 Shoreham Street, Sheffield, South Yorkshire, S1 4SQ ☎ 07828 131423 ⊕ triplepointbrewing.co.uk

Father and son operated, modern brewery and bar conversion, of what was formerly a carpet showroom. The brewery is clearly visible from the drinking area which operates as the taproom for the brewery. The taproom is open daily. Convenient for Bramall Lane football ground. ‼ ✦

Gold (ABV 4%) GOLD
S.IPA (ABV 4.5%) PALE

Debut (ABV 5.5%) IPA

Triumph

39 Hawthorn Lane, Tile Hill, Coventry, CV4 9LB
☎ 07903 131512 ✉ triumphbrewing@aol.com

Triumph is a nanobrewery offering brew days to the public who want to try homebrewing with professional standard equipment.

True North SIBA

47 Eldon Street, Sheffield, South Yorkshire, S1 4GY
☎ (0114) 272 0569

Office: 127-129 Devonshire Street, Sheffield, S3 7SB
⊕ truenorthbrewco.uk

True North began brewing in 2012 using spare capacity at Welbeck Abbey Brewery (qv). It opened its own plant in Sheffield in 2016. Dean Hollingworth is head brewer, supplying 11 pubs owned by the company plus other independent outlets.

Best Bitter (ABV 3.8%) BITTER
Blonde (ABV 4%) GOLD
Polaris (ABV 4.3%) BITTER

Truman's SIBA

New Queens Yard Brewery, Unit 14a, Queens Yard, White Post Lane, Hackney Wick, London, E9 5EN
☎ (020) 8533 3575

Office: 1 Priestley Way, Walthamstow, E17 6AL
⊕ trumansbeer.co.uk

A glorious name in the history of British brewing – at one time the greatest output of any brewery in the world! Once operating from 1666 to 1989, it was reborn in 2013 and has since flourished. In 2020 it moved into a new site in Hackney Wick in the former Crate brewery. Acknowledging its heritage, the brewery still uses the original Truman's yeast recovered from the National Collection of Yeast Cultures. ♦LIVE♦

Swift (ABV 3.9%) GOLD
Well-balanced, refreshing golden ale with citrus and sweet digestive biscuit on the palate and nose. Spicy, hoppy lingering finish.
Runner (ABV 4%) BITTER
Easy-drinking session bitter with spicy hoppy aroma and flavour, fading in the dry aftertaste. Marmalade fruit on the palate.
Zephyr (ABV 4.4%) PALE
Pale brown, smooth beer with a slightly dry roasted character on palate and bitterish finish. Touch of orange and hops.

Truth Hurts

c/o MSS City Mills, Peel Street, Morley, Leeds, West Yorkshire, LS27 8QL
☎ (0113) 238 0382 ☎ 07950 567341
⊕ truthhurts.co.uk

⊕Established in 2016 as Blue Square Brewery and rebranded as Truth Hurts in 2019. It produces one-off brews from its four-barrel plant in a split level building that is part of a mill complex. ⛟♦

Tryst

Lorne Road, Larbert, FK5 4AT
☎ (01324) 554 000 ⊕ trystbrewery.co.uk

The brewery started production in 2003. A large range of beers is available, in cask and bottle. Beers for Clockwork Beer Co are also produced. ‼⛟♦LIVE

Brockville Pale (ABV 3.9%) PALE
Hop Trial (ABV 3.9%) BITTER
Carronade Pale Ale (ABV 4.2%) PALE
Drovers 80/- (ABV 4.3%) OLD
Chocolate and Coconut Porter (ABV 4.4%) PORTER
Double Chocolate Porter (ABV 4.4%) SPECIALITY
Sherpa Porter (ABV 4.4%) PORTER
German Hops Pils (ABV 4.5%) SPECIALITY
V.I.P (ABV 4.5%) BITTER
RAJ IPA (ABV 5.5%) IPA

Tudor SIBA

Unit A, Llanhilleth Industrial Estate, Llanhilleth, NP13 2RX
☎ (01495) 214808 ☎ 07498 734896
⊕ tudorbrewery.co.uk

☺Tudor began brewing in 2007 in Abergavenny. The family who now own it acquired it in 2011 and moved it to Llanilleth in 2012. Several local pubs are supplied, in addition to others further afield. There is a bar and function room in the office suite above the brewery, for which it has recently acquired a full license (previously it was only for one-off events). It also started contract brewing during the pandemic. LIVE♦

Blorenge (ABV 3.8%) PALE
Black Mountain Stout (ABV 4%) STOUT
IPA (ABV 4%) PALE
Skirrid (ABV 4.2%) MILD
Super Hero (ABV 4.5%) PALE
Sugarloaf (ABV 4.7%) BITTER
Black Rock (ABV 5.6%) PORTER

Turk's Head (NEW)

⊟ Turk's Head, 202 High Street, Exeter, Devon, EX4 3EB
☎ (01392) 706013 ⊕ turksheadexeter.com

A historic public house, refurbished by City Pub Group during 2020/2021, brewing a range of up to five real ales. The range is expected to increase. ♦

Turning Point SIBA

Unit 3, Grimbald Park, Wetherby Road, Knaresborough, North Yorkshire, HG5 8LJ
☎ (01423) 869967 ⊕ turningpointbrewco.com

Two friends, Cameron Brown and Aron McMahon, began brewing in Kirkbymoorside in 2017, before relocating to the former Roosters brewery in Knaresborough in 2019. The expansion into the new brewery means a brew length over 40 hectolitres, with fermenting capacity of 340 hectolitres. All beers are unfined and unfiltered. A partnership with Fossgate Tap in York designates it as the brewery tap. ♦V♦

Wavelength (ABV 4.5%) GOLD
Lucid Dream (ABV 5%) SPECIALITY
Disco King (ABV 5.1%) PALE

Turnstone

The Old Post Office, Vicarage Road, Wingfield, Suffolk, IP21 5RB ☎ 07807 262662
✉ turnstoneales@outlook.com

⊠ Turnstone Ales is a small, home-based brewery set up in 2014 in Kent, which has now relocated to Suffolk. Beers are available from local farmers markets and local shops selling bottled local beers. LIVE

Turpin

Turpins Lodge, Lodge Farm, Tadmarton Heath Road, Hook Norton, Oxfordshire, OX15 5DQ
☎ (01608) 737033
✉ turpinbrewery@btconnect.com

⊗ Brewing started in 2013, with brewing capacity extended in 2019. A number of local pubs are supplied regularly, as well as a few pubs further afield in Oxford, Rugby and Birmingham. ♦

Golden Citrus (ABV 4.2%) GOLD

Turpin's SIBA

Unit 13b Sawston Trade Park, London Road, Pampisford, Cambridgeshire, CB22 3EE
☎ (01223) 833883 ● turpinsbrewery.co.uk

⊗ Turpin's is a vibrant, modern brewery based in Pampisford, near Cambridge, established in 2015 and brewing a wide variety of beers. The brewery hosts open days (see social media for details). ♦

Dragon's Den (ABV 3.9%) GOLD
Mozart (ABV 3.9%) GOLD
Single Hop Range (ABV 3.9%) GOLD
Mango Milkshake Pale Ale (ABV 4.3%) PALE
Meditation (ABV 4.3%) PALE
Cambridge Black (ABV 4.6%) STOUT
NAPA (ABV 5%) PALE
Celebration (ABV 5.5%) SPECIALITY

Twice Brewed SIBA

▤ Twice Brewed Inn, Bardon Mill, Hexham, NE47 7AN
☎ (01434) 344534 ● twicebrewedbrewhouse.co.uk

☺Brewing commenced on a five-barrel plant in 2017. Due to the close proximity of Hadrian's Wall, beer names have a Roman theme. Beers are available at the Twice Brewed Inn as well as other outlets. ‼️🍺♦V◢

Gallia (ABV 3.7%) GOLD
Best Bitter (ABV 3.8%) BITTER
Sycamore Gap (ABV 4.1%) PALE
Ale Caesar (ABV 4.2%) BITTER
Steel Rigg (ABV 4.9%) PORTER
Nox (ABV 5%) STOUT
Vindolanda Excavation IPA (ABV 5.3%) PALE

Twickenham SIBA

Unit 6, 18 Mereway Road, Twickenham, TW2 6RG
☎ (020) 8241 1825 ● twickenham-fine-ales.co.uk

⊗ Established in 2004, Twickenham Fine Ales is London's oldest, independent standalone brewery. Operating a 25-barrel plant, the styles are traditional with a modern twist and output is predominantly cask. It opens on match days for the rugby fans going to the nearby stadium. ‼️🍺♦◢

Grandstand Bitter (ABV 3.8%) BITTER
Sessionable, pale brown beer with peach, citrus, a little caramelised toffee and hop fading in the bitter, slightly dry finish.
Red Sky (ABV 4.1%) RED
Naked Ladies (ABV 4.4%) BLOND
Refreshing, dark golden ale with aromas and flavours of biscuit, stone fruit, pine and citrus. Long-lasting, slightly astringent, bitter finish.

Twin Taff

8 Jenkins Place, Twynrodyn, Merthyr Tydfil, CF47 0ND
☎ 07564 187945 ✉ twintaffbrewery@outlook.com

☺Twin Taff was established in 2018 by twin brothers Darryl and Daniel Williams. It is Merthyr Tydfil's first town centre microbrewery. Brewing is currently suspended.

Twisted SIBA

Unit 8, Commerce Business Centre, Commerce Close, Westbury, Wiltshire, BA13 4LS
☎ (01373) 864441 ● twisted-brewing.com

⊗ Twisted began brewing in 2014. It is an independent brewery producing traditional ales with a modern twist. ♦

Three & Sixpence (ABV 3.6%) PALE
Rider/Three Lions (ABV 4%) BITTER
Pirate (ABV 4.2%) BITTER
Urban Legend (ABV 4.3%) GOLD
Canteen Cowboy (ABV 4.5%) GOLD
Gaucho/Half Fly (ABV 4.6%) BITTER

Twisted Barrel

Unit 11, Fargo Village, Far Gosford Street, Coventry, CV1 5ED
☎ (024) 7610 1701 ● twistedbarrelale.co.uk

⊗ Founded in 2013 in a garage, the brewery moved in 2015 to Fargo Village, home to artisanal businesses and to arts and music events. It has since relocated to larger premises on the same site. With a capacity of 5,200 litres, and an on-site bar, the brewery hosts a variety of events and a dynamic homebrew club. Beers are distributed throughout the UK and abroad. A canning machine was purchased in 2021 giving greater flexibility. ‼️🍺◆LIVE V

Gotta Light (ABV 3%) PALE
Beast Of A Midlands Mild (ABV 3.5%) MILD
Pixel Juice (ABV 4%) GOLD
The Great Went (ABV 4%) SPECIALITY
Detroit Sour City (ABV 4.5%) SPECIALITY
God's Twisted Sister (ABV 4.5%) STOUT
Sine Qua Non (ABV 4.5%) IPA
Vurt (ABV 4.5%) PALE
Naido (ABV 5%) IPA
Kazan (ABV 5.5%) IPA
Lonely Souls (ABV 6.3%) SPECIALITY

Twisted Kettle

Deadman's Island, Donaghadee, County Down

An independent nanobrewery producing small-batch beers.

Twisted Magnolia

▤ Magnolia Belgian Beer Bar & Bistro, 33 Lake Road, Keswick, Cumbria, CA12 5DQ
☎ (017687) 44343 ● magnoliabarbistro.co.uk

Brewing began in 2019. This café bar produces a small, interesting range of beers.

Twisted Oak SIBA

Yeowood Farm, Iwood Lane, Wrington, BS40 5NU
☎ (01934) 310515 ● twistedoakbrewery.co.uk

⊗ Twisted Oak began brewing in 2012 using a five-barrel plant, crafting small batches of unique ales. It is situated in a former agricultural building on a working farm in the North Somerset countryside. Beer is available in several local outlets. ♦LIVE

Fallen Tree (ABV 3.8%) BITTER

Superb, bittersweet, session bitter. Aroma and flavour of hops and ripe fruit. Complex and satisfying bitter, astringent finish.

Crack Gold (ABV 4%) BITTER
Balanced golden ale. Hints of honey on the nose, flavours of malt biscuit and hops, and a short, hoppy ending.

Wild Wood (ABV 4%) BITTER
Little aroma. Very smooth, with flavours of hops and fruit and a little malt. Minimal aftertaste.

Crack Hops (ABV 4.2%) PALE
Hops on the nose, pale malt with fruity orange and grapefruit hints on the palate leaving a balanced, bittersweet aftertaste.

Old Barn (ABV 4.5%) RED
Fruity red ale. Well-balanced flavour with a very long, bitter finish.

Spun Gold (ABV 4.5%) GOLD
Classic golden ale with a soft mouthfeel. Spicy notes to the fruity malt aroma and flavour. Hops in the aroma develop into a bitter finish.

Leveret (ABV 4.6%) BITTER
Amber best bitter with light citrus aroma. Initial pale malt flavours combine with hoppy bitterness that lingers in the aftertaste.

Solstice (ABV 4.7%) BITTER
Sheriff Fatman (ABV 5%) GOLD
Amber-coloured ale with hops dominant on both the nose and the slightly citrus palate, also in the bitter finish.

Slippery Slope (ABV 5.3%) PORTER
Aromas of roast malt and coffee, flavours of black toffee and hints of dark fruits, rather dry and moreish ending.

Ghost Town (ABV 5.7%) STOUT

Twisted Wheel

Unit 11, Easter Court, Europa Boulevard, Warrington, Cheshire, WA5 7ZB
☎ (01925) 714019 ⊕ twistedwheelbrewco.co.uk

Twisted Wheel began brewing in 2020 using a 10-barrel brew plant. In late 2020 it moved from Standish to its new home in Warrington, adding a canning line within the new 20-barrel brewhouse. An extensive range of beer is available in can, keg and cask. All beers are unfined. ‼🍴♦V

Sunday Sessions (ABV 3.8%) PALE
Technicolour Beat (ABV 4.3%) PALE
Speed Wobble (ABV 4.7%) PALE
Hoodoo Voodoo (ABV 6.5%) IPA
Soul City (ABV 6.5%) IPA

Two Bob (NEW)

Correspondence: 10 Abbots Close, Datchworth, Hertfordshire, SG3 6TA ✉ twobobbrewco@gmail.com

Two Bob Brewing Co is a nanobrewery in North East Hertfordshire producing small batch hand crafted ales using traditional methods and natural ingredients.

Two by Two

Unit 28, Point Pleasant Industrial Estate, Wallsend, NE28 6HA ☎ 07723 959168

Office: 14 Albany Gardens, Whitley Bay, NE26 2DY ✉ twobytwobrewing@gmail.com

Brewing began in 2014 using a five-barrel plant in Wallsend on Tyneside. At the end of 2018 an additional five-barrel plant was installed, increasing capacity to 10 barrels. LIVE

Session IPA (ABV 4%) PALE

Leap Frog (ABV 4.1%) PALE
Foxtrot Pale (ABV 4.5%) PALE
Snake Eyes Pale (ABV 4.6%) PALE
Dragonfly (ABV 5.5%) IPA
Sitting Duck (ABV 5.7%) STOUT
American Pale Ale (ABV 5.8%) IPA
South Paw IPA (ABV 6.2%) IPA

Two Cocks

Church Lane, Enborne, Berkshire, RG20 0HB
☎ (01635) 37777 ⊕ twococksbrewery.com

⊗ Under the same ownership and sharing the same kit as Swamp Bog brewery (qv), Two Cocks was established in 2011, after wild hops were found growing in the farm's hedgerows. A 180-feet deep borehole supplies water for the brewery. During the English Civil War, the first Battle of Newbury (1643) was fought on the surrounding land and most of the beer names refer to it in some way.

Diamond Lil' (ABV 3.2%) GOLD
1643 Cavalier (ABV 3.8%) GOLD
1643 Leveller (ABV 3.8%) BITTER
1643 Musket Bitter (ABV 3.8%) PALE
1643 Roundhead (ABV 4.2%) BITTER
1643 Puritan (ABV 4.5%) STOUT
1643 Viscount (ABV 5.6%) BITTER

Two Rivers SIBA

2 Sluice Bank, Denver, Downham Market, Norfolk, PE38 0EQ
☎ (01366) 858365 ☎ 07518 099868
⊕ denverbrewery.co.uk

⊗ Two Rivers was established in 2012. Bottled-conditioned ales have been available since the establishment of the brewery and cask ales have been produced since 2013. It now has six established ales and one seasonal. Experimental brews are available on an ad-hoc basis. The brewery also brews three regular house ales for the Wellington, Feltwell, and will brew bottled or cask ale on commission. The Blackstone Engine Bar at Denver Windmill is the brewery tap. ‼🍴♦LIVE

Miners Mild (ABV 3.1%) MILD
Hares Hopping (ABV 4.1%) BITTER
Kiwi Kick (ABV 4.1%) GOLD
Denver Diamond (ABV 4.4%) BITTER
Porters Pride (ABV 5%) PORTER
Windmill Wheat (ABV 5%) SPECIALITY
Norfolk Stoat (ABV 5.8%) STOUT

Two Thirsty Men

The Brewery, Grantown on Spey, PH26 3EL
☎ (01479) 872246 ⊕ twothirstymen.com

Brewing began in 2016 in a garage at the back of a café bar.

Spey IPA (ABV 3.5%) PALE
No74 (ABV 4.5%) BITTER

Two Towers SIBA

29 Shadwell Street, Birmingham, B4 6HB
☎ (0121) 439 3738 ☎ 07795 247059
⊕ twotowersbrewery.co.uk

⊗ Established in 2010 on a site in the Jewellery Quarter, the 10-barrel brewery is located behind its taphouse, the Gunmakers Arms, and is visible from the beer garden. Frequent specials and bespoke beers supplement the core range. ‼🍴♦LIVE V

Baskerville Bitter (ABV 3.8%) BITTER
Hockley Gold (ABV 4.1%) GOLD
Complete Muppetry (ABV 4.3%) BITTER
Chamberlain Pale Ale (ABV 4.5%) PALE
Peaky Blinders Mild (ABV 4.5%) MILD
Jewellery Porter (ABV 5%) STOUT

Two Towns Down

c/o 36-40 Bellfield Street, Dundee, DD1 5HZ
⊕ twotownsdown.com

Two Towns Down is a brewing project founded in 2019 by Sandy McKelvie, formerly of Hanging Bat, Fallen and Black Isle breweries. Spare capacity is used at 71 Brewing (qv).

Two Tribes

Unit 4, Tileyard Studios, Tileyard Road, Barnsbury, London, N7 9AH
☎ (020) 3955 6782 ⊕ twotribes.co.uk

Brewing started in the old King's Brewery in Horsham in 2015, moving to the new London brewery north of King's Cross in 2018. It brews both on-site, and using third parties. The name is based on the idea of collaboration. Beers are sold around London, Horsham and Leeds as well as in its new taproom (adjacent) which offers outside drinking in shipping containers with camp fires and 'live-fire' food plus music events. No real ale. ☒♦

Twt Lol SIBA

Unit B27, Trefforest Industrial Estate, Pontypridd, CF37 5YB ☎ 07966 467295 ⊕ twtlol.com

Established in 2015 using a 10-barrel plant, the brewery has a capacity of 80 firkins a week, with the potential to expand to 160. All of its branding is produced in both Welsh and English. The brewery is now open on the first weekend of each month. ‼☒♦

Bwgan Brain / Scarecrow (ABV 3.5%) BITTER
Buwch Goch Gota / Little Red Cow (ABV 3.7%) RED
Glog (ABV 4%) BITTER
Twti Ffrwti (ABV 4%) GOLD
Cwrw'r Afr Serchog / Horny Goat Ale (ABV 4.2%) GOLD
Cymryd y Pyst (ABV 4.4%) BITTER
Lol! (ABV 4.4%) GOLD
Glo in the Dark (ABV 4.5%) PORTER
Blŵbri (ABV 4.6%) SPECIALITY
Pewin Ynfytyn / Crazy Peacock (ABV 4.8%) PALE
Pyncio Pioden IPA / Pretty Fly For A Magpie (ABV 5%) PALE
Dreigiau'r Diafol / Diablo Dragons (ABV 5.5%) IPA

Tydd Steam SIBA

Manor Barn, Kirkgate, Tydd Saint Giles, Cambridgeshire, PE13 5NE
☎ (01945) 871020 ☎ 07932 726552
⊕ tyddsteam.co.uk

☒ Established in 2007 in a converted agricultural barn, the brewery is named after two farm steam engines. A 15-barrel plant was installed in 2011. Around 70 outlets are supplied direct. ‼♦LIVE

Barn Ale (ABV 3.9%) BITTER
A golden bitter that has good biscuity malt aroma and flavour, balanced by spicy hops. Long, dry, fairly astringent finish.

Scoundrel (ABV 4%) BITTER

A dry, pale amber bitter with a gentle malty and hoppy aroma, plenty of hop bitterness with fruity hints in the taste and a persistent dry aftertaste.

Piston Bob (ABV 4.6%) BITTER
Amber bitter with malt and faint hop aroma, a malty flavour balanced by hops and fruit then a dry finish.

Tyne Bank SIBA

375 Walker Road, Newcastle upon Tyne, NE6 2AB
☎ (0191) 265 2828 ⊕ tynebankbrewery.co.uk

☒ The brewery, with its adjacent taproom, is now firmly established on the Newcastle real ale scene, and forms an important venue on the Ouseburn circuit. Beers are available in cask, keg, bottles and cans, with most being vegan-friendly. New beers are regularly produced. ‼☒♦V♦

Castle Gold (ABV 3.8%) GOLD
Summer Breeze (ABV 3.9%) SPECIALITY
West Coast IPA (ABV 4%) PALE
Monument Bitter (ABV 4.1%) BITTER
Northern Porter (ABV 4.5%) PORTER
Silver Dollar (ABV 4.9%) GOLD
Helix (ABV 5%) SPECIALITY
Cherry Stout (ABV 5.2%) SPECIALITY

Tyton

54 Bradshaw's Lane, Ainsdale, PR8 3LQ ☎ 07487 598787 ✉ tytonbrewing@gmail.com

Brewing began in 2018.

Uffa

⊟ White Lion Inn, Lower Street, Lower Ufford, Suffolk, IP13 6DW
☎ (01394) 460770 ⊕ uffabrewery.co.uk

Uffa began brewing in 2011 using a 2.5-barrel plant. It is situated next to the White Lion pub in a converted coach house. ♦

Ugly Lovely

See 3 Lamps

Uley

The Old Brewery, 31 The Street, Uley, Gloucestershire, GL11 5TB
☎ (01453) 860120 ⊕ uleybrewery.com

☒ Brewing at Uley began in 1833 as Price's brewery. After a long gap, the premises were restored and Uley Brewery opened in 1985. Now operating a 10-barrel plant, it uses its own spring water. Uley delivers to 40-50 outlets in the Cotswolds area. ☒♦

Uley Pale (ABV 3.8%) PALE
Bitter (ABV 4%) BITTER
A copper-coloured beer with hops and fruit in the aroma and a malty, fruity taste, underscored by a hoppy bitterness. The finish is dry, with a balance of hops and malt.

Old Ric (ABV 4.5%) BITTER
A full-flavoured, hoppy bitter with some fruitiness and a smooth, balanced finish. Distinctively copper-coloured, this is the house beer for the Old Spot Inn, Dursley.

Taverner (ABV 4.5%) BITTER
Old Spot Prize Strong Ale (ABV 5%) BITTER
A ruby ale with an initial strong malty sweetness that develops into a smooth dry malty finish. A beer that is deceptively easy to drink.

Pig's Ear Strong Beer (ABV 5%) PALE

A golden pale ale with an initial refreshing taste with a hint of fruitiness that develops into a light malty finish. A smooth, quaffable, strong ale.

Ulverston

Lightburn Road, Ulverston, Cumbria, LA12 0AU
☎ (01229) 586870 ☎ 07840 192022
⊕ ulverstonbrewingcompany.co.uk

⊛The brewery occupies the octagonal bullring of the old livestock market. There is a bar that overlooks the brew-plant, which opens by prior arrangement and during some local festivals. Some beers have a Laurel and Hardy theme: Stan Laurel was born in Ulverston. ‼☰♦⌀

Flying Elephants (ABV 3.7%) PALE
Clean, refreshing, yellow bitter, sweet and fruity with a dry, citrus finish.
Celebration Ale (ABV 3.9%) PALE
Yellow fruity bitter with hints of tangerine and a notably sustained, dry finish.
Harvest Moon (ABV 3.9%) BLOND
A well-balanced, pale, hoppy bitter.
Laughing Gravy (ABV 4%) BITTER
Smooth and grainy brown bitter with a good mix of flavours.
Lonesome Pine (ABV 4.2%) BLOND
A fresh and fruity pale gold beer; honeyed, lemony and resiny with an increasingly bitter finish.
Fra Diavolo (ABV 4.3%) MILD

Unbarred

Elder Place, Brighton, East Sussex, BN1 4GF ☎ 07850 070471

Office: 33 Bolsover Road, Hove, BN3 5HQ
⊕ unbarredbrewery.com

⊗ UnBarred was born and bred in Brighton and Hove, established in 2014 in the shed of founder and head brewer, Jordan. It now has a brewery and taproom in central Brighton. Beers are brewed with creativity and passion, with the brewery best known for its NEIPA's and stout styles. LIVE ♦

Unbound (NEW) SIBA

Lenches Road, Colne, BB8 8EU ☎ 07886 062825
⊕ unboundbrew.co.uk

Brewing commenced early 2021.

Unity SIBA

23-27 Princes Street, Northam, Southampton, SO14 5RP
☎ (023) 8178 2627 ⊕ unitybrewingco.com

Founded in 2016, Unity Brewing Co produces beers influenced by Belgian and North East American styles, using traditional techniques and modern ingredients. Output is mainly keg or cans with occasional special releases in cask. In 2019 it expanded and moved into a brand new, crowd-funded, 12-barrel brewery with a modern taproom on-site. ☰♦

Unsworth's Yard SIBA

4 Unsworth's Yard, Ford Road, Cartmel, Cumbria, LA11 6PG ☎ 07810 461313 ⊕ unsworthsyard.co.uk

⊛Unsworth's Yard opened in 2011, brewing on a five-barrel plant. The brewery produces beers named after historic figures and legends associated with the Cartmel area. Beers are available in Cartmel pubs and other local outlets as well as the brewery's tap bar. ‼☰♦

Peninsula Best (ABV 3.8%) BITTER
Crusader Gold (ABV 4.1%) GOLD
Eel River IPA (ABV 4.3%) PALE
Sir Edgar Harrington's Last Wolf (ABV 4.5%) BROWN
Well-balanced, rich, fruity, tawny ale with gentle bitterness.
The Flookburgh Cockler (ABV 5.5%) PORTER

Untapped

Unit 6, Little Castle Farm Business Park, Raglan, NP15 2BX
☎ (01291) 690074 ⊕ untappedbrew.com

Established in 2009, 2013 saw Untapped move to its current premises. It has a regular range of filtered beers and (except for 'Triple S') all are vegan-friendly. ‼☰♦LIVE V

Border Bitter (ABV 3.8%) BITTER
Sundown (ABV 4%) GOLD
Monnow (ABV 4.2%) BITTER
Whoosh (ABV 4.2%) BITTER
Diolch (ABV 4.4%) PALE
UPA (ABV 4.5%) PALE
Triple S (ABV 4.9%) STOUT
Crystal (ABV 6%) SPECIALITY

Up Front

Office: 1 / 1, 27 Skirving Street, Glasgow, G41 3AB
☎ 07526 088973 ⊕ upfrontbrewing.com

Founded in 2015 by former homebrewer Jake Griffin, Up Front is a gypsy brewery primarily using spare capacity at Overtone Brewing Co (qv), plus that at other local breweries. Predominantly producing canned beers and speciality bottles, cask-conditioned beers are available on rare occasions.

Up the Creek

☰ Up the Creek Comedy Club, 302 Creek Road, Greenwich, London, SE10 9SW
☎ (020) 8858 4581 ⊕ up-the-creek-brewery.co.uk

Brewing began in 2018 as Greenwich Brewery, using a three-barrel plant and is situated in the front part of the bar area of the Up the Creek Comedy Club. Beers are available in the bar. Please note that entrance may be restricted to ticket holders for some events in the club area.

Uprising

See Windsor & Eton

Urban Alchemy

York Road, New Barnet, EN5 1LJ ☎ 07894 452263
⊕ urban-alchemy-brewing.co.uk

⊗ Urban Alchemy started brewing commercially in 2019 and was established by a group of friends with years of brewing experience between them. A bespoke three-barrel plant is used. Beers are supplied to local pubs and beer festivals and are suitable for vegans. Bottle-conditioned beers are available for delivery locally or nationally. LIVE V

Fat Labrador (ABV 5.2%) SPECIALITY
Crumbling Ghost (ABV 5.4%) BITTER
Elephants Graveyard (ABV 6.7%) STOUT

Urban Chicken

Ilkeston, Derbyshire, DE7 5EH ☎ 07976 913395
⊕ urbanchickenale.co.uk

One-barrel brewery producing small batches of beer for local pubs, restaurants, bottle shops and beer festivals. Registered as a commercial brewery in 2016. Cask and bottle, unfined.

Mad Van Mild (ABV 4.2%) MILD
Rooster Juice (ABV 4.3%) PALE
Earthquake (ABV 5.6%) STOUT
Insane in the Henbrain (ABV 5.9%) GOLD
Chick Weed Revenge (ABV 6.3%) IPA
Pit Pony Plus (ABV 6.5%) STOUT

Urban Island SIBA

Unit 28, Limberline Industrial Estate, Limberline Spur, Portsmouth, Hampshire, PO3 5DZ
☎ (023) 9266 8726 ⊕ urbanislandbrewing.uk

⊠ Urban Island began production in 2015 and now has a capacity of 10 barrels. The range is distributed throughout Hampshire and neighbouring counties. Some of the range is available in cans and KeyKeg. Canned beers can be ordered online and delivered nationwide. ‼▰V◆

Urban Pale (ABV 3.8%) GOLD
An unfined, yellow ale an aroma of orange and pink grapefruit, leading to a robust, hoppy taste and softer finish.
Mosaic (ABV 4%) GOLD
Great use of Mosaic hops. Dry and hoppy with pronounced citrus and grapefruit flavours throughout and a refreshing, bitter finish.
Ammo (ABV 4.5%) GOLD
DSB (Dolly's Special Beer) (ABV 4.6%) BITTER
A well-balanced refreshing bitter, with hints of strawberry and some bitterness in the finish.
Porter 28 (ABV 5%) PORTER
Dark berry aromas build into a roast chocolatey flavour and pleasing tartness in the mouth, and a dry, bitter finish.
High & Dry (ABV 5.5%) IPA
Urban Graffiti (ABV 6%) IPA
A cross between stout and Black IPA. Bursting with flavour throughout from chocolate malt to hops and plums to oranges.

Utopian SIBA

Unit 4, Clannaborough Business Units, Bow, Crediton, EX17 6DA
☎ (01392) 769765 ⊕ utopianbrewing.com

Utopian began brewing in 2019 producing craft lagers. No real ale.

Uttoxeter SIBA

26b Carter Street, Uttoxeter, Staffordshire, ST14 8EU
☎ 07734 392321 ⊕ uttoxeterbrewingcompany.com

Established in 2016, The Uttoxeter Brewing Company is a microbrewery producing hand-crafted real ales. A combination of passion, knowledge and hard work produces ales demonstrating distinctive aromas and delicious flavours, exploiting the famous Burton-Upon-Trent hard water. ▰◆

Bunting's Blonde (ABV 3.7%) BLOND
Dark Horse Mild (ABV 3.7%) MILD
Ground Breaker (ABV 4%) GOLD
? (Question Mark) (ABV 4.5%) PALE
Admiral Gardner (ABV 4.5%) GOLD

Dr Johnson's Contrafibularity (ABV 4.5%) PALE
Earthmover (ABV 4.5%) GOLD
Final Furlong (ABV 4.5%) BITTER
Sargeant's Special Ale (ABV 4.6%) PALE
Chinook (ABV 4.7%) PALE
Earthmover Gold (ABV 4.7%) PALE
Full Gallop (ABV 4.7%) BROWN
Paddock Porter (ABV 4.8%) PORTER
Uxonian (ABV 4.9%) BITTER
American IPA (ABV 5.2%) PALE
Yogi Beer (ABV 6.1%) IPA

Vaguely

15 Lune Way, Bingham, Nottinghamshire, NG13 8YX
☎ 07969 137248 ⊕ vaguelybrewing.co.uk

⊠ Vaguely Brewing launched as a commercial nanobrewery in 2019 following four years of homebrewing and recipe development. It produces vaguely traditional beers that are naturally-conditioned, unfiltered and unfined. LIVE V

Bitter (ABV 4.2%) BITTER
Hazy (ABV 4.5%) PALE
Porter (ABV 4.7%) STOUT
Pale Ale (ABV 6%) IPA

Vale SIBA

Tramway Business Park, Ludgershall Road, Brill, Buckinghamshire, HP18 9TY
☎ (01844) 239237 ⊕ valebrewery.co.uk

⊠ Established in 1995 and initially based in Haddenham, Vale moved to Brill in 2007. In 2010 it expanded to a 20-barrel brew plant. Three pubs are owned, including the Hop Pole, where sister brewery the Aylesbury Brewhouse operated from 2011 to 2019. When it closed, brewing moved back to Vale. ‼▰◆LIVE

Brill Gold (ABV 3.5%) GOLD
Best IPA (ABV 3.7%) BITTER
This pale amber beer starts with a slight fruit aroma. This leads to a clean, bitter taste where hops and fruit dominate. The finish is long and bitter with a slight hop note.
Black Swan Mild (ABV 3.9%) MILD
Wychert Ale (ABV 3.9%) BITTER
VPA (Vale Pale Ale) (ABV 4.2%) PALE
Red Kite (ABV 4.3%) BITTER
Black Beauty Porter (ABV 4.4%) PORTER
A very dark ale, the initial aroma is malty. Roast malt dominates initially and is followed by a rich fruitiness, with some sweetness. The finish is increasingly hoppy and dry.
Gravitas (ABV 4.8%) PALE

Vault City SIBA

Unit 2, A1 Industrial Park, Sir Harry Lauder Road, Edinburgh, EH15 2QA ⊕ vaultcity.co.uk

Launched as a kitchen brewery in Edinburgh in 2018, Vault City Brewing relocated to share facilities at 71 Brewing in Dundee in 2019 before moving back to Edinburgh. Making fruit-forward, modern sour beers, the monthly Farm to Fermenter series utilises local fruits. Available in bottles and kegs.

Vaux (NEW)

Unit 2, Monk Street, Sunderland, SR6 0DB
☎ (0191) 580 5770 ⊕ vaux.beer

Vaux Brewery is a name synonymous with life in Sunderland, since first launching in 1837, right up until its closure in 1999. In 2019, plans were made to relaunch the brewery, and following contract brewing at breweries in the North East it moved into its own premises in Sunderland. 🍺◆

Vendetta

28 Usk Road, Aveley, South Ockendon, Essex, RM15 4PB ✉ info@vendettabrewing.co.uk

Established in 2017, this microbrewery uses both traditional and modern brewing methods.

Mild (ABV 3.8%) MILD
Gold (ABV 4%) GOLD
Best Bitter (ABV 4.2%) BITTER
Session IPA (ABV 4.5%) PALE

Ventile (NEW)

Unit 4, Spur Mill, Broadstone Hall Road South, Stockport, SK5 7BY ⊕ ventilebrew.co

Ventile Brew Co began brewing in 2021 and is a modern small-batch microbrewery.

Verdant

Unit 30, Parkengue, Kernick Road, Penryn, Cornwall, TR10 9EP
☎ (01326) 619117 ⊕ verdantbrewing.co

Brewery established by keen homebrewers in 2014. It moved to new premises in 2020 with the aid of crowdfunding, and upgraded from a 10-barrel to a new 20-barrel plant. No real ale.

Verse (NEW)

⬢ 1a Piccadilly Place, London Road, Bath, BA1 6PL
☎ (01225) 446195

Verse Brewing began production in 2021 and is based in the Chapter One pub. 🍺

Veterans

Unit 0, Dundyvan Enterprise Park, Dundyvan Way, Coatbridge, ML5 4AQ
☎ (01236) 425281

South East: 35 Carden Hill, Brighton, East Sussex, BN1 8AA ⊕ veteransbrewing.uk

Established on Armistice Day 2014, Veterans Brewing is owned and run by, and supporting veterans. Initially based only in Scotland, a second depot was launched in Brighton in 2018, with its beers contract brewed at Franklins (qv).

Vibrant Forest

The Purlieu Centre, Units 3-6, Hardley Industrial Estate, Hardley, Hampshire, SO45 3NQ
☎ (023) 8200 2200 ☎ 07921 753109
⊕ vibrantforest.co.uk

⊗ Vibrant Forest Brewery began commercial brewing in 2011 as a one-barrel plant. This gradually increased to 10 barrels over the next five years at Lymington. It relocated to a four unit brewery at Hardley and increased in size to a 12-barrel plant, with its own canning machine, plus taproom. ‼🍺◆V◆

Summerlands (ABV 3.5%) PALE
PUPA (ABV 4.5%) PALE
Farmhouse (ABV 5%) SPECIALITY
Single Hop Pale Ale (ABV 5%) PALE
Kick-Start (ABV 5.7%) SPECIALITY

Metropolis (ABV 6%) IPA
Intense, resinous hoppiness dominate this Black IPA. Complex, with chocolate notes and tropical fruits lead to a dry, hoppy finish.
Kaleidoscope (ABV 6.5%) IPA
Umbral Abyss (ABV 8.8%) SPECIALITY

Victoria Inn

⬢ Victoria Inn, Roch, Haverfordwest, SA62 6AW
☎ (01437) 710426 ☎ 07814 684975
⊕ thevictoriainnroch.com

⊗ A small brewery on the site of the Victoria Inn, which also offers B&B. ‼◆V

Village Brewer

See Hambleton

Village Brewer: Brew 22

⬢ 22 Coniscliffe Road, Darlington, DL3 7RG
☎ (01325) 354590 ⊕ villagebrewer.co.uk

⊚One-barrel microbrewery, established in 2013, which has been brewing on a regular basis since 2015. The plant is also used to produce the malt wash for the distilling of gin and vodka on-site. The beer strength and style varies from brew to brew.

Villages

21-22 Resolution Way, Deptford, London, SE8 4NT
☎ (020) 3489 1143 ⊕ villagesbrewery.com

Established in 2016 by brothers Archie and Louis Village. Predominantly keg and canned beers available, although some cask may be available. 🍺◆

Vine

⬢ Vine, 27-29 High Street, Tarring, Worthing, West Sussex, BN14 7NN
☎ (01903) 201121 ✉ thevinepub@hotmail.com

⊗ Brewery established in 2018 in the barn at the rear of the Vine pub. Beer is brewed monthly and sold exclusively at the pub.

Vine Inn

⬢ Vine Inn & Brewery, Sheep Fair, Rugeley, Staffordshire, WS15 2AT
☎ (01889) 574443 ✉ oli@thevinebrewery.com

⊗ The Vine Brewery is based in Rugeley, within the Vine Inn public house, parts of which date back to the 16th century. The brewery's beers can be found in a number of pubs in the Cannock Chase area.

Vittles

Hull Trinity Market, Trinity House Lane, Hull, East Yorkshire, HU1 2JH ☎ 07598 098632
⊕ vittlesandcompany.co.uk

Vittles & Co started brewing in 2018 at the Trinity Market, Hull. The site can produce just 50 litres at a time. The brewery name comes from the fact that the owner loves to pair beer and food, hence the old name for food, vittles. 🍺

Vocation

Unit 8, Craggs Country Business Park, New Road, Cragg Vale, Hebden Bridge, West Yorkshire, HX7 5TT
☎ (01422) 410810 ⊕ vocationbrewery.com

Ⓥ Vocation began brewing in 2015 and is located high above Hebden Bridge. Brewing capacity continues to increase at pace as it expands UK and Worldwide markets with a wide range of beer styles. This includes barrel-aged and a single hop series, as well as collaboration brews. It has local bars in Hebden Bridge called Vocation & Co, and Assembly Underground in Leeds. 🍺♦V

Bread & Butter (ABV 3.9%) GOLD
A feast of floral hops with citrus aroma and taste. Robust bitter aftertaste.

Heart & Soul (ABV 4.5%) GOLD
A golden ale with a strong citrus aroma. Hops dominate taste and aftertaste.

Pride & Joy (ABV 5.3%) PALE
Flavoursome IPA packed with citrus hoppiness. A hint of sweetness gives way to a mellow aftertaste.

Naughty & Nice (ABV 5.9%) STOUT

Life & Death (ABV 6.5%) IPA

VOG

Unit 8a, Atlantic Trading Estate, Barry, CF63 3RF
☎ (01446) 730757 ⊕ vogbrewery.co.uk

Ⓥ Created in 2005, the founders handed over the reins to a new team in 2015 who rebranded the brewery and refreshed the beer range. VOG's beers can be found frequently in a number of South Wales pubs, as well as occasionally throughout the country thanks to the brewery's beer swaps. The brewery has recently opened two taphouse outlets and has six associated gastropubs. ♦LIVE

Paradigm Shift (ABV 4.2%) BITTER
South Island (ABV 4.2%) PALE
Dark Matter (ABV 4.4%) SPECIALITY
Speak Easy IPA (ABV 4.6%) PALE
Lady Liberty (ABV 4.8%) PALE

Volden SIBA

77 Malham Road, Forest Hill, London, SE23 1AH
☎ (020) 8684 4492 ⊕ volden.co.uk

⊗ Volden produce cask beer for the Antic pub group. Originally taking over the Clarence & Fredericks brewery in Croydon in 2015, a new brewery was installed in Forest Hill in 2020. The two core beers are supplemented by seasonally-named specials along with a clutch of football-focused pales. ♦

Session Ale (ABV 3.8%) BITTER
Amber bitter with caramel malt and orange aroma. Fruit, hops and sweetish, malty biscuit fading to a bitter, dryish finish.

Pale Ale (ABV 4.6%) GOLD
Gold beer with floral hop flavour with slight hint of fresh orange peel and biscuit, becoming more bitter on drinking.

Volunteer Tavern (NEW)

🏠 9 New Street, Old Market, Bristol, BS2 9DX
☎ (0117) 955 8498 ⊕ volunteertavern.co.uk

Brewing commenced in 2020 in a shipping container located in the garden of the Volunteer Tavern, a 17th century pub tucked away in a quiet street. Two ales are regularly available in the pub. ♦V

Wadworth SIBA IFBB

Northgate Brewery,, Devizes, Wiltshire, SN10 1JW
☎ (01380) 723361 ⊕ wadworth.co.uk

⊗ Established in 1875 by Henry Alfred Wadworth, this impressive, family-owned brewery has a modern brewhouse and a microbrewery, which enables it to create unique, small batch beers. Its traditional horse-drawn drays deliver beer daily around Devizes. Wadworth has more than 150 pubs in the South-West of England. ‼🍺♦LIVE✦

Henry's IPA (ABV 3.6%) BITTER
Horizon (ABV 4%) BITTER
6X (ABV 4.1%) BITTER
Copper-coloured ale with a malty and fruity nose, and some balancing hop character. The flavour is similar, with some bitterness and a lingering malty, but bitter finish.

Swordfish (ABV 5%) SPECIALITY

Wagtail

New Barn Farm, Wilby Warrens, Old Buckenham, Norfolk, NR17 1PF
☎ (01953) 887133 ⊕ wagtailbrewery.com

Wagtail Brewery went into full-time production in 2006. All beers are only available bottle-conditioned. This is a chemical-free brewery. No chemicals are on-site and all cleaning is done with hot water and 'elbow grease'. LIVE

Walled City

🏠 70 Ebrington Square, Londonderry, BT47 6FA
☎ (028) 7134 3336 ⊕ walledcitybrewery.com

Restaurant-based brewery established in Derry in 2015. Beers are brewed on-site, and a member of staff is usually happy to show you around.

Izaac Walton

Whitehouse Farm, Cold Norton, Staffordshire, ST15 0NS
☎ (01785) 760780 ☎ 07496 097883
✉ steve@iwbrewhouse.co.uk

Brewing began in 2017.

Grayling (ABV 3.9%) PALE
Rainbow Trout (ABV 4.2%) MILD
Gudgeon (ABV 4.5%) BITTER
King Carp (ABV 4.8%) PALE
Gentle gold beer. Gentle hoppy taste but deceptively strong.

Pike (ABV 6%) MILD

Wander Beyond

98 North Western Street, Manchester, M12 6JL
☎ (0161) 661 3676 ⊕ wanderbeyondbrewing.com

Wander Beyond launched in 2017 in a railway arch under Piccadilly Station. The range of beer available can vary, each beer is brewed for only a short period so the range is constantly changing. Styles and ingredients are unusual and sometimes unique. 🍺V✦

Peak (ABV 3.8%) PALE

Wanderlust

See Magpie

Wantsum SIBA

Kent Barn, St Nicholas Court Farm, Court Road, St Nicholas at Wade, Kent, CT7 0PT
☎ (01227) 910135 ⊕ wantsumbrewery.co.uk

⊗ Wantsum Brewery, established by James Sandy in 2009, takes its name from the nearby Wantsum Channel. Located in St Nicholas at Wade just outside Canterbury. Wantsum brews a wide range of traditional and modern craft ale styles packaged in cask, keg, minikegs, polypins, bottles and cans, supplied to outlets throughout the south of England. An on-site taproom/shop showcases a wide selection of the beers. It has an online shop which ships nationwide. ‼️☞♦LIVE ✦

More's Head (ABV 3.7%) SPECIALITY
Ruby golden brown beer with fruity American hops and rye.
1381 (ABV 3.8%) PALE
Black Prince (ABV 3.9%) MILD
Imperium (ABV 4%) BITTER
Montgomery (ABV 4%) PALE
An amber-coloured, light, easy, summer session beer with American hops that are light and refreshing. Spicy finish.
Hurricane (ABV 4.1%) GOLD
One Hop (ABV 4.2%) GOLD
Dynamo (ABV 4.3%) GOLD
Turbulent Priest (ABV 4.4%) BROWN
Fortitude (ABV 4.6%) BITTER
Black Pig (ABV 4.8%) PORTER
Black porter with a sweet aroma. The flavour is of sweet malt, roasty chocolate and fruit that fade in the finish.
Golgotha (ABV 5.5%) STOUT
Smooth, rich, dry, roasty stout with dark fruits and malt throughout.
Ravening Wolf (ABV 5.9%) SPECIALITY

Ward & Houldsworth

Office: 62 Drakehouse Lane West, Beighton, South Yorkshire, S20 1FX ☎ 07912 028880 ⊕ ifinfused.com

Former Kelham Island brewer Paul Ward together with Darren Houldsworth established the company in 2019. Beers are contract brewed at Pheasantry (qv) and distributed from storage in Sheffield.

Warwickshire SIBA

Bakehouse Brewery, Queen Street, Cubbington, Leamington Spa, Warwickshire, CV32 7NA ☎ (01926) 450747 ⊕ warwickshirebeer.co.uk

A six-barrel brewery in a former village bakery which has been in operation since 1998. Bottled beers are available from local farm shops, garden centres, wine specialists and supermarkets, as well as from the brewery direct and its four pubs. More unusual craft beers are available under the Bakehouse Brewery brand name. ☞♦LIVE

SPA (Spa Pale Ale) (ABV 3.8%) PALE
Darling Buds (ABV 4%) PALE
Duck Soup (ABV 4.2%) BITTER
Lady Godiva (ABV 4.2%) GOLD
Yer Bard (ABV 4.3%) BITTER

Brewed under the Bakehouse Brewery name:
Liquid Bread (ABV 4.5%) GOLD

Wash House

See Allanwater

Wasted Degrees

Unit 11, Sawmill Yard, Blair Atholl, PH18 5TL ⊕ wasteddegrees.com

Leaving the degrees and day jobs behind, Wasted Degrees began small-batch brewing commercially in 2017 before expanding to a 1000-litre brewhouse in Blair Atholl in 2019. A barrel-ageing programme was established in 2018. ‼️☞✦

Watermill

See Windermere

Tomos Watkin SIBA

Unit 3, Alberto Road, Century Park, Valley Way, Swansea Enterprise Park, Swansea, SA6 8RP ☎ (01792) 797280 ⊕ tomoswatkin.com

⊛Brewing began in 1995, originally in Llandeilo behind the Castle Hotel. The brewery moved to Swansea in 2000 and was taken over by Hurns Mineral Water Company in 2002. More than 60% of production is bottled beer (not bottle-conditioned). ‼️☞♦✦

Delilah (ABV 4%) GOLD
Swansea Jack (ABV 4%) GOLD
OSB (Old Style Bitter) (ABV 4.5%) BITTER
Amber-coloured with an inviting aroma of hops and malt. Full-bodied; hops, fruit, malt and bitterness combine to give a balanced flavour continuing into the finish.
IPA (ABV 4.8%) PALE
Pecker Wrecker (ABV 5%) BITTER

Watson's

Old Heath, Colchester, Essex, CO1 2HD ☎ 07804 641267 ⊕ watsonsbrewery.co.uk

⊠ Small batch, home brewery set up in 2016 using a 100-litre brew plant. Local pubs, festivals and bottle shops are supplied with one-off beers.

Watts & Co (NEW)

Gardeners Road, Debenham, Suffolk, IP14 6RX ☎ 07764 906886 ⊕ watts.fm

Watts and Co was established in 2015 and brew a range of traditional and modern beers from its tiny brewhouse in the heart of Suffolk. Each brew produces just 300 pints, with a range of traditional and modern beers, all handcrafted.

Waveney

☰ Queen's Head, Station Road, Earsham, Norfolk, NR35 2TS ☎ (01986) 892623 ✉ lyndahamps@aol.com

⊠ Established at the Queen's Head in 2004, the five-barrel brewery produces three beers, regularly available at the pub along with other free trade outlets. ♦

Way Outback

144 Seabourne Road, Southbourne, Bournemouth, Dorset, BH5 2HZ ⊕ thewayoutback.co.uk

Started in 2017 and born in a shed, Way Outback is based in Southbourne. It is run by owner and head brewer Richard Brown (with help from his four-legged assistant Arthur), and specialises in beers using high quality ingredients with provenance. ✦

Wayoh (NEW) SIBA

3 Lodge Bank, Horwich, BL6 5HY ☎ 07799 410540 ⊕ wayohbrewing.co.uk

⊛The brewery launched in 2019 and is named after the local reservoir. It specialises in small batch craft beer using a 2.5-barrel kit. A taproom is located at the brewery (open Thu-Sat). ♦✦

Oatmeal Stout (ABV 4.2%) STOUT
Golden Ale (ABV 5%) GOLD

Saxon Cross ESB (ABV 5.9%) BITTER

Weal SIBA

Unit 6, Newpark Business Park, London Road, Chesterton, Newcastle under Lyme, Staffordshire, ST5 7HT
☎ (01782) 565635 ☎ 07980 606966
⊕ wealales.co.uk

Weal Ales is a multiple SIBA award-winning microbrewery supplying events and independent outlets both locally and nationally. Established in 2014 by husband and wife team Paul and Andrea Wealleans, it uses a six-barrel plant and bottles many of its beers. Its taphouse, Wellers, in Newcastle under Lyme, opened in 2016. ☏LIVE V◆

This is the Modern Weal (ABV 3.8%) PALE
Wagon Weal (ABV 4.1%) BITTER
Wealy Hopper (ABV 4.2%) PALE
Weller Weal (ABV 4.6%) PALE
Weal Noir (ABV 4.8%) PORTER
Sweet aroma from this black as black beer. Sweet tastes with lots of liquorice and smoky notes. Balanced between sweet, smoke and hoppy undertones. A moreish finish for another mouthful.
Centwealial Milk Stout (ABV 4.9%) STOUT
Weally Wonka (ABV 5.4%) PALE
Ginger Weal (ABV 5.5%) SPECIALITY
Lemon & Ginger Weal (ABV 5.5%) SPECIALITY

Weard'ALE

⬛ Hare and Hounds, 24 Front Street, Westgate, DL13 1RX
☎ (01388) 517212

Brewing commenced in the Hare & Hounds in 2010. The beers are mainly sold on the premises but some have found their way to nearby beer festivals and other local pubs.

Weatheroak

Unit 7, Victoria Works, Birmingham Road, Studley, Warwickshire, B80 7AP
☎ (01527) 854 433 ☎ 07771 860645

Office: Weatheroak Tap House, 21a High Street, Studley, B80 7HN ⊕ weatheroakbrewery.co.uk

⊠ The brewery was set up in 1997 at Weatheroak Hill. It is now in a spacious factory unit in Studley. Weatheroak supplies 20 outlets. Off-sales available for all beers at the Tap House on the High street in Studley. 18 and 36 pint polypins are available with notice. ‼◆

Light Oak (ABV 3.6%) BITTER
Bees Knees (ABV 3.7%) BITTER
This straw-coloured quaffing ale has lots of hoppy notes on the tongue and nose, and a fleetingly sweet aftertaste.
Victoria Works (ABV 4.3%) PALE
Redwood (ABV 4.4%) BITTER
Keystone Hops (ABV 5%) BITTER
A golden yellow beer that is surprisingly easy to quaff given the strength. Fruity hops are the dominant flavour without the commonly associated astringency.

Weatheroak Hill

Coach & Horses, Weatheroak Hill, Alvechurch, Worcestershire, B48 7EA
☎ (01564) 823386 ☎ 07496 289924
✉ weatheroakhillbrewery@gmail.com

Established in 2008, Weatheroak Hill Brewery has been supplying the Coach & Horses with quality beers brewed on-site for over a decade, travelling a mere 10 meters from grain to glass. The free trade and CAMRA festivals are also supplied and customers can order online for pick up and delivery. ‼◆

IPA (Icknield Pale Ale) (ABV 3.8%) PALE
Impossible IPA (ABV 4.1%) PALE
Cofton Common (ABV 4.9%) SPECIALITY

Weetwood SIBA

The Brewery, Common Lane, Kelsall, Cheshire, CW6 0PY
☎ (01829) 752377 ⊕ weetwoodales.co.uk

☺Weetwood Ales were founded in a barn back in 1992 but now operate out of a modern 30-barrel plant close to Kelsall. The broad range of beers is available across the north-west and North Wales. Besides regular brewery tours and an on-site shop, a distillery (an enterprise totally complementary to the brewery) produces a range of spirits including gin and vodka, with plans for a single malt release in 2022. ‼☏

Southern Cross (ABV 3.6%) GOLD
Best Bitter (ABV 3.8%) BITTER
Pale brown beer with an assertive bitterness and a lingering, dry finish. Despite initial sweetness, peppery hops dominate throughout.
Mad Hatter (ABV 3.9%) RED
A typical red beer, malty aromas lead to a fruity, sweet middle, backed up with a bitter finish.
Cheshire Cat (ABV 4%) GOLD
Pale, dry bitter with a spritzy lemon zest and a grape aroma. Hoppy aroma leads through to the initial taste before fruitiness takes over. Smooth creamy mouthfeel and a short, dry finish.
Eastgate (ABV 4.2%) PALE
Well-balanced and refreshing clean amber beer. Citrus fruit flavours predominate in the taste and there is a short, dry aftertaste.
Oregon Pale (ABV 4.3%) PALE
Old Dog (ABV 4.5%) BITTER
Robust, well-balanced, amber beer with a slightly fruity aroma. Rich malt and fruit flavours are balanced by bitterness. Some sweetness and a hint of sulphur on nose and taste.
Jester IPA (ABV 4.8%) PALE

Weighbridge

See BrightBeer

Weird Beard SIBA

Units 5 & 9, Boston Business Park, Trumpers Way, Hanwell, London, W7 2QA
☎ (020) 3645 2711 ⊕ weirdbeardbrewco.com

⊠ Brewing began in 2013 on an industrial estate in Hanwell. The plant has expanded a few times, including into the adjacent unit. The eye catching artwork and inventive beer names complement the range of modern styles (available in cask, keg, cans and bottles). LIVE V

Black Perle (ABV 3.8%) SPECIALITY
Coffee milk stout with roast notes throughout this full-favoured, sweetish black beer with some red fruits. Bitterish, dry finish.
Little Things That Kill (ABV 3.9%) GOLD
Hoppy, fruity golden ale which varies in flavour as the hops that are used can alter.
Bat Oat of Hell (ABV 4%) PALE
Kill Pills (ABV 5%) SPECIALITY

Mariana Trench (ABV 5.3%) GOLD
Passionfruit and citrus are noticeable throughout this malty, sweet, golden beer. Bitterness builds and lingers overlaid by dryness.
Five O'clock Shadow (ABV 7%) IPA
Golden ale with appley nose and palate. Sweet biscuit and resinous spicy hops dominating. Dry sweet aftertaste fading to spicy.

Weird Dad (NEW)

🏠 Filling Station, 23-23a Caerleon Road, Newport, NP19 7BU ✉ weirddadbrewery@gmail.com

A quirky nanobrewery located in central Newport, established on the principles of enjoying the art of crafting beer and the pleasures of sharing the results with old and new friends. ‼🛒

Weird Sisters

24 Timworth Heath Cottages, Great Barton, Suffolk, IP31 2QH ☎ 07827 923923

⊗ A nanobrewery established by a father and three daughters (the weird sisters) in 2018. The brewery has one core beer and mainly produces seasonal beers to mark the eight seasonal festivals of the wheel of the year. Beers can be found at festivals, morris dancing events and in specialist beer shops.

Slaphead (ABV 6.7%) IPA

Welbeck Abbey SIBA

Brewery Yard, Welbeck, Nottinghamshire, S80 3LT
☎ (01909) 512539 ☎ 07921 066274
⊕ welbeckabbeybrewery.co.uk

Welbeck Abbey Brewery opened in 2011. The microbrewery is housed in a listed barn at the centre of the traditional landed Welbeck estate. General manager Claire Monk trained at the Kelham Island Brewery after studying microbiology at Sheffield University. The brewery produces six regular cask ales and monthly specials. Beer is also brewed for Stocks Brewing Co. ‼♦

Henrietta (ABV 3.6%) GOLD
Red Feather (ABV 3.9%) BITTER
Kaiser (ABV 4.1%) SPECIALITY
Harley (ABV 4.3%) PALE
Portland Black (ABV 4.5%) PORTER
Black ale with a roast malt aroma and taste throughout and a well-balanced bitterness.
Cavendish (ABV 5%) BLOND
Golden in colour with a smooth, hoppy and malty mouthfeel and a lingering, hoppy bitter finish.

Contract brewed for Stocks Brewing Co:
St Leger Gold (ABV 4.1%) BARLEY
Old Horizontal (ABV 5.3%) BARLEY

Weldon

Bencroft Grange, Bedford Road, Rushden, Northamptonshire, NN10 0SE
☎ (01536) 601016

Office: 12 Chapel Road, Weldon, NN17 3HP
⊕ weldonbrewery.co.uk

Weldon Brewery originally started brewing in 2014 on a two-barrel plant at the Shoulder of Mutton, after which the brewery was originally named. In 2016 the brewery acquired the premises and 3.5-barrel kit of the former Copper Kettle brewery in Rushden and became the main production facility, with the brewery being renamed Weldon. The original plant at the Shoulder of Mutton has

been retained and is used for small runs and test batches. ♦V

Diab-Lo (ABV 3.7%) PALE
Essanell (ABV 3.8%) MILD
Dragline (ABV 3.9%) GOLD
Stahlstadt (ABV 4%) BLOND
Galvy Stout (ABV 4.2%) STOUT
Weldon Windmill (ABV 4.2%) BITTER
Mad Max (ABV 4.4%) PALE
Paradisium (ABV 4.4%) PALE
Roman Mosaics (ABV 4.6%) PALE

Well Drawn SIBA

Unit 5, Greenway Workshops, Bedwas House Industrial Estate, Caerphilly, CF83 8HW
⊕ welldrawnbrewing.co.uk

This six-barrel brewery opened in 2017 in a small industrial unit near Caerphilly. It supplies direct to local pubs as well as through a number of regional wholesalers. ‼🛒♦LIVE⊘

WD Pale Ale (ABV 3.8%) BITTER
Bedwas Bitter (ABV 4.2%) BITTER
Caerphilly Pale (ABV 4.2%) BITTER
Oatmeal Stout (ABV 4.4%) STOUT
WD Gold (ABV 4.4%) GOLD
Providence Pale (ABV 4.5%) PALE
Pontcanna Pale (ABV 4.6%) SPECIALITY
2nd Breakfast IPA (ABV 5.1%) BITTER

Welland

Cradge Bank, Spalding, Lincolnshire, PE11 3AN
☎ (07732) 33702 ⊕ wellandbrewery.co.uk

Welland Brewery commenced in 2018 and was set up by Tom Bradshaw and Dave Jackson, assisted by the owner and brewer of nearby Austendyke Ales, Charlie Rawlings. A brewery taphouse is planned.

Shipshape Blonde (ABV 3.7%) GOLD
Sneaky St.oat (ABV 3.9%) STOUT
Fen Tiger (ABV 4%) GOLD
Flatland Bitter (ABV 4%) BITTER
Pale RyeNo (ABV 4.1%) SPECIALITY
YFM (ABV 4.2%) GOLD
Jack Rawlshaw (ABV 4.4%) BITTER
Black Cow (ABV 4.7%) STOUT
Rusty Giraffe (ABV 5%) BITTER
Mad Cow (ABV 5.4%) STOUT
Lincoln Red (ABV 6.2%) RED
Red Tsar (ABV 10%) STOUT

Wensleydale SIBA

Unit 4, Badger Court, Leyburn, North Yorkshire, DL8 5BF
☎ (01969) 622463 ☎ 07765 596666
⊕ wensleydalebrewery.co.uk

🌐Wensleydale was set up in 2003 and has since moved to larger premises in Leyburn utilising a 10-barrel plant. Around 200 outlets are supplied direct in Yorkshire and Co Durham. ‼🛒♦⊘

Falconer (ABV 3.9%) BITTER
Semer Water (ABV 4.1%) PALE
Gamekeeper (ABV 4.3%) BITTER
Black Dub (ABV 4.4%) STOUT
High Fives (ABV 5.7%) IPA

Weobley

🏠 Jules Restaurant, Portland Street, Weobley, Herefordshire, HR4 8SB

☎ (01544) 318206 ☎ 07493 269189
⊕ theweobleybrewing.co

Commercial brewing began in 2019 at this nanobrewery, which is part of Jules restaurant in the village of Weobley and is run by chef and head brewer Tom Evans. Four beers are regularly brewed along with two occasional beers, available from the brewery, restaurant and other local outlets and pubs.

Werewolf (NEW) SIBA

🏠 Rose & Crown, 71-73 Torriano Avenue, Kentish Town, London, NW5 2SG
☎ (020) 7267 4305 ⊕ werewolfbeer.com

First cuckoo brewed in 2020 at Little Creatures, Kings Cross. Towards the end of the year a nanobrewery was installed in the basement of the Rose & Crown. There are plans to install a larger brewery in a railway arch in Camden Town. No real ale.

Wessex

Rye Hill Farm, Longbridge Deverill, BA12 7DE
☎ (01985) 844532 ✉ wessexbrewery@gmail.com

⊠ This four-barrel brewery, hidden away on a farm industrial complex in the West Wiltshire Area of Outstanding Natural Beauty, was established in 2001. The brewery sources its malt from the nearby Warminster Maltings. Around 2010 two new fermenters were installed. A handful of regular outlets are supplied, with wider availability via selected wholesalers. The brewery is able to brew beer for other concerns when capacity permits. Beers are occasionally brewed for Isle of Avalon (qv). ♦

Stourton Pale Ale (ABV 3.5%) PALE
Mild (ABV 3.9%) MILD
Kilmington Best (ABV 4.2%) BITTER
Deverill's Advocate (ABV 4.5%) GOLD
Maltings Gold (ABV 4.5%) GOLD
Warminster Warrior (ABV 4.5%) BITTER
Golden Apostle (ABV 4.8%) GOLD
Beast of Zeals (ABV 6.6%) BARLEY
Festive Ferret (ABV 7%) STOUT

WEST

🏠 Binnie Place, Glasgow Green, Glasgow, G40 1AW
☎ (0141) 550 0135 ⊕ westbeer.com

Brewery producing artisan lagers and ales in strict accordance with the German Purity Law of 1516, which also has an on-site beer hall, restaurant and events venue. All beers are unpasteurised. ‼♦

West Berkshire SIBA

The Old Dairy, Frilsham Farm, Yattendon, Berkshire, RG18 0XT
☎ (01635) 767090 ⊕ wbbrew.com

⊠ West Berkshire Brewery was established in 1995. In 2018, following investment from new shareholders and crowdfunding, the brewery moved to a new, purpose-built facility (its fourth expansion). Capacity was increased tenfold to 50,000 hectolitres. The state-of-the-art brewery is located in a former dairy farm building and, since opening, has expanded to take over the whole building, covering 68,000sq ft. The site includes a shop, taproom and kitchen. Beers are available throughout the south of England and beyond. ‼🍺♦🍴

Mister Chubb's (ABV 3.4%) BITTER

A drinkable, balanced, session bitter. A malty caramel note dominates aroma and taste and is accompanied by a nutty, bittersweetness and a hoppy aftertaste.
Maggs' Mild (ABV 3.5%) MILD
Silky, full-bodied, dark mild with a creamy head. Roast malt aroma is joined in the taste by caramel, sweetness and mild, fruity hoppiness. Aftertaste of roast malt with balancing bitterness.
Good Old Boy (ABV 4%) BITTER
Tawny-coloured, session bitter with malty aroma, then a balanced flavour with hops and fruit, leading to a long, dry, bitter aftertaste.
Gold Star (ABV 4.1%) GOLD
Maharaja IPA (ABV 5.1%) PALE

West by Three

See Freetime

West Coast Rock

🏠 1877 The Brew Room, 137-139 Church Street, Blackpool, FY1 3NX
☎ (01253) 319165 ⊕ thebrewroom1887.co.uk

☺Historic Blackpool pub, which reopened as a specialist beer outlet in 2017 and first brewed in 2018 using a six-barrel plant. Many of the beers have a Blackpool Football Club theme, the club being founded in the pub in 1887. ‼♦

West Coast

See Conwy

West End

🏠 68-70 Braunstone Gate, Leicester, LE3 5LG
☎ 07875 745302 ⊕ thewestendbrewery.co.uk

☺The West End Brewery is Leicester city centre's original brewpub, which opened in 2016 using a 2.5-barrel plant. Total capacity doubled to five barrels in 2019. Beers are available in the pub and occasionally in other local outlets. 🍺♦LIVE🍴

Westerham SIBA

Beggars Lane, Westerham, Kent, TN16 1QP
☎ (01732) 864427 ⊕ westerhambrewery.co.uk

⊠ Having moved in 2017 to a new, purpose-built brewery, Westerham recently opened a new taproom with 12 taps serving beer straight from the maturation tank. The brewery benefits from the supply of Greensand aquifer water from an on-site borehole. It also utilises original heritage yeasts from the former Black Eagle Brewery, thus maintaining a link to the Kent style of the past. More than 500 outlets are supplied in Kent, Surrey, Sussex and London. ‼🍺♦LIVE🍴

Grasshopper Kentish Bitter (ABV 3.8%) BITTER
Summer Perle (ABV 3.8%) GOLD
Spirit of Kent (ABV 4%) GOLD
British Bulldog (ABV 4.1%) BITTER
1965 – Special Bitter Ale (ABV 4.8%) BITTER
Audit Ale (ABV 6.2%) BITTER

Westmorland

Kendal, Cumbria ☎ 07554 562662

Office: Mint Street, Kendal, LA9 6DS
✉ westmorlandbrewery@gmail.com

Westmorland began brewing in 2016 using a one-barrel plant.

Wetherby

🍺 Beer Station, York Road Estate, York Road, Wetherby, LS22 7SU
☎ (01937) 584637 ☎ 07725 850654
⊕ wetherbybrewco.com

⊗Wetherby Brew Co was established in 2017 and is located a short walk from the town centre. It is independently-owned and operated, and brews on a 1.25-barrel plant. The brewery incorporates an on-site taproom and bottle shop. Regular events are held and half day brewing experiences are offered. 🛒♦✦

Wharfe

See Hambleton

Wharfedale

🍺 Back Barn, 16 Church Street, Ilkley, West Yorkshire, LS29 9DS
☎ (01943) 609587 ⊕ wharfedalebrewery.com

⊗Wharfedale began brewing in 2012 using spare capacity at Five Towns brewery in Wakefield. Brewing moved to Ilkley in 2013 using a 2.5-barrel plant located at the rear of the Flying Duck pub, creating Wharfedale's first brewpub.

Whim

Whim Farm, Hartington, Derbyshire, SK17 0AX
☎ (01298) 84991 ⊕ whimales.co.uk

Whim Ales began brewing in 1993 in an outstanding location at Whim Farm near Hartington in the Derbyshire Dales, Peak District. It produces cask ales using the finest ingredients, Derbyshire hill water and its own yeast. The beers are available in 50-70 outlets and the brewery's tied house, Wilkes Head, Leek. ♦

Marynka (ABV 3.3%) GOLD
Arbor Light (ABV 3.6%) GOLD
Hartington Bitter (ABV 4%) PALE
Earl Grey Bitter (ABV 4.2%) BITTER
Hartington IPA (ABV 4.5%) PALE
Flower Power (ABV 5.3%) GOLD

Whitacre

🍺 Dog Inn, Dog Lane, Nether Whitacre, Warwickshire, B46 2DU
☎ (01675) 481318 ☎ 07977 393833
⊕ thedoginnwhitacre.co.uk

Established in 2017 by licencees Gary and Joanne Webb to supply the adjacent Dog Inn. The nine-gallon brewery is situated in an outbuilding. All the beer names are dog themed as the owners are Shih Tzu dog owners. ✦

Whitby SIBA

East Cliff, Whitby, North Yorkshire, YO22 4JR
☎ (01947) 228871 ☎ 07516 116377
⊕ whitby-brewery.com

Whitby Brewery was established in 2012 under the Conquest name by a local team who built the brewery from scratch. It expanded in 2016 to a new site in the shadow of Whitby Abbey, with a 20-barrel capacity. Music events are hosted occasionally at weekends. Beers are distributed across Yorkshire and the North East. ‼🛒♦LIVE V✦

Abbey Blonde (ABV 3.8%) BLOND
Whitby Whaler (ABV 4%) PALE
Saltwick Nab (ABV 4.2%) RED

Smugglers Gold (ABV 4.2%) BITTER
Jet Black (ABV 4.5%) PORTER
IPA (ABV 5.2%) BITTER
Black Death (ABV 6.6%) STOUT

White Hart

🍺 White Hart Hotel & Restaurant, 15 High Street, Halstead, Essex, CO9 2AP
☎ (01787) 475657 ⊕ whitehartbrewery.co.uk

⊗ Brewing began in 2017 in old stables at the back of the White Hart. Both the brewery and pub are owned by father and son, Charles and Hugo Townsend. Beers are available in the pub and at local beer festivals.

White Hart Tap

🍺 White Hart Tap, 4 Keyfield Terrace, St Albans, Hertfordshire, AL1 1QJ
☎ (01727) 860974 ⊕ whiteharttap.co.uk

Brewing began in 2015. Beers are only available in the pub. Brewing is currently suspended.

White Horse SIBA

3 Ware Road, White Horse Business Park, Stanford in the Vale, Oxfordshire, SN7 8NY
☎ (01367) 718700 ⊕ whitehorsebrewery.co.uk

⊗White Horse was founded in 2004. In 2018 a new management team took over the running of the brewery. It has major outlets in Oxfordshire, as well as supplying other outlets nationally. In addition to its regular beers, a range of seasonal monthly beers is brewed. A number of one-off beers are brewed under the Luna brand name. ‼🛒♦

WHB – White Horse Bitter (ABV 3.7%) BITTER
Black Beauty (ABV 3.9%) MILD
Stable Genius (ABV 4%) BITTER
Village Idiot (ABV 4.1%) GOLD
Dark Blue Oxford University Ale (ABV 4.3%) BITTER
Wayland Smithy (ABV 4.4%) BITTER

White Rabbit

Unit 15A, Weston Industrial Estate, Honeybourne, Worcestershire, WR11 7GB ☎ 07713 952807
✉ whiterabbit@aol.co.uk

⊗ Housed in a refurbished nissen hut on an industrial estate in Honeybourne, and incorporating the former Cannon Royall brewery, White Rabbit started brewing in 2018. The 15-barrel plant produces beers for its own pub, the Red Lion in Evesham, as well as the local free trade.

Brown Bess (ABV 3.5%) MILD
Aunt Lucy (ABV 3.7%) SPECIALITY
Opal (ABV 4%) BITTER
Elwood's Dark (ABV 4.1%) MILD
Dark brown porter, small creamy head, coffee and chocolate aromas continue with smoky, stone fruit flavours finishing with a slightly sweet, then peaty, slightly bitter finish.
Jammers Ale (ABV 4.3%) BITTER
Old Ale (ABV 4.6%) OLD

Brewed under the Cannon Royall brand name:
Black Betty (ABV 3.5%) MILD
Black Coffee (ABV 3.7%) MILD
Fruiterers Mild (ABV 3.7%) MILD
Fruity aroma with a hint of damsons, slightly sweet, fruity taste balanced with roasted malt. Fruity finish with smoky malt undertones.
Hunny Bear (ABV 3.8%) SPECIALITY
King's Shilling (ABV 3.8%) BITTER

Light Beer (ABV 3.8%) BITTER
Amber, session bitter, malty aroma with hints of toffee, initial hoppiness revealing a biscuit malt base, a slight grassiness and a lingering, bitter finish.
Pioneer (ABV 3.8%) BITTER
Arrowhead Bitter (ABV 3.9%) BITTER
Well-balanced, fruity aroma with hints of banana, fruit and hops with mango and peach on the palate, followed by a long, sweet, hoppy finish.
Muzzle Loader (ABV 4.2%) BITTER
Flavoursome, full-bodied, amber best bitter. A fruity nose with hints of butterscotch and apple continues into the taste, with a long, bitter finish.
Arrowhead Extra (ABV 4.3%) BITTER
Foxy Lady (ABV 4.3%) BITTER
Light-bodied, amber bitter, sweetshop aroma, moderate sweet malt taste with faint hops and a short, bitter finish.
Paddington (ABV 4.3%) BITTER
Silver Fox (ABV 4.3%) PALE
Teddy Bear (ABV 4.3%) BITTER
Son of Bertie (ABV 5%) STOUT
Bertie's Stout (ABV 6.7%) STOUT

Cannon Royall
Best Bitter (ABV 4.2%) BITTER
Amber best bitter, floral caramel aroma, initial hints of grapefruit and apple give way to complex hoppy bitterness then an initially flowery hoppiness in a long, bitter finish.

White Rose
Premises R/0, 7 Doncaster Road, Mexborough, South Yorkshire, S64 0HL
☎ (0114) 2466334

Office: 119 Chapel Road, Burncross, Chapeltown, Sheffield, S35 1QL
✉ whiterose.brewery@btinternet.com

☺Established in 2007 by Gary Sheriff, former head brewer at Wentworth Brewery. Formerly sharing premises with Little Ale Cart, White Rose then brewed in Mexborough, sharing premises with Imperial Brewery (qv). In 2018 it moved to its own premises using a new seven-barrel plant. ‼♦

Original Blonde (ABV 4%) BLOND
Stairlift to Heaven (ABV 4.2%) BLOND
Raven (ABV 4.9%) STOUT

Whitechapel
See Haworth Steam

Whitefaced
14 Market Street, Penistone, Sheffield, South Yorkshire, S36 6BZ ☎ 07894 532456

Established in 2017 producing bottled and keg beers, the brewery moved into cask production in 2019, winning CAMRA awards the same year. Cans were introduced in 2020. Originally brewing from his residence, owner/brewer David Hampshaw has recently relocated the two-barrel brewery into a new tap house in Penistone town centre. The brewery is named after the highly-prized, local, whitefaced woodland sheep. ♦LIVE

Painted Tiles (ABV 4%) PALE
First Flight (ABV 6%) STRONG

Whitewater
Lakeside Brae Clarkhill Road, Castlewellan, Northern Ireland, BT31 9RH
☎ (028) 4377 8900 ⊕ whitewaterbrewery.com

Established in 1996, Whitewater is now the biggest brewery in Northern Ireland. ‼♦

Copperhead (ABV 3.7%) BITTER
Belfast Black (ABV 4.2%) STOUT
Belfast Ale (ABV 4.5%) BITTER
Maggie's Leap IPA (ABV 4.7%) PALE
Clotworthy Dobbin (ABV 5%) PORTER

Whitley Bay
▤ **2-4 South Parade, Whitley Bay, NE26 2RG** ☎ 07392 823480 ✉ whitleybaybrewingcompany@gmail.com

☺Brewing commenced in 2016 on a five-barrel plant and relocated to larger premises, a new brewery tap, in the centre of Whitley Bay in 2018. Around 40 local outlets are supplied. V

Slow Joe (ABV 3.9%) SPECIALITY
Warrior (ABV 3.9%) PALE
Spanish City Blonde (ABV 4.2%) BLOND
Dark Knight (ABV 4.3%) BROWN
Ghost Ships (ABV 4.3%) PALE
Equinox (ABV 5%) PALE
Texas Cleggy (ABV 5%) BITTER
55 Degrees North (ABV 5.5%) SPECIALITY

Whitstable SIBA
Little Telpits Farm, Woodcock Lane, Grafty Green, Kent, ME17 2AY
☎ (01622) 851007 ⊕ whitstablebrewery.co.uk

Whitstable Brewery was founded in 2003. It currently provides all the beer for the Whitstable Oyster Company's three restaurants, its hotel and a brewery tap, as well as supplying pubs all over Kent, London and Surrey. ♦

Native Bitter (ABV 3.7%) BITTER
A classic, copper-coloured, Kentish, session bitter with hoppy aroma and a long, dry, bitter hop finish.
Renaissance Ruby Mild (ABV 3.7%) MILD
East India Pale Ale (ABV 4.1%) PALE
A well-hopped, golden IPA with good grapefruit aroma hop character and lingering, bitter finish.
Oyster Stout (ABV 4.5%) STOUT
Pearl of Kent (ABV 4.5%) BLOND
Winkle Picker (ABV 4.5%) BITTER
Kentish Reserve (ABV 5%) BITTER

Why Not
27 Redfern Road, Thorpe St Andrew, Norwich, Norfolk, NR7 9RB
☎ (01603) 300786 ⊕ thewhynotbrewery.co.uk

Why Not began brewing in 2005 on a 1.5-barrel plant located to the rear of the house of proprietor Colin Emms. In 2006 the brewery was extensively upgraded, doubling in capacity. In 2011 the brewery was moved to a new location in Thorpe St Andrew. LIVE

Wally's Revenge (ABV 4%) BITTER
An overtly bitter beer with a hoppy background. The bitterness holds on to the end as an increasing astringent dryness develops.
Roundhead Porter (ABV 4.5%) PORTER
Cavalier Red (ABV 4.7%) BITTER
Explosive fruity nose belies the gentleness of the taste. The summer fruit aroma dominates this red-gold brew. A sweet, fruity start disappears under a quick, bitter ending.
Norfolk Honey Ale (ABV 5%) SPECIALITY
Chocolate Nutter (ABV 5.5%) OLD

Whyte Bar

c/o 25 Paris Street, Exeter, Devon, EX1 2JB

Whyte Bar, pronounced Whyte Bear, was founded in 2018 as a cuckoo brewery by Andy Whyte and Joel Barnard. Brewing also takes place at other local breweries, such as Many Hands and Topsham (qv). Its own bar, Cuckoo Bar, is due to open.

Wibblers SIBA

Goldsands Road, Southminster, Essex, CM0 7JW
☎ **(01621) 772044 ⊕ wibblers.com**

⊗ Wibblers was established in 2007 and expanded to a 20-barrel plant in 2009. In 2016 the brewery moved to new premises in Southminster with a taproom. In 2018 the taproom was expanded four-fold, along with capacity. Craft beers and ciders are now produced, as well as seasonal specials. Wibblers supply numerous outlets throughout East Anglia, London and Kent in addition to exporting to mainland Europe. **!! ▆ ♦ LIVE ⬦**

IPA (ABV 3.6%) PALE
Apprentice (ABV 3.9%) BITTER
Dark (ABV 4%) MILD
Gold (ABV 4%) GOLD
Hop Black (ABV 4%) BITTER
Beneath the Embers (ABV 4.7%) PALE
Crafty Stoat (ABV 5.3%) STOUT

Wicked Hathern

See Staffordshire

Wickham House

Church Lane, Conisholme, Louth, Lincolnshire, LN11 7LX ☎ 07817 467303
✉ **bearplumb64@gmail.com**

⊕ Wickham House was formed in 2018 as a small artisan brewery concentrating on traditional ales produced in small batches.

Wickham (NEW)

⧉ Five Bells, Baydon Road, Wickham, Berkshire, RG20 8HH
☎ **(01488) 657300 ⊕ fivebellswickham.co.uk**

A brewpub which started in 2020, on the same site and using the kit as previously used by INNformal brewery, which moved to Hungerford in 2019. The brewhouse was built by the previous owners behind the Five Bells in 2015. A borehole in the pub garden supplies water for the 2.5-barrel plant and 0.5-barrel test kit.

Wickwar

Old Brewery, Station Road, Wickwar, Gloucestershire, GL12 8NB
☎ **(01454) 292000 ⊕ wickwarbrewing.co.uk**

Wickwar was established as a 10-barrel brewery in 1990. In 2004 it expanded to 50 barrels. Moles Brewery and pubs were acquired in 2017, bringing its pub estate up to 20. This has now been rationalised to 16. 350 outlets are supplied on a regular basis and the beers are available nationally through most distributors and SIBA. Beers are contract brewed by an unknown third party. **♦**

BOB (ABV 4%) BITTER
Amber-coloured, this has a distinctive blend of hop, malt and apple/pear citrus fruits. The slightly sweet taste turns into a fine, dry bitterness, with a similar malty-lasting finish.

Cotswold Way (ABV 4.2%) BITTER
Amber-coloured, it has a pleasant aroma of pale malt, hop and fruit. Good dry bitterness in the taste with some sweetness. Similar though less sweet in the finish, with good hop content.
Falling Star (ABV 4.2%) GOLD
Stand-Up IPA (ABV 4.6%) PALE
Station Porter (ABV 6.1%) PORTER

Brewed for Moles Brewery:
Gold (ABV 3.8%) GOLD
Golden-coloured hoppy beer with a subtle citrus fruit aroma and flavour and a malty background.
Best (ABV 4%) BITTER
An amber-coloured bitter, clean, dry and malty with some bitterness, and delicate floral hop flavour.
Elmo's (ABV 4.4%) PALE
Medium-bodied bitter with subtle fruit aroma and flavours, leading to a long bitter finish.

Wigan Brewhouse

The Old Brewery, Brewery Yard, off Wallgate, Wigan, WN1 1JU
☎ **(01942) 234976 ☎ 07764 936410**
⊕ **wiganbrewhouse.co.uk**

⊕ Wigan Brewhouse commenced brewing in 2018 after local businessman Martin Blythe leased the now-defunct AllGates Brewery premises, including the acquisition of beers formerly brewed by AllGates. Beers are also brewed to its own recipes, developed by head brewer Jonathan Provost with Martin's input. **!! ♦**

Pretoria (ABV 3.6%) BLOND
California (ABV 3.9%) PALE
A pale yellow beer with a restrained hoppy and fruity aroma. It is clean and fresh-tasting, with hops and fruit in the mouth and a bitter, hoppy finish.
Casino (ABV 3.9%) BITTER
Wigan Junction (ABV 3.9%) BITTER
Dry Bones (ABV 4%) GOLD
Slider (ABV 4%) BITTER
Tempo (ABV 4.1%) GOLD
Blue Sky Tea (ABV 4.2%) SPECIALITY
Kicker IPA (ABV 4.2%) PALE
Allnighter (ABV 4.3%) PALE
Station Road Stout (ABV 4.5%) MILD
Dark brown beer with a malty, fruity aroma. Creamy and malty in taste, with blackberry fruits and a satisfying aftertaste.

Wild Barn

The Old Barn, Annat, PH33 7NA ☎ 07387 268193

Office: 14 Torr an Eas, Glenfinnan, PH37 4LS
✉ **delvauxsimon6@hotmail.com**

⊕ Launched in 2019 and rebranded in 2020, Wild Barn is a nanobrewery owned and operated by Simon Delvaux and Freja MacDougall, a Belgian and a Highlander. Beers with a strong nod to Simon's Belgian heritage are produced on a 500-litre kit. Brewing is currently suspended. **!! ♦ LIVE**

Wild Beer SIBA

Lower Westcombe Farm, Evercreech, Somerset, BA4 6ER
☎ **(01749) 838742**

Lovington: The Old Cheese Dairy, Hornblotton, Lovington, Castle Cary, BA7 7PS ☎ (01963) 240551
⊕ **wildbeerco.com**

Brewing began in 2012 using a 24-hectolitre plant (15 barrels). Set on a Somerset farm, it shares premises with

Westcombe Dairy in an adjacent building. A wide range of beers are produced, including sour beers, using alternative fermentation methods, unorthodox yeasts, alongside barrel-ageing and a blending program. It also forages seasonal, wild ingredients. Two pub restaurants are owned. Wild Beer purchased the former Cottage Brewing site and all brewing equipment. ♦LIVE

Bibble (ABV 4.2%) PALE

Wild Boar

🍺 Wild Boar, Crook Road, Bowness-on-Windermere, Cumbria, LA23 3NF
☎ (0845) 850 4604 ⊕ englishlakes.co.uk/the-wild-boar

⊗ Brewing began in 2013 at the Wild Boar, a large, traditional Lakeland luxury hotel. The hotel is part of the English Lakes Hotels group and supplies beers to hotels within the group. ♦

Wild Card SIBA

Unit 2, Lockwood Way, Blackhorse Road, Walthamstow, London, E17 5RB
☎ (020) 8935 5560 ⊕ wildcardbrewery.co.uk

⊗ Wild Card began brewing in 2013, initially using spare capacity at several breweries in and around London. After brewing at its Ravenswood site, production moved to Lockwood in 2018 along with increasing the capacity of the brewery. Both sites remain popular taprooms at the weekend. Real ale was introduced during 2021. 🍴♦

Wild Horse SIBA

Unit 4, Cae Bach Builder Street, Llandudno, LL30 1DR
☎ (01492) 868292 ⊕ wildhorsebrewing.co.uk

Small brewery concentrating on supplying KeyKeg, bottled and canned beers to local bars and off-licences. All products are unfiltered and unpasteurised. Occasional one-off casks are produced. ♦✦

Wild Weather SIBA

Unit 19, Easter Park, Benyon Road, Silchester, Aldermaston, Berkshire, RG7 2PQ
☎ (0118) 970 1837 ⊕ wildweatherales.com

⊗ Established in 2012, this is a 12-barrel plant brewing a vast array of beer styles, distributed throughout the UK. Many of the beers are one-off or collaborations. The Weather Station pub/taproom, Reading, opened in 2019. ‼🍴♦V✦

King Street Pale (ABV 4.2%) PALE
Shepherd's Warning (ABV 5.6%) IPA

Wildcraft

Wildcraft Brewery Ltd, Coltishall Road, Buxton, Norfolk, NR10 5JD
☎ (01603) 278054 ☎ 07584 308850
⊕ wildcraftbrewery.co.uk

⊗ Wildcraft was set up in 2016 and uses as much foraged and locally-sourced ingredients as possible to produce its beers. ‼🍴

Wild Eye P.A. (ABV 3.8%) PALE
Wild Norfolk (ABV 4.2%) PALE
Strong cut grass and citrus hop aroma. Full-bodied with lemon, sweet biscuit and a dry bitterness. Increasingly astringent finish.
Wild Bill Hiccup (ABV 4.5%) BITTER
Wild Summer (ABV 4.5%) PALE

Wild Ride (ABV 5%) GOLD
Wild Stallion Stout (ABV 5%) STOUT

Wilde Child

Unit 5, Armley Road, Leeds, West Yorkshire, LS12 2DR
☎ (0113) 244 6549 ☎ 07908 419028
⊕ wildechildbrewing.co.uk

Established as one of the smallest breweries in Leeds in 2016, Keir McAllister-Wilde took his operation from a one-barrel plant in a garage to a 10-barrel operation in a 2,000 sq ft unit, within two years. There are a large number of different ales in Wilde Child's portfolio, all are unfined. As well as distributing nationwide, beers are being sent to Holland, Spain and Finland. ✦

Opaque Reality (ABV 5.9%) SPECIALITY

Wilderness

Unit 54, Mochdre Industrial Estate, Newtown, SY16 4LE
☎ (01686) 449020 ⊕ wildernessbrew.co.uk

Wilderness began brewing in 2018 using a custom-made, five-barrel plant. The brewery focuses on seasonal, barrel-aged and mixed fermentation beers. Belgian and farmhouse-style beers make up the majority of the range. V

Motueka Grisette (ABV 3.8%) SPECIALITY
Southern Pale (ABV 4.3%) PALE
Keller Weiss (ABV 5.1%) SPECIALITY
Equinox Saison (ABV 5.2%) SPECIALITY
Mandarina Pale (ABV 5.9%) IPA

Wildside

See Brightside

Williams Bros SIBA

New Alloa Brewery, Kelliebank, Alloa, FK10 1NT
☎ (01259) 725 511 ⊕ williamsbrosbrew.com

☺A brotherhood of brewers, creating unique beers. Bruce and Scott Williams started brewing Heather Ale in 1988. A range of indigenous, historic ales have been added since. Hundreds of cask ale outlets are supplied worldwide. ‼♦

Fraoch Heather Ale (ABV 4.1%) SPECIALITY
The unique taste of heather flowers is noticeable in this beer. A fine floral aroma and spicy taste give character to this drinkable speciality beer.
Birds & Bees (ABV 4.3%) GOLD
March of the Penguins (ABV 4.9%) STOUT
Joker IPA (ABV 5%) PALE
Seven Giraffes (ABV 5.1%) SPECIALITY

Willy's

🍺 17 High Cliff Road, Cleethorpes, Lincolnshire, DN35 8RQ
☎ (01472) 602145

The brewery opened in 1989 to provide beer mainly for its in-house pub in Cleethorpes, although some beer is sold in the free trade. It has a five-barrel plant with maximum capacity of 15 barrels a week. The brewery can be viewed at any time from pub or street. ‼♦

Wily Fox SIBA

1 Kellet Close, Wigan, WN5 0LP
☎ (01942) 215525 ⊕ wilyfoxbrewery.co.uk

THE BREWERIES

A bespoke 20-barrel brewery, set up in 2016. Head brewer Dave Goodwin previously worked for Thwaites and Samuel Smith. ‼

Blonde Vixen (ABV 3.8%) BLOND
Light-bodied, fruity beer.
Prohibition APA (ABV 3.9%) PALE
Hoppy beer with citrus character throughout.
Crafty Fox (ABV 4%) BITTER
Well-balanced, bitter and malty sweetness, with fruity hops. Creamy mouthfeel, and bitter finish.
The Fox Hat (ABV 4.2%) GOLD
Fruity aroma. Citrus hop taste and bitter, hoppy aftertaste.
Karma Citra (ABV 4.3%) GOLD
Citrus fruit in aroma and taste with balanced bitterness, and a dry finish.
Dark Flagon (ABV 4.4%) PORTER

Wimbledon SIBA

8 College Fields, Prince George's Road, Colliers Wood, London, SW19 2PT
☎ (020) 3674 9786 ⊕ wimbledonbrewery.com

⊠ Set up by Mark Gordon after a 23 year career in the City, Wimbledon began production in 2015, with former Young's and Fuller's brewer Derek Prentice at the helm of a brand new, 30-barrel plant. The brewery expanded in 2017 with two new 60-barrel fermenters, and further expanded in 2018 with an additional 60-barrel fermenter. Some beers are inspired by the original Wimbledon Brewery, destroyed by fire in 1889. ‼ ⇶ ♦ LIVE ⬧

Common Pale Ale (ABV 3.7%) BITTER
Well-balanced, easy-drinking, gold-coloured bitter with mandarin and hoppy aroma and flavour overlaying a biscuit sweetness. Lingering, dry bitterness.
Copper Leaf Ale (ABV 4%) RED
Caramelised toffee, roast, raisins and citrus is complemented by a growing dry, spicy bitterness. Aroma has a touch of marmalade.
SW19 (ABV 4%) BLOND
Easy-drinking, pale ale with honeyed citrus and a gentle hopping flavour, becoming peppery in the subtle, dry finish.
Quartermaine IPA (ABV 5.8%) IPA
Well-balanced, amber beer with an underlying sweetness complementing citrus, fruit cake and spicy hops in aroma and dry, bitter finish.

Wincle SIBA

Tolls Farm Barn, Dane Bridge, Wincle, Cheshire, SK11 0QE
☎ (01260) 227777 ⊕ winclebeer.co.uk

⊕ Wincle Beer Co was set up in 2008 on a farm, close to its present location. It now has a 15-barrel plant in Wincle, adjacent to the River Dane, just inside Cheshire, and within the Peak District National Park. The beers are brewed using water from its own borehole. A brewery shop is housed in a converted stable next to the brewery. An annual beer festival is held at the end of June and an open tap night with a guest caterer once a month. ‼ ⇶ ♦

Waller (ABV 3.8%) PALE
Rambler (ABV 4%) BITTER
Sir Philip (ABV 4.2%) BITTER
Wibbly Wallaby (ABV 4.4%) BITTER
Burke's Special (ABV 5%) BITTER

Windermere SIBA

 Watermill Inn, Ings, Cumbria, LA8 9PY

☎ (01539) 821309 ☎ 07831 873300
⊕ lakelandpub.co.uk

⊕ Originally known as Watermill, the brewery was established in 2006 in a purpose-built extension to the inn. The beers have a doggy theme – dogs are allowed in the main bar. Windermere Brewing was originally a separate brand but all beers are now brewed under the name. ‼ ♦

Windmill Hill SIBA

Unit 1 Eastfield Farm, Deppers Bridge, CV47 2SU
☎ (01926) 355450 ⊕ whbrewery.co.uk

Windmill Hill is an independent microbrewery using a one-barrel plant, brewing small batch beers. Around 30 outlets are supplied direct.

Table Beer (ABV 2.9%) BITTER
Amber Post (ABV 4.2%) BITTER
The Chesterton (ABV 4.2%) BITTER
Grindstone (ABV 4.5%) GOLD

Windmill

c/o Unit 10, Castle Mills, Aynam Road, Kendal, Cumbria, LA9 7DE
☎ (01539) 726800 ☎ 07885 171210
⊕ bownessbaybrewing.co.uk

⊕ Brewing began in 2016 in converted farm buildings near Standish. Run by the owner of the Windmill pub in Parbold to supply the Windmill and other local free trade outlets mainly in Merseyside, West Lancashire and Wigan. The brewery was purchased by Bowness Bay Brewing in 2019 and all production moved there. ‼ ♦

Windsor & Eton SIBA

Unit 1, Vansittart Estate, Duke Street, Windsor, Berkshire, SL4 1SE
☎ (01753) 854075 ⊕ webrew.co.uk

⊠ Four friends, including two fully-qualified brewers, set up the brewery in 2010 though their brewing experience goes back to the original Courage Brewery. In 2018 it was granted a Royal Warrant as Brewer to Her Majesty the Queen. The purpose-built plant is 18 barrels, which supplies around 300 outlets in London and the Thames Valley area, while wholesalers distribute nationally. Beers are also produced under the Uprising brand name. ‼ ⇶ ♦ LIVE ⬧

Knight of the Garter (ABV 3.8%) GOLD
Session golden ale with a citrusy hop aroma, joined by some sweetness in the taste, followed by bitterness in the finish.
Windsor Knot (ABV 4%) BITTER
Guardsman (ABV 4.2%) BITTER
Eton Boatman (ABV 4.3%) GOLD
Session golden ale with tropical fruit and citrus hop aroma, continuing into the taste with some sweetness and subtle bitter finish.
Father Thames (ABV 4.8%) BITTER
Conqueror (ABV 5%) BROWN
Dark brown ale with an aroma of dark malts and citrus hops. Malt dominates the taste with citrus and spice. Dry, malty finish.

Windswept SIBA

Unit B, 13 Coulardbank Industrial Estate, Lossiemouth Moray, Lossiemouth, IV31 6NG
☎ (01343) 814 310 ⊕ windsweptbrewing.co.uk

Windswept Brewing Co was established in 2012 and is situated near the gates of RAF Lossiemouth. It is run by two former Tornado pilots who are CAMRA members. The brewery has developed to include a bar, shop and regular tours. Bottle-conditioned, seasonal and barrel-aged beers are produced. ‼ ▪️LIVE V

Blonde (ABV 4%) PALE
Smooth, golden, citrus hoppy brew with hints of peach. Slight malty background.
APA (ABV 5%) PALE
Good mix of malts and grapefruit hop throughout. Tangy finish.
Weizen (ABV 5.2%) SPECIALITY
Cloudy wheat beer full of bananas and pear drops with a hint of spices.
Wolf (ABV 6%) OLD
Dark, strong-tasting, slightly sweet, roasted malty brew with chocolate and a vanilla coffee background and a bitter finish.

Windy

▪ **Volunteer Inn, New Road, Seavington St Michael, Somerset, TA19 0QE**
☎ (01460) 240126 ⊕ thevolly.co.uk

The brewery was established at the Volunteer Inn in 2011 using a four-barrel plant. The name stems from the time when alterations were carried out to the back of the pub and the workmen suffered extremes of varying weather conditions. All beers are named with a weather theme. ‼ ♦

Wingtip

The Grain Shed, Ford Lane, Ashurst, West Sussex, BN44 3AT
☎ (0333) 224 4888 ⊕ wingtipbrewing.com

⊠ Established in 2015, Wingtip is influenced by the history of Shoreham Airport and its founders experience of aviation and travel. Beers are available in pubs and bars around Sussex and London.

Autopilot (ABV 3.9%) BLOND

Winster Valley

See Handsome

Winter's

See Mr Winter's (under M)

Winton

Hospital Road, 10 Station Yard Industrial Estate, Haddington, EH41 3PP ⊕ wintonbrewery.com

After a spell brewing at Top Out (qv), Winton moved to a site adjacent to Thistly Cross Cider and are producing a range of distinctive beers, mainly in cask and can. In 2020 it took over the Station Yard micropub, Dunbar. It relocated from West Barns to Haddington in 2021. ♦

Wintrip

7 Copenhagen Street, Worcester, WR1 2HB
☎ (01905) 612808 ☎ 07964 196194
⊕ wintripbrew.co

Wintrip began brewing in 2014 as Three Shires Brewery on a hand-built plant in Worcester before moving to new premises at the Oil Basin Brewhouse and subsequent name change. Local outlets are supplied.

Butchers Beastly Best (ABV 4%) BITTER
Salt Mine Stout (ABV 4.6%) SPECIALITY

Wiper and True SIBA

2-8 York Street, St Werburghs, Bristol, BS2 9XT
☎ (0117) 941 2501 ⊕ wiperandtrue.com

Originally launched in 2012 by Michael Wiper as a gypsy brewery, Wiper and True has operated since 2015 using its own 20-barrel plant. Producing an ever-changing range of seasonal specials along with several core beers. A proportion of its output goes into cask. The beers are available locally in Bristol and Bath, nationally and internationally. ‼ ▪️LIVE ♦

Wishbone

2a Worth Bridge Industrial Estate, Chesham Street, Keighley, West Yorkshire, BD21 4NS
☎ (01535) 600412 ☎ 07867 419445
⊕ wishbonebrewery.co.uk

Established in 2015 and run by a husband and wife team with many years previous experience in the brewing industry, beers are brewed on a modern, 10-barrel plant. ♦

Blonde (ABV 3.6%) BLOND
A hoppy, golden ale with with a strong citrus character. A bitter hoppy and slightly astringent finish.
Drover (ABV 3.9%) GOLD
Volk (ABV 3.9%) BITTER
Flux (ABV 4.1%) PALE
Tiller Pin (ABV 4.2%) GOLD
Abyss (ABV 4.3%) STOUT
Caramel and coffee bean aroma in a stout of chocolate and liquorice leading into a malty finish.
Gumption (ABV 4.5%) BITTER
Well-balanced, amber best bitter. Look for hints of dried fruit, biscuit and nuts, underpinned by dry hoppiness, leading to a bitter finish.

Witham

c/o The Chicken Sheds, Upp Hall Farm, Salmons Lane, Coggeshall, Essex, CO6 1RY
☎ (01376) 563123 ☎ 07824 698235
✉ glennackerman15@gmail.com

Brewing started in 2012, using a 0.5-barrel plant at the Woolpack Inn, Witham. In 2015 it began using spare capacity at the Red Fox Brewery. The beer continues to be available at the Woolpack, Witham. ▪️

Scruffy (ABV 3.9%) MILD
Witham Gold (ABV 4.1%) GOLD
No Name (ABV 4.3%) BITTER
Capt. Keebles Ramming Speed (ABV 4.5%) BITTER

Withnell's SIBA

Artisan House, 101 Anderton Street, Chorley, Lancashire, PR7 2AY
☎ (01257) 460535 ☎ 07787 567471
⊕ withnells.co.uk

⊕Withnell's is an independent small batch brewery, established in 2016 using a five-barrel plant. Its taproom, Artisan Ale House, opened in 2021 and is situated downstairs next to the brewery. Upstairs is the Lancashire Bottle Shop. Beers are supplied direct to pubs within a 20-mile radius of the brewery. ♦

Invincibles Ale (ABV 3.7%) GOLD
Blonde Summit (ABV 4%) BLOND
Hoppy Fettler (ABV 4.3%) PALE
Push Iron (ABV 4.5%) GOLD
Pike Stone IPA (ABV 5.5%) IPA

Wobbly

Unit 22c, Beech Business Park, Tillington Road, Hereford, HR4 9QJ
☎ (01432) 355496 ⊕ wobblybrewing.co

Wobbly began brewing in 2013, as an offshoot of AJP Process Pipework, in a small business park in Hereford, and is closely linked with its sister canning company Wecan Solutions. The brewery has a tap house open Thursday, Friday and Saturday evenings. Contract brewing, canning and the brewing of its six core cask-conditioned ales remain the main lines of business. A new canning line has been installed, greatly increasing capacity. !! ➡ ♦ LIVE ✔

WABBIT (ABV 4%) PALE
Gold (ABV 4.2%) GOLD
American Amber ale (ABV 4.5%) BITTER
Crow (ABV 4.5%) STOUT
Welder (ABV 4.8%) BITTER
INDIA PALE ALE No3 (ABV 6%) IPA

Wold Top SIBA

Hunmanby Grange, Wold Newton, Driffield, East Yorkshire, YO25 3HS
☎ (01723) 892222 ⊕ woldtopbrewery.co.uk

☺An integral part of Hunmanby Grange Farm, Wold Top brewed its first ale in 2003. It uses home and Wolds-grown malting barley and chalk-filtered water from the farm's own borehole. Now brewing on a 40-barrel plant, the range includes special edition cask and bottled beers plus three gluten-free beers. The brewery installed a bottling line in 2007 and contract bottles for other breweries. !! ➡ ♦

Bitter (ABV 3.7%) BITTER
Anglers Reward (ABV 4%) PALE
Wolds Way (ABV 4%) PALE
Headland Red (ABV 4.3%) BITTER
Against the Grain (ABV 4.5%) BLOND
Wold Gold (ABV 4.8%) GOLD

Wolf SIBA

Decoy Farm, Old Norwich Road, Besthorpe, Attleborough, Norfolk, NR17 2LA
☎ (01953) 457775 ⊕ wolfbrewery.com

⊠ The brewery was founded in 1995 on a 20-barrel plant, which was upgraded to a 25-barrel plant in 2006. It moved to its current site in 2013. More than 300 outlets are supplied. ➡ ♦

Edith Cavell (ABV 3.7%) GOLD
Hoppy, peppery nose flows into taste. Malt, caramel and bitterness give depth and complexity. Crisp finish with a hoppy edge.
Golden Jackal (ABV 3.7%) GOLD
Gentle lemon citrus aroma. A balanced mix of malt and hop with a crisp bitter tang. Burgeoning bitter swansong.
Wolf in Sheep's Clothing (ABV 3.7%) MILD
Strong fruity nose with roast. A strong caramel beginning with a bitter roast counterpoint. Gently tapering finish. Increasing raspberry sweetness.
Lavender Honey (ABV 3.8%) SPECIALITY
Malty caramel aroma leads into a bittersweet beginning with background honey notes. A long drying finish.
Battle of Britain (ABV 3.9%) BITTER
Wolf Ale (ABV 3.9%) BITTER
Copper-coloured with a smooth mix of biscuit and hop. A growing, grainy bitterness gives contrast to the long finale.
Lupus Lupus (ABV 4.2%) PALE

Hoppy throughout with malt and lemon. Increasing bitterness overcomes the initial sweetness although the beer is easy-drinking and balanced.
Sirius Dog Star (ABV 4.4%) RED
Rich tapestry of malt, roast and caramel with interwoven hop hints. Sweetness and bitterness provide a light but growing undercurrent.
Sly Wolf (ABV 4.4%) BLOND
Straw Dog (ABV 4.5%) SPECIALITY
Delicately-flavoured with a fruity character. A redcurrant aroma gives way to marmalade and hops. A strong, increasingly bitter finale.
Mad Wolf (ABV 4.7%) RED
Well-rounded, malty foundation with chocolate and chestnut support. A bittersweet hoppiness provides depth and balance. Full-bodied and lasting.
Granny Wouldn't Like It (ABV 4.8%) BITTER
Complex, with a malty bouquet. Increasing bitterness is softened by malt as a gentle, fruity sweetness adds depth.
Woild Moild (ABV 4.8%) MILD
Heavy and complex with malt, vine fruit, bitterness and roast notes vying for dominance. Increasingly dry finish.

Contract brewed for City of Cambridge Brewery:
Boathouse (ABV 3.7%) BITTER
Hobson's Choice (ABV 4.2%) GOLD
Atom Splitter (ABV 4.5%) GOLD
Parkers Piece (ABV 5%) BITTER

Wood SIBA

Wistanstow, Shropshire, SY7 8DG
☎ (01588) 672523 ⊕ woodbrewery.co.uk

The brewery opened in 1980 in buildings next to the Plough Inn, the brewery's only tied house. Steady growth over the years included the acquisition of the Sam Powell Brewery in 1991. The brewery was sold to drinks firm Yarrawaddie in 2018 and continues to operate, supplying around 200 outlets. !! ♦

Parish Bitter (ABV 3.8%) BLOND
A blend of malt and hops with a bitter aftertaste. Pale brown in colour.
Shropshire Lass (ABV 4%) GOLD
Beauty (ABV 4.2%) BITTER
Shropshire Lad (ABV 4.5%) BITTER

Tom Wood

See Lincolnshire Craft

Woodcote

Woodland Road, Dodford, Worcestershire, B61 9BT
☎ 07779 166174

⊠ Opened in 2015 as Woodcote Manor in former dairy outbuildings attached to the brewer's house, the name was shortened to Woodcote in 2020. The original one-barrel plant has now expanded to seven barrels at new premises nearby, with a new mash tun and copper. The regular beers are distributed to a number of local pubs. ♦ LIVE V

SSS (ABV 3.8%) GOLD
Half Cut (ABV 4.2%) PALE
Single Hop (ABV 4.4%) GOLD
Well-balanced golden bitter, light hop aromas with subtle melon, the initial sweetness is followed by a hint of ginger with hops predominating. Long and smooth hoppy finish.
Weavers Exclusive (ABV 4.4%) GOLD
IPA (ABV 4.6%) GOLD

Golden, well-balanced and hoppy, grapefruit aromas are followed by a pronounced hop and slightly spicy taste, with a lingering bitter finish.

Oatmeal Stout (ABV 4.9%) STOUT
Dark in colour, roasted malt, chocolate and coffee tones are evident in the aroma and flavour, leading to a satisfying slightly, bitter finish.

Cap'n Will's Rum & Raisin Stout (ABV 6%) SPECIALITY

Woodford Experiment

See Three Hills

Woodforde's SIBA

Broadland Brewery, Woodbastwick, Norfolk, NR13 6SW
☎ (01603) 720353 ⊕ woodfordes.co.uk

⊠ Founded in 1981 by two members of the Homebrewers' Society. Woodforde's is named after Parson Woodforde, the 18th century Norfolk diarist with a penchant for real ale. In 1989 the brewery moved to its current home at Woodbastwick. It has its own boreholes and brews using locally-grown Maris Otter. Investment in 2001 and 2008 more than doubled the production capacity. Brewery tap, the Fur & Feather, is located next door, and more than 800 outlets are supplied on a regular basis. ‼️ ▤ ◆ LIVE

Wherry (ABV 3.8%) BITTER
A sweet biscuit base with strawberry and a contrasting hoppy bitterness. Long and well-balanced with a noticeable citrusy encore.

Reedlighter (ABV 4%) GOLD
Well-balanced hop and grapefruit backbone with a sweet biscuity undercurrent. Full-bodied with a pronounced bittersweet ending.

Bure Gold (ABV 4.3%) GOLD
Singularly citrus throughout with a succinct hop garland. Sweet biscuit floats in the background over a bitter footing.

Nelson's (ABV 4.5%) BITTER
Malt, hop and vine fruits dominate this full-bodied, well-balanced brew. Caramel and bitterness add depth and contrast.

Volt (ABV 4.5%) PALE
Rollicking mix of lemon, lime, hop and biscuit. Slightly astringent, resinous notes add crispness and character at the end.

Nog (ABV 4.6%) OLD
Echoes of Pontefract cake dominate. A plummy sweetness is aided by a dry bitterness and a hint of caramel.

Woodman's

Unit 3, Moorland Road Business Park, Indian Queens, Cornwall, TR9 6GX
☎ (01726) 869004 ⊕ woodmanswildale.co.uk

Wild food forager, Stuart Woodman, started brewing in 2016. He brews a core range of speciality beers, plus seasonal and special brews, with most featuring fruits and herbs. Having sold the brewery to Louis Simpson, Stuart remains as head brewer, and is trialling a number of new beers. A new set of regular beers will result, alongside the continuing and diverse seasonal and short-term brews. ‼️ ◆ LIVE

Woodstock (NEW)

24 Shipton Road, Woodstock, Oxfordshire, OX20 1LL
☎ 07481 569419 ⊕ woodstockbrewery.co.uk

A new nanobrewery which started in mid-2021 on 70-litre brewing kit. A range of bottle-conditioned beers are produced, which are sold online, at local pubs and shops and at local markets through the Thames Valley Farmers' Market cooperative. LIVE

WooHa

Upper Hempriggs Farm, Kinloss, IV36 2UB
☎ (01667) 459929 ☎ 07811 260732
⊕ woohabrewing.com

Wooha opened in 2015 using a 10 barrel plant. It specialises in producing bottle-conditioned beers with cask-conditioned ales being brewed on demand for beer festivals. Pubs and retail outlets are supplied locally in Nairn, and across Scotland. In 2017 the brewery moved to larger premises and in 2021 it was sold to the US-based North Coast Brewing Co. LIVE

Wookey (NEW)

Albion Dockside Building, Hanover Place, Bristol, BS1 6UT ⊕ wookeyale.co.uk

Wookey Ale was established in 2020 by Samuel and Simon to create a local beer for the famous village of Wookey Hole. ◆ V

Witch Way Home (ABV 4%) PALE

Woolybutt

31 Alexandra Road, Hull, East Yorkshire, HU5 2NS
☎ 07966 511242 ⊕ woolybuttbrewshed.co.uk

⊛Woolybutt Brew Shed is a two-barrel brewery. Rob Sutherland moved to commercial brewing after years of homebrewing experience.

English Pale Ale (ABV 4.4%)

Worcester

Arch 49, Cherry Tree Walk, Worcester, WR1 3AU
☎ 07906 432049 ⊕ worcesterbrewingco.co.uk

A small brewery in the heart of Worcester and home to Sabrina Ales. A range of beers is brewed in rotation using traditional British hops, named with a loose association to the English Civil War.

Holy Ground (ABV 4.2%) BITTER
Powick Porter (ABV 4.5%) PORTER
1651 (ABV 5.1%) BITTER
Sabrina's Dark Ruby Ale (ABV 5.5%) BITTER

Working Hand

🍴 Three Horseshoes, Pit House Lane, Leamside, DH4 6QQ
☎ (0191) 5842394 ☎ 07703 337556
⊕ threehorseshoesleamside.co.uk

Brewing began in 2012 using a 2.5-barrel plant. Beers are available at the Three Horseshoes as well as the four other pubs in the group. The brewery was renamed the Working Hand Brewery in 2016 when Matthew Booth took over the brewing. In 2018 it upgraded to a seven-barrel plant. Brewing is currently suspended.

World's End

🍴 Crown Inn, 60 Wilcot Road, Pewsey, Wiltshire, SN9 5EL
☎ (01672) 562653 ⊕ thecrowninnpewsey.com

⊠ World's End Ales was established in 2009 on a one-barrel plant at the rear of the Crown Inn, Pewsey. World's

THE BREWERIES

End is the 18th century name for the area in which the brewery is located. ‼♦

Worsthorne SIBA

Unit 11 Siberia Mill, Holgate Street, Briercliffe, Lancashire, BB10 2HQ
☎ (01282) 422588 ☎ 07815 708289
⊕ worsthornebrewingcompany.co.uk

Worsthorne began brewing in 2011 using a 5.5-barrel plant. The brewery moved to larger premises behind the original building in 2014. An expansion to a 10-barrel plant was carried out in 2016, including a licensed visitor centre. More than 150 outlets are supplied. ‼♦

Gold (ABV 3.6%) GOLD
Packhorse (ABV 3.7%) BITTER
Palamino (ABV 3.9%) BLOND
Some Like It Blonde (ABV 3.9%) BLOND
Summer Nights (ABV 3.9%) BLOND
Chestnut Mare (ABV 4%) BITTER
Chinook (ABV 4%) BITTER
Great White (ABV 4.2%) GOLD
Red Man (ABV 4.2%) GOLD
Old Trout (ABV 4.5%) RED
Blackthorne Stout (ABV 4.9%) STOUT
Colliers Clog (ABV 5.5%) PALE

Worthington's

See Heritage

Wrexham Lager

42 St Georges Crescent, Wrexham, LL13 8DB
☎ (01978) 266222 ⊕ wrexhamlager.co.uk

Lager was first brewed in Wrexham in 1882 and returned to the town in 2011, following the closure in 2000 of the original Wrexham Lager brewery. This new German-built, 50-hectolitre brewery produces keg and bottled lagers but no cask beers are produced.

Wriggle Valley SIBA

Unit 4, The Sidings, Station Road, Stalbridge, Dorset, DT10 2SS
☎ (01963) 363343 ☎ 07599 677139
⊕ wrigglevalleybrewery.co.uk

Wriggle Valley began brewing in 2014 using a three-barrel plant in a converted garage. It relocated to Stalbridge in 2017 to an industrial unit and changed hands in 2020. Beers are mainly supplied within a 20-mile radius of the brewery. A taproom was opened at the brewery in 2019. ➤♦LIVE♦

Dorset Nomad (ABV 3.8%) BITTER
Golden Bear (ABV 4%) BLOND
Golden ale with fruit notes in the aroma and taste leading to a dry, slightly astringent finish.
Dorset Pilgrim (ABV 4.2%) BITTER
A traditional best bitter with some malt and fruit in the aroma developing hop and bitterness in the taste with a more bitter, balanced finish.
Copper Hoppa (ABV 4.5%) BITTER
Light malt and hop aroma with a relatively sweet taste predominated by fruit and caramel which linger in a pleasant aftertaste along with slight bitterness coming forward.
Valley Gold (ABV 4.5%) GOLD
Golden ale with some fruit and hop in the aroma with bitterness and astringency developing with a light citrus note in the taste and through to a bitter aftertaste.

Wriggly Monkey SIBA

B.131 Motor Transport Yard, Bicester Heritage Centre, Bicester, Oxfordshire, OX26 5HA
☎ (01869) 246599 ☎ 07590 749062
⊕ wrigglymonkeybrewery.com

Established in 2018 on a 1.25-barrel kit, the brewery and its taproom are based in an old motor transport workshop at an automotive centre on the old RAF Bicester site. It is named after the compartment of a chain-drive mechanism of the Fraser Nash car. ‼➤♦

Super Sports (ABV 3.2%) PALE
Gullwing Lager (ABV 4%) BLOND
Full Tilt (ABV 4.2%) BITTER
Charabanc (ABV 5.3%) BITTER
Ambassador (ABV 5.5%) IPA

Wrong Side of the Tracks

South Park Crescent, Catford, London, SE6 1JW
☎ 07493 499494 ⊕ wrongsideofthetracks.beer

A small scale home brewer selling bottled beers commercially to local bottle shops and from its webshop with delivery to the local area.

Wrytree

Unit 1, Wrytree Park, Greenhead, Northumberland, CA8 7JA

Brewing commenced in 2015 as Pit Top Brewery. The name changed to Wrytree in 2019.

Gold (ABV 3.9%) GOLD
Copper (ABV 4%) BITTER

Wychwood

Eagle Maltings, The Crofts, Witney, Oxfordshire, OX28 4DP
☎ (01993) 890800 ⊕ wychwood.co.uk

Wychwood brewery is located in the Cotswold market town of Witney. The brewers take inspiration from the myths and legends associated with the ancient medieval Wychwood forest. Part of Carlsberg Marston's Brewing Co. ‼➤♦LIVE♦

Hobgoblin Gold (ABV 4.2%) GOLD
Hobgoblin Ruby (ABV 4.5%) BITTER

Wye Valley Meadery (NEW)

Unit 5F, Severn Bridge Industrial Estate, Caldicot, NP26 5PR ☎ 07402 983998

Office: 19 River View, School Hill, Chepstow, NP16 5AX ✉ hey@wyevalleymeadery.co.uk

Brewing began in 2021. The brewery offers beers infused with honey from its own hives. Bottles and casks are available. Some output may be under the name of Hive Mind Brewery.

Wye Valley SIBA IFBB

Stoke Lacy, Herefordshire, HR7 4HG
☎ (01885) 490505 ☎ 07970 597937
⊕ wyevalleybrewery.co.uk

Founded in 1985 in the back of a village pub, this award-winning brewery is now producing around 250,000 pints per week and delivers direct to more than 1,200 pubs, including eight of its own. Its products are also available through selected wholesale and retail stockists. ‼➤♦LIVE

Bitter (ABV 3.7%) BITTER

A beer whose aroma gives little hint of the bitter hoppiness that follows right through to the aftertaste.
The Hopfather (ABV 3.9%) BITTER
HPA (ABV 4%) PALE
A pale, hoppy, malty brew with a hint of sweetness before a dry finish.
Butty Bach (ABV 4.5%) BITTER
Wholesome Stout (ABV 4.6%) STOUT
A smooth and satisfying stout with a bitter edge to its roast flavours. The finish combines roast grain and malt.

Wylam

Palace of Arts, Exhibition Park, Newcastle upon Tyne, NE2 4PZ ⊕ wylambrewery.co.uk

Wylam commenced brewing in 2000 on a 4.5-barrel plant. Originally brewing in Heddon-on-the-Wall in Northumberland, the brewery moved to Newcastle upon Tyne in 2016 with a new 30-barrel brew kit with an on-site brewery tap. ‼♦⬥

Galatia (ABV 3.9%) PALE
Gold Tankard (ABV 4%) GOLD
Fresh, clean flavour, full of hops. This golden ale has a hint of citrus in the finish.
Collingwood (ABV 4.1%) BITTER
Swipe Right (ABV 4.7%) SPECIALITY
Puffing Billy (ABV 5.5%) IPA
Jakehead IPA (ABV 6.3%) IPA

Wylde Sky

Unit 8a, The Grip, Hadstock Road, Linton, Cambridgeshire, CB21 4XN
☎ (01223) 778350 ⊕ wyldeskybrewing.com

Established in 2018, the brewery has a purpose-built, 10-barrel plant, brewing small batches of innovative beers in a range of styles from around the world. All beers are unfined, unfiltered and unpasteurised. A number of outlets are supplied in the area and an on-site taproom is open Wednesdays to Sundays (some seasonal variations.) ‼▬♦⬥

Wyre Piddle

See Ambridge

XT SIBA

Notley Farm, Chearsley Road, Long Crendon, Buckinghamshire, HP18 9ER
☎ (01844) 208310 ⊕ xtbrewing.com

XT started brewing in 2011 using an 18-barrel plant. It supplies direct to pubs across southern England and the Midlands. The brewery taproom and shop sell draught and bottled beers to drink in or take out. A range of limited edition, but ever-changing, one-off brews is produced under the Animal Brewing Co name.
‼▬♦LIVE⬥

Four (ABV 3.8%) BITTER
Hop Kitty (ABV 3.9%) GOLD
One (ABV 4.2%) BLOND
Three (ABV 4.2%) PALE
Eight (ABV 4.5%) PORTER
Fifteen (ABV 4.5%) PALE
Squid Ink (ABV 5.5%) STOUT

Xtreme

Unit 21-22 Alfric Square, Maxwell Road, Woodston, Peterborough, Cambridgeshire, PE2 7JP ☎ 07825 680932 ⊕ xtremeales.com

The Hunt brothers took over Xtreme Ales in 2020. The core range of ales is retained, along with some of the popular seasonals, but a number of new brews have also been added. Bumbling Brewery beers are also brewed for the Bumble Inn micropub, Peterborough. ‼♦

PiXie APA (ABV 3.7%) PALE
Pigeon Ale 20 (ABV 4.3%) BITTER
Red FoX (ABV 4.5%) RED
OatiX Stout (ABV 4.6%) STOUT
GalaXy IPA (ABV 5%) IPA
Special Bitter (ABV 5%) BITTER
Triple Hop Xtra IPA (ABV 5%) PALE
XPorter (ABV 6%) PORTER
SaXquatch (ABV 8.6%) OLD

XYLO

⬛ Unit 1 2-14 High Street, Margate, Kent, CT9 1AT
☎ (01843) 229403 ⊕ xylobrew.com

Neil Wright and Ben Atkins set up the XYLO brewery and pub in 2019 using a four-barrel brew plant built in the pub cellar. ‼

Yard of Ale

⬛ Surtees Arms, Chilton Lane, Ferryhill, DL17 0DH
☎ (01740) 655933 ☎ 07540 733513
⊕ thesurteesarms.co.uk

Established in 2008, the 2.5-barrel microbrewery supplies ales to its brewery tap, the Surtees Arms, beer festivals and to a growing number of pubs. ‼▬♦LIVE

Yardsman

See Hercules

Yates' SIBA

Unit 4c, Langbridge Business Centre, Newchurch, Isle of Wight, PO36 0NP
☎ (01983) 867878 ⊕ yates-brewery.co.uk

Brewing started in 2000 on a five-barrel plant at the Inn at St Lawrence. In 2009 it moved to Newchurch and upgraded to 10-barrel plant. The brewery was moved on the same site in 2015 to sit alongside the wholesale unit at Newchurch. ‼♦

Golden Bitter (ABV 4%) GOLD
Beachcomber (ABV 4.3%) BLOND
Holy Joe (ABV 4.9%) SPECIALITY
Dark Side of the Wight (ABV 5%) SPECIALITY

Yelland Manor

Lower Yelland Farm, Yelland, Barnstaple, Devon, EX31 3EN ☎ 07770 267592
✉ yellandmanor@gmail.com

Located on the Taw Estuary and close to the Tarka Trail, this five-barrel plant in a converted milking parlour was established in 2013. It supplies a small number of local pubs and hotels, although the majority of sales are now made from the premises, either as takeaways or for consumption as part of a 'brewery experience'. Small functions are also catered for, together with regular steak, and fish n' chip evenings. ♦

The Tarka Special (ABV 4.1%) BITTER
Standard (ABV 4.2%) BITTER

Yeovil SIBA

Unit 5, Bofors Park, Artillery Road, Lufton Trading Estate, Yeovil, Somerset, BA22 8YH

☎ (01935) 414888 ⊕ yeovilales.com

⊗ Yeovil Ales was established in 2006 using an 18-barrel plant. More than 300 pubs are supplied in the South West. ‼ ≋ ♦ V

Hopkandi (ABV 3.8%) GOLD
Star Gazer (ABV 4%) BITTER
Easy-drinking, tawny, standard bitter. Malt and toffee in the aroma lead to a predominantly sweet flavour. Short bitter finish.
Summerset (ABV 4.1%) BLOND
Ruby (ABV 4.5%) BITTER
POSH IPA (ABV 5.4%) PALE

Yetman's

Bayfield Farm Barns, Bayfield Brecks Farm, Bayfield, Norfolk, NR25 7DZ ☎ 07774 809016 ⊕ yetmans.net

A 2.5-barrel plant built by Moss Brew was installed in restored medieval barns near Holt in 2005. The brewery supplies local free trade outlets. LIVE

Red (ABV 3.8%) BITTER
A plummy malt carapace with a balanced hop and caramel undercoat. Full-bodied and long lasting. Bittersweet notes slowly intercede.
Amber (ABV 4.2%) BITTER
Orange (ABV 4.2%) BITTER
Stout (ABV 4.2%) STOUT
Green (ABV 4.8%) BITTER

Yonder

The Workshop, Rookery Farm, Binegar, Radstock, Somerset, BA3 4UL
☎ (01749) 681378 ⊕ brewyonder.co.uk

A farmhouse-style brewery founded by Stuart Winstone and Jasper Tupman, formally of Wild Beer fame, in 2018. Yonder focuses on wild yeasts, foraged ingredients and barrel-aging. All ingredients are sourced locally, within about 40 minutes of the brewery. ♦

York

c/o Black Sheep Brewing, Wellgarth, Masham, Ripon, North Yorkshire, HG4 4EN ⊕ york-brewery.co.uk

York started production in 1996 and was bought out of administration by Black Sheep Brewery (qv) in 2018. Four pubs are owned in York and Leeds. Brewing of all York Brewery beers is temporarily taking place at Black Sheep until new premises can be found. ‼ ♦

Yorkshire Brewhouse

Matrich House, Goulton Street, Hull, East Yorkshire, HU3 4DD
☎ (01482) 755199 ⊕ yorkshirebrewhouse.com

☺ Founded in 2017 by friends Jon Constable and Simon Cooke as a weekend family venture. The brewery started with a 200 litre capacity and has now expanded to 2,500 litre per batch. It supplies cask, bag in box and bottle-conditioned ale to East Yorkshire pubs and outlets, and online. Most of the beers are given names that mirror Yorkshire dialect or have a local connection. LIVE V

1904 (ABV 3.8%) BITTER
Reet (ABV 3.8%) BITTER
EYPA (ABV 3.9%) PALE
Tenfoot (ABV 3.9%) BARLEY
Ey Up (ABV 4%) BITTER
Faithful (ABV 4.5%) STOUT
Flippin Eck (ABV 4.6%) OLD
Red Robin (ABV 4.6%) STOUT

Well Chuffed (ABV 4.9%) PALE

Yorkshire Coast

▤ 105 Hilderthorpe Road, Bridlington, East Yorkshire, YO15 3ET ⊕ yorkshire-coast-brewery.com

Established in the basement of the Funny Onion pub in 2019, Yorkshire Coast Brew Co was launched commercially in 2020. With 30 years experience of brewing, head brewer Steve Golden brews small batches of traditional ales. ‼

Yorkshire Dales

Abbey Works, Askrigg, North Yorkshire, DL8 4LP
☎ (01969) 622027 ☎ 07818 035592
⊕ yorkshiredalesbrewery.com

☺ Situated in the heart of the Yorkshire Dales, brewing started in a converted milking parlour in 2005. In 2016 the brewery moved to larger premises. More than 150 pubs are supplied throughout the north of England. A tap and bottle shop opened at the brewery in 2017.
‼ ♦ LIVE ✦

Butter Tubs (ABV 3.7%) GOLD
Askrigg Bitter (ABV 3.8%) BITTER
Bainbridge Blonde (ABV 3.8%) BLOND
Buckden Pike (ABV 3.9%) BLOND
Nappa Scar (ABV 4%) GOLD
Muker Silver (ABV 4.1%) BLOND
Askrigg Ale (ABV 4.3%) PALE
Garsdale Smokebox (ABV 5.6%) SPECIALITY

Yorkshire Heart SIBA

The Vineyard, Pool Lane, Nun Monkton, North Yorkshire, YO26 8EL
☎ (01423) 330716 ☎ 07838 030067
⊕ yorkshireheart.com

☺ Yorkshire Heart has been brewing since 2011 and is situated near to York adjacent to the Yorkshire Heart vineyard and winery run by the same family. The brewery uses a five-barrel plant. ‼ ≋ ♦

Hearty Bitter (ABV 3.7%) BITTER
Rhubarbeer (ABV 3.7%) SPECIALITY
Blonde (ABV 3.9%) BLOND
SilverHeart IPA (ABV 4%) PALE
Blackheart Stout (ABV 4.8%) STOUT
Platinum EPA (ABV 5%) PALE
Ghost Porter (ABV 5.4%) PORTER

Young's

See Eagle

Zapato

Unit 1a, Holme Mills, West Slaithwaite Road, Marsden, Huddersfield, West Yorkshire, HD7 6LS
☎ (01484) 841201 ☎ 07788 513432
⊕ zapatobrewery.co.uk

Small company, established in 2016, that nomadic brewed in the Leeds and Manchester areas prior to establishing a permanent home in Marsden. It produces innovative beers based in traditional European styles. Collaboration brews are a staple part of its output. ✦

Zepto

Graig Fawr Lodge, Blackbrook Road, Caerphilly, CF83 1NF ☎ 07951 505524 ⊕ zeptobrew.co.uk

Established in 2016, Zepto is a 100-litre brewery set up by CAMRA member Chris Sweet. Although production is mainly bottled, cask-conditioned beers are occasionally brewed. Brewing is currently suspended.

Zerodegrees SIBA

Blackheath: 29-31 Montpelier Vale, Blackheath, London, SE3 0TJ
☎ (020) 8852 5619

Bristol: 53 Colston Street, Bristol, BS1 5BA ☎ (0117) 925 2706

Cardiff: 27 Westgate Street, Cardiff, CF10 1DD
☎ (029) 2022 9494

Reading: 9 Bridge Street, Reading, RG1 2LR ☎ (0118) 959 7959 ⏺ zerodegrees.co.uk

Brewing started in 2000 in Blackheath, London, and now four brewpubs are owned, each incorporating a computer-controlled, German plant producing unfiltered and unfined ales and lagers. All beers use natural ingredients, are suitable for vegetarians, and are served from tanks using air pressure (not CO2).

Zest SIBA

Heath Lane, Barkston Heath, Lincolnshire, NG32 2DE
☎ (01476) 572135

⏺In 2020 Zest was rebranded from Oldershaw Brewrey, which had been brewing since 1997. Owned and run by brewster Kathy Britton, Zest produces a core range of beers in both traditional and contemporary styles, as well as seasonal ales. Bespoke bottled and cask beers can be created to order and a mobile bar service is also available. ‼️🍺♦

Heavenly Blonde (ABV 3.8%) BITTER
Newton's Drop (ABV 4.1%) BITTER
Balanced malt and hops but with a strong bitter, lingering taste in this mid-brown beer.

Blond Bombshell (ABV 4.3%) GOLD
Mosaic Blonde (ABV 4.3%) BLOND
Atomic IPA (ABV 4.5%) GOLD
Blonde Volupta (ABV 5%) BLOND

Zoo SIBA

Excal House, Capel Hendre Industrial Estate, Ammanford, SA14 3SJ ☎ 07889 592614
⏺ zoo-brew.com

Zoo Brew was established in 2019. It produces a small range of cask-conditioned and bottled ales. Beer is mainly supplied to local pubs plus home deliveries.

Amman Eagle (ABV 4.4%) GOLD
Towy Tiger (ABV 5%) BITTER
Merlin's Own (ABV 5.2%) PALE

Zulu Alpha

51b Symondscliffe Way, Caldicot, NP26 5PW ☎ 07578 196275 / 07899 794294
✉ info@zulualphabrewing.co.uk

Brewing since 2018, Zulu Alpha Brewing consists of a seven-barrel brewhouse with four fermenters. Open days are held at the brewery, which has a licensed bar. One of the ales is a regular at the Cellar, Caldicot.

New Horizon (ABV 4%) SPECIALITY
Voyager (ABV 4.8%) PALE
Evolution (ABV 5.2%) PALE

Zymurgorium

Unit 19, Irlam Business Centre, Soapstone Way, Irlam, M44 6RA ⏺ zymurgorium.com

The UK's first craft meadery and Manchester's first distillery. In combination with the brewery it was established in Irlam in 2013. Most of its output is in bottled form.

Towering ambitions

There are several references in the Guide's breweries section to 'tower breweries'. They were buildings designed in Victorian times along strict utilitarian lines, with the brewing process flowing logically from floor to floor, without the need for pumps and electrical devices. The system is best exemplified today by the Hook Norton Brewery in Oxfordshire.

Tanks on the top floor hold water or 'brewing liquor'. Below the tanks are the malt and hop stores that hold the vital raw materials needed for the brewing process. Mills crush the malt into grist, made up of fine cereal powder and coarser parts of the grain that act as a filter during the mashing stage of brewing.

The grain drops down a floor into the mash tuns, where it is thoroughly mixed with heated liquor. During the mashing period, natural enzymes in the malt convert starch into fermentable sugar or maltose. One floor down, the sweet sugary extract, known as wort, is transferred to coppers where it is vigorously boiled with hops. Hops not only add bitterness to beer but also impart delightful piny, resiny, spicy, peppery and floral aromas and flavours.

At the end of the copper boil, the hopped wort is cooled in a type of refrigeration unit known as a paraflow, then run into fermenting vessels one floor down, where yeast is added. During the course of seven days, the yeast consumes the malt sugars and creates both alcohol and carbon dioxide. When the yeast has finished its work, the beer is stored in conditioning tanks for a few days to purge itself of rough alcohols and is then run to the ground floor where it is racked into casks prior to delivery to pubs. At this stage, additional hops may be added to the cask for aroma with a dosage of brewing sugar to encourage a strong second fermentation.

THE BREWERIES

Closed breweries

The following breweries have closed or gone out of business since the 2021 Guide was published:

3 Piers, Poulton-le-Fylde, Lancashire
Abington, Buckingham, Bucks
Arcadian, Cardiff, Glamorgan
Arrow, Kington, Herefordshire
Ashleyhay, Wirksworth, Derbyshire
Bad Joke, Amersham, Buckinghamshire
Bell Street, Henley-on-Thames, Oxfordshire
Bellinger's, Grove, Oxfordshire
Bexar County, Peterborough, Cambridgeshire
Biggar, Barrow-in-Furness, Cumbria
Bilbrough Top, Bilbrough, North Yorkshire
Bodachra, Potterton, Aberdeen & Grampian
Box Social, Newburn, Tyne & Wear
Bullmastiff, Cardiff, Glamorgan
Burton Old Cottage, Burton-upon-Trent, Staffordshire
Bute, Rothesay: Isle of Bute, Argyll & the Isles
Cellar Boys, SE16: Bermondsey, Greater London
Cheadle, Cheadle, Greater Manchester
Cotleigh, Wiveliscombe, Somerset
Craft, The, Southport, Merseyside
Craft Academy, SE24: Herne Hill, Greater London
Credence, Amble, Tyne & Wear
Croft, Bristol, Gloucestershire & Bristol
Derventio, Darley Abbey, Derbyshire
Eel Pie, Twickenham, Greater London
Elixir, Edinburgh, Edinburgh & the Lothians

Engineer, High Hurstwood, East Sussex
Epic Brewing, Manchester, Greater Manchester
Eyeball, Dunbar, Edinburgh & the Lothians
Faringdon, Faringdon, Oxfordshire
Fintry, Fintry, Loch Lomond, Stirling & the Trossachs
Granite Rock, Penryn, Cornwall
Halfpenny, Lechlade-on-Thames, Gloucestershire & Bristol
Haresfoot, Aston Clinton, Buckinghamshire
Hay Rake, Littleborough, Greater Manchester
Heidrun, Glasgow, Greater Glasgow & Clyde Valley
Hillside, Longhope, Gloucestershire & Bristol
Holy Well, Bolton, Greater Manchester
Hop Therapy, Draycote Cerne, Wiltshire
Hopburst, Darlington, Durham
Hungry Bear, Leeds, West Yorkshire
John Thompson, Melbourne, Derbyshire
Keppels, Rochford, Essex
Kirrie, Kirriemuir, Tayside
Late Night Hype, Clydebank, Greater Glasgow & Clyde Valley
Maldon, Maldon, Essex
Mechanic, E1: Bethnal Green, Greater London
Moseley, Moseley, West Midlands
Mr Grundy's, Derby, Derbyshire
Nutbrook, West Hallam, Derbyshire
Odcombe, Odcombe, Somerset

Old Moll Spring, Honley, West Yorkshire
Old Windsor, Windsor, Berkshire
Plot Five, Biggleswade, Bedfordshire
Project 88, NW2: Willesden Green, Greater London
Providence, Preston, Lancashire
Purple Cow, Kettering, Northamptonshire
RAN, Stoke-on-Trent, Staffordshire
Range, Lympne, Kent
Red Dragon, New Inn, Gwent
Red Moon, Solihull, West Midlands
Remedy, Stockport, Greater Manchester
Rocket Town, Darlington, Durham
Roundhill, Stockton-on-Tees, Durham
Scribbler's, Stapleford, Nottinghamshire
Strata, Whitworth, Lancashire
Summershed, Wigginton, Hertfordshire
Tantum, Poole, Cheshire
Tunnel, Hinckley, Leicestershire
Two Finches, N3: Finchley, Greater London
Watling Street, N17: Tottenham, Greater London
Watts Brewing?, Stockport, Greater Manchester
Websters, Wollaston, West Midlands
Weltons, Horsham, West Sussex
White Rock, St Sampsons: Guernsey, Channel Islands

Future breweries

The following new breweries have been notified to the Guide and will start to produce beer during 2021/2022. In a few cases they were in production during the summer of 2021 but were too late for a full listing:

Azvex, Derby, Derbyshire

Billy Ruffian's, Plymouth, Devon

Bishop Auckland, Bishop Auckland, Durham

Bishy, Bishopthorpe, North Yorkshire

Black Box, Southend on Sea, Essex

Bredy, Burton Bradstock, Dorset

Brewhouse & Kitchen, Worthing, West Sussex

Clovelly, Bideford, Devon

Common Rioters, SE18: Plumstead, Greater London

Dargavel, Langbank, Greater Glasgow & Clyde Valley

Dookit, Glasgow, Greater Glasgow & Clyde Valley

Drum & Monkey, Stamford, Lincolnshire

Epochal, Glasgow, Greater Glasgow & Clyde Valley

Good Name, Loughborough, Leicestershire

House, Bedford, Bedfordshire

Ingol Village, Preston, Lancashire

Maverick, Farnham, Surrey

Mine, St Ives, Cornwall

Monkey, Lymington, Hampshire

Pinkers, Weston-super-Mare, Somerset

St Felix, SE1: Southwark, Greater London

Shed Brewery, Horsham, West Sussex

Sommar, Birmingham, West Midlands

Three Hounds, Beckenham, Greater London

West Coast, Bispham, Lancashire

Yaptown, Arundel, West Sussex

Breweries for sale

The following breweries are reported as being for sale:

Double Top, Worksop, Nottinghamshire

Fool Hardy, Heaton Norris, Greater Manchester

Geeves, Barnsley, South Yorkshire

Goodall's, Alsager, Staffordshire

Hop Stuff, SE28: Thamesmead, Greater London

Oxted, Oxted, Surrey

Salamander, Bradford, West Yorkshire

Shropshire Brewer, Longden Common, Shropshire

Silver Street, Bury, Greater Manchester

Trinity Ales, Gisleham, Suffolk

Violet Cottage, Gwaelod y Garth, Glamorgan

Hook Norton brewery, Oxfordshire, still uses shire horses to deliver to local pubs

Indexes & Further Information

Beers index

These beers refer to those in bold type in the breweries section (beers in regular production) and so therefore do not include seasonal, special or occasional beers that may be mentioned elsewhere in the text.

Black IPA Incredible *726*
  Isca *728*
Black Jack Porter Cliff Quay *665*
  Milltown *755*
Black Jack Hunters *725*
Black Katz Burnside *655*
Black Knight Ludlow *747*
Black Lion Porter Goldmark *705*
Black Listed IBA Farr Brew *691*
Black Magic IPA Snowhill *801*
Black Mass Abbeydale *617*
Black Moth Tipples *818*
Black Mountain Stout Tudor *824*
Black Noise Dorking *680*
Black Ops Rother Valley *790*
  Taw Valley *812*
Black Panther Mill Valley *755*
  Panther *773*
Black Pear Malvern Hills *750*
Black Pearl Milestone *754*
Black Peggy Shottle Farm *798*
Black Perle Weird Beard *833*
Black Pheasant Pheasantry *776*
Black Pig Wantsum *832*
Black Pike Clouded Minds *666*
Black Port Blackedge *640*
Black Porter Captain Cook *659*
Black Prince Wantsum *832*
Black Ram Stout Kinver *734*
Black Rat Rat *783*
Black Road East NEIPA St Ives *792*
Black Road Stout Grey Trees *709*
Black Rock Noss Beer Works *766*
  Tudor *824*
Black Ryeno Crafty Little *672*
Black Sabbath Brunswick *653*
Black Sail Hesket Newmarket *718*
Black Spell Porter Forest, The *697*
Black Stag Peak *774*
Black Stallion Arundel *624*
Black Star Keswick *733*
  Phipps *776*
Black Sun Potbelly *780*
Black Swan Mild Vale *829*
Black Taxi to the Moon Angels &
  Demons *621*
Black Troll Tillingbourne *817*
Black Ven Gyle 59 *711*
  Lyme Regis (Gyle 59) *711*
Black Volt Shortts *797*
Black Widow 8 Sail *616*
  Brew Monster *647*
Black William Adur *618*
Black Blackedge *640*
  Boss *644*
  Castle Eden *660*
  Chiltern *663*
  Lancaster *737*
  Tatton *812*
Blackbeerble Stout
  Beerblefish *632*
Blackberry Porter Elgood's *687*
  Mauldons *752*
  S&P *791*
Blackbird Pig & Porter *777*
Blackeyed Susan Kissingate *735*
Blackfoot Brunning & Price
  (Tombstone) *820*
Blackhall English Stout
  Hexhamshire *719*
Blackheart Stout Yorkshire
  Heart *846*
Blackheath Stout Fixed Wheel *695*
Blackhorse Brick *650*
Blackjack Mild AJ's *618*

Blackmoor Goose Eye *705*
Blacksmith Handsome *713*
Blacksmith's Gold Little
  London *742*
Blacksmiths Ale Coniston *668*
Blackthorne Stout Worsthorne *844*
Blackwater Mild Crouch Vale *674*
Blade Prior's Well *781*
Blanco Blonde Sheffield *796*
Blaven Isle of Skye *729*
Blaydon Brick Firebrick *694*
Blaze Boss *644*
Blea Moor Porter Three Peaks *816*
BLH4 Newark *763*
Blighty Ben's *634*
  Northern Whisper *766*
The Blind Butler Posh Boys *780*
Blind Poet New River *763*
Blind Side Crafty Brewing *671*
Blind Tiger Springhead *804*
Blindside Front Row *700*
Blisland Gold Dow Kammel *682*
Blitzen Platform 5 *779*
Blizzard Atlas (Orkney) *770*
Blodeuwedd Lleu *743*
Blodwen Gwaun Valley *711*
Blond Bombshell Zest *847*
Blond Moment Stamps *804*
Blond Witch Moorhouse's *758*
Blond Castle Eden *660*
  Outstanding *772*
Blonde Ale Atom *625*
  Fuddy Duck *700*
  Quirky *783*
Blonde Ambition GT *710*
  Tonbridge *820*
Blonde Bach Big Bog *635*
Blonde Bear Little Critters *741*
Blonde Beauty Dark Horse *675*
Blonde Bird Greyhound *710*
Blonde Bombshell Old Mill *768*
Blonde Knight Eden River *686*
The Blonde Maid Posh Boys *780*
Blonde Session Ale Nene Valley
  (NVB) *762*
Blonde Star Anarchy *620*
  Silhill *798*
Blonde Summit Withnell's *841*
Blonde Vixen Wily Fox *840*
Blonde Volupta Zest *847*
Blonde Voyage Campervan *659*
Blonde 3 Brewers of St Albans *615*
  Acorn *617*
  Arran *623*
  Backyard *626*
  Black Isle *639*
  Black Storm *639*
  Blackedge *640*
  Born *643*
  Boss *644*
  Bosun's *644*
  Bridgehouse *650*
  Cerne Abbas *661*
  Clevedon *665*
  Coach House *666*
  Daleside *675*
  Derwent *678*
  Dovedale *681*
  Dukeries *683*
  Elland *687*
  Ennerdale *688*
  Forge *697*
  Freewheelin' *699*
  Great Corby *708*
  Green Duck *709*

  Healey's *716*
  Ilkley *726*
  Jolly Boys *731*
  Lakeland *736*
  Lancaster *737*
  Ludlow *747*
  Lytham *747*
  Mordue (Blue) *641*
  Neepsend *761*
  Pig Iron *777*
  Quartz *782*
  River Leven *787*
  Rock Solid *789*
  Saltaire *794*
  Settle *795*
  Stancill *804*
  Tatton *812*
  True North *824*
  Windswept *841*
  Wishbone *841*
  Yorkshire Heart *846*
Blonde+ Stod Fold *806*
Blonded Snowhill *801*
Blondie Shortts *797*
  TOPS (The Olde Potting
  Shed) *821*
Blood Revenge Black Metal *639*
Bloodhound Hairy Dog *712*
Blorenge Tudor *824*
Blue Ensign Breakwater *647*
Blue Hills Bitter Driftwood
  Spars *683*
Blue Sky Drinking Arbor *622*
Blue Sky Tea Wigan
  Brewhouse *838*
Blue Top Old Dairy *768*
Blue Atlantic *625*
Bluebeary Beartown *630*
Bluebell Best 360° *615*
Blueberry Classic Bitter Coach
  House *666*
Blueberry Hill Porter Big Bog *636*
Blueberry Porter Muirhouse *760*
Blueberry and Vanilla Oatmeal
  Stout Tarn Hows *812*
Bluebird Bitter Coniston *668*
Bluebird Premium XB
  Coniston *668*
Bluebird Lenton Lane *739*
Bluenette Church Hanbrewery *664*
Blues Briggs Signature *651*
  Rother Valley *790*
Bluesbreaker Cheshire
  Brewhouse *663*
Blunderbus Coach House *666*
Blunderbuss Clavell & Hind *665*
Blẃbri Twt Lol *827*
Boadicea Rother Valley *790*
Boar D'eau Slaughterhouse *800*
Boardwalk Beatnikz Republic *631*
Boathouse Blonde
  Brack'N'Brew *645*
Boathouse Premium Blonde Beer
  Camerons *659*
Boathouse Wolf *842*
Bob 'ole 3P's *615*
BOB (Best of Both) Shottle
  Farm *798*
BOB Wickwar *838*
Bobbin's Bitter Three B's *814*
Boc Ban Ardgour *623*
Boc na Braiche Ardgour *623*
Bodicacia IV Corinium *669*
Bog Standard Bitter Big Bog *635*
Bog Trotter Poachers *779*

California Common Ale Fengate *693*
California Dreaming Hemlock *717*
California Steam Beer Draycott (Derbyshire) *682*
California Steam Tollgate *819*
California Wigan Brewhouse *838*
Calisto Elusive *687*
Call Me Blondie Hemlock *717*
Calmer Chameleon Brew York *648*
Cambrian Gold Stonehouse *807*
Cambridge Best Bitter Moonshine *757*
Cambridge Bitter Elgood's *687*
Cambridge Black Turpin's *825*
Cambridge Fellow Fellows *693*
Cambridge Pale Ale Moonshine *757*
Camouflage Black IPA Stealth *805*
Campania Team Toxic (Liverpool Brewing) *743*
Campfire Hophurst *723*
Camphillisner Ampersand *620*
Camps Comfort Roughacre *790*
Canary Pale Ale Headstocks (Rufford Abbey) *791*
Candelriggs Drone Valley *683*
Candidate US Session Pale Revolutions *786*
Candlewick Torrside *821*
Candy Soup No Frills Joe *764*
Cannonball Redcastle *785*
Canteen Cowboy Twisted *825*
The Cap Bitter Ampersand *620*
Cap'n Will's Rum & Raisin Stout Woodcote *843*
CAPA Elmesthorpe *687*
Capability Brown Rooster's *790*
Capitalist Hippie – Far Out Gyle 59 *711*
Capitalist Hippie – Skinny Gyle 59 *711*
Capitalist Hippie – Summer of Love Gyle 59 *711*
Cappuccino Stout Titanic *819*
Capt. Keebles Ramming Speed Witham *841*
Capt Lawrence Oates Gilbert White's *703*
Captain Bob Mighty Oak *754*
Captain Hopbeard Totally Brewed *821*
Captain Morrison IPA Five Kingdoms *695*
Captain Smith's Strong Ale Titanic *819*
Car Park Cuddle IVO *730*
Caradog Grey Trees *709*
Caramel Stout Grafton *706*
Cardi Bay Penlon *775*
Cariad Bang-On *627*
Carlisle Bell Carlisle *660*
Carlisle State Bitter Derwent *678*
Carpe Diem Roman Way *789*
Carpenter's Cask Crafty Beers *671*
Carr Lane Black Label Drone Valley *683*
Carronade Pale Ale Tryst *824*
Cart Blanche Kelburn *732*
Cart Noir Kelburn *732*
Cartway Gold Severn Valley *796*
Carver Doone Fat Belly *692*

Cascade IPA Burton Town *656*
Mighty Oak *754*
Robinsons *788*
Cascade Pale Bricknell *650*
Cascade Blackedge *640*
Gloucester *704*
Gwaun Valley *711*
Liverpool Brewing *742*
Nailmaker *760*
Saltaire *794*
Stockport *806*
Cascadia Harbour *714*
Casemate IPA Southsea *802*
Casino Wigan Brewhouse *838*
Cask Ale Banks's *627*
Cass 2CV Tigertops *817*
Cast Iron Stout Iron Pier *728*
Castle Black Merlin *753*
Castle Gold Tintagel *818*
Tyne Bank *827*
Castle on the Hill Breakwater *647*
Castle Hill Dukeries *683*
Dunham Massey *684*
Castle Arundel *624*
Castletown Bitter Bushy's *656*
Cat Nap Barngates *628*
Catbells Hesket Newmarket *718*
Catcher Pale Ale Flack Manor *695*
Cat's Eyes Darkland *676*
Cathedral Ale Hill Island *720*
Cat's Whiskers Colchester *666*
Caudle Bitter Langton *737*
Causeway Cornish Crown *669*
Cavalier Red Why Not *837*
Cave-Man Manning *750*
Cavegirl Bitter Kinver *734*
Cavendish Red Roughacre *790*
Cavendish Welbeck Abbey *834*
Celebration Ale Ulverston *828*
Celebration Maypole *753*
Turpin's *825*
Celestial Love Out There *771*
Cell Phone Zombies Anarchy *621*
Celtic Gold Hereford *718*
Celtic Pride Felinfoel *692*
Cemetery Gates Crafty Monkey *672*
Centaurus Stockport *806*
Centennial Bingley *637*
Chadkirk *661*
Centurion II Corinium *669*
Centurion Pale Ale Parker *774*
Centurion Dow Bridge *681*
Centurion's Ghost Ale York (Black Sheep) *639*
Century Gold Fixed Wheel *695*
Century Flagship *696*
Centwealial Milk Stout Weal *833*
Cerberus Stout Fox *698*
Chaff Farm Yard *691*
Chain Mail Pale Three Castles *815*
Chain Reaction Pale Ale Fixed Wheel *695*
Chained Oak Peakstones Rock *774*
Chairman Dave Amwell Springs *620*
Chalk Stream Ramsbury *783*
Raven Hill *784*
Challenger Ales of Scilly *618*
Kingstone *734*
ChamAleon Crafty Little *672*
Chamberlain Pale Ale Two Towers *827*
Chameleon Hop Kettle *722*
Chapel Rock Skinner's *799*

Chapel Street Porter Billericay *637*
Chapmans Map Dukeries *683*
Chapter 1 New Beginnings Fuggle Bunny *700*
Chapter 2 Cotton Tail Fuggle Bunny *700*
Chapter 3 Orchard Gold Fuggle Bunny *700*
Chapter 4 24 Carrot Fuggle Bunny *700*
Chapter 5 Oh Crumbs Fuggle Bunny *700*
Chapter 6 Hazy Summer Daze Fuggle Bunny *700*
Chapter 7 Russian Rare-Bit Fuggle Bunny *700*
Chapter 8 Jammy Dodger Fuggle Bunny *700*
Chapter 9 La La Land Fuggle Bunny *700*
Charabanc Wriggly Monkey *844*
Charcoal Burner High Weald *719*
Charisma Alechemy *618*
Charismatic Beermats *633*
Charon Ride *787*
Charrington IPA Heritage *718*
Charrington Oatmeal Stout Heritage *718*
Charter Lacons *736*
Chase Buster Beowulf *634*
Chaser Winster Valley (Handsome) *713*
Chasewater Bitter Beowulf *634*
Chatsworth Gold Peak *774*
Cheeky Blonde Bridgetown *650*
Cheeky Monkey Parkway *774*
Cheltenham Flyer Humpty Dumpty *724*
Cheltenham Gold Goff's *704*
Chennai Kissingate *735*
Chequered Flag Prescott (Hanlons) *713*
Silverstone *798*
Cheriton Porter Flower Pots *696*
Cherokee Tombstone *820*
Cherry Choc Bridgehouse *650*
Cherry Dark Titanic *819*
Cherry Raven Magpie *749*
Cherry Stout Tyne Bank *827*
Cheru Kol Brentwood *647*
Chesapeake Newby Wyke *763*
Cheshire Cat Weetwood *833*
Cheshire Gap Cheshire Brewhouse *663*
Cheshire Gold Coach House *666*
Cheshire IPA Dunham Massey *684*
Chesn't Cabin *657*
Chester Gold Oaks *767*
The Chesterton Windmill Hill *840*
Chestnut Mare Worsthorne *844*
Cheswold Doncaster *680*
Chew Chew Fallen *691*
Chick Weed Revenge Urban Chicken *829*
Chief Jester Farr Brew *691*
Chieftains Export Burnside *655*
Chiffchaff Digfield *679*
Chikara Lazy Bay *737*
Chilli Porter Billericay *637*
Chilli Hopstar *723*
Chimera IPA Downton *682*
Chinook & Grapefruit Bollington *643*
Chinook Blonde Goose Eye *706*

BEERS INDEX

Cotswold Best North Cotswold *765*
Cotswold Way Wickwar *838*
Cotton Clouds Craft Ale
  Donkeystone *680*
Country Bitter McMullen *748*
Country Bumpkin Country Life *670*
Country Wobbler Dartford
  Wobbler *676*
Countryman Tonbridge *820*
County Best Exeter *689*
Courthill Redcastle *785*
Courthouse Porter New
  Buildings *763*
Coventry Bitter Byatt's *657*
Covert Stealth *805*
Cowcatcher American Pale Ale
  East London *685*
Cowgirl Gold Fallen Angel *691*
Cowjuice Milk Stout
  Breakwater *647*
Crack Gold Twisted Oak *826*
Crack Hops Twisted Oak *826*
Crackatoa IPA CrackleRock *671*
Cracker Barngates *628*
  Quartz *782*
Crackerjack CrackleRock *671*
Craft Pale Boilerhouse (JW
  Lees) *738*
Crafty Flanker Front Row *700*
Crafty Fox Wily Fox *840*
Crafty Mild Kirkby Lonsdale *734*
Crafty One Crafty Brewing *671*
Crafty Shag CrackleRock *671*
Crafty Stoat Wibblers *838*
Crag Fell *692*
Cragg Bitter Little Valley *742*
Craigmill Mild Strathaven *807*
Craven Bitter Dark Horse *675*
Crazy Daze Potbelly *780*
Crazy Like a Fox Totally
  Brewed *821*
Cream Stout St Peter's *793*
Creation Pale Ale Altarnun *620*
Cregennan Cader *657*
Creme Bearlee Beartown *630*
Crex Squawk *804*
Crib Goch Cold Black Label *667*
Cricket Grasshopper *707*
Cricklade Ordinary Bitter Hop
  Kettle *722*
Criffel Sulwath *808*
Crimson Rye'd GT *710*
Crispin Ale Mad Cat *748*
Crispin's Ommer Fownes *698*
Crispy Pig Hunters *725*
Critical Temperature Atom *625*
Crofters FILO *693*
Cromwell Best Milestone *754*
Cromwells Best Bitter Coach
  House *666*
Crooked Hooker Towcester
  Mill *821*
Crop Circle Hop Back *721*
Cross Collar Marble *751*
Cross Pacific Pale Ale Firebrand
  (Altarnun) *620*
Crosspale Crosspool Alemakers
  Society *673*
Crouch Front Row *699*
Crow Black Hattie Brown's *716*
Crow Potton *780*
  Wobbly *842*
Crowlas Bitter Penzance *775*
Crown & Glory Cheddar *663*
Crown Best Bitter Stockport *806*

Crown Imperial Stout
  Goacher's *704*
Crows-an-Wra Penzance *775*
Crowstone Leigh on Sea *739*
Crucible Best Sheffield *796*
Cruck House New Buildings *763*
Crumbling Ghost Urban
  Alchemy *828*
Crusader Gold Unsworth's Yard *828*
Crusader Milestone *754*
  Redcastle *785*
Crystal Ship Papworth *773*
Crystal Quartz *782*
  Untapped *828*
Cub Moody Fox *757*
Cubbio Damage Marble *751*
Cuil Hill Sulwath *808*
Cuillin Beast Isle of Skye *730*
Cult Leader Anarchy *620*
Culture Vulture Lazy Bay *737*
Cumberland Ale Jennings *730*
Cumbria Way Robinsons *788*
Cumbrian Bitter Carlisle *660*
Cumbrian Five Hop
  Hawkshead *716*
Cunning Stunt Fuzzy Duck *701*
The Cure Shortts *797*
Curiously Dark Dartford
  Wobbler *676*
Cushie Butterfield Firebrick *694*
Cuthberts Church End *664*
Cwm Gwaun Porter Gwaun
  Valley *711*
Cwrw Caradog Ogwen *767*
Cwrw Coch Crafty Dragon *672*
Cwrw Eryri/Snowdonia Ale Purple
  Moose *782*
Cwrw Glaslyn/Glaslyn Ale Purple
  Moose *782*
Cwrw Glyndwr Llyn *743*
Cwrw Gorslas/Bluestone Bitter
  Glamorgan *703*
Cwrw Gwyn Gwaun Valley *711*
Cwrw Madog/Madog's Ale Purple
  Moose *782*
Cwrw Melyn Gwaun Valley *711*
Cwrw Teifi Mantle *751*
Cwrw Ysgawen/Elderflower Ale
  Purple Moose *782*
Cwrw Evan Evans *689*
Cwrw'r Afr Serchog / Horny Goat
  Ale Twt Lol *827*
Cwrw'r Ddraig Aur Robinsons *788*
Cwtch Tiny Rebel *818*
Cyclops Milton *755*
Cymryd y Pyst Twt Lol *827*

D
D Day Dodger Martland Mill *752*
Déjà Brewed Snaggletooth *801*
Daemon Red Ale Brew
  Monster *647*
Dafen IPA Tinworks *818*
Daggers Ale Three Daggers *815*
Daggers Blonde Three
  Daggers *815*
Daggers Edge Three Daggers *815*
Daily Bread Abbeydale *617*
Daisy Gold Brightwater *651*
Dale Strider Richmond *787*
Dales Way IPA Dent *678*
Dalliance Bad Seed *626*
Dam Strong Ale Lymm *747*
Damn Gates Burton *702*

Damson Porter 8 Sail *616*
  Burton Bridge *655*
Dancing Dragonfly Pheasantry *776*
Danish Dynamite Stonehenge *807*
The Dankness Bullhouse *654*
Dark & Seedy Little Ox *742*
Dark Ages Copper Street *669*
Dark Ale Tremethick *823*
Dark Arts Magic Rock *749*
Dark Beacons Cold Black Label *667*
Dark Blue Oxford University Ale
  White Horse *836*
Dark Denomination Flipside *696*
Dark Destroyer CrackleRock *671*
Dark Drake Dancing Duck *675*
Dark Dunkel Barnaby's *628*
Dark Flagon Wily Fox *840*
Dark Forest Rockingham *789*
Dark Fox Hornes *723*
Dark Heart Mantle *751*
Dark Horse Mild Uttoxeter *829*
Dark Horse Stout Elmtree *687*
Dark Horse Belvoir *634*
  Blythe *642*
  GT *710*
  Hepworth *717*
  Winster Valley
  (Handsome) *713*
Dark Island Orkney *770*
Dark Knight Hopstar *723*
  Independent Lakeland
  (Strands) *807*
  Redcastle *785*
  Whitley Bay *837*
Dark Magic Merlin *754*
Dark Magus Milk Stout Three
  Sods *816*
Dark Masquerade Half Moon *712*
Dark Matter Atom *625*
  Bridge *650*
  Tiny Vessel *818*
  VOG *831*
Dark Mild 3 Brewers of St
  Albans *615*
  Artefact *623*
  Bank Top *627*
  Blackedge *640*
  Boxcar *645*
  Harvey's *715*
  Healey's *716*
  High Weald *719*
  Timothy Taylor *812*
Dark Moor Kelburn *732*
Dark Munro Swannay *810*
Dark Necessities BAD *626*
Dark Night Southport *802*
Dark Nights Porter Jolly Sailor *731*
Dark Peak Howard Town *724*
Dark Porter Fuddy Duck *700*
  Stod Fold *806*
Dark Raven Beowulf *634*
Dark Ruby Mild Bridge *650*
  Consall Forge *668*
  Sarah Hughes *724*
Dark Ruby Blythe *642*
Dark Rum Blackedge *640*
Dark Side of the Moon
  Bullfinch *654*
Dark Side of the Toon Three
  Kings *816*
Dark Side of the Wight Yates' *845*
Dark Side Fosse Way *697*
  Three Fiends *815*
Dark Spartan Stout Parker *774*
Dark Star Original Dark Star *676*

Drakkar Darkland *676*
Draught Bass Marston's *752*
Draught Burton Ale Burton
　Bridge *655*
Draymans Draught Bank Top *627*
Dreadnought Cliff Quay *665*
　Nottingham *766*
Dream Machine Bone
　Machine *643*
Dreamland IPA No Frills Joe *764*
Dreigiau'r Diafol / Diablo
　Dragons Twt Lol *827*
Drift Jaw *730*
Drone Valley IPA Drone Valley *683*
Dronfield Best Drone Valley *683*
Dronny Bottom Bitter Drone
　Valley *683*
Drop Bar Pale Ale Tring *823*
Drop of the Black Stuff
　Springhead *804*
Drop Squint Caffle *658*
Drop Jaw *730*
Drover Wishbone *841*
Drover's Return Cotswold Lion *670*
Drovers 80/- Tryst *824*
Drummer Boy Grey Trees *709*
Dry Bones Wigan Brewhouse *838*
The Dry Road Beeston *633*
Dry Stone Stout Hawkshead *716*
Dryfe Blonde Lowland *746*
DSB (Dolly's Special Beer) Urban
　Island *829*
Duchess Anne Strathaven *807*
Duck & Dive Green Duck *709*
Duck 'n' Dive Mallard *749*
Duck Soup Warwickshire *832*
Duckling Mallard *750*
Due South Strathbraan *808*
Duffel Goat Little Goat *741*
Duffield Amber Tollgate *820*
Duke IPA Swannay *810*
The Duke Ben's *634*
Dukey's Delight AJ's *618*
Duncansby John O'Groats *731*
Duneham Ale Downham Isle *681*
Dunham Dark Dunham
　Massey *684*
Dunham Gold Dunham
　Massey *684*
Dunham Milk Stout Dunham
　Massey *684*
Dunham Porter Dunham
　Massey *684*
Dunham Stout Dunham
　Massey *684*
Dunham XPA Dunham Massey *684*
Dunstable Giant B&T (3 Brewers of
　St Albans) *615*
Durdle Door Dorset (DBC) *681*
Dusty Penny Flipside *696*
DV US Deeply Vale *677*
DV8 Deeply Vale *677*
Dynamo Wantsum *832*

E
The Eagle has Landed Eagles
　Crag *685*
Eagle of Darkness Eagles Crag *685*
Eagle of Kindness Eagles Crag *685*
The Eagle's Feather Eagles
　Crag *685*
EAPA (East Anglian Pale Ale)
　Humpty Dumpty *724*
Earl de Grey IPA Aitcheson's *618*

Earl Grey Bitter Whim *836*
Earl Grey IPA Marble *751*
Earl Grey PA Atlantic *625*
Earls RDA Island *729*
Early Rider Headstocks (Rufford
　Abbey) *791*
Earth Koomor *735*
Earthmover Gold Uttoxeter *829*
Earthmover Uttoxeter *829*
Earthquake Urban Chicken *829*
East the Beast Lacada *735*
East Coast IPA Poppyland *780*
East India Pale Ale Dunham
　Massey *684*
　Whitstable *837*
East Kent Gold Breakwater *647*
East Star Hop Kettle *722*
East Street Cream Pitchfork
　(Epic) *688*
Eastern Nights Bollington *643*
Eastgate Weetwood *833*
Easton IPA Dawkins *677*
Easy Geez Amwell Springs *620*
Easy Life Eight Arch *686*
Easy Pale Citra Stardust *805*
Easy Rider Kelham Island *732*
EB Enfield (Enfield) *688*
Ebb & Flow Brewis *649*
Ebb Rock Noss Beer Works *766*
Ebony Mild Goldmark *705*
Echo Beach Dovedale *681*
Echo Chamber Alter Ego *620*
Eclipse Clay Brow *665*
　Franklins *698*
　Navigation *761*
Ed Porter Dove Street *681*
Eddystone South Hams *802*
Eden Atomic Blonde Eden
　River *686*
Eden Best Eden River *686*
Eden Dynamite Eden River *686*
Eden First Emperor Eden River *686*
Eden Fuggle Eden River *686*
Eden Gold Eden River *686*
Edge Hopper Swamp Bog *809*
Edge Kinver *734*
　Sandstone *794*
Edinburgh Castle 80/-
　Caledonian *658*
Edinburgh Gold Stewart *806*
Edith Cavell Wolf *842*
Edmonton Best Bitter
　Beerbleflish *632*
Edwin Taylor's Extra Stout B&T (3
　Brewers of St Albans) *615*
Eel River IPA Unsworth's Yard *828*
Effortless RedWillow *786*
Egbert's Stone Copper Street *669*
Egret Great Oakley *708*
Egyptian Cream Nene Valley
　(NVB) *762*
Egyptian Goose Thames Side *813*
Eight Grain Porter Brew Shack *647*
Eight Shilling Shottle Farm *798*
Eight XT *845*
Eighty Shilling Bellfield *633*
Ein Stein Lymestone *747*
Eisenbrau Wheat Beer
　Nailmaker *761*
El Dorado Bridge *650*
　Lazy Bay *737*
Elder Pale Brimstage *651*
Elder Statesman Firebrick *694*
Elderflower Blonde Atlantic *625*
Elderquad Downton *682*

Electric Eye Pale Ale Big
　Smoke *636*
Electric Landlady Bakers
　Dozen *626*
Electric Trail Star Wing *805*
Elemental Porter Tempest *813*
Elephant Hawk IPA Thirst Class *814*
Elephant Juice NE Pale
　Manchester *750*
Elephant Riders Fownes *698*
Elephants Graveyard Urban
　Alchemy *828*
Elevation Raven Hill *784*
Eleven APA Blimey! *640*
Elisir Clouded Minds *666*
Elixir Guisborough *710*
Elizabeth Ale Earl Soham *685*
Ella Ella Ella Beath *631*
Ellensberg Harbour *714*
Elmers Flying Monk *697*
Elmo's Moles (Wickwar) *838*
Elsi Pale Dukeries *683*
Elsie Mo Castle Rock *660*
Elterwater Gold Langdale *737*
Elwood's Dark White Rabbit *836*
Elysian Fields Spartan *803*
Elysium Amber Ale Chapel-en-le-
　Frith *662*
Elysium Mobberley *756*
Emotional Blackmail Mad Cat *748*
Emotional Support Hamster
　Nightjar *764*
Empire IPA Spitting Feathers *803*
Empire George's *702*
Encore Lacons *736*
Endeavour Bingley *637*
　Captain Cook *659*
Endless Summer Black Iris *639*
Engel's Best Bitter Opa Hay's *770*
Engels Fruity Little Number Opa
　Hay's *770*
Engine Vein Cheshire
　Brewhouse *663*
England's Finest Hour
　Consortium *668*
English Best Bitter Three Acre *814*
English Bitter Stardust *805*
English Garden Franklins *698*
English IPA Barnaby's *628*
　Botley *644*
　Severn *795*
English Lore Gritchie *710*
English Pale Ale Artefact *623*
　Clark's *664*
　Woolybutt *843*
English Stout 4Ts *616*
Enigma Ad Hop *617*
　Townhouse *822*
Entire Stout Hop Back *722*
Entire Cronx *673*
　Olde Swan *769*
EPA Centenary Harwich Town *715*
EPA 4Ts *616*
　Inveralmond *728*
　Marston's *751*
　Pig Iron *777*
Epic IPA Settle *795*
Epiphany Littleover *742*
Equator Ridgeside *787*
Equilibrium Consall Forge *668*
　Deeply Vale *677*
Equinox Saison Wilderness *839*
Equinox Ad Hop *617*
　Whitley Bay *837*
Equinoxity Golden Triangle *705*

Forager's Gold Indigenous 727
Force Four Isle of Purbeck 729
Forest Gold Bespoke 635
  Rockingham 789
Foresters Black Dawkins 677
Forever Godstone 704
Format Beermats 633
Fortitude Bristol Beer Factory 652
  Wantsum 832
Fortune Teller Origami 770
Fortyniner Ringwood 787
Fosse Ale Dow Bridge 681
Fosse Framework 698
Fosseway Flanker North
  Cotswold 765
Fossil Fuel Isle of Purbeck 729
Fossil Madrigal 749
Foundation Bitter East London 685
Foundation Stone Lymestone 747
Founder's JW Lees 738
Fountain Dale Lincoln Green 740
Four Acre Arcadia Star Wing 805
Four Freedoms Clarkshaws 665
Four Hopmen of the Apocalypse
  Totally Brewed 821
Four Kings Battledown 630
Four Sons Creaton Grange 672
Four XT 845
Fox Brown Ale Great Corby 708
Fox Dark Keswick 733
The Fox Hat Wily Fox 840
Fox Pale Keswick 733
Fox Paw Framework 698
Fox Exmoor 690
Foxtrot Pale Two by Two 826
Foxtrot Premium Ale Great North
  Eastern 708
Foxy Lady Cannon Royall (White
  Rabbit) 837
FPA Pale Ale Fat Belly 692
Fra Diavolo Ulverston 828
Fragile X Spotlight 803
Franc in Stein Flipside 696
Franconia Torrside 821
Frank Morris Escape 689
Frank the Tank Bullhouse 654
Franken's Curse Taw Valley 812
Fraoch Heather Ale Williams
  Bros 839
Free Style Fine Tuned 694
Freebird Deeply Vale 677
Freedom Hiker Gyle 59 711
Friday Gold Friday Beer 699
Friday St IPA Framework 698
Frigate Irving 728
Friggin' in the Riggin' Nelson 761
Frisky Mare Indigenous 727
Frizzle British IPA Hop Shed 722
Froglet 8 Sail 616
Front Runner Ascot 624
Frost Hammer Fownes 698
Frothingham Best Great
  Newsome 708
Fruit Bat B&T (3 Brewers of St
  Albans) 615
Fruiterers Mild Cannon Royall
  (White Rabbit) 836
Fruits of the Forest
  Rockingham 789
Fryer's Thirst Exe Valley 689
FSB (Forest Strong Bitter) Forest,
  The 697
Fudge Unit Three Fiends 815
Fuggle Stone Hop Back 721
Fuggle-Dee-Dum Goddards 704

Full Bore Hunters 725
Full Gallop Uttoxeter 829
Full Measure Porter
  Aitcheson's 618
Full Moon Porter Canopy 659
Full Moon Chantry 661
Full Tilt Wriggly Monkey 844
Full Whack Peerless 775
Fum Little Giant 741
Fun Sponge Furnace 701
Funk Beat 631
Funky Monkey Frome 699
Funky Town Beath 631
Funny Farm Blindmans 641
Fursty Ferret Hall & Woodhouse
  (Badger) 712
Fusee Chain Drop The Anchor 683
Fusion Hartshorns 715
Fusioneer Mr Winter's 759
Fuster Cluck Bang-On 627
fyi Paradigm 773
Fyrds Gold Battle 630

G

Gadds' Black Pearl Ramsgate
  (Gadds') 783
Gadds' Faithful Dogbolter Porter
  Ramsgate (Gadds') 783
Gadds' Hoppy Pale Ramsgate
  (Gadds') 783
Gadds' No. 3 Kent Pale Ale
  Ramsgate (Gadds') 783
Gadds' No. 5 Best Bitter Ale
  Ramsgate (Gadds') 783
Gadds' No. 7 Bitter Ale Ramsgate
  (Gadds') 783
Gadds' Seasider Ramsgate
  (Gadds') 783
Gadds' SheSells SeaShells
  Ramsgate (Gadds') 783
Galapagos Darwin 676
Galatia Wylam 845
Galaxy Australian Pale Ale
  Frome 699
GalaXy IPA Xtreme 845
Gallia Twice Brewed 825
Galloway Gold Sulwath 808
Gallows Gold Park Brewery 773
Galvy Stout Weldon 834
Game Over Leatherbritches 738
Game On JW Lees 738
Gamekeeper Wensleydale 834
Ganges Harwich Town 715
Gannet Mild Earl Soham 685
Garden Shed Outhouse
  Brewing 772
Garland Madrigal 749
Garsdale Smokebox Yorkshire
  Dales 846
Garside Gold Grafton 706
Gate Hopper Maypole 753
Gates Burton Ale (GBA) Gates
  Burton 702
Gaucho Tomos a Lilford 820
Gaucho/Half Fly Twisted 825
GB Best Grainstore 707
GB Golden Blonde Ale
  Brumaison 653
Geekhunter Gorgeous 706
Gem Bath 629
General Picton Rhymney 786
Genesis Pale Ale Fable 690
Genesis Goody 705
George Shaw Premium 4Ts 616

German Ale Altbier Fuddy
  Duck 700
German Hops Pils Tryst 824
GFB Hop Back 721
Ghost Porter Yorkshire Heart 846
Ghost Ship Adnams 617
Ghost Ships Whitley Bay 837
Ghost Town Cromarty 672
  Twisted Oak 826
Ghyll Fell 692
Gibraltar Porter Cheshire
  Brewhouse 663
Giggle & Titter Parkway 774
Gigglemug Bang The Elephant 627
Gilt Complex Surrey Hills 809
Gilt Trip Surrey Hills 809
Ginger & Chilli IPA Art Brew 623
Ginger Beer Blue Bee 641
  Enville 688
  Fallen Angel 691
Ginger Brew Bollington 643
Ginger Ninja Dancing Duck 675
Ginger Panther Panther 773
Ginger Stout Angel Ales 621
Ginger Tinge Stockport 806
Ginger Weal Weal 833
Ginger Blackedge 640
  Tipples 818
Give it Some Healey's 716
GL12 Lucifer 747
Glacier Beartown 630
Gladiator Dow Bridge 681
  Three Engineers 815
Gladstone Guzzler Dove Street 681
Gladstone Strong Ale
  Townhouse 822
Glasgow Cross IPA Broughton 653
Glo in the Dark Twt Lol 827
Glog Twt Lol 827
Glorious Devon Isca 728
Glory Barnet 628
Glowfly Gorgeous 706
Glyder Fawr Cold Black Label 667
GNE Stout Great North Eastern 708
Go Your Own Way Don Valley 680
Goat Walk Topsham 821
Goat's Leap Cheddar 663
Goat's Milk Church End 664
Gobble Great Oakley 708
Gobhar Odhar Ardgour 623
Gobhar Reamhar Ardgour 623
God's Twisted Sister Twisted
  Barrel 825
Going Off Half-Cocked
  Bespoke 635
Gold (Also known as Yella Belly
  Gold) Batemans 629
Gold Beacons Cold Black Label 667
Gold Cup Ascot 624
Gold Digger Blueball 642
Gold Dust Born 643
Gold Leaf Lymm 747
Gold Muddler Andwell 621
Gold Parachute One More Than
  Two 770
Gold Rush Blythe 642
  Cabin 657
  CrackleRock 671
  Dynamite Valley 684
  Lenton Lane 739
Gold Star Strong Ale Goacher's 704
Gold Star Phipps 776
  Shipstone's 797
  Silhill 798
  West Berkshire 835

Greensand IPA Surrey Hills 809
Greenstede High Weald 719
Greet Ale Mallard 749
Gresham Hopper Titsey 819
Grey Ghost IPA Silver 798
Greyfriars Stout Richmond 787
Griffin IPA Reedley Hallows 786
Griffin Brampton 646
Grindstone Windmill Hill 840
Grizzly Bear Fox 698
Frisky Bear 699
Groat Hybrid 725
Grosvenor Gold Affinity 618
Ground Breaker Uttoxeter 829
Grounded Devon Earth 678
GSB Goldmark 705
GTF Hybrid 725
Guardian of the Forest Totally
Brewed 821
Guardian Cold Black Label 667
Guardsman Windsor & Eton 840
Gubbins Lord Conrad's 745
Gudgeon Izaac Walton 831
Guell Cross Bay 673
Guerrilla Blue Monkey 641
Guid Ale Arran 623
Guinea Guzzler Dartford
Wobbler 676
Guji Coffee Stout Tarn Hows 812
Gulf IPA Farm Yard 691
Gullwing Lager Wriggly
Monkey 844
Gulp IPA Frome 699
Gulping Fellow Fellows 693
Gumption Wishbone 841
Gun Dog Oscars 771
Teignworthy 813
Gundog Bitter Richmond 786
Gunhild Fownes 698
Gunners Gold Loose Cannon 745
Gunpowder Mild Coach House 666
Gunpowder Gorgeous 706
Gunslinger Beer Brothers 632
Tombstone 820
Gunsmoke Dukeries 683
Gunson Loxley 746
Gurt Coconuts Rum Stout Cerne
Abbas 661
Gurt Stout Cerne Abbas 661
Gutenberg Beer Ink 632
Guzzler Fat Belly 692
York (Black Sheep) 639
Gwydion Lleu 743

H _____

H!PA Helmsley 717
Habit Flying Monk 697
Hackney Blonde Tollgate 819
Hackney TNT Beerblefish 632
Hair of the Dog Pennine 775
Hairy Helmet Leatherbritches 738
Haka Slater's 800
Halcyon Daze Gyle 59 711
Half Bore Hunters 725
Half Centurion Kinver 734
Half Cut Woodcote 842
Half Nelson Papworth 773
Half Rats Bang The Elephant 627
Half Wit Three Blind Mice 815
Half-Time Front Row 700
Halfway Dead Anarchy 620
Halliday Loxley 746
Halo Cross Bay 673
Halt Hilden 719

Hammer Best Bitter
Metalhead 754
Hammerstone IPA Bluestone 642
Hampsfell Shaws of Grange 796
Hampshire Pale Ale Botley 644
Hampshire Rose Itchen Valley 730
Hancock Shaker Northdown 765
Hancocks HB Molson Coors
(Brains) 646
Hang Hill Hazy Forest, The 697
Hang Ten Tenby 813
Hanged Man Madrigal 749
Hanged Monk Tipples 818
Hanging Around Six Hills 799
Happy Chappy Cromarty 672
Happy People Shiny 797
Harbour Pale Harbour 714
Harbour Special Tintagel 818
Harbour Wall Cheviot 663
Harbour Combe 667
Hard Graft Axholme (Docks) 679
Hard Yards Chapeau 662
Hardrock Cheddar 663
Hare Raiser Hetton Law 719
Hares Hopping Two Rivers 826
Harlech Castle Cold Black
Label 667
Harley Welbeck Abbey 834
Harpers Great Oakley 708
Harrier Thames Side 813
Harrogate Pale Harrogate 714
Harry Hop McCanns (Angels &
Demons) 621
Harry's Heifer Church Farm 664
Hartington Bitter Whim 836
Hartington IPA Whim 836
Harvard Southwark 803
Harvest Ale Malt 750
Harvest Moon Mild
Moonshine 757
Harvest Moon Hemlock 717
Ulverston 828
Harvest Pale Castle Rock 660
Harvey George Samuel 702
Hat Trick IPA Muirhouse 760
Hat Trick Kelchner 732
Magic Rock 749
Havok Big Hand 636
Hawthorn Gold Staffordshire 804
Hay Tomos a Lilford 820
Haybob Farm Yard 691
Hayles' Ale Golden Duck 704
Haystacks Hesket Newmarket 718
Haze of Thunder Brew York 648
Hazelnutter Clouded Minds 666
Hazy Vaguely 829
HBA Hattie Brown's 716
HBB Hogs Back 720
HBC Best Bitter Horsham 724
HE-BRU IPA Northdown 765
Heacham Gold Fox 698
Head East Strathbraan 808
Head Otter 771
Headland Red Wold Top 842
Headlander Southbourne 802
Headless Dog College (Hilden) 719
Headless RedWillow 786
Headmaster Old School 769
heads up Paradigm 773
Headstock Redcastle 785
Heanor Pale Ale Bottle Brook 644
Heart & Soul Vocation 831
Heart Quartz 782
Heartbreak Stout Barefaced 627
Heartland Pennine 775

Hearty Bitter Yorkshire Heart 846
Heathen Abbeydale 617
Heather Honey Ale Penlon 775
Heather Honey Black Isle 639
Heavenly Blonde Zest 847
Heavenly Matter Moonshine 757
Heavy on the Chips IVO 730
Heavy Cross Borders 673
Hebden's Wheat Little Valley 742
Hedge Monkey Glastonbury
(Parkway) 774
HedgeHopper Mobberley 756
Hedgerow Hop Lord Conrad's 745
Hedonism Potbelly 780
Heel Stone Stonehenge 806
Helix Tyne Bank 827
Hell Cat Fat Cat 692
Hella Pale St Ives 792
Helles Lager Grasmere 707
Hellfire Corner Breakwater 647
Hellhound IPA Clarkshaws 665
Hello Darkness Scarborough 795
Hellstown West Coast IPA
Harbour 714
Helm Brewis 649
Helter Skelter Cornish Crown 670
Helvellyn Gold Hesket
Newmarket 718
Hen Harrier Bowland 644
Henrietta Welbeck Abbey 834
Henry's IPA Wadworth 831
Her Majes Tea Lord Conrad's 745
Herald Meanwood 753
Herefordshire Light Ale (HLA)
Hereford 718
Herefordshire Owd Bull
Hereford 718
Heresy Bishop Nick 638
Heritage Pale Bruha 653
Heritage Trail Ale Lymm 747
Heritage XX Firebird 694
Heritage Gentlewood 702
Three Castles 815
Herm Island Gold Liberation 740
Heroes Bitter Beowulf 634
Heron Ale Thames Side 813
Herr Keith Keith 731
Hetton Harlot Hetton Law 719
Hetton Hermit Hetton Law 718
Hetton Howler Hetton Law 718
Hetton Pale Ale Dark Horse 675
Hibernation Stealth 805
Hicks St Austell 792
Hidden Howler Penlon 775
High & Dry Urban Island 829
High Five Thirst Class 814
High Fives Wensleydale 834
High Pike Hesket Newmarket 718
High Speed Barnet 628
High Street Bitter Tollgate 820
High Time Melwood 753
High Tor Matlock Wolds Farm 752
High Wire Magic Rock 749
Highland Cow Strathcarron 808
Highland IPA Cairngorm 658
Highlander Fyne 701
Highway 51 Rooster's 790
Hill Climb Prescott (Hanlons) 713
Hillfoot Best Bitter Blue Bee 641
Hindsight Hybrid 725
Hinkypunk Big Bog 635
Hip Hop Ards 623
Briggs Signature 651
Langham 737
Quirky 783

Misfit Brass Castle 647
Missenden Pale Malt 750
Mister Chubb's West Berkshire 835
Mister Squirrel Mad Squirrel 748
Misty Law Kelburn 732
Mocha Choc Stout Lucifer 747
Mocha Porter St Andrews
Brewing 792
Mocha Heathen 717
Moderation Malt 750
Modern Bitter Donkeystone 680
Liverpool Brewing 743
Modern Helles Tempest 813
Modwena Burton Town 656
Moel Famau Ale Hafod 712
Mogul West Country IPA
Breakwater 647
MOHO Mantle 751
Mok Titi Three Fiends 815
Moldbreaker Hafod 712
Moletrap Bitter Mauldons 752
Molly's LoveBeer 746
Moloko Mocha Porter Nightjar 764
Mon Cheri IPA Three Sods 816
Money for Old Rope Bespoke 635
Moneypenny EPA Crafty
Monkey 672
Monkey Hanger Poachers 779
Monkey Magic Gorilla 706
Monkey Wrench Daleside 675
Monkey's Fist Madrigal 749
Monkeytown Mild Phoenix 777
Monk's Gold Howard Town 724
Monkholme Premium Reedley
Hallows 786
Monnow Untapped 828
Monocle Indigenous 727
Monster Hop Redcastle 785
Monterey Hop Maypole 753
Montgomery Wantsum 832
Monument Bitter Tyne Bank 827
Monumental Blonde Kirkby
Lonsdale 734
Moon Lore Gritchie 710
Moon Kissingate 735
To the Moon Lord's 745
Moonbeam Kings Clipstone 734
Moondance Melwood 753
Triple fff 823
Moongazing Tring 823
Moonlight Serious 795
Moonlite Hattie Brown's 716
Moonraker JW Lees 738
Moonrocket Tipples 818
Moonshine Abbeydale 617
Moonstruck Mild Rowton 790
Moonstruck Downton 682
Indigenous 727
Moor Ale Little Valley 742
Moor Top Buxton 657
Moose River Great Western 708
Morast Big Bog 636
More's Head Wantsum 832
Moreton Mild North Cotswold 765
Morrisman Elusive 687
Mosaic Blonde Zest 847
Mosaic City Golden Triangle 705
Mosaic Gluten Free Arbor 622
Mosaic IPA Farmageddon 691
Mosaic Pale Ale Grey Trees 710
North Riding (Brewery) 765
Thirst Class 814
Mosaic Pale Hawkshead 716
Red Cat 784

Mosaic Session IPA Burning
Soul 655
Mosaic Adnams 617
Ashton 624
Brewsmith 649
Cheshire Brewhouse 663
Exit 33 690
Horsforth 723
Nailmaker 761
Neptune 762
Urban Island 829
Mosaica Mile Tree 754
Mosquito IPA Roughacre 790
Mosquito Three Engineers 815
Motueka Grisette Wilderness 839
Motueka Chadkirk 661
Moturiki – Blowhole Pale Ale
Downham Isle 681
Mouldings Porter Stow Fen 807
Moulin D'Etienne Wit Bier
Burwell 656
Mount Helix West Coast Pale
Lord's 745
Mountain Mild Facer's 690
Mourne Gold Mourne
Mountains 759
Mouse-low Mild Mouselow
Farm 759
Moving the Goalposts Six Hills 799
Mowdy Pale Ale Tractor Shed 822
Mozart Turpin's 825
MPA Monty's 756
Mr Badman Three Fiends 815
Mr B's Anniversary Pale
Moonface 757
Mr Brown Alter Ego 620
Mr M's Porter Red Cat 784
Mr P's Clay Brow 665
Mr Sheppard's Crook Exe
Valley 689
Mr Swifts Barnet 628
Mrs P's Clay Brow 665
Mrs Simpson's Thriller in Vanilla
Porter Brown Cow 653
Muck 'n' Straw Holsworthy 721
Muckle Moss Stout Muckle 760
Mucky Duck Fuzzy Duck 701
Mud City Stout Sadler's
(Hawkshead) 716
Muggy Porter Northdown 765
Muker Silver Yorkshire Dales 846
Mumbai Bridge 650
Murder of Crows Kissingate 735
Murmelt Mumbles 760
Mustang Sally Hattie Brown's 716
Mustang Three Engineers 815
Mutineer Derwent 678
Mutiny on the Bounty
Campervan 659
Mutley's Revenge Hereford 718
Mutts Nuts Hereford 718
Muzzle Loader Cannon Royall
(White Rabbit) 837
Muzzleloader Musket 760
My Green is Earl Hush 725
My Horse Came Fourth
Horsforth 723
My Milk Stout Furnace 701
Myricale Treboom 823
Mystery Tor Glastonbury
(Parkway) 774
Mystic Cotswold Spring
(Severn) 795
Mythic IPA Merlin 754

N

N1 Hammerton 713
N18 Clouded Minds 666
N253 Clouded Minds 666
N29 Clouded Minds 666
N7 Hammerton 713
Naido Twisted Barrel 825
Naked Ladies Twickenham 825
Nano Cask Moor 757
NAPA Turpin's 825
Nappa Scar Yorkshire Dales 846
NASHA IPA S&P 791
Native Bitter Whitstable 837
Natural Blonde Isla Vale 729
Natural Gold Pennine 775
Natural Selection Good
Chemistry 705
Natural Spring Water Brolly 652
Naughty & Nice Vocation 831
Navigator Captain Cook 659
Navvy Phoenix 777
The Naze Big Stone 637
Neap Tide Teignworthy 813
Neddy Donkeystone 680
Neddy's Anstey 622
Neil, Neil Orange Peel Beccles 631
Nektar Cronx 673
Nel's Best High House Farm 719
Nelson Blonde Downham Isle 681
Nelson's Blood Fox 698
Nelson's Delight Downton 682
Nelsons Blood Nelson 761
Nelson's Tree Beccles 631
Nelson's Woodforde's 843
Nemesis Peakstones Rock 774
Neon Kiss Slater's 800
Neptune's Hill Island 719
Nero Milton 755
Nessies Monster Mash
Cairngorm 658
Nettle IPA Gyle 59 711
Nettlethrasher Elland 687
Never Say Die Axholme
(Docks) 679
New Age Crisis Anarchy 620
New Alchemy Plan B 779
The New Black Kent 732
New Bostal Gilbert White's 703
New Dawn Pale Navigation 761
New Devon Ale New Devon 763
New England IPA Gloucester 704
New Era Crafty Monkey 672
New Forest Ale Downton 682
New Hampshire Itchen Valley 730
New Horizon Zulu Alpha 847
New Horizons Hop Studio 722
New Laund Dark Reedley
Hallows 786
New Normal Box Steam 645
New Session IPA Plan B 779
New Wave Beat 631
New World Shiny 797
New York Pale Chantry 661
New Zealand Gold Harbour 714
New Zealand Pale Avid 625
Brewsmith 649
Chadkirk 661
Reedley Hallows 786
Newark IPA Cat Asylum 660
Newbird Lenton Lane 739
Newport Pale Ale Plan B 779
Newton's Drop Zest 847
Nibbler Moon Gazer 757
Nice Weather Dancing Duck 675
Nicholas De Luda Consortium 668

Riverbed Red New River *763*
Rivet Catcher Great North Eastern *708*
Road Apple Strong Drinkstone *683*
Road Crew Camerons *659*
Road Trip Bullhouse *654*
Roadie All-Night Signature *798*
Roadrunner Bottle Brook *644*
RoadRunner Mobberley *756*
Roaring Meg Springhead *804*
Roasted Nuts·Rebellion *784*
Roasted JackRabbit *730*
Robbie's Red Adur *618*
Robin Goodfellow Papworth *773*
Robusta Ad Hop *617*
Rock & Roll Briggs Signature *651*
Rock Ale Bitter Beer Nottingham *766*
Rock Ale Mild Beer Nottingham *766*
Rock Ape Poachers *779*
Rock the Kazbek Redemption *785*
Rock Steady Bull of the Woods *654*
Mantle *751*
Rocka Beat *631*
Rockabilly Shortts *797*
Rocket Brunswick *653*
Rocketeer Bluestone *642*
Roebuck Bitter Roebuck *789*
Roebuck Blonde Roebuck *789*
Roebuck IPA Roebuck *789*
Rogue Wave Cromarty *672*
Roister Brumaison *653*
Rokerite North Pier *765*
Rollin Pale Ale One More Than Two *770*
Rolling Hills Big River *636*
Rolling Hitch Darwin *676*
Rolling Maul Snaggletooth *801*
Rolling Stone 8 Sail *616*
Roman Gold Castor *660*
Roman Mosaic Castor *660*
Roman Mosaics Weldon *834*
Roman Road Towcester Mill *821*
Romsey Gold Flack Manor *695*
Rooi Kabouter Red Ale Three Sods *816*
Rook Wood Clavell & Hind *665*
Room No. 6 Posh Boys *780*
Rooster Juice Urban Chicken *829*
Root Thirteen Downlands *681*
Ropetackle Golden Ale Adur *618*
Rorschach Mr Winter's *759*
Rosemary Ale Tomos a Lilford *820*
Rosetta's Comet Polarity *779*
Rotten End Shalford *796*
Rough Rock Big Stone *637*
Roughtor Altarnun *620*
Rouleur Chapeau *662*
Round The Wrekin St Annes *792*
Roundhead Porter Why Not *837*
Routemaster Red Southwark *803*
Royal Fanfare Top-Notch *820*
Royal Hunt Hunters *725*
Royal Stag Stout Kings Clipstone *734*
Royal Lytham *748*
RPA (Riviera Pale Ale) Riviera *788*
RPA Craft Brews *671*
Rubis Horsforth *724*
Ruby Duck Fuzzy Duck *701*
Ruby English Ale 3 Brewers of St Albans *615*
Ruby Mild Rudgate *791*
Ruby O'Reilly Blueball *642*

Ruby Porter Severn *795*
Ruby Red Mild Red Fox *785*
Ruby Red St Peter's *793*
Ruby Revolution Three Brothers *815*
Ruby Riding Hood One More Than Two *770*
Ruby Ruby Ruby Ruby Crafty Monkey *672*
Ruby Sunset Combe *667*
Ruby AJ's *618*
Freewheelin' *699*
Quirky *783*
Yeovil *846*
Rucked Front Row *700*
Rude Not To Amwell Springs *620*
Ruffled Feathers Swan *810*
Rufford Poacher Rufford Abbey *791*
Rufus Crooked *673*
Rum Porter Stamps *804*
Rumour Gower *706*
Run Hop Run Rigg & Furrow *787*
Runner Truman's *824*
Running With the Big Dog Six Hills *799*
Rush Hour Spitting Feathers *803*
Rushmoor Ripper Tilford *817*
Ruskins Bitter Kirkby Lonsdale *734*
Russian Imperial Stout Battle *630*
Russian Rouble Flipside *696*
Rustic Tonbridge *820*
Rusty Giraffe Welland *834*
Rusty's Ale Godstone *704*
Rutland Beast Grainstore *707*
Rutland Bitter Grainstore *707*
Rutland Osprey Grainstore *707*
Rutland Panther Grainstore *707*
Rutterkin Brewsters *649*
Ryc Ogwen *767*
The Ryddler Bowler's *645*
Rye the Hell Not Chapel-en-le-Frith *662*
Rye IPA Slater's *800*
Rye Pale Ale Townhouse *822*
Ryestone Hornes *723*

S

S.IPA Triple Point *823*
Séance Full Mash *700*
S'more Fire Alter Ego *620*
S'more Porter Three Brothers *815*
SA Gold Brains *646*
SA Brains *646*
Saaz Blonde Hopstar *723*
Sabrina's Dark Ruby Ale Worcester *843*
Saddle Tank Marston's *751*
Saddleback Best Bitter Slaughterhouse *800*
Saffron Sun Roughacre *790*
St Ayles Ale Ovenstone 109 *772*
St Edmunds Greene King *709*
St George Holsworthy *721*
St Leger Gold Stocks (Welbeck Abbey) *834*
Saint Louis Big River *636*
St Margaret's Ale Pumphouse Community *782*
St. Modwen Golden Ale Heritage *718*
St Nonna's Altarnun *620*
Saint or Sinner Boss *644*

Saint Petersburg Imperial Russian Stout Thornbridge *814*
St Wulfrum's IPA Cat Asylum *660*
The Saintly One Roughacre *790*
Saison Langham *737*
Salem Porter Batemans *629*
Salt Mine Stout Wintrip *841*
Salt's Burton Ale Tower *822*
Saltwick Nab Whitby *836*
Salvation Charnwood *662*
Salvation! One Mile End *769*
Same Again Ramsbury *783*
Samson Maxim *753*
Samuel Engels Meister Pils (SEMP) Opa Hay's *770*
San Francisco Conwy *669*
Sanctuary Pale Ale Camerons *659*
Sanctuary Applecross *622*
Sand House Doncaster *680*
Sand in the Wind Bottle Brook *644*
Sand Martin Hatherland *715*
Sand Storm Cold Black Label *667*
Sandbanks Bitter Sandbanks *794*
Sandgrounder Bitter Southport *802*
Sandpiper Light Ale Brimstage *651*
Sandstorm BritHop *652*
Sandygate Crosspool Alemakers Society *673*
Santa Fe Tombstone *820*
Santas Little Helper Little Goat *741*
SAORSA Blonde Ale Seagate *795*
Saracen Pilgrim *778*
Sargeant's Special Ale Uttoxeter *829*
Saturday's Blonde Consortium *668*
Sauvignon Blonde Crafty Beers *671*
Saved by the Bell Bespoke *635*
Savinjski Chapel-en-le-Frith *662*
Saviour Navigation *761*
Saxon Archer Three Castles *815*
Saxon Bronze Alfred's *619*
Saxon Cross ESB Wayoh *833*
Saxon Cross Rockingham *789*
Saxon Gold Copper Street *669*
Saxon Red Ale Parker *774*
SaXquatch Xtreme *845*
SBA Donnington *680*
Scafell Blonde Hesket Newmarket *718*
Scapa Special Swannay *810*
Scapegoat Little Goat *741*
Scar Top Stout Three Peaks *816*
Scaramanga Gun *710*
Scarecrow Bitter Brimstage *651*
Scaredy Cat Moorhouse's *758*
Scene Deleted Lazy Bay *737*
Schiehallion Harviestoun *715*
The Schil Cheviot *663*
Schmankerl Top Out *821*
Scholar Oxford *772*
School Night Nightjar *764*
Rock Mill *788*
Schooner Black Dog (Hambleton) *712*
Captain Cook *659*
Schrodingers Cat Atom *625*
Schwarz Rose Horsforth *723*
Scilly Stout Penzance *775*
Scottish Maiden Morton *758*
Scotts 1816 Copper Dragon *669*
Scoundrel Leatherbritches *738*
Tydd Steam *827*
Scrabo Gold Ards *623*

Skew Sunshine Ale Bowman 645
Skiddaw Hesket Newmarket 718
Skiffle Shortts 797
Skin Deep Anarchy 620
Skinful Beartown 630
SkIPA Emsworth 688
Skippers Mersea Island 754
Skipper's Ticket Lerwick 739
Skippy Captain Cook 659
Skirp Gold Caffle 658
Skirrid Tudor 824
Skrimshander IPA
  Hopdaemon 722
Skull Splitter Orkney 770
Skydiver Steamin' Billy
  (Belvoir) 634
Skye Black Isle of Skye 729
Skye Blonde Isle of Skye 730
Skye Gold Isle of Skye 729
Skye IPA Isle of Skye 729
Skye Red Isle of Skye 729
Skyelight Isle of Skye 729
Skylarking Pig & Porter 777
Skyline Kettlesmith 733
  Peerless 775
Slap in the Face Totally
  Brewed 821
Slap N'Tickle Lord Conrad's 745
Slaphead Weird Sisters 834
Slasher Piddle 777
Slate Grain 707
Slave to the Money Pig &
  Porter 777
Sleck Dust Great Newsome 708
Sleeper Heavy Beer Engine 632
Sleepless RedWillow 786
Sleepy Badger Little Critters 741
Slider Wigan Brewhouse 838
Slingshot to Mars Six Hills 799
Slip Stream Chapeau 662
Slippery Slope Twisted Oak 826
Slipway IPA St Ives 792
Slipway Captain Cook 659
Slow Joe Whitley Bay 837
Slumbering Monk Joule's 731
Slumdog Leadmill 738
Sly Wolf Wolf 842
Small Axe Bullhouse 654
Smelter's Stout Kissingate 735
Smild Rother Valley 790
Smiling Assassin Falstaff 691
The Smoked Brown Anspach &
  Hobday 622
Smoked Porter Hesket
  Newmarket 718
  Slater's 800
  Top Out 821
Smokeless RedWillow 786
Smokestack Lightnin' Dorking 680
Smokey Jack Ferry Brewery 693
Smokey Joe's Black Beer
  Hopstar 723
Smooth Hoperator Calvors 658
Smuggler Rebellion 784
Smugglers Gold Whitby 836
Snake Charmer Crafty Little 672
Snake Eyes Pale Two by Two 826
Snake Eyes Black Iris 639
Snake Oil Stout Hop Monster
  (George's) 702
The Snake Soul 801
Snakecharmer One Mile End 769
Snapper Canopy 659
Sneaky St.oat Welland 834
Sneaky Steamer Riverside 787

Sneaky Wee Orkney Stout
  Swannay 810
Sniper Mr Grundy's (Black
  Hole) 638
So.LA Dark Revolution 675
So You've Travelled Barefaced 627
SOD B&T (3 Brewers of St
  Albans) 615
Soft Mick Northern Whisper 766
Solar Power Isle of Purbeck 729
Solar Clun 666
Solaris Session Pale Ale Big
  Smoke 636
Solaris Newbridge 763
Solstice Boot (Burton Bridge) 656
  Mobberley 756
  Twisted Oak 826
Solution Fresh Standard 699
Solway Mist Sulwath 808
Soma Tapstone 811
Sombrero Brentwood 647
Some Like It Blonde
  Worsthorne 844
Some Might Say Session IPA
  Manchester 762
Son of a Beach Tenby 813
Son of Bertie Cannon Royall (White
  Rabbit) 837
Son of my Brother Reckless
  Dweeb 784
Son of Pale Face Blimey! 640
Son of Zeus Spartan 803
Sonic Dark Revolution 675
Sonoma Track 822
Sons of Liberty APA Bang The
  Elephant 627
Sons Pale Ale Lennox 739
Soul Citra Atlantic 625
Soul City Twisted Wheel 826
Soul Mate Beermats 633
Soul Train Box Steam 645
Sound Bitter Roam 788
Soundwave IPA Siren 799
The Source Tillingbourne 817
South Island Pale Stockport 806
South Island Saltaire 794
  VOG 831
South Paw IPA Two by Two 826
Southern Cross Weetwood 833
Southern Gold Sherfield
  Village 797
Southern Pale Wilderness 839
Southern Summit Loch
  Lomond 743
Southwold Bitter Adnams 617
Sovereign Gold Burton Bridge 655
SPA (Shefford Pale Ale) B&T (3
  Brewers of St Albans) 615
SPA (Spa Pale Ale)
  Warwickshire 832
SPA 4Ts 616
  AJ's 618
  Cornish Crown 670
Space Dog Oscars 771
Space is the Place Dig 679
  Out There 771
Spangle Hattie Brown's 716
Spanish City Blonde Whitley
  Bay 837
Spank Blueball 642
Spankers IPA Park Brewery 773
Spanky McDanky Brolly 652
Spark IPA Tollgate 820

Sparky's Dream Hemlock 717
SPARS Driftwood Spars 683
Sparta Milton 755
Speak Easy IPA VOG 831
Speak Easy Transatlantic Pale Ale
  Powderkeg 781
Speak Out Barefaced 627
Specduckular Mallard 750
Special Ale Black Sheep 639
  Spitting Feathers 803
Special Bitter Keswick 733
  Xtreme 845
Special English Ale 3 Brewers of St
  Albans 615
Special Oatmeal Stout
  Coniston 668
Special Reserve Axholme
  (Docks) 679
  Chantry 662
Special Holden's 720
  Lister's 740
Special/House Ale Goacher's 704
Speciale Brampton 646
Spectrum Spotlight 803
Speculation Enfield (Enfield) 688
Speed Wobble Twisted Wheel 826
Spellbinder Elusive 687
Spellbound Merlin 753
Spey IPA Two Thirsty Men 826
Spey Stout Spey Valley 803
Spey's Hopper Spey Valley 803
Spiffing Wheeze Lord Conrad's 745
Spike Island Stout Bexley 635
Spike's Gold Small World 800
Spin Drift Gun 711
Spingo Middle Blue Anchor 641
Spingo Special Blue Anchor 641
Spinner's Gold Martland Mill 752
Spiral Stout Boudicca (S&P) 791
Spire Ale Stonehenge 806
Spire Light Star Wing 805
Spirit of Kent Westerham 835
Spitfire Gold Shepherd Neame 797
Spitfire Shepherd Neame 797
Spitting Feathers
  Leatherbritches 738
Spokes Crooked 673
Spot Light Old Spot 769
Spot O'Bother Old Spot 769
Spotland Gold Phoenix 777
Sprilly Maid Caffle 658
Spring Tide Teignworthy 813
Springwell Goose Eye 705
Spud's Milltown 755
Spun Gold Carlisle 660
  Twisted Oak 826
Square Hammer Chasing
  Everest 662
Square Logic Eight Arch 686
Squid Ink XT 845
The Squirrels Nuts Beeston 633
SS Brussels Harwich Town 715
SS9 Leigh on Sea 739
SSS Woodcote 842
ST01 Artisan 624
Stable Genius White Horse 836
Staffie Blythe 642
Stag Cairngorm 658
  Exmoor 690
Stage Coach Reserve
  Tombstone 820
Stagecoach Tombstone 820
Stahlstadt Weldon 834
Stain Glass Blue Star Wing 805
Stainless Stancill 804

Super Sharp Shooter Three Fiends *815*
Super Sports Wriggly Monkey *844*
Super Star Silhill *798*
Super Tidy Big Hand *636*
Superior IPA Fyne *701*
Supernova Black Hole *638*
   JW Lees *738*
   Nightjar *764*
Supreme Nottingham *766*
Surf Bum IPA Dynamite Valley *684*
Surf Jaw *730*
Surfer Rosa Madrigal *749*
Surreptitious Stealth *805*
Surrex Gold Red Fox *785*
Surrey Nirvana Hogs Back *720*
Surrey XPA Dorking *680*
Surrey Pilgrim *778*
Sussex Best Bitter Harvey's *715*
Sussex Gold Arundel *624*
Sussex IPA Arundel *624*
Sussex Pride Long Man *745*
Sussex Wild Hop Harvey's *715*
Sussex Kissingate *735*
SVA Severn Valley *796*
SW19 Wimbledon *840*
SwAle Richmond *786*
Swallowtail Humpty Dumpty *724*
Swampy Big Bog *636*
Swan Black Bowness Bay *645*
Swan Blonde Bowness Bay *645*
   Swan *810*
Swan Gold Bowness Bay *645*
Swansea Jack Tomos Watkin *832*
Swedish Blonde Maxim *753*
Sweeney Todd Colchester *666*
Sweet Chestnut Ale Poppyland *780*
Sweet Symphony BritHop *652*
Swelkie John O'Groats *731*
Swift Best Bowness Bay *645*
Swift Nick Peak *774*
Swift One Bowman *645*
Swift Bullfinch *654*
   Truman's *824*
Swingball Session IPA Tapestry *811*
Swipe Right Wylam *845*
Switch Revolutions *786*
Swoon Chocolate Fudge Milk Stout Revolutions *786*
Swordfish Wadworth *831*
Swords & Sandals Spartan *803*
Swordsman Beowulf *634*
Sy Fy Lazy Bay *737*
Sycamore Gap Twice Brewed *825*
SYL First Chop *694*
System of a Brown Bakers Dozen *626*

T

T'errmmm-inator Strands *807*
T'owd Tup Dent *678*
Tabaknakas Kings Clipstone *734*
Table Beer Windmill Hill *840*
Table Bitter Golden Triangle *705*
Tag Lag Barngates *628*
Taiheke Sun Great North Eastern *708*
Tailshaker Great Oakley *708*
Taiphoon Hop Back *722*
Taipur 4Ts *616*
Take It Easy Gyle 59 *711*
Talisman IPA Pictish *777*

Tally Ho! Palmers *772*
Talyllyn Pale Ale Cader *657*
Tamar Black Holsworthy *721*
Tamar Source Forge *697*
Tamar Summerskills *809*
Tambourine Man Treboom *823*
Tangerine Dream Lord Conrad's *745*
Tanglefoot Hall & Woodhouse (Badger) *712*
Tango with a Mango Grafton *706*
Tap House Tipple Draycott (Derbyshire) *682*
Tar Gan Yam *701*
Tarasgeir Isle of Skye *729*
Target Snowhill *801*
The Tarka Special Yelland Manor *845*
Taverner Uley *827*
Tavy Best Bitter Roam *788*
Tavy Gold Roam *788*
Tavy IPA Roam *788*
Tavy Porter Roam *788*
Taw Head IPA Taw Valley *812*
Tawny Stratton Lane *808*
Tawton Session Ale Taw Valley *812*
TBC (Thwaites Best Cask) Thwaites *817*
Tea Kettle Stout Tring *823*
TEA Hogs Back *720*
Team Mates Beermats *633*
Technicolour Beat Twisted Wheel *826*
Techno Briggs Signature *651*
Teddy Bear Cannon Royall (White Rabbit) *837*
Tedi Boy Poachers *779*
Telegraph Session Crafty Monkey *672*
Tell No Tales Bosun's *644*
Tempest Stout Blue Bee *641*
Temple Team Toxic (Liverpool Brewing) *743*
Templer Teignmouth *813*
Tempo Wigan Brewhouse *838*
Temptation North Yorkshire *765*
TEN DDH APA Cryo Blimey! *640*
Ten Fifty Grainstore *707*
Ten Topsham *821*
Tenfoot Yorkshire Brewhouse *846*
Tenterhook Crankshaft *672*
Tequila Blonde Bridgehouse *650*
Terminus George Samuel *702*
Tern IPA Bowness Bay *645*
Terra Nova Ovenstone 109 *772*
Testbed v4 Crankshaft *672*
Tether Blond Wharfe (Hambleton) *712*
Tetherdown Wheat Saison Muswell Hillbilly *760*
Teuchter Strathaven *807*
Tewdric's Tipple Kingstone *734*
Texas Cleggy Whitley Bay *837*
Texas Jack Tombstone *820*
Textbook Old School *769*
THAIPA Hill Island *720*
ThaIPA Three Brothers *815*
Thanks Pa Consortium *668*
That Burton Beer Burton Town *656*
There is a Light Hemlock *717*
There's Something in the Water Beer Hut *632*
Thieves & Fakirs Dartford Wobbler *676*

Thieving Rogue Magpie *749*
Third Eye Blind Mad Dog *748*
Thirst Aid Kit Rock & Roll *788*
Thirst Aid Exit 33 *690*
Thirst Celebration Keswick *733*
Thirst of Many GT *710*
Thirst Quencher Keswick *733*
Thirst Rescue Keswick *733*
Thirst Run Keswick *733*
Thirstquencher Spitting Feathers *803*
Thirsty Moon Phoenix *777*
Thirsty Walker Dove Street *681*
Thirteen Blimey! *640*
Thirty Three Brighton Bier *651*
This is the Modern Weal Weal *833*
This is the One Boyz Reckless Dweeb *784*
This Splendid Ale Facer's *690*
Thomas Lift Langton *737*
Thomas Miller 1785 Ferry Brewery *693*
Thomas Sykes Burton Bridge *655*
Thomcat Burton Town *656*
Thoroughbred Bad Ram Haywood Bad Ram *716*
Thoroughbred IPA Hambleton *712*
Thoroughbred Gyle 59 *711*
Three & Sixpence Twisted *825*
Three Amigos Snaggletooth *801*
Three Beacons Cold Black Label *667*
Three Bridges Ferry Brewery *693*
Three Counties Roughacre *790*
Three Erics St Annes *792*
Three Sisters Atlas (Orkney) *770*
Three Swords Kirkstall *735*
Three Tails Boudicca (S&P) *791*
Three Threads Fengate *693*
Three XT *845*
ThreeOneSix Grain *706*
Thriller Cappuccino Porter Glastonbury (Parkway) *774*
Through and Off Fixed Wheel *695*
Thrupenny Bitter Phipps *776*
Thunderbird Glamorgan *703*
Thunderbridge Stout Small World *800*
Thurlton Gold People's *776*
Thurstein Pilsner Coniston *668*
Tiamat IPA Brew Monster *647*
Tickle Muckle *760*
Tidal Moon Northdown *765*
Tidal Pool Northdown *765*
Tidal Wave Hop Studio *722*
Tidy Bang-On *627*
Tiffield Thunderbolt Great Oakley *708*
Tiffin Gold Kirkby Lonsdale *734*
Tiger Rut Millstone *755*
Tiger Tom Ruby Mild Cerne Abbas *661*
Tiger Everards *689*
Tigers Tail Milltown *755*
Tiller Pin Wishbone *841*
Timeline Kettlesmith *733*
Tin Plate Irwell Works *728*
Tinder Box Inferno *727*
Tinderbox IPA Fell *692*
Tiny Dancer Pale Ale Flash House *696*
Tip Top Citra London Beer Lab *744*
Tipsy Fisherman Steamin' Billy (Belvoir) *634*
Tipsy Tup Penlon *775*

Readers' recommendations

Suggestions for pubs to be included or excluded

All pubs are regularly surveyed by local branches of the Campaign for Real Ale to ensure they meet the standards required by the *Good Beer Guide*. If you would like to comment on a pub already featured, or on any you think should be featured, please fill in the form below (or a copy of it), and send it to the address indicated. Alternatively, email **gbgeditor@camra.org.uk**. Your views will be passed on to the branch concerned. Please mark your envelope/email with the county where the pub is, which will help us to direct your comments efficiently.

Pub name:

Address:

Reason for recommendation/criticism:

Pub name:

Address:

Reason for recommendation/criticism:

Pub name:

Address:

Reason for recommendation/criticism:

Your name and address:

Please send to: [Name of county] Section, Good Beer Guide,
230 Hatfield Road, St Albans, Hertfordshire AL1 4LW

HOW BEER IS BREWED

The brewer's art sees raw ingredients transformed into a wide variety of styles of beer. Follow their journey from field to glass with this general look at how beer is brewed.

THE KEY INGREDIENTS OF BEER

While brewers will experiment and make use of the cornucopia of ingredients available to them, there are four key elements most beers have in common: water, yeast, malt and hops, although, increasingly brewers are playing with extra ingredients that impart unusual and exciting flavours, aromas or consistency into a beer. Lactose, and heather, for example, have historically been used as additions, but more and more brewers are now employing honey, flowers, spices, fruits, and even meat in specialty ales.

Differing preparation methods, and varietals can create a spectrum of beer – from the very pale, to the near black; from clean, simple aromas, to deep coffee notes, or a fruity punch on the nose; and gentle, sessionable flavours that comfort the palate, to those that assault and challenge your taste buds.

Some breweries will have their own specific way of doing things, and each brewery set-up is individual, but the process is broadly the same. Use the flow chart overleaf to discover how brewers take the four key ingredients below and use them to create one of the most diverse drinks on the planet.

🌾 MALT

The mix of malts used in making a beer contribute to the colour, flavour and strength of the beer. Malted barley is most common, but other grains, such as wheat, oats, or rye can be used. Once harvested, maltsters steep barley in water to absorb moisture, then spread it on heated floors or inside rotating drums where it will start to germinate. It is then kilned to dry. The temperature determines the type of malt produced – from pale, through to black. Common flavours and aromas derived include Ovaltine, oatmeal biscuits, Ryvita, almonds/nuts, honey, butterscotch, caramel, tobacco and vanilla.

🌿 HOPS

Hops can be used either as dried whole flowers or ground and compressed into pellets. Hops – via their oils and resins – impart aroma and flavour (including bitterness) into a beer, and are added into the copper/kettle, but can also be added later in the process. 'Dry-hopping', for example, is the process of adding a small amount of hops to a cask before it leaves the brewery en route to the pub, for additional aroma. Delicate aromas that can be destroyed during the boil can be retained in this way. While New World hops have become increasingly popular for their tropical fruit explosion in the last few years, UK hops provide the basis of more traditional beers.

💧 WATER

Water used for the brewing process is called liquor. Pure water can come from springs, bore holes or from the public supply. And while some breweries will treat their water to achieve a certain profile (adding sulphates such as gypsum and magnesium), or to remove potential off-flavour-causing compounds, others have embraced the natural, distinct quality of the local water – such as world-renowned Burton water. This water trickles through bands of gypsum and gives the resulting beer the world-famous, sought-after 'Burton snatch'.

⚗️ YEAST

Every brewery will have its own yeast culture and often this will be a closely guarded asset. Yeast are living organisms that consume sugars, turning them in to alcohol and carbon dioxide. Traditionally most yeast used in UK beer production would have been 'ale yeast' which rises to the surface during fermentation and is therefore known as 'top-fermenting'. Other commonly-used yeasts are lager yeast, known as 'bottom-fermenting', and wild yeasts which create 'spontaneous fermentation', when beer in open vats is exposed to wild yeast in the air. Yeast produces natural chemical compounds called esters that give off aromas reminiscent of apples, oranges, pear drops, banana, liquorice, molasses and, in especially strong beers, fresh leather.

START

When malted barley reaches the brewery, it's ground in a mill into a powder called grist.

Grist and pure hot water, also called liquor, flow into the mash tun, where the porridge-like mixture of grain and water starts the brewing process.
The mixture is left to stand in the mash tun for around two hours, and during that time enzymes in the malt convert the remaining starch into fermentable sugar.

Malt mill   Mash tun   Liquor tank

Casks have to be vented to allow some of the natural gas to escape. A cask has two openings: a bung at the flat end where a tap is inserted to serve the beer; and a shive hole on top. A soft porous peg of wood, known as a spile or peg, is knocked into the shive, enabling some of the CO_2 to escape. As fermentation dies down, the soft spile is replaced after 24 hours by a hard one that leaves some gas in the cask: this gives the beer its natural sparkle, known as 'condition'.
Inside the cask, finings sink to the bottom, attracting the yeast in suspension.

When the publican is satisfied that the beer has 'dropped bright', plastic tubes or 'lines' are attached to the tap and the beer is drawn by a suction pump activated by a handpump on the bar. Some pubs and beer festivals may serve the beer straight from the cask.

FINISH

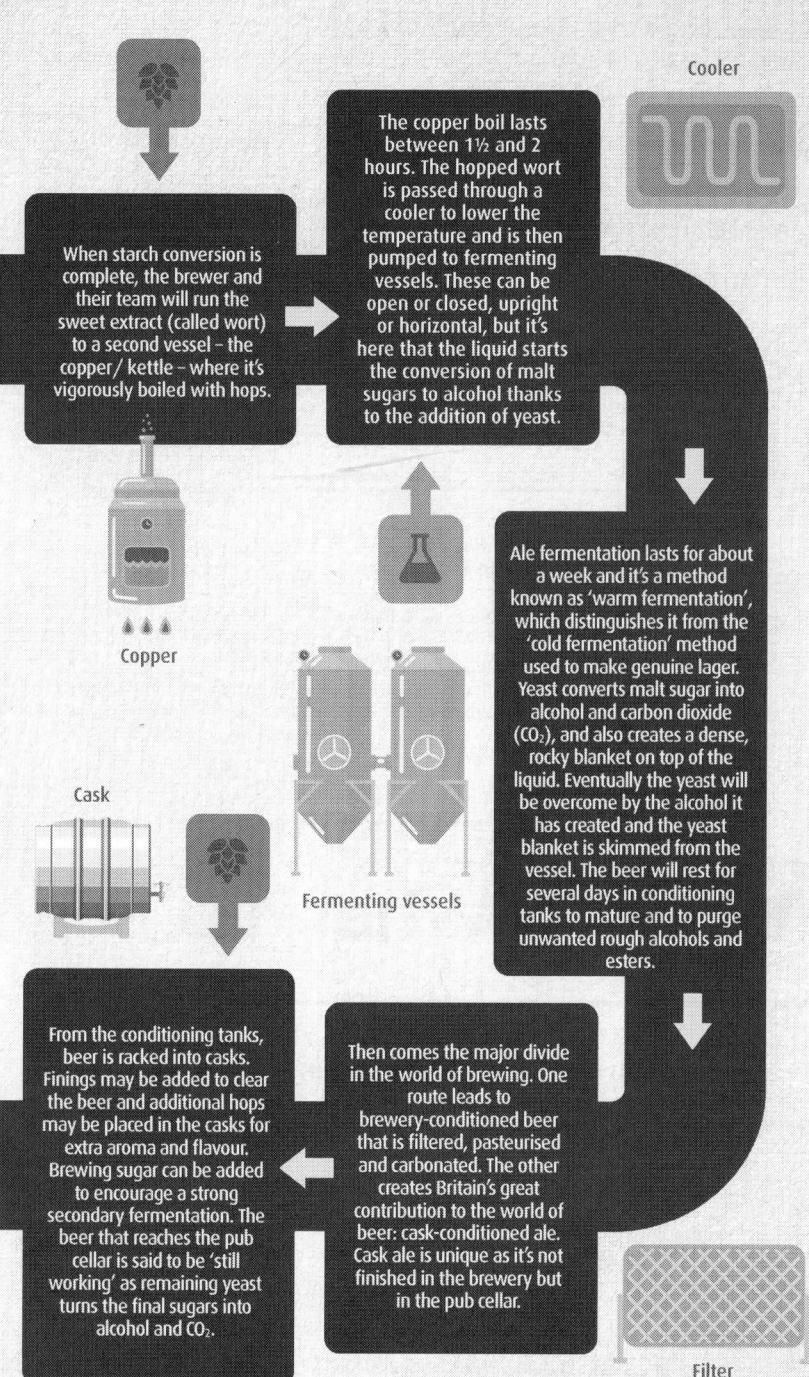

Cooler

When starch conversion is complete, the brewer and their team will run the sweet extract (called wort) to a second vessel – the copper/ kettle – where it's vigorously boiled with hops.

The copper boil lasts between 1½ and 2 hours. The hopped wort is passed through a cooler to lower the temperature and is then pumped to fermenting vessels. These can be open or closed, upright or horizontal, but it's here that the liquid starts the conversion of malt sugars to alcohol thanks to the addition of yeast.

Copper

Cask

Fermenting vessels

Ale fermentation lasts for about a week and it's a method known as 'warm fermentation', which distinguishes it from the 'cold fermentation' method used to make genuine lager. Yeast converts malt sugar into alcohol and carbon dioxide (CO_2), and also creates a dense, rocky blanket on top of the liquid. Eventually the yeast will be overcome by the alcohol it has created and the yeast blanket is skimmed from the vessel. The beer will rest for several days in conditioning tanks to mature and to purge unwanted rough alcohols and esters.

From the conditioning tanks, beer is racked into casks. Finings may be added to clear the beer and additional hops may be placed in the casks for extra aroma and flavour. Brewing sugar can be added to encourage a strong secondary fermentation. The beer that reaches the pub cellar is said to be 'still working' as remaining yeast turns the final sugars into alcohol and CO_2.

Then comes the major divide in the world of brewing. One route leads to brewery-conditioned beer that is filtered, pasteurised and carbonated. The other creates Britain's great contribution to the world of beer: cask-conditioned ale. Cask ale is unique as it's not finished in the brewery but in the pub cellar.

Filter

ADDITIONAL RESOURCES

The *Good Beer Guide* is also available in digital formats, including a mobile app and a sat-nav Points of Interest (POI) download. Together, these offer the perfect solution to pub-finding on the move. See **shop1.camra.org.uk** for further information.

GOOD BEER GUIDE APP

The *Good Beer Guide* mobile app provides detailed information on the latest *Good Beer Guide* pubs, breweries and beers wherever you are or wherever you are going. It also provides information for more than 31,000 other real ale pubs all over the UK, collated by CAMRA. Social media integration lets you share your beer experiences with other users and you can record your pub visits, tasted beers and personal reviews. For more information visit **gbgapp.camra.org.uk**

CAMRA'S NATIONAL BEER SCORING SYSTEM

CAMRA's National Beer Scoring System (NBSS) is used by members across the country to help them identify outlets that serve consistently good beer. The system uses a 0–5 scale that can be submitted online. Any member can submit a beer score by visiting **whatpub.com**, logging in as a member and selecting 'Submit Beer Scores' or by using the beer scoring function on the Good Beer Guide app.

The NBSS is also used to select beers for the annual Champion Beer of Britain competition.

See **camra.org.uk/NBSS** for details.

JOIN CAMRA'S GOOD BEER GUIDE PRIVILEGE CLUB

CAMRA members can take advantage of an even bigger discount on the *Good Beer Guide*, and get further benefits, by joining the Good Beer Guide Privilege Club.

- Pay just £11 (RRP £15.99) for your copy, with free p&p
- Receive your copy hot off the press and in advance of other purchasers
- Receive occasional special Club offers and discounts on other CAMRA books and merchandise
- Stay up-to-date every year with The Good Beer Guide as everything is taken care of with one simple Direct Debit
- Help to fund CAMRA directly, allowing us to continue to campaign for real ale and community pubs

For further details and to sign up visit **camra.org.uk/gbg-privilege-club** and follow the online instructions.

BOOKS AND MERCHANDISE

CAMRA's online shop is the idea place to visit for anyone looking for beer-and pub-related books, clothing or merchandise for themselves or fellow beer lovers.

Books on beer, brewing, pubs, and breweries have been exploding onto our bookshelves in more numbers than ever before in recent years. Alongside a rise in the 'craft' beer movement the books on beer have taken on a much more eclectic and varied approach to the subject. Beer and cooking, brewing your own with a myriad of ingredients and the most exotic places to drink beer, have all been covered in one form or another. CAMRA books are keen to embrace this newfound desire to explore the quirky and exciting aspects of beer but with 50 years of publishing and a combined membership life experience of over 9 million years, we are much more inclined to approach these subjects with the long term in mind. As an authority on beer, we are very much concerned with preserving it in its purest form and celebrating the changes and innovations for their benefits.

- Browse the full range of CAMRA Books titles within categories including beer knowledge; beer travel; history & culture, heritage, home brewing and pub walks & travel
- Discover our growing selection of beer-related titles from other publishers
- Shop our expanding range of clothing and merchandise
- Get upcoming CAMRA titles in advance of publication at special pre-order prices
- As a CAMRA member, log in to receive further discounts

Visit us at: **shop1.camra.org.uk**

Modern British Beer

Matthew Curtis

Matthew Curtis maps the evolution of Modern British Beer through the intricate stories of individual regional beers. He gives a personal insight into the eclectic and exciting world of Modern British Beer from a choice of 86 influential brews; from how they taste, how their ingredients are sourced, to the engaging stories of the people behind the scenes working hard to bring exciting beer to drinkers all over Britain.

"A beauty and a triumph... An incredibly engaging read." - *Claire Bullen, Editor-in-Chief, Good Beer Hunting*

RRP: £15.99 **ISBN:** 978-1-85249-370-7

For this and other books on beer and pubs visit CAMRA's online bookshop at **shop1.camra.org.uk** or call 01727 867201.

Discounts are available for CAMRA members.

A Year in Beer
The Beer Lover's Guide to the Seasons
Jonny Garrett

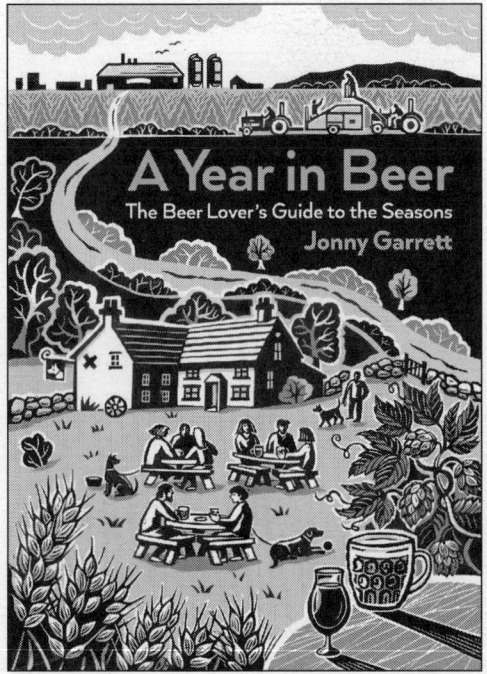

A Year in Beer is a bold and exciting new look at beer, encouraging drinkers to reconnect our favourite beverage with the world around us.

Taking us through the hop and malt harvests of late summer, the joyful fireside drinks and slow cooking of Autumn, the glut of Christmas beers and a cheese boards of winter, and the wild and fresh burst of new life and brewing in spring, A Year in Beer explains why drinking seasonally might just teach us more about what we drink and why.

The book is peppered with delicious food recipes, explorations of the UK's modern brewing scene and deep dives into the histories and unlikely origins of our favourite styles – all bringing it back to the context in which we enjoy them – not just the season, not just the weather, but the people and the places that make them unique.

Written by 2019 Beer Writer of the Year Jonny Garrett this book will change how we look at brewing and drinking beer, and increase our enjoyment of both.

RRP: £15.99 **ISBN:** 978-1-85249-372-1

For this and other books on beer and pubs visit CAMRA's online bookshop at **shop1.camra.org.uk** or call 01727 867201.

Discounts are available for CAMRA members.

Modern British Cider

Gabe Cook

Gabe Cook, The Ciderologist, shines a light on the complex, contemporary story of cider.

Cider is one of the world's oldest drinks, with a heritage dating back at least 2,000 years. It has formed an integral part of the landscape, economy and culture of many rural parts of the UK for centuries.

Both beer and cider now face a new change in the drinking landscape of Britain – the rise of 'craft' and modern, discerning drinkers with different needs, habits and spending opportunities.

Now is the time for CAMRA to produce a cider guide that sheds light on the incredible diversity that exists within cider in the UK today.

The best of cider-making talent is celebrated in Modern British Cider. From Aberdeen to Anglesey and Yeovil to Yorkshire, 101 cider makers from across England, Scotland and Wales are featured, along with producers from Guernsey, Northern Ireland and the Republic of Ireland. It reflects on what the cider industry looks like in this modern age, where it has come from, and what key events over the past 60 years have informed the trends that are being experienced now.

RRP: £15.99 **ISBN:** 978-1-85249-371-4

For this and other books on beer and pubs visit CAMRA's online bookshop at **shop1.camra.org.uk** or call 01727 867201.

Discounts are available for CAMRA members.